W9-BVG-786

Hoover's Handbook of

Private Companies

2021

Hoover's Handbook of Private Companies 2021 is intended to provide readers with accurate and authoritative information about the enterprises covered in it. Hoover's researched all companies and organizations profiled, and in many cases contacted them directly so that companies represented could provide information. The information contained herein is as accurate as we could reasonably make it. In many cases we have relied on third-party material that we believe to be trustworthy, but were unable to independently verify. We do not warrant that the book is absolutely accurate or without error. Readers should not rely on any information contained herein in instances where such reliance might cause financial loss. The publisher, the editors, and their data suppliers specifically disclaim all warranties, including the implied warranties of merchantability and fitness for a specific purpose. This book is sold with the understanding that neither the publisher, the editors, nor any content contributors are engaged in providing investment, financial, accounting, legal, or other professional advice.

The financial data (Historical Financials sections) in this book are from a variety of sources. Mergent Inc., provided selected data for the Historical Financials sections of publicly traded companies. For private companies and for historical information on public companies prior to their becoming public, we obtained information directly from the companies or from trade sources deemed to be reliable. Hoover's, Inc., is solely responsible for the presentation of all data.

Many of the names of products and services mentioned in this book are the trademarks or service marks of the companies manufacturing or selling them and are subject to protection under US law. Space has not permitted us to indicate which names are subject to such protection, and readers are advised to consult with the owners of such marks regarding their use. Hoover's is a trademark of Hoover's, Inc.

10 9 8 7 6 5 4 3 2 1

Publishers Cataloging-in-Publication Data

Hoover's Handbook of Private Companies 2021

Includes indexes.

ISBN: 978-1-64972-058-0

ISSN 1073-6433

1. Business enterprises — Directories. 2. Corporations — Directories.

HF3010 338.7

U.S. AND WORLD BOOK SALES

Mergent Inc.

580 Kingsley Park Drive
Fort Mill, SC
29715
Phone: 704-559-6961
e-mail: skardon@ftserussell.com
Web: www.mergentbusinesspress.com

Mergent Inc.

Executive Managing Director: John Pedernales

Publisher/Managing Director of Print Products: Thomas Wecera

Director of Print Products: Charlot Volny

Quality Assurance Editor: Wayne Arnold

Production Research Assistant: Davie Christna

Data Manager: Jason Horvat

MERGENT CUSTOMER SERVICE-PRINT
Support & Fulfillment: Stephanie Kardon
Phone: 704-559-6961
e-mail: skardon@ftserussell.com
Web: www.mergentbusinesspress.com

ABOUT MERGENT INC.

For over 100 years, Mergent, Inc. has been a leading provider of business and financial information on public and private companies globally. Mergent is known to be a trusted partner to corporate and financial institutions, as well as to academic and public libraries. Today we continue to build on a century of experience by transforming data into knowledge and combining our expertise with the latest technology to create new global data and analytical solutions for our clients. With advanced data collection services, cloud-based applications, desktop analytics and print products, Mergent and its subsidiaries provide solutions from top down economic and demographic information, to detailed equity and debt fundamental analysis. We incorporate value added tools such as quantitative Smart Beta equity research and tools for portfolio building and measurement. Based in the U.S., Mergent maintains a strong global presence, with offices in New York, Charlotte, San Diego, London, Tokyo, Kuching and Melbourne. Mergent, Inc. is a member of the London Stock Exchange plc group of companies. The Mergent business forms part of LSEG's Information Services Division, which includes FTSE Russell, a global leader in indexes.

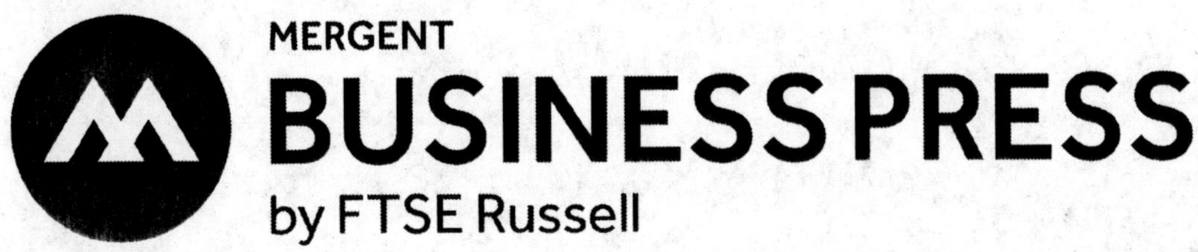

Abbreviations

AFL-CIO – American Federation of Labor and Congress of Industrial Organizations
AMA – American Medical Association
AMEX – American Stock Exchange
ARM – adjustable-rate mortgage
ASP – application services provider
ATM – asynchronous transfer mode
ATM – automated teller machine
CAD/CAM – computer-aided design/computer-aided manufacturing
CD-ROM – compact disc – read-only memory
CD-R – CD-recordable
CEO – chief executive officer
CFO – chief financial officer
CMOS – complementary metal oxide silicon
COO – chief operating officer
DAT – digital audiotape
DOD – Department of Defense
DOE – Department of Energy
DOS – disk operating system
DOT – Department of Transportation
DRAM – dynamic random-access memory
DSL – digital subscriber line
DVD – digital versatile disc/digital video disc
DVD-R – DVD-recordable
EPA – Environmental Protection Agency
EPS – earnings per share
ESOP – employee stock ownership plan
EU – European Union
EVP – executive vice president
FCC – Federal Communications Commission
FDA – Food and Drug Administration
FDIC – Federal Deposit Insurance Corporation
FTC – Federal Trade Commission
GATT – General Agreement on Tariffs and Trade
GDP – gross domestic product
HMO – health maintenance organization
HR – human resources
HTML – hypertext markup language
ICC – Interstate Commerce Commission
IPO – initial public offering
IRS – Internal Revenue Service
ISP – Internet service provider
kWh – kilowatt-hour
LAN – local-area network
LBO – leveraged buyout
LCD – liquid crystal display
LNG – liquefied natural gas
LP – limited partnership
Ltd. – limited
mips – millions of instructions per second
MW – megawatt
NAFTA – North American Free Trade Agreement
NASA – National Aeronautics and Space Administration
NASDAQ – National Association of Securities Dealers Automated Quotations
NATO – North Atlantic Treaty Organization
NYSE – New York Stock Exchange
OCR – optical character recognition
OECD – Organization for Economic Cooperation and Development
OEM – original equipment manufacturer
OPEC – Organization of Petroleum Exporting Countries
OS – operating system
OSHA – Occupational Safety and Health Administration
OTC – over-the-counter
PBX – private branch exchange
PCMCIA – Personal Computer Memory Card International Association
P/E – price to earnings ratio
RAID – redundant array of independent disks
RAM – random-access memory
R&D – research and development
RBOC – regional Bell operating company
RISC – reduced instruction set computer
REIT – real estate investment trust
ROA – return on assets
ROE – return on equity
ROI – return on investment
ROM – read-only memory
S&L – savings and loan
SEC – Securities and Exchange Commission
SEVP – senior executive vice president
SIC – Standard Industrial Classification
SOC – system on a chip
SVP – senior vice president
USB – universal serial bus
VAR – value-added reseller
VAT – value-added tax
VC – venture capitalist
VoIP – Voice over Internet Protocol
VP – vice president
WAN – wide-area network

Contents

Companies Profiled

Companies Profiled (continued)

Companies Profiled (continued)

Companies Profiled (continued)

Companies Profiled (continued)

Companies Profiled (continued)

Companies Profiled (continued)

Companies Profiled (continued)

Companies Profiled (continued)

Companies Profiled (continued)

Companies Profiled (continued)

Companies Profiled (continued)

About Hoover's Handbook of Private Companies 2021

Finding current relevant information about non-public companies can be a challenge, as many of these organizations see secrecy as a competitive strategy. In this edition of *Hoover's Handbook of Private Companies,* we have done for you the tough work of compiling these hard-to-find facts.

We consider this volume to be one of the premier sources of business information on privately held enterprises in the US. It features the facts on 900 of the largest and most influencial of those enterprises. Entries feature overviews of company operations, up to five years of financial information, product information, and lists of company executives as found in Hoover's huge database of company information. Some larger and more visable companies will feature an additional History section.

HOOVER'S ARCHIVES FOR BUSINESS NEEDS

In addition to the 2,550 companies featured in our handbooks, comprehensive coverage of more than 6 years of Hoovers Books are published in the Hoovers Archives.. Our goal is to provide one site that offers authoritative, updated intelligence on US and global companies, industries, and the people who shape them. Stay with the Hoovers famaily of products and History and package the books with the archives products.

We welcome the recognition we have received as a provider of high-quality company information — online, electronically, and in print — and continue to look for ways to make our products more available and more useful to you.

Hoover's Handbook of Private Companies is one of our four-title series of handbooks that covers, literally, the world of business. The series is available as an indexed set, and also includes *Hoover's Handbook of American Business, Hoover's Handbook of World Business,* and *Hoover's Handbook of Emerging Companies.* This series brings you information on the biggest, fast-growing, and most influential enterprises in the world.

We believe that anyone who buys from, sells to, invests in, lends to, competes with, interviews with, or works for a company should know all there is to know about that enterprise. Taken together, this book and the other Hoover's products and resources represent the most complete source of basic corporate information readily available to the general public.

HOW TO USE THIS BOOK

This book has four sections:

1. "Using Hoover's Handbooks" describes the contents of our profiles and explains the ways in which we gather and compile our data.
2. "A List-Lover's Compendium" contains lists of the largest and fastest-growing private companies. The lists are based on the information in our profiles, or compiled from well-known sources.
3. The company profiles section makes up the largest and most important part of the book — 900 profiles of major private enterprises, arranged alphabetically.
4. Three indexes complete the book. The first sorts companies by industry groups, the second by headquarters location. The third index is a list of all the executives found in the Executives section of each company profile.

Using Hoover's Handbooks

SELECTION OF THE COMPANIES PROFILED

The 900 enterprises profiled in this book include the largest and most influential companies in America. Among them are:

- private companies, from the giants (Cargill and Koch) to the colorful and prominent (Bad Boy Entertainment and L.L. Bean)
- mutuals and cooperative organizations owned by their customers (State Farm Insurance, Ace Hardware, Ocean Spray Cranberries)
- not-for-profits (Red Cross, Kaiser Permanente, Smithsonian Institution)
- joint ventures (Motiva Enterprises, Dow Corning)
- partnerships (PricewaterhouseCoopers, Baker & McKenzie)
- universities (Columbia, Harvard, University of California)
- government-owned corporations (US Postal Service and New York City's Metropolitan Transportation Authority)
- and a selection of other enterprises (National Basketball Association, AFL-CIO, Texas Lottery Commission).

ORGANIZATION

The profiles are presented in alphabetical order. You will find the commonly used name of the enterprise at the beginning of the profile; the full, legal name is found in the Locations section. If a company name is also a person's name, such as Henry Ford Health System or Mary Kay, it will be alphabetized under the first name; if the company name starts with initials, for example, L.L. Bean or S.C. Johnson, look for it under the combined initials (in the above examples, LL and SC, respectively).

Basic financial data are listed under the heading Historical Financials. The annual financial information contained in the profiles is current through fiscal year-ends occuring as late as January 2021. We have included certain nonfinancial developments , such as officer changes, through January 2021.

OVERVIEW

In the first section of the profile, we have tried to give a thumbnail description of the company and what it does. The description will usually include information on the company's strategy, reputation, and ownership. We recommend that you read this section first.

HISTORY

This extended section, which is available for some of the larger and more well-known companies, reflects our belief that every enterprise is the sum of its history and that you have to know where you came from in order to know where you are going. While some companies have limited historical awareness, we think the vast majority of the enterprises in this book have colorful backgrounds. We have tried to focus on the people who made the enterprises what they are today. We have found these histories to be full of twists and ironies; they make fascinating reading.

EXECUTIVES

Here we list the names of the people who run the company, insofar as space allows. In the few cases where available, we have shown the ages and pay of key officers. In some instances the published data is for the previous year, although the company has announced promotions or retirements since year-end. The pay represents cash compensation, including bonuses, but excludes stock option programs.

Although companies are free to structure their management titles any way they please, most modern corporations follow standard practices. The ultimate power in any corporation lies with the shareholders, who elect a board of directors, usually including officers or "insiders" as well as individuals from outside the company. The chief officer, the person on whose desk the buck stops, is usually called the chief executive officer (CEO). Often, he or she is also the chairman of the board.

As corporate management has become more complex, it is common for the CEO to have a "right-hand person" who oversees the day-to-day operations of the company, allowing the CEO plenty of time to focus on strategy and long-term issues. This right-hand person is usually designated the chief operating officer (COO) and is often the president of the company. In other cases one person is both chairman and president.

A multitude of other titles exists, including chief financial officer (CFO), chief administrative officer, and vice chairman. We have always tried to include the CFO, the chief legal officer, and the chief human resources or personnel officer.

The people named in the Executives section are indexed at the back of the book.

The Executives section also includes the name of the company's auditing (accounting) firm, where available.

LOCATIONS

Here we include the company's full legal name and its headquarters, street address, telephone and fax numbers, and Web site, as available. The back of the book includes an index of companies by headquarters locations.

In some cases we have also included information on the geographic distribution of the company's business, including sales and profit data. Note that these profit numbers, like those in the Products/Operations section below, are usually operating or pretax profits rather than net profits. Operating profits are generally those before financing costs (interest income and payments) and before taxes, which are considered costs attributable to the whole company rather than to one division or part of the world. For this reason the net income figures (in the Historical Financials section) are usually much lower, since they are after interest and taxes. Pretax profits are after interest but before taxes.

Headquarters for companies that are incorporated in Bermuda, but whose operational headquarters are in the US, are listed under their US address.

PRODUCTS/OPERATIONS

This section contains selected lists of products, services, brand names, divisions, subsidiaries, and joint ventures. We have tried to include a company's major lines and most familiar brand names.

The nature of this section varies by company and the amount of information contained in Hoover's storehouse of business information. If the company publishes sales and profit information by type of business, we have included it.

COMPETITORS

In this section we have listed companies that compete with the profiled company. This feature is included as a quick way to locate similar companies and compare them. The universe of competitors includes all public companies and all private companies with sales in excess of $500 million. In a few instances we have identified smaller private companies as key competitors.

HISTORICAL FINANCIALS

Here we have tried to present as much data about each enterprise's financial performance as we could compile in the allocated space. The information varies somewhat from industry to industry and is less complete in the case of private companies that do not release data. (We have always tried to provide annual sales and employment, although in some instances those numbers are simply not available). There are a few industries, venture capital and investment banking, for example, for which revenue numbers are not reported as a rule. In the case of private companies that do not publicly disclose financial information, we have statistics when reliable sources are available.

The following information is generally present.

A five-year table, with relevant annualized compound growth rates, covers:

- Sales — fiscal year sales (year-end assets for most financial companies)
- Net income — fiscal year net income (before accounting changes)
- Net profit margin — fiscal year net income as a percent of sales (as a percent of assets for most financial firms)
- Employees — fiscal year-end or average number of employees

The information on the number of employees is intended to aid the reader interested in knowing whether a company has a long-term trend of increasing or decreasing employment. As far as we know, we are the only company that publishes this information in print format.

The numbers on the left in each row of the Historical Financials section give the month and the year in which the company's fiscal year actually ends. Thus, a company with a March 31, 2020, year-end is shown as 3/19. The last item in the Financials section is a graph, which for private companies shows net income, or, if that is unavailable, sales.

Key year-end statistics are included in this section for insurance companies and companies required to file reports with the SEC. They generally show the financial strength of the enterprise, including:

- Debt ratio (long-term debt as a percent of shareholders' equity)
- Return on equity (net income divided by the average of beginning and ending common shareholders' equity)
- Cash and cash equivalents
- Current ratio (ratio of current assets to current liabilities)
- Total long-term debt (including capital lease obligations)
- Fiscal year sales for financial institutions

Hoover's Handbook of

Private Companies

A List-Lover's Compendium

The 300 Largest Private Companies by Sales 2021

Rank	Company	Sales ($ mil.)
1	STATE OF CALIFORNIA	$255,725
2	CHINESE HOSPITAL ASSOCIATION	$226,958
3	STATE OF TEXAS	$115,336
4	COMMONWEALTH OF PENNSYLVANIA	$78,418
5	ALBERTSONS COMPANIES, INC.	$62,455
6	STATE OF ILLINOIS	$62,452
7	STATE OF OHIO	$60,384
8	STATE OF MICHIGAN	$54,684
9	COMMONWEALTH OF MASSACHUSETTS	$53,391
10	STATE OF WASHINGTON	$50,993
11	NOVARTIS PHARMACEUTICALS CORPORATION	$49,436
12	STATE OF NORTH CAROLINA	$48,977
13	MCLANE COMPANY, INC.	$48,016
14	STATE OF GEORGIA	$45,109
15	STATE OF MINNESOTA	$41,741
16	COMMONWEALTH OF VIRGINIA	$40,939
17	DHPC TECHNOLOGIES, INC.	$38,584
18	JOHNSON CONTROLS, INC.	$37,179
19	STATE OF INDIANA	$36,470
20	STATE OF ARIZONA	$34,554
21	STATE OF TENNESSEE	$32,779
22	STATE OF WISCONSIN	$31,684
23	STATE OF LOUISIANA	$30,034
24	STATE OF OREGON	$28,230
25	COMMONWEALTH OF KENTUCKY	$27,091
26	STATE OF MISSOURI	$25,749
27	STATE OF SOUTH CAROLINA	$24,768
28	STATE OF ALABAMA	$23,698
29	STATE OF COLORADO	$22,950
30	ASCENSION HEALTH ALLIANCE	$22,633
31	CANDID COLOR SYSTEMS, INC.	$21,742
32	COUNTY OF LOS ANGELES	$21,191
33	BNSF RAILWAY COMPANY	$20,747
34	UPMC	$20,609
35	STATE OF OKLAHOMA	$19,784
36	STATE OF NEW MEXICO	$18,370
37	TRINITY HEALTH CORPORATION	$18,345
38	STATE OF IOWA	$18,007
39	STATE OF MISSISSIPPI	$16,887
40	WHOLE FOODS MARKET, INC.	$16,030
41	STATE OF KANSAS	$14,988
42	KAISER FOUNDATION HOSPITALS INC	$14,795
43	PROVIDENCE HEALTH & SERVICES	$14,434
44	STATE OF UTAH	$14,316
45	GENERAL ELECTRIC INTERNATIONAL, INC.	$14,100
46	STATE OF ARKANSAS	$13,821
47	ALLEGIS GROUP, INC.	$13,583
48	DAIRY FARMERS OF AMERICA, INC.	$13,528
49	STATE OF WEST VIRGINIA	$12,469
50	STATE OF ALASKA	$12,422
51	LELAND STANFORD JUNIOR UNIVERSITY	$12,262
52	GOVERNMENT OF DISTRICT OF COLUMBIA	$12,096
53	TEXAS DEPARTMENT OF TRANSPORTATION	$12,070
54	MAYO CLINIC HOSPITAL-ROCHESTER	$11,993
55	ADVENTIST HEALTH SYSTEM/SUNBELT, INC.	$11,892
56	WAKEFERN FOOD CORP.	$11,871
57	KIEWIT CORPORATION	$11,826
58	U.S. GENERAL SERVICES ADMINISTRATION	$11,785
59	STATE OF HAWAII	$11,744
60	MASS GENERAL BRIGHAM INCORPORATED	$11,666
61	WHEATLAND UNION HIGH SCHOOL DISTRICT	$11,465
62	PETER KIEWIT SONS', INC.	$11,220
63	ADVENTIST HEALTH SYSTEM SUNBELT HEALTHCARE CORPORATION	$10,974
64	HY-VEE, INC.	$10,673
65	THE CLEVELAND CLINIC FOUNDATION	$10,560
66	THE TURNER CORPORATION	$10,524
67	TURNER CONSTRUCTION COMPANY INC	$10,516
68	ROBERT BOSCH LLC	$10,474
69	STATE OF NEVADA	$10,436
70	CAMERON INTERNATIONAL CORPORATION	$10,381
71	SHI INTERNATIONAL CORP.	$10,372
72	TMV CORP.	$10,310
73	UNIVERSITY OF PENNSYLVANIA	$10,094
74	LIMETREE BAY TERMINALS LLC	$10,048
75	EQUINOR MARKETING & TRADING (US) INC.	$9,874
76	ASSOCIATED WHOLESALE GROCERS, INC.	$9,704
77	NEW YORK CITY HEALTH AND HOSPITALS CORPO	$9,551
78	ALTICOR INC.	$9,460
79	STATE OF NEBRASKA	$9,322
80	BAYLOR SCOTT & WHITE HOLDINGS	$9,084
81	METROPOLITAN TRANSPORTATION AUTHORITY	$9,043
82	DIGNITY HEALTH	$8,958
83	ONEOK PARTNERS, L.P.	$8,918
84	INTERMOUNTAIN HEALTH CARE INC	$8,812
85	THE HERTZ CORPORATION	$8,803
86	THE PRIDDY FOUNDATION	$8,792
87	CHEVRON PHILLIPS CHEMICAL COMPANY LLC	$8,769
88	GROWMARK, INC.	$8,745
89	BON SECOURS MERCY HEALTH, INC.	$8,718
90	STATE OF IDAHO	$8,616
91	JARDEN LLC	$8,604
92	NEW YORK UNIVERSITY	$8,500
93	THE NEW YORK AND PRESBYTERIAN HOSPITAL	$8,484
94	OCHSNER CLINIC FOUNDATION	$8,405
95	SOLSTICE HOLDINGS INC.	$8,235
96	STATE OF MAINE	$8,156
97	STATE OF DELAWARE	$8,125
98	U.S. VENTURE, INC.	$8,076
99	UPMC PRESBYTERIAN SHADYSIDE	$8,046
100	REGENTS OF THE UNIVERSITY OF MICHIGAN	$7,956
101	STATE OF NORTH DAKOTA	$7,861
102	CFJ PROPERTIES LLC	$7,672
103	R. DIRECTIONAL DRILLING & UNDERGROUND	$7,668
104	COMPUTER SCIENCES CORPORATION	$7,607
105	CITY & COUNTY OF SAN FRANCISCO	$7,562
106	STATE OF RHODE ISLAND AND PRO. PLANTATIONS	$7,547
107	ATRIUM HEALTH FOUNDATION	$7,511
108	ALLIED UNIVERSAL HOLDCO LLC	$7,461
109	FEDERAL-MOGUL HOLDINGS LLC	$7,434
110	HEALTHPARTNERS, INC.	$7,252
111	CITY OF LOS ANGELES	$7,196
112	COMMONSPIRIT HEALTH	$7,170
113	FLORIDA DEPARTMENT OF LOTTERY	$7,158
114	GEISINGER HEALTH	$7,122
115	THE JOHNS HOPKINS HEALTH SYSTEM CORP	$7,110
116	CHEVRON PHILLIPS CHEMICAL COMPANY LP	$7,106
117	PRECISION CASTPARTS CORP.	$7,002
118	IHC HEALTH SERVICES, INC.	$6,947
119	EATON CORPORATION	$6,925
120	SPECTRUM HEALTH SYSTEM	$6,884
121	THE PENNSYLVANIA STATE UNIVERSITY	$6,796
122	STATE OF MONTANA	$6,741
123	WORLD WIDE TECHNOLOGY HOLDING CO., LLC	$6,702
124	AEROTEK, INC.	$6,662
125	CITY OF PHILADELPHIA	$6,647
126	MERCY HEALTH	$6,520
127	SSM HEALTH CARE CORPORATION	$6,497
128	JOHNS HOPKINS UNIVERSITY	$6,471
129	ALLY BANK	$6,427
130	NIELSEN HOLDINGS PLC	$6,172
131	FAIRVIEW HEALTH SERVICES	$6,050
132	STATE UNIVERSITY OF NEW YORK	$5,961
133	STATE OF NEW HAMPSHIRE	$5,955
134	CGB ENTERPRISES, INC.	$5,955
135	ZEN-NOH GRAIN CORPORATION	$5,931
136	WORLD WIDE TECHNOLOGY, LLC	$5,928
137	STATE OF VERMONT	$5,869
138	HENRY FORD HEALTH SYSTEM	$5,854
139	MEMORIAL HERMANN HEALTH SYSTEM	$5,792
140	MEDSTAR HEALTH, INC.	$5,789
141	ACE HARDWARE CORPORATION	$5,717
142	HENSEL PHELPS CONSTRUCTION CO.	$5,677
143	HILL/AHERN FIRE PROTECTION, LLC	$5,669
144	CHALMETTE REFINING, L.L.C.	$5,648
145	CONSOLIDATED GRAIN & BARGE COMPANY	$5,640
146	LEVI STRAUSS & CO.	$5,575
147	STANFORD HEALTH CARE	$5,568
148	BOARD OF REGENTS OF THE UNIV. SYS OF GA	$5,532
149	THE WHITING-TURNER CONTRACTING COMPANY	$5,522
150	UNIVERSITY OF WASHINGTON INC	$5,511
151	NOVANT HEALTH, INC.	$5,435
152	ADVOCATE HEALTH CARE NETWORK	$5,393
153	TEXAS PERMANENT SCHOOL FUND MGE CO INC.	$5,375
154	AURORA HEALTH CARE, INC.	$5,334
155	ADVOCATE HEALTH AND HOS.	$5,310
156	AIRGAS, INC.	$5,305
157	NEW YORK STATE CATHOLIC HEALTH PLAN, INC.	$5,305
158	BOARD OF EDUCATION OF CITY OF CHICAGO	$5,273
159	HOUSTON METHODIST HOSPITAL	$5,226
160	THE METHODIST HOSPITAL	$5,226
161	NEW YORK CITY TRANSIT AUTHORITY	$5,061
162	UNIVERSITY OF COLORADO HEALTH	$5,055
163	UAW RETIREE MEDICAL BENEFITS TRUST	$5,051
164	ST. JOSEPH HEALTH SYSTEM	$4,956
165	PLACID REFINING COMPANY LLC	$4,929
166	PLACID HOLDING COMPANY	$4,929
167	TEKSYSTEMS, INC.	$4,928
168	SPECTRA ENERGY CORP	$4,916
169	GILBANE BUILDING COMPANY	$4,899
170	MERCY HEALTH	$4,860
171	TAUBER OIL COMPANY	$4,831
172	SANFORD HEALTH	$4,819
173	FAIRFAX COUNTY VIRGINIA	$4,806
174	BATTELLE MEMORIAL INSTITUTE	$4,775
175	LUKOIL PAN AMERICAS, LLC	$4,746
176	BEAUMONT HEALTH	$4,703
177	BALFOUR BEATTY, LLC	$4,690
178	TEXAS HEALTH RESOURCES	$4,689
179	COUNTY OF SAN DIEGO	$4,657

SOURCE: MERGENT, INC., DATABASE, FEBRUARY 2021

The 300 Largest Private Companies by Sales 2021(continued)

Rank	Company	Sales ($ mil.)
180	SANFORD	$4,639
181	BIOURJA TRADING, LLC	$4,622
182	DUKE UNIVERSITY	$4,612
183	MARYLAND DEPARTMENT OF TRANSPORTATION	$4,609
184	MCCARTHY HOLDINGS, INC.	$4,591
185	HOBBY LOBBY STORES, INC.	$4,544
186	MCCARTHY BUILDING COMPANIES, INC.	$4,513
187	NEW YORK PRESBYTERIAN HOSPITAL WEILL CORNELL UNIVERSITY MEDICAL CENTER	$4,506
188	MEMORIAL SLOAN-KETTERING CANCER CENTER	$4,499
189	ADVENTIST HEALTH SYSTEM/WEST, CORPORATION	$4,434
190	THE PRESIDENT AND FELLOWS OF HARVARD COL	$4,409
191	UNIVERSITY OF MARYLAND MEDICAL SYS	$4,364
192	COBANK, ACB	$4,321
193	SWINERTON INCORPORATED	$4,305
194	ALLINA HEALTH SYSTEM	$4,279
195	SWINERTON BUILDERS, INC.	$4,272
196	YALE UNIVERSITY	$4,247
197	THE REGENTS OF THE UNIVERSITY OF COI	$4,240
198	THE SCOULAR COMPANY	$4,226
199	CHRISTUS HEALTH	$4,212
200	MONTGOMERY COUNTY, MARYLAND	$4,203
201	IOWA HEALTH SYSTEM	$4,157
202	BRIGHTSTAR US, LLC	$4,138
203	COUNTY OF ORANGE	$4,105
204	WINCO HOLDINGS, INC.	$4,104
205	UNIVERSITY OF COLORADO	$4,098
206	VANDERBILT UNIVERSITY MEDICAL CENTER	$4,086
207	CHS MCPHERSON REFINERY INC.	$4,081
208	AVAYA HOLDINGS CORP.	$4,081
209	XMED OXYGEN & MEDICAL EQUIPMENT, LP	$4,061
210	THE INCOME FUND OF AMERICA INC	$4,051
211	NEW YORK UNIVERSITY	$4,017
212	SHAMROCK FOODS COMPANY	$4,016
213	CORNELL UNIVERSITY	$4,014
214	HMH HOSPITALS CORPORATION	$4,000
215	CITY OF BOSTON	$3,953
216	THOMAS JEFFERSON UNIVERSITY	$3,952
217	DUKE UNIVERSITY HEALTH SYSTEM, INC.	$3,952
218	MASSACHUSETTS INSTITUTE OF TECHNOLOGY	$3,951
219	THE SCHOOL BOARD OF MIAMI-DADE COUNTY	$3,948
220	STATE OF SOUTH DAKOTA	$3,946
221	CAPITAL INCOME BUILDER	$3,912
222	ALASKA PERMANENT FUND CORPORATION	$3,907
223	VCU HEALTH SYSTEM AUTHORITY	$3,896
224	DANONE US, INC.	$3,866
225	BALFOUR BEATTY CONSTRUCTION GROUP, INC.	$3,853
226	AMERICAN TIRE DISTRIBUTORS HOLDINGS, INC.	$3,839
227	BALFOUR BEATTY CONSTRUCTION, LLC	$3,809
228	COUNTY OF SAN BERNARDINO	$3,807
229	MONTEFIORE MEDICAL CENTER	$3,763
230	THE WASHINGTON UNIVERSITY	$3,750
231	UNIVERSITY SYSTEM OF MARYLAND	$3,749
232	SANFORD HEALTH	$3,741
233	API GROUP INC.	$3,730
234	CEDARS-SINAI MEDICAL CENTER	$3,648
235	KWIK TRIP, INC.	$3,640
236	TEMPLE UNIV. COMMONWEALTH SYS. OF HI ED.	$3,629
237	CLARK COUNTY SCHOOL DISTRICT	$3,617
238	SUTTER VALLEY HOSPITALS	$3,614
239	UNIVERSITY OF WISCONSIN SYSTEM (INC)	$3,614
240	TRINITY HEALTH-MICHIGAN	$3,596
241	UTI, (U.S.) HOLDINGS, INC.	$3,568
242	SCRIPPS NETWORKS INTERACTIVE, INC.	$3,562
243	THE PARSONS CORPORATION	$3,561
244	HCL AMERICA INC.	$3,559
245	BARNES & NOBLE, INC.	$3,553
246	HARTFORD HEALTHCARE CORPORATION	$3,542
247	COUNTY OF NASSAU	$3,523
248	LONG ISLAND POWER AUTHORITY	$3,516
249	NATIONAL RAILROAD PASSENGER CORPORATION	$3,504
250	BLACK & VEATCH HOLDING COMPANY	$3,480
251	PROVIDENCE HEALTH & SERVICES - OREGON	$3,479
252	KIEWIT INDUSTRIAL GROUP INC	$3,474
253	THE SCHOOL DISTRICT OF PHILADELPHIA	$3,474
254	SCHWAB CHARITABLE FUND	$3,466
255	THE WALSH GROUP LTD	$3,462
256	BEARINGPOINT, INC.	$3,456
257	CALIFORNIA INSTITUTE OF TECHNOLOGY	$3,434
258	THE OHIO STATE UNIVERSITY WEXNER MED.	$3,433
259	THE GOLUB CORPORATION	$3,427
260	AG PROCESSING INC A COOPERATIVE	$3,411
261	THE UNIVERSITY OF IOWA	$3,404
262	SHARP HEALTHCARE ACO, LLC	$3,397
263	OHIOHEALTH CORPORATION	$3,388
264	COUNTY OF SUFFOLK	$3,378
265	MONSTER BEVERAGE 1990 CORPORATION	$3,369
266	BVH, INC.	$3,364
267	NOBLE HOLDING (U.S.) CORPORATION	$3,352
268	USG CORPORATION	$3,336
269	OREGON HEALTH & SCIENCE UNIVERSITY	$3,313
270	FRANCISCAN ALLIANCE, INC.	$3,303
271	COUNTY OF CLARK	$3,301
272	PRODUCTION TECHNOLOGIES, INC.	$3,289
273	DRIVETIME AUTOMOTIVE GROUP, INC.	$3,267
274	ESTES EXPRESS LINES	$3,259
275	RAYMOND JAMES & ASSOCIATES INC	$3,256
276	AMERICAN BALANCED FUND, INC.	$3,255
277	CITY OF HOUSTON	$3,253
278	VIRGINIA DEPARTMENT OF TRANSPORTATION	$3,240
279	PHILADELPHIA CONSOLIDATED HOLDING CORP.	$3,234
280	MULTICARE HEALTH SYSTEM	$3,234
281	KAISER FDN HEALTH PLAN OF COLORADO	$3,197
282	PROVIDENCE HEALTH & SERVICES-WASHINGTON	$3,178
283	THE UNIVERSITY OF IOWA	$3,177
284	TRUMAN ARNOLD COMPANIES	$3,174
285	ATLANTIC HEALTH SYSTEM INC.	$3,163
286	REGAL ENTERTAINMENT GROUP	$3,163
287	RALEY'S	$3,162
288	SKF USA INC.	$3,139
289	LEHIGH VALLEY HEALTH NETWORK, INC.	$3,130
290	SALT RIVER PROJECT AGRIC.IMP. AND POWER	$3,121
291	COUNTY OF SACRAMENTO	$3,115
292	DYNCORP INTERNATIONAL LLC	$3,101
293	UNIVERSITY OF CHICAGO	$3,092
294	THE CHILDREN'S HOSPITAL OF PHILADELPHIA	$3,057
295	BONNEVILLE POWER ADMINISTRATION	$3,055
296	BIG WEST OIL, LLC	$3,053
297	TEXAS COUNTY AND DISTRICT RETIRE.	$3,030
298	FRANCISCAN MISSIONARIES OF OUR LADY	$3,007
299	AXEL JOHNSON INC.	$2,982
300	MASSACHUSETTS DEPARTMENT OF TRANS	$2,958

The 300 Largest Private Companies by Employees 2021

Rank	Company	Employees
1	ALBERTSONS COMPANIES, INC.	270,000
2	STATE OF CALIFORNIA	208,580
3	RYMAN HOSPITALITY PROPERTIES,	177,000
4	KAISER FOUNDATION HOSPITALS INC	175,668
5	STATE OF TEXAS	144,175
6	ASCENSION HEALTH ALLIANCE	111,719
7	ASCENSION HEALTH	109,000
8	JOHNSON CONTROLS, INC.	105,000
9	COMMONWEALTH OF VIRGINIA	100,000
10	COUNTY OF LOS ANGELES	100,000
11	WHOLE FOODS MARKET, INC.	95,000
12	COMMONWEALTH OF PENNSYLVANIA	89,207
13	STATE UNIVERSITY OF NEW YORK	88,024
14	ALLIED UNIVERSAL HOLDCO LLC	88,000
15	ALLEGIS GROUP, INC.	85,000
16	HY-VEE, INC.	83,000
17	STATE OF COLORADO	81,349
18	UPMC	80,000
19	ADVENTIST HEALTH SYSTEM SUNBELT HEALTHCARE CORPORATION	78,000
20	COMMONSPIRIT HEALTH	72,500
21	STATE OF NORTH CAROLINA	69,869
22	STATE OF SOUTH CAROLINA	67,816
23	METROPOLITAN TRANSPORTATION AUT	67,457
24	STATE OF GEORGIA	67,139
25	MASS GENERAL BRIGHAM INCOR	67,000
26	COMPUTER SCIENCES CORPORATION	66,000
27	ATRIUM HEALTH FOUNDATION	62,000
28	MAYO FOUNDATION FOR MEDICAL EDUCATION AND RESEARCH	60,000
29	STATE OF ILLINOIS	59,659
30	COMMONWEALTH OF MASSACHUSETTS	59,253
31	STATE OF WASHINGTON	57,659
32	STATE OF OHIO	57,631
33	ST MARY'S MEDICAL CENTER	56,605
34	DIGNITY HEALTH	55,494
35	STATE OF MICHIGAN	55,416
36	THE UNIVERSITY OF NORTH CAROLINA	55,000
37	ALLIED SECURITY HOLDINGS LLC	53,760
38	FEDERAL-MOGUL HOLDINGS LLC	53,700
39	STATE OF MISSOURI	51,488
40	PILOT CORPORATION	51,337
41	TRINITY HEALTH CORPORATION	51,100
42	SANFORD	50,000
43	NEW YORK CITY TRANSIT AUTHORITY	47,956
44	STATE OF LOUISIANA	47,937
45	ADVENTIST HEALTH SYSTEM/SUNBELT	46,960
46	STATE OF HAWAII	44,201
47	THE CLEVELAND CLINIC FOUNDATION	44,000
48	THE PENNSYLVANIA STATE UNIVERSITY	44,000
49	NIELSEN HOLDINGS PLC	43,061
50	BNSF RAILWAY COMPANY	41,000
51	CITY OF LOS ANGELES	41,000
52	COUNTY OF BROWARD	40,500
53	BOARD OF REG OF THE UNIV OF GA	40,000
54	THE HERTZ CORPORATION	38,000
55	STATE OF TENNESSEE	37,737
56	STATE OF ALABAMA	37,659
57	STATE OF OKLAHOMA	37,613
58	JOHNS HOPKINS UNIVERSITY	37,600
59	CLARK COUNTY SCHOOL DISTRICT	37,361
60	STEWARD HEALTH CARE SYSTEM LLC	37,000
61	STATE OF OREGON	36,176
62	NEW YORK CITY HEALTH AND HOSP	35,700
63	STATE OF WISCONSIN	35,522
64	STATE OF MINNESOTA	35,217
65	INTERMOUNTAIN HEALTH CARE INC	35,000
66	MERCY HEALTH	35,000
67	BEAUMONT HEALTH	35,000
68	THE OHIO STATE UNIVERSITY WEXNER MEDICAL CENTER	35,000
69	MAXIM HEALTHCARE SERVICES, INC.	35,000
70	GOOD SAMARITAN HOSPITAL	35,000
71	REGENTS OF THE UNIV OF MICH	34,624
72	GOVERNMENT OF DISTRICT OF COL.	34,600
73	STATE OF ARIZONA	34,161
74	COMMONWEALTH OF KENTUCKY	34,000
75	STATE OF INDIANA	33,000
76	MEDSTAR HEALTH, INC.	33,000
77	MAYO CLINIC HOSPITAL-ROCHESTER	32,271
78	MOSAIC HEALTH SYSTEM	32,000
79	BROWARD COUNTY PUBLIC SCHOOLS	31,174
80	UNIVERSITY OF MISSOURI SYSTEM	30,282
81	PRECISION CASTPARTS CORP.	30,106
82	UNIVERSITY HOSPITALS HEALTH SYS.	30,099
83	CITY & COUNTY OF SAN FRANCISCO	30,000
84	AURORA HEALTH CARE, INC.	30,000
85	CITY OF BROCKTON	30,000
86	CITY OF PHILADELPHIA	29,862
87	STATE OF UTAH	29,821
88	NPC RESTAURANT HOLDINGS, LLC	29,000
89	THE SD OF WEST PALM BEACH COUNTY	28,910
90	STATE OF ARKANSAS	28,272
91	UNIVERSITY SYSTEM OF MARYLAND	28,000
92	STATE OF MISSISSIPPI	27,775
93	UNIVERSITY OF WASHINGTON INC	27,228
94	ALLINA HEALTH SYSTEM	26,400
95	CITY OF BALTIMORE	26,400
96	OREGON UNIVERSITY SYSTEM	26,000
97	ROBINSON HEALTH SYSTEM, INC.	26,000
98	CHRISTUS HEALTH	25,700
99	REGAL ENTERTAINMENT GROUP	25,359
100	ADVOCATE HEALTH CARE NETWORK	25,000
101	HILLSBOROUGH CTY SCHOOL DISTRICT	25,000
102	SCHOOL BOARD OF ORANGE CTY FL	25,000
103	CITY OF SCOTTSDALE	25,000
104	DALLAS INDEPENDENT SD	24,937
105	BARNABAS HEALTH, INC.	24,600
106	STATE OF IOWA	24,304
107	SSM HEALTH CARE CORPORATION	24,230
108	BARNES & NOBLE, INC.	24,000
109	THE ORANGE COUNTY PUBLIC SD	24,000
110	THE EVANGELICAL LUTHERAN GOOD SAMARITAN SOCIETY	24,000
111	THE NEW YORK AND PRES.HOSPITAL	23,709
112	CITY OF HOUSTON	23,235
113	CAMERON INTERNATIONAL CORP.	23,000
114	HENRY FORD HEALTH SYSTEM	23,000
115	HOBBY LOBBY STORES, INC.	23,000
116	ORLANDO HEALTH, INC.	23,000
117	ACCENTCARE, INC.	23,000
118	YALE NEW HAVEN HEALTH SERV.	22,490
119	HOUSTON INDEPENDENT SD	22,440
120	STATE OF KANSAS	22,375
121	STATE OF NEW MEXICO	22,217
122	HEALTHPARTNERS, INC.	22,000
123	YALE NEW HAVEN HOSPITAL, INC.	22,000
124	PRINCE GEORGE'S CTY PUBLIC SCH.	22,000
125	TEXAS HEALTH RESOURCES	21,277
126	THE SCHOOL DISTRICT OF PHIL.	21,065
127	DAIRY FARMERS OF AMERICA, INC.	21,000
128	NEW YORK UNIVERSITY	21,000
129	COUNTY OF ORANGE	21,000
130	SCHOOL BOARD OF PALM BEACH CTY	21,000
131	THE VANDERBILT UNIVERSITY	21,000
132	MCLANE COMPANY, INC.	20,128
133	BATTELLE MEMORIAL INSTITUTE	20,000
134	LARSEN & TOUBRO INFOTECH LIMITED	20,000
135	BAYCARE HEALTH SYSTEM, INC.	20,000
136	NORTHWESTERN MEM. HEALTHCARE	20,000
137	AMC ENTERTAINMENT INC.	19,700
138	AVAYA HOLDINGS CORP.	19,601
139	ADVENTIST HEALTH SYSTEM/WEST,	19,512
140	THE GOLUB CORPORATION	19,500
141	OREGON HEALTH & SCIENCE UNIV.	19,500
142	STATE OF WEST VIRGINIA	19,357
143	BON SECOURS MERCY HEALTH, INC.	19,000
144	VANDERBILT UNIV. MEDICAL CENTER	19,000
145	FRANCISCAN ALLIANCE, INC.	19,000
146	OCHSNER HEALTH SYSTEM	19,000
147	IOWA HEALTH SYSTEM	18,923
148	PAREXEL INTERNATIONAL CORP	18,900
149	CITY OF BOSTON	18,760
150	STATE OF NEBRASKA	18,653
151	NATIONAL RAILROAD PASSENGER CORP	18,650
152	UNIVERSITY OF NEW MEXICO	18,362
153	WILLIAM BEAUMONT HOSPITAL	18,050
154	FAIRVIEW HEALTH SERVICES	18,000
155	THE UNIVERSITY OF UTAH	18,000
156	METROPOLITAN GOVERNMENT OF NASHVILLE & DAVIDSON COUNTY	18,000
157	WHEATON FRANCISCAN SERVICES, INC.	18,000
158	CHILDREN'S HOSPITAL MED.CENTER	18,000
159	ASCENSION SOUTHEAST MICHIGAN	17,806
160	UNIVERSITY OF GEORGIA	17,800
161	UNIVERSITY OF CALIFORNIA, DAVIS	17,741
162	MAIN LINE HEALTH SYSTEM	17,485
163	INDIANA UNIVERSITY HEALTH, INC.	17,242
164	CEC ENTERTAINMENT, INC.	17,200
165	JARDEN LLC	17,000
166	AIRGAS, INC.	17,000
167	COUNTY OF SAN DIEGO	17,000
168	THE UNIVERSITY OF IOWA	17,000
169	SCOTTSDALE HEALTHCARE CORP.	17,000
170	WAKE COUNTY PUBLIC SCHOOL SYSTEM	17,000
171	SPECTRUM HEALTH SYSTEM	16,996
172	THE RESEARCH FOUNDATION FOR THE STATE UNIVERSITY OF NEW YORK	16,330
173	THE SALVATION ARMY	16,168
174	UNIVERSITY OF SOUTH FLORIDA	16,165

SOURCE: MERGENT, INC., DATABASE, FEBRUARY 2021

The 300 Largest Private Companies by Employees 2021 (continued)

Rank	Company	Employees
175	ST. JOSEPH'S HEALTH, INC.	16,132
176	HOUCHENS INDUSTRIES, INC.	16,000
177	TRUSTEES OF INDIANA UNIVERSITY	16,000
178	ROCHESTER REGIONAL HEALTH	16,000
179	ALSCO INC.	16,000
180	INOVA HEALTH SYSTEM FOUNDATION	16,000
181	UNIVERSITY SYSTEM OF NEW HAMP	16,000
182	BAPTIST HEALTH SOUTH FLORIDA, INC.	16,000
183	SPECTRUM HEALTH PRIMARY CARE PAR	16,000
184	MINNETONKA INDEPENDENT SCHOOL DISTRICT 276	16,000
185	LEVI STRAUSS & CO.	15,800
186	COBB COUNTY PUBLIC SCHOOLS	15,796
187	COUNTY OF MARICOPA	15,751
188	DST SYSTEMS, INC.	15,700
189	THE PARSONS CORPORATION	15,633
190	BEARINGPOINT, INC.	15,200
191	NEBRASKA MEDICINE GUILD	15,200
192	BOARD OF REGENTS OF THE UNIVERSITY OF NEBRASKA	15,200
193	LELAND STANFORD JUNIOR UNIVERSITY	15,000
194	THE METHODIST HOSPITAL	15,000
195	OHIOHEALTH CORPORATION	15,000
196	PITT COUNTY MEMORIAL HOSPITAL	15,000
197	AKAL SECURITY, INC.	15,000
198	BUHLER INC.	15,000
199	MINNESOTA STATE COLLEGES AND UNI	15,000
200	SCHOOL DISTRICT 1 IN THE CITY DENVER AND THE STATE OF COLORADO	14,965
201	STATE OF NEVADA	14,790
202	TEXAS DEPARTMENT OF TRANSPORT	14,720
203	PETER KIEWIT SONS', INC.	14,700
204	HOSPITAL SISTERS HEALTH SYSTEM	14,676
205	UNIVERSITY OF CINCINNATI	14,600
206	COUNTY OF NASSAU	14,500
207	COUNTY OF SANTA CLARA	14,500
208	WORLDWIDE MEDIA SERVICES GROUP	14,375
209	ALMOST FAMILY, INC.	14,200
210	ADVANCE SERVICES, INC.	14,200
211	MILWAUKEE PUBLIC SCHOOLS (INC)	14,154
212	STANFORD HEALTH CARE	14,100
213	UNIVERSITY OF ARKANSAS SYSTEM	14,025
214	ALTICOR INC.	14,000
215	SOLSTICE HOLDINGS INC.	14,000
216	MEMORIAL HERMANN HEALTH SYSTEM	14,000
217	WINCO HOLDINGS, INC.	14,000
218	SHARP HEALTHCARE ACO, LLC	14,000
219	ESTES EXPRESS LINES	14,000
220	RALEY'S	14,000
221	NAVY EXCHANGE SERVICE COMMAND	14,000
222	CITY OF PHOENIX	14,000
223	HONORHEALTH	14,000
224	THE HEALTH CARE AUTHORITY OF THE CITY OF HUNTSVILLE	14,000
225	JEFFERSON COUNTY BOARD OF ED	14,000
226	MORTON HOSPITAL AND MEDICAL CENTER STAFF. LLC	14,000
227	NOVANT HEALTH, INC.	13,800
228	NORTHSIDE INDEPENDENT SD	13,698
229	STATE OF RHODE ISLAND AND PROVIDENCE PLAN-TATIONS	13,535
230	THE CHILDREN'S HOSPITAL OF PHIL.	13,519
231	THE FINISH LINE INC	13,500
232	FLORIDA STATE UNIVERSITY	13,497
233	COUNTY OF KING	13,300
234	RECTOR & VISITORS OF THE UNIVERSITY OF VIR-GINIA	13,300
235	UNIVERSITY OF MASSACHUSETTS	13,196
236	GEISINGER HEALTH	13,030
237	U.S. GENERAL SERVICES ADMINI	13,000
238	THE JOHNS HOPKINS HEALTH SYSTEM	13,000
239	INOVA HEALTH CARE SERVICES	13,000
240	CYPRESS-FAIRBANKS INDEPENDENT SD	13,000
241	DUVAL COUNTY PUBLIC SCHOOLS	13,000
242	CITY OF TRENTON	13,000
243	THE REGENTS OF THE UNIV OF CO	12,980
244	COUNTY OF SUFFOLK	12,814
245	UNIVERSITY OF HOUSTON SYSTEM	12,608
246	BAPTIST HEALTHCARE SYSTEM, INC.	12,601
247	THE FRESH MARKET INC	12,600
248	NORTH CAROLINA BAPTIST HOSPITAL	12,563
249	HARTFORD HEALTHCARE CORPORATION	12,500
250	STATE OF NEW HAMPSHIRE	12,280
251	CORNELL UNIVERSITY	12,207
252	UNIVERSITY OF NORTH CAROLINA AT CHAPEL HILL	12,204
253	BOARD OF EDUCATION-MEMPHIS CITY SCHOOLS	12,015
254	STATE OF MAINE	12,000
255	FAIRFAX COUNTY VIRGINIA	12,000
256	UNIV MARYLAND MEDICAL SYSTEM COR	12,000
257	MASSACHUSETTS INSTIT. OF TECH	12,000
258	LEHIGH VALLEY HEALTH NETWORK	12,000
259	METALDYNE PERFORMANCE GROUP INC.	12,000
260	JOHNS HOPKINS HOSPITAL	12,000
261	THE MOSES H CONE MEMORIAL HOS	12,000
262	CITY OF SAN ANTONIO	12,000
263	NATIONWIDE CHILDREN'S HOSPITAL	12,000
264	MISSION HEALTH SYSTEM, INC.	12,000
265	WESTCHESTER COUNTY HEALTH CARE	12,000
266	THE GEISINGER CLINIC	12,000
267	UNIVERSITY OF TENNESSEE	12,000
268	JEFFERSON COUNTY SD NO. R-1	12,000
269	UNIVERSITY OF HAWAII SYSTEMS	12,000
270	TESLA ENERGY OPERATIONS, INC.	12,000
271	CHICAGO TRANSIT AUTHORITY (INC)	12,000
272	BODDIE-NOELL ENTERPRISES, INC.	12,000
273	UNIVERSITY OF PUERTO RICO	12,000
274	PORTLAND ADVENTIST MEDICAL CENT	12,000
275	HCL AMERICA INC.	11,993
276	ASCENSION VIA CHRISTI HEALTH, INC	11,970
277	THE PRESIDENT AND FELLOWS OF HARVARD COL-LEGE	11,500
278	METHODIST LE BONHEUR HEALTHCARE	11,459
279	CITY OF SAN DIEGO	11,200
280	LESTER E. COX MEDICAL CENTERS	11,170
281	MICHIGAN STATE UNIVERSITY	11,100
282	YALE UNIVERSITY	11,000
283	MONTEFIORE MEDICAL CENTER	11,000
284	SPECTRUM HEALTH HOSPITALS	11,000
285	DALLAS COUNTY HOSPITAL DISTRICT	11,000
286	BAYSTATE HEALTH INC.	11,000
287	PUBLIC HEALTH TRUST OF MIAMI DADE	11,000
288	VIRGINIA COMMONWEALTH UNIV	11,000
289	COUNTY OF VOLUSIA	11,000
290	BEAUMONT UNIFIED SCHOOL DISTRICT PUBLIC FACILITIES CORPORATION	11,000
291	ST. MARYS DEAN VENTURES, INC	11,000
292	COUNTY OF SACRAMENTO	10,968
293	CITY OF AUSTIN	10,922
294	BALTIMORE CITY PUBLIC SCHOOLS	10,800
295	MAIN LINE HEALTH, INC.	10,800
296	VIRGINIA DEPARTMENT OF TRANS	10,737
297	MED AMERICA HEALTH SYSTEMS CORP	10,700
298	LEGACY HEALTH	10,675
299	THOMAS JEFFERSON UNIVERSITY	10,625
300	RICH PRODUCTS CORPORATION	10,536

The 100 Largest Private Companies by Net Income 2021

Rank	Company Headquarters	Net Income ($mil)
1	BNSF RAILWAY COMPANY	$12,119
2	AMERICAN MUTUAL FUND	$9,525
3	COMMONSPIRIT HEALTH	$9,008
4	NEW WORLD FUND	$8,315
5	AMERICAN FUNDS PORTFOLIO SERIES	$6,853
6	NOVARTIS PHARMACEUTICALS CORPORATION	$6,698
7	CAPITAL INCOME BUILDER	$5,826
8	STATE OF CALIFORNIA	$4,799
9	THE PRESIDENT AND FELLOWS OF HARVARD COLLEGE	$4,608
10	TEXAS PERMANENT SCHOOL FUND MANAGEMENT CO. INC.	$4,155
11	STATE OF NEW MEXICO	$3,033
12	BON SECOURS MERCY HEALTH, INC.	$2,593
13	CANDID COLOR SYSTEMS, INC.	$2,535
14	UNIVERSITY OF PENNSYLVANIA	$2,327
15	STATE OF ALASKA	$2,276
16	AMERICAN BALANCED FUND, INC.	$2,254
17	AMERICAN FUNDS COLLEGE TARGET DATE SERIES	$2,243
18	THE CLEVELAND CLINIC FOUNDATION	$2,239
19	STATE OF OREGON	$2,142
20	ST. JOSEPH HEALTH SYSTEM	$2,083
21	LELAND STANFORD JUNIOR UNIVERSITY	$1,961
22	STATE OF NORTH DAKOTA	$1,955
23	STATE OF TEXAS	$1,883
24	THE BOND FUND OF AMERICA INC	$1,775
25	STATE OF SOUTH CAROLINA	$1,775
26	TEXAS COUNTY AND DISTRICT RETIREMENT SYSTEM	$1,761
27	STATE OF OHIO	$1,717
28	CHEVRON PHILLIPS CHEMICAL COMPANY LLC	$1,687
29	JOHNSON CONTROLS, INC.	$1,679
30	AMERICAN FUNDS MORTGAGE FUND	$1,673
31	ASCENSION HEALTH ALLIANCE	$1,639
32	STATE OF OKLAHOMA	$1,637
33	ADVENTIST HEALTH SYSTEM/SUNBELT, INC.	$1,607
34	STATE OF ILLINOIS	$1,596
35	PERMANENT UNIVERSITY FUND	$1,550
36	SCHWAB CHARITABLE FUND	$1,549
37	STATE OF ARIZONA	$1,497
38	COMMONWEALTH OF VIRGINIA	$1,481
39	MASSACHUSETTS INSTITUTE OF TECHNOLOGY	$1,448
40	THE SUNDERLAND FOUNDATION	$1,429
41	SUNOCO PIPELINE L.P.	$1,420
42	ALASKA PERMANENT FUND CORPORATION	$1,406
43	STATE OF LOUISIANA	$1,386
44	TRINITY HEALTH CORPORATION	$1,359
45	DHPC TECHNOLOGIES, INC.	$1,320
46	CHEVRON PHILLIPS CHEMICAL COMPANY LP	$1,301
47	HOUSTON METHODIST HOSPITAL	$1,276
48	THE METHODIST HOSPITAL	$1,276
49	ALLY BANK	$1,273
50	AMCAP FUND INC	$1,249
51	STATE OF GEORGIA	$1,235
52	ATRIUM HEALTH FOUNDATION	$1,223
53	INTERMOUNTAIN HEALTH CARE INC	$1,212
54	COBANK, ACB	$1,191
55	UAW RETIREE MEDICAL BENEFITS TRUST	$1,176
56	PUBLIC EMPLOYEE RETIREMENT SYSTEM, IDAHO	$1,145
57	TEXAS DEPARTMENT OF TRANSPORTATION	$1,108
58	ONEOK PARTNERS, L.P.	$1,072
59	NEW YORK CITY TRANSIT AUTHORITY	$1,050
60	AMERICAN FUNDS INFLATION LINKED BOND FUND	$1,046
61	STATE OF MINNESOTA	$1,041
62	SPECTRA ENERGY CORP	$1,020
63	STATE OF ARKANSAS	$998
64	STATE OF INDIANA	$987
65	CORNELL UNIVERSITY	$986
66	BARNABAS HEALTH, INC.	$926
67	RECTOR & VISITORS OF THE UNIVERSITY OF VIRGINIA	$909
68	JOHNS HOPKINS UNIVERSITY	$904
69	IHC HEALTH SERVICES, INC.	$888
70	PERMIAN EXPRESS PARTNERS LLC	$880
71	TEXAS HEALTH RESOURCES	$870
72	MAYO CLINIC HOSPITAL-ROCHESTER	$856
73	CAMERON INTERNATIONAL CORPORATION	$848
74	STATE OF NORTH CAROLINA	$836
75	STATE OF MICHIGAN	$833
76	SANTA CLARA VALLEY TRANSPORTATION AUTHORITY	$830
77	EATON CORPORATION	$821
78	MONSTER BEVERAGE 1990 CORPORATION	$821
79	PRECISION CASTPARTS CORP.	$817
80	SCRIPPS NETWORKS INTERACTIVE, INC.	$814
81	KIEWIT CORPORATION	$796
82	STATE OF KANSAS	$795
83	WHEATLAND UNION HIGH SCHOOL DISTRICT	$789
84	MILTON HERSHEY SCHOOL & SCHOOL TRUST	$785
85	PLAINS PIPELINE, L.P.	$783
86	PROVIDENCE HEALTH & SERVICES - OREGON	$781
87	STATE OF MISSISSIPPI	$774
88	NORTHERN BORDER PIPELINE COMPANY	$766
89	STATE OF TENNESSEE	$755
90	AMERICAN HONDA FINANCE CORPORATION	$753
91	THE BLOOMBERG FAMILY FOUNDATION INC	$737
92	EQUINOR NATURAL GAS LLC	$722
93	95 EXPRESS LANES LLC	$722
94	THE WASHINGTON UNIVERSITY	$719
95	INOVA HEALTH SYSTEM FOUNDATION	$717
96	THOMAS JEFFERSON UNIVERSITY	$700
97	STATE OF UTAH	$696
98	STATE OF WISCONSIN	$693
99	TRUSTEES OF DARTMOUTH COLLEGE	$691
100	CHS MCPHERSON REFINERY INC.	$687

SOURCE: MERGENT DATA FEBRUARY 2021

The 100 Largest Private Companies by Total Assets 2021

Rank	Company Headquarters	Net Income ($bil)
1	CHINESE HOSPITAL ASSOCIATION	$362,951
2	STATE OF CALIFORNIA	$333,689
3	STATE OF TEXAS	$323,008
4	COBANK, ACB	$139,016
5	TEXAS DEPARTMENT OF TRANSPORTATION	$134,159
6	STATE OF OHIO	$130,570
7	NOVARTIS PHARMACEUTICALS CORPORATION	$130,124
8	AMERICAN BALANCED FUND, INC.	$129,091
9	STATE OF NORTH CAROLINA	$127,399
10	ALLY BANK	$123,548
11	COMMONWEALTH OF VIRGINIA	$121,329
12	THE INCOME FUND OF AMERICA INC	$111,706
13	COMMONWEALTH OF PENNSYLVANIA	$109,100
14	STATE OF WASHINGTON	$108,197
15	STATE OF ALASKA	$103,389
16	METROPOLITAN TRANSPORTATION AUTHORITY	$91,569
17	COMMONWEALTH OF MASSACHUSETTS	$87,795
18	STATE OF GEORGIA	$84,078
19	BNSF RAILWAY COMPANY	$83,098
20	STATE OF MINNESOTA	$76,714
21	STATE OF MICHIGAN	$75,388
22	STATE OF ILLINOIS	$74,914
23	ALASKA PERMANENT FUND CORPORATION	$70,049
24	AMERICAN HONDA FINANCE CORPORATION	$69,854
25	THE PRESIDENT AND FELLOWS OF HARVARD COLLEGE	$69,810
26	STATE OF SOUTH CAROLINA	$67,044
27	STATE OF INDIANA	$66,689
28	AMCAP FUND INC	$65,323
29	STATE OF TENNESSEE	$65,315
30	STATE OF WISCONSIN	$64,256
31	CITY OF LOS ANGELES	$63,512
32	STATE OF OREGON	$61,712
33	STATE OF ALABAMA	$61,075
34	COMMONWEALTH OF KENTUCKY	$60,521
35	UAW RETIREE MEDICAL BENEFITS TRUST	$60,353
36	AMERICAN MUTUAL FUND	$60,172
37	STATE OF MISSOURI	$58,195
38	LELAND STANFORD JUNIOR UNIVERSITY	$57,803
39	STATE OF LOUISIANA	$56,246
40	STATE OF ARIZONA	$54,629
41	STATE OF NEW MEXICO	$51,929
42	STATE OF UTAH	$51,687
43	NEW YORK CITY TRANSIT AUTHORITY	$49,670
44	STATE OF COLORADO	$47,974
45	STATE OF OKLAHOMA	$47,955
46	SIGNATURE FINANCIAL LLC	$47,365
47	DORMITORY AUTHORITY - STATE OF NEW YORK	$45,583
48	YALE UNIVERSITY	$44,696
49	U.S. GENERAL SERVICES ADMINISTRATION	$44,681
50	TEXAS PERMANENT SCHOOL FUND MANAGEMENT CO. INC.	$44,517

Rank	Company Headquarters	Net Income ($bil)
51	THE BOND FUND OF AMERICA INC	$44,114
52	CITY & COUNTY OF SAN FRANCISCO	$42,701
53	NEW WORLD FUND	$42,218
54	AMERICAN FUNDS PORTFOLIO SERIES	$42,026
55	COMMONSPIRIT HEALTH	$40,625
56	MASSACHUSETTS DEPARTMENT OF TRANSPORTATION	$40,195
57	COUNTY OF LOS ANGELES	$39,892
58	SPECTRA ENERGY CORP	$36,842
59	STATE OF MISSISSIPPI	$34,821
60	STATE OF IOWA	$34,600
61	ASCENSION HEALTH ALLIANCE	$34,320
62	STATE OF NORTH DAKOTA	$33,816
63	THE TRUSTEES OF PRINCETON UNIVERSITY	$33,030
64	STATE OF HAWAII	$32,695
65	AGFIRST FARM CREDIT BANK	$32,487
66	MISSOURI DEPARTMENT OF TRANSPORTATION	$31,573
67	MASSACHUSETTS INSTITUTE OF TECHNOLOGY	$30,506
68	STATE OF KANSAS	$30,503
69	STATE OF WEST VIRGINIA	$29,967
70	STATE OF ARKANSAS	$29,920
71	JOHNSON CONTROLS, INC.	$29,673
72	COUNTY OF CLARK	$28,914
73	CITY OF HOUSTON	$27,927
74	CITY OF SAN ANTONIO	$27,901
75	EATON CORPORATION	$27,466
76	GGP, INC.	$27,282
77	UNIVERSITY OF PENNSYLVANIA	$26,415
78	TEXAS COUNTY AND DISTRICT RETIREMENT SYSTEM	$26,387
79	TRINITY HEALTH CORPORATION	$26,196
80	STATE OF NEBRASKA	$25,700
81	PERMANENT UNIVERSITY FUND	$25,199
82	BARCLAYS BANK DELAWARE	$25,013
83	FARM CREDIT SERVICES OF AMERICA	$24,773
84	ALBERTSONS COMPANIES, INC.	$24,735
85	REGENTS OF THE UNIVERSITY OF MICHIGAN	$24,233
86	KAISER FOUNDATION HOSPITALS INC	$22,753
87	MARYLAND DEPARTMENT OF TRANSPORTATION	$22,510
88	BROOKFIELD PROPERTIES RETAIL INC.	$21,973
89	FARM CREDIT BANK OF TEXAS	$21,222
90	GOVERNMENT OF DISTRICT OF COLUMBIA	$21,155
91	STATE OF IDAHO	$21,019
92	KNIGHTS OF COLUMBUS	$20,534
93	PRECISION CASTPARTS CORP.	$20,497
94	VIRGINIA DEPARTMENT OF TRANSPORTATION	$20,173
95	THE HERTZ CORPORATION	$20,058
96	NEW JERSEY TRANSPORTATION TRUST FUND AUTHORITY	$20,053
97	THE CLEVELAND CLINIC FOUNDATION	$19,974
98	BONNEVILLE POWER ADMINISTRATION	$19,669
99	CITY OF PHILADELPHIA	$19,633
100	GENERAL ELECTRIC INTERNATIONAL, INC.	$19,615

SOURCE: MERGENT DATA FEBRUARY 2021

Hoover's Handbook of

Private Companies

The Companies

1199 SEIU NATIONAL BENEFIT FUND FOR HEALTH AND HUMAN SERVICE EMPLOYEES

Auditors: KPMG LLP NEW YORK NY

LOCATIONS

HQ: 1199 SEIU NATIONAL BENEFIT FUND FOR HEALTH AND HUMAN SERVICE EMPLOYEES , NEW YORK, NY 10108
Phone: 646 473-6020

HISTORICAL FINANCIALS

Company Type: Private

Income Statement — FYE: December 31

	REVENUE ($ mil.)	NET INCOME ($ mil.)	NET PROFIT MARGIN	EMPLOYEES
12/17	1,642	45	2.8%	2
12/09	1,167	(19)	—	—
Annual Growth	4.4%	—	—	—

2017 Year-End Financials

Return on assets: 5.3%
Return on equity: 8.2%
Current ratio: 8.70
Cash ($ mil.): 47

21ST CENTURY ONCOLOGY HOLDINGS, INC.

EXECUTIVES

Ceo, Kimberly Commins-Tzoumakas
Chb, Robert L Rosner
Pres-Ceo, William R Spalding
Cfo, Leanne M Stewart
Cmo, Constantine A Mantz
Sr V Pres-Cao-Contrl-asst Trea, Joseph Biscardi
Sr V Pres US Oprs, Gary Delanois
Coo, Charlie Powell
Manager, Kasha Holt
Auditors: DELOITTE & TOUCHE LLP MIAMI

LOCATIONS

HQ: 21ST CENTURY ONCOLOGY HOLDINGS, INC. 2270 COLONIAL BLVD, FORT MYERS, FL 339071412
Phone: 239 931-7254
Web: WWW.21CO.COM

HISTORICAL FINANCIALS

Company Type: Private

Income Statement — FYE: December 31

	REVENUE ($ mil.)	NET INCOME ($ mil.)	NET PROFIT MARGIN	EMPLOYEES
12/14	1,026	(343)	—	3,930
12/13	736	(78)	—	—
12/12	693	(151)	—	—
Annual Growth	21.6%	—	—	—

2014 Year-End Financials

Return on assets: (-29.0%)
Return on equity: —
Current ratio: 1.40
Cash ($ mil.): 99

95 EXPRESS LANES LLC

EXECUTIVES

Mng MBR, Michael Kulper

LOCATIONS

HQ: 95 EXPRESS LANES LLC 6440 GENERAL GREEN WAY, ALEXANDRIA, VA 223122413
Phone: 571 419-6100

HISTORICAL FINANCIALS

Company Type: Private

Income Statement — FYE: June 30

	REVENUE ($ mil.)	NET INCOME ($ mil.)	NET PROFIT MARGIN	EMPLOYEES
06/20	975	722	74.1%	1
06/19	1,047	786	75.1%	—
06/18	92	32	35.6%	—
06/17	83	25	30.6%	—
Annual Growth	126.9%	204.7%	—	—

2020 Year-End Financials

Return on assets: 14.1%
Return on equity: 19.7%
Current ratio: 3.50
Cash ($ mil.): 332

A-1 SPECIALIZED SERVICES & SUPPLIES, INC.

EXECUTIVES

Pres, Suresh Khosla
V Pres*, Om Perkash
SEC*, Ashok Kumar
SEC*, Ashok K Khosla
Treas*, Leena Khosla
Auditors: MEENA JERATH CPA MED MBA

LOCATIONS

HQ: A-1 SPECIALIZED SERVICES & SUPPLIES, INC. 347 MOUNT PLEASANT AVE # 200, WEST ORANGE, NJ 070522744
Phone: 215 788-9200
Web: WWW.NORTHAM.CO.ZA

HISTORICAL FINANCIALS

Company Type: Private

Income Statement — FYE: December 31

	REVENUE ($ mil.)	NET INCOME ($ mil.)	NET PROFIT MARGIN	EMPLOYEES
12/10	1,359	7	0.6%	66
12/09	1,205	2	0.2%	—
12/08	2,637	15	0.6%	—
Annual Growth	(28.2%)	(28.9%)	—	—

2010 Year-End Financials

Return on assets: 1.5%
Return on equity: 12.5%
Current ratio: 1.10
Cash ($ mil.): 8

AAA COOPER TRANSPORTATION

AAA Cooper Transportation (ACT) is a trucking company offering freight hauling services primarily in the Southwest Southeast and Midwest. ACT offers less-than-truckload (LTL) hauling in 21 states (LTL carriers combine freight from multiple shippers into a single truckload). The company also offers freight brokerage services dedicated contract carriage and fleet maintenance services through 40 locations. The company's International Services division offers cross-border services to Canada and Mexico. ACT can also facilitate transportation in Puerto Rico and the US Virgin Islands. The company's fleet includes 3000 tractors and 6500 trailers.

Operations

The company's five primary service offerings are LTL Services dedicated services international services (including port services) managed services and fleet maintenance services.

Less than Truckload (LTL) services provides transportation to shipments typically falling between 50 and 10000 pounds. These shipments are commingled to ensure that these small sized shipments do not solely bear the full cost of transportation. Dedicated Services provides for the provisioning and dedication of transportation resources directly to a specific logistics need. International services offers cross border service to Canada and Mexico. Its system ensures seamless service complete control and single invoicing for shipments from origin to destination.

Managed services provides additional services which support and enhance shipping experience. These services are all offered through current sales associate. Some of fleet maintenance services include maintenance services to all type of diesel engines including CAT VOLVO INTERNATIONAL DETROIT CUMMINS among others and all types of trailing equipment PM flat rates are available based on requirements and engine part specifications and major repair work such as engine and transmission overhauls.

Geographic Reach

Through more than 70 locations ACT offers less-than-truckload (LTL) hauling in 21 states. The company also facilitates transportation in Puerto Rico Canada Mexico and the US Virgin Islands.

Sales and Marketing

The company markets their products and services through websites such Less that Truckload Services (LTL)Data Exchange In additions the company provides dedicated services for the provisioning and dedication of transportation resources directly to a specific logistics need such as technology data exchange route planning asset tracking reporting & customized billing and customer portal.

Company Background

ACT was founded in 1955.

EXECUTIVES

President And Coo, Reid Dove
Vp Administration Cfo Treasurer And Corporate Secretary, Steve Roy
Evp And Coo, Charles (Charlie) Prickett
Vp Strategic Services, Lee McMillan
Vp Information Services, Dan Christian
Senior Vice President Finance, Mark Griffis
National Account Manager, David Hunt
Vice President Enterprise Development, John Hammons
National Account Manager, Bob Mazzeffi
National Account Manager, Christopher Holden

LOCATIONS

HQ: AAA COOPER TRANSPORTATION
1751 KINSEY RD, DOTHAN, AL 363035877
Phone: 334 793-2284
Web: WWW.AAACOOPER.COM

PRODUCTS/OPERATIONS

Selected Services

Dedicated
Company branding
Specialized equipment
International LTL
LTL
Port
Consolidation
Drayage
Transloading

COMPETITORS

ArcBest
Averitt Express
Estes Express
FedEx Freight
Old Dominion Freight
R+L Carriers
Saia
Southeastern Freight Lines
UPS Freight
YRC Worldwide

HISTORICAL FINANCIALS

Company Type: Private

Income Statement — FYE: January 1

	REVENUE ($ mil.)	NET INCOME ($ mil.)	NET PROFIT MARGIN	EMPLOYEES
01/17	592	17	3.0%	4,933
01/16*	595	14	2.4%	—
12/14	576	20	3.5%	—
Annual Growth	1.3%	(6.4%)	—	—

*Fiscal year change

2017 Year-End Financials

Return on assets: 4.9%
Return on equity: 9.9%
Current ratio: 1.40
Cash ($ mil.): —

AARP

Turn 50 and the doors of the AARP will open for you as they have for nearly 38 million current members. On behalf of its members the not-for-profit AARP acts as an advocate on public policy issues such as health care and financial security publishes information (the monthly AARP Bulletin and the bimonthly AARP The Magazine and through social media channels) promotes community service and works with business partners to offer products and services. The group is organized into more than 800 local chapters throughout the US Puerto Rico and Virgin Islands. Contributions from members account for about half of the group's revenue.

Operations

It may not be the most exclusive club around but AARP is one of the most powerful. As the largest advocacy group in the US it has a loud voice in elections the organization provides information to its members so they can choose candidates who best fit their views and values. AARP through its Foundation organization is focused on medicine and nutritious food for seniors. To this end the organization operates Government Watch an interactive website designed to allow older Americans to hold Congress and the President's administration accountable on key issues that affect them.

AARP oversees volunteer services as well. The AARP Experience Corps is for volunteers aged 50+ who want to tutor and mentor youth in their communities primarily literacy for children in kindergarten through third grade. It operates in about 25 cities across the country.

Overall AARP generate about 50% of its revenue from contributions followed by government grants which gives more than 30% and the rest comes from in-kind contribution and return on investments.

Geographic Reach

Washington D.C-based AARP boasts staffed offices in all 50 US states Puerto Rico and the US Virgin Islands.

Financial Performance

Cash held by company at the end of 2019 increased by $11.0 million to $23.1 million compared from the prior year with $12.1 million. Cash provided by operations was $27.8 million while cash used for investing activities was $16.8 million mainly for purchase of investments.

EXECUTIVES

Evp And Cfo, Robert R. Hagans
Ceo, Jo Ann C. Jenkins
Evp And President Life Reimagined, Emilio Pardo
Evp And Chief Of Staff, Kevin Donnellan
Evp State And National Group, Nancy A. LeaMond
President And Ceo Aarp Services Inc., John J. Wider
Evp Membership And Integrated Value, Steve Cone
Evp Multicultural Markets And Engagement, Lorraine Cortés-V ́zquez
Evp States And Communities, Harroll (Hop) Backus
Evp And Cio, Hollis (Terry) Bradwell
Evp Policy Strategy And International Affairs, Debra Whitman
President Aarp Foundation, Lisa M. Ryerson
Executive Vice President Of Media, Beth Ellard
Chief Operating Officer, Scott Frisch
Executive Vice President Chief Human Resources Officer, Richard Randazzo
Senior Vice President Editorial Director, Myrna Blyth
Vice President And National Director, Julie Lee
Vice President Quality And Compliance, Michael Lewis
Senior Vice President Media Relations, Jeffrey Davis
Vice President Distribution, John Minniti
Executive Vice President And General Counsel, Cindy Lewin
Vice President Portfolio Strategy, Carey Kyler
Vice President And Associate General Counsel, Sarah Shaw
Senior Vice President And Senior Associate General Counsel, David Morales
Vice President Distribution Ne Region, James Bayer
Vice President Grants And External Initiatives, Marc Mcdonald
Senior Vice President Campaigns, John Hishta
Experience Corps. Rsvp Project Manager, Ellen Acevedo
Vice President Enterprise Performance Management, Walter Harris
Vice President, Daphne Kwok
Regional Vice President Central Region, Sarah Jennings
Vice President Financial Planning And Analysis, Chuck Ullan
Senior Vice President For Public, Susan Reinhard
Vice President Of Operations, Kathryn Tefft-Keller
Vice President Multicultural Leadership, Yvette Pena
Vice President, Margaret Mannix
2nd Vice President, Callie Herd
Vice President Experience Insights, Chuck Berman
Vice President Talent Development, Donna Gupton
Vice President Associate General Counsel, Laurel Gillis
Vice President Secretary Treasurer, Lee W Hammond
Vice President Data And Analytic Strategy, Garland Bond
Vp Distribution Ne Region, Jim Bayer
Senior Vice President And Treasurer, Karen Mercer
Vice President Corporate And Foundation Relations, Stephen Venute
Vice President Communications Strategies And Outreach, Paul Anderson
Senior Vice President Litigation, William Rivera
Senior Vice President Strategy And Innovation Aarp Serv, Kimberly Moorehead
Vice President Strategic Partnership Development And Relations, Shani Hosten
Solution Delivery Vice President Customer Service, Mark La Croix
Vice President Of Investment Management, Chuck Curtis
Vice President Digital Strategy, Kyle Murdoch
Senior Vice President, Jon Dauphine
Vice President Marketing, Stephen Driscoll
Vp Distribution Midwest Region, Bernie Buonanno
Vp Enterprise Strategy And Innovation, Anne Kilgallon
Vice President Direct Response, Steven Delvecchio
Senior Vice President, Alison Bryant
Chairman, Carol Raphael
Vice Chairman, Ronald E. Daly
Board Member Treasurer Administration Executive, Joan Ruff
Member Board Of Directors, Libby Sartain
Board Member, Jewell Hoover
Auditors: GRANT THORNTON LLP WASHINGTON

LOCATIONS

HQ: AARP
601 E ST NW, WASHINGTON, DC 200490003
Phone: 202 434-2277
Web: WWW.AARP.ORG

PRODUCTS/OPERATIONS

2016 sales

	$ mil.	% of total
Royalties	880	55
Membership dues	299	19
Publications advertising	150	9
Contributions	96	6
Grant	97	6
Program income	73	5
Other	5	-
Total	**1,603**	**100**

Selected Operations & Programs

AARP Bulletin (monthly news update)
AARP Driver Safety (classroom refresher)
AARP Foundation Experience Corps
AARP Legal Services Network
AARP Services (taxable product management marketing and e-commerce subsidiary)
AARP The Magazine (bimonthly magazine)
Back to Work 50+
Financial Planning
Public Policy Institute
Research Information Center
Senior Community Service Employment Program (SCSEP)
Tax-Aide

HISTORICAL FINANCIALS

Company Type: Private

Income Statement	REVENUE ($ mil.)	NET INCOME ($ mil.)	NET PROFIT MARGIN	EMPLOYEES
FYE: December 31				
12/17	1,643	279	17.0%	1,800
12/16	1,604	141	8.8%	—
12/14	1,399	84	6.0%	—
12/13	1,438	408	28.4%	—
Annual Growth	3.4%	(9.1%)	—	—

2017 Year-End Financials

Return on assets: 6.5%
Return on equity: 16.2%
Current ratio: —
Cash ($ mil.): 460

ABINGTON MEMORIAL HOSPITAL INC

Abington Memorial Hospital brings health care to residents of southeastern Pennsylvania. The not-for-profit community hospital has some 670 beds. In addition to general medical and surgical care the hospital offers specialized care centers for cancer and cardiovascular conditions operates high-tech orthopedic and neurological surgery units and serves as a regional trauma care facility. It also runs an inpatient pediatric unit in affiliation with The Children's Hospital of Philadelphia. Abington Memorial also known as Abington Health operates the neighboring 125-bed Lansdale Hospital and several area outpatient facilities.

Operations

The not-for-profit community hospital has some 670 beds and employs about 1400 physicians. Its specialty units include the Pilla Heart Center the Rosenfeld Cancer Center the Diamond Stroke Center as well as a level II trauma center and institutes for senior health and bariatric surgeries. Abington Memorial is affiliated with several medical schools including the Temple University School of Medicine and offers residency programs and postgraduate medical education.

In addition to its hospitals Abington Memorial operates an extensive outpatient care facility named Abington Health Center-Warminster. The Warminster facility is located in Bucks County and features an inpatient hospice center. Other outpatient facilities include Abington Health Center-Schilling (in Willow Grove) Abington Health Center-Blue Bell and Abington Physicians at Montgomeryville.

Altogether the organization's facilities handle 677000 outpatient visits and 33000 inpatient admissions each year.

Additionally Abington Memorial operates a nursing school and a clinical research center.

Geographic Reach

Abington Memorial provides care to residents of southeastern Pennsylvania. The hospital serves Montgomery Bucks and Philadelphia counties.

Strategy

Abington Memorial began using the Abington Health moniker to reflect its larger network of facilities after it acquired Lansdale Hospital which was previously known as Central Montgomery Medical Center from Universal Health Services in 2008. Abington Memorial has since invested in a number of improvements at the acquired hospital. The main Abington Memorial facility has also been enhanced including a new hybrid operating room for cardiac procedures in 2013.

Mergers and Acquisitions

In 2013 Abington Memorial acquired a home health agency the North Penn Visiting Nurse Association (NPVNA). The purchase expanded the geographic reach of Abington Memorial's home health operations.

Company Background

Abington Memorial first opened its doors in 1914.

EXECUTIVES

President Abington Hospitals, Margaret M. (Meg) McGoldrick
Chief Medical Officer, John J. Kelly
Respiratory Therapy Director, Kathy Sebastian
Director Of Radiology, Kristin Crisci
Medical Director Of Labor And Delivery, Amy Mackey
Vice President Oncologist, Michael S Yoon
Vice President Of Administration, Regina Harte
Secretary, Jennifer Meixsell

LOCATIONS

HQ: ABINGTON MEMORIAL HOSPITAL INC
1200 OLD YORK RD, ABINGTON, PA 190013788
Phone: 215 481-2000
Web: WWW.ABINGTONHEALTH.ORG

PRODUCTS/OPERATIONS

Selected Facilities

Abington Health Center ; Blue Bell Campus (Blue Bell PA)
Abington Health Center ; Schilling Campus (Willow Grove PA)
Abington Health Center ; Warminster Campus (Warminster PA)
Abington Memorial Hospital (Abington PA)
Abington Physicians at Montgomeryville (North Wales PA)
Lansdale Hospital (Lansdale PA)

COMPETITORS

Albert Einstein Healthcare Network
Aria Health
Crozer-Keystone Health System
Doylestown Hospital
Grand View
Main Line Health System
Memorial Hospital (PA)
Mercy Health System
Moses Taylor Hospital
North Philadelphia Health System
TUHS
Tenet Healthcare
University of Pennsylvania Health System
Virtua Memorial

HISTORICAL FINANCIALS

Company Type: Private

Income Statement	REVENUE ($ mil.)	NET INCOME ($ mil.)	NET PROFIT MARGIN	EMPLOYEES
FYE: June 30				
06/16	740	35	4.8%	4,018
06/15	697	28	4.1%	—
06/14	697	0	0.1%	—
06/13	708	20	2.9%	—
Annual Growth	1.5%	19.2%	—	—

2016 Year-End Financials

Return on assets: 4.5%
Return on equity: 87.7%
Current ratio: 2.00
Cash ($ mil.): 176

ACCESS BUSINESS GROUP LLC

Somehow all those Amway products have to get from factories to the sales floor and that's where Access Business Group (ABG) comes in. The company manufactures and distributes cosmetics nutritional supplements home care and personal care products for its sister company Amway. (Both companies are units of Alticor.) It also offers contract manufacturing services for third-party consumer goods companies but to a lesser extent. Other offerings include product packaging services as well as catalog and direct mail printing services. In addition the company operates R&D labs that develop and test products for Amway. Alticor is the parent company of Access Business Group as well as Amway and is a holding company for Amway's non-direct selling companies

Geographic Reach

ABG owns and operates seven manufacturing plants.

The company's main office was located in Ada Michigan and an additional office in Buena Park California.

Sales and Marketing

The company offers its products through distributors and retailers both in North America and Internationally.

EXECUTIVES

Vice President Brand Management, Jackie Nickel
Vice President, Rob Hunter

LOCATIONS

HQ: ACCESS BUSINESS GROUP LLC
7575 FULTON ST E, ADA, MI 493550001
Phone: 616 787-6000
Web: WWW.ACCESSBUSINESSGROUP.COM

PRODUCTS/OPERATIONS

Selected Services and Products

Beauty
- Blushes
- Eye shadows
- Lipsticks
- Mascara
- Skin care

Fulfillment
- A-Frame
- B2B & B2C
- Customized order picking at the store level
- High volume pick pack & ship
- Pick-to-light
- Tilt tray sorter

Home Care
- Household cleaners
- Plastic bottles
- Powder and liquid dish washing detergents
- Powder and liquid laundry detergents

Nutrition
- Antioxidants/supplements/herbals
- Food bars
- Granulation
- Multiminerals/multivitamins
- OTC tableting
- Powdered drinks

Personal Care
- Bar soaps
- Bath oils
- Body mist
- Conditioners
- Lotions
- Plastic bottles
- Shampoos
- Shower gels
- Styling products

Print
- Catalogs
- Corrugated cases
- Fine printing
- Labels
- L-Boards
- Paperboard packaging

COMPETITORS

AppTech
Berry Global
Botanical Laboratories
Essential Nutrition
Johnson & Johnson
Pfizer
Procter & Gamble
Strathmore
UPS Supply Chain Solutions

HISTORICAL FINANCIALS

Company Type: Private

Income Statement FYE: December 31

	REVENUE ($ mil.)	NET INCOME ($ mil.)	NET PROFIT MARGIN	EMPLOYEES
12/15	1,009	0	—	3,000
12/14	1,068	0	—	—
12/13	1,135	0	—	—
Annual Growth	(5.7%)	—	—	—

ACE HARDWARE CORPORATION

In an age of big-box home improvement centers (Home Depot Lowes) wholesaler Ace makes the case for the local hardware store. By sales it is the leading hardware cooperative in the US. Ace Hardware is a retailer-owned hardware cooperative in the world with more than 5300 locally owned and operated hardware stores in approximately 70 countries. The overall home improvement industry is consists of a broad range of products and services including lawn and garden products paint and sundries certain building supplies and general merchandise. Ace also provides value-added services such as advertising market research merchandising assistance and store location and design services. Ace was founded in 1924 by a group of Chicago hardware store owners.

HISTORY

A group of Chicago-area hardware dealers — William Stauber Richard Hesse Gern Lindquist and Oscar Fisher — decided in 1924 to pool their hardware buying and promotional costs. In 1928 the group incorporated as Ace Stores named in honor of the superior WWI fliers dubbed aces. Hesse became president the following year retaining that position for the next 44 years. The company also opened its first warehouse in 1929 and by 1933 it had 38 dealers.

The organization had 133 dealers in seven states by 1949. In 1953 Ace began to allow dealers to buy stock in the company through the Ace Perpetuation Plan. During the 1960s Ace expanded into the South and West and by 1969 it had opened distribution centers in Georgia and California — its first such facilities outside Chicago. In 1968 it opened its first international store in Guam.

By the early 1970s the do-it-yourself market began to surge as inflation pushed up plumber and electrician fees. As the market grew large home center chains gobbled up market share from independent dealers such as those franchised through Ace. In response Ace and its dealers became a part of a growing trend in the hardware industry — cooperatives.

Hesse sold the company to its dealers in 1973 for $6 million (less than half its book value) and the following year Ace began operating as a cooperative. Hesse stepped down in 1973. In 1976 the dealers took full control when the company's first Board of Dealer-Directors was elected.

After signing up a number of dealers in the eastern US Ace had dealers in all 50 states by 1979. The co-op opened a plant to make paint in Matteson Illinois in 1984. By 1985 Ace had reached $1 billion in sales and had initiated its Store of the Future Program allowing dealers to borrow up to $200000 to upgrade their stores and conduct market analyses. Former head coach John Madden of the National Football League's Oakland Raiders signed on as Ace's mouthpiece in 1988.

A year later the co-op began to test ACENET a computer network that allowed Ace dealers to check inventory send and receive e-mail make special purchase requests and keep up with prices on commodity items such as lumber. In 1990 Ace established an International Division to handle its overseas stores. (It had been exporting products since 1975.) EVP and COO David Hodnik became president in 1995. That year the co-op added a net of 67 stores including a three-store chain in Russia. Expanding further internationally Ace signed a five-year joint-supply agreement in 1996 with Canadian lumber and hardware retailer Beaver Lumber. Hodnik added CEO to his title in 1996.

Ace fell further behind its old rival True Value in 1997 when ServiStar Coast to Coast and True Value merged to form TruServ (renamed True Value in 2005) a hardware giant that operated more than 10000 outlets at the completion of the merger.

Late in 1997 Ace launched an expansion program in Canada. (The co-op already operated distribution centers in Ontario and Calgary.) In 1999 Ace merged its lumber and building materials division with Builder Marts of America to form a dealer-owned buying group to supply about 2700 retailers. Ace gained 208 member outlet stores in 2000 but saw 279 member outlets terminated. The next year it gained 220 but lost 255.

Sodisco-Howden bought all the shares of Ace Hardware Canada in February 2003. To better serve international members Ace opened its first international buying office in Hong Kong in April 2004.

In all the company added 131 new stores in 2005. That year after 33 years with the company David F. Hodnik retired as president and CEO of Ace Hardware. He was succeeded by COO Ray A. Griffith.

In 2007 Griffith sent a letter to Ace's retailers saying the company was considering changing from a cooperative to a traditional corporation to become more competitive and to better fuel growth. Shortly after the company announced an accounting shortfall of about $150 million or nearly half of its equity which was uncovered while Ace prepared to convert formats. The error turned out to be an accident by a mid-level employee.

In 2009 Ace launched Aisle411 a free product-location service that can be accessed via phone similar to dialing for information. The company launched the service after learning that shoppers who were unable to find a product either left (about 20% of the time) or asked store associates for assistance (about 60%) which created a high demand for staff attention. Dedicated to pleasing its shoppers Ace was ranked "Highest in Customer Satisfaction among Home Improvement Stores" by J.D. Power and Associates in 2007 2008 and 2009.

In mid-2010 the hardware store chain became the first retailer — outside of Sears and Kmart stores — to sell Craftsman brand tools.

In January 2011 the company reorganized its international division into a stand-alone entity: Ace Hardware International Holdings. Ace Hardware owns about 78% of the newly-created entity.

In December 2012 Ace exited the paint manufacturing business with the sale of its paint manufacturing division including two paint manufacturing plants near Chicago to Valspar Corp. for about $45 million. Under the terms of the sale Valspar will continue to make and supply Ace-branded paint under a long-term supply agreement. Also it will supply a comprehensive line of Valspar-branded paints to Ace retail stores.

EXECUTIVES

President And Ceo, John S. Venhuizen, age 50
Vp Information Technology And Cio, Karen Fedyszyn
Evp Cfo And Chief Risk Officer, Bill Guzik
Vice President Merchandising, Frank Carroll
Associate Vice President, James Mallaney
Svp Of Marketing, Brian Wyborg
Vice President, Carolyn Scherbarth
Vice President International Finance, Edward Dentzman
Vice President, Bruce Paris
Vice President Advertising Marketing And Company, Michael Bodzewski
Vice President, David Murch
Vice President Of Information Technology, Alan Sommer
Vice President, Dale Ganz
Vice President Information Technology, Brian Huesers
Vp Retail Operations And New Business, John Tovar
Svp And Chief Marketing Officer, Kim Lefko
Vice President Of Merchandising, John Sommers
Vice President Secretary, Tim Novac
Vice President Information Technology, William Smith
Vice President, Michael Upchurch

Vice President, Sue Stepler
Vice President, Maxine Parker
Vice President, Lynn Duke-jednet
Gm Vp, Rodney Persons
Vice President, Kirsti Kimball
Vice President, Ralph Viola
Vice President, Ed Dinaro
Vice President, Frank Nelson
Executive Vice President, Joanne Laskowski
Vice President, Everett Spear
Vice President, Dan Bolthouse
Vice President, Troy Rex
Vice President, Gregory Korte
Vice President, David Korte
Vice President, David Lozon
Vice President, Harold Crump
Vice President, Tami Dosch
Vice President, Joseph Bennis
Vice President, Donna Sims
Vice President, Paul Childress
Vice President, Steven Korte
Vice President, Pennie Martin
Vice President, Todd Steadman
Vice President, Don Cergizan
Vice President, Loren Schemper
Vice President, John Kay
Chairman, Jim Ackroyd
Assistant Treasurer, Petrina Rauzi
Secretary, Kenneth Easton
Treasurer, Jennifer Kelly
Secretary Treasurer, Judy Touchtone
Secretary, Peggy Steadman
Secretary Treasurer, Elsie Weir
Treasurer, Kay Stokes
Sec Treas, Vickie Murray
Secretary Treasurer, Corrine Mathis
Sec Treas, Teresa Smith
Sec Treas, Michele Peterson
Secretary Treasurer, Clarienda Abbott
Secretary, Juanita Spradlin
Secretary, Thomas Bacon
Secretary, Frances Alam
Sec Treas, Richard Pryde
Secretary, Helen Napp
Secretary, Kathy Ward
Secretary, Brandon Baynes
Secretary, Yvonne Schemper
Secretary Treasurer, Eugene Stephenitch
Secretary, Jeanne Halleman
Auditors: ERNST & YOUNG LLP CHICAGO IL

LOCATIONS

HQ: ACE HARDWARE CORPORATION
2200 KENSINGTON CT, OAK BROOK, IL 605232100
Phone: 630 368-3393
Web: WWW.ACEHARDWARE.COM

PRODUCTS/OPERATIONS

2014 Sales

	$ mil.	% of total
Wholesale Revenues	4,466	95
Retail Revenues	233	5
Total	**4,700**	**100**

Selected Services

Assembly
Automotive chip key cutting
Blade sharpening
Glass & Acrylic sheet cutting
Glass Repair
Hunting/Fishing license
In-store lock servicing

Selected Brands

ACCO BRANDS
ACE
ACME
ADANAC
BIG BENBIL
COEUREKA
EVEREADY

COMPETITORS

84 Lumber
Akzo Nobel
BMC Stock
Costco Wholesale
Do it Best
Fastenal
Grossman's
Home Depot
Kmart
Lowe's
McCoy Corp.
Menard
Northern Tool
Orgill
Sutherland Lumber
True Value
United Hardware Distributing
Wal-Mart

HISTORICAL FINANCIALS

Company Type: Private

Income Statement — FYE: December 29

	REVENUE ($ mil.)	NET INCOME ($ mil.)	NET PROFIT MARGIN	EMPLOYEES
12/18	5,717	128	2.2%	4,500
12/17	5,388	147	2.7%	—
12/16*	5,125	161	3.1%	—
01/16	5,045	156	3.1%	—
Annual Growth	4.3%	(6.4%)	—	—

*Fiscal year change

2018 Year-End Financials

Return on assets: 6.2%
Return on equity: 22.6%
Current ratio: 1.40
Cash ($ mil.): 25

ADVANCED TECHNOLOGY INTERNATIONAL

EXECUTIVES

Ceo, Chris Van Metre
Treas*, Julia Martin
Prin*, Caitlin Kunkle
Senior Contracts Administrator, Amanda Ballou
Scientist, Gerry Graves
Purchasing Administrator, Dee Green
Senior Project Manager, Jenny Swygert
Vlc Chief Administrative Offic, Morgan Odonnell
Technical Director Advanced Te, Nick Melillo
Senior Program Manager, Dick Tiano
Senior Program Manager, Jim Welborn
Auditors: BDO USA LLP RALEIGH NC

LOCATIONS

HQ: ADVANCED TECHNOLOGY INTERNATIONAL
315 SIGMA DR, SUMMERVILLE, SC 294867790
Phone: 843 760-4500
Web: WWW.ATI.ORG

HISTORICAL FINANCIALS

Company Type: Private

Income Statement — FYE: September 30

	REVENUE ($ mil.)	NET INCOME ($ mil.)	NET PROFIT MARGIN	EMPLOYEES
09/19	2,086	7	0.3%	117
09/18	1,190	0	0.1%	—
09/17*	718	(11)	—	—
06/16	423	(2)	—	—
Annual Growth	70.2%	—	—	—

*Fiscal year change

2019 Year-End Financials

Return on assets: 0.8%
Return on equity: 50.9%
Current ratio: 1.00
Cash ($ mil.): 554

ADVENTIST HEALTH SYSTEM SUNBELT HEALTHCARE CORPORATION

EXECUTIVES

Pres-Ceo, Terry Shaw
Cfo, Paul Rathdun
Asst SEC, Louis Mark Block
Coordinator, Pennie Moore
Regional Laboratory Administra, Dhobie Wong
Information Security, Teresa Majors
Admin Director Strategic Plann, Belinda Grant
Podiatrist, Tara Fussell
Administrator, Adnan Chowdhury
Erp It Security Analyst, Aubrey Alleyne
Senior Telecommunications Anal, Becky Beranek
Auditors: ERNST & YOUNG LLP ORLANDO FL

LOCATIONS

HQ: ADVENTIST HEALTH SYSTEM SUNBELT HEALTHCARE CORPORATION
900 HOPE WAY, ALTAMONTE SPRINGS, FL 327141502
Phone: 407 357-1000
Web: WWW.ADVENTHEALTH.COM

HISTORICAL FINANCIALS

Company Type: Private

Income Statement — FYE: December 31

	REVENUE ($ mil.)	NET INCOME ($ mil.)	NET PROFIT MARGIN	EMPLOYEES
12/18	10,974	635	5.8%	78,000
12/17	10,083	1,167	11.6%	—
12/16	9,651	806	8.4%	—
12/14	519	26	5.1%	—
Annual Growth	114.4%	121.7%	—	—

2018 Year-End Financials

Return on assets: 4.0%
Return on equity: 6.2%
Current ratio: 3.60
Cash ($ mil.): 576

ADVENTIST HEALTH SYSTEM/SUNBELT, INC.

Adventist Health System/Sunbelt one of the country's largest faith-based hospital systems runs about 45 hospitals 15 nursing homes 25 home health care agencies and approximately 40 Centra Care-branded urgent care centers in about 10 states (mostly in the Southeast). The not-for-profit system's acute care hospitals have some 8100 beds combined; its long-term care facilities offer around

1900 beds. The company's Florida division includes about two dozen hospitals as well as home health agencies and nursing homes. Adventist Health is sponsored by the Seventh-Day Adventist Church as part of that denomination's legacy of providing health care.

Geographic Reach

Adventist Health operates in 10 states: Colorado Florida Georgia Illinois Kansas Kentucky North Carolina Tennessee Texas and Wisconsin. Its largest market is Orlando.

Strategy

Adventist Health strives to provide "whole person" care combining medical spiritual and social services to its communities. The system has launched a number of initiatives to help it meet federal standards as the US government encourages hospital systems to improve health care quality safety and expenses. Among the new types of offerings it has embraced are telemetry monitoring of at-risk patients and art therapy for cancer patients.

Adventist improves its existing facilities through expansion and renovation projects. In 2018 the company broke ground on a new 76-bed patient tower at its Florida Hospital Celebration Health facility. The previous year it completed the $3.2 million renovation of its cancer unit at the Florida Hospital for Children in Orlando.

Furthermore the company increases its already hefty size through acquisitions and through affiliation agreements (particularly in markets where it doesn't have a major presence). For example in mid-2018 the company acquired Munroe Regional Medical Center in West Florida adding more than 400 beds to its portfolio. Earlier that year it acquired Bayfront Health Dade City Hospital from Community Health Systems; it renamed the hospital Florida Hospital Dade City. In Texas Adventist Health partners with St. David's Healthcare at Adventist Health's Central Texas Medical Center and the system has a separate agreement with Scott & White Healthcare to grow medical services at Adventist Health's Metroplex Health System. Adventist is also partnering with Texas Health Resources to build a $150 million hospital campus in Mansfield Texas.

Mergers and Acquisitions

Adventist Health adds to its portfolio through regular acquisitions. In mid-2018 the company acquired Munroe Regional Medical Center in West Florida adding more than 400 beds to its holdings. Earlier that year it acquired Bayfront Health Dade City Hospital from Community Health Systems; it renamed that hospital Florida Hospital Dade City.

EXECUTIVES

Senior Vice President, Jeffrey Bromme
Cio And Director, Brent G. Snyder
President And Ceo Mid-america Region; President And Ceo Shawnee Mission Medical Center, Samuel H. (Sam) Turner
Executive Vice President President/ceo Multi-state Division, Richard K. (Rich) Reiner
Executive Vice President President/ceo Florida Division, Lars D. Houmann
Evp Florida Division; Evp Florida Hospital, Des D. Cummings
President And Ceo Appalachia Region; President And Ceo Park Ridge Hospital, Jimm A. Bunch
Evp Florida Division; President And Ceo Florida Region, Michael H. Schultz
President And Ceo Metroplex Health System, Carlyle Walton
President Ceo, Kenneth A. (Ken) Finch
President And Ceo Takoma Regional Hospital, Daniel Wolcott
President And Ceo Midwest Region; President And Ceo Adventist Midwest Health, David L. Crane
Cfo, David W. Evans
Chief Technology Officer, Michael Emmons
Vice President And Chief Nursing Officer, Ellen Lenkevich
Medical Director, Steven Dukes
Vice President Marketing And Brand Strategy, Kevin Edgerton
Vice President Managed Care, John Brownlow
Senior Vice President Chief Strategy Officer Florida Hospital, Josef Ghosn
I:iadvenlist Vice President Medical Mission, Ted Hamilton
Senior Vice President And Chief Clinical Officer, Carlene Jamerson
Assistant Vice President Materiel Management, Lowell Church
Assistant Vice President, Harry Janke
Vice President Facilities And Construction, Jody Barry
Senior Vice President, Mark Martin
Vice President Of Population Health And Care Innovation Information Technology Solutions, Jennifer Jackson
Vice President, Russ Weaver
Vice President Of Regional Operations, Cary Smith
Director Of Nursing, Angela Jacobson
Vice President Finance And Chief Officer, Andrew Jahn
Associate Vice President Of Human Resources, Jeni Hasselbrac
Vice President Of Treasury, Jeff Graff
Corporate Vice President And Chief Information Officer, Alan Soderblom
Assistant Vice President Public Relations, Jacobs Lanell
Physical Therapy Director, RAY OWENS
Head Nurse, Madelyn Smith
Medical Records Director, KEVIN CARPENTER
Dir Of Home Healthcare Srv, CHRISTINA HARWOOD
Medical Director, Pamela Huang
Vpres, Ryan Small
Medical Director, Dipti Mehta
Vp Operations, Kathy Roberts
Director Of Nursing, Janet Redhi
Health Care Director, Richelle Cheek
Health Care Director, Beth Rowe
Director Of Radiology, John Mckissack
Operating Room Dir, Carolyn Hopper
Vice President, Pamela Hodges
Auditors: ERNEST & YOUNG LLP ORLANDO

LOCATIONS

HQ: ADVENTIST HEALTH SYSTEM/SUNBELT, INC.
900 HOPE WAY, ALTAMONTE SPRINGS, FL 327141502
Phone: 407 357-1000
Web: WWW.ADVENTISTHEALTHSYSTEM.COM

Selected Facilities

Colorado
Avista Adventist Hospital (Louisville)
Littleton Adventist Hospital
Parker Adventist Hospital
Porter Adventist Hospital (Denver)

Florida
Florida Hospital Altamonte (Altamonte Springs)
Florida Hospital Apopka
Florida Hospital Carrollwood (Tampa)
Florida Hospital Celebration Health (Celebration)
Florida Hospital DeLand
Florida Hospital East Orlando
Florida Hospital Fish Memorial (Orange City)
Florida Hospital Flagler (Palm Coast)
Florida Hospital Heartland Medical Center (Sebring)
Florida Hospital Kissimmee
Florida Hospital Lake Placid
Florida Hospital Memorial Medical Center (Daytona Beach)
Florida Hospital North Pinellas (Tarpon Springs)
Florida Hospital Oceanside (Ormond Beach)
Florida Hospital Orlando
Florida Hospital Pepin Heart Institute (Tampa)
Florida Hospital Tampa
Florida Hospital Waterman (Tavares)
Florida Hospital Wauchula
Florida Hospital Winter Park Memorial Hospital
Florida Hospital Zephyrhills

Georgia
Gordon Hospital (Calhoun)
Emory-Adventist Hospital (Smyrna)

Illinois
Adventist Bolingbrook Hospital
Adventist GlenOaks Hospital (Glendale Heights)
Adventist Hinsdale Hospital
Adventist La Grange Memorial Hospital

Kansas
Shawnee Mission Medical Center

Kentucky
Manchester Memorial Hospital

North Carolina
Park Ridge Hospital (Fletcher)

Tennessee
Jellico Community Hospital
Takoma Regional Hospital (Greeneville)

Texas
Central Texas Medical Center (San Marcos)
Huguley Memorial Medical Center (Fort Worth)
Metroplex Adventist Hospital (Killeen)
Rollins Brook Community Hospital (Lampasas)

Wisconsin
Chippewa Valley Hospital (Durand)

PRODUCTS/OPERATIONS

Selected Products

Behavioral Health
Cardiovascular
Diabetes
Digestive Health
Emergency
Eye Care Center
Family Practice
Home Health/Home Care
Imaging Services
Mammography/Breast Center/Breast Care
Minimally Invasive/Robotic Surgery
Neurology
Neurosurgery
NICU
OB/Birth Care
Oncology/Cancer
Orthopedics
Outpatient Surgery
Pain Medicine
Pediatrics
Psychology
Rehab
Senior Care
Sleep Center
Stroke Care/Stroke Center
Surgery
Therapy Services
Urology
Wellness Center
Women's Services
Wound Care

COMPETITORS

Ascension Health
BayCare Health System
CHRISTUS Health
Catholic Health Initiatives
Community Health Systems
Encompass Health
HCA
Kindred Healthcare
Mount Sinai Medical Center of Florida
Orlando Health
Tenet Healthcare
Universal Health Services

HISTORICAL FINANCIALS

Company Type: Private

Income Statement				FYE: December 31
	REVENUE ($ mil.)	NET INCOME ($ mil.)	NET PROFIT MARGIN	EMPLOYEES
12/19	11,892	1,607	13.5%	46,960
12/09*	0	0	—	—
10/08	145	(8)	—	—
Annual Growth	49.2%	—	—	—

*Fiscal year change

2019 Year-End Financials

Return on assets: 8.7%
Return on equity: 13.6%
Current ratio: 3.40
Cash ($ mil.): 184

ADVENTIST HEALTH SYSTEM/WEST, CORPORATION

Not content to wait around for the advent of good health Adventist Health System/West operates about 20 hospitals in the western US. Its health care facilities sprinkled throughout California Hawaii Oregon and Washington also include more than 260 physicians' clinics. Additionally the not-for-profit organization runs more than a dozen home health care agencies and a handful of retirement centers. The system has more than 5000 physicians on staff. Adventist Health maintains strong ties to the Seventh-day Adventist Church but is independently owned. A sister organization Adventist Health System operates in the central and southern parts of the country.

Operations

Adventist Health System/West works with its own churches and those of other denominations to offer such preventive health services as medical screenings immunizations and health education. The majority of Adventist Health's acute care hospitals are concentrated in California with the rest scattered throughout Hawaii Oregon and Washington. The system's nearly 300 clinics vary from small one or two provider offices to large facilities with primary care specialty medical services dental behavioral health perinatal and other services. Other facilities include home care agencies and four retirement centers.

Annually Adventist Health System/West has more than 150000 admissions 685000 emergency department visits and 2.9 million outpatient visits.

Geographic Reach

Adventist Health System/West serve patients throughout California Hawaii and Oregon. It also has a retirement center in Washington.

Financial Performance

In fiscal 2016 Adventist Health System/west received $3.95 billion in net revenue including patient care income and other sources of income. Its operating expenses totaled $3.77 billion that year.

Strategy

Adventist Health System/West often partners with others including organizations related to the Seventh-day Adventist church to enhance and grow its health care offerings. In early 2018 for example it joined forces with another not-for-profit health system Rideout Health (which operates acute care hospital Rideout Regional Medical Center). The partners aim to improve the wellness of California's Yuba City/Marysville community by providing expanded health care services.

EXECUTIVES

Vice President, Douglas E Rebok
Vice President Clinical Effectiveness, Keith R Doram
Svp And Cfo, Jack W. Wagner
President And Ceo Southern California Region, Beth D. Zachary
President And Ceo Glendale Adventist Medical Center, Scott Reiner
President And Ceo Central California Region, Wayne Ferch
President And Ceo Northern California Region, Jeff Eller
President And Ceo Northwest Region, Joyce Newmyer
Evp And Coo, Bill Wing
Vice President Finance, Dale Northorp
Vice President, John G Raffoul
Senior Vice President, Kirby McKague
Vice President Of Finance, Carlton Jacobson
Vice President, Meredith Jobe
Corporte Director Of Pharmacy, Thomas Jacobsen
Regional Vice President Of Marketing St Helena Adventist Health, Joshua Cowan
Vice President Information Technology Operations, Harry – Janke
Assistant Vice President Corporate Compliance Officer, Kevin Longo
Vice President, Janae Bowles
Senior Vice President, Teresa M Day
Second Vice President, Rebecca Williams
Vice President, Christopher Smith
Medical Director, John Zweifler
Medical Director Employee Health Plan, Martha Miller
Vp Support Services, Hal Chilton
Vice President Of Advocacy And Public Policy, Michael Griffin
Vice President Human Resources, Don Jones
Vice President Of Treasury, Jeffrey Graff
Vice President Finance, Ryan Ashlock
Vice President System Controller, Jay Lipps
Secretary, Kirk Iverson
Secretary, Joan Rusche
Treasurer, Brandon Seibold

LOCATIONS

HQ: ADVENTIST HEALTH SYSTEM/WEST, CORPORATION
1 ADVENTIST HEALTH WAY, ROSEVILLE, CA 956613266
Phone: 844 574-5686
Web: WWW.ADVENTISTHEALTH.ORG

COMPETITORS

Community Health Systems
Dignity Health
HCA
Hawai'i Pacific Health
John Muir Health
Kuakini Health System
Legacy Health System
LifePoint Health
Memorial Health Services
Providence St. Joseph Health
Queen's Medical Center
Shasta Regional Medical Center
Sisters of Charity of Leavenworth
Stanford Health Care
Sutter Health
Tenet Healthcare
UCSF Medical

HISTORICAL FINANCIALS

Company Type: Private

Income Statement				FYE: December 31
	REVENUE ($ mil.)	NET INCOME ($ mil.)	NET PROFIT MARGIN	EMPLOYEES
12/18	4,434	544	12.3%	19,512
12/17	4,114	199	4.9%	—
12/16	3,945	185	4.7%	—
12/15	251	10	4.3%	—
Annual Growth	160.3%	267.8%	—	—

2018 Year-End Financials

Return on assets: 9.4%
Return on equity: 19.3%
Current ratio: 2.90
Cash ($ mil.): 700

ADVENTIST HEALTHCARE, INC.

From the newest newborn to the most senior senior Adventist HealthCare takes care of residents in the Washington DC region. The not-for-profit system with more than 1880 physicians and medical providers is home to four acute care hospitals and about 446000 outpatient visits. Its acute care hospitals are Adventist HealthCare Shady Grove Medical Center and Adventist Rehabilitation. Adventist HealthCare which is affiliated with the Seventh-day Adventist Church has been in operation since 1907.

Operations

Adventist HealthCare's Lourie Center for Children's Social & Emotional Wellness promotes the emotional health of parent-child relations through education training research early prevention and intervention. Its offerings include an early head start program to benefit low-income families parent-child programs a therapeutic nursery. The company operates mental health services home health agencies physician networks urgent care centers and imaging centers.

The system has about 161000 emergency visits about 446600 outpatient visits and delivers some 6500 babies a year.

Geographic Reach

Adventist HealthCare operates facilities in Maryland and Washington DC. Its headquarters is located in Gaithersburg Maryland.

Strategy

Adventist HealthCare is dedicated to being the safest place to receive care and to deliver superior clinical outcomes. It recently unveiled plans to create a health destination in southern Prince George's County that will offer comprehensive specialty and preventative care services. The Harbor expansion aligns with Adventist's strategy to provide quality compassionate care throughout the metropolitan area. The health destination will serve as a link between nearby Adventist HealthCare Fort Washington Medical Center and its new primary care facility minutes away from the hospital. Together the facilities will provide critical services that are essential to meeting the healthcare needs of the community.

Adventist HealthCare also recently opened a new outpatient clinic in the White Oak Medical Pavilion in late 2020. Expanding its integrated multi-specialty rehabilitation services further fulfills the organization's commitment to providing innovative and compassionate care to help patients in the local community return to the life they want to live.

The system is moving its Washington Adventist Hospital to an integrated campus currently under construction in White Oak Maryland. The new campus opened in 2019 and features 180 private patient rooms. It was renamed Adventist HealthCare White Oak Medical Center.

In addition Adventist HealthCare Shady Grove Medical Center became one of the first hospitals in Maryland to perform spine surgery using the Mazor X Robotics Guidance Platform in early 2019. The tool brought surgeons new capabilities when treating patients with debilitating spine conditions.

Adventist HealthCare Home Health Services also expanded its in-home healthcare services to residents of Frederick County Maryland in early 2019. The expansion was another step toward Adventist Home Health's vision of broadening its service area to more residents in its region.

Company Background

In 1907 Washington Sanitarium opens in Takoma Park later to become Washington Adventist Hospital.

EXECUTIVES

President Adventist Healthcare Behavioral Health And Wellness Services, Kevin Young
President And Ceo, Terry Forde
Evp And Coo; President Adventist Healthcare Shady Grove Medical Center, John Sackett
Evp And Cfo, James G. Lee
Vp Public Relations And Marketing, Thomas Grant
Vp And Cio, Christopher Ghion
President Adventist Healthcare Washington Adventist Hospital, Erik Wangsness
Svp Physician Integration Strategy; President Adventist Medical Group, Patrick Garrett
Senior Vice President And Chief Human Resources Officer, Marta Perez
Vice President, Kristen Pulio
Radiology Director, Mike Calhoun
Vice President Of Operations, David Smith
Vice President And Chief Medical Officer, Kevin Smothers
Vice President Mission And Spiritual Care, Ann Roda
Director Of Clinical Services, Jason Martin
Senior Vp, Marta Brito Perez
Trustee, David E. Weigley
Vice Chairman, Robert T. Vandeman
Secretary Ii, Diane Snider
Unit Secretary, Swazenne Drew
Secretary Facilities Management, Malissa Clements
Auditors: BAKER TILLY VIRCHOW KRAUSE L

LOCATIONS

HQ: ADVENTIST HEALTHCARE, INC.
820 W DIAMOND AVE STE 600, GAITHERSBURG, MD 208781469
Phone: 301 315-3030
Web: WWW.ADVENTISTHEALTHCARE.COM

PRODUCTS/OPERATIONS

Selected Home Health Services

Nursing and Home Health
- Adult nursing
- Diabetes management
- Maternal/child care
- Nutrition management
- Pediatric nursing
- Personal care
- Pre- and post-op care
- Rehabilitation
- Wound care

Home Assistance
- Laundry and linens
- Light housekeeping
- Meal preparation
- Medication reminders
- Personal care

COMPETITORS

Bon Secours Health
Calvert Memorial Hospital
Dimensions Healthcare
Frederick Memorial
GBMC
Johns Hopkins Health System
MedStar Health
Trinity Health (Novi)
University of Maryland Medical System

HISTORICAL FINANCIALS

Company Type: Private

Income Statement — FYE: December 31

	REVENUE ($ mil.)	NET INCOME ($ mil.)	NET PROFIT MARGIN	EMPLOYEES
12/19	862	32	3.8%	5,236
12/18	820	21	2.6%	—
12/17	723	31	4.4%	—
12/16	779	0	0.1%	—
Annual Growth	3.4%	250.9%	—	—

2019 Year-End Financials

Return on assets: 2.4%
Return on equity: 6.9%
Current ratio: 1.90
Cash ($ mil.): 25

ADVOCATE HEALTH AND HOSPITALS CORPORATION

EXECUTIVES

Pres, James H Skogsbergh
Vp, Patricia Smith-Calascibetta
Director of Professional Devel, Linda Plewniak
Social Worker, Alberto Godinez
Supervisor, Damir Radisic
Rn, Elizabeth Wilson
Director, Jeremiah Stevens
Family Practitioner, Jignasa Puri
Coordinator Perioperative Mate, Paul Cnor
Director, Faheem Uraizee
Human Resource Coordinator Adv, Jessica Olague
Auditors: ERNST & YOUNG US LLP CHICAGO

LOCATIONS

HQ: ADVOCATE HEALTH AND HOSPITALS CORPORATION
3075 HIGHLAND PKWY, DOWNERS GROVE, IL 605151288
Phone: 630 572-9393
Web: WWW.ADVOCATEGIVING.ORG

HISTORICAL FINANCIALS

Company Type: Private

Income Statement — FYE: December 31

	REVENUE ($ mil.)	NET INCOME ($ mil.)	NET PROFIT MARGIN	EMPLOYEES
12/17	5,310	243	4.6%	4,110
12/13	4,072	392	9.6%	—
12/12	3,645	419	11.5%	—
12/01	2,014	114	5.7%	—
Annual Growth	6.2%	4.8%	—	—

2017 Year-End Financials

Return on assets: 2.9%
Return on equity: 4.8%
Current ratio: 0.50
Cash ($ mil.): 229

ADVOCATE HEALTH AND HOSPITALS CORPORATION

Advocate Lutheran General Hospital also known simply as Lutheran General provides acute and long-term medical and surgical care to the residents of Park Ridge Illinois and the surrounding northern suburban Chicago area. As one of the largest hospitals in the region Lutheran General boasts nearly 640 beds and a Level I trauma center. Its operations also include a complete children's hospital and pediatric critical care center. Lutheran General serves as a teaching hospital and its specialized programs include oncology cardiology women's health emergency medicine and hospice care. Lutheran General is part of the Advocate Health Care network.

Operations

Lutheran General the sixth largest hospital in the Chicago area is a not-for-profit faith-based organization related to the Evangelical Lutheran Church in America and the United Church of Christ. With some 1150 physicians representing more than 50 specialties and subspecialties Advocate Lutheran General saw 62500 patients in its emergency department in 2012.

That year the company reported more than 29000 admissions 19000 surgeries and more than 4000 births.

Geographic Reach

The hospital system is the primary academic referral hospital for northwest Chicago and north Greater Chicago.

Strategy

Increase its services to meet specific demographics in 2012 Lutheran General opened a new South Asian Cardiovascular Center in the Midwest; it also launched Expressions a program aimed at helping seniors in the early stages of Alzheimer's disease.

That year thee hospital introduced a new Pet Therapy program to the Adult Oncology unit. It also launched of its neuroendovascular program to expand Lutheran General's acute stroke care to provide advanced acute stroke care to patients throughout the northern Chicago area.

Company Background

Lutheran General serves those who live in the northern suburban Chicago area specifically Park Ridge Illinois.

The hospital was founded in 1897.

EXECUTIVES

Medical Director, Clifford Spanierman
Secretary, Lily DeLaCruz
Secretary Communications, Hazel Ferrin
Secretary, Silvia De La Roca

LOCATIONS

HQ: ADVOCATE HEALTH AND HOSPITALS CORPORATION
1775 DEMPSTER ST, PARK RIDGE, IL 600681143
Phone: 847 723-6610
Web: WWW.ADVOCATECHILDRENSHOSPITAL.COM

Selected Hospitals

Advocate BroMenn Medical Center
Advocate Children's Hospital - Oak Lawn
Advocate Children's Hospital - Park Ridge
Advocate Christ Center for Breast Care
Advocate Christ Medical Center
Advocate Christ Medical Center - Physical Rehabilitation Center Center for Hearing and Sleep Center
Advocate Christ Outpatient Center

Advocate C

Advocate Condell Medical Center
Advocate Eureka Hospital
Advocate Good Samaritan Hospital
Advocate Good Shepherd Hospital
Advocate Illinois Masonic Medical Center
Advocate Lutheran General Hospital
Advocate South Suburban Hospital
Advocate Trinity Hospital

PRODUCTS/OPERATIONS

Selected Services

Adult Day Hospital
Adult Down Syndrome Center
Anticoagulation Center
Behavioral Health
Caldwell Breast Center
Cancer Care
Center for Fetal Care
Children's Services
The Comprehensive Continence Center
Emergency Services
Heart and Vascular
Hyperbaric Treatment
Interventional Radiology
Joint Reconstruction & Replacement
Nutrition Services Opthamology
Outpatient Testing Prep Instructions
Pain Management Center
Rehabilitation
Senior Services
Sleep Disorders
Surgical Services
The Center for Robotic Surgery
Women's Services
Wound Care

COMPETITORS

Children's Hopsital of Chicago
Gottleib Memorial Hospital
NorthShore University HealthSystem
Northwest Community Healthcare
Northwestern Lake Forest Hospital
Northwestern Memorial HealthCare
Rush System for Health
University of Chicago Medical Center

HISTORICAL FINANCIALS

Company Type: Private

Income Statement — FYE: December 31

	REVENUE ($ mil.)	NET INCOME ($ mil.)	NET PROFIT MARGIN	EMPLOYEES
12/17	790	79	10.0%	4,818
12/16	785	118	15.1%	—
12/15	752	104	13.9%	—
12/14	741	107	14.5%	—
Annual Growth	2.1%	(9.6%)	—	—

2017 Year-End Financials

Return on assets: 0.9%
Return on equity: 1.6%
Current ratio: 1.00
Cash ($ mil.): 229

ADVOCATE HEALTH CARE NETWORK

EXECUTIVES

Evp And Chief Medical Officer; President Advocate Physician Partners, Lee B. Sacks
Svp Cfo Treasurer, Dominic J. Nakis
President Advocate South Suburban Hospital, Ann Errichetti
President Advocate Good Shepherd Hospital, Karen A. Lambert
President Advocate Home Health Services, Denise M. Keefe
President Advocate Physician Partners, Martin F. (Marty) Manning
President Advocate Medical Group, James R. Dan
President Recognized Associates, John Bruss
Svp And Chief Marketing Officer, Kelly Jo Golson
President Dreyer Clinic, Donna Copper
President Acl Laboratories, Barbara Bigler
Coo, Dana Gilbert
Vice President Support Operations, Laura Neiberg
Vice President Advocate Operating System, Alex Andrade
Vice President Corporate Is Physician Services, John Norenberg
Vice President Of Clinical Effectiveness, Debra Oconnor
Vice President Clinical Information, Anupam Goel
Vice President Operations, Joe Skvara
Vice President Of Medical Management, Richard Multack
Medical Director, Martin Doot
Vice President Public Affairs, Lisa Lesniak
Vice President Comm Health Faith Outreach, Bonnie Condon
Svp Coordinator Public Affairs Marketing, Sarah Scroggins
Medical Director Of Women And Childrens Services, Julie Ms
Director Of Pharmacy, Sheila Grasso
Vp Associate General Counsel, Perry Kusakabe
Medical Director Cardiac Mri, Nayla Chaptini
Vice President Revenue Cycle, Dave Szandzik
Vice President Security Services, Deborah Somers Larney
Vice President Human Resources, Kristin Landini
Vice President Dio, William Werner
Manager Government Relations, Shauna Mccarthy
Secretary Iii, Schmeski Cathy
Secretary I, Madelyn Correa
Vice Chair Department Of Emergency Medicine Advocate Christ Medical Center, Mila Felder
Secretary Iii, Denise Turner-stewart
Auditors: ERNST & YOUNG LLP CHICAGO IL

LOCATIONS

HQ: ADVOCATE HEALTH CARE NETWORK
3075 HIGHLAND PKWY FL 6, DOWNERS GROVE, IL 605155563
Phone: 630 572-9393
Web: WWW.ADVOCATEHEALTH.COM

PRODUCTS/OPERATIONS

Selected Locations

Advocate BroMenn Medical Center (Normal Illinois) - 221 beds
Advocate Christ Medical Center (Oak Lawn Illinois) - 695 beds
Advocate Condell Medical Center (Libertyville Illinois) - 281 beds
Advocate Good Samaritan Hospital (Downers Grove Illinois) -340 beds
Advocate Eureka Hospital (Eureka Illinois)- 25 beds
Advocate Good Shepherd Hospital (Barrington Illinois) - 183 beds
AdvoAdvocate Hope Children's Hospital (Oak Lawn Illinois)
Advocate Illinois Masonic Medical Center (Chicago Illinois) -408 beds
Advocate Lutheran General Hospital (Park Ridge Illinois) - 639 beds
Advocate Sherman Hospital (ElginIllinois)- 225 beds
Advocate South Suburban Hospital (Hazel Crest Illinois) - 284 beds
Advocate Trinity Hospital (Chicago Illinois) - 250 beds

COMPETITORS

Alexian Brothers Health System
Central DuPage Hospital
Children's Hopsital of Chicago
Covenant Ministries
Elmhurst Memorial Healthcare
Gottleib Memorial Hospital
HCA
Hospital Sisters Health System
KishHealth
Loyola University Health System
Mercy Hospital and Medical Center
NorthShore University HealthSystem
Northwest Community Healthcare
Northwestern Lake Forest Hospital
Northwestern Memorial HealthCare
Pronger Smith
Rush System for Health
SSM Health Care
Silver Cross Hospital
Sinai Health System
University of Chicago Medical Center

HISTORICAL FINANCIALS

Company Type: Private

Income Statement — FYE: December 31

	REVENUE ($ mil.)	NET INCOME ($ mil.)	NET PROFIT MARGIN	EMPLOYEES
12/15	5,392	60	1.1%	25,000
12/06	3,268	286	8.8%	—
12/05	2,973	140	4.7%	—
12/04	2,779	143	5.2%	—
Annual Growth	6.2%	(7.6%)	—	—

2015 Year-End Financials

Return on assets: 0.6%
Return on equity: 1.1%
Current ratio: 0.90
Cash ($ mil.): 203

AEROTEK, INC.

Aerotek a unit of staffing powerhouse Allegis Group offers commercial and technical staffing services throughout North America Europe and Asia Pacific. Through several divisions Aerotek staffs workers such as engineers mechanics scientists and technical professionals as well as administrative staff members general laborers and tradespeople. The company also provides training and support services. Along with aerospace auto and engineering companies Aerotek's clients include companies from the construction energy manufacturing health care and finance industries.

Operations

Aerotek solutions include staffing services workforce management engineering support and government services. Its staffing services provide short-term

Aerotek solutions include staffing services sciences support workforce management engineering support government services and managed resources. Its staffing services provide short-term seasonal high-volume and niche contract support. It also offers contract-to-hire talent for project-based positions with the option to hire contractors as permanent employees.

Workforce management services comprise customized support for complex projects and business lines with specific timelines. Sciences support includes clinical and lab services across a range of industries through various delivery models. Aerotek also provides support and services to the government and government subcontractors with capabilities focused on contracts security compliance business development program management and finance.

seasonal high-volume and niche contract support. It also offers contract-to-hire talent for project-based positions with the option to hire contractors as permanent employees.

Workforce management services comprise customized support for complex projects and business lines with specific timelines. Sciences support includes clinical and lab services across a range of industries through various delivery models. Aerotek also provides support and services to the government and government subcontractors with capabilities focused on contracts security compliance business development program management and finance.

Geographic Reach

Aerotek is headquartered in Hanover MD. The company has office locations in Asia Pacific (Australia Hong Kong China and Japan) Europe (Belgium France Germany Netherlands Sweden Switzerland and UK) and North America (Canada and the US). Aerotek also operates a network of more than 250 non-franchised offices.

Sales and Marketing

Aerotek serves a wide variety of industries approximately 20000 clients and more than 300000 contract employees every year.

The company serves a wide variety of industries including accounting administrative & support services aerospace aviation & defense architecture & design automotive construction customer service energy & utilities engineering environmental financial services government & public administration healthcare manufacturing pharmaceutical sciences and warehouse & distribution.

Strategy

Aerotek realigned its business operations into three specialized business units. The business units reflect Aerotek's core areas of expertise ? Engineering & Sciences Industrial and Professional ? and led by dedicated leadership teams. Aerotek's business units also include its companies Aston Carter and EASi.

Company Background

Aerotek was founded in 1983 in Baltimore MD by entrepreneurs Steve Bisciotti and Jim Davis. It got its start by providing engineering staffing for the aerospace and defense industries and later for automotive manufacturers and suppliers. In 1990 the company formed Telecommunications Services now known as TEKsystems which has been recognized as the top information technology staffing firm in the US by the IT Services Business Report.

In 1993 Aerotek acquired Onsite Engineering & Management focused on environmental and energy services staffing. It later branched out to include staffing for other industries including biotechnology pharmaceuticals healthcare light industrial and light technical. It opened its first European office in 1993 and two years later expanded into Canada with an office in Mississauga Ontario.

In 1998 Allegis Group was formed as the parent entity of several operating companies including Aerotek TEKsystems and Onsite. In 2001 Aerotek and Onsite merged to become Onsite Companies and in 2004 Onsite Companies changed its name to Aerotek Inc. to leverage the reputation of the Aerotek name.

EXECUTIVES

Vp Technical And Professional Services, Mark Cooper
President, Todd M. Mohr
Cfo, Thomas B. (Tom) Kelly
Svp Operations, John Flanigan
Regional Vp Northeast, John Rudy
Regional Vp Midwest, Marty Schager
Regional Vp Central, Mike Hansen
Regional Vp West, Tony Bartolucci
Regional Vp Northwest, Brooks Wells
Vp Canada, Bryan Toffey
Regional Vp Southwest, Brad Kennedy
Regional Vp Mid-atlantic, Jeff Colvin
Regional Vp Southeast, Greg Jones
Vice President Client Delivery, Vinayak Nayak
Vice President Of Finance, James Mann
Regional Vice President, Anthony Bartolucci
Auditors: PRICEWATERHOUSECOOPERS LLP B

LOCATIONS

HQ: AEROTEK, INC.
7301 PARKWAY DR, HANOVER, MD 210761159
Phone: 410 694-5100
Web: WWW.AEROTEK.COM

PRODUCTS/OPERATIONS

INDUSTRIES SERVED

Accounting
Administrative & Support Services
Aerospace Aviation & Defense
Architecture & Design
Automotive
Construction
Customer Service
Energy & Utilities
Engineering
Environmental
Financial Services
Government & Public Administration
Healthcare
Manufacturing
Pharmaceutical
Sciences
Warehouse & Distribution

COMPETITORS

AMN Healthcare
Adecco
Bryant Bureau
CDI
COMFORCE
Insight Global
Integrity Staffing
Kelly Services
Kforce
MSX International
ManpowerGroup
On Assignment
Pinnacle Staffing
Randstad Holding
Robert Half
Roth Staffing

HISTORICAL FINANCIALS

Company Type: Private

Income Statement — FYE: December 31

	REVENUE ($ mil.)	NET INCOME ($ mil.)	NET PROFIT MARGIN	EMPLOYEES
12/19	6,662	0	—	4,200
12/18	6,586	0	—	—
12/17	6,070	0	—	—
12/16	5,565	0	—	—
Annual Growth	6.2%	—	—	—

2019 Year-End Financials

Return on assets: —
Return on equity: —
Current ratio: 4.40
Cash ($ mil.): 13

AFFILIATED FOODS MIDWEST COOPERATIVE, INC.

Affiliated Foods Midwest Cooperative is a wholesale food distribution cooperative that supplies more than 800 independent grocers in some 15 states in the Midwest. From its handful of distribution centers in Kansas Nebraska and Wisconsin the co-op distributes fresh produce meats deli items baked goods dairy products and frozen foods as well as general merchandise and equipment. It distributes goods under the Shurfine brand (from Topco Associates) and IGA labels. Additionally Affiliated Foods Midwest provides marketing merchandising and warehousing support services for its members. The cooperative was formed in 1931 to make wholesale purchases for a group of retailers in Nebraska.

Geographic Reach

Norfolk Nebraska-based Affiliated Foods Midwest Cooperative has distribution centers in Norfolk Elwood Kansas and Kenosha Wisconsin. It serves customers in 15 states across the Midwest.

Financial Performance

Affiliated Foods Midwest rang up an estimated $1.6 billion in sales in fiscal 2013 (ended June).

Auditors: BKD LLP LINCOLN NEBRASKA

LOCATIONS

HQ: AFFILIATED FOODS MIDWEST COOPERATIVE, INC.
1301 W OMAHA AVE, NORFOLK, NE 687015872
Phone: 402 371-0555
Web: WWW.AFMIDWEST.COM

PRODUCTS/OPERATIONS

Selected Private-Label Brands

CharKing
ChuckWagon (pet food)
Clear Value
Cow Belle Creamery (ice cream)
Domestix (household products)
Full Circle (organic natural products)
IGA
PAWS Premium (pet products)
Shurfine
TopCare (OTC drugs health and beauty)
Valu Time
Wide Awake Coffee Co. (coffee)
World Classics Trading Company

COMPETITORS

Associated Wholesale Grocers
C&S Wholesale
Central Grocers
Certco
Dearborn Wholesale Grocers
Kroger
McLane
SUPERVALU
Wal-Mart

HISTORICAL FINANCIALS

Company Type: Private

Income Statement — FYE: June 26

	REVENUE ($ mil.)	NET INCOME ($ mil.)	NET PROFIT MARGIN	EMPLOYEES
06/15	1,527	1	0.1%	850
06/14	1,477	2	0.2%	—
06/13	1,391	2	0.2%	—
06/12	1,486	2	0.2%	—
Annual Growth	0.9%	(19.5%)	—	—

AFFILIATED FOODS, INC.

This company helps keep pantries stocked in the Texas Panhandle and elsewhere. Affiliated Foods is a leading wholesale distribution cooperative that supplies grocery stores and restaurants in about a half a dozen states including Texas New Mexico and Oklahoma. It distributes fresh produce meat and non-food products as well as dairy products and beverages through its Plains Dairy unit. Its Tri State Baking Company supplies bread and other baked goods. In addition Affiliated Foods owns a stake in private-label products supplier Western Family Foods. The company was founded in 1946 as Panhandle Associated Grocers which merged with South Plains Associated Grocers to form Affiliated Foods in 1968.

Geographic Reach

Based in Amarillo Texas Affiliated Foods supplies grocery stores and restaurants in Texas Oklahoma Kansas New Mexico Colorado Arizona and Arkansas.

Financial Performance

While privately-owned Affiliated Foods doesn't report its financial results the cooperative reported an estimated $1.5 billion in sales in fiscal 2012 (ends October).

EXECUTIVES

National Account Manager, Yolanda Davis
Vice President Of Food Service Sales, Doug Street
Executive Vice President, David Engelhaupt
Auditors: JOHNSON & SHELDON PLLC AMARI

LOCATIONS

HQ: AFFILIATED FOODS, INC.
1401 W FARMERS AVE, AMARILLO, TX 791186134
Phone: 806 372-3851
Web: WWW.AFIAMA.COM

PRODUCTS/OPERATIONS

Selected Subsidiaries

Affiliated Food Service (restaurant supply)
Plains Dairy (Amarillo Texas)
Tri-State Baking Co. (Amarillo Texas)

COMPETITORS

Affiliated Foods Midwest
Associated Wholesale Grocers
C&S Wholesale
GSC Enterprises
IGA
McLane
SUPERVALU

HISTORICAL FINANCIALS

Company Type: Private

Income Statement				FYE: September 28
	REVENUE ($ mil.)	NET INCOME ($ mil.)	NET PROFIT MARGIN	EMPLOYEES
09/19	1,450	2	0.1%	1,200
09/17*	1,421	1	0.1%	—
10/16	1,440	0	0.1%	—
09/06	1,137	0	0.0%	—
Annual Growth	1.9%	11.0%	—	—

*Fiscal year change

2019 Year-End Financials

Return on assets: 1.0%
Return on equity: 2.9%
Current ratio: 1.30
Cash ($ mil.): 8

AFJ, LLC

EXECUTIVES

Chairman, J Phillip Adams
Committee Member*, James A Baker
Committee Member*, Richard D Peterson
Commitee Member*, Andre Lortz
Contl, Robert Inkley

LOCATIONS

HQ: AFJ, LLC
1104 COUNTRY HILLS DR, OGDEN, UT 844032400
Phone: 801 624-1000

HISTORICAL FINANCIALS

Company Type: Private

Income Statement				FYE: January 31
	REVENUE ($ mil.)	NET INCOME ($ mil.)	NET PROFIT MARGIN	EMPLOYEES
01/07	661	(0)	—	735
01/06	574	(2)	—	—
01/05	401	3	0.8%	—
Annual Growth	28.4%	—	—	—

2007 Year-End Financials

Return on assets: (-0.3%)
Return on equity: (-0.6%)
Current ratio: 0.40
Cash ($ mil.): —

AG PROCESSING INC A COOPERATIVE

Soy far soy good for Ag Processing (AGP) the largest farmer-owned soybean processor in the world and roughly the fourth-largest soybean processor in the US based on capacity. It purchases and processes more than 5.5 million acres of members' soybeans per year. The farmer-owned cooperative is also a leading supplier of refined vegetable oil in the US. It procures processes markets and transports grains and grain products ranging from human food ingredients to livestock feed to renewable fuels. AGP is owned by about 180 local and regional cooperatives and represents more than 250000 farmers in 15 states throughout the US.

Operations

In addition to its soybean processing and vegetable oil refining facilities AGP operates a merchandising and trading group called Ag Products subdivided into three areas of focus: Grain Protein and Export. Ag Products Grain focuses on marketing grain for members seeking to better compete in the global grain industry. Ag Products Protein markets soybean meal and soy hulls; it also manufactures AMINOPLUS a protein that improves milk production. Ag Products Export offers international marketing of soybean meal oilseeds grains and other bulk agricultural commodities. Its main gateway to the fast growing Pacific Rim market is through a West Coast export shipping terminal in Washington state.

AGP also holds investment stakes in Masterfeeds a Canadian feed manufacturing business and in Protinal/Proagro Venezuela's largest poultry processor and one of country's largest animal feed producers.

Geographic Reach

AGP operates nine soybean processing plants including six located in Iowa. Other soybean processing plants are located in Minnesota Missouri and Nebraska. The company operates a growing ethanol plant in Nebraska to serve the renewable fuels market and soybean methyl ester plants in Iowa and Missouri. (Soy methyl ester an alternative to petroleum-based products is a byproduct that is used in everything from biodiesel to solvents.)

Financial Performance

AGP recorded its fourth best earnings year in the company's history in fiscal 2011. Its earnings from continuing operations (before income taxes) nearly doubled from 2010. Soybean processing rebounded from the previous year partly due to more aggressive export efforts. The company's vegetable oil business had its most profitable year yet as a result of improved demand from the soy biodiesel market improved oil quality and improved plant efficiency. Its renewable fuels business (ethanol and biodiesel) started slowly but finished 2011 strong posting improved earnings over 2010.

Strategy

With evolving EPA mandates the potential is still strong for integrated biodiesel producers like AGP which led it to acquire a 60-million gallon biodiesel plant in Algona Iowa in 2011. The acquisition doubled AGP's biodiesel production capacity now totaling about 120 million gallons.

Another major component of AGP's strategy is investing in expanding upgrading and modernizing various facilities for improved capacity and efficiency. In 2011 the company initiated major upgrade and modernization projects at soy processing plants in Sergeant Bluff Iowa and Dawson Minnesota. It also undertook a multi-million dollar expansion project at its Aberdeen Washington-based export terminal as overseas shipments to Pacific Rim countries increases.

In 2012 Ag Processing merged its Masterfeeds subsidiary with the Canadian commercial feed business (Feed-Rite) of Ridley to form the second-largest feed provider in Canada Masterfeeds LP. The new entity operates 22 manufacturing plants across the Quebec Ontario and Prairie provinces. Ridley and Ag Processing each own relative shares in Masterfeeds LP.

EXECUTIVES

Group Vice President, Scott Simmelink
Senior Vice President And General Counsel, Dave Wilwerding
Senior Vice President Transportation, Greg Twist
Senior Vice President, Mark Craigmile
Senior Vice President Of Operations, Ernie Kiley
Group Vice President And Chief Operating Officer, Cal Meyer
Senior Vice President, Chris Schaffer
Senior Vice President, Mark Sandeen

LOCATIONS

HQ: AG PROCESSING INC A COOPERATIVE
12700 W DODGE RD, OMAHA, NE 681546102
Phone: 402 496-7809
Web: WWW.AGP.COM

PRODUCTS/OPERATIONS

Selected Brands

Masterfeeds

AMINOPLUS (dairy cattle feed additive)
DIRECTOR (dairy cattle feed additive)
FUSION (horse feed additive)

Proagro/Protinal

Corral (Prepared chicken products Venezuela only)

SOYGOLD (bio-diesel fuel additives herbicides solvents surfacants fuel additives)

Selected Exported Products

Barley
Corn
Distillers dried grains (DDGS)
Feeding peas
High-protein soybean meal
Lecithin
Low-protein soybean meal
Oats
Soybean hulls
Soybean oil
Soybeans
Sunflowers
Wheat

Selected Operations and Products

Animal feed
Corn processing
Corn-based ethanol
Grain processing merchandising and sales
Industrial products (ethanol and methyl esters)
Soybean processing
Soybean oil
Soybean biodiesel
Prepared chicken products (Venezuela only)

COMPETITORS

ACH Food Companies
ADM
Bunge Limited
CGB
CGC
CHS
Cargill
ConAgra
J-OIL MILLS
Land O'Lakes Purina Feed
Liberty Vegetable Oil
Luckey Farmers
Marfrig
POET
Smucker
South Dakota Soybean Processors
Spectrum Foods
West Central Co-op
Zeeland Farm

HISTORICAL FINANCIALS

Company Type: Private

Income Statement				FYE: August 31
	REVENUE ($ mil.)	NET INCOME ($ mil.)	NET PROFIT MARGIN	EMPLOYEES
08/16*	3,410	134	3.9%	1,456
12/10	3	0	1.3%	—
08/06	2,360	62	2.7%	—
Annual Growth	3.7%	7.9%	—	—

*Fiscal year change

2016 Year-End Financials

Return on assets: 9.9%
Return on equity: 15.3%
Current ratio: 2.80
Cash ($ mil.): 210

AGFIRST FARM CREDIT BANK

The expenses involved in equipping and operating a farm add up quickly which is where AgFirst Farm Credit Bank comes in. AgFirst is one of a half-dozen members of the Farm Credit System a federally chartered network of agricultural and rural lending cooperatives. Boasting $30 billion in assets the bank provides financing to 19 farmer-owned agricultural credit associations. The associations in turn offer mortgages and loans to some 80000 farmers agribusinesses and rural homeowners through 280 branches in 15 eastern states and Puerto Rico. They also offer crop insurance credit-related life insurance and financial planning services. Instead of accepting deposits AgFirst raises money by selling bonds and notes on the capital markets.

Operations

AgFirst's capital markets arm arranges participates in and sells loan syndications for agribusinesses. Its correspondent lending unit buys sells and services agricultural and rural home loans throughout the US. About 68% of the bank's loan portfolio consisted of direct notes in 2014 while purchased participations/syndications made up another 19% of loan assets. The rest of the portfolio consisted of correspondent lending (12%) and loans to OFIs (less than 1%).

The bank makes almost all of its money from interest income. About 79% of its total revenue came from loan interest in 2014 with another 18% of revenue coming from interest on investment securities and other assets. The remainder of its revenue mostly came from loan fees.

Geographic Reach

Columbia South Carolina-based AgFirst serves 15 eastern US states and Puerto Rico. Its largest markets are in Florida North Carolina Georgia Virginia and Pennsylvania. The bank is also active in Alabama Delaware the District of Columbia Kentucky Louisiana Maryland Mississippi Ohio South Carolina Tennessee West Virginia and Puerto Rico.

Financial Performance

AgFirst Farm Credit Bank has struggled to grow its annual revenues and profits over the past several years as its loan assets have not increased and as interest margins continue to be squeezed in the low-interest environment.

The bank's revenue fell 7% to $703.8 million during 2014 as its loan assets barely grew to $20.9 billion or about the same levels as they've been since 2010.

Revenue declines in 2014 coupled with a rise in insurance fund premiums and salaries caused AgFirst's net income to shrink 17% to $380.3 million for the year. The bank's operating cash levels fell sharply to $370.9 million on lower cash earnings and unfavorable working capital changes mostly related to changes in accounts receivables balances.

Strategy

AgFirst has focused on maintaining strong personal relationships with its local customer base. It's also been investing more in security-based IT investments to protect its customers from security breaches. In 2015 it built a modern Data Center to accommodate the bank's growth with 1 Petabyte of data.

Company Background

The Farm Credit System was established by Congress in 1916 to provide a reliable source of credit for US farmers and ranchers.

EXECUTIVES

Ceo, Leon T. (Timmy) Amerson
Svp And Cfo, Charl L. Butler
Svp And Cio, Benjamin F. Blakewood
Senior Vice President, David Bridges
Vice President Executive Account Manager, Michael Mancini
Vice President Capital Markets, Neda Beal
Vice President Capital Mkts, John Burnside
Vice President Human Resources, Jeffery Payne
Vice President Chief Audit Officer, William Beckham
Executive Vice President, Larry Doyle
Senior Vice President And General Counsel, Isvara Wilson
Vice President, Steven Oshea
Vice President, Katie Hane
Vice President Finance, Steve Mcclam
Vice President Of Investments And Funding, Richard Wilkins
Vice President: Marketing Customer Support Corpo, Ann Lamar Tuten
Vice Chairman, Dale R. Hershey
Chairman, Robert H. Spiers
Board Member, Robert Holden
Auditors: PRICEWATERHOUSECOOPERS LLP MI

LOCATIONS

HQ: AGFIRST FARM CREDIT BANK
1901 MAIN ST, COLUMBIA, SC 292012443
Phone: 803 799-5000
Web: WWW.AGFIRST.COM

PRODUCTS/OPERATIONS

2014 Sales

	$ mil.	% of total
Interest		
Loans	566	79
Investment securities & other	127	18
Non-interest		
Loan fees	8	2
Building lease income	3	-
Net other-than-temporary impairment losses	(1.4)	-
Gains (losses) on called debt	(7.7)	-
Gains (losses) on investments net	0	-
Gains (losses) on other transactions	0	-
Other	7	1
Total	703	100

COMPETITORS

AgriBank
Bank of America
COUNTRY Financial
Cat Financial
Farm Family Holdings
First National of Nebraska
Rabo AgriFinance

HISTORICAL FINANCIALS

Company Type: Private

Income Statement				FYE: December 31
	ASSETS ($ mil.)	NET INCOME ($ mil.)	INCOME AS % OF ASSETS	EMPLOYEES
12/17	32,487	344	1.1%	530
12/15	30,620	336	1.1%	—
Annual Growth	3.0%	1.2%	—	—

2017 Year-End Financials

Return on assets: 1.1%
Return on equity: 15.4%
Sales ($ mil): 883

AGTEGRA COOPERATIVE

Who loves you a bushel and a peck? South Dakota Wheat Growers may; it is an agricultural co-op comprising some 6800 member-farmers. It provides a grain warehouse along with grain marketing services intended to compete with big food and ag companies. In addition to storage and drying Wheat Growers offers agronomy spreading and spraying and transportation. It supplies feed fertilizer chemicals and other farm-related provisions for members in and around counties in North and South Dakota. Wheat Growers generates more than half of its revenues through marketing some 160 million bushels of grain (corn wheat and soybeans) each year. Remaining revenues are made through agronomy and retail sales and services.

EXECUTIVES

Senior Vice President Organizational And Member Development, Judy Stulken
Vice President Safety Environmental Regulatory Affairs, William Spreeman
Auditors: GARDINER THOMSEN PC DES MOIN

LOCATIONS

HQ: AGTEGRA COOPERATIVE
908 LAMONT ST S, ABERDEEN, SD 574015515
Phone: 605 225-5500
Web: WWW.WHEATGROWERS.COM

Selected Counties of Operation

North Dakota
Dickey
LaMoure
Stutsman
South Dakota
Aurora
Beadle

Brown
Brule
Clark
Corson
Day
Edmunds
Faulk
Hand
Hyde
Jerauld
Lyman
Marshall
Sanborn
Spink

COMPETITORS

ADM
CHS
Cargill
North Central Farmers Elevator
Northern Growers

HISTORICAL FINANCIALS

Company Type: Private

Income Statement — FYE: July 31

	REVENUE ($ mil.)	NET INCOME ($ mil.)	NET PROFIT MARGIN	EMPLOYEES
07/19	1,509	(5)	—	638
07/18	1,544	32	2.1%	—
07/17	1,275	22	1.8%	—
07/16	1,209	6	0.6%	—
Annual Growth	7.7%	—	—	—

2019 Year-End Financials

Return on assets: (-0.6%)
Return on equity: (-1.7%)
Current ratio: 1.20
Cash ($ mil.): 6

AIDS HEALTHCARE FOUNDATION

EXECUTIVES

Ceo, Michael Arthur Weinstein
M.D., Chairman*, Rodney L Wright
Cfo*, Lyle Honig
Sr V Pres*, Peter Reis
Prin*, Scott Carruthers
Coordinator, Santiago Leal
Director of Contracts Administ, Charity MPA
Supply Chain Manager, David Fitzpatrick
Senior Payroll Specialist, Johnny Nguyen
Director, Robert Heglar
Georgia Regional Director, Tiffany Roan
Auditors: VASQUEZ & COMPANY LLP LOS ANG

LOCATIONS

HQ: AIDS HEALTHCARE FOUNDATION
6255 W SUNSET BLVD FL 21, LOS ANGELES, CA 900287422
Phone: 323 860-5200
Web: WWW.AIDSHEALTH.ORG

HISTORICAL FINANCIALS

Company Type: Private

Income Statement — FYE: December 31

	REVENUE ($ mil.)	NET INCOME ($ mil.)	NET PROFIT MARGIN	EMPLOYEES
12/16	1,163	40	3.5%	2,331
12/15	1,039	56	5.4%	—
12/14	879	30	3.5%	—
12/13	772	16	2.1%	—
Annual Growth	14.6%	35.2%	—	—

2016 Year-End Financials

Return on assets: 10.0%
Return on equity: 15.1%
Current ratio: 1.90
Cash ($ mil.): 63

AIR METHODS CORPORATION

It's a bird it's a plane ... it's an ambulance! With a fleet of more than 450 medically equipped aircraft mainly helicopters Air Methods is one of the largest providers of emergency medical air-transportation services in the US. The company operates through three divisions. A community-based operating company Air Methods offers transportation and in-flight medical care from hubs in some four dozen states. It also provides tourism operations around Hawaiian Islands through Blue Hawaiian Helicopters. The smallest division United Rotorcraft designs manufactures and installs aircraft medical-transport products.

Operations

The company mainly provides air medical transportation services throughout the US and designs manufactures and installs medical aircraft interiors and other aerospace and medical transport products.

Geographic Reach

The company has about 300 bases of operations that serve about 50 states in the US. It operates eight maintenance centers throughout the country and a national communications center.Air Methods' corporate headquarters is located at Greenwood Village Colorado.

Sales and Marketing

Air Methods serves healthcare tourism and aerospace industries.

Strategy

In October 2020 Air Methods announced that it has partnered with MountainStar Healthcare and will open a base in Ogden Utah in November 3 as AirLife Utah. The base will serve Ogden Regional Medical Center Cache Valley Hospital Brigham City Hospital Pleasant View Emergency Center and Lakeview Hospital and other surrounding community hospitals to provide emergency air medical services throughout northern Utah southern Idaho and southwest Wyoming.

Also in 2020 Air Methods has rebranded its Florida program in the greater Tampa Bay area as AirLife Florida. The local crews and aircraft formerly operated as Bayflite and will continue to serve the region as AirLife Florida with bases in Tampa North Port and Inverness. This rebranding went into effect in April 1.

EXECUTIVES

Ceo And Director, Aaron D. Todd, $765,000 total compensation
President Sundance Helicopters, James (Jim) Greiner
President Domestic Air Medical Services, Michael D. Allen, $459,000 total compensation
Vp Information Technology, Doni Perry
Director Operations, Dennis McCall
Evp Business Development, David M. Doerr, $408,000 total compensation
Cfo And Treasurer, Peter P. Csapo
President Tourism Division, David Doerr
Senior Vice President Patient Business Services, Mark Keene
Senior Vice President General Counsel And Secretary, Crystal L Gordon
Senior Vice President, Jonathan Collier
Senior Vice President Process Improvement, Kevin Campbell
Svp, Tina Giangrasso
V Pres Internal Audit, Beth Womersley
Vice President, David Poulsen
Vp Safety, Mark Rambis
Medical Director, Janelle Martin
Chairman, C. David Kikumoto
Auditors: KPMG LLP DENVER COLORADO

LOCATIONS

HQ: AIR METHODS CORPORATION
5500 S QUEBEC ST STE 300, GREENWOOD VILLAGE, CO 801111926
Phone: 303 792-7400
Web: WWW.AIRMETHODS.COM

PRODUCTS/OPERATIONS

2014 Sales

	$ mil.	% of total
AMS	863	85
Tourism	116	11
United Rotorcraft	36	4
Corporate Activities	86	0
Adjustments	(11.4)	-
Total	**1,004**	**100**

Fleets

Fleets
AS 350
EC 135
EC 130
Bell 407
EC 145
Bell 429
BK 117
A-109
SA 365
Bell 222
Bell 430
Bell 206
MD 902
King Air
PC 12
Agusta 119Kx

Services

AirCom
Complete Billing Solutions
DirectCall
TAMMA
United Rotorcraft
LifeShield Alliance

COMPETITORS

Acadian Ambulance Service Inc.
Bristow Group Inc
CHC Group
Evergreen Holdings
PHI Inc.

HISTORICAL FINANCIALS

Company Type: Private

Income Statement				FYE: December 31
	REVENUE ($ mil.)	NET INCOME ($ mil.)	NET PROFIT MARGIN	EMPLOYEES
12/15	1,085	109	10.1%	5,133
12/14	1,004	95	9.5%	—
12/13	881	62	7.0%	—
Annual Growth	11.0%	32.7%	—	—

2015 Year-End Financials

Return on assets: 7.0%
Return on equity: 19.0%
Current ratio: 3.20
Cash ($ mil.): 5

AIRGAS, INC.

Airgas safely and reliably provides products services and expertise to industries through its more than 18500 associates in more than 1400 locations robust e-Business platform and Airgas Total Access telesales channel. Airgas distributes argon carbon dioxide hydrogen nitrogen oxygen and a variety of specialty gases as well as welding products tools and equipment dry ice and protective equipment (hard hats goggles). The company serves more than 1 million customers in various industries. The company is owned by Air Liquide SA.

Operations

Airgas operates through five product categories: Gases Gas equipment Safety products Tools and hardware and Welding products.

Its Gases include industrial application gases such as acetylene argon and helium; medical gases such as carbon dioxide nitrogen and oxygen; and specialty gases such as gas mixtures.

Gas equipment include balloon regulators; specialty gas equipment; welding gas equipment such as torches burning bars spark lighters and flints; and gas equipment accessories such as adapters and fittings cylinder carts hoses cable reels gas containers and valves.

Safety products include barricades clothing footwear gloves fire equipment first aid and head eye and face protection.

Tools and hardware products include abrasives cutting tools industrial brushes machine tools air compressors and plant maintenance equipment.

Welding products include fluxes and powders gas welding rods wires solders welders accessories such as plasma torches and cutters and welding support equipment such as blankets curtains pads and screens.

Geographic Reach

Headquartered in Radnor Pennsylvania the Airgas' US network covers more than 900 retail locations and is present in over 1400 locations in all 50 states.

Sales and Marketing

Airgas serves customers in a range of industries including manufacturing and metal fabrication power utilities and materials construction life sciences and healthcare food beverage and retail energy and chemical production and distribution basic materials and services. It also has government defense and aerospace clients. It interacts with customers through phone online and in physical stores. The company's network includes airgas.com.

Strategy

In 2019 Airgas announced the grand opening of its new liquid carbon dioxide and dry ice facility in Stockton California. The facility which was engineered to have minimal environmental impact is a zero runoff/discharge site. Technology at the site will capture and recycle all process and rain water that comes in contact with the equipment. The plant converts gaseous carbon dioxide that would otherwise be discarded as a byproduct of ethanol manufacturing it into approximately 500 tons of liquid carbon dioxide per day. The adjoining Airgas Dry Ice facility will convert up to 250 tons per day of liquid carbon dioxide into dry ice which is used for safe transport in food and agriculture applications and a variety of life science and industrial processes.

Airgas acquired Tech Air a large independent distributor of industrial gases and welding supplies serving various geographies in the US. This transaction enables Airgas to further strengthen its network in the US with a complementary footprint to better serve customers while generating significant efficiencies. Leveraging Air Liquide's integrated model the acquisition will deliver significant efficiencies. Moreover customers will benefit from an expanded offering as well as a wider distribution network and a leading digital platform. Over the years Airgas has successfully acquired and integrated companies' operations and associates to create an industry-leading distribution network in the US serving a variety of customers safely and reliably.

Mergers and Acquisitions

In early 2019 Air Liquide announced that Airgas has completed the acquisition of TA Corporate Holdings Inc. a large independent distributor of industrial gases and welding supplies serving various geographies in the United States. This transaction enables Airgas to further strengthen its network in the United States with a complementary footprint to better serve customers while generating significant efficiencies. Terms of this transaction were not disclosed.

HISTORY

In the early 1980s Peter McCausland was a corporate attorney involved in mergers and acquisitions for Messer Griesheim a large German industrial gas producer. When the German firm declined McCausland's recommendation in 1982 to buy Connecticut Oxygen he raised money from private sources and bought it himself. He acquired other distributors and then left Messer Griesheim in 1987 to run Airgas full-time.

Airgas began buying mostly small local and regional gas distributors in the US. By 1994 strategy shifted to purchasing larger "superregional" distributors such as Jimmie Jones Co. and Post Welding Supply of Alabama which added about $70 million combined to the company's revenues.

Airgas then began "rolling up" additional similar businesses. In 1995 it bought more than 25 companies and two years later it added more than 20 gas distributors. Also in 1997 Airgas expanded its manufacturing capabilities by building five plants that could fast-fill whole pallets of gas cylinders (the old manual system rolls cylinders two at a time). By 2000 the company had about 100 cylinder fill plants.

Struggling to integrate acquisitions while dealing with softening markets Airgas began a companywide realignment in 1998. To that end it sold its calcium carbide and carbon products operations to former partner Elkem ASA later that year; the company also consolidated 34 hubs into 16 regional companies and sold its operations in Poland and Thailand to Germany-based Linde in 1999.

In 2000 Airgas acquired distributor Mallinckrodt's Puritan-Bennett division (gas products for medical uses) with 36 locations in the US and Canada. The company also acquired the majority of Air Products' US packaged gas business excluding its electronic gases and magnetic resonance imaging-related helium operations in 2002.

In 2004 and 2005 it bought units from giants like Air Products and Chemicals BOC and LaRoche Industries. In 2006 Airgas continued to build with the purchase of 10 businesses including Union Industrial Gas which supplies Texas and much of the Southwest and then Linde's US bulk gas business for $495 million the next year. Linde in the process of integrating its 2006 acquisition of BOC then sold to Airgas a portion of its US packaged gas business for $310 million.

Rival Air Products had made a major bid to buy Airgas in 2010 but was rebuffed. Air Products extended its tender offer to Airgas stockholders several times and made a "best and final offer" of $70 a share (almost $6 billion) in December 2010. Airgas said it was holding out for $78 a share and rejected that offer too. In early 2011 a Delaware judge ruled for Airgas in a suit brought by Air Products to set aside a "poison pill" defense used by the Airgas board to fend off the takeover try. Following the verdict Air Products dropped its bid.

Airgas acquired six businesses in 2010 including Tri-Tech an independent distributor with 16 locations throughout Florida Georgia and South Carolina and annual sales of $31 million.

In 2011 Airgas reorganized its 12 regional segments into four new business support divisions — North South Central and West — to leverage a new SAP information systems platform in 2011. Each of the units is headed by a division president. The new company structure is designed to accelerate sales growth and pricing management and create operating efficiencies.

In fiscal 2012 the company added eight businesses with total annual sales of about $106 million. The largest of the businesses acquired were ABCO Gases Welding and Industrial Supply Company (ABCO); Pain Enterprises; and Industrial Welding Supplies of Hattiesburg (doing business as Nordan Smith). Connecticut-based ABCO has 12 industrial and gas welding supply locations throughout New England. Indiana-based Pain operates 20 dry ice and liquid carbon dioxide production and distribution sites. Mississippi-based Nordan Smith has 17 locations that distribute industrial medical and specialty gases and supplies thoughout Alabama Arkansas and Mississippi.

In 2013 Airgas retained Chicago-based Acquity Group as a key partner in helping the company continue to provide new online digital customer platforms. As one of the leading digital marketing companies the Acquity Group will provide its e-channel expertise in leading the design and implementation of Airgas' new content-rich website.

In 2013 Airgas acquired two US-based industrial gas and welding supply distributors that complement the Airgas portfolio of products and services. Combined annual revenues for the two acquired businesses are more than $30 million.

In fiscal 2013 the company also acquired Illinois-based The Encompass Gas Group (one of the largest privately-owned suppliers of industrial medical and specialty gases and related hardgoods in the US) with about $55 million in annual revenues in 2012.

EXECUTIVES

Coo, Andrew R. (Andy) Cichocki, $296,936 total compensation

Svp Human Resources, Pamela J. (Pam) Claypool

Vice President Construction, John Appolonia

Svp Sales And Marketing, Ronald J. (Ron) Stark

Svp And Cio, Robert A. Dougherty, $263,779 total compensation
President Airgas South, John F. Sheehan
Svp And Cfo, Robert M. (Bob) McLaughlin, $470,453 total compensation
Division President Gases Production, Thomas S. Thoman
Division President West, Douglas L. (Doug) Jones
Svp And General Counsel, Robert H. Young, $397,272 total compensation
Division President Central, Terry L. Lodge
President East Region, Jack Appolonia
Ceo, Pascal Vinet
Vice President Area Sales, Ross Jones
Vice President Of Information Technology Airgas Mid South, George Turner
Vice President Central Division, Don Berndsen
Vice President Safety And Compliance, Jim McCarthy
Vice President Business Development, Bruce Woerner
Regional Vice President Healthcare, Linda Wissink
Vice President, James Cook
Regional Vice President Of Finance, Jana Bittinger
National Sales Manager, Jerry Anderskow
Vice President Finance, Monica Garza
Vice President Of Plant Operations, Roger Weber
Vice President Of Bulk Operations, Steve Scheuring
Vice President, Ted Schulte
Vice President Construction Markets, Jason Vetterick
Vice President Of Finance, Jennifer Mihaljcic
Vice President Strategic Accounts, Otto Gaus
Area Vice President, Jeff Mann
Assistant Vice President, Brian Blackwood
Assistant Vice President Corporate Development, Brian Shammo
Vice President Hardgoods, David Levin
Regional Vice President Usa East, Adam Needles
Vice President, Chris Brazell
Assistant Vice President And Corporate Controller, Jeffrey Cornwell
Division Vice President Of Sales, Mark Johnston
Vice President, Wayne Wilson
Vice President Bulk Gases, Ziba Behnam
National Account Manager, Don Wallenfelsz
Area Vice President, Gene Klein
Area Vice President, Ron Weber
National Account Manager, Victoria Ektarian
Vice President Internal Audit, E Coyne
Vice President Supply Chain Management, Ken McDowell
National Account Manager, Earl Dyck
Vice President Of Sales, Marcelo Feistauer
Vice President Gulf Coast Region, Scott Koonce
Vice President Area, Luke Aass
Vice President Bulk Sales And Operations, Thomas Archie
Vice President Credit And Collections, Ed Burke
National Account Manager, Thomas White
Area Vice President, Beth Medford
National Account Manager, Daniel Christenson
Vice President Total Access, Kerrie Sodano
Vice President Bulk Sales And Operations, Richard Cassano
Vice President Distribution And Logistics, Eric Parker
Vp Manufacturing, Jill Barth
Vice President Finance, Kyle Douglas
Vice President Of Food And Beverage, Bill Baker
Vice President Of Safety And Compliance, Chris Herbert
Division Vice President Human Resources, Stamy Paul
Svp Healthcare Life Sciences And Specialty Gases, Christophe Tardieu
Vp Safety And Compliance, Curtis Henson
Vice President Safety And Compliance North Division, Benson Scott
Executive Vice President, Steve Shupe
Chairman, Pierre Dufour
Vice Chairman, Michael J. (Mike) Graff
Auditors: KPMG LLP PHILADELPHIA PENNSY

LOCATIONS

HQ: AIRGAS, INC.
259 N RADNOR CHESTER RD # 100, RADNOR, PA 190875240
Phone: 610 687-5253
Web: WWW.AIRGAS.COM

PRODUCTS/OPERATIONS

Selected Products and Services

Products
Carbon dioxide
Dry ice
Industrial gases
Argon
Helium
Hydrogen
Liquid oxygen
Nitrogen
Nitrous oxide
Oxygen
Safety equipment
Specialty gases
Services
Container rental
Welding equipment rental

Selected Subsidiaries

Airgas Canada
Airgas Carbonic
Airgas East
Airgas Great Lakes
Airgas Intermountain
Airgas Medical Services
Airgas Mid America
Airgas Mid South
Airgas Nitrous Oxide
Airgas Nor Pac
Airgas North Central
Airgas Northern California & Nevada
Airgas Refrigerant
Airgas Safety
Airgas South
Airgas Southwest
Airgas Specialty Gases
Airgas Specialty Products
Airgas West
National Welders Supply Company dba Airgas National Welders
Nitrous Oxide Corp.
Red-D-Arc
WorldWide Welding LLC

COMPETITORS

Air Products
Lincoln Electric
Matheson Tri-Gas
Praxair Distribution
Valley National Gases
W.W. Grainger

HISTORICAL FINANCIALS

Company Type: Private

Income Statement — FYE: March 31

	REVENUE ($ mil.)	NET INCOME ($ mil.)	NET PROFIT MARGIN	EMPLOYEES
03/15	5,304	368	6.9%	17,000
03/13	4,957	340	6.9%	—
Annual Growth	3.4%	3.9%	—	—

2015 Year-End Financials

Return on assets: 6.2%
Return on equity: 17.1%
Current ratio: 1.30
Cash ($ mil.): 50

AKRON GENERAL MEDICAL CENTER INC

Akron General Medical Center the flagship hospital of Akron General Health System is a not-for-profit teaching hospital that boasts more than 530 acute care beds. The hospital serves the residents of Northeast Ohio as a regional referral center in a number of medical specialties including cardiovascular disease heart surgery cancer care women's health orthopedics sports medicine and trauma care. Akron General Medical also operates Edwin Shaw Rehab the area's only rehabilitation hospital. Edwin Shaw has 35 beds and treats patients who have experienced stroke head trauma and other critical injuries. Akron General Medical was founded in 1914 as Peoples Hospital.

Operations

Akron General is a level I trauma center and holds the county's first certified chest pain and primary stroke centers. It also offers a level III obstetric unit and it operates a freestanding outpatient surgery center. As a major teaching hospital with more than 1000 physicians as well as 3400 professional and support staff members Akron General Medical offers medical students about a dozen residency programs. It does so through its affiliations with Northeastern Ohio Medical University which serves as the medical college for University of Akron Youngstown State University and Kent State University. Residencies include those in family medicine OB-GYN psychiatry and breast cancer.

Geographic Reach

Akron General Medical Center serves communities across the counties of Summit Medina Portage Stark and Wayne located in Northeast Ohio. In addition to facilities in Akron the hospital has satellite locations in Green Stow and Tallmadge. Edwin Shaw Rehab is located in the nearby town of Cuyahoga Falls. The center serves an area with a population of some 1.2 million people.

Strategy

The hospital conducts facility and equipment upgrades to meet the needs of a growing population in Northeast Ohio. Akron General enhanced its neurosurgical capabilities in 2012 as part of the establishment of its Neurosciences Institute. The center includes new Brainlab CT and MRI imaging systems for use during minimally invasive surgical procedures. The hospital is also upgrading its heart and vascular center which was certified as a heart failure clinic in 2013. In addition Akron General is working to upgrade IT systems to improve physician and patient resources.

EXECUTIVES

Chb, F William Steere
Director, Mary Beth Carroll
Director of Nursing, Phillip G Moser
Scientist, Barbara Klimonek
Scientist, Tookie Dunnie
Executive of Information Techn, Richard J Streck
Security Staff, Chris J Voller
Information Specialist, Paul Hayslip
Coordinator, Karen Orndorf
Emergency Medicine Specialist, David Peter
Director, Lee Sahadi
Auditors: LB BLUE & CO LLC COLUMBUS OH

LOCATIONS

HQ: AKRON GENERAL MEDICAL CENTER INC
1 AKRON GENERAL AVE, AKRON, OH 443072432
Phone: 330 344-6000
Web: WWW.MY.CLEVELANDCLINIC.ORG

Selected Locations and Affiliates
Akron General Medical Center
Akron Health Center
Edwin Shaw Rehabilitation Institute
Green Health Center
Health and Wellness Centers (West North and Green)
Hospice Center
Lodi Community Hospital
Tallmadge Health Center

PRODUCTS/OPERATIONS

Selected Centers and Services

Anesthesiology

Audiology
Bariatric Surgery
Breast Health Center
Cancer Center
Community Health
Corporate Wellness
Critical Care Center
Diabetes Center
Diagnostic Services
Emergency Medicine/Level 1 Trauma Center
Endocrinology
Endoscopy
Executive Health Program
Family Medicine
Food and Nutrition Services
Gastroenterology
Health and Wellness
Heart and Vascular Center
Heartburn Center
Hyperbaric Medicine
Infectious Disease
Internal Medicine
Lab Services
Maternity Services
Nephrology
Neuroscience Institute
Nuclear Medicine
Occupational Therapy
Orthopedic Center
Osteoporosis Prevention
Pain Management
Physical Therapy
Primary Care
Psychiatry and Behavioral Sciences
Pulmonary Medicine
Radiology
Rehabilitation
Senior Services
Sleep Center
Speech and Language Pathology
Sports Medicine
Surgery
Urology
Women's Center
Wound Center

COMPETITORS

Akron Children's Hospital
Community Health Systems
OhioHealth
Regency Hospital
Sharon Regional Health System
Summa Health System
Trinity Health System
University Hospitals Health System

HISTORICAL FINANCIALS

Company Type: Private

Income Statement — FYE: December 31

	REVENUE ($ mil.)	NET INCOME ($ mil.)	NET PROFIT MARGIN	EMPLOYEES
12/14	544	47	8.7%	875
12/13	507	22	4.4%	—
12/12	486	10	2.2%	—
12/04	0	0	—	—
Annual Growth	—	—	—	—

2014 Year-End Financials

Return on assets: 10.3%
Return on equity: 35.3%
Current ratio: 0.40
Cash ($ mil.): 20

ALASKA HOUSING FINANCE CORP

EXECUTIVES

Chb, Frank Roppel
Ceo, Daniel R Fauske
Cfo, Joseph M Dubler
Coordinator, Tammie Robertson
Human Resources Director, Elaine Hodl
Accounting Staff, Joanne McClure
Rural, John Anderson
Personnel Technician, Jill Smart
Compliance Officer, Kim Coy
Planner, Andy Petroni
Senior Programmer Analyst, Colin Coker

LOCATIONS

HQ: ALASKA HOUSING FINANCE CORP
4300 BONIFACE PKWY # 130, ANCHORAGE, AK 995044387
Phone: 907 338-6100
Web: WWW.AHFC.US

HISTORICAL FINANCIALS

Company Type: Private

Income Statement — FYE: June 30

	ASSETS ($ mil.)	NET INCOME ($ mil.)	INCOME AS % OF ASSETS	EMPLOYEES
06/20	4,609	35	0.8%	152
06/19	4,322	32	0.8%	—
06/06	5,229	306	5.9%	—
06/05	4,762	(23)	—	—
Annual Growth	(0.2%)	—	—	—

2020 Year-End Financials

Return on assets: 0.8%
Return on equity: 2.2%
Sales ($ mil): 251

ALASKA NATIVE TRIBAL HEALTH CONSORTIUM

The Alaska Native Tribal Health Consortium (ANTHC) brings good health to Alaska Natives. The company is a not-for-profit statewide health care organization managed by regional tribal governments and their respective regional health organizations. The organization connects disparate medical providers by providing a range of health programs and services including community health care public health advocacy and education initiatives health research (including water and sanitation) and medical supply distribution. The 150-bed Alaska Native Medical Center (ANMC) a native-owned hospital is jointly managed by ANTHC and Southcentral Foundation a regional health corporation based in the Cook Inlet region.

Operations

ANMC's services are reserved primarily for Alaska Native Tribal groups with the exception of its Urgent Care centers and Emergency Room. (Emergency rooms are compelled to take patients of all types under US fair care guidelines.) The hospital handles about 8000 patient admissions each year as well as 300000 outpatient and 57000 emergency room visits. It also conducts some 11000 surgeries and 1600 births. ANMC has about 100 physicians.

The organization's primary mission is to improve the health of Alaska natives through health sanitation technology and advocacy services. It conducts a number of community outreach programs and it works to create a continuum of care for its members so they can move smoothly through the health care process (including initial specialist and follow-up care visits). The hospital is the regional hub of that health care continuum offering general and specialist care in a range of fields. ANTHC also operates outpatient care centers and it operates an extensive telemedicine network (allow providers to care for and consult with patients in outlying areas).

ANTHC provides administrative support to Alaska's Tribal health groups and it supports state legislative efforts such as the reauthorization of the Indian Health Care Improvement Act. The consortium formed in 1997 also works to improve the Alaskan health system by participating in strategic summit meetings and sponsoring electronic health record initiatives.

Geographic Reach

ANTHC and ANMC are located in Anchorage Alaska. The organization provides services throughout the state.

Financial Performance

The company's 2014 revenues stood at $643 million about 33% of which came from patient revenues. Other major operating segments include compact revenue (25% of sales) and grant and project income (17%).

Strategy

Infrastructure and service expansions are a key means of growth for ANTHC.

In 2015 ANTHC awarded Neeser Construction Inc. a contract to build the new ANMC patient housing facility on the Alaska Native Health Campus in Anchorage. The building will house patients and their families travelling to ANMC for medical care. The a new patient housing facility is expected to open in fall 2016. It will have 202 private rooms and six floors with a dedicated floor for new families.

In 2015 Alaska Governor Walker introduced legislation declaring his plan for Medicaid reform and expansion. ANTHC supports the Governor's efforts to expand Medicaid coverage to more than 41000 Alaskans.

Company Background

In 2012 ANMC expanded its maternal child health and neurosurgery departments due to increasing patient populations in the Anchorage area. In 2010 the medical center opened the only Level II trauma center in Alaska making it a referral hospital for major trauma cases.

The organization has also improved its health care technology resources; it expanded the use of electronic health records at ANMC in 2012 and it is expanding its telemedicine operations (as telemedicine is becoming an increasingly popular way for specialists to see patients without the expense of a personal visit). It has increased other community outreach efforts as well such as smoking cessation and behavioral health programs.

EXECUTIVES

Vp Professional And Support Services Alaska Native Medical Center Hospital, Vivian Echavarria
Cfo, Garvin Federenko
Ceo And Administrator, Roald Helgesen
Cio, Stewart Ferguson
Chief Medical Officer, Paul Franke
Chief Nursing Executive Alaska Native Medical Center Hospital, Richard Hall
Chairman And President, Andy Teuber
Vice Chairman, Lincoln A. Bean
Auditors: BDO USA LLP ANCHORAGE AK

LOCATIONS

HQ: ALASKA NATIVE TRIBAL HEALTH CONSORTIUM
4000 AMBASSADOR DR, ANCHORAGE, AK 995085909
Phone: 907 729-1900
Web: WWW.ANTHC.ORG

PRODUCTS/OPERATIONS

2014 Sales

	$ mil.	% of total
Patient revenue	213	33
Compact revenue	161	25
Grant & project revenue	109	17
Warehouse revenue	22	3
Investment income	4	1
Other	133	21
Total	**643**	**100**

Selected Services

Ear Nose Throat
Emergency and Trauma
Family Medicine
Imaging and Laboratory Services
Internal Medicine Clinic
Maternal Fetal Medicine
OB/GYN Services
Oncology
Orthopedics Clinic
Pediatric ICU
Pediatrics
Pharmacy Services
Pregnancy and Childbirth
Primary Care Services
Respiratory Care

COMPETITORS

HCA
Immediate Care
PeaceHealth
Providence St. Joseph Health
South Peninsula Hospital
Tenet Healthcare

HISTORICAL FINANCIALS

Company Type: Private

Income Statement — FYE: September 30

	REVENUE ($ mil.)	NET INCOME ($ mil.)	NET PROFIT MARGIN	EMPLOYEES
09/16	587	72	12.4%	1,850
09/15	511	3	0.7%	—
09/14	618	154	24.9%	—
09/13	459	21	4.6%	—
Annual Growth	8.5%	50.5%	—	—

2016 Year-End Financials

Return on assets: 10.8%
Return on equity: 13.8%
Current ratio: 1.60
Cash ($ mil.): 121

ALASKA PERMANENT FUND CORPORATION

EXECUTIVES

Ceo, Angela Rodell
Coo*, Marcus Frampton
Chief Financial Officer*, Valerie Mertz
Information Specialist, Andrew Loney
Principal, Chris Poag
Communications Manager, Paulyn Swanson
Portfolio Manager, Timothy Andreyka
Human Resources Director, Chad Brown
Investment Officer Real Estate, Christi Grussendorf
Senior Associate Private Marke, Jared Brimberry
Senior Associate, Maria Skuratovskaya
Auditors: KPMG LLP ANCHORAGE AK

LOCATIONS

HQ: ALASKA PERMANENT FUND CORPORATION
801 W 10TH ST STE 302, JUNEAU, AK 998011878
Phone: 907 796-1500
Web: WWW.APFC.ORG

HISTORICAL FINANCIALS

Company Type: Private

Income Statement — FYE: June 30

	ASSETS ($ mil.)	NET INCOME ($ mil.)	INCOME AS % OF ASSETS	EMPLOYEES
06/19	70,049	1,405	2.0%	50
06/18	67,671	5,109	7.6%	—
06/17	61,824	6,675	10.8%	—
06/16	55,346	(30)	—	—
Annual Growth	8.2%	—	—	—

ALBANY MEDICAL CENTER

Albany Medical Center (AMC) provides medical care in upstate New York. Serving residents of northeastern New York and western New England the health system has at its heart the 730-bed Albany Medical Center Hospital. The general medical-surgical facility also provides specialty care in such areas as oncology rehabilitation and organ transplantation. AMC also features a children's hospital an outpatient surgery center and a group medical practice. It employs some 400 full-time physicians. Its Albany Medical College is one of the nation's first private medical schools. It offers undergraduate and graduate medical degrees and residency programs as well as fellowships and continuing medical education.

Operations

AMC's assets includes a biomedical research enterprise and one of the region's largest physicians practices with more than 400 doctors. Its physicians have extensive training and experience in 34 subspecialties of pediatric medicine. The system's subsidiaries include the Albany Medical Center Kidskeller Corporation a not-for-profit day care facility and Madison Avenue Services Corporation a taxable corporation.

AMC is affiliated with several community physician groups including Albany Vascular Group Capital Cardiology Associates and Capital Region Orthopaedic Group.

In 2013 the system reported some 33000 admissions 581000 outpatient visits 28000 surgical cases and 68000 emergency department visits.

Geographic Reach

AMC offers services in 25 counties in northeastern New York and western New England. In addition to treating patients at the main site in Albany providers also treat patients at community-based locations throughout the region including Clifton Park Latham Malta North Greenbush Delmar and others.

Sales and Marketing

HMOs account for around a third of net patient revenue while Medicare and Medicaid represent about 20% and 15% respectively.

Financial Performance

The company's revenues grew by 3% to $752 million in 2013 (versus $728 million in 2012) due to an increase in net patient revenue; this was partially offset by declines in interest income dividends and other revenue. Net income grew 21% to $63 million in 2013 as net realized gains on sales of securities and impairment charges rose. Other gains were made in pension-related changes and net unrealized gains and losses in investments.

Cash flow from operations fell 55% that year to $37 million as more was used in receivables and other liabilities.

Strategy

AMC grows through organic expansion partnerships and product initiatives. The company is in the midst of a $360 million expansion including a new patient tower with more than 100 beds and increased intensive care resources. The project – expected to last several years – will also increase Albany Medical Center Hospital's bed count to more than 700.

In 2014 The Neurology Group and The Endocrine Group joined AMC's Albany Med Faculty Physician Group.

AMC and Union Graduate College joined forces in 2013 to offer a new joint degree combining medical school with an MBA.

That year AMC and Saratoga Hospital formed a joint venture and opened the $17.5 million Malta Med Emergent Care to provide area residents an alternative to hospital emergency rooms for all but the most serious medical circumstances.

On the product innovation side in 2013 AMC introduced advanced imaging technologies in a pair of its new Patient Pavilion operating rooms that provide for greater precision and patient safety during brain and spinal surgeries.

Also that year the company opened a Chronic Kidney Disease Clinic as the sole source for comprehensive care for 6000 people in its service area suffering from the slow loss of kidney function.

AMC also engages in research and development of new pharmaceuticals through partnerships with companies like Aegis Therapeutics with which it is developing an anti-obesity peptide to benefit patients with type 2 diabetes. The college's research department is also studying brain mapping techniques as well as Alzheimer's disease vascular disease and cancer and multiple sclerosis treatments.

Company Background

AMC which produced Nobel prize winners in both 2009 and 2011 annually awards its own $500000 prize the largest monetary award in medicine and biomedical research in the US. In 2010 combined federal-state entities awarded the center $10 million the center's largest grant since its founding which will be used to expand research labs at Albany Medical College.

AMC's status as the Capital Region's reigning health care giant was toppled by the 2011 merger of four locals hospitals to form St. Peter's Health Partners with nearly 12000 employees vs. 6000 at AMC. Post merger the newly-merged group has nearly 50% of the Capital Region market while AMC has 25%. While AMC is no longer the area's largest hospital as the region's trauma center and only medical school it continues to draw many patients from outside the four-county area.

Albany Medical College was formed in 1839; the hospital's predecessor was formed in 1849. The two combined under the AMC umbrella in 1982.

EXECUTIVES

President And Ceo, James J. Barba
Coo, Gary J. Kochem
Evp And Cfo, William C. Hasselbarth
Svp And Cio, George T. Hickman
Evp Ids And Hospital Systems General Director, Steven M. Frisch
Evp Policy Planning And Communications, Kim Fine
Svp Hospital Business Services And Coo Hospital, Bernadette Pedlow

Dean And Evp Health Affairs, Vincent Verdile
Svp And Chief Nursing Officer, Mary Ellen Plass
Senior Vice President And Chief Compliance Officer, Noel Hogan
Vice President Information Systems, Arthur Gross
Vice President Finance, Cooper Matthew
Physical Therapy Director, Louann Kuntz
Vice President For Communications, Jeffrey Gordon
Vice President Patient Financial Services, Carol Mcdonald
Vice President Of Facility Operations, Don Stichter
Vice President, Anjali Singla
Vice President, Michael Gruenthal
Senior Vice President Of Integrated Delivery Systems And Hospital Director, Stephen Frisch
Vice President Finance, Matt Cooper
Vice President Community Development, Pamela Brown
Chairman, Robert Cushing
Auditors: KPMG LLP ALBANY NEW YORK

LOCATIONS

HQ: ALBANY MEDICAL CENTER
43 NEW SCOTLAND AVE, ALBANY, NY 122083478
Phone: 518 262-3125
Web: WWW.AMC.EDU

PRODUCTS/OPERATIONS

2013 Sales

	$ mil.	% of total
Net patient service	720	96
Inter-institutional	8	1
Interest & dividends	2	-
Other	17	2
Net assets released from restrictions	3	1
Total	**752**	**100**

2013 Net Patient Service Revenue

	% of total
Health maintenance organizations	32
Medicare	19
Medicaid	15
Blue Cross and Blue Shield	14
Commercial carriers	9
No fault & worker's compensation	5
Private pay	2
Other third-party payors	4
Total	**100**

Selected Services

Cancer center
Children's Hospital
Center for Donation and Transplant
Diabetes service
Emergency medical services
Hearing center
HIV medicine
Pain management
Perinatal
Physical therapy
Radiology
Rheumatology
Surgical
Trauma center
Women's wellness center

COMPETITORS

Berkshire Health Systems
Ellis Hospital
SUNY Upstate Medical University
Southwestern Vermont Health Care
St. Joseph's Hospital Health Center
St. Peter's Health Partners
United Health Services Hospitals

HISTORICAL FINANCIALS

Company Type: Private

Income Statement — FYE: December 31

	REVENUE ($ mil.)	NET INCOME ($ mil.)	NET PROFIT MARGIN	EMPLOYEES
12/17	664	267	40.2%	7,000
12/16	317	77	24.5%	—
12/15	1,167	5	0.5%	—
12/13	980	115	11.7%	—
Annual Growth	(9.3%)	23.4%	—	—

2017 Year-End Financials

Return on assets: 36.5%
Return on equity: 84.3%
Current ratio: 2.20
Cash ($ mil.): 113

ALBANY MEDICAL CENTER HOSPITAL

EXECUTIVES

Pres, James J Barba
Coo*, Gary J Kochem
SEC*, Sabine Needham
Risk Manager, Vickey Masta
Patient Care Director, Diane Carey
Cardiac Physician, Mohammad Hajjar
Auditors: KPMG LLP ALBANY NY

LOCATIONS

HQ: ALBANY MEDICAL CENTER HOSPITAL
43 NEW SCOTLAND AVE, ALBANY, NY 122083478
Phone: 518 262-3125
Web: WWW.AMC.EDU

HISTORICAL FINANCIALS

Company Type: Private

Income Statement — FYE: December 31

	REVENUE ($ mil.)	NET INCOME ($ mil.)	NET PROFIT MARGIN	EMPLOYEES
12/19	1,133	86	7.6%	1,568
12/17	1,017	38	3.8%	—
12/16	960	46	4.8%	—
12/15	893	16	1.9%	—
Annual Growth	6.1%	50.3%	—	—

2019 Year-End Financials

Return on assets: 7.2%
Return on equity: 16.2%
Current ratio: 3.10
Cash ($ mil.): 158

ALBERICI CONSTRUCTORS, INC.

EXECUTIVES

Pres, Gregory J Kozicz
V Pres, John S Alberici
V Pres, Leroy Stromberg
Cfo, Gregory T Hesser
Sr Acct, Sherry Morrow
Chief Information Officer, Frank C Kropiunik
Quality Manager, Brian Miller
Subcontract Administration, Erin Yaeger
Executive Assistant, Gail Thompson
Chief Structural Engineer, Gary Broccard
Superintendent, Greg Forshee

LOCATIONS

HQ: ALBERICI CONSTRUCTORS, INC.
8800 PAGE AVE, SAINT LOUIS, MO 631146106
Phone: 314 733-2000
Web: WWW.ALBERICI.COM

HISTORICAL FINANCIALS

Company Type: Private

Income Statement — FYE: December 31

	REVENUE ($ mil.)	NET INCOME ($ mil.)	NET PROFIT MARGIN	EMPLOYEES
12/17	782	0	—	2,000
12/16	960	0	—	—
12/15	1,028	0	—	—
12/14	729	0	—	—
Annual Growth	2.4%	—	—	—

2017 Year-End Financials

Return on assets: —
Return on equity: —
Current ratio: 1.20
Cash ($ mil.): 76

ALBERICI CORPORATION

Alberici helped shape the St. Louis skyline; it now sets its sights – or its construction sites – across North America. As the parent company of Alberici Constructors the company encompasses a group of enterprises with a presence in North America Central America South America and Europe. Operations include construction services building materials and steel fabrication and erection units. Alberici offers general contracting design/build construction management demolition and specialty contracting services while also offering facilities management. Founded in 1918 the Alberici family still holds the largest share of the employee-owned firm.

Operations

The company boasts more than a dozen operating companies in the US Canada and Mexico that serve the automotive energy health care industrial manufacturing and wastewater treatment markets. Its Gunther-Nash subsidiary provides construction services to the mining industry. Another division Vertegy specializes in construction consulting for green and sustainable projects.

Geographic Reach

Alberici is active throughout North America and has offices in St. Louis Missouri; Detroit Michigan; Atlanta Georgia; Topeka Kansas; Burlington and Cambridge Ontario; Saskatoon Saskatchewan; and Léon Mexico.

Sales and Marketing

Alberici serves a range of different companies including those that are automotive building energy healthcare heavy industrial industrial process mining infrastructure or water-related.

Some of Alberici's completed projects include casinos for Ameristar modernization and new facilities for Anheuser-Busch and factories for Boeing. Nearly 80% of its revenue comes from repeat clients.

Financial Performance

While full financial information was not available for the privately held company Alberici reports that its annual revenue typically exceeds $1 billion. In 2013 the company took home $1.9 billion and was ranked the 46th largest contractor in the US by the Engineering News-Record .

In 2012 the company reported more than $530 million in industrial-related revenue thanks to a recovering economy supporting demand for major industrial projects in the US and Canada.

Strategy

In recent years the heavy construction firm has pursued acquisitions to better diversify its business both geographically and by entering new specialty markets. In 2013 for example Alberici purchased contractor Flintco LLC to broaden its reach into new markets in the southern and southwestern regions of the US. In early 2012 Alberici acquired a water treatment facility specialist to expand its service offerings in the water plant construction market.

Alberici has also become a recognized contractor in recent years which could help give the company a higher profile and thus more exposure to new potential clients. In 2013 the Associated General Contractors of St. Louis awarded Alberici with top prizes at its 16th Annual Keystone Awards for the company's work on the Seabrook Gates Complex and the Knights of Columbus Child Development Center. To date Alberici has won 14 Keystone Awards more than any other general contractor.

So far its high standing hasn't hurt business. In July 2014 Alberici was chosen to lead in the engineering procurement and construction of a major air quality improvement project – with the goal of installing environmental controls and reducing sulfur dioxide emissions by 90% – at one of the generating stations owned and operated by Alliant Energy's Wisconsin utility Wisconsin Power and Light Company.

Mergers and Acquisitions

Expanding it range of capabilities in January 2012 Alberici acquired water treatment facility specialist CAS Construction. The addition of CAS which has built facilities throughout the central and western US strengthens Alberici's capabilities in the water market. The company was renamed CAS Constructors.

In early 2013 Alberici closed on its acquisition of Flintco LLC a century-old Native American-owned contractor based in Tulsa Oklahoma. With offices in Oklahoma New Mexico Texas Arkansas and California Flintco presented an attractive geographic diversification opportunity for Alberici.

EXECUTIVES

Executive Vice President, Chris Hermann
Vice President Alberici Constructors Ltd., Sean Thibeault
Executive Vice President, Kevin Williams

LOCATIONS

HQ: ALBERICI CORPORATION
8800 PAGE AVE, SAINT LOUIS, MO 631146106
Phone: 314 733-2000
Web: WWW.ALBERICI.COM

PRODUCTS/OPERATIONS

Selected Markets

Automotive

Building

Energy
Green building
Health care
Industrial
Manufacturing/Food and Beverage
Mining infrastructure
Steel fabrication
Water and Wastewater Treatment

Selected Subsidiaries and Brands

Alberici Global Group GmbH
Alberici Constructors Ltd. (Canada)
Alberici Construcciones S.A. de C.V. (Mexico)
Alberici Group Inc.
Alberici Constructors Inc.
Alberici Global Automotive Constructors (automotive construction)
Alberici Healthcare Constructors
Alberici Industrial LLC
CAS Construction LLC (water wastewater)
Flintco LLC (Native American-owned contractor)
Gunther-Nash Inc. (shaft slope and tunnel construction for mining industry)
Hillsdale Fabricators (steel fabrication)
Kienlen Constructors (structural concrete structural steel)
Vertegy (green building consulting)

COMPETITORS

Barton Malow
Bechtel
Black & Veatch
DPR Construction
Fluor
Hensel Phelps Construction
Hoffman Corporation
Hunt Construction
Jacobs Engineering
McCarthy Building
Parsons Corporation
Peter Kiewit Sons'
TIC Holdings
Tutor Perini
Walbridge Aldinger
Walsh Group
Zachry Inc.

HISTORICAL FINANCIALS

Company Type: Private

Income Statement — FYE: December 31

	REVENUE ($ mil.)	NET INCOME ($ mil.)	NET PROFIT MARGIN	EMPLOYEES
12/17	1,531	0	—	2,080
12/16	1,742	0	—	—
12/15	1,885	0	—	—
12/14	1,532	0	—	—
Annual Growth	(0.0%)	—	—	—

2017 Year-End Financials

Return on assets: —
Return on equity: —
Current ratio: 1.40
Cash ($ mil.): 182

ALBERICI GROUP, INC.

EXECUTIVES

Ceo, Gregory J Kozicz
Chb*, John S Alberici
Coo*, Leroy J Stromberg Jr
Exe V Pres*, Michael W Burke
Coordinator, Keeley Vickers
Safety Project Coordinator, Matt Walters
Director of Preconstruction, Frederick Biermann

LOCATIONS

HQ: ALBERICI GROUP, INC.
8800 PAGE AVE, SAINT LOUIS, MO 631146106
Phone: 314 733-2000
Web: WWW.ALBERICI.COM

HISTORICAL FINANCIALS

Company Type: Private

Income Statement — FYE: December 31

	REVENUE ($ mil.)	NET INCOME ($ mil.)	NET PROFIT MARGIN	EMPLOYEES
12/17	838	0	—	2,000
12/16	1,036	0	—	—
12/15	1,124	0	—	—
12/14	729	0	—	—
Annual Growth	4.8%	—	—	—

2017 Year-End Financials

Return on assets: —
Return on equity: —
Current ratio: 1.20
Cash ($ mil.): 105

ALBERT EINSTEIN MEDICAL ASSOCIATES, INC.

EXECUTIVES

Pres, Barry Freedman
V Pres, Penny Rezet
Treas, Gerard McKee
Cfo, Brian Derrick
Pres, Herbert S Waxman
Treas, John Murino
Coordinator, Nicole Amrik
Coordinator, Monica Rollerson
Staff, John Skanse
Coordinator, Kelsey Kriebel
Health Professional, Mel Hanick

LOCATIONS

HQ: ALBERT EINSTEIN MEDICAL ASSOCIATES, INC.
5501 OLD YORK RD STE 1, PHILADELPHIA, PA 191413018
Phone: 215 456-7890
Web: WWW.EINSTEIN.EDU

HISTORICAL FINANCIALS

Company Type: Private

Income Statement — FYE: June 30

	REVENUE ($ mil.)	NET INCOME ($ mil.)	NET PROFIT MARGIN	EMPLOYEES
06/09	670	0	—	5,251
06/08	693	33	4.9%	—
06/07	785	63	8.0%	—
06/06	718	29	4.1%	—
Annual Growth	(2.3%)	—	—	—

2009 Year-End Financials

Return on assets: —
Return on equity: —
Current ratio: 0.40
Cash ($ mil.): 82

ALBERT EINSTEIN MEDICAL CENTER

EXECUTIVES

Pres, Richard Greenberg
Administrator, Christine Wambold
Telehealth Project Manager, Gaesenee Kongsubto
Managing Director Hospitalist, Anita Govil
Administrator, Donna Brown
Osteopathy, Sandra S Jones
Treasurer, Gerard McKee
Analyst, Joann Vanderslice
Payroll, Carole Sinclair
Director, David Tebbens
Research, Joseph Herres

LOCATIONS

HQ: ALBERT EINSTEIN MEDICAL CENTER
5501 OLD YORK RD STE 1, PHILADELPHIA, PA 191413098
Phone: 215 456-7890
Web: WWW.EINSTEIN.EDU

HISTORICAL FINANCIALS

Company Type: Private

Income Statement FYE: June 30

	REVENUE ($ mil.)	NET INCOME ($ mil.)	NET PROFIT MARGIN	EMPLOYEES
06/19	829	(51)	—	48
06/18	820	7	1.0%	—
06/16	746	9	1.3%	—
06/15	679	38	5.7%	—
Annual Growth	5.1%	—	—	—

2019 Year-End Financials

Return on assets: (-6.1%)
Return on equity: (-17.7%)
Current ratio: 1.30
Cash ($ mil.): 17

ALBERTSONS COMPANIES, INC.

Albertsons Companies is one of the biggest supermarket retailers in the US with nearly 2250 stores in some 35 states and the District of Columbia. In addition to traditional grocery items many of the stores offer pharmacies and coffee shops and over 400 include adjacent gas stations. The company operates under some 20 banners including Albertsons Vons Pavilions Randalls Tom Thumb Carrs Jewel-Osco Shaw's/Star Market Safeway Market Street Haggen and United. It also owns meal kit company Plated. Albertsons Companies which traces its roots to 1939 is owned by Cerberus Capital Management which has been looking to take the company public for quite some time. In 2018 the retailer called off its pending acquisition of the Rite Aid pharmacy chain amid investor pushback.

HISTORY

J. A. "Joe" Albertson Leonard Skaggs (whose family ran Safeway) and Tom Cuthbert founded Albertson's Food Center in Boise Idaho in 1939. Albertson who left his position as district manager for Safeway to run the store thought big from the start. The 10000-sq.-ft. store was not only eight times the size of the average competitor it also offered an in-store butcher shop and bakery one of the country's first magazine racks and homemade "Big Joe" ice-cream cones. The men ended their partnership in 1945 the year Albertson's was incorporated and by 1947 it operated six stores in Idaho.

The company opened its first combination food store and drugstore a 60000-sq.-ft. superstore in 1951 and began locating stores in growing suburban areas. Albertson's went public to raise expansion capital in 1959 and by 1960 had 62 stores in Idaho Oregon Utah and Washington. The food retailer acquired Greater All American Markets (1964) a grocery chain based in Downey California and Semrau & Sons (1965) of Oakland which aided the company's thrust into the California market.

Albertson's and the Skaggs chain (by this time run by L. S. Skaggs Jr.) reunited temporarily in 1969 financing six Skaggs-Albertson's food-and-drug-combination stores. (The partnership dissolved in 1977 with each side taking half of the units.) By 1986 the company had reached $5 billion in sales a fivefold increase over 1975.

The company purchased 74 Jewel Osco combination food stores and drugstores (mostly in Arkansas Florida Oklahoma and Texas) from American Stores in 1992. Co-founder Albertson died in 1993 at age 86.

In 1997 the United Food and Commercial Workers union which represents supermarket employees sued Albertson's alleging the company forced employees to work overtime without pay. (It was settled in 1999 resulting in a $22 million charge.) Also in 1997 Albertson's began selling gasoline at a few stores. Acquisitions the next year (including Buttrey Food and Drug Stores) added stores and states. That year the company began serving online customers in the Dallas-Fort Worth area.

In 1999 the grocer revisited its roots when it acquired American Stores (Skaggs' successor) which operated more than 1550 stores in 26 states. To obtain regulatory approval for the $12 billion deal Albertson's sold 145 stores in overlapping markets in three states (most were in California).

In 2001 Larry Johnston former CEO of GE Appliances took over as chairman and CEO of Albertson's. Facing increasing competition (especially from Wal-Mart) Johnston announced in March 2002 aggressive restructuring plans that included job cuts and closing 95 stores in under-performing markets specifically Memphis and Nashville Tennessee and Houston and San Antonio Texas.

Already allowing customers to order drugs online (from its online drugstore Savon.com) and groceries in Seattle Albertson's expanded its online operations to San Diego in 2001 and in early 2002 to Los Angeles San Francisco and parts of Oregon and Washington. Albertson's exited the New England drugstore market in 2002 when it sold 80 New England Osco stores to Brooks Pharmacy.

In February 2004 Albertson's launched its "Blue Ribbon" brand of beef a private-label line of roasts and steaks. Also in February the company consolidated its Southwest Intermountain Northwest and Rocky Mountain divisions to form a new Intermountain West Division and combined the Acme and Florida divisions into a new Eastern Division.

A four-and-a-half month strike by grocery workers in Southern California ended in March 2004. The dispute pitted workers' demands for continued generous health care coverage vs. management's call for cost cuts to remain profitable in the face of Wal-Mart's entry into the Southern California grocery market. In April Albertson's completed the acquisition of JS USA Holdings which runs Shaw's and Star Markets stores in New England from UK grocer J Sainsbury. The deal to buy Shaw's was worth about $2.4 billion (cash and leases). In September Albertson's gained a toehold in the gourmet-food market with the purchase of Bristol Farms the operator of about a dozen upscale food markets in Southern California. In October Albertson's combined its Northern and Southern California food divisions into a single business unit the newly formed California Food Division. In an effort to improve efficiency Albertson's reorganized its supply chain food operations and Six Sigma Quality functions in May 2005.

In June 2006 Albertson's was sold to a consortium that included SUPERVALU CVS Cerberus Capital Management and Kimco for about $9.7 billion. Following the acquisition and the divvying up of Albertson's assets the surviving company went private and changed its name to Albertsons LLC. Concurrently Johnston left Albertsons and was succeeded by Robert Miller chairman of drugstore chain Rite Aid and the former head of Fred Meyer for eight years in the 1990s. Of the company's 27 price-impact Super Saver stores 25 closed their doors in mid-2006. Also in June the company put about 45 stores on the auction block. (It was announced in late 2006 that discount apparel retailer Ross Stores would acquire these stores.) In July the company shut down its online shopping service Albertsons.com.

In February 2007 Albertsons sold 132 grocery stores and two distribution centers in Northern California and Nevada to Save Mart Supermarkets for an undisclosed amount. Other recent closings include stores in Texas in the Dallas-Fort Worth Austin and Longview markets; Colorado; and Oklahoma.

Albertsons also sold eight of its stores in Wyoming to SUPERVALU in January 2008. The divestments continued in September with the sale of 49 supermarkets in Florida to Publix Super Markets for about $500 million. Also in 2008 Albertsons sold about 100 of its Express fuel centers in Arizona Colorado Florida Louisiana and Texas to Valero Energy and Reb Oil.

EXECUTIVES

Evp And General Counsel, Robert A. (Bob) Gordon
Coo, Wayne A. Denningham
Chief Marketing & Merchandising Officer, Shane Sampson
President Jewel Osco, Mike Withers
President Seattle Division, Karl Schroeder
President Houston Division, Sidney Hopper
Chairman And Ceo, Robert G. (Bob) Miller
Chief Administrative Officer, Justin Dye
President Southwest Division, Shane Dorcheus
President United, Robert Taylor
Evp And Cio, Anuj Dhanda
President Portland Division, Greg McNiff
President Southern Division, Dennis Bassler
Evp East Operations, Susan Morris
President Shaws, Paul Gossett
President Southern California Division, Lori Raya
President Acme Markets Division, Dan Croce
Evp And Cfo, Bob Dimond
Evp West Region Operations, Jim Perkins
Evp Human Resources Labor Relations Public Affairs And Government Relations, Andrew (Andy) Scoggin
Evp Corporate Development And Real Estate, Justin Ewing
President Eastern Division, Dan Valenzuela
President Northern California Division, Tom Schwilke
President Denver Division, Todd Broderick
President Intermountain Division, Brad Street
Svp Merchandising, Dennis Clark
Senior Vice President Digital And Ecommerce, Narayan Iyengar
Evp And Chief Data And Analytics Officer, Gautam Kotwal

Vice President Merchandising Strategy, Merritt Mccoy
Pharmacy Manager, Jim Mayes
Group Vice President Corporate Law, Laura Donald
Auditors: DELOITTE & TOUCHE LLP BOISE

LOCATIONS

HQ: ALBERTSONS COMPANIES, INC.
250 E PARKCENTER BLVD, BOISE, ID 837063999
Phone: 208 395-6200
Web: WWW.ALBERTSONSCOMPANIES.COM

PRODUCTS/OPERATIONS

2018 Sales

	$ mil.	% of total
Non-perishables	26,372	44
Perishables	24,921	41
Pharmacy	4,987	8
Fuel	3,456	6
Other	799	1
Total	**60,535**	**100**

COMPETITORS

ALDI
Amazon.com
Costco Wholesale
Fry's Food
H-E-B
Kroger
Lidl
Publix
Quality Food
Roundy's
Stater Bros.
Target Corporation
Wal-Mart
Wegmans
Winn-Dixie

HISTORICAL FINANCIALS

Company Type: Private

Income Statement — FYE: February 29

	REVENUE ($ mil.)	NET INCOME ($ mil.)	NET PROFIT MARGIN	EMPLOYEES
02/20	62,455	466	0.7%	270,000
02/19	60,534	131	0.2%	—
02/18	59,924	46	0.1%	—
Annual Growth	2.1%	217.4%	—	—

2020 Year-End Financials

Return on assets: 1.9%
Return on equity: 20.5%
Current ratio: 1.00
Cash ($ mil.): 470

ALBUQUERQUE MUNICIPAL SCHOOL DISTRICT NUMBER 12

EXECUTIVES

Supt, Jason Martinez
Superintendent, Raquel Martinez Reedy
Benefits Specialist, Ann Johnson
Substitute Teacher, Alysa Louton
Voip Telecommunications Manage, Brian Thompson
Teacher, Cara Chavez
Teacher, Cicely Ryan
Truancy Social Worker, Danielle Burnett
Para Educator, Donna Huling
Secretary, Doris Smith
Teacher, Heather Worf
Auditors: MOSS ADAMS LLP ALBUQUERQUE N

LOCATIONS

HQ: ALBUQUERQUE MUNICIPAL SCHOOL DISTRICT NUMBER 12
6400 UPTOWN BLVD NE, ALBUQUERQUE, NM 871104202
Phone: 505 880-3700
Web: WWW.APS.EDU

HISTORICAL FINANCIALS

Company Type: Private

Income Statement — FYE: June 30

	REVENUE ($ mil.)	NET INCOME ($ mil.)	NET PROFIT MARGIN	EMPLOYEES
06/19	1,006	(35)	—	10
06/18	954	50	5.3%	—
06/17	946	57	6.0%	—
06/16	998	11	1.2%	—
Annual Growth	0.3%	—	—	—

2019 Year-End Financials

Return on assets: (-1.4%)
Return on equity: —
Current ratio: 2.50
Cash ($ mil.): 62

ALDINE INDEPENDENT SCHOOL DISTRICT

EXECUTIVES

Supt, Dr Latonya Goffney
Principal, Ruth Dimmick
Principal, Jeannette Ross
Information Technology/Interne, Jamila Ashmeade-Brown
Assistant, Sonia Pace
Assistant, Akua Twumasi
Human Resources, Esther Hinojosa
Operations Manager, Rosana Barton
Registrar, Christine Lemons
Assistant Director of Public I, Debbie Willett
Teacher, Alicia Cerda
Auditors: WHITLEY PENN LLP HOUSTON TX

LOCATIONS

HQ: ALDINE INDEPENDENT SCHOOL DISTRICT
2520 WW THORNE BLVD, HOUSTON, TX 770733406
Phone: 281 449-1011
Web: WWW.ALDINEISD.ORG

HISTORICAL FINANCIALS

Company Type: Private

Income Statement — FYE: June 30

	REVENUE ($ mil.)	NET INCOME ($ mil.)	NET PROFIT MARGIN	EMPLOYEES
06/20	814	(3)	—	7,000
06/19	791	106	13.5%	—
06/18	757	33	4.5%	—
06/17	743	(276)	—	—
Annual Growth	3.1%	—	—	—

2020 Year-End Financials

Return on assets: (-0.2%)
Return on equity: —
Current ratio: —
Cash ($ mil.): 48

ALEGENT HEALTH-BERGAN MERCY HEALTH SYSTEM

EXECUTIVES

Ceo, Cliff Robertson
Pres, Lawrence Beckman
Sr V Pres, Bonnie Burnett
Cfo, Jeanette Wojtalewicz
V Pres, Leigh Bertholf
Coo, Joan Neuhaus
Director, Ann Tuohy
Diagnostic Radiologist, Michael Schuster
Chief Officer, Devin Fox
Pacs Administrator, Lisa McCarty
Patient Accounts Manager, Judy Rising

LOCATIONS

HQ: ALEGENT HEALTH- BERGAN MERCY HEALTH SYSTEM
7500 MERCY RD, OMAHA, NE 681242319
Phone: 402 398-6060
Web: WWW.CHIHEALTH.COM

HISTORICAL FINANCIALS

Company Type: Private

Income Statement — FYE: June 30

	REVENUE ($ mil.)	NET INCOME ($ mil.)	NET PROFIT MARGIN	EMPLOYEES
06/18	695	60	8.7%	1
06/17	727	23	3.2%	—
06/14	543	88	16.3%	—
Annual Growth	6.3%	(9.1%)	—	—

2018 Year-End Financials

Return on assets: 5.7%
Return on equity: 7.4%
Current ratio: —
Cash ($ mil.): 7

ALEX LEE, INC.

The Alex Lee family of companies includes Lowes Foods and Merchants Distributors (MDI). Alex Lee grew out of Merchants Produce Company which was founded in 1931 by Alex and Lee George. MDI supplies food and general merchandise to more than 600 retailers with food and non-food items in over 10 Eastern states. MDI's own Consolidation Services business provides warehousing and logistics services. As part of its business Alex Lee also operates Lowe's Food Stores a chain of about 75 grocery stores located in the Carolinas and Virginia. Alex and Lee George started the company in 1931The George family continues to control Alex Lee.

Operations

Alex Lee named after Lebanese immigrant founder Moses George's two sons Alex and Lee boasts two operating companies: Merchants Distributors Inc. and Lowe's Food Stores Inc. Run as a division of MDI Consolidation Services operates under the Alex Lee and MDI umbrellas.

In addition one of its brands is seeking North Carolina products across many categories including seafood and packaged products and it is actively working with farmers to get their products through the distribution system of a large grocery chain.Alex Lee named after Lebanese immigrant founder Moses George's two sons Alex and Lee boasts two operating companies: Merchants Distributors Inc. and Lowe's Food Stores Inc. Run as a division of MDI Consolidation Services operates under the Alex Lee and MDI umbrellas.In addition one of its brands is seeking North Carolina products across many categories including seafood and packaged products and it is actively working with farmers to get their products through the distribution system of a large grocery chain.

Geographic Reach

Headquartered in Hickory North Carolina the company's reach extends to about a dozen US states. Alex Lee operates its Merchants Distributors Inc. (MDI) retail distribution unit across the Carolinas Georgia Tennessee Virginia Alabama Virginia Ohio Florida Pennsylvania and Kentucky. Regional supermarket chain Lowe's Food Stores serves customers in Virginia South Carolina and North Carolina.

Sales and Marketing

One of the brands of the company has a complete retail wholesale operation supplying over 650 stores and caters to the SMB market.

Strategy

In 2019 Alex Lee acquired W. Lee Flowers & Co. a wholesale and retail grocery company based in Scranton S.C. The acquisition of W. Lee Flowers enables Alex Lee to expand its geographic footprint enhance operations in new markets and offer consumers a greater variety of products at competitive costs.

Mergers and Acquisitions

In late 2019 Alex Lee Inc. announced that it has completed its acquisition of W. Lee Flowers & Co. a wholesale and retail grocery company based in Scranton S.C. The acquisition of W. Lee Flowers which distributes to more than 75 grocery stores in the Carolinas and Georgia including 50 stores that it owns and operates enables Alex Lee to expand its geographic footprint enhance operations in new markets and offer consumers a greater variety of products at competitive costs. Terms were not disclosed.

EXECUTIVES

Chairman And Ceo, Boyd L. George, age 78
President Lowe's Food Stores, Steve Hall
President, Brian George
Svp And Cfo, Joyce Reto
Vice President, Roger Henderson
Auditors: RSM US LLP CHARLOTTE NORTH C

LOCATIONS

HQ: ALEX LEE, INC.
120 4TH ST SW, HICKORY, NC 286022947
Phone: 828 725-4424
Web: WWW.ALEXLEE.COM

PRODUCTS/OPERATIONS

Selected Operations

Lowe's Food Stores Inc.
Merchants Distributors Inc.
Consolidation Services Inc.

COMPETITORS

ALDI
Associated Wholesale Grocers
Ben E. Keith
C&S Wholesale
Food Lion
H. T. Hackney
Harris Teeter Supermarkets
Ingles Markets
K-VA-T Food Stores
Kroger
MAINES
McLane
Meadowbrook Meat Company
SUPERVALU
Southeastern Grocers
Sysco
US Foods
Wal-Mart
Winn-Dixie

HISTORICAL FINANCIALS

Company Type: Private

Income Statement — FYE: September 28

	REVENUE ($ mil.)	NET INCOME ($ mil.)	NET PROFIT MARGIN	EMPLOYEES
09/19	2,286	25	1.1%	9,550
09/18	2,238	14	0.7%	—
09/17*	2,261	4	0.2%	—
10/16	2,229	8	0.4%	—
Annual Growth	0.8%	43.7%	—	—

*Fiscal year change

2019 Year-End Financials

Return on assets: 2.8%
Return on equity: 5.1%
Current ratio: 1.30
Cash ($ mil.): 3

ALFRED I.DUPONT HOSPITAL FOR CHILDREN

EXECUTIVES

Ceo, Thomas Ferry
V Pres*, Stephen T Lawless
Cfo*, William Britton
Editor, Dustin Samples
Coordinator, Carol Eade-Viele
Coordinator, Julia Morrison

LOCATIONS

HQ: ALFRED I.DUPONT HOSPITAL FOR CHILDREN
1600 ROCKLAND RD, WILMINGTON, DE 198033607
Phone: 302 651-4000
Web: WWW.NEMOURS.ORG

HISTORICAL FINANCIALS

Company Type: Private

Income Statement — FYE: December 31

	REVENUE ($ mil.)	NET INCOME ($ mil.)	NET PROFIT MARGIN	EMPLOYEES
12/18	553	16	3.0%	3,068
12/17	525	34	6.6%	—
12/16	516	(31)	—	—
12/15	450	28	6.4%	—
Annual Growth	7.1%	(16.3%)	—	—

2018 Year-End Financials

Return on assets: 2.5%
Return on equity: 2.7%
Current ratio: 1.90
Cash ($ mil.): —

ALIEF INDEPENDENT SCHOOL DISTRICT

EXECUTIVES

Supt, H D Chambers
Cfo*, Deanna Wentz
Administrative Assistant, Brian Pilgreen
Management Info Dir, Doug Brown
Administration Manager, Jonell Keller
Coordinator, Laura Klubert
Operations Manager, Karen Coleman
Assistant, Adan C Morales
Health Coordinator, Carleen Johnson
Teacher, Debra Kelly
Teacher English, Easton Riley Massie
Auditors: NULL-LAIRSON PC HOUSTON TX

LOCATIONS

HQ: ALIEF INDEPENDENT SCHOOL DISTRICT
4250 COOK RD, HOUSTON, TX 770721115
Phone: 281 498-8110
Web: WWW.ALIEFISD.NET

HISTORICAL FINANCIALS

Company Type: Private

Income Statement — FYE: August 31

	REVENUE ($ mil.)	NET INCOME ($ mil.)	NET PROFIT MARGIN	EMPLOYEES
08/19	553	35	6.3%	6,000
08/18	535	(25)	—	—
08/17	519	(5)	—	—
08/16	514	38	7.5%	—
Annual Growth	2.5%	(3.0%)	—	—

2019 Year-End Financials

Return on assets: 3.9%
Return on equity: 50.8%
Current ratio: —
Cash ($ mil.): 184

ALLAN MYERS, INC.

American Infrastructure provides heavy civil construction services for projects in the Mid-Atlantic. Operating as Allan A. Myers in Pennsylvania and Delaware and as American Infrastructure in Maryland and Virginia the family-run business builds and reconstructs highways water treatment plants medical facilities and shopping centers and offers site development for homebuilders. Its quarries and asphalt plants operate under the Independence Construction Materials (ICM) subsidiary which supplies aggregates asphalt and ready-mixed concrete to its construction companies. The company is ranked by Engineering News-Record as 25th on the country's Top 50 list of heavy civil contractors.

Operations

American Infrastructure builds projects ranging from $100000 to more than $100 million per project.

As a land developer interested in conservation American Infrastructure offers a unique all-terrain tree spade vehicle that is designed to carry large mature trees harvested from heavily wooded sites intended to be replanted on developed sites. The process allows mature trees to be saved and relocated on a developed site.

Geographic Reach

American Infrastructure and its subsidiaries operate in the Mid-Atlantic region through about 20 locations (including quarries and plants) in Pennsylvania Maryland Virginia Delaware and Washington DC as well as four satellite offices in the region. The company also has 15 materials mining and/or asphalt production facilities in four states.

Sales and Marketing

American Infrastructure serves private developers general contractors departments of transportation utilities local and state governments and federal military customers throughout the Mid-Atlantic region.

Customers include CRB Military Housing Frederick Winchester Service Authority O'Brien & Gere Delaware Department of Transportation The Goldenberg Group Morgan-Keller Construction Forest Park Water Uniwest Construction Divinity Trucking Nardi Construction Hunt Building Company the City of Wilmington and Maryland State Highway Administration.

Strategy

American Infrastructure's financial capacity is strengthened by a bonding capacity of $800 million which allows it to tackle major projects. Selected projects includes Richmond Airport Connector Route 715/40 Interchange Virginia SR 29 Bridge Jersey Shore Pump Station Aberdeen Test Track Argonne Drive Bridge MARC Wedge Railyard Nicodemus Bridge Route 52 Ballenger McKinney wastewater treatment plant and Mount Holly wastewater treatment plant.

Company Background

Some past projects include Eagle Heights at Dover Air Force Base ($13.3 million) Cool Springs Reservoir ($18.6 million) and MD 43 ($46.7 million) in Baltimore County Maryland.

The company was established in 1939 as Allan A. Myers and Son a local hauling company in the suburbs of Philadelphia.

EXECUTIVES

Vice President And Corporate General Counsel, Nunzio Ruggeri
Vice President General Manager, Brock Myers
Vice President General Manager, Mark Carroll
Vice President Human Resources, Heather Peters
District Vice President, Jamie Kirby
Vice President Technology, Jim Edmunds
Executive Vice President Of Construction, Rich Dungan
Treasurer And Director Of Partnership Accounting, Craig Little
Auditors: PRICEWATERHOUSECOOPERS LLP PH

LOCATIONS

HQ: ALLAN MYERS, INC.
1805 BERKS RD, WORCESTER, PA 19490
Phone: 610 222-8800
Web: WWW.ALLANMYERS.COM

PRODUCTS/OPERATIONS

Selected Services

Site Development
- Concrete flatwork
- Excavation and grading
- Hauling
- Large-diameter tree relocation
- Milling and paving
- Rock drilling and blasting
- Soft dig capabilities
- Stone and curb
- Stormwater management
- Survey and stakeout
- Underground utilities

Transportation
- Asphalt paving
- Box culverts
- Bridges and structures
- Concrete paving
- Maintenance of traffic

Water Resources
- New water/wastewater treatment plants
- Reservoirs and dams
- Underground reservoirs
- Water and sewer transmission lines
- Wetland mitigation and reconstruction

Selected Subsidiaries

Allan A. Myers Inc.
American Infrastructure-Maryland
American Infrastructure-Virginia
Independence Construction Materials

COMPETITORS

Angelo Iafrate
Balfour Beatty Infrastructure
Barnhill Contracting
Branch Group
Cherry Hill Construction
English Construction Company
Lane Construction
Peter Kiewit Sons'
Skanska USA Civil
Traylor Bros.
Vecellio & Grogan

HISTORICAL FINANCIALS

Company Type: Private

Income Statement — FYE: December 31

	REVENUE ($ mil.)	NET INCOME ($ mil.)	NET PROFIT MARGIN	EMPLOYEES
12/19	989	48	5.0%	2,000
12/17	751	21	2.8%	—
12/16	756	15	2.0%	—
12/15	519	0	—	—
Annual Growth	17.5%	—	—	—

2019 Year-End Financials

Return on assets: 8.3%
Return on equity: 45.3%
Current ratio: 0.90
Cash ($ mil.): 129

ALLEGHENY GENERAL HOSPITAL INC

If there is a critical trauma anywhere near Pittsburgh Allegheny General Hospital (AGH) is ready to take it on. The roughly 630-bed hospital is the Level I Shock Trauma Center for the five-state region surrounding Steel City. AGH offers traditional medical and surgical services as well as cardiology care and organ transplants. The hospital also is engaged in research in areas such as neuroscience oncology trauma and genetics. AGH which treats nearly 22000 patients each year has about 800 physicians on its staff. The hospital which is affiliated with Philadelphia's Drexel University College of Medicine is a subsidiary of Allegheny Health System which itself is owned by Highmark Inc.

Operations

AGH receives more than 50000 emergency visits each year as well as had 300000 outpatient visits and more than 21000 surgical procedures. In order to receive those emergencies in an expedient manner the hospital also operates a LifeFlight aero medical service.

The hospital's cancer center provides programs for a wide range of diseases such as lung breast colon prostate brain and liver cancer.

AGH also operates a smaller satellite facility in the northern Pittsburgh suburb of McCandless as well as an outpatient facility in suburban Pittsburgh.

Strategy

In 2014 AGH proposed investing part of $175 million from Highmark Inc. in renovations and technology upgrades at its AGH and West Penn hospitals anticipating that they will accommodate more patients when Highmark insurance subscribers lose in-network access to the University of Pittsburgh Medical Center in 2015.

Company Background

AGH first opened in 1885.

EXECUTIVES

Chair Department Of Pathology, Jan Silverman
President And Ceo, Michael Harlovic
Vice President Of Finance, Rick Fries
Chief Operating Officer, Ronald Andro
Vice President Of Research And Development, Stephanie Kladakis
Vice President Of Clinical Sciences, Janet Vargo
Professor And Vice Chair Department Of Psychiatry Allegheny Health Network Drexel University College Of Medicine, Anthony Mannarino

LOCATIONS

HQ: ALLEGHENY GENERAL HOSPITAL INC
320 E NORTH AVE, PITTSBURGH, PA 152124772
Phone: 412 359-3131
Web: WWW.AHN.ORG

COMPETITORS

Butler Health System
Excela Health
Heritage Valley Health
Jefferson Regional Medical Center of Pennsylvania
Ohio Valley General
St. Clair Health
The Western Pennsylvania Hospital
UPMC
UPMC Mercy
Weirton Medical Center

HISTORICAL FINANCIALS

Company Type: Private

Income Statement — FYE: June 30

	REVENUE ($ mil.)	NET INCOME ($ mil.)	NET PROFIT MARGIN	EMPLOYEES
06/16	720	73	10.2%	5,064
06/15	700	107	15.4%	—
Annual Growth	2.8%	(31.7%)	—	—

2016 Year-End Financials

Return on assets: 19.5%
Return on equity: —
Current ratio: 1.20
Cash ($ mil.): 1

ALLEGIS GROUP, INC.

Allegis Group is one of the world's largest staffing and recruitment firms. Among its group of staffing companies are Aerotek (engineering automotive and scientific professionals) Aston Carter (recruitment for accounting finance and professional skills) and TEKsystems (information technology staffing and consulting). Other Allegis Group units include sales support outsourcer MarketSource. Allegis Group operates through more than 500 locations worldwide. Chairman Jim Davis helped found the company (originally known as Aerotek) in 1983 to provide contract engineering personnel to two clients in the aerospace industry.

Operations

Operating through a group of about 10 companies Allegis Group serves businesses and organizations from the engineering automotive finance IT life sciences and other industries. The company also serves government agencies and subcontractors. Aerotek and TEKsystems are among the group's largest and most established companies; other Allegis companies provide niche services including disability recruitment through its Getting Hired unit and legal recruitment though Major Lindsey & Africa.

Allegis Group's core services include staffing and recruitment (screening onboarding and retention) search (CEO and board member services) talent advisory (executive report data file and segment analysis) managed delivery and workforce management.

Geographic Reach

Hanover Maryland-based Allegis Group operates in more than 500 locations around the globe including offices throughout the US the UK and Europe as well as in the Middle East Asia and Asia Pacific region.

Sales and Marketing

Allegis Group has served approximately 20000 clients.

Company Background

In 1983 Stephen Bisciotti and Jim Davis founded the company (originally known as Aerotek) in Maryland. At the time the founders' firm matched job seekers with aeronautics engineering and light industrial positions. In the late 1980s the company expanded into the IT application markets.

Aerotek extended its reach into commercial environmental and energy industries through its 2001 acquisition of Onsite Companies. The company later changed its name to Allegis Group while the other divisions remained separate companies until eventually consolidating under the Allegis Group banner.

EXECUTIVES

It Vice President Of Finance, Celeste Slifer
Cfo, Paul J. Bowie
President, Andy Hilger
Senior Vice President, Mary Pat Smith
Vice President National Account Director At Allegis Rpo, John Markey
Vice President Human Resources, Tanya Axenson
Chairman, James C. (Jim) Davis
Auditors: PRICEWATERHOUSECOOPERS LLP B

LOCATIONS

HQ: ALLEGIS GROUP, INC.
7301 PARKWAY DR, HANOVER, MD 210761159
Phone: 410 579-3000
Web: WWW.ALLEGISGROUP.COM

PRODUCTS/OPERATIONS

Selected Subsidiaries

Aerotek
- Aerotek Aviation LLC
- Aerotek Canada
- Aerotek Scientific LLC

Allegis Group Canada
Allegis Group India
Major Lindsey & Africa
MarketSource Inc
Stephen James Associates
TEKsystems
- TEKsystems Canada
- TEKsystems Netherlands
- TEKsystems United Kingdom

COMPETITORS

ASG Renaissance
Adecco
CDI
Curran Partners
ExecuNet
Heidrick & Struggles
Horton International
Innovative Management Solutions Group
Kelly Services
Korn/Ferry
ManpowerGroup
RDL Corporation
Randstad Holding
Robert Half
Snelling Staffing
Volt Information

HISTORICAL FINANCIALS

Company Type: Private

Income Statement — FYE: December 31

	REVENUE ($ mil.)	NET INCOME ($ mil.)	NET PROFIT MARGIN	EMPLOYEES
12/19	13,583	0	—	85,000
12/18	13,402	0	—	—
12/17	12,296	0	—	—
12/16	11,502	0	—	—
Annual Growth	5.7%	—	—	—

2019 Year-End Financials

Return on assets: —
Return on equity: —
Current ratio: 3.90
Cash ($ mil.): 841

ALLEGRO MICROSYSTEMS, LLC

Allegro MicroSystems' chips don't need touch to make contact. The company is one of the world's top makers of Hall-effect sensors which reduce mechanical wear by using magnets to produce contactless sensors. Automakers use these specialized components – named after an electromagnetic phenomenon called "the Hall effect" – in braking steering suspension and other systems. Allegro also makes power integrated circuits (ICs) used in portable electronics along with driver controller and power interface ICs used in a variety of applications. The company is a subsidiary of Sanken Electric.

Operations

Allegro also offers linear and angle position sensors transmission sensors ICs and various types of switches and latches

Geographic Reach

Allegro is headquartered in Manchester New Hampshire. The company has more than 15 offices located in Argentina Uruguay Italy the UK Czech Republic France Germany the Philippines South Korea Taiwan Thailand China and Japan.

Sales and Marketing

Its products are sold primarily to OEMs through a sales channel that includes a direct sales force manufacturers representatives and distributors such as Digi-Key.

Strategy

Allegro has continued its investment in R&D to produce innovative better offerings to customers. In 2020 the company launched the world's first standalone Hall-based coreless current sensor the industry's first fully-integrated back-biased GMR transmission speed and direction sensor and the ACS37002 family of advanced Hall-effect current sensors.

The company also acquired Voxtel to leverage its significant laser and imaging expertise in the production of Allegro's next generation Advanced Driver Assistance Systems (ADAS).

Mergers and Acquisitions

In 2020 Allegro acquired Voxtel Inc a privately held company specializing in advanced photonic and 3D imaging technology including long-range eye-safe Light Detection and Ranging (LiDAR). This acquisition brings together Voxtel's significant laser and imaging expertise with Allegro's automotive leadership and scale to enable the next generation of Advanced Driver Assistance Systems (ADAS).

EXECUTIVES

Ceo, Ravi Vig
Cfo*, Mark A Feragne
V Pres*, Andre G Labrecque
Exec V Pres*, Yoshihiro Suzuki
V Pres*, Steven Miles
Treas*, Diane Macaluso
Marketing Manager, Walter Sullivan Jr
Assistant Engineer, Nathan B Baribeau
Layout, Peter Van Hoesen
Assistant Engineer, Patricia Borglund
Tech, Edward Beaudoin

LOCATIONS

HQ: ALLEGRO MICROSYSTEMS, LLC
955 PERIMETER RD, MANCHESTER, NH 031033353
Phone: 603 626-2300
Web: WWW.ALLEGROMICRO.COM

PRODUCTS/OPERATIONS

Selected Products

Current sensor integrated circuits (ICs)
- Conductor sensor chips
- High-side hot-swap Hall-effect current monitor chips

Magnetic digital position sensor chips
- Bipolar switches
- Dual-element switches
- Hall-effect latches and bipolar switches
- Hall-effect unipolar switches
- Micropower switches and latches

Magnetic linear and angular position sensor chips
- Angular position sensor chips
- Linear position sensor chips

Magnetic speed sensor ICs (camshaft crankshaft transmission and wheel-speed sensor ICs)
Motor driver and interface ICs
- Bipolar stepper motor drivers
- Brushless DC motor drivers
- Photo and ion smoke detector ICs

Regulators and lighting
- LED drivers for backlighting and lighting
- Regulators (single-output multiple output low-noise block)
- Xenon photoflash drivers

COMPETITORS

Fairchild Semiconductor
Honeywell International
Infineon Technologies
Maxim Integrated Products
Micronas Semiconductor
Micropac Industries
NVE
NXP Semiconductors
ON Semiconductor
Optek Technology
Power Integrations
STMicroelectronics
Sypris Solutions
Texas Instruments
Toshiba Semiconductor & Storage Products
Vishay Intertechnology

HISTORICAL FINANCIALS

Company Type: Private

Income Statement — FYE: March 30

	REVENUE ($ mil.)	NET INCOME ($ mil.)	NET PROFIT MARGIN	EMPLOYEES
03/18	654	72	11.1%	3,500
03/17	600	65	10.9%	—
03/16	526	43	8.3%	—
03/13	489	45	9.3%	—
Annual Growth	6.0%	9.7%	—	—

2018 Year-End Financials

Return on assets: 12.1%
Return on equity: 14.8%
Current ratio: 3.40
Cash ($ mil.): 114

ALLEN LUND COMPANY, LLC

The Allen Lund Company (ALC) knows loads; it matches shippers' loads with a network of truckload and less-than-truckload (LTL) carriers. (LTL carriers collect consolidate and haul freight from multiple shippers.) The brokerage firm arranges the transport of dry refrigerated (predominantly produce) and flatbed cargo. It operates from 30 offices throughout more than 20 US states. ALC Logistics ALC Perishable Logistics and ALC International (an international division) assist shippers in managing transportation costs tracking and tracing shipments managing appointments and executing freight forward management services overseas. The company was founded in 1976 by Allen Lund and his wife Kathie Lund.

Operations

ALC has a Logistics & Software division ALC Logistics.

Geographic Reach

The company's international division provides transportation services worldwide along with transportation to and from the US including Puerto Rico Hawaii Alaska and ground transportation for Canada and Mexico.

Strategy

In an effort to expand its operation in 2012 the company opened a new office in Joplin Missouri and another in McAllen Texas which mainly focuses on handling heavy haul flatbed particularly in and out of Mexico. In addition the company opened four additional offices in 2012.

Mergers and Acquisitions

In an effort to grow its business in early 2014 ALC acquired Wisconsin based Northern Freight Service Inc. a company provides truckload LTL and intermodal services to the customers ranging from small shippers to FORTUNE 500 shippers.

EXECUTIVES

Vice President Sales And Branch Operations, Ed Lund

Vice President Of Operations, Kenneth Lund

LOCATIONS

HQ: ALLEN LUND COMPANY, LLC
4529 ANGELES CREST HWY, LA CANADA FLINTRIDGE, CA 910113247

Phone: 818 790-8412

Web: WWW.ALLENLUND.COM

PRODUCTS/OPERATIONS

Selected Services

Software and Logistics
- LTL Freight
- Scheduling
- Spot Pricing and Bid Management
- Truck Load

Transportation Services
- Dry Van
- Flatbed Trucking
- International Freight Shipping
- LTL Freight
- Refrigerated Transportation

COMPETITORS

C.H. Robinson Worldwide
CEVA Logistics
Ryder System
Universal Logistics

HISTORICAL FINANCIALS

Company Type: Private

Income Statement — FYE: December 31

	REVENUE ($ mil.)	NET INCOME ($ mil.)	NET PROFIT MARGIN	EMPLOYEES
12/18	661	20	3.0%	310
12/17	515	10	2.0%	—
12/16	426	12	2.9%	—
12/15	457	13	2.9%	—
Annual Growth	13.1%	15.1%	—	—

2018 Year-End Financials

Return on assets: 19.6%
Return on equity: 44.0%
Current ratio: 1.70
Cash ($ mil.): 32

ALLIANCE LAUNDRY HOLDINGS LLC

Laundry day can't come often enough for Alliance Laundry Holdings (ALH). Through its wholly owned subsidiary Alliance Laundry Systems the company designs makes and markets commercial laundry equipment used in Laundromats multi-housing laundry facilities (such as apartments dormitories and military bases) and on-premise laundries (hotels hospitals and prisons). Its washers and dryers are sold under the brands Speed Queen UniMac Huebsch IPSO and Cissell. They're sold primarily in the US and Canada but also overseas. Investment firm BDT Capital Partners controls the company which was founded in 1908.

Operations

Commercial laundry equipment service and parts account for 98% of the firm's revenue. It also operates an equipment financing business which accounts for the rest.

Geographic Reach

North America is Wisconsin-based ALH's largest market accounting for about 70% of sales. Europe and Asia each represent about 10% of sales. The remainder comes from markets in Latin America the Middle East and Africa. The company's manufacturing facilities are located in Wisconsin and Wevelgem Belgium.

Sales and Marketing

ALH relies on an expansive distribution network to bring its goods to market. The company's more than 550 distributors in North America and 150-plus international distributors serve its Laundromat and on-premise laundry customers. Its multi-family housing laundry customers are served by ALH's roster of more than 100 route operators.

Financial Performance

The company's sales topped $505 million in 2012 a 10% increase compared with 2011. Net income fell 30% over the same period to $16.4 million as a result of a loss from early retirement of debt and higher expenses. The company attributed the gain in sales (its third in as many years) to increases across all of its markets with the exception of Europe. Increased sales volumes and price increases primarily in the US and Canada drove results. The strong performance over the past three years pushed sales to an all-time high following a drop-off during the recession.

Strategy

Despite difficult economic conditions globally ALH has seen its business strengthen driven by resilience in North America and international expansion. (The company is fortunate that consumers view clean clothes as an necessity with economic conditions historically having limited effect on frequency of use of commercial laundry equipment.) In the US and Canada the equipment financing business is posting higher earnings and demand for commercial laundry equipment is rising. Markets in Latin America including Colombia Peru and Venezuela are driving double-digit sales growth in the region. Expansion in Asia in such markets as Australia China the Philippines and Thailand is another growth driver.

In pursuit of future growth in 2013 the company completed a $23 million investment to increase production capacity for current and new products and to purchase tooling and equipment for its plant in Wisconsin. The expansion added more than 20000 square feet to the plant's existing assembly metal stampingand press shop facilities. The project increased ALH's production capacity for small chassis washers and dryers by more than 40% enabling the company to meet increasing consumer demand for its products.

EXECUTIVES

MBR, Thomas F Lesperance
MBR, Bruce Rounds
MBR, William Przybysz
MBR, Scott Gaster
MBR, Robert T Wallace
Procurement Coordinator, Caitlyn Smith
Customer Support Representativ, Dan Miracle
Desktop Administrator, Elvis Rosario
Sales Assistant, Jennifer Dych
Associate Payables Clerk, Jill Jahn
Warranty Coordinator, Jodi Deford
Auditors: PRICEWATERHOUSECOOPERS MILWAU

LOCATIONS

HQ: ALLIANCE LAUNDRY HOLDINGS LLC
221 SHEPARD ST, RIPON, WI 549711390

Phone: 920 748-3121

Web: WWW.ALLIANCELAUNDRY.COM

COMPETITORS

BSH Bosch und Siemens Hausger ote
Electrolux
GE Appliances & Lighting
Haier Group
Miele
Whirlpool

HISTORICAL FINANCIALS

Company Type: Private

Income Statement — FYE: December 31

	REVENUE ($ mil.)	NET INCOME ($ mil.)	NET PROFIT MARGIN	EMPLOYEES
12/14	726	29	4.1%	2,100
12/12	505	16	3.2%	—
12/09	393	16	4.2%	—
Annual Growth	13.1%	12.3%	—	—

2014 Year-End Financials

Return on assets: 2.4%
Return on equity: 31.0%
Current ratio: 1.40
Cash ($ mil.): 48

ALLIED SECURITY HOLDINGS LLC

Better than a blanket Allied Security Holdings gives customers a sense of security. One of the largest private contract security firms in the US it does business as AlliedBarton Security Services. It recruits and employs trained security guards to serve thousands of customers (some of which are large FORTUNE 500 companies) and their facilities. They include government facilities hospitals offices ports residential communities shopping centers and universities. The firm also provides employment and background screening services through its HR Plus subsidiary. In mid-2016 AlliedBarton merged with Universal Services of America to create Allied Universal North America's largest security services group.

EXECUTIVES

Vice President Information Technology, Betty Ritts
Regional Vice President, Jason Stapleton
Regional Vice President, Rafael Sorto

LOCATIONS

HQ: ALLIED SECURITY HOLDINGS LLC
161 WASHINGTON ST STE 600, CONSHOHOCKEN, PA 194282083
Phone: 484 351-1300
Web: WWW.ALLIEDBARTON.COM

COMPETITORS

AFI International	Kroll
Asset Protection & Security Services	Securitas
Command Security	TransNational Security
G4S Secure Solutions	Walden Security
Guardsmark	Whelan Security

HISTORICAL FINANCIALS

Company Type: Private

Income Statement — FYE: December 31

	REVENUE ($ mil.)	NET INCOME ($ mil.)	NET PROFIT MARGIN	EMPLOYEES
12/14	2,149	24	1.1%	53,760
12/13	2,042	51	2.5%	—
12/12	1,923	43	2.3%	—
Annual Growth	5.7%	(25.0%)	—	—

2014 Year-End Financials

Return on assets: 2.6%
Return on equity: —
Current ratio: 1.80
Cash ($ mil.): 51

ALLIED UNIVERSAL HOLDCO LLC

EXECUTIVES

Ceo, Steve Jones
Regional Vice President, Craig Demartini
Client Manager, Anders Siverling
Site Supervisor, Bryan Overton
Supervisor, Dustin Rost
Operations Manager, Eric Hartley
Branch Manager, Herbert Morency
Human Resources Coordinator, Jill English
Director of Security, John Lopez
Site Supervisor Raytheon Sas O, Jose Rincon
Account Manager (security Spec, Joseph Nelson

LOCATIONS

HQ: ALLIED UNIVERSAL HOLDCO LLC
1551 N TUSTIN AVE STE 650, SANTA ANA, CA 927058664
Phone: 866 877-1965
Web: WWW.AUS.COM

HISTORICAL FINANCIALS

Company Type: Private

Income Statement — FYE: December 31

	ASSETS ($ mil.)	NET INCOME ($ mil.)	INCOME AS % OF ASSETS	EMPLOYEES
12/19	6,432	(381)	—	88,000
12/17	4,451	(69)	—	—
Annual Growth	20.2%	—	—	—

2019 Year-End Financials

Return on assets: (-5.9%)
Return on equity: (-77.7%)
Sales ($ mil): 7,461

ALLINA HEALTH SYSTEM

Allina Health System is a not-for-profit health care system that works to protect people's #1 asset – their good health. The system owns and operates a dozen hospitals a network of nearly 100 clinics and specialty centers and a whole bunch of pharmacies. It has licensed bed capacity of 2451 acute care beds. Its vast system of provider locations serve residents throughout Minnesota and western Wisconsin providing disease prevention programs along with specialized inpatient and outpatient services. Allina's Aspen Medical Group division also operates a range of outpatient clinics providing primary and specialty care.

Operations

Allina has 12 hospitals (about 1800 beds) more than 90 clinics and 15 pharmacies. The largest hospital in the group is Abbott Northwestern Hospital (600 beds) followed by United Hospital which has about 570 beds. Five of Allina's hospitals are in the Minneapolis/St. Paul metropolitan area (where the system has more than a 30% share of the health care market) five are scattered throughout the rest of Minnesota and one is in western Wisconsin. The health system reported more than 103000 inpatient admissions in 2016; it also had some 1.4 million outpatient admissions. Each year it has around 360000 emergency care visits about 16000 births and more than 7 million clinic visits.

Regina Hospital has a 57-bed acute care hospital a 61-bed skilled care nursing home and a 134-bed assisted living facility. It also operates three outpatient multi-specialty clinics. Located in Minneapolis/St. Paul District One Hospital provides a broad range of health care services to Faribault and the surrounding communities.

Geographic Reach

The health care system's hospitals are located in Burnsville Champlin Coon Rapids Edina Inver Grove Heights Maplewood Plymouth St. Paul Shakopee and Woodbury in Minnesota and in River Falls in Wisconsin.

Financial Performance

In 2016 Allina Health had $3.9 billion in revenue a 4% increase over the prior year thanks to a 3% gain on hospital net patient revenue. A nurse's strike cut into operating income and the system reported a $27.4 million operating loss in 2016 (versus operating income of $155.3 million in 2015). Among the striking nurses' complaints was the Minnesota Nurses Association's allegations that estimate Allina Health has lost $80 million investing in interest-rate swaps – $80 million that could have been used to improve pay benefits and patient care.

Strategy

Despite Allina's already hefty size the system has a partnership with retail clinic provider MinuteClinic which offers basic health care at CVS Health stores. The hospital also has a multi-year collaboration with HealthPartners designed to reduce total medical costs at both hospitals.

In early 2017 Allina Health and insurance giant Aetna created a health plan joint venture – Allina Health and Aetna Insurance Company – to serve employers and individuals in the Minneapolis/St. Paul area. The venture is designed to streamline the patient experience by coordinating health care services with insurance benefits and administrative services.

The system's wide-ranging locations combined with its huge number of facilities have prompted Allina to embark on a multi-year initiative to install electronic medical records (EMR) at all of its hospitals and clinics. The installation gives medical providers the ability to track a patient's progress through any of the myriad health care settings operated by Allina. The EMR also gives patients access to coordinated care between the different providers as well as the ability to see portions of their medical records and lab results online. Patients can also schedule appointments and make use of a number of health and wellness tools all via the internet.

Allina was the first Minnesota health care organization to earn the Davies Award the industry's preeminent award for health information technology.

EXECUTIVES

System Vp; President Mercy Hospital, Sara Criger
Evp Clinics And Home Care Services, Robert A. Wieland
Ceo, Penny Ann Wheeler
System Vp; President Abbott Northwestern Hospital, Ben Bache-Wiig
System Vp; President United Hospital, Thomas (Tom) O'Connor
Evp Administration And Cfo, Duncan P. Gallagher
Evp Hospital And Specialty Services, Daniel McGinty
Pharmacy Manager, Matthew Wolf
Director Of Pharmacy, Jill Strykowski
Director Of Pharmacy Ambulatory, Lee Mork
Vice President Of Marketing, Cathy Runck
Director Of Nursing, Karen Tennis
Vice President Of Information Technology, Adrian Lewis
Senior Vice President And Chief Information Office, Jonathan Shoemaker
Medical Director, John Mageli
Vice President Of Patient Care Services, Maribeth Olson
Senior Vice President Finance And Treasury, Richard Magnuson
Vice President Payor Contract Reimb, Margaret Hasbrouck
Medical Director, Walter Galicich
Medical Director, Mahmoud Nagib
Senior Vice President, Lisa Smith
Vice President Patient Care Services, Sue Miller
Vice President Of Medical Affairs, Ryan Else
Vice President Of Cardiovascular Services, Mike Rasmussen
Vice President Medical Affairs, Dennis O'hare

Vice President Medical Staff Services Resources And Administration, Jacqueline Moen
Medical Director, Amy Mcdaniel
Medical Director, Tara Bizily
Chairman, Mark S. Jordahl
Treasurer, Anne Uttermark
Auditors: KPMG LLP MINNEAPOLIS MINNESO

LOCATIONS

HQ: ALLINA HEALTH SYSTEM
2925 CHICAGO AVE, MINNEAPOLIS, MN 554071321
Phone: 612 262-5000
Web: WWW.ALLINAHEALTH.ORG

PRODUCTS/OPERATIONS

Selected Services

Care at home
Chronic and advanced illness
Clinics
Home oxygen and medical equipment
Hospitals
Lab services
Medical Services
Medical transportation
Pharmacies
Providers
Specialty services
Urgent care

Selected Hospitals

Abbott Northwestern Hospital (Minneapolis MN)
Buffalo Hospital (Buffalo MN)
Cambridge Medical Center (Cambridge MN)
District One Hospital (Faribault MN)
Mercy Hospital (Coon Rapids MN)
New Ulm Medical Center (New Ulm MN)
Owatonna Hospital (Owatonna MN)
Phillips Eye Institute (Minneapolis MN)
Regina Hospital (Hastings MN)
River Falls Area Hospital (River Falls WI)
St. Francis Regional Medical Center (Shakopee MN)
United Hospital (St. Paul MN)
Unity Hospital (Fridley MN)

COMPETITORS

Bethesda Hospital
Catholic Health Initiatives
CentraCare Health
Children's Hospitals and Clinics of Minnesota
Fairview Health
Hazelden Betty Ford
HealthEast Care System
Mayo Clinic
Methodist Hospital (MN)
North Memorial Health Care
Park Nicollet Health Services
Regions Hospital
St. John's Hospital (Minnesota)
University of Minnesota Medical Center

HISTORICAL FINANCIALS

Company Type: Private

Income Statement — FYE: December 31

	REVENUE ($ mil.)	NET INCOME ($ mil.)	NET PROFIT MARGIN	EMPLOYEES
12/17	4,279	173	4.0%	26,400
12/16	3,947	74	1.9%	—
Annual Growth	8.4%	131.3%	—	—

2017 Year-End Financials

Return on assets: 3.8%
Return on equity: 6.4%
Current ratio: 0.60
Cash ($ mil.): 36

ALLWAYS HEALTH PARTNERS, INC.

Neighborhood Health Plan (NHP) is a not-for-profit health plan provider that offers health insurance products and related services to more than 300000 members in Massachusetts. The organization is a leading provider of managed health care for members of MassHealth the state's Medicaid program for low-income and disabled residents. But it also provides commercial health plans for small businesses as well as low-cost and no-cost family and individual plans for people who qualify for subsidized health coverage under Massachusetts' 2006 health care reform law. NHP maintains a provider network of more than 4300 primary care physicians 13000 specialists and dozens of hospitals. The company was founded in 1986.

Sales and Marketing

NHP markets its products to individuals families and employers.

Its care network includes primary care providers specialists and hospitals such as Massachusetts General Hospital and Boston Children's Hospital. It also includes community health centers across the state.

In 2015 NHP hired Mechanica to manage its marketing branding and advertising efforts.

Strategy

The company's Partnership for Community Health initiative with Partners HealthCare with the Massachusetts League of Community Health Centers announced $6 million in grants for community health centers throughout Massachusetts.

In 2013 NHP was granted approval to expand coverage into Greater Plymouth County.

EXECUTIVES

President And Ceo, David Segal
Chief Medical Officer, Paul Mendis
Vp Operations And Cio, Marilyn Daly
Vp Operations, Katie Catlender
Interim Cfo, Doug Thompson
Vice President Of Clinical Operations, Deb Bonin
Senior Medical Director, Jim Glauber
Chairman, Matthew E. Fishman
Board Member, Pablo Rodriguez

LOCATIONS

HQ: ALLWAYS HEALTH PARTNERS, INC.
399 REVOLUTION DR, SOMERVILLE, MA 021451444
Phone: 617 772-5500
Web: WWW.NHP.ORG

COMPETITORS

Aetna
Blue Cross and Blue Shield of Massachusetts
CIGNA
ConnectiCare
Fallon Community Health Plan
Harvard Pilgrim
Health New England
MVP Health Plan
Tufts Health Plan
UnitedHealth Group

HISTORICAL FINANCIALS

Company Type: Private

Income Statement — FYE: December 31

	REVENUE ($ mil.)	NET INCOME ($ mil.)	NET PROFIT MARGIN	EMPLOYEES
12/15	2,178	(22)	—	340
12/14	1,743	(108)	—	—
12/13	1,380	(68)	—	—
Annual Growth	25.6%	—	—	—

2015 Year-End Financials

Return on assets: (-4.9%)
Return on equity: (-11.6%)
Current ratio: 0.90
Cash ($ mil.): 120

ALLY BANK

Ally Bank is on your side when it comes to banking. Formerly known as GMAC Bank Ally Bank (which is a subsidiary of government-backed Ally Financial) offers savings and money market accounts as well as traditional and no-penalty CDs. The online bank also offers interest checking accounts. The bank offers its services online and over the phone; it operates no physical branch locations. Clients also can use any ATM in the US and Ally will reimburse any fees charged by other banks. Ally Bank was revamped and renamed in 2009 in the midst of GM's (very public) financial difficulties. Predecessor GMAC Bank had been in operation since 2001.

EXECUTIVES

Chb-Pres-Ceo, Diane E Morais
Exec V Pres, Jeffrey J Brown
Cfo, James N Young
SEC, Cathy L Quenneville
Director of Remarketing Sales, Mark Juday
Area Sales Manager, Anthony Stoothoff
CRA Officer, Jan Bergeson
Senior Credit Manager, Anthony Zimmer
Bank Compliance Manager, Brett Hoskin

LOCATIONS

HQ: ALLY BANK
6985 S UNION PARK CTR # 435, MIDVALE, UT 840474177
Phone: 801 790-5005
Web: WWW.ALLY.COM

COMPETITORS

Bank of America
BofI
Charles Schwab
Citibank
E*TRADE Bank
State Farm

HISTORICAL FINANCIALS

Company Type: Private

Income Statement — FYE: December 31

	ASSETS ($ mil.)	NET INCOME ($ mil.)	INCOME AS % OF ASSETS	EMPLOYEES
12/16	123,547	1,273	1.0%	42
12/07*	28,472	291	1.0%	—
06/06	3,586	0	0.0%	—
Annual Growth	38.0%	114.3%	—	—

*Fiscal year change

2016 Year-End Financials

Return on assets: 1.0%
Return on equity: 7.2%
Sales ($ mil): 6,427

ALMOST FAMILY, INC.

EXECUTIVES

Pres, Steven Guenthner
Graphic Designer, Lisa Landers
Senior Living Coordinator, Jackie Alexander
Account Executive, Bob Magowan
Quality Director Clinical Serv, Carol Morley
Team Lead, Holly Pardo
Desktop Support Specialist, Jordan Logsdon
Corporate Marketing Manager, Marygen Boley
AP Specialist, Antonette Moore
Account Executive, Ashley Amundsen
Authorization, Betty Muller
Auditors: ERNST & YOUNG LLP LOUISVILLE

LOCATIONS

HQ: ALMOST FAMILY, INC.
9510 ORMSBY STATION RD # 300, LOUISVILLE, KY 402235016
Phone: 502 891-1000
Web: WWW.ALMOSTFAMILY.COM

COMPETITORS

Amedisys	HCR ManorCare
Apria Healthcare	Home Instead
Capital Senior Living	Hooper Holmes
Chemed	LHC Group
Continucare	NHC
Diversicare Healthcare Services	National Home Health
Gentiva	Odyssey HealthCare
Girling Health Care	Providence Service
	U.S. Physical Therapy

HISTORICAL FINANCIALS

Company Type: Private

Income Statement FYE: December 29

	REVENUE ($ mil.)	NET INCOME ($ mil.)	NET PROFIT MARGIN	EMPLOYEES
12/17	796	20	2.6%	14,200
12/16*	623	18	2.9%	—
01/16	532	19	3.7%	—
12/14	495	13	2.7%	—
Annual Growth	17.1%	14.7%	—	—

*Fiscal year change

2017 Year-End Financials

Return on assets: 2.8%
Return on equity: 4.0%
Current ratio: 2.00
Cash ($ mil.): 11

ALPINE SCHOOL DISTRICT

EXECUTIVES

Supt, Vern Henshaw
Supt, Samuel Y Jarman
Coordinator, Alex Goold
Accounting Staff, Steven Reese
Public Information Director, David Stephenson
Coordinator, Barbara Langford
Director, Adam Dajany
Research/Development Director, David Mower
Director of Teacher Personnel, John Spencer
Administrative Vice President, Jim Melville
Transportation Director, DOT Dean
Auditors: SQUIRER & COMPANY PC OREM U

LOCATIONS

HQ: ALPINE SCHOOL DISTRICT
575 N 100 E, AMERICAN FORK, UT 840031758
Phone: 801 610-8400
Web: WWW.ALPINESCHOOLS.ORG

HISTORICAL FINANCIALS

Company Type: Private

Income Statement FYE: June 30

	REVENUE ($ mil.)	NET INCOME ($ mil.)	NET PROFIT MARGIN	EMPLOYEES
06/20	757	(78)	—	8,000
06/19	726	(44)	—	—
06/18	680	77	11.4%	—
06/17	638	129	20.3%	—
Annual Growth	5.9%	—	—	—

ALRO STEEL CORPORATION

Alro Steel runs its service centers like a grocery store for metals keeping what customers need in easy reach. The service center operator which has a dozen facilities in the US Northeast Midwest and Southeast provides processing services such as aluminum circle cutting CNC flame cutting forming and machining. The company carries an extensive inventory of steel products along with industrial tools and supplies. It also offers plastic sheet rod tube and film through its Alro Plastics division and distributes industrial tools and materials through subsidiary Alro Industrial Supplies.

Operations

Led by its steel activities Alro Steel operates several other businesses: Alro Metals Service Center Alro Metals Plus (steel bars plates and sheet and brass copper aluminum and other products); Alro Plastics (fiberglass acrylics nylon urethanes and other); and Alro Industrial Supplies (threading milling boring holemaking reaming and other machinery and equipment).

Geographic Reach

Alro Steel has more than 50 facilities in 12 US states (Florida Illinois Indiana Kentucky Michigan Missouri New York North Carolina Ohio Oklahoma Pennsylvania and Wisconsin).

Sales and Marketing

The company distributes metals industrial supplies and plastics through its online store.

Strategy

Alro Steel is expanding its operations to meet demand.

In 2014 the company expanded its presence in Greensboro North Carolina by opening a 42000-sq.-ft. facility. It plans to potentially double the work force there within five years.

In 2013 it opened a new 70000 sq. ft. facility in St. Louis to provide regional manufacturers with Alro's broad range of metal products and extensive processing capabilities. That year the company also opened a new 98000 sq. ft. facility in Imperial Pennsylvania to serve manufacturers in western and central Pennsylvania and northern West Virginia.

Company Background

The company was established in 1948.

EXECUTIVES

Board Member, Jason Cook
Auditors: DELOITTE & TOUCHE LLP DETRO

LOCATIONS

HQ: ALRO STEEL CORPORATION
3100 E HIGH ST, JACKSON, MI 492036413
Phone: 517 787-5500
Web: WWW.MADEINJACKSON.COM

COMPETITORS

Carlisle Companies	Mill Steel
Central Steel & Wire	Peerless Steel
Contractors Steel	
Flame Metals Processing	

HISTORICAL FINANCIALS

Company Type: Private

Income Statement FYE: May 31

	REVENUE ($ mil.)	NET INCOME ($ mil.)	NET PROFIT MARGIN	EMPLOYEES
05/20	1,941	149	7.7%	2,400
05/19	2,213	198	9.0%	—
05/18	1,989	165	8.3%	—
Annual Growth	(1.2%)	(5.1%)	—	—

ALSCO INC.

Alsco has built a big business outfitting its customers in uniforms linens and related products. Operating from more than 180 branches in more than 10 countries worldwide the company rents and sells uniforms linens towels napkins and soft blankets to approximately 355000 customers worldwide. It also manages janitorial services provides washroom supplies and soap and sanitizer service. In addition Alsco provides professional textile rental services and offers First aid that is fresh and budget friendly. The company was founded in 1889 by George Steiner and is still owned and operated by the Steiner family. It is headquartered in Utah has locations in Australia Brazil Canada China Germany Italy New Zealand Singapore Malaysia Thailand and the US.

Sales and Marketing

Alsco serves customers in various industries including automotive food processing facilities healthcare restaurant and industrial sector. The company sell its products through its retail stores located across North America.

Strategy

In July 2020 Alsco announced the construction of a new state-of-the-art processing facility which will employ 200 people and include over 95000 square feet of advanced improvements. The new facility comprises cutting?edge technology to reduce Alsco's impact on the environment. This includes a ceramic filtration system that promotes water savings and energy reduction by allowing the plant to reuse approximately 70% of its water. The new facility will be located in and continue to serve the greater Houston Texas area allowing Alsco to keep pace with the expected growth in the metropolitan area.

EXECUTIVES

Vice President Finance And Chief Financial Officer, Jim Kearns
Treasurer, Jennifer Whitt-duke

LOCATIONS

HQ: ALSCO INC.
505 E 200 S STE 101, SALT LAKE CITY, UT 841022053
Phone: 801 328-8831
Web: WWW.ALSCO.COM

PRODUCTS/OPERATIONS

Selected Products and Services

Clean room garments
Gown room management
Hospitality/restaurant apparel
Laundry services
Linens
Mats
Mops
Napkins
Restroom service
Towels
Uniform rental and sales
Vacuum filters
Washroom supplies

COMPETITORS

ARAMARK
Angelica Corporation
Berendsen
Cintas
Crothall Healthcare
Diversey
Ecolab
G&K Services
Healthcare Services
ISS A/S
Rentokil Initial
ServiceMaster
Sodexo USA
Superior Uniform Group
Swisher Hygiene
Tranzonic
UniFirst

HISTORICAL FINANCIALS

Company Type: Private

Income Statement — FYE: December 31

	REVENUE ($ mil.)	NET INCOME ($ mil.)	NET PROFIT MARGIN	EMPLOYEES
12/18	922	25	2.7%	16,000
12/17	892	64	7.2%	—
12/16	704	38	5.5%	—
12/15	683	30	4.5%	—
Annual Growth	10.5%	(6.5%)	—	—

2018 Year-End Financials

Return on assets: 2.2%
Return on equity: 3.8%
Current ratio: 1.70
Cash ($ mil.): 34

ALSTON CONSTRUCTION COMPANY, INC.

Panattoni Construction Inc. (PCI) is in the business of building businesses. The design/build general contractor specializes in commercial and industrial construction projects which include manufacturing and distribution facilities master-planned business parks and office and retail buildings. The company provides construction management services for such clients as Clorox Amazon.com PetSmart and Whirlpool.The company's project portfolio ranges from smaller 2500 sq. ft offices to large warehouses spanning more than one million sq. ft. PCI operates from 20 offices in Arizona California Colorado Florida Georgia Illinois Indiana Missouri Nevada New Jersey Oregon Tennessee Texas and Washington.

EXECUTIVES

Vice President, Jim Wegman
Vice President General Manager, William Hancock
Auditors: CAMPBELL TAYLOR WASHBURN ROSE

LOCATIONS

HQ: ALSTON CONSTRUCTION COMPANY, INC.
8775 FOLSOM BLVD STE 201, SACRAMENTO, CA 958263725
Phone: 916 340-2400
Web: WWW.ALSTONCO.COM

COMPETITORS

Alter Group
Balfour Beatty Construction
Bechtel
Fluor
H and M Construction
KPRS Construction
Skanska USA Building
Turner Corporation

HISTORICAL FINANCIALS

Company Type: Private

Income Statement — FYE: December 31

	REVENUE ($ mil.)	NET INCOME ($ mil.)	NET PROFIT MARGIN	EMPLOYEES
12/19	1,271	18	1.5%	200
12/18	909	14	1.6%	—
12/17	865	13	1.6%	—
12/15	642	6	1.1%	—
Annual Growth	18.6%	28.4%	—	—

2019 Year-End Financials

Return on assets: 5.8%
Return on equity: 54.2%
Current ratio: 1.10
Cash ($ mil.): 50

ALTICOR INC.

Where there's a will (and an army of independent sales representatives) there's Amway. Operated through holding company Alticor Amway is the world's top direct-selling company with millions of individual ABOs (Amway Business Owners) pitching everything from air filters to vitamins. The company makes some 450 unique products across the categories of nutrition (which generates about half of sales) beauty and personal care and home. It is active in more than 100 countries across the globe with Asia (led by China) its largest market. Alticor is controlled by the families of Rich DeVos and Jay Van Andel who founded Amway in 1959.

Operations

Nutrition products (supplements skin care products weight management programs) account for about 50% of total Amway sales. Beauty and personal care items (makeup shampoo toothpaste) generate about a quarter of sales and home products (water and air filters cookware cleaners) contribute about 20%. The company's top products include Nutrilite supplements Artistry color cosmetics eSpring water treatment systems and XS energy drinks.

Geographic Reach

Based in Ada Michigan Amway operates in more than 100 countries. Its top markets by sales are China the US and South Korea; other leading markets include India Japan Malaysia Russia Taiwan and Thailand.

The company has manufacturing facilities farms and warehouses in Brazil China Hungary India Japan Mexico the Netherlands Poland Russia South Korea Taiwan Thailand Vietnam and the US.

Sales and Marketing

Amway's 450-plus products are marketing worldwide by more than 3 million independent distributors who purchase the products and resell them. The company provides a host of support services including personal mentors brand centers online learning tools and call centers.

Financial Performance

While privately-owned Alticor doesn't report full results Amway reported global sales of $8.6 billion in 2017 down from $8.8 billion in 2016.The company points to a challenging Chinese market for its revenue decline over the past few years

Strategy

Amway's strategy is pretty straight-forward: continue to enhance and expand its line of products to serve more markets and appeal to more customers and create tools that make selling those products easier for the 3+ million ABOs (Amway Business Owners).

In 2017 Amway introduced a new formula for its Nutrilife Double X product one of the best-selling supplements in the world that includes a phytonutrient blend designed to help the body fight free radicals. Other additions to the company's product portfolio that year include a reformulated Essentials by Artistry skincare line and its first in-car air filtration system Atmosphere Drive. Amway also pushed its XS brand of energy drinks into new countries in 2017 including China and India with more launches planned for 2018. The company has more than 800 patents worldwide and another 250 pending applications.

Direct selling of course looks a lot different in the age of Amazon than it did some 60 years ago when Amway was founded. The company has been making significant investment in tools and technologies in recent years to enable its ABOs to better compete. It has spent some $70 million in mobile apps for ABOs including the flagship Amway MyBiz app which provides back office data and analytics. In addition Amway has boosted its own customer service capabilities with instant messaging bots and other technologies to help it handle the more than 12 million annual customer requests. Other recent initiatives include a content sharing app for ABOs in the Philippines a beauty app for customers in South Korea and a one-stop product education and purchase portal in for ABOs in China.

EXECUTIVES

President And Director; President Amway; And President Quixtar, Doug DeVos
Vice President Information Service, Richard Holwill
Executive Vice President Of Sales Amway Regions, Jim Payne
General Vice President Attorney, Scott Balfour
Vice President Regulatory Affairs And Quality Assurance, John Coyle
Vice President Internal Audit, Nick Thole
Vp Human Resources, Kelly Savage
Vice President, Louis Huey
Chairman, Steve Van Andel
Treasurer, William G Roth
Tres, Jeffery C Tuori

LOCATIONS

HQ: ALTICOR INC.
7575 FULTON ST E, ADA, MI 493550001
Phone: 616 787-1000
Web: WWW.AMWAY.COM

PRODUCTS/OPERATIONS

2017 Sales

	% of total
Nutrition	50
Beauty & personal care	26
Home	21

Other	3
Total	**100**

Selected Brands

Nutrition
  Nutrilite
Beauty & personal care
  Artistry
  G&H
  Glister
  Satinique
Home
  Amway Home
  Atmosphere Sky
  eSpring
  iCook
Other
  XS

COMPETITORS

Avon
Bath & Body Works
Bluestem Brands
Colgate-Palmolive
Estée Lauder
Forever Living
GNC
Herbalife Ltd.
Johnson & Johnson
L'Oréal
Mary Kay
Melaleuca
New Avon
Newell Brands
Nikken
Nu Skin
Procter & Gamble
Revlon
Shaklee
Tupperware Brands
Unilever PLC

HISTORICAL FINANCIALS

Company Type: Private

Income Statement — FYE: December 31

	REVENUE ($ mil.)	NET INCOME ($ mil.)	NET PROFIT MARGIN	EMPLOYEES
12/15	9,459	0	—	14,000
12/14	10,804	0	—	—
12/13	11,754	0	—	—
Annual Growth	(10.3%)	—	—	—

2015 Year-End Financials

Return on assets: —
Return on equity: —
Current ratio: 1.20
Cash ($ mil.): 1,300

ALTISOURCE SOLUTIONS, INC.

EXECUTIVES

Ceo, William B Shepro
Cfo, Michelle Esterman
Coo, Marcello Mastioni
Facilities, CFM Herman
Supervisor, Gloria Luberger
Recruiting Coordinator, Theresa Strenio
Regional Field Manage, Andrew Davis
Director Infrastructure, Eric Placencia
Chief Revenue Officer, John A Vella
Chief Administration, Kevin J Wilcox
Auditors: DELOITTE & TOUCHE LLP ATLANT

LOCATIONS

HQ: ALTISOURCE SOLUTIONS, INC.
1000 ABERNATHY RD STE 200, ATLANTA, GA 303285604
Phone: 770 612-7007
Web: WWW.ALTISOURCE.COM

HISTORICAL FINANCIALS

Company Type: Private

Income Statement — FYE: December 31

	ASSETS ($ mil.)	NET INCOME ($ mil.)	INCOME AS % OF ASSETS	EMPLOYEES
12/13	724	133	18.5%	700
12/12	429	115	27.0%	—
Annual Growth	68.9%	15.4%	—	—

2013 Year-End Financials

Return on assets: 18.5%
Return on equity: 84.8%
Sales ($ mil): 768

ALTRU HEALTH SYSTEM

Altru Health System provides medical care throughout northeastern North Dakota and northwestern Minnesota. The integrated health care network administers everything from primary care to inpatient medical and surgical care through its Altru Hospital (with roughly 265 beds) and about a dozen primary care clinics. It also operates a cancer center a rehabilitation center dialysis facilities and home health providers. For area seniors Altru Health operates Parkwood Place a senior living facility that provides several levels of care to residents depending on need. The not-for-profit center was formed in 1997 by the integration of Grand Forks Clinic and United Health Services.

Operations

The system employs more than 200 physicians and serves over 200000 residents. Altru Hospital with a Level II Trauma designation has a 16-bed critical care unit a 10-bed surgical critical care unit pulmonary and sleep labs and cardio and pulmonary rehabilitation facilities.

In 2013 Altru Health System had 12603 inpatient discharges 275000 outpatient discharges 1600 births and some 29000 emergency visits.

Sales and Marketing

Medicare and Medicaid payments accounted for more than 50% of net patient revenue in 2013; Blue Cross accounted for more than 30%. Self-pay and other third-party accounts represented the rest of patient revenue.

In 2013 the system paid $901799 for advertising up from $892641 in 2012.

Financial Performance

Altru Health System's net revenue increased 1% to $457 million in 2013 due to increased patient services charges. Net income also rose 5% to $26 million due to gains on investments. Cash flow also held steady rising 3% to $40 million due to a decline in cash used in receivables plus an increase in cash generated from accounts payable and accrued expenses.

Strategy

The system looks for opportunities to expand both its locations and its services. To that end it is building a new hospital in Grand Forks to replace Altru. The replacement will be built in three stages and is expected to be complete by 2020. The replacement for its main clinic is expected to be operational by 2022.

Altru opened its newest hospital the 45-bed Altru Specialty Center in Grand Forks North Dakota in 2014. The center has four operating rooms and offers such services as elective orthopedic and podiatry surgeries joint replacement and inpatient rehabilitation.

In 2013 Altru opened clinics in Thief River Falls Minnesota and East Grand Fork; it also expanded a clinic in Devils Lake North Dakota.

Company Background

The system was created in 1997 when United Hospital merged with the Grand Forks Clinic.

EXECUTIVES

Ceo, David Molmen
Cfo, Dwight Thompson
President, Eric Lunn
Administrative Director Primary Care, Renee Axtman
Chief Nurse Executive, Margaret Reed
Administrative Director Information Services, Mark Waind
Administrative Director Medical Specialty Care, Kerry Carlson
Coo, Brad Wehe
Executive Director Altru Health Foundation, Jon Green
Medical Director Primary Care, Colleen Swank
Medical Director Surgical Services, Scott Charette
Administrative Director Cardiology And Musculoskeletal Services, Kelly Hagen
Administrative Director Surgical Services, Joseph Myers
Health Care Director, Donna Bazey
Chairman, John Snustad
Vice Chairman, Kris Compton

LOCATIONS

HQ: ALTRU HEALTH SYSTEM
1200 S COLUMBIA RD, GRAND FORKS, ND 582014044
Phone: 701 780-5000
Web: WWW.ALTRU.ORG

PRODUCTS/OPERATIONS

2013 Sales

	$ mil.	% of total
Net patient service	426	93
Other operating revenue	31	7
Total	**457**	**100**

2013 Net Patient Revenue

	% of total
Medicare	41
Blue Cross	31
Medicaid	11
Other third party	14
Patients	3
Total	**100**

Selected Centers

Bariatric Center
Breast Center
Cancer Center
Diabetes Center
Family Birthing Center
Grief Center
Hand Therapy Center
Hearing Center
Heart and Vascular Center
Joint Replacement Center
Medical Fitness Center
Outpatient Procedure Center
Pre-Admission Center
Psychiatry Center
Truyu Aesthetic Center

COMPETITORS

Avera Health
Catholic Health Initiatives
First Care
Sanford Health-MeritCare
St. Alexius Medical Center
St. Mary's Innovis Health

HISTORICAL FINANCIALS

Company Type: Private

Income Statement				FYE: December 31
	REVENUE ($ mil.)	NET INCOME ($ mil.)	NET PROFIT MARGIN	EMPLOYEES
12/19	589	10	1.8%	3,800
12/18	566	(13)	—	—
12/17	549	20	3.7%	—
12/16	549	10	1.9%	—
Annual Growth	2.3%	0.1%	—	—

2019 Year-End Financials

Return on assets: 1.7%
Return on equity: 4.0%
Current ratio: 2.50
Cash ($ mil.): 60

AMC ENTERTAINMENT INC.

EXECUTIVES

Manager, Beth Olson
Vice President Investor Relations, John Merriwether
Vice President And Chief Audit Executive, Kathy Weekley
Vice President Guest Engagement, Julius Lai
Vice President Social Media And Content, Pamela Sandler
Vice President Benefits And Employment Practices, Rosalind Reeves
Vice President Government Affairs, Robert Bruchman
Vice President Leasing (legal), Ron Herman
Board Member, Lloyd Hill
Auditors: KPMG LLP KANSAS CITY MISSOUR

LOCATIONS

HQ: AMC ENTERTAINMENT INC.
11500 ASH ST, LEAWOOD, KS 662117804
Phone: 913 213-2000
Web: WWW.AMCTHEATRES.COM

HISTORICAL FINANCIALS

Company Type: Private

Income Statement				FYE: December 31
	REVENUE ($ mil.)	NET INCOME ($ mil.)	NET PROFIT MARGIN	EMPLOYEES
12/15	2,946	103	3.5%	19,700
12/14	2,695	64	2.4%	—
12/13	2,749	364	13.3%	—
12/12	811	(37)	—	—
Annual Growth	53.7%	—	—	—

2015 Year-End Financials

Return on assets: 2.0%
Return on equity: 6.7%
Current ratio: 0.60
Cash ($ mil.): 209

AMCAP FUND INC

EXECUTIVES

President, Marry Clemeson
Treas, Mary C Hall
Sr V Pres, Gordon Crawford
Sr V Pres, Paul G Haaga Jr
SEC, Julie Williams
Principal, Walter Stern

LOCATIONS

HQ: AMCAP FUND INC
333 S HOPE ST STE LEVB, LOS ANGELES, CA 900713003
Phone: 213 486-9200
Web: WWW.CAPITALGROUP.COM

HISTORICAL FINANCIALS

Company Type: Private

Income Statement				FYE: February 28
	ASSETS ($ mil.)	NET INCOME ($ mil.)	INCOME AS % OF ASSETS	EMPLOYEES
02/19	65,322	1,248	1.9%	300
02/18	64,019	9,994	15.6%	—
02/16	44,148	(2)	—	—
Annual Growth	14.0%	—	—	—

AMERICA CHUNG NAM (GROUP) HOLDINGS LLC

America Chung Nam (ACN) sells recovered fiber sources to Chinese paper mills where it can be converted into fiberboard cardboard and packaging. It also collects and exports a number of grades of post-consumer plastics. The company sources its materials through exclusive relationships with recycling facilities. Founder Yan Cheung and Ming Chung Liu own the company. It was founded in 1990.

Operations

ACN makes and supplies recovered paper (Mixed ONP DLK Magazines OCC Office Paper and other paper grades) recyclable plastics (including PET HDPE LDPE PS ABS Commingled Plastic and other engineering plastics).

It annually exports more than seven million tons of paper annually. In terms of logistics services the company has strong relationships with ocean trucking and trans-loading partners to enable access to rails shipping routes and ports all over the world.

ACN is partnered with Nine Dragons. It is an environmentally-friendly recovered paper based paper manufacturer based on production capacity.

The company helps the environment every year by saving 153 million trees. It also saves barrels of oil gallons of water and acres of landfill.

Geographic Reach

The company has operations in North America Asia and Europe. It has offices in the US (Jersey City and California) Europe (the Netherlands and the UK) and Asia (China South Korea and Japan).

Sales and Marketing

The relationship between ACN and its major customer Nine Dragons Paper Group is a tremendous advantage for the company's suppliers enabling ACN to provide business continuity regardless of fluctuations in the global market.

Company Background

America Chung Nam was founded in 1990 by Yan Cheung and Ming Chung Liu. Recognizing the demand for packaging materials driven by China's product exports and having a ready source for fiber materials through America Chung Nam Cheung established Nine Dragons Paper in 1996.

EXECUTIVES

Chief Executive Officer Worldwide Marketing, Peter Wang
Deputy Ceo Asia Pacific Region, Teresa Cheung
President And Ceo, Yan Cheung

LOCATIONS

HQ: AMERICA CHUNG NAM (GROUP) HOLDINGS LLC
1163 FAIRWAY DR, CITY OF INDUSTRY, CA 917892846
Phone: 909 839-8383
Web: WWW.ACNI.NET

COMPETITORS

Caraustar Recovered Fiber Group
Guanwei Recycling
International Paper
Weyerhaeuser

HISTORICAL FINANCIALS

Company Type: Private

Income Statement				FYE: December 31
	REVENUE ($ mil.)	NET INCOME ($ mil.)	NET PROFIT MARGIN	EMPLOYEES
12/18	1,711	216	12.6%	70
12/09	1,125	16	1.5%	—
12/08	1,363	7	0.6%	—
12/07	1,088	9	0.9%	—
Annual Growth	4.2%	32.5%	—	—

2018 Year-End Financials

Return on assets: 30.1%
Return on equity: 45.7%
Current ratio: 2.90
Cash ($ mil.): 42

AMERICAN ASSOCIATED PHARMACIES

EXECUTIVES

Pres-Ceo, Jon Copeland
SEC-Treas, Kevin Foshee
Territory Manager, Jim Kilborn
Territory Manager, Richard Nastasi
Director of Sales Central Regi, Mark Wegelin
Territory Manager, Brian Weglarz
Vice President of Merchandisin, Mark Metzger
Director of Human Resources, Brandy Hooper
Director of Marketing, Emily Harris
Territory Manager, James Lovelady
Member Support Manager, Nova Sisk
Auditors: GANT CROFT ASSOCIATES PC SC

LOCATIONS

HQ: AMERICAN ASSOCIATED PHARMACIES
201 LNNIE E CRAWFORD BLVD, SCOTTSBORO, AL 357697408
Phone: 256 574-7521
Web: WWW.RXAAP.COM

HISTORICAL FINANCIALS

Company Type: Private

Income Statement				FYE: December 31
	REVENUE ($ mil.)	NET INCOME ($ mil.)	NET PROFIT MARGIN	EMPLOYEES
12/15	642	(0)	—	220
12/14	513	0	0.0%	—
12/13	498	0	0.0%	—
12/12	476	0	0.1%	—
Annual Growth	10.5%	—	—	—

2015 Year-End Financials

Return on assets: (-0.1%)
Return on equity: (-1.1%)
Current ratio: 1.00
Cash ($ mil.): 34

AMERICAN BALANCED FUND, INC.

EXECUTIVES

Chb-Ceo, Robert G O'Donnell
Pres, Paul G Haaga Jr
V Pres, Hilda L Applbaum
Sr V Pres, Abner Goldstine
Sr V Pres, John H Smet
V Pres, J Dale Harvey
V Pres, Jeffrey T Lager
Asst Treas, R Marcia Gould
SEC, Patrick F Quan
Auditors: DELOITTE & TOUCHE LLP COSTA M

LOCATIONS

HQ: AMERICAN BALANCED FUND, INC.
1 MARKET, SAN FRANCISCO, CA 941051596
Phone: 707 864-3945

HISTORICAL FINANCIALS

Company Type: Private

Income Statement				FYE: December 31
	ASSETS ($ mil.)	NET INCOME ($ mil.)	INCOME AS % OF ASSETS	EMPLOYEES
12/18	129,090	2,254	1.7%	9
12/17	128,462	23,932	18.6%	—
12/15	87,394	4,903	5.6%	—
12/00	6,203	832	13.4%	—
Annual Growth	18.4%	5.7%	—	—

2018 Year-End Financials

Return on assets: 1.7%
Return on equity: 1.8%
Sales ($ mil): 3,254

AMERICAN CHEMICAL SOCIETY,

This group has a lot of chemistry. With more than 152000 members the American Chemical Society (ACS) is the world's largest scientific society. The not-for-profit organization provides information career development and educational resources to member chemists chemical engineers and technicians. ACS also publishes magazines journals and books. Its Chemical Abstract Service provides accurate and authoritative chemistry content curated and quality-controlled by hundreds of Ph.D. scientists from around the world. ACS also serves as an advocate for its members on public policy issues. The ACS Member Insurance Program provides insurance plans to its members. The company was founded in 1876.

Operations

ACS has about 70 Journals more than 45 million Chemical Abstracts records; around 150 million CAS REGISTRY organic and inorganic substances; more than 155 million ACS journal article downloads; and $17.7 million Petroleum Research Grants with roughly 175 research grants. It has 185 local sections. The society offers members the opportunity to participate in more than 30 specialty divisions ranging from food and agriculture to industrial and engineering chemistry.

Overall ACS programs account for more than 95% of the total sales. While PRF (Petroleum Research Fund) accounts for about 5%.

Geographic Reach

Based in Washington DC it has more than 152000 members in 140+ countries. The Society's international membership exceeds 28000. More than 60% of the content and articles published in ACS journals and abstracts originates from outside the US.

ACS sponsors or promotes a number of international activities such as joint conferences with chemical societies in India and other countries and the International Chemical Congress of Pacific Basin Societies (PacifiChem) a weeklong scientific meeting held once every five years in conjunction with ACS counterparts in Australia Canada Japan Korea New Zealand and China.

Sales and Marketing

The company accumulates its sales from fees and booth sales license of electronic devices and membership grants.

Financial Performance

Cash held by the company at the end of 2019 decreased by $1.6 million to $105.9 million compared from the prior year with $106.7 million. Cash provided by operations and financing activities were $64.6 million and $1.2 million respectively. Cash used for investing activities was $67.5 million mainly for purchases of investments.

Company Background

ACS was founded in 1876 and chartered by the US Congress in 1937.

EXECUTIVES

Executive Director And Ceo, Thomas M. (Tom) Connelly
Cfo And Treasurer, Brian Bernstein
President Acs Publications Division, Brian Crawford
Director Member And Scientific Advancement Division, Denise Creech
President Chemical Abstracts Service (cas), Manuel Guzman
Director Education Division, Mary Kirchhoff
Cio Washington It Operations, John Sullivan
President, Diane Grob Schmidt
Vice President Sales And Marketing, Brandon Nordin
Vice President Of Sales, Sean Evans
Vice President, Celia Henry
Vice President Global Editorial And Author Services, Sarah Tegen
Vice President, Jeffrey Long
Vice President International Human Resources, Pablo Soria
Vice President, Robert Lipyanek
Chair, Pat N. Confalone
Secretary, Flint Lewis
Assistant Treasurer And Director Of Investments, Jordan Levine
Assistant Treasurer Pubs Bus Sup, Robert Beard
Secretary, Christine Ausherman
Auditors: IT KPMG LLP MC LEAN VA

LOCATIONS

HQ: AMERICAN CHEMICAL SOCIETY,
1155 16TH ST NW, WASHINGTON, DC 200364892
Phone: 202 872-4600
Web: WWW.ACS.ORG

HISTORICAL FINANCIALS

Company Type: Private

Income Statement				FYE: December 31
	REVENUE ($ mil.)	NET INCOME ($ mil.)	NET PROFIT MARGIN	EMPLOYEES
12/13	568	62	11.0%	2,000
12/08	451	(38)	—	—
12/05	411	26	6.4%	—
Annual Growth	4.1%	11.3%	—	—

2013 Year-End Financials

Return on assets: 4.8%
Return on equity: 7.0%
Current ratio: 0.60
Cash ($ mil.): 37

AMERICAN CRYSTAL SUGAR COMPANY

Sugarbeet cooperative American Crystal Sugar is owned by some 2600 growers in the Red River Valley of North Dakota and Minnesota who farm more than 400000 acres of cropland. Through five processing plants crops are converted into sugar and other products such as molasses and sugarbeet pulp. The cooperative's products are sold in the US and other markets to industrial users and retail and wholesale customers under the Crystal name as well as under private labels through marketing co-ops United Sugars and Midwest Agri-Commodities. American Crystal Sugar also provides sugarbeet processing for third parties and owns 51% of a corn wet-milling plant leased to agriculture giant Cargill.

Operations

Sugar production accounts for about 90% of American Crystal Sugar's total revenue; industrial usage (by confectioners cereal makers bakeries and others) makes up the largest portion of sugar sales with wholesale and retail usage (under the Crystal Sugar brand) accounting for the rest.

The company generates about 10% of total revenue from the production of molasses sugarbeet pulp and other agri-products.

Other operations include Sidney Sugars which provides processing services for third parties and corn-sweetener joint venture ProGold which leases its corn wet-milling facility to Cargill for the production of high-fructose corn syrup.

Geographic Reach

American Crystal Sugar generates its revenue primarily in the US although it does export sugarbeet pulp to Japan and parts of Europe.

The Moorhead Minnesota-based cooperative has cropland in the Red River Valley of North Dakota and Minnesota and five processing facilities in the same two states (Crookston East Grand Forks and Moorhead Minnesota and Drayton and Hillsboro North Dakota).

Sales and Marketing

American Crystal Sugar markets its sugar through United Sugars Corporation a marketing cooperative owned by the company and others; its agri-products are marketed by Midwest Agri-Commodities Company which the company also owns with others.

Company Background

In 1973 sugarbeet growers organized to acquire the business and assets of the American Crystal Sugar Company which was a publicly held New Jersey corporation founded in 1899. It has been a cooperative ever since.

EXECUTIVES

President And Ceo, Thomas S. Astrup, $259,902 total compensation
Vice President Finance, Teresa Warne
Chairman, Francis L. Kritzberger
Vice Chairman, Neil C. Widner
Treasurer, Steve Rosenau
Board Member, David Mueller
Auditors: CLIFTONLARSONALLEN LLP STEVEN

LOCATIONS

HQ: AMERICAN CRYSTAL SUGAR COMPANY
101 3RD ST N, MOORHEAD, MN 565601990
Phone: 218 236-4400
Web: WWW.CRYSTALSUGAR.COM

COMPETITORS

Alexander & Baldwin
Amalgamated Sugar
American Sugar Refining
C&H Sugar
Cargill
Cumberland Packing
Florida Crystals
Imperial Sugar
M. A. Patout
Merisant
Michigan Sugar Company
Nippon Beet Sugar
NutraSweet
SMBSC
Sterling Sugars
Sugar Cane Growers Cooperative of Florida
Sugar Foods
S dzucker
Tate & Lyle
U.S. Sugar
Western Sugar Cooperative

HISTORICAL FINANCIALS

Company Type: Private

Income Statement — FYE: August 31

	REVENUE ($ mil.)	NET INCOME ($ mil.)	NET PROFIT MARGIN	EMPLOYEES
08/19	1,528	624	40.9%	1,365
08/18	1,515	650	43.0%	—
08/17	1,420	511	36.0%	—
08/16	1,290	561	43.5%	—
Annual Growth	5.8%	3.6%	—	—

2019 Year-End Financials

Return on assets: 61.6%
Return on equity: 151.4%
Current ratio: 1.20
Cash ($ mil.): 1

AMERICAN ELECTRIC POWER SERVICE CORPORATION

EXECUTIVES

Chb, Nicholas K Akins
Ex Vp Policy-Fin-Strat Plannin, Susan Tomasky
Deputy Gen Counsel, Jeffrey D Cross
Sr Vp Reg Svcs, J Craig Baker
Vp Corp Comm, Dale E Heydlauff
Exec V Pres- Cfo, Holly Koeppel
Svp Gen Counsel & SEC, John B Keane
Executive Vice President, Donald M Clements Jr
Dir Federal Agency Relations, Sabrina V Campbell
Vice-President, Van Der Walde
Information Specialist, Carole Root

LOCATIONS

HQ: AMERICAN ELECTRIC POWER SERVICE CORPORATION
1 RIVERSIDE PLZ FL 1 # 1, COLUMBUS, OH 432152373
Phone: 614 716-1000
Web: WWW.AEP.COM

HISTORICAL FINANCIALS

Company Type: Private

Income Statement — FYE: December 31

	REVENUE ($ mil.)	NET INCOME ($ mil.)	NET PROFIT MARGIN	EMPLOYEES
12/16	1,348	0	—	2,152
12/05	12,111	1,037	8.6%	—
12/02	1,391	0	—	—
Annual Growth	(0.2%)	—	—	—

2016 Year-End Financials

Return on assets: —
Return on equity: —
Current ratio: 0.40
Cash ($ mil.): 16

AMERICAN FUNDS PORTFOLIO SERIES

EXECUTIVES

Mgr, Alan N Berro
Auditors: DELOITTE & TOUCHE LLP COSTA

LOCATIONS

HQ: AMERICAN FUNDS PORTFOLIO SERIES
333 SUTH HOPE ST FL 55 FLR 55, LOS ANGELES, CA 90071
Phone: 213 486-9200
Web: WWW.CAPITALGROUP.COM

HISTORICAL FINANCIALS

Company Type: Private

Income Statement — FYE: October 31

	REVENUE ($ mil.)	NET INCOME ($ mil.)	NET PROFIT MARGIN	EMPLOYEES
10/19	860	6,852	796.0%	2
10/18	684	(112)	—	—
Annual Growth	25.9%	—	—	—

AMERICAN FURNITURE WAREHOUSE CO INC

Tony the Tiger hawking home furnishings might give some marketers pause but the combination seems to work for American Furniture Warehouse. American Furniture's television commercials often spotlight white-haired president and CEO Jake Jabs (who has become a well-known personality in the state as well as in the home furnishings industry) accompanied by baby exotic animals mostly tigers. The company sells furniture electronics and decor at discounted prices. It boasts about a dozen retail locations in Colorado and Arizona and sells through its website which also features bridal and gift registries. The company has built a reputation as a home-spun local furniture retailer. Jabs bought the company in 1975.

Geographic Reach

American Furniture has locations in the Colorado cities of Aurora Englewood Centennial Lakewood Thornton Westminster Colorado Springs Firestone/Longmont Fort Collins Glenwood Springs Pueblo and Grand Junction. In Arizona it has locations in Phoenix Gilbert and Glendale. It serves customers in the neighboring states of Wyoming Utah Kansas Nevada and New Mexico.

Financial Performance

American Furniture's 2013 sales reached more than $390 million.

Strategy

In 2013 the company made its first move outside Colorado when it opened a 630000-sq.-ft. store in Gilbert Arizona (near Phoenix). It opens another store – in Glendale Arizona – in late 2014. American Furniture hopes to net $3.4 million in direct revenue from the Glendale store during its first year in operation. The furniture retailer also has an eye on expanding into north Scottsdale.

EXECUTIVES

Vice President, Jackie Brookshire
Auditors: WIPFLI LLP DENVER COLORADO

LOCATIONS

HQ: AMERICAN FURNITURE WAREHOUSE CO INC
8820 AMERICAN WAY, ENGLEWOOD, CO 801127056
Phone: 303 799-9044
Web: WWW.AFW.COM

PRODUCTS/OPERATIONS

Selected Products

Decorative accessories
Electronics
Furniture
- Bedroom
- Chairs
- Dining room
- Home office
- Indoor/outdoor
- Living room
- Occasional tables
- Sectionals
- Sofas
- Youth bedroom

Lighting
Mattresses
Rugs

COMPETITORS

Ashley Furniture
Big Lots
Costco Wholesale
Kmart
Pier 1 Imports
Rooms To Go
Target Corporation
Wal-Mart

HISTORICAL FINANCIALS

Company Type: Private

Income Statement FYE: March 31

	REVENUE ($ mil.)	NET INCOME ($ mil.)	NET PROFIT MARGIN	EMPLOYEES
03/20	740	21	2.9%	3,500
03/19	694	29	4.3%	—
03/18	673	28	4.2%	—
03/17	652	25	3.9%	—
Annual Growth	4.3%	(5.8%)	—	—

2020 Year-End Financials

Return on assets: 5.0%
Return on equity: 5.8%
Current ratio: 2.40
Cash ($ mil.): 38

AMERICAN HIGH INCOME TRUST

EXECUTIVES

President, Larry Clemmenson
V Pres-Treas, Mary C Cremin
V Pres, Michael J Downer
SEC, Julie F Williams
Auditors: DELOITTE & TOUCHE LLP COSTA M

LOCATIONS

HQ: AMERICAN HIGH INCOME TRUST
333 S HOPE ST STE 5200, LOS ANGELES, CA 900713061
Phone: 949 766-6305
Web: WWW.CAPITALGROUP.COM

HISTORICAL FINANCIALS

Company Type: Private

Income Statement FYE: September 30

	ASSETS ($ mil.)	NET INCOME ($ mil.)	INCOME AS % OF ASSETS	EMPLOYEES
09/19	16,645	25	0.2%	1
09/18	16,817	577	3.4%	—
09/16	17,336	1,555	9.0%	—
Annual Growth	(1.3%)	(74.7%)	—	—

2019 Year-End Financials

Return on assets: 0.2%
Return on equity: 0.2%
Sales ($ mil): 1,113

AMERICAN HONDA FINANCE CORPORATION

If you're fonda the idea of driving a Honda you might want to call on American Honda Finance. Operating as Honda Financial Services the company provides retail financing in the US for Honda and Acura automobiles motorcycles all-terrain vehicles power equipment and outboard motors. Its American Honda Service division administers service contracts while Honda Lease Trust offers leases on new and used vehicles. Honda Financial Services also offers dealer financing and related dealer services. Ancillary services include servicing loans and securitizing and selling loans into the secondary market. A subsidiary of American Honda Motor the company began as a wholesale motorcycle finance provider in 1980.

Operations

American Honda Finance (AHF) acquires retail installment contracts and closed-end vehicle lease contracts from purchasers and lessees and authorized Honda and Acura dealers. It also provides these authorized dealers with wholesale flooring and commercial loans.

AHF also acquires used auto loans of non-Honda and non-Acura vehicles and provides these third-party dealers iwth wholesale loans. Additionally the company offers vehicle service contracts services underwriting and pricing of consumer financing services and incentive financing programs for Honda and Acura products.

Geographic Reach

The company is headquartered in Torrance California and operates nine regional offices that support all authorized Honda and Acura dealers across North America.

Financial Performance

While full financials of the subsidiary were not available American Honda Finance's (AHF) revenue has been on the uptrend as auto sales continue to strengthen along with the US economy. Revenue in fiscal 2014 (ended March 31 2014) grew by 22% to 5.97 trillion ($58.1 billion) thanks to larger revenues from its parent company's auto business and positive foreign currency exchange rates.

Despite higher selling general and administrative expenses and R&D expenses AHF's operating income also increased 39% to 290.9 billion ($2.83 billion) in 2014 after the company continued its cost reduction measures.

Strategy

American Honda Finance Corp. (AHFC) exists to provide stability to support sales of new and used Honda and Acura vehicles throughout North America Honda Motor's largest market. To that end AHFC seeks to preserve funding diversity balanced liquidity and maintain a prudent maturity profile. To spur growth of its US business in 2012 the company opened its ninth regional office a 25000-square-foot facility in Charlotte North Carolina to serve Honda buyers in the Carolinas Maryland Tennessee Virginia and West Virginia.

EXECUTIVES

Ceo, Hideo Tamaka
Sr V Pres*, Stephan Smith
V Pres-Cfo*, John Weisickle
Information Specialist, Hung Le
Information Technology Directo, David Newallis
Information Technology Directo, John Thompson
Export Territory Manager, Dave Huerta
Dealer Relations Manager, Paul Arbios
Regional Manager, Dean Hardesty
Marine OEM Sales Manager, Dennis Ashley
General Manager, Glenn Yamamoto
Auditors: KPMG LLP LOS ANGELES CALIFO

LOCATIONS

HQ: AMERICAN HONDA FINANCE CORPORATION
1919 TORRANCE BLVD, TORRANCE, CA 905012722
Phone: 310 972-2239
Web: WWW.HONDAFINANCIALSERVICES.COM

Selected Offices

Alpharetta GA
Charlotte NC
Cypress CA
Elgin IL
Holyoke MA
Irving TX
San Ramon CA
Torrance CA
Wilmington DE

COMPETITORS

Ally Financial
Automotive Finance Corporation
Bank of America
Credit Acceptance
Ford Motor Credit
Mercedes-Benz Financial Services USA
Mitsubishi Motors Credit of America
Toyota Motor Credit

HISTORICAL FINANCIALS

Company Type: Private

Income Statement FYE: March 31

	ASSETS ($ mil.)	NET INCOME ($ mil.)	INCOME AS % OF ASSETS	EMPLOYEES
03/17	69,854	753	1.1%	1,000
03/16	66,653	910	1.4%	—
03/08	50,526	(45)	—	—
03/07	41,431	394	1.0%	—
Annual Growth	5.4%	6.7%	—	—

2017 Year-End Financials

Return on assets: 1.1%
Return on equity: 5.9%
Sales ($ mil): 2,066

AMERICAN LEBANESE SYRIAN ASSOCIATED CHARITIES, INC.

EXECUTIVES

Pres-Ceo, Rick Shadyac Jr
Cmo, Emily Callahan
Chief Admin Ofcr, Emily S Greer
CIO, Robert Machen
Cfo, Jeffrey T Pearson
Svp-Ceo Ops, Betty Macdougall
Sharepoint Administrator, Justin Cooper
Senior Applications Analyst, Tina Currie
Strategic Partnerships, Tracy Nilles
Sr Regional Repres, Caitlin O'Brien-Rice
Director, Chase Carter
Auditors: DELOITTE & TOUCHE LLP MEMPHIS

LOCATIONS

HQ: AMERICAN LEBANESE SYRIAN ASSOCIATED CHARITIES, INC.
501 SAINT JUDE PL, MEMPHIS, TN 381051905
Phone: 901 578-2000
Web: WWW.STJUDE.ORG

HISTORICAL FINANCIALS

Company Type: Private

Income Statement FYE: June 30

	REVENUE ($ mil.)	NET INCOME ($ mil.)	NET PROFIT MARGIN	EMPLOYEES
06/17	1,741	658	37.8%	1,300
06/16	1,161	(27)	—	—
06/15	1,182	251	21.2%	—
06/13	976	210	21.5%	—
Annual Growth	15.6%	33.0%	—	—

2017 Year-End Financials

Return on assets: 15.8%
Return on equity: 16.1%
Current ratio: —
Cash ($ mil.): 178

AMERICAN MITSUBA CORPORATION

EXECUTIVES

Pres-Ceo-Coo, Masayoshi Shirato
V Pres*, Hideaki Fujii
V Pres*, Takashi Ichinokawa
V Pres*, Hiroshi Naito
Sr V Pres*, David Stevens
Sr V Pres*, Mishel Ashtary
Acctng Mgr, Ken Garber
Auditors: PLANTE & MORAN PLLC AUBURN

LOCATIONS

HQ: AMERICAN MITSUBA CORPORATION
2945 THREE LEAVES DR, MOUNT PLEASANT, MI 488584596
Phone: 989 779-4962
Web: WWW.AMERICANMITSUBA.COM

HISTORICAL FINANCIALS

Company Type: Private

Income Statement — FYE: December 31

	REVENUE ($ mil.)	NET INCOME ($ mil.)	NET PROFIT MARGIN	EMPLOYEES
12/16	697	(2)	—	765
12/15	687	9	1.4%	—
12/14	558	5	0.9%	—
12/13	557	17	3.1%	—
Annual Growth	7.7%	—	—	—

2016 Year-End Financials

Return on assets: (-0.9%)
Return on equity: (-2.0%)
Current ratio: 1.70
Cash ($ mil.): 24

AMERICAN MUNICIPAL POWER, INC.

Power to the Public is the motto of American Municipal Power (AMP). The non-profit membership organization supplies wholesale power to more than 80 community-owned distribution utilities in Ohio 30 in Pennsylvania 6 in Michigan 5 in Virginia 3 in Kentucky 2 in West Virginia 1 in Indiana and 1 in Delaware (a joint action agency). AMP and its members own and operate plants that generate more than 1500 MW of power. The company also handles projects on behalf of the Ohio Municipal Electric Generating Agency (OMEGA) Joint Ventures program (jointly owned generation and transmission projects). The power generation company is owned by its member municipalities. AMP member utilities serve some 635000 customers.

Operations

The company provides electric capacity and energy and furnishes other services to its members on a cooperative basis. As part of its joint venture responsibilities American Municipal Power also operates the Belleville Hydroelectric Plant a 42 MW plant located in Belleville West Virginia. AMP's wholly-owned subsidiary AMPO provides assistance in establishing electric and gas aggregation programs to benefit local consumers.

Geographic Reach

Ohio-based American Municipal Power serves 130 members - 129 member municipal electric communities in the states of Ohio Pennsylvania Michigan Indiana Virginia Kentucky and West Virginia as well as the Delaware Municipal Electric Corporation a joint action agency headquartered in Smyrna Delaware.

Financial Performance

American Municipal Power (AMP) reported $982.5 million in revenue in 2013 representing a 19% increase over 2012. Rising electric revenues and service fees up 19% and 44% respectively drove growth in 2013. AMP's net margin expanded to $5.3 million from $1.9 million over the same period.

Strategy

Expanding into Indiana in 2014 AMP gained its newest member the city of Cannelton.

Implementing a strategy to reduce carbon emissions the company is building six hydroelectric projects on the Ohio River. The Meldahl plant (with 105 MW of capacity) will be the largest hydroelectric plant on the Ohio River. American Municipal Power also has a deal to develop up to 300 MW of solar power with solar panel company Standard Energy. It also has wind power and landfill gas operations. Indeed AMP members' projected energy resource mix will be approximately 21% renewable by 2015.

In 2013 American Municipal Power and the Vermont Energy Investment Corporation agreed to extend the operation of Efficiency Smart beyond the end of the year. The program provides a broad range of energy efficiency services for the power coop's member utilities. Some 49 member communities in Ohio Pennsylvania and Michigan participated in Efficiency Smart in 2013.

Company Background

To replace lost capacity in 2011 it acquired the Fremont Energy Center in Fremont Ohio from FirstEnergy for $500 million. The 707-MW natural gas combined-cycle facility commenced commercial operation in early 2012. In 2010 American Municipal Power also secured a 368-MW ownership stake in the Prairie State Energy Campus in Illinois.

Expanding geographically American Municipal Power moved into a seventh state in 2011 when it made Delaware Municipal Electric its 129th member.

American Municipal Power was founded in 1971.

EXECUTIVES

Senior Vice President Of Generation Operations, Scott Kiesewetter
Assistant Vice President Energy Policy, Randell Corbin
Vice President Of Power Supply Planning, Mike Migliore
Assistant Vice President Of Finance And Member Cre, Chris Deeter
Auditors: PRICEWATERHOUSECOOPERS LLP CO

LOCATIONS

HQ: AMERICAN MUNICIPAL POWER, INC.
1111 SCHROCK RD STE 100, COLUMBUS, OH 432291155
Phone: 614 540-1111
Web: WWW.AMPPARTNERS.ORG

PRODUCTS/OPERATIONS

2013 Sales

	% of total
Electric revenues	97
Service fees	1
Programs & other	2
Total	**100**

Selected Services

Aggregation
Business Development
Clean Energy & Conservation
Community Outreach
Financial
Legislative Regulatory & Legal
Power Supply / AMP Energy Control Center
Safety Programs
Scholarship Programs
Technical Services

COMPETITORS

Dominion Energy
Duke Energy Ohio
Ohio Valley Electric

HISTORICAL FINANCIALS

Company Type: Private

Income Statement — FYE: December 31

	REVENUE ($ mil.)	NET INCOME ($ mil.)	NET PROFIT MARGIN	EMPLOYEES
12/19	1,170	5	0.5%	229
12/15	1,127	5	0.5%	—
12/14	1,039	2	0.2%	—
12/13	982	5	0.5%	—
Annual Growth	3.0%	(0.0%)	—	—

2019 Year-End Financials

Return on assets: 0.1%
Return on equity: 5.9%
Current ratio: 1.50
Cash ($ mil.): 118

AMERICAN MUTUAL FUND

EXECUTIVES

Chb, Jonathan B Lovelace Jr
Chb-Ceo*, James K Dunton
V Chb*, James W Ratzlaff
Pres*, Robert G O'Donnell
V Pres*, Joyce Gordon
V Pres*, Joanna F Jonsson
SEC*, Vince Carti
Treas*, Mary C Hall
Treasurer, Mary Hall
Auditors: DELOITTE & TOUCHE LLP COSTA M

LOCATIONS

HQ: AMERICAN MUTUAL FUND
333 S HOPE ST FL 51, LOS ANGELES, CA 900711420
Phone: 213 486-9200
Web: WWW.CAPITALGROUP.COM

HISTORICAL FINANCIALS

Company Type: Private

Income Statement — FYE: October 31

	ASSETS ($ mil.)	NET INCOME ($ mil.)	INCOME AS % OF ASSETS	EMPLOYEES
10/19	60,172	9,524	15.8%	200
10/18	50,526	3,375	6.7%	—
Annual Growth	19.1%	182.2%	—	—

2019 Year-End Financials

Return on assets: 15.8%
Return on equity: 15.9%
Sales ($ mil): 1,506

AMERICAN TIRE DISTRIBUTORS HOLDINGS, INC.

Business for American Tire Distributors starts where the rubber meets the road. The company is the largest independent tire wholesaler in North America. Its offerings include flagship brands Bridgestone Continental Pirelli and Michelin as well as budget brands and private-label tires. ATD also markets custom wheels and tire service equipment. Its network of 140-plus distribution centers serves independent tire dealers retail chains and auto service centers across the US and Canada. The company is owned by private equity firm TPG Capital.

Operations

Passenger and light truck tires contribute most of American Tire Distributors' sales; the company also supplies tires for medium trucks farm vehicles and specialty vehicles.

Beyond tires ATD distributes wheels and other automotive products. Its brands include Cruiser Alloy Drifz O.E. Performance and ICW Racing.

Geographic Reach

North Carolina-based American Tire Distributors has a strong position in North America. It rings up most of its sales in the US where it has some 115 distribution centers. The company has nearly 25 distribution centers across Canada.

Sales and Marketing

American Tire Distributors sells tires to local regional and national independent tire retailers as well as mass merchandisers warehouse clubs tire-manufacturer-owned stores automotive dealerships and web-based markets.

Financial Performance

As a privately held entity American Tire Distributions does not publicly release financials. Estimates place annual revenue at $5 billion-plus.

Strategy

As with many industries the auto parts industry is being disrupted by online and mobile retailing and other technologies. In addition manufacturers are looking to sell directly to end-users thereby removing distributors from the supply chain. American Tire Distributors is grappling with both trends as it sees online behemoth Amazon strengthen its position in the tire replacement market and it loses distribution rights to one of the world's largest tire brands.

In 2018 Amazon announced a partnership with Sears through which customers who purchase replacement tires from Amazon can have them installed for a fee at Sears Auto Centers. Also that year Goodyear one of the largest tire manufacturers in the world announced ATD would no longer distribute its tires as it is forming its own tire distribution joint venture with a subsidiary of Bridgestone. That follows an earlier tire distribution joint venture between Michelin North America and Sumitomo.

In the face of competition from Amazon ATD touts its nearly 10-year history of online sales. It also continues to invest in innovation including the recent transition of ATD Online to a new platform with enhanced tools and superior service. As more manufactures get in the distribution game themselves the company is emphasizing and working to improve its value-added services. ATD positions itself not just as a distributor but as a partner to tire dealers offering industry-leading technology sourcing training and insights and category management.

In addition ATD continues to strengthen its operations in Canada. In 2017 its Canadian subsidiary National Tire Distributors added three Quebec-based distribution centers via an acquisition.

EXECUTIVES

Senior Vice President Eastern Division Manager, Keith Calcagno

Evp General Counsel And Secretary, J. Michael (Mike) Gaither, $400,000 total compensation

Evp And Cfo, Jason T. Yaudes, $400,000 total compensation

President And Ceo, Stuart Schuette

Evp Product Strategy And Supply, Jason Shannon

Vice President Of Human Resources, Laurie Heavner

Svp Proprietary Brands, Joshua Simpson

Vice President Hercules Brand Marketing, Jedd Emans

Regional Vice President, John Reid

Vice President Business Development And Strategy, Donald Gualdoni

Senior Vice President Supply Chain, Mark Chandler

Chief People Officer, Rebecca Sinclair

Vice President Financial Planning And Analysis, Ryan Walsh

Senior Vice President Sales Operations, Mark Lindsey

Senior Vice President Of Transportation, Baltazar-huntersville Nelson

Vice President Operations East Coast, Peter Holm

Svp Applications Technology, Murali Bandaru

Vice President Of Supply Chain, Randal Arthur

Auditors: PRICEWATERHOUSECOOPERS LLP CH

LOCATIONS

HQ: AMERICAN TIRE DISTRIBUTORS HOLDINGS, INC.
12200 HERBERT WAYNE CT # 150, HUNTERSVILLE, NC 280786397

Phone: 704 992-2000

Web: WWW.ATD-US.COM

PRODUCTS/OPERATIONS

Selected Brands

Tires
- Alliance
- BFGoodrich
- Continental
- Dunlop
- Firestone
- IronMan
- Michelin
- Toyo Tires
- UniRoyal

Wheels
- Center Line
- ICW Racing
- Konig
- Motiv
- Pacer
- Ultra Motorsports

Supplies
- Blaster
- Chicago Pneumatic
- Ingersoll-Rand
- Ken-Tool
- SuperSprings
- Stoner
- Western Pacific Storage Solutions

COMPETITORS

Amazon.com
Bridgestone
Dealer Tire
Goodyear Tire & Rubber
Sears Holdings
Sumitomo Corporation of America
TCI Tire Centers
Tire Distribution Systems
Tire Group International Inc.
Wal-Mart

HISTORICAL FINANCIALS

Company Type: Private

Income Statement — FYE: December 28

	REVENUE ($ mil.)	NET INCOME ($ mil.)	NET PROFIT MARGIN	EMPLOYEES
12/13	3,839	(6)	—	1,072
12/12	3,455	(14)	—	—
12/11	3,050	0	0.0%	—
Annual Growth	12.2%	—	—	—

2013 Year-End Financials

Return on assets: (-0.2%)
Return on equity: (-0.9%)
Current ratio: 1.90
Cash ($ mil.): 35

AMERICAN TRANSMISSION COMPANY, LLC

American Transmission Company is an entrepreneur in the US power grid business — a for-profit multi-state transmission-only utility. Connecting electricity producers to distributors American Transmission owns operates monitors and maintains 9480 miles of high-voltage electric transmission lines and 529 substations in portions of Illinois Michigan Minnesota and Wisconsin. The company a member of the Midwest Independent Transmission System Operator (MISO) regional transmission organization operates the former transmission assets of some of its shareholders. About 30 utilities municipalities electric companies and cooperatives in its service area have an ownership stake in American Transmission.

Operations

Unlike most other power utilities American Transmission is not engaged in the generation distribution or marketing of electricity. Its duties include reliable operation of the transmission system growing the system to meet current and future needs and upgrading and maintain the transmission equipment as needed.

American Transmission is a member of the MISO regional transmission organization and provides nondiscriminatory service to all customers supporting effective competition in energy markets without favoring any market participant.

Geographic Reach

American Transmission meets the power needs of about 5 million people in 72 counties in Illinois Michigan Minnesota and Wisconsin. It operates North central Wisconsin Michigan's Upper Peninsula and Northern Wisconsin South Central/Southwest Wisconsin and North Central Illinois Northeast Wisconsin and Southeast Wisconsin.

Sales and Marketing

The company's customers include local electric distribution companies municipal utilities and co-operative utilities (that procure primary network transmission service and are interconnected or plan on interconnecting to its transmission system) local and national marketers generators and utilities (that procure primarily point-to-point transmission service generators and other transmission systems that want to interconnect with American Transmission's system).

Financial Performance

American Transmission reported revenues of about $603 million in 2012 a 6% increase over 2011 revenues.

Strategy

The company is trying to use its single focus on power transmission to win more customers. American Transmission has invested more than $2.8 billion on infrastructure upgrades (since 2001) including 2305 miles of power line. It has also built more 560 miles of new lines during this time period. By 2021 the company plans to spend a further $3.9-$4.8 billion on infrastructure improvement with a focus on adding new renewable sources to its expanded grid.

In 2014 American Transmission filed applications with the Public Service Commission of Wisconsin to rebuild a 12.5 mile 138000-volt transmission line in western Kenosha County at a cost $12.2 million and a 69000-volt transmission line between Dyckesville Wisconsin and Sturgeon Bay Wisconsin (for $23 million).

In 2013 American Transmission received authorizing to build two new 138-kilovolt transmission lines needed to improve electric system reliability in western Milwaukee County and began construction activities on a new 5.8-mile 345-kilovolt electric transmission line to strengthen the electric system in southeastern Wisconsin and northeastern Illinois. That year it energized the 32-mile 345-kilovolt Rockdale-West Middleton Transmission Line; and placed in service. In 2013 American Transmission

In 2012 it teamed up with ALLETE to study transmission options for transporting Midwestern wind energy as well as Canadian hydroelectric power into Minnesota Wisconsin and Michigan to help local utilities enhance reliability and meet renewable energy goals. To further enable movement of renewable energy that year the company and Minnesota Power agreed to develop a 50-mile double-circuit 345-kilovolt transmission line from the Mesabi Iron Range to the companies' jointly owned Arrowhead Substation in Duluth. The project is due to come into service in 2020.

Company Background

In 2010 it signed two agreements with the Department of Energy to access $12.7 million in investment grants for incorporating smart grid technologies into its transmission system.

In 2011 it announced a plan to build seven new transmission line projects (1800 miles of new line) aimed at filling gaps in the existing transmission grid improving grid reliability and enabling increased delivery of renewable power in Iowa Wisconsin Illinois Indiana and Ohio. The projects in total will cost about $4 billion. It also agreed to purchase of the Zephyr Power Transmission Project (950 miles of transmission line between Wyoming and southern Nevada) in another $4 billion deal.

Boosting its transmission assets in 2011 American Transmission formed a transmission utility joint venture with Duke Energy. Duke-American Transmission Co. builds owns and operates new power transmission infrastructure across North America.

American Transmission is one of the first for-profit transmission companies formed (in 2001) when the US market deregulated in the early 2000s. It is 88% owned by investor-owned utilities and 12% owned by municipalities municipal electric companies and electric cooperatives.

EXECUTIVES

Vice President Human Capital, Lori Lorenz
Vice President It, Scott Herbst
Auditors: DELOITTE & TOUCHE LLP MILWAU

LOCATIONS

HQ: AMERICAN TRANSMISSION COMPANY, LLC
W234N2000 RDGVIEW PKY CT, WAUKESHA, WI 531881022
Phone: 262 506-6700
Web: WWW.ATCLLC.COM

PRODUCTS/OPERATIONS

Contributing Owners

Adams-Columbia Electric Cooperative
Alger Delta Cooperative Electric Association
Badger Power Marketing Authority
Central Wisconsin Electric Cooperative
City of Algoma
City of Columbus
City of Kaukauna
City of Menasha
City of Oconto Falls
City of Plymouth
City of Reedsburg
City of Sheboygan Falls
City of Sturgeon Bay
City of Sun Prairie
City of Wisconsin Rapids
Cloverland Electric Cooperative
Edison Sault Electric Company
Madison Gas & Electric Company
Manitowoc Public Utilities
Marshfield Electric and Water Department
Ontonagon County Rural Electrification Association
Rainy River Energy
Rock Energy Cooperative
Stoughton Utilities
Upper Peninsula Public Power Agency
Wisconsin Electric Power Company
Wisconsin Power & Light Company
Wisconsin Public Service Corporation
WPPI Energy

COMPETITORS

AES
Ameren
Duke Energy
Exelon
FirstEnergy

HISTORICAL FINANCIALS

Company Type: Private

Income Statement — FYE: December 31

	REVENUE ($ mil.)	NET INCOME ($ mil.)	NET PROFIT MARGIN	EMPLOYEES
12/18	687	172	25.0%	547
12/17	714	172	24.2%	—
12/16	650	147	22.7%	—
12/15	615	200	32.5%	—
Annual Growth	3.7%	(5.0%)	—	—

2018 Year-End Financials

Return on assets: 3.5%
Return on equity: 14.2%
Current ratio: 0.20
Cash ($ mil.): —

AMERICAN TRANSMISSION SYSTEMS, INCORPORATED

EXECUTIVES

Pres, Richard R Grigg
Director, Richard A Ziegler

LOCATIONS

HQ: AMERICAN TRANSMISSION SYSTEMS, INCORPORATED
76 S MAIN ST, AKRON, OH 443081812
Phone: 330 761-4370
Web: WWW.FIRSTENERGYCORP.COM

HISTORICAL FINANCIALS

Company Type: Private

Income Statement — FYE: December 31

	REVENUE ($ mil.)	NET INCOME ($ mil.)	NET PROFIT MARGIN	EMPLOYEES
12/17	656	165	25.2%	1
12/16	540	133	24.7%	—
Annual Growth	21.6%	23.8%	—	—

AMERICARES FOUNDATION, INC.

AmeriCares Foundation provides emergency medical aid around the world. The not-for-profit charitable organization helps victims of natural disasters and supports long-term humanitarian programs by collecting medical supplies in the US and overseas and delivering them to places where they are needed. AmeriCares has provided aid in more than 90 countries worldwide. In the US the organization offers medical assistance runs a camp for kids with HIV/AIDS and conducts HomeFront a program that renovates housing for the needy in parts of Connecticut and New York. Robert C. Macauley founded AmeriCares in 1982.

Geographic Reach

The company has presence in US Latin America Caribbean Asia and Eurasia Africa and Middle East.

Financial Performance

AmeriCares' revenue decreased 9% to $572 million in 2014 due to a decline in public support and loss on investments.

EXECUTIVES

Pres-Ceo, Michael Nyenhuis
Svp-Operations*, Richard K Trowbridge Jr
Vp-US Programs & Partnership, Lindsay O'Brien
Auditors: GRANT THORNTON LLP NEW YORK

LOCATIONS

HQ: AMERICARES FOUNDATION, INC.
88 HAMILTON AVE STE 1, STAMFORD, CT 069023100
Phone: 203 658-9500
Web: WWW.AMERICARES.ORG

HISTORICAL FINANCIALS

Company Type: Private

Income Statement — FYE: June 30

	REVENUE ($ mil.)	NET INCOME ($ mil.)	NET PROFIT MARGIN	EMPLOYEES
06/19	976	(101)	—	231
06/15	742	101	13.7%	—
06/14	560	(4)	—	—
06/12	526	5	1.1%	—
Annual Growth	9.2%	—	—	—

2019 Year-End Financials

Return on assets: (-44.0%)
Return on equity: (-46.9%)
Current ratio: 26.70
Cash ($ mil.): 17

AMES CONSTRUCTION, INC.

Ames Construction aims right for the heart of heavy construction. The company is a general contractor providing heavy civil and industrial construction services to the transportation mining and power industries mainly in the West and Midwest. The family-owned company works on highways airports bridges rail lines mining facilities power plants and other infrastructure projects. Ames also performs flood control environmental remediation reclamation and landfill work. Additionally the firm builds golf courses and undertakes commercial and residential site development projects. Ames typically partners with other companies to perform the engineering and design portion of construction jobs.

Operations

Some of Ames Construction's project include the Arlington Power Plant Dry Fork Station Unit 1 Site Work and Substructure Construction Rentech ClearFuels Cortez Hills Mine and Mills Site and Airport Extension Projects such as its MSP International Airport work.

Geographic Reach

Ames Construction has offices in the US in Minnesota Arizona California Colorado Nevada and Utah as well as in Canada.

Strategy

Through its subcontracting activities Ames Construction contributed to the construction of the Minnesota Twins ballpark and served as subcontractor and partner in a joint venture with Fluor and Balfour Beatty Rail that that undertook a $1 billion design/build portion of a rail line project for the Denver Regional Transit District.

EXECUTIVES

Vice President Of Management Services, Roger L Mcbride
Regional Vice President Of Engineering, Robert Gillis
Vice President, Nick Ruba
Auditors: CLIFTONLARSONALLEN LLP MINNE

LOCATIONS

HQ: AMES CONSTRUCTION, INC.
2500 COUNTY ROAD 42 W, BURNSVILLE, MN 553376911
Phone: 952 435-7106
Web: WWW.AMESCONSTRUCTION.COM

Selected Locations
Arizona
California
Canada
Colorado
Minnesota
Nevada
Utah

PRODUCTS/OPERATIONS

Selected Markets

Commercial
Commercial site development
Environmental remediation/ landfills
Residential site development
Mining
Contract mining
Leach pad construction
Mine development
Mine infrastructure
Mine reclamation/remediation
Mine tailings dam
Power
Coal fired
Combined-cycle/natural gas
Nuclear
Transmission
Wind
Transportation
Airports
Bridges
Highways
Railroads
Water resources
Dams reservoirs and flood control
Wastewater/water treatment
Water delivery
Water retention structures

COMPETITORS

American Civil Constructors Holdings
Balfour Beatty Construction
Clyde Companies
Granite Construction
Meadow Valley
Peter Kiewit Sons'
SEMA Construction
Skanska USA Civil
Sterling Construction
Tutor-Saliba

HISTORICAL FINANCIALS

Company Type: Private

Income Statement — FYE: November 30

	REVENUE ($ mil.)	NET INCOME ($ mil.)	NET PROFIT MARGIN	EMPLOYEES
11/19	1,248	61	4.9%	2,500
11/16	845	2	0.3%	—
11/15	1,068	5	0.5%	—
11/14	1,074	26	2.4%	—
Annual Growth	3.1%	18.7%	—	—

2019 Year-End Financials

Return on assets: 14.8%
Return on equity: 43.7%
Current ratio: 1.30
Cash ($ mil.): 70

ANCHORAGE SCHOOL DISTRICT

EXECUTIVES

Supt, Ed Graff
Supt*, Carol Comeau
SEC Accounting*, Lois Hartsfield
Exe SEC*, Vanessa Blake
Doctor*, Deena Bishop
Substitute Teacher, Carla Goldberg
Cafeteria Manager, Shani Pritchard
Teacher, Ardy Robertson
Administrative Assistant, Chekedia Rias
School Nurse, Amy Belmear
Business Analyst, Andria Johannes
Auditors: BDO USA LLP ANCHORAGE ALASK

LOCATIONS

HQ: ANCHORAGE SCHOOL DISTRICT
5530 E NTHRN LIGHTS BLVD, ANCHORAGE, AK 99504
Phone: 907 742-4000
Web: WWW.ASDK12.ORG

HISTORICAL FINANCIALS

Company Type: Private

Income Statement — FYE: June 30

	REVENUE ($ mil.)	NET INCOME ($ mil.)	NET PROFIT MARGIN	EMPLOYEES
06/12	834	(8)	—	5,039
06/11	822	(2)	—	—
06/10	774	(19)	—	—
Annual Growth	3.8%	—	—	—

2012 Year-End Financials

Return on assets: (-0.6%)
Return on equity: (-1.3%)
Current ratio: —
Cash ($ mil.): 162

ANCHORAGE, MUNICIPALITY OF (INC)

Anchorage is Alaska's largest city in both size and population. The city encompasses almost 2000 sq. mi. of land – almost the size of Delaware. Anchorage had a 2010 population of about 290000 residents or about a quarter of the state's population. Anchorage is located in the south central part of the state and sits on the Gulf of Alaska.

EXECUTIVES

Medical Director, Michael Levy
Vice President Information Technology, Bill Chadwick
Secretary, Linda Luebke

LOCATIONS

HQ: ANCHORAGE, MUNICIPALITY OF (INC)
632 W 6TH AVE STE 810, ANCHORAGE, AK 995016312
Phone: 907 343-6610
Web: WWW.MUNI.ORG

HISTORICAL FINANCIALS

Company Type: Private

Income Statement — FYE: December 31

	REVENUE ($ mil.)	NET INCOME ($ mil.)	NET PROFIT MARGIN	EMPLOYEES
12/19	800	21	2.7%	3,680
12/18	740	26	3.6%	—
12/17	816	(33)	—	—
12/16	766	(26)	—	—
Annual Growth	1.5%	—	—	—

2019 Year-End Financials

Return on assets: 0.3%
Return on equity: 0.5%
Current ratio: 1.80
Cash ($ mil.): 396

ANDERSON AND DUBOSE, INC.

You might say this company keeps the Big Mac big and the Happy Meals happy. Anderson-DuBose Pittsburgh is a leading wholesale distributor that supplies food and non-food items to McDonald's and Chipotle fast-food restaurants in Ohio Pennsylvania New York and West Virginia. It serves about 500 Golden Arches locations with frozen meat and fish dairy products and paper goods and packaging as well as toys for Happy Meals. One of the largest black-owned companies in the US Anderson-DuBose was started in 1991 by Warren Anderson and Stephen DuBose who purchased control of a McDonald's distributorship from Martin-Brower. Anderson became sole owner in 1993 when he bought out his partner's stake in the business.

EXECUTIVES

Pres, Warren Anderson
Customer Staff, Nancy Wilson
Human Resources Generalist, Linsey Gray
Account Manager, Ray Bonner
Executive Assistant, Rhonda McAllister

LOCATIONS

HQ: ANDERSON AND DUBOSE, INC.
5300 TOD AVE SW, WARREN, OH 444819767
Phone: 440 248-8800
Web: WWW.A-D.US

COMPETITORS

Golden State Foods
Gordon Food Service
Keystone Foods
MAINES
Martin-Brower
Meadowbrook Meat Company
Reinhart FoodService
Sysco
US Foods

HISTORICAL FINANCIALS

Company Type: Private

Income Statement — FYE: December 27

	REVENUE ($ mil.)	NET INCOME ($ mil.)	NET PROFIT MARGIN	EMPLOYEES
12/19	598	4	0.7%	100
12/18	577	3	0.7%	—
12/16	518	2	0.4%	—
12/15	546	2	0.4%	—
Annual Growth	2.3%	16.1%	—	—

2019 Year-End Financials

Return on assets: 10.1%
Return on equity: 23.5%
Current ratio: 1.10
Cash ($ mil.): 2

ANMED HEALTH

EXECUTIVES

Pres-Ceo, John A Miller Jr
Dir, Jimmy Kimbell
Compliance Staff, Chandra Snyder
Data Coordinator, Donna Hamby
Telecommunications Technician, Freddy McGee
Pharmacy Director, George Reid
Hematologist Oncologist, Jay Nayak
Associate, Sandra Coronel
Account Director, Sonya Gould
Anesthesiologist, Amy Weaver
Director Nursing, Bryan Kennedy
Auditors: DIXON HUGHES GOODMAN LLP GREE

LOCATIONS

HQ: ANMED HEALTH
800 N FANT ST, ANDERSON, SC 296215708
Phone: 864 512-1000
Web: WWW.ANMEDHEALTH.ORG

HISTORICAL FINANCIALS

Company Type: Private

Income Statement — FYE: December 31

	REVENUE ($ mil.)	NET INCOME ($ mil.)	NET PROFIT MARGIN	EMPLOYEES
12/18	543	(15)	—	2,600
12/17	513	41	8.0%	—
12/16	504	40	8.0%	—
12/15	590	(1)	—	—
Annual Growth	(2.7%)	—	—	—

2018 Year-End Financials

Return on assets: (-1.7%)
Return on equity: (-2.8%)
Current ratio: 1.90
Cash ($ mil.): 49

ANN & ROBERT H. LURIE CHILDREN'S HOSPITAL OF CHICAGO

When it comes to caring for kids Ann & Robert H. Lurie Children's Hospital of Chicago has the Windy City covered. Founded in 1882 the not-for-profit hospital provides a full range of pediatric services with acute and specialty care. Lurie Children's provides services through its main hospital campus with about 300 beds and outpatient centers in Chicago's Lincoln Park neighborhood and through more than a dozen suburban outpatient centers and outreach partner locations in the greater Chicago area. A leader in pediatric research the hospital operates the Children's Hospital of Chicago Research Center and is the pediatric teaching facility of Northwestern University's Feinberg School of Medicine.

Operations

Lurie Children's serves roughly 150000 patients each year and employs some 1350 pediatric specialists with expertise in 70 different specialties. The hospital is one of only about a dozen children's hospitals nationwide to perform more than 1000 liver transplants. The center performs on average 50 solid organ and 50 stem cell transplants annually.

A major research center Lurie Children's is one of nearly 30 interdisciplinary research centers and institutes belonging to the hospital's academic partner — Feinberg School of Medicine. Its research arm Stanley Manne Children's Research Institute employs some 200 physician-scientists and research investigators who in 2014 were awarded more than $40 million in external funding.

Geographic Reach

Based in Chicago Lurie Children's has cared for patients from throughout the US and about 50 countries around the globe.

Financial Performance

Lurie Children's saw revenues increase by 8% to $826 million in fiscal 2014 (ended August). That growth was attributed to a rise in patient care revenues and other earnings. Net income increased 198% to $128 million that year largely due to the higher revenue as well as strong investment returns.

Cash flow from operations rose 36% to $124.5 million in fiscal 2014.

Strategy

The hospital has all-private rooms even in the neonatal intensive care unit; private rooms are said to speed healing by reducing hospital-acquired infection and minimize noise. Lurie Children's is working to enhance its specialist services and has upgraded its information technology systems. In 2013 it implemented a Voalte system that allows nurses to communicate through rapid-response systems including text messages and high-definition voice calls. Also that year it opened the first pediatric gender identity clinic. In 2015 the hospital acquired the fourth-generation da Vinci Xi robotic system for use in minimally invasive surgery.

In 2014 Lurie Children's Health Partners (composed of Lurie Children's and two groups of pediatricians) launched the Clinically Integrated Network the first health care network in Chicago to focus exclusively on children and their families. Its areas of focus include care coordination obesity asthma immunizations and child development.

EXECUTIVES

Assistant Vice President Corporate Giving, Erin Coleman
Vice President Revenue Cycle, Susan Pfister
Vice President And Chief Of Staff, Wayne Magdziarz
Assistant Vice President Capital Planning, Michael Loftsgaarden
Executive Vice President And Chief Development Officer, Grant Stirling
Vice President Human Resources Chro Chief Diversity Inclusion Officer, Winifred Williams
Medical Director, Gregory Gruener
Vice President Of Information Technology, Laura Bagus

LOCATIONS

HQ: ANN & ROBERT H. LURIE CHILDREN'S HOSPITAL OF CHICAGO
225 E CHICAGO AVE, CHICAGO, IL 606112991
Phone: 312 227-4000
Web: WWW.LURIECHILDRENS.ORG

Selected Illinois Locations

Lurie Children's at Cadence Health (Winfield)
Main Hospital (Chicago)
Outpatient Center in Arlington Heights (Arlington Heights)
Outpatient Center in Glenview (Glenview)
Outpatient Center in Lake Forest (Lake Forest)
Outpatient Center in Lincoln Park (Chicago)
Outpatient Center in New Lenox (New Lenox)
Outpatient Center in Westchester (Westchester)
Outpatient Services in Grayslake (Grayslake)
Outpatient Services in Gurnee (Gurnee)
Outpatient Services in Lincoln Square (Chicago)
Pediatrics - Uptown (Chicago)
Rehabilitation Services at Westbrook (Westchester)

PRODUCTS/OPERATIONS

2014 Sales

	$ mil.	% of total
Patient care revenues	706	85
Grants gifts & endowment income	62	8
Other revenues	57	7
Total	**825**	**100**

Selected Services

Adolescent Medicine
Allergy and Immunology
Anesthesiology
Audiology
Autonomic Medicine
Brain Tumor
Cancer and Blood Disorders
Cardiology (Heart Center)
Child Abuse Pediatrics
Child and Adolescent Psychiatry
Clinical Nutrition
Convenient Care
Critical Care

Cystic Fibrosis
Dentistry and Oral Surgery
Dermatology
Emergency Medicine
Endocrinology
Epilepsy
Fetal Health
Gastroenterology Hepatology and Nutrition (Digestive Disorders)
Gender and Sex Development
General Pediatric Surgery
General Pediatrics
Genetics Birth Defects and Metabolism
Heart Failure and Transplants
HIV/AIDS Prevention
Infectious Diseases
Intestinal Transplants
Kidney Diseases
Kidney Transplants
Liver Transplants
Medical Imaging (Radiology)
Neonatology
Neurology
Neurosurgery
Occupational Therapy
Ophthalmology
Orthopaedic Surgery
Orthotics/Prosthetics
Otolaryngology (ENT)
Palliative Care
Pathology and Laboratory Medicine
Physical Therapy
Plastic and Reconstructive Surgery
Pulmonary Medicine
Rehabilitative Services
Rheumatology
Speech-Language Pathology
Spina Bifida Center
Sports Medicine
Stem Cell Transplants
Transitioning to Adult Care
Transplantation
Urology

COMPETITORS

Advocate Health Care
Advocate Lutheran General Hospital
Alexian Brothers Health System
Covenant Ministries
HCA
Loyola University Health System
Mercy Hospital and Medical Center
NorthShore University HealthSystem
Northwestern Lake Forest Hospital
Northwestern Memorial HealthCare
Rush System for Health
SSM Health Care
Sinai Health System
University of Chicago Medical Center

HISTORICAL FINANCIALS

Company Type: Private

Income Statement — FYE: August 31

	REVENUE ($ mil.)	NET INCOME ($ mil.)	NET PROFIT MARGIN	EMPLOYEES
08/13	694	28	4.2%	2,800
08/10	599	52	8.8%	—
08/09	533	(5)	—	—
Annual Growth	6.8%	—	—	—

2013 Year-End Financials

Return on assets: 1.4%
Return on equity: 2.0%
Current ratio: 2.90
Cash ($ mil.): 92

ANNE ARUNDEL COUNTY BOARD OF EDUCATION

EXECUTIVES

Pres, Stacy Korbelak
Teacher, Matt Heist
Auditors: CLIFTONLARSONALLEN LLP BALTIM

LOCATIONS

HQ: ANNE ARUNDEL COUNTY BOARD OF EDUCATION
2644 RIVA RD, ANNAPOLIS, MD 214017427
Phone: 410 222-5000
Web: WWW.AACPS.ORG

HISTORICAL FINANCIALS

Company Type: Private

Income Statement — FYE: June 30

	REVENUE ($ mil.)	NET INCOME ($ mil.)	NET PROFIT MARGIN	EMPLOYEES
06/13	1,147	3	0.3%	130
06/04	712	0	0.1%	—
06/03	701	50	7.1%	—
Annual Growth	5.1%	(23.0%)	—	—

2013 Year-End Financials

Return on assets: 0.3%
Return on equity: 0.6%
Current ratio: —
Cash ($ mil.): 166

ANNE ARUNDEL MEDICAL CENTER, INC.

The ill and infirm get the royal treatment at Anne Arundel Medical Center. The full-service acute-care hospital serves the residents of Anne Arundel Calvert Prince George's and Queen Anne counties in Maryland. With about 425 beds the hospital administers care for women's health oncology pediatrics (it has a level III neonatal intensive care unit) neurology orthopedics and cardiovascular care. The medical center also has weight loss sleep disorder and rehabilitation centers. Anne Arundel which opened its doors in 1902 and is part of the Anne Arundel Health System has expanded its service offerings through various affiliations with regional specialty and primary care clinics. It also has a partnership with Johns Hopkins Medicine.

Operations

With more than 1000 staff members Anne Arundel handles some 26000 inpatient visits and 102000 outpatient visits per year. It also manages more than 5000 births and 93000 emergency room visits.

Johns Hopkins and the not-for-profit Anne Arundel share some services faculty and patients through their collaboration. They also operate a joint outpatient urgent-care facility. Additionally the two organizations work together to perform clinical research projects and conduct physician graduate medical education programs.

Geographic Reach

In addition to its 57-acre Annapolis campus Anne Arundel has outpatient centers in Bowie Kent Island Odenton Pasadena and Waugh Chapel.

Sales and Marketing

In 2014 Medicare payments accounted for about one-third of net patient revenues.

Financial Performance

In 2014 revenue grew 3% to $591 million as net patient services revenues increased. However net income fell 23% to $42 million due to a decline in non-operating income (investment earnings). Cash flow from operations spike 188% to $56 million as cash generated from patient receivables prepaid expenses and other sources rose.

Strategy

Anne Arundel has in recent years added new facilities to better keep up with a continued growth in demand for health care services throughout its service area. In 2015 it opened the second phase of its Pasadena Pavilion adding physical therapy orthopedics and sports medicine capabilities. It also opened a new FastCare walk-in clinic in a grocery store/pharmacy in Annapolis. In 2014 the system opened an outpatient mental health clinic in Annapolis which provides services for patients 13 years of age and older.

In 2013 Anne Arundel opened a training center – the James and Sylvia Earl Simulation to Advance Innovation and Learning (SAIL) Center – to enhance its medical education programs and improve the quality and safety of care in the region. It also opened the Hackerman-Patz House that year to provide an affordable and convenient housing option for families of patients.

Also in 2013 the organization was designated as a Medicare accountable care organization (ACO) by the US government. ACOs work to coordinate care for Medicare patients to improve quality and reduce expenses.

EXECUTIVES

Vp Cancer Services, Cathy Copertino
Vice President Corporate Services, Carolyn Cole
Vice President Finance, Marc Brassard
Vice President Of Human Resources, Julie McGovern
Medical Director Perioperative Services, Sohail Zaidi
Vice President Strategic Planning And Marketing And Communications, Josh Jacobs
Vice President Of Finance, Catherine Yurkon
Vice President, Steve Clarke
Director Of Pharmacy, James Caldwell
Vice President, Barbara Jacobs
Vice President, Peter Odenwald
Secretary Treasurer, Robert Reilly
Auditors: SC&H TAX & ADVISORY SERVICES L

LOCATIONS

HQ: ANNE ARUNDEL MEDICAL CENTER, INC.
2001 MEDICAL PKWY, ANNAPOLIS, MD 214013773
Phone: 443 481-1000
Web: WWW.AAHS.ORG

PRODUCTS/OPERATIONS

Selected Centers and Services

Blood Donor Center
Breast Center
Cardiac Cath Lab
Chest Pain Center
DeCesaris Cancer Institute
Diabetes Wound and Hyperbaric Center
Diagnostic Imaging
Heart and Vascular Institute
Joint Center
Laboratory
Pediatrics
Rehabilitation

Research Institute
Sleep Disorder Center
Spine Center
Stroke Center
Surgery
Women's and Children's Center

COMPETITORS

Ascension Health
Bon Secours Health
Dimensions Healthcare
Franklin Square Hospital Center
GBMC
Harbor Hospital
Johns Hopkins Health System
Johns Hopkins Medicine
LifeBridge Health
MedStar Health
Sinai Hospital of Baltimore
St. Agnes HealthCare
University of Maryland Medical System

HISTORICAL FINANCIALS

Company Type: Private

Income Statement FYE: June 30

	REVENUE ($ mil.)	NET INCOME ($ mil.)	NET PROFIT MARGIN	EMPLOYEES
06/19	579	17	2.9%	1,890
06/15	526	39	7.6%	—
06/14	492	20	4.1%	—
06/13	493	16	3.4%	—
Annual Growth	2.7%	0.3%	—	—

2019 Year-End Financials

Return on assets: 1.8%
Return on equity: 4.0%
Current ratio: 0.90
Cash ($ mil.): 9

ANOKA-HENNEPIN SCHOOL DIST NO 11

EXECUTIVES

Supt, David Law
Accounting Mgr*, Renee Rodewald
Cfo*, Michelle Vargas
Coordinator, Jeff Mueller
Coordinator, Dorothy Olsen
Coordinator, James Greer
Coordinator, Mark Hansen
Coordinator, Noella Fath
Coordinator, Tim Dahlheimer
Site Leader, Chrisanne Way
Site Leader, Donna Riley
Auditors: MALLOY MONTAGUE KARNOWSKI RA

LOCATIONS

HQ: ANOKA-HENNEPIN SCHOOL DIST NO 11
2727 N FERRY ST, ANOKA, MN 553031650
Phone: 763 506-1000
Web: WWW.AHSCHOOLS.US

HISTORICAL FINANCIALS

Company Type: Private

Income Statement FYE: June 30

	REVENUE ($ mil.)	NET INCOME ($ mil.)	NET PROFIT MARGIN	EMPLOYEES
06/19	574	(88)	—	6,100
06/18	550	151	27.5%	—
Annual Growth	4.3%	—	—	—

ANR PIPELINE COMPANY

ANR Pipeline keeps natural gas in line a pipeline that is. The company operates one of the largest interstate natural gas pipeline systems in the US. A subsidiary of TransCanada Corp. ANR controls about 10350 miles of pipeline and delivers more than 1 trillion cu. ft. of natural gas per year. The company primarily serves customers in the Midwest but through its network is capable of connecting to all major gas basins in North America. In tandem with its ANR Storage and Blue Lake Gas Storage subsidiaries ANR Pipeline also provides natural gas storage services and has ownership interests in more than 250 billion cu. ft. of underground natural gas storage capacity.

Operations

The ANR System is part of TransCanada's network 37000 miles of wholly owned and 4900 miles of partially owned pipelines connecting major supply basins with major markets all across North America.

Geographic Reach

ANR transports natural gas from producing fields in Texas and Oklahoma from offshore and onshore regions of the Gulf of Mexico and from the US midcontinent for delivery mainly to Illinois Indiana Michigan Ohio and Wisconsin.

Strategy

To create greater operating efficiency in 2012 ANR Pipeline Company sold assets and certain related onshore facilities to its wholly owned subsidiary TC Offshore LLC.

To support the growing natural gas production in the Haynesville Shale play in Texas and Louisiana the company is developing the ANR Haynesville Lateral Project to transport up to 1.8 billion cu. ft. of natural gas a day. The Haynesville Lateral pipeline enables producers to transport shale gas to markets in the Southeast Midwest and Northeast.

Company Background

ANR Pipeline was founded as Michigan-Wisconsin Pipe Line Company in 1945 and adopted its current name in 1984.

El Paso Corp. sold ANR Pipeline to TransCanada in 2007. The deal gave TransCanada a regulated natural gas pipeline and storage assets that complemented its other North American gas transmission operations.

EXECUTIVES

Vice President Commercial Services And Design, Norm Bowman
Vice President Gulf Coast Asset Manager, Betsy Mcmahon
Vice President, Lance Coulter
Vice President Tax Services, Beth Carley
Board Member, John Smith
Board Member, Alan Resnick
Board Member, Angela Panzarella
Board Member, Richard Harrison
Board Member, Gary Haseley

LOCATIONS

HQ: ANR PIPELINE COMPANY
700 LOUISIANA ST STE 700 # 700, HOUSTON, TX 770022873
Phone: 832 320-2000
Web: WWW.ANRPL.COM

COMPETITORS

Alliance Pipeline
Buckeye Pipe Line
Columbia Gulf Transmission
Duke Energy
OGE Energy
ONEOK Partners
Panhandle Eastern Pipe Line
Transcontinental Gas Pipe Line
Vector Pipeline
Williams Companies
Williston Basin Interstate Pipeline

HISTORICAL FINANCIALS

Company Type: Private

Income Statement FYE: December 31

	REVENUE ($ mil.)	NET INCOME ($ mil.)	NET PROFIT MARGIN	EMPLOYEES
12/17	758	139	18.5%	1,000
12/16	686	54	8.0%	—
12/06	540	152	28.1%	—
12/05	548	147	26.8%	—
Annual Growth	2.7%	(0.4%)	—	—

2017 Year-End Financials

Return on assets: 4.6%
Return on equity: 10.4%
Current ratio: 1.30
Cash ($ mil.): —

API GROUP INC.

Holding company APi Group has a piece of the action in two main sectors: fire protection systems and industrial and specialty construction services. APi boasts about 40 subsidiaries which operate as independent companies across the US (nearly half of them in Minnesota) the UK and Canada. Services provided by the company's construction subsidiaries include HVAC and plumbing system installation; electrical industrial and mechanical contracting; industrial insulation; and garage door installation. Safety-focused units install a host of fire sprinkler detection security and alarm systems. The family-owned company was founded in 1926 by Reuben Anderson father of chairman Lee Anderson.

Operations

Through its various companies APi Group is involved in engineering designing constructing and installing LEED green-building certification program projects. Its divisions include Architectural Roofing and Mechanical Classic Industrial Services APi Construction APi Distribution and Industrial Fabricators among others.

Geographic Reach

Minnesota-based APi Group operates companies throughout North America and the UK.

Sales and Marketing

APi Group serves several sectors such as security and defense education commercial industrial medical oil and gas and residential.

Strategy

Although APi Group companies are independent they often pool resources and work together to service clients.

Mergers and Acquisitions

The highly acquisitive APi Group regularly acquires new companies to strengthen its growing group.

In 2013 the company's Western States Fire Protection (WSFP) acquired Advanced Fire an Oklahoma City-based fire-suppression company that specializes in military work. Buying Advanced Fire extends the company's reach in the fire protection industry and boosts its market share within Oklahoma City and the surrounding area. APi Group's Delta Fire Systems acquired Idaho's 3-D Fire which provides full-fire-system design fabrication installation testing and certification capabilities for commercial and private projects.

APi Group previous purchases include Dynamic Fire Protection LLC (DFP) Omlid & Swinney Fire Protection and Security Canada-based Fire Stop Enterprises Ohio-based 3S and Kansas-based mainline pipeline contractor Jomax Construction.

EXECUTIVES

Pres-Ceo, Russell Becker
Treas-Cfo, Gregory Keup
SEC, William M Beadie
Project Manager, Adam Tollefson
Administrator, Bill Ziobro
Corporate Safety Director, Bryan Thayer
It Manager, Carole Roden
Assistant Controller, Chris Otto
Operations Manager, Christie Pletscher
Voice, Clint Latz
Project Manager, Cori Prokopowicz
Auditors: KPMG

LOCATIONS

HQ: API GROUP INC.
1100 OLD HIGHWAY 8 NW, SAINT PAUL, MN 551126447
Phone: 651 636-4320
Web: WWW.APIGROUPINC.COM

PRODUCTS/OPERATIONS

Selected Subsidiaries

Fire Protection Systems
- Alliance Fire Protection Inc.
- APi National Service Group
- Davis-Ulmer Sprinkler Company
- Delta Fire Systems Inc.
- Grunau Company
- Halon Banking Systems
- International Fire Protection Inc.
- Island Fire Sprinkler Inc.
- Reliance Fire Protection
- Rich Fire Protection Co Inc.
- Security Fire Protection Company
- United States Fire Protection Company
- VFP Fire Systems Inc.
- Viking Automatic Sprinkler Company
- Vipond Fire Protection Inc. (Canada)
- Vipond Fire Protection Ltd. (UK)
- Western States Fire Protection Inc.

Industrial and Specialty Construction Services

3S Incorporated
- Anco Products Inc.
- APi CAD Services
- APi Construction Company
- APi Distribution Inc.
- APi Electric
- APi Supply Inc.
- Classic Industrial Services Inc.
- Doody Mechanical Inc.
- Garage Door Store
- Grunau Company Inc.
- Industrial Contractors Inc.
- Industrial Fabricators Inc.
- Jamar Company
- Jomax Construction Co.
- LeJeune Steel Company
- NYCO Inc.
- Tessier's Inc.
- Twin City Garage Door Company

Low Voltage
- APi Systems Group Inc.
- APi Systems Integrators
- Vipond Systems Group

COMPETITORS

Comfort Systems USA
EMCOR
IES Holdings
Irex
John E. Green
TDIndustries
Team
Turner Industries
Tyco Fire & Security

HISTORICAL FINANCIALS

Company Type: Private

Income Statement — FYE: December 31

	REVENUE ($ mil.)	NET INCOME ($ mil.)	NET PROFIT MARGIN	EMPLOYEES
12/18	3,730	122	3.3%	4,237
12/17	3,046	112	3.7%	—
12/16	2,608	104	4.0%	—
12/15	2,448	106	4.3%	—
Annual Growth	15.1%	5.0%	—	—

2018 Year-End Financials

Return on assets: 6.2%
Return on equity: 21.3%
Current ratio: 1.10
Cash ($ mil.): 54

APPALACHIAN REGIONAL HEALTHCARE, INC.

Under-the-weather coal miners (and their daughters) can turn to Appalachian Regional Healthcare (ARH) for medical services. The not-for-profit health system serves residents of eastern Kentucky and southern West Virginia through a dozen hospitals with more than 1000 beds as well as dozens of clinics home health care agencies HomeCare Stores and retail pharmacies. Its largest hospital in Hazard Kentucky has 310 beds and features an inpatient psychiatric unit that serves as the state mental health facility. Several of the system's hospitals are Critical Access Hospitals a federal government designation for rural community hospitals that operate in medically underserved areas.

Operations

ARH's HomeCare Stores provide home medical equipment and oxygen delivery as well as 24-hour support through eight respiratory therapists. Its HomeCare Stores are supported by the ARH Home Health Agencies which provide access to nursing care occupational and physical therapy and social services.

Among the system's hospitals are Beckley ARH Hospital a not-for-profit 173-bed acute-care facility; Harlan ARH Hospital a state-licensed 150-bed acute-care facility; and Mary Breckinridge ARH Hospital a critical access facility.

ARH is the largest provider of care and single largest employer in southeastern Kentucky and the third-largest private employer in southern West Virginia. It employs almost 5000 people and has a network of more than 600 medical staff members. In 2013 the system had 153000 emergency department visits 482000 outpatient visits some 1500 births and about 12000 outpatient surgeries.

Geographic Reach

ARH serves residents of eastern Kentucky and southern West Virginia. It has hospitals in Harlan Hazard Hyden Martin McDowell Middlesboro Morgan County South Williamson and Whitesburg Kentucky; and in Beckley and Summers County West Virginia.

Strategy

As the primary provider of health care to medically underserved populations ARH doles out millions of dollars in uncompensated care each year to un- or underinsured residents of the Appalachian region.

Along with a larger population of uninsured patients and the resulting unpaid medical bills that come along with them rural health care providers face a number of hardships not encountered by their urban brethren. For example physician recruitment is more difficult at rural hospitals especially for some higher-risk specialties such as obstetrics. In order to attract and retain doctors ARH and other rural health care providers have to offer more competitive compensation packages pay for relocation and invest in technology and facility upgrades.

Also patients in rural areas are more likely to suffer from chronic health problems such as diabetes and obesity which can become a significant drain on a health system's resources. ARH is one of many health care providers looking to benefit from changes to the health care system outlined in Affordable Care Act especially the requirement that all US citizens carry health insurance.

To keep up with patient demand ARH also focuses on building and acquiring new facilities as well as investing in new technology and medical capacities.

Beckley ARH Hospital is undergoing a nearly $7 million renovation project that will add 19 more private rooms decrease utility costs and improve patient flow processes. In 2014 ARH completed a $47 million expansion project at the Hazard ARH Regional Medical Center that added an additional 100000 sq. ft. to the medical center including a new patient tower a new 24-bed emergency department on the first floor a dedicated 16-bed cardiac critical care unit and 34 private rooms. Hazard ARH is now the largest hospital in southeastern Kentucky.

Mergers and Acquisitions

In 2018 Appalachian Regional Healthcare acquired its twelfth hospital – the 25-bed Saint Joseph Martin Hospital – and its clinics. That facility now operates as ARH Our Lady of the Way.

Company Background

Appalachian Regional Healthcare was formed in 1956 by the United Mine Workers of America but became an independent not-for-profit entity in the early 1960s.

EXECUTIVES

Vice President Sales And Marketing, Holly Harris
Vice President Corporate Strategy, Hollie Harris
Director Of Radiology, Jeremy Willis
Medical Director, Jim Maynard
Director Of Admissions, David Slone
Vice President, Jim Parker
Vice Chair, Leslie Combs
Auditors: MCM CPA'S & ADVISORS LLP LOU

LOCATIONS

HQ: APPALACHIAN REGIONAL HEALTHCARE, INC.
2260 EXECUTIVE DR, LEXINGTON, KY 405054808
Phone: 859 226-2440
Web: WWW.ARH.ORG

PRODUCTS/OPERATIONS

Selected Facilities

- Beckley ARH Hospital (Beckley West Virginia)
- Hazard ARH Regional Medical Center (Hazard Kentucky)
- Harlan ARH Hospital (Harlan Kentucky)
- McDowell ARH Hospital (McDowell Kentucky)
- Middlesboro ARH Hospital (Middlesboro Kentucky)
- Morgan County ARH Hospital (West Liberty Kentucky)
- Summers County ARH Hospital (Hinton West Virginia)
- Tug Valley ARH Regional Medical Center (South Williamson Kentucky)
- Whitesburg ARH Hospital (Whitesburg Kentucky)

Selected Services

Bariatrics

Behavioral Health
Cancer Care
Clinics
Emergency
Heart Care
Home Health
HomeCare Stores
Imaging
Laboratory
Medical Spa
Nephrology
Obstetrics and Gynecology
Pediatrics
Pharmacy
Rehabilitation Therapy
Respiratory Therapy
Rheumatology
Senior Care
Skilled Nursing
Sleep Lab
Surgery
Swing Beds

COMPETITORS

Baptist Health
Bon Secours Health
Carilion Clinic
Catholic Health Initiatives
Community Health Systems
Highlands Health
Jewish Hospital & St. Mary's HealthCare
Kindred Healthcare
Mercy Medical Center (NY)
Montgomery Regional Hospital
Norton Healthcare
Pikeville Medical Center
University of Kentucky Chandler Hospital
University of Virginia Health System

HISTORICAL FINANCIALS

Company Type: Private

Income Statement — FYE: June 30

	REVENUE ($ mil.)	NET INCOME ($ mil.)	NET PROFIT MARGIN	EMPLOYEES
06/19	760	1	0.2%	4,520
06/18	689	65	9.4%	—
06/17	657	43	6.6%	—
06/16	653	17	2.6%	—
Annual Growth	5.2%	(59.2%)	—	—

2019 Year-End Financials

Return on assets: 0.1%
Return on equity: 0.4%
Current ratio: 0.90
Cash ($ mil.): 76

APPLE HOSPITALITY REIT, INC.

EXECUTIVES

Pres-Ceo, Justin G Knight
Exec Chb*, Glade M Knight
Exec V Pres-Coo, Kristian M Gathright
Evp-Cfo, Bryan Peery
Exec V Pres-Clo, David P Buckley
Exec V Pres-CIO, Nelson G Knight
Manager Director, Debra Quin
Board Member, Jon Fosheim
Executive Chairman, Glade Knight
Director, Justin Knight
Senior Vice President of Asset, Kc Gallagher
Auditors: ERNST & YOUNG LLP RICHMOND V

LOCATIONS

HQ: APPLE HOSPITALITY REIT, INC.
814 E MAIN ST, RICHMOND, VA 232193306
Phone: 804 344-8121
Web: WWW.APPLEHOSPITALITYREIT.COM

HISTORICAL FINANCIALS

Company Type: Private

Income Statement — FYE: December 31

	REVENUE ($ mil.)	NET INCOME ($ mil.)	NET PROFIT MARGIN	EMPLOYEES
12/14	803	6	0.9%	171
12/13	387	115	29.7%	—
12/12	365	75	20.6%	—
12/11	320	69	21.8%	—
Annual Growth	35.9%	(54.0%)	—	—

ARCTIC SLOPE REGIONAL CORPORATION

The Inupiat people have survived the rigors of the Arctic for centuries and now surviving in the business world. The Inupiat-owned Arctic Slope Regional Corporation (ASRC) is a locally owned and operated business in Alaska. It gets the bulk of its sales from energy services (ASRC Energy Services) and petroleum refining and marketing unit (Petro Star). Other operations include construction (ASRC Construction Holding) governmental services (ASRC Federal Holding) economic development (Alaska Growth Capital BIDCO) local services (Eskimos Inc.) and tourism (Tundra Tours).

Operations

ASRC owns title to nearly 5 million acres of land on Alaska's North Slope which contain a high potential for oil gas coal and base metal sulfides. It also owns subsurface and surface rights to certain lands.

The company seeks to adhere to traditional Inupiat values of protecting the land the environment and the native culture while developing economic programs.

It operates in six diverse major business segments: petroleum refining and marketing government contract services energy support services industrial services resource development and construction industries. Petro Star has two refineries (strategically positioned along the Trans-Alaska Pipeline) and serves Interior Alaska South Central Alaska Kodiak and Dutch Harbor. Its North Pole facility supplies the mining industry in the interior region of Alaska and provides home heating oil to several communities.

ASRC Federal Holding Company provides professional and technical services to the federal government (including defense and intelligence agencies engineering IT infrastructure support professional and technical services to civil).

ASRC Energy Services offers oilfield engineering operations maintenance construction fabrication regulation and permitting and other services to oil and gas companies. The company provides services to the energy industry throughout Alaska and the Gulf of Mexico.

ASRC Construction Holding Company provides construction services to commercial and government clients in Alaska the Lower 48 and in other countries.

ASRC Industrial Services (AIS) is a people-oriented organization of complementary yet diverse services focusing on the industrial end-use customers nationwide.

Geographic Reach

ASRC represents approximately 13000 members/shareholders in eight villages on the North Slope of Alaska: Anaktuvuk Pass Atqasuk Kaktovik Nuiqsut Point Hope Point Lay Utqiógvik and Wainwright. ASRC has its head office in Utqiógvik with a major administrative office in Anchorage. It has other subsidiary offices in the Lower 48 states.

Strategy

ASRC is issuing the following statement regarding its decision to drop its membership of the Alaska Federation of Natives or AFN. With this decision ASRC intends to focus on the various needs within Alaska's North Slope where there is an increased degree of alignment as well as additional efficiencies related to shared geography and other interests.

In 2019 the company acquired the National Environmental Group (NEG) and Niles Construction Services (NCS) through its wholly-owned subsidiary ASRC Industrial Services LLC (AIS). Working with the teams at NEG and NCS will build on the companies' well-earned reputations and the process provide additional opportunities for their talented workforces bring additional services to customers and ultimately deliver meaningful benefits to ASRC's shareholders.

Mergers and Acquisitions

In late 2019 ASRC announced the acquisition of Northwest Demolition & Dismantling (NWDD) by its wholly-owned subsidiary ASRC Industrial Services LLC (AIS). Oregon-based NWDD provides services throughout the US Canada and the Pacific islands. It has over 60 years in demolition decommissioning environmental remediation and specialty consulting services. The company will join AIS's Remediation and Response Services (RRS) operating group. Financial terms were not disclosed.

Company Background

ASRC was set up to own and manage 5 million acres on Alaska's North Slope after the Alaska Native Claims Settlement Act in 1971 cleared the way for oil development in the area.

In 2010 ASRC protested the US Fish and Wildlife Service's designation of Alaskan North Slope oil-producing areas as a critical habitat for endangered polar bears claiming it would cost ASRC millions of dollars in lost oil revenues. In 2011 it led a coalition of Native groups to sue the Department of the Interior over this issue.

In 2012 ASRC Construction Holding expanded into southeast Alaska with the acquisition of native-Alaskan owned McGraw's Custom Construction.

EXECUTIVES

Evp Lands And Natural Resources, Richard K. Glenn
President And Ceo, Rex A. Rock
Chairman And Evp Shareholder Community Programs, Crawford Patkotak
Evp And General Counsel, Denali Kemppel
Evp And Coo, Butch Lincoln
Evp And Cfo, Charlie Kozak
Vice President Tax, Mark Hamilton
Executive Vice President Human Resources, Debbie Akpik
Vice President Corporate Controller, Walter Williams
Vice Chairman, George Sielak

LOCATIONS

HQ: ARCTIC SLOPE REGIONAL CORPORATION
3900 C ST STE 801, ANCHORAGE, AK 995035963
Phone: 907 339-6000
Web: WWW.ASRC.COM

PRODUCTS/OPERATIONS

Selected Businesses

Energy Services
- ASRC Energy Services Inc.
- Arctic Inupiat Offshore LLC.

Petroleum Refining and Marketing
- Petro Star Inc.

Government Services
- ASRC Federal Holding Company

Construction
- ASRC Construction Holding Company LLC

Resource Development
- Little Red Services
- Petrochem

COMPETITORS

Alaska Communications Systems
Baker Hughes
Halliburton
Nabors Industries
Noble
Schlumberger
T-Mobile USA
Tesoro

HISTORICAL FINANCIALS

Company Type: Private

Income Statement — FYE: December 31

	REVENUE ($ mil.)	NET INCOME ($ mil.)	NET PROFIT MARGIN	EMPLOYEES
12/08	2,297	151	6.6%	6,700
12/07	1,777	207	11.7%	—
12/06	1,700	206	12.1%	—
12/05	1,566	127	8.1%	—
Annual Growth	13.6%	5.8%	—	—

2008 Year-End Financials

Return on assets: 11.7%
Return on equity: 19.0%
Current ratio: 1.70
Cash ($ mil.): 302

ARIZONA STATE LOTTERY

EXECUTIVES

Dep Dir, Karen Emery
Director*, Gregory Edgar
Info Tech Specialist, Benita Martinez
Auditors: HENRY & HORNE LLP CASA GRAND

LOCATIONS

HQ: ARIZONA STATE LOTTERY
4740 E UNIVERSITY DR, PHOENIX, AZ 850347400
Phone: 480 921-4400
Web: WWW.ARIZONALOTTERY.COM

HISTORICAL FINANCIALS

Company Type: Private

Income Statement — FYE: June 30

	REVENUE ($ mil.)	NET INCOME ($ mil.)	NET PROFIT MARGIN	EMPLOYEES
06/20	1,097	5	0.5%	112
06/19	1,076	9	0.9%	—
06/17	853	0	0.0%	—
06/97	254	84	33.2%	—
Annual Growth	6.6%	(11.1%)	—	—

2020 Year-End Financials

Return on assets: 4.5%
Return on equity: 26.8%
Current ratio: 0.90
Cash ($ mil.): 57

ARIZONA STATE UNIVERSITY

Sun lovers and knowledge seekers can turn to Arizona State University (ASU) for a well-rounded college education. The research university offers a wide variety of bachelor's master's and doctoral degree programs with more than 300 majors through some 18 schools teaching a range of disciplines including nursing journalism and engineering. It has an enrollment of more than 98100 undergraduate graduate and professional students on its six campuses in metropolitan Phoenix; most students attend the Tempe campus. The university has a student-teacher ratio of 23:1. ASU was founded in 1885 as a teachers college and has become widely known for its extensive research programs.

Operations

ASU offers more than 90 undergraduate and graduate degrees and certificates online through some of its colleges including the W. P. Carey School of Business Mary Lou Fulton Teachers College College of Nursing and Health Innovation and the Ira A. Fulton School of Engineering. ASU also partners with Pearson Digital Learning to administer online courses; Pearson also monitors and analyzes student performance trends.

The university's extensive research programs cover a variety of fields in life science medicine and physical science categories. In addition subsidiary Arizona Technology Enterprises (AzTE) manages technology ventures for ASU. AzTE manages the university's intellectual property (much of which is the result of its research programs) and facilitates startup businesses which have led to the formation of 80 companies and attracted $500 million in funding between 2002 and 2016.

Geographic Reach

ASU has an enrollment of students from more than 130 countries.

Financial Performance

The university's revenues increased by 11% (or $162 million) to $1.6 billion in fiscal 2016 primarily due a 10% increase in enrollment including a 23% growth in nonresident enrollment. Research grants and contracts revenue primarily funded by federal agencies rose by 7%.

Operating expenses grew by $143 million (or 7%) that year largely related to the increase in enrollment. Instruction and academic support expenses experienced the largest rise of $81 million.

Strategy

The university is working to become a top research university in interdisciplinary fields of science and technology. As part of that goal ASU is seeking to expand its AzTE entrepreneur business through additional technology discoveries and startup formations. It also seeks to help stimulate the Arizona economy by reaching out to local businesses and encouraging startups that will maintain a presence in the state.

ASU is also working to improve graduation rates increase graduate enrollment and enhance individual learning programs. The university intends to increase the quality of its academic programs and its student facilities.

In 2015 and 2016 the US News & World Report named ASU as the most innovative school in the US.

In 2016 the school opened the $130 million Arizona Center for Law and Society at its downtown campus. The center provides law students with greater access to Arizona's judicial political and economic centers. Other planned facilities include new educational and research centers near Phoenix's Mayo Clinic Hospital; they will deepen ASU's partnership with the Mayo Clinic and provide learning opportunities for ASU students.

In 2014 the university launched a partnership with Starbucks to provide tuition reimbursement to employees nationwide attending ASU online.

EXECUTIVES

Evp Treasurer And Cfo, Morgan R. Olsen
President, Michael M. Crow, age 65
Cio And Professor Of Parctice, Lev S. Gonick, age 60
Svp And President Asu Alumni Association, Christine K. Wilkinson
Evp And University Provost, Mark Searle
Cio, Gordon Wishon
Evp Knowledge Enterprise Development And Chief Research & Innovation Officer, Sethuraman (Panch) Panchanathan
Svp And Chief Marketing Officer, Daniel Dillon
Dean Educational Initiatives And Ceo Edplus, Philip Regier
Ceo And Director General Thunderbird School Of Global Management And Professor Of Global Strategy And Leadership, Allen Morrison
Auditors: LINDSEY PERRY CPA CFE PHOEN

LOCATIONS

HQ: ARIZONA STATE UNIVERSITY
300 E UNIVERSITY DR # 410, TEMPE, AZ 852812061
Phone: 480 965-2100
Web: WWW.WEBLOGIN.ASU.EDU

PRODUCTS/OPERATIONS

2014 Sales

	$ mil.	% of total
Tuition & fees	896	67
Research grants and contracts	244	18
Auxiliary enterprises	140	10
Other operating revenues	66	5
Total	**1,348**	**100**

Selected Colleges and Schools

Barrett Honors College
College of Health Solutions
College of Liberal Arts and Sciences
College of Nursing and Health Innovation
College of Public Programs
College of Technology and Innovation
Graduate College
Herberger Institute for Design and the Arts
Ira A. Fulton Schools of Engineering
Mary Lou Fulton Teachers College
New College of Interdisciplinary Arts and Sciences
Sandra Day O'Connor College of Law
School of Letters and Sciences
School of Sustainability
Thunderbird School of Global Management
University College
Walter Cronkite School of Journalism and Mass Communication
W.P. Carey School of Business

HISTORICAL FINANCIALS

Company Type: Private

Income Statement — FYE: June 30

	REVENUE ($ mil.)	NET INCOME ($ mil.)	NET PROFIT MARGIN	EMPLOYEES
06/19	2,048	85	4.2%	8,000
06/18	1,915	63	3.3%	—
06/17	1,782	99	5.6%	—
06/16	1,644	108	6.6%	—
Annual Growth	7.6%	(7.7%)	—	—

2019 Year-End Financials

Return on assets: 1.9%
Return on equity: 6.3%
Current ratio: 1.00
Cash ($ mil.): 239

ARIZONA STATE UNIVERSITY

LOCATIONS

HQ: ARIZONA STATE UNIVERSITY
951 S PALM WALK, TEMPE, AZ 852870001
Phone: 480 965-4385
Web: WWW.ASU.EDU

HISTORICAL FINANCIALS

Company Type: Private

Income Statement FYE: June 30

	REVENUE ($ mil.)	NET INCOME ($ mil.)	NET PROFIT MARGIN	EMPLOYEES
06/15	1,482	92	6.2%	26
06/14	1,348	103	7.7%	—
Annual Growth	9.9%	(10.7%)	—	—

2015 Year-End Financials

Return on assets: 6.4%
Return on equity: 6.2%
Current ratio: 0.60
Cash ($ mil.): 47

ARKANSAS CHILDREN'S HOSPITAL

As the only pediatric medical center in the state Arkansas Children's Hospital (ACH) serves the youngest Razorbacks from birth to age 21. The not-for-profit hospital with its 370 beds specializes in childhood cancer pediatric orthopedics and neonatology. Besides acute care services it operates more than 80 specialty clinics and outpatient centers. One of the US's largest pediatric hospitals ACH is also engaged in teaching and medical research through its affiliation with the University of Arkansas for Medical Sciences. Its Arkansas Children's Hospital Research Institute focuses on biological mechanisms underlying birth defects diabetes-related complications and childhood diseases.

Operations

ACH each year performs more than 14500 operations and boasts 55000-plus emergency department visits nearly 330000 outpatient visits and about 14800 inpatient admissions.

ACH's Circle of Friends clinic treats more than 20000 patients annually. The clinic which opened in 2008 provides primary care as well as a broad range of specialty care services related to endocrinology dermatological conditions hemophilia and tuberculosis.

The hospital also offers community outreach services that include help for children of domestic abuse and wellness programs as well as a number of clinics to support those with eating disorders and diabetes.

As a prime destination for treatment ACH also runs Angel One Transport an intensive care medical transportation system that brings critically ill and injured infants children and adolescents as well as adult burn patients from throughout Arkansas and the surrounding states to ACH. It also boasts a high risk obstetric transport program in partnership with the University of Arkansas for Medical Sciences.

ACH has a staff of 500 physicians including 95 residents in pediatrics and pediatric specialties. Its mobile clinics annually serve more than 6000 patients and provide more than $3 million in dental treatment.

Geographic Reach

Based in Little Rock Arkansas on a campus that extends nearly 30 city blocks ACH serves children nationwide as one of the largest pediatric hospitals in the US. It has several locations across Arkansas in Little Rock Jonesboro and Lowell.

Financial Performance

The hospital gets about 82% of its net sales from net patient service revenues.

Strategy

In 2015 ACH announced plans to build a $184 million hospital in Springdale. The 24-bed hospital will be located on 37 acres of land near Arvest Ballpark. The hospital is targeted to be completed in 2018.

In 2013 ACH inked a contract with Aetna health insurance under which patients with Aetna health insurance will be able to seek in-network care at ACH. The contract allows the company to reach more families throughout the region.

Company Background

The hospital opened a new $121 million south wing in mid-2012 that added more than 50 inpatient beds to the hospital's capacity. The nearly 260000-sq.-ft. four-story building features telemedicine technology (for remote patient care) new trauma rooms a dedicated orthopedics suite and a decontamination unit.

To its benefit ACH became the state's only pediatric Level I trauma center in 2010 after receiving a four-year designation from the Arkansas Department of Health. The designation means that the hospital is equipped for and capable of taking care of children with the most severe of traumas. Level I trauma centers serve as referral locations for hospitals that are unable to provide the same level of care.

EXECUTIVES

President Ceo And Director, Jonathan R. (Jon) Bates
Evp, Scott R. Gordon
President Arkansas Childrens Hospital Research Institute, Richard F. Jacobs
Svp And Cio, Darrell T. Leonhardt
Svp And Cfo, Gena G. Wingfield
Svp And Coo, David T. Berry
President Ach Foundation, Fred Scarborough
Senior Vice President Chief Quality Officer, Jayant K. Deshpande
Senior Vice President Medical Director, W. Robert Morrow
Vice President Operations, Jennifer Carlisle
Nursing Director, Terri Songer
Director Of Pharmacy, Marita Q Nazarian
Vice President Of Ancillary Services, Cindy Holland
Vice President Finance, Cindy Hill
Director Of Nursing, Rebecca Kersten
Nursing Director, Kim Moore
Director Of Nursing, Amy Huett
Vice President Performance Improvement, Angela Green
Nursing Director, Amy Allen
Nursing Director Of The Special Staffing Team, Jenny Janisko
Senior Vice President Chief Strategy Officer, Robert Steele
Senior Vice President Of Human Resource, Kimberly Frisbee
Vice President, Curtis Summers
Medical Director, Stephen Schexnayder
Respiratory Therapy Director, Patty Burge
Nursing Director, Tammy Wells
Senior Vice President Chief Strategy Officer, Bob Steele
Senior Vice President And Chief Information Officer, Jonathan Goldberg
Vice President Ambulatory Care Services, Lee A Eddy
Nursing Director, Tammy R Diamond-wells
Secretary To Vice President Human Resources, Charlotte Johnson
Secretary Iii, Pamela Chumley
Secretary Iii, Sharon Mitchell
Secretary Iii Manged Care, Susan Henson
Secretary Iii, Debbie Chumley
Secretary Ii, Kim Nelson
Secretary, Conee Corning-banks
Auditors: KPMG LLP MEMPHIS TN

LOCATIONS

HQ: ARKANSAS CHILDREN'S HOSPITAL
1 CHILDRENS WAY, LITTLE ROCK, AR 722023500
Phone: 501 364-1100
Web: WWW.ARCHILDRENS.ORG

PRODUCTS/OPERATIONS

Selected Services

Ambulatory Surgery
Audiology
Center for Good Mourning
Cleft Clinic
Dennis Developmental Center
Dental Clinic
ECMO
Gastroenterology Clinic
Genetic and Metabolic Clinic
Infectious Diseases
Neuroscience Unit
Physical Medicine & Rehab Outreach Clinics
Sleep Disorders Center
Volunteer Services
WHAM (Wellness Health Action & Motivation) Clinic

COMPETITORS

Arkansas Heart Hospital
Baptist Health (Arkansas)
Children's Healthcare of Atlanta
Children's Medical Center of Dallas
Children's Mercy Hospital
Children's National Medical Center
Cook Children's Health Care System
Dell Children's Medical Center
East Tennessee Children's Hospital
Jefferson Regional Medical Center of Arkansas
Methodist Healthcare
Shriners Hospitals For Children
St. Joseph's Mercy Health Center
St. Jude Children's Research Hospital
St. Vincent Health System
Texas Children's Hospital
Universal Health Services
White County Medical Center

HISTORICAL FINANCIALS

Company Type: Private

Income Statement FYE: June 30

	REVENUE ($ mil.)	NET INCOME ($ mil.)	NET PROFIT MARGIN	EMPLOYEES
06/19	703	93	13.3%	3,700
06/18	660	57	8.7%	—
06/17	615	59	9.7%	—
06/16	585	70	12.1%	—
Annual Growth	6.3%	9.6%	—	—

2019 Year-End Financials

Return on assets: 6.0%
Return on equity: 7.2%
Current ratio: 8.20
Cash ($ mil.): 101

ARKANSAS ELECTRIC COOPERATIVE CORPORATION

Having access to power is the natural state in the Natural State thanks to Arkansas Electric Cooperative Corporation (AECC) the sole wholesale power provider for 17 Arkansas electric distribution cooperatives. The company operates power plants with 3418 MW of generating capacity owns transmission assets and buys wholesale power to meet its members' demands. Affiliate Arkansas Electric Cooperatives Inc. (AECI) provides administrative and maintenance services to the distribution companies. The distribution utilities serve about 500000 customers in more than 60% of Arkansas. AECC and AECI along with the state's 17 electric distribution cooperatives are known as the Electric Cooperatives of Arkansas.

Operations

AECC's diverse generation assets include three hydropower plants three natural gas/oil-based plants and three natural gas-based-only plants. It also co-owns portions of four low-cost coal-based plants and has a long-term power purchase agreement for 51 MW wind energy. The coop also has four transmission lines.

Sales and Marketing

In fiscal 2013 co-op members Mississippi County Electric Cooperative First Electric Cooperative Carroll Electric Cooperative and Arkansas Valley Electric Corporation together accounted for 59% of AECC's total revenues.

Financial Performance

Thanks to a rebounding economy and growing demand for power the company saw its revenues grow by 13% in fiscal 2013.

Net income declined by 37% in fiscal 2013 due to higher operations maintenance generation and transmission expenses as well as an increase in administration and general expenses.

Strategy

AECC is ramping up its renewable energy resources in order to meet state and federal clean energy power requirements.

In 2013 the company signed a long-term deal to buy 150 MW of wind energy from RES America Developments Inc. a subsidiary of Renewable Energy Systems Americas Inc.

In 2012 it reached a long-term purchase power agreement for 51 MW of wind energy from the Flat Ridge 2 South Wind Farm in Kansas. AECC's 51 MW of capacity is part of 470 MW of potential generation provided by the farm's 294 GE wind turbines. BP and Sempra U.S. Gas & Power are equal joint venture partners for the facility which has a combined investment of more than $800 million. A wholly-owned affiliate of BP Wind Energy will monitor and maintain the farm

Mergers and Acquisitions

In another move to cut back on the use of coal-fired power plants in 2012 AECC bought a 746-MW combined cycle natural gas-fired power plant near Magnet Cove for $240 million.

Company Background

The first electric cooperative in Arkansas was formed in Jacksonville in 1938 as part of the Roosevelt Administration's national rural electrification drive.

EXECUTIVES

Vice President Of Human Resources, Maria Smedley
Vice President External Affairs, Sandra Byrd
Vice President Of Planning, Andrew Lachowsky
Auditors: BKD LLP LITTLE ROCK ARKANSA

LOCATIONS

HQ: ARKANSAS ELECTRIC COOPERATIVE CORPORATION
1 COOPERATIVE WAY, LITTLE ROCK, AR 722095493
Phone: 501 570-2200
Web: WWW.AECC.COM

HISTORICAL FINANCIALS

Company Type: Private

Income Statement — FYE: October 31

	REVENUE ($ mil.)	NET INCOME ($ mil.)	NET PROFIT MARGIN	EMPLOYEES
10/19	790	24	3.1%	220
10/18*	827	38	4.7%	—
12/15	462	35	7.7%	—
12/14	455	30	6.6%	—
Annual Growth	11.7%	(3.8%)	—	—

*Fiscal year change

2019 Year-End Financials

Return on assets: 1.4%
Return on equity: 4.1%
Current ratio: 0.90
Cash ($ mil.): 154

ARKANSAS ELECTRIC COOPERATIVES, INC.

EXECUTIVES

Pres, Duane Highley
Plant Manager, Mark Folsland
Information Technology Enginee, Nathaniel Collier
Associate Editor, Sheila Yount
Department Admin Assistant, Stacy Rinehart
Title Field Sales Representat, Thomas Schwab
Senior Analyst, Willie Brooks
Manager, David Henthorne
Manager, Kelli Hobbs
Title Manager, Heith Barger
Distribution Shipping Transpor, Jonathan Oliver
Auditors: BKD LLP LITTLE ROCK ARKANSA

LOCATIONS

HQ: ARKANSAS ELECTRIC COOPERATIVES, INC.
1 COOPERATIVE WAY, LITTLE ROCK, AR 722095493
Phone: 501 570-2200
Web: WWW.AECC.COM

HISTORICAL FINANCIALS

Company Type: Private

Income Statement — FYE: December 31

	REVENUE ($ mil.)	NET INCOME ($ mil.)	NET PROFIT MARGIN	EMPLOYEES
12/18	679	50	7.4%	840
12/17	564	44	7.8%	—
12/15	462	35	7.7%	—
12/13	416	32	7.7%	—
Annual Growth	10.3%	9.4%	—	—

2018 Year-End Financials

Return on assets: 13.8%
Return on equity: 18.5%
Current ratio: 3.60
Cash ($ mil.): 101

ARLINGTON INDEPENDENT SCHOOL DISTRICT (INC)

EXECUTIVES

Supt, Marcelo Bavazls
Principal, Webb Elementary, Michael Martin
Coordinator, Kathy Hitt
Tech Prep Coordinator, Ed Cannady
Sp Ed Teacher, Daisy Segovia
Chemistry Teacher, Israel Iyoke
Social Media Marketing, Becky Volk
Auditors: WHITLEY PENN LLP HOUSTON TEX

LOCATIONS

HQ: ARLINGTON INDEPENDENT SCHOOL DISTRICT (INC)
1203 W PIONEER PKWY, ARLINGTON, TX 760136246
Phone: 682 867-4611
Web: WWW.AISD.NET

HISTORICAL FINANCIALS

Company Type: Private

Income Statement — FYE: June 30

	REVENUE ($ mil.)	NET INCOME ($ mil.)	NET PROFIT MARGIN	EMPLOYEES
06/19	688	(87)	—	8,000
06/18	680	(28)	—	—
06/17	641	(35)	—	—
06/16	636	115	18.1%	—
Annual Growth	2.7%	—	—	—

2019 Year-End Financials

Return on assets: (-6.8%)
Return on equity: —
Current ratio: —
Cash ($ mil.): 443

ASCENSION HEALTH ALLIANCE

EXECUTIVES

Pres-Ceo, Joseph Impicciche
Pres-Ceo, Joseph R Impicciche
Sr Exec Advsr, Sister Bernice Coreil DC
Evp, John D Doyle
Evp, Robert J Henkel
Evp, Susan Nestor Levy
Evp, Sister Maureen McGuire DC
Evp, David B Pryor
Executive Administrative Assis, Teresa Hatton
Regional Director, Andrew Gwin
Cco Clinical & Network Svs, Richard Fogel
Auditors: ERNST & YOUNG LLP ST LOUIS

LOCATIONS

HQ: ASCENSION HEALTH ALLIANCE
101 S HANLEY RD STE 450, SAINT LOUIS, MO 631053463
Phone: 314 733-8000
Web: WWW.ASCENSION.ORG

HISTORICAL FINANCIALS

Company Type: Private

Income Statement				FYE: June 30
	ASSETS ($ mil.)	NET INCOME ($ mil.)	INCOME AS % OF ASSETS	EMPLOYEES
06/17	34,320	1,638	4.8%	111,719
06/16	32,469	(339)	—	—
06/15	30,963	(42)	—	—
Annual Growth	5.3%	—	—	—

2017 Year-End Financials

Return on assets: 4.8%
Return on equity: 8.0%
Sales ($ mil): 22,633

ASCENSION PROVIDENCE HOSPITAL

Providence Hospital and Medical Centers provides health care in the Motor City and surrounding areas. The main Providence Hospital is a 408-bed teaching facility that has been recognized for its cardiology program and clinical expertise in behavioral medicine. It offers a variety of other services ranging from cancer treatment and neurosurgery to orthopedics and women's health. The network also includes dozens of affiliated general practice and specialty health clinics. The not-for-profit medical center founded in 1845 as St. Vincent's Hospital in Detroit by the Daughters of Charity is part of Catholic health ministry St. John Health (itself a subsidiary of Ascension Health).

Operations

As part of its health care system Providence Hospital and Medical Centers operates a host of hospitals and medical centers across the metropolitan Detroit area. They include Providence Southfield and four namesake Providence Medical Center locations in Farmington Hills Livonia Dearborn Heights and South Lyon. Across its system the medical facilities employ some 1500 physicians and enlist the help of about 300 active volunteers.

Carroll Manor is a skilled nursing center that provides short- and long-term medical care and rehabilitation services. The system's behavioral health division Seton House provides alcohol and addiction treatment in Washington DC.

Providence Hospital and Medical Centers had more than 41600 emergency department visits in 2013.

Strategy

In order to provide better services the hospital renovated and expanded its emergency department in 2014. Also that year its family medicine division opened a new office in the Glenn Dale/Bowie area.

EXECUTIVES

Pres-Ceo, Brant Russell
Prin, Diane Radloff
Internal Medicine Practitioner, Zaid Yaldo
Chief Operating Officer, Vijay Mittal
Internal Medicine Practitioner, Elias Zeine
Internal Medicine Practitioner, Michael J Di Loreto
Coordinator, Tiffany Tscherne
Internist, Gurbir Singh
Administrative Assistant, Leslie Tippett
Director, Lou Bischoff
Internist, Mousa Shukr
Auditors: DELOITTE TAX LP CINCINNATI O

LOCATIONS

HQ: ASCENSION PROVIDENCE HOSPITAL
16001 W 9 MILE RD, SOUTHFIELD, MI 480754818
Phone: 248 849-3000
Web: WWW.PROVIDENCEOBGYNRESIDENCY.COM

Selected Hospitals and Medical Centers

Providence Southfield-Southfield
Providence Medical Center-Farmington Hills
Providence Medical Center-Livonia
Providence Medical Center-Dearborn Heights
Providence Medical Center-South Lyon

PRODUCTS/OPERATIONS

Selected Primary Services

Cancer clinical trials
Cardiac rehabilitation
Childbirth
Congenital heart disease clinic
Emergency
Oncology
Orthopedics
Senior services
Surgery
Women's health

COMPETITORS

Beaumont Health System
Crittenton Hospital
Detroit Medical Center
Henry Ford Health System
McLaren Health Care
Trinity Health (Novi)
University of Michigan Health System

HISTORICAL FINANCIALS

Company Type: Private

Income Statement				FYE: June 30
	REVENUE ($ mil.)	NET INCOME ($ mil.)	NET PROFIT MARGIN	EMPLOYEES
06/16	703	21	3.1%	4,700
06/15	654	25	3.9%	—
06/14	659	53	8.1%	—
06/11	706	27	3.9%	—
Annual Growth	(0.1%)	(4.9%)	—	—

2016 Year-End Financials

Return on assets: 0.5%
Return on equity: 3.2%
Current ratio: 1.20
Cash ($ mil.): 3

ASI COMPUTER TECHNOLOGIES INC

ASI offers an extensive line of products components and services and also provides ISO-9001 compliant system integration and value add contract assembly. ASI Computer Technologies is a national distributor of IT software and hardware products. It offers more than 15000 products including PCs scanners security surveillance and data storage devices. The company has rapidly grown to become the partner of choice for over 20000 VARs throughout North America. Its vendor partners include companies the likes of AMD Intel Microsoft and Western Digital. ASI's services include custom systems integration. It also markets PCs and notebooks under its own brands: Pegatron and Nspire. Furthermore it caters to various industries such as retail and the SMB market The company was established in 1987 by president and owner Cristine Liang.

Operations

ASI offers an extensive line of products components and services and also provides ISO-9001 compliant system integration and value add contract assembly. More specifically it has other products including but not limited to cables drones desktops mount USBs software hard drives and printers. In addition it provides Converged Infrastructure Solutions and server solutions for different platforms.

The company has services such as hardware and software testing pre-sales system design and configuration assistance and bios and driver updates among others. The company has partnerships with Samsung ASUS AMD Intel Microsoft and Western Digital to name a few.

Geographic Reach

Based in California ASI operates nationwide as well as in Canada. To support its business the wholesaler operates regional offices in Atlanta Chicago Dallas Los Angeles Portland Kansas and New Jersey. Its Canadian offices are in Montreal Toronto and Vancouver. In Mexico ASI has offices in Monterrey and Nuevo Laredo.

Sales and Marketing

ASI's diverse portfolio of products and services allow it to service a broad customer base (it counts over 8000 customers) which includes VARs systems integrators OEMs and retailers.

EXECUTIVES

President Of Asi Computer Systems, Dave Wirth
Auditors: MARCUM LLP SAN FRANCISCO CA

LOCATIONS

HQ: ASI COMPUTER TECHNOLOGIES INC
48289 FREMONT BLVD, FREMONT, CA 945386510
Phone: 510 226-8000
Web: WWW.ASIPARTNER.COM

PRODUCTS/OPERATIONS

Selected Products

Accessories

Cables

Cameras

Cases

CD-ROM drives
Central processing units
Controller cards
DVD drives
Fans
Floppy drives
Hard drives
Keyboards
Memory
Mice
Modems
Monitors
Motherboards
MP3 players
Multimedia products
Network connectivity products
Notebooks
Optical drives
PCs
Power supplies
Printers
Projectors
Removable drives and media
Scanners
Software
Sound cards
Speakers
Storage devices
Tape back-up products
Video cards
Zip drives

COMPETITORS

ASCII Group
Agilysys
Arrow Electronics
Avnet
Avnet Technology
CompuCom
Continental Resources
D & H Distributing
En Pointe
Flextronics
Ingram Micro
MTM Technologies
Merisel
MicroAge
New Age Electronics
SED International
SHI International
SYNNEX
Softmart
Supercom
Tech Data

HISTORICAL FINANCIALS

Company Type: Private

Income Statement FYE: December 31

	REVENUE ($ mil.)	NET INCOME ($ mil.)	NET PROFIT MARGIN	EMPLOYEES
12/13	1,746	17	1.0%	700
12/04	1,057	12	1.2%	—
12/03	982	13	1.3%	—
12/02	865	10	1.2%	—
Annual Growth	6.6%	4.9%	—	—

2013 Year-End Financials

Return on assets: 5.4%
Return on equity: 1.0%
Current ratio: 1.10
Cash ($ mil.): 28

ASPIRUS WAUSAU HOSPITAL, INC.

EXECUTIVES

Ceo, Duane Erwin
Pres*, Darrell Lentz
Scientist, Cindy Geiss
Director of Gastroenterology, Raymond Hartke
Information Specialist, Mark Chickering
Chief of Medicine, Erik Anderson
Quality Assurance Director, Deb Zahrt
Nurse, Debra Knapp
Coordinator, Wayne Pierce
Coordinator, Rhnea Cornils
Director, Bonnie M Samuelson
Auditors: WIPFLI LLP EAU CLAIRE WISCON

LOCATIONS

HQ: ASPIRUS WAUSAU HOSPITAL, INC.
425 PINE RIDGE BLVD # 1, WAUSAU, WI 544014122
Phone: 715 847-2019
Web: WWW.ASPIRUS.ORG

HISTORICAL FINANCIALS

Company Type: Private

Income Statement FYE: June 30

	REVENUE ($ mil.)	NET INCOME ($ mil.)	NET PROFIT MARGIN	EMPLOYEES
06/20	565	7	1.3%	3,500
06/19	543	70	12.9%	—
06/18	497	8	1.7%	—
06/16	456	51	11.4%	—
Annual Growth	5.5%	(38.6%)	—	—

2020 Year-End Financials

Return on assets: 1.2%
Return on equity: 2.0%
Current ratio: 1.80
Cash ($ mil.): 4

ASPIRUS, INC.

Aspirus aspires to provide care for Midwesterners in need. The health system provides a comprehensive range of health and medical services to residents in a 14-county region of central and northern Wisconsin as well as Michigan's Upper Peninsula. Aspirus operates the Aspirus Wausau Hospital a 325-bed multi-specialty regional health center and seven smaller community hospitals. Its hospitals and network of community clinics provide specialized primary and emergency care. Aspirus also operates imaging centers hospice services home health care long-term care facilities and an outpatient dialysis center.

Operations

Other facilities in Aspirus' network include the 25-bed Aspirus Medford Hospital the Catholic Aspirus Langlade Hospital specialist hospital Riverview Family Clinic and 25-bed critical care access hospitals Aspirus Ontonagon and NORTHSTAR. In all it operates four hospitals in Michigan and four in Wisconsin as well as 50 clinics home health and hospice care helicopter transport nursing homes and pharmacies.

Sales and Marketing

Aspirus takes payments from most health plans and payers in the region in which it operates. It also contracts directly with employers and community business coalitions.

Mergers and Acquisitions

Michigan-based NORTHSTAR Health System became an Aspira subsidiary in 2014. It added a 25-bed critical access hospital as well as clinics to Aspira's network.

EXECUTIVES

President And Ceo, Duane L. Erwin, age 69
Senior Vice President Of Finance And Cfo Aspirus Wausau Hospital Aspirus Inc., Sidney Sczygelski
Executive Director Aspirus Network Inc., Joel Rueber
Interim President/coo Aspirus Wausau Hospital, Marita Hattem
President Of Aspirus Clinics And Chief Clinical Integration Officer For Aspirus, Bud Chumbley
Vice President Of Patient Care/chief Nursing Officer, Kathy Drengler
Ceo Of Aspirus Grand View, Carol Goffnett
Vice President Marketing And Planning, Rick L. Nevers
Executive Director Of Aspirus Health Foundation, Kalynn Pempek
Vice President Of Information Technology/chief Information Officer, Todd Richardson
Senior Vice President Of Business Development, Eric Anderson
Physical Therapy, Nathan Weiler
Vice President Of Compliance, Lori Peck
Vice President, Jean Burgener
Clinical Director, Rae Kaare
Nursing Director, Ann Line
Director Of Pharmacy, Jill Michaud
Medical Director, Kristine Flowers
Medical Records Director, Shelley Stokosa
Vice President Of Patient Care Chief Nursing Officer, Jeannine Nosko
Nursing Director, Barbara Lato
Pharm D, Debbie Kitch
Pharmacy Manager, Stacy PharmD
Respiratory Therapy Director, Kevin Foley
Nursing Director, Sherry Bunten
Secretary Treasurer, Sid Sczygelski
Auditors: WIPFLI LLP EAU CLAIRE WISCO

LOCATIONS

HQ: ASPIRUS, INC.
2200 WESTWOOD DR, WAUSAU, WI 544017806
Phone: 715 847-2121
Web: WWW.ASPIRUS.ORG

Selected FacilitiesU.P. of MichiganAspirus Grand View Aspirus Keweenaw HospitalAspirus Ontonagon HospitalNORTHSTAR Health System WisconsinAspirus Wausau HospitalAspirus Langlade HospitalAspirus Medford HospitalRiverview Hospital

PRODUCTS/OPERATIONS

Selected Services
Alzheimer's & Memory Disorders
Anesthesia Services
Angioplasty
Anticoagulation Clinic
Cardiac Electrophysiology
Cardiac Rehab
Cardioversion
Dentistry
Oral & Maxillofacial Surgery
Prosthodontics
Psychiatry
Psychology
Pulmonary Medicine
Sleep Disorders

COMPETITORS

Dean Health Systems Inc.
Howard Young Health Care
Luther Midelfort
ThedaCare Inc.
University of Wisconsin Hospital and Clinics

HISTORICAL FINANCIALS

Company Type: Private

Income Statement FYE: June 30

	REVENUE ($ mil.)	NET INCOME ($ mil.)	NET PROFIT MARGIN	EMPLOYEES
06/20	1,090	169	15.5%	7,100
06/19	996	102	10.3%	—
06/18	911	78	8.6%	—
06/13	536	47	8.9%	—
Annual Growth	10.7%	19.7%	—	—

2020 Year-End Financials

Return on assets: 9.3%
Return on equity: 14.4%
Current ratio: 2.50
Cash ($ mil.): 328

ASSOCIATED FOOD STORES, INC.

This business makes sure there's plenty of grub for the Wild West. Associated Food Stores (AFS) is a leading regional cooperative wholesale distributor that supplies groceries and other products to some 500 independent supermarkets in about eight Western states. It also offers support services for its member-owners including market research real estate analysis store design technology procurement and training. In addition AFS owns a stake in Western Family Foods a grocery wholesalers' partnership that produces Western Family private-label goods. The co-op formed in 1940 also operates 40-plus corporate stores in Utah under five different banners including Fresh Market.

Operations

In addition to its wholesale business AFS's retail arm — Associated Retail Operations — owns and operates corporate stores in Utah under five different formats and banners: Macey's; Fresh Market; Dan's Fresh Market in Salt Lake City; Lin's Fresh Market; and Dick's Fresh Market. The retail business accounts for about 35% of AFS's annual revenue.

The grocery distributor supplies independent supermarkets with over 3600 products. Products comprise a wide array including baking breakfast cereals frozen foods household supplies and even pet food and supplies. In early 2013 Associated closed its distribution centers in Helena and Billings Montana and consolidated warehouse operations for its nearly 100 Montana and Wyoming customers at its facility in Farr West Utah.

Geographic Reach

Salt Lake City-based Associated Food Stores has operations in Arizona Colorado Idaho Montana Nevada Oregon Utah and Wyoming. The

Financial Performance

While privately-owned Associated Food Stores doesn't report its financial results the company logged an estimated $2.2 billion in sales in fiscal 2013 (ended March) versus $2.1 billion in sales the previous year.

EXECUTIVES

Director Of Pharmacy Administration, Eliseo Faz
Director Of Pharmacy Operations, Shawna Hanson
Treasurer, Bob Obray
Auditors: DELOITTE & TOUCHE LLP SALT L

LOCATIONS

HQ: ASSOCIATED FOOD STORES, INC.
1850 W 2100 S, SALT LAKE CITY, UT 841191304
Phone: 801 973-4400
Web: WWW.AFSTORES.COM

PRODUCTS/OPERATIONS

Selected Brands
Western Family
Full Circle
Shur Saving

Selected Retail Banners
Dan's Fresh Market
Dick's Fresh Market
Fresh Market
Lin's Fresh Market
Macey's

COMPETITORS

AMCON Distributing
C&S Wholesale
GSC Enterprises
Kroger
McLane
SUPERVALU
Safeway
URM Stores
Wal-Mart

HISTORICAL FINANCIALS

Company Type: Private

Income Statement — FYE: March 31

	REVENUE ($ mil.)	NET INCOME ($ mil.)	NET PROFIT MARGIN	EMPLOYEES
03/12	2,011	5	0.3%	300
03/11	1,953	(6)	—	—
03/10	1,785	(2)	—	—
Annual Growth	6.1%	—	—	—

2012 Year-End Financials

Return on assets: 1.0%
Return on equity: 5.4%
Current ratio: 0.90
Cash ($ mil.): 105

ASSOCIATED WHOLESALE GROCERS, INC.

Associated Wholesale Grocers (AWG) knows its customers can't live on bread and milk alone. The second-largest retailer-owned distribution cooperative in the US (behind Wakefern Food Corporation) AWG supplies more than 3800 grocery retail outlets in more than half of the US states from 10 distribution centers which collectively have some 7 million square feet of space. In addition to its wholesale grocery operation AWG offers a variety of business services to its members including marketing and merchandising programs retail accounting supermarket development and access to low-cost merchandise through its Value Merchandisers subsidiary. AWG was founded by a group of independent grocers in 1924.

Geographic Reach

Kansas City-headquartered Associated Wholesale Grocers began in Missouri and its operations are generally centered on that state. It operates ten wholesale divisions in Missouri Nebraska Kansas Oklahoma Louisiana Alabama Tennessee and Wisconsin. Its distribution activities extend into another 25 states.

AWG's Valu Merchandisers subsidiary is gaining a foothold in non-US regions such as the Caribbean Central & South America and the Middle East.

Sales and Marketing

As a cooperative AWG serves the needs of its members who collectively determine how best to utilize the co-ops operations. Its board of directors is made up of nearly 20 people each a key executive at a grocer retail chain which receives products from AWG.

AWG serves up several private label brands to stores. They include Superior Selections Clearly Organic Best Choice Always Save and IGA.

Financial Performance

Associated Wholesale Grocers (AWG) has grown net sales in recent years from $7.8 billion in 2016 to more recent results exceeding $9.0 billion. Net income has trended positively over the same period from $175 million in 2012 to a spiked of more than $225 million in 2014 to a current result near $190 million.

For the year 2016 net sales grew 3% to $9.2 billion. Product price deflation pushed sales lower as did the loss of Albertsons' membership in the distribution co-op. AWG gained 800 new member stores in conjunction with its unification with Affiliated Foods Midwest which increased sales sufficiently to overcome the negative influencers.

Net income for the year was $190 million 4% lower than the prior year due to a corresponding increase in the co-op's general and administrative expenses.

Strategy

As a supplier to primarily independent and non-national grocers the co-op must retain size in order to compete with larger corporate firms. Years 2016 and 2017 saw its size shrink in Texas particularly in the hotly contested Dallas-Fort Worth market. Associated Wholesale Grocers lost two key members Albertsons (owner of Tom Thumb's and Safeway) and WinCo. It countered this by uniting with Affiliated Foods Midwest a distribution co-op with some 800 retail stores but the loss of such notable members is expected influence AWG's posturing within the North Texas area.

AWG continues to build sales of its billion-dollar private-label products line which includes the Best Choice IGA and Always Save brands. In addition to marketing the products as lower-cost alternatives to brand-name products the co-op has been investing in efforts to make sure the quality of its private-label items matches competing national brands. The company also owns and operates the Value Merchandisers Company (VMC) which offers some 22000 nonfood items to its members including health and beauty care general merchandise and seasonal and promotional products.

Operating in a fragmented business AWG competes with a large number of local and regional suppliers as well as distributors of specialty items. The food wholesale business also has its share of national giants including C & S Wholesale Nash-Finch and wholesale grocery and retail company SUPERVALU.

EXECUTIVES

Svp And Division Manager Nashville, Mike Danes
Evp And Chief Marketing Officer, Steve Arnold
Svp And Division Manager Memphis, Gary Jennings
Svp Finance, David Carl
Svp Distribution, Richard Kearns
Svp And Cio, Jon Payne
Svp And Division Manager Fort Worth, Linda Lawson
Svp Springfield, Tim Bellanti
Evp Division Operations, David Smith
Svp And Division Manager Oklahoma City, Danny Lane
Svp Grocery Products, Dan Funk
Svp Perishables, Jerry Edney
Svp And Division Manager Gulf Coast, Bob Durand
President Valu Merchandisers Company (vmc), Dave Sutton
President Always Fresh, Michael Schumacher
Vp Sales And Merchandising Memphis Division, David Gates
Senior Vice President, Maurice Henry
Vice President Of Sales Great Lakes, Sonny Leon
Vice President Of Fresh Merchandising Bakery Deli And Food Service, Daniel Koch
Vice President Of Corporate Distribution, Mark Wilson
Director, Bob Hufford
Vice Chairman, Don Woods

LOCATIONS

HQ: ASSOCIATED WHOLESALE GROCERS, INC.
5000 KANSAS AVE, KANSAS CITY, KS 661061135
Phone: 913 288-1000
Web: WWW.AWGINC.COM

COMPETITORS

Affiliated Foods
Affiliated Foods Midwest
Albertsons
Alex Lee
C&S Wholesale
Central Grocers
Dearborn Wholesale Grocers
GSC Enterprises
H. T. Hackney
McLane
SUPERVALU
SpartanNash
Wakefern Food
Wal-Mart
WinCo Foods

HISTORICAL FINANCIALS

Company Type: Private

Income Statement — FYE: December 31

	REVENUE ($ mil.)	NET INCOME ($ mil.)	NET PROFIT MARGIN	EMPLOYEES
12/17	9,703	199	2.1%	5,500
12/15	8,935	198	2.2%	—
12/14	8,934	226	2.5%	—
12/13	8,380	192	2.3%	—
Annual Growth	3.7%	0.8%	—	—

2017 Year-End Financials

Return on assets: 12.3% | Cash ($ mil.): 166
Return on equity: 39.4%
Current ratio: 1.20

ATHENE ANNUITY & LIFE ASSURANCE COMPANY

EXECUTIVES

Ceo, James R Belardi
Pres, Chip Smith
V Pres Fin, Cfo, David Attaway
Evp, Matthew Easley
Pres, Guy H Smith
Exec V Pres, Christopher Grady
Sr V Pres, Rod Mims

LOCATIONS

HQ: ATHENE ANNUITY & LIFE ASSURANCE COMPANY
2000 WADE HAMPTON BLVD, GREENVILLE, SC 296151037
Phone: 864 609-1000
Web: WWW.ATHENE.COM

HISTORICAL FINANCIALS

Company Type: Private

Income Statement — FYE: December 31

	ASSETS ($ mil.)	NET INCOME ($ mil.)	INCOME AS % OF ASSETS	EMPLOYEES
12/13	11,775	49	0.4%	120
12/12	10,481	11	0.1%	—
Annual Growth	12.3%	330.4%	—	—

2013 Year-End Financials

Return on assets: — | Sales ($ mil): 217
Return on equity: 22.8%

ATLANTIC DIVING SUPPLY, INC.

Atlantic Diving Supply (doing business as ADS) is geared toward gearing up the military. Serving agencies in the Federal Government the company specializes in helping customers procure tactical and operational military equipment. Like a retailer it sells over 46220 products manufactured by over 2445 suppliers including Camelbak FLIR L3 Harris and Oakley but its niche offering is its supply management services. These services which are tailored to military customers include kitting (packaging related products in groups) assembly training operational equipment procurement support and program management. Other customers include the navy and space force.

Operations

ADS Inc. provides equipment procurement logistics and supply chain solutions. Products include apparel nylon equipment surveillance and sensors robotics and aviation equipment among others.

Geographic Reach

The company is headquartered in Virginia.

Sales and Marketing

ADS' customers are within the Department of Defense and the Federal Government other customers are Air Force Army and Army Reserves Coast Guard Marine Corps National Guardm Navy Space Force and U.S. Partner Nation.

EXECUTIVES

Executive Vice President, Bruce Dressel
Chairman And Ceo, Luke Hillier
President, Daniel Clarkson
Cfo, Patricia Bohlen
Coo, Jason S. Wallace
Evp, Donald L. Sayre
Vice President Sales (verticals), Craig Doren
Vice Chairman, Dan Clarkson

LOCATIONS

HQ: ATLANTIC DIVING SUPPLY, INC.
621 LYNNHVEN PKWY STE 160, VIRGINIA BEACH, VA 23452
Phone: 757 481-7758
Web: WWW.ADSINC.COM

PRODUCTS/OPERATIONS

Selected Products

Apparel
Bags packs and cases
Eyewear
Footwear
Hydration systems
Knives
Lighting
Medical
Tools
Training aids

COMPETITORS

Amazon.com
Army and Air Force Exchange
Kmart
Navy Exchange
Target Corporation
Wal-Mart

HISTORICAL FINANCIALS

Company Type: Private

Income Statement — FYE: December 31

	REVENUE ($ mil.)	NET INCOME ($ mil.)	NET PROFIT MARGIN	EMPLOYEES
12/10	1,327	77	5.8%	360
12/09	938	54	5.8%	—
12/08	650	40	6.2%	—
Annual Growth	42.8%	38.7%	—	—

2010 Year-End Financials

Return on assets: 28.7% | Cash ($ mil.): 1
Return on equity: 676.2%
Current ratio: 1.10

ATLANTIC HEALTH SYSTEM INC.

Got a gash or gout in the Garden State? Atlantic Health System has more than 1600 beds for you to get better in. The not-for-profit Atlantic Health System (AHS) operates about dozen urgent care hospital providing general medical and surgical services to residents of northern New Jersey. Its flagship Morristown Medical Center serves as a regional trauma center and provides specialty care in a number of areas including oncology pediatrics and cardiac care. The system's Overlook Medical Center houses the Atlantic Neuroscience Institute; home to the Comprehensive Stroke Center. Its smaller Newton Medical Center serves patients in two New Jersey counties as well as counties in Pennsylvania and New York.

Operations

The system's corporate health division provides employee assistance programs as well as a full range of corporate-related medical services including physicals smoking cessation work injury and travel medicine services.

In addition to its hospitals AHS operates home care and hospice units that serve Essex Morris Somerset and Union counties.

AHS provides educational that includes continuing medical education classes and residency programs in pharmacy and nursing to keep its medical staff current on medical technologies and techniques. Annually the hospital system teaches more than 250 medical residents through about a dozen residency programs in emergency and family medicine surgery and pediatrics among others.

Geographic Reach

Atlantic Health System hospitals provides services to Northern New Jersey and surrounding areas.

Sales and Marketing

Atlantic Health System serves more than half the state of New Jersey including about a dozen counties and about 5 million people.

EXECUTIVES

Vp Of Resident Council, Natasha Mamdani
Vice President Integrated Care, Carol Vargas
Auditors: PRICEWATERHOUSECOOPERS LLP FL

LOCATIONS

HQ: ATLANTIC HEALTH SYSTEM INC.
475 SOUTH ST, MORRISTOWN, NJ 079606459
Phone: 973 660-3100
Web: WWW.ATLANTICHEALTH.ORG

PRODUCTS/OPERATIONS

Selected Operations

Atlantic Home Care
Atlantic Hospice
Atlantic Neuroscience Institute (Overlook Hospital)
Carol G. Simon Cancer Center (Morristown and Overlook hospitals)
Chilton Medical Center
Gagnon Cardiovascular Institute (Morristown Hospital)
Goryeb Children's Hospital
Morristown Medical Center
Newton Medical Center
Overlook Medical Center

COMPETITORS

Children's Specialized Hospital
Chilton Medical Center
Community Health Systems
East Orange General Hospital
JFK Medical Center
Newark Beth Israel Medical Center
Raritan Bay Medical Center
Robert Wood Johnson University Hospital at Rahway
Saint Barnabas Medical
St. Joseph's Healthcare System
The Valley Hospital
Trinitas Regional Medical Center

HISTORICAL FINANCIALS

Company Type: Private

Income Statement — FYE: December 31

	REVENUE ($ mil.)	NET INCOME ($ mil.)	NET PROFIT MARGIN	EMPLOYEES
12/19	3,163	476	15.0%	3,100
12/17	0	(0)	—	—
Annual Growth	8917.8%	—	—	—

2019 Year-End Financials

Return on assets: 11.0% Cash ($ mil.): 465
Return on equity: 19.8%
Current ratio: 2.10

ATLANTICARE REGIONAL MEDICAL CENTER

EXECUTIVES

Ceo, David Tilton
V Pres-Coo*, Lori Herndon
Senior Buyer, Nicole Hagan
Registered Nurse, Eunice Creamer
Anesthesiologist, Nicholas Incandela
Pathologist, Bruno Dantas
Gynecologist, Diane Timms
Cardiologist, Mitul Kanzaria
Psychiatrist, Syed Tirmazi
Chief of Orthopedic Surgery, Alvin Ong
Vice President, Linda Valente Rose

LOCATIONS

HQ: ATLANTICARE REGIONAL MEDICAL CENTER
65 W JIMMIE LEEDS RD, POMONA, NJ 082409102
Phone: 609 652-1000
Web: WWW.ATLANTICARE.ORG

HISTORICAL FINANCIALS

Company Type: Private

Income Statement FYE: December 31

	REVENUE ($ mil.)	NET INCOME ($ mil.)	NET PROFIT MARGIN	EMPLOYEES
12/14	718	64	9.0%	249
12/08	560	(58)	—	—
12/05	457	51	11.3%	—
Annual Growth	5.1%	2.5%	—	—

2014 Year-End Financials

Return on assets: 6.4% Cash ($ mil.): —
Return on equity: 14.0%
Current ratio: 0.50

ATLAS OIL COMPANY

EXECUTIVES

Ceo, Sam Simon
Pres*, Robert Kenyon
Cfo*, Joseph Rivera
Coo*, Michael Devoe
Vp-Wholesale & Real Estate, Jacob Leatherman
Pres of Truck & Rig Fueling, Michael Meredith
Vp of Business Development, Jeremiah Whiddon
Vp of Supply and Logistics, Clinton Werth
V Pres For Crude Hauling, Samuel Carmicheal
Vp-Technology, Mark Kryska
Director of Human Resources, Dawn Thomson
Auditors: ERNST & YOUNG LLP DETROIT M

LOCATIONS

HQ: ATLAS OIL COMPANY
24501 ECORSE RD, TAYLOR, MI 481801641
Phone: 313 292-5500
Web: WWW.ATLASOIL.COM

HISTORICAL FINANCIALS

Company Type: Private

Income Statement FYE: December 31

	REVENUE ($ mil.)	NET INCOME ($ mil.)	NET PROFIT MARGIN	EMPLOYEES
12/08	1,153	1	0.1%	453
12/07	717	1	0.1%	—
12/06	617	0	0.1%	—
Annual Growth	36.7%	99.7%	—	—

2008 Year-End Financials

Return on assets: 1.6% Cash ($ mil.): 3
Return on equity: 8.6%
Current ratio: 1.00

ATLAS WORLD GROUP, INC.

Willing to carry the weight of a moving world agent-owned Atlas World Group is the holding company for Atlas Van Lines one of the largest moving companies in the US. Atlas Van Lines' more than 500 agents transport household goods domestically and between the US and Canada; it also offers specialized transportation of items such as trade show exhibits fine art and electronics. Atlas Van Lines International provides international corporate relocation and freight forwarding services. Its Atlas Canada unit moves household goods in that country while American Red Ball International specializes in military relocations and serves van lines outside Atlas' network.

Operations

Atlas World Group oversees a family of companies that deliver transportation and related services globally through a network agents and select service partners. Several of its key locations are concentrated in Evansville Indiana.

Strategy

The company continues to grow by adding offices and regional moving agents. In 2013 Atlantic Relocation Systems the second largest agency group within the Atlas Van Lines' US network expanded both its national footprint as well as its local service area in Colorado by opening a new office in Colorado Springs.

EXECUTIVES

Vice President, Steve Hermann
Vice President Human Resources, Nancy Priebe
Auditors: ERNST & YOUNG LLP INDIANAPOLI

LOCATIONS

HQ: ATLAS WORLD GROUP, INC.
1212 SAINT GEORGE RD, EVANSVILLE, IN 477112364
Phone: 812 424-2222
Web: WWW.ATLASVANLINES.COM

PRODUCTS/OPERATIONS

Selected Companies

American Red Ball International (international freight forwarding)
American Vanpac Carriers (international freight forwarding)
Atlas Terminal Company (relocation-related supplies and equipment)
Atlas Van Lines (transportation services)
Atlas Van Lines (Canada) (transportation services)
Atlas Van Lines International (transportation services)
Atlas World Class Travel (travel agency)
Avail Move Management (management programs)
AWG Logistics (transportation warehousing and distribution)
Cornerstone Relocation Group (relocation services)
Smart Move Transportation (containerized shipping)
Titan Global Distribution (logistics)

COMPETITORS

A-Mrazek Moving
ALTAIR Global Relocation
AMERCO
Bekins
Budd Van Lines
Business Products Group
Graebel
Penske Truck Leasing
SIRVA
Starving Students
UniGroup

HISTORICAL FINANCIALS

Company Type: Private

Income Statement FYE: December 31

	REVENUE ($ mil.)	NET INCOME ($ mil.)	NET PROFIT MARGIN	EMPLOYEES
12/19	906	9	1.1%	726
12/18	900	10	1.1%	—
12/17	842	4	0.6%	—
12/16	795	6	0.8%	—
Annual Growth	4.5%	15.0%	—	—

2019 Year-End Financials

Return on assets: 3.8% Cash ($ mil.): 11
Return on equity: 6.7%
Current ratio: 2.20

ATMEL CORPORATION

Atmel is a leading maker of microcontrollers which are used in a wide range of products from computers and mobile devices (smartphones tablets e-readers) to automobile motor control systems television remote controls and solid-state lighting. In addition the company offers touchscreen controllers and sensors nonvolatile memory devices and radio frequency (RF) and wireless components. Its chips are used worldwide in consumer communications industrial military and networking applications. Most of Atmel's sales come from customers outside the US. In mid-2016 the company was bought by Microchip a chip maker for $3.6 billion.

Operations

In 2014 Atmel realigned its business segments for allocation of resources and focus on core its markets. The company created the Multi-Market and Other segment while eliminating the former Application Specific Integrated Circuit (ASIC) segment.

But it's the Microcontroller segment that leads the way for Atmel accounting for 70% of the company's sales. The segment includes Atmel's general purpose microcontroller and microprocessor families AVR 8-bit and 32-bit products SMART ARM-based products Atmel's 8051 8-bit products and designated commercial wireless products including low power radio and SOC products.

The Nonvolatile Memory segment 12% of sales includes electrically erasable programmable read-only erasable programmable read-only memory ('EPROM') devices and secure cryptographic products. The Automotive segment 11% makes devices for automotive electronics including products using radio frequency technology. The new segment Multi-Market and Other is 7% of sales and includes application specific and standard products for aerospace applications and legacy products.

Geographic Reach

The company generates about 60% of its sales from Asia including about a third from China and Hong Kong. After China and Hong Kong the US is Atmel's largest market accounting for 15% of sales with sales in Germany at 14%.

Sales and Marketing

Atmel markets its products to original equipment manufacturers (OEMs) via a direct sales force as well as through distribution partners; each method accounts for about half of revenue. Arrow Electronics and Samsung Electronics each account for more than 10% of sales.

End-market customers include some of the leading names in the fields of communications (Alcatel Lucent Cisco Ericsson) computer and consumer electronics (Acer Dell Motorola Nokia) automotive (Delphi Visteon) and military and aerospace (BAE Systems Airbus Honeywell Lockheed Martin).

Financial Performance

Revenue rose 2% to $1.4 billion in 2014 from $1.39 billion in 2013 boosted by a 4% increase in microcontroller sales. The unit experienced demand from industrial automotive and communications markets. The addition of Newport Media acquired in mid-2014 also abetted microcontroller revenue. Sales in the nonvolatile memory segment were up 9% for the year.

On the bottom line Atmel went from a $22 million loss in 2013 to a $32 million profit in 2014. Profit was pushed by revenue growth as well as a lack of charges the company contended with in 2013. Cash flow from operations jumped 41% higher in 2014 to about $180 billion from $127 million in 203.

Strategy

Looking to pursue a "fab-lite" strategy of streamlining existing facilities and relying more on silicon foundries (contract manufacturers of semiconductors) Atmel has sold most of its manufacturing plants and now operates only one fab located in Colorado. Wafer fabs are highly expensive to build and maintain mostly due to the cost of semiconductor production equipment and pushing some of those costs off on the foundries many of which have state-of-the-art plants is attractive.

Atmel has increased the release of new products in the past three years aiming to provide customers with high performing microcontrollers than use little power. The company has found a place for its products within the Internet of Things the conglomeration of devices that communicate through the Internet.

The company also has pushed its line of maXTouch products for touchscreens in smartphones and tables. The products have found acceptance in automotive consumer and industrial markets. While that line thrives Atmel sold its XSense line of touch sensors to UniPixel in 2015. Atmel maintained possession of the XSense patent portfolio which it licensed to UniPixel.

With its sale to Dialog Atmel gets access to a range of new customers within Atmel's portfolio. Dialog expects to benefit from Atmel's products primed for the Internet of Things. The combined company would have about $2.7 billion sales annually. The deal is expected to close in the 2016 first quarter.

Mergers and Acquisitions

In agreeing to be bought by Microchip Atmel ended a deal to be purchased by Dialog. Atmel management said company shareholders would get a better return from the Microchip deal. Atmel was on the hook for a $137 million termination fee to be paid to Dialog. The Dialog offer had been valued at $4.6 billion when it was made but the value of Atmel stock has declined since then. The Atmel-Microchip deal enables the companies to gather competitive strength with complementary technologies and products.

In 2014 Atmel acquired Newport Media Inc. a provider of advanced Wi-Fi and Bluetooth products. This acquisition expands Atmel's wireless portfolio with the addition of 802.11n Wi-Fi and Bluetooth. Those product should speed up Atmel's introduction of low-energy Bluetooth products.

HISTORY

George Perlegos — a former Intel design engineer and co-founder of chip maker SEEQ Technology (later acquired by LSI Logic now LSI Corp.) — founded Atmel in 1984. (The name was short for Advanced Technology for Memory and Logic.) The enterprise started with a $30000 investment and a $5.1 million design contract from General Instrument; it soon added military and corporate contracts. In 1991 the company went public and introduced the first three-volt flash memory.

Atmel built its business by developing fast power-efficient chips — perfect for portable electronics. It acquired Concurrent Logic a maker of field-programmable gate arrays (user-programmable chips) in 1993. One year later Atmel became the #1 producer of EEPROMs (electrically erasable programmable ROM chips) when it bought SEEQ's chip business.

To strengthen its product line in 1995 Atmel licensed SRAM (static random-access memory) technology in an alliance with Paradigm Technology (now part of IXYS) for use in creating multimedia chips. It purchased RISC chip technology (which uses shorter instruction sets for faster processing) from Norwegian chip maker Nordic VLSI in 1996.

EXECUTIVES

Svp And Cfo, Stephen A. (Steve) Skaggs, $444,462 total compensation
Evp Office Of The President, Tsung-Ching Wu, $509,200 total compensation
Coo, Jalil Shaikh
Svp And General Manager Automotive Aerospace And Memory Business Units, Robert (Rob) Valiton, $393,000 total compensation
Svp And Chief Legal Officer, Scott M. Wornow, $397,538 total compensation
Vp And General Manager Touch Business Unit, Vegard Wollan
Svp Worldwide Operations, Shahin Sharifzadeh
Vp Corporate Marketing, Sander Arts
Svp And General Manager Microcontroller Business Unit, Reza Kazerounian, $453,365 total compensation
Svp And Cto; General Manager Touch Business Unit, Stanley A. (Stan) Swearingen

LOCATIONS

HQ: ATMEL CORPORATION
1600 TECHNOLOGY DR, SAN JOSE, CA 951101382
Phone: 408 735-9110
Web: WWW.MICROCHIP.COM

2014 Sales

	$ mil.	% of total
Asia/Pacific		
China (including Hong Kong)	435	31
South Korea	119	9
Taiwan	60	4
Singapore	55	4
Japan	37	3
Other countries	102	7
Europe		
Germany	204	14
France	15	1
Other countries	139	10
US	211	15
Other regions	30	2
Total	**1,413**	**100**

PRODUCTS/OPERATIONS

2014 Sales

	$ mil.	% of total
Microcontrollers	994	70
Nonvolatile memory	166	12
Automotive	153	11
Multi-Market and others	99	7
Total	**1,413**	**100**

Selected Products and Applications

Application-Specific Integrated Circuits (ASICs)
- Cell-based ASICs
- Complex ASIC cores
- Gate arrays/embedded arrays

Application-Specific Standard Products (ASSPs)
- Aerospace and military
- Communications
- Cellular corded and cordless phones
- Internet appliances and voice over Internet Protocol (VoIP)
- Wireless datacom
- Industrial
- Industrial controls
- Power metering
- Multimedia
- Audio
- Video
- Power management
- Security and smart card
- Biometrics
- PC security
- Radio-frequency identification (RFID)
- Secure memories
- Secure microcontrollers
- USB controllers

Logic
- Field-programmable gate arrays (FPGAs)
- Programmable logic devices (PLDs)

Microcontrollers (MCUs)
- 4- 8- 16- and 32-bit microcontrollers
- ARM microprocessor architecture-based MCUs
- Flash MCUs

Nonvolatile Memory
- EPROMs (erasable programmable read-only memories)
- Flash memory chips
- Parallel EEPROMs (electrically erasable PROMs)
- Serial EEPROMs

COMPETITORS

Cypress Semiconductor
Fairchild Semiconductor
Fujitsu Semiconductor
Hitachi
Infineon Technologies
Intel
Microchip Technology
Micron Technology
NXP Semiconductors
ON Semiconductor
Renesas Electronics
STMicroelectronics
Samsung Electronics
Silicon Labs
Synaptics
Texas Instruments

HISTORICAL FINANCIALS

Company Type: Private

Income Statement — FYE: December 31

	REVENUE ($ mil.)	NET INCOME ($ mil.)	NET PROFIT MARGIN	EMPLOYEES
12/14	1,413	35	2.5%	5,200
12/13	1,386	(22)	—	—
12/12	1,432	30	2.1%	—
Annual Growth	(0.7%)	7.5%	—	—

2014 Year-End Financials

Return on assets: 2.6%
Return on equity: 4.0%
Current ratio: 2.70
Cash ($ mil.): 206

ATRIUM HEALTH FOUNDATION

The medical facilities under the watchful eye of the Charlotte-Mecklenburg Hospital Authority care for the injured and infirmed. As the largest health care system in the Carolinas the organization operating as Carolinas HealthCare System (CHS) owns or manages more than 30 affiliated hospitals. It also operates long-term care facilities research centers rehabilitation facilities surgery centers home health agencies radiation therapy facilities and other health care operations. Collectively CHS facilities have more than 6400 beds and affiliated physician practices employ more than 1700 doctors. The network's flagship facility is the 875-bed Carolinas Medical Center in Charlotte North Carolina.

EXECUTIVES

Assistant Vice President, Luann Bailey
Group Vice President Levine Childrens Atrium Health Medical, Jennifer Terry
Assistant Vice President Of Human Resources, Dana Burnette
Assistant Vice President, Melissa Snuggs
Director Of Pharmacy, Chris Barringer
Executive Vice President And Chief Strategy Officer, Rasu Shrestha
Assistant Vice President Of Human Resources, Nehemie Owen
Vice President Diversity And Inclusion, Kinneil Coltman
Auditors: KPMG LLP CHARLOTTE NORTH CAR

LOCATIONS

HQ: ATRIUM HEALTH FOUNDATION
1000 BLYTHE BLVD, CHARLOTTE, NC 282035812
Phone: 704 355-2000
Web: WWW.CAROLINASHEALTHCARE.ORG

PRODUCTS/OPERATIONS

2010 Revenue

	% of total
Tertiary & acute care services	72
Physicians' services	16
Post-acute care services	3
Specialty services	2
Other services & non-operating activities	7
Total	**100**

Selected Hospitals and Health Care Pavilions

AnMed Health Medical Center
AnMed Health Rehabilitation Hospital
AnMed Health Women's and Children's Hospital
Anson Community Hospital
Bon Secours/St. Francis Hospital
Cannon Memorial Hospital
Carolinas Medical Center
Carolinas Medical Center - Kannapolis (health care pavilion)
Carolinas Medical Center - Lincoln
Carolinas Medical Center - Mercy
Carolinas Medical Center - NorthEast
Carolinas Medical Center - Pineville
Carolinas Medical Center - Steele Creek (health care pavilion)
Carolinas Medical Center - Union
Carolinas Medical Center - University
Carolinas Medical Center - Waxhaw (health care pavilion)
Carolinas Rehabilitation
Carolinas Rehabilitation - Mount Holly
Cleveland Regional Medical Center
CMC - Randolph
Columbus Regional Healthcare System
Crawley Memorial Hospital
Grace Hospital
Kings Mountain Hospital
Levine Children's Hospital
MedWest - Harris
MedWest - Haywood
MedWest - Swain
Roper Hospital
Roper St. Francis - Mount Pleasant Hospital
Scotland Memorial Hospital
Stanly Regional Medical Center
St. Luke's Hospital
Valdese Hospital
Wallace Thomson Hospital
Wilkes Regional Medical Center

COMPETITORS

Alamance Regional Medical Center
CaroMont
Community Health Systems
Cone Health
Conway Medical Center
Cumberland County Hospital System
Davis Regional Medical Center
Duke University Health System
FirstHealth of the Carolinas
Georgetown Hospital System
Grand Strand Regional Medical Center
HCA
Haywood Regional
High Point Regional Health System
McLeod Health
Mission Hospitals
Morehead Memorial Hospital
New Hanover Regional Medical Center
Novant Health
Palmetto Health
Presbyterian Healthcare
Rex Healthcare
Soliant Health
Tenet Healthcare
UNC Hospitals
Upstate Affiliate
Vidant Health
WakeMed

HISTORICAL FINANCIALS

Company Type: Private

Income Statement — FYE: December 31

	REVENUE ($ mil.)	NET INCOME ($ mil.)	NET PROFIT MARGIN	EMPLOYEES
12/19	7,510	1,223	16.3%	62,000
12/18	6,228	(69)	—	—
12/17	5,991	829	13.9%	—
12/16	5,676	493	8.7%	—
Annual Growth	9.8%	35.3%	—	—

2019 Year-End Financials

Return on assets: 9.7%
Return on equity: 16.0%
Current ratio: 1.10
Cash ($ mil.): 377

ATRIUS HEALTH, INC.

Not-for-profit multi-specialty group Atrius Health provides health care services in Boston and surrounding regions. The 900-physician (and some 6000 other health care professionals) medical group operates more than 30 offices throughout eastern Massachusetts providing primary and specialty care to some 720000 adult and pediatric patients. For acute health care services Harvard Vanguard patients have access to more than a dozen hospitals including Beth Israel-Deaconess Hospital Boston Children's Hospital and Emerson Hospital.

Operations

Atrius Health's network of doctors represent more than 50 medical specialties including primary care oncology cardiology and neurology. In addition to providing health care services the group conducts research in health systems clinical trials and epidemiological studies.Members of Atrius Health include Dedham Medical Associates Granite Medical Group Harvard Vanguard Medical Associates and PMG Physician Associates. Subsidiary VNA Care provides home health and hospice services.

Geographic Reach

Atrius Health has almost five locations in the City of Boston about 25 locations in Greater Boston and two administrative offices in Newton and Needham.

Sales and Marketing

Atrius Health accepts insurance from most major health plans including Aetna Blue Cross and Blue Shield of Massachusetts CIGNA Coventry Health Care Harvard Pilgrim Health Care AllWays Health Partners and Tufts Health Plan.

Strategy

Atrius Health has collaborated with Kyruus to help consumers connect with the right providers for their care online.

Dedicated to its vision to transform care to improve lives Atrius Health undertook a series of digital initiatives aimed at streamlining and modernizing access to its network of more than 1100 providers. As a first step the Atrius Health team worked with Kyruus to build enhanced profile information for Atrius Health providers in the KyruusOne provider data management platform which included matching Kyruus' robust proprietary clinical taxonomy to providers' clinical areas of focus. The taxonomy maps clinical terms to common synonyms facilitating patient-provider matching based on consumer-friendly search terms.

Company Background

Atrius Health was founded in 2004 by medical groups including Dedham Medical Associates and Harvard Vanguard Medical Associates; Granite Medical Group joined a short time later in 2005.The companies work together to coordinate care in a number of ways including sharing an electronic medical records system. In 2015 the groups merged to create one not-for-profit group named Atrius Health. Reliant Medical Group Southboro Medical Group and South Shore Medical Center were no longer affiliated with the group after the transformation. In 2017 PMG Physician Associates joined Atrius Health adding seven new office locations to our practice.

EXECUTIVES

Cfo Atrius Health And Harvard Vanguard Medical Associates, Thomas M. Congoran
Coo, Mary Dawley
Vp Nursing, Deborah S. Morsi
Interim President And Interim Ceo, H. Eugene (Gene) Lindsey
Chief Information Officer, Daniel Moriarty
Evp And Interim Chief Medical Officer, Michael Pinnolis
Interim Chief Medical Officer, Steven Lampert
Medical Director Of Analytics And Report, Joe Kimura
Vice President General Counsel, Kimberly Nelson
Medical Director Of Patient Safety And Risk Management, Martin November
Vice President Network Services, Rick Weisblatt
Auditors: PKF PC QUINCY MA

LOCATIONS

HQ: ATRIUS HEALTH, INC.
275 GROVE ST STE 3300, AUBURNDALE, MA 024662274
Phone: 617 559-8444
Web: WWW.ATRIUSHEALTH.ORG

PRODUCTS/OPERATIONS

Selected Specialty Affiliations

Massachusetts Eye and Ear Infirmary
New England Baptist Hospital

Selected OB/GYN Affiliations

Beth Israel Deaconess Medical Center

Beth Israel Deaconess Hospital - Milton
Emerson Hospital
Lowell General Hospital
Mount Auburn Hospital
Newton-Wellesley Hospital
South Shore Hospital

Selected Services
Allergy
Andrology
Audiology
Behavioral Health
Cardiology
Central Patient Registration
Complex Chronic Care Program
Cosmetic Dermatology
Dermatology
Developmental and Behavioral Pediatrics
Ear Nose & Throat
Endocrinology
Endoscopy
Eye Care
Family Medicine
Fertility & Reproductive Health
Gastroenterology
Genetics
Geriatrics
Hematology/Oncology
Imaging/Radiology
Infectious Disease
Internal Medicine
Interpreter Services
Laboratory
Medical Billing
Medical Records
Minimally-Invasive GYN Surgery
Nephrology
Neurology
Nutrition
Obstetrics/Gynecology
Occupational
Hand Therapy
Orthopedics & Sports Medicine
Pain Management
Palliative Care
Pediatrics
Pharmacy
Physical Therapy
Podiatry
Pulmonology
Rheumatology
Speech and Language Therapy
Surgery
Travel Medicine
Urgent Care
Urology
Weight Management/HMR®; Program

COMPETITORS

Boston Medical Center
Hallmark Health
Massachusetts General Hospital
St. Elizabeth's Medical Center
Winchester Healthcare

HISTORICAL FINANCIALS

Company Type: Private

Income Statement — FYE: December 31

	REVENUE ($ mil.)	NET INCOME ($ mil.)	NET PROFIT MARGIN	EMPLOYEES
12/17	1,872	39	2.1%	3,906
12/15	1,577	(28)	—	—
12/14	28	(0)	—	—
12/01	0	0	—	—
Annual Growth	—	—	—	—

2017 Year-End Financials

Return on assets: 6.0%
Return on equity: 17.0%
Current ratio: 0.90
Cash ($ mil.): 153

ATTORNEY GENERAL, TEXAS

The Office of the Attorney General of Texas defends the state Constitution represents the state in litigation and approves public bond issues. The office is legal counsel to state government boards and agencies and issues legal opinions when requested by the Governor and agency heads. The Attorney General also sits as an ex-officio member of state committees and commissions and defends state laws and suits against agencies and state employees. Other roles include enforcing health safety and consumer regulations; protecting elderly and disabled residents' rights; collecting court-ordered child support; and administering the Crime Victims' Compensation Fund. Greg Abbott was elected Attorney General in 2002.

EXECUTIVES

Chief Sales Officer, Karen Simmons

LOCATIONS

HQ: ATTORNEY GENERAL, TEXAS
300 W 15TH ST, AUSTIN, TX 787011649
Phone: 512 475-4375
Web: WWW.TEXASATTORNEYGENERAL.GOV

HISTORICAL FINANCIALS

Company Type: Private

Income Statement — FYE: August 31

	REVENUE ($ mil.)	NET INCOME ($ mil.)	NET PROFIT MARGIN	EMPLOYEES
08/16	659	45	6.8%	4,200
08/15	561	8	1.5%	—
08/14	571	(6)	—	—
08/06	0	0	—	—
Annual Growth	—	—	—	—

2016 Year-End Financials

Return on assets: 13.1%
Return on equity: 16.5%
Current ratio: 4.20
Cash ($ mil.): 87

AUBURN UNIVERSITY

Most of us bleed red but students and alumni of this university bleed auburn. One of the largest schools in the South Auburn University has an enrollment of more than 30000 students on two campuses and offers bachelors master's and doctoral degrees in more than 140 different fields of study through about a dozen colleges and schools. Fields of study include agriculture business education construction forestry and mathematics and science as well as medical fields including nursing pharmacy and veterinary medicine. Auburn has 1200 faculty members and a student-to-teacher ratio of 18:1.

Operations

Unique research institutes at Auburn include the Space Research Institute the National Center for Asphalt Technology the Alabama Agricultural Experiment Station and the Canine and Detection Research Institute.

Geographic Reach

Auburn's main campus is in Auburn Alabama. The university also has a branch campus in Montgomery Alabama. More than 800 students participate in the university's study abroad programs each year.

Financial Performance

Auburn reported a 5% rise in revenues to some $602 million in 2012 due to increased income from tuition and fees state and local grants and contracts and sales and services from educational departments. Net income fell 12% to $87 million in 2012 however due to higher operating expenses from benefits and compensation as well as due to the absence of federal stimulus funds (streamed through the state during 2011).

Company Background

Auburn was founded by the Alabama Conference of the Methodist Episcopal Church in 1856 as the East Alabama Male College. It became a state land-grant institution in 1872 (known as the Agricultural and Mechanical College of Alabama) and adopted its current name in 1960. The university is governed by a board of trustees appointed by the Alabama governor.

EXECUTIVES

Executive Vice President Of Initiatives, Austin Chandler
Executive Vice President Of Programs, Patrick Starr
Auditors: PRICEWATERHOUSECOOPERS LLP B

LOCATIONS

HQ: AUBURN UNIVERSITY
107 SAMFORD HALL, AUBURN, AL 368490001
Phone: 334 844-4650
Web: WWW.AUBURN.EDU

PRODUCTS/OPERATIONS

Selected Colleges and Schools
College of Agriculture
College of Architecture Design and Construction
College of Business
College of Education
College of Human Sciences
College of Liberal Arts
College of Sciences and Mathematics
College of Veterinary Medicine
Graduate School
Harrison School of Pharmacy
Honors College
Samuel Ginn College of Engineering
School of Forestry and Wildlife Sciences
School of Nursing

HISTORICAL FINANCIALS

Company Type: Private

Income Statement — FYE: September 30

	REVENUE ($ mil.)	NET INCOME ($ mil.)	NET PROFIT MARGIN	EMPLOYEES
09/19	897	78	8.8%	6,000
09/18	876	78	9.0%	—
09/17	805	79	9.9%	—
09/16	775	129	16.8%	—
Annual Growth	5.0%	(15.3%)	—	—

2019 Year-End Financials

Return on assets: 2.1%
Return on equity: 6.2%
Current ratio: 1.10
Cash ($ mil.): 246

AUGUSTANA HEALTH CARE CENTER OF APPLE VALLEY

EXECUTIVES

Pres, Timothy H Tucker
Coordinator, Alice Svihel
Quality Control Director, Diane Newman

LOCATIONS

HQ: AUGUSTANA HEALTH CARE CENTER OF APPLE VALLEY
14650 GARRETT AVE, SAINT PAUL, MN 551247543
Phone: 952 431-7700
Web: WWW.APPLEVALLEYCAMPUS.ORG

HISTORICAL FINANCIALS

Company Type: Private

Income Statement — FYE: September 30

	REVENUE ($ mil.)	NET INCOME ($ mil.)	NET PROFIT MARGIN	EMPLOYEES
09/09	1,505	30	2.0%	280
09/05	6	(0)	—	—
Annual Growth	287.7%	—	—	—

2009 Year-End Financials

Return on assets: 162.0% Cash ($ mil.): 1
Return on equity: 784.9%
Current ratio: 3.10

AURORA HEALTH CARE METRO, INC

EXECUTIVES

President, Marie Golanowski
Project Sys Dev, Shafei Fahim
Specialist, John Halverson
Chief of Medicine, Scott Hardin
Project Manager S, Alison Marianacci
Administrative Assistant, Annette Kachelmeyer
Supervisor Food, Jeffrey Gavitt
Administrative Assistant Senio, Jody Knoble
Diagnostic Radiologist, Joshua Lechusz
Manager Clinic Operations, Kathleen Olson
Diagnostic Radiologist, Mohammad Madani

LOCATIONS

HQ: AURORA HEALTH CARE METRO, INC
2900 W OKLAHOMA AVE, MILWAUKEE, WI 532154330
Phone: 414 649-6000

HISTORICAL FINANCIALS

Company Type: Private

Income Statement — FYE: December 31

	REVENUE ($ mil.)	NET INCOME ($ mil.)	NET PROFIT MARGIN	EMPLOYEES
12/17	1,428	141	9.9%	4,000
12/16	1,416	164	11.6%	—
Annual Growth	0.8%	(14.0%)	—	—

2017 Year-End Financials

Return on assets: 5.4% Cash ($ mil.): 1,804
Return on equity: 6.2%
Current ratio: 19.70

AURORA HEALTH CARE, INC.

EXECUTIVES

Manager of Talent Aquisition, Diane Turner
Appl Sys Administrator, John Kerkhoff
Social Worker, Lindsey Fabian
Human Resources Assistant, Stacey Hunter
Chief Pharmacist, Jessica Small
Pediatrician, Jeffery Garland
Clinical Assistant Professor, Nanette Kloth
Sr Research Nurse Coordinator, Bonnie Hughes
Director of Inpatient Operatio, Cheryl Michler
Family Practitioner, Dale Jacobson
Network Manager, Dan Klug
Auditors: DELOITTE & TOUCHE LLP MILWAUK

LOCATIONS

HQ: AURORA HEALTH CARE, INC.
750 W VIRGINIA ST, MILWAUKEE, WI 532041539
Phone: 800 326-2250
Web: WWW.AURORAHEALTHCARE.ORG

HISTORICAL FINANCIALS

Company Type: Private

Income Statement — FYE: December 31

	REVENUE ($ mil.)	NET INCOME ($ mil.)	NET PROFIT MARGIN	EMPLOYEES
12/17	5,334	437	8.2%	30,000
12/16	5,124	385	7.5%	—
12/15	4,930	428	8.7%	—
Annual Growth	4.0%	1.1%	—	—

2017 Year-End Financials

Return on assets: 7.7% Cash ($ mil.): 192
Return on equity: 14.4%
Current ratio: 3.50

AUSTIN INDEPENDENT SCHOOL DISTRICT (INC)

EXECUTIVES

Supt, Stephanie S Elizalde
Cfo*, Nicole Conley Johnson
Prin*, Teri Garcia
Coordinator, Artra Luckett
Executive Officer, Debbie Coco
Accounting Staff, Brenda Niles
Accounting Staff, Nancy Zuraitis
Occupational Specia, Gemma Cercone
Occupational Specia, Mary Coneway
Assistant Superintendent, Gilbert Hicks
Teacher, Joyce Brisco
Auditors: RSM US LLP AUSTIN TEXAS

LOCATIONS

HQ: AUSTIN INDEPENDENT SCHOOL DISTRICT (INC)
4000 S IH 35 FRONTAGE RD, AUSTIN, TX 78704
Phone: 512 414-1700
Web: WWW.AUSTINISD.ORG

HISTORICAL FINANCIALS

Company Type: Private

Income Statement — FYE: June 30

	REVENUE ($ mil.)	NET INCOME ($ mil.)	NET PROFIT MARGIN	EMPLOYEES
06/19	1,703	208	12.3%	9,200
06/18	1,534	(117)	—	—
06/16	1,231	110	9.0%	—
Annual Growth	11.4%	23.5%	—	—

2019 Year-End Financials

Return on assets: 8.9% Cash ($ mil.): 1
Return on equity: 355.8%
Current ratio: —

AVAYA HOLDINGS CORP.

Avaya Holdings Corp. is the holding company that owns enterprise communications equipment and services provider Avaya Inc.. Spun off from Lucent Technologies in 2000 Avaya was a publicly traded company until 2007 when it was taken private by Silver Lake Partners and TPG Capital for more than $8 billion. After four years of unprofitable private ownership its investors are looking for an exit and Avaya Holdings Corp. was created to make a second bid for listing on a US stock exchange filing for an initial public offering in 2011. The IPO is on hold however and Avaya has been expanding its business and product line through acquisitions.

EXECUTIVES

National Account Manager, Tom Hicks
Auditors: PRICEWATERHOUSECOOPERS LLP SA

LOCATIONS

HQ: AVAYA HOLDINGS CORP.
4655 GREAT AMERICA PKWY, SANTA CLARA, CA 950541236
Phone: 908 953-6000
Web: WWW.AVAYA.COM

COMPETITORS

Alcatel-Lucent
Aspect Software
Cisco Systems
Fujitsu
Hitachi
Huawei Technologies
Logitech
Mitel Networks
NEC
NSN
ShoreTel
Tellabs
ZTE

HISTORICAL FINANCIALS

Company Type: Private

Income Statement — FYE: September 30

	REVENUE ($ mil.)	NET INCOME ($ mil.)	NET PROFIT MARGIN	EMPLOYEES
09/15	4,081	(168)	—	19,601
09/14	4,371	(253)	—	—
09/13	4,708	(376)	—	—
09/11	5,547	(863)	—	—
Annual Growth	(7.4%)	—	—	—

2015 Year-End Financials

Return on assets: (-2.5%) Cash ($ mil.): 323
Return on equity: —
Current ratio: 0.80

AVERITT EXPRESS, INC.

Small loads add up at Averitt Express. The company provides less-than-truckload (LTL) freight transportation service. (LTL carriers combine freight from multiple shippers into a single trailer.) . Averitt Express directly serves the southern US and Mexico and it provides service elsewhere in North America through partnerships with other carriers such as Lakeville Motor Express and DATS. The company also offers truckload and expedited freight transportation along with logistics warehousing and international freight forwarding.

Geographic Reach

Averitt Express has a total of about 100 facilities that serve thousands of points throughout the Southern US (in around 20 states) Canada Mexico and the Caribbean.

EXECUTIVES

President And Ceo, Gary D. Sasser
Evp And Coo, Wayne Spain
Evp Sales And Marketing, Phil Pierce
Evp And Cfo, George Johnson
Auditors: DUNCAN WHEELER & WILKERSON P

LOCATIONS

HQ: AVERITT EXPRESS, INC.
1415 NEAL ST, COOKEVILLE, TN 385014328
Phone: 931 526-3306
Web: WWW.AVERITTEXPRESS.COM

PRODUCTS/OPERATIONS

Selected Services

Cross-border/domestic offshore (Canada Mexico Puerto Rico/Virgin Islands)
Dedicated
Expedited
Intermodal
International ocean/air (ocean/air Asia-Memphis Express)
LTL (regional nationwide distribution/consolidation)
Portside
Retail specialized services
Transportation management
Truckload (dry van flatbed brokerage)
Warehousing

COMPETITORS

AAA Cooper Transportation
ArcBest
C.H. Robinson Worldwide
Estes Express
FedEx Freight
J.B. Hunt
Old Dominion Freight
R+L Carriers
Schneider National
Southeastern Freight Lines
Swift Transportation
UPS Freight
YRC Worldwide

HISTORICAL FINANCIALS

Company Type: Private

Income Statement — FYE: December 31

	REVENUE ($ mil.)	NET INCOME ($ mil.)	NET PROFIT MARGIN	EMPLOYEES
12/18	1,292	77	6.0%	8,208
12/16	1,088	45	4.1%	—
12/15	1,091	44	4.1%	—
Annual Growth	5.8%	19.8%	—	—

2018 Year-End Financials

Return on assets: 7.5%
Return on equity: 9.4%
Current ratio: 5.00
Cash ($ mil.): 203

AVERITT INCORPORATED

EXECUTIVES

Pres, Gary D Sasser
Exec V Pres, Phil Pierce
Exec V Pres, George Johnson
Site Operations Manager, Matthew Clark
Human Resources Application An, Amber Glover
Accounts Payable, Gwen Johnson
Maintenance Shop Front Line Le, Nathan Gideon
Senior Manager Supply Chain Di, Marilyn Jones
Compliance Specialist, Maria Wright
Auditors: DUNCAN WHEELER & WILKERSON P

LOCATIONS

HQ: AVERITT INCORPORATED
1415 NEAL ST, COOKEVILLE, TN 385014328
Phone: 931 526-3306
Web: WWW.AVERITTEXPRESS.COM

HISTORICAL FINANCIALS

Company Type: Private

Income Statement — FYE: December 31

	REVENUE ($ mil.)	NET INCOME ($ mil.)	NET PROFIT MARGIN	EMPLOYEES
12/18	1,292	86	6.7%	8,210
12/17	1,157	93	8.1%	—
12/16	1,097	52	4.8%	—
12/15	1,104	52	4.8%	—
Annual Growth	5.4%	17.7%	—	—

2018 Year-End Financials

Return on assets: 7.6%
Return on equity: 9.9%
Current ratio: 3.20
Cash ($ mil.): 96

AVI-SPL HOL6DINGS, INC.

EXECUTIVES

Ceo, John Zettel
Coo, John Murphy
Cfo, Steve Palmer
Treas, Jean Constant
Treasury Mgr, Ed Bewley
Corporate Controller, Bill McGann
Training & Manager, Jennifer Schwartzberg
Controller, Mary Schaffel
Director Logistics, Rob Scott
Vp Strategic Accounts, Randy Bonham
Auditors: ERNST & YOUNG LLP TAMPA FL

LOCATIONS

HQ: AVI-SPL HOLDINGS, INC.
6301 BENJAMIN RD STE 101, TAMPA, FL 336345115
Phone: 866 708-5034
Web: WWW.AVISPL.COM

HISTORICAL FINANCIALS

Company Type: Private

Income Statement — FYE: December 31

	REVENUE ($ mil.)	NET INCOME ($ mil.)	NET PROFIT MARGIN	EMPLOYEES
12/11	555	5	1.1%	4,936
12/10	505	(0)	—	—
12/09	421	3	0.7%	—
Annual Growth	14.8%	38.5%	—	—

2011 Year-End Financials

Return on assets: 1.8%
Return on equity: 4.2%
Current ratio: 1.50
Cash ($ mil.): 2

AVIO INC.

LOCATIONS

HQ: AVIO INC.
270 SYLVAN AVE STE 130, ENGLEWOOD CLIFFS, NJ 076322545
Phone: 201 816-2720
Web: WWW.AVIOUSA.COM

HISTORICAL FINANCIALS

Company Type: Private

Income Statement — FYE: December 31

	REVENUE ($ mil.)	NET INCOME ($ mil.)	NET PROFIT MARGIN	EMPLOYEES
12/12	1,310	7	0.6%	34
12/05	293	0	0.2%	—
12/04	387	8	2.1%	—
12/03	1,817	0	—	—
Annual Growth	—	—	—	—

2012 Year-End Financials

Return on assets: 12.3%
Return on equity: 0.6%
Current ratio: 0.60
Cash ($ mil.): 42

AXEL JOHNSON INC.

The Johnson family of Stockholm Sweden has an investment arm that stretches across the ocean. Axel Johnson owns and operates North American businesses on behalf of the Johnson dynasty. The investment firm focuses on several industries such as energy medical device manufacturing and water treatment. Its portfolio includes Sprague Energy Parkson Corp. and Kinetico Incorporated. Axel Johnson's companies boast about $4 billion in annual revenues. Axel Johnson along with Axel Johnson AB and AXFast are all affiliated with Sweden-based Axel Johnson Group but are independent. Established in 1873 the Johnson family of companies is in its fourth generation of family ownership.

Operations

Axel Johnson which was formed in 1920 is a long-term investor that typically holds on to its companies for about 20 years. Some companies have been a part of Axel Johnson's portfolio for more than 40 years. Two of its holdings Parkson and Kinetico are part of Axel Johnson's AxWater Group which was formed in 2000.

Financial Performance

Following the economic downturn the company has seen sales increase for several years. Axel Johnson's revenue rose by 6% in 2012 to $4.2 billion as compared to 2011. Energy product sales generated the largest portion of the company's revenue. The results were powered by higher commodity prices and growth at Kinetico Cadence and Mountain Lumber; the first two along with ConforMis and Walk2Campus reported record sales in 2012.

Strategy

Through NewtrAX Axel Johnson makes minority investments in smaller businesses. NewtrAX has stakes in Cadence a manufacturer of cutting and piercing instruments used for the medical and industrial applications. It also owns portions of wood reclamation company Mountain Lumber Co. and Walk2Campus a real estate management and acquisition company. The company in late 2011 invested some $15 million in ConforMIS which develops and markets customized medical devices for the treatment of osteoarthritis and joint damage.

EXECUTIVES

Pres-Chb, Michael D Milligan
Chb, Antonia Axson Johnson
Exec V Pres, Ben J Hennelly
Exec V Pres, John Pascale
Vice President, Sally Sarsfield
V Pres, Clare Peeters
Chief Information Security Off, Janie Wintermyer
Administrative Assistant, Stephanie Moots
Director Benefits, Lawrence Haynes
Accounting Manager, Sylwia Majewski
Manager of Corporate Finance, Erika Cafarella
Auditors: ERNST & YOUNG LLP NEW YORK N

LOCATIONS

HQ: AXEL JOHNSON INC.
155 SPRING ST FL 6, NEW YORK, NY 100125254
Phone: 646 291-2445
Web: WWW.AXELJOHNSON.COM

PRODUCTS/OPERATIONS

Selected Portfolio Companies

Cadence Incorporated
ConforMIS Inc.
Decisyon Inc.
Kinetico Incorporated
Mountain Lumber Company
Parkson Corporation
Sprague Energy Corp.
Walk2Campus Holdings LLC

COMPETITORS

CCMP Capital
Court Square Capital Partners
Enterprise Partners
KKR
Menlo Ventures
Sevin Rosen

HISTORICAL FINANCIALS

Company Type: Private

Income Statement — FYE: December 31

	REVENUE ($ mil.)	NET INCOME ($ mil.)	NET PROFIT MARGIN	EMPLOYEES
12/10	2,982	15	0.5%	1,200
12/09	2,598	11	0.5%	—
12/08	4,312	8	0.2%	—
Annual Growth	(16.8%)	35.5%	—	—

2010 Year-End Financials

Return on assets: 1.4%
Return on equity: 5.2%
Current ratio: 1.70
Cash ($ mil.): 9

AXOS BANK

EXECUTIVES

Ceo, Greg Garrabants
Sr V Pres-Cfo, Andrew Micheletti
Evp-Chief Credit Offr-Chief RE, Tom Constantine
Gen Counsel, Eshel Bar-Adon
Exec V Pres, Brian Swanson
Executive Vice-President, Adriaan Van Zyl
Assistant Vice-President, Joel Kodish
Human Resources Manager, Maria Dews
Assistant Vice-President, Danielle Austin
Vice President, Gilbert Gomez
Underwriter, Jessica Montoya

LOCATIONS

HQ: AXOS BANK
4350 LA JOLLA VILLAGE DR, SAN DIEGO, CA 921221243
Phone: 858 350-6200
Web: WWW.AXOSBANK.COM

HISTORICAL FINANCIALS

Company Type: Private

Income Statement — FYE: December 31

	ASSETS ($ mil.)	NET INCOME ($ mil.)	INCOME AS % OF ASSETS	EMPLOYEES
12/17	8,908	150	1.7%	102
12/16	8,162	137	1.7%	—
12/15	6,656	104	1.6%	—
12/14	5,190	71	1.4%	—
Annual Growth	19.7%	28.1%	—	—

2017 Year-End Financials

Return on assets: 1.7%
Return on equity: 17.3%
Sales ($ mil): 483

B.L. HARBERT HOLDINGS, L.L.C.

EXECUTIVES

Ceo-Chm, Billy Harbert
Exe V Pres-Cfo-Sec, R Alan Hall
V Pres-Cao, James Stewart
V Pres-Risk MGT-Cco, William Lalor
Contrl-Treas-Asst SEC, John Rives
Senior Project Manager, Justin Allred
Auditors: CROWE HORWATH LLP ATLANTA GE

LOCATIONS

HQ: B.L. HARBERT HOLDINGS, L.L.C.
820 SHADES CREEK PKWY # 3000, BIRMINGHAM, AL 352094564
Phone: 205 802-2800
Web: WWW.BLHARBERT.COM

HISTORICAL FINANCIALS

Company Type: Private

Income Statement — FYE: December 31

	REVENUE ($ mil.)	NET INCOME ($ mil.)	NET PROFIT MARGIN	EMPLOYEES
12/14	807	53	6.7%	2,000
12/05	361	0	—	—
12/04	203	0	—	—
Annual Growth	14.8%	—	—	—

2014 Year-End Financials

Return on assets: 6.8%
Return on equity: 6.7%
Current ratio: 0.60
Cash ($ mil.): 191

B.L. HARBERT INTERNATIONAL, L.L.C.

My way or the highway? For Harbert it's my way and the highway. B. L. Harbert International Group provides highway and heavy construction services for commercial industrial and public projects throughout the world but primarily in the Southeast US. The design/build company's portfolio includes commercial and institutional buildings research facilities hotels and condominiums water and wastewater treatment plants dams and highways and pipelines. B. L. Harbert International has offices in the US and Dubai. CEO Billy Harbert Jr. leads the family-owned company which traces its roots to the 1949 founding of Harbert Construction by brothers Bill and John Harbert.

Geographic Reach

The Alabama-based company's international business consists of building US embassies around the world. To date Harbert has built or is building more than 20 embassies in locations including Nigeria Republic of the Congo Sudan Pakistan and Morocco. In the US the company in 2013 completed construction on a 900000-square-foot logistics center in Vance Alabama for Mercedes-Benz US International. In 2011 the firm was selected to build a $50 million 300000-square-foot facility in Auburn Alabama for GE Aviation in 2011.

Financial Performance

Privately-owned B.L. Harbert International posted revenue of $582 million in 2012 compared with $617 million in 2011.

Strategy

Harbert International is building its portfolio and filling its coffers by constructing embassies around the globe. In 2013 the firm was awarded a $292-million-contract to provide design-and-build services for the new US embassy compound in Jakarta Indonesia and a $115-million contract for a new embassy in Paramaribo Suriname. Also in 2013 the US Navy awarded Harbert a $150 million design-build contract for the P-688 Forward Operating Base at Camp Lemonnier in Djibouti Africa.

EXECUTIVES

Senior Vice President International Oper, Charles Bohn
Senior Vice President International Group, Matt Devalk
Auditors: CROWE HORWATH LLP ATLANTA GE

LOCATIONS

HQ: B.L. HARBERT INTERNATIONAL, L.L.C.
820 SHADES CREEK PKWY # 3000, BIRMINGHAM, AL 352094564
Phone: 205 802-2800
Web: WWW.BLHARBERT.COM

PRODUCTS/OPERATIONS

Selected Services

Building information modeling
Construction management
Design-build
General contracting
Owner services
Preconstruction

Selected Operations

US
- Civil/Industrial
- Commercial
- Government
- Health care
- Public/Private Venture division

International

Civil/Industrial
Commercial
Government

COMPETITORS

Barton Malow
Bechtel
Beck Group
Black & Veatch
Bouygues
Brasfield & Gorrie
Brice Building
Choate Construction
Fluor
Gray Construction
H.J. Russell
Hardin Construction
McCarthy Building
Peter Kiewit Sons'
Skanska
Turner Corporation
Whiting-Turner

HISTORICAL FINANCIALS

Company Type: Private

Income Statement — FYE: December 31

	REVENUE ($ mil.)	NET INCOME ($ mil.)	NET PROFIT MARGIN	EMPLOYEES
12/14	807	57	7.2%	1,400
12/08	554	33	6.0%	—
Annual Growth	6.5%	9.7%	—	—

2014 Year-End Financials

Return on assets: 6.8%
Return on equity: 7.2%
Current ratio: 0.90
Cash ($ mil.): 182

BALFOUR BEATTY CONSTRUCTION GROUP, INC.

Balfour Beatty Construction is deep in the heart of Texas – and beyond. The company provides start-to-finish project management pre-construction and related services for commercial construction projects. Offerings include site evaluation and analysis general contracting cost consulting process equipment installation turnkey medical facility development capital equipment planning and closeout services. The company works on a range of facilities including hotels office buildings civic centers airports hospitals schools public buildings and retail locations. UK firm Balfour Beatty plc acquired the company then named Centex Construction from Centex Corp. in 2007.

Operations

Balfour Beatty Construction ranks as the fifth largest general builder in the US. The firm is also active in the construction services infrastructure investment and professionals and support services markets.

Geographic Reach

Dallas-based Balfour Beatty Construction has locations in the West Mid-Atlantic and Southeast.

Strategy

The US arm of the international infrastructure group Balfour Beatty Construction is poised to profit from the recovery of the US economy. Indeed the US market has seen a quicker return to growth that its UK counterpart with more private and complex construction projects coming to the market. To that end the construction service firm is expanding its Houston Division to capitalize on growing demand from the energy and multifamily housing markets in the Houston area. To build its Campus Solutions business which specializes in the construction of education facilities Balfour Beatty Construction absorbed Charter Builders a specialist in educational facilities in 2012. Recent student housing projects include a 1274-bed student housing project at Texas A&M University. Construction of the $104 million project began in mid-2014 with completion and occupancy set for August 2015.

Some of the company's more notable projects include NASA Mission Control (Houston) Texas Stadium (home of the Dallas Cowboys) the Mayo Clinic The James Madison Library of Congress One America Plaza Miami International Airport and Cinderella's Castle at Walt Disney World.

EXECUTIVES

Exec V Pres, John Woodcock
Auditors: KPMG LLP DALLAS TX

LOCATIONS

HQ: BALFOUR BEATTY CONSTRUCTION GROUP, INC.
3100 MCKINNON ST FL 10, DALLAS, TX 752017007
Phone: 214 451-1000
Web: WWW.BALFOURBEATTYUS.COM

PRODUCTS/OPERATIONS

Selected Key Markets

Airports
Defense housing
Education
Health care
Judicial & institutional
Rail
Roads

Selected Projects

Air Force Memorial (Arlington VA)
Army/Air Force Exchange Shopping Center (Fort Jackson SC)
Bank of America (Charlotte NC)
Broward County Convention Center (Fort Lauderdale FL)
Burger King corporate headquarters (Miami)
Cape Coral Parkway Expansion (Cape Coral FL)
Carnival Cruise Lines corporate headquarters (Miami)
Children's Hospital & Health Center (San Diego CA)
Cisco Systems corporate headquarters (Research Triangle Park NC)
Disney's Wilderness Lodge Resort (Lake Buena Vista FL)
Duke University Levine Science Research Center (Durham NC)
Harrah's Casino (New Orleans)
Harris Methodist Hospital (Fort Worth TX)
James Madison Memorial Building Library of Congress (Washington DC)
J.P. Morgan International Plaza (Dallas)
Lucayan Beach Resort (Grand Bahama Island Bahamas)
Mescalero Apache K-12 (Mescalero NM)
Music City Central MTA Bus Facility (Nashville TN)
NASA Space Station Control Center (Houston)
Osceoloa County Courthouse (Kissimmee FL)
Port of Miami (Miami)
Southwest Airlines corporate headquarters (Dallas)
United Spirit Arena (Lubbock TX)
Vanderbilt University Medical Center (Nashville TN)
Walter Reed Army Medical Center military housing (Silver Spring MD)
White Sands Missile Range military housing (White Sands NM)

COMPETITORS

American Constructors
Ames Construction
Axis Construction
Bechtel
Cutler Associates
Engelberth Construction
Falkenberg Construction
Fluor
G. A. Johnson & Son
Hardaway Construction
LeChase Construction
M & H Enterprises
MW Builders
McGough Construction
Panattoni Construction
Rayco Construction
Satterfield & Pontikes
Skanska USA Building
Turner Construction

HISTORICAL FINANCIALS

Company Type: Private

Income Statement — FYE: December 31

	REVENUE ($ mil.)	NET INCOME ($ mil.)	NET PROFIT MARGIN	EMPLOYEES
12/15	3,852	(14)	—	2,200
12/14	3,932	17	0.4%	—
12/13	3,816	24	0.6%	—
12/12	3,459	19	0.6%	—
Annual Growth	3.7%	—	—	—

2015 Year-End Financials

Return on assets: (-0.9%)
Return on equity: (-3.0%)
Current ratio: 1.20
Cash ($ mil.): 69

BALFOUR BEATTY CONSTRUCTION, LLC

EXECUTIVES

MBR, Mark Layman
MBR, John Woodcock
MBR, Eric Stenman
MBR, Richard Jaggers
MBR, Glenn Burns
MBR, John Parolisi
MBR, John Tarpey
Performance Awareness Cnsltnt, Patricia Laprade
Project Coordinator, Leonicio Alonzo
Assistant Controller, Colleen Anderson
Senior Project Manager, Titus Rodriguez
Auditors: KPMG LLP DALLAS TX

LOCATIONS

HQ: BALFOUR BEATTY CONSTRUCTION, LLC
3100 MCKINNON ST FL 10, DALLAS, TX 752017007
Phone: 214 451-1000
Web: WWW.BALFOURBEATTYUS.COM

HISTORICAL FINANCIALS

Company Type: Private

Income Statement — FYE: December 31

	REVENUE ($ mil.)	NET INCOME ($ mil.)	NET PROFIT MARGIN	EMPLOYEES
12/16	3,809	13	0.3%	2,190
12/13	3,816	23	0.6%	—
12/12	3,365	8	0.3%	—
12/10	0	0	—	—
Annual Growth	—	—	—	—

2016 Year-End Financials

Return on assets: 0.8%
Return on equity: 2.8%
Current ratio: 1.20
Cash ($ mil.): 53

BALFOUR BEATTY, LLC

EXECUTIVES

Mng MBR-Pres, Mark Crouser
V Pres, Peter Zinkin
V Pres, Leslie Cohn

V Pres-Asst SEC, Joanne Bonfiglio
Treas, Barry Crozier
SEC, Christine Schiltz
Asst Treas, Vicki Sizemore
Vp and Business Unit Leader Fo, Ed Prendergast
Intern, Kara Fugate
Project Coordinator, Allyn Wingfield
Senior Project Engineer, Brady Logan
Auditors: DELOITTE & TOUCHE LLP DALLAS

LOCATIONS

HQ: BALFOUR BEATTY, LLC
1011 CENTRE RD STE 322, WILMINGTON, DE 198051266
Phone: 302 573-3873

HISTORICAL FINANCIALS

Company Type: Private

Income Statement — FYE: December 31

	REVENUE ($ mil.)	NET INCOME ($ mil.)	NET PROFIT MARGIN	EMPLOYEES
12/15	4,690	(18)	—	2,200
12/12	4,378	43	1.0%	—
12/11	4,078	58	1.4%	—
Annual Growth	3.6%	—	—	—

2015 Year-End Financials

Return on assets: (-0.5%)
Return on equity: (-1.0%)
Current ratio: 1.70
Cash ($ mil.): 391

BALLAD HEALTH

EXECUTIVES

Chm-Pres-Ceo, Alan Levine
Cfo, Lynn Krutak
Coo, Marvin Eichorn
Svp-CIO, Pam Austin
Cipo, Jamie Swift
Cmo Northwest Division, Herb Ladley
Vp Oncology Services, Tony Dotson
Human Resources Generalist, Kasey Guy
Marketing Coordinator, Lori English
Operating Room Dir, Ruth Morelock
Manager, Al Salama
Auditors: PYA PC KNOXVILLE TENNESSE

LOCATIONS

HQ: BALLAD HEALTH
400 N STATE OF FRNKLIN RD, JOHNSON CITY, TN 376046035
Phone: 423 431-6561
Web: WWW.BALLADHEALTH.ORG

HISTORICAL FINANCIALS

Company Type: Private

Income Statement — FYE: June 30

	REVENUE ($ mil.)	NET INCOME ($ mil.)	NET PROFIT MARGIN	EMPLOYEES
06/20	2,077	(69)	—	6,114
06/19	2,106	99	4.7%	—
Annual Growth	(1.4%)	—	—	—

2020 Year-End Financials

Return on assets: (-1.9%)
Return on equity: (-4.2%)
Current ratio: 1.90
Cash ($ mil.): 427

BALTIMORE CITY PUBLIC SCHOOLS

EXECUTIVES

Ceo, Sonja B Santelises
Ceo, Bonnie S Copeland
Chief School Supports Officer, Karl E Perry
Chief Achievement and Accounta, Theresa Jones
Accounting Staff, Michele Hayes
Teacher, George Kessler
Director, E Hope
Elementary School Teacher, Jaime Clough
Esol Teacher, Laura Oxenreiter
Manager, Andrew Monger
Information Technology Manager, Chanelle Floyd
Auditors: CLIFTONLARSONALLEN LLP BALTIM

LOCATIONS

HQ: BALTIMORE CITY PUBLIC SCHOOLS
200 E NORTH AVE, BALTIMORE, MD 212025984
Phone: 443 984-2000
Web: WWW.BCPS.K12.MD.US

HISTORICAL FINANCIALS

Company Type: Private

Income Statement — FYE: June 30

	REVENUE ($ mil.)	NET INCOME ($ mil.)	NET PROFIT MARGIN	EMPLOYEES
06/12	1,480	(18)	—	10,800
06/02	988	(23)	—	—
Annual Growth	4.1%	—	—	—

2012 Year-End Financials

Return on assets: (-2.0%)
Return on equity: (-3.6%)
Current ratio: —
Cash ($ mil.): 183

BANNER-UNIVERSITY MEDICAL CENTER TUCSON CAMPUS LLC

Banner - University Medicine (formerly The University of Arizona Health Network) heals Arizonans and trains Wildcats. It operates three academic medical centers in Phoenix and Tucson serving as the primary teaching hospital for the University of Arizona (UA) and offering medical treatment research and education services. The not-for-profit center provides cancer cardiology geriatric respiratory transplant and dialysis care as well as general practice and home health services. Specialty services include burn care behavioral health integrative medicine sports medicine and level I trauma care. The network merged with Banner Healthcare in 2015.

Operations

The University of Arizona Health Network merged with Banner Health to create Banner - University Medicine. The division includes three hospitals: Banner - University Medical Center Tucson Banner - University Medical Center South and Banner - University Medical Center Phoenix. The network also includes Banner - University Medical Group (formerly named University of Arizona Physicians) a group of Tucson-based physicians.

Geographic Reach

Banner - University Medicine serves patients in and around Phoenix and Tucson Arizona.

Strategy

In 2015 Banner - University Medical Center Phoenix broke ground on a new $160 million emergency department that will have the capacity to serve an additional 20000 patients each year. Expected to open in mid-2017 the new facility will include 60 private exam rooms a new trauma unit and 40 observation beds.

Company Background

The University of Arizona Health Network was formed in 2010 when University Physicians Hospital merged with University Medical Center.

LOCATIONS

HQ: BANNER-UNIVERSITY MEDICAL CENTER TUCSON CAMPUS LLC
1501 N CAMPBELL AVE, TUCSON, AZ 857240001
Phone:
Web: WWW.UAHEALTH.IXT.COM

COMPETITORS

John C. Lincoln Health Network
Northern Arizona Healthcare
Phoenix Children's Hospital
Scottsdale Healthcare
Sun Health
Yuma Regional Medical Center

HISTORICAL FINANCIALS

Company Type: Private

Income Statement — FYE: June 30

	REVENUE ($ mil.)	NET INCOME ($ mil.)	NET PROFIT MARGIN	EMPLOYEES
06/09	541	0	—	3,000
06/08	512	27	5.3%	—
06/05	708	0	0.0%	—
Annual Growth	(6.5%)	—	—	—

2009 Year-End Financials

Return on assets: 16.3%
Return on equity: —
Current ratio: —
Cash ($ mil.): 3

BAPTIST HEALTH

For those seeking medical salvation Baptist Health may be the answer to their prayers. The organization provides health services through about 175 points of care scattered throughout in Arkansas. Its facilities include seven hospitals and a number of rehabilitation facilities family clinics and therapy and wellness centers. Arkansas Health Group a division of Baptist Health runs more than 20 physician clinics across the state. Specialized services include cardiology women's health orthopedics rehabilitation and home and hospice care. Baptist Health's Parkway Village is a 90-acre retirement community for active seniors located close to Baptist Health Medical Center - Little Rock.

Operations

In addition to its hospitals the company has 47 physician clinics 20 therapy centers and 53 other centers and service locations. Its Baptist Health Mobile Health Unit travels the state to provide a temporary facility for health screenings health education and first-aid (emergent care) services.

Along with the standard roster of health care services Baptist Health also offers Little Rock residents nine programs of health care study through its Baptist Health Schools Little Rock division. The school coordinates with Arkansas Tech University to offer Baptist Health RN graduates an online option to complete their Bachelor of Science in Nursing degree. Its average enrollment is about 900 students each semester.

Geographic Reach

Baptist Health serves patients across Arkansas. Baptist Health's hospitals include Baptist Health Extended Care Hospital Baptist Health Medical Center - Arkadelphia Baptist Health Medical Center - Heber Springs Baptist Health Medical Center - Little Rock Baptist Health Medical Center - North Little Rock Baptist Health Medical Center - Stuttgart and Baptist Health Medical Center - Hot Spring County.

Sales and Marketing

Baptist Health works with a number of insurance policies and organizations including Aetna AMCO PPO Arkansas Blue Cross and Blue Shield Arkansas Municipal League Care Improvement Plus CIGNA Coventry/First Health PPO and GEHA.

Strategy

The hospital system has been growing to meet the needs of its customers. In 2013 it began leasing Hot Spring County Medical Center in Malvern. The 72-bed acute care hospital was renamed Baptist Health Medical Center Hot Spring County. Baptist Health also bought nearly 40 acres in Conway and began construction on a medical center to serve Faulkner county.

To improve operating efficiency in 2013 Baptist Health formed a new organization – Baptist Health Physician Partners a clinical integration program with more than 200 physician partners.

EXECUTIVES

Medical Director, Nancy Rector
Vice President Of It, Chris Parker
Nursing Director, Christopher Cox
Operating Room Dir, Deborah Branson
Vice President Operations, Mark Truman
Secretary Ii, Tammera Worden
Auditors: BKD LLP LITTLE ROCK ARKANSA

LOCATIONS

HQ: BAPTIST HEALTH
9601 BAPTIST HEALTH DR # 109, LITTLE ROCK, AR 722056323
Phone: 501 202-2000
Web: WWW.BAPTIST-HEALTH.COM

Selected Locations in Arkansas

Arkansas Health Group (statewide)
BH Extended Care (Little Rock)
BHMC Arkadelphia
BHMC Heber Springs
BHMC Hot Spring County
BHMC Little Rock
BHMC North Little Rock
BHMC Stuttgart
Baptist Health Rehabilitation Institute (Little Rock)
Parkway Village (Little Rock)

PRODUCTS/OPERATIONS

Selected Services

Behavioral Health
Cardiac Rehab
Diabetes Treatment & Management
Eye Center
Hospice & Home Health
Home Infusion Services
Imaging Services
Laboratory
MedFlight
Men's Health
Pastoral Care
Sleep Disorder
Transplant
Weight Loss Program
Wound Care Center

COMPETITORS

Arkansas Children's Hospital
Arkansas Heart Hospital
Baxter Regional Medical Center
Conway Regional Health System
Jefferson Regional Medical Center of Arkansas
Saline Memorial
Sparks Health System
St. Joseph's Mercy Health Center
St. Vincent Health System
White County Medical Center

HISTORICAL FINANCIALS

Company Type: Private

Income Statement — FYE: December 31

	REVENUE ($ mil.)	NET INCOME ($ mil.)	NET PROFIT MARGIN	EMPLOYEES
12/18	1,215	(45)	—	7,000
12/17	875	49	5.6%	—
12/09	924	64	7.0%	—
Annual Growth	3.1%	—	—	—

2018 Year-End Financials

Return on assets: (-2.9%)
Return on equity: (-5.5%)
Current ratio: 1.70
Cash ($ mil.): 58

BAPTIST HEALTH SOUTH FLORIDA, INC.

Baptist Health South Florida (BHSF) is a faith-based not-for-profit enterprise operating about a dozen acute-care hospitals in the Miami area. Its flagship facility Baptist Hospital has about 730 beds and provides a comprehensive range of medical and surgical services. The system also includes Bethesda Hospital (480 beds) South Miami Hospital (440 beds) a children's hospital and other community hospitals in surrounding areas. In all BHSF hospitals contain about 2650 beds. In addition to inpatient services the organization provides ambulatory surgery primary and urgent care diagnostic imaging rehabilitation and home health services from more than 100 outpatient centers and physician practices.

Strategy

BHSF's strategic goals focus on expansion through new construction and additions acquisitions and select partnerships. Additionally the health system works to improve patient care through medical equipment and information technology upgrades.

The company looks to attract patients seeking specialty care by maintaining specialist centers with state-of-the-art medical technologies and skilled physicians. For instance the organization opened a new multidisciplinary skin cancer clinic featuring a 3D whole-body imaging system at its Miami Cancer Institute facility in 2019. Other specialist centers include the Miami Cardiac and Vascular Institute the Miami Cancer Institute the Baptist Health Neuroscience Center and the Miami Orthopedic and Sports Medicine Institute.

BHSF is also expanding its global alliances through its Baptist Health International unit. In 2019 Baptist Health International formed a partnership with ProHealth Urgent Care to open an urgent care center in St. Croix US Virgin Islands.

Mergers and Acquisitions

As part of an ongoing wave of consolidation among hospital operators BHSF acquired another South Florida-based health care organization the not-for-profit Boca Raton Regional Hospital in 2019. The acquired entity operates a 400-bed hospital and related outpatient facilities in the Boca Raton area.

Company Background

Baptist Hospital opened in 1960 and the Baptist Health organization was formed in 1990.

The company added a number of hospitals through acquisitions and construction efforts over the years. It opened the West Kendall Baptist Hospital in 2011. In 2017 the system merged with the not-for-profit Bethesda Health adding two hospitals (Bethesda East and Bethesda West) in Boynton Beach. It also added the Fishermen's Community Hospital that year.

EXECUTIVES

Evp And Cfo, Ralph E. Lawson
President And Ceo, Brian E. Keeley
Ceo And Executive Medical Director Miami Cancer Institute, Michael J. Zinner
Evp And Coo, D. Wayne Brackin
Evp And Chief Physician Executive, Jack A. Ziffer
Evp And Chief Administrative Officer, Joe Natoli
Corporate Vice President Real Estate, Kathy Moorman
Medical Director Medical Education, Arturo Fridman
Medical Director, James Benenati
Senior Vice President Of Network, Eric Shatnof
Vice President, DAVID VITTORIA
Chairman, Rev. William W. White
Unit Secretary, Rosario Sol
Auditors: DELOITTE & TOUCHE LLP MIAMI

LOCATIONS

HQ: BAPTIST HEALTH SOUTH FLORIDA, INC.
6855 S RED RD, SOUTH MIAMI, FL 331433647
Phone: 305 596-1960
Web: WWW.CIRUGIAOCULARBAPTIST.COM

PRODUCTS/OPERATIONS

2013 Sales

	$ mil.	% of total
Managed Care	1,655	69
Medicare	278	12
Medicaid	122	5
Other	331	14
Total		**100**

Selected Florida Facilities

Baptist Hospital of Miami (Kendall)
Baptist Cardiac & Vascular Institute
Baptist Children's Hospital
Doctors Hospital (Coral Gables)
Homestead Hospital (Homestead)
Mariners Hospital (Tavernier)
South Miami Hospital (South Miami)
West Kendall Baptist Hospital (Kendall)

Selected Services

Addiction treatment
Behavorial medicine
Blood conservation program
Cancer services
Cardiovascular services
Care and counseling services
Children's health
Community wellness
Critical care center
Diabetes
eICU LifeGuard
Emergency
Endoscopy
Executive health
Gamma knife center
Heart surgery
Home care
Hyperbaric services

Imaging
Intensive care unit
International services
Interventional/surgical Services
Laboratory
Maritime medical services
Neonatal
Neuroscience
Nutrition counseling services
Occupational health
Online appointments
Orthopedics
Outpatient/diagnostic services
Pain center
Pastoral care
Pediatric
Pelvic health
Physical and speech therapy
Pregnancy and childbirth
Progressive care unit
Prostate cancer
Pulmonary services
Radiation oncology
Rehabilitation services
Robotic surgery
Senior services
Sleep diagnostic center
Sports medicine and orthopedic programs
Stroke services
Surgery
Weight-loss surgery
Wellness Center
Women's health
Wound care

COMPETITORS

Adventist Health System Sunbelt Healthcare
Boca Raton Regional Hospital
Broward Health
HCA
Holy Cross Hospital Fort Lauderdale
Jackson Health System
Lakeland Regional Medical Center
Miami Children's Hospital
Mount Sinai Medical Center of Florida
South Broward Hospital District
Tenet Healthcare
The Cleveland Clinic
University of Miami Hospital

HISTORICAL FINANCIALS

Company Type: Private

Income Statement FYE: September 30

	REVENUE ($ mil.)	NET INCOME ($ mil.)	NET PROFIT MARGIN	EMPLOYEES
09/17	608	244	40.2%	16,000
09/15	846	137	16.2%	—
09/09*	616	121	19.7%	—
12/08	2	(1)	—	—
Annual Growth	83.2%	—	—	—

*Fiscal year change

2017 Year-End Financials

Return on assets: 5.1%
Return on equity: 7.1%
Current ratio: 1.50
Cash ($ mil.): 106

BAPTIST HEALTH SYSTEM, INC.

Even if you don't root for the Jacksonville Jaguars you can still seek care from Baptist Health System. Baptist Health serves the Jacksonville Florida area through four acute care hospitals and a children's hospital with a combined total of more than 1000 beds. Baptist Medical Center its flagship facility is a full-service hospital that also houses Baptist Heart Hospital. Across the street Wolfson Children's Hospital also cares for the city's youngest residents. The system's satellite acute-care facilities include Baptist Medical Center Beaches Baptist Medical Center Nassau and Baptist Medical Center South.

Operations

Baptist Health's flagship tertiary care hospital Baptist Medical Center is centrally located in Jacksonville and is a full-service medical center representing nearly all major health care specialties. Its Baptist Heart Hospital offers comprehensive cardiovascular care.

In addition to its hospitals Baptist Health System operates a network of about 200 outpatient centers including primary and specialty care physician practices and clinics (including cardiology and cancer care centers) as well as urgent care rehabilitation pharmacy and occupational health locations. In total Baptist Health System has 1200 physicians and handles some 51000 inpatient stays nearly 250000 emergency visits 44000 surgeries and 7000 births each year.

Financial Performance

In 2014 Baptist Health's net revenues increased by 3% due to higher net patient service revenues less provision for bad debts. Net patient service revenue by major payor source was: Medicare 40%; Blue Cross 23%; Medicaid 7%; other third-party payors 25%; and self pay 5%.

The hospital incurred a net loss of $8.9 million in 2014 (a 190% drop compared to 2013) despite the increase in net revenues.

Cash outflow decreased by 102% compared to 2013.

Strategy

Baptist Health is expanding certain programs to cater to targeted population segments in the Jacksonville area. For instance it is expanding its Baptist AgeWell Institute program at the Jacksonville hospital as well as the pastoral care program in Nassau. It is also enhancing its emergency room at the Beaches hospital and is conducting community outreach programs for low-income families.

In 2015 Baptist Health and The University of Texas MD Anderson Cancer Center moved forward with multidisciplinary cancer care for adult patients throughout their region by opening the Baptist MD Anderson Cancer Center.

Company Background

A major construction project was completed in late 2012 with the opening of a new 11-story patient tower at Baptist Jacksonville. The new $200 million tower features all private patient rooms and high-tech surgical suites.

Baptist Health was founded in 1955.

EXECUTIVES

Evp And Coo, John F. Wilbanks
Hospital President Baptist Medical Center South, Ron Robinson
Hospital President Wolfson Childrens Hospital, Michael D. Aubin
President And Ceo, A. Hugh Greene
Hospital President Baptist Beaches; President Transitional Care, Joseph M. (Joe) Mitrick
Svp Medical Affairs And Clinical Effectiveness; Chief Medical Officer, Keith L. Stein
Svp And Cfo, Scott Wooten
Hospital President Baptist Medical Center Jacksonville, Michael A. Mayo
Svp And Chief Nursing Officer, Diane S. Raines
President Physician Integration, Edward Sim
Svp And Cio, Roland Garcia
Chief Medical Officer Wolfson Children's Hospital, Jerry A. Bridgham
Hospital President Baptist Medical Center Nassau, Stephen Lee
Medical Director, Mark Stich
Medical Director, David Ross
Vice President Of Operations, Keon Falkner
Pharmacy Manager, Michael Brooks
Vice President Of Community Investment And Impact, Melanie Patz
Medical Director, Ted Glasser
Vice President Legal, Terry Hayes
Secretary, Mariza Ortiz
Auditors: ERNST & YOUNG LLP JACKSONVIL

LOCATIONS

HQ: BAPTIST HEALTH SYSTEM, INC.
800 PRUDENTIAL DR, JACKSONVILLE, FL 322078202
Phone: 904 202-2000
Web: WWW.BAPTISTJAX.COM

PRODUCTS/OPERATIONS

Selected facilities

Baptist Medical Center Beaches (Jacksonville Beach Florida)
Baptist Medical Center Jacksonville (Jacksonville Florida)
Baptist Heart Hospital
Baptist Medical Center Nassau (Fernandina Beach Florida)
Baptist Medical Center South (Jacksonville Florida)
Wolfson Children's Hospital (Jacksonville Florida)

COMPETITORS

Bay Medical Center
Brooks Rehabilitation
Florida Hospital Tampa Bay Division
Florida Hospital Waterman
HCA
Mayo Clinic Jacksonville
Munroe Regional Health System
Nemours Foundation
Orlando Health
St. Vincent's Health System
UF Health Jacksonville

HISTORICAL FINANCIALS

Company Type: Private

Income Statement FYE: September 30

	REVENUE ($ mil.)	NET INCOME ($ mil.)	NET PROFIT MARGIN	EMPLOYEES
09/19	1,923	176	9.2%	7,000
09/18	1,736	252	14.5%	—
09/17	1,630	304	18.7%	—
Annual Growth	8.6%	(23.8%)	—	—

2019 Year-End Financials

Return on assets: 4.7%
Return on equity: 6.9%
Current ratio: 1.20
Cash ($ mil.): 190

BAPTIST HEALTH SYSTEM, INC.

EXECUTIVES

Ceo, Keith Parrott
Cfo*, Greg Johnston
CIO*, Scott Fenn
Chro*, Beth Francis
Cmo*, Elizabeth Ennis
CIO*, Chris Davis
Health Professional, Syed A Ali
Chief of Medicine, Lynn Crawford
Vice-President Human Resources, Le Roy Walker
General, Steve Brooks
Nursing Director, Tiffany Garza
Auditors: WARREN AVERETT LLC BIRMINGHAM

LOCATIONS

HQ: BAPTIST HEALTH SYSTEM, INC.
1130 22ND ST S STE 3200, BIRMINGHAM, AL 352052867
Phone: 205 715-5000
Web: WWW.BAPTISTHEALTHALABAMA.ORG

HISTORICAL FINANCIALS

Company Type: Private

Income Statement FYE: December 31

	REVENUE ($ mil.)	NET INCOME ($ mil.)	NET PROFIT MARGIN	EMPLOYEES
12/14	565	(35)	—	4,300
12/12	528	(15)	—	—
12/11*	587	(34)	—	—
06/10	1,220	0	—	—
Annual Growth	—	—	—	—

*Fiscal year change

2014 Year-End Financials

Return on assets: (-4.5%)
Return on equity: (-17.0%)
Current ratio: 0.90
Cash ($ mil.): 1

BAPTIST HEALTHCARE SYSTEM, INC.

Baptist Healthcare System which goes by Baptist Health wants to keep all its followers healthy. The system owns eight acute -care hospitals one a long-term facility in Kentucky with a total capacity of more than 2100 beds. The not-for-profit health system's largest facility is Baptist Hospital East a 520-bed hospital in Louisville that provides a wide range of health services with special expertise in cardiology rehabilitation and women's health. In addition to its owned facilities Baptist Health manages Hardin Memorial a 300-bed hospital located in Elizabethtown and Russell County Hospital with 25 beds.The growing Baptist Health was founded as a single hospital in Louisville in 1924.

Operations

Along with inpatient acute care services Baptist Health offers home health care services runs two outpatient surgery centers provides urgent care through a handful of clinics and operates a regional physicians' practice group. It also runs a community-based not-for-profit health care plan Baptist Health Plan which operates across the state and into parts of Indiana and Tennessee. Baptist Health plans to shut the struggling health plan down in 2018.

Strategy

Baptist Health faced major losses during 2017 and laid off more than 500 employees that year. It announced plans to realign its structure and shut down its not-for-profit Baptist Health Plan.

Mergers and Acquisitions

In mid-2017 Baptist Health agreed to buy Hardin Memorial for an undisclosed amount. Hardin Memorial (which Baptist Health already manages) operates some 50 outpatient facilities as well as its 300-bed hospital.

EXECUTIVES

President And Ceo Bluegrass Family Health, James S. Fritz
President Baptist Hospital East, David L. Gray
President Central Baptist Hospital, William G. Sisson
President Baptist Hospital Northeast, Christopher M. (Chris) Roty
President Baptist Regional Medical Center, Larry W. Gray
President Hardin Memorial Hopsital, Dennis Johnson
Vice President And General Counsel, Janet Norton
Ceo, Stephen C. Hanson
Chief Clinical Officer, Timothy Jahn
Cio, David J. Bensema
Cfo, Carl G. Herde
Chief Health Integration Officer; President Baptist Health Medical Group, Isaac J. Myers
President Baptist Health Richmond, C. Todd Jones
Regional Executive And President Baptist Health Paducah, William A. Brown
President Baptist Health Madisonville, Michael A. Baumgartner
Vice President Marketing, Carla Conklin
Clinic Manager, Sean Sullivan
Vice President Human Resources And Development, Sue Christopher
Director Of Pharmacy, Michael Anderson
Vice President Human Resources Baptist Health Lexi, Lynette Walker
Auditors: DELOITTE & TOUCHE LLP LOUISVI

LOCATIONS

HQ: BAPTIST HEALTHCARE SYSTEM, INC.
2701 EASTPOINT PKWY, LOUISVILLE, KY 402234166
Phone: 502 896-5000
Web: WWW.BAPTISTHEALTH.COM

PRODUCTS/OPERATIONS

Selected Facilities and Operations (Kentucky)

Hospitals

Managed
Baptist Health Corbin
Baptist Health La Grange
Baptist Health Lexington
Baptist Health Louisville
Baptist Health Richmond
Baptist Health Madisonville
Baptist Health Paducah
ContinueCARE Hospital (Corbin)
Owned
Hardin Memorial Hospital (Elizabethtown)
Russell County Hospital (Russell Springs)

Other operations

Baptist East Milestone Wellness Center (Louisville)
Baptist Express Care (various Walmarts in state)
Baptist Medical Associates (medical practice group Louisville area)
Baptist Urgent Care (Louisville)
Bluegrass Family Health (provider-sponsored insurance)

COMPETITORS

Appalachian Regional Healthcare
Catholic Health Initiatives
Jewish Hospital & St. Mary's HealthCare
Kindred Healthcare
Norton Healthcare
Pikeville Medical Center
University Health Care
University of Kentucky Chandler Hospital

HISTORICAL FINANCIALS

Company Type: Private

Income Statement FYE: August 31

	REVENUE ($ mil.)	NET INCOME ($ mil.)	NET PROFIT MARGIN	EMPLOYEES
08/19	2,878	122	4.2%	12,601
08/18	2,725	149	5.5%	—
08/17	2,688	5	0.2%	—
08/16	2,331	1	0.0%	—
Annual Growth	7.3%	373.0%	—	—

2019 Year-End Financials

Return on assets: 3.5%
Return on equity: 6.2%
Current ratio: 2.50
Cash ($ mil.): 162

BAPTIST HOSPITAL OF MIAMI, INC.

Baptist Hospital of Miami can treat many vices for Miami residents. The flagship facility of the Baptist Health South Florida health system provides residents of the city with a full range of health care services including pediatric cancer home health rehabilitation neurology and cardiovascular care. The hospital has more than 680 beds and includes the Baptist Children's Hospital which offers a pediatric emergency room and a neonatal intensive care unit. Baptist Hospital of Miami also includes the Baptist Cardiac & Vascular Institute a regional cancer program and a diabetes care center. Baptist Hospital of Miami was founded in 1960.

Operations

Baptist Children's Hospital offers 24-hour emergency care as well as two intensive care units and specialist services including pediatric cancer care. Baptist Hospital of Miami also contains the Baptist Cardiac and Vascular Institute which conducts treatment and research programs. The hospital's international care unit provides services to patients from the Caribbean Latin America and other regions. Other specialist divisions include a sleep diagnostic center and a spine care facility as well as a maternity ward. Baptist Hospital of Miami also operates several wellness centers.

As part of Baptist Health South Florida the Baptist Hospital of Miami is part of a network of six hospitals including South Miami Hospital Doctors Hospital and the West Kendall Baptist Hospital. In addition the health system includes outpatient care clinics including emergency surgery imaging and primary care centers.

Strategy

Controlling expenses through data management quality and wellness initiatives and other measures becomes increasingly important for the hospital and its affiliates as the cost of medical care in the US market continues to skyrocket. Maintaining an efficient organization is also imperative as the level of charity care provided by the system's facilities continues to rise in the face of economic difficulties.

As the largest hospital in the Baptist Health system Baptist Hospital of Miami takes a leading role in technology programs such as medical equipment and data management system upgrades. The Baptist Health network is in the process of installing an electronic health record (EHR) system to connect patient records across its facilities.

In 2012 Baptist Hospital of Miami launched a $90 million construction effort to expand the Cardiac and Vascular Institute. The new expanded institute facility will open in 2016 and will include centers for aneurysm treatment structural heart therapy and endovascular therapy. The project also includes expansion efforts on the hospital's surgery center which will have enhanced capabilities for neurological cardiac and robotic surgery procedures.

EXECUTIVES

Prin, William W White
Chm*, Calvin Babcock
Cfo*, Ralph Lawson
Treas*, Manuel Lasaga
Coordinator, Suzanne Balbosa
Pulmonary Disease Specialist, Mark J Hauser
Internal Medicine Practitioner, Ivette Acosta-Trant
Nuclear Medicine Specialist, Jason Samii
Information Specialist, Jorge Perez
Internist, Rania Albataineh
Manager Engineering, Richard Johenning

LOCATIONS

HQ: BAPTIST HOSPITAL OF MIAMI, INC.
8900 N KENDALL DR, MIAMI, FL 331762197
Phone: 786 596-1960
Web: WWW.BAPTISTHEALTH.NET

PRODUCTS/OPERATIONS

Selected Centers and Services

Baptist Cardiac & Vascular Institute (Heart Care)
Baptist Children's Hospital (Pediatrics)
Breast Care
Cancer Services
Center for Spine Care
Children's Cancer Services
Children's Emergency Center
Clinical Research Trials
Community Wellness
Critical Care/eICU LifeGuard
Diabetes Care
Diagnostic Imaging
Emergency Services
Endoscopy
Gynecology
Home Care
Intensive Care
International Services
Interventional
Maternity
Neonatal Intensive Care Unit
Neuroscience Center
Neurosurgery
Orthopedic Services
Pain Management
Physical & Speech Therapy
Pulmonary Services
Rehabilitation Services
Robotic Surgery
Senior Services
Sleep Diagnostic Center
Spine Care
Stroke Services
Surgery
Women's Services

COMPETITORS

Broward Health
H. Lee Moffitt Cancer Center & Research Institute
HCA
Jackson Health System
Larkin Community Hospital
Miami Children's Hospital
Mount Sinai Medical Center of Florida
South Broward Hospital District
University of Miami Hospital

HISTORICAL FINANCIALS

Company Type: Private

Income Statement — FYE: September 30

	REVENUE ($ mil.)	NET INCOME ($ mil.)	NET PROFIT MARGIN	EMPLOYEES
09/18*	1,169	143	12.3%	4,200
12/17	1,004	73	7.3%	—
09/16	867	39	4.6%	—
09/15	889	108	12.2%	—
Annual Growth	9.5%	9.8%	—	—

*Fiscal year change

2018 Year-End Financials

Return on assets: 14.1%
Return on equity: 44.5%
Current ratio: 0.90
Cash ($ mil.): —

BAPTIST MEMORIAL HOSPITAL

When most of us think of Memphis we think of Elvis Presley. When doctors think of Memphis they think of Elvis and Baptist Memorial Hospital-Memphis. As the flagship facility of Baptist Memorial Health Care the 710-bed hospital often simply called Baptist Memphis offers patients the full spectrum of health care services including cancer treatment orthopedics surgical services and neurology. The campus also features the Baptist Heart Institute for cardiovascular care and research a pediatric emergency room a skilled nursing facility and the Plaza Diagnostic Pavilion for outpatient health care. Baptist Memphis established in 1979 is one of the state's highest volume hospitals.

Operations

Doctors at the hospital see more than 27000 admissions 54000 emergency department visits and nearly 116000 outpatient visits each year. The emergency department houses more than 30 treatment bays. In addition Baptist Memphis' skilled nursing center includes 30 beds. The hospital also operates a 30-bed rehabilitation hospital and a 165000 sq. ft. heart institute for diagnostic and surgical cardiac care. The facility boasts advanced surgical systems including the CyberKnife radiation system for cancerous and non-cancerous tumor removal.

EXECUTIVES

Exec V Pres, David Hogan
Sr Vice Pres-Cfo*, Don Pounds
Exec V Pres*, Robert Gordon
Ceo*, Jason Little
Information, Dick Escue
Human Resources Representative, Larry Braughton
Scientist, Denitrea Palmer
Scientist, Mary Robison
Chief of Medicine, Mike Abutineh
Staff Pharmacist, Robert Smith
Food Director, Julie Craig

LOCATIONS

HQ: BAPTIST MEMORIAL HOSPITAL
6019 WALNUT GROVE RD, MEMPHIS, TN 381202113
Phone: 901 226-5000
Web: WWW.BAPTISTONLINE.ORG

COMPETITORS

Methodist Healthcare
Parkwest Medical Center
Shelby County Health Care
St. Jude Children's Research Hospital
Tenet Healthcare

HISTORICAL FINANCIALS

Company Type: Private

Income Statement — FYE: September 30

	REVENUE ($ mil.)	NET INCOME ($ mil.)	NET PROFIT MARGIN	EMPLOYEES
09/15	691	(1)	—	6,000
09/14	663	(47)	—	—
09/13	504	17	3.4%	—
09/12	697	15	2.2%	—
Annual Growth	(0.3%)	—	—	—

2015 Year-End Financials

Return on assets: (-0.2%)
Return on equity: (-0.5%)
Current ratio: 1.40
Cash ($ mil.): 28

BARCLAYS BANK DELAWARE

Spending money is a rewarding experience for holders of Barclays Bank Delaware cards. With co-branded credit cards from Barclays Bank Delaware (aka Barclays US) customers accumulate points that can be redeemed for air travel hotel stays and other perks. The company a division of Barclays issues Visa and MasterCard credit cards in addition to co-branded credit cards through partnerships with over 25 top companies including Priceline Choice Privileges Carnival World and JetBlue. Founded as Juniper Financial in 2000; it became a part of Barclays in 2004.

Operations

The company creates customized co-branded credit card programs for some of the country's most successful travel entertainment retail cash-back business expenses and financial institutions. Barclays also offer personal loans by invitation to some customers.

Geographic Reach

Barclays US is headquartered in Wilmington Delaware and has customers and clients across 40 countries.

Sales and Marketing

Barclays US collaborates with over 25 top companies to deliver an array of consumer and small business credit card programs uses partnerships to expand its business. Some of its major partners include Barnes & Noble Frontier Airlines Priceline.com Wyndham Holland America and Diamond Resorts World.

Strategy

Barclays US has been growing in recent years as the global economy improves and it continues to play a pivotal role in furthering innovation and shared growth for all as it evolves the future of banking.

Barclays US continues to focus on next-generation payment technology and digital safety for its customers. Its website and mobile app now utilize a new simplified log-in process to verify one's identity. It added a verification method a SecurPass code to help customers confirm their identity when they attempt to log in on an unknown device as well as Fraud Text Alerts that help protect customers' card in real time.

Company Background

In 1966 Barclays launches Barclaycard the first credit card in the UK. Following that year it introduces the world's first ATM. Barclays acquires Juniper Bank a credit card company formed in 2000 and creating Barclaycard US in 2004. In 2009 Barclaycard becomes a top-10 credit card issuer in the U.S. It launches the first mobile app for card members in 2011. In 2018 Barclaycard rebrands to Barclays in the U.S. offering a range of personal banking products to U.S. consumers.

EXECUTIVES

Managing Director Corporate Communications, Kevin M. Sullivan
Ceo, Amer Sajed
Cfo, Gerald (Jerry) Pavelich
Chief Credit Officer, Michael Mayer
Assistant Vp Strategic Cost Management, Glenn Watson
Vp Data Science And Advanced Analytics, Vishal Morde

LOCATIONS

HQ: BARCLAYS BANK DELAWARE
100 S WEST ST, WILMINGTON, DE 198015015
Phone: 302 255-8000
Web: WWW.BARCLAYCARDUS.COM

PRODUCTS/OPERATIONS

Selected Card Partnerships
Ameriprise
Bank Atlantic
Barnes & Noble
BJ's
Frontier
L.L. Bean
US Airways
Best Western
Priceline.com
Payless
Travelocity
Virgin America

COMPETITORS

Alliance Data Systems
American Express
Bank of America
Capital One
Citibank
Discover
JPMorgan Chase

HISTORICAL FINANCIALS

Company Type: Private

Income Statement — FYE: December 31

	ASSETS ($ mil.)	NET INCOME ($ mil.)	INCOME AS % OF ASSETS	EMPLOYEES
12/14	25,012	239	1.0%	349
12/13	19,055	331	1.7%	—
12/08	12,418	20	0.2%	—
12/07	7,470	0	—	—
Annual Growth	18.8%	—	—	—

2014 Year-End Financials

Return on assets: 1.0%
Return on equity: 7.5%
Sales ($ mil): 2,245

BARNABAS HEALTH, INC.

EXECUTIVES

Ceo-Pres, Barry Ostrowsky
Cao, Stephen Jones
Program Director, Anthony Carlino
Doctor, Isabel Roberti
Nurse, Lisa Depta
Administrative Assistant, Kelly Feteira
Director Neonatology, Shyan Sun
Purchasing Manager, Al Coleman
Diagnostic Radiologist, Alan Dembner
Internal Medicine, Alvin Bell
Director Information Technolog, Brian Keene

LOCATIONS

HQ: BARNABAS HEALTH, INC.
95 OLD SHORT HILLS RD, WEST ORANGE, NJ 070521008
Phone: 973 322-5000
Web: WWW.BARNABASHEALTH.ORG

HISTORICAL FINANCIALS

Company Type: Private

Income Statement — FYE: December 31

	REVENUE ($ mil.)	NET INCOME ($ mil.)	NET PROFIT MARGIN	EMPLOYEES
12/19	793	926	116.6%	24,600
12/18	730	(131)	—	—
12/17	624	293	47.0%	—
12/02	2,159	(92)	—	—
Annual Growth	(5.7%)	—	—	—

2019 Year-End Financials

Return on assets: 16.8%
Return on equity: 126.5%
Current ratio: 0.20
Cash ($ mil.): 777

BARNES & NOBLE, INC.

Barnes & Noble does business by the book and the NOOK. As one of the largest bookstore chains in the US it operates over 620 Barnes & Noble superstores in all 50 states and Washington DC. Stores range in size of stock between 19000 and 133000 book titles. It also sells books and other media online. The company's digital subsidiary NOOK Media develops supports and creates digital content and products for the digital reading and digital education markets. The struggling company has been restructuring for several years having spun off its education division among other initiatives. In 2019 Barnes & Noble was acquired by private equity firm Elliott Management.

Change in Company Type

In mid-2019 private equity firm Elliott Management bought Barnes & Noble for about $683 million including debt. The struggling bookseller had been exploring a possible sale since 2018 as one option to turn the company around. It has been hit hard by competition from Amazon which owns nearly half the market for new book sales.

Under Elliott's control newly private Barnes & Noble will have greater flexibility to restructure and make needed investments.

Operations

The Company's two operating segments are B&N Retail and NOOK.

The B&N retail segment includes almost 630 bookstores offering comprehensive trade book title base a café departments dedicated to Kids and Young Adults Toys & Games DVDs Music & Vinyl Gift Magazine and Bargain products. This segment includes the Company's e-Commerce website www.barnesandnoble.com and its publishing operation Sterling Publishing. This segment accounts for around 95% of the company's total sales in 2019.

NOOK represents the Company's digital business including the development and support of the Company's NOOK® product offerings. The digital business includes digital content such as eBooks digital newsstand and sales of NOOK® devices and accessories to B&N Retail. It accounts for about 5% of B&N sales.

Geographic Reach

New York-based Barnes & Noble owns two distribution centers one in Monroe Township New Jersey and another in Reno Nevada.

Its bookstores are scattered all over the United States.

Sales and Marketing

Barnes & Noble distributes its own books which enables direct purchasing by vendors rather than wholesalers. Using the Company's own distribution centers rather than wholesalers lowers distribution costs per unit increases inventory turns and improves product margins.

Additionally the Company believes its reinvigorated marketing efforts which include improved email campaigns and new advertising campaigns can help improve store traffic trends.

Financial Performance

For the past five years B&N's revenue growth showed a downward trend. Net income for the same period also fluctuated.

In fiscal 2019 the company reported revenue of $3.6 billion down 3% from the prior year. Sales for both the Retail and NOOK segments declined.

The company eeked out a profit of $3.8 million that year a significant improvement from the $125.5 million loss in fiscal 2018.

Cash at the end of fiscal 2019 was $9.4 million a decline of $1.3 million from the prior year. Cash from operations contributed $106 million to the coffers while investing activities used $113.7 million mainly for capital expenditures. Financing activities added $6.4 million as a result of proceeds from credit.

Strategy

To improve its performance the Company's strategic plan is focused on strengthening its core business by enhancing its customer value proposition; improving profitability through an aggressive expense management program which will be redeployed to fund growth initiatives; and innovating for the future which will position the Company for long-term growth.

To strengthen its core business the Company is focused on enhancing its customer value proposition by improving its merchandise offerings enriching the overall shopping experience increasing the value of its Membership Program and expanding its omni-channel capabilities. The Company will continue to leverage the strength of its Barnes & Noble brand knowledgeable booksellers vast book selection omni-channel offering (free Wi-Fi connectivity for NOOK customers) and retail footprint to attract customers and grow sales.

Company Background

Barnes & Noble dates back to 1873 when Charles Barnes went into the used-book business in Wheaton Illinois.

After growing organically and through acquisitions and changing hands several times Barnes & Noble – by then a booming book superstore chain – went public in 1993.

In 2019 after years of struggle brought on by online book giant Amazon and other retail headwinds Barnes & Noble was purchased by private equity firm Elliott Management.

HISTORY

Barnes & Noble dates back to 1873 when Charles Barnes went into the used-book business in Wheaton Illinois. By the turn of the century he was operating a thriving bookselling operation in Chicago. His son William took over as president in 1902. William sold his share in the firm in 1917 (to C. W. Follett who built Follett Corp.) and moved to New York City where he bought an interest in established textbook wholesalers Noble & Noble. The company was soon renamed Barnes & Noble. It first sold mainly to colleges and libraries providing textbooks and opening a large Fifth Avenue shop. Over the next three decades Barnes & Noble became one of the leading booksellers in the New York region.

Enter Leonard Riggio who worked at a New York University bookstore to help pay for night school. He studied engineering but got the itch for bookselling. In 1965 at age 24 he borrowed $5000 and opened Student Book Exchange NYC a college bookstore. Beginning in the late 1960s he expanded by buying other college bookstores.

In 1971 Riggio paid $1.2 million for the Barnes & Noble store on Fifth Avenue. He soon expanded the store and in 1974 he began offering jaw-dropping competitor-maddening discounts of up to 40% for best-sellers. Acquiring Marlboro Books five years later the company entered the mail-order and publishing business.

By 1986 Barnes & Noble had grown to about 180 outlets (including 142 college bookstores). Along with Dutch retailer Vendex that year it bought Dayton Hudson's B. Dalton mall bookstore chain (about 800 stores) forming BDB Holding Corp. (Vendex had sold its shares by 1997.) In 1989 the company acquired the Scribner's Bookstores trade name and the Bookstop/Bookstar superstore chain. BDB began its shift to superstore format and streamlined its operations to integrate Bookstop and Doubleday (acquired in 1990) into its business.

BDB changed its name to Barnes & Noble in 1991. With superstore sales booming the retailer went public in 1993 (the college stores remained private). It bought 20% of Canadian bookseller Chapters (now Indigo Books) in 1996 (sold in 1999).

The bookseller went online in 1997 and in 1998 sold a 50% stake in its Web operation subsidiary to Bertelsmann (which it re-purchased in 2003) in an attempt to strengthen both companies in the battle against online rival Amazon.com.

Also in 1998 Barnes & Noble agreed to buy #1 US book distributor Ingram Book Group but the deal was called off in 1999 because of antitrust concerns. Also in 1999 barnesandnoble.com went public and Barnes & Noble bought small book publisher J.B. Fairfax International USA which included coffee-table book publisher Michael Friedman Publishing Group. Later that year the company bought a 49% stake in book publishing portal iUniverse.com (later reduced to 22%). It also bought Riggio's financially struggling Babbage's Etc. a chain of about 500 Babbage's Software Etc. and GameStop stores for $215 million.

Subsidiary Babbage's Etc. (renamed GameStop Inc.) acquired video game retailer Funco for $161.5 million in 2000. In 2001 Barnes & Noble joined barnesandnoble.com in acquiring a majority stake in magazine subscription seller enews.com.

The company completed an IPO of its GameStop unit in 2003 reducing its ownership interest to about 63%. Leonard also handed over the CEO title to his brother Steve Riggio. Another development during that busy year included shutting down enews.com due to repeated quarterly losses.

In 2003 the company beefed up its self-publishing efforts with the purchase of Sterling Publishing a specialist in how-to and craft books. In addition Barnes & Noble's half-owned BOOK magazine shut down. The next year saw Barnes & Noble exit the video game retailing business when it spun off its remaining shares in GameStop.

In 2009 the firm sold its majority interest in Calendar Club for $7 million.

CEO Steve Riggio was replaced by William Lynch president of Barnes&Noble.com in 2010. Riggio remained chairman of the company. Barnes & Noble closed the last of its small-format B. Dalton bookstores in early 2010. (B. Dalton which once numbered more than 900 stores had been closing stores since 1989.) Later in the year hedge fund manager William Ackman offered to finance a $960 million merger of Barnes & Noble and its smaller rival Borders but nothing came of it.

CEO Lynch resigned in mid-2013 following an earnings report that underscored Barnes & Noble's failed attempt at building up its Nook division. CFO Michael Huseby was appointed chief executive of the Nook division and president of Barnes & Noble.

EXECUTIVES

Ceo And Director, Demos Parneros
Cfo, Allen W. Lindstrom, $545,385 total compensation
Evp Sterling Publishing, Theresa Thompson
Cio, William E. (Bill) Wood
Vp And Chief Digital Officer, Frederic D. (Fred) Argir, $378,846 total compensation
Vp Stores, Michael Ladd
Chief Merchandising Officer, Mary Amicucci
Executive Vice President, William Maloney
Vice President Internet Marketing, Mark Vottini
Vice President Of Marketing, Janine Juergensonn
Vice President Enterprise Operations, Jim Ferguson
Vice President Marketing, Deb Hallberg
Svp Corporate Communications And Public Affairs, Mary Ellen Keating
Chairman, Leonard S. (Len) Riggio
Auditors: ERNST & YOUNG LLP NEW YORK N

LOCATIONS

HQ: BARNES & NOBLE, INC.
122 5TH AVE FL 2, NEW YORK, NY 100115693
Phone: 212 633-3300
Web: WWW.BARNESANDNOBLEINC.COM

2018 Stores

	No.
California	69
Texas	51
Florida	39
New York	38
Illinois	26
Pennsylvania	26
Virginia	25
New Jersey	22
North Carolina	21
Other states	310
Total	**627**

PRODUCTS/OPERATIONS

2019 Sales

	$ mil.	% of total
Retail	3,481	97
NOOK	92	3
Adjustments	(21.3)	-
Total	**3,552**	**100**

COMPETITORS

Amazon.com
Apple Inc.
Books-A-Million
Buy.com
Costco Wholesale
Powell's Books
Target Corporation
Wal-Mart
eBay

HISTORICAL FINANCIALS

Company Type: Private

Income Statement — FYE: April 27

	REVENUE ($ mil.)	NET INCOME ($ mil.)	NET PROFIT MARGIN	EMPLOYEES
04/19	3,552	3	0.1%	24,000
04/18	3,662	(125)	—	—
04/17	3,894	22	0.6%	—
04/16	4,163	(24)	—	—
Annual Growth	(5.2%)	—	—	—

2019 Year-End Financials

Return on assets: 0.2%
Return on equity: 0.8%
Current ratio: 1.20
Cash ($ mil.): 9

BARNES-JEWISH HOSPITAL

LOCATIONS

HQ: BARNES-JEWISH HOSPITAL
1 B J HOSPITAL PLAZA DR, SAINT LOUIS, MO 63110
Phone: 314 747-3000
Web: WWW.BARNESJEWISH.COM

HISTORICAL FINANCIALS

Company Type: Private

Income Statement — FYE: December 31

	REVENUE ($ mil.)	NET INCOME ($ mil.)	NET PROFIT MARGIN	EMPLOYEES
12/15	1,726	68	4.0%	30
12/14	1,664	83	5.0%	—
Annual Growth	3.7%	(18.2%)	—	—

2015 Year-End Financials

Return on assets: 5.1%
Return on equity: 5.7%
Current ratio: 3.00
Cash ($ mil.): —

BARRICK ENTERPRISES, INC.

EXECUTIVES

President, Robert L Barrick
Auditors: CROSKEY LANNI PC ROCHESTER

LOCATIONS

HQ: BARRICK ENTERPRISES, INC.
4338 DELEMERE BLVD, ROYAL OAK, MI 480731876
Phone: 248 549-3737
Web: WWW.BARRICKENT.COM

HISTORICAL FINANCIALS

Company Type: Private

Income Statement				FYE: December 31
	REVENUE ($ mil.)	NET INCOME ($ mil.)	NET PROFIT MARGIN	EMPLOYEES
12/18	573	2	0.5%	35
12/17	534	0	0.1%	—
12/16	491	3	0.6%	—
12/15	552	3	0.7%	—
Annual Growth	1.2%	(8.8%)	—	—

2018 Year-End Financials

Return on assets: 8.5%
Return on equity: 11.4%
Current ratio: 2.00
Cash ($ mil.): 10

BARRY-WEHMILLER GROUP, INC.

With Barry-Wehmiller you get the whole package. The company manufactures and supplies packaging corrugating paper converting filling and labeling automation equipment for a broad range of industries. It conducts business around the world through nine operating companies that together own about 90 subsidiaries such as Accraply (labeling machinery) Design Group (automation and control systems) Winkler and Dunnebier (postage services and paper towels) and Synerlink (ultra-clean packaging for milk products and desserts). Other divisions manufacture paper converting machinery and offer engineering/design consulting services. Berry-Wehmiller is privately owned by the Chapman family who took over from Fred Wehmiller in 1963.

Operations

Barry-Wehmiller's operations comprise four segments and nine divisions: BW Packaging Systems (Accraply BW Flexible Systems BW Integrated systems Pneumatic Scale Angelus and Synerlink); BW Paper Systems Platform (BW Papersystems); BW Converting Platform (Paper Converting Machine Company and Winkler + D nnebier); and BW Engineering and IT Consulting (Design Group).

Geographic Reach

St. Louis-based Barry-Wehmiller has operations in about 30 countries in some 100-plus locations spanning Asia Australia Europe and the Americas.

Sales and Marketing

Barry-Wehmiller's manufacturing technology and services serve a wide range of industries including packaging paper converting sheeting corrugating engineering and IT consulting.

Strategy

Barry-Wehmiller's mantra is expansion through organic growth and acquisitions. The company has purchased more than 95 companies over approximately 25 years creating a mosaic of time and money-saving products and services in locations around the globe. In the same vein its businesses' operations are built upon lean manufacturing practices whereby employees are empowered and resources optimized to contribute to the end product's value.

Barry-Wehmiller rationalized its messy list of subsidiaries which included confusing legacy brands like FleetwoodWydardGoldco and PneumaticScaleAngelus. Their branding was brought under Barry-Wehmiller's nine divisions and four "platforms."

Company Background

Originally a provider of conveying equipment to St. Louis malt houses Barry-Wehmiller was founded by Thomas Barry and Alfred Wehmiller in 1885. Ownership passed from the Wehmiller family to the Chapman family in 1963 and the Chapmans continue as the majority owners.

EXECUTIVES

Chairman And Ceo, Robert H. (Bob) Chapman
Vp And Cfo, James W. (Jim) Lawson
Cio, Craig Hergenroether
President, Tim Sullivan
Vice President Senior Partner _ Product Development Solutions, James Webb
Corporate Vice President Global Supply Chain, Mark Green
Vice President Global It For The Packaging Platform, Jim Southwick
Vp Of Finance, William Kuhn
Senior Vice President, Richard George
Auditors: ERNST & YOUNG LLP

LOCATIONS

HQ: BARRY-WEHMILLER GROUP, INC.
8020 FORSYTH BLVD, SAINT LOUIS, MO 631051707
Phone: 314 862-8000
Web: WWW.BARRYWEHMILLER.COM

PRODUCTS/OPERATIONS

Selected Operations

BW Engineering and IT Consulting
- Design Group

BW Converting Platform
- Paper Converting Machine Company (PCMC)
- Winkler +

BW Packaging Systems
- Accraply Inc. (packaging label machinery)
- PneumaticScaleAngelus (fillers cappers seamers and labelers)
- BW Flexible Systems
- BW Integrated Systems
- Synerlink

BW Papersystems

COMPETITORS

Bradman Lake
Gilbreth
Industria Macchine Automatiche
Kl ¶ckner-Werke
STT Enviro
Sencorp Inc
Tetra Laval
Traco Manufacturing

HISTORICAL FINANCIALS

Company Type: Private

Income Statement				FYE: September 30
	REVENUE ($ mil.)	NET INCOME ($ mil.)	NET PROFIT MARGIN	EMPLOYEES
09/19	2,856	77	2.7%	4,500
09/18	3,037	85	2.8%	—
09/11	1,240	0	—	—
09/10	1,097	0	—	—
Annual Growth	11.2%	—	—	—

2019 Year-End Financials

Return on assets: 4.0%
Return on equity: 17.6%
Current ratio: 1.40
Cash ($ mil.): 199

BARTON MALOW COMPANY

Barton Malow scores by building end zones and home plates. The construction management and general contracting firm which has built its share of sporting facilities also focuses on projects such as schools hospitals offices and plants. Across the eastern US and Mexico the company offers design/build and program management services ranging from the pre-planning stage to completion. Projects have included the Detroit Institute of Arts and Cultural Center and the Baltimore Orioles stadium. Affiliate Barton Malow Design provides architecture and engineering services while Barton Malow Rigging installs process equipment and machinery. Carl Osborn Barton founded the employee-owned firm as C.O. Barton Company in 1924.

Operations

Barton Malow is a general contractor and construction manager. It provides a variety of building services including building information modeling (BIM) planning & scheduling service conceptual and hard dollar estimating services. It specializes in several areas such as routine boiler installation & service foundation & architectural concrete forming machinery moving & equipment installation and procurement & erection of steel building framework.

The company addresses niche markets in its geography focusing on energy health industrial and sports industries along with K-12 education and government institutions.

Geographic Reach

Michigan-based Barton Malow operates about a dozen offices in the eastern third of the US. It also has an office in San Luis Potosi Mexico.

Financial Performance

A private company Barton Malow provides little financial information. However Forbes Magazine estimates its revenue to be $2.4 billion in 2016.

Strategy

Headquartered in a Detroit suburb Barton Malow has historically maintained a healthy relationship with the steel and auto industries. It is somewhat atypical in that it maintains a staff of workers to perform its trade-based services as with boiler servicing and steel erection; other firms commonly hire out such work.

In 2017 the company received a Best Projects award from trade magazine Engineering News-Record (ENR) for its work on a MATS (Mercury and Air Toxics Standards) compliance project with energy client DTE Energy. In that same year the company completed a complete redesign of Bloomfield Hills (Michigan) High School which involved a partial demolition and partial renovation of existing structures and the design and buildout of a new open-plan educational campus.

EXECUTIVES

Evp And Corporate Secretary, Doug Maibach
Chairman And Ceo, Ben C. Maibach
Vp Central Region, Michael (Mike) Stobak
Vp Central Region, Todd Ketola
Svp Eastern Region, Phil Kirby
Vp Eastern Region And Virginia, Carrie Shaeffer
Vp Florida, David Price
Vp National Sports, Len Moser
President, Ryan Maibach
General Manager Quality Concrete, Chuck Binkowski
Svp And Cfo, Michael Dishaw
Vp Health Facilities, Rod Creach

Vp Central Region, Dan Kovoch
Vice President, Jennifer Brown
Vice President, Joe Benvenuto
Vice President, Matt Lentini
Senior Vice President, Bob Grottenthaler
Vice President, Sheryl Maibach
Executive Vice President, Rick Vanderpoel
Auditors: PRICEWATERHOUSECOOPERS LLP DE

LOCATIONS

HQ: BARTON MALOW COMPANY
26500 AMERICAN DR, SOUTHFIELD, MI 480342252
Phone: 248 436-5000
Web: WWW.BARTONMALOW.COM

Selected Locations

Atlanta

Baltimore

Charlottesville

Chicago

Columbus

Fairfax

Jacksonville
Oak Park
Orlando
Richmond
Southfield

PRODUCTS/OPERATIONS

Selcted Services
Architecture and planning
Building Information Management (BIM)
Concrete trade services
Construction management
Design/build
Facility audits
Facility services
Administration
Engineering
Maintenance repair and operations
General contracting
Interior design
Interior trade services
Preconstruction
Program management
Rigging
Special projects
Technology consulting

COMPETITORS

Alberici
Clark Enterprises
Gilbane
H.J. Russell
Hensel Phelps Construction
Hunt Construction
KBR Building Group
M. A. Mortenson
McCarthy Building
Miron Construction
Skanska USA Building
Turner Corporation
Walbridge Aldinger
Walsh Group
Whiting-Turner

HISTORICAL FINANCIALS

Company Type: Private

Income Statement — FYE: March 31

	REVENUE ($ mil.)	NET INCOME ($ mil.)	NET PROFIT MARGIN	EMPLOYEES
03/20	1,971	11	0.6%	1,600
03/19	1,634	8	0.5%	—
03/18	2,502	11	0.4%	—
03/17	2,361	0	0.0%	—
Annual Growth	(5.8%)	202.9%	—	—

2020 Year-End Financials

Return on assets: 1.7%
Return on equity: 15.3%
Current ratio: 1.10
Cash ($ mil.): 94

BARTON MALOW ENTERPRISES, INC.

EXECUTIVES

Pres, Benjamin C Maibach III
SEC-Exec V Pres, Douglas L Maibach
Treas-Cfo, Michael F Dishaw
V Pres, Ronald J Torbert
Dir, Sheryl B Maibach
Senior Vice President Sports F, Harvey Oliva
Project Accountant, Jim Morse
Vice President, Lars Luedeman
Marketing Coordinator, Eliot Dolgin
Project Engineer, Gretchen Stadler
Safety Manager, Anthony Allam
Auditors: PRICEWATERHOUSECOOPERS LLP DE

LOCATIONS

HQ: BARTON MALOW ENTERPRISES, INC.
26500 AMERICAN DR, SOUTHFIELD, MI 480342252
Phone: 248 436-5000
Web: WWW.BARTONMALOW.COM

HISTORICAL FINANCIALS

Company Type: Private

Income Statement — FYE: March 31

	REVENUE ($ mil.)	NET INCOME ($ mil.)	NET PROFIT MARGIN	EMPLOYEES
03/20	1,972	19	1.0%	2,000
03/18	2,502	18	0.7%	—
03/17	2,361	14	0.6%	—
03/16	1,777	9	0.6%	—
Annual Growth	2.6%	17.6%	—	—

2020 Year-End Financials

Return on assets: 2.6%
Return on equity: 17.1%
Current ratio: 1.10
Cash ($ mil.): 111

BASIN ELECTRIC POWER COOPERATIVE

Ranges at home on the range depend on Basin Electric Power Cooperative as do other electric-powered items in nine states from Montana to Iowa to New Mexico. The consumer-owned power generation and transmission co-op provides power to 138 rural electric member systems which serve about 2.8 million people. It had generating capacity of 5478 MW (mostly coal-fired) in 2014. Basin Electric's subsidiaries include Dakota Gasification (which produces natural gas from coal) Dakota Coal (markets lignite and limestone) Basin Telecommunications (Internet access) Basin Co-operative Services (property management) PrairieWinds (wind power) and Souris Valley Pipeline (CO2 pipeline).

Operations

The company maintains about 2250 miles of high-voltage transmission 70 switchyards and about 150 telecommunication locations. It generates about 990 MW for participants in the Missouri Basin Power Project (a group of six regional consumer-owned energy entities that built the Laramie River Station in Wyoming). Its generation portfolio includes 4913 MW of wholesale electric generating capacity.

Geographic Reach

Basin Electric serves customers in Colorado Iowa Minnesota Montana Nebraska New Mexico North Dakota South Dakota and Wyoming. The enterprise's generation facilities are located in Iowa Minnesota Montana North Dakota South Dakota and Wyoming.

Financial Performance

In 2013 Basin Electric's revenues grew by 12% due to higher members sales as a result of an increase in higher electricity resales.

The coop's net income decreased by 62% that year as the result of to higher operating expenses caused by an increase in depreciation and amortizations.

The company's operating cash inflow decreased to $306.56 million in 2013 (from $354.18 million in 2012) due to lower net income and a change in working capital as a result of higher customer account receivables and inventories.

Strategy

Basin Electric like all power utilities is under regulatory pressure to lower the carbon emissions from its power production. As part of its commitment to cleaner energy production the company has established two wind power subsidiaries to build wind farms in the Dakotas.

In 2013 Basin Electric signed two power purchase agreements with California-based Infinity Wind Power associated with the development of two new wind projects in North Dakota with a combined capacity is 278 MW.

Company Background

The company generated 437 MW of its total capacity of 482 MW of renewable energy in 2012 from wind power sources. That year about 16% of Basin Electric's generating capacity came from renewable sources.

In 2011 Basin Electric opened the Crow Lake Wind Project (Nebraska) its largest renewable project to date with 162 MW of power generating capacity. Basin Electric's operations are overseen by a 10-member board of directors elected by and representing individual membership districts. Dakota Gasification and Dakota Coal have separate boards.

The not-for-profit generation and transmission cooperative was formed in 1961.

EXECUTIVES

Coo And Svp Dakota Coal Company And Montana Limestone Company, Robert J. Bartosh
Svp Financial Services And Cfo, Paul Sukut
Svp Transmission, Michael Risan
Coo And Svp Dakota Gasification Company, Dave Sauer
Svp Generation, Matt Greek
Vp Marketing And Trading, Kenneth S. Rutter
Vice President Basin Electric Board, Kermit Pearson
President Basin Electric Board, Wayne Peltier
Auditors: DELOITTE & TOUCHE LLP MINNEAP

LOCATIONS

HQ: BASIN ELECTRIC POWER COOPERATIVE
1717 E INTERSTATE AVE, BISMARCK, ND 585030564
Phone: 701 223-0441
Web: WWW.BASINELECTRIC.COM

PRODUCTS/OPERATIONS

2013 Power Generation Fuel Mix

	% of total
Coal	60
Renewables	15
Natural gas	14
Hydro	6
Oil	4
Nuclear	1
Total	**100**

2012 Sales

	% of total
Utility	62
Synthetic gas	13
Lignite coal	7
Byproducts co-products & other	18
Total	**100**

Regional Member Cooperatives

Regional Member Cooperatives
Central Montana Electric Power Cooperative (District 6)
Beartooth Electric Cooperative (Red Lodge MT)
Big Flat Electric Cooperative (Malta MT)
Fergus Electric Cooperative (Lewistown MT)
Hill County Electric Cooperative (Havre MT)
Marias River Electric Cooperative (Shelby MT)
Mid-Yellowstone Valley Electric Cooperative (Hysham MT)
Northern Electric Cooperative (Opheim MT)
Park Electric Cooperative (Livingston MT)
Sun River Electric Cooperative (Fairfield MT)
Tongue River Electric Cooperative (Ashland MT)
Valley Electric Cooperative (Glasgow MT)
Vigilante Electric Cooperative (Dillon MT)
Yellowstone Valley Electric Cooperative (Huntley MT)
Central Power Electric Cooperative (District 3)
Capital Electric Cooperative (Bismarck ND)
Dakota Valley Electric Cooperative (Milnor ND)
McLean Electric Cooperative (Garrison ND)
North Central Electric Cooperative (Bottineau ND)
Northern Plains Electric Cooperative (Carrington ND)
Verendrye Electric Cooperative (Velva ND)
Corn Belt Power Cooperative (Humboldt IA)
District 9
Grand Electric Cooperative (Bison SD)
KEM Electric Cooperative (Linton ND)
Minnesota Valley Cooperative Light & Power Association (Montevideo MN)
Mor-Gran-Sou Electric Cooperative (Flasher ND)
Oliver-Mercer Electric Cooperative (Hazen ND)
Rosebud Electric Cooperative (Gregory SD)
Wright-Hennepin Cooperative Electric Association (Rockford MN)
Wyoming Municipal Power Agency (Lusk WY)
East River Electric Power Cooperative (District 1)
Bon Homme-Yankton Electric Association (Tabor SD)
Central Electric Cooperative
Charles Mix Electric Association (Lake Andes SD)
Clay-Union Electric Corp. (Vermillion SD)
Codington-Clark Electric Cooperative (Watertown SD)
Dakota Energy Cooperative (Huron SD)
Douglas Electric Cooperative (Armour SD)
FEM Electric Association (Ipswich SD)
H-D Electric Cooperative (Clear Lake SD)
Kingsbury Electric Cooperative (De Smet SD)
Lake Region Electric Association (Webster SD)
Lyon-Lincoln Electric Cooperative (Tyler MN)
McCook Electric Cooperative (Salem SD)
Northern Electric Cooperative (Bath SD)
Oahe Electric Cooperative (Blunt SD)
Renville-Sibley Cooperative Power Association (Danube MN)
Sioux Valley-Southwestern Cooperative (Colman SD)
Southeastern Electric Cooperative (Marion SD)
Traverse Electric Cooperative (Wheaton MN)
Union County Electric Cooperative (Elk Point SD)
Whetstone Valley Electric Cooperative (Milbank SD)
Flathead Electric Cooperative (Kalispell MT)
L & O Power Cooperative (District 2)
Lyon Rural Electric Cooperative (Rock Rapids IA)
Osceola Electric Cooperative (Sibley IA)
Northwest Iowa Power Cooperative (NIPCO) (District 4)
Harrison County Electric Cooperative (Woodbine)
Iowa Lakes Electric Cooperative (Estherville)
Nishnabotna Valley Rural Electric Cooperative (Harlan)
North West Rural Electric Cooperative (Orange City)
Western Iowa Municipal Electric Association (Manning)
Western Iowa Power Cooperative
Woodbury County Rural Electric Cooperative (Moville)
Powder River Energy Corp. (District 10 Sundance WY)
Rushmore Electric Power Cooperative (District 7)
Butte Electric Cooperative (Newell SD)
Cam Wal Electric Cooperative (Selby SD)
Cherry-Todd Electric Cooperative (Mission SD)
Lacreek Electric Association (Martin SD)
Moreau-Grand Electric Cooperative (Timber Lake SD)
West Central Electric Cooperative (Murdo SD)
West River Electric Association (Wall SD)
Tri-State Generation and Transmission Association (District 5)
Big Horn Rural Electric Co. (Basin WY)
Carbon Power & Light (Saratoga WY)
Central New Mexico Electric Cooperative (Mountainair NM)
Chimney Rock Public Power District (Bayard NE)
Columbus Electric Cooperative (Deming NM)
Delta-Montrose Electric Association (Delta CO)
Empire Electric Association (Cortez CO)
Garland Light & Power Co. (Powell WY)
Gunnison County Electric Association (Gunnison CO)
Highline Electric Association (Holyoke CO)
High Plains Power Inc. (Thermopolis and Riverton WY)
High West Energy (Pine Bluffs WY)
Jemez Mountains Electric Cooperative (Hernandez NM)
K. C. Electric Association (Hugo CO)
Kit Carson Electric Cooperative (Taos NM)
La Plata Electric Association (Durango CO)
Midwest Electric Cooperative Corp. (Grant NE)
Morgan County Rural Electric Association (Fort Morgan CO)
Mountain Parks Electric (Granby CO)
Mountain View Electric Association (Limon CO)
Niobrara Electric Association (Lusk WY)
Northern Rio Arriba Electric Cooperative (Chama NM)
Northwest Rural Public Power District (Hay Springs NE)
Panhandle Rural Electric Membership Association (Alliance NE)
Poudre Valley Rural Electric Association (Fort Collins CO)
Roosevelt Public Power District (Mitchell NE)
San Isabel Electric Association (Pueblo CO)
San Luis Valley Rural Electric Cooperative (Monte Vista CO)
San Miguel Power Association (Nucla CO)
Sangre De Cristo Electric Association (Buena Vista CO)
Sierra Electric Cooperative Inc. (Elephant Butte NM)
Southeast Colorado Power Association (La Junta)
Springer Electric Cooperative (Springer MN)
United Power (Brighton CO)
Wheat Belt Public Power District (Sidney NE)
Wheatland Rural Electric Association (Wheatland WY)
White River Electric Association (Meeker CO)
Wyrulec Co. (Lingle WY)
Y-W Electric Association (Akron CO)
Upper Missouri Generation and Transmission Electric Cooperative (District 8)
Burke-Divide Electric Cooperative (Columbus ND)
Goldenwest Electric Cooperative (Wibaux MT)
Lower Yellowstone Rural Electric Association (Sidney MT)
McCone Electric Cooperative (Circle MT)
McKenzie Electric Cooperative (Watford City ND)
Mountrail-Williams Electric Cooperative (Williston ND)
Sheridan Electric Cooperative (Medicine Lake MT)
Slope Electric Cooperative (New England ND)
Southeast Electric Cooperative (Ekalaka MT)
West Plains Electric Cooperative (Dickinson ND)
????

COMPETITORS

Alliant Energy
Berkshire Hathaway Energy
Black Hills
MDU Resources
Nebraska Public Power
NorthWestern
Omaha Public Power
Otter Tail
Xcel Energy

HISTORICAL FINANCIALS

Company Type: Private

Income Statement — FYE: December 31

	REVENUE ($ mil.)	NET INCOME ($ mil.)	NET PROFIT MARGIN	EMPLOYEES
12/19	2,253	76	3.4%	1,579
12/18	2,436	64	2.6%	—
12/17	2,112	72	3.4%	—
12/16	1,561	54	3.5%	—
Annual Growth	13.0%	12.0%	—	—

2019 Year-End Financials

Return on assets: 1.0%
Return on equity: 5.1%
Current ratio: 1.00
Cash ($ mil.): 154

BATTELLE MEMORIAL INSTITUTE

EXECUTIVES

BR Mgr, Jeffrey Wadsworth
Geologist, Joel Main
Researcher, Anthony Gutierrez
Research Scientist, Stephanie Eastwood
Research Scientist, Thomas Vinci
Program Manager, William Burke
Research Engineer, Charles Miele
Research In Public Health Lead, Marcia Nishioka
Research Leader, Richard Davis
Closeout Analyst, Olivia Bunders
Auditors: DELOITTE & TOUCHE LLP COLUMBU

LOCATIONS

HQ: BATTELLE MEMORIAL INSTITUTE
2555 INTERNATIONAL ST, COLUMBUS, OH 432284604
Phone: 800 201-2011
Web: WWW.BATTELLE.ORG

HISTORICAL FINANCIALS

Company Type: Private

Income Statement — FYE: September 30

	REVENUE ($ mil.)	NET INCOME ($ mil.)	NET PROFIT MARGIN	EMPLOYEES
09/14	4,775	(95)	—	20,000
09/13	4,795	(7)	—	—
09/12	5,228	(20)	—	—
Annual Growth	(4.4%)	—	—	—

2014 Year-End Financials

Return on assets: 2.7%
Return on equity: (-2.0%)
Current ratio: 0.70
Cash ($ mil.): 117

BAYHEALTH MEDICAL CENTER, INC.

EXECUTIVES

Pres, Terry Murphy
Warehouse Manager, David Webb
Health Care Director, Nadine Pieniaszek
Physician, James Everette
Family Practice, Kenny Vu
Director of Orthopedic, Stephen Manifold
MD, Zi Xu
Public Relations, Leigh Coleman
Chief Information Officer, Lynn Gold
Chief Operations Officer, Mike Metzing
Network Engineer, Kevin Seiwell
Auditors: GRANT THORNTON LLP PHILADELPH

LOCATIONS

HQ: BAYHEALTH MEDICAL CENTER, INC.
640 S STATE ST, DOVER, DE 199013530
Phone: 302 422-3311
Web: WWW.BAYHEALTH.ORG

HISTORICAL FINANCIALS

Company Type: Private

Income Statement — FYE: June 30

	REVENUE ($ mil.)	NET INCOME ($ mil.)	NET PROFIT MARGIN	EMPLOYEES
06/20	725	35	4.9%	2,790
06/19	677	58	8.7%	—
06/18	615	87	14.2%	—
06/17	583	86	14.9%	—
Annual Growth	7.5%	(25.7%)	—	—

2020 Year-End Financials

Return on assets: 2.6%
Return on equity: 3.8%
Current ratio: 1.30
Cash ($ mil.): 151

BAYLOR SCOTT & WHITE HOLDINGS

EXECUTIVES

Ceo, Jim Hinton
ADM, Jared Kastriner
Auditors: PRICEWATERHOUSECOOPERS LLP DA

LOCATIONS

HQ: BAYLOR SCOTT & WHITE HOLDINGS
301 N WASHINGTON AVE, DALLAS, TX 752461754
Phone: 214 820-3151
Web: WWW.BSWHEALTH.COM

HISTORICAL FINANCIALS

Company Type: Private

Income Statement — FYE: June 30

	REVENUE ($ mil.)	NET INCOME ($ mil.)	NET PROFIT MARGIN	EMPLOYEES
06/17	9,084	630	6.9%	1
06/15	7,535	356	4.7%	—
Annual Growth	9.8%	33.0%	—	—

2017 Year-End Financials

Return on assets: 5.7%
Return on equity: 11.6%
Current ratio: 2.00
Cash ($ mil.): 1,189

BAYLOR UNIVERSITY

Don't mess with Texas and don't mess around at Baylor University. The world's largest Baptist institution of higher learning requires its more than 15000 students to follow a strict code of conduct. The university has approximately 150 undergraduate degree programs as well as about 75 masters and more than 30 doctoral programs. With a student-to-faculty ratio of 15:1 the private co-educational university also offers degrees from its law school (juris doctor) and theological seminary (master of divinity and doctor of ministry) as well as extensive research programs. Founded in 1845 the college is affiliated with the Baptist General Convention of Texas.

EXECUTIVES

Assistant Vice President Of Operations, Sandra Lene
Auditors: GRANT THORNTON LLP DALLAS TX

LOCATIONS

HQ: BAYLOR UNIVERSITY
700 S UNIV PKS DR STE 67, WACO, TX 767061003
Phone: 254 710-1561
Web: WWW.BAYLOR.EDU

PRODUCTS/OPERATIONS

Selected Colleges and Schools

College of Arts and Sciences
George W. Truett Theological Seminary
Graduate School
Hankamer School of Business
Honors College
Law School
Louise Herrington School of Nursing
School of Education
School of Engineering and Computer Science
School of Music
School of Social Work

Selected Institutes

Allbritton Art Institute
Institute for Air Science
Institute for Faith and Learning
Institute for Oral History
Institute of Biblical and Related Languages
Institute of Biomedical Studies
J. M. Dawson Institute of Church-State Studies

HISTORICAL FINANCIALS

Company Type: Private

Income Statement — FYE: May 31

	REVENUE ($ mil.)	NET INCOME ($ mil.)	NET PROFIT MARGIN	EMPLOYEES
05/20	791	142	18.0%	2,500
05/19	710	19	2.8%	—
05/18	674	96	14.3%	—
05/16	656	(20)	—	—
Annual Growth	4.8%	—	—	—

2020 Year-End Financials

Return on assets: 4.8%
Return on equity: 6.8%
Current ratio: —
Cash ($ mil.): 228

BAYLOR UNIVERSITY MEDICAL CENTER

Baylor University Medical Center at Dallas is the flagship institution of the Baylor Health Care System. The medical center (known as Baylor Dallas) serves more than 300000 patients annually with more than 1000 inpatient beds and some 1200 physicians. It offers general medical and surgical services to specialty care in a wide range of fields including oncology cardiovascular disease and neuroscience. The hospital also features a Level I trauma center neonatal ICU and organ transplantation center. Founded in 1903 the Baylor Dallas campus includes the Charles A. Sammons Cancer Center and the Baylor Research Institute which conducts basic and clinical research across numerous medical specialties.

Operations

The Baylor University Medical Center campus consists of 20 specialty centers for treating a range of medical conditions. Primary facilities include the Charles A. Sammons Cancer Center Neuroscience Center Annette C. and Harold C. Simmons Transplant Institute James M. and Dorothy D. Collins Womens and Children's Center and the George Truett James Orthopaedic Institute as well as a top trauma center digestive care program and heart and vascular unit. The Heart and Vascular Institute conducts more than 50 research studies a year.

Strategy

The hospital received a boost in 2011 when Texas A&M's Health Science Center struck an affiliation with Baylor Health Care System. The two parties agreed to make Baylor Dallas a primary teaching hospital for A&M's third and fourth-year medical students. No hospital in the Baylor Health Care System held such a designation after it became independent from Baylor University in 1997.

As one of only two adult Level 1 trauma centers in the region Baylor Dallas has worked to bolster its emergency services to keep up with increasing demand. To this end it has broadened its Level 1 trauma capabilities increased the size of its minor emergency care area and added more patient care areas. The Riggs Emergency Department treats some 67000 patients each year.

Baylor Dallas' transplant program is considered a national leader in solid organ transplantation and in partnership with the program at Baylor All Saints Medical Center is one of only three programs worldwide to have performed more than 3000 adult liver transplants. The program is also known for its kidney pancreas heart and lung small bowel and blood and marrow transplants.

EXECUTIVES

Vice President Finance Decision Support Services, Lavone Neal

LOCATIONS

HQ: BAYLOR UNIVERSITY MEDICAL CENTER
2001 BRYAN ST STE 2200, DALLAS, TX 752013024
Phone: 214 820-3151
Web: WWW.BSWHEALTH.MED

Selected Locations

A. Webb Roberts Hospital
Baylor Charles A. Sammons Cancer Center
Baylor Jack and Jane Hamilton Heart and Vascular Hospital
Carr P. Collins Hospital
Erik and Margaret Jonsson Medical and Surgical Hospital
George W. Truett Memorial Hospital
Karl and Esther Hoblitzelle Memorial Hospital
Baylor Specialty Hospital
Our Children's House at Baylor

PRODUCTS/OPERATIONS

Selected Speciality Centers

Baylor Cancer Hospital
Baylor Center for Pain Management
Baylor Diagnostic Imaging Centers
Baylor George Truett James Orthopaedic Institute
Baylor Geriatric and Senior Center
Baylor Heart and Vascular Institute
Baylor Heart Failure Program
Baylor Motion and Sports Performance Center
Baylor Neuroscience Center
Baylor Radiosurgery Center
Baylor Ruth Collins Diabetes Center
Baylor Sammons Bone Tumor Center
Baylor Sammons Lung Cancer Center
Baylor Spine Center
Baylor SportsCare
Comprehensive Wound Center

Darlene G. Cass Women's Imaging Center
Digestive Care Services
Ernie's Appearance Center
Gastrointestinal and Endoscopy Laboratory
Hereditary Cancer Risk Program
Infectious Disease Center
James M. and Dorothy D. Collins Women and Children's Center
Kimberly H. Courtwright and Joseph W. Summers Institute of Metabolic Disease
Louise Gartner Center for Hyperbaric Medicine
Martha Foster Lung Care Center
Non-invasive Heart and Vascular Laboratory
Reuben H. Adams Family Health Center
Simply Mom's Mother and Baby Boutique
Sleep Center
TINY TOTS Clinic
Virginia R. Cvetko Cancer Patient Education Center
Visual Function Testing Center
W.H. and Peggy Smith Baylor Sammons Breast Center
Weight Loss Surgery Program

COMPETITORS

CHRISTUS Health
Children's Medical Center of Dallas
Dynacq Healthcare
Harris Methodist Fort Worth Hospital
Parkland Health & Hospital System
Presbyterian Hospital of Dallas
Southwestern Medical Center
Texas Health Denton
Texas Health Resources
The Methodist Health System

HISTORICAL FINANCIALS

Company Type: Private

Income Statement FYE: June 30

	REVENUE ($ mil.)	NET INCOME ($ mil.)	NET PROFIT MARGIN	EMPLOYEES
06/15	1,394	378	27.2%	5,003
06/09	1,072	0	—	—
06/08	155	16	10.3%	—
06/06	937	114	12.2%	—
Annual Growth	4.5%	14.3%	—	—

2015 Year-End Financials

Return on assets: 18.8%
Return on equity: 19.5%
Current ratio: 3.10
Cash ($ mil.): —

BAYSTATE HEALTH INC.

Baystate Medical Center is the flagship facility of the not-for-profit Baystate Health System. It is a tertiary care facility and Level I trauma center that provides comprehensive acute care services to residents of Springfield Massachusetts and the surrounding region. The more than 700-bed medical center is also a teaching hospital serving as a secondary campus for Tufts University School of Medicine. The Baystate Medical Center campus includes Baystate Children's Hospital a 110-bed/57-bassinette unit that boasts neonatal and pediatric ICUs. Other Baystate Medical Center operations include specialty programs in radiology cardiac care cancer and neurology.

Operations

As the only Level I trauma center in western Massachusetts Baystate Medical Center is responsible for treating the most critical and urgent cases in the region. The hospital is also home to the second-busiest emergency department in the state. Along with performing its own research activities Baystate Medical Center collaborates with the University of Massachusetts Amherst on biomedical technology research projects through the Pioneer Valley Life Sciences Institute. The center is home to one of only about 40 American College of Surgeons-accredited Level I Comprehensive Education Institutes in the world.

Other Baystate Health System facilities include Baystate Franklin Medical Center and Baystate Mary Lane Hospital.

Strategy

In partnership with nine other area not-for-profit hospitals Baystate Medical Center is working to improve its region's access to health care services and overall well-being. Social and economic factors impeding access to care include the community's poverty levels poor housing conditions and lack of transportation. Health conditions include high rates of obesity diabetes asthma and cardiovascular disease as well as the growing incidence of opioid overdoses. The coalition of hospitals aims to improve matters by working together combining resources to increase care capabilities.

EXECUTIVES

President And Ceo, Mark A. Keroack
Svp Coo And Chief Nursing Officer, Nancy Shendell-Falik
Medical Director Emergency Department, Rakesh Talati
Medical Director, Kathleen Mahoney
Medical Director Hospital Medicine, Venkatrao Medarametla
Vice President, Chris Shirtcliff
Vice President, Paul Judd
Vice President, Neil Kudler
Vice President Diagnostic Services, Jason Newmark
Director Of Pharmacy, Aaron J Michelucci
Vice President Marketing, Walter Hollihan
Senior Vice President Human Resources, Paula Squires
Vice President Of Information Technology, Philip Lacombe
Trustee Senior Vice President Med Affairs, Loring Flint
Director Of Nursing, Townsend Vernette
Senior Vice President Division Academic Affairs, Paul Friedmann
Medical Director, Boos Stephen
Medical Director, Julio Martinez-silvestrini
Medical Director, Andrew Fay
Vice President Clinical Informatics And Re Engineering, Joan Sullivan
Vice President Strategic Accounts, Odonnell Marleen
Vice President, Lisa Demko
Vice President Strategic Planning And Business Development, Jean Ahn
Vice President Human Resources Business Partners, LouAnn Muir
Vice President Marketing And Communications, Suzanne Hendery
Associate Medical Director, Anant Shenoy
Medical Director, Dan Engelman
Vice President Human Resources, Beverly Fein
Director Of Health Information Management, Walter Houlinan
Vice President Regulatory Affair, Fabrizio Pluchino
Vice President, Randi Nichols
Director Of Radiology Services, Lynda Zukowski
Medical Director, Bruce Tallman
Nursing Director, Madonna Weiland
Treasurer, Kieth Mclean-shinaman
Secretary, Nancy Melanson
Auditors: DELOITTE & TOUCHE LLP BOSTON

LOCATIONS

HQ: BAYSTATE HEALTH INC.
759 CHESTNUT ST, SPRINGFIELD, MA 011991001
Phone: 413 794-0000
Web: WWW.BAYSTATEHEALTH.ORG

PRODUCTS/OPERATIONS

Selected Programs and Services

Baystate Children's Hospital
Baystate Heart & Vascular Program
Baystate Regional Cancer Program
Department of Surgery
Regional Sleep Program
Women's Health

COMPETITORS

Berkshire Health Systems
Boston Medical Center
CareGroup
Children's Hospital Boston
Connecticut Children's Medical Center
Harrington Memorial Hospital
Hartford Health Care
Hospital of Central Connecticut
Partners HealthCare
Saint Francis Hospital and Medical Center
St. Elizabeth's Medical Center
University of Connecticut Health Center
Yale New Haven Health System

HISTORICAL FINANCIALS

Company Type: Private

Income Statement FYE: September 30

	REVENUE ($ mil.)	NET INCOME ($ mil.)	NET PROFIT MARGIN	EMPLOYEES
09/18	1,284	62	4.9%	11,000
09/17	1,217	107	8.8%	—
09/16	1,095	108	9.9%	—
09/15	1,048	76	7.3%	—
Annual Growth	7.0%	(6.4%)	—	—

2018 Year-End Financials

Return on assets: 4.6%
Return on equity: 7.6%
Current ratio: 3.50
Cash ($ mil.): 79

BAYSTATE HEALTH SYSTEM HEALTH SERVICES, INC.

Patients in need of medical care can dock at this bay. Not-for-profit Baystate Health is the largest health care services provider in western Massachusetts. The system operates five acute-care and specialty hospitals with a total of approximately 1000 beds including the flagship Baystate Medical Center which operates a Level 1 Trauma Center and a specialized children's hospital. Baystate Health also offers ancillary medical services such as cancer care respiratory care infusion therapy visiting nurse and hospice services through its regional clinics and agencies. The system controls for-profit health plan provider Health New England as well as clinical pathology firm Baystate Reference Laboratories.

Operations

Baystate Medical Center accounts for more than 700 of the system's beds. Its other four acute care hospitals are Baystate Franklin Medical Center (89 beds) Baystate Wing Hospital (74 beds) Baystate Noble Hospital (97 beds) and Baystate Mary Lane Hospital (25 beds). The system also runs a physicians group Baystate Medical Practices which operates more than two dozen physician practices in several surrounding counties and towns. Other outpatient centers include surgery centers imaging and radiology clinics and neighborhood health centers. Altogether its facilities serve a population of 750000 western New England residents and admit more than 45000 inpatients perform some 34000 surgeries handle about 4500 births and conduct 1.4 million outpatient visits each year.

Baystate Health provides academic and community educational programs as well as conducting basic clinical and biomedical research. For instance the Baystate Medical Center is a teaching hospital that serves as the western campus of the Tufts University School of Medicine. Baystate Health also partners with a number of regional colleges to offer nursing programs.

In the research realm Tufts and Baystate Health work on biomedical studies through the Tufts Clinical and Translational Science Institute. Baystate Medical Center also has a partnership with the University of Massachusetts that forms the Pioneer Valley Life Sciences Institute. Areas of research include clinical care quality of care and diabetes and metabolism. The Baystate Health system receives about $10 million per year in research funding from the National Institutes of Health and other agencies.

Geographic Reach

Baystate Health has some 60 locations serving western Massachusetts including Berkshire Franklin Hampden Hampshire and Worcester counties.

Sales and Marketing

Patient service revenue accounts for a majority (about 60%) of the hospital system's sales; Medicare and Medicaid reimbursements make up 57% of patient service payments. Other sources include commercial insurers and private-pay customers.

Financial Performance

In fiscal 2015 (ended September) Baystate Health revenues grew 17% to $1.2 billion; this was driven by a growth in premiums as well as net patient service revenue. However that year the system reported a net loss of $78 million due to higher medical claims and capitation as well as losses on investments and pension adjustments.

Following net income's suit cash flow from operations dropped 38% to $51 million in fiscal 2015.

Strategy

Baystate Health has been conducting expansion and renovation efforts at its facilities in recent years including medical technology and information system upgrades. The system's largest effort was the construction of a $300 million clinical building on the Baystate Medical Center Campus.

Other facilities and divisions are undergoing expansion as well: The system is adding new space to house a pharmacy and nearly 100 modern inpatient rooms at its flagship campus while a new surgical center is being added to Baystate Franklin Medical Center in Greenfield. Baystate Medical Practices continues to grow by adding new practices on a regular basis. Baystate Health is also upgrading its medical equipment and its information technology systems.

Mergers and Acquisitions

Baystate Health acquired Noble Hospital (now Baystate Noble Hospital) a 97-bed not-for-profit community hospital in 2015. The year before that it added another acute care facility when it bought the 74-bed Wind Memorial Hospital (now Baystate Wing Hospital) from UMass Memorial Healthcare.

EXECUTIVES

Svp Community Hospitals Cfo And Treasurer, Dennis W. Chalke

Interim President And Chief Administrative Officer Baystate Health Eastern Region, Michael F. Moran

President And Ceo Health New England Inc., Maura C. McCaffrey

Ceo Baycare Health Partners, Stephen J. Sweet

Vp And Chief Information Officer, Joel L. Vengco

President And Ceo, Mark A. Keroack

Svp Coo And Chief Nursing Office Baystate Medical Center, Nancy Shendell-Falik

President Baystate Medical Practices And Chief Physician Executive, John R. Schreiber

President Eastern Region, Charles E. Cavagnaro

Auditors: ERNST & YOUNG LLP BOSTON MAS

LOCATIONS

HQ: BAYSTATE HEALTH SYSTEM HEALTH SERVICES, INC.
280 CHESTNUT ST, SPRINGFIELD, MA 011991000
Phone: 413 794-9939

Selected Locations

Baystate Medical Center (Springfield)
Baystate Children's Hospital (Springfield)
Baystate Franklin Medical Center (Greenfield)
Baystate Mary Lane Hospital (Ware)
Baystate Noble Hospital (Westfield)
Baystate Wing Hospital (Palmer)
Outpatient Centers
Baystate Home Infusion & Respiratory Services
Baystate Medical Practices
Baystate Radiology and Imaging (BRI)
Baystate Reference Laboratories (BRL)
Baystate Visiting Nurse Association & Hospice
Brightwood Health Center
Chestnut Surgery Center
D'Amour Center for Cancer Care
High Street Center (adult and pediatrics)
Mason Square Neighborhood Health Center
Neurodiagnostics & Sleep Center
Orthopedic Surgery Center
Wesson Women & Infants Health Center

PRODUCTS/OPERATIONS

2015 Sales

	$ mil.	% of total
Net patient service revenue	1,222	57
Premiums	822	39
Other	94	4
Total	**2,138**	**100**

Selected Services

Ambulance
Anesthesiology
Behavioral health services
Birthing services
Cancer
Cardiovascular
Emergency medicine
Endoscopy
Home care and home medical supplies
Hospital medicine
Neurosciences
Obstetrics and gynecology
Pain management center
Pathology
Pediatrics
Radiology
Rehabilitation care
Reproductive medicine
Sleep program
Surgery
Weight management
Women's health

COMPETITORS

Berkshire Health Systems
Cambridge Health Alliance
Cape Cod Healthcare
CareGroup
Harrington Memorial Hospital
Partners HealthCare
Shriners Hospitals For Children
Southcoast Hospitals Group
Steward Health Care
Universal Health Services

HISTORICAL FINANCIALS

Company Type: Private

Income Statement — FYE: September 30

	REVENUE ($ mil.)	NET INCOME ($ mil.)	NET PROFIT MARGIN	EMPLOYEES
09/07	1,286	125	9.7%	5,000
09/06	1,209	83	6.9%	—
09/05	0	0	—	—
09/04	0	0	—	—
Annual Growth	—	—	—	—

2007 Year-End Financials

Return on assets: 5.4%
Return on equity: 9.7%
Current ratio: 0.70
Cash ($ mil.): 61

BEALL'S, INC.

Residents of the Sun Belt have been known to leave their homes with Beall's on. The retail holding company operates through subsidiaries Beall's Department Stores Beall's Outlet and Burke's Outlet Stores in a dozen states. The multi-brand retailer has more than 530 department and outlet stores (about 200 are in Florida) located throughout states in the southern and western US including Arizona California Georgia Louisiana and Texas. Products range from off-price clothing and footwear for men and women to cosmetics gifts and housewares. Each chain has its own online shopping destination. The family-owned company was founded in 1915 by the grandfather of chairman Robert Beall (pronounced "bell").

Operations

Beall's Inc. oversees operations of its three operating companies. Beall's Florida operates some 190 stores in the Sunshine State. Beall's Outlet operates about 300 stores in Arizona Florida Texas and Georgia while Burke's Outlet operates more than 190 stores in 16 states.

Geographic Reach

Beall's trio of chain's operate stores in Alabama Arkansas Arizona California Florida Georgia Kentucky Louisiana Mississippi Nevada New Mexico North Carolina South Carolina Tennessee Texas Virginia and West Virginia.

Financial Performance

Privately-owned Beall's rings ups more than $1 billion in sales annually.

Strategy

The company has aspirations to transform itself into a major discount retailer much like its larger rivals TJX and Ross Stores. To that end the company plans to add new stores outside its traditional markets with an eye on establishing a national retail presence. Targets include adding 30 to 50 stores a year for the next several years and raising brand awareness beyond Florida.

With many of its stores in Arizona Florida and California (three of the states hit hardest by the housing crisis and deep recession) Beall's Inc. should have been in a heap of retail trouble. However its largest chain — Beall's Outlet —proved to be quite popular during this recession. Indeed the budget-priced outlet chain outperformed its two sister chains as well as more moderately priced department stores. The retailer has also benefited from the demise of other retailers including Goody's Linens 'n Things and Mervyn's.

The three operating companies share resources provided by Beall's Inc. such as distribution finance loss prevention and information systems. Conversely each chain is responsible for its purchasing product development real estate and advertising activities.

Company Background

Stores operating under the Bealls name in Alabama New Mexico and Texas are owned by Stage Stores and are not affiliated with Beall's Inc.

EXECUTIVES

Dvp Merchandise Support, Pam Meyer
Senior Vice President Chief Merchant, Tianne Doyle
Dvp Of Merchandise Process, Trina Gladwell
Vice President Of Real Estate, Wade Laufenberg
Divisional Vice President Gmm, Eric Kozlowski
Auditors: CHRISTOPHER SMITH LEONARD B

LOCATIONS

HQ: BEALL'S, INC.
E R BALL CTR 700 13TH AVE, BRADENTON, FL 34208
Phone: 941 747-2355
Web: WWW.BEALLSINC.COM

PRODUCTS/OPERATIONS

Selected Retail Operations

Bealls Department Stores (Florida)
Bealls Outlet (deep-discount outlet stores in Arizona Florida Georgia)
Burke's Outlet (11 southern states)

COMPETITORS

Bed Bath & Beyond
Costco Wholesale
Dillard's
J. C. Penney Company
Kohl's
Macy's
Nordstrom
Ross Stores
Stage Stores
TJX Companies
Target Corporation
The Gap
Wal-Mart

HISTORICAL FINANCIALS

Company Type: Private

Income Statement — FYE: August 1

	REVENUE ($ mil.)	NET INCOME ($ mil.)	NET PROFIT MARGIN	EMPLOYEES
08/15*	1,321	25	1.9%	9,700
07/12	1,232	14	1.1%	—
07/11	1,166	15	1.3%	—
Annual Growth	3.2%	12.8%	—	—

*Fiscal year change

2015 Year-End Financials

Return on assets: 4.5%
Return on equity: 8.7%
Current ratio: 1.60
Cash ($ mil.): 107

BEARINGPOINT, INC.

EXECUTIVES

Ceo, F Edwin Harbach
Chb, Roderick C McGeary
Cfo, Kenneth A Hiltz
Coo, David Hunter
Svp Comm & Media Practice, Michael Reuschel
Director, Gov't Relations, Charles Cantus
Vp-Mgr Dir/Bus Dev, Jose Garcia
National Mgr Dir, Mark Gembicki
Sr. Administrative Assistant,, Alicia Flakes-Cuffee
Managing Director, Andrew Smith
Vice President, Business Devel, Bettina Smilo
Auditors: ERNST & YOUNG LLP MCLEAN VI

LOCATIONS

HQ: BEARINGPOINT, INC.
100 CRESCENT CT STE 700, DALLAS, TX 752012112
Phone: 214 459-2770

HISTORICAL FINANCIALS

Company Type: Private

Income Statement — FYE: December 31

	REVENUE ($ mil.)	NET INCOME ($ mil.)	NET PROFIT MARGIN	EMPLOYEES
12/07	3,455	(362)	—	15,200
12/06	3,444	(177)	—	—
Annual Growth	0.3%	—	—	—

2007 Year-End Financials

Return on assets: (-18.0%)
Return on equity: —
Current ratio: 1.40
Cash ($ mil.): 468

BEAUMONT HEALTH

Beaumont Health is an eight-hospital regional health system in southeastern Michigan. The health system boasts about 3400 hospital beds 150 outpatient sites and 5000 affiliated physicians. Outpatient facilities include community medical centers nursing homes a home health agency a research institute and primary and specialty care clinics as well as rehabilitation cardiology and cancer centers. Beaumont is the exclusive clinical teaching site for the Oakland University William Beaumont School of Medicine; it also has affiliations with Michigan State University College of Osteopathic Medicine and Wayne State University School of Medicine. In 2019 it agreed to acquire Ohio hospital operator Summa Health.

EXECUTIVES

Executive Vice President Business Development, Jack Devaney
Senior Vice President And Chief Development Officer, Margaret Casey
Senior Vice President Chief Medical Officer Beaumont Hospital Troy, James Lynch
Senior Vice President, Leslie Rocher
Vice President Information Technology, Karie Lyon
Senior Vice President And Associate Chief Medical Officer Acute Care, Malcolm Henoch
Senior Vice President And Executive Director Beaumont Medical Group, Michael Herbert
Vice President, Ryan Daly
Vice President Finance, Mark Leonard
Vice President Finance, Steve Collard
Executive Vice President Quality Safety Clinical Effectiveness, Sam Flanders
Vice President Information Technology Service Delivery And Crm, Neha Yale
Director Of Nursing, Dahlia Klein
Vice President, Jennifer Post
Vice President Human Resources, Ronald Lilek
Senior Vice President And Chief Compliance Officer, Dawn Geisert
Senior Vice President Supply Chain Management, Ed Hardin
Vice President Acute Care And Ancillary Applications, Marge Mathews
Executive Vice President And Chief Nursing Officer, Susan Grant
Vice President Financial Operations And Corporate Accounting, Donna Zuk
Executive Vice President Chief Operating Officer, Carolyn Wilson
Executive Vice President Chief Financial Officer, John Kerndl
Senior Vice President Chief Human Resources Officer, Aaron Gillingham
Svp Government Relations And Community Affairs, Mary Zatina
Senior Vice President, David Walters
Vice President, Margaret Lightner
Vice President Of Clinical Outcomes, Linda Fitzgerald-mays
Vice President Revenue Cycle, Denise Waters
Associate Vice President, Elizabeth Lent
Unit Secretary, Barbara Bullion
Secretary Employee Health Services, Debbie Show

LOCATIONS

HQ: BEAUMONT HEALTH
3601 W 13 MILE RD, ROYAL OAK, MI 480736712
Phone: 248 898-5000
Web: WWW.BEAUMONT.ORG

Selected Michigan Locations

Lake Orion
Macomb
Rochester Hills
Royal Oak
St. Clair Shores
Sterling Heights
Warren
West Bloomfield

PRODUCTS/OPERATIONS

Selected Michigan Facilities

Health Wellness and Outpatient Care
- Beaumont Bon Brae Center (fitness; St. Clair Shores)
- Beaumont Health and Wellness Center (Rochester Hills)
- Beaumont Health Center (outpatient services; Royal Oak)
- Beaumont Medical Centers

Hospitals
- Beaumont Hospital Grosse Pointe
- Beaumont Hospital Royal Oak
- Beaumont Hospital Troy

Nursing and Rehabilitation
- Evergreen Health and Living Center (Southfield)
- Shelby Nursing Center (Shelby Township)
- ShorePointe Nursing Care (St. Clair Shores)
- ShorePointe Village Assisted Living (St. Clair Shores)
- West Bloomfield Nursing Center
- Woodward Hills Nursing Center (Bloomfield Hills)

Research and Education
- Oakland University William Beaumont School of Medicine (Royal Oak)

Selected Centers of Excellence

Cancer
Children's Hospital
Digestive health
Heart and vascular
Neuroscience
Orthopedics
Women's health

COMPETITORS

Children's Hospital of Michigan
Crittenton Hospital
Detroit Medical Center
Garden City Hospital
Henry Ford Health System
Kindred Healthcare
Mayo Clinic
McLaren Health Care
Mount Clemens Regional Medical Center
Providence Hospital and Medical Centers
Sinai-Grace Hospital
St. John Health
St. John Hospital & Medical Center
Trinity Health (Novi)
University of Michigan Health System

HISTORICAL FINANCIALS

Company Type: Private

Income Statement FYE: December 31

	REVENUE ($ mil.)	NET INCOME ($ mil.)	NET PROFIT MARGIN	EMPLOYEES
12/19	4,703	401	8.5%	35,000
12/18	4,659	142	3.0%	—
12/17	4,438	392	8.8%	—
12/16	4,373	286	6.6%	—
Annual Growth	2.5%	11.8%	—	—

2019 Year-End Financials

Return on assets: 6.8%
Return on equity: 13.5%
Current ratio: 2.20
Cash ($ mil.): 519

BEAVERTON SCHOOL DISTRICT

EXECUTIVES

Supt, Jerome Colonna
Asst Supt*, Sarah Boly
Asst Supt*, Bud Moore
Cfo*, Janice Essenberg
CIO*, Stephen Langford
Coordinator, Jill Bogle
Project Coordinator, Jay Dwyer
Project Coordinator, Krista Hawkins
Information Technology/Interne, Sheila Bell
Information Technology Team ME, Kathy Panchot
Teacher, Susan Rosenbaum
Auditors: GROVE MUELLER & SWANK PC

LOCATIONS

HQ: BEAVERTON SCHOOL DISTRICT
16550 SW MERLO RD, BEAVERTON, OR 970035179
Phone: 503 591-8000
Web: WWW.BEAVERTON.K12.OR.US

HISTORICAL FINANCIALS

Company Type: Private

Income Statement FYE: June 30

	REVENUE ($ mil.)	NET INCOME ($ mil.)	NET PROFIT MARGIN	EMPLOYEES
06/19	611	(93)	—	4,000
06/18	584	(97)	—	—
06/17	529	119	22.5%	—
06/16	513	(137)	—	—
Annual Growth	6.0%	—	—	—

BELLIN HEALTH SYSTEMS, INC.

EXECUTIVES

Pres, George Kerwin
Cfo*, Jim Dietsche
Controller, Kevin Mc Gurk
Coordinator, Diane Koepke
Vice-President Business Develo, Randy Vanstraten
Executive Officer, John Rocheleau
Information Specialist, Teresa Krause
Account Executive, Amanda Verhagen
Staff, Brian Knapp
Health Professional, Linda Falk
Telecommunications Coordinator, Christopher Taft
Auditors: WIPFLI LLP GREEN BAY WISCONS

LOCATIONS

HQ: BELLIN HEALTH SYSTEMS, INC.
744 S WEBSTER AVE, GREEN BAY, WI 543013505
Phone: 920 433-3500
Web: WWW.BELLIN.ORG

HISTORICAL FINANCIALS

Company Type: Private

Income Statement FYE: September 30

	REVENUE ($ mil.)	NET INCOME ($ mil.)	NET PROFIT MARGIN	EMPLOYEES
09/18	608	24	4.0%	2,300
09/17	571	43	7.6%	—
09/16	533	31	6.0%	—
09/15	502	27	5.5%	—
Annual Growth	6.6%	(4.5%)	—	—

2018 Year-End Financials

Return on assets: 3.7%
Return on equity: 5.2%
Current ratio: 2.50
Cash ($ mil.): 71

BELLIN MEMORIAL HOSPITAL, INC.

EXECUTIVES

Pres, George Kerwin
Cfo*, Jim Dietsche
Internal Medicine Practitioner, Andrea Akpoguma
Administrator, Kevin J McGurk
Security Staff, Tom Brault
Accounting Staff, Ann Tedrick
Registered Nurse, Luann Woodland
Information Specialist, Thomas Brault
Icu Ccu Director, Parnell Pierce
Network Administrator, Westley Pruetting
Vice President Chief Financial, James Dietsche
Auditors: WIPFLI LLP GREEN BAY WISCONS

LOCATIONS

HQ: BELLIN MEMORIAL HOSPITAL, INC.
744 S WEBSTER AVE, GREEN BAY, WI 543013581
Phone: 920 433-3500
Web: WWW.CARE.BELLIN.ORG

HISTORICAL FINANCIALS

Company Type: Private

Income Statement FYE: September 30

	REVENUE ($ mil.)	NET INCOME ($ mil.)	NET PROFIT MARGIN	EMPLOYEES
09/18	561	26	4.7%	1,725
09/17	571	42	7.5%	—
09/16	488	32	6.7%	—
09/15	462	27	6.0%	—
Annual Growth	6.7%	(1.7%)	—	—

2018 Year-End Financials

Return on assets: 4.4%
Return on equity: 6.3%
Current ratio: 2.70
Cash ($ mil.): 65

BENCO DENTAL SUPPLY CO.

Benco Dental Supply is a one-stop shop for the tooth doc. Through regional showrooms and distribution centers Benco provides dental and dentistry supplies to more than 30000 dental professionals throughout the US. Its offerings include dental hand pieces furniture and disposable supplies. Its BencoNET division develops and distributes custom computers and proprietary programming and networking systems for dentists. Other services include dental office design practice consulting financing and real estate planning wealth management and equipment repairs.

Operations

Benco offerings range from large equipment to small supplies made by a broad range of manufacturers. The company supplies more than 80000 products including dental cement impression supplies and curing lights made by manufacturers such as 3M Dentsply Sirona Sybron (Kerr) Hu-Friedy and more. It also sells products under its own Benco Dental brand.

Support services include offers inventory management services and hand piece equipment and upholstery repair.

Benco Dental's practice management services include staff recruitment assistance product training programs for dentists peer-to-peer networking solutions and continuing medical education programs.

Geographic Reach

Benco Dental's main headquarters and showroom is located in Pittston Pennsylvania. It also operates another CenterPoint Experience (large-scale) showroom in Costa Mesa California and it has a network of about 50 smaller regional showrooms and five distribution centers (in Pittston; Dallas; Fort Wayne Indiana; Jacksonville Florida; and Reno Nevada) across the US that serve customers in all 50 US states.

Although most of its operations are in the US the company also ships products to overseas customers.

Sales and Marketing

Benco markets its products and services directly to dental practices. It also increasing the number of orders placed through its online ordering system (Painless) and it promotes services to dentists through affiliations with dental organizations and associations (including the American Academy of Dental Group Practice and the American Association of Orthodontists). The company has more than 400 sales representatives. To support sales it also has about 300 factory-trained service technicians.

Financial Performance

Benco increased net sales by 9% in 2012 due to new product sales launches and increased sales of existing products in fields including 3D imaging equipment and digital sensors.

Strategy

Benco tends to expand its operations through organic growth initiatives including offering new products and services to a wider customer base. In addition the company grows through acquisitions in key growth regions. The company launched 14 Benco branded products during 2012 as well as 3800 new products made by its vendor partners. It also added about 50 new sales reps that year to meet rising customer demands. The company estimated that it grew market share to some 11% of the US market that year (placing itself among the top three dental supply distributors).

Benco increased sales to community health centers that year through its partnership with PSS. To expand its educational programs in 2012 the company also formed a partnership with the Kois Center which offers a nine-course program on topics including aesthetic and restorative dentistry.

To reach additional customers and expand its capacity the company opened its fifth distribution center – a 120000-sq. ft. facility in Reno Nevada – in 2011. It also opened a new sales branch office in Los Angeles to serve the Southern California market in 2012.

Benco Dental moved into its CenterPoint headquarters and showroom in Pittston Pennsylvania in early 2010. The facility is one of the largest dental equipment showrooms in the US with exhibits including more than two dozen dental rooms 14 digital X-ray units three sterilization centers and other oral surgery and orthodontic units as well as an office design concept suite and a training and education center. Following the success of that location the company opened a second CenterPoint Experience showroom in Costa Mesa California in 2012.

EXECUTIVES

V Pres, George Rable
V Pres, Paul Jackson
Vice President Business Innovation, Julie Radzyminski
Vp Operations, Louis Mangino
Vice President Of Sales And Branch Operations, Kari Taylor
Auditors: COHEN AND CO CLEVELAND OHIO

LOCATIONS

HQ: BENCO DENTAL SUPPLY CO.
295 CENTERPOINT BLVD, PITTSTON, PA 186406136
Phone: 570 602-7781
Web: WWW.BENCO.COM

Selected Distribution Center Locations

Dallas Texas
Fort Wayne Indiana
Jacksonville Florida
Pittston Pennsylvania
Reno Nevada

PRODUCTS/OPERATIONS

Selected Brands

Large Equipment
A-dec
Belmont
BIOLASE
Cadent
Gendex
Instrumentarium
Marus
Midmark
Pelton & Crane
Sirona
Soredex
Vatech
Small Equipment
Accutron
Aceton
Air Techniques
Cadent
KaVo
Midmark
Midwest
Tuttnauer
W&H
Supplies and technology (Benco brands)
BencoNET
BluChip rewards
BluPrint (dental impression material)
fas-TRACT
HD
Iris (dental pit and fissure sealant)
Natural Extensions (nitrile gloves)
Painless
ValuGrip (latex gloves)
Vision XR (oral x-ray film)
XLR8 (dental equipment)
Z3

COMPETITORS

Burkhart Dental
Cardinal Health
Darby Dental
Dentsply Sirona
Discus Dental
Henry Schein
McKesson
Owens & Minor
Patterson Companies
Sybron Dental

HISTORICAL FINANCIALS

Company Type: Private

Income Statement — FYE: January 4

	REVENUE ($ mil.)	NET INCOME ($ mil.)	NET PROFIT MARGIN	EMPLOYEES
01/14*	620	8	1.4%	1,600
12/12	600	7	1.2%	—
12/07	389	5	1.3%	—
Annual Growth	8.1%	10.0%	—	—

*Fiscal year change

2014 Year-End Financials

Return on assets: 4.9%
Return on equity: —
Current ratio: 1.60
Cash ($ mil.): —

BENEFIS HOSPITALS, INC

EXECUTIVES

Ceo-Cfo, John Goodnow
Pres*, Laura Goldhahn
V Pres*, Steven Ballock
Dentist, Will Daniels DDS
Vice-President Information Ser, Alexander N Chung
Vice-President Information Ser, Mary Davis
General Practitioner, Justin Madill
Director, Patty Harris
Assistant Vice President Plann, Linda Simonich
Safety Director, Louis Dantuono
Internist, Jamina Charles

LOCATIONS

HQ: BENEFIS HOSPITALS, INC
1101 26TH ST S, GREAT FALLS, MT 594055161
Phone: 406 455-5000
Web: WWW.BENEFIS.ORG

HISTORICAL FINANCIALS

Company Type: Private

Income Statement — FYE: December 31

	REVENUE ($ mil.)	NET INCOME ($ mil.)	NET PROFIT MARGIN	EMPLOYEES
12/16	865	26	3.0%	2,419
12/15	860	20	2.4%	—
12/14*	363	14	4.0%	—
05/06	86	9	10.5%	—
Annual Growth	23.3%	10.1%	—	—

*Fiscal year change

BERRY GLOBAL FILMS, LLC

Making plastic cling is this company's thing. AEP Industries manufactures plastic packaging films – more than 15000 types – including stretch wrap for industrial pallets packaging for foods and beverages and films for agricultural uses such as wrap for hay bales. AEP also makes dispenser-boxed plastic wraps which are sold to consumers as well as institutions ranging from schools to hospitals. Other industries courted by AEP are packaging transportation food autos chemicals textiles and electronics. The company operates in the US and in Canada. In the summer of 2016 AEP agreed to be acquired by rival Berry Plastics Group.

Change in Company Type

AEP agreed to be acquired by Berry Plastics Group in mid-2016 in a deal valued at $765 million a price that includes AEP's debt load. AEP will be combined with Berry's Engineered Materials Division.

Geographic Reach

AEP conducts about 95% of its business in the US market. Remaining sales take place in Canada. It has about 15 manufacturing facilities in the US (about 11 states) and Canada. The company also exports its products to Latin America through its office in Waxahachie Texas.

Sales and Marketing

About two-thirds of AEP's sales are made to distributors and the remainder directly to end-users of its products. It serves about 3000 customers. The company works to maintain customer relationships and it provides technical training to its sales personal so that they are able to provide customer support and communicate customer needs to the company's product development team. Distribution functions are mostly contracted to third parties.

Financial Performance

AEP's revenues have fluctuated over the years. After peaking at $1.19 billion in 2014 revenues fell by 4% to $1.14 billion in 2015. The revenue decrease for 2015 was fueled by a 3% dip in average selling prices primarily due to the pass-through of lower resin costs negatively affecting net sales by $31 million.

The company in 2015 also experienced a 1% decrease in sales volumes attributed to volatility in the resin markets. This resulted in soft customer demand in certain stock product lines customer bankruptcies and the impact of exiting certain low-margin businesses during fiscal 2014.

After experiencing a net loss of $6 million in 2014 AEP posted positive net income of $29 million in 2015. This was the result of a decline in costs coupled with a larger amount of income tax benefits.

Strategy

With little product differentiation among plastic film producers AEP positions itself as the low-cost source with technological expertise to customize value-added flexible films to satisfy myriad manufacturing and processing applications. The company aims to provide long-term value to shareholders by becoming the preferred provider of flexible packaging products in the North American market.

To strengthen its finances and increase manufacturing output and productivity AEP is investing heavily in capital improvements. During the last decade it has purchased or leased new equipment and made equipment upgrades intended to optimize its manufacturing footprint in high-growth product categories.

The company looks for success in its sales and distribution model by establishing long-term relationships with its customers. To mitigate the volatility of raw material prices the company pursues volume raw material rebates by making most of its purchases from three primary suppliers.

Company Background

Brendan Barba a former salesman for polyethylene film maker PPD formed Flexible Plastics in 1967 in Lodi New Jersey. In 1970 his partner bought him out. That year Barba founded AEP Industries briefly called Automatically Extruded Products. In 1982 the company moved into the specialty and premium films market. It established a plant in Waxahachie Texas in 1985 and went public a year later.

EXECUTIVES

Vp Manufacturing Polyvinyl Chloride Products, Richard Boyette
Evp Operations, Paul C. Vegliante, $317,300 total compensation
President And Coo, John J. Powers, $349,300 total compensation
Evp Finance Cfo And Director, Paul M. Feeney, $463,800 total compensation
Chairman President And Ceo, J. Brendan Barba, $958,700 total compensation
Evp National Accounts, Robert Cron
Vp Custom Films Division, Robert Covella
Division Manager Resinite Products, Steve Firmery
Vp Stretch Film Division, Brian Ochsner
Vp Proformance Films Products, Gary Bobko
Vp Ipd Division, Philip A. Hernberg
Vice President Engineering, Carl Opperman
Vice President Of Information Technology, Ken Ribe

LOCATIONS

HQ: BERRY GLOBAL FILMS, LLC
95 CHESTNUT RIDGE RD, MONTVALE, NJ 076451801
Phone: 201 641-6600
Web: WWW.BERRYPLASTICS.COM

2015 Sales

	$ mil.	% of total
US	1,073	94
Canada	68	6
Total	**1,141**	**100**

PRODUCTS/OPERATIONS

2015 Sales

	$ mil.	% of total
Custom films	357	31
Stretch (pallet) wrap	332	29
Food contact	165	14
Canliners	144	13
PROformance films	63	6
Printed & converted films specialty films & other	77	7
Total	**1,141**	**100**

Selected Products

Canliners
Kitchen and standard garbage bags
Custom films (polyethylene co-extruded and monolayer custom designed film)
  Drum box carton pail liners
  Films to cover high value products
  Furniture and mattress bags
  Magazine overwrap
PROformance films (co-extruded and monolayer polyolefin films)
  Cereal box liners
  Fresh cut produce packaging
  Frozen foods
  Medical
Polyvinyl chloride wrap
  Food and freezer wrap
Printed and converted films (polyethylene)
  Printed laminated converted films for flexible packaging to consumer markets
  Printed shrink films
Stretch (pallet) wrap (polyethylene)
  Pallet wrap
Other products and specialty films (unplasticized polyvinyl chloride polyethylene)
  Agricultural films
  Battery labels
  Canliners
  Credit card laminate
  Retail and institutional films and products
  Table covers aprons bibs and gloves
  Twist wrap

COMPETITORS

Acme Packaging	Pactiv
Ampac	Plastic Suppliers
Bemis	Primex Plastics
Berry Global	Printpack
Dow Chemical	S.C. Johnson
FlexSol Packaging	Sealed Air Corp.
Griffon	Sigma Plastics
Inteplast	Tredegar
Intertape Polymer	

HISTORICAL FINANCIALS

Company Type: Private

Income Statement — FYE: October 31

	REVENUE ($ mil.)	NET INCOME ($ mil.)	NET PROFIT MARGIN	EMPLOYEES
10/15	1,141	28	2.5%	2,600
10/14	1,192	(5)	—	—
10/13	1,143	10	0.9%	—
Annual Growth	(0.1%)	63.8%	—	—

2015 Year-End Financials

Return on assets: 6.6%
Return on equity: 32.2%
Current ratio: 2.10
Cash ($ mil.): 20

BEST PETROLEUM CORPORATION

EXECUTIVES

Pres, Antonio De Jesus Nieves
Head of Business Development, Manuel F Rojas
Auditors: JESUS OYOLA CUADRADO BAYAMON

LOCATIONS

HQ: BEST PETROLEUM CORPORATION
KM 20 HM 5 RR 2, TOA BAJA, PR 00951
Phone: 787 251-6218
Web: WWW.BESTPETROLEUMCORP.COM

HISTORICAL FINANCIALS

Company Type: Private

Income Statement — FYE: December 31

	REVENUE ($ mil.)	NET INCOME ($ mil.)	NET PROFIT MARGIN	EMPLOYEES
12/18	673	32	4.8%	130
12/17	547	26	4.8%	—
12/16	439	16	3.7%	—
12/15	479	11	2.4%	—
Annual Growth	12.0%	41.5%	—	—

2018 Year-End Financials

Return on assets: 18.8%
Return on equity: 21.2%
Current ratio: 8.10
Cash ($ mil.): 110

BETH ISRAEL DEACONESS MEDICAL CENTER, INC.

Beth Israel Lahey Health (formerly Beth Israel Deaconess Medical Center or BIDMC) is a Boston-based health system with 13 hospitals across Massachusetts. Its flagship location is the hospital for Major League Baseball's Red Sox but it's perhaps best known for being a teaching hospital of Harvard Medical School. The facility has about 675 beds and provides general medical and surgical care as well as outpatient services at its facilities. The health system traces its roots to Deaconess Hospital founded in 1896 and Beth Israel Hospital established in 1916. In 2019 BIDMC merged with Lahey Health to create a stronger rival to Massachusetts' largest system Partners HealthCare.

Operations

Beth Israel Lahey Health's operations include the hospitals previously owned by BIDMC and Lahey Health as well as Anna Jaques Hospital Mount Auburn Hospital Baptist Hospital and several medical offices.

Many of the system's physicians hold faculty appointments at Harvard Medical School. Along with helping students become doctors Beth Israel Lahey Health provides clinical education to students in social work radiology and pharmacy.

The Carl J. Shapiro Institute for Education and Research provides medical students and physicians in training with an on-site centralized educational facility.

Financial Performance

Beth Israel Lahey Health is very active in medical research and consistently ranks among the top recipients of biomedical research funding from the National Institutes of Health totaling nearly $200 million annually. The health system is also home to the Harvard-Thorndike Laboratory the nation's oldest clinical research laboratory.

Strategy

Being on the forefront of medical education goes hand-in-hand with using cutting-edge technology and Beth Israel Lahey Health does just that with its Carl J. Shapiro Institute for Education and Research administers training for learners at all levels and from all disciplines using progressive teaching methods to replicate real-life patient care situations from routine procedures to acute management crises. The institute features a range of technologically advanced educational resources including realistic models simulators virtual reality experiences computer-based materials ultrasound technology and filmed operations.

In late 2017 the hospital announced plans to build a 10-story patient tower its largest such project in more than 20 years. The facility will have private patient rooms operating rooms imaging suites and a landing pad for helicopters.

Mergers and Acquisitions

In early 2017 BIDMC agreed to merge with Lahey Health to become Massachusetts' second-largest health system (after Partners HealthCare). The merger was official in March 2019. Other hospitals joined the combined system including Anna Jaques Hospital of Newburyport New England Baptist Hospital and Mount Auburn Hospital. Now named Beth Israel Lahey Health the system has 13 hospitals.

EXECUTIVES

Svp Information Systems And Cio, John D. Halamka, age 57
Svp Finance And Cfo, Steven Fischer
President And Ceo Beth Israel Deaconess Hospital Plymouth, Peter J. Holden
Coo, Nancy Formella
President And Ceo Affiliated Physicians Group, John Christoforo
Chairman Department Of Medicine, Mark L. Zeidel
President Ceo And Director, Kevin Tabb
Chief Nursing Officer And Svp Patient Care Services, Marsha Maurer
President And Ceo Beth Israel Deaconess Hospital - Needham, John Fogarty
President And Ceo Beth Israel Deaconess Hospital Milton, Peter Healy
Svp Communications And Marketing, Paul Donovan
Interim President And Ceo Beth Israel Deaconess Care Organization, Jeff Hulburt
President And Ceo Harvard Medical Faculty Physicians, Stuart Rosenberg
Deputy Cio/cto, Manu Tandon
Medical Director Of Cytogenetics, Christine Bryke
Vice President Research Operations, Randy Mason
Clinical Nursexecutive Vice Presidentractitioner, Julie Knopp
Nurse Endoscopy And Infusion, Jill Sullivan
Director, Ronald P. (Ron) O'Hanley, age 63
Vice Chair, Margaret A. McKenna, age 75
Vice Chair, Edward H. (Ted) Ladd
Director, Daniel Jick

LOCATIONS

HQ: BETH ISRAEL DEACONESS MEDICAL CENTER, INC.
330 BROOKLINE AVE, BOSTON, MA 022155400
Phone: 617 667-7000
Web: WWW.BIDMC.ORG

PRODUCTS/OPERATIONS

Centers and Departments
Cancer Center
CardioVascular Institute
Digestive Disease Center
Spine Center
Transplant Institute
Clinical Departments
Anesthesia Critical Care and Pain Medicine
Dermatology
Emergency Medicine
Medicine
Neonatology
Neurology
Obstetrics and Gynecology
Orthopedic Surgery
Pathology
Psychiatry
Radiation Oncology
Radiology
Rehabilitation Services
Surgery

Selected Facilities
Beth Israel Deaconess HealthCare-Chelsea
Beth Israel Deaconess HealthCare-Chestnut Hill
Beth Israel Deaconess HealthCare-Lexington
Beth Israel Deaconess Hospital-Milton
Beth Israel Deaconess Hospital-Needham
Beth Israel Deaconess Hospital-Plymouth

COMPETITORS

Boston Medical Center
Brigham and Women's Hospital
Cambridge Health Alliance
Care New England
Children's Hospital Boston
Dana-Farber
Massachusetts General Hospital
Newton-Wellesley Hospital
Northeast Health System
Partners HealthCare
Southcoast Hospitals Group
Spaulding Rehabilitation Hospital
Steward Health Care

HISTORICAL FINANCIALS

Company Type: Private

Income Statement — FYE: September 30

	REVENUE ($ mil.)	NET INCOME ($ mil.)	NET PROFIT MARGIN	EMPLOYEES
09/18	1,394	51	3.7%	6,500
09/17	1,335	37	2.8%	—
09/16	1,279	28	2.3%	—
09/15	1,198	44	3.7%	—
Annual Growth	5.2%	4.8%	—	—

2018 Year-End Financials

Return on assets: 2.3%
Return on equity: 4.6%
Current ratio: 3.00
Cash ($ mil.): 70

BETH ISRAEL MEDICAL CENTER

Residents of New York City's Lower East Side look to Beth Israel Medical Center to keep them healthy. A member of Continuum Health Partners the tertiary care medical facility has more than 1100 inpatient beds at two facilities in the New York area – its main location in Manhattan and another in Brooklyn. It also operates outpatient care centers and physician offices. Along with its patient care operations Beth Israel Medical Center maintains medical residency programs through its affiliation with Yeshiva University's Albert Einstein College of Medicine. The hospital also conducts institutional medical research with Rockefeller University and offers a nursing degree through its Phillips Beth Israel School of Nursing.

Operations

The main campus in Petrie has about 900 beds and hosts several major specialist units while the Brooklyn location has more than 210 beds and provides general medicine surgery radiology and intensive care services. Outpatient centers include the Phillips Ambulatory Care Center in Manhattan and the Beth Israel Ambulatory Surgi-Center in Brooklyn which provide diagnostic and ambulatory surgery services. Another affiliated clinic the Continuum Center for Health and Healing provides primary and specialty care as well as alternative services including acupuncture. The Beth Israel Medical Group operates several primary and specialty care physician clinics in Manhattan.

Altogether the Beth Israel Medical Center facilities handle about 59000 inpatient encounters annually. It also manages about 107000 emergency room visits 3500 births 11000 inpatient surgeries and 21000 outpatient surgeries. The center employs about 2300 medical and dental staff members.

Geographic Reach

The hospital's main campus in Manhattan is known as the Beth Israel Medical Center-Petrie Campus. The Brooklyn location is known as Beth Israel Brooklyn; prior to 2012 the campus was known as the Beth Israel Medical Center-Kings Highway Division.

Strategy

Continuum Health is investing in upgrades to Beth Israel Medical Center's facilities. For instance it added a new endoscopy suite at the Brooklyn campus in 2012. The main Petrie campus is renovating its emergency room and various inpatient units are increasing quality programs.

In 2012 a major expansion project was launched at the Continuum Center for Health and Healing to expand access to outpatient care for area residents; the program will add services including dermatology cardiology and podiatry. In addition the hospital opened a new cancer center in Manhattan in 2010 and a deluxe unit for high-income patients having orthopedic and other surgeries in 2008. Continuum Health is also upgrading some of Beth Israel Medical Center's IT functions including its radiology data management systems.

EXECUTIVES

President, Harris M. Nagler
The Alfred And Gail Engelberg Department Of Family Medicine, Robert M. Schiller
Chairman Medicine, Henry C. Bodenheimer
Clinical Director Continuum Heart Institute, Steven R. Bergmann
Co-director Institue For Head And Neck Cancer, Roy B. Sessions
Senior Vice President Business Development, Marc Hall
Medical Director, Bernard Brahm
Vice President Administration, Timothy Day
Occupational Medicine, Sabrina Perry
Vice President, Kenneth R Holden
Chairman, Steven Hochberg
Vice Chairman, Sorrell Mathes
Treasurer Vice President, Stacey Resk
Secretary, Esther Sanchez
Auditors: PRICEWATERHOUSECOOPERS LLP NE

LOCATIONS

HQ: BETH ISRAEL MEDICAL CENTER
281 1ST AVE, NEW YORK, NY 100032925
Phone: 212 420-2000
Web: WWW.BETHISRAELNY.ORG

PRODUCTS/OPERATIONS

Selected Centers and Services
AIDS Services
Allergy and Immunology
Anesthesiology
Appel-Venet Comprehensive Breast Service
Asian Services
Beth Israel ALS Center
Beth Israel Hernia Center
Beth Israel Medical Group
Betty & Morton Yarmon Stroke Center
Brief Psychotherapy Research Program
Cancer Center (Oncology)
Center for Blood Management and Bloodless Medicine and Surgery
Center for Endovascular Surgery
Center for Health and Healing
Craniofacial and Cleft Palate Center
Cystic Fibrosis Center
Dermatology
Endocrinology and Metabolism
Epilepsy
Friedman Diabetes Institute
Genetics
Geriatrics
Heart Institute (Cardiology)
Hematology
Hospice

Hyman Newman Institute for Neurology and Neurosugery (INN)
The Chris and Morton P. Hyman Patient Care Unit
Hyperhidrosis Program
Incontinence
Integrative Medicine
Interventional Neuroradiology
Israeli Health Program
Karpas Health Information Center
Latino Health Institute
Live Well New York
Louis Armstrong Center for Music and Medicine:
Lung Nodule Center
Maternity Services
Methadone Maintenance Treatment Program
Midwifery
Nephrology
Neurology
Orthopedics
Ostomy Program
Pain Medicine and Palliative Care
Pediatrics
Phillips Beth Israel School of Nursing
Primary Care
Psychiatry
Pulmonary and Critical Care Medicine
Radiation Oncology
Radiology
Rheumatology
Senior Health
Sleep Health
Speech-Language and Learning Center
Spine Institute
Sports Medicine
Stroke Centers
Styuvesant Square Chemical Dependency Services
Surgery
Urology
Vascular and Birthmarks Institute of New York
Women's Health
Women's Heart NY
Wound Healing Center

COMPETITORS

Bronx-Lebanon Hospital
Catholic Healthcare System
Kingsbrook Jewish Medical Center
Lutheran HealthCare
Maimonides Medical Center
MediSys Health Network
Memorial Sloan-Kettering
Montefiore Medical
NYU Hospital for Joint Diseases
New York City Health and Hospitals
NewYork-Presbyterian Healthcare
Northwell Health
SUNY Downstate

HISTORICAL FINANCIALS

Company Type: Private

Income Statement — FYE: December 31

	REVENUE ($ mil.)	NET INCOME ($ mil.)	NET PROFIT MARGIN	EMPLOYEES
12/09	1,256	15	1.2%	8,100
12/08	932	(59)	—	—
Annual Growth	34.8%	—	—	—

2009 Year-End Financials

Return on assets: 1.6%
Return on equity: 5.6%
Current ratio: 0.50
Cash ($ mil.): 98

BETHESDA HOSPITAL, INC.

From modest beginnings as a informal cottage hospital Bethesda North Hospital has grown into the fourth largest medical center in Cincinnati Ohio. Bethesda North is a full-service acute care hospital with some 360 beds for adults and 60 for children. It provides comprehensive medical and surgical care including maternity and fertility services emergency care and diagnostic imaging. The hospital joined with fellow Cincinnati health care provider Good Samaritan Hospital in 1995 to form TriHealth. Together the two hospitals offer care at some 80 locations including primary care offices fitness centers and occupational health facilities.

Operations

The full-service 420-bed acute care hospital handles some 24000 inpatient admissions each year as well as 260000 outpatient visits 77000 emergency room visits and 4000 births. It employs 165 full-time doctors and dentists and provides more than $30 million in community outreach efforts (including charity care programs) each year.

Specialty units at Bethesda North Hospital include institutes for cancer heart surgical and digestive care as well as centers for outpatient imaging breast stroke obstetrics-gynecology orthopedics and emergency trauma care. As a regional teaching center the hospital offers residency programs in a number of specialties including family medicine internal medicine OB-GYN and surgery.

Geographic Reach

Bethesda North is located in northern Cincinnati Ohio and serves as a regional trauma center as well as a major teaching hospital in the area.

Strategy

Parent organization TriHealth has aligned skilled physicians specialists surgeons and its staff to create specialty institutes offering best-of-class medical assistance in fields including heart and cancer care. To further enhance its facilities in 2013 the organization renovated the labor and delivery wing at Bethesda North Hospital. Other recent projects include the addition of a seven-story patient tower and a new outpatient imaging center.

Additionally the company has invested in TriHealth Connect the electronic medical records system that will help access accurate patient information.

Company Background

In early 2012 TriHealth unveiled a new logo.

Bethesda North traces it roots to 1896 and a cottage occupied by seven German Methodist deaconesses ministering to the poor and sick.

EXECUTIVES

Pres, John Prout
Cfo*, Craig Rucker
Controller, Brian Krause
Client Administrator, Kim Hill
Clinical Staff Pharmacist, Jessica Bennett
Logistics Management Lead Tech, Judy Booker-Westerfi
Physician, Ken Zwergel
Associate Program Director, Scott Woods
Hr Director, Sharon Hancock
Benefits Consultant, Tracy Ford
Auditors: LB BKD LLP CINCINNATI OH

LOCATIONS

HQ: BETHESDA HOSPITAL, INC.
4750 WESLEY AVE, CINCINNATI, OH 452122244
Phone: 513 569-6100
Web: WWW.TRIHEALTH.COM

PRODUCTS/OPERATIONS

List of Selected Services

Breast health
Cancer care
Digestive diseases
Heart and vascular care
Maternity (OB-GYN childbirth)
Orthopedics
Outpatient imaging
Pallative Care
Pharmacy
Robotic-assisted surgery
Stroke care
Trauma/Emergency services

COMPETITORS

Cincinnati Children's Hospital
Deaconess Associations
Kettering Health Network
Miami Valley Hospital
Premier Health Partners
St. Elizabeth Healthcare
The Christ Hospital Corporation
UC Health

HISTORICAL FINANCIALS

Company Type: Private

Income Statement — FYE: June 30

	REVENUE ($ mil.)	NET INCOME ($ mil.)	NET PROFIT MARGIN	EMPLOYEES
06/20	643	(36)	—	3,000
06/19	624	32	5.2%	—
06/18	639	52	8.2%	—
06/15	551	71	13.0%	—
Annual Growth	3.1%	—	—	—

2020 Year-End Financials

Return on assets: (-2.8%)
Return on equity: (-5.8%)
Current ratio: 0.80
Cash ($ mil.): —

BETHESDA, INC.

EXECUTIVES

Pres, J James Pearce Jr
V Pres, Chip Crowther
SEC, Ellen Katz
Treas, William A Tsacalis
V Chm, Michael F Haverkamp
Officer, Lynn Meyer
Associate Director Divi, Steven Kleeman
MD, Phillip F Oblinger
Psychiatrist, Melvin Gale
MD, Craig Eisentrout
Staffing Coordinator, Jule Williams
Auditors: BKD LLP CINCINNATI OH

LOCATIONS

HQ: BETHESDA, INC.
619 OAK ST 7N, CINCINNATI, OH 452061613
Phone: 513 569-6400
Web: WWW.TRIHEALTH.COM

HISTORICAL FINANCIALS

Company Type: Private

Income Statement — FYE: June 30

	REVENUE ($ mil.)	NET INCOME ($ mil.)	NET PROFIT MARGIN	EMPLOYEES
06/20	667	(37)	—	5,543
06/19	651	28	4.4%	—
06/18	679	78	11.6%	—
06/17	615	91	14.8%	—
Annual Growth	2.8%	—	—	—

2020 Year-End Financials

Return on assets: (-2.3%)
Return on equity: (-4.0%)
Current ratio: 0.90
Cash ($ mil.): —

BI-MART ACQUISITION CORP.

EXECUTIVES

Pres-Coo, Richard Truett
SEC, David B Zientara
Cfo, Dan Chen
Exec Admin, Jodie Murchy
Auditors: DELOITTE & TOUCHE LLP PORTLAN

LOCATIONS

HQ: BI-MART ACQUISITION CORP.
220 SENECA RD, EUGENE, OR 974022725
Phone: 541 344-0681
Web: WWW.BIMART.COM

HISTORICAL FINANCIALS

Company Type: Private

Income Statement — FYE: February 23

	REVENUE ($ mil.)	NET INCOME ($ mil.)	NET PROFIT MARGIN	EMPLOYEES
02/08	721	10	1.4%	3,300
02/07	694	11	1.7%	—
02/06	665	6	1.0%	—
02/05	648	7	1.1%	—
Annual Growth	3.6%	12.8%	—	—

2008 Year-End Financials

Return on assets: 5.6%
Return on equity: 105.3%
Current ratio: 1.90
Cash ($ mil.): 3

BIG RIVER RESOURCES, LLC.

EXECUTIVES

Ceo-Pres, Raymond E Defenbaugh
Coo, Jim Leiting
Cfo, Jim Hall
MBR-Treas, Les Allen
MBR-V Pres, Andy Brader
MBR, Gene Youngquist
Scientist, Jeannette Peterson
Water Treatment Coordinator, Jim Dutton
Operations Manager, Jim Gunter
Financial Staff Accountant, Heather Rabong
Grain Elevator Operations Mana, Jerry Borg
Auditors: CHRISTIANSON PLLP WILLMAR M

LOCATIONS

HQ: BIG RIVER RESOURCES, LLC.
211 N GEAR AVE STE 200, WEST BURLINGTON, IA 526551027
Phone: 319 753-1100
Web: WWW.BIGRIVERRESOURCES.COM

HISTORICAL FINANCIALS

Company Type: Private

Income Statement — FYE: December 31

	REVENUE ($ mil.)	NET INCOME ($ mil.)	NET PROFIT MARGIN	EMPLOYEES
12/19	823	17	2.2%	250
12/18	802	20	2.5%	—
12/17	817	33	4.2%	—
12/16	851	74	8.8%	—
Annual Growth	(1.1%)	(38.1%)	—	—

2019 Year-End Financials

Return on assets: 5.0%
Return on equity: 5.9%
Current ratio: 2.70
Cash ($ mil.): 40

BIG RIVERS ELECTRIC CORPORATION

EXECUTIVES

Ceo, Robert Berry
Chm*, Wayne Elliott
V Chm*, Larry Elder
SEC/Treas*, Paul Edd Butler
Dir*, James Sills
Dir/Acctg/Fin*, Donna Windhaus
Analyst, Tony Howard
Accounting Staff, Julia Book
Manager, Roger Hickman
Plant Manager, Keith Scott
Public Relations Manager, Nick Castlen

LOCATIONS

HQ: BIG RIVERS ELECTRIC CORPORATION
201 3RD ST, HENDERSON, KY 424202979
Phone: 270 827-2561
Web: WWW.BIGRIVERS.COM

HISTORICAL FINANCIALS

Company Type: Private

Income Statement — FYE: December 31

	REVENUE ($ mil.)	NET INCOME ($ mil.)	NET PROFIT MARGIN	EMPLOYEES
12/12	568	11	2.0%	599
12/11	561	5	1.0%	—
12/10	527	6	1.3%	—
Annual Growth	3.8%	27.0%	—	—

2012 Year-End Financials

Return on assets: 0.7%
Return on equity: 2.8%
Current ratio: 1.70
Cash ($ mil.): —

BIG WEST OF CALIFORNIA, LLC

EXECUTIVES

Member, Fred Greener
Member, Eugene Cotten
Member, Robert Payne
Manager, Eric Byers

LOCATIONS

HQ: BIG WEST OF CALIFORNIA, LLC
1104 COUNTRY HILLS DR, OGDEN, UT 844032400
Phone: 801 296-7890
Web: WWW.BIGWESTOIL.COM

HISTORICAL FINANCIALS

Company Type: Private

Income Statement — FYE: January 31

	REVENUE ($ mil.)	NET INCOME ($ mil.)	NET PROFIT MARGIN	EMPLOYEES
01/07	1,438	(32)	—	260
01/06	1,109	23	2.1%	—
Annual Growth	29.6%	—	—	—

BIG WEST OIL, LLC

Big West Oil keeps the wagon trains rolling across the big West – at least the station wagons. The company is in the oil processing and products business centered around its 35000 barrels-a-day refinery in North Salt Lake Utah to its fleet of tanker trucks that gather crude oil from the refinery and other purchases and deliver to wholesale customers and gas station/convenience stores in seven Western states including Colorado Idaho Nevada Utah and Wyoming. The company's refinery processes crude oil produced in Utah Wyoming and Canada. Big West Oil is a subsidiary of FJ Management.

EXECUTIVES

Pres, Fred L Greener
Manager of Crude Oil Supply, Ed Hatch
Executive Assistant, Kris Barkdull
Process Safety Management Coor, Laura Plummer
It Technical Manager, Orson Thornton
Compliance Manager, Stuart Smith
Pricing, Tawna Cruz
Project Engineer, Andrew Springer
Unit Supervisor, John Stoops
Safety, Dusty Ott
Safety Manager, Nickolas Skabelund

LOCATIONS

HQ: BIG WEST OIL, LLC
333 W CENTER ST, NORTH SALT LAKE, UT 840542805
Phone: 801 624-1000
Web: WWW.BIGWESTOIL.COM

COMPETITORS

HollyFrontier
Marathon Petroleum
Sinclair Oil
Tesoro

HISTORICAL FINANCIALS

Company Type: Private

Income Statement — FYE: January 31

	REVENUE ($ mil.)	NET INCOME ($ mil.)	NET PROFIT MARGIN	EMPLOYEES
01/08	3,053	191	6.3%	460
01/07	2,399	89	3.7%	—
01/06	2,014	102	5.1%	—
01/05	735	50	6.9%	—
Annual Growth	60.7%	55.6%	—	—

2008 Year-End Financials

Return on assets: 19.9%
Return on equity: 50.4%
Current ratio: 1.20
Cash ($ mil.): 6

BIG-D CONSTRUCTION CORP.

Big-D builds big things. Founded in 1967 by Dee Livingood (who carried the nickname "Big-Dee") the family-run construction firm offers design/build services to customers in a dozen states from offices in Utah Arizona California and Wyoming. Known for its work on projects in the food and beverage sector Big-D also works on light commercial office and retail properties manufacturing health care and hospitality projects among others. Its clients have included Hampton and Marriott. Big-D's Signature Group division builds high-end luxury homes as well as condominiums spas and other special projects in resort communities. Its Self-Performed Services unit works on parking garage architectural and structural projects. Big-D ranked 2nd in Top Utah General Contractor by Utah Design & Construction Magazine (rankings are based on revenues).

Operations

Big-D generates around $1.5 billion in revenues per year and staffs about 1500 employees on average. The company has completed nearly 75 LEED projects and over 800 projects using construction management/general contractor and design-build services.

The contractor operates four main divisions. The Commercial division serves commercial and industrial customers that offers construction management and design-build services for projects exceeding $5 million in scope while the Light Commercial division offers more streamlined construction services for tenant improvement commercial and light industrial clients with smaller projects (less than $5 million in scope).

The Self-Performed Services division works on concrete (like parking garages) carpentry and specialty construction projects. The Signature division mostly works on higher-end housing and resort-related projects for private estate and resort property owners.

Geographic Reach

The Salt Lake City-based contractor serves clients with offices in a dozen of states. Its other offices are in Ogden Lindon and Park City in Utah; Pleasanton California; Tempe Arizona; Jackson Wyoming; Las Vegas Nevada; Bozeman Montana; Rexburg Idaho; and St. Paul Minnesota.

Sales and Marketing

Big-D serves industries from industrial/mining hospitality federal/state technology retail commercial education healthcare warehouse/distribution manufacturing and food/beverage.

Some of Big-D's clients Salt Lake City Public Library Crown Plaza Marriott University of Utah Kenco Freedman Hershey Dannon Yogurt and Malt-O-Meal among others.

Financial Performance

Big-D Construction reports an average yearly revenue of $1.5 billion.

Strategy

Big-D Construction applies management techniques that maintain a frictionless team environment at every stage of the building process.

The company also utilizes a "Design?Build" delivery system that enables clients to contract with a single entity to complete both the design and construction phases of the project. As all the elements of its clients' projects are facilitated through Big-D it is able to more readily control costs and schedules including offering a Guaranteed Maximum Price.

Big-D has taken on new projects in recent years. In mid-2020 it broke ground on a new Post House project. Big-D is working with Lowe Property Group Q Factor BCG Holdings and Bridge Investment Group to provide Construction Management and General Contracting services (CM/GC) for this monumental project.

Big-D also has a joint venture project with Holder Construction which is the new Salt Lake City Airport Redevelopment program. This major project has been in the works for the past six and a half years and is officially opening in late 2020. In early 2020 Big-D reported that this project was ahead of schedule due to the significant drop in the number of travelers. The enhanced construction opportunity saved hundreds of millions of dollars and has allowed the project to finish years ahead of schedule.

Company Background

Big-D courted more government projects as a way to weather the economic downturn which has put a halt on many commercial jobs. Among those public projects was the Utah Museum of Natural History at The University of Utah and the Wallace F. Bennett Federal Building in Salt Lake City. Big-D also is focusing on developing its eco-friendly construction business.

EXECUTIVES

Cfo, Larry Worrell
President Mountain West Group, Forrest McNabb
President Big-d Construction, Rob Moore
President Big-d Pacific, Ken Mitchell
Svp, Cory Moore
Vp And Managing Director Southwest, Jeff Arnold
Vp And Managing Director Signature, Michael Kerby
Evp, Troy Thompson
Ceo, Jack Livingood
Auditors: GRANT THORNTON LLP SALT LAKE

LOCATIONS

HQ: BIG-D CONSTRUCTION CORP.
404 W 400 S, SALT LAKE CITY, UT 841011108
Phone: 801 415-6000
Web: WWW.BIGDCORP.COM

Selected Markets

Arizona
Arkansas
California
Colorado
Georgia
Hawaii
Idaho
Montana
Nevada
New Mexico
North Carolina
North Dakota
Oklahoma
Oregon
South Dakota
Tennessee
Texas
Utah
Washington

PRODUCTS/OPERATIONS

Selected Services

Construction management
Design/build
Field services
 Architectural concrete
 Finish carpentry
 Rough framing
 Structural concrete
General contracting
Green and Leadership in Energy and Environmental Design

Selected Industry Specializations

Commercial/public spaces (governmental educational and office complexes; mixed-use projects)
Food processing and distribution
Health care
Hospitality and resort
Manufacturing
Retail

COMPETITORS

Bechtel
Hensel Phelps Construction
J.F. Shea
Jacobsen Construction
Jaynes Companies
Layton
Okland Construction
Swinerton

HISTORICAL FINANCIALS

Company Type: Private

Income Statement FYE: December 31

	REVENUE ($ mil.)	NET INCOME ($ mil.)	NET PROFIT MARGIN	EMPLOYEES
12/12	541	0	—	574
12/11	554	0	—	—
12/10	259	0	—	—
Annual Growth	44.4%	—	—	—

2012 Year-End Financials

Return on assets: —
Return on equity: —
Current ratio: 1.40
Cash ($ mil.): 38

BILLINGS CLINIC

Billings Clinic is an integrated health care system that serves the residents of Big Sky Country. Through a group of more than 450 doctors and other providers the clinic caters a vast region covering much of Montana northern Wyoming and the western Dakotas. It offers 50-plus specialties such as emergency and trauma cancer orthopedics birthing cardiovascular neurosciences dialysis and pediatrics. Its operations include a more than 300-bed hospital and the organization's main clinic. Additionally Billings Clinic has nearly 15 regional partnerships including management agreements with more than 10 Critical Access Hospitals and a joint venture in Community Medical Center (Missoula MT) with RegionalCare Hospital Partners. The not-for-profit health care system is owned by the community.

Operations

With its vast service area the health care system provides a MedFlight advanced life support fixed-wing aircraft service that transports critically ill or injured patients from rural communities.

As part of its operations Billings Clinic runs a Level II emergency and trauma center 20-suite family birthing center Level III neonatal intensive care unit inpatient cancer care unit and surgery centers. The health care system's cancer center provides both inpatient and outpatient care in Billings.

Billings Clinic is led by a physician CEO Billings Clinic is governed by a board of community members nurses and physicians.

Billings Clinic's Community Benefit totalled more than $38 million including $9.9 million in financial assistance provided to nearly 11000 patients.

Geographic Reach

As the largest health care organization in the area Billings Clinic's service area extends 260000 miles to provide specialty care for residents of rural

Montana (headquarters) Wyoming and North Dakota.

Strategy

Billings Clinic works with pharmaceutical sponsors on a variety of clinical research trials in various phases and indications.

In October 2019 Billings Clinic and Broadwater Health Center officially signed an affiliation agreement to partner together to provide essential health care services to the people of Townsend Montana. Earlier that month the Hospital District Board also voted in favor of the transaction for the hospital and ambulance service.

It also signed another affiliation agreement with Powell Valley Healthcare (PVHC) in early 2020 concluding a three-year long process of creating a new governance arrangement between the two organizations. In the new affiliation Billings Clinic will provide management services for PVHC.

Company Background

The Billings Clinic evolved from the general practice of Dr. Arthur J. Movius who founded his Billings practice in 1911.

It expanded its capacity for infusions in 2012 when its Billings Clinic Cody location opened an infusion center. In late 2012 the organization also opened a new Stillwater Billings Clinic medical facility which combines Stillwater Community Hospital and Billings Clinic Columbus and integrates the billing process for the two health care facilities.

EXECUTIVES

Vp And Cio, Chris Stevens
Physician In Chief, Mark C. Rumans
President Billings Clinic Foundation, Jim Duncan
Vp Hospital Operations, Lu Byrd
Cfo, Connie F. Prewitt
Ceo, Randall Gibb
Director Of Radiology, Douglas Bell
Director Of Medical Records, Lorraine Jelle
Vice President Regional Operations, Vern Carda
Vice President, Erik Wood
Treasurer And Director, J. Scott Millikan
Vice Chairman, David Brown
Board Certified Member, Stacy Shomento

LOCATIONS

HQ: BILLINGS CLINIC
2800 10TH AVE N, BILLINGS, MT 591010703
Phone: 406 657-4000
Web: WWW.BILLINGSCLINIC.COM

PRODUCTS/OPERATIONS

Selected Services

Advance Medical Directives
Allergy Asthma Immunology
Aspen Meadows - Skilled Nursing and Assisted Living
Anticoagulation Clinic
Breast Center
Cancer Center
Cardiovascular Services
Cardiovascular Surgery
Children's Services
Continence Center
Community Training Center
Cosmetic Surgery
da Vinci Surgical System
Dermatology Center
Diabetes Management Center
Diagnostic Imaging
Diabetes
Dialysis Center
Eldercare Solutions
Emergency & Trauma Center
Emmi Educational Videos
Employer Services - Occupational Health
Endocrinology
Eye Center
Facial Plastic Surgery
Family Medicine
Family Birth Center
Gastroenterology
General Surgery
Genetic Counseling
Geriatric Assessment Program
Gynecologic Cancer
Heart Services
Heart Surgery
Home Oxygen & Medical Equipment
Hospitalist Program
Infectious Diseases
Insurance Finder
Internal Medicine
Laboratory Services
LifeFit
Maternal-Fetal Medicine
MedFlight Air Ambulance
Mental Health Services
Metabolism Center
Mohs Surgery
Nutrition Services
Neurosciences
Obstetrics & Gynecology
Occupational Health - Employer Services
Ophthalmology
Orthopedics & Sports Medicine
Palliative Care
Pediatrics
  Pediatric Center
  Pediatric Cancer
  Pediatric Diabetes
  Pediatric Gastroenterology
  Pediatric Pulmonology
  Rehabilitation (Therapy)
Pharmacy
Physical Medicine & Rehabilitation
Plastic Surgery
Primary Care for Adults
Pulmonary Rehabilitation Program
Radiology Services
Reproductive Medicine and Fertility Care
Robotic Surgery
SameDay Care
Senior Services
Sleep Disorders Center
Sports Medicine
Sports Specific Camps
Stroke Care
Surgery Center
Transitional Care Unit
Urology Services
Vascular Surgery
Vein Clinic
Women's Free Screenings
Women's and Children's Services

Selected Affiliate Hospitals and Clinics

Beartooth Billings Clinic - Red Lodge
Colstrip Medical Center - Colstrip
Daniels Memorial Healthcare - Scobey
Livingston HealthCare - Livingston
North Big Horn Hospital - Lovell
Pioneer Medical Center - Big Timber
Roundup Memorial Healthcare - Roundup
Sheridan Memorial Hospital Association
Stillwater Billings Clinic

COMPETITORS

Glendive Medical Center
St. Alexius Medical Center
St. James Healthcare
St. Patrick Hospital
Wyoming Medical Center

HISTORICAL FINANCIALS

Company Type: Private

Income Statement — FYE: June 30

	REVENUE ($ mil.)	NET INCOME ($ mil.)	NET PROFIT MARGIN	EMPLOYEES
06/16	586	(2)	—	3,300
06/15	565	30	5.4%	—
06/14	593	38	6.6%	—
06/13	560	14	2.6%	—
Annual Growth	1.6%	—	—	—

2016 Year-End Financials

Return on assets: (-0.3%)
Return on equity: (-0.6%)
Current ratio: 1.80
Cash ($ mil.): 13

BIOMEDICAL RESEARCH FOUNDATION OF NORTHWEST LOUISIANA

EXECUTIVES

Chb, Stephen F Skrivanos
V Pres*, James D Dean
V Pres*, Dennis Lower
Prin*, John F George Jr
SEC*, Johnette Magner
Treas*, Arthur Thompson
Director, Joseph Sarpy Jr
Director, John F Sharp
Director, Virginia K Shehee
Director, Elaine Joyce Simpkins PHD
Director, W Juan Watkins
Auditors: POSTLETHWAITE & NETTERVILLE B

LOCATIONS

HQ: BIOMEDICAL RESEARCH FOUNDATION OF NORTHWEST LOUISIANA
2031 KINGS HWY, SHREVEPORT, LA 711033600
Phone: 318 716-4190
Web: WWW.BIOMED.ORG

HISTORICAL FINANCIALS

Company Type: Private

Income Statement — FYE: September 30

	REVENUE ($ mil.)	NET INCOME ($ mil.)	NET PROFIT MARGIN	EMPLOYEES
09/15	564	14	2.6%	50
09/14	502	(1)	—	—
09/13*	10	(5)	—	—
12/09	15	0	2.1%	—
Annual Growth	81.9%	88.0%	—	—

*Fiscal year change

2015 Year-End Financials

Return on assets: 3.8%
Return on equity: 24.4%
Current ratio: 1.10
Cash ($ mil.): 8

BIOURJA TRADING, LLC

EXECUTIVES

Chm-Ceo, Amit Bhandari
Vp Hr*, Arpita Bhandari
Head of Ethanol Trading*, Jordan Fife
Law Specialist, Varinder Gill
Head of Human Resources, Steve Sfamenos
Manager, Paras Shah
Auditors: CARR RIGGS & INGRAM LLC HOUST

LOCATIONS

HQ: BIOURJA TRADING, LLC
1080 ELDRIDGE PKWY # 115, HOUSTON, TX 770772576
Phone: 832 775-9000
Web: WWW.BIOURJA.COM

HISTORICAL FINANCIALS

Company Type: Private

Income Statement FYE: December 31

	REVENUE ($ mil.)	NET INCOME ($ mil.)	NET PROFIT MARGIN	EMPLOYEES
12/13	4,622	26	0.6%	72
12/12	2,992	11	0.4%	—
12/11	3,842	13	0.4%	—
Annual Growth	9.7%	38.6%	—	—

2013 Year-End Financials

Return on assets: 16.9%
Return on equity: 57.0%
Current ratio: 1.40
Cash ($ mil.): 15

BLACK & VEATCH CORPORATION

Black & Veatch (BV) is one of the world's top global engineering procurement consulting and construction firms specializing in infrastructure development for the energy oil and gas water environmental and telecommunications industries and governments. BV offers microconsulting experts on demand engineering consulting and management consulting. The employee-owned contractor has offices in more than 20 countries including coal nuclear and combustion turbine plants; drinking water and coastal water operations; and wireless and broadband installations. The company was founded by engineers E. B. Black and Tom Veatch in 1915.

Operations

The company offers services such as asset management construction consulting engineering environmental master planning procurement and program and risk management.

Geographic Reach

Black & Veatch operates in more 20 countries in Americas Asia Pacific Europe Middle East and Africa regions. Its headquarters is located in Overland Park Kansas.

Sales and Marketing

The company offer its services to certain industries such as commercial data centers governments industrial and manufacturing mining oil and gas power telecommunications transportation and water industries.

Strategy

In 2020 Black & Veatch and Hexagon's PPM division had a new technology partnership that will advance engineering design further into the digital age. To accomplish this goal Black & Veatch's oil and gas business has focused on maximizing the functionalities of Hexagon's Intergraph Smart® suite of engineering design tools. Black & Veatch is working to fully leverage Hexagon technology throughout the construction value chain to create faster more seamless communication quicker updates and smoother integration with project partner vendors and subcontractors.

The company also had a strategic partnership with ENACT Systems Inc. to elevate its commercial solar project management to new heights in Southeast Asia.

EXECUTIVES

Ceo Energy Business, O. H. (Dean) Oskvig
Cfo, Karen L. Daniel
President Federal Services Division, William R. (Bill) Van Dyke
President Telecommunications, Martin G. Travers
President Water Business, Cindy Wallis-Lage
Chief Administrative Officer; President Administrative Division, James R. (Jim) Lewis
Svp B&v Energy Asia Middle East India Europe And B&v Water Asia Pacific, Hoe Wai Cheong
President Management Consulting, John Chevrette
Evp Energy, Steven L. Edwards
President Construction & Procurement, John E. Murphy
Assistant Vp Enterprise Risk Management And Project Management Office, Lisa Terry
Associate Vice President, Adrienne Mickells
Senior Vice President, Ernie Wright Ernie Wright
Vice President Finance, Angela Hoffman
Vice President Tax Counsel, Jeffrey Stamm
Vice President Senior Project Director, Jim Doull
Vice President Of Service, Emily Vijayakirthi
Associate Vice President Mechanical Department Manager Energy, Joel Lundquist
Associate Vice President And Project Manager, Larry Lee
Vice President Of Enterprise Systems, Bob Brnilovich
Associate Vice President, Scott Roesle
Senior Vice President Assistant General Counsel And Chief Compliance Manager, Peter Loftspring
Vice President, Lyle White
Vice President Projects Service Area, Doug Anderson
Associate Vice President Project Manager, David Lefebvre
Vice President Administration, Joy Johnson
Vice President Marketing, Peter Sheckleford-lister
Vice President And Project Director Power Business, Jeffrey Kurtz
Associate Vice President, Norman Song
Associate Vice President Construction Group Leader, Mike Baker
Vice President, Scott Kinner
Associate Vice President, Christopher Mueller
Associate Vice President And Division Counsel, Curtis J Martin
Associate Vice President Asset Management Services, David Brill
Associate Vp And Project Manager For Global Energy Business, Mark Mcdermott
Vice President Public Safety, Chris Krafft
Vice President, Dave Abrams
Associate Vice President, Matt Bond
Associate Vice President, Donnie Griffin
Associate Vice President Director Wastewater Treatment Technology President Mark Steichen Process Engineer. J Associate Vice, Mark Steichen
Department Head, Dan Nelson
Vice President, Richard Jacober
Associate Vice President, Derek Cambridge
Associate Vice President Asset Management, David Price
Associate Vice President Asset Management, David C Price
Vice President And Project Director, Charles Mitchell
Associate Vice President, John H Johnson
Associate Vice President Director Of Finance And Administration B And V Water Americas, Mike Goff
Senior Vice President Mining, James Spenceley
Vice President Client Director, Peter Cohlmia
Senior Vice President And Managing Direc, James Schnieders
Associate Vice President Project Director, Jim Morley
Vice President Business Development, Julie Cronin
Associate Vice President, Craig Brown
Senior Vice President, Patrick Jameson
Secretary, Cheryl Toske

LOCATIONS

HQ: BLACK & VEATCH CORPORATION
11401 LAMAR AVE, OVERLAND PARK, KS 662111598
Phone: 913 458-2000
Web: WWW.BV.COM

PRODUCTS/OPERATIONS

Market Sectors

Energy
- Air quality control
- Coal
- Combustion turbine
- Gas oil and chemicals
- Hydropower
- IGCC
- Nuclear
- Power delivery
- Renewables

Environmental
- Air quality
- Compliance management
- Due diligence
- Field studies/investigations
- Permitting
- Prevention plans
- Remediation
- Watershed analysis and restoration
- Water/wastewater

Federal
- Civil works
- Disaster support
- Facilities
- Federal design-build
- Management programs
- Security

Management consulting
- Integrated strategy development
- Process improvement
- Technology application services

Services
- Asset management
- Climate change solutions
- Construction
- Design/build
- Engineering and design
- Engineering consulting
- Infrastructure planning
- Management consulting
- Procurement
- Program management
- SAP services
- Smart utility
- Water spares

Telecommunications
- Broadband wireline
- Cyber and physical security
- Site acquisition services
- Telecom for smart utilities
- Utility automation
- Utility telecommunications
- Wireless

Water
- Conveyance systems and tunneling services
- Drinking water
- Hydropower
- River and coastal management
- Wastewater
- Water resources

COMPETITORS

AECOM
ARCADIS
Amec Foster Wheeler
Balfour Beatty Infrastructure
Bechtel
Burns & McDonnell
Burns and Roe
Costain
EA Engineering
Fluor
HNTB Companies
Louis Berger
MWH Global
McDermott
Michael Baker
Mott MacDonald
Parsons Brinckerhoff
Parsons Corporation
SNC-Lavalin
TIC Holdings
Tetra Tech
Zachry Inc.

HISTORICAL FINANCIALS

Company Type: Private

Income Statement — FYE: December 31

	REVENUE ($ mil.)	NET INCOME ($ mil.)	NET PROFIT MARGIN	EMPLOYEES
12/09	1,163	58	5.0%	4,065
12/08	1,267	16	1.3%	—
12/07	1,287	33	2.6%	—
Annual Growth	(4.9%)	31.7%	—	—

2009 Year-End Financials

Return on assets: 6.9%
Return on equity: 21.8%
Current ratio: 1.30
Cash ($ mil.): 16

BLACK & VEATCH HOLDING COMPANY

EXECUTIVES

Chb-Pres-Ceo, Steven L Edwards
Evp-Cfo, Kenneth L Williams
Svp-Treasurer, Michael Williams
Exec V Pres-SEC, Timothy W Triplett
Asst SEC, Andrea C Bernica
IBEW General Foreman, William Ayers
Project Engineer, Ian Grant
Employee, Kevin Bryant
Associate, Michael Miglioretti
Employee, Michelle Duck
Electrical Engineer, Badrinarayana Sankaran
Auditors: KPMG LLP KANSAS CITY MISSOUR

LOCATIONS

HQ: BLACK & VEATCH HOLDING COMPANY
11401 LAMAR AVE, OVERLAND PARK, KS 662111598
Phone: 913 458-2000
Web: WWW.BV.COM

HISTORICAL FINANCIALS

Company Type: Private

Income Statement — FYE: December 28

	REVENUE ($ mil.)	NET INCOME ($ mil.)	NET PROFIT MARGIN	EMPLOYEES
12/18	3,479	80	2.3%	8,495
12/17	3,364	87	2.6%	—
12/16*	3,207	75	2.3%	—
01/16	2,955	109	3.7%	—
Annual Growth	5.6%	(9.7%)	—	—

*Fiscal year change

2018 Year-End Financials

Return on assets: 4.9%
Return on equity: 54.7%
Current ratio: 1.10
Cash ($ mil.): 383

BLACK & VEATCH INTERNATIONAL COMPANY

EXECUTIVES

Chb, Steve Edwards
President, Mario Azar
Evp-SEC, Timothy W Triplett
Evp-Cfo, Kenneth L Williams
Svp-Treasurer, Michael Williams
Svp-Asset SEC, Peter D Loftspring
Asst Secretary, Andrea C Bernica
Engineer, Jeff Coggins
Associate Vice President, Donnie Ginn
Auditors: KPMG LLP KANSAS CITY MO

LOCATIONS

HQ: BLACK & VEATCH INTERNATIONAL COMPANY
11401 LAMAR AVE, OVERLAND PARK, KS 662111598
Phone: 913 458-2000
Web: WWW.BV.COM

HISTORICAL FINANCIALS

Company Type: Private

Income Statement — FYE: December 31

	REVENUE ($ mil.)	NET INCOME ($ mil.)	NET PROFIT MARGIN	EMPLOYEES
12/09	711	43	6.1%	283
12/08	711	43	6.1%	—
12/07	1	(0)	—	—
12/06	1	(0)	—	—
Annual Growth	754.9%	—	—	—

2009 Year-End Financials

Return on assets: 8.5%
Return on equity: 37.5%
Current ratio: 1.10
Cash ($ mil.): 39

BLOUNT INTERNATIONAL, INC.

Folks at Blount International have their work cut out for them. The manufacturer produces cutting chain guide bars sprockets and accessories for chainsaws concrete-cutting equipment and lawnmower blades. Blount's lineup is sold under brands Oregon Carlton and KOX to outdoor equipment OEMs and the replacement and retail markets. Other subsidiaries supply log splitters and other agriculture add-ons. End users are professionals and consumers engaged in forestry lawn and garden farming and construction activities. The company's manufacturing facilities dot Brazil Canada China and the US. Blount was founded in 1947 as Oregon Saw Chain Company by Joe Cox.

Operations

Blount sells its products across two markets: forestry lawn and garden (FLAG) and farm ranch and agriculture (FRAG). It also operates a concrete cutting and finishing (CCF) equipment business.

The company produces saw chains bars and sprockets and outdoor equipment accessories and parts for the garden and landscape industry. Blount offers these products under the brand names OREGON Carlton and KOX.

Blount manufactures high-quality attachments and implements log splitters and other agriculture-related products as well as distributor of aftermarket parts. These products are marketed under the brand names Woods Speeco Alitec Central Fabricators Gannon Wain-Roy and WoodsCare.

The company also manufactures and markets diamond-cutting chains assembles and markets concrete cutting chain saws and purchases other concrete cutting products that are marketed to the construction and utility industries.

Geographic Reach

Oregon-based Blount sells its products in more than 110 countries around the world.

Sales and Marketing

The company sells its products through a global sales and distribution network of over 300 distributors 30000 dealers direct sales companies and mass merchants which sell to the global forestry lawn and garden; farm ranch and agriculture; and construction products end markets. The company also sells through nearly 100 original equipment manufacturers.

Company Background

Blount was founded in 1947 as Oregon Saw Chain Company by Joe Cox.

EXECUTIVES

Svp And Cfo, Calvin E. Jenness, age 64, $385,000 total compensation
Ceo And Chairman, Joshua L. (Josh) Collins, age 55, $565,000 total compensation
President Frag Division, Gerald D. (Jerry) Johnson, $350,000 total compensation
Vp Flag Manufacturing Operations, William C. Alford
President And Coo, David A. Willmott, age 50, $500,000 total compensation
Svp Global Supply Chain, David K. Parrish
Vp And Cio, Kevin M. Trepa
Svp Global Sales And Marketing Flag Division, Dave P. Gillrie
Vice President Marketing, Alan Lofurno
Vice President Supply Chain, Michael Ritter
Vice President, Valdir R Viana
National Account Manager, Chris Seeman
National Account Manager, Casey Cecil
Auditors: KPMG LLP PORTLAND OREGON

LOCATIONS

HQ: BLOUNT INTERNATIONAL, INC.
4909 SE INTERNATIONAL WAY, PORTLAND, OR 972224679
Phone: 503 653-8881
Web: WWW.BLOUNT.COM

PRODUCTS/OPERATIONS

Selected Products

Chain drive sprockets
Chainsaw guide bars
Concrete-cutting chainsaws and circular saws (gasoline and hydraulic powered)
Cutting chain (for chainsaws)
Diamond-segmented chain (for cutting concrete)
Farm accessories
Lawn and garden cutting attachments
Lawnmower and edger cutting blades
Log splitters
Maintenance tools (for chainsaws and mechanical timber harvesting equipment)
Tractor driven post-hole diggers
Tractor three-point linkage parts

COMPETITORS

Alamo Group
Ariens
Briggs & Stratton
Caterpillar
Champion Cutting Tool
Deere
Dover Corp.
Emak Group
Great Plains Manufacturing
Husqvarna
Kubota
MTD Products
Metso
STIHL Incorporated
Terex

HISTORICAL FINANCIALS

Company Type: Private

Income Statement FYE: December 31

	REVENUE ($ mil.)	NET INCOME ($ mil.)	NET PROFIT MARGIN	EMPLOYEES
12/15	828	(49)	—	4,000
12/14	944	36	3.9%	—
12/13	900	4	0.5%	—
12/12	927	39	4.3%	—
Annual Growth	(3.7%)	—	—	—

2015 Year-End Financials

Return on assets: (-7.2%)
Return on equity: (-45.1%)
Current ratio: 2.60
Cash ($ mil.): 25

BLUE BUFFALO PET PRODUCTS, INC.

Blue Buffalo Pet Products is converting pet parents into what it refers to as "True Blue Believers" with its wholesome pet food offerings. The company makes natural dog and cat food using whole meats fruits and vegetables with no by-products or artificial ingredients; some products are also grain-free. By riding the wave of people forking over big bucks for natural and wholesome food for themselves and their families Blue Bufallo has positioned dogs and cats as members of the family and has risen to be the #1 brand in the Wholesome Natural pet food market segment. The company sells its products internationally but the majority of net sales remains in the US. Bill Bishop started the company when his dog Blue developed cancer but recovered after eating food he formulated. Cereal giant General Mills bought Blue Buffalo in 2018.

Change in Company Type

In mid-2018 consumer packaged goods company General Mills paid some $8 billion for Blue Buffalo in its quest to reshape its portfolio with more natural and organic brands. Blue Buffalo will operate as an independent subsidiary while taking advantage of the supply chain distribution and sales capabilities of its new parent.

Operations

Blue Buffalo operates its business in one reportable segment. It makes five main lines of pet food covering different product types diet types breed sizes for dogs and life stages.

The company has traditionally sold its products through specialty channels such as pet stores in the past but has recently expanded its distribution into the food drug and mass (FDM) markets (such as grocery stores) in the US where it now generates more than half its revenues.

The company produces 55% of its dry food in its own food production facility in Joplin MO and plans to open a new facility in Richmond IN by the end of 2018. Blue Buffalo hopes to handle 85% of its dry food production at these two sites over the next several years. The remainder of food production is through third-party contract manufacturers.

Geographic Reach

Blue Bufallo's BLUE brand products are sold in the US Canada Japan and Mexico. The US accounts for more than 95% of net sales.

Sales and Marketing

Blue Buffalo BLUE products are sold through multiple distributors who also provide logistics services and some in-field sales support. Products appear in specialty channels such as national and regional pet stores farm and feed stores e-commerce retailers and select grocery stores. The company has minimal sales through veterinary clinics and hospitals. Its sales teams are organized by type of retail accounts they sell to — National Accounts Regional Accounts eCommerce and Food-Drug-Mass (FDM).

The company promotes and markets its products through television internet and print advertisements produced by an in-house agency. Blue Buffalo has increased its advertising spend about 60% in the past three years ($132.3 million in 2016 $101.2 million in 2016 and $83.6 million in 2015).

In 2017 almost 60% of Blue Buffalo's sales were generated from its two largest customers PetSmart and Petco. Other customers include Tractor Supply Company Pet Supermarket Target Kroger Meijer and Publix.

Financial Performance

Blue Buffalo has enjoyed double digit growth over the past several years with sales in 2017 amounting to $1.3 billion (an 11% increase over 2016). Net sales were driven by a favorable product mix growth in sales in national pet superstores and expansion in farm and feed stores and e-commerce retailers.

Net income increased 49% to $193.5 million in 2017 compared with $130.2 million in 2016 mainly due to increased volume supply chain efficiencies and lower tax rates.

Cash at the end of fiscal 2017 was $282.2 million a decrease of $10.3 million from the prior year. Cash from operations contributed $193.9 billion to the coffers while investing activities used $171.0 million mainly for capital expenditures for a three-year program to expand its internal manufacturing capabilities. Financing activities used another $33.5 million for repurchases of common stock.

Strategy

Blue Buffalo touts its extensive product line and continuous innovation as differentiators for the company. It also includes educating "pet parents" as part of the company's strategy for attracting new customers; it uses part-time employees it calls Pet Detectives to interact with and market directly to customers shopping for pet food in stores in the US and Canada. The company has also significantly increased spending on advertising over the past three years. Some of Blue Buffalo's key initiatives going forward include expanding distribution in the US growing its FDM business expanding the wet food and pet treat lines and increasing its focus on e-commerce sales.

The company is leveraging General Mills' resources and expertise to expand its FDM distribution in the US and refine its supply chain and category management operations. It will also capitalize on General Mills' customer relationship management (CRM) capabilities to to increase communication with customers.

In the pet specialty channel Blue Buffalo is investing in media advertising to support sales as well as new packaging and products in the wet food and treats categories an area it feels is currently underdeveloped.

The company aims to continue manufacturing operations at both company-owned as well as co-manufacturing facilities. It will open a new facility in Richmond IN in 2018 and a new treat facility at its existing location in Joplin MO.

EXECUTIVES

Evp Cfo And Treasurer, Michael (Mike) Nathenson, $318,270 total compensation
Ceo, William (Billy) Bishop, $269,088 total compensation
Board Member, Raymond Debbane
Board Member, Michael Eck
Auditors: KPMG LLP STAMFORD CONNECTICU

LOCATIONS

HQ: BLUE BUFFALO PET PRODUCTS, INC.
11 RIVER RD STE 103, WILTON, CT 068976011
Phone: 203 762-9751
Web: WWW.BLUEBUFFALO.COM

PRODUCTS/OPERATIONS

2017 Sales

	$ mil.	% of total
Dry foods	1,013	80
Wet foods treats and other	261	20
Total	**1,274**	**100**

Selected Product Lines

BLUE Life Protection Formula
BLUE Wilderness
BLUE Basics
BLUE Freedom
BLUE Natural Veterinary Diet

COMPETITORS

Big Heart Pet Brands
Breeder's Choice
Hill's Pet Nutrition
Iams
Mars Incorporated
Nestlé Purina PetCare
Nutro Products
OurPet's Co.
Pet Supermarket
Pet Valu
Procter & Gamble
Royal Canin
Simmons Foods
WellPet

HISTORICAL FINANCIALS

Company Type: Private

Income Statement FYE: December 31

	REVENUE ($ mil.)	NET INCOME ($ mil.)	NET PROFIT MARGIN	EMPLOYEES
12/17	1,274	193	15.2%	1,800
12/16	1,149	130	11.3%	—
12/15	1,027	89	8.7%	—
Annual Growth	11.4%	47.1%	—	—

2017 Year-End Financials

Return on assets: 22.8%
Return on equity: 64.7%
Current ratio: 3.70
Cash ($ mil.): 282

BLUE CROSS & BLUE SHIELD ASSOCIATION

Blue insurers prefer to sing a happy healthy tune. Health plan providers affiliated with the Blue Cross and Blue Shield Association (BCBSA) — known as "the Blues" — serve some 106 million members nationwide. The association is a federation of about 40 independent health insurance companies who license the Blue Cross and Blue Shield brand names. Member companies own the rights to sell Blue-branded health plans within defined regions. BCBSA coordinates some national programs such as BlueCard which allows members of one franchisee to have coverage in other service areas and the Federal Employee Program (FEP) which covers more than half of federal government employees retirees and their families. The company traces its roots back to 1929.

HISTORY

Blue Cross was born in 1929 when Baylor University official Justin Kimball offered schoolteachers 21 days of hospital care for $6 a year. A major plan feature was a community rating system that based premiums on the community claims experience rather than members' conditions.

The Blue Cross symbol was devised in 1933 by Minnesota plan executive E. A. van Steenwyck. By 1935 many of the 15 plans in 11 states used the symbol. Many states gave the plans not-for-profit status and in 1936 the American Hospital Association formed the Committee on Hospital Service (renamed the Blue Cross Association in 1948) to coordinate them.

As Blue Cross grew state medical societies sponsored prepaid plans to cover doctors' fees. In 1946 they united under the aegis of the American Medical Association (AMA) as the Associated Medical Care Plans (later the Association of Blue Shield Plans).

In 1948 the AMA thwarted a Blue Cross attempt to merge with Blue Shield. But the Blues increasingly cooperated on public policy matters while competing for members and each Blue formed a not-for-profit corporation to coordinate its plan's activities.

Blue Cross insured about a third of the US by 1960. Over the next decade the Blues started administering Medicare and other government health plans and by 1970 half of Blue Cross' premiums came from government entities.

In the 1970s the Blues adopted such cost-control measures as review of hospital admissions; many plans even abandoned the community rating system. Most began emphasizing preventive care in HMOs or PPOs. The two Blues finally merged in 1982 to form the Blue Cross and Blue Shield Association (BCBSA) but this had little effect on the associations' bottom lines as losses grew.

By the 1990s the Blues were big business. Some of the state associations offered officers high salaries and perks but still insisted on special regulatory treatment.

But as lower-cost plans attracted the hale and hearty the Blues' customers became older sicker and more expensive. With their quasi-charitable status and outdated rate structures many Blues plans lost market share.

The Blues fought back by updating their technology and rate structures merging among themselves creating for-profit subsidiaries forming alliances with for-profit enterprises or (in some cases) dropping their not-for-profit status and going public – while still using the Blue Cross Blue Shield name.

Blue Cross of California became the first chapter to give up its tax-free status when it was bought by WellPoint Health Networks a managed care subsidiary it had founded in 1992. In a 1996 deal WellPoint became the chapter's parent and converted it to for-profit status assigning all of the stock to a public charitable foundation which received the proceeds of its subsequent IPO. WellPoint also bought the group life and health division of Massachusetts Mutual Life Insurance.

The for-profit switches picked up in 1997. Blue Cross of Connecticut merged with insurance provider Anthem and other mergers followed. Half the nation's Blues formed an alliance called BluesCONNECT (now BlueCard) competing with national health plans by offering employers one nationwide benefits organization. BCBSA also pursued overseas licensing agreements in Europe South America and Asia assembling a network of Blue Cross-friendly caregivers aiming for worldwide coverage.

In 1998 Blues in more than 35 states sued the nation's big cigarette companies to recoup costs of treating smoking-related illnesses. In a separate lawsuit Blue Cross and Blue Shield of Minnesota received nearly $300 million from the tobacco industry. In 1999 Anthem moved to acquire or affiliate with Blues in Colorado Maine Nevada and New Hampshire.

After years of discussions in 2000 the New York attorney general permitted Empire Blue Cross and Blue Shield to convert to for-profit status. The pace of for-profit conversions slowed down in following years however as state regulators became increasingly wary of signing off on the procedure. The improved financial situation of most of the not-for-profit Blues also took away a key incentive for for-profit conversion – access to capital markets.

In 2004 Anthem and WellPoint Health Networks merged and Anthem's name changed to Wellpoint (though it continued to use the Anthem brand name in certain markets) becoming the largest for-profit health insurer in the nation. WellPoint acquired Empire Blue Cross and its parent WellChoice as well as non-Blue consumer-driven plan provider Lumenos in 2005. In addition to snapping up Blues providers the for-profit WellPoint acquired a number of non-Blue subsidiaries such as American Imaging Management while meeting the requirement that it get two-thirds of its insurance revenue from Blue products to keep its BCBSA license. (Wellpoint changed its name back to Anthem in 2012.)

Consolidation among Blues plans continued when Health Care Service Corporation added its fourth not-for-profit Blues plan (Blue Cross and Blue Shield of Oklahoma) in 2005.

In 2007 BCBSA was approved under a Federal Savings Bank charter to provide health-related banking services through its Blue Healthcare Bank.

Two licensees Highmark and Independence Blue Cross had agreed to merge in 2008 but the deal was terminated in early 2009 after long delays and heavy regulatory concern that the merger would create an unfair advantage in the Pennsylvania market. Some consolidation continued however as Triple-S which operates under the Blue Shield brand in Puerto Rico acquired and absorbed Blue Cross licensee La Cruz Azul from Independence Blue Cross in 2009.

Highmark reached a formal affiliation agreement (including shared administrative and IT resources) with Blue Cross Blue Shield of Delaware in 2011.

Another regional Blues provider Cambia Health Solutions (formerly Regence Group) changed its name in 2011 to signify its diversification efforts though its BCBS subsidiaries continue to operate under the Regence name.

Three Blues companies – Anthem Health Care Service Corp. (HCSC) and BCBS of Michigan– joined together in 2011 to invest in a commercial insurance exchange (Bloom Health) designed to allow businesses to contribute to employees' selected health coverage. The venture was part of the Blues' efforts to meet the changing US insurance needs under health reform laws.

BCBSA launched a new wellness rewards program for FEP participants in 2012.

EXECUTIVES

President And Ceo, Scott P. Serota, $1,307,804 total compensation
Evp And Cfo, Robert J. (Bob) Kolodgy
Svp Operations And Cio, Doug Porter
Evp And Chief Of Staff, Jennifer Vachon
Chief Medical Officer, Trent Haywood
Svp Commercial Markets, Kari Hedges
Vp And Cto, Nasir Khan
Senior Vice President National Programs, Steve Gammarino
Senior Vp, Matthew Collins
Vice President Finance, Mitch Helfand
Vice President Brand Strategy, Julie Koewler
Vice President Human Resources, Kelly Williams
Vice President Information Security, Brenda Callaway
Vice President Corporate Human Resources, Patrick Oconnor
Senior Vice President, David Pankau
Senior Vice President And Chief Network Officer, Ronald Mornelli
Chairman, Daniel J. Hilferty
Auditors: PRICEWATERHOUSECOOPERS LLP PH

LOCATIONS

HQ: BLUE CROSS & BLUE SHIELD ASSOCIATION
225 N MICHIGAN AVE FL 5, CHICAGO, IL 606017658
Phone: 312 297-6000
Web: WWW.BCBS.COM

PRODUCTS/OPERATIONS

Selected Blue Cross and Blue Shield Licensees
Arkansas Blue Cross and Blue Shield
Blue Cross and Blue Shield of Alabama
Blue Cross and Blue Shield of Arizona
Blue Cross and Blue Shield of Delaware
Blue Cross and Blue Shield of Florida
Blue Cross and Blue Shield of Kansas
Blue Cross and Blue Shield of Kansas City
Blue Cross and Blue Shield of Louisiana
Blue Cross and Blue Shield of Massachusetts
Blue Cross and Blue Shield of Michigan
Blue Cross and Blue Shield of Minnesota
Blue Cross and Blue Shield of Mississippi
Blue Cross and Blue Shield of Montana
Blue Cross and Blue Shield of Nebraska
Blue Cross and Blue Shield of North Carolina
Blue Cross and Blue Shield of North Dakota
Blue Cross and Blue Shield of Rhode Island
Blue Cross and Blue Shield of South Carolina
Blue Cross and Blue Shield of Tennessee
Blue Cross and Blue Shield of Vermont
Blue Cross and Blue Shield of Wyoming
Blue Cross of Idaho Health Service
Blue Cross of Northeastern Pennsylvania
California Physicians' Service (dba Blue Shield of California)
Cambia Health Solutions Inc. (formerly The Regence Group)
  Regence BlueCross and BlueShield of Oregon
  Regence BlueCross BlueShield of Utah
  Regence BlueShield of Idaho
  Regence BlueShield (Washington)
Capital BlueCross (Pennsylvania)
CareFirst
  CareFirst Blue Cross and Blue Shield (District of Columbia)
  CareFirst Blue Cross and Blue Shield of Maryland
Excellus BlueCross BlueShield of New York
Hawaii Medical Service Association
Health Care Service Corporation
  Blue Cross and Blue Shield of Illinois
  Blue Cross and Blue Shield of New Mexico
  Blue Cross and Blue Shield of Oklahoma
  Blue Cross and Blue Shield of Texas
HealthNow New York
  BlueCross and BlueShield of Western New York
  BlueShield of Northeastern New York
Highmark Blue Cross Blue Shield (Pennsylvania)
  Mountain State Blue Cross and Blue Shield (West Virginia)
Horizon Healthcare Services (dba Horizon Blue Cross and Blue Shield of New Jersey)
Independence Blue Cross (Pennsylvania)
Premera Blue Cross (Alaska and Washington)
Triple-S (Puerto Rico)
Wellmark
  Wellmark Blue Cross and Blue Shield of Iowa
  Wellmark Blue Cross and Blue Shield of South Dakota

WellPoint
Anthem Blue Cross and Blue Shield of Colorado
Anthem Blue Cross and Blue Shield of Connecticut
Anthem Blue Cross and Blue Shield of Indiana
Anthem Blue Cross and Blue Shield of Kentucky
Anthem Blue Cross and Blue Shield of Maine
Anthem Blue Cross and Blue Shield of Nevada
Anthem Blue Cross and Blue Shield of New Hampshire
Anthem Blue Cross and Blue Shield of Ohio
Anthem Blue Cross and Blue Shield of Virginia
Blue Cross and Blue Shield of Georgia
Blue Cross and Blue Shield of Missouri (dba Anthem Blue Cross and Blue Shield)
BlueCross BlueShield of Wisconsin (dba Anthem Blue Cross and Blue Shield)
California Blue Cross (Anthem Blue Cross)
Empire Blue Cross and Blue Shield of New York
International plans
Blue Cross & Blue Shield de Uruguay
BlueCross BlueShield of Panama

COMPETITORS

AMERIGROUP
Aetna
CIGNA
Centene
Health Net
Humana
Kaiser Foundation Health Plan
Molina Healthcare
Principal Financial
UnitedHealth Group
WellCare Health Plans

HISTORICAL FINANCIALS

Company Type: Private

Income Statement				FYE: December 31
	REVENUE ($ mil.)	NET INCOME ($ mil.)	NET PROFIT MARGIN	EMPLOYEES
12/17	591	(1)	—	1,880
12/06	320	14	4.5%	—
12/05	275	8	3.0%	—
12/04	270	11	4.3%	—
Annual Growth	6.2%	—	—	—

2017 Year-End Financials

Return on assets: (-0.2%)
Return on equity: (-1.5%)
Current ratio: 1.00
Cash ($ mil.): 486

BLUE CROSS AND BLUE SHIELD OF ARIZONA, INC.

Blue Cross Blue Shield of Arizona (BCBSAZ) provides health insurance products and services to nearly 1.5 million Arizonans. The not-for-profit company offers a variety of managed care plans to small and large employer groups individuals and families including PPO HMO and high-deductible health plans. It also provides dental vision and prescription drug coverage as well as supplemental health plans for Medicare beneficiaries. Additionally BCBSAZ's HealthyBlue wellness and disease management programs give members information and services that encourage healthy lifestyles. Founded in 1933 the company is an independent licensee of the Blue Cross and Blue Shield Association.

Geographic Reach

BCBSAZ serves customers throughout the state of Arizona (headquarters) from its offices in Chandler Flagstaff Phoenix and Tucson.

Sales and Marketing

BCBSAZ offers insurance services to individuals and families seniors employers brokers and consultants and health care professionals through agents.

Its Select Network comprises contracted hospitals and doctors that are part of Phoenix Children's Hospital and Dignity Health.

BCBSAZ offers health insurance and related services to nearly 1.5 million customers.

Strategy

BCBSAZ opened facilities and partnered with institutions to help improve its customers' lives as well as those who are just in need. For instance BCBSAZ and Fiesta Bowl Organization collaborated to create the Empowering Diversity Scholarship. The company also opened a fitness center that will be utilized by both students and staff of Brunson-Lee Elementary School in Phoenix.

Mergers and Acquisitions

In 2020 Blue Cross Blue Shield of Arizona (BCBSAZ) announced that after securing all regulatory approvals it has completed its acquisition of Steward Health Choice Arizona LLC. In addition to its individual employer and Medicare plans BCBSAZ will now provide health coverage and related services to Arizonans eligible for Medicaid and those who are dual-eligible for Medicare and Medicaid. This includes the Arizona Health Care Cost Containment System (AHCCCS) Complete Care plan and the "Generations" Medicare health plan. Terms were not disclosed.

EXECUTIVES

President And Ceo, Richard L. (Rich) Boals
Evp External Operations, Susan H. Navran
Evp Internal Operations, Sandra Lee Gibson
Cio, Elizabeth A. Messina
Svp And Cfo, Karen Abraham
Svp Health Services And Chief Medical Officer, Vishu Jhaveri
Svp Strategy Sales And Marketing, Jeff Stelnik
Ceo Blue Cross Blue Shield Of Arizona Advantage, Dave Firdaus
Chairman, Harry A. Papp
Vice Chairman, Alton J. Washington

LOCATIONS

HQ: BLUE CROSS AND BLUE SHIELD OF ARIZONA, INC.
2444 W LAS PALMARITAS DR, PHOENIX, AZ 850214860
Phone: 602 864-4100
Web: WWW.AZBLUE.COM

PRODUCTS/OPERATIONS

Selected Plans

Family and Individual Medical Plans
BlueBasic Plus PPO
BlueEssential Plus PPO
BlueOptimum Plus PPO
BluePortfolio Plus (high deductible PPO with HSA)
BlueValue Plus PPO
Medicare Part D
Medicare Supplement
Group Medical Plans
BlueAlliance benefit
BluePreferred PPO
BluePreferred HSA Plus (high deductable PPO with HSA)
BlueSelect HMO
Dental plans
Eyewear plans
GeoBlue Expat

COMPETITORS

Aetna
CIGNA HealthCare of Arizona
First Dental Health
Health Net
Humana
Southwest Catholic Health Network
UnitedHealth Group
Western Dental Services

HISTORICAL FINANCIALS

Company Type: Private

Income Statement				FYE: December 31
	ASSETS ($ mil.)	NET INCOME ($ mil.)	INCOME AS % OF ASSETS	EMPLOYEES
12/09	1,059	64	6.1%	1,278
12/08	975	71	7.4%	—
Annual Growth	8.6%	(9.9%)	—	—

BLUE TEE CORP.

Handling a variety of steel products and scrap materials suits Blue Tee to a tee. The holding company which operates through two primary subsidiaries distributes steel building materials and scrap metal. Blue Tee's Brown-Strauss Steel subsidiary is one of the largest distributors of wide flange beam and structural steel products (beams pipe and tubing) in North America. The metal distributor's other primary business is Azcon a leading scrap processor broker and mill services management company which handles scrap metal sales rail cars and other steel parts.

Operations

Azcon is a major scrap processor broker and mill services management company. Brown-Strauss Steel distributes steel products.

Azcon buys collects warehouses and distributes a wide variety of rail and track accessories for the railroad industry across North America. Its core businesses include Processing Yard Mill Scrap Management and Brokerage. Other product lines include Relaying and Re-rolling Rail Railroad Equipment and Railroad Parts.

Brown-Strauss Steel's focus is on the distribution of new steel (wide flange beam and structural steel tubing) across the US.

Geographic Reach

The company has major offices in Denver Kansas City Longview (Washington) New York City Phoenix Salt Lake City and Stockton and Fontana (California). It has additional locations in Alton Chicago and Sterling (Illinois); Austin Texas; Duluth Minnesota; and Sharpsburg Pennsylvania.

In Canada Blue Tee has offices in Edmonton Calgary Grande Prairie Grimshaw Kamloops Prince George and Red Deer.

Sales and Marketing

Blue Tee serves a range of industries including construction forestry road building mining farming power oil and gas solid waste water waste management highway transportation environmental and groundwater monitoring.

Strategy

The company is focusing its resources developing Azcon and Brown-Strauss Steel. Brown-Strauss is looking to grow its product offerings to include structural tubing; it also plans to expand its facilities. In this regard in 2012 Blue Tee Corp (through Brown-Strauss) purchased a 69190 sq. ft. industrial building in Aurora Colorado from The Lowenberg Corp. for $6 million.

Company Background

Blue Tee is owned by its employees through an employee stock ownership plan.

In 2011 Blue Tee divested subsidiaries GEFCO (an OEM of portable drilling rigs and other industrial equipment) and STECO (transfer and dump-truck trailers) to Astec Industries for about $30.8 million.

The move to axe its GEFCO and STECO subsidiaries followed another sale. Blue Tee sold its pump parts subsidiary Texas-based Standard Alloys to German pump manufacturer KSB in mid-2010.

The Blue Tee holding company was founded in 1986. Azcon was formed in 1863 and Brown-Strauss Steel was established in 1905.

EXECUTIVES

Pres-Ceo, William M Kelly
Sr V Pres-Cfo-Chb, David P Alldian
Exec Dir, Annette Marino D'Arienzo
Real Estate Conultant, Cristina Hungria
Assistant Controller, Annette Marino
Controller, Thomas Caruso
Auditors: DELOITTE & TOUCHE LLP NEW YO

LOCATIONS

HQ: BLUE TEE CORP.
387 PARK AVE S FL 5, NEW YORK, NY 100161495
Phone: 212 598-0880
Web: WWW.BLUETEE.COM

PRODUCTS/OPERATIONS

Selected Subsidiaries

Azcon Corporation (ferrous and nonferrous scrap; rail cars locomotives and parts; relay and reroll rail)
Brown-Strauss Steel (steel distribution including angles beams channels pipe and tubing)

Selected Azcon Services

Barge Services
Brokerage Services
Demolition Services
Foundries - Scrap Management
Industrial Plants - Scrap Management
Mill Service
Mine Services
Railroad Industry Services
Steel Mills - Scrap Management

Selected Brown-Strauss Steel Products and Services

Products:
Structural Angle
Structural Channels
Structural Pipe
Structural Tubing
Wide Flange Beams

Services:

Cambering
Inventory Stocking program
Length/cutting optimization program
Mill Brokerage
Saw Cutting
Track Torch Cutting

COMPETITORS

A. M. Castle
APi Group
Dover Corp.
Metals USA
OmniSource
Pacesetter Steel
Reliance Steel
Russel Metals
Ryerson
TTX
Wescast Industries

HISTORICAL FINANCIALS

Company Type: Private

Income Statement — FYE: December 31

	REVENUE ($ mil.)	NET INCOME ($ mil.)	NET PROFIT MARGIN	EMPLOYEES
12/10	809	14	1.8%	900
12/09	564	(10)	—	—
12/08	1,549	33	2.1%	—
Annual Growth	(27.7%)	(34.4%)	—	—

2010 Year-End Financials

Return on assets: 3.7%
Return on equity: 8.2%
Current ratio: 2.10
Cash ($ mil.): 8

BNSF RAILWAY COMPANY

BNSF Railway operates one of the largest railroad networks in North America. A wholly-owned subsidiary of Burlington Northern Santa Fe itself a unit of Berkshire Hathaway the company provides freight transportation over a network of about 32500 route miles of track across some 30 US states and three provinces in Canada. BNSF Railway owns or leases a fleet of about 8000 locomotives. It also has some 25 intermodal facilities that help to transport agricultural consumer and industrial products as well as coal. In addition to major cities and ports BNSF Railway serves smaller markets in alliance with short-line partners.

Operations

BNSF Railway transports a wide range of products and commodities through its four main product segments.

The Consumer Products segment generates about 35% of revenue and consists of the Domestic Intermodal International Intermodal and Automotive business units. The Industrial Products segment provides about 25% of revenue and comprises five business units: Construction Products Petroleum Products Building Products Chemicals and Plastics Products and Food and Beverages.

Agricultural Products represents 20% of revenue and includes the transportation of commodities like corn wheat ethanol soybeans fertilizer oil seeds flour and other grains. The Coal business (less than 20%) is primarily BNSF's operations that originate from the Powder River Basin of Wyoming and Montana.

The company also generates about 5% of revenue from its wholly-owned non-rail logistics subsidiary BSNF Logistics LLC through logistics and transportation services such as storage as well as demurrage (detention fees for delays in loading and unloading of freight).

Geographic Reach

Headquartered in Fort Worth TX BNSF Railway's network spreads across about 30 US states and three Canadian provinces.

Sales and Marketing

BNSF Railway serves smaller markets by working closely with 200 shortline partners. It also forms marketing agreements with other rail carriers expanding the marketing reach for each railroad and its customers.

Financial Performance

BNSF has seen steady growth in recent years with revenue reaching $23.9 billion in 2018 a 12% increase compared with $21.4 billion in 2017. The increase in 2018 was mainly due to increased volume and increased rates per car as well as tight truck capacity in the transportation sector which converted some business from highway to rail.

Net income however plummeted to $5.2 billion less than half that of the previous year. This was primarily due to an increased tax liability as a result of the Tax Cuts and Jobs Act.

Cash at the end of fiscal 2018 was $2.0 billion about the same as the prior year. Cash from operations contributed $7.9 billion to the coffers while investing activities used $3.2 billion mainly for capital expenditures related to equipment purchases. Financing activities used another $4.7 billion primarily for cash distributions to its parent company.

Strategy

BNSF plans capital spending of about $3.5 billion in 2019 for network maintenance and replacement of assets to ensure safe and reliable operations. These include expansion and efficiency projects focused on key growth areas along its Southern and Northern Trancon routes. The company faces challenges in its supply chain environment with competition from improving productivity in the trucking industry. Another hurdle is consumers' expectations for quicker and quicker delivery as online shopping continues to grow. In response BSNF is focusing on providing consistent reliable and efficient transportation services to its customers.

Company Background

BNSF's traces its roots to 1849 when the Aurora Branch Railroad was founded in Illinois with 12 miles of track. Over the years additional rail lines were built including Atchison Topeka & Santa Fe;Burlington Northern; Chicago Burlington & Quincy; Frisco; Great Northern; Northern Pacific; and Spokane Portland & Seattle.

BNSF was created in 1995 when Burlington Northern Inc. (the parent company of Burlington Northern Railroad) merged with Santa Fe Pacific Corporation (parent company of the Atchison Topeka & Santa Fe Railway). The company was acquired by Berkshire Hathaway in 2010 and BNSF now operates as a subsidiary of that company.

EXECUTIVES

President And Ceo, Carl R. Ice, age 63
Evp Law And Corporate Affairs, Roger Nober, age 55
Evp And Cfo, Julie A. Piggott
Evp And Chief Marketing Officer, Stevan B. Bobb
Evp Operations, Gregory C. Fox
Vice President Federal Government Affairs, Amy Hawkins
Executive Vice President Law And Government Affairs And Secretary, Jeffrey Moreland
Vice President Network Strategy, Dean Wise
Vice President Controller, Dannis Johnson
Executive Chairman, Matthew K. (Matt) Rose, age 61
Auditors: DELOITTE & TOUCHE LLP FORT WO

LOCATIONS

HQ: BNSF RAILWAY COMPANY
2650 LOU MENK DR, FORT WORTH, TX 761312830
Phone: 800 795-2673
Web: WWW.BNSF.COM

PRODUCTS/OPERATIONS

2018 Sales

	$ mil.	% of total
Consumer Products	7,902	33
Industrial Products	5,967	25
Agricultural Products	4,697	20
Coal	4,012	17
Other revenues	1,277	5
Total	23,855	100

COMPETITORS

CSX
Canadian National Railway
Canadian Pacific Railway
Kansas City Southern Railway
Norfolk Southern
Union Pacific Railroad

HISTORICAL FINANCIALS

Company Type: Private

Income Statement — FYE: December 31

	REVENUE ($ mil.)	NET INCOME ($ mil.)	NET PROFIT MARGIN	EMPLOYEES
12/17	20,747	12,119	58.4%	41,000
12/16	19,278	4,260	22.1%	—
12/14	22,714	4,397	19.4%	—
12/13	21,552	4,271	19.8%	—
Annual Growth	(0.9%)	29.8%	—	—

2017 Year-End Financials

Return on assets: 14.6%
Return on equity: 19.3%
Current ratio: 1.00
Cash ($ mil.): 516

BOARD OF EDUCATION FOR THE CITY OF SAVANNAH AND THE COUNTY OF CHATHAM (INC)

EXECUTIVES

Pres, Jolene Byrne
Contrl, Beth Stanford
Auditors: KRT CPAS PC SAVANNAH GEORG

LOCATIONS

HQ: BOARD OF EDUCATION FOR THE CITY OF SAVANNAH AND THE COUNTY OF CHATHAM (INC)
208 BULL ST, SAVANNAH, GA 314013843
Phone: 912 395-1000
Web: WWW.SAVANNAH.COM

HISTORICAL FINANCIALS

Company Type: Private

Income Statement — FYE: June 30

	REVENUE ($ mil.)	NET INCOME ($ mil.)	NET PROFIT MARGIN	EMPLOYEES
06/19	569	86	15.2%	4,781
06/18	525	41	7.8%	—
06/17	500	(30)	—	—
06/16	493	21	4.3%	—
Annual Growth	4.9%	59.4%	—	—

BOARD OF EDUCATION OF CITY OF CHICAGO

EXECUTIVES

Pres, Frank Clark
Technology, James V Dispensa
Coordinator, Samantha Treworgy
Auditors: MCGLADREY LLP CHICAGO ILLINO

LOCATIONS

HQ: BOARD OF EDUCATION OF CITY OF CHICAGO
42 W MADISON ST FL 2, CHICAGO, IL 606024309
Phone: 773 553-1600
Web: WWW.CPSBOE.ORG

HISTORICAL FINANCIALS

Company Type: Private

Income Statement — FYE: June 30

	REVENUE ($ mil.)	NET INCOME ($ mil.)	NET PROFIT MARGIN	EMPLOYEES
06/16	5,272	(381)	—	5,151
06/12	5,760	324	5.6%	—
06/11	5,660	238	4.2%	—
06/08	17	(0)	—	—
Annual Growth	103.8%	—	—	—

BOARD OF EDUCATION-MEMPHIS CITY SCHOOLS

LOCATIONS

HQ: BOARD OF EDUCATION-MEMPHIS CITY SCHOOLS
160 S HOLLYWOOD ST, MEMPHIS, TN 381124801
Phone: 901 416-5300

HISTORICAL FINANCIALS

Company Type: Private

Income Statement — FYE: June 30

	REVENUE ($ mil.)	NET INCOME ($ mil.)	NET PROFIT MARGIN	EMPLOYEES
06/13	1,157	(12)	—	12,015
06/12	1,169	(2)	—	—
06/11*	1,173	(5)	—	—
12/09	449	(64)	—	—
Annual Growth	37.1%	—	—	—

*Fiscal year change

2013 Year-End Financials

Return on assets: —
Return on equity: (-1.1%)
Current ratio: —
Cash ($ mil.): 177

BOARD OF PUBLIC EDUCATION SCHOOL DISTRICT OF PITTSBURGH (INC)

EXECUTIVES

Pres, Thomas Sumpter
SEC*, Cindy Polis
Coordinator, Susan Chersky
Auditors: MAHER DUESSEL PITTSBURGH PEN

LOCATIONS

HQ: BOARD OF PUBLIC EDUCATION SCHOOL DISTRICT OF PITTSBURGH (INC)
341 S BELLEFIELD AVE, PITTSBURGH, PA 152133516
Phone: 412 622-3500
Web: WWW.PGHSCHOOLS.ORG

HISTORICAL FINANCIALS

Company Type: Private

Income Statement — FYE: December 31

	REVENUE ($ mil.)	NET INCOME ($ mil.)	NET PROFIT MARGIN	EMPLOYEES
12/14	631	13	2.1%	5,016
12/13	624	19	3.1%	—
12/12	613	3	0.6%	—
12/11	631	(14)	—	—
Annual Growth	(0.0%)	—	—	—

2014 Year-End Financials

Return on assets: 1.8%
Return on equity: 4.9%
Current ratio: 2.70
Cash ($ mil.): 89

BOARD OF REGENTS OF THE UNIVERSITY OF NEBRASKA

The University of Nebraska has sprouted four campuses out in the fields of the Cornhusker State. Founded in 1869 the university confers bachelor's master's and doctoral degrees in more than 200 majors including agriculture business education and engineering at its campuses in Kearney Lincoln and Omaha. The university's Medical Center in Omaha trains doctors performs research and is affiliated with a nearly 720-bed teaching hospital. The school also operates research and extension services across the state. More than 51420 students attend classes in the system that has a student-teacher ratio of about 17:1. It was founded as a land-grant university just two years after the Nebraska became a state.

EXECUTIVES

Svp Business And Finance, David E. Lechner
Chancellor University Of Nebraska Lincoln, Harvey S. Perlman
Chancellor University Of Nebraska Kearney, Douglas A. (Doug) Kristensen
Chancellor University Of Nebraska Omaha, John Christensen
Evp And Provost, Susan M. Fritz
Interim President, James Linder
Chancellor University Of Nebraska Medical Center, Jeffrey P. Gold
Cio, Walter Weir
President, Hank M. Bounds
Assistant Vice President And Director Human Resources, Ed Wimes
Assistant Vp And Director Federal Relations, Matt Hammons
Vice President, Elbert Dickey
Vice Chancellor And Vice President, Ronnie Green
Vice President Of Accounting, Keith Auber
Assistant Vp Global Strategy And International Initiatives, Steven Duke

Vice President And General Counsel, James P Pottorff
Department Head, Martha Mamo
Chairman, Howard L. Hawks
Vice Chairman, Bob Phares
Auditors: MARK AVERY CPA LINCOLN NEBR

LOCATIONS

HQ: BOARD OF REGENTS OF THE UNIVERSITY OF NEBRASKA
3835 HOLDREGE ST, LINCOLN, NE 685031435
Phone: 402 472-3906
Web: WWW.NEBRASKA.EDU

PRODUCTS/OPERATIONS

University Campuses
The University of Nebraska at Kearney
The University of Nebraska-Lincoln
The University of Nebraska Medical Center
The University of Nebraska at Omaha

HISTORICAL FINANCIALS

Company Type: Private

Income Statement FYE: June 30

	REVENUE ($ mil.)	NET INCOME ($ mil.)	NET PROFIT MARGIN	EMPLOYEES
06/16	1,490	215	14.5%	15,200
06/15	1,405	221	15.8%	—
06/14	1,333	222	16.7%	—
06/13	1,313	254	19.4%	—
Annual Growth	4.3%	(5.4%)	—	—

2016 Year-End Financials

Return on assets: 4.3%
Return on equity: 6.0%
Current ratio: 2.80
Cash ($ mil.): 613

BOARD OF REGENTS OF THE UNIVERSITY SYSTEM OF GEORGIA

EXECUTIVES

Chancellor, Hank Huckaby
Director For Grants Accounting*, Jennifer Shaw
Administrative Coordinator, Linda Pickering
Assistant Professor, Ling Xue
Associate Director of Informat, Lisa Baldwin
Manager, Mark Bryan
Business Analyst 2, Mark Walters
Doctor, May Gao
Associate Sports Communication, Mike Holmes
Research Associate, Noah Tobin
Administrator, Paul Keck
Auditors: GREG S GRIFFIN ATLANTA GEORG

LOCATIONS

HQ: BOARD OF REGENTS OF THE UNIVERSITY SYSTEM OF GEORGIA
270 WASHINGTON ST SW, ATLANTA, GA 303349056
Phone: 404 962-3050
Web: WWW.USG.EDU

HISTORICAL FINANCIALS

Company Type: Private

Income Statement FYE: June 30

	REVENUE ($ mil.)	NET INCOME ($ mil.)	NET PROFIT MARGIN	EMPLOYEES
06/19	5,532	426	7.7%	40,000
06/18	5,210	221	4.3%	—
06/17	5,100	57	1.1%	—
06/15	4,704	124	2.6%	—
Annual Growth	4.1%	36.1%	—	—

2019 Year-End Financials

Return on assets: 3.0%
Return on equity: 21.0%
Current ratio: 2.70
Cash ($ mil.): 1,385

BOARD OF TRUSTEES OF STATE INSTITUTIONS OF HIGHER LEARNING

EXECUTIVES

Comm'r, Hank Bounds
Coordinator, Tonya Neely
Security Staff, Ivy Babb
Director, Jim Steil
Senior Designer, Pete Halverson
Marketing Team Member, Holly Johnson
Data, Kathy Burgess
Director, Pete Walley
Administrative Assistant, Sharon Scott
Auditors: KPMG LLP JACKSON MISSISSIPP

LOCATIONS

HQ: BOARD OF TRUSTEES OF STATE INSTITUTIONS OF HIGHER LEARNING
3825 RIDGEWOOD RD, JACKSON, MS 392116453
Phone: 601 432-6198
Web: WWW.MISSISSIPPI.EDU

HISTORICAL FINANCIALS

Company Type: Private

Income Statement FYE: June 30

	REVENUE ($ mil.)	NET INCOME ($ mil.)	NET PROFIT MARGIN	EMPLOYEES
06/19	2,720	103	3.8%	65
06/18	2,588	(5)	—	—
06/17	2	0	1.1%	—
06/16	2,539	173	6.8%	—
Annual Growth	2.3%	(15.8%)	—	—

2019 Year-End Financials

Return on assets: 1.5%
Return on equity: 4.8%
Current ratio: 3.00
Cash ($ mil.): 615

BOARDRIDERS, INC.

Boardriders rides the wave of youth appeal. Formerly Quiksilver the company caters to the young and athletic with surfwear snowboardwear sportswear and swimwear sold under the Quiksilver Billabong Element VonZipper and Roxy names among others. It also owns the DC Shoes brand of footwear and apparel for young men and juniors. It sells its apparel footwear and accessories in specialty and department stores worldwide as well as through its own network of about 630 retail stores. It emerged from Chapter 11 bankruptcy protection in 2016 and is now owned by Oaktree Capital Management; in 2018 it bought rival Billabong.

Geographic Reach

Boardriders serves customers in more than 110 countries; it has e-commerce capabilities in about 35 countries and company-owned retail stores in nearly 30. More than 60% of revenue comes from outside North America.

Strategy

To grow sales and return to profitability after emerging from bankruptcy Boardriders is focused on strengthening its brands; expanding its business in emerging markets; and driving operational efficiencies. The company has also invested in improving its e-commerce platform and growing its store network.

It owns a portfolio of the leading brands in surf and sportswear including Quiksilver DC Shoes Element and Billabong. The company is dedicated to preserving and promoting each of these distinctive historic brands.

In addition Boardriders is pushing its brands into new product areas including personal care (Roxy and Quiksilver sun care and other products through an agreement with Inter Parfums) and hotels (Quiksilver and Roxy have partnered with Accor's Jo&Joe a new hotel chain targeting millennials).

To help it focus the company has divested noncore business to focus on its most iconic brands. Jettisoned brands include Surfdome (sold to SurfStitch) Mervin Manufacturing (sold to Extreme Holdings) and skateboarder Tony Hawk's Hawk Designs (sold to Cherokee).

Mergers and Acquisitions

In April 2018 Boardriders completed the acquisition of Australian rival Billabong which owns Element VonZipper Billabong and other brands that make surf and action sports apparel and accessories. The deal valued around $155 million creates one of the world's largest action sports companies.

EXECUTIVES

Evp Global Human Resources, Carol E. Scherman
Evp And Cio, Michael B. Tasooji
President Quiksilver Europe, Pierre Agnes, $617,500 total compensation
President Americas, Nate Smith
Evp New Business Development; President Quiksilver Americas, Robert (Rob) Colby, $400,000 total compensation
Cfo, Richard Shields, $522,900 total compensation
President Asia Pacific (apac), Greg Healy
Senior Vice President Of Global Sourcing, Christopher Dubes
Vice President Worldwide Controller, Michael Henry
Vice President Of Merchandising And Design, Guy Stagman
Senior Vice President Of Marketing, Ryan Scanlon
Chairman, Bob McKnight
Auditors: DELOITTE & TOUCHE LLP COSTA M

LOCATIONS

HQ: BOARDRIDERS, INC.
5600 ARGOSY AVE STE 100, HUNTINGTON BEACH, CA 926491063
Phone: 714 889-2200
Web: WWW.BOARDRIDERS.COM

PRODUCTS/OPERATIONS

Selected Brands

Billabong
DC Shoes
Element
Kustom
Palmers
Quiksilver
Roxy
RVCA
VonZipper
Xcel

COMPETITORS

Abercrombie & Fitch
Bleach Group
Body Glove
Burton
Calvin Klein
Columbia Sportswear
FUBU
Fat Face
Foot Locker
Head N.V.
Levi Strauss
NIKE
Nautica Apparel
Oakley
Skullcandy
Sole Technology
St ssy
Tecnica
Tommy Hilfiger
Under Armour
VF Corporation
Volcom
Warnaco Swimwear
adidas

HISTORICAL FINANCIALS

Company Type: Private

Income Statement FYE: October 31

	REVENUE ($ mil.)	NET INCOME ($ mil.)	NET PROFIT MARGIN	EMPLOYEES
10/14	1,570	(320)	—	600
10/13	1,810	(233)	—	—
10/12	2,013	(9)	—	—
Annual Growth	(11.7%)	—	—	—

2014 Year-End Financials

Return on assets: (-25.0%)
Return on equity: (-556.7%)
Current ratio: 2.10
Cash ($ mil.): 46

BON SECOURS MERCY HEALTH, INC.

Bon Secours Mercy Health (formerly Bon Secours Health System) is a Roman Catholic health care organization. Sponsored by the Bon Secours Ministries it is home to 43 hospitals with more than 2100 physicians. First founded in 1919 its facilities are in seven states in the eastern US from New York to Florida. In addition to its acute care hospitals the not-for-profit system operates a psychiatric hospital numerous nursing homes and assisted-living facilities as well as hospices and home health care agencies. Bon Secours merged with Cincinnati-based Mercy Health to create Bon Secours Mercy Health in 2018. The combined entity expanded into Ireland in 2019.

Geographic Reach

Bon Secours Mercy Health has hospitals in Florida Kentucky Maryland New York Ohio South Carolina and Virginia.

Sales and Marketing

Medicare and Medicaid payments account for around 35% of Bon Secours Mercy Health's total net patient revenue.

Strategy

Bon Secours Mercy Health plans to continue to grow its operations in existing and new communities targeting expansion in ambulatory care elderly services and home health and hospice. The health system has opened several new ambulatory care centers in existing service territories and it is conducting renovation and expansion efforts at some of its hospital facilities.

The system has also initiated information technology restructuring efforts; it has developed a new clinical information management system (electronic medical records) ConnectCare which is being implemented at its facilities in gradual stages.

The company branched out internationally through the purchase of Irish hospital operator Bon Secours Health System in 2019. Additionally its Global Ministry Initiative provides outreach for health care and social services in developing countries particularly Haiti Peru and South Africa.

Mergers and Acquisitions

Bon Secours MercyHealth in 2019 agreed to acquire three hospitals in southeastern Virginia expanding its operations in the region by some 500 beds. The hospitals are Southside Regional Medical Center in Petersburg Southampton Memorial Hospital in Franklin and Southern Virginia Regional Medical Center in Emporia. The hospitals are affiliates of Community Health Systems Inc. a hospital company selling facilities as it deal with financial difficulties.

In 2018 Bon Secours and Cincinnati-based Mercy Health joined forces to create a system with 43 hospitals in seven states. The combined entity has more than 2100 physicians and clinicians working in more than 1000 locations.

The following year Bon Secours Mercy Health acquired Ireland-based Bon Secours Health System which operates five hospitals and other health facilities.

EXECUTIVES

President Ceo And Director, Richard J. (Rich) Statuto
Svp And Cio, Skip Hubbard
Evp, Mark S. Nantz
Evp, Janice Burnett
Evp, Samuel L. Ross
Ceo Bon Secours St. Francis Health System, R. Craig McCoy
Ceo Bon Secours Charity, Mary Leahy
Senior Vice President Of Mission, Pam Phillips
Vice President Revenue Cycle Services, Vickie Kleski
Vice President Financial Planning And Analysis, James Siegel
Senior Vice President Human Resources, Fernando Fleites
Director Of Admissions, Carrie Newcomb
Vice President Ancillary Amb Services, Johnna S Reed
Vice President Revenue Cycle, Sheila Kuenzle
Vice President Treasury Services, Pamela Schmidt
Director Of Nursing Resources, Candace Porter
Senior Vice President Of Services, Robert Rosenthal
Medical Director And Residency Director, John Unkel
Medical Director And Physician, Mark Miranda
Pharmacy Manager, Ryan Cann
Director Of Pharmacy, Terri Spearman
Medical Director, Janet Eddy
Director Of Radiology, William Long
Medical Director Emergency Services, Adrienne Wasserman
Vice President Patient Care Cne, Sophie Crawford-Rosso
Vice President Service Line Strategy, Leigh Sewell
Vice President Corporate Communications, Terri Mcnorton
Senior Vice President Provider Networks, Wael Haidar
Vice President Patient Care Services, Leana Fox
Director Of Pharmacy, Kerri Musselman
Medical Director Clinical Ethics, Kelly Stuart
Vice President Bon Secours Hampton Roads Foundations, Judy Bilicki
Senior Vice President, Archuleta Bob
Vice President, Rose Marie Jasinski
Assistant Vice President Quality And Patient Safety, Kathleen Geisinger
Executive Vice President Chief Administrative Officer, Tim Davis
Radiology Director, Alan Bailey
Medical Records Director, Susan Griffith
Director Of Radiology, Hill Michael
Vice President Of Patient Services And Chief Nursing Executive, Brandi Fields
Vice President Of Clinical Operations, Jude Ade
Chairman, Charles H. Brown
Secretary, Maria Sorice
Unit Secretary, Corie Miller
Unit Secretary, Noel Townes
Secretary Admin, Huff Brenda
Senior Medical Secretary, Brian Raymond
Unit Secretary, Tamara Pearson
Unit Secretary, Eva White
Auditors: KPMG LLP BALTIMORE MD

LOCATIONS

HQ: BON SECOURS MERCY HEALTH, INC.
1701 MERCY HEALTH PL, CINCINNATI, OH 452376147
Phone: 410 442-5511
Web: WWW.BSMHEALTH.ORG

Selected Facilities

Florida
Bon Secours St. Petersburg Health System
Bon Secours - Maria Manor Nursing Care and Rehabilitation Center
Bon Secours Place at St. Petersburg
Bon Secours St. Petersburg Home Care Services
Kentucky
Bon Secours Kentucky Health System
Our Lady of Bellefonte Hospital (Ashland)
Maryland
Bon Secours Baltimore Health System
Bon Secours Hospital
Bon Secours Washington Village
Community Institute of Behavioral Sciences
Hollins Terrace/Benet House
New York
Bon Secours Charity Health System
Bon Secours Community Hospital (Port Jervis)
Good Samaritan Hospital (Suffern)
St. Anthony Community Hospital (Warwick)
Bon Secours New York Health System
Schervier Nursing Care Center (Riverdale)
Pennsylvania
Altoona Regional Health System (joint venture)
South Carolina
Bon Secours St. Francis Health System Inc.
St. Francis Hospital (Downtown and Eastside Campuses Greenville)
Roper St. Francis Healthcare (Charleston joint venture)
Virginia
Bon Secours Hampton Roads Health System
Bon Secours Maryview Nursing Care Center (Suffolk)
DePaul Medical Center (Norfolk)
Mary Immaculate Hospital (Newport News)
Maryview Medical Center (Portsmouth)
Province Place (Norfolk and Portsmouth)
St. Francis Nursing Care Center (Newport News)
Bon Secours Richmond Health System (joint venture)
Memorial Regional Medical Center (Mechanicsville)
Richmond Community Hospital
St. Francis Medical Center (Midlothian)
St. Mary's Hospital (Richmond)

Selected Affiliations

Cosponsoring Congregational Relationships
Bernardine Sisters of the Third Order of St. Francis (Newport News Virginia)
Sisters of Charity of Saint Elizabeth of Convent Station (New Jersey and New York)
Affiliated Organizations

Health Corporation of Virginia (Richmond)
Medical Society of South Carolina and Carolinas Health Care System (Charleston)
Life Care Services (Florida and Virginia)

PRODUCTS/OPERATIONS

2014 Sales

	$ mil.	% of total
Net Patient Service Revenue	3,328	96
Other revenue	133	4
Total	**3,461**	**100**

COMPETITORS

Adventist HealthCare
Albany Medical Center
Albert Einstein Healthcare Network
Appalachian Regional Healthcare
Carilion Clinic
Catholic Health Initiatives
Centra Health Inc.
Christiana Care
Community Health Systems
Conemaugh Health System
Franklin Square Hospital Center
GBMC
HCA
Highlands Health
Inova
Johns Hopkins Medicine
MedStar Health
MediSys Health Network
New York City Health and Hospitals
Novant Health
Riverside Health System (Virginia)
Sentara Healthcare
St. Agnes HealthCare
University of Maryland Medical System
University of Miami Hospital
Upstate Affiliate
Virginia Hospital Center

HISTORICAL FINANCIALS

Company Type: Private

Income Statement — FYE: December 31

	REVENUE ($ mil.)	NET INCOME ($ mil.)	NET PROFIT MARGIN	EMPLOYEES
12/19*	8,717	2,593	29.7%	19,000
08/10	3,084	(41)	—	—
08/09	2,895	(291)	—	—
08/08	187	51	27.6%	—
Annual Growth	41.8%	42.7%	—	—

*Fiscal year change

2019 Year-End Financials

Return on assets: 19.1%
Return on equity: 34.1%
Current ratio: 1.00
Cash ($ mil.): 453

BONNEVILLE POWER ADMINISTRATION

Bonneville Power Administration (BPA) keeps the lights on in the Pacific Northwest. The US Department of Energy power marketing agency operates a transmission grid (with more than 15000 miles of high-voltage lines) that delivers about 30% of the electrical power consumed in the region. The electricity that BPA wholesales is generated primarily by around 30 federal hydroelectric dams (operated by the US Army Corp of Engineers) and one nonfederal nuclear facility and several small nonfederal power plants.

Operations

BPA operates and maintains about three-fourths of the high-voltage transmission in its service territory. It promotes energy efficiency renewable resources and new technologies. The agency also funds regional efforts to protect and rebuild fish and wildlife populations affected by hydroelectric power development in the Columbia River Basin.

Overall power accounts to about 70% of total sales transmission accounts for some 25% and US Treasury credits and others account for the rest.

Geographic Reach

Headquartered in Portland Oregon BPA's service territory includes Idaho Oregon Washington western Montana and small parts of eastern Montana California Nevada Utah and Wyoming.

Sales and Marketing

The company serves consumer-owned electric cooperatives municipalities public utility districts and tribal utilities.

It also sells wholesale power and transmission to entities that buy and sell non-federal power in the region in-region purchasers of federal power generators marketers and utilities that seek to transmit power into out of or through the region.

Financial Performance

BPA's 2019 revenue is similar to its 2018 revenue ($3.7 billion).

Cash and cash equivalents at the end of the year were $846.5 million 62% higher than in the previous year. Cash provided by operating activities was $972.3 million. Investing activities used $543.9 million primarily for Investment in utility plant including AFUDC while financing activities used $105.8 million primarily for repayment of borrowings from US Treasury.

Strategy

Technology and energy markets are changing rapidly impacting how BPA operates the transmission grid and hydropower plants it together with its federal partners are entrusted with managing. Its asset management program maximizes the value it derives from these and other assets including facilities and IT equipment. NIE is continually growing and updating its program to help maintain Bonneville's competitive edge in the marketplace enable industry change deliver on its public responsibilities and strengthen financial health by effectively managing asset lifecycle costs. This year NIE strengthened the tie between its strategic asset management plans and its financial planning process and it began implementing a common risk methodology to base all asset decisions on five dimensions of risk: financial reliability compliance safety and environmental.

It is also making significant headway in its effort to modernize BPA's systems and operations in response to new and changing markets. Out of a portfolio of 35 grid modernization projects six were completed this year three were completed in FY 2019 and all but one of the others are in flight. This work is essential for the agency to remain the region's wholesale power provider of choice by helping the company identify surplus capacity available on the power and transmission systems for additional sales manage grid congestion more efficiently and reliably and provide valuable insights into how best to invest in the system. Projects are already delivering significant value to BPA and our customers such as through a new program called One BPA Outage.

Company Background

In 2012 BPA bought electricity from a number of wind projects and had more than 4000 MW of wind power capacity tied in to its transmission grid. BPA harnessed and integrated about 6000 MW of wind power by the end of 2013.

BPA is also expanding its transmission grid building three new 500-kilovolt transmission lines to cater to expanding Columbia Gorge wind power. In this regard in 2011 the company began building a new high-voltage transmission line and substation (the Big Eddy-Knight Transmission Project) that would add more than 1150 MW of capacity to its transmission grid and accommodate new wind energy sources. In 2012 it completed a separate 79-mile $216-million line along the Columbia River east of the gorge.

BPA was founded in 1937.

EXECUTIVES

Chief Administrative Officer, John L. Hairston
Evp Corporate Strategy, Elliot Mainzer
Evp Corporate Strategy, Cathy Ehli
Svp Power Services, Mark O. Gendron
Evp And General Counsel, Mary Jensen
Deputy Administrator, Greg Delwiche
Svp Transmission Services, Richard Shaheen
Evp And Cfo, Javier Fernandez
Vice President Power Services, Joel Cook
Auditors: PRICEWATERHOUSECOOPERS LLP PO

LOCATIONS

HQ: BONNEVILLE POWER ADMINISTRATION
905 NE 11TH AVE, PORTLAND, OR 972324169
Phone: 503 230-3000
Web: WWW.BPA.GOV

PRODUCTS/OPERATIONS

2014 Sales

	$ mil.	% of total
Power	2,572	71
Transmission	892	25
US Treasury credits for fish	104	3
Other	70	1
Adjustments	(38)	-
Total	**3,600**	**100**

COMPETITORS

AEP
AES
Avista
Black Hills
CenterPoint Energy
Duke Energy
IDACORP
NW Natural
PG&E Corporation
PacifiCorp
Portland General Electric
Puget Energy
Sempra Energy

HISTORICAL FINANCIALS

Company Type: Private

Income Statement — FYE: September 30

	REVENUE ($ mil.)	NET INCOME ($ mil.)	NET PROFIT MARGIN	EMPLOYEES
09/10	3,055	(127)	—	3,100
09/09	2,870	(101)	—	—
09/08	3,036	264	8.7%	—
Annual Growth	0.3%	—	—	—

2010 Year-End Financials

Return on assets: (-0.6%)
Return on equity: (-0.9%)
Current ratio: 1.20
Cash ($ mil.): 1,078

BOSCOV'S, INC.

EXECUTIVES

Ceo, Albert Boscov
Pres, Kenneth S Lakin
Evp Finance, Cao*, Russell C Diehm
Exec V Pres, Toni Miller
V Pres, Peter D Lakin
Prin, Edwin A Lakin
Pres*, Sam Flamholz
Cfo*, Jason Curtis
Staff, Ronnie Eddinger
Sales Staff, Chantal Van Bauwel
Sales and Marketing Staff, Emile De Cordier
Auditors: KPMG LLP PHILADELPHIA PA

LOCATIONS

HQ: BOSCOV'S, INC.
4500 PERKIOMEN AVE, READING, PA 196063946
Phone: 610 779-2000
Web: WWW.BOSCOVS.COM

HISTORICAL FINANCIALS

Company Type: Private

Income Statement — FYE: February 1

	REVENUE ($ mil.)	NET INCOME ($ mil.)	NET PROFIT MARGIN	EMPLOYEES
02/20	1,241	41	3.3%	10,003
02/19	1,215	47	3.9%	—
02/18*	1,192	37	3.2%	—
01/17	1,139	32	2.8%	—
Annual Growth	2.9%	8.6%	—	—

*Fiscal year change

2020 Year-End Financials

Return on assets: 7.3%
Return on equity: 13.7%
Current ratio: 2.80
Cash ($ mil.): 117

BOSTON MEDICAL CENTER CORPORATION

Located in Boston's South End neighborhood Boston Medical Center (BMC) offers a full spectrum of health care services from prenatal care and obstetrics to surgery and rehabilitation. BMC is also the city's largest provider of indigent care spending millions of dollars annually on care for uninsured patients and offering free screenings and other community outreach programs. The not-for-profit hospital boasts nearly 500 licensed beds more than 700 physicians and includes a Level 1 trauma center acute rehabilitation facilities and neonatal and pediatric intensive care units. The center is the primary teaching hospital of Boston University's School of Medicine.

Operations

BMC also operates Boston HealthNet a network affiliation of the medical center Boston University School of Medicine and more than a dozen community health centers. Boston HealthNet provides outreach prevention primary care and specialty care and dental services at sites located throughout the community.

Hand-in-hand with being a major teaching hospital is engaging in extensive medical research. BMC oversees more than 590 research and service projects and conducts both biomedical and clinical research programs exploring infectious disease cardiology vascular biology Parkinson's disease geriatrics and endocrinology among other areas. With Boston University BMC also operates a 16-acre research and business park called BioSquare that serves as a collaborative center for the development and commercialization of new biomedical technologies.

In 2015 BMC had more than 712 000 outpatient clinic visits 204000 outpatient ancillary visits 125000 emergency department visits and 24000 admissions.

Sales and Marketing

In addition to its medical and research services BMC provides health insurance through its BMC HealthNet Plan a managed care plan that has more than 240000 Medicaid and low-cost health plan members. The center markets its services through social media.

Financial Performance

BMC received more than $119 million in sponsored research funding in fiscal 2015; it oversees 594 research and service projects separate from research activities at Boston University School of Medicine.

Strategy

In late 2014 BMC's Center for Regenerative Medicine and Boston University were awarded a $2.7 million grant from the National Heart Lung and Blood Institute to establish a stem cell repository that researchers across the US can access for free. The first-of-its-kind repository will help promote stem cell research particularly in the area of lung disease.

EXECUTIVES

Svp Finance And Cfo, Richard Silveria
President And Ceo, Kate E. Walsh
Svp And Chief Nursing Officer, Nancy Gaden
Svp And Chief Medical Officer, Ravin Davidoff
Coo, Alastair Bell
President And Ceo Faculty Practice Foundation, William Creevy
Svp Quality Safety And Technology; Chief Quality Officer, Stanley Hochberg
Senior Vice President, David Beck
Associate Vice President For Human Resources, Manuel Monteiro
Senior Vice President Chief Financial Officer, Chuck Orlando
Senior Vice President For Quality, Stanley Md
Chairman, James S. Phalen, age 69
Auditors: BMC HEALTH SYSTEM INC BOSTO

LOCATIONS

HQ: BOSTON MEDICAL CENTER CORPORATION
1 BOSTON MEDICAL CTR PL # 1, BOSTON, MA 021182999
Phone: 617 414-5000
Web: WWW.BMC.ORG

PRODUCTS/OPERATIONS

Selected Services and Programs

Alzheimer's Disease Center
Anesthesiology
Boston HealthNet
Boston University Affiliated Physicians
Boston University Cosmetic and Laser Center
Cardiovascular Center
Care Management
Dermatology
Diabetes
Elders Living at Home Program
Emergency Medicine
Facial Plastic and Reconstructive Surgery
General Internal Medicne / Primary Care
Geriatrics
Head and Neck Cancer Center of Excellence
Hematology & Medical Oncology
Immigrant & Refugee Health Program
Integrative Medicine
LocoMotor Training
Mattapan Community Health Center
Melanoma Program
Neurosurgery
Nursing
Ophthalmology
Oral and Maxillofacial Surgery
Pediatrics - bWell Center
Pediatrics
Rehabilitation Therapies
Renal Medicine
South End Community Health Center
Special Kids Special Help
Thoracic Surgery
Transplant Surgery
Uphams Corner Health Center
Urology
Vascular Center
Vascular and Endovascular Surgery
Weight Loss Surgery (Bariatric Surgery)
Whittier Street Health Center

COMPETITORS

Beth Israel Deaconess Medical Center
Brigham and Women's Hospital
Cambridge Health Alliance
Care New England
CareGroup
Children's Hospital Boston
Dana-Farber
Massachusetts General Hospital
Newton-Wellesley Hospital
Northeast Health System
Partners HealthCare
Shriners Hospitals For Children
Spaulding Rehabilitation Hospital
St. Elizabeth's Medical Center
Steward Health Care

HISTORICAL FINANCIALS

Company Type: Private

Income Statement — FYE: September 30

	REVENUE ($ mil.)	NET INCOME ($ mil.)	NET PROFIT MARGIN	EMPLOYEES
09/17	1,089	12	1.2%	4,200
09/15	1,004	7	0.8%	—
09/12	886	2	0.3%	—
Annual Growth	4.2%	38.0%	—	—

2017 Year-End Financials

Return on assets: 0.6%
Return on equity: 1.0%
Current ratio: 1.90
Cash ($ mil.): 125

BOSTON UNIVERSITY

EXECUTIVES

Pres, Robert Brown
Cfo*, Martin Howard
V Pres*, Todd Klipp
Scientist, Jeffrey Baumgardner
Scientist, Karen Hirsch
Coordinator, Lisa Murphy
Assistant Professor, Francois Gourio
Assistant Professor, Ksenija Borojevic
Administrator, Barbara Passoff
Boston University Dean, Tobe Berkovitz
Assistant Professor, Bing Liu

LOCATIONS

HQ: BOSTON UNIVERSITY
590 COMMONWEALTH AVE # 255, BOSTON, MA 022152521
Phone: 617 353-2600
Web: WWW.BU.EDU

HISTORICAL FINANCIALS

Company Type: Private

Income Statement — FYE: June 30

	REVENUE ($ mil.)	NET INCOME ($ mil.)	NET PROFIT MARGIN	EMPLOYEES
06/18	2,018	517	25.6%	70
06/17	1,895	507	26.8%	—
Annual Growth	6.5%	2.0%	—	—

2018 Year-End Financials

Return on assets: 8.1%
Return on equity: 13.2%
Current ratio: —
Cash ($ mil.): 148

BOZZUTO'S, INC.

Bozzuto's is a leading wholesale grocery distribution company that supplies food and household products to retailers in New Jersey New York Pennsylvania and in New England. The company distributes a full line of grocery items including meat products produce and floral and grocery dairy and frozen food as well as seasonal and GM/HBC and specialty and organics. It carries goods sold under both the IGA and Hy-Top labels in addition to national brands. Bozzuto's also owns about five distribution centers in Connecticut and Pennsylvania. The company was founded in 1945.

Operations

Bozzuto's Inc. is a total service wholesale distributor of food and household products to retailers. Its services are grocery dairy frozen bakery and deli fresh meat and seafood produce and floral seasonal and GM/HBC and specialty and organics.

In terms of brands the customers can choose from IGA brand products or Hy-Top brand products. The company also offers a growing line of store brand organics called Seven Farms.

Geographic Reach

Cheshire Connecticut-based Bozzuto's operates a pair of distribution centers in Cheshire as well as facilities in North Haven Connecticut and Allentown Pennsylvania. In terms of its clients it also has its presence in New England.

Sales and Marketing

The company has sales associates and distributes its products to retailers.

Company Background

The company founded in 1945 is owned and operated by the Bozzuto family including chairman and CEO Michael Bozzuto.

EXECUTIVES

Vice President Human Resources, Bonnie Sirois
Svp Business Technology Systems And Services, John Keeley
Evp Retail Development, George Motel
Chairman President And Ceo, Michael A. Bozzuto
Vice President Finance, Jim Beaudreault
Vice President Ecommerce Retail Technology, Stephen Methvin
Vice President Information Technology, John Martin
Vice President Customer Service, Gail Handley
Vice President Wholesale Business Information Systems, Samar Saha
Vice President Of Chain Sales, Rob Thatford
Vice President Of Center Store, Jeff King
Vice President Informationtechnologies, Jhon Kelly
Vice President Of Transportation, Steven Schwartz
Vice President Trade Relations, Carol Forshee
Executive Vice President Finance, Chris Sferruzzo
Vice President Human Resources, Scott Grove
Vice President Business Performance Coated And Specialties And Pulp And Lumber Operations, Craig B Stevens
Auditors: FEDERMAN LALLY & REMIS LLC F

LOCATIONS

HQ: BOZZUTO'S, INC.
275 SCHOOLHOUSE RD, CHESHIRE, CT 064101257
Phone: 203 272-3511
Web: WWW.BOZZUTOS.COM

PRODUCTS/OPERATIONS

Selected Services

New store site and demographic analysis
Retail merchandising specialists and sales support
Retail financial services accounting and payroll
Operational analysis
Shelf management programs
Market/pricing strategies
Employee training seminars and workshops
Profit building ideas
Retail technology

COMPETITORS

Associated Grocers of New England
C&S Wholesale
Krasdale Foods
McLane
Pine State Trading
SUPERVALU
Shaw's
Stop & Shop
Wakefern Food

HISTORICAL FINANCIALS

Company Type: Private

Income Statement — FYE: September 27

	REVENUE ($ mil.)	NET INCOME ($ mil.)	NET PROFIT MARGIN	EMPLOYEES
09/08	1,243	(5)	—	3,100
09/07	1,180	(0)	—	—
09/06	955,449	0	0.0%	—
Annual Growth	(96.4%)	—	—	—

2008 Year-End Financials

Return on assets: 7.0%
Return on equity: (-0.5%)
Current ratio: 0.60
Cash ($ mil.): 1

BRANDSMART USA OF HENRY COUNTY, LLC

EXECUTIVES

Pres, Michael Pearlman
Exec V Pres, Larry Sinewgz
Cfo, Eric Beazley
General Manager, Kenneth Nadelman
Inside Sales Representative, Mendez Michael
Auditors: KAUFMAN ROSSIN AND CO

LOCATIONS

HQ: BRANDSMART USA OF HENRY COUNTY, LLC
3200 SW 42ND ST, FORT LAUDERDALE, FL 333126808
Phone: 954 797-4000
Web: WWW.BRANDSMARTUSA.COM

HISTORICAL FINANCIALS

Company Type: Private

Income Statement — FYE: September 25

	REVENUE ($ mil.)	NET INCOME ($ mil.)	NET PROFIT MARGIN	EMPLOYEES
09/10	800	7	0.9%	1
09/09	826	8	1.0%	—
Annual Growth	(3.2%)	(12.4%)	—	—

2010 Year-End Financials

Return on assets: 2.4%
Return on equity: 4.4%
Current ratio: 1.00
Cash ($ mil.): 2

BRAZOS ELECTRIC POWER COOPERATIVE, INC.

Brazos means "arms" in Spanish and the generation and transmission arms of Brazos Electric Power Cooperative reach across 68 Texas counties. It serves 16 member/owner distribution cooperatives and one municipality in Northern and Central Texas. Brazos Electric Power annually generates (through its four power stations) and/or accesses from other power marketers some 3655 MW of electric power. The cooperative's members include Comanche Electric Cooperative Association Heart of Texas Electric Co-op (McGregor) Mid-South Synergy (Navasota) United Coop Services (Cleburne) and Wise Electric (Decatur).

EXECUTIVES

Vice President, Johnny York
Vice President Technology, Lynn Gustafson
Vp Supply Chain, Josh Clevenger
Secretary, Lois Anderson
Auditors: PRICEWATERHOUSECOOPERS LLP KA

LOCATIONS

HQ: BRAZOS ELECTRIC POWER COOPERATIVE, INC.
7616 BAGBY AVE, WACO, TX 767126924
Phone: 254 750-6500
Web: WWW.BRAZOSELECTRIC.COM

Brazos Electric Power Cooperative has operations in 68 counties in northern and Central Texas.

PRODUCTS/OPERATIONS

Member/Owners

Barlett Electric Cooperative
BEPC
Comanche Electric Cooperative
Cooke County Electric Cooperative
CoServ Electric
Fort Belknap Electric Cooperative
Hamilton County Electric Cooperative
Heart of Texas Electric Cooperative
HILCO Electric Cooperative
J-A-C Electric Cooperative
Mid-South Synergy
Navarro County Electric Cooperative
Navasota Valley Electric Cooperative
South Plains Electric Cooperative
Tri-County Electric Cooperative
United Cooperative Services
Wise Electric Cooperative

COMPETITORS

AEP
CenterPoint Energy
El Paso Electric
Entergy
LCRA

HISTORICAL FINANCIALS

Company Type: Private

Income Statement — FYE: December 31

	REVENUE ($ mil.)	NET INCOME ($ mil.)	NET PROFIT MARGIN	EMPLOYEES
12/17	905	58	6.5%	366
12/09	963	56	5.9%	—
12/99	307	6	2.3%	—
Annual Growth	6.2%	12.6%	—	—

2017 Year-End Financials

Return on assets: 1.9%
Return on equity: 7.4%
Current ratio: 15.30
Cash ($ mil.): 353

BRG SPORTS, INC.

BRG Sports is helmet and shoulder pads above the field. The company's Riddell brand is one of the main providers of helmets and shoulder pads worn by players of American football at all levels from junior leagues to the NFL. Riddell is the official helmet and protective gear provider of USA Football and American Youth Football. As concerns about football and brain injuries have risen Riddell has responded with research to development new helmet models. BRG is a corporate holding company of leading brands that design develop and market innovative sports equipment smart helmet technology team apparel and accessories.

Operations

BRG's helmets and pads are worn by athletes in other sports where protection is desired such as ice hockey baseball and softball.

Geographic Reach

BRG Sports is based in Illinois and has approximately 10 facilities worldwide.

Sales and Marketing

BRG serves youth sports equipment and apparel institutional/scholastic sports equipment and apparel professional football equipment industries.

EXECUTIVES

Cfo, Mark A. Tripp, $316,875 total compensation
President Easton Sports, Christopher (Chris) Zimmerman
President And Chief Operating Officer, Timothy P. (Tim) Mayhew
President Ceo And Director, Paul E. Harrington, $715,385 total compensation
Executive Chairman And Chief Executive Officer, Terry G. Lee
President Riddell, Daniel J. (Dan) Arment, $337,038 total compensation
Chief Operations Officer President Of Giro Easton Cycling, Donna L. Flood, $339,692 total compensation
Evp And General Manager Mass Division And Action Sports Sales, Steven T. Bigelow
Evp And General Manager Of Giro/easton Cycling, Greg Shapleigh
Evp And General Manager Of Bell/blackburn, Jessica Klodnicki
President Easton, Mike Zlaket
Auditors: ERNST & YOUNG LLP LOS ANGELE

LOCATIONS

HQ: BRG SPORTS, INC.
1700 E HIGGINS RD STE 500, DES PLAINES, IL 600183800
Phone: 224 585-5200
Web: WWW.BRGSPORTS.COM

2013 Sales

	$ mil.	% of total
North America	667	85
Europe	84	11
Other	28	4
Total	780	100

PRODUCTS/OPERATIONS

Selected Products

Riddell helmets
Riddell shoulder pads
Riddell padded shirts
Riddell game pants
Riddell compression shirts and pants

COMPETITORS

Amer Sports
Bauer Hockey
Merrithew
NIKE
Rawlings Sporting Goods
Reebok-CCM Hockey
Russell Brands
Under Armour
Wilson Sporting Goods
adidas

HISTORICAL FINANCIALS

Company Type: Private

Income Statement — FYE: December 29

	REVENUE ($ mil.)	NET INCOME ($ mil.)	NET PROFIT MARGIN	EMPLOYEES
12/12	827	(3)	—	2,370
12/11*	834	10	1.2%	—
01/11	772	8	1.1%	—
Annual Growth	3.5%	—	—	—

*Fiscal year change

2012 Year-End Financials

Return on assets: (-0.3%)
Return on equity: (-0.9%)
Current ratio: 2.50
Cash ($ mil.): 40

BRIDGEPORT HOSPITAL

EXECUTIVES

Pres-Ceo, William M Jennings
Sr V Pres-Med Staff, Bruce Mc Donald
V Pres-Hr*, Joseph E Janell
SEC*, Norman Roth
Dir, David Bindelglass
Chief Medical Officer-Svp Med*, Victor Morris
Human Resources Coordinator, Maria Alicea
Pediatrician, Mary Gaeta
Engineer, Peter Romano
Director, Susan French
Doctor, Armand J Wolff

LOCATIONS

HQ: BRIDGEPORT HOSPITAL
267 GRANT ST, BRIDGEPORT, CT 066102870
Phone: 203 384-3000
Web: WWW.BRIDGEPORTHOSPITAL.ORG

HISTORICAL FINANCIALS

Company Type: Private

Income Statement — FYE: September 30

	REVENUE ($ mil.)	NET INCOME ($ mil.)	NET PROFIT MARGIN	EMPLOYEES
09/18	550	72	13.2%	200
09/17	482	25	5.4%	—
09/16	470	46	9.9%	—
09/15	466	55	11.9%	—
Annual Growth	5.7%	9.4%	—	—

2018 Year-End Financials

Return on assets: 12.0%
Return on equity: 27.6%
Current ratio: 2.00
Cash ($ mil.): 78

BRIGHTSTAR US, LLC

EXECUTIVES

Mng MBR, Joe Kalinoski
MBR*, Catherine Smith
MBR*, Jack Negro
MBR*, Chad Meadinger
Information Technology, Chris Goebbert
Metric Analyst, Ronna Barger

LOCATIONS

HQ: BRIGHTSTAR US, LLC
9725 NW 117TH AVE STE 300, MEDLEY, FL 331781213
Phone: 305 421-6000
Web: WWW.BRIGHTSTAR.COM

HISTORICAL FINANCIALS

Company Type: Private

Income Statement — FYE: December 31

	REVENUE ($ mil.)	NET INCOME ($ mil.)	NET PROFIT MARGIN	EMPLOYEES
12/16	4,137	52	1.3%	225
12/15	4,418	50	1.1%	—
Annual Growth	(6.4%)	2.8%	—	—

BRODER BROS., CO.

Selling clothes had been in the genes of sportswear distributor Broder Bros. for years. Begun as a haberdashery in 1919 the company evolved from making hats and gloves into a leading distributor of imprintable sportswear distributing 40000-plus SKUs across more than 40 retail brands including adidas Golf Champion Russell Athletic alternative Dickies and private labels. It operates under the Broder Alpha and NES divisions. Private labels include Devon & Jones Chestnut Hill and Harriton. Customers mostly small US retailers order merchandise through seasonal catalogs or online. Private investment firm Bain Capital has held a majority interest in the company since 2000 when the Broder family sold the company.

Operations

Broder Bros.' business comprises eight distribution facilities nationwide as well as 10 Express locations that offer pickup services to customers. Express facilities ship through ground parcel service to more than 80% of the continental US population within one business day and to more than 98% of the continental US population within two business days.

Its two primary markets are imprintable sportswear and accessories. Typically undecorated or blank items such as sweatshirts polo shirts fleece outerwear caps bags and other imprintable accessories are bought from Broder Bros. and decorated for the purposes of advertising and promotion. Decorator customers are offered value-added merchandising marketing and promotional support to help them grow their businesses.

Geographic Reach

Based in Pennsylvania Broder Bros. boasts the industry's largest distribution network. It provides its products to customers across the continental US.

Sales and Marketing

The company which caters to more than 70000 customers relies on a handful of suppliers such as Gildan Hanes and Fruit of the Loom.

In general Broder Bros. clients include advertising specialty companies screen printers embroiderers and specialty retailers that purchase Broder Bros. products (blank T-shirts sweatshirts polo shirts outerwear caps bags and more) to embellish for their own clients. Broder Bros. distributes popular brands such as Anvil Jerzees Hanes Fruit of the Loom and Gildan.

Strategy

Broder Bros. has seen its business pick up on the heels of a tough selling environment. One way it has turned its business around is by ensuring that it had in stock the most popular products while it rebuilt its inventory of proprietary brands. It also strengthened its commitment not to be undersold by rivals. To ensure that its dozen distribution centers were bustling with business Broder Bros. also recruited a senior sales and marketing executive to review and fine-tune how the company sells its products help to decide which product assortment is ideal going forward and figure out how to attract a wider customer base from the imprintable sportswear market.

Mergers and Acquisitions

Looking to post more than $900 million in sales and $50 million in pro forma EBITDA in 2013 Broder Bros. bought Denver-based Imprints Wholesale one of the top wholesale clothing distributors in the Rocky Mountain region. The deal is Broder Bros.' first acquisition since 2006 and first since private investment firm Littlejohn & Co. took over control of the board of directors in mid-2012.

EXECUTIVES

Regional Vice President, Jason Buchanan
Vice President Of Customer Service, Dave Null Hance
Executive Vice President Sales, Hays Lindstrom

LOCATIONS

HQ: BRODER BROS., CO.
6 NESHAMINY INTERPLEX DR 6T, TREVOSE, PA 190536964
Phone: 215 291-0300
Web: WWW.ALPHABRODER.COM

PRODUCTS/OPERATIONS

Selected Products

Accessories

Bags
Decoration supplies
Fleece
Headwear
Pants
Shorts
Sport shirts
T-shirts
Woven shirts

Selected Brands
Trade
Adams Cap
American Apparel
Anvil
Bella
Canvas
Cross Creek
Fruit of the Loom
Gildan
Hanes
Izod
Outer Banks
Van Heusen
Weatherproof
Yupoong
Retail
adidas Golf
Champion
Dickies Chef
Dickies Workwear
Rossignol Pure Mountain Company
Private-label
Chestnut Hill
Harriton
Devon & Jones
HYP
Harvard Square

COMPETITORS

Anvil Holdings
Concept One Accessories
Delta Apparel
Fruit of the Loom
Gildan Activewear
Hanesbrands
M. J. Soffe
PremiumWear
Russell Brands
VF Corporation

HISTORICAL FINANCIALS

Company Type: Private

Income Statement — FYE: December 26

	REVENUE ($ mil.)	NET INCOME ($ mil.)	NET PROFIT MARGIN	EMPLOYEES
12/09	705	(13)	—	1,826
12/08	926	(68)	—	—
12/07	929	(124)	—	—
Annual Growth	(12.9%)	—	—	—

2009 Year-End Financials

Return on assets: (-4.5%)
Return on equity: —
Current ratio: 2.10
Cash ($ mil.): 3

BRONSON HEALTH CARE GROUP, INC.

Bronson Health Care Group has a strong presence as a provider of a wide range of medical services in southern Michigan and northern Indiana. The company operates several regional hospitals and health clinics including Bronson Methodist Hospital (some 400 beds) Bronson Battle Creek (220 beds) and Bronson Lakeview Hospital (35 beds). The not-for-profit health care system's facilities provide general and specialty services including trauma stroke burn cancer and cardiac care as well as emergency medicine pediatrics obstetrics rehabilitation and home health care.

Operations

Bronson Health Care Group serves about 24000 patients each year at more than 60 locations. The medical system offers a full range of services from primary care to critical care; it has more than 1000 medical staff members and 812 licensed beds.

The hospital group provides $94 million in community benefits a year including charity care for under-insured or uninsured patients.

Geographic Reach

Bronson Health Care Group operates hospitals clinics and physician practice facilities in Kalamazoo Calhoun and Van Buren counties in southwestern and south central Michigan; its locations also serve patients from areas of northern Indiana.

Strategy

Expanded its infrastructure to meet demand in 2013 the company opened Bronson Commons a rehabilitation and skilled nursing community in Mattawan. The all-private room healthcare facility has the capacity to serve 100 patients.

That year 2013 Bronson Battle Creek opened a new outpatient center on Beckley Road.

Mergers and Acquisitions

In 2013 HealthCare Midwest a multidisciplinary physician group (with 80 doctors) serving southwest Michigan joined the Bronson family of companies and became Bronson HealthCare Midwest. That year Associated Internal Medicine Specialists a medical practice focused on internal medicine and rheumatology joined Bronson Battle Creek and was renamed Bronson Internal Medicine & Rheumatology.

In 2012 Colon and Rectal Surgery Center PC joined the Bronson network and became Bronson Center for Colon & Rectal Diseases.

Company Background

To expand its services and geographic reach in 2011 Bronson Health Care System acquired the Battle Creek Health System (now named Bronson Battle Creek located in south central Michigan. The purchase added acute care inpatient mental health cancer care occupational health and other specialized services in the region.

The not-for-profit health care system was founded in 1900.

EXECUTIVES

Vp Cno, Denise Neely
Senior Vice President Strategy And Communication, Sue Birch
Vice President Contracting And Clinically Integrated Network, Nancy Vannest
Medical Secretary, Nicole Blain
Auditors: PLANTE & MORAN PLLC GRAND RA

LOCATIONS

HQ: BRONSON HEALTH CARE GROUP, INC.
301 JOHN ST, KALAMAZOO, MI 490075295
Phone: 269 341-6000
Web: WWW.BRONSONHEALTH.COM

PRODUCTS/OPERATIONS

Selected Facilities
Bronson Athletic Club
Bronson Battle Creek
Bronson Commons
Bronson Health Foundation
Bronson HealthCare Midwest
Bronson Home Health Care
Bronson LakeView Hospital
Bronson LakeView Outpatient Center
Bronson Lifestyle Improvement & Research Center
Bronson Medical Group
Bronson Methodist Hospital
Bronson Vicksburg Outpatient Center
Van Buren Emergency Medical Services

COMPETITORS

Ascension Health
Gerber Memorial
Hayes Green Beach Memorial Hospital
Mercy Health Hackley
Sheridan Community Hospital
Spectrum Health

HISTORICAL FINANCIALS

Company Type: Private

Income Statement — FYE: December 31

	REVENUE ($ mil.)	NET INCOME ($ mil.)	NET PROFIT MARGIN	EMPLOYEES
12/17	1,233	63	5.1%	4,180
12/16	1,136	28	2.5%	—
12/09	119	16	13.8%	—
12/08	588	(62)	—	—
Annual Growth	8.6%	—	—	—

2017 Year-End Financials

Return on assets: 4.5%
Return on equity: 9.4%
Current ratio: 5.60
Cash ($ mil.): 103

BRONSON METHODIST HOSPITAL INC

From your leg bone to your knee bone; your neck bone to your head bone Bronson Methodist Hospital has the specialists to cure what ails you. The 435-bed hospital is the flagship facility of the Bronson Healthcare Group a not-for-profit health care system. Bronson Methodist provides care in just about every specialty including orthopedics surgery and oncology. The hospital also contains specialist units for critical care (level I trauma center) neurology (primary stroke center) cardiology (Chest pain emergency center) women's health (BirthPlace) and pediatrics (children's hospital).

EXECUTIVES

Cio And Svp Information Technology, Ashutosh Goel
Director Of Nursing, Kathy Cheesebro
Vice President Of Finance And Human Resources, Erica Nagra
Director Of Nursing, Tresa Kruis
Auditors: PLANTE & MORAN PLLC CHICAGO

LOCATIONS

HQ: BRONSON METHODIST HOSPITAL INC
601 JOHN ST STE E-012, KALAMAZOO, MI 490075346
Phone: 269 341-7654
Web: WWW.BRONSONHEALTH.COM

PRODUCTS/OPERATIONS

Selected Services

Anticoagulation

Bereavement
Breast Health
Burn
Cancer Care
Critical Care
Diabetes
Flu
Heart and Vascular
Home Health
Hyperbaric Oxygen Therapy
Infusion
Laboratory
Medical and Surgical Weight Management
Neurosciences
Nutrition
Occupational Health
Orthopedics
Palliative Care
Pediatrics
Pharmacy
Pregnancy and Childbirth
Rehabilitation
Respiratory Care
Sleep
Surgery
Stomal Therapy
Testing and Imaging
Trauma and Emergency
Women's Health
Wound

COMPETITORS

Ascension Health
Borgess Health
Bronson Battle Creek Community Hospital
Elkhart General Healthcare System
Hayes Green Beach Memorial Hospital
Holland Hospital
Spectrum Health
Trinity Health (Novi)
Zeeland Community Hospital

HISTORICAL FINANCIALS

Company Type: Private

Income Statement — FYE: December 31

	REVENUE ($ mil.)	NET INCOME ($ mil.)	NET PROFIT MARGIN	EMPLOYEES
12/18	864	26	3.1%	2,861
12/17	864	85	9.8%	—
12/15	726	69	9.5%	—
12/13	647	(8)	—	—
Annual Growth	6.0%	—	—	—

2018 Year-End Financials

Return on assets: 2.8%
Return on equity: 4.2%
Current ratio: 9.40
Cash ($ mil.): 109

BRONXCARE HEALTH SYSTEM

Bronx-Lebanon Hospital Center cares for patients in the central and south Bronx no doubt while rooting for the Yankees a few blocks away. The health care provider maintains more than 970 beds across its two campuses as well as psychiatric and nursing home facilities. Hospital specialty units include chest pain orthopedic cancer and women's health centers. Bronx-Lebanon also manages a network of about 70 owned and affiliated medical practices (under the BronxCare brand). This network includes primary care doctors and specialty clinics as well as rehabilitation facilities. The hospital is also a primary teaching hospital for the Albert Einstein College of Medicine.

Operations

Aside from its two major hospitals Bronx-Lebanon operates a psychiatric facility a pair of specialized long-term care facilities and the BronxCare network of medical practices that include Dr. Martin Luther King Jr. Health Center and a 51-unit facility to house seniors and low-income residents. Bronx-Lebanon cares for those with mental or substance abuse problems through the Family Wellness Center. It also operates a 240-bed Special Care Center and the 90-bed Highbridge Woodycrest Center to provide long term health care to geriatric AIDS and disabled residents. Its ER Department responds to about 141000 patient visits a year.

Geographic Reach

The hospital system's 37 locations serve residents of central and south Bronx in New York.

Sales and Marketing

In 2013 the company spent about $144000 on advertising.

Financial Performance

The Hospital Center is supported primarily by patient service fees paid by Medicaid Medicare and commercial insurance carriers. In 2013 the Medicaid contributed 63% of the revenue whereas Medicare contributed 28% and the rest 9% was contributed other third-party insurance carriers.

In 2013 Bronx-Lebanon's net revenues increased by about 5% due to a rise in patient service revenues and grants partially offset by a decrease in auxiliary services.

The company's net income increased by more than 790% in 2013 as the result of an increase in revenues.

Bronx-Lebanon's operating cash flows increased by 53% thanks to higher income.

Strategy

Bronx-Lebanon emphasizes its role as a community health care provider not only through its BronxCare network but through a number of community outreach and service efforts including school-based programs mobile health units free health screening and even a weekly live television show that discusses health issues.

To accommodate the growing population in and around the Bronx the hospital system has expanded in recent years with a new children's wing for inpatient and outpatient services; a nine-story ambulatory care facility; and an extensive emergency room modernization. Bronx-Lebanon also maintains a short stay observation unit in the emergency room area to monitor and evaluate patients in cardiac distress prior to admission or discharge.

Bronx-Lebanon is one of many hospital organizations to have joined a regional health information organization (RHIO) to allow medical professionals to access a patient's medical records at any number of health care locations. Other members of the Bronx RHIO include Montefiore Medical Center Jacobi Medical Center St. Barnabas Hospital and Hebrew Home at Riverdale.

Bronx-Lebanon is also one of the few hospitals in New York that is fully computerized with a complete inpatient and outpatient electronic medical record.

The hospital center's expansion plans include a $42 million 60000 sq. ft ambulatory care facility and a $34 million 56000 sq. ft. life recovery center for chemical dependency services.

In 2014 the company completed the construction of its Health and Wellness Center a new state-of-the-art outpatient facility with general and specialty services and new treatment rooms and diagnostic equipment. It also completed the construction of its Life Recovery Center to combine inpatient outpatient and residential services for individuals suffering from chemical dependency.

The company also expanded its Emergency room adding a new 11-bay treatment area.

In the same year it also relocated and expanded its main Dentistry Practice adding 39 dental chairs (a 50% increase).

EXECUTIVES

Medical Director, Soni Mathew
Vice President, Milton A Gumbs
Vice Chairman Department Of Otolaryngology Head And Neck Surgery, Srinivasan Krishna

LOCATIONS

HQ: BRONXCARE HEALTH SYSTEM
1276 FULTON AVE, BRONX, NY 104563402
Phone: 718 590-1800
Web: WWW.BRONX-LEB.ORG

PRODUCTS/OPERATIONS

Selected Services

Anesthesiology

Asthma
Adult
Pediatric
Cardiology
Dentistry
Diabetes
Adult
Pediatric
Ear Nose & Throat
Gastroenterology
Hematology & Oncology
Neonatology
Neurology
Ophthalmology
Orthopaedics
Pediatrics

Physical Medicine
Psychiatry
Radiology
Special Care Center
Urology & Men's Health

Selected Academic Affiliations

Albert Einstein College of Medicine
Bronx Community College
Hostos Community College
Lehman College City University of New York
State University of New York at Stony Brook

COMPETITORS

Beth Israel Medical Center
Catholic Healthcare System
Continuum Health Partners
Lenox Hill Hospital
Maimonides Medical Center
Memorial Sloan-Kettering
Montefiore Medical
New York City Health and Hospitals
NewYork-Presbyterian Healthcare
Northwell Health
Winthrop-University Hospital

HISTORICAL FINANCIALS

Company Type: Private

Income Statement FYE: December 31

	REVENUE ($ mil.)	NET INCOME ($ mil.)	NET PROFIT MARGIN	EMPLOYEES
12/17	750	12	1.6%	4,000
12/16	641	6	1.0%	—
12/15	631	18	3.0%	—
12/14	598	(34)	—	—
Annual Growth	7.9%	—	—	—

2017 Year-End Financials

Return on assets: 2.4%
Return on equity: 19.6%
Current ratio: 0.70
Cash ($ mil.): 117

BROOKFIELD PROPERTIES RETAIL INC.

EXECUTIVES

Director, Cheryl Casanova
Senior Director of Big Box Lea, Chris Milkie
Site Manager, Ken Hesse
Administrative Assistant, Adriana Imbert
Director, Kyrie Bonadies
Business, Marc Wolfer
Auditors: DELOITTE & TOUCHE LLP CHICAGO

LOCATIONS

HQ: BROOKFIELD PROPERTIES RETAIL INC.
350 N ORLEANS ST STE 300, CHICAGO, IL 606541607
Phone: 312 960-5000
Web: WWW.BROOKFIELDPROPERTIESRETAIL.COM

HISTORICAL FINANCIALS

Company Type: Private

Income Statement FYE: December 31

	REVENUE ($ mil.)	NET INCOME ($ mil.)	NET PROFIT MARGIN	EMPLOYEES
12/19	1,563	480	30.7%	87
12/18	2,064	4,163	201.7%	—
Annual Growth	(24.2%)	(88.5%)	—	—

2019 Year-End Financials

Return on assets: 2.2%
Return on equity: 14.6%
Current ratio: —
Cash ($ mil.): 197

BROTHER INTERNATIONAL CORPORATION

Brother International is part of one big global family. A subsidiary of Japan-based Brother Industries Brother International sells a host of products – including inkjet and laser printers fax machines scanners typewriters sewing machines gear motors and machine tools – manufactured by its parent company. Its products are marketed to consumers and businesses in North America and across Latin America. Through its subsidiaries Brother International operates production and sales facilities in some 30 countries worldwide; it serves customers in about 100 countries. The business was formed in 1954.

Strategy

Although it provides a range of products for office and home use including home appliances such as sewing machines Brother International is increasingly focused on office equipment technology and document management. In 2019 it partnered with software firm Accusoft by integrating Accusoft's OnTask SaaS workflow platform into select Brother devices allowing for remote collaboration improved visibility and tracking of documents and shortened turnaround times.

EXECUTIVES

Chairman Brother International Corporation, Tadashi Ishiguro
Vice President, Bill Henderson
Vice President Distribution Operations, Steve Gadd

LOCATIONS

HQ: BROTHER INTERNATIONAL CORPORATION
200 CROSSING BLVD FL 1, BRIDGEWATER, NJ 088072861
Phone: 908 704-1700
Web: WWW.BROTHER-USA.COM

PRODUCTS/OPERATIONS

Selected Services

Brother Business Solutions
Brother Cloud

Selected Products

Fax machines
Garment printers
Gear motors
Home sewing & embroidery
Industrial printing & sewing
Labeling systems
Machine tools
Mobile products (portable scanners printers industrial labelers)
Printers
Scanners
Sewing and embroidery machines
Stamp-making systems
Typewriters
Web conferencing

COMPETITORS

Canon USA
Epson
HP
IBM
Kyocera Document Solutions America
Microsoft
OKI Data Americas
Oracle
RISO Inc.
Retail Holdings
Ricoh Americas
Xerox

HISTORICAL FINANCIALS

Company Type: Private

Income Statement FYE: March 31

	REVENUE ($ mil.)	NET INCOME ($ mil.)	NET PROFIT MARGIN	EMPLOYEES
03/18	1,751	33	1.9%	2,000
03/15	1,852	3	0.2%	—
03/14	1,826	26	1.5%	—
Annual Growth	(1.0%)	6.1%	—	—

2018 Year-End Financials

Return on assets: 4.2%
Return on equity: 6.0%
Current ratio: 3.30
Cash ($ mil.): 29

BROWARD COUNTY PUBLIC SCHOOLS

EXECUTIVES

Supt, Robert W Runcie
Acct*, Paul Purrier
Executive of Information Techn, Sharon Simmons
Customer Staff, Kendra Demme
Director, Angela St Hubert
Teacher, Joann Hoy
Director, Judy Zinn
Office Manager, Kathryn McArthur
Administrative Assistant, Nicoletta Williams
Teacher, Adriana Cardoso
Management, Alden B Davis

LOCATIONS

HQ: BROWARD COUNTY PUBLIC SCHOOLS
600 SE 3RD AVE, FORT LAUDERDALE, FL 333013125
Phone: 754 321-0000
Web: WWW.BROWARDSCHOOLS.COM

HISTORICAL FINANCIALS

Company Type: Private

Income Statement FYE: June 30

	REVENUE ($ mil.)	NET INCOME ($ mil.)	NET PROFIT MARGIN	EMPLOYEES
06/16	2,630	(37)	—	31,174
06/15	2,536	186	7.3%	—
06/11	2,515	(37)	—	—
Annual Growth	0.9%	—	—	—

2016 Year-End Financials

Return on assets: (-0.9%)
Return on equity: (-6.4%)
Current ratio: 1.50
Cash ($ mil.): 671

BROWN UNIVERSITY IN PROVIDENCE IN THE STATE OF RHODE ISLAND AND PROVIDENCE PLANTATIONS

Ivy isn't always green — particularly when it's Brown. Founded in 1764 Brown University is both an Ivy League college and one of the oldest universities in the US. About 8700 undergraduate graduate and medical students have about 70 undergraduate and 70 graduate programs of study at their disposal in areas ranging from acting to pharmacology and from history to business administration. The university's specialty programs include the Warren Alpert Medical School and the Brown School of Engineering; it also has continuing education and online learning programs. Brown has some 700 faculty members giving it a student-teacher ratio of about 8:1. It has an endowment of more than $3 billion.

Operations

Nearly all applicants to Brown have graduated in the top 10% of their high school class. Undergraduate tuition and fees at Brown run at more than $62000 per year and as such nearly half of its students receive needs-based scholarships.

Brown's medical school partners with a number of area medical facilities to provide specialized medical training as well as specialized health care services to the public in addition to research in a variety of disease and treatment areas.

In fiscal 2015 Brown spent $152 million on research expenditures funded by both government and private sources.

Geographic Reach

Brown's students come from all 50 US states as well as from more than 115 other countries. The university campus is located in Providence Rhode Island and consists of 235 buildings on nearly 140 acres. It also has study abroad partnerships with schools in countries including Scotland and China.

Financial Performance

Brown University's endowment was up to nearly $3 billion until 2009 when the troubled economy caused it to lose more than a quarter of its value leading Brown to cut its operating budget in subsequent year. The university has recovered some of the lost funds through rebounding markets and a diverse investment strategy (including traditional stocks and fixed-income securities as well as alternative investment funds) with the endowment rising to just over $2.5 billion in 2012. By fiscal 2015 the endowment reached a new peak at $3.3 billion.

Also that year revenue increased 5% to $808 million on an equal amount of growth in net tuition and fees as well as growth in contributions and grants and auxiliary enterprises. However net income declined steeply falling $334 million to $67 million in 2015. This was a result of lower investment earnings and higher operating expenses (salaries supplies etc.). Operating cash outflow increased 8% to $73 million due to changes in accounts payable and accrued liabilities.

Strategy

To enhance its students' educational experience Brown is looking to expand its campus facilities and grow its portfolio of programs. Of its three professional schools (public health medical and engineering) two were established within the past five years. In 2015 Brown introduced a new master's program in social analysis and research.

In terms of physical facilities the university is also making additions and changes. It recently completed projects updating the mathematics (2015) and sports (2014) departments and it is expanding the engineering school complex.

Company Background

Founded in 1764 as the College of Rhode Island the university was renamed Brown University in 1804 for benefactor Nicholas Brown. Brown was the the first Ivy League school to appoint an African-American to the position president; Ruth Simmons was president of the university from 2001-2012. Simmons was also the university's first female president.

EXECUTIVES

Evp Finance And Administration, Elizabeth C. Huidekoper
Evp Planning And Policy, Russell C. Carey
Dean Of Admission, James Miller
Dean Medicine And Biological Sciences, Jack A. Elias
Provost, Mark S. Schlissel
Vp And Cio For Computing And Information Services, Michael Pickett
Dean Of The Faculty, Kevin McLaughlin
Dean Graduate School, Peter Weber
Dean Engineering, Lawrence Larson
President, Christina H. Paxson
Vp And Chief Investment Officer, Joseph L. Dowling
Dean Continuing Education, Karen Sibley
Vp And General Counsel, Eileen Goldgeier
Vice Chancellor, Jerome C. Vascellaro
Chancellor, Thomas J. Tisch
Secretary, Marshall Jiang
Treasurer Trustee, Alison Ressler
Auditors: KPMG LLP PROVIDENCE RI

LOCATIONS

HQ: BROWN UNIVERSITY IN PROVIDENCE IN THE STATE OF RHODE ISLAND AND PROVIDENCE PLANTATIONS
1 PROSPECT ST, PROVIDENCE, RI 029129100
Phone: 401 863-1000
Web: WWW.BROWN.EDU

PRODUCTS/OPERATIONS

2015 Revenues

	$ mil.	% of total
Net tuition & fees	289	36
Grants & contracts	151	18
Endowment income	142	18
Contributions	98	12
Auxiliary enterprises	90	11
Other	36	5
Total	**808**	**100**

Selected Programs

Africana Studies Department of
American Studies Department of
Anthropology Department of
Applied Mathematics Division of
Archaeology and the Ancient World Joukowsky Institute for
Behavioral and Social Sciences Department of
Biology & Medicine Division of
Biomedical Engineering Center for
Biostatistics Department of
Biotechnology Graduate Program
Brown-Pfizer MA Program in Biology
Chemistry Department of
Classics Department of
Cognitive Linguistic and Psychological Sciences Department of
Commerce Organizations & Entrepreneurship C.V. Starr Program in
Comparative Literature Department of
Computational Biology Center for
Computer Science Department of
Development Studies Program in

HISTORICAL FINANCIALS

Company Type: Private

Income Statement — FYE: June 30

	REVENUE ($ mil.)	NET INCOME ($ mil.)	NET PROFIT MARGIN	EMPLOYEES
06/13	732	289	39.6%	5,100
06/12	704	(69)	—	—
06/11	666	359	53.9%	—
Annual Growth	4.8%	(10.2%)	—	—

2013 Year-End Financials

Return on assets: 6.6%
Return on equity: 8.4%
Current ratio: —
Cash ($ mil.): 14

BRUCE OAKLEY, INC.

From little acorns mighty Oakleys grow. Bruce Oakley provides road and river (barge) transportation of dry bulk commodities as well as grain storage and bulk fertilizer sales. The company's trucking division which uses both end-dump and pneumatic tank trailers serves the continental US and Canada. Overall Bruce Oakley operates some 450 trailers. It maintains about half a dozen ports in Arkansas Louisiana and Missouri on the Arkansas Mississippi and Red rivers and the company's river barge transportation unit operates on those and other inland and intracoastal waterways. Grain storage services are available in five ports in Arkansas. Bruce Oakley was founded in 1968.

EXECUTIVES

Vice President, Edward Bubba Vance
Vice President, Shane Smith
Vice President, Josh Childress
Vice President Sales Division, Russell Vallance
Vice President, Autumn Whiting
Vice President Fuel, Tim Lloyd
Senior Vice President Intermodal Finance, Austin Downey

LOCATIONS

HQ: BRUCE OAKLEY, INC.
3400 GRIBBLE ST, NORTH LITTLE ROCK, AR 721146406
Phone: 501 945-0875
Web: WWW.BRUCEOAKLEY.COM

PRODUCTS/OPERATIONS

Selected Products and Services

Bagging

Barges
Bulk fertilizer
Grain and grain storage
Oakley vessel freight
River ports and stevedoring
Trucking

COMPETITORS

American Commercial Lines
Bulkmatic
Comcar
GrainCorp
Groendyke Transport
Kansas City Southern
Superior Bulk Logistics

HISTORICAL FINANCIALS

Company Type: Private

Income Statement FYE: September 25

	REVENUE ($ mil.)	NET INCOME ($ mil.)	NET PROFIT MARGIN	EMPLOYEES
09/08	1,160	31	2.8%	720
09/07	526	11	2.2%	—
09/06	419	13	3.2%	—
Annual Growth	66.3%	53.6%	—	—

2008 Year-End Financials

Return on assets: 21.7%
Return on equity: 34.6%
Current ratio: 2.50
Cash ($ mil.): 3

BRUCKNER TRUCK SALES, INC.

EXECUTIVES

Pres, Brian M Bruckner
Exec V Pres*, Chris B Bruckner
Sec-Treas-Cfo*, Wesley L Lawhorn
V Pres*, Keith Martin
V Pres*, Brian Murphy
Truck, Colt Bothel
Truck, Drew Wilkens
Outside Parts Sales, Johnny Arellano
Outside Parts Sales Representa, Liz Anderson
Used Truck Sales Coordinator, Mason Moore
Used Truck Sales, Robyn Penland
Auditors: CLIFTON LARSON ALLEN LLP DALL

LOCATIONS

HQ: BRUCKNER TRUCK SALES, INC.
9471 E INTERSTATE 40, AMARILLO, TX 791186960
Phone: 806 376-6273
Web: WWW.BRUCKNERTRUCK.COM

HISTORICAL FINANCIALS

Company Type: Private

Income Statement FYE: June 30

	REVENUE ($ mil.)	NET INCOME ($ mil.)	NET PROFIT MARGIN	EMPLOYEES
06/15	580	10	1.8%	900
06/14	490	10	2.1%	—
06/10	200	2	1.1%	—
Annual Growth	23.8%	37.9%	—	—

2015 Year-End Financials

Return on assets: 3.5%
Return on equity: 12.9%
Current ratio: 1.20
Cash ($ mil.): 31

BRYAN MEDICAL CENTER

Bryan Medical Center is the centerpiece of a not-for-profit health care system serving residents of Lincoln Nebraska and surrounding communities. The medical center which operates as part of Bryan Health features two acute-care hospitals (Bryan East and Bryan West) housing a combined 670 beds. In addition to providing general medical and surgical care it serves as a regional trauma center and provides specialty care in areas such as cancer orthopedics and cardiology. The Bryan Health organization also includes a rural hospital and several outpatient clinics and it provides medical training home health care services and wellness programs.

Operations

In addition to Bryan Medical Center the Bryan Health organization operates the Crete Area Medical Center a 25-bed community hospital. Outpatient facilities include the Bryan Heart Institute (cardiology and cardiothoracic surgery) the Bryan Physician Network (family practice urgent care and specialist locations) and Bryan LifePointe (wellness and fitness programs). In addition the network includes the Bryan College of Health Sciences which provides bachelor's and master's degrees in nursing and health professional fields and the Bryan Foundation. It also conducts community education activities.

In the latest year for which data is available the hospital had 5912 inpatient visits; 6650 outpatient surgeries; and 68352 emergency department visits.

Geographic ReachBryan Medical Center serves patients throughout Nebraska as well as portions of neighboring states including Kansas Iowa and Missouri with clinics in more than 30 communities including Lincoln Columbus and Hastings.

Sales and Marketing

Bryan Medical Center advertises through magazines and through the Internet.

Strategy

In 2015 the hospital became the first in Nebraska to utilize the CardioMEMS HF System a miniaturized and wireless monitoring device to manage heart failure and reduce hospital admissions. That year it also began using the Kiva VCF Treatment System for the treatment of patients with vertebral compression fractures.

Company Background

The BryanLGH system was formed through the 1997 combination of Bryan Memorial Hospital (named after populist firebrand William Jennings Bryan) and Lincoln General Hospital. Bryan Health is part of the Heartland Health Alliance a group of about 40 Nebraska hospitals that work together to improve rural health care services through shared services and best practices.

In 2012 the health organization rebranded itself to reflect its expanded position in the region's health care market. BryanLGH Medical Center was renamed Bryan Medical Center and the broader health organization changed its name from the BryanLGH Health System to simply Bryan Health.

EXECUTIVES

Pharmacy Manager, Jeff Weber
Auditors: CROWE HORWATH LLP SIMSBURY C

LOCATIONS

HQ: BRYAN MEDICAL CENTER
1600 S 48TH ST, LINCOLN, NE 685061283
Phone: 402 481-1111
Web: WWW.BRYANHEALTH.COM

PRODUCTS/OPERATIONS

Selected Services

Bariatrics
Cardiac Services
Cancer
Cardiothoracic Surgery
Childbirth/Family Birthplace
Corporate & Community Wellness
Diabetes Center
Early Detection
Emergency Department
Heart Valve Center of Excellence
Hospitalists
Independence Center
Inpatient Rehabilitation
Neuroscience
Mental Health
Orthopedics
Outpatient Specialty Clinic
Radiation Oncology
Radiology
Rehabilitation/Therapy
Robotic Surgery
Sleep Medicine
StarCare Air Ambulance
Substance Abuse
Trauma Center
Urgent Care
Vascular Services
Women's & Children's

COMPETITORS

Catholic Health Initiatives
Children's Hospital & Medical Center
Madonna Rehabilitation Hospital
Methodist Health System
Nebraska Medical Center

HISTORICAL FINANCIALS

Company Type: Private

Income Statement FYE: December 31

	REVENUE ($ mil.)	NET INCOME ($ mil.)	NET PROFIT MARGIN	EMPLOYEES
12/19	785	129	16.5%	3,970
12/17	606	74	12.3%	—
12/16	586	60	10.3%	—
12/15	558	43	7.8%	—
Annual Growth	8.9%	31.2%	—	—

2019 Year-End Financials

Return on assets: 9.9%
Return on equity: 13.0%
Current ratio: 2.20
Cash ($ mil.): 108

BUFFALO CITY SCHOOL DISTRICT

EXECUTIVES

Supt, Kriner Cash
Coordinator, Shannon Standing
Coordinator, Jeanine Groll
Assistant Superintendent, Mary Jo Conrad
Associate Superintendent For T, Anne Botticelli
Assistant, Catherine Dulak

Central Cse Coordinator, Dawn Haring
General Counsel, Nathaniel Kuzma
Food Director, Brigitte O'Brien-Wood
Junior Buyer Bureau of Purchas, Jason Giglio
Coordinator Team Lead, Jason Guzzetta
Auditors: FREEDMAXICK CPAS PC BUFFALO

LOCATIONS

HQ: BUFFALO CITY SCHOOL DISTRICT
712 CITY HALL, BUFFALO, NY 142027537
Phone: 716 816-3575
Web: WWW.BUFFALOSCHOOLS.ORG

HISTORICAL FINANCIALS

Company Type: Private

Income Statement — FYE: June 30

	REVENUE ($ mil.)	NET INCOME ($ mil.)	NET PROFIT MARGIN	EMPLOYEES
06/12	868	(194)	—	3,700
06/05	0	0	1.4%	—
Annual Growth	215.8%	—	—	—

2012 Year-End Financials

Return on assets: (-11.0%)
Return on equity: —
Current ratio: —
Cash ($ mil.): 348

BVH, INC.

EXECUTIVES

Ceo-Chb-Pres, Steve L Edwards
Evp-SEC, Timothy W Triplett
Evp-Cfo, Kenneth L Williams
Svp-Treasurer, Michael Williams
Water Project Manager, Andrew Mally
Gasification Consultant, Anthony Black
Marketing Coordinator, Belinda Walk
Mechanical Engineer, Ben Connell
Planning Manager Ener, Brent Burklund
Ops Manager, Bruce Chow
Associate Vice President, Carl Petz
Auditors: KPMG LLP KANSAS CITY MO

LOCATIONS

HQ: BVH, INC.
11401 LAMAR AVE, OVERLAND PARK, KS 662111508
Phone: 913 458-2000
Web: WWW.BV.COM

HISTORICAL FINANCIALS

Company Type: Private

Income Statement — FYE: December 29

	REVENUE ($ mil.)	NET INCOME ($ mil.)	NET PROFIT MARGIN	EMPLOYEES
12/17	3,363	87	2.6%	8,495
12/16*	3,207	75	2.4%	—
01/16	2,955	108	3.7%	—
01/15	3,029	113	3.7%	—
Annual Growth	3.6%	(8.3%)	—	—

*Fiscal year change

2017 Year-End Financials

Return on assets: 5.6%
Return on equity: 73.5%
Current ratio: 1.10
Cash ($ mil.): 344

C.R. ENGLAND, INC.

The world's top refrigerated trucking company and one of North America's largest transportation firms C.R. England hauls refrigerated and dry cargo throughout the US. The family-owned company also serves parts of Canada and through alliances points in Mexico. C.R. England's fleet includes more than 3500 Freightliner Peterbilt Volvo and International tractors and 8000 trailers. Besides for-hire freight hauling C.R. England offers dedicated contract carriage in which drivers and equipment are assigned to a customer long-term; logistics services including freight brokerage; and intermodal railroad service.

Operations

The company's operations include national US US regional and Mexican truckload service as well as dedicated (customized) truck contracts and intermodal service.

In addition to freight brokerage C.R. England's England Logistics unit offers intermodal service for refrigerated cargo in which customers' containerized freight is shuttled between truck and railroad facility. The logistics unit also arranges the transportation of less-than-truckload quantities of freight and provides ground transportation of ocean containers for shipping lines.

This unit also provides global logistics - international shipping and freight forwarding solutions); supply chain management (freight management) and carrier services (factoring solutions fuel discounts tire discounts and other services).

C.R. England's business also benefits from operating five truck driving schools in the US and a course on becoming a freight broker. The school helps improve driver safety as well as provides a pool of qualified truck drivers for hire.

Geographic Reach

The company operates primarily in California Illinois Texas and Utah.

Strategy

Greening its fleet C. R. England has announced a multi-year liquefied natural gas (LNG) bulk fueling agreement with Shell. C.R. England will replace existing diesel trucks with LNG-powered trucks servicing southern California the most mature US market for fueling LNG-powered trucks.

The company is focusing on innovation in its intermodal and dedicated operations. The intermodal division has more than 1000 TempStack 53 ft. temperature-controlled containers which can be double-stacked on the flatcars of its partner railroad reducing customer costs increasing shipping capacity and efficiency and lowering fuel costs.

C.R. England is also beefing up its trucking operations working to deliver faster more secure shipments for its customers in its national and regional divisions.

Company Background

C.R. England was founded in 1920 by Chester Rodney England and is run by his descendants.

EXECUTIVES

President Mexico Division, David (Dave) Akers
Evp Maintenance, Todd D. England
Evp Operations Support, Corey D. England
Ceo, Chad England
President, Josh England
Coo, Brandon Harrison
Evp Corporate Sales And Marketing, David A. Kramer
Coo; President England Logistics, Zach England
Corporate Vp Compliance And Safety, Dustin England
President National And Regional, Sam Scott
President Intermodal, Coby Bullard
President Dedicated, Tracy Brown
Cfo, TJ McGeean
Executive Vice President Human Resources, Lisa Callister
Vice President Of Recruiting, Wayne Cederholm
Vice President Information Technology, Rich Farr
Chairman And President, Daniel E. (Dan) England
Ceo, Dean D. England
Auditors: TANNER LLC SALT LAKE CITY UT

LOCATIONS

HQ: C.R. ENGLAND, INC.
4701 W 2100 S, SALT LAKE CITY, UT 841201223
Phone: 800 421-9004
Web: WWW.CRENGLAND.COM

PRODUCTS/OPERATIONS

Selected Operations

Trucking
National - Long haul truckload service
Mexico - Shipments in and out of Mexico
Regional - Short haul truckload service positioned in the West Midwest and Texas and surrounding areas (AR LA OK)
Dedicated - Tailor-made services dedicating trucks and drivers to specific customer needs
Intermodal - Expedited priority rail service using TempStack 53' refrigerated containers
England Logistics

COMPETITORS

C.H. Robinson Worldwide
Central Refrigerated Service
Covenant Transportation
Crete Carrier
Frozen Food Express
J.B. Hunt
KLLM Transport Services
Landstar System
Marten Transport
Navajo Shippers
Prime Inc.
Stevens Transport
Swift Transportation
Willis Shaw Express

HISTORICAL FINANCIALS

Company Type: Private

Income Statement — FYE: December 31

	REVENUE ($ mil.)	NET INCOME ($ mil.)	NET PROFIT MARGIN	EMPLOYEES
12/12	1,579	56	3.6%	6,500
12/11	1,315	55	4.3%	—
12/07	829	41	5.0%	—
Annual Growth	13.7%	6.2%	—	—

2012 Year-End Financials

Return on assets: 7.4%
Return on equity: 24.7%
Current ratio: 1.40
Cash ($ mil.): 15

CABELL HUNTINGTON HOSPITAL INC

EXECUTIVES

Pres-Ceo, Brent A Marsteller
V Pres, David Graley
SEC, Steven L Burton
Treas, Floyd Eharlow Jr
Dir, Carolyn L Bagby
Executive Officer, Judith Riley
Chief of Medicine, Ross Patton
Anesthesiologist, Don Gross
Patient Account Supervisor, Michelle Hampton

Analyst, Jason Hill
Director, Jack Taylor
Auditors: BAKER TILLY VIRCHOW KRAUSE LL

LOCATIONS

HQ: CABELL HUNTINGTON HOSPITAL INC
1340 HAL GREER BLVD, HUNTINGTON, WV 257013804
Phone: 304 526-2000
Web: WWW.CABELLHUNTINGTON.ORG

HISTORICAL FINANCIALS

Company Type: Private

Income Statement — FYE: September 30

	REVENUE ($ mil.)	NET INCOME ($ mil.)	NET PROFIT MARGIN	EMPLOYEES
09/17	587	76	13.0%	2,300
09/16	559	18	3.2%	—
09/15	473	17	3.8%	—
09/14	417	8	2.0%	—
Annual Growth	12.0%	109.3%	—	—

2017 Year-End Financials

Return on assets: 12.2%
Return on equity: 26.1%
Current ratio: 2.20
Cash ($ mil.): 70

CALGON CARBON CORPORATION

Calgon Carbon wants impurities in water and air gone. A global leader in activated carbons and purification systems it offers purification and a variety of industrial and commercial manufacturing processes. Services include ballast water treatment ultraviolet light disinfection and advanced ion-exchange technologies used in the treatment of drinking water wastewater odor control pollution abatement and a variety of industrial and commercial manufacturing processes. Its products find usage more than 700 discrete market applications including air drinking water foods and pharmaceuticals purification and the removal of mercury emissions from coal-powered electrical plants.

Operations

Calgon Carbon operates in three division?Activated Carbon Applications and Products.

Activated Carbon makes granular and powdered activated carbon to remove organic compounds from liquids and gases.

Products include Granular Activated Carbon Reactivation Services Powdered Activated Carbon UV Technologies ION Exchange Activated Carbon Pellets Activated Carbon Cloth and Equipment.

Applications services include Manila and Environmental Water Treatment Air Treatment Mercury Removal Industrial Processes Food & Beverage Personal Protection Equipment Metals Recovery Medical/Pharmaceutical and Energy Storage.

Geographic Reach

Pennsylvania-based Calgon Carbon operates in a geographically diverse array of markets. It operates over 20 production plants in Belgium China France the UK and the US.

Sales and Marketing

Calgon Carbon offer carbon technologies used in over 700 distinct market applications from purifying air and drinking water to purifying foods and pharmaceuticals to separating gas and removing mercury emissions from coal-fired power plants.

Strategy

Calgon Carbon aims to develop and apply activated carbon technologies to protect people and the environment from contaminants in water air food and industrial processes while developing and maintaining a highly motivated workforce that has a strong commitment to its customers shareholders and society.

The company will maintain worldwide marketing manufacturing and technology leadership in the production use and recycling of activated carbon; develop or acquire products or services which are complementary to its existing business and organization; continue to develop the technology of its products and services to meet ever-changing customer needs; stress quality and professionalism in all areas of its business its people its products and services and its business conduct; earn income which will support the growth of its business and provide an above-average return to its shareholders; and expand the applicability of its technology to all appropriate markets including commercial and consumer markets.

Calgon Carbon decided to expand its Mississippi activated carbon plant in mid-2020. The expansion is expected to add 38 jobs at the plant when complete. The estimated investment in the additional production line will be $185 million. When completed Calgon Carbon's virgin granular activated carbon capacity will exceed 200 million pounds per year. the expansion enables its activated carbon products to be more broadly used to clean the world's air and water on an even larger scale.

Company Background

In 1942 the Company produced an activated carbon product using bituminous coal and that was the beginning of the firm now known as Calgon Carbon Corporation.

EXECUTIVES

Evp And Coo, Robert P. (Bob) O'Brien, age 70, $378,325 total compensation
Evp Advanced Materials Manufacturing And Equipment Division, Stevan R. Schott, age 57, $322,500 total compensation
Chairman President And Ceo, Randall S. (Randy) Dearth, age 57, $560,000 total compensation
Evp Core Carbon And Services Division, James A. Coccagno, age 49
Svp And Cfo, Robert Fortwangler
National Accounts Manager, Michael Prevade
Senior Vice President Global Procurement And Strategic Initiatives, Jim Coccagno
Senior Vice President General Counsel Secretary, Chad Whalen
Vice President Specialty Products Business Unit, Bill Zinsser
Auditors: DELOITTE & TOUCHE LLP PITTSBU

LOCATIONS

HQ: CALGON CARBON CORPORATION
3000 GSK DR, MOON TOWNSHIP, PA 151081381
Phone: 412 787-6700
Web: WWW.CALGONCARBON.COM

2015 sales

	$ mil.	% of total
United States	288	53
United Kingdom	43	8
Japan	35	7
France	20	4
China	17	3
Germany	17	3
Canada	17	3
South Korea	12	2
Belgium	10	2
Singapore	9	2
Netherlands	5	1
Denmark	4	1
Switzerland	3	1
Spain	3	1
Thailand	3	1
Other	41	8
Total	**535**	**100**

PRODUCTS/OPERATIONS

2015 Sales

	$ mil.	% of total
Activated Carbon & Service	486	91
Equipment	39	7
Consumer	9	2
Total	**535**	**100**

Selected Products

Ballast Water Treatment
Energy Storage
Environmental Air Treatment
Environmental Water Treatment
Food and Beverage
Industrial Processes
Medical
Mercury Removal
Metals Recovery
Municipal Water Treatment
Personal Protection Equipment
Residential Point of Use/Entry

COMPETITORS

3M Purification
ITT Water & Wastewater Herford
Met-Pro
Norit
Siemens Water Technologies
Trojan Technologies

HISTORICAL FINANCIALS

Company Type: Private

Income Statement — FYE: December 31

	REVENUE ($ mil.)	NET INCOME ($ mil.)	NET PROFIT MARGIN	EMPLOYEES
12/17	619	21	3.4%	1,334
12/16	514	13	2.7%	—
12/15	535	43	8.1%	—
12/14	555	49	8.9%	—
Annual Growth	3.7%	(24.7%)	—	—

2017 Year-End Financials

Return on assets: 2.5%
Return on equity: 5.0%
Current ratio: 2.60
Cash ($ mil.): 42

CALIFORNIA DEPARTMENT OF WATER RESOURCES

The California Department of Water Resources knows that water is gold. The agency is dedicated to managing the state's water resources in partnership with other agencies. Its core areas include designing the State Water Project (which supplies water to some 25 million farms businesses and residents) providing legislative guidance creating recreational opportunities educating the public and offering technical and financial support for local planning and regional water management. The department also provides flood control and dam safety services as well as plans for future water needs for the state.

Operations

The company has 3 branches of Government; Executive Legislative and Judicial.

The California government's executive branch is overseen by the Office of the Governor and includes elected officials and administrators.

The California Legislature has two branches the State Assembly and the Senate. The Legislature vote on state laws and draft legislation.

The judicial branch includes the California Supreme Court and all the lower courts in the state and it interprets and applies laws at state and local levels.

Geographic Reach

The company has 2640 Data sets in California Data.

EXECUTIVES

Chief Deputy Director, Susan Sims
Director, Mark Cowin

LOCATIONS

HQ: CALIFORNIA DEPARTMENT OF WATER RESOURCES
1416 9TH ST, SACRAMENTO, CA 958145511
Phone: 916 653-9394
Web: WWW.CA.GOV

HISTORICAL FINANCIALS

Company Type: Private

Income Statement — FYE: June 30

	REVENUE ($ mil.)	NET INCOME ($ mil.)	NET PROFIT MARGIN	EMPLOYEES
06/19	1,149	(27)	—	3,000
06/18	1,206	0	—	—
06/17	1,223	0	—	—
06/05	0	0	—	—
Annual Growth	—	—	—	—

2019 Year-End Financials

Return on assets: (-0.3%)
Return on equity: (-2.4%)
Current ratio: 1.50
Cash ($ mil.): 708

CALIFORNIA INSTITUTE OF TECHNOLOGY

The California Institute of Technology (Caltech) has an enlightened perspective on science. The institute enrolls more than 2235 students and offers about two dozen majors across six academic divisions focused on biology chemistry engineering geology humanities and physics. Caltech has a very low student-teacher ratio of 3:1. The school receives about 90% of its operating revenue through research grants and contracts. Caltech operates the Jet Propulsion Laboratory (JPL) which supervises robotic Mars exploration programs and other interplanetary missions under contract to NASA. The school was founded in 1891.

Operations

Caltech's most popular majors are engineering computer and information science and support services physical sciences; mathematics and statistics; and biological and biomedical sciences. The school also owns and operates large-scale research facilities such as the Seismological Laboratory and a global network of astronomical observatories including the Palomar and W. M. Keck Observatories; and cofounded and comanages LIGO.

The JPL lab has more than 100 research and mission collaborations with Caltech faculty.

Geographic Reach

Caltech's about 125-acre campus is located in Pasadena California. In addition to its facilities in California the institute has astronomy observatories across the US and Chile.

Financial Performance

Caltech's cash and cash equivalents at the end of the year were $6.5 million 5% higher compared to $6.2 million in the previous year. Cash used by operating activities was $59.4 million. Investing activities provided $32 million primarily from proceeds from sales and maturities of investments while financing activities provided $27.7 million primarily from contributions restricted for long-term investment and capital projects.

Company Background

Caltech's professors and graduates have snared more than 30 Nobel Prizes. Other alumni include filmmaker Frank Capra and Apollo 17 astronaut Harrison Schmitt.

EXECUTIVES

Provost, Edward M. Stolper
Vp Business And Finance, Dean W. Currie
Cio, Richard E. (Rich) Fagen
Vp; Director Jet Propulsion Laboratory, Charles Elachi, age 73
Vice Provost Research, Stephen L. Mayo
President, Thomas F. Rosenbaum
Chief Investment Officer, Scott Richland
Chair Chemistry And Chemical Engineering Division, Jacqueline K. Barton
Chair Physics Mathematics And Astronomy Division, B. Thomas Soifer
Chair Engineering And Applied Science Division, Guruswami Ravichandran
Chair Geological And Planetary Sciences Division, John P. Grotzinger
Chair Humanities And Social Sciences Division, Jean-Laurent Rosenthal
Vice President Of Operations, Luisa Avila
Senior Vice President Financial Investigations Unit, Bob Binnie
Vice President, Kevin Vu
Chairman, David L. Lee, age 64
Vice Chairman, Ronald K. Linde
Secretary, Zachary Erickson
Auditors: PRICEWATERHOUSECOOPERS LLP LO

LOCATIONS

HQ: CALIFORNIA INSTITUTE OF TECHNOLOGY
1200 E CALIFORNIA BLVD, PASADENA, CA 911250001
Phone: 626 395-6811
Web: WWW.CALTECH.EDU

PRODUCTS/OPERATIONS

Selected Academic Divisions

Academics
Biology
Chemistry and Chemical Engineering
Engineering and Applied Science
Geological and Planetary Sciences
Humanities and Social Sciences
Physics Mathematics and Astronomy
Jet Propulsion Laboratory (NASA partnership)
Galaxy Evolution Explorer Science Center
Infrared Processing and Analysis Center
NASA Exoplanet Science Institute
NASA Herschel Science Center
Spitzer Space Telescope Science Center

HISTORICAL FINANCIALS

Company Type: Private

Income Statement — FYE: September 30

	REVENUE ($ mil.)	NET INCOME ($ mil.)	NET PROFIT MARGIN	EMPLOYEES
09/19	3,434	(11)	—	9,808
09/18	3,303	165	5.0%	—
09/17	2,894	412	14.3%	—
09/16	2,561	203	7.9%	—
Annual Growth	10.3%	—	—	—

2019 Year-End Financials

Return on assets: (-0.2%)
Return on equity: (-0.3%)
Current ratio: —
Cash ($ mil.): 6

CALIFORNIA STEEL INDUSTRIES, INC.

California Steel Industries (CSI) doesn't use forensic evidence but its work does involve a steel slab. The company uses steel slab produced by third parties to manufacture steel products such as hot-rolled and cold-rolled steel galvanized coils and sheets and electric resistance weld (ERW) pipe. Its customers include aftermarket automotive manufacturers oil and gas producers roofing makers tubing manufacturers and building suppliers. CSI serves the western region of the US. The company operates slitting shearing coating and single-billing services for third parties. Japan's JFE Holdings and Brazilian iron ore miner Vale SA each own 50% of CSI.

Operations

CSI has an annual production capacity of 2.8 million metric tons of flat rolled steel and pipe. It is the leading producer of flat rolled steel in the Western US and the only West Coast steel supplier capable of producing more than 2 million tons of steel in five different product lines: hot rolled pickled and oiled galvanized and cold rolled sheet and electric resistance welded pipe.

Geographic Reach

At its California plant the company processes steel slab purchased from suppliers around the world including Brazil Mexico Australia Japan Europe and the US.

CSI buys more than two-thirds of its steel slab from ArcelorMittal subsidiary Lazaro Cardenas in Mexico; ArcelorMittal Tubar o in Brazil; and Australia's Bluescope Steel. The purchased slab is transported to the Port of Los Angeles and then sent by train to CSI's facilities.

Sales and Marketing

Most of CSI's product lines are also sold to service distribution centers throughout the Western and Midwestern US with some product also sold worldwide through the export market. Its steel framing studs roofing decking and metal lath products are used in the home and commercial building industries. Other uses include water gas and oil pipelines automotive pans tubing (used by construction and furniture makers) and heating and cooling parts.

Strategy

In 2014 CSI built a new pipe mill on its site near Fontana California. The mill produces high-strength electrical resistance welded pipe up to 24 inches in diameter and up to 80 feet in length. Its existing pipe mill was limited to 16-inch diameter and 60-foot lengths.

Since 1992 CSI has invested more than $1 billion on its facilities to maintain modernize and expand operations.

Company Background

The company was formed in 1983.

EXECUTIVES

Vice President, Brett Guge
Secretary, Beverly Sprinkle
Auditors: ERNST & YOUNG LLP LOS ANGELES

LOCATIONS

HQ: CALIFORNIA STEEL INDUSTRIES, INC.
14000 SAN BERNARDINO AVE, FONTANA, CA 923355259
Phone: 909 350-6300
Web: WWW.CALIFORNIASTEEL.COM

PRODUCTS/OPERATIONS

Selected Steel Products

Cold Rolled
ERW Pipe
Galvanized
Hot Rolled
Pickled and Oiled

COMPETITORS

AK Steel Holding Corporation
Evraz Inc. NA
Nucor
O'Neal Steel
Steel Dynamics
Steelscape
Ternium Mexico
USS-POSCO Industries

HISTORICAL FINANCIALS

Company Type: Private

Income Statement	REVENUE ($ mil.)	NET INCOME ($ mil.)	NET PROFIT MARGIN	EMPLOYEES
				FYE: December 31
12/09	551	(13)	—	1,095
12/08	1,510	13	0.9%	—
Annual Growth	(63.5%)	—	—	—

2009 Year-End Financials

Return on assets: (-2.2%)
Return on equity: (-4.4%)
Current ratio: 4.30
Cash ($ mil.): 61

CALIFORNIA'S VALUED TRUST

EXECUTIVES

Exec Dir, Valerie Cornuelle
Exec Dir, David Vaughn
Helpdesk Analyst, James Mason
Business Analyst, Nolan Clinard

LOCATIONS

HQ: CALIFORNIA'S VALUED TRUST
520 E HERNDON AVE, FRESNO, CA 937202907
Phone: 559 437-2960
Web: WWW.CVTRUST.ORG

HISTORICAL FINANCIALS

Company Type: Private

Income Statement	ASSETS ($ mil.)	NET INCOME ($ mil.)	INCOME AS % OF ASSETS	EMPLOYEES
				FYE: September 30
09/18	157	(3)	—	1
09/17	157	21	13.3%	—
09/15	136	(5)	—	—
Annual Growth	4.9%	—	—	—

CAMERON INTERNATIONAL CORPORATION

Cameron is a leading manufacturer provider and servicer of oil and gas industry equipment. The company makes products that control pressure at oil and gas wells including blowout preventers chokes controls wellheads measurement tools and valves. The company's products are used for offshore onshore and subsea applications. Cameron is a wholly owned subsidiary of oilfield product and services giant Schlumberger (a major provider of technology for reservoir characterization drilling production and processing services to the oil and gas industry).

Financial Performance

Cameron generates about 15% of Schlumberger's sales. The subsidiary's revenue declined 4% to $6.5 billion on lower sales for its OneSubsea and Valves & Measurements product segments. OneSubsea offers products and services for subsea oil and gas companies including wellheads subsea trees control systems and production system optimization. The company's Valves & Measurements products span valves and measurement systems for oil and gas flow for the upstream midstream and downstream sectors.

Strategy

To keep pace with rivals increasingly adopting automation technology Schlumbeger formed a joint venture in 2019 with Rockwell Automation to form Sensia. Sensia combines Cameron's sensor and measurement products with Rockwell's industrial automation technology and analytics capabilities. The new company's offerings will facilitate automated oilfield operations and connect equipment with software to gather data from sensors and devices. About two-fifths of the JV's revenue is expected to derive from North America.

EXECUTIVES

President Cameron Group, Olivier Le Peuch
Auditors: ERNST & YOUNG LLP HOUSTON TE

LOCATIONS

HQ: CAMERON INTERNATIONAL CORPORATION
4646 W SAM HOUSTON PKWY N, HOUSTON, TX 770418214
Phone: 713 939-2282
Web: WWW.SLB.COM

PRODUCTS/OPERATIONS

Selected Mergers and Acquisitions

COMPETITORS

ABB Inc.
Aker Solutions
Atlas Copco
CIRCOR International
Dresser-Rand
Dril-Quip
Ebara
FMC
Flotek
GE Oil
Ingersoll-Rand Industrial Technologies
McDermott
National Oilwell Varco
Weatherford International

HISTORICAL FINANCIALS

Company Type: Private

Income Statement	REVENUE ($ mil.)	NET INCOME ($ mil.)	NET PROFIT MARGIN	EMPLOYEES
				FYE: December 31
12/14	10,381	848	8.2%	23,000
12/13	9,838	724	7.4%	—
12/12	8,502	750	8.8%	—
Annual Growth	10.5%	6.3%	—	—

2014 Year-End Financials

Return on assets: 6.6%
Return on equity: 15.6%
Current ratio: 1.80
Cash ($ mil.): 1,513

CAMPUS CRUSADE FOR CHRIST INC

EXECUTIVES

Ceo-Pres, Stephen B Douglass
Dir*, Vonette Z Bright
Director, Marc Rutter
Coordinator, Matthew Anderson
Security Staff, Russ Licht
Assistant Director of Treasury, Steve Hackney
Audio Operations Manager, David Quiroz
Customer Manager, Anjelina Maldonado
National Director College Prep, Ben Burns
Executive, Irv Klaschus
Campus Human Resources, Alan Penman

LOCATIONS

HQ: CAMPUS CRUSADE FOR CHRIST INC
100 LAKE HART DR, ORLANDO, FL 328320100
Phone: 407 826-2000
Web: WWW.CRU.ORG

HISTORICAL FINANCIALS

Company Type: Private

Income Statement	REVENUE ($ mil.)	NET INCOME ($ mil.)	NET PROFIT MARGIN	EMPLOYEES
				FYE: August 31
08/17	598	26	4.4%	7,688
08/08	7	1	25.1%	—
08/05	0	0	—	—
08/04	423	414	97.7%	—
Annual Growth	2.7%	(19.0%)	—	—

2017 Year-End Financials

Return on assets: 7.4% Cash ($ mil.): 45
Return on equity: 10.8%
Current ratio: 0.70

CANDID COLOR SYSTEMS, INC.

EXECUTIVES

Pres-Ceo, Jack E Counts Jr
SEC-Treas, Beverly Ellis
Designer, David J Wall
Chief Financial Officer, Clayton Sliger
Customer Support Manager, Cristina Oconnor
Customer Support Manager, Cristina O'Connor
Bankruptcy Automation Manager, Jack Smiley

LOCATIONS

HQ: CANDID COLOR SYSTEMS, INC.
1300 METROPOLITAN AVE, OKLAHOMA CITY, OK 731082042
Phone: 405 947-8747
Web: WWW.CANDID.COM

HISTORICAL FINANCIALS

Company Type: Private

Income Statement FYE: July 31

	REVENUE ($ mil.)	NET INCOME ($ mil.)	NET PROFIT MARGIN	EMPLOYEES
07/07	21,742	2,534	11.7%	300
07/05	22	1	8.3%	—
07/04	21	2	10.9%	—
07/03	21	1	9.4%	—
Annual Growth	467.2%	498.3%	—	—

2007 Year-End Financials

Return on assets: 999.0% Cash ($ mil.): 2
Return on equity: 999.9%
Current ratio: 2.30

CAPE COD HEALTHCARE, INC.

Cape Cod Healthcare (CCHC) is a not-for-profit healthcare organization that operates two acute care hospitals (Cape Cod Hospital and Falmouth Hospital) with a total of more than 350 beds. Specializations include heart and vascular women's health bones and muscles cancer care and brain spine and nerves. CCHC also operates a home health services agency (Visiting Nurse Association of Cape Cod) primary and specialized care clinics a 130-bed skilled nursing and rehabilitation facility (JML Care Center) and a 60-unit assisted living facility (Heritage at Falmouth). The health care system has an affiliation with UMass Medical School whereby students can receive hands-on training at Cape Cod Hospital.

Operations

CCHC is the Cape's largest private employer with nearly 5000 staff members including more than 450 physicians. The system has about 120000 emergency department visits each year and facilitates about 1200 births and performs more than 14000 surgical procedures annually.

Financial Performance

CCHC's net patient revenue numbers have been increasing over the past five years. In fiscal 2016 it increased 8% to $817 million. Like most hospitals net patient revenue represents the bulk of CCHC's total revenue.

Strategy

While CCHC enjoys a strong market share in the Cape Cod region it also struggles with seasonal fluctuations and high Medicare and Medicaid numbers within its patient load. As such the company could be impacted by reform measures that could decrease Medicare reimbursement levels. CCHC plans to continue its efforts to control costs and increase efficiencies to keep its operations nimble and keep pace with the changing health care environment.

Faced with rising operating costs and lower reimbursement rates the system in 2017 agreed to sell its outreach lab services operations to Quest Diagnostics. As a focused lab services provider Quest is able to provide testing at a lower cost than the typical hospital-based laboratory. The two companies will partner to provide an expanded array of diagnostics to the Cape Cod community.

EXECUTIVES

President And Ceo, Michael K. (Mike) Lauf, age 49
Coo, Michael Bundy
Svp Communications And Business Development, Patrick Kane
Svp Finance And Cfo, Michael L. Connors
Chief Medical Officer, Donald A. Guadagnoli
Svp And Cio, Jeanne M. Fallon
President And Ceo Vna Of Cape Cod, Dianne C. Kolb
Marketing And Government Relations Director, Van Northcross
Senior Vice President Of Managed Care, Jack Lipomi
Vice President Patient Financial Services, Victor Oliveira
Senior Vice President And Chief Quality Officer, Kevin Mulroy
Senior Vice President And Chief Development Officer, Kevin Ralph
Medical Director, Vladimir Koren
Vice President Nursing Jml Care Center, Cynthia Lehtinen
Chairman, William Zammer
Vice Chairman, DeWitt Davenport
Treas, Michael A Loffredo
Auditors: PRICEWATERHOUSECOOPERS LLP BO

LOCATIONS

HQ: CAPE COD HEALTHCARE, INC.
27 PARK ST, HYANNIS, MA 026015230
Phone: 508 862-5030
Web: WWW.CAPECODHEALTH.ORG

PRODUCTS/OPERATIONS

Selected Massachusetts Facilities

Bourne Health Center
Cape Cod Hospital (Hyannis)
Davenport Mugar Cancer Center (Hyannis)
Falmouth Hospital
Clark Cancer Center
Fontaine Medical Center (Harwich)
Heritage at Falmouth
JLM Care Center (Falmouth)
Mashpee Health Center
Sandwich Health Center
Wilkins Outpatient Medical Complex (Hyannis)

COMPETITORS

Baystate Health
Boston Medical Center
Cambridge Health Alliance
Care New England
CareGroup
Milford Regional Medical Center
Northeast Health System
Partners HealthCare
Southcoast Hospitals Group
Steward Health Care
Universal Health Services
Winchester Healthcare

HISTORICAL FINANCIALS

Company Type: Private

Income Statement FYE: September 30

	REVENUE ($ mil.)	NET INCOME ($ mil.)	NET PROFIT MARGIN	EMPLOYEES
09/19	978	29	3.0%	1,850
09/18	921	80	8.7%	—
09/17	872	74	8.5%	—
09/16	837	74	8.9%	—
Annual Growth	5.3%	(26.9%)	—	—

2019 Year-End Financials

Return on assets: 2.5% Cash ($ mil.): 41
Return on equity: 3.6%
Current ratio: 1.70

CAPE COD HOSPITAL

Get too much sun or eat too much lobster while visiting Cape Cod? Never fear Cape Cod Hospital can treat whatever ails you. Cape Cod Hospital a subsidiary of Cape Cod Healthcare is a 260-bed acute care hospital that serves the Cape Cod Massachusetts area. Its specialty services include pediatrics maternity care cancer treatment and infectious disease therapeutics. The not-for-profit Cape Cod Hospital also includes a specialty cardiovascular center a psychiatry unit a surgical pavilion and a diagnostic imaging facility as well as outpatient medical offices.

Operations

Cape Cod Hospital's emergency department treats about 85000 patients each year. The medical center also performs more than 12500 surgeries and 1000 birth procedures each year as well as about 2 million laboratory tests. Its 20-bed Cape Psych Center provides inpatient and outpatient mental and behavioral services. The campus also includes more than a dozen medical offices buildings and a community health center. Cape Cod Hospital's staff includes about 300 physicians.

Geographic Reach

Cape Cod Hospital is located on a 40-acre campus on the shoreline of Hyannis Massachusetts.

Strategy

To keep its facilities modern and efficient in 2015 the company opened a new emergency center located adjacent to the existing emergency center. The 18-month $22 million project added 25000 sq. ft. of space and 72 patient treatment rooms.

In 2013 Cape Cod Hospital reopened the renovated and expanded Intensive Care Unit. That project cost $4.9 million and doubled the size of the original area.

To control the cost of providing hospital care parent Cape Cod Healthcare has also been expanding its outpatient and ambulatory care services. It is adding new urgent care centers and surgery centers both near the hospital and in surrounding communities.

Company Background

Cape Cod Hospital was established in Hyannis in 1920.

EXECUTIVES

Medical Director, Kelsey Rezendes
Medical Records Director, Tim Greene
Director Of Nursing, Dian Birch
Vice President Ofperioperative Andsurgical Services, Cynthia Marlin-mha
Auditors: POWERHOUSECOOPERS LLP BOSTON

LOCATIONS

HQ: CAPE COD HOSPITAL
27 PARK ST, HYANNIS, MA 026015203
Phone: 508 771-1800
Web: WWW.CAPECODHEALTH.ORG

PRODUCTS/OPERATIONS

Selected Services

Allergy and Immunology
Behavioral Health
Blood Center
Dermatology
Foot Care & Surgery
Hand Surgery
Orthopedics
Pregnancy & Birth
Sports Medicine
Women's Health

COMPETITORS

Baystate Health
Boston Medical Center
Cambridge Health Alliance
Care New England
CareGroup
Children's Hospital Boston
Milford Regional Medical Center
Northeast Health System
Partners HealthCare
Southcoast Hospitals Group
Steward Health Care
Sturdy Memorial
Universal Health Services
Winchester Healthcare

HISTORICAL FINANCIALS

Company Type: Private

Income Statement FYE: September 30

	REVENUE ($ mil.)	NET INCOME ($ mil.)	NET PROFIT MARGIN	EMPLOYEES
09/19	599	25	4.3%	1,700
09/18	564	46	8.3%	—
09/17	526	47	9.0%	—
09/16	515	43	8.4%	—
Annual Growth	5.1%	(15.7%)	—	—

2019 Year-End Financials

Return on assets: 4.0%
Return on equity: 5.5%
Current ratio: 2.20
Cash ($ mil.): 11

CAPE FEAR VALLEY MEDICAL CENTER

LOCATIONS

HQ: CAPE FEAR VALLEY MEDICAL CENTER
1638 OWEN DR, FAYETTEVILLE, NC 283043424
Phone: 910 615-4000
Web: WWW.CAPEFEARVALLEY.COM

HISTORICAL FINANCIALS

Company Type: Private

Income Statement FYE: September 30

	REVENUE ($ mil.)	NET INCOME ($ mil.)	NET PROFIT MARGIN	EMPLOYEES
09/15	630	23	3.8%	2,711
09/14	590	40	6.8%	—
09/13	823	398	48.4%	—
Annual Growth	(12.5%)	(75.5%)	—	—

2015 Year-End Financials

Return on assets: 2.6%
Return on equity: 5.1%
Current ratio: 2.80
Cash ($ mil.): 38

CAPITAL DISTRICT PHYSICIANS' HEALTH PLAN, INC.

Capital District Physicians' Health Plan (CDPHP) is an independent not-for-profit health plan serving some 448000 members in two dozen New York counties. It offers employer-sponsored and individual managed care plans (including HMO PPO and consumer-directed plans) as well as a Medicare Advantage plan for seniors. The company's coverage include full coverage for some preventative medical services as well as options for covering prescription drugs dental work and vision services. CDPHP also provides wellness programs that help members with weight loss smoking cessation and chronic disease management.

Operations

In addition to its commercial and Medicare offerings CDPHP provides health plans under several state-subsidized insurance programs including Family Health Plus and Child Health Plus (intended for residents who don't qualify for Medicaid) and Healthy NY (intended for small businesses and sole proprietors). Altogether the CDPHP provider network includes more than 10000 physicians and facilities.

The company's classifies its products in three lines of business: Health Maintenance Organization (HMO) products (which includes Healthy New York Medicare Choices Medicaid Child Health Plus and Family Health Plus) provided by CDPHP; Preferred Provider Organization (PPO) products (which include PPO High Deductible PPO Medicare Choices Exclusive Provider Organization -EPO- and High Deductible EPO products) provided by CDPHP Universal Benefits Inc.; and the Administrative Services Organization (ASO) plans (which includes ASO and self-insured plans) provided by Capital District Physicians' Healthcare Network Inc.

In 2013 CDPHP's membership increased by about 38000.

Geographic Reach

CDPHP serves customers in 24 New York counties: Albany Broome Chenango Columbia Delaware Dutchess Essex Fulton Greene Hamilton Herkimer Madison Montgomery Oneida Orange Otsego Rensselaer Saratoga Schenectady Schoharie Tioga Ulster Warren and Washington.

Financial Performance

CDPHP reported a 13% increase in revenues in 2013 due to an increase in membership and in earned premiums.

The company suffered a loss of $43 million in 2013 (a decrease of more than 375%) due to an increase in claims and general expenses.

Strategy

CDPHP's self-proclaimed strategy is to use the majority of its premium income to pay out medical claims while maintaining necessary reserve levels to keep its solid financial performance and to comply with federal medical loss-ratio guidelines. It earmarks a small amount of income for operational expenses as well as to fund growth and wellness initiatives.

In mid-2014 the company teamed upewith Independent Health to build innovative products tools and services for providers employers and individuals across New York State. The partnership will focus on developing new tools technology and products along with recruiting new physicians.

In the early 2013 the company opened a new CDPHP Service Center location at Latham New York and a health and fitness center inside an Albany supermarket.

CDPHP also works to lower medical expenses by partnering with other regional care and plan providers.

Company Background

In 2011 CDPHP partnered with Trendshift in 2011 to provide a new group funding management system for employers.

An association of local Albany physicians founded CDPHP in 1984.

EXECUTIVES

Vice President Of Medical Affairs Operations, Tracy Langlais
Vice President Application Management, Sigrid Cerio
Senior Vice President Government And External Relations, Robert Hinckley
Medical Director Behavioral Health, Kelly J Clark
Senior Vice President Chief Information Officer, Linda Navarra
Medical Director, Anne Fernandez
Senior Vice President Medical Affairs And Chief Medical Officer, Richard Dal Col
Vice President Information Technology Infrastructure Management, George Waghorn

LOCATIONS

HQ: CAPITAL DISTRICT PHYSICIANS' HEALTH PLAN, INC.
500 PATROON CREEK BLVD, ALBANY, NY 122061057
Phone: 518 641-3700
Web: WWW.CDPHP.COM

PRODUCTS/OPERATIONS

Selected Products

Dental and Vision Health Plans
- CVS ExtraCare Health Card
- Delta Dental

Government Plans
- Child Health Plus
- Family Health Plus
- Medicaid Select Plan
- Medicare Choices (HMO)

Group Health Plans
- Embrace Health
- Exclusive Provider Organization (EPO)
- Group Medicare
- High Deductible Health Plans (HDHP)
- Health Maintenance Organization (HMO)
- Healthy Direction
- Lifestyle Riders
- Preferred Provider Organization (PPO)
- Transitional Health Plans
- Health Funding Arrangements
- Flexible Spending Accounts

Health Reimbursement Arrangement
Health Savings Account
Individual Health Plans
Healthy New York
Non-Group Health Plans

COMPETITORS

Aetna
Anthem
CIGNA
EmblemHealth
Fidelis Care New York
Humana
Independent Health
MVP Health Plan
UnitedHealth Group
excellus bluecross blueshield rochester region
healthnow new york inc

HISTORICAL FINANCIALS

Company Type: Private

Income Statement — FYE: December 31

	REVENUE ($ mil.)	NET INCOME ($ mil.)	NET PROFIT MARGIN	EMPLOYEES
12/13	1,314	22	1.7%	700
12/09	1,037	33	3.2%	—
12/03	818	(1)	—	—
Annual Growth	4.9%	—	—	—

2013 Year-End Financials

Return on assets: 4.4%
Return on equity: 7.0%
Current ratio: 0.80
Cash ($ mil.): 61

CAPITAL INCOME BUILDER

EXECUTIVES

Chm Ceo, Tim Armour
Vchm, Rob Lovelace
Pres, Phil De Toledo
Coo, Rob Klausner
Head Fixed Incm Glob Tradng, Mike Gitlin
Chm Ceo NA Distribution, Matt O'Connor
Auditors: PRICEWATERHOUSECOOPERS LLP LO

LOCATIONS

HQ: CAPITAL INCOME BUILDER
333 S HOPE ST FL 55, LOS ANGELES, CA 900713061
Phone: 213 486-9200
Web: WWW.CAPITALGROUP.COM

HISTORICAL FINANCIALS

Company Type: Private

Income Statement — FYE: October 31

	ASSETS ($ mil.)	NET INCOME ($ mil.)	INCOME AS % OF ASSETS	EMPLOYEES
10/19	107	5,826	5441.8%	2
10/18	102,648	(7,919)	—	—
10/16	100,286	2,628	2.6%	—
Annual Growth	(89.8%)	30.4%	—	—

CARDINAL LOGISTICS HOLDINGS, LLC

EXECUTIVES

Ceo, Tom Hostetler
Exec Chm, Leo Suggs
Exec Chb, Tom White
Chm, Vin McLoughlin
Pres, Jerry Bowman
Exec V Pres-Treas, Robert C Larose
Sr V Pres-Gen Counsel-Sec, John Hove
V Pres-Chief Risk Offcr, Jeff Lester
V Pres-Contrl, Michael Skipworth
V Pres, Dan Curtis
Cfo, Michael Roberts
Auditors: KPMG LLP CHARLOTTE NORTH CAR

LOCATIONS

HQ: CARDINAL LOGISTICS HOLDINGS, LLC
5333 DAVIDSON HWY, CONCORD, NC 280278478
Phone: 704 789-2000
Web: WWW.CARDLOG.COM

HISTORICAL FINANCIALS

Company Type: Private

Income Statement — FYE: December 31

	REVENUE ($ mil.)	NET INCOME ($ mil.)	NET PROFIT MARGIN	EMPLOYEES
12/18	804	(16)	—	3,040
12/17	791	(10)	—	—
Annual Growth	1.7%	—	—	—

2018 Year-End Financials

Return on assets: (-6.7%)
Return on equity: (-12.7%)
Current ratio: 1.60
Cash ($ mil.): 56

CARE NEW ENGLAND HEALTH SYSTEM INC

Care New England Health System take pains to ease its patients' pain. The system operates four hospitals: Kent Hospital a general acute care facility with about 360 beds; the 290-bed Memorial Hospital of Rhode Island; psychiatric facility Butler Hospital; and Women & Infants Hospital of Rhode Island which specializes in obstetrics gynecology and newborn pediatrics. All told the system has more than 963 licensed beds. Care New England formed in 1996 by three member hospitals also operates a home health agency and outpatient care facilities. In late 2016 the system dropped its plans to merge with Southcoast Health. The following year it agreed to be acquired by Partners HealthCare which is expanding outside of Massachusetts.

EXECUTIVES

Vice President Human Resources Kent Hospital, Dean Carlson
Auditors: PRICEWATERHOUSECOOPERS LLP BO

LOCATIONS

HQ: CARE NEW ENGLAND HEALTH SYSTEM INC
45 WILLARD AVE, PROVIDENCE, RI 029053218
Phone: 401 453-7900
Web: WWW.CARENEWENGLAND.ORG

COMPETITORS

Baystate Health
Community Health Systems
Lifespan Corporation
Partners HealthCare
Roger Williams Medical Center
Southcoast Hospitals Group
Tenet Healthcare
Universal Health Services
Yale New Haven Health System

HISTORICAL FINANCIALS

Company Type: Private

Income Statement — FYE: September 30

	REVENUE ($ mil.)	NET INCOME ($ mil.)	NET PROFIT MARGIN	EMPLOYEES
09/19	1,146	(30)	—	6,500
09/17	1,132	21	1.9%	—
09/16	1,154	(63)	—	—
09/15	126	(8)	—	—
Annual Growth	73.4%	—	—	—

2019 Year-End Financials

Return on assets: (-3.5%)
Return on equity: (-12.3%)
Current ratio: 1.30
Cash ($ mil.): 74

CAREOREGON, INC.

EXECUTIVES

Pres, Chris Krenk
Exec Dir*, Mylia Christensen
Coordinator, Crystal Page
Customer Representativ, Brian M McManus
Personnel Assistant, Vicki Greenwald
Network Technician, Ross Ludeman
Claims Examiner Supervisor, Jeremy Brown
Human Resources Benefits Speci, Shannon Clesceri
Senior Administrative Assistan, Deborah Haren
Qnxt Administrator, Herb Kaaihue
Accounting Manager, Kinh Reynolds
Auditors: LB KPMG LLP SEATTLE WA

LOCATIONS

HQ: CAREOREGON, INC.
315 SW 5TH AVE STE 900, PORTLAND, OR 972041703
Phone: 503 416-4100
Web: WWW.CAREOREGON.ORG

HISTORICAL FINANCIALS

Company Type: Private

Income Statement — FYE: December 31

	REVENUE ($ mil.)	NET INCOME ($ mil.)	NET PROFIT MARGIN	EMPLOYEES
12/16	886	(9)	—	140
12/14	851	87	10.3%	—
12/13	564	(0)	—	—
12/08	343	22	6.5%	—
Annual Growth	12.6%	—	—	—

2016 Year-End Financials

Return on assets: (-2.3%)
Return on equity: (-3.3%)
Current ratio: 5.40
Cash ($ mil.): 49

CARILION MEDICAL CENTER

EXECUTIVES

Ceo, Nancy Howell Agee
Pres*, Steve Arner
SEC*, Briggs Andrews
V Pres-Treas*, Rob Vaughan
Treas*, George Robert Vaughan Jr
Cfo*, Donald E Lorton
Prin*, Edward Murphy
Department SEC, Donna Webb
Pathologist, Robert White
Internist, Bruce Johnson
Human Resources Coordinator, Carrie Boggess
Auditors: DELOITTE & TOUCHE LLP CHARLOT

LOCATIONS

HQ: CARILION MEDICAL CENTER
1906 BELLEVIEW AVE SE, ROANOKE, VA 240141838
Phone: 540 981-7000
Web: WWW.CARILIONCLINIC.ORG

HISTORICAL FINANCIALS

Company Type: Private

Income Statement FYE: September 30

	REVENUE ($ mil.)	NET INCOME ($ mil.)	NET PROFIT MARGIN	EMPLOYEES
09/19	1,380	(137)	—	6,390
09/18	1,281	134	10.5%	—
09/17	1,232	134	10.9%	—
09/16	1,177	4	0.4%	—
Annual Growth	5.4%	—	—	—

2019 Year-End Financials

Return on assets: (-9.0%)
Return on equity: (-26.4%)
Current ratio: 1.30
Cash ($ mil.): 2

CARILION NEW RIVER VALLEY MEDICAL CENTER

EXECUTIVES

Pres, Donald Halliwill
Ceo*, John Piatkowski
Bus Anylst, Mike Bunker
Coordinator, Becky Garnett

LOCATIONS

HQ: CARILION NEW RIVER VALLEY MEDICAL CENTER
2900 LAMB CIR STE 150, CHRISTIANSBURG, VA 240736341
Phone: 540 731-2000
Web: WWW.CARILIONCLINIC.ORG

HISTORICAL FINANCIALS

Company Type: Private

Income Statement FYE: September 30

	REVENUE ($ mil.)	NET INCOME ($ mil.)	NET PROFIT MARGIN	EMPLOYEES
09/13	896	116	12.9%	800
09/05	30	2	6.5%	—
09/04	115	18	16.0%	—
09/03	88	11	13.5%	—
Annual Growth	26.1%	25.5%	—	—

2013 Year-End Financials

Return on assets: 10.9%
Return on equity: 27.1%
Current ratio: 1.20
Cash ($ mil.): —

CARILION SERVICES, INC.

EXECUTIVES

Pres, Bill Flattery
SEC, Briggs Andrew
Prin, Carolyn Brown
Prin, Lawrence G Hincker
Prin, William J Flattery
Recruiter, Jill Lusher
Senior Vice President, Curtis Mills
Downtown Roanoke Site Manager, Aaron Washington
Sales Representative, Chris Deel
Aquatics Manager, Grace Milauskas
Aquatics Manager, Kayla Burnette
Auditors: DELOITTE & TOUCHE LLP CHARLOT

LOCATIONS

HQ: CARILION SERVICES, INC.
213 S JEFFERSON ST # 633, ROANOKE, VA 240111700
Phone: 540 981-7000
Web: WWW.CARILIONCLINIC.ORG

HISTORICAL FINANCIALS

Company Type: Private

Income Statement FYE: September 30

	REVENUE ($ mil.)	NET INCOME ($ mil.)	NET PROFIT MARGIN	EMPLOYEES
09/08	1,221	(147)	—	935
09/05	87	(2)	—	—
09/04	228	(23)	—	—
09/03	205	17	8.3%	—
Annual Growth	42.8%	—	—	—

2008 Year-End Financials

Return on assets: (-8.4%)
Return on equity: (-18.4%)
Current ratio: 0.90
Cash ($ mil.): 1

CARLE FOUNDATION HOSPITAL

Carle Foundation Hospital is a 393-bed acute-care facility that serves the residents of east central Illinois. The hospital includes the region's only Level I trauma center as well as a Level III perinatal center a neonatal ICU and centers devoted to cardiac and cancer care. It also runs a handful of specialty centers in the region. Carle Foundation Hospital is the primary teaching hospital for the University of Illinois College of Medicine at Urbana-Champaign. It is controlled by the not-for-profit Carle Foundation; sister company Carle Physician Group which boasts more than 400 physicians representing 80 specialties is one of the nation's largest private physician groups.

Operations

The hospital averages more than 22000 annual patient admissions and treats 63000-plus emergency room patients. It offers services related to bariatrics stroke sports medicine women's health and heart and cancer care.

Geographic Reach

Carle Foundation Hospital's service area spans 14 communities across east-central Illinois.

Sales and Marketing

Revenue increased 12% to $2 billion in 2014 as patient service earnings and rental income grew. However due to an increase in medical benefits of insured and pension-related changes net income fell 65% to $112 million that year.

Despite the lower net income cash flow from operations rose 20% to $193 million on changes in medical claims payable as well as an increase in cash generated fro third-party payor settlements.

Strategy

Construction has been key to Carle Foundation Hospital's growth in recent years. The hospital built a $6 million center for children with hearing loss; the center houses the Expanding Children's Hearing Opportunities Center and the Carle Auditory Oral School. Carle Foundation Hospital Research Institute opened an $11-million Biomedical Research Center that houses hospital and University of Illinois staff conducting research in breast cancer gastrointestinal and cardiovascular disease and neuroscience.

The hospital in 2013 added a $200 million seven-story patient tower that houses the heart and vascular institute. The new patient capacity replaced patient beds in older parts of the hospital and provides for future growth opportunities. Carle Foundation Hospital now plans to build a new facility to address the region's needs for increased orthopedic and sports medicine services.

In 2015 Crawford Memorial Hospital and Carle Foundation Hospital entered into an affiliation agreement. Crawford's 25-bed facility joined Carle's network of rural care centers to better provide care for patients in the area.

EXECUTIVES

President And Ceo, James C. Leonard
Vice President Of Facility, Scott Harding
Medical Director, Andy Arwari
Associate Medical Director Emergency Department, Benjamin Davis
Vice President Medical Affairs, Napoleon Knight
Medical Records Director, Tricia Truscott
Vice President Corporate Counsel, Kurt Leifheit
Occupational Medicine, Laura Shanks
Vice President Of Human Resources, Lauren Schmid

Vice President Revenue Cycle Operations, Dawn Walden
Vice President Information Management And Analytics, Cheryl Gerow
Medical Director, Thomas Scaggs
Radiology Director, Tim Sapyta
Occupational Medicine, Martina Stika
Vice President And Medical Director, Kirk Moberg
Vice President, Ashley Hummel
Vice President, Matthew Kolb
Vice President And Chief Academic Officer, King Li
Vice President Research, Jennifer Eardley
Board Member, Sean Grambart

LOCATIONS

HQ: CARLE FOUNDATION HOSPITAL
611 W PARK ST, URBANA, IL 618012529
Phone: 217 326-2900
Web: WWW.CARLE.ORG

PRODUCTS/OPERATIONS

2014 Sales

	$ mil.	% of total
Net premium revenue-health insurance	1,296	63
Net patient service revenue	709	34
Rental income	15	1
Net assets released from restrictions	1	-
Other	34	2
Loss on the disposal of property & equipment	(2.8)	-
Total	**2,054**	**100**

Selected Medical Services

Bariatrics
Cancer
Cancer
Cardiology & Heart Surgery
Diabetes & Endocrinology
Ear Nose & Throat
Gastroenterology & GI Surgery
Geriatrics
Gynecology
Heart
Nephrology
Neurology & Neurosurgery
Sports Medicine
Stroke
Women's Health

COMPETITORS

Advocate BroMenn
Decatur Memorial Hospital
Hospital Sisters Health System
Iroquois Memorial Hospital
Memorial Health System
Morris Hospital
OSF Healthcare System
Sarah Bush Lincoln Health Center
Silver Cross Hospital
St. Elizabeth Regional Health
St. John's Hospital (Illinois)
Union Hospital (Indiana)

HISTORICAL FINANCIALS

Company Type: Private

Income Statement — FYE: December 31

	REVENUE ($ mil.)	NET INCOME ($ mil.)	NET PROFIT MARGIN	EMPLOYEES
12/18	937	216	23.1%	2,500
12/17	900	247	27.5%	—
12/16	812	185	22.8%	—
12/15	754	163	21.7%	—
Annual Growth	7.5%	9.8%	—	—

CARNEGIE MELLON UNIVERSITY

Carnegie Mellon University is known around the world for churning out award-winning actors such as Holly Hunter from its highly regarded drama school. Drama isn't all Carnegie teaches though – the school has seven colleges and schools that offer academic programs in areas such as psychology computer science engineering biology and public policy. It has more than 14500 students and 4000 faculty and staff and it has a relatively small student-teacher ratio of 13:1. Carnegie Mellon was founded by philanthropist and industrialist Andrew Carnegie who established the Carnegie Technical Schools in 1900 for the sons and daughters of Pittsburgh's blue-collar workers.

Operations

Along with its undergraduate and graduate degree programs Carnegie offers working adults a chance to continue their learning through the Professional & Distance Learning arm of the school. Students there can hone their international business management skills and bone up on information technology health systems and human resources among other topics.

Carnegie prides itself on its innovation efforts and to support them operates more than 100 research institutes and centers across its campus. Carnegie's CyLab is one of the largest university-based cybersecurity education and research centers in the country. Cylab focuses on seven primary areas of research and development spanning a wide range of technologies and systems and users.

Tuition for residential undergraduates in 2019 totaled more than $55000.

The school's alumni network includes about 20 Nobel Prize laureates some 125 Emmy Award winners and 10 Academy Award winners.

Geographic Reach

The school's main campus nearly 150 acres with more than 100 buildings is located in Pittsburgh; Carnegie Mellon also has branch campuses in Qatar and Silicon Valley California. Additionally the university offers degrees in about 20 locations around the world including Australia Greece Japan Mexico Portugal and Singapore.

Financial Performance

Carnegie Mellon's revenue increased to $1.3 billion in fiscal 2018 an approximately 4% increase from the year prior. Investment income and tuition revenue rose 13% and 4% respectively offset by a 7% decline in contributions revenue. The university's net assets increased 6.5% to $3.4 billion primarily driven by an operating surplus and increases from both favorable investment returns and contributions with donor restrictions.

Expenses grew 5% in fiscal 2018 to $1.1 billion.Cash provided by operating activities was $111.1 million in 2018 while investing activities used $152.6 million. Financing activities provided another $74.9 million. The company ended fiscal 2018 with $514.7 million in cash and cash equivalents.

Strategy

Carnegie Mellon continues to follow its Strategic Plan 2025 which includes a number of initiatives designed to enhance the university. One of the plan's projects was completed in 2018. The David A. Tepper Quadrangle the largest building on campus debuted in 2018. The 315000-square-foot building which cost $200 million and took three years to plan and construct is the home of Tepper School of Business and serves as a hub to promote cross-campus collaboration.

The university also announced a new president in 2018. Farnam Jahanian who had served as the university's provost and chief academic officer was installed in October 2018 replacing Subra Suresh.

Company Background

Carnegie Tech merged with the Mellon Institute of Research to become Carnegie Mellon University in 1967.

EXECUTIVES

Provost, Farnam Jahanian
Ceo Software Engineering Institute, Paul D. Nielsen, age 69
Dean Student Affairs, Gina Casalegno
Dean Qatar Campus, Ilker Baybars
President, Subra Suresh
Dean Heinz College, Ramayya Krishnan
Chief Investment Officer, Charles A. Kennedy
Vp Finance And Cfo, Amir Rahnamay-Azar
Dean College Of Engineering, James H. Garrett
Dean College Of Fine Arts, Dan Martin
Dean Mellon College Of Science, Fred Gilman
Dean Tepper School Of Business, Robert M. Dammon
Vp Marketing And Communications, Steve Kloehn
Interim Cio, David Baisley
Dean School Of Computer Science, Andrew Moore
Dean Dietrich College Of Humanities And Social Sciences, Richard Scheines
Dean Of Admission, Michael Steidel
Dean University Libraries, Keith Webster
Department Head, Terry Hurlbert
Senior Management (senior Vice President General Manager Director), Gretchen Beck
Vice President Institutional Advancement And Assistant Secretary, Neel Kishan
Vice President Of Mentorship, Adrian Galarza
Department Head, Patsy McCarthy
Vice President, Chinmayi Bhavanishankar
Vice President Of Investment Banking, Samantha Speer
Vice President Of Communications, Ted Lee
Assistant Vice President For Research Compliance, Ann Mathias
Vice President Of Treasury, Kaijie Hu
Vice President Of Education, Anjali Guatam
Vice President Of External Affairs, Carolyn Commer
Deputy General Counsel And Associate Vice President, James Mercolini
Vice President Of Technology, Daniel Dallala
Vice President Of Finance, Peter Tran
Vice President Of Finance, Jorge Carvallo
Vice President Of Finance, Sam Phong
Vice President Of Technology Education, Silvio Tannert
Vice President Finance, Maneesh Lekkala
Co Vice President Of Finance, Sahil Jain
Vice President Of Education Technology, Georgia Tech
Vice President Of Finance, Kevin Gallagher
Vice President Of Finance And Technology, Daniel Robinson
Vice President, Egon Balas
Assistant Vice President For Planning, Keith Cook
Vice President, John Hooker
Vice President, Javier Pena
Associate Vice President For Academic Affairs And Dean Of Graduate Studies, Rodney Mcclendon
Ifc Vice President Recruitment, Thomas Preite
Vice President Of Operations, Rodney P Mcclendon
Vice President, Kailin Dong
Associate Vice President, Mark Delos Reyes Davis
Chairman, James E. (Jim) Rohr, age 72
Vice Chairman, Tod S. Johnson
Vice Chairman, Edward H. (Ed) Frank, age 63
Secretary, Alice Yochum

Assistant Secretary, Karen Khan
Department Secretary, Nancy Watson
Secretary, Ginger Placone
Treasurer, Fred Jacquet
Auditors: KPMG LLP PITTSBURG PA

LOCATIONS

HQ: CARNEGIE MELLON UNIVERSITY
5000 FORBES AVE, PITTSBURGH, PA 152133890
Phone: 412 268-2000
Web: WWW.CMU.EDU

Selected Locations

Adelaide Australia
Athens Greece
Aveiro and Coimbra Portugal
Doha Qatar
Kobe Japan
Lisbon Portugal
Los Angeles
Madeira Portugal
Minho and Porto Portugal
Mexico
Silicon Valley
Singapore

PRODUCTS/OPERATIONS

2015 Sales

	$ mil.	% of total
Tuition and other educational fees revenue net of financial aid	450	39
Sponsored projects revenue	376	32
Contributions revenue	136	12
Auxiliary services revenue	57	5
Investment income	37	3
Other sources	109	9
Total	**1,168**	**100**

Selected Departments

Chemical Engineering
Civil and Environmental Engineering
Energy Science Technology & Policy
Electrical and Computer Engineering
Engineering and Public Policy
Engineering & Technology Innovation Management
Information Networking Institute
Materials Science Engineering
Mechanical Engineering
Software Engineering and
Software Management
Architecture
Art
Design
Drama
Master of Arts Management
Master of Entertainment Industry Management
Music
English
History
Modern Languages
Philosophy
Psychology
Social and Decision Sciences
Statistics

Selected Schools

Carnegie Institute of Technology
School of Computer Science
College of Fine Arts
College of Humanities & Social Sciences
H. John Heinz III College
Mellon College of Science
Tepper School of Business

HISTORICAL FINANCIALS

Company Type: Private

Income Statement — FYE: June 30

	REVENUE ($ mil.)	NET INCOME ($ mil.)	NET PROFIT MARGIN	EMPLOYEES
06/19	1,363	207	15.2%	4,913
06/18	1,313	296	22.6%	—
06/17	1,229	556	45.2%	—
06/13	1,106	182	16.5%	—
Annual Growth	3.5%	2.1%	—	—

2019 Year-End Financials

Return on assets: 4.7%
Return on equity: 6.1%
Current ratio: —
Cash ($ mil.): 514

CAROLINA HEALTHCARE CENTER OF CUMBERLAND LP

Auditors: RSM MCGLADREY CHARLOTTE NC

LOCATIONS

HQ: CAROLINA HEALTHCARE CENTER OF CUMBERLAND LP
4600 CUMBERLAND RD, FAYETTEVILLE, NC 283062412
Phone: 910 429-1690
Web: WWW.CAROLINA-HEALTH.COM

HISTORICAL FINANCIALS

Company Type: Private

Income Statement — FYE: September 30

	REVENUE ($ mil.)	NET INCOME ($ mil.)	NET PROFIT MARGIN	EMPLOYEES
09/09	1,019	62	6.2%	150
09/03	6	(0)	—	—
Annual Growth	132.0%	—	—	—

2009 Year-End Financials

Return on assets: 771.0%
Return on equity: 999.9%
Current ratio: 0.60
Cash ($ mil.): —

CAROLINAS MEDICAL CENTER NORTHEAST

LOCATIONS

HQ: CAROLINAS MEDICAL CENTER NORTHEAST
920 CHURCH ST N, CONCORD, NC 280252927
Phone: 704 783-3000
Web: WWW.ATRIUMHEALTH.ORG

HISTORICAL FINANCIALS

Company Type: Private

Income Statement — FYE: December 31

	REVENUE ($ mil.)	NET INCOME ($ mil.)	NET PROFIT MARGIN	EMPLOYEES
12/17	576	158	27.4%	4,500
12/16	552	130	23.6%	—
12/15	557	117	21.0%	—
Annual Growth	1.7%	16.3%	—	—

2017 Year-End Financials

Return on assets: 10.1%
Return on equity: 10.3%
Current ratio: 23.20
Cash ($ mil.): —

CARTER-JONES COMPANIES, INC.

EXECUTIVES

Pres-Ceo, Neil Sackett
Sr V Pres-Cfo*, Jeffrey Donley
SEC*, Judy Lee
Controller*, Brian Horning
Auditors: BDO USA LLP AKRON OHIO

LOCATIONS

HQ: CARTER-JONES COMPANIES, INC.
601 TALLMADGE RD, KENT, OH 442407331
Phone: 330 673-6100
Web: WWW.CARTERLUMBER.COM

HISTORICAL FINANCIALS

Company Type: Private

Income Statement — FYE: December 31

	REVENUE ($ mil.)	NET INCOME ($ mil.)	NET PROFIT MARGIN	EMPLOYEES
12/19	1,504	45	3.0%	3,225
12/18	1,482	39	2.7%	—
12/17	1,365	29	2.1%	—
12/16	1,241	15	1.2%	—
Annual Growth	6.6%	43.6%	—	—

2019 Year-End Financials

Return on assets: 5.8%
Return on equity: 11.1%
Current ratio: 2.30
Cash ($ mil.): 5

CARY OIL CO., INC.

EXECUTIVES

Pres-Ceo, Craig Stephenson
Chb*, Don Stephenson
V Pres*, Betty Phillips
V Pres*, Jim Bosworth
V Pres*, Mark Maddox
Asst SEC-Treas*, Rick Stephenson
V Pres-Chief Fin Officer*, Jason Holt
Vp Strategy & Innovation, Adam Stephenson
Sales Representative, Jim Pendergast
Director Operations Support, David Taylor
L Credit Analyst, Kristy Bishop
Auditors: BATCELOR TILLERY & ROBERTS L

LOCATIONS

HQ: CARY OIL CO., INC.
110 MACKENAN DR STE 300, CARY, NC 275117901
Phone: 919 462-1100
Web: WWW.CARYOIL.COM

HISTORICAL FINANCIALS

Company Type: Private

Income Statement — FYE: December 31

	REVENUE ($ mil.)	NET INCOME ($ mil.)	NET PROFIT MARGIN	EMPLOYEES
12/12	1,647	2	0.2%	100
12/11	1,608	2	0.1%	—
12/10	1,177	1	0.1%	—
Annual Growth	18.3%	28.2%	—	—

2012 Year-End Financials

Return on assets: 4.8% Cash ($ mil.): 4
Return on equity: 25.1%
Current ratio: 1.00

CASE WESTERN RESERVE UNIVERSITY

Looking for a research-oriented university? Case Western Reserve University (CWRU) is an independent research school with an enrollment of about 11465 students from all US states and around 90 countries more than half of whom are graduate and professional students. CWRU offers about 230 undergraduate and graduate degree programs from its eight colleges and schools ? management engineering law arts and sciences dentistry social work nursing and medicine ? as well as a graduate school at its campus in Cleveland. The university has approximately 3695 faculty members and a student-to-teacher ratio of 11:1.

Operations

The school receives close to $400 million in external funding each year to pay for its various research enterprises. CWRU provides research opportunities to roughly 4000 undergraduates and partners with corporations foundations and other universities to operate more than 100 research centers and institutes. Some of its priority research initiatives include energy and the environment culture creativity and design social justice and ethics. Medical studies are conducted in coordination with health care entities; its most predominant partner is the Cleveland Clinic.

The university generates revenue from grants and contracts for about 35% of sales student tuition and fees for nearly 30% gifts and pledges investment FHBO and operational returns and facilities and administrative cost recovery for nearly 10% each and auxiliary services and others accounts the remainder.

Geographic Reach

CWRU is located at more than 265-acre campus in Cleveland's University Circle; a 400-acre farm located in Hunting Valley Ohio; and houses approximately 40 educational medical cultural social and religious institutions. CWRU's students come from all 50 US states and around 90 countries.

Financial Performance

In 2019 the University reported $1.2 billion in total revenue a $40 million or a 3% increase over the fiscal year 2018.

The University's net income decreased to $7.7 million mainly due to lower retained surplus use.

Cash held by the University decreased by $24.8 million to $80.6 million in 2019 compared to the prior year with $105.4 million. Cash provided by operations and financing activities were $1.5 million and $15.5 million respectively. Cash used for investing activities was $41.8 million mainly for purchase of investments.

Strategy

The University's fiscal year 2019 financial plan continued to focus on maintaining momentum in core operating results strengthening the balance sheet and generating new funding for strategic capital projects by philanthropy. The results were a $61 million or 6% operating margin on a Generally Accepted Accounting Principles basis; an increase in total net assets of $45 million; and another successful year in attainment with $182 million in new gifts and pledges.

Company Background

The university's origins date back to 1826 in the Ohio region then known as the Western Reserve of Connecticut; its current structure was formed in 1967 with the combination of neighboring Case Institute of Technology and Western Reserve College.

EXECUTIVES

Vice President, Carolyn Gregory
Vice President For Campus Services, Dick Jamieson
Vice President, Glenn Nicholls
Director Media Relations, Lisa Chiu
President, Barbara R. Snyder, age 64
Dean School Of Graduate Studies, Charles Rozek
Dean Undergraduate Studies, Jeffrey Wolcowitz
Chief Investment Officer, Sally J. Staley
Dean School Of Dental Medicine, Kenneth B. Chance
Dean Mandel School Of Applied Social Sciences, Grover C. (Cleve) Gilmore
Provost And Evp, William A. (Bud) Baeslack
Svp Finance And Cfo, John F. Sideras
Dean School Of Medicine, Pamela Bowles Davis
Dean College Of Arts And Sciences, Cyrus Taylor
Vp University Marketing And Communications, Chris Sheridan
Dean Case School Of Engineering, Jeffrey Duerk
Dean Weatherhead School Of Management, Robert E. Widing
Dean Bolton School Of Nursing, Mary E. Kerr
Vp Information Technology Services And Cio, Sue B. Workman
Dean School Of Law, Jessica Berg
Dean School Of Law, Michael P. Scharf
Medical Director Professor, Kingman Strohl
Vice President Information Services, Lev Gonick
Assistant Vice President For Research, Diane Domanovics
Vice President Of Marketing, Marlene Gambatese
Vice President Government And Foundation Relations, Julie Rehm
Associate Vice President For Operations And Planning, Dennis Rupert
Krieger Mueller Associate Professor Of Applied History Krieger Mueller Historian Vice President For Collections Wrhs, John Grabowski
Deputy Vice President, Sonia Winner
Chair Department Of Nutrition, Henri Brunengraber
Director Of Nursing University Health Service, Timothy Eppich
Associate Vice President Office Of Student Affairs, Donald Kamalsky
Medical Director, ELIZABETH CLICK
Chief Information Security Officer Office Of The Vice President Of Information Technology Services, Tom Siu
Second Vice President, Clare Rimnac
Vice President, Meredith Sorenson
Vice President Of Communications, Emily Kugel
Vice President Of Recruitment, Arjun Gopinath
Vice President Of Membership Development, Akash K Menon
Vice President Finance, Shreenath Nedungadi
Vice President University Relations, Lara Kalafatis
Vice President, Raymond Neff
Vice President, Jacqueline Musacchia
Cvp Chief Operation Officer, Eric W Bower
Vice President Of Finance And Administration, Nancy Suttenfield
Second Vice President, Katherine Lanese
Medical Director Clinical Microbiology, Michael Jacobs
Vice President Its, Dean Bianchi
Vice President Technology, Karmar Clifton
Vice President, Tom Mullen
Vice President For Development, Lawrence Gibson
Vice President, Don Kamalsky
Senior Vice President Secretary And General Counsel, Elizabeth Keefer
Vice President Of Operations, Ronald Dziedzicki
Vice President Of Marketing, Juanita Cutler
Assistant Vice President Technology Transfer, Catherine Porto
Vice President, Casandra Tice
Medical Director, Barbara Gripshover
Vice President Corporate Solutions, Ryan Terry
Vice President, Marissa Morgan
Vice President, Ranjith Ramachandran
Vp Physician Network And Clinical Operations, Danielle Chickerella
Vice President, Ray Braun
Associate Vice President For University Planning And Administration, Victoria Wright
Vice President Finance Director Of Finance And Suppo, Sonia Salvino
Medical Director, Karen Olness
Vice President Of Sales, Lee Thornton
Chairman, Charles D. (Chuck) Fowler
Board Member, Fred Collopy
Treasurer, Robert Brown
Secretary, Ellen Rothchild
Vice Chair Of Research And Professor, Irina Pikuleva
Secretary, Susan Grimm
Secretary, Kimberly Racut
Treasurer, Mark Chapman
Treasurer, Robert Thompson
Secretary, Meghan Gallagher
Secretary, Krystle Elder
Treasurer, Paul Simmons
Auditors: PRICEWATERHOUSECOOPERS LLP CL

LOCATIONS

HQ: CASE WESTERN RESERVE UNIVERSITY
10900 EUCLID AVE, CLEVELAND, OH 441064901
Phone: 216 368-6062
Web: WWW.CASE.EDU

PRODUCTS/OPERATIONS

2014 Sales

	$ mil.	% of total
Grants and contracts	249	27
Student tuition and fees	218	24
Gifts and pledges	85	9
CCLCM grants and contracts	83	9
Facilities and administrative cost recovery	72	8
Others	217	23
Total	**926**	**100**

Selected Schools and Programs

Case School of Engineering
College of Arts and Sciences
Cleveland Clinic (part of the School of Medicine)
Frances Payne Bolton School of Nursing
Mandel Center for Nonprofit Organizations
Mandel School of Applied Social Sciences
School of Dental Medicine
School of Graduate Studies
School of Law
School of Medicine
Weatherhead School of Management

HISTORICAL FINANCIALS

Company Type: Private

Income Statement FYE: June 30

	REVENUE ($ mil.)	NET INCOME ($ mil.)	NET PROFIT MARGIN	EMPLOYEES
06/20	1,075	(49)	—	6,599
06/18	1,016	111	10.9%	—
06/17	1,022	208	20.4%	—
06/15	1,093	48	4.4%	—
Annual Growth	(0.3%)	—	—	—

2020 Year-End Financials

Return on assets: (-1.5%) Cash ($ mil.): 108
Return on equity: (-2.1%)
Current ratio: —

CATHOLIC HEALTH INITIATIVES - IOWA, CORP.

EXECUTIVES

Ceo, David Vellinga
Coordinator, Kelli Cain
Coordinator, Valerie Diehl
Midwest Regional Sales Manager, Jeff Johnston
Buyer Purchaser, Debbie Soloman
Emergency Medicine Specialist, Benjamin Sweet
Family Practitioner, Butool Abdullah
Internist, Daniela Frankova
Registered Nurse, Elizabeth Hanson
Internist, Moanis Omar
Internist, Tagore Sunkara
Auditors: CATHOLIC HEALTH INITIATIVES E

LOCATIONS

HQ: CATHOLIC HEALTH INITIATIVES - IOWA, CORP.
1111 6TH AVE, DES MOINES, IA 503142613
Phone: 515 247-3121
Web: WWW.MERCYONE.ORG

HISTORICAL FINANCIALS

Company Type: Private

Income Statement — FYE: June 30

	REVENUE ($ mil.)	NET INCOME ($ mil.)	NET PROFIT MARGIN	EMPLOYEES
06/16	804	58	7.3%	6,100
06/14	733	(14)	—	—
06/10	691	39	5.8%	—
06/08	577	36	6.3%	—
Annual Growth	4.2%	6.2%	—	—

2016 Year-End Financials

Return on assets: 6.9%
Return on equity: 9.5%
Current ratio: 3.60
Cash ($ mil.): 82

CATHOLIC HEALTH INITIATIVES COLORADO

EXECUTIVES

Pres, Gregory H Burfitt
Corporate Revenue Integrity, Shelly Vendemo
Chief Officer, Terry Orourke
Orsos Reimbursement Coordinato, Terry Walb
Vice President of Operations, Geoffrey Lawton Pharmd
Chief Operating Officer, Jameson Smith Fache
Senior Vice President, Nick Barto
Knowledge Director, Jeff Sauvie
Vice President of Finance, Jerry Francis
Application Analyst III, Julie Vaccari
Applications Analyst III, Kimberly Fitzgerald
Auditors: LB CATHOLIC HEALTH INITIATIVES

LOCATIONS

HQ: CATHOLIC HEALTH INITIATIVES COLORADO
9100 E MINERAL CIR, CENTENNIAL, CO 801123401
Phone: 303 290-6500
Web: WWW.CATHOLICHEALTHINITIATIVES.ORG

HISTORICAL FINANCIALS

Company Type: Private

Income Statement — FYE: June 30

	REVENUE ($ mil.)	NET INCOME ($ mil.)	NET PROFIT MARGIN	EMPLOYEES
06/15	1,735	101	5.8%	8,000
06/14	1,689	96	5.7%	—
06/10	1,307	50	3.9%	—
06/09	1,226	24	2.0%	—
Annual Growth	6.0%	26.4%	—	—

2015 Year-End Financials

Return on assets: 5.4%
Return on equity: 7.2%
Current ratio: 1.50
Cash ($ mil.): 45

CATHOLIC MEDICAL MISSION BOARD INC

EXECUTIVES

Pres, John F Galbraith
Pres, Bruce Wilkinson
Senior Vice-President, Marivette Cannon
Vice-Chairman, F W Smullen
Program Manager, Syndie Saint Hilaire
Senior Specialist Information, Isaac Roldan
Assistant To President, Lois Harrigan
Vice President, Meseret Ansebo
Marketing Manager, Carmina Perez
Country Director, John Perry
Director of Direct Marketing, Tim Beresnyak
Auditors: MARKS PANETH & SHRON LLP NEW

LOCATIONS

HQ: CATHOLIC MEDICAL MISSION BOARD INC
100 WALL ST FL 9, NEW YORK, NY 100055765
Phone: 212 242-7757
Web: WWW.CMMB.ORG

HISTORICAL FINANCIALS

Company Type: Private

Income Statement — FYE: September 30

	REVENUE ($ mil.)	NET INCOME ($ mil.)	NET PROFIT MARGIN	EMPLOYEES
09/18	740	105	14.2%	38
09/17	603	19	3.2%	—
09/16	371	(12)	—	—
09/15	290	(3)	—	—
Annual Growth	36.7%	—	—	—

2018 Year-End Financials

Return on assets: 48.2%
Return on equity: 49.6%
Current ratio: —
Cash ($ mil.): 5

CATHOLIC RELIEF SERVICES - UNITED STATES CONFERENCE OF CATHOLIC BISHOPS

EXECUTIVES

Ceo, Sean Callahan
Exec V Pres, Schuyler Thorup
Exec V Pres, Joan Rosenhauer
Exec V Pres, Annemarie Reilly
Exec V Pres-Dir, Mark Melia
Exec V Pres-Dir, Shawn Mood
Cfo-Dir, James Bond
Assistant II, Andrea Hamilton
Assistant I, Alexandra Charles
Data Analyst, Alicen McCarrick
Communications Officer (latin, Beatriz Afanador
Auditors: RSM US LLP GAITHERSBURG MARY

LOCATIONS

HQ: CATHOLIC RELIEF SERVICES - UNITED STATES CONFERENCE OF CATHOLIC BISHOPS
228 W LEXINGTON ST, BALTIMORE, MD 212013422
Phone: 410 625-2220
Web: WWW.CRS.ORG

HISTORICAL FINANCIALS

Company Type: Private

Income Statement — FYE: September 30

	REVENUE ($ mil.)	NET INCOME ($ mil.)	NET PROFIT MARGIN	EMPLOYEES
09/19	940	(21)	—	7,100
09/18	989	(3)	—	—
09/17	978	20	2.1%	—
09/16	917	(47)	—	—
Annual Growth	0.8%	—	—	—

2019 Year-End Financials

Return on assets: (-4.2%)
Return on equity: (-13.2%)
Current ratio: 1.00
Cash ($ mil.): 64

CEB INC.

EXECUTIVES

Ceo, Thomas L Monahan III
Cfo*, Richard S Lindahl
Cao*, J Barron Anschutz
Information Specialist, Gary Banks
Executive Officer, Christoffer Ellehuus
Head, Corporate Strategy and D, Jesse Levin
Chief Administrative Officer, Melody L Jones
Staff, Kevin Hoyle
Managing Director, Andrew Blaisdell
Managing Director, Ashley Tatum
Controller, Barron Anschutz
Auditors: ERNST & YOUNG LLP MCLEAN VIR

LOCATIONS

HQ: CEB INC.
1201 WILSON BLVD STE 1800, ARLINGTON, VA 222092316
Phone: 571 303-3000
Web: WWW.CEBGLOBAL.COM

COMPETITORS

Accenture
Booz Allen
Boston Consulting
Conference Board
Kantar Group
McKinsey & Company

HISTORICAL FINANCIALS

Company Type: Private

Income Statement				FYE: December 31
	REVENUE ($ mil.)	NET INCOME ($ mil.)	NET PROFIT MARGIN	EMPLOYEES
12/16	949	(34)	—	4,600
12/15	928	92	10.0%	—
12/14	908	51	5.6%	—
12/13	820	31	3.9%	—
Annual Growth	5.0%	—	—	—

2016 Year-End Financials

Return on assets: (-2.5%)
Return on equity: —
Current ratio: 0.80
Cash ($ mil.): 134

CEC ENTERTAINMENT, INC.

Don't let the mouse mascot fool you: This amusement kingdom is founded on the power of pizza. CEC Entertainment operates the Chuck E. Cheese's chain of pizza parlors with more than 610 locations in over 45 states and approximately 15 foreign countries and territories. The restaurants cater mostly to families with children and feature a broad array of entertainment offerings including arcade-style and skill-oriented games rides live entertainment shows. Entertainment and merchandise account for some 55% of sales. The menu features pizzas wings appetizers salads and desserts. CEC Entertainment owns and operates more than 550 of the pizza and fun joints while the rest are franchised.

Bankruptcy

CEC Entertainment Inc. a nationally recognized leader in family entertainment and dining announced that in order to overcome the financial strain resulting from prolonged COVID-19 related venue closures and position the company for long-term success CEC Entertainment and its domestic affiliates have filed for voluntary protection under Chapter 11 of the U.S. Bankruptcy Code. The company expects to use the time and legal protections made available through the Chapter 11 process to continue discussions with financial stakeholders as well as critical conversations with its landlords to achieve a comprehensive balance sheet restructuring that supports its re-opening and longer-term strategic plans.

Operations

Chuck E. Cheese is a highly recognized brand that appeals to primary guest base of families with children between below 5 and 12 years of age. Each venue includes approximately 75 games rides and attractions for kids of all ages including classic skill games such as arcade basketball skee-ball and Whack-a-Mole along with the Ticket Blaster machine. Chuck E. Cheese menu features fresh hand-made pizza boneless and bone-in chicken wings desserts and beverages including beer and wine at most locations.

Peter Piper Pizza serves fresh handcrafted food and beverages including craft beer and wine and offers state-of-the-art games for all ages. Venues feature a bold design and contemporary layout with open kitchens such as fresh mozzarella being shredded off the block vegetables being hand-chopped wings being hand-tossed and its Certified Dough Masters crafting pizzas with made-from-scratch dough. The company's open dining areas provide an enjoyable atmosphere for families and group events with attentive staff dedicated to providing an enjoyable and memorable experience to each guest.The company's entertainment and merchandise generate approximately 55% of sales food and beverage generate about 45% of sales and franchise fees and royalties generate the remaining.

Geographic Reach

The company and its franchisees operate a system of more than 600 Chuck E. Cheese and more than 120 Peter Piper Pizza venues with locations in over 45 states and more than 15 foreign countries and territories.

Peter Piper Pizza's office is located in Phoenix Arizona. The company also has a warehouse building in Topeka Kansas which primarily serves as a storage distribution and refurbishing facility for venue fixtures and game equipment. The company's headquarter is located in Irving Texas.

Sales and Marketing

The Chuck E. Cheese's concept has successfully cemented a place in the family dining market by focusing on the entertainment options available at its restaurants and marketing itself as a safe and convenient place for parents to take the kids. The company's advertising expenses were $45 million and $48.2 million for 2019 and 2018 respectively.

Financial Performance

After a dip in revenue in 2017 the company was back on its tracks and have increased revenue for three consecutive years. The net income for the last five years has been mostly in black. Only in 2017 did they reported a positive income.Net revenue in 2019 increased by 2% to $890 million. The increase in company venue sales was primarily attributable to a 2.7% increase in comparable venue sales partially offset by a $2.6 million decrease in company venue sales from its non-comparable venues primarily due to a net reduction of seven company-operated venues over the last two years. Net income loss incurred by the company in 2019 was $28.9 million. The decrease in income were due to higher operating costs and expenses and higher interest expense. Cash at the end of 2019 was $34.8 million. Cash generated by operations was $111.1 million. Investing and financing activities used $87.6 and $52.1 million respectively. Main cash uses for 2019 were for property and equipment purchases repayments of loans and repurchases of senior notes.

Strategy

The company's strategic objectives are focused on becoming "the world's leading family - friendly entertainment restaurant brands" by entertaining and inspiring kids around the world and ensuring that every guest is happy. This strategic plan is centered on the following six growth pillars: Increasing traffic to its venues through marketing and sales promotions; Drive in-store guest spending; Pursuing a programmatic approach to our domestic remodel program; Expanding the global franchise network; Launching a division to focus on entertainment & licensing efforts; and Increasing efficiencies and lower operating costs with tight controls.

Also as part of its long-term growth strategy the company plans to upgrade the games rides and entertainment in most of its existing venues remodel certain of its existing venues and open additional new venues in selected markets. Over the years the company has made significant changes to its marketing and advertising strategy including the introduction of an updated Chuck E. Cheese character; change in the mix of its media expenditures increase in advertising directed to parents and promoting its brand and reasons to visit on television and online.

Company Background

The Chuck E. Cheese's concept was created by Nolan Bushnell founder of video game pioneer Atari Corporation in 1977. Showbiz Pizza acquired the chain in 1984 and changed its name to CEC Entertainment 1998.

EXECUTIVES

Cfo, Dale R. Black
President, J. Roger Cardinale, $408,846 total compensation
Evp And Director Operations, Randy G. Forsythe, $257,500 total compensation
Svp And Coo International Operations, Mark K. Gordon, $225,000 total compensation
Ceo And Director, Thomas (Tom) Leverton, $232,692 total compensation
Vp Operations, Chris Kelly
Auditors: DELOITTE & TOUCHE LLP DALLAS

LOCATIONS

HQ: CEC ENTERTAINMENT, INC.
1707 MARKET PL STE 200, IRVING, TX 750638049
Phone: 972 258-8507
Web: WWW.CHUCKECHEESE.COM

2016

	Company-Owned Stores.	Franchised Stores	Total
Domestic			
Chuck E. Cheese's	512	29	541
Peter Piper Pizza	32	62	94
International			
Chuck E. Cheese's	12	39	51
Peter Piper Pizza	-	46	46
Total		176	732

PRODUCTS/OPERATIONS

2016 Sales

	$ mil.	% of total
Company store sales		
Entertainment and merchandise sales	497	54
Food and beverage sales	408	44
Franchise fees and royalties	17	2
Total	922	100

COMPETITORS

Brinker
Buffets Inc
Burger King
California Pizza Kitchen
Carlson Restaurants
Cheesecake Factory
Darden
Dave & Buster's
Denny's
Domino's
In-N-Out Burgers
McDonald's
Papa John's
Pizza Hut
Red Robin
Shakey's
Sonic Corp.
Wendy's

HISTORICAL FINANCIALS

Company Type: Private

Income Statement				FYE: December 29
	REVENUE ($ mil.)	NET INCOME ($ mil.)	NET PROFIT MARGIN	EMPLOYEES
12/19	912	(28)	—	17,200
12/18	896	(20)	—	—
12/17*	886	53	6.0%	—
01/17	923	(3)	—	—
Annual Growth	(0.4%)	—	—	—

*Fiscal year change

2019 Year-End Financials

Return on assets: (-1.4%)
Return on equity: (-13.5%)
Current ratio: 0.60
Cash ($ mil.): 34

CEDARS-SINAI MEDICAL CENTER

Many a star has been born literally at Cedars-Sinai Medical Center. The 886-bed teaching and research hospital is located right where Los Angeles meets Beverly Hills and West Hollywood and has tended to the medical needs of a number of celebrities since its founding in 1902. However the center is also a major teaching hospital for UCLA's David Geffen School of Medicine and is engaged in hundreds of research programs in areas such as cancer neuroscience and genetics. It also includes two multi-specialty physician associations Cedars-Sinai Medical Group and Ceders-Sinai Health Associates and operates a number of community health centers and outreach programs (such as mobile health clinics).

Operations

The not-for-profit hospital's more than 2100 physicians represent just about every clinical specialty out there. Cedars-Sinai is consistently listed as a top-ranked hospital by U.S. News & World Report in such specialties as cancer cardiology endocrinology gastrointestinal disorders gynecology heart surgery kidney disease neurology orthopaedics and respiratory disorders.

Cedars-Sinai is the only private hospital with a Level 1 trauma center in Los Angeles County; as such the hospital sees about 1600 trauma patients a year. The hospital also provides a number of outpatient services.

Federal funding from the National Institutes of Health and other sources have provided the hospital with some $40 million towards research. Cedars-Sinai currently has some 1300 research projects.

The hospital sees some 660000 outpatient visits and 85000 emergency department visits each year.

Geographic Reach

Cedars-Sinai's hospital is located in Los Angeles; it has an administrative office in Beverly Hills California.

Financial Performance

Revenues from patient care and other sources totaled nearly $2.77 billion in fiscal 2015 while net income amounted to $472.9 million.

Strategy

To meet increasing patient demand and expand its capacity for research projects Cedars-Sinai added nearly 7000 sq. ft. of space to house the Cedars-Sinai Biobank and Translational Research Core Facility in 2015. The previous year it opened a new clinic dedicated to the evaluation of heart and vascular disease patients for participation in stem cell medical studies.

EXECUTIVES

Senior Vice President Human Resources And Organization Development, Jeanne Flores
Senior Vice President Legal Affairs, Peter Braveman
President And Ceo, Thomas M. (Tom) Priselac
Evp Finance And Cfo, Edward M. Prunchunas
Evp Hospital Operations And Coo Medical Center, Mark R. Gavens
Evp Academic Affairs And Dean Of The Faculty, Shlomo Melmed
Svp Medical Affairs And Chief Medical Officer, Michael L. Langberg
Evp System Development And Chief Strategy Officer, Richard B. Jacobs
Svp Enterprise Information Systems And Cio, Darren Dworkin
Evp Medical Network, John Jenrette
Vice President Legal Affairs, James Laur
Vice President Strategic Planning And Business Development, Lori Weise
Medical Director, Roy Artal
Vice President Of Marketing And Public Relations, Richard Elbaum
Medical Director Liver Transplant, Tram Tran
Medical Director Genrisk Adult Genetic, Ora Gordon
Senior Vice President Medical Network, Thomas D Gordon
Medical Director, Spencer Koerner
Senior Vice President Community Relations, Arthur Ochoa
Director Of Radiology, Lynne Roy
Medical Director, Jaime Moriguchi
Medical Director, Syed Naqvi
Vice President Of Medical Affairs, Neil Romanoff
Medical Director Enterprise Information Systems, Lisa Masson
Legal Secretary To Vice President For Legal Affairs And Two Associate Attorneys, Nancy Ogg
Vice President Service Line Operations, Bryan Croft
Medical Director Partial Hospitalization Program, David Callander
Mph Chc Vice President Corporate Integrity Program, Ginny Kim
Medical Director, Edward Wolin
Senior Vice President And Chief Nursing Executive, David R Marshall
Vp Clinical Operations Medical Network, Prasanna Mohanty
Medical Director, Howard Moss
Senior Vice President Legal Affairs, Terri Wagner Cammarano
Medical Director, David Cannom
Chairman, Marc H. Rapaport
Vice Chair, Steven Romick
Auditors: ERNST & YOUNG LLP LOS ANGELES

LOCATIONS

HQ: CEDARS-SINAI MEDICAL CENTER
8700 BEVERLY BLVD, WEST HOLLYWOOD, CA 900481804
Phone: 310 423-3277
Web: WWW.CEDARS-SINAI.ORG

PRODUCTS/OPERATIONS

Selected Centers and Services

Ambulatory Care Center
Cedars-Sinai Center for Chest Disease
Cedars-Sinai Center for Digestive Diseases
Cedars-Sinai Heart Institute
Cedars-Sinai Institute Spine Center
Cedars-Sinai Health Associates (affiliated independent physician association)
Cedars-Sinai Medical Group (multi-specialty physicians group)
Cedars-Sinai Orthopedic Center
Diagnostic imaging center
Emergency department and trauma center
Hospice services
Kidney and pancreas transplant center
Neuroscience services
Pediatric services
Psychiatry and mental health services
Samuel Oschin Comprehensive Cancer Institute
Surgical services
Organ and bone marrow transplantation
Radiation therapy
Radiology
Stroke program
Pain management services
Women's health services

COMPETITORS

Adventist Health System West
Brotman Medical Center
Childrens Hospital Los Angeles
City of Hope
Community Health Systems
Dignity Health
Eisenhower Medical Center
Glendale Adventist Medical Center
Glendale Memorial Hospital
Golden State Health Centers
Good Samaritan Hospital (IN)
HCA
Hollywood Presbyterian Medical Center
Newhall Memorial Hospital
Pasadena Hospital Association
Providence Health System Southern California
Scripps Health
Tenet Healthcare
UCSF Medical
White Memorial Medical Center

HISTORICAL FINANCIALS

Company Type: Private

Income Statement — FYE: June 30

	REVENUE ($ mil.)	NET INCOME ($ mil.)	NET PROFIT MARGIN	EMPLOYEES
06/20	3,647	443	12.2%	8,000
06/19	3,649	389	10.7%	—
06/18	3,470	418	12.0%	—
06/17	3,788	380	10.0%	—
Annual Growth	(1.2%)	5.3%	—	—

2020 Year-End Financials

Return on assets: 6.0%
Return on equity: 8.7%
Current ratio: 4.60
Cash ($ mil.): 1,140

CENTERPOINT ENERGY SERVICES RETAIL LLC

EXECUTIVES

Pres-Ceo, David McClanahan
Auditors: GRANT THORNTON LLP TULSA OKL

LOCATIONS

HQ: CENTERPOINT ENERGY SERVICES RETAIL LLC
1111 LA ST FL 20 FLR 20, HOUSTON, TX 77002
Phone: 800 752-8036
Web: WWW.INFUSEENERGY.COM

HISTORICAL FINANCIALS

Company Type: Private

Income Statement — FYE: December 31

	REVENUE ($ mil.)	NET INCOME ($ mil.)	NET PROFIT MARGIN	EMPLOYEES
12/14	695	8	1.2%	35
12/13	549	9	1.7%	—
Annual Growth	26.6%	(11.9%)	—	—

CENTIMARK CORPORATION

Shout it from the rooftops Centimark is one of the commercial and industrial roofing contractors in the US Canada and Mexico. The company provides roof installation inspection repair and emergency leak service. Centimark typically works on flat roofs using EPDM rubber thermoplastic bitumen metal and coatings. Its QuestMark division offers commercial industrial and retail flooring do-it-yourself (DIY) products and floor maintenance and cleaning products. The company has more than 85 offices throughout US Canada and Mexico.

Operations

The company offers roof services roof replacement roof repairs roof cleaning preventative maintenance programs asset alert and asset management. Centimark also provides systems such as thermoplastic solutions sprayed polyurethane foams roof coatings modified bitumen and built-up roofing metal products and steep slope products.

QuestMark a division of Centimark offers materials for commercial retail and industrial floors. It specializes in DiamondQuest polished concrete flooring epoxy flooring floor repair materials floor maintenance and floor cleaning products.

Centimark's Asset Management service provides extensive roof surveys roof life expectancy models return-on-investment analysis for roof repairs and evaluations for roof repair or roof replacement.

Geographic Reach

Canonsburg Pennsylvania-based Centimark also does business in Canada through subsidiary Centimark Ltd. which has offices in Calgary Edmonton Toronto and Vancouver.

Sales and Marketing

The company serves customers in different segments including retail industrial general contractors and education.

Company Background

Chairman and CEO Edward Dunlap founded Centimark as an industrial cleaning business in 1967. Centimark is owned by its employees.

EXECUTIVES

Vice President Applications, Joe Filtz
Vice President, Thor Dicesare
Chairman And Ceo, Edward B. Dunlap
President And Coo, Timothy M. Dunlap
Evp And Northern Group Director, Robert J. Rudzik
Evp And Western Group Director, Steven M. Ferencz
Evp National And Regional Sales, John T. Godwin
Evp And Cfo, John L. Heisey
Evp And Southern Group Director, Sherman L. Gaskins
Evp And Questmark Flooring Group Director, John P. Scanlon
Svp And Eastern Group Director, Mark A. Cooper
Evp And Canada Group Director Centimark Ltd, Robert T. Penney
Svp And Southern Group Director, Keith Battenfield
Evp Service, Kenneth W. Zmich
National Accounts Manager, Cindy Molnar
Vice President Of Human Resources, Landon Connolly
National Account Manager, Robert Marinkoski
Vice President Marketing, Patrick Dunlap
National Account Manager, Eric Gorman
National Accounts Manager, Keith O'brien
National Account Manager, Ryan Alyea
Executive Vice President, John Rudzik
Vice President Of Litigation Department, John Liekar
National Account Manager, Shaun Bynum
National Accounts Manager, Chuck Blair
National Account Manager, Kevin Russell
National Account Manager, Tony Crawford
National Account Manager, Brian Short
National Account Manager, John Luck
National Accounts Manager, Bob Roche
Vice President National Accounts, Thomas Vehrs
National Account Manager, Dean Morrison
National Accounts Manager, David Schulze
Auditors: SCHNEIDER DOWNS & CO INC P

LOCATIONS

HQ: CENTIMARK CORPORATION
12 GRANDVIEW CIR, CANONSBURG, PA 153178533
Phone: 724 514-8700
Web: WWW.CENTIMARK.COM

PRODUCTS/OPERATIONS

Selected Operations

CentiMark (roofing)
CentiMark ltd. (Canada roofing)
QuestMark (flooring)

Selected Systems

Roof Systems
EPDM
Green Roofing
Metal Roofs
Modified Bitumen and Built-Up Roofs
Roof Coatings
SPF
Steep Slope
TPO & PVC
Floor Systems
Chemical Resistant Systems
Decorative Broadcast
Decorative Concrete
Electric Static Dissipative
Heavy Duty Resurfacer
High Build Coating
Polished Concrete
Thin Mil

COMPETITORS

Armstrong World Industries
Cabral Roofing & Waterproofing
D. C. Taylor
Duro-Last Roofing
Garcia Roofing
Holland Roofing
Pickens Roofing
Tecta America

HISTORICAL FINANCIALS

Company Type: Private

Income Statement — FYE: April 30

	REVENUE ($ mil.)	NET INCOME ($ mil.)	NET PROFIT MARGIN	EMPLOYEES
04/19	723	62	8.6%	3,500
04/18	670	54	8.1%	—
04/17	625	51	8.2%	—
04/15	540	46	8.7%	—
Annual Growth	7.6%	7.3%	—	—

2019 Year-End Financials

Return on assets: 12.1%
Return on equity: 16.1%
Current ratio: 4.60
Cash ($ mil.): 205

CENTRA HEALTH, INC.

Centra Health is a constellation of hospitals and medical practices targeting the health care needs of residents in central and southern Virginia. At the not-for-profit entity's core are two acute care facilities in Lynchburg: the 358-bed Lynchburg General which is the region's main emergency center and specializes in orthopedic pediatric and cardiac care; and Virginia Baptist a 161-bed facility focused on surgery women's health infant care mental health and rehabilitation. Centra also operates a nearby community hospital and an array of primary care physician practices home health agencies retirement centers and other physical and behavioral health businesses.

Operations

In addition to Lynchburg General and Virginia Baptist Centra's acute care facilities include Southside Community Hospital (Farmville). Southside Community Hospital serves as a central acute care and birthing facility for an eight-county region. Centra also operates the Bedford Memorial Hospital through a partnership with Carilion Health System; it plans to buy out Carilion's shares in the partnership.

Outside of its acute care operations Centra Health administers senior care services through The Summit assisted living and independent living facilities. The Summit offers senior residents private apartments medical care and personal assistance. Centra also operates a network of treatment centers for patients of all ages with behavioral and psychiatric disorders. The network includes facilities that specialize in treating children and adolescents with emotional and behavioral disorders.

Altogether the network handles more than 300000 patient visits each year including more than 90000 emergency room visits and more than 5000 cardiac procedures. Its hospitals have a medical staff of about 500 doctors who perform more than 6300 inpatient and 9300 outpatient surgeries annually. Centra also operates the Centra Medical Group which includes about 140 primary care and specialist physicians.

Geographic Reach

Centra Health serves Lynchburg and surrounding communities in central Virginia including Farmville (located in Prince Edward County) Bedford Danville/Gretna and Moneta/Smith Mountain Lake Virginia.

Strategy

Centra Health is expanding its breadth of services as well as its network of facilities. Recent additions include new behavioral health facilities and an expansion of Bedford Memorial's orthopedic center. In 2015 it announced plans to buy out Carilion Clinic's shares of Bedford Memorial Hospital and the Oakwood Health and Rehabilitation Center for $11 million.

Company Background

Centra Health was founded in 1987 through the merger of Lynchburg General and Virginia Baptist. Southside Community Hospital joined the network in 2006.

EXECUTIVES

Chairman Centra Foundation, George A. Hurt
President And Ceo, E. W. Tibbs
Vp And Ceo Centra Southside Community Hospital, William L. Bass
Medical Director, Peter Betz
Vice President Of Nursing Operations, Carolyn Jacques
Medical Director, James Cure
Vice President Operational Finance, Julie Sledd
Director Of Him, Bise Rhonda
Chairman, Walker P. Sydnor
Vice Chairman, Amy G. Ray
Secretary, Kelly Overstreet

LOCATIONS

HQ: CENTRA HEALTH, INC.
1920 ATHERHOLT RD, LYNCHBURG, VA 245011120
Phone: 434 200-3204
Web: WWW.CENTRAHEALTH.COM

PRODUCTS/OPERATIONS

Selected Facilities
Bedford Memorial Hospital (Bedford Virginia; partnership with Carilion Health System)
Lynchburg General Hospital (Lynchburg Virginia)
Virginia Baptist Hospital (Lynchburg Virginia)
Southside Community Hospital (Farmville Virginia)
Physician Practices
Altavista Medical Center (Altavista Virginia)
Big Island Medical Center (North Big Island Virginia)
Brookneal Family Medical Center (Brookneal Virginia)
Gretna Medical Center (Gretna Virginia)
Lynchburg Family Medicine Center (Lynchburg Virginia)
Other Facilities
Bridges Treatment Center (Lynchburg Virginia)
Fairmont Crossing Health and Rehabilitation Center (Amherst Virginia)
Guggenheimer Health and Rehabilitation Center (Lynchburg Virginia)
Piedmont Psychiatric Center (Lynchburg Virginia)
Rivermont Schools (regional)
The Summit (regional)

COMPETITORS

Alleghany Regional Hospital
Bon Secours Health
Carilion Clinic
Clinch Valley Medical Center
Danville Regional Medical Center
Encompass Health
Martha Jefferson Hospital
Mary Washington Healthcare
Montgomery Regional Hospital
Sentara Healthcare
University of Virginia Health System

HISTORICAL FINANCIALS

Company Type: Private

Income Statement — FYE: December 31

	REVENUE ($ mil.)	NET INCOME ($ mil.)	NET PROFIT MARGIN	EMPLOYEES
12/15	742	25	3.4%	6,000
12/14	553	63	11.5%	—
12/09	534	16	3.1%	—
12/08	419	33	7.9%	—
Annual Growth	8.5%	(3.9%)	—	—

2015 Year-End Financials

Return on assets: 2.6%
Return on equity: 4.5%
Current ratio: 0.50
Cash ($ mil.): 25

CENTRACARE HEALTH SYSTEM

EXECUTIVES

Pres, Kenneth Holmen
Health Professional, Saul S Singh
Manager of Management Informat, Dawn Adelman
Scientist, Christy Emerson
Research Analyst, Cheryl Kelley
Psychologist, Barbara Carver
Psychologist, Jennifer Harris
Administrative Assistant, Abby Foley
Physical Therapist Personal Tr, Audra Zastrow
Manager, David Covington
Purchasing, Debbie Sadergaski
Auditors: RSM US LLP MINNEAPOLIS MINN

LOCATIONS

HQ: CENTRACARE HEALTH SYSTEM
1406 6TH AVE N, SAINT CLOUD, MN 563031900
Phone: 320 251-2700
Web: WWW.CENTRACARE.COM

HISTORICAL FINANCIALS

Company Type: Private

Income Statement — FYE: June 30

	REVENUE ($ mil.)	NET INCOME ($ mil.)	NET PROFIT MARGIN	EMPLOYEES
06/19	1,695	50	3.0%	4,957
06/15	176	(15)	—	—
06/13	115	27	23.8%	—
06/11	48	(6)	—	—
Annual Growth	55.8%	—	—	—

2019 Year-End Financials

Return on assets: 2.2%
Return on equity: 4.1%
Current ratio: 1.40
Cash ($ mil.): 112

CENTRAL CRUDE, INC.

EXECUTIVES

Ceo, Steve Jordan
Pres*, George Jordan
V Pres*, Joe Milazzo
Health Professional, Lisa Gustas
Vice-President Business Develo, Kevin Hickey
Treasurer, Katy Bertrand
Auditors: MCELROY QUIRK & BURCH

LOCATIONS

HQ: CENTRAL CRUDE, INC.
4187 HIGHWAY 3059, LAKE CHARLES, LA 706153310
Phone: 337 436-1000
Web: WWW.CENTRALCRUDE.COM

HISTORICAL FINANCIALS

Company Type: Private

Income Statement — FYE: March 31

	REVENUE ($ mil.)	NET INCOME ($ mil.)	NET PROFIT MARGIN	EMPLOYEES
03/09	637	1	0.2%	50
03/08	635	0	0.1%	—
03/06	280	0	0.1%	—
Annual Growth	31.5%	56.2%	—	—

2009 Year-End Financials

Return on assets: 2.4%
Return on equity: 40.0%
Current ratio: 1.00
Cash ($ mil.): —

CENTRAL ELECTRIC POWER COOPERATIVE, INC.

EXECUTIVES

Ceo, Ronald J Calcaterra
Sr V Pres*, Art Fusco
Sr V Pres*, Jim Lamb
Dir*, David Logeman
Cfo*, John Brantley
Prin*, John Tiencken
Program Manager, Scott Hammond
Information Technology Manager, Mike Kelly
Pricing Manager, Cole Price
Director of Power Supply Opera, Gerald Fleming
Engineer, Kale Ford

LOCATIONS

HQ: CENTRAL ELECTRIC POWER COOPERATIVE, INC.
20 COOPERATIVE WAY, COLUMBIA, SC 292103112
Phone: 803 779-4975
Web: WWW.CEPCI.ORG

HISTORICAL FINANCIALS

Company Type: Private

Income Statement — FYE: December 31

	REVENUE ($ mil.)	NET INCOME ($ mil.)	NET PROFIT MARGIN	EMPLOYEES
12/15	1,220	0	0.0%	44
12/14	1,254	0	0.0%	—
12/13	1,198	0	0.0%	—
12/09	1,037	1	0.2%	—
Annual Growth	2.8%	(33.9%)	—	—

2015 Year-End Financials

Return on assets: —
Return on equity: 0.4%
Current ratio: —
Cash ($ mil.): 8

CENTRAL GROCERS, INC.

In a city of big stores Central Grocers helps keep neighborhood markets stocked. Founded in 1917 the cooperative wholesale food distributor is owned by some 225 members. It supplies 40000 food items and general merchandise to more than 400 independent grocery stores serving several states such as Illinois Indiana Iowa Michigan and Wisconsin. Central Grocers distributes products under both national brands and its own Centrella brand which is marketed exclusively to its member stores. The co-op also operates about 30 stores under a handful of banner names including Strack & Van Til Town & Country Key Market and the low-cost Ultra Foods chain.In 2017 the company filed for Chapter 11 bankruptcy protection.

Bankruptcy

In May 2017 Central Grocers filed for Chapter 11 bankruptcy protection. The company intends to sell its Strack & Van Tilstores and its Joliet Ill. distribution warehouse as its seeks to exit its wholesale distribution business.

Operations

As part of its business Central Grocers caters to its customers with the help of a fleet of 100 refrigerated trucks 300 dry trailers and about 70 Freightliner tractors.

Sales and Marketing

Central Grocers services a wide variety of store formats and ethnic groups including Hispanic Italian and African Americans. Besides older and smaller 5000-sq.-ft. stores its clients include large-scale warehouse discount stores that measure 75000 sq. ft. and large conventional stores that average 70000 sq. ft.

Financial Performance

While privately-owned Central Grocers doesn't report financial results. The co-op rings up an estimated $2 billion in sales and it returns (in the form of dividends) to its members about $243 million.

Strategy

Central Grocers the 7th largest grocery cooperative in the US boasts the second-largest market share in the Chicago area. It specializes in serving Chicago independent supermarkets. Central Grocers supplies them with a comprehensive menu of groceries produce fresh meat service deli items frozen foods ice cream and items from its own Centrella brand.

Central Grocers expanded its distribution center by 15000-sq.-ft. to 940000-sq.-ft. of storage capacity in 2011. The reason for expansion was due to demand for produce and fresh meats.

LOCATIONS

HQ: CENTRAL GROCERS, INC.
2600 HAVEN AVE, JOLIET, IL 604338467
Phone: 815 553-8800
Web: WWW.CENTRAL-GROCERS.COM

PRODUCTS/OPERATIONS

Selected Products

Fresh meat
Frozen foods
Groceries
Ice cream
Produce
Service deli items

COMPETITORS

ALDI
Albertsons
Alex Lee
Associated Wholesale Grocers
C&S Wholesale
Certco
Dearborn Wholesale Grocers
Kroger
Meijer
SUPERVALU
Safeway
Schnuck Markets
Wal-Mart
Winkler

HISTORICAL FINANCIALS

Company Type: Private

Income Statement — FYE: July 28

	REVENUE ($ mil.)	NET INCOME ($ mil.)	NET PROFIT MARGIN	EMPLOYEES
07/07	1,197	(10)	—	2,300
07/06	1,108	5	0.5%	—
07/05	1,103	4	0.4%	—
07/04	1,047	3	0.3%	—
Annual Growth	4.5%	—	—	—

2007 Year-End Financials

Return on assets: (-3.8%)
Return on equity: (-35.2%)
Current ratio: 1.00
Cash ($ mil.): —

CENTRAL HUDSON GAS & ELECTRIC CORPORATION

EXECUTIVES

Chb-ceo, Stephen Lant
Executive Vice President, James Laurito
Executive Vice President Sustainability And Chief Human Resource Officer, Nora Duke
Vice President Human Resources And Safety, Sharon A Mcginnis

LOCATIONS

HQ: CENTRAL HUDSON GAS & ELECTRIC CORPORATION
284 SOUTH AVE DEPT 100, POUGHKEEPSIE, NY 126014839
Phone: 845 452-2700
Web: WWW.CENHUD.COM

HISTORICAL FINANCIALS

Company Type: Private

Income Statement — FYE: December 31

	REVENUE ($ mil.)	NET INCOME ($ mil.)	NET PROFIT MARGIN	EMPLOYEES
12/17	671	55	8.2%	869
12/16	640	52	8.2%	—
/ 0	0	—	—	
Annual Growth	—	—	—	—

2017 Year-End Financials

Return on assets: 2.5%
Return on equity: 8.8%
Current ratio: 1.80
Cash ($ mil.): 14

CENTRAL IOWA HOSPITAL CORP

EXECUTIVES

Ceo, Eric Crowell
Executive Director-Finance*, Kara Dunham
Chief of Urology, Markham J J Anderson
Regional Vice-President, Jean Shelton

LOCATIONS

HQ: CENTRAL IOWA HOSPITAL CORP
1200 PLEASANT ST, DES MOINES, IA 503091406
Phone: 515 241-6212
Web: WWW.APDAPARKINSON.ORG

HISTORICAL FINANCIALS

Company Type: Private

Income Statement — FYE: December 31

	REVENUE ($ mil.)	NET INCOME ($ mil.)	NET PROFIT MARGIN	EMPLOYEES
12/17	832	3	0.4%	3,495
12/16	573	153	26.8%	—
12/15	548	152	27.9%	—
12/14	534	145	27.2%	—
Annual Growth	15.9%	(71.6%)	—	—

2017 Year-End Financials

Return on assets: 0.3%
Return on equity: 0.4%
Current ratio: 3.20
Cash ($ mil.): 2

CENTRAL STEEL AND WIRE COMPANY

When it comes to metal service center Central Steel & Wire Company (CS&W) can shape up and ship out. CS&W distributes ferrous and nonferrous metals in a variety of shapes and forms including bars coils plates sheets structurals tubing and wire. Among the company's processing services are annealing blanking computer numerical control (CNC) laser cutting galvanizing and structural fabrication. CS&W distributes its products throughout North America from five facilities that are located primarily in the Midwestern US. The company has metallurgical engineers on its staff to support customers with metal specifications and interpretation expertise.

Operations

The company distributes processed and unprocessed ferrous and nonferrous metals which are are generally obtained from rolling mills in many forms and distributed from CS&W's warehouses.

Geographic Reach

CS&W is based in Chicago. It has stocking facilities in Cincinnati Detroit Milwaukee Greensboro (North Carolina). Its Central Coil Processing unit is in Portage Indiana.

Financial Performance

In 2013 CS&W's revenues decreased by 10% due to lower prices caused by excess mill capacity and a 4% drop in tons shipped caused by lower net sales.

The company's net income decreased by 79% that year primarily due to a decline in revenues.

CS&W's operating cash inflow increased to $11 million (compared to $10 million in 2012) due to cash generated from inventories and receivables.

Strategy

In 2013 the company launched a new web based material test reporting feature increasing its ability to service customers more efficiently through an additional channel when material certifications are required.

Company Background

In 2011 CS&W added pre-painted steel and aluminum coil to its full-line inventory of metal products. The pre-paint program includes material stocked and processed to customer specific specifications for next day delivery. The main intent of this expansion is to develop inventory management programs to reduce total costs and support short-dated delivery requirements.

CS&W was founded in 1909. The company is majority-owned by a trust set up by a former chairman the late James Lowenstein.

EXECUTIVES

Ceo, Stephen E Fuhrman
Cfo*, Kevin G Powers
Assistant Manager Order Proces, Cindy Lambros
Customer Rep, Hilda Villalobos
Inside Sales, Jenna Romano
Inside Sales Representative, Jordan Alvarez
Territory Sales Manager, Kimberly Witkowski
Administrative Assistant, Laura Phipps

Transportation, Michael Hawkins
Coordinator, Steve Wilson
Payroll, Maria Liakopoulos

LOCATIONS

HQ: CENTRAL STEEL AND WIRE COMPANY
3000 W 51ST ST, CHICAGO, IL 606322198
Phone: 773 471-3800
Web: WWW.CENTRALSTEEL.COM

PRODUCTS/OPERATIONS

Selected Products

Alloy bars
Aluminum
Bar and structural shapes
Brass and copper
CF bars/flat wire
Grating/Morton products
HR bars
Steel plates
Steel sheets/strapping
Stainless steel
Steel tubing/pipe
Wire/drill rod/tool steel

Selected Processing Capabilities

Angle Rings
Annealing
Annodizing
Band Saw Cutting
Beam Splitting
Blanking
Burning - Oxyfuel
Centerless Grinding
Circle Shearing
CNC Laser Cutting
CNC Plasma Cutting
CNC Punching
CNC Waterjet Cutting
Coil Blanking
Coil Cut To Length
Cold Sawing Bar
Cold Sawing Plate
Contour Sawing
Deep Hole Drilling
Drilling & Tapping
F&D Heads
Facing & Centering
Forming
Galvanizing
Grinding
Heat Treating
Honing
Lathe Cut Tube/Pipe
Machining
Mech Descale and Oil
Miter Cutting
Normalizing
Painting
Perforating
Pickling & Oiling
Plate and Struct Rolling
Plating
Polishing
Precision Plasma
Precision Sawing
Protex Covering
Sand/Shot Blasting
SCS Finishing
Seam Planishing
Seam Welding
Shearing
Slitting
Straightening
Stress Relieving
Struct Fabrication
Threading
Tube/Pipe Fabrication
Tumble Deburring
Ultrasonic Testing
Welding
Wire Brush Deburr

COMPETITORS

Alro
Macsteel Service Centers USA
Metals USA
Olympic Steel
Precision Steel
Reliance Steel
Ryerson
Worthington Industries

HISTORICAL FINANCIALS

Company Type: Private

Income Statement — FYE: December 31

	REVENUE ($ mil.)	NET INCOME ($ mil.)	NET PROFIT MARGIN	EMPLOYEES
12/14	698	(2)	—	1,075
12/13	678	2	0.3%	—
12/12	750	10	1.4%	—
Annual Growth	(3.6%)	—	—	—

2014 Year-End Financials

Return on assets: (-1.3%)
Return on equity: (-1.8%)
Current ratio: 7.10
Cash ($ mil.): 28

CERTCO, INC.

Certco has built a business serving about 200 independent grocers in Minnesota Wisconsin Iowa and Illinois. The food distribution cooperative offers customers an inventory of more than 57000 items including bakery goods frozen foods meat products produce and general merchandise. It distributes products under the Shurfine Shurfresh and Top Care labels. Additionally Certco offers its member-operators such services as advertising accounting client data services warehousing merchandising store planning and design and other business support services. The cooperative was founded in 1930 as Central Wisconsin Cooperative Food Stores.

Operations

To support its business Certco operates a nearly 1 million-sq.-ft. distribution center. Its brands include Shurfine Shurfresh Value Time Full Circle Topco and Top Care.

Geographic Reach

Based in Madison Wisconsin Certco operates in Minnesota and Wisconsin with an extended reach into parts of Iowa and Illinois.

Sales and Marketing

Many of Certco's clients are Fortune 500 companies. It distributes the national brands of major companies such as Kraft General Mills Procter & Gamble and Johnson & Johnson. The company also distributes specialty items under the names Amy's Hodgson Mills Bob's Red Mill and Annie's that are only available through direct-store-delivery suppliers.

Company Background

Certco was established in 1930 when five Madison-area retailers formed an alliance to boost their combined purchasing muscle.

EXECUTIVES

Treasurer Vice President, David Ryman
Auditors: SATTELL JOHNSON APPEL & CO

LOCATIONS

HQ: CERTCO, INC.
5321 VERONA RD, FITCHBURG, WI 537116050
Phone: 608 271-4500
Web: WWW.CERTCOINC.COM

PRODUCTS/OPERATIONS

Selected Brands

Full Circle
Shurfine
Shurfresh
Top Care
Topco
Value Time

Selected Services

Advertising
Client data services
Retail accounting
Retail meetings/seminars
Retail support
Retail technology
Store planning & design
Trade shows
Value added services
Warehouses
Web architecture

COMPETITORS

Affiliated Foods Midwest
Associated Wholesale Grocers
C&S Wholesale
Central Grocers
Dearborn Wholesale Grocers
Kroger
Roundy's
Winkler

HISTORICAL FINANCIALS

Company Type: Private

Income Statement — FYE: April 26

	REVENUE ($ mil.)	NET INCOME ($ mil.)	NET PROFIT MARGIN	EMPLOYEES
04/14	640	5	0.9%	325
04/13	607	5	0.9%	—
04/12	569	5	0.9%	—
Annual Growth	6.0%	5.6%	—	—

2014 Year-End Financials

Return on assets: 5.0%
Return on equity: 8.4%
Current ratio: 2.00
Cash ($ mil.): 11

CFJ PROPERTIES LLC

EXECUTIVES

Chb, Crystal Call Maggelet
Exec Committee MBR*, Andre Lortz
Exec Committee MBR*, Richard D Peterson
Executive Committee MBR, Richard Peterson
Senior Corporate Counsel, Tom Schofield
Auditors: KPMG LLP SALT LAKE CITY UTAH

LOCATIONS

HQ: CFJ PROPERTIES LLC
5508 LONAS DR, KNOXVILLE, TN 379093221
Phone: 801 624-1000
Web: WWW.PILOTFLYINGJ.COM

HISTORICAL FINANCIALS

Company Type: Private

Income Statement — FYE: January 31

	REVENUE ($ mil.)	NET INCOME ($ mil.)	NET PROFIT MARGIN	EMPLOYEES
01/09	7,672	157	2.1%	6,250
01/07	6,769	50	0.7%	—
01/06	6,166	48	0.8%	—
Annual Growth	7.6%	47.7%	—	—

2009 Year-End Financials

Return on assets: 18.7%
Return on equity: 47.1%
Current ratio: 0.60
Cash ($ mil.): 37

CGB ENTERPRISES, INC.

The farmer in the delta relies on CGB Enterprises. Located in Louisiana near the shores of Lake Pontchartrain and the mouth of the Mississippi River the agricultural company provides US farmers with a range of services including grain handling storage and merchandising. It offers inland grain transportation by barge rail and truck and also markets and sells seeds agricultural products and insurance. CGB's Consolidated Terminals and Logistics Co. (CTLC) subsidiary provides transportation logistics and bulk commodity services for both agricultural and non-agricultural customers. The company operates more than 170 locations across the US. Japanese trading conglomerates ITOCHU and ZEN-NOH own CGB.

Operations

The company provides an array of services for grain farmers from buying storing selling and shipping of the crop to financing and risk management. The company's entrepreneurial approach has thrived over 45 years as CGB has expanded in many new directions. Natural extensions have included the addition of soybean processing and fertilizer products.

CGB's divisions include Consolidated Grain and Barge Co. AgriFinancial (services more than $2 billion in loans across the country) Diversified Services Soybean Processing CTLC CGB Marine (an operating business unit under the CTLC division directly involved in over 12000 barge loads of cargo annually) Feed Ingredients (source Dried Distiller's Grains (DDGs) and other feed ingredients for export and domestic markets) and Container Shipping.

Geographic Reach

From its headquarters in the city of Covington Louisiana CGB operates its business through more than 170 locations nationwide including over 100 grain elevators and terminals. It boasts grain facilities in more than 10 states including Nebraska Oklahoma Arkansas Iowa Illinois and Missouri. CGB Marine has facilities located on the Lower Mississippi River near the Gulf of Mexico the St. Louis Harbor Cairo and various other locations on the Mississippi the Ohio and the Illinois Rivers.

Sales and Marketing

Besides its core services of inland grain transportation via barge rail and truck CGB markets and sells its products beyond the agricultural industry. Its Soybean Processing's main customers include feed mills poultry manufacturers hog farmers cattle farms dairies edible oil manufactures as well and bio-fuel producers.

Strategy

Consolidated Grain and Barge Co. (CGB) announced in August 2020 the development of a new organic-specific grain and oilseed business. CGB is currently purchasing organic crops into two facilities with additional locations expected to be announced in the future. Organic production in the northern plains is growing and the need for readily accessible markets is becoming more and more important. Its goal is to provide producers with an efficient and reliable option to market organic crops. Initially it will be dealing mainly in feed commodities but it expects to establish a robust food program as well in order to further expand the available marketing options to growers.

Earlier in June CGB announced it signed a definitive agreement to lease nine facilities located in the heart of the deep south from Big River Rice and Grain a wholly owned subsidiary of Agspring. This transaction allows Agspring to focus on its value-added businesses including Thresher Artisan Wheat Firebird Artisan Mills and Agforce Transport Services.

Mergers and Acquisitions

In 2020 Consolidated Grain and Barge Co. a wholly-owned subsidiary of CGB Enterprises announced the acquisition of four facilities located in the heart of the Mississippi Delta from The Scoular Company of Omaha Nebraska. These facilities are a natural extension of CGB's existing grain origination network further in the deep south. The acquisition includes three river terminals with six million bushels of grain storage capacity. Terms of the transaction were not announced.

EXECUTIVES

Vice President, Doug Debelak
Vice President, Gerard Brechtel
President And Ceo, Kevin D. Adams
Vp Grain Group, Gregory Beck
General Manager Diversified Services, Rodney L. Clark
General Manager Agri Financial Services, Alan Singleton
Manager Cgb Fertilizer, George Porvaznik
Vp Ctlc And Marine, Scott Leininger
General Manager Feed Ingredients, Mark Cruse
Vice President Manager Director, Cindi Ernest
Senior Vice President, Steve O'nan
Vice President Baseball, Selking Jason
Vice President Of Sales, Greg Brubaker
Auditors: KPMG LLP NEW ORLEANS LOUISIA

LOCATIONS

HQ: CGB ENTERPRISES, INC.
1127 HWY 190 E SERVICE RD, COVINGTON, LA 704334929
Phone: 985 867-3500
Web: WWW.CGB.COM

PRODUCTS/OPERATIONS

Selected Business Units
Feed Ingredients
Fertilizer
Financial Services
Grain
Marine
Premium Grains
Risk Management
Soybean Processing
Terminals & Logistics

COMPETITORS

ADM
Ag Processing Inc.
Alabama Farmers Cooperative
Canal Barge Company
Cargill
Crosby Tugs
Jimmy Sanders
Kirby Corporation
Southern States
Tennessee Farmers Co-op

HISTORICAL FINANCIALS

Company Type: Private

Income Statement — FYE: May 31

	REVENUE ($ mil.)	NET INCOME ($ mil.)	NET PROFIT MARGIN	EMPLOYEES
05/20	5,955	50	0.8%	3,250
05/19	6,498	67	1.0%	—
05/18	6,801	110	1.6%	—
Annual Growth	(6.4%)	(32.7%)	—	—

2020 Year-End Financials

Return on assets: 1.6%
Return on equity: 9.4%
Current ratio: 1.10
Cash ($ mil.): 17

CHALMETTE REFINING, L.L.C.

EXECUTIVES

Ceo, Thomas J Nimbley
Manager, Eric Beam

LOCATIONS

HQ: CHALMETTE REFINING, L.L.C.
500 W SAINT BERNARD HWY, CHALMETTE, LA 700434821
Phone: 504 281-1212
Web: WWW.CHALMETTEREFINING.COM

HISTORICAL FINANCIALS

Company Type: Private

Income Statement — FYE: December 31

	REVENUE ($ mil.)	NET INCOME ($ mil.)	NET PROFIT MARGIN	EMPLOYEES
12/07	5,647	364	6.4%	600
12/06	5,020	423	8.4%	—
12/05	3,462	264	7.6%	—
12/04	3,130	221	7.1%	—
Annual Growth	21.7%	18.1%	—	—

2007 Year-End Financials

Return on assets: —
Return on equity: 6.4%
Current ratio: 0.50
Cash ($ mil.): 302

CHARLESTON AREA MEDICAL CENTER, INC.

CAMC Health System is a catalyst for care in Charleston. The health network includes flagship facility Charleston Area Medical Center (CAMC) which is the largest hospital in West Virginia and consists of three campuses with some 840 beds total. The system also includes the CAMC Health Education and Research Institute which coordinates education programs for medical students from West Virginia University. In addition the health system operates smaller rural hospital CAMC Teays Valley and several urgent care and family practice clinics. CAMC Health System operates an online medical information system and physician services company Integrated Health Care Providers.

Operations

The three campuses of CAMC include CAMC General Hospital CAMC Memorial Hospital and CAMC Women and Children's Hospital all of which are located in Charleston. Specialty services at the hospitals include cardiology kidney transplants trauma and pediatrics. The CAMC Institute conducts graduate and continuing education courses; it also connects education and health care through clinical research projects in areas such as cancer and cardiovascular clinical science studies. The Teays Valley Hospital is a 70-bed facility located in nearby Hurricane West Virginia.

CAMC General Hospital is home to the highest level Trauma Center nationally-accredited Medical Rehabilitation and Stroke Centers The Center for Joint Replacement Neurosciences Center one of two Facial Surgery Centers Charleston's only accredited Sleep Center and West Virginia's only kidney transplant program affiliated with the Cleveland Clinic.

CAMC Memorial Hospital hosts one of highest volume heart programs in the US which performs 8000 procedures in the cardiac catheterization labs and more than 1600 open-heart bypass surgeries a year.

CAMC Women and Children's Hospital facilitates the birth of more than 3000 babies (including many high-risk births) per year.

Teays Valley Hospital is a not-for-profit 70-bed hospital. More than 100 doctors are authorized to practice at the hospital.

CAMC serves as a clinical training site for 700 additional learners per year through educational affiliations with regional colleges and universities.

Sales and Marketing

Commercial insurance providers and other third parties accounted for more than half of CAMC's net patient revenue in 2013; Medicare and Medicaid account for 30% and 13% respectively.

Financial Performance

The company's revenue grew by 4% to $969 million in 2013 due to higher net patient revenues and investment income. Net income fell 8% to $86 million though as expenses including salaries and employee benefits rose. Cash flow from operations dropped 48% to $33 million both as a result of the lower net income and an increase in cash used in short-term trading investments.

Strategy

In 2013 CAMC teamed up with The Ohio State University University of Michigan and West Virginia University to raise awareness and educate the community about cervical cancer. Community Awareness Resources and Education (CARE) is one of OSU Cancer Center's programs sponsored by the National Cancer Institute that focuses on an important health disparity among an underserved Appalachian population.

The following year CAMC teamed with Alliance Oncology a division of Alliance HealthCare Services to work on establishing a department of radiation therapy at CAMC Cancer Center.

Upgrading its infrastructure in 2013 Teays Valley Hospital completed a $3.7 million ICU expansion project.

EXECUTIVES

Vice President, Jeff Goode
Director Of Radiology, John J Anton
Director Of Pharmacy Operations, Tracy Hall
Director Of Radiology, Michael E Anton
Interim Vice President For Medical Affairs, Joan Phillips
Director Of Radiology, Jeffrey C Dameron
Vice President Chief Medical Officer, Pinckney Mcilwain
Respiratory Therapy Director, April Bostic
Board Member, Gail Pitchford
Secretary And Receptionist, Diana Gallik
Auditors: DELOITTE TAX LLP CHICAGO IL

LOCATIONS

HQ: CHARLESTON AREA MEDICAL CENTER, INC.
501 MORRIS ST, CHARLESTON, WV 253011326
Phone: 304 348-5432
Web: WWW.CAMC.ORG

PRODUCTS/OPERATIONS

2013 Net Patient Revenue

	% of total
Commercial insurance & other third-party payment programs	51
Medicare	30
Medicaid	13
Self-pay	1
PEIA	5
Total	**100**

2013 Sales

	$ mil.	% of total
Net patient revenue less provision for bad debts	876	91
Investment income	49	5
Other revenue	41	4
Net assets released from restrictions	1	-
Total	**968**	**100**

Selected Service Areas

Behavioral health
Cancer
Cardiac
Children's medicine
Craniofacial surgery
Endoscopy
Fertility
Gynecology
Hemophilia
Kidney transplant
Orthopedics
Palliative care
Perinatal
Plastic surgery
Stroke
Trauma
Urology
Vascular

COMPETITORS

Charleston Hospital
Ohio Valley Medical Center
Princeton Community Hospital
St. Mary's Medical Center
WVUHS
Weirton Medical Center
West Virginia University Hospitals

HISTORICAL FINANCIALS

Company Type: Private

Income Statement — FYE: December 31

	REVENUE ($ mil.)	NET INCOME ($ mil.)	NET PROFIT MARGIN	EMPLOYEES
12/16	1,044	(17)	—	4,000
12/15	932	36	4.0%	—
12/14	877	42	4.9%	—
12/13	861	54	6.3%	—
Annual Growth	6.6%	—	—	—

2016 Year-End Financials

Return on assets: (-1.8%)
Return on equity: (-4.7%)
Current ratio: 0.80
Cash ($ mil.): 106

CHARTER MANUFACTURING COMPANY, INC.

Charter Manufacturing's magna carta calls for it to make steel products. The family-owned company manufactures such steel products as special bar quality (SBQ) bar rod wire and stainless steel rod. The company also supplies precision cold-rolled custom profiles and engineered components including driveline engine and transmission parts for the automotive industry. It operates primarily in the US but also in Europe and Asia through subsidiaries Charter Steel (general steel products) Charter Wire (precision cold-rolled custom profiles flat wire and standard shapes) Charter Dura-Bar (cast iron bar and bronze alloys) and Charter Automotive (engineered components for automotive applications).

Operations

The company manufactures special bar quality bar rod and wire as well as precision cold-rolled custom profiles flat wire and standard shapes and engineered components for use in engines transmissions and drivelines. Charter Steel is an integrated producer of special bar quality bar rod and wire products has an annual coil-making capacity of 1.2 million tons; Charter Dura-Bar is a leading producer of continuous cast iron bar stock and a distributor (through Dura-Bar Metal Services) of Dura-Bar products and bronze alloys; Charter Wire supplies precision cold-rolled custom profiles flat wire and standard shapes; while Charter Automotive supplies of engineered components for engine driveline and transmission applications.

Geographic Reach

Charter Manufacturing serves customers around the world and has plants in the US (Illinois North Carolina Ohio Pennsylvania and Wisconsin) China (one plant) and the UK (two plants).

Sales and Marketing

Charter Manufacturing sells its products through its operating subsidiaries and sales representatives.

Strategy

The company is looking to expand both geographically and in terms of product offerings. Growing its global footprint in 2012 the company expanded its European operations with the purchase of a 57000 sq.-ft. manufacturing plant in Burntwood UK. The expansion strengthens Charter Automotive's position as a global supplier to OEM automotive and powertrain industries and helps it meet the growing demands of customers in Europe and elsewhere.

Mergers and Acquisitions

In 2012 the company acquired Wells Manufacturing Company (owner of Dura-Bar and DuraBar Metal Services). The acquired assets (which added a fourth division to Charter Manufacturing's family of companies — Charter Dura-Bar) focus on producing specialty iron bar and distributing bronze alloy products.

Company Background

Facing tough market conditions Charter Automotive closed part of its steelmaking operations in Milwaukee Wisconsin in 2010. The company ceased making steel dipsticks and tubes for cars and trucks as part of a wider response to global market trends. The company which kept its engine components operations elsewhere in Milwaukee active sold the Heather Avenue plant idled by this move.

Charter Manufacturing was established in 1936 and is owned by the family of founder Alfred Mellowes.

EXECUTIVES

Senior Business Intelligence Developer, Jason Odrzywolski
Vice President Of Human Resources Safety And Environmental Charter Steel, Bill Fiorelli
Vice President Information Technology, Sarah Urban
Auditors: DELOITTE & TOUCHE LLP MILWAU

LOCATIONS

HQ: CHARTER MANUFACTURING COMPANY, INC.
12121 CORPORATE PKWY, MEQUON, WI 530923332
Phone: 262 243-4700
Web: WWW.CHARTERMFG.COM

PRODUCTS/OPERATIONS

Selected Operating Units

Charter Automotive
Charter Dura-Bar
Charter Steel
Charter Wire

Selected Mergers and Acquisitions

COMPETITORS

AK Steel Holding Corporation
Federal-Mogul
Gerdau Ameristeel
Nucor
Republic Steel
Timken
United States Steel

HISTORICAL FINANCIALS

Company Type: Private

Income Statement — FYE: December 31

	REVENUE ($ mil.)	NET INCOME ($ mil.)	NET PROFIT MARGIN	EMPLOYEES
12/10	903	74	8.3%	2,000
12/09	517	2	0.4%	—
12/08	996	26	2.7%	—
Annual Growth	(4.8%)	66.8%	—	—

2010 Year-End Financials

Return on assets: 14.4%
Return on equity: 24.7%
Current ratio: 1.60
Cash ($ mil.): 85

CHEMIUM INTERNATIONAL CORP.

EXECUTIVES

Pres, Ofer Levy
V-Pres, Thomas Holzmann
Software Developer, Nicolas Folgado
Vice-President, Sanjeev Vora
Accounting Team Member, Jimena Ferrufino
Financial Analyst, Daniela Weir
Head of Crude, Ed More
Director of Global Business De, Jack Nicholas
Human Resources, Zoyla Hernandez
Manager, Steve Williams
Independent Representative, Cesar Calvo

LOCATIONS

HQ: CHEMIUM INTERNATIONAL CORP.
3773 RICHMOND AVE STE 600, HOUSTON, TX 770463725
Phone: 713 622-7766
Web: WWW.CHEMIUMCORP.COM

HISTORICAL FINANCIALS

Company Type: Private

Income Statement — FYE: December 31

	REVENUE ($ mil.)	NET INCOME ($ mil.)	NET PROFIT MARGIN	EMPLOYEES
12/15	2,015	3	0.2%	24
12/06	450	3	0.9%	—
12/03	103	0	—	—
Annual Growth	28.1%	—	—	—

2015 Year-End Financials

Return on assets: 2.9%
Return on equity: 0.2%
Current ratio: 0.80
Cash ($ mil.): 5

CHENEGA CORPORATION

An Alaska Native Corporation Chenega Corporation has gone from landowner to business titan. Representing the Chenega people residing in the central Alaskan Prince William Sound region it operates mostly through its subsidiaries. Chenega Integrated Systems and Chenega Technology Services offer information technology security training manufacturing research and development network engineering and military operation support services. Chenega Corporation's clients have included the Department of Defense Department of Homeland Security and EPA.

Geographic Reach

The company's headquarters are located in Anchorage Alaska. Chenega Corporation and its subsidiaries operate in 45 states and 11 countries.

Strategy

Government contracts are a source of revenue growth. Chenega Corporation began to participate in the Government Services marketplace in 1997. By 2012 it was performing on more than 158 prime contracts and 100 principal sub-contracts through a combination of competitive and negotiated best-value awards.

EXECUTIVES

Director Of Government Relations, Kristina Woolston
Senior Vice President Of Finance Chief Financial Officer, Robb A Milne
Executive Vice President Chief Operating Officer, Jeff Hueners
Vice President And Director, Lloyd Kompkoff
Executive Vice President Application Development, Charles Totemoff
Senior Vice President Corporate Compliance, Renee Hagen
Vice President, Kathy Ward
Vice President Business Services Ps, Susan Friesz
Senior Vice President, Ken Bishop
Board Member, Amy Steele Arm

LOCATIONS

HQ: CHENEGA CORPORATION
3000 C ST STE 301, ANCHORAGE, AK 995033975
Phone: 907 277-5706
Web: WWW.CHENEGA.COM

PRODUCTS/OPERATIONS

Selected Services

Base operations and maintenance
Environmental management
Information technology
Intel and military operations
Light manufacturing
Logistics support
Telecommunications
Tourism and hospitality
Training services
Security services

COMPETITORS

Akal Security
Arctic Slope Regional Corporation
Computer Sciences Corp.
HP Enterprise Services
Halliburton
IBM Global Services
Parsons Corporation
TKC Communications
chugach alaska

HISTORICAL FINANCIALS

Company Type: Private

Income Statement — FYE: September 30

	REVENUE ($ mil.)	NET INCOME ($ mil.)	NET PROFIT MARGIN	EMPLOYEES
09/19	871	19	2.3%	4,500
09/18	829	19	2.3%	—
09/17	875	12	1.4%	—
09/16	926	14	1.5%	—
Annual Growth	(2.0%)	11.6%	—	—

2019 Year-End Financials

Return on assets: 4.6%
Return on equity: 9.0%
Current ratio: 2.30
Cash ($ mil.): 28

CHEROKEE NATION BUSINESSES LLC

EXECUTIVES

MBR-Ceo, Shawn Slaton
Chb*, Bill John Baker
MBR*, Gary Cooper
MBR-Cfo*, Doug Evans
MBR-Board MBR*, Bob Berry
Snr Dir Fin*, Kimberly Barnette
Information Specialist, Aaron Lowther
Information Specialist, Cody Hardy
Information Specialist, Curtis Starling
Information Specialist, Daniel Basden
Regional Vice-President, David Mullen
Auditors: BKD LLP TULSA OK

LOCATIONS

HQ: CHEROKEE NATION BUSINESSES LLC
777 W CHEROKEE ST, CATOOSA, OK 740153235
Phone: 918 384-7474
Web: WWW.CHEROKEENATIONBUSINESSES.COM

HISTORICAL FINANCIALS

Company Type: Private

Income Statement — FYE: September 30

	REVENUE ($ mil.)	NET INCOME ($ mil.)	NET PROFIT MARGIN	EMPLOYEES
09/19	1,183	48	4.1%	3,117
09/18	1,098	65	5.9%	—
09/17	1,018	40	4.0%	—
09/16	1,021	50	4.9%	—
Annual Growth	5.0%	(1.5%)	—	—

2019 Year-End Financials

Return on assets: 4.3%
Return on equity: 5.2%
Current ratio: 2.30
Cash ($ mil.): 237

CHEROKEE NATION ENTERTAINMENT, LLC

EXECUTIVES

Ceo, David Stewart
Prin*, Shawn Slaton
Coordinator, Amber Steele
Manager Strategic Marketing, John M Whitney
Marketing Supervisor Cherokee, Kathryn Hemphill
Executive Recruiter, Lydia Horner
Purchasing Manager, Stacyee Hall
Safety Manager, Steve Falling
Buyer II, Carrie Souter
Information Technology Support, Gene Garvin
Surveillance Technology Manage, John Underwood
Auditors: BKD LLP TULSA OK

LOCATIONS

HQ: CHEROKEE NATION ENTERTAINMENT, LLC
777 W CHEROKEE ST, CATOOSA, OK 740153235
Phone: 918 384-7800
Web: WWW.CHEROKEECASINO.COM

HISTORICAL FINANCIALS

Company Type: Private

Income Statement FYE: September 30

	REVENUE ($ mil.)	NET INCOME ($ mil.)	NET PROFIT MARGIN	EMPLOYEES
09/19	686	(14)	—	3,100
09/17	666	25	3.9%	—
Annual Growth	1.5%	—	—	—

2019 Year-End Financials

Return on assets: (-1.9%)
Return on equity: (-2.1%)
Current ratio: 2.30
Cash ($ mil.): 55

CHEVRON PHILLIPS CHEMICAL COMPANY LLC

Among the world's largest petrochemical firms Chevron Phillips Chemical (CPChem) produces ethylene propylene polyethylene and polypropylene – sometimes used as building blocks for the company's other products such as pipes and food containers. CPChem also produces aromatics such as benzene and styrene specialty chemicals such as acetylene black (a form of carbon black) and mining chemicals. Chevron Phillips Chemical Company LP is CPChem's wholly-owned primary US operating subsidiary. CPChem is 50% owned by Chevron U.S.A. Inc. an indirect wholly-owned subsidiary of Chevron Corporation and 50% by wholly-owned subsidiaries of Phillips 66.

Operations

CPChem divides its operations into two segments: Olefins & Polyolefins and Specialties Aromatics and Styrenics.

The Olefins & Polyolefins segment produces ethylene polyethylene normal alpha olefins polyalphaolefins propylene and high-density polyethylene pipe and conduit and pipe fittings.

The Specialties Aromatics and Styrenics segments makes cyclohexane styrene polystyrene benzene mining chemicals Soltex drilling mud additive scentinel mercaptans specialty organosulfur compounds racing fuels and E-Series acetylene hydrogenation catalysts.

CPChem generates some 55% of sales from petrochemicals products one-third form polymers and more than 10% from specialty products.

The company's chemical products are used in more than 70000 consumer and industrial products. Its brands include Marlex Aromax Scentinel Soltex and K-Resin.

Geographic Reach

CPChem operates about 30 factories across Belgium Colombia Qatar Saudi Arabia Singapore and the US. It has two R&D and quality control centers in Bartlesville Oklahoma and Kingwood Texas. CPChem is active in Qatar Saudia Arabia and Singapore through joint venture

Sales and Marketing

CPChem serves a range of markets including Adhesives and Sealants Agricultural Appliances Automotive Building and Construction Chemical Manufacturing Drycleaning Textiles Pharmaceuticals Paint and Coatings Imaging and Photography Packaging and Electronics.

It holds the leading market position in the US for polyethelyne piping and is the world's largest marketer of cyclohexane. Subsidiary America Styrenics holds a nearly 30% market share in US polystyrene.

Financial Performance

CPChem has recorded growing sales over the past three years. In 2018 revenue climbed 25% to $11.3 billion. Profits dipped in 2017 but rebounded in 2018 growing 43% to $2.1 billion.

Strategy

External pressures on the petrochemicals industry including slowing growth the trade war between the US and China and a consumer backlash against plastic use have ushered in a period of consolidation. To diversify its output and geographic spread Chevron Phillips (CPChem) bid for Nova Chemicals in 2019 in a move that would make CPChem the third-largest producer of polyethylene in North America and the largest producer of high-density polyethylene.

Company Background

A coin toss determined whose name would go first when Chevron and Phillips Petroleum (now Phillips 66) formed 50-50 joint venture Chevron Phillips Chemical Company in 2000.

EXECUTIVES

Svp Petrochemicals, D. S. (Dave) Smith
President And Ceo, Mark E. Lashier
Vp And Cio, Peggy Colsman
Svp Cfo And Controller, Tim D. Leveille
Svp Projects And Supply Chain, R. E. (Ron) Corn
Svp Manufacturing, M. S. (Scott) Sharp
Svp Polymers, David Morgan
Vice President Of Business Development, John Lupe
Vice President, Linda Tolman
Vice President Controller, G Maxwell
National Account Manager, Steve Faggard
Vice President Manufacturing, Todd Monette
Senior Vice President Of Technology Research, Don Lycette
Auditors: ERNST & YOUNG LLP HOUSTON TX

LOCATIONS

HQ: CHEVRON PHILLIPS CHEMICAL COMPANY LLC
10001 SIX PINES DR, THE WOODLANDS, TX 773801498
Phone: 832 813-4100
Web: WWW.CPCHEM.COM

PRODUCTS/OPERATIONS

Selected Products

Olefins and polyolefins
- Ethylene
- Polyethylene
- Polyethylene pipe
- Polypropylene
- Propylene

Aromatics and styrenics
- Benzene
- Cumene
- Cyclohexane
- Paraxylene
- Styrene

Specialty products
- Acetylene black
- Alpha olefins
- Dimethyl sulfide
- Drilling specialty chemicals
- High-purity hydrocarbons and solvents
- Mining chemicals
- Neohexene
- Performance and reference fuels
- Polyalpha olefins
- Polystyrene

Selected Joint Ventures

Americas Styrenics (50%)
Chevron Phillips Singapore Chemicals (Private) Limited (50%)
KR Copolymer Co. Ltd. (60% South Korea)
Qatar Chemical Company Ltd. (Q-Chem 49%)
Saudi Chevron Phillips Company (50%)
Shanghai Golden Phillips Petrochemical Co. Ltd. (40%)

COMPETITORS

Dow Chemical	SABIC
ExxonMobil Chemical	Sasol
LyondellBasell	Total Petrochemicals
NOVA Chemicals	Westlake Chemical

HISTORICAL FINANCIALS

Company Type: Private

Income Statement FYE: December 31

	REVENUE ($ mil.)	NET INCOME ($ mil.)	NET PROFIT MARGIN	EMPLOYEES
12/16	8,769	1,687	19.2%	6,472
12/15	9,859	2,651	26.9%	—
12/14	14,148	3,288	23.2%	—
Annual Growth	(21.3%)	(28.4%)	—	—

2016 Year-End Financials

Return on assets: 10.9%
Return on equity: 14.7%
Current ratio: 1.90
Cash ($ mil.): 587

CHEVRON PHILLIPS CHEMICAL COMPANY LP

EXECUTIVES

Ceo, Peter Cella
Exec V Pres, Mark Lashier
Sr V Pres, Ron Corn
Sr V Pres, Tim Hill
V Pres, Mitch Eichelberger
Coordinator, Aprile Turner
Staff, Aaron Evitts
Coordinator, Tom Shomette
Safety Manager, Carolyn Rogers
Information Specialist, Marie Newhouse
Operations Manager, Art Orscheln
Auditors: ERNST & YOUNG LLP HOUSTON T

LOCATIONS

HQ: CHEVRON PHILLIPS CHEMICAL COMPANY LP
10001 SIX PINES DR, THE WOODLANDS, TX 773801498
Phone: 832 813-4100
Web: WWW.CPCHEM.COM

HISTORICAL FINANCIALS

Company Type: Private

Income Statement				FYE: December 31
	REVENUE ($ mil.)	NET INCOME ($ mil.)	NET PROFIT MARGIN	EMPLOYEES
12/16	7,106	1,301	18.3%	6,472
12/15	7,990	2,020	25.3%	—
12/14	11,758	2,444	20.8%	—
Annual Growth	(22.3%)	(27.0%)	—	—

2016 Year-End Financials

Return on assets: 11.1%
Return on equity: 13.5%
Current ratio: 1.30
Cash ($ mil.): 422

CHG FOUNDATION

EXECUTIVES

Director, Sheila Martz
High Risk Case Manager Supervi, Mark David
Auditors: MOSS ADAMS LLP SAN FRANCISCO

LOCATIONS

HQ: CHG FOUNDATION
740 BAY BLVD, CHULA VISTA, CA 919105254
Phone: 619 422-0422
Web: WWW.CHGSD.COM

HISTORICAL FINANCIALS

Company Type: Private

Income Statement				FYE: December 31
	REVENUE ($ mil.)	NET INCOME ($ mil.)	NET PROFIT MARGIN	EMPLOYEES
12/16	1,098	206	18.8%	1
12/14	622	34	5.5%	—
12/13	323	(11)	—	—
12/09	133	1	1.0%	—
Annual Growth	35.1%	106.8%	—	—

2016 Year-End Financials

Return on assets: 28.0%
Return on equity: 53.6%
Current ratio: —
Cash ($ mil.): 659

CHICAGO TRANSIT AUTHORITY (INC)

The Chicago Transit Authority (CTA) is focused on making its ETA. The CTA operates one of the largest public transportation system in the US. On a typical weekday CTA passengers take about 1.6 million rides on the agency's buses and trains which travel in and around Chicago and about 35 suburbs. The CTA operates a fleet of some 1865 buses on almost 130 routes. Its rail system includes eight rail lines with over 1490 rail cars operating on 224 miles of track at more than 145 stations. The agency created by the Illinois legislature in 1947 is part of the state's Regional Transportation Authority which also oversees Metra (commuter rail system) and Pace (suburban bus system).

Operations

CTA's services are provided by two modes: bus and rail.

Most rides on CTA are taken by bus. It makes over 25000 trips daily and serves nearly 12000 bus stops throughout the region. CTA bus routes serve communities locally move people across town and a number of express services are provided. Several routes also provide 24-hour service known as "Owl Service."

The company's rail system known as "The 'L'" consists of train lines spanning the city and neighboring communities. The service provided is described as "heavy rail rapid transit" also referred to as a "subway" or "metro". During late night and early morning hours major rail lines and some of CTA's bus routes offer "Night Owl" service much of it with connecting schedules and routing.

In addition the company offers advertising in which other companies can advertise service product or business. Advertising on CTA trains buses and rail stations is a great way to have other company's message seen by millions of people every day.

Overall the company generates almost 55% of total revenue from its Farebox followed by Pass with more than 35%. Advertising & Concessions and others account the rest.

Geographic Reach

The company is based in Illinois. The routes are mainly in Chicago and connected to Midway Airport and O'Hare Airport.

Sales and Marketing

CTA has a Small Business Program. The program is designed to give certified small businesses an opportunity to bid as primes on CTA contracts under $3 million with sufficient Small Business availability. Under the program selected contracts will be set aside for small businesses to bid on as prime contractors.

Furthermore MillerCoors is the official sponsor of CTA's Free Rides on New Year's Eve program which provides free rides on New Year's Eve to encourage safe and responsible celebration of the holiday.

Financial Performance

The agency generates the majority of its revenue from bus and rail passenger fares. The CTA also recognizes revenue from rental fees received from concessionaires the fees collected from advertisements on CTA property and miscellaneous operating revenues.

The company's net revenue increased in the last three years (2017-2019). In fiscal 2019 revenues were $654 million a minimal decrease from $656.1 million the year prior. Farebox revenue declined that year as well as its advertising and concessions revenue.

CTA's net loss increased 15% to $886.2 million in 2019 from $771 million the year prior due to the decrease in revenue and a rise in operating expenses and provision for depreciation.

Cash at the end of the year was $161.7 million. Operating activities used $762.3 million while financing activities used another $228.3 million. Investing activities provided $117.7 million from investment account withdrawals. CTA's main cash uses in 2019 were acquisition and construction of capital assets interest payments on bonds and repayment of bonds payable.

Strategy

CTA delivers quality affordable transit services that link people jobs and communities.

The CTA Metra and Pace released a new completely redesigned version of the Ventra mobile app the widely used app to buy fares and manage travel on the region's transit systems. The new app features a brand-new look and a host of customer-friendly features and improvement?all designed to make it easier and more convenient for customers to ride trains and buses throughout the region.

As part of ongoing efforts to provide a safer healthier travel environment the CTA upgraded and expanded it is recently launched Ridership Information Dashboard to include dynamic rail crowding data. The upgrade and expansion is the latest step in its ongoing efforts to keep its customers better informed and to continuously evolve its operations during this unprecedented time.

Company Background

The RTA was established in 1974 to oversee local transportation operators in the six-county Chicago metropolitan area. Illinois state law requires the three RTA service boards? CTA Metra (the suburban rail system) and Pace (the suburban bus system) ? to recover collectively at least 50 percent of operating costs from farebox and other system revenues.

EXECUTIVES

Cfo And Treasurer, Karen Walker, $180,000 total compensation
Inspector General, Paul Sidrys, $160,000 total compensation
Coo, Peter Ousley
President, Forrest Claypool
Chairman, Terry Peterson
Auditors: CROWE LLP CHICAGO ILLINOIS

LOCATIONS

HQ: CHICAGO TRANSIT AUTHORITY (INC)
567 W LAKE ST STE CTA, CHICAGO, IL 606611465
Phone: 312 664-7200
Web: WWW.TRANSITCHICAGO.COM

PRODUCTS/OPERATIONS

2014 Sales

	$ mil.	% of total
Farebox	364	57
Pass	219	35
Advertising & Concessions	27	4
Other Revenue	22	4
Total	633	100

HISTORICAL FINANCIALS

Company Type: Private

Income Statement				FYE: December 31
	REVENUE ($ mil.)	NET INCOME ($ mil.)	NET PROFIT MARGIN	EMPLOYEES
12/19	654	(115)	—	12,000
12/16	625	(79)	—	—
12/10	548	(323)	—	—
12/05	448	(153)	—	—
Annual Growth	2.7%	—	—	—

2019 Year-End Financials

Return on assets: (-1.8%)
Return on equity: —
Current ratio: 0.70
Cash ($ mil.): 111

CHILDREN'S HOSPITAL

EXECUTIVES

Pres, Kurt Newman
Chief Officer, Denice Cora-Bramble
Senior Vice President, Robin Steinhorn
Executive Vice President, Alec H King
Psychologist, Jesse Olague
Graduate Research Assistant, Sandra Kirsch
Chief Real Estate, Charles Weinstein
Pediatrician, Lily Chattopadhyay
Psychologist, Melissa Balderrama
Neonatologist, Rachel Chapman
Center For Autism Spectrum Dis, Anne Inge
Auditors: GRANT THORNTON LLP MC LEAN V

LOCATIONS

HQ: CHILDREN'S HOSPITAL
111 MICHIGAN AVE NW, WASHINGTON, DC 200102916
Phone: 202 232-0521
Web: WWW.CHILDRENSNATIONAL.ORG

HISTORICAL FINANCIALS

Company Type: Private

Income Statement FYE: June 30

	REVENUE ($ mil.)	NET INCOME ($ mil.)	NET PROFIT MARGIN	EMPLOYEES
06/15	1,076	118	11.0%	6,000
06/14	983	43	4.4%	—
Annual Growth	9.4%	174.2%	—	—

2015 Year-End Financials

Return on assets: 11.2%
Return on equity: 20.9%
Current ratio: 0.60
Cash ($ mil.): 114

CHILDREN'S HOSPITAL COLORADO

Rocky Mountain rugrats can count on Children's Hospital Colorado. The not-for-profit organization runs a network of health facilities in Colorado anchored by its nearly 50-acre main campus in Aurora. The campus includes a 260-bed inpatient hospital and numerous outpatient clinics. Children's Hospital Colorado also operates more than a dozen satellite locations in and around Denver that specialize in providing children with emergency and specialty care. Affiliated with the University of Colorado Denver School of Medicine the hospital provides medical training and performs a wide range of research into pediatric illnesses including cancer and HIV/AIDS.

Operations

The main hospital is located on the Anschutz Medical Campus with the medical school and the University of Colorado Hospital Authority's 620-bed acute care center. With help from its medical staff of 2330 Children's Hospital Colorado had 18500 inpatient admissions; 21000 surgeries 527000 outpatient visits and about 158000 emergency department visits in 2014.

The hospital boasts two additional emergency locations at Exempla Saint Joseph Hospital in Denver and Centura's Parker Adventist Hospital in Parker. Children's Hospital Colorado provides urgent care through three nearby community locations: Centura Littleton Adventist Hospital Children's Hospital North Campus at Broomfield and Exempla Lutheran Medical Center in Wheat Ridge. In addition it has about 10 specialty care clinics in the Denver area that provide cancer pulmonary and surgery services.

The health care facility's research initiatives are conducted at the Children's Hospital Colorado Research Institute. Along with its affiliation with the university the Children's Hospital works with the Pediatric Clinical Translational Research Center to conduct research and clinical trials in a number of fields including cardiology gastroenterology oncology orthopedics pulmonology and psychiatry.

Geographic Reach

Children's Hospital Colorado established in 1908 serves a seven-state region through its Level 1 trauma center. Its other facilities cater to residents of the Denver metropolitan area.

Sales and Marketing

Medicaid accounted for 47% of the hospital's net patient revenue in 2014; managed care accounted for 45%.

Financial Performance

Gross patient services revenue totaled $2.2 billion in 2014; other operating revenue totaled $60.7 million.

Strategy

Children's Hospital Colorado boasts the capacity to handle the most challenging emergencies as the only dedicated Level 1 trauma center in a seven-state region. Through its affiliation with the University of Colorado the hospital conducts physician assistant residency fellowship and internship programs in a variety of fields including anesthesiology orthopedics dentistry and neurology. It also provides continuing education programs for doctors and nurses.

The health care facility is expanding its footprint in the Colorado Springs area as the region experiences noteworthy growth. To this end it is building a new $110 million hospital on the University of Colorado Health Memorial North campus that will house 100 inpatient beds an emergency room neonatal and pediatric intensive care units and operating rooms. The complex is expected to open in 2018.

EXECUTIVES

President And Ceo Children's Hospital Colorado Foundation, Steve Winesett
President Ceo And Director, James E. Shmerling, age 66
Svp Patient Care Services And Chief Nursing Officer, Kelly M. Johnson
Surgeon-in-chief, Timothy M. Crombleholme
Pediatrician-in-chief, Stephen Daniels
Chief Medical Officer, Joan Bothner
President And Ceo, Jena Hausmann
Svp And Cio, Mary Anne Leach
Svp And Cfo, Jeff Harrington
Chief Research Officer, Frederick J. Suchy
Medical Director Pediatric Sports Medicine, Aaron Provance
Nursing Director, Norine Hemphill
Ambulatory Operations Manager For Occupational And Physical Therapy, Felicia Latsko
Medical Director, Lalit Bajaj
Finance Vice President, Jeffrey Harrington
Medical Director, George Wang
Vice President Of Support Services, Dan Coxall
Senior Vice President, Cary Larger
Medical Director Of Clinical Chemistry And Point Of Care Testing Transfusion Medicine Physician, Melkon DomBourian
Physical Therapy, Terri Carry
Chairman, Kevin Reidy
Secretary, Nancy Krebs

LOCATIONS

HQ: CHILDREN'S HOSPITAL COLORADO
13123 E 16TH AVE, AURORA, CO 800457106
Phone: 720 777-1234
Web: WWW.CHILDRENSCOLORADO.ORG

Selected Locations

Children's Hospital Colorado Main Campus
Children's Hospital Colorado at Saint Joseph Hospital
Children's Hospital Colorado KidStreet
Children's Hospital Colorado Orthopedic Care Centennial
Children's Hospital Colorado Outpatient Specialty Care Centennial
Children's Hospital Colorado Outpatient Specialty Care Colorado Springs
Children's Hospital Colorado Outpatient Specialty Care Parker
Children's Hospital Colorado Therapy Care Parker
Children's Hospital Colorado Therapy Care Pueblo
Children's Hospital Colorado Urgent and Outpatient Specialty Care Wheat Ridge

PRODUCTS/OPERATIONS

Selected Departments

Adolescent Medicine Program
Adult Congenital Heart Disease Program
Aerodigestive Program
Allergy Program
Arrhythmia Center
Asthma Program
Audiology Speech and Learning Program
Bill Daniels Center for Children's Hearing
Bone Marrow Transplant Program
Breathing Institute
Burn program
Cardiac Anesthesia
Cardiac Catheterization
Cardiology Clinic
Cardiology Outreach Programs
Cardiomyopathy Program
Center for Cancer and Blood Disorders
Center for Celiac Disease
Child Abuse Services
Child Development Unit
Child Health Clinic
Colorado Fetal Care Center
Colorado Institute for Maternal and Fetal Health
Colorectal and Complex Pelvic Floor Disorders Program
Complex Congenital Heart Disease and Development Clinic
Craniofacial Center
Critical Care
Cystic Fibrosis Research and Care Center
Dental
Dermatology
Digestive Health Institute
Ear Nose and Throat
Eating Disorder Program
Emergency Department
Endocrinology
Endoscopy Clinic (ATECh)
Experimental Therapeutics Program
Extracorporeal Membrane Oxygenation (ECMO) Program
Eye
Fetal Cardiology Program
Fiberoptic Endoscopic Evaluation of Swallowing (FEES) Clinic
Flight for Life
Gastroenterology
Gastrointestinal Eosinophilic Diseases
Genetics Program
Gynecology
Healthy Expectations Perinatal Mental Health Program
Heart Institute
Heart Surgery
Heart Transplant Program
HOPE Clinic for Cancer Survivors
Hospitalist Services

COMPETITORS

Banner Health
Catholic Health Initiatives
Centura Health
Denver Health and Hospital Authority
Exempla Healthcare
HealthONE
North Colorado Medical Center
Presbyterian/St. Luke's Medical Center
Rose Medical Center
Shriners Hospitals For Children
The Memorial Hospital

HISTORICAL FINANCIALS

Company Type: Private

Income Statement — FYE: December 31

	REVENUE ($ mil.)	NET INCOME ($ mil.)	NET PROFIT MARGIN	EMPLOYEES
12/18	1,102	138	12.6%	2,200
12/17	960	76	8.0%	—
12/16	911	50	5.5%	—
12/15	908	25	2.8%	—
Annual Growth	6.7%	75.3%	—	—

2018 Year-End Financials

Return on assets: 8.4%
Return on equity: 18.3%
Current ratio: 2.10
Cash ($ mil.): 135

CHILDREN'S HOSPITAL MEDICAL CENTER

Cincinnati Children's Hospital Medical Center has a special place in its heart for kids. The pediatric health care facility offers specialty treatments for children and adolescents suffering from just about any malady including ailments of the heart and liver as well as blood diseases and cancer. Cincinnati Children's Hospital has some 600 beds and operates about a dozen outpatient care centers. Founded in 1883 the not-for-profit hospital runs the only level I pediatric trauma center in the region and serves as a teaching and research facility for the University of Cincinnati College of Medicine. It is also ranked in the top 10 for all 10 pediatric specialties by U.S. News & World Report .

Operations

With a staff of some 1500 physicians Cincinnati Children's Hospital serves more than 1 million patients each year including about 100000 emergency room visits and 32000 surgical procedures. Its outpatient centers include community urgent and emergency care facilities and general and specialty physician practices as well as laboratory radiology dentistry and physical therapy clinics.

The Cincinnati Children's Research Foundation conducts research and clinical trials of pediatric medical innovations including new vaccines and surgical techniques. It has research partnerships with hospitals in Africa Asia Latin America and the Middle East. The hospital and research foundation's contributions to pediatric medicine include the rotavirus vaccine and Albert Sabin's discovery of the oral polio vaccine (first tested in 1960).

The hospital's educational programs are also renowned.

Geographic Reach

Reaching beyond Cincinnati Cincinnati Children's Hospital also provides services to communities in southeastern Indiana and northern Kentucky through its network of outpatient clinics. The hospital serves patients from all 50 US states as well as from about 60 international countries. It has international research collaborations with institutions in Bangladesh Brazil China Honduras Israel Malawi Mexico Nepal and the United Arab Emirates.

Financial Performance

In 2014 revenue grew 10% to $2.1 billion as the center saw rises in revenue from net patient services capitation professional services and other operations. Net income rose 13% to $172 million due to the higher revenue.

Strategy

Cincinnati Children's Hospital regularly expands its facilities to improve medical services and enhance research and education programs. In 2015 it opened a new 15-story clinical research building at its main campus in Avondale. In 2014 it opened a new urgent care center at its Liberty Campus.

In addition the institution forms collaborations to expand its operations. In 2015 it signed a three-year partnership with Shire to research rare diseases. The partners will work to discover and develop novel therapies to treat these diseases.

The hospital has remained on the forefront of the digital revolution that has swept the health care industry. In recent years the organization has linked its emergency inpatient radiology pharmacy and specialty department patient data together to create an electronic medical record (EHR). The EHR system helps to reduce patient errors (such as medication errors) and improves communication between departments.

To prepare for health reform measures Cincinnati Children's Hospital is also reducing costs through workflow purchasing and care delivery improvement programs.

EXECUTIVES

Vice President Family Relations, David Anderson
President And Ceo, Michael Fisher, age 61
Evp And Coo, Scott J. Hamlin
Svp Information Services And Cio, Marianne F. James
Cfo, Mark D. Mumford, age 58
Chief Medical Officer, Margaret Hostetter
Vice President For Medical Affairs, Melodie Blacklidge
Medical Director, Jennifer Ehrhardt
Vice President Facilities Management, Thomas Kinman
Medical Director, Jennifer McAllister
Medical Director, Douglas Rose
Medical Director, Vivek Narendran
Assistant Vice President, Carolyn Karageorges
Clinical Director, Victoria Decastro
Svp Strategy And Growth, Jennifer Dauer
Clinical Director, Natalie Elsbrock
Assistant Vice President, Melissa Saladonis
Assistant Vice President, Stephanie Ebken
Assistant Vice President Patient Service, Deborah Browning
Clinical Director, Anna Sheets
Clinical Director, Julie Clark
Pharmacy Manager, John Hingl
Clinical Director, Wendy Ungard
Clinical Director, Julie Zix
Medical Director Cv Surgeon, Angela Lorts
Assistant Vice President Information Services, Terri Price
Clinical Director, Thomas Cahill
Vice President Business Development, Jim Barter
Clinical Director, Dolores Puthoff
Associate Vice President Supply Chain, Cmrp Nirody
Assistant Vice President, Maria Britto
Clinical Director, Michael Sorter
Medical Director, Alessandro De alarcon
Clinical Director, Lois Curtwright
Clinical Director, Linda Richey
Clinical Director, Kahne Springborn
Medical Director, Carina Braeutigam
Clinical Director, Kandice Ferdon
Clinical Director, Laurie Gregor
Clinical Director, Barbara Valerius
Assistant Vice President Business Intelligence, Mike Naber
Senior Vice President Human Resources, Chris Browning
Clinical Director, Angie White-cole
Clinical Director, Travee Sanderson
Clinical Director, Megan Isley
Senior Business Intelligence Developer, Brad Blackmore
Vice President Information Technology, Tyler Jones
Vp Budget And Finance, Sidney Norton
Medical Director Of Transfusion Services, Stephanie Kinney
Clinical Director, Andrea Shaffer Ellis
Vice President, David Krier
Vice President Research Operations And Management, Kristine Justus
Chair, Thomas G. Cody, age 78
Assistant Treasurer, Alex Miller

LOCATIONS

HQ: CHILDREN'S HOSPITAL MEDICAL CENTER
3333 BURNET AVE, CINCINNATI, OH 452293039
Phone: 513 636-4200
Web: WWW.CINCINNATICHILDRENS.ORG

PRODUCTS/OPERATIONS

Selected Locations

Anderson

Batesville

Burnet Campus
Children's
College Hill Campus
Drake
Eastgate
Fairfield
Harrison
Hopple Street Center
Kenwood
Liberty Campus
Lindner Center of Hope (Mason)
Mason Campus
Northern Kentucky
Oak Campus

Selected Treatment Areas

Abdomen and Digestive Tract
Allergy Asthma Immunology
Anesthesia
Arthritis and Rheumatology
Babies / Infants
Bones Joints and Muscles
Brain Spinal Cord and Nerves
Cancer
Cerebral Palsy
Chest and Lungs
Craniofacial Anomalies
Dental and Oral Health
Developmental Disabilities
Ear Nose Throat
Endocrine Metabolism and Diabetes
Eyes
Genetics
Growth and Development
Heart
Hemangiomas and Vascular Malformations
Hematology and Blood
Infectious Diseases
Injuries and Poisonings
Kidney Bladder and Genitals
Liver
Medications
Mental Health
Nutrition and Diet
Pain Management
Rehabilitation

Safety and Injury Prevention
Skin
Speech
Sports Medicine
Surgery
Teen Health
X-Ray / Radiology

COMPETITORS

Bethesda North
Children's Hospital of Philadelphia
Deaconess Associations
Kettering Health Network
Nationwide Children's Hospital
Nemours Foundation
Premier Health Partners
Shriners Hospitals For Children
St. Elizabeth Healthcare
St. Jude Children's Research Hospital
The Christ Hospital Corporation
TriHealth
UC Health

HISTORICAL FINANCIALS

Company Type: Private

Income Statement — FYE: June 30

	REVENUE ($ mil.)	NET INCOME ($ mil.)	NET PROFIT MARGIN	EMPLOYEES
06/16	1,597	213	13.4%	18,000
06/15	1,527	209	13.7%	—
06/14	2,116	140	6.6%	—
06/11	1,693	53	3.2%	—
Annual Growth	(1.2%)	32.0%	—	—

2016 Year-End Financials

Return on assets: 8.3%
Return on equity: 20.6%
Current ratio: 1.70
Cash ($ mil.): 148

CHILDREN'S HOSPITAL OF WISCONSIN, INC

EXECUTIVES

Pres-Coo, Cindy Christensen
Treas*, Timothy L Birkenstock
V Pres-CIO*, Michael Jones
Corp V Pres of Hr*, Marge Nienen
Coordinator, Laurie Smrz
Cardiac Physician, Michele Frommelt
Acting Director, Rhonda Nowakowski
Hematologist, Mary K Hintermeyer
Talent Acquisition Manager, Julie Okoro
Director of Supply Chain, Lisa Fohey
Director, Karen Gralton

LOCATIONS

HQ: CHILDREN'S HOSPITAL OF WISCONSIN, INC
999 N 92ND ST STOP 1, MILWAUKEE, WI 532264876
Phone: 414 266-2000
Web: WWW.CHILDRENSWI.ORG

HISTORICAL FINANCIALS

Company Type: Private

Income Statement — FYE: December 31

	REVENUE ($ mil.)	NET INCOME ($ mil.)	NET PROFIT MARGIN	EMPLOYEES
12/13	600	57	9.6%	2,045
12/12	34	(0)	—	—
12/09	588	74	12.7%	—
Annual Growth	0.5%	(6.2%)	—	—

2013 Year-End Financials

Return on assets: 4.1%
Return on equity: 5.8%
Current ratio: 3.20
Cash ($ mil.): 86

CHILDREN'S MEDICAL CENTER OF DALLAS

Children's Medical Center of Dallas (operating as Children's Health) treats children with various medical needs from birth to age 18. Specialties include craniofacial deformities cystic fibrosis gastroenterology cancer and heart disease. Children's is also a major pediatric center for heart kidney bone marrow and other transplant procedures. The not-for-profit hospital has about 600 beds and is the pediatric teaching facility for UT Southwestern Medical. Children's also operates a network of about 20 primary care and specialty clinics in and around Dallas in addition to its two full-service campuses.

Operations

The Children's system serves patients through two full-service hospitals a specialty care center in Southlake and a network of primary care offices called MyChildren's located throughout the Metroplex. As the primary pediatric teaching facility for UT Southwestern Children's supports a three-year residency program for physicians and academic fellowships in numerous subspecialties.

Children's Health's Dallas campus operates the city's only pediatric emergency room and the region's only pediatric-centered teaching hospital. It was also the first Level I trauma center for pediatrics in the state. Together the Dallas and Plano hospital campuses serve some 800000 patients annually and provide more than 50 sub-specialty programs. Additionally the organization provides primary health care services to the county's children living in under-served areas; some of these care services are provided through academic programs for doctors in training.

The system's research and development areas includes cancer cardiothoracic neonatology kidney disease infectious disease pharmacology sickle cell disease and psychiatry. It also provides Level IV Neonatal Intensive Care Unit.

In 2014 Children's logged some 173000 patient visits in its emergency departments in Dallas and Plano.

Geographic Reach

Children's main hospital campuses are in Dallas and Plano Texas. It has a handful of specialty centers and 16 primary care locations in the Dallas suburbs and area communities including Southlake.

Financial Performance

Children's receives revenues from a mix of third-party payers including HMOs and PPOs as well as Medicaid and Medicare and the state Children's Health Insurance Program (CHIP). It also relies heavily on private donations and fundraising efforts but provides a hefty amount of charity care each year for the region's uninsured children.

Strategy

Children's introduced its Children's Health brand in 2014. The new identity serves to reflect its operations as an integrated health system beyond the two primary campus locations.

At any given time it seems that Children's is building or opening one facility or another. In 2015 it opened the nation's second Pitt Hopkins Syndrome clinic treating a rare genetic condition that can cause development delays intellectual disabilities breathing issues and seizures.

Mergers and Acquisitions

In 2015 the system bought Our Children's House which provides rehabilitative and transitional care to children with special needs from Baylor Scott & White. Children's took over operations of Our Children's House's inpatient and outpatient facilities as well as eight outpatient clinics.

Company Background

In the four-year period between 2001 and 2005 the center spent more than $250 million on new construction and expansion projects. It opened a 72-bed Children's Legacy Hospital in nearby Plano in 2008 and in 2009 Children's completed construction of a new $150 million tower on its main Dallas campus to house its heart center cancer center and neonatal intensive care unit.

The company was founded in 1913.

EXECUTIVES

Evp And Chief Administrative Officer Corporate Services, Michele Chulick
Chief Clinical Officer And Evp, W. Robert (Bob) Morrow
Evp Population Health And Business Development, Peter W. Roberts
President Children's Medical Center Dallas Foundation And Evp Children's Health System Texas, Kern Wildenthal
President And Ceo, Christopher J. Share
President And Coo, Douglas G. Share

LOCATIONS

HQ: CHILDREN'S MEDICAL CENTER OF DALLAS
1935 MEDICAL DISTRICT DR, DALLAS, TX 752357701
Phone: 214 456-7000
Web: WWW.CHILDRENS.COM

Children's Medical Center Selected Locations

Chase Bank Building Specialty Center (Dallas)
Children's Medical Center and Ambulatory Care Pavilion at Legacy (Plano)
Children's Medical Center of Dallas Main Campus
Dallas Ambulatory Care Pavilion
Irving Specialty Center
Mesquite Specialty Center
MyChildren's Primary Care (about 16 locations)
Pediatric Urology Clinic at Rockwall
Southlake Specialty Care Center
Walnut Hill Urology Clinic

PRODUCTS/OPERATIONS

Children's Medical Center Selected Services

Allergy/Immunology/Asthma

Audiology
Cystic fibrosis
Day surgery
Dentistry
Dermatology
Diabetes
Ear/Nose/Throat
Endocrinology
Gastroenterology
General surgery
Genetics/Metabolism
International adoption medicine
Laboratory services
Neurology
Nutrition
Obesity program
Occupational therapy
Ophthalmology
Orthodontics
Orthopaedics
Physical therapy
Plastic Surgery
Pulmonary function lab
Pulmonology
Radiology
Rheumatology

Sickle cell treatment
Sleep disorders
Speech therapy
Trauma
Urology

COMPETITORS

Baylor University Medical Center
Cook Children's Health Care System
Dell Children's Medical Center
HCA
Parkland Health & Hospital System
Tenet Healthcare
Texas Children's Hospital

HISTORICAL FINANCIALS

Company Type: Private

Income Statement — FYE: December 31

	REVENUE ($ mil.)	NET INCOME ($ mil.)	NET PROFIT MARGIN	EMPLOYEES
12/15	712	(185)	—	5,318
12/14	1,120	135	12.1%	—
12/13	1,111	166	15.0%	—
12/08	744	(4)	—	—
Annual Growth	(0.6%)	—	—	—

2015 Year-End Financials

Return on assets: (-7.7%)
Return on equity: (-6.6%)
Current ratio: 4.70
Cash ($ mil.): 9

CHILDRENS HOSPITAL

EXECUTIVES

Prin, Kurt Newman
Doctor, Ashley D Hill
Dentist, Edwin Zechman DDS
Manager, David Thibodeau
Director of Mis/Is, Gary Manion
Quality Assurance Manager, Lorna Riach
Auditors: GRANT THORNTON LLP MC LEAN V

LOCATIONS

HQ: CHILDRENS HOSPITAL
1917 C ST NE, WASHINGTON, DC 200026753
Phone: 202 476-5000
Web: WWW.CHILDRENSNATIONAL.ORG

HISTORICAL FINANCIALS

Company Type: Private

Income Statement — FYE: June 30

	REVENUE ($ mil.)	NET INCOME ($ mil.)	NET PROFIT MARGIN	EMPLOYEES
06/13	970	24	2.5%	41
06/10	806	66	8.2%	—
Annual Growth	6.4%	(28.3%)	—	—

2013 Year-End Financials

Return on assets: 2.5%
Return on equity: 6.0%
Current ratio: 0.50
Cash ($ mil.): 59

CHILDRENS HOSPITAL MEDICAL CENTER OF AKRON

Akron Children's Hospital is the largest pediatric health care system in northeast Ohio. The health system operates through more than 80 locations scattered around the state including its flagship 253-bed hospital in Akron. Among Children's specialized services are cardiology orthopedics rehabilitation and home care. It also has a second 50-bed inpatient hospital called the Akron Children's Beeghly Campus. The main hospital's emergency department treats nearly 70000 patients each year. Its regional burn center sees about 3700 visits per year. Akron Children's Hospital started as a nursery more than 100 years ago.

Operations

Each year Akron Children's Hospital sees some 800000 outpatients performs more than 15000 surgeries and admits more than 10000 inpatients.

Geographic Reach

Akron Children's Hospital is a major teaching facility affiliated with Northeastern Ohio Medical University and offering nearly a dozen subspecialty fellowship training programs. Children's also runs one of the state's largest pediatric primary care networks with 15 offices in seven counties including Cuyahoga Medina Wayne Tuscawaras and Portage.

Sales and Marketing

In 2014 Medicaid payments accounted for 52% of gross patient service revenue while commercial payments accounted for 44%.

Financial Performance

The hospital's net revenue was about $701000 in fiscal 2014 with about 90% of that coming from patient services revenues.

Strategy

The system has expanded its campuses and opened new facilities to broaden its care offerings. In 2014 it opened its first location in Columbiana County opened a pediatric specialty care office in Mansfield and expanded its sports rehabilitation hours and services at LifeCenter Plus in Hudson.

EXECUTIVES

President And Ceo, William H. (Bill) Considine
Vp Medical Services; Clinical Leader Ohio Children's Hospitals Solutions For Patient Safety, Michael Bird
Vp Managed Care, Karen Richter
Vp Operations And Coo, Grace Wakulchik
Evp, Shawn Lyden
Vp Akron Children's Hospital Foundation, John Zoilo
Noah Miller Chair Department Of Pediatrics, Norman C. Christopher
Vp Akron Children's Mahoning Valley, Sharon Hrina
Cfo, Michael Trainer
Vp Patient Services And Chief Nursing Officer, Lisa Aurilio
Cio, Tom Ogg
Vp Department Of Pediatrics, Cindy Dormo
Chief Medical Information Officer, Amy Maneker
Vp Surgical Subspecialty Practices, Craig McGhee
Chief Medical Officer, Robert McGregor
Director Of Pharmacy, John Lepto
Nursing Director, Beth Carr
Vice President Marketing, Carolyn Davis
Medical Director, Ilka Warshawsky
Physical Therapy Director, Mary Marino
Medical Director Of The Locust Pediatric Care Group, Cooper White
Director Of Pharmacy, Todd Grisez
Nursing Director, Diane Sprankle
Vice President Of Public Policy And Government Affairs, Rhonda Perkins
Pharmacy Manager, Maryann Allen
Medical Director, Julia Papouras
Department Secretary, Lori Podojil
Secretary, Alice Smiley
Secretary, Stephanie Knox
Secretary For Clincal Administration, Sue Good
Department Secretary, Carolyn Carr
Auditors: ERNST & YOUNG LLP CLEVELAND

LOCATIONS

HQ: CHILDRENS HOSPITAL MEDICAL CENTER OF AKRON
1 PERKINS SQ, AKRON, OH 443081063
Phone: 330 543-1000
Web: WWW.AKRONCHILDRENS.ORG

COMPETITORS

Akron General Medical Center
Aultman Health Foundation
Lake Health
Mercy Medical Center (NY)
MetroHealth System
Nationwide Children's Hospital
OhioHealth
Parma Community General Hospital
Robinson Memorial Hospital
Summa Health System
The Cleveland Clinic
University Hospitals Health System

HISTORICAL FINANCIALS

Company Type: Private

Income Statement — FYE: December 31

	REVENUE ($ mil.)	NET INCOME ($ mil.)	NET PROFIT MARGIN	EMPLOYEES
12/14	701	93	13.3%	4,763
12/13	623	80	13.0%	—
12/12	579	46	8.1%	—
Annual Growth	10.0%	41.2%	—	—

2014 Year-End Financials

Return on assets: 7.9%
Return on equity: 15.2%
Current ratio: 1.60
Cash ($ mil.): 42

CHINESE HOSPITAL ASSOCIATION

EXECUTIVES

Ceo, Brenda Yee
Cfo*, Thomas Bolger
Coo*, Linda Schumacher
Chief of Medicine, Joseph Woo
Director of Finance, Amy Wong
Lab Technician, Lisa Glaser
Training Manager, Josephine Lee
Executive Director, Angela Sun
Internal Medicine, Roderick Snow
Director, Scott Huang
Vice President, Chee Tong
Auditors: MOSS & ADAMS LLP SAN FRANCISC

LOCATIONS

HQ: CHINESE HOSPITAL ASSOCIATION
845 JACKSON ST, SAN FRANCISCO, CA 941334899
Phone: 415 982-2400
Web: WWW.CHINESEHOSPITAL-SF.ORG

HISTORICAL FINANCIALS

Company Type: Private

Income Statement FYE: December 31

	REVENUE ($ mil.)	NET INCOME ($ mil.)	NET PROFIT MARGIN	EMPLOYEES
12/19	226,958	(10,648)	—	285
12/18	216	(28)	—	—
12/17	123	(11)	—	—
12/16	202	(13)	—	—
Annual Growth	938.3%	—	—	—

2019 Year-End Financials

Return on assets: (-2.9%)
Return on equity: (-6.2%)
Current ratio: 1.10
Cash ($ mil.): 21,386

CHRISTUS HEALTH

In CHRISTUS there is no east or west but plenty of care nonetheless. The not-for-profit Catholic health care system operates about 350 medical facilities from its more than 60 hospitals including general hospitals and long-term acute care facilities to clinics and outpatient centers. It operates mostly in Louisiana and Texas where its hospitals are but also has facilities in Arkansas Georgia Iowa Missouri and New Mexico and in six states in Mexico and one in Chile. In addition to its acute care facilities CHRISTUS runs medical groups home health and hospice agencies and senior living facilities. Specialized services include oncology pediatrics rehabilitation and women's and children's health care.

Operations

In addition to its more than 30 hospitals CHRISTUS also operates about 20 long-term care facilities 175 clinics and outpatient centers and dozens of other "health ministries" including mobile clinics fitness centers and daycare centers for adults and children.

Geographic Reach

CHRISTUS has a dozen hospitals in Texas and Louisiana one in Puebla Mexico and one in Santiago Chile. Its clinics outpatient centers long-term care facilities (under the Dubois and Advanced Care names) are found in Texas Louisiana Iowa Georgia Missouri and New Mexico in the US and in the Mexican states of Chihuahua Coahuila Nuevo Le n Puebla San Luis Potos and Tamaulipas.

Financial Performance

In 2013 CHRISTUS reported a 3% increase in revenue from $3.6 billion to $3.7 billion based on increased net patient and premium revenues. Net income was $261 million against net loss in 2012 due to an increase in investment returns.

Strategy

CHRISTUS has been expanding its Continuing Care division which includes non-acute care operations like home care hospice palliative care residential facilities and fitness centers.

Another goal of CHRISTUS Health is to reduce overcrowding and such misuses as patients being seen for routine illnesses in its emergency rooms. To that end and to make primary care a bit more accessible the company has opened immediate care clinics in a number of Texas Wal-Mart stores. CHRISTUS Health has plans to expand the clinics into Wal-Marts in Louisiana.

CHRISTUS Health has taken other steps to try to offset some costs of indigent care including pushing for the establishment of hospital districts to pay for charity care costs in some of its markets. It has also sold some of it facilities.

The organization has been focused on growing its operations in Mexico where it operates about a dozen clinics in six states. CHRISTUS Health's Mexico operations are a majority-owned partnership with Monterrey-based Muguerza. The organization's main Monterrey facility became the first Mexican hospital to win accreditation from the Joint Commission International a unit of the organization that certifies US hospitals.

Because Mexican citizens overwhelmingly rely on public hospitals run by the national health care system CHRISTUS Muguerza markets itself as a "medical tourism" destination where Americans can go for cheaper and lower-hassle medical care. Services include acute and primary care dental care urgent care and post-surgical rehabilitation.

Company Background

CHRISTUS Health was formed through the 1999 merger of Incarnate Word Health System and Sisters of Charity Health System. Both systems have their roots in the religious order Sisters of Charity of the Incarnate Word founded when three French nuns arrived in Texas in 1866 to care for the poor and sick.

EXECUTIVES

Vice President, Mary Lynch
Evp And Chief Clinical Officer, John A. Gillean
President And Ceo, Ernie W. Sadau
Evp And Chief Administrative Officer, Linda McClung
Svp And Cio, George S. Conklin
Evp And Coo, Jeffrey M. (Jeff) Puckett
Evp And Cfo, Randolph W. Safady
Evp And Chief Strategy And Health Network Officer, Paul Generale
Evp Corporate Services And Chief Human Resources Officer, Marty Margetts
President And Ceo Good Shepherd Hospital Longview, Todd Hancock
Vice President, Melissa Williams
Senior Vice President, Theresa Mcgrath
Vice President And Litigation Counsel, Maria Ganson
Vice President Of Marketing, Linda Clung
Respiratory Therapy Director, SHELLEY COOPER
Vice President, Jamesha Bell
Vice President, James Colbert
Medical Director, Kris Bhat
Operating Room Dir, Tammy Martin
Chairman, Arthur M. Southam
Vice Chair, Maricela S. Moore
Board Member, Jennifer Galysh
Auditors: ERNST & YOUNG LLP DALLAS TX

LOCATIONS

HQ: CHRISTUS HEALTH
919 HIDDEN RDG, IRVING, TX 750383813
Phone: 469 282-2000
Web: WWW.CHRISTUSHEALTH.ORG

PRODUCTS/OPERATIONS

2015 Payor Mix

	% of total
Managed care organizations	47
Medicare	22
Self-pay	14
Medicaid	9
Commercial insurance	8
Total	**100**

2015 Revenues

	$ mil.	% of total
Patient services	3,233	90
Premium revenue	161	4
Other revenue	188	5
Equity in income of unconsolidated organizations	25	1
Total	**3,609**	**100**

Selected Facilities in Texas

CHRISTUS HomeCare - Corpus Christi
CHRISTUS HomeCare - Texarkana
CHRISTUS Hospital - St. Elizabeth
CHRISTUS Hospital - St. Mary
CHRISTUS Jasper Memorial Hospital
CHRISTUS Santa Rosa Alamo Heights Imaging Center
CHRISTUS Santa Rosa Ambulatory Surgery Center
CHRISTUS Santa Rosa Cancer Center
CHRISTUS Santa Rosa Children's Hospital
CHRISTUS Santa Rosa Hospital - City Centre
CHRISTUS Santa Rosa Hospital - Medical Center
CHRISTUS Santa Rosa Hospital - New Braunfels
CHRISTUS Santa Rosa Hospital - Westover Hills
CHRISTUS Santa Rosa Imaging Center
CHRISTUS Santa Rosa Outpatient Rehabilitation Center
CHRISTUS Santa Rosa Rehabilitation Hospital
CHRISTUS Santa Rosa Rehabilitation Services - Downtown
CHRISTUS Santa Rosa Rehabilitation Services - Medical Center
CHRISTUS Santa Rosa Wound Care and Hyperbaric Center - Downtown
CHRISTUS Santa Rosa Wound Care and Hyperbaric Center - Medical Center
CHRISTUS Spohn Family Center Northside
CHRISTUS Spohn Family Health Center
CHRISTUS Spohn Family Health Center Falfurrias
CHRISTUS Spohn Family Health Center Padre Island
CHRISTUS Spohn Family Health Center Robstown
CHRISTUS Spohn Family Health Center San Diego
CHRISTUS Spohn Family Health Center Westside
CHRISTUS Spohn Health System
CHRISTUS Spohn Hospital Alice
CHRISTUS Spohn Hospital Beeville
CHRISTUS Spohn Hospital Corpus Christi - Memorial
CHRISTUS Spohn Hospital Corpus Christi - Shoreline
CHRISTUS Spohn Hospital Corpus Christi - South
CHRISTUS Spohn Hospital Kleberg
CHRISTUS Spohn Medical Group - Obstetrics and Gynecology Associates
CHRISTUS St. Catherine Hospital
CHRISTUS St. John Hospital
CHRISTUS St. Michael Health System
CHRISTUS St. Michael Rehabilitation Hospital
CHRISTUS Transplant Institute
CHRISTUS Visiting Nurse Association - Houston
CHRISTUS Visiting Nurse Association - Nassau Bay
CHRISTUS Visiting Nurse Association - San Antonio
David Christopher Goldsbury Center for Children and Families
Dubuis Hospital of Beaumont
Dubuis Hospital of Bryan Texas
Dubuis Hospital of Corpus Christi
Dubuis Hospital of Houston Texas (long-term acute care)
Dubuis Hospital of Paris
Dubuis Hospital of Port Arthur Texas (long-term acute care)
Dubuis Hospital of Texarkana

Selected Other US Facilities

Advance Care Hospital of Fort Smith (Arkansas)
Advance Care Hospital of Hot Springs (Arkansas)
CHRISTUS Coushatta Health Care Center (Coushatta Louisiana)
CHRISTUS HomeCare - Jennings (Louisiana)
CHRISTUS HomeCare - Lake Charles (Louisiana)
CHRISTUS HomeCare - Shreveport (Louisiana)
CHRISTUS Hospice and Palliative Care - Alexandria (Louisiana)
CHRISTUS Schumpert Health System (Shreveport Louisiana)
CHRISTUS Schumpert Highland (Shreveport Louisiana)
CHRISTUS Schumpert St. Mary Place (Shreveport Louisiana)
CHRISTUS St. Frances Cabrini Hospital (Alexandria Louisiana)
CHRISTUS St. Patrick Hospital (Lake Charles Louisiana)
CHRISTUS St. Vincent (Santa Fe New Mexico)
Dubuis Hospital of Alexandria (Louisiana)
Dubuis Hospital of Lake Charles (Louisiana)

Dubuis Hospital of Shreveport (Louisiana)
Dubuis Hospital of St. Louis (Chesterfield Missouri)
Natchitoches Parish Hospital (Louisiana)
Southern Crescent Hospital for Specialty Care (Riverdale Georgia)

Selected Facilities in Mexico

CHRISTUS MUGUERZA Hospital Alta Especialidad (Monterrey Nuevo Leon)
CHRISTUS MUGUERZA Hospital Conchita (Monterrey Nuevo Leon)
CHRISTUS MUGUERZA Hospital Del Parque (Chihuahua)
CHRISTUS MUGUERZA Hospital Reynosa (Tamaulipas+; C.P.)
CHRISTUS MUGUERZA Hospital Saltillo (Coahuila)
CHRISTUS MUGUERZA Hospital Sur (Monterrey Nuevo Leon)
CHRISTUS MUGUERZA Hospital UPAEP (Puebla)

COMPETITORS

Ascension Health
Catholic Health Initiatives
Community Health Systems
HCA
Intermountain Health Care
LifePoint Health
MD Anderson Cancer Center
Memorial Health Services
Memorial Hermann Healthcare
Mercy Health
Methodist Hospital System
St. Luke's Episcopal Hospital
Tenet Healthcare
Texas Children's Hospital
Universal Health Services
University of Utah Hospitals & Clinics

HISTORICAL FINANCIALS

Company Type: Private

Income Statement — FYE: June 30

	REVENUE ($ mil.)	NET INCOME ($ mil.)	NET PROFIT MARGIN	EMPLOYEES
06/16	4,212	149	3.6%	25,700
06/15	658	(44)	—	—
06/14	673	25	3.8%	—
06/13	646	124	19.3%	—
Annual Growth	86.7%	6.3%	—	—

2016 Year-End Financials

Return on assets: 2.9%
Return on equity: 5.1%
Current ratio: 2.50
Cash ($ mil.): 483

CHRISTUS SANTA ROSA HEALTH CARE CORPORATION

EXECUTIVES

Pres, Don Beeler
Pres, Patrick B Carrier
Dir, Melissa Krause
Coo, Renato Baciarelli
Cfo, Kenneth Kolb
Coordinator, Carl Zepeda
Coordinator, Amy Lopez
Chief of Emergency Room, Greg Roth
Chief of Medicine, Hugo Castaneda
Executive of Information Techn, Ron Love
Coordinator, Bernice Avilez
Auditors: ERNST & YOUNG US LLP INDIANAP

LOCATIONS

HQ: CHRISTUS SANTA ROSA HEALTH CARE CORPORATION
333 N SANTA ROSA ST, SAN ANTONIO, TX 782073108
Phone: 210 704-2011
Web: WWW.CHRISTUSHEALTH.ORG

HISTORICAL FINANCIALS

Company Type: Private

Income Statement — FYE: June 30

	REVENUE ($ mil.)	NET INCOME ($ mil.)	NET PROFIT MARGIN	EMPLOYEES
06/15	656	(14)	—	3,700
06/14	635	6	1.1%	—
06/13	612	2	0.4%	—
06/10	577	(19)	—	—
Annual Growth	2.6%	—	—	—

2015 Year-End Financials

Return on assets: (-2.0%)
Return on equity: (-4.1%)
Current ratio: 2.70
Cash ($ mil.): 2

CHRISTUS TRINITY MOTHER FRANCES HEALTH SYSTEM

EXECUTIVES

Pres, Chris Glenney
Cmo, Steve Keuer
Coo*, Jason Proctor
Cfo*, Elizabeth Tulliam
Chief Nursing Officer, Shelly Welch
Exec Asst, Susan Wilson
Physician, Donald Knarr
Office Manager III, Haley Clark
Registered Nurse, Jamie Slagle
Lactation Consultant, Jennifer Dean
Office Assistant, Jessica Hornsby
Auditors: ERNST & YOUNG LLP DALLAS TX

LOCATIONS

HQ: CHRISTUS TRINITY MOTHER FRANCES HEALTH SYSTEM
800 E DAWSON ST, TYLER, TX 757012036
Phone: 903 593-8441
Web: WWW.CHRISTUSHEALTH.ORG

HISTORICAL FINANCIALS

Company Type: Private

Income Statement — FYE: June 30

	REVENUE ($ mil.)	NET INCOME ($ mil.)	NET PROFIT MARGIN	EMPLOYEES
06/17	789	42	5.4%	4,000
06/15	752	48	6.4%	—
Annual Growth	2.5%	(5.6%)	—	—

CHS MCPHERSON REFINERY INC.

Cooperation is a refined art and refining a co-operative art for the National Cooperative Refinery Association (NCRA) which provides its member owners farm supply cooperatives CHS GROWMARK and MFA Oil with gasoline and diesel fuel through its oil refinery in McPherson Kansas. The refinery's production rate is 85000 barrels per day. Fuel from the refinery is allocated to member/owners on the basis of ownership percentages. In addition to the refinery NCRA owns Jayhawk Pipeline stakes in two other pipeline companies and an underground oil storage facility.

Operations

NCRA's logistical system includes 76 trucks. (In 2012 almost 40000 barrels per day of crude was gathered from more than 6000 oil wells mainly in Kansas and transported to the McPherson refinery by truck.)

The system also includes more than 1000 miles of pipelines to move crude oil and finished products from its refinery to tanks and terminals. Its Conway Texas underground storage facility has 1.5 million barrels of refined products capacity. NCRA also has two refined products terminals (in McPherson Kansas and Council Bluffs Iowa).

Strategy

The cooperative's primary strategy is to gather oil and gas and make diesel and gasoline to serve it members (and the farms of rural America) while maintaining and upgrading its systems in order to stay competitive with better resourced private sector refining rivals.

In 2011 NCRA announced a $555 million investment to build a new Delayed Coking Unit at its McPherson refinery. The new facility will allow the refiner to process a larger variety of crude oils. It is scheduled to be completed in 2015 and will replace a unit that was built in 1952.

In 2012 the company agreed to pay $700000 in federal and state penalties to settle violations of environmental laws at its McPherson petroleum refinery and underground storage facility.

Company Background

The enterprise has its origins in 1943 when five regional farm supply cooperatives tired of wartime fuel shortages created the NCRA to buy the Globe oil refinery in McPherson Kansas.

EXECUTIVES

Exec V Pres-, Shirley Cunningham
Exec V Pres-Coo*, Jay Debertin
Exec V Pres-Cfo*, Timothy Skidmore
Exec V Pres*, Lisa Zell
Coordinator, Maury Hoefer
Information Technology Manager, Jason Beckman
Accountant II, Anika Polzin
Admin, Jeanne Whitenack
Project Engineer, Kelly Long
Specialist, Phillip Boesker
Terminal Manager, Quinton Hett
Auditors: PRICEWATERHOUSECOOPERS LLP MI

LOCATIONS

HQ: CHS MCPHERSON REFINERY INC.
2000 S MAIN ST, MCPHERSON, KS 674609402
Phone: 620 241-2340

COMPETITORS

BP
CVR Refining
Chevron
Exxon Mobil
HollyFrontier
Marathon Petroleum
Tesoro
Valero Energy

HISTORICAL FINANCIALS

Company Type: Private

Income Statement				FYE: August 31
	REVENUE ($ mil.)	NET INCOME ($ mil.)	NET PROFIT MARGIN	EMPLOYEES
08/13	4,081	686	16.8%	700
08/12	4,045	705	17.4%	—
08/11	3,405	378	11.1%	—
Annual Growth	9.5%	34.7%	—	—

2013 Year-End Financials

Return on assets: 32.8%
Return on equity: 51.0%
Current ratio: 1.60
Cash ($ mil.): 386

CHUGACH ALASKA CORPORATION

At the heart of Chugach Alaska Corporation is a vision of indigenous people running their own businesses on their own land. Chugach Alaska was formed following the activation of the Alaska Native Claims Settlement Act (which was passed by the US Congress in 1971) to provide land management services for the 928000-acre Chugach region of Alaska. The company derives the bulk of its sales from oil and gas production mining commercial timber and tourist activities that occur in the region and from its engagement in military base construction projects at more than 30 locations in Alaska the US Pacific Northwest and the Western Pacific. Chugach Alaska's shareholders consist of Aleut Eskimo and Indian natives.

Operations

In 2011 the company's Chugach World Services unit secured a $32 million contract (with the option for an additional $33 million) for housing and maintenance operations at Naval Base Guam and Andersen Air Force Base Guam.

In late 2010 the Chugach Alaska Services unit won a renewal of its existing oil spill prevention and response contract with Alyeska Pipeline Service Company. The new contract to service the Alaska Pipeline runs from 2011 to 2016.

Geographic Reach

With operations in Alaska the Pacific Northwest and the Western Pacific the company has major offices in Alabama Alaska Hawaii and Nevada.

Financial Performance

To raise cash in 2013 Chugach Alaska sold its three-story former headquarters building in downtown Anchorage.

Strategy

Developing and sustaining multiple revenues streams has been a key to the company's growth. Chugach Alaska is looking to continue to grow its Alaskan gas natural gas projects while diversifying into markets that are not traditional for the company such as the niche market of environmentally responsible guided tourism.

Expanding its global engineering footprint in 2012 the company acquired bankrupt Hawaii-based engineering firm Heide & Cook LLC.

Company Background

Chugach Alaska was founded in 1972 as an Alaska Native Claims Settlement Act Corporation. A nine-person board of directors elected from the corporation's more than 2300 shareholders oversees Chugach Alaska's management and operations. The company has gone from filing bankruptcy protection in 1990 (in the wake of the Exxon Valdez oil spill and a major cannery fire) to generating about $1 billion in annual revenues.

EXECUTIVES

Senior Vice President Of Operations, Scott Davis
Svp Business Development, Tim Hopper
Vice President Cultural, John Johnson
Vice President Finance, Kathleen Grimes

LOCATIONS

HQ: CHUGACH ALASKA CORPORATION
3800 CNTRPINT DR STE 1200, ANCHORAGE, AK 99503
Phone: 907 563-8866
Web: WWW.CHUGACH.COM

PRODUCTS/OPERATIONS

Selected Services

Base Operating Services
Construction Services
Educational Services
Engineering Services
IT/Telecommunications
Manufacturing Services
Oil and Gas Services

Selected Subsidiaries

Chugach Alaska Services Inc. (CASI)
Chugach Education Services Inc. (CESI)
Chugach Federal Solutions Inc. (CFSI)
Chugach Government Services Inc. (CGSI)
Chugach Industries Inc. (CII)
Chugach Information Technology Inc. (CITI)
Chugach Management Services Inc. (CMSI)
Chugach McKinley Inc. (CMI)
Chugach Support Services Inc. (CSSI)
Chugach Systems Integration Llc (CSI)
Chugach World Services Inc. (CWSI)
Heide & Cook LLC. (H&C)
Wolf Creek Federal Services Inc. (WCFS)

COMPETITORS

ConocoPhillips Alaska
Doyon
Fluor
Freegold Ventures
Jacobs Engineering
Sealaska

HISTORICAL FINANCIALS

Company Type: Private

Income Statement				FYE: December 31
	REVENUE ($ mil.)	NET INCOME ($ mil.)	NET PROFIT MARGIN	EMPLOYEES
12/17	919	20	2.3%	4,822
12/16	842	35	4.2%	—
12/15	758	22	3.0%	—
12/14	7	(12)	—	—
Annual Growth	387.6%	—	—	—

2017 Year-End Financials

Return on assets: 4.5%
Return on equity: 6.5%
Current ratio: 2.60
Cash ($ mil.): 66

CIC GROUP, INC.

CIC Group can see clearly that its future (like its present) is in heavy manufacturing and construction. Its group of commercial and industrial subsidiaries specialize in the manufacture maintenance and repair of equipment for the crude oil natural gas coal and other energy industries. Its largest subsidiary is Nooter/Eriksen which supplies heat recovery steam generators for combustion gas turbines worldwide. CIC's Nooter Construction is a construction contractor serving the refining petrochemical pulp and paper and power industries among others. The employee-owned holding company was formed in 2002.

Operations

CIC through its 20 subsidiaries is engaged in the heavy industrial construction of refineries and petrochemical and power plants. It also designs and builds heat recovery systems for power plants.

Sales and Marketing

Some of the company's largest customers include Ameren Calpine Chevron ConocoPhillips Exxon Mobil Florida Power & Light and Royal Dutch Shell.

Financial Performance

Although privately held the company reported 2012 revenue of $1.2 billion up 30% from 2011. CIC anticipates revenue of $2 billion by 2017 or 2018.

Strategy

The company is taking advantage of the low price and abundance of natural gas in the US which has encouraged companies to shift the manufacture of petrochemical plants to the US from the Middle East and Asia.

However CIC is also strengthening its position in the growth markets of Eastern Europe and Asia. In 2012 the company announced plans to work on photovoltaic projects for Chinese solar manufacturer LDK Solar and to act as a distributor for the company.

EXECUTIVES

Vice President Of Operations, Don Majchrowski

LOCATIONS

HQ: CIC GROUP, INC.
1509 OCELLO DR, FENTON, MO 630262406
Phone: 314 682-2900
Web: WWW.CICGROUP.COM

PRODUCTS/OPERATIONS

Selected Subsidiaries

ArcMelt
Delta Nooter
Megamet Sold Metals Co.
Nooter Construction
Nooter/Eriksen s.r.l.
Pressline Services
RMF Nooter
Schoeller Bleckmann Nooter GmbH
St. Louis Metallizing
Superior Corporate Travel
Wyatt Field Service Co.
Wyatt Virgin Islands

COMPETITORS

BWX Technologies
Clarkson Construction
Fluor
Fred Weber
Jacobs Engineering
Mitsubishi Heavy Industries
Phillips-Medisize
U.S. Pipe

HISTORICAL FINANCIALS

Company Type: Private

Income Statement				FYE: November 30
	REVENUE ($ mil.)	NET INCOME ($ mil.)	NET PROFIT MARGIN	EMPLOYEES
11/11	838	0	—	1,500
11/10	758	0	—	—
11/08	1,120	0	—	—
Annual Growth	(9.2%)	—	—	—

2011 Year-End Financials

Return on assets: —
Return on equity: —
Current ratio: 1.70
Cash ($ mil.): 136

CIMA ENERGY, LP

EXECUTIVES

Pres, Thomas K Edwards
Cfo, Michael D Rupe
Accounting Staff, Audrey Blum
Senior Financial Analyst, Benjamin Porche
Business, Kyoichi Miyazaki
Developer, Andretti Medina
Accounting, Emily Smith
Director of Information Techno, Roger Heiniluoma
Auditors: DELOITTE & TOUCHE LLP HOUSTON

LOCATIONS

HQ: CIMA ENERGY, LP
1221 MCKINNEY ST STE 3700, HOUSTON, TX 770102046
Phone: 713 209-1112
Web: WWW.CIMA-ENERGY.COM

HISTORICAL FINANCIALS

Company Type: Private

Income Statement — FYE: December 31

	REVENUE ($ mil.)	NET INCOME ($ mil.)	NET PROFIT MARGIN	EMPLOYEES
12/07	1,195	8	0.7%	65
12/06	902	11	1.3%	—
12/05	872	0	—	—
12/04	569	4	0.8%	—
Annual Growth	28.0%	19.1%	—	—

2007 Year-End Financials

Return on assets: 5.6%
Return on equity: 26.2%
Current ratio: 1.20
Cash ($ mil.): 16

CINCINNATI PUBLIC SCHOOLS

EXECUTIVES

Spdt, Laura Mitchell
SEC*, Denae Coco
Cfo-Treas*, Jonathan Boid
Facilities, Michael L Burson
Coordinator, Melvina Stokes
Network Administrator, Christine Shields
Instructor, Gerald Powell
Education Assistant, Leah Runyon
Teacher, Lisa Shelly
Assistant, Michael Allison
Teacher, Monique Wallace
Auditors: PLATTENBURG & ASSOCIATES INC

LOCATIONS

HQ: CINCINNATI PUBLIC SCHOOLS
2651 BURNET AVE, CINCINNATI, OH 452192551
Phone: 513 363-0000
Web: WWW.CPS-K12.ORG

HISTORICAL FINANCIALS

Company Type: Private

Income Statement — FYE: June 30

	REVENUE ($ mil.)	NET INCOME ($ mil.)	NET PROFIT MARGIN	EMPLOYEES
06/17	703	17	2.5%	7,070
06/16	650	13	2.1%	—
06/15	654	(0)	—	—
06/05	402	0	—	—
Annual Growth	4.8%	—	—	—

CITIZENS ENERGY GROUP

Hoosiers are happy to have their homes provided with gas and water services by Public Utilities of the City of Indianapolis (dba Citizens Energy and CWA Authority public charitable trusts). Its Citizens Water unit provides water and wastewater services to 300000 customers in Indianapolis; Citizens Gas serves more than 266000 gas customers. Citizens Energy also provides steam heating and chilled water cooling services to about 250 customers through Citizens Thermal Energy. The regional utility also has a small oil production unit (Citizens Oil Division). Its Citizens Resources unit has joint venture stakes in some companies not regulated by the Indiana Utility Regulatory Commission such as ProLiance Energy.

EXECUTIVES

Vice President Information Technology, John Lucas
Vice President And Controller, Sabine Karner
Vice President Capital Programs And Engineering, Mark C Jacob
Vice President Of Information Technology, Ravi Chittaranjan

LOCATIONS

HQ: CITIZENS ENERGY GROUP
2020 N MERIDIAN ST, INDIANAPOLIS, IN 462021306
Phone: 317 924-3341
Web: WWW.CITIZENSENERGYGROUP.COM

PRODUCTS/OPERATIONS

2012 Sales

	$ mil.	% of total
Utility	650	93
Non-utility	45	7
Total	696	100

2012 Sales

	% of total
Citizens Gas	37
Water	24
Wastewater	22
Steam	9
Chilled Water	6
Oil	1
Resources	1
Total	100

COMPETITORS

American States Water
Duke Energy
Indiana Municipal Power Agency
NIPSCO
Vectren
Veolia Environnement

HISTORICAL FINANCIALS

Company Type: Private

Income Statement — FYE: September 30

	REVENUE ($ mil.)	NET INCOME ($ mil.)	NET PROFIT MARGIN	EMPLOYEES
09/12	696	(11)	—	1,100
09/11	463	32	7.0%	—
09/10	440	(1)	—	—
Annual Growth	25.7%	—	—	—

2012 Year-End Financials

Return on assets: (-0.3%)
Return on equity: (-10.5%)
Current ratio: 1.50
Cash ($ mil.): 393

CITY & COUNTY OF HONOLULU

With a population of almost 1 million people Honolulu County located on the island of Oahu is the largest city and county in Hawaii. The city and county are governed by a mayor and a nine-member legislative council. Honolulu's largest industry is tourism but the city is also the financial center of Hawaii.

EXECUTIVES

Vice Chair District 3, Ikaika Anderson
Prvt. Secretary, L Morita
Treasurer, Dustin Timm
Private Secretary To The, Aileen Nagamine
Auditors: ACUITY LLP HONOLULU HAWAII

LOCATIONS

HQ: CITY & COUNTY OF HONOLULU
530 S KING ST RM 300, HONOLULU, HI 968133019
Phone: 808 768-4141
Web: WWW.HONOLULU.GOV

HISTORICAL FINANCIALS

Company Type: Private

Income Statement — FYE: June 30

	REVENUE ($ mil.)	NET INCOME ($ mil.)	NET PROFIT MARGIN	EMPLOYEES
06/19	2,013	315	15.6%	8,000
06/18	1,848	482	26.1%	—
06/17	1,728	(89)	—	—
06/16	1,657	(216)	—	—
Annual Growth	6.7%	—	—	—

2019 Year-End Financials

Return on assets: 1.8%
Return on equity: 7.6%
Current ratio: —
Cash ($ mil.): 727

CITY & COUNTY OF SAN FRANCISCO

The City of San Francisco is the 14th largest in the US and its dense population geographic detachment and cultural diversity have made San Francisco a favorite with both tourists and residents. San Francisco's government is a consolidated city-county bureaucracy with both entities led by an elected mayor. The government includes an executive branch led by the mayor and consisting of other elected officials and city departments and a legislative branch consisting of an 11-member Board of Supervisors. The city is also home to several federal institutions including the Federal Reserve Bank and the US Mint.

EXECUTIVES

Legal Secretary, Pamela Cheeseborough
Medical Director, Jan Gurley
Legal Secretary Labor Division, Sylvia Angelo
Legal Secretary, Catheryn Daly
Director Of Nursing, Lissette Waterman
Secretary, Vinnie Lew
Board Member, Niki Solis
Office Of The Treasurer And Tax Collector, Romualdo Castro
Board Member, Esther Lane
Auditors: MACIAS GINI & O'CONNELL LLP

LOCATIONS

HQ: CITY & COUNTY OF SAN FRANCISCO
1 DR CARLTON B GOODLETT P, SAN FRANCISCO, CA 941024604
Phone: 415 554-7500
Web: WWW.SFGOV.ORG

HISTORICAL FINANCIALS

Company Type: Private

Income Statement — FYE: June 30

	REVENUE ($ mil.)	NET INCOME ($ mil.)	NET PROFIT MARGIN	EMPLOYEES
06/19	7,561	563	7.4%	30,000
06/18	6,411	1,172	18.3%	—
06/17	5,971	569	9.5%	—
06/16	5,789	546	9.4%	—
Annual Growth	9.3%	1.0%	—	—

CITY CENTER HOLDINGS, LLC

Auditors: DELOITTE & TOUCHE LLP LAS VE

LOCATIONS

HQ: CITY CENTER HOLDINGS, LLC
3950 LAS VEGAS BLVD S, LAS VEGAS, NV 891191005
Phone: 702 632-9800
Web: WWW.CITIZENSLASVEGAS.COM

HISTORICAL FINANCIALS

Company Type: Private

Income Statement — FYE: December 31

	REVENUE ($ mil.)	NET INCOME ($ mil.)	NET PROFIT MARGIN	EMPLOYEES
12/12	1,189	(510)	—	—
12/11	1,081	(502)	—	—
Annual Growth	10.0%	—	—	—

2012 Year-End Financials

Return on assets: (-5.6%)
Return on equity: (-8.3%)
Current ratio: 1.20
Cash ($ mil.): 252

CITY OF ALBUQUERQUE

Albuquerque is by far New Mexico's largest city with a 2015 estimated population of 561380 (about 970680 in the greater metropolitan area). Albuquerque is located in the central part of the state and is home to The University of New Mexico. While Pueblo Indians lived in the general area for several centuries Spanish explorers arrived in the 16th century. The city of Albuquerque was founded in 1706 and named after the Spanish town of Albuquerque (with an extra "r"). The City of Albuquerque is administered by a Mayor and a nine-person City Council.

EXECUTIVES

Legal Secretary, Shannon Triplett
City Treasurer, Cilia Aglialoro
Auditors: MOSS ADAMS LLP ALBUQUERQUE N

LOCATIONS

HQ: CITY OF ALBUQUERQUE
400 MARQUETTE AVE NW, ALBUQUERQUE, NM 871022117
Phone: 505 768-3000
Web: WWW.CABQ.GOV

HISTORICAL FINANCIALS

Company Type: Private

Income Statement — FYE: June 30

	REVENUE ($ mil.)	NET INCOME ($ mil.)	NET PROFIT MARGIN	EMPLOYEES
06/19	825	20	2.5%	6,500
06/18	722	45	6.2%	—
06/17	709	(5)	—	—
06/16	691	53	7.8%	—
Annual Growth	6.1%	(27.4%)	—	—

2019 Year-End Financials

Return on assets: 0.4%
Return on equity: 0.6%
Current ratio: 2.90
Cash ($ mil.): —

CITY OF ALEXANDRIA

Historically a wartime victim of occupying forces modern Alexandria is home to many Defense Department contractors and employees. It uses a council-manager form of government wherein the mayor is part of the six-member city council (all elected at large) which determines city policy. The city manager works to carry out the policy and run the day-to-day operations of Alexandria. In addition to the city manager the council also appoints the city attorney city clerk and members of various commissions and boards. Alexandria's more than 30 departments operate on an annual budget of about $400 million and serve about 130000 citizens. The city was founded in 1749.

EXECUTIVES

Mayor, Allison Silberberg
City Mgr*, Mark Jinks
Deputy Cty Mgr*, Emily A Baker
U.S. Attorney, Tyler McGaughey
Coordinator Is To Build On Tha, Azuree Bowman
Management, Steven F Bloomfield
Account Clerk III, Susana Ibarra
Assistant City, Dori Martin
Program Manager, Helen Lee
Maintenance Worker, Keith Cpsi
Police Sergeant, Nick Ruggiero
Auditors: CLIFTONLARSONALLEN LLP ARLING

LOCATIONS

HQ: CITY OF ALEXANDRIA
301 KING ST, ALEXANDRIA, VA 223143211
Phone: 703 746-4000
Web: WWW.ALEXANDRIAVA.GOV

HISTORICAL FINANCIALS

Company Type: Private

Income Statement — FYE: June 30

	REVENUE ($ mil.)	NET INCOME ($ mil.)	NET PROFIT MARGIN	EMPLOYEES
06/20	910	167	18.4%	2,375
06/19	880	(8)	—	—
06/18	842	108	12.9%	—
06/16	751	15	2.0%	—
Annual Growth	4.9%	82.1%	—	—

2020 Year-End Financials

Return on assets: 7.4%
Return on equity: 46.7%
Current ratio: —
Cash ($ mil.): 422

CITY OF ANAHEIM

Anaheim is a city in sunny southern Orange County California. The state's 10th largest city is home to Disneyland Resort one of Walt Disney Parks and Resorts' theme parks. The city also features a number of professional sports franchises such as the Anaheim Ducks hockey team and the Angels baseball team. Anaheim was founded in 1857.

EXECUTIVES

Secretary, Leticia Hurtado
Auditors: KPMG LLP IRVINE CALIFORNIA

LOCATIONS

HQ: CITY OF ANAHEIM
200 S ANAHEIM BLVD, ANAHEIM, CA 928053820
Phone: 714 765-5162
Web: WWW.ANAHEIM.NET

HISTORICAL FINANCIALS

Company Type: Private

Income Statement FYE: June 30

	REVENUE ($ mil.)	NET INCOME ($ mil.)	NET PROFIT MARGIN	EMPLOYEES
06/19	592	12	2.2%	3,100
06/18	566	27	4.9%	—
06/17	602	92	15.4%	—
06/16	558	60	10.8%	—
Annual Growth	2.0%	(40.3%)	—	—

2019 Year-End Financials

Return on assets: 0.2%
Return on equity: 0.7%
Current ratio: —
Cash ($ mil.): 105

CITY OF ATLANTA

City of Atlanta leaders have a dream to improve Atlantans' quality of life. The birthplace of civil rights activist Martin Luther King Jr. Atlanta is run by a mayor and a 16-member council. With a metropolitan population of more than 5 million Atlanta is the most populous city in Georgia. It's also the state capital and home to such major companies as The Coca-Cola Company The Home Depot and UPS. In addition Atlanta has a number of professional sports franchises namely the Atlanta Braves Hawks and Falcons.

EXECUTIVES

National Sales Manager, Melissa Legaux
Treasurer, Stephen Thomas
Auditors: KPMG LLP ATLANTA GA

LOCATIONS

HQ: CITY OF ATLANTA
55 TRINITY AVE SW # 3900, ATLANTA, GA 303033543
Phone: 404 330-6100
Web: WWW.ALLATLANTA.ORG

HISTORICAL FINANCIALS

Company Type: Private

Income Statement FYE: June 30

	REVENUE ($ mil.)	NET INCOME ($ mil.)	NET PROFIT MARGIN	EMPLOYEES
06/17	1,044	146	14.0%	8,885
06/15	920	274	29.8%	—
06/14	883	9	1.0%	—
06/13	850	14	1.7%	—
Annual Growth	5.3%	79.0%	—	—

2017 Year-End Financials

Return on assets: 0.8%
Return on equity: 2.0%
Current ratio: 3.20
Cash ($ mil.): 48

CITY OF AUSTIN

Deep in the heart of Texas you'll find Austin the capital of the state and self-proclaimed Live Music Capital of the World. The city covering more than 300 square miles follows the council/manager model where the mayor and six city council members all elected to three-year terms enact policy and the city manager carries it out. The manager's office oversees about 30 departments/offices the municipal court system city utilities and the city's airport. Austin has a city population of more than 820000 and a greater metro population of more than 1.8 million. Stephen F. Austin brought the first Anglo settlers to the area in 1821.

EXECUTIVES

Vice President Information Technology, Amanda Gomez
Vice President Energy Market Operations, Khalil Shalabi
Auditors: DELOITTE & TOUCHE LLP AUSTIN

LOCATIONS

HQ: CITY OF AUSTIN
301 W 2ND ST, AUSTIN, TX 787014652
Phone: 512 974-2000
Web: WWW.AUSTINTEXAS.GOV

Selected Departments and Offices

Austin Resource Recovery
Animal Services Office
Austin Convention Center Department
Austin Water Utility
Aviation Department
Capital Planning Office
Code Compliance Department
Communications and Public Information Office
Contract Management Department
Economic Growth and Redevelopment Services Office
Emergency Medical Services Department
Fire Department
Health and Human Services Department/Medical Director
Human Resources
Labor Relations Office
Law Department
Library Department
Neighborhood Housing and Community Development
Office of Homeland Security and Emergency Management
Office of Police Monitor
Office of Real Estate Services
Parks and Recreation Department
Planning and Development Review Department
Police Department
Public Works Department
Small and Minority Business Resources Department
Sustainability Office
Transportation Department
Watershed Protection Department

HISTORICAL FINANCIALS

Company Type: Private

Income Statement FYE: September 30

	REVENUE ($ mil.)	NET INCOME ($ mil.)	NET PROFIT MARGIN	EMPLOYEES
09/19	1,352	33	2.5%	10,922
09/18	1,279	67	5.2%	—
09/17	1,186	28	2.4%	—
09/16	1,148	65	5.7%	—
Annual Growth	5.6%	(19.8%)	—	—

2019 Year-End Financials

Return on assets: 0.2%
Return on equity: 0.9%
Current ratio: 2.60
Cash ($ mil.): 9

CITY OF BALTIMORE

EXECUTIVES

Mayor, Bernard C Young
Dep Chief of Operations*, Khalil Zaied
Chief Information Officer-Chie*, Frank Johnson
Architect, Joseph L Henley
Mayor, Catherine E Pugh
Crime Fighting Strategist, Pol, Baltimore City of
Fire Battalion Chief, Mark Ruff
Licensed Clinical Social Worke, Patricia Pencil
Chief of Staff, Bruce H Williams
Acting Police Commissioner, Michael S Harrison
Human Resources Business Partn, Catherine B Phr
Auditors: KPMG LLP WASHINGTON DC

LOCATIONS

HQ: CITY OF BALTIMORE
100 HOLLIDAY ST STE 250, BALTIMORE, MD 212023459
Phone: 410 396-3835
Web: WWW.BALTIMORECITY.GOV

HISTORICAL FINANCIALS

Company Type: Private

Income Statement FYE: June 30

	REVENUE ($ mil.)	NET INCOME ($ mil.)	NET PROFIT MARGIN	EMPLOYEES
06/19	2,413	133	5.5%	26,400
06/18	2,147	126	5.9%	—
06/17	2,167	63	2.9%	—
06/16	2,081	30	1.5%	—
Annual Growth	5.1%	62.8%	—	—

2019 Year-End Financials

Return on assets: 0.9%
Return on equity: 3.3%
Current ratio: —
Cash ($ mil.): 1,518

CITY OF BOSTON

Boston's legacy includes a famous Tea Party Paul Revere's Ride and clam chowder. With about 625000 residents Boston has been called the economic and cultural hub of New England. The Greater Boston metro area is home to about 4.6 million people making it the 10th largest city in the US. Boston also boasts world class educational institutions (Harvard Massachusetts Institute of Technology) champion sports teams (Red Sox Celtics Patriots) and a rich cultural and historical identity. Boston is also the capital of Massachusetts.

EXECUTIVES

Vice President, Peter Derosa
Auditors: KPMG LLP BOSTON MA

LOCATIONS

HQ: CITY OF BOSTON
1 CITY HALL SQ STE 242, BOSTON, MA 022011020
Phone: 617 635-4545
Web: WWW.CITYOFBOSTON.GOV

HISTORICAL FINANCIALS

Company Type: Private

Income Statement FYE: June 30

	REVENUE ($ mil.)	NET INCOME ($ mil.)	NET PROFIT MARGIN	EMPLOYEES
06/19	3,953	213	5.4%	18,760
06/17	3,542	93	2.7%	—
06/16	3,393	138	4.1%	—
06/15	3,278	79	2.4%	—
Annual Growth	4.8%	28.1%	—	—

CITY OF BRIDGEPORT

EXECUTIVES

Mayor, Bill Finch
City Clerk*, Fleeta A Hudson
Town Clerk*, Hector Diaz
Dir of Finance*, Jerome I Baron
City Attorney*, Mark Anastasi
School Superintendent*, James B Connelly
Treas*, Sharon D Lemdon
Comptroller*, Michael Lupkas
Assistant Special Projects Man, Christopher Anastasi
Chief Administrative Officer, Andrew Nunn
Chief Financial Officer Comptr, Kenneth Flatto
Auditors: BLUM SHAPIRO & COMPANY PC

LOCATIONS

HQ: CITY OF BRIDGEPORT
999 BROAD ST STE 2, BRIDGEPORT, CT 066044320
Phone: 203 576-3964
Web: WWW.BRIDGEPORTCT.GOV

HISTORICAL FINANCIALS

Company Type: Private

Income Statement FYE: June 30

	REVENUE ($ mil.)	NET INCOME ($ mil.)	NET PROFIT MARGIN	EMPLOYEES
06/19	686	26	3.9%	3,646
06/18	767	23	3.1%	—
06/16	781	0	0.0%	—
06/15	723	35	4.9%	—
Annual Growth	(1.3%)	(7.0%)	—	—

2019 Year-End Financials

Return on assets: 1.4%
Return on equity: —
Current ratio: 1.80
Cash ($ mil.): 198

CITY OF CAMBRIDGE

The City of Cambridge houses an abundance of prominent minds. Part of the Greater Boston area it is home to prestigious universities Harvard and the Massachusetts Institute of Technology (MIT). With a population of more than 100000 the city covers just seven square miles. Most of its commercial districts are major street intersections (which act as neighborhood centers) which has given rise to its nickname "City of Squares." They include: Central Harvard Inman Kendall Lechmere and Porter Squares. Cambridge's city government is a bit unusual. The city manager (appointed by its nine city council members) rather than the mayor (also elected by the council) serves as the chief executive of the city.

EXECUTIVES

City Mgr, Robert W Healy
Budget Analyst, David Holland
Administrator, Elizabeth Lewis
Disability Project Coordinator, Michael Muehe
Executive Director, Nancy Tauber
Auditors: KPMG LLP BOSTON MA

LOCATIONS

HQ: CITY OF CAMBRIDGE
795 MASSACHUSETTS AVE, CAMBRIDGE, MA 021393219
Phone: 617 349-4260
Web: WWW.CAMBRIDGEMA.GOV

HISTORICAL FINANCIALS

Company Type: Private

Income Statement FYE: June 30

	REVENUE ($ mil.)	NET INCOME ($ mil.)	NET PROFIT MARGIN	EMPLOYEES
06/19	754	38	5.1%	2,000
06/18	726	65	9.0%	—
06/17	667	55	8.3%	—
06/16	635	18	2.9%	—
Annual Growth	5.9%	27.2%	—	—

CITY OF CHARLOTTE

You can bank on Charlotte ... the nation's second-largest banking center (behind New York City). The City of Charlotte delivers public services and promotes safety and health among residents. Policies are set by a mayor and 11 council members elected for two-year terms. The day-to-day operations are handled by a city manager. Charlotte has a population of more than 750000 and covers about 280 square miles. It's home to a handful of Fortune 500 companies including Bank of America Family Dollar and Duke Energy as well as the Carolina Panthers and Charlotte Motor Speedway. It also boasts some 700 places of worship earning it the nickname "The City of Churches."

EXECUTIVES

Mayor, Vi Lyles
Sergeant, Beth Boggess
Captain, Greg Collins
Program Inspector, David Barley
Sergeant, Michael Smith
Assistant Chief, Scott Eaton
Project, Eric Howard
Program Inspector, George Lee
Captain, Tom Seifert
Portfolio Manager Real Estate, Angela Hagerman
Keep Charlotte Beautiful Progr, Denise Coleman
Auditors: CHERRY BEKAERT LLP CHARLOTTE

LOCATIONS

HQ: CITY OF CHARLOTTE
600 E 4TH ST, CHARLOTTE, NC 282022816
Phone: 704 336-7600
Web: WWW.CHARLOTTENC.GOV

HISTORICAL FINANCIALS

Company Type: Private

Income Statement FYE: June 30

	REVENUE ($ mil.)	NET INCOME ($ mil.)	NET PROFIT MARGIN	EMPLOYEES
06/19	1,065	148	13.9%	5,011
06/18	997	(10)	—	—
06/17	945	(36)	—	—
06/16	929	56	6.1%	—
Annual Growth	4.7%	37.7%	—	—

CITY OF CHESAPEAKE

The City of Chesapeake attracts both beachcombers and history buffs. Located about 20 miles from Virginia Beach Chesapeake was established in 1963 through the merging of the city of South Norfolk and Norfolk County which was created in 1691. The first English settlement in the area began around 1620 along the banks of the Elizabeth River. The mayor vice mayor and seven city council members (elected for four-year terms) govern the city which has a population of more than 233370. The third-largest city in Virginia Chesapeake is home to the College of William and Mary and Hampton University.

EXECUTIVES

Vice President Application Development, Jenkins Steven
Board Member, Lisa Wagenbrenner
Vice Chair, Sandi Hutchinson
Auditors: CHERRY BEKAERT LLP VIRGINIA B

LOCATIONS

HQ: CITY OF CHESAPEAKE
306 CEDAR RD, CHESAPEAKE, VA 233225597
Phone: 757 382-6586
Web: WWW.CITYOFCHESAPEAKE.NET

HISTORICAL FINANCIALS

Company Type: Private

Income Statement FYE: June 30

	REVENUE ($ mil.)	NET INCOME ($ mil.)	NET PROFIT MARGIN	EMPLOYEES
06/16	621	14	2.4%	2,893
06/15	595	4	0.8%	—
06/14	0	4	—	—
06/13	570	4	0.7%	—
Annual Growth	2.9%	52.4%	—	—

CITY OF CINCINNATI

Founded in 1788 Cincinnati is home to almost 300000 people and covers roughly 80 square miles. It is the third-largest city in Ohio trailing behind Columbus and Cleveland. The city's government consists of the mayor and nine city council members (elected at large). Council committees deal with a wide range of issues including public education health economic concerns and community development. The city is also home to two major-league sports franchises – baseball's Cincinnati Reds and football's Cincinnati Bengals.

EXECUTIVES

Mayor, John Cranley
Prin*, Roxanne Qualls
Pres*, Wendell Young
Vice Mayor*, Christopher Smitherman
Coordinator, Chris Eilerman
Real Estate Consultant, Andrea Yang
Coordinator, Lynn Melzer
Human Resources Senior Analyst, Lisa Auciello
Council President Pro Tem, Tamaya Dennard
Acting City Manager, Patrick Duhaney
Recycling Coordinator, Sue Magness
Auditors: DAVE YOST COLUMBUS OHIO

LOCATIONS

HQ: CITY OF CINCINNATI
801 PLUM ST RM 246, CINCINNATI, OH 452025704
Phone: 513 352-3221
Web: WWW.CINCINNATI-OH.GOV

HISTORICAL FINANCIALS

Company Type: Private

Income Statement — FYE: June 30

	REVENUE ($ mil.)	NET INCOME ($ mil.)	NET PROFIT MARGIN	EMPLOYEES
06/19	769	25	3.3%	5,964
06/18	728	(22)	—	—
06/17	708	10	1.5%	—
Annual Growth	4.2%	52.5%	—	—

2019 Year-End Financials

Return on assets: 0.6%
Return on equity: 2.0%
Current ratio: 2.40
Cash ($ mil.): 93

CITY OF CLEVELAND

It's only rock and roll but Cleveland residents like it. The City of Cleveland Ohio (C-Town) is home to the Rock and Roll Hall of Fame and is the nation's 45th largest city and Ohio's second largest (behind Columbus). C-Town with more than 390000 residents is run by a mayor-council form of government. The legislative branch consists of a 21-member council and the executive branch comprises the mayor his adjunct offices advisors and the city's administrative departments. The mayor is the city's CEO and is elected to enforce its charter ordinances and state laws. The Village of Cleveland was incorporated in 1814.

EXECUTIVES

Legal Secretary, Tara Hoffman
Auditors: CLARK SCHAEFER HACKETT & CO

LOCATIONS

HQ: CITY OF CLEVELAND
601 LAKESIDE AVE E RM 210, CLEVELAND, OH 441141015
Phone: 216 664-2000
Web: WWW.CITY.CLEVELAND.OH.US

HISTORICAL FINANCIALS

Company Type: Private

Income Statement — FYE: December 31

	REVENUE ($ mil.)	NET INCOME ($ mil.)	NET PROFIT MARGIN	EMPLOYEES
12/19	839	31	3.7%	8,073
12/17	801	75	9.5%	—
12/15	706	20	3.0%	—
12/12	738	46	6.2%	—
Annual Growth	1.9%	(5.5%)	—	—

2019 Year-End Financials

Return on assets: 0.4%
Return on equity: 1.2%
Current ratio: —
Cash ($ mil.): 1,351

CITY OF COLUMBUS

So what if European explorer Christopher Columbus didn't sail the Scioto River? Columbus the capital of Ohio is located smack dab in the middle of the state. With a population of almost 836000 people Columbus is the largest city in the Buckeye State. (Cleveland and Cincinnati however have larger populations in their greater metropolitan areas.) Columbus is home to a handful of Fortune 500 companies including Nationwide Insurance and retailer L Brands. While the area had been home to European fur trappers since the 1700s and Native Americans for centuries Columbus became a city in 1812.

EXECUTIVES

Legal Secretary, Kathleen Addlesperger
Medical Director, David Keseg
Auditors: PLANTE & MORAN PLLC COLUMBUS

LOCATIONS

HQ: CITY OF COLUMBUS
90 W BROAD ST RM B33, COLUMBUS, OH 432159061
Phone: 614 645-7671
Web: WWW.COLUMBUS.GOV

HISTORICAL FINANCIALS

Company Type: Private

Income Statement — FYE: December 31

	REVENUE ($ mil.)	NET INCOME ($ mil.)	NET PROFIT MARGIN	EMPLOYEES
12/19	1,630	29	1.8%	8,385
12/18	1,478	94	6.4%	—
12/17	1,442	(1)	—	—
12/16	1,342	97	7.2%	—
Annual Growth	6.7%	(33.0%)	—	—

2019 Year-End Financials

Return on assets: 0.3%
Return on equity: 1.1%
Current ratio: —
Cash ($ mil.): 1,250

CITY OF EL PASO

Out in the West Texas Town of El Paso the sprawling metropolis is administered by the City of El Paso. The sixth-largest city in Texas with a population of about 650000 (2.5 million in the region including Ciudad Ju˘rez Mexico) El Paso is built around the base of the Franklin Mountains across the Rio Grande from Ju˘rez. Its city government consists of the mayor and eight council members (elected to four-year terms) along with a hired city manager. US Army post Fort Bliss and The University of Texas at El Paso are among the city's largest employers.

Financial Performance

In the budget of 2015 the City of El Paso had estimated revenues of $841.1 million with a major increase in Franchises Fees and Service Revenues offsetting a decline in Intergovernmental Revenues.

The increase in Franchises Fees was due to increase in the customer base (including El Paso Water Utilities International Bridges Crossing Fees) offset by lower decreases in the AT&T Electric Company and Gas Franchise Fees.

Service revenues grew thanks to higher mass transit revenues (due to an increase in fares and new transit projects) and higher revenues from solid waste services (thanks to a growth in customer accounts).

Strategy

The City is looking to leverage the region's position as one of the largest manufacturing centers in North America (with the largest bilingual and bi-cultural workforce in the Western Hemisphere) to further attract industries and new job growth. It is also seeking to boost tourism.

EXECUTIVES

Mayor, Dee Margo
City Manager, Tommy Gonzalez
Mgr, Leesy McCorgary
Director, Information Technolo, Enrique Martinez Jr
Chief Financial Officer, Robert Cortinas
Library Branch Manager, Michael Pitterman
Facilities Superintendent, Rivera Victor
Comptroller, Patricia Degman
Applications Admini, Richard Campos
Sports Manager, Andrea Schiechl
Human Resources, Mary Michel
Auditors: BKD LLP DALLAS TX

LOCATIONS

HQ: CITY OF EL PASO
300 N CAMPBELL ST, EL PASO, TX 799011402
Phone: 915 212-0000
Web: WWW.EPPENSION.ORG

HISTORICAL FINANCIALS

Company Type: Private

Income Statement — FYE: August 31

	REVENUE ($ mil.)	NET INCOME ($ mil.)	NET PROFIT MARGIN	EMPLOYEES
08/19	638	64	10.0%	6,500
08/18	609	(89)	—	—
08/17	569	(41)	—	—
08/16	550	270	49.2%	—
Annual Growth	5.1%	(38.2%)	—	—

2019 Year-End Financials

Return on assets: 1.3%
Return on equity: 5.6%
Current ratio: —
Cash ($ mil.): 67

CITY OF HARTFORD

EXECUTIVES

Mayor, Luke Bronin
City Treas*, Kathleen Plam
City Manager*, Sandra Kee Borges
Spokesperson, Lily Richardson
Public Relations Executive, Maribel La Luz
Police Officer, Chris Van Wey
Senior Project Manager, Claude Trapp
CPA, Joseph Caruso
Deputy Director, Kiley Gosselin
Mayors Scheduling Assistant, Latoya Aitcheson
Registrar of Voters, Sheila Hall
Auditors: RSM US LLP NEW HAVEN CONNECT

LOCATIONS

HQ: CITY OF HARTFORD
550 MAIN ST STE 1, HARTFORD, CT 061032913
Phone: 860 757-9311
Web: WWW.HPSCHOICE.COM

HISTORICAL FINANCIALS

Company Type: Private

Income Statement — FYE: June 30

	REVENUE ($ mil.)	NET INCOME ($ mil.)	NET PROFIT MARGIN	EMPLOYEES
06/19	948	5	0.6%	10,000
06/18	940	(11)	—	—
06/17	885	(75)	—	—
06/16	875	21	2.4%	—
Annual Growth	2.7%	(34.8%)	—	—

2019 Year-End Financials

Return on assets: 0.3% — Cash ($ mil.): 156
Return on equity: 1.3%
Current ratio: —

CITY OF HOUSTON

It is bigger in Texas when you consider the City of Houston. As the largest city in the state and one of the largest cities nationwide Houston is more than an oil town. Founded in 1836 and home to Rice University and the Astros it also has a noteworthy museum district and operates the Texas Medical Center one of the world's largest health care facilities. While a mayor oversees Houston's management 14 council members (elected for two-year terms) have the power to enact and enforce city ordinances. With a population of more than 2 million Houston operates through some 20 departments including health and human services police and parks and recreation. It has an annual budget of about $2 billion.

Geographic Reach

Houston reaches more than 656 square miles and comprises Harris Fort Bend and Montgomery counties. The larger area of Houston Sugar Land and Baytown with some 6.5 million residents makes up the fifth-largest metropolitan area in the US.

Strategy

Looking to provide staff with flexible transportation options the City of Houston partnered with car-sharing network Zipcar in 2012 to launch Houston Fleet Share. As part of the program the city maintains an owned fleet of 50 plug-in electric and hybrid vehicles that are outfitted with Zipcar's car-sharing technology. Houston Fleet Share is funded by the State Energy Conservation Office American Recovery and Reinvestment Act (SECO-ARRA) transportation program.

Company Background

Houston's operations were battered when Hurricane Ike — called the worst storm to hit Texas in nearly 50 years — rolled through the city in 2008. Water and electricity services were interrupted for days and municipal services were severely limited in the aftermath of the storm.

Houston gained national attention soon after by electing the first openly gay mayor of a major US city Annise Parker. She is Houston's second female mayor and served as an at-large member of the Houston City Council from 1997-2003 and City Controller from 2004-2009.

EXECUTIVES

Mayor, Sylvester Turner
Dir*, Tina Paez
Acting Cfo*, Tantri Emo
Chief of Staff*, Marvalette Hunter
Senior Assistant City, Cell Price
Assistant City, Charles Miers
Program Coordinator, Jason Jeffries
Assistant City, Mayura Ramanna
Assistant To Jill Jewett, Mayo, Veronica Juarez
Theater Event Coordinator, Anna Cardona
Council Member, District B, Carol Mims Galloway
Auditors: MCCONNELL & JONES LLP BANKS

LOCATIONS

HQ: CITY OF HOUSTON
901 BAGBY ST, HOUSTON, TX 770022049
Phone: 832 393-1000
Web: WWW.HOUSTONTX.GOV

PRODUCTS/OPERATIONS

Selected City Sites
Art Car Parade
Baylor College of Medicine
Houston Auto Show
Houston Greek Festival
Houston Livestock Show and Rodeo
Houston Theater District
Lyndon B. Johnson Space Center
MD Anderson Cancer Center
Memorial Hermann Hospital
Museum District
Rice University
Theater District
University of Houston
Uptown District
UT Health Science Center

HISTORICAL FINANCIALS

Company Type: Private

Income Statement — FYE: June 30

	REVENUE ($ mil.)	NET INCOME ($ mil.)	NET PROFIT MARGIN	EMPLOYEES
06/19	3,253	98	3.0%	23,235
06/18	3,110	52	1.7%	—
06/17	494	128	25.9%	—
06/16	2,946	(14)	—	—
Annual Growth	3.4%	—	—	—

2019 Year-End Financials

Return on assets: 0.4% — Cash ($ mil.): 854
Return on equity: 7.1%
Current ratio: —

CITY OF JACKSONVILLE

In Jacksonville residents and visitors can enjoy the Florida wilderness. The city which offers some 57000 acres of parks provides more land for recreation than any other city in the US. Its 19 city council members (five at-large members and 14 representing geographic districts) enact the legislation for the Jacksonville. Elected for four-year terms the mayor oversees the administration of the central government and appoints directors for its 10 departments. The 14th-largest city in the US Jacksonville has a population of more than 850000 residents.

EXECUTIVES

Mayor, Alvin Brown
General Legal Practice, Deborah D Walters
Payroll Staff, Tina Rehmel
Customer Staff, Ken Roper
Officer, Alex Mack
Internal Auditor, Mitchell Perin
Customer Representativ, Amy Maddox
Director of Intra Governmental, Craig Thompson
Animal Placement Supervisor, Daniel Clavel
Teen Court Program Case Manage, Danielle Felton
Communications Director, David Chapman
Auditors: CARR RIGGS & INGRAM LLC JACKS

LOCATIONS

HQ: CITY OF JACKSONVILLE
117 W DUVAL ST FL MESS, JACKSONVILLE, FL 322023737
Phone: 904 630-1776
Web: WWW.COJ.NET

HISTORICAL FINANCIALS

Company Type: Private

Income Statement — FYE: September 30

	REVENUE ($ mil.)	NET INCOME ($ mil.)	NET PROFIT MARGIN	EMPLOYEES
09/18	1,599	64	4.0%	7,908
09/17	1,560	12	0.8%	—
09/16	1,493	33	2.3%	—
09/15	1,414	50	3.6%	—
Annual Growth	4.2%	8.7%	—	—

2018 Year-End Financials

Return on assets: 0.4% — Cash ($ mil.): 187
Return on equity: 2.5%
Current ratio: —

CITY OF LAS VEGAS

Some 585000 people call Sin City home. Las Vegas Nevada's largest city is the gaming capital of the US. The city is overseen by a mayor an appointed city manager and six elected city council members. Its largest industry is tourism; the casino resorts attract visitors seeking business and pleasure — Las Vegas hosts almost 20000 conventions every year.

EXECUTIVES

Legal Secretary, Cindy Kelly
Manager Health And Human Services, William Federson
Secretary, Paul Harrison
Auditors: PIERCY BOWLER TAYLOR & KERN L

LOCATIONS

HQ: CITY OF LAS VEGAS
495 S MAIN ST, LAS VEGAS, NV 891012986
Phone: 702 229-6321
Web: WWW.LASVEGASNEVADA.GOV

HISTORICAL FINANCIALS

Company Type: Private

Income Statement FYE: June 30

	REVENUE ($ mil.)	NET INCOME ($ mil.)	NET PROFIT MARGIN	EMPLOYEES
06/19	857	58	6.9%	2,500
06/18	782	69	8.9%	—
06/17	688	10	1.6%	—
06/16	704	248	35.3%	—
Annual Growth	6.8%	(38.1%)	—	—

CITY OF LONG BEACH

It's a city it's a port it's Long Beach. The City of Long Beach boasts the Port of Long Beach one of the busiest ports in the nation. With a population of more than 460000 Long Beach is part of the greater Los Angeles metropolitan area. The city uses a charter form of government with an elected mayor and city council as well as an appointed city manager. It's also known for its large oil reserves managed by the Long Beach Gas & Oil Department.

EXECUTIVES

City Treasurer, David Nakamoto
Secretary, Jessica Rosa
Secretary, Nina Anaya
Auditors: KPMG LLP LOS ANGELES CALIFOR

LOCATIONS

HQ: CITY OF LONG BEACH
411 W OCEAN BLVD, LONG BEACH, CA 908024664
Phone: 562 570-6450
Web: WWW.LONGBEACH.GOV

HISTORICAL FINANCIALS

Company Type: Private

Income Statement FYE: September 30

	REVENUE ($ mil.)	NET INCOME ($ mil.)	NET PROFIT MARGIN	EMPLOYEES
09/19	864	36	4.3%	5,028
09/18	779	26	3.4%	—
09/17	716	9	1.3%	—
09/16	675	(1)	—	—
Annual Growth	8.6%	—	—	—

2019 Year-End Financials

Return on assets: 0.3%
Return on equity: 0.7%
Current ratio: 2.80
Cash ($ mil.): 581

CITY OF LOS ANGELES

Los Angeles may be a Mecca for the rich and famous but there is little glamour in running a city of more than 4 million people. Governing responsibilities are shared among the city's mayor and city council while various commissions departments and bureaus see to the daily operations that keep the wheels spinning. Elected every four years the mayor appoints most commission members (subject to approval by the city council) and serves as the city's executive officer. The City of Los Angeles is located in the County of Los Angeles.

EXECUTIVES

Medical Director Pathology And Lab Medicine Children's Hospital Los Angeles, Paul Pattengale
Vp Of Programming, Noah Silver
Managing Director. Candidate 2020, Kush Gaur
Head Secretary, Rosie Aldaz

LOCATIONS

HQ: CITY OF LOS ANGELES
200 N SPRING ST STE 303, LOS ANGELES, CA 900123239
Phone: 213 978-0600
Web: WWW.LACITY.ORG

HISTORICAL FINANCIALS

Company Type: Private

Income Statement FYE: June 30

	REVENUE ($ mil.)	NET INCOME ($ mil.)	NET PROFIT MARGIN	EMPLOYEES
06/16	7,196	231	3.2%	41,000
06/09*	6,281	(285)	—	—
12/08	0	0	—	—
Annual Growth	274.6%	—	—	—

*Fiscal year change

2016 Year-End Financials

Return on assets: 0.4%
Return on equity: 1.2%
Current ratio: —
Cash ($ mil.): 7,446

CITY OF MEMPHIS

Home to Graceland and Beale Street Memphis has both feet entrenched in the world of music. With a population of more than 670000 it is located in the southwestern corner of the state and stretches over 300 square miles. Serving the largest urban population in Tennessee it is run by a mayor and 13 city council members (elected from nine districts). City government is responsible for economic development public education housing public utilities homeland security and landmark preservation. Set atop the eastern bank of the Mississippi River and named after the ancient capital of Egypt Memphis was founded in 1820.

EXECUTIVES

Vice President, Alicia McAnally
Vice Chair, Amber Floyd
Auditors: BANKS FINLEY WHITE & CO ME

LOCATIONS

HQ: CITY OF MEMPHIS
125 N MAIN ST STE 628, MEMPHIS, TN 381032032
Phone: 901 676-6657
Web: WWW.MEMPHISTN.GOV

HISTORICAL FINANCIALS

Company Type: Private

Income Statement FYE: June 30

	REVENUE ($ mil.)	NET INCOME ($ mil.)	NET PROFIT MARGIN	EMPLOYEES
06/16	906	8	0.9%	6,000
06/15	863	1	0.2%	—
06/14	840	26	3.2%	—
06/13	845	(25)	—	—
Annual Growth	2.3%	—	—	—

2016 Year-End Financials

Return on assets: 0.1%
Return on equity: 0.3%
Current ratio: —
Cash ($ mil.): 285

CITY OF MIAMI

Thankfully the City of Miami is much more than Dolphins sound-machines and vice cops. With a population of more than 400000 the city has little trouble attracting tourists and residents alike to the bustling international hub of business entertainment and culture. Thanks to its status as a transportation hub and the businesses that make the city home to international operations the city is also known as the Gateway to Latin America. The city government consists of its elected mayor five commissioners a city manager and the heads of Miami's various public services departments.

EXECUTIVES

Mayor, Francis X Suarez
Commissioner*, Mark Sarnoff
Manager, Rasha Cameau
Administrative Aide II, Elsa Fernandez
Mayor, Tomas Regalado
Human Resources Technician I, Katia Dorneval
Director of Architecture and D, Brian Zeltsman
Budget Director, Chris Rose
Park Manager II, Patrice Jackson
Admin Assistant I, Roberto Santana
City Manager, Aniska Elliott
Auditors: RSM US LLP MIAMI FLORIDA

LOCATIONS

HQ: CITY OF MIAMI
3500 PAN AMERICAN DR FL 2, MIAMI, FL 331335595
Phone: 305 250-5300
Web: WWW.MIAMIGOV.COM

HISTORICAL FINANCIALS

Company Type: Private

Income Statement FYE: September 30

	REVENUE ($ mil.)	NET INCOME ($ mil.)	NET PROFIT MARGIN	EMPLOYEES
09/16	837	15	1.8%	3,000
09/15	792	(1)	—	—
09/12	675	(18)	—	—
09/09	691	(30)	—	—
Annual Growth	2.8%	—	—	—

CITY OF MINNEAPOLIS

One half of Minnesota's famed Twin Cities Minneapolis is a combination of the Sioux word for water with the Greek word for city. With 20 lakes and wetlands plus the Mississippi River waterfront and many creeks and streams the City of Minneapolis is known as the City of Lakes. It is governed by a mayor and city council with 13 members representing the city's wards. The mayor appoints the chief of police but has little other power. Independent boards oversee public housing the tax office and public parks and libraries. The city's more than 80 parks serve as a model for city park systems nationwide. Formed in 1856 Minneapolis is now home to a population of almost 400000.

EXECUTIVES

Mayor, Jacob Frey
City Clerk*, Steve Ristuben
Councilman*, Andrea Jenkins
Program Inspector, Michael Kjos
Director of Economic Policy, David Frank
Deputy Controller, Dawn Koenig
Executive Committee Member, Jeff Sands
Transportation Planning Intern, Katie Page
Internal Auditor, Travis Kamm
Manager, Anita Birmingham
Employee, Ann Kjos
Auditors: REBECCA OTTO SAINT PAUL MN

LOCATIONS

HQ: CITY OF MINNEAPOLIS
350 S 5TH ST STE 325M, MINNEAPOLIS, MN 554151315
Phone: 612 673-3000
Web: WWW.MINNEAPOLISMN.GOV

HISTORICAL FINANCIALS

Company Type: Private

Income Statement — FYE: December 31

	REVENUE ($ mil.)	NET INCOME ($ mil.)	NET PROFIT MARGIN	EMPLOYEES
12/19	916	85	9.3%	5,000
12/18	858	84	9.8%	—
12/17	846	36	4.3%	—
12/16	807	11	1.4%	—
Annual Growth	4.3%	95.4%	—	—

2019 Year-End Financials

Return on assets: 1.8%
Return on equity: 3.0%
Current ratio: —
Cash ($ mil.): 1,038

CITY OF NEW HAVEN

EXECUTIVES

Mayor, John Destefano Jr
Coordinator, Bill Macmullen
Coordinator, Tomi Veale
Executive Director, Karyn Gilvarg
Program Manager Youth, Gwendolyn Busch
Education, Typhanie Jackson
Librarian, David Simon
Assistant, Gerald Bennett
Director of Aging, Migdalia Castro
Alderman, Alberta Witherspoon
Executive Administrative Asst, Dawn Lewis
Auditors: MCGLADREY LLP NEW HAVEN CONN

LOCATIONS

HQ: CITY OF NEW HAVEN
165 CHURCH ST FL 2, NEW HAVEN, CT 065102010
Phone: 203 946-8200
Web: WWW.NEWHAVENCT.GOV

HISTORICAL FINANCIALS

Company Type: Private

Income Statement — FYE: June 30

	REVENUE ($ mil.)	NET INCOME ($ mil.)	NET PROFIT MARGIN	EMPLOYEES
06/18	776	10	1.3%	4,500
06/17	819	5	0.7%	—
06/16	811	10	1.3%	—
06/15	738	3	0.5%	—
Annual Growth	1.7%	45.2%	—	—

2018 Year-End Financials

Return on assets: 0.5%
Return on equity: —
Current ratio: —
Cash ($ mil.): 96

CITY OF NEW ORLEANS

New Orleans is a city with a story. The city was founded in 1718 and became famous for its architecture music food and parties. The city is home to a major port the New Orleans Saints the French Quarter and is the regarded as the birthplace of jazz. Devastated by Hurricane Katrina and the flooding which ensued in 2005 the city has undertaken a massive rebuilding and recovery effort utilizing state and federal assistance. The city of New Orleans is governed by a city council consisting of seven members and an elected mayor.

EXECUTIVES

Director Of Health, Sheila Webb
Auditors: POSTLETHWAITE & NETTERVILLE N

LOCATIONS

HQ: CITY OF NEW ORLEANS
1300 PERDIDO ST BSMT FL2, NEW ORLEANS, LA 701122128
Phone: 504 658-4900
Web: WWW.NOLA.GOV

HISTORICAL FINANCIALS

Company Type: Private

Income Statement — FYE: December 31

	REVENUE ($ mil.)	NET INCOME ($ mil.)	NET PROFIT MARGIN	EMPLOYEES
12/18	1,056	1	0.1%	6,658
12/17	901	(74)	—	—
12/16	881	39	4.5%	—
12/15	905	65	7.2%	—
Annual Growth	5.2%	(71.4%)	—	—

2018 Year-End Financials

Return on assets: —
Return on equity: 0.1%
Current ratio: —
Cash ($ mil.): 318

CITY OF NEWPORT NEWS

There are nearly as many theories on where the unusual city name came from as there are citizens of Newport News Virginia. Whether it was founded on land chosen by Sir William Newce or the point where Captain Newport delivered good news to early settlers Newport News today boasts a population of some 193000. The mayor and six-member city council (representing three districts) work together to serve residents and visitors backed by an annual budget of about $750 million. The council sets up city policies and controls funding while the city manager attorney and clerk carry out the day-to-day administration of Newport News. The city which was settled around 1621 is well known as a military shipbuilding hub.

EXECUTIVES

Mayor, McKinley Price
City Mgr*, Edgar Maroney
City Mgr*, Hilde Brandt
Prin*, James M Bourey
Project Coordinator, Aaron Shivers
Project Coordinator, Wendy Ledford
Sergeant, Xavier O Falero
Chief Television Engineer, Ishrat Mohammad
Production Specialist, Wade Harrington
Sr Production Specialist, John Corriere
Administrative Assistant II, Maria Tisdale
Auditors: CHERRY BEKAERT LLP RICHMOND

LOCATIONS

HQ: CITY OF NEWPORT NEWS
2400 WASHINGTON AVE MAIN, NEWPORT NEWS, VA 236074300
Phone: 757 926-8411
Web: WWW.LEEHALL.ORG

HISTORICAL FINANCIALS

Company Type: Private

Income Statement — FYE: June 30

	REVENUE ($ mil.)	NET INCOME ($ mil.)	NET PROFIT MARGIN	EMPLOYEES
06/20	598	(30)	—	5,000
06/19	602	50	8.4%	—
06/17	563	33	5.9%	—
06/16	544	10	1.9%	—
Annual Growth	2.4%	—	—	—

2020 Year-End Financials

Return on assets: (-1.3%)
Return on equity: (-4.9%)
Current ratio: —
Cash ($ mil.): 332

CITY OF NORFOLK

You could say that the City of Norfolk Virginia is at home on the water. The second-largest city in Virginia with a population of more than 245400 Norfolk sports miles of lake river and bay front as well as a bustling international port and the world's largest naval base. The city was founded in 1682 and offers such attractions as the battleship USS Wisconsin the National Maritime Center and Old Dominion University. Norfolk Southern Railway's corporate headquarters are also located in the city.

Norfolk city government consists of its seven-member city council and mayor. The city manager serves as the city's COO and is appointed by the city council.

EXECUTIVES

Mayor, Kenneth Cooper Alexander
City Mgr*, Regina V K Williams
Cmo*, Michael G Brown
Attorney, Charles Prentace
Attorney, Bernard A Pishko
Communications, Amanda Howie
Assistant City Engineer, Chuck Joyner
Public Information Officer, Jo Hughes
Prosecutor, Phil Evans
Design Engineer, Tammy Halstead
Police Captain, Todd Williams
Auditors: KPMG LLP NORFOLK VA

LOCATIONS

HQ: CITY OF NORFOLK
810 UNION ST STE 508, NORFOLK, VA 235108048
Phone: 757 664-7300
Web: WWW.NORFOLK.GOV

HISTORICAL FINANCIALS

Company Type: Private

Income Statement — FYE: June 30

	REVENUE ($ mil.)	NET INCOME ($ mil.)	NET PROFIT MARGIN	EMPLOYEES
06/19	751	162	21.6%	4,364
06/18	730	73	10.0%	—
06/17	702	22	3.3%	—
06/16	684	(119)	—	—
Annual Growth	3.2%	—	—	—

CITY OF OAKLAND

Joining San Francisco and San Jose Oakland makes up one-third of Northern California's Golden Triangle . Founded in 1852 Oakland boasts of a diverse population numbering more than 390000 residents a Mediterranean climate and thriving hip arts scene. The city is a hub for the port of San Francisco Bay as well as for the business elite and the higher educated. Environmental policies have helped propel Oakland to stand among the top green economies in the US. The city is served by a mayor and eight council members who oversee a budget of almost $1 billion. It is home to the NBA's Golden State Warriors NFL's Oakland Raiders and national landmark Lake Merritt.

EXECUTIVES

Mayor, Libby Schaaf
City Mgr*, Deborah Edgerly
Film Coordinator, AMI Zins
Staff, Joseph Feiccabrino
Captain, Brian Oftedal
Sergeant, Bryan Hubbard
Captain, Drennon Lindsey
Captain, Leronne Armstrong
Human Resources Analyst, Lisette Del Pino
Coordinator, Mary Costello
Sergeant, Mary Guttormson
Auditors: MACIAS GINI & O'CONNELL LLP W

LOCATIONS

HQ: CITY OF OAKLAND
1 FRANK H OGAWA PLZ 2ND, OAKLAND, CA 946121904
Phone: 510 238-3280
Web: WWW.OAKLANDCA.GOV

HISTORICAL FINANCIALS

Company Type: Private

Income Statement — FYE: June 30

	REVENUE ($ mil.)	NET INCOME ($ mil.)	NET PROFIT MARGIN	EMPLOYEES
06/19	1,211	28	2.3%	4,000
06/18	1,164	184	15.8%	—
06/17	1,071	100	9.4%	—
06/16	1,020	28	2.8%	—
Annual Growth	5.9%	(0.5%)	—	—

CITY OF OKLAHOMA CITY

Oklahoma City was born overnight as a boomtown named Oklahoma Station in 1889 during the celebrated land rush in Oklahoma Territory. It became in time the state capital and largest city (with a population approaching 600000) and is headquarters of oil and gas companies Chesapeake Energy and Devon Energy as well as electric utility OGE Energy and service station operator Love's Truck Stops. City government is headed by a mayor and council members representing eight wards. The city captured its first top-rank sports franchise when the Oklahoma City Thunder NBA team began play in 2008.

EXECUTIVES

Mayor, Mick Cornett
City Manager, James D Couch
City Clerk, Frances Kersey
Asst Fin Dir, Kenton Tsoodle
Coordinator, Yolinda Washington
Associate Planner, Donna Cervantes
Auditors: ALLEN GIBBS & HOULIK LC W

LOCATIONS

HQ: CITY OF OKLAHOMA CITY
100 N WALKER AVE, OKLAHOMA CITY, OK 731022230
Phone: 405 297-2506
Web: WWW.OKC.GOV

HISTORICAL FINANCIALS

Company Type: Private

Income Statement — FYE: June 30

	REVENUE ($ mil.)	NET INCOME ($ mil.)	NET PROFIT MARGIN	EMPLOYEES
06/18	865	112	13.0%	4,500
06/17	806	(21)	—	—
06/16	800	26	3.3%	—
06/15	803	65	8.2%	—
Annual Growth	2.5%	19.5%	—	—

2018 Year-End Financials

Return on assets: 1.6%
Return on equity: 3.1%
Current ratio: 4.40
Cash ($ mil.): 76

CITY OF OMAHA

Owing it name to one the tribes living in the area the City Omaha was once bypassed by the Lewis and Clark expedition. Founded in 1854 Omaha has become the 42nd largest city in the U.S. with a population of almost 409.000 in an area measuring little more than 130 square miles. The city is ruled by a mayor-council consisting of of an "at-large" mayor and 7 district councilmembers. The City of Omaha is home for megacompanies Berkshire Hathaway ConAgra Peter Kiewit Sons Mutual of Omaha TD Ameritrade Union Pacific West Corporation Valmont Industries and Werner Enterprises.

EXECUTIVES

Vice President, Kenneth Smith
Director Of Nursing, Marti Christensen
Auditors: BKD LLP OMAHA NEBRASKA

LOCATIONS

HQ: CITY OF OMAHA
1819 FARNAM ST RM 300, OMAHA, NE 681831000
Phone: 402 444-5000
Web: WWW.CITYOFOMAHA.ORG

HISTORICAL FINANCIALS

Company Type: Private

Income Statement — FYE: December 31

	REVENUE ($ mil.)	NET INCOME ($ mil.)	NET PROFIT MARGIN	EMPLOYEES
12/19	636	1	0.2%	2,800
12/18	593	(29)	—	—
12/17	589	24	4.2%	—
Annual Growth	3.9%	(76.6%)	—	—

CITY OF PHILADELPHIA

Known as the City of Brotherly Love Philadelphia is the fifth largest city in the nation with a population of more than 1.5 million. The city which covers 135 square miles operates through some 50 departments boards offices and other units that include emergency medical services sanitation services and street maintenance. Founded in 1682 by William Penn Philadelphia has a mayor 10 districts and 17 council members. The city which hosts millions of tourists each year is home to the Phillies the Eagles the Flyers the 76ers Bryn Mawr College the Liberty Bell and the National Constitution Center. The City of Philadelphia has an annual budget of more than $3.5 billion.

EXECUTIVES

Senior Vice Presiden, John Ryan
Vice President Operations, Bob Brown
Auditors: CHRISTY BRADY CPA PHILADELPH

LOCATIONS

HQ: CITY OF PHILADELPHIA
215 CITY HALL, PHILADELPHIA, PA 191073214
Phone: 215 686-2181
Web: WWW.PHILA.GOV

PRODUCTS/OPERATIONS

Selected Units
Behavioral Health
Board of Pensions and Retirement

Board of Revision of Taxes
City Controllers Office
City Planning Commission
City Treasurer
Civil Service Commission
Commerce
Department of Human Services
Ethics Board
Finance
Fire
Fleet Management
Health Department
Historical Commission
Human Relations
Inspector General
Labor Relations
Law
Library
Licenses and Inspections
Parking Authority
Philadelphia International Airport
Police
Procurement
Recreation
Records Department
Redevelopment Authority
Water Revenue Bureau

HISTORICAL FINANCIALS

Company Type: Private

Income Statement — FYE: June 30

	REVENUE ($ mil.)	NET INCOME ($ mil.)	NET PROFIT MARGIN	EMPLOYEES
06/17	6,646	20	0.3%	29,862
06/16	6,264	(64)	—	—
06/15	6,070	(92)	—	—
06/14	5,947	(10)	—	—
Annual Growth	3.8%	—	—	—

2017 Year-End Financials

Return on assets: 0.1% — Cash ($ mil.): 1,744
Return on equity: —
Current ratio: —

CITY OF PHOENIX

Phoenix the capital of Arizona has a population of about 1.4 million and is the sixth largest city in the US. Located in the south-central portion of the state Phoenix covers a sprawling 500 square miles and is geographically larger than Los Angeles. The City of Phoenix operates through some 30 departments including street transportation water services human services and public transit. Eight city council members (representing eight districts) and the mayor make up the city council which develop laws and policy for governing the city. Phoenix was incorporated in 1881.

EXECUTIVES

Mayor, Thelda Williams
Sales and Marketing Executive, Lexie Van Haren
Sergeant, Dale Skjerping
Sergeant, Tom Osborne
Information Specialist, James Baran
Counsel, Diego Leal
Management Assistant II, Amy Hartle
Career Advisor, Angela Boozer
Officer, Mark Aker
Staff, Alberto N Mejia
Aviation Program Manager, Anne Kurtenbach
Auditors: BKD LLP DALLAS TEXAS

LOCATIONS

HQ: CITY OF PHOENIX
200 W WASHINGTON ST FL 11, PHOENIX, AZ 850031611
Phone: 602 262-7111
Web: WWW.PHOENIX.GOV

HISTORICAL FINANCIALS

Company Type: Private

Income Statement — FYE: June 30

	REVENUE ($ mil.)	NET INCOME ($ mil.)	NET PROFIT MARGIN	EMPLOYEES
06/19	2,588	54	2.1%	14,000
06/18	2,521	(34)	—	—
06/17	2,318	198	8.6%	—
06/16	2,136	(1)	—	—
Annual Growth	6.6%	—	—	—

2019 Year-End Financials

Return on assets: 0.3% — Cash ($ mil.): 604
Return on equity: 0.9%
Current ratio: —

CITY OF PITTSBURGH

Take one look at the skyline and it's no wonder Pittsburgh's been nicknamed "The City of Bridges." With more than 440 bridges 150 skyscrapers and a countless number of steel behemoths Pittsburgh is Pennsylvania's second largest city (behind Philadelphia) with a population of more than 305700. The city is composed of nine districts each represented by a council member while the mayor rounds out the executive side. Its annual budget goes toward enhancements to health care and retirement as well as hiring police and fire prevention personnel; most of its revenue comes from real estate taxes. Pittsburgh was founded in 1758.

EXECUTIVES

Mayor, William Peduto
Prin*, Sara Deroy
Sr Bdgtg Anlst, Kathleen Butter
Program Inspector, Alan Asbury
Chief of Staff, Dan Gilman
Commission Representative, Leanne Davis
Police Officer, Steve Mescan
Information Technology Manager, Thomas Vennero
Assistant City Solicitor, Kelly Mistick
Project Management Administrat, Tracy Sowinski
Commissioner, Amanda Neatrour
Auditors: MAHER DUESSEL PITTSBURGH PEN

LOCATIONS

HQ: CITY OF PITTSBURGH
414 GRANT ST, PITTSBURGH, PA 152192409
Phone: 412 255-2640
Web: WWW.PITTSBURGHPA.GOV

HISTORICAL FINANCIALS

Company Type: Private

Income Statement — FYE: December 31

	REVENUE ($ mil.)	NET INCOME ($ mil.)	NET PROFIT MARGIN	EMPLOYEES
12/19	651	48	7.4%	3,500
12/18	635	2	0.3%	—
12/14	537	22	4.2%	—
12/13	542	(30)	—	—
Annual Growth	3.1%	—	—	—

2019 Year-End Financials

Return on assets: 2.1% — Cash ($ mil.): 432
Return on equity: —
Current ratio: 2.70

CITY OF PORTLAND

A rose by any other name would smell as sweet may be only way to tell this city from 18 other Portlands in the US. Portland has been known as the City of Roses since 1888 and has hosted an annual rose festival since 1905.

EXECUTIVES

Treasurer, Terry Black
Auditors: MOSS ADAMS LLP PORTLAND ORE

LOCATIONS

HQ: CITY OF PORTLAND
1221 SW 4TH AVE RM 340, PORTLAND, OR 972041900
Phone: 503 823-4120
Web: WWW.NPNSCOMMUNITY.ORG

HISTORICAL FINANCIALS

Company Type: Private

Income Statement — FYE: June 30

	REVENUE ($ mil.)	NET INCOME ($ mil.)	NET PROFIT MARGIN	EMPLOYEES
06/20	1,648	269	16.3%	5,684
06/19	1,604	138	8.6%	—
06/18	1,483	110	7.5%	—
06/17	1,379	94	6.9%	—
Annual Growth	6.1%	41.8%	—	—

CITY OF PROVIDENCE

EXECUTIVES

Mayor, Jorge O Elorza
Coordinator, Rita Murphy
Officer, Paul Renzi
Deputy Chief of Staff, Marisa O'Gara
City Council, David Salvatore
Chief of Staff, Emily Martineau
Human Resources Director, Emmanuel Echevarria
City, Jeffrey Padwa
Emergency Director, Kevin Kugel
Court Clerk, Paul Jabour
Detective, Shawn Maxwell
Auditors: MARCUM LLP PROVIDENCE RI

LOCATIONS

HQ: CITY OF PROVIDENCE
25 DORRANCE ST UNIT 1, PROVIDENCE, RI 029031738
Phone: 401 421-7740
Web: WWW.PROVIDENCERI.GOV

HISTORICAL FINANCIALS

Company Type: Private

Income Statement — FYE: June 30

	REVENUE ($ mil.)	NET INCOME ($ mil.)	NET PROFIT MARGIN	EMPLOYEES
06/19	853	7	0.8%	2,800
06/18	836	15	1.9%	—
06/17	821	5	0.6%	—
06/16	790	6	0.8%	—
Annual Growth	2.6%	5.1%	—	—

2019 Year-End Financials

Return on assets: 0.4%
Return on equity: —
Current ratio: 1.80
Cash ($ mil.): 175

CITY OF RICHMOND

Music legends Joan Baez and Jerry Garcia both sang about seeing Richmond fall but these days Richmond is rising. The city which made its living on tobacco and slave trading early in its history now thrives on business law and the research center at the Virginia Biotechnology Research Park. Richmond is home to several major corporations including CarMax Dominion Resources Genworth Financial and MeadWestvaco. It's also home to more than 200000 people who are governed by a city council representing nine districts along with an at-large mayor. The city follows a council-manager system and the mayor is not part of the council. Richmond which was founded in 1737 has an annual budget of about $1.4 billion.

EXECUTIVES

Legal Secretary, Robinson Victrena Vickie
City Treasurer, Nichole Armstead
Auditors: CLIFTONLARSONALLEN LLP ARLING

LOCATIONS

HQ: CITY OF RICHMOND
900 E BROAD ST STE 201, RICHMOND, VA 232191907
Phone: 804 646-7970
Web: WWW.RICHMONDGOV.COM

HISTORICAL FINANCIALS

Company Type: Private

Income Statement — FYE: June 30

	REVENUE ($ mil.)	NET INCOME ($ mil.)	NET PROFIT MARGIN	EMPLOYEES
06/20	824	(6)	—	5,315
06/19	800	72	9.0%	—
06/18	757	(41)	—	—
06/17	786	51	6.6%	—
Annual Growth	1.6%	—	—	—

2020 Year-End Financials

Return on assets: (-0.1%)
Return on equity: (-0.6%)
Current ratio: 2.10
Cash ($ mil.): 599

CITY OF ROCHESTER

Known as "The World's Image Center" the City of Rochester situated on the south of Lake Ontario encompasses some 37 sq. mi. The city incorporated in 1703 was one of the first "boomtowns" in the US due to a large number of flour mills. Rochester is now a center of higher education medical and technological research with University of Rochester Rochester Institute of Technology Bausch & Lomb and Kodak calling it home. Xerox still has a large presence in the city. A population of over 200000 makes the city the third largest in the state. The government is a "strong mayor" style with 4 district and 5 at-large council members. Previously known as "The Flower City" it hosts an annual lilac festival.

EXECUTIVES

Mayor, Lovely A Warren
Sergeant, Michael Lesniak
Director of Financial Audits, Jacqueline Farabell
Architectural Drafting Technic, Luigi Ianniello
Purchasing, Ella Harbison
Asar Release Administrators, John Rowe
Branch Manager, Bruce Tehan
Associate Digital Communicatio, Carlet Cleare
Commander, Elena Correia
Branch Manager, Erin Clarke
Commander, Fabian Rivera
Auditors: FREED MAXICK CPAS PC ROCHE

LOCATIONS

HQ: CITY OF ROCHESTER
30 CHURCH ST, ROCHESTER, NY 146141206
Phone: 585 428-6755
Web: WWW.CITYOFROCHESTER.GOV

HISTORICAL FINANCIALS

Company Type: Private

Income Statement — FYE: June 30

	REVENUE ($ mil.)	NET INCOME ($ mil.)	NET PROFIT MARGIN	EMPLOYEES
06/19	577	(3)	—	3,200
06/18	584	17	2.9%	—
06/17	581	(19)	—	—
06/16	555	(12)	—	—
Annual Growth	1.3%	—	—	—

2019 Year-End Financials

Return on assets: (-0.1%)
Return on equity: —
Current ratio: —
Cash ($ mil.): 306

CITY OF SACRAMENTO

With its Mediterranean climate and location at the foot of the Sierra Nevadas living in the city of Sacramento is no sacrifice. Founded in 1849 Sacramento is the oldest incorporated city in the state and its seventh most populated comprising about 470000 residents. California's capital city uses a council-manager form of government with council members from eight districts elected to four-year terms. The council sets up city policies approves contracts and a budget of nearly $800 million as well as hears appeals of city decisions. The four council-appointed officers that carry out the city's business are the city manager attorney treasurer and clerk. A Legislative Affairs Unit supports the council.

EXECUTIVES

Mayor, Darrell Steinberg
Chief Innovation Officer*, Louis Stewart
Administrative Analyst, Beverly Coleman
Customer Staff, Thompson Raquel
Auditors: VAVRINEK TRINE DAY & CO LL

LOCATIONS

HQ: CITY OF SACRAMENTO
915 I ST FL 5, SACRAMENTO, CA 958142622
Phone: 916 808-5300
Web: WWW.CITYOFSACRAMENTO.ORG

HISTORICAL FINANCIALS

Company Type: Private

Income Statement — FYE: June 30

	REVENUE ($ mil.)	NET INCOME ($ mil.)	NET PROFIT MARGIN	EMPLOYEES
06/19	838	86	10.3%	4,500
06/18	723	2	0.3%	—
06/17	694	46	6.7%	—
06/16	709	91	12.9%	—
Annual Growth	5.7%	(1.9%)	—	—

CITY OF SAN ANTONIO

When you "Remember the Alamo" don't forget San Antonio! The second-largest Texas city (behind Houston) with a population of about 1.5 million San Antonio was the site of the Battle of the Alamo. Today it's home to major tourist attractions like the River Walk SeaWorld and Six Flags Fiesta Texas as well as the San Antonio Spurs NBA franchise and more than 50 golf courses. It has a huge military presence with three major Army and Air Force bases. San Antonio is run by a mayor and 10 district representatives who pass laws and establish policies for the city. Its city manager oversees day-to-day operations including nearly 40 departments. San Antonio has an annual budget of more than $2 billion.

EXECUTIVES

Vice President Of Marketing, Martin Rodriguez
Legal Secretary, Maria Urbano
National Sales Manager, Tanya Espalin
Auditors: GRANT THORNTON LLP HOUSTON T

LOCATIONS

HQ: CITY OF SAN ANTONIO
CITY HALL 100 MLITARY PLZ, SAN ANTONIO, TX 78205
Phone: 210 207-6000
Web: WWW.SANANTONIO.GOV

HISTORICAL FINANCIALS

Company Type: Private

Income Statement — FYE: September 30

	REVENUE ($ mil.)	NET INCOME ($ mil.)	NET PROFIT MARGIN	EMPLOYEES
09/19	2,150	192	9.0%	12,000
09/18	2,056	284	13.8%	—
09/16	0	0	—	—
09/15	1,742	(96)	—	—
Annual Growth	5.4%	—	—	—

2019 Year-End Financials

Return on assets: 0.7%
Return on equity: 2.1%
Current ratio: 3.80
Cash ($ mil.): 507

CITY OF SAN DIEGO

The City of San Diego offers more than just warm weather and beautiful beaches. The second-largest city in California (with a population of more than 1.3 million) known as Telecom Valley is also one of the centers in the US for technological manufacturing. Its council members each represent one of its nine districts. Founded in 1769 San Diego is the home to 3 universities as well as professional sports teams Padres of MLB and Chargers of the NFL. The city operates through some 50 programs and departments including environmental services homeland security parks and recreation and the commission for arts and culture. The City of San Diego has an annual budget of approximately $3 billion.

EXECUTIVES

Public Information Clerk Office Of The City Treasurer, Juan Anguiano
Auditors: MACIAS GINI & O'CONNELL LLP S

LOCATIONS

HQ: CITY OF SAN DIEGO
202 C ST, SAN DIEGO, CA 921013860
Phone: 619 236-6330
Web: WWW.SANDIEGO.GOV

HISTORICAL FINANCIALS

Company Type: Private

Income Statement FYE: June 30

	REVENUE ($ mil.)	NET INCOME ($ mil.)	NET PROFIT MARGIN	EMPLOYEES
06/19	2,283	62	2.7%	11,200
06/18	2,021	(82)	—	—
06/16	1,978	263	13.3%	—
06/15	1,882	273	14.5%	—
Annual Growth	4.9%	(31.0%)	—	—

CITY OF SAN JOSE

Do you know the way to San José? If so you're probably a high tech worker and hopefully one with a salary to match its real estate prices. The city is known for its Silicon Valley location and technology-driven economy. More than 500 tech firms are the major employers in the area which is also known for its premium home prices (median $495000). San José was founded in 1777 and incorporates some 180 square miles. 950000 residents make San José the third largest city in the state. The city government uses the council/manager model wherein the council made up of the mayor (elected at large) and the 10 council members (one from each district) sets policy and the council-appointed city manager carries it out.

EXECUTIVES

Vice President, Rachel Vanderveen
Auditors: MACIAS GINI & O'CONNELL LLP

LOCATIONS

HQ: CITY OF SAN JOSE
200 E SANTA CLARA ST, SAN JOSE, CA 951131905
Phone: 408 535-3500
Web: WWW.SANJOSECA.GOV

HISTORICAL FINANCIALS

Company Type: Private

Income Statement FYE: June 30

	REVENUE ($ mil.)	NET INCOME ($ mil.)	NET PROFIT MARGIN	EMPLOYEES
06/19	1,731	134	7.8%	7,500
06/18	1,629	9	0.6%	—
06/17	1,526	48	3.1%	—
06/16	1,452	43	3.0%	—
Annual Growth	6.0%	45.6%	—	—

CITY OF SEATTLE

In the Emerald City it's not just the name that's green. The City of Seattle is known for rain-fed lush greenery but also for its environmentalism. It uses a charter form of government which features an elected mayor and city council along with a city attorney. The nine council members are elected at large annually. Among some 25 other departments Seattle has an Office of Sustainability and Environment it's restoring salmon habitat and it celebrates Earth Month rather than just Earth Day. The city serves a population of more than 600000 with an annual budget of around $4 billion. It was first settled by Europeans in 1851 and takes its name from Chief Seattle a local tribal leader.

EXECUTIVES

Mayor, Jenny Durkan
Information Integratio, Corrie Martin
Assistant Management, Michelle Honeycutt
Information Integratio, Mike Miller
Senior Information Ana, Stephen Burke
Captain, Gene Zimmerman
Coordinator, James Bush
Information Specialist, Barbara Lundstrom
Coordinator, Chris Wiley
Coordinator, Kenya Fredie
Scientist, Alan Tomita
Auditors: JAN M JUTTE CPA CGFM OLYMP

LOCATIONS

HQ: CITY OF SEATTLE
700 5TH AVE STE 5500, SEATTLE, WA 981045016
Phone: 206 684-7999
Web: WWW.SEATTLE.GOV

HISTORICAL FINANCIALS

Company Type: Private

Income Statement FYE: December 31

	REVENUE ($ mil.)	NET INCOME ($ mil.)	NET PROFIT MARGIN	EMPLOYEES
12/19	2,549	115	4.5%	10,000
12/18	2,395	44	1.9%	—
12/17	2,210	120	5.5%	—
12/16	2,099	123	5.9%	—
Annual Growth	6.7%	(2.4%)	—	—

2019 Year-End Financials

Return on assets: 0.7%
Return on equity: 1.8%
Current ratio: 2.90
Cash ($ mil.): 2,044

CITY OF SPRINGFIELD

EXECUTIVES

Mayor, Domenic J Sarno
Treasurer*, Ehsanul Bhuiya
Tresauer*, Stephen Lonergan
Web Developer, Eileen Foley
Coordinator, Judy Dziobek
Coordinator, Ramon Planas
Coordinator, Tony Pettaway
Auditing Manager, Yong No
Sergeant, Phil Tarpey
Administrative Assistant, Queen Withee
Assessor, Rene Jenkins
Auditors: POWERS & SULLIVAN LLC WAKEFI

LOCATIONS

HQ: CITY OF SPRINGFIELD
36 COURT ST, SPRINGFIELD, MA 011031687
Phone: 413 736-3111
Web: WWW.SPRINGFIELD-MA.GOV

HISTORICAL FINANCIALS

Company Type: Private

Income Statement FYE: June 30

	REVENUE ($ mil.)	NET INCOME ($ mil.)	NET PROFIT MARGIN	EMPLOYEES
06/17	813	40	5.0%	6,107
06/14	765	(10)	—	—
06/13	751	(19)	—	—
06/12	0	0	—	—
Annual Growth	—	—	—	—

2017 Year-End Financials

Return on assets: 3.6%
Return on equity: —
Current ratio: 2.50
Cash ($ mil.): 207

CITY OF ST. LOUIS

The Gateway to the West is bordered by the Mississippi River on the east and occupies approximately 62 square miles with a population of more than 300000. The government of the City of St. Louis is comprised of the city's mayor and a Board of Aldermen (made up of 28 elected members in addition to the board president). Unlike most city governments the mayor shares executive authority with other independent citywide elected officials such as the treasurer and comptroller. During the 21st century St. Louis has transitioned from a manufacturing and industrial economy to one heavily dependent on medicine biotechnology and other sciences. It is home to MLB's St. Louis Cardinals and NFL's St. Louis Rams.

EXECUTIVES

Armory Secretary, Emily Russo
Auditors: KPMG LLP ST LOUIS MO

LOCATIONS

HQ: CITY OF ST. LOUIS
1200 MARKET ST RM 212, SAINT LOUIS, MO 631032805
Phone: 314 622-3201
Web: WWW.STLOUIS-MO.GOV

HISTORICAL FINANCIALS

Company Type: Private

Income Statement				FYE: June 30
	REVENUE ($ mil.)	NET INCOME ($ mil.)	NET PROFIT MARGIN	EMPLOYEES
06/19	870	111	12.8%	4,500
06/18	848	50	5.9%	—
06/17	796	14	1.8%	—
06/16	773	7	0.9%	—
Annual Growth	4.0%	148.6%	—	—

2019 Year-End Financials

Return on assets: 2.9%
Return on equity: 22.1%
Current ratio: —
Cash ($ mil.): 252

CITY OF STAMFORD

EXECUTIVES

Mayor, David Martin
Sergeant, Diedrich Hohn
Project Coordinator, Laura Labosky
Coordinator, Sharon Wade
Risk Manager, Ann Mones
Special Education Teacher, Julie Kazi
Gis Coordinator, Cindy Barber
Teacher, Janet Inzitari
Director of Finance, Robert Robitaille
School Counselor, Betsy Benenson
Assistant Corporation Counsel, Burt Rosenberg
Auditors: BLUM SHAPIRO & COMPANY PC W

LOCATIONS

HQ: CITY OF STAMFORD
888 WASHINGTON BLVD, STAMFORD, CT 069012924
Phone: 203 977-4150
Web: WWW.BRENNANGOLF.COM

HISTORICAL FINANCIALS

Company Type: Private

Income Statement				FYE: June 30
	REVENUE ($ mil.)	NET INCOME ($ mil.)	NET PROFIT MARGIN	EMPLOYEES
06/18	709	(6)	—	2,878
06/17	678	5	0.8%	—
06/16	648	29	4.5%	—
06/15	627	19	3.0%	—
Annual Growth	4.2%	—	—	—

2018 Year-End Financials

Return on assets: (-0.5%)
Return on equity: (-3.9%)
Current ratio: —
Cash ($ mil.): 67

CITY OF SYRACUSE

Syracuse New York is located in the center of the state but it is a world apart from the " Big Apple". Named after the Sicilian city of Syracuse the city owes much of its growth and history to two things— salt and the Erie Canal. Although neither is as important as it once was to the city Syracuse is still a regional transportation hub and the city has managed to weather the economic trends supplanting a salt-centric economy with industrial manufacturing before evolving to a service industry centered economy. The city has a population of about 150000 and is governed by its mayor and a ten-person Common Council.

EXECUTIVES

Mayor, Stephanie Miner
Information Manager, Randy Scott
Project Records Manager, Emma Patterson
Director, Janet Burke
City Manager, William Ryan
Assistant To Deputy Commission, Debbie Ramsey-Burns
Executive Assistant To May, Elizabeth Dejoseph
Civil Engineer II, Kim Kelchner
Sustainability Coordinator, Rebecca Klossner
Chief Data Officer, Sam Edelstein
District Chief, Steve McLaughlin
Auditors: TESTONE MARSHALL & DISCENZA

LOCATIONS

HQ: CITY OF SYRACUSE
233 E WSHNGTN ST STE 231, SYRACUSE, NY 132021423
Phone: 315 448-8005
Web: WWW.SYRACUSE.NY.US

HISTORICAL FINANCIALS

Company Type: Private

Income Statement				FYE: June 30
	REVENUE ($ mil.)	NET INCOME ($ mil.)	NET PROFIT MARGIN	EMPLOYEES
06/19	775	16	2.1%	6,456
06/18	758	122	16.2%	—
06/17	741	6	0.8%	—
06/16	722	(14)	—	—
Annual Growth	2.4%	—	—	—

2019 Year-End Financials

Return on assets: 1.0%
Return on equity: —
Current ratio: —
Cash ($ mil.): 142

CITY OF TAMPA

Disregarded by its first owners the Spanish in 1517 and the British in 1763 Tampa is now a thriving city on the Gulf Coast of Florida. It joins Clearwater and St. Petersburg in forming the Tampa Bay Area. The city uses a mayor-council form of government with seven council members one from each of four districts and three at-large. The mayor and council members are elected to four year terms. They set policy and the chief of staff carries it out by running the day-to-day operations of the city. In addition to tourism and the port of Tampa major area industry includes agriculture construction health care and military operations. Tampa which has a population of about 350000 was incorporated in 1855.

EXECUTIVES

Mayor, Jane Castor
Procurement Staff, Celeste Gibbons-Peoples
Project, Kevin Henika
Senior Programmer Analyst, Karen Romo
Wastewater Department Operatio, Ocea Lattimore
Captain, Mike Stout
Teacher, Lloyd Zweben
Human Resources Executive, Carrie Ortolano
Gis Analyst, Mark Jolley
Assistant City, Ursula Richardson
City Bicycle, Calvin Thornton
Auditors: RSM US LLP TAMPA FLORIDA

LOCATIONS

HQ: CITY OF TAMPA
306 E JACKSON ST, TAMPA, FL 336025223
Phone: 813 274-8211
Web: WWW.TAMPAGOV.NET

HISTORICAL FINANCIALS

Company Type: Private

Income Statement				FYE: September 30
	REVENUE ($ mil.)	NET INCOME ($ mil.)	NET PROFIT MARGIN	EMPLOYEES
09/19	610	33	5.5%	4,500
09/18	558	64	11.5%	—
09/17	491	(8)	—	—
09/16	467	105	22.5%	—
Annual Growth	9.3%	(31.5%)	—	—

CITY OF TUCSON

There's no such thing as too much sun in Tucson. The City of Tucson Arizona enjoys 360 sunny days a year is divided into six wards each represented by a council member. Together with the mayor the members form the Tucson City Council which sets city policies; a city manager leads all departments in implementing these policies. Tucson has about half a million residents and a culture that blends Native American and Mexican influences. It's home to The University of Arizona Davis-Monthan Air Force Base and The National Optical Astronomy Observatories. The Arizona Diamondbacks are based in Tucson and the Chicago White Sox hold spring training here. The city has an annual budget of greater than $2 billion.

EXECUTIVES

Vice President, Joan Tracey
Auditors: CLIFTON LARSON ALLEN LLP TUCS

LOCATIONS

HQ: CITY OF TUCSON
255 W ALAMEDA ST, TUCSON, AZ 857011362
Phone: 520 791-4561
Web: WWW.TUCSONAZ.GOV

HISTORICAL FINANCIALS

Company Type: Private

Income Statement				FYE: June 30
	REVENUE ($ mil.)	NET INCOME ($ mil.)	NET PROFIT MARGIN	EMPLOYEES
06/19	903	58	6.4%	5,900
06/16	763	19	2.5%	—
06/15	723	(16)	—	—
06/14	728	31	4.4%	—
Annual Growth	4.4%	12.8%	—	—

2019 Year-End Financials

Return on assets: 1.2%
Return on equity: 3.2%
Current ratio: 2.40
Cash ($ mil.): 392

CITY OF VIRGINIA BEACH

Whether you're looking for seaside peace and seclusion or bustling boardwalk adventure Virginia Beach is the spot. With nearly 40 miles of Chesapeake Bay and Atlantic Ocean coastline the city's economy thrives largely on travel and tourism and supports a population of more than 435000 people. Virginia Beach's city council consists of 11 elected members (including its mayor) and is responsible for legislative duties including levying taxes adopting an annual budget and appointing a city manager. The city manager carries out executive and administrative tasks in this city's Council-Manager government.

EXECUTIVES

Mayor, Robert M Dyer
City Manager, David L Hansen
Law, Kalfus Nachman
Real Estate Conultant, Charlie Mills
Coordinator, Candace Blue
Coordinator, Christina Uperti
Prin, Allison Bouillon
Prin, Amanda Bryan
Prin, Amanda Kidder
Prin, Angel Fogle
Public Safety Portfolio Projec, Anthony Fox
Auditors: CLIFTONLARSONALLEN LLP ARLIN

LOCATIONS

HQ: CITY OF VIRGINIA BEACH
2401 COURTHOUSE DR 13R, VIRGINIA BEACH, VA 234569120
Phone: 757 385-3111
Web: WWW.VBGOV.COM

HISTORICAL FINANCIALS

Company Type: Private

Income Statement — FYE: June 30

	REVENUE ($ mil.)	NET INCOME ($ mil.)	NET PROFIT MARGIN	EMPLOYEES
06/19	1,379	(70)	—	7,500
06/18	1,356	61	4.5%	—
06/17	1,308	7	0.6%	—
06/16	1,295	46	3.6%	—
Annual Growth	2.1%	—	—	—

CITY OF WATERBURY

EXECUTIVES

Mayor, Neil M O'Leary
Executive Secretory, Laina Dibona
Information Technology/Interne, Bruce Watts
Payroll Staff, Alyce Cass
Information Specialist, Andrea Nixon
Project Coordinator, Samuel Bowens
and Board of Alderma, Joe Begnal
Hris Analyst, Laura Webb-Beers
Alderman, Sandra Martinez-Mccart
Staff, Angela Juliani
Maintenance Manager, Art Daigle
Auditors: BLUM SHAPIRO & COMPANY PC

LOCATIONS

HQ: CITY OF WATERBURY
235 GRAND ST, WATERBURY, CT 067021915
Phone: 203 574-6712
Web: WWW.WATERBURYCT.ORG

HISTORICAL FINANCIALS

Company Type: Private

Income Statement — FYE: June 30

	REVENUE ($ mil.)	NET INCOME ($ mil.)	NET PROFIT MARGIN	EMPLOYEES
06/17	558	(16)	—	3,200
06/16	536	22	4.1%	—
06/15	530	(20)	—	—
06/08	505	(15)	—	—
Annual Growth	1.1%	—	—	—

2017 Year-End Financials

Return on assets: (-1.7%)
Return on equity: —
Current ratio: 3.90
Cash ($ mil.): 25

CITY OF WORCESTER

EXECUTIVES

Mayor, Joseph M Petty
City Mgr*, Edward Augustus Jr
Assistant Treasurer*, Kathy Johnson
Coordinator, Sharon Arnold
Coordinator, Nancy E Moses
Mayor, Joseph Petty
Sergeant, Richard Cipro
Assistant Chief, Stephen Rolle
Mayor, Konstantina Lukes
Assistant City Clerk, Aj Pottle
Staff Assistant II, Effy Larkin
Auditors: CLIFTONLARSONALLEN LLP BOSTON

LOCATIONS

HQ: CITY OF WORCESTER
455 MAIN ST RM 112, WORCESTER, MA 016081805
Phone: 508 799-1049
Web: WWW.GREENHILLGC.COM

HISTORICAL FINANCIALS

Company Type: Private

Income Statement — FYE: June 30

	REVENUE ($ mil.)	NET INCOME ($ mil.)	NET PROFIT MARGIN	EMPLOYEES
06/13	726	9	1.3%	5,637
06/12	703	(15)	—	—
Annual Growth	3.3%	—	—	—

2013 Year-End Financials

Return on assets: 0.7%
Return on equity: 4.0%
Current ratio: —
Cash ($ mil.): 145

CITY OF YONKERS

The city of Jonk Herr (Dutch for young gentleman) has gone through many changes since its founding in 1670. Incorporated in 1872 the City of Yonkers now has a population of almost 200000 nestled into an area of about 20 sq. mi. overlooking the Hudson River. Home to Sarah Lawrence College Yonkers' mayor/council style of government is run by an "at large" mayor and seven district councilmembers.

EXECUTIVES

Vice President Regional Credit Manager, Steve Kearney
Vice President General Manager, Evelyn Arauz
Vice President And General Manager Gulf States Region, Connie Braun
Auditors: O' CONNOR DAVIES LLP HARRISO

LOCATIONS

HQ: CITY OF YONKERS
40 S BROADWAY STE 1, YONKERS, NY 107013715
Phone: 914 377-6000
Web: WWW.YONKERSNY.GOV

HISTORICAL FINANCIALS

Company Type: Private

Income Statement — FYE: June 30

	REVENUE ($ mil.)	NET INCOME ($ mil.)	NET PROFIT MARGIN	EMPLOYEES
06/20	1,219	69	5.7%	2,500
06/19	1,263	(41)	—	—
06/18	1,199	(6)	—	—
06/17	1,171	(15)	—	—
Annual Growth	1.4%	—	—	—

2020 Year-End Financials

Return on assets: 3.5%
Return on equity: —
Current ratio: —
Cash ($ mil.): 120

CITY PUBLIC SERVICES OF SAN ANTONIO

CPS Energy (formerly City Public Service of San Antonio) serves about 860935 electricity customers and some 358495 natural gas customers in the greater San Antonio Texas area. The utility has a generating capacity of some 7370 MW from its gas coal nuclear battery wind solar and landfill gas power plants.

Operations

CPS Energy is the nation's largest municipally owned energy utility providing both natural gas and electric service. Over 90% of sales were generated from electric sales while gas and nonoperating sales account for the rest.

Geographic Reach

CPS Energy serves customers in the greater San Antonio Texas area where it is headquartered including Bexar County.

Sales and Marketing

Throughout its service territory CPS Energy provides electric and natural gas services for residential and commercial customers. It serves more than 840750 electric customers and 352585 natural gas customers.

Financial Performance

CPS Energy's revenue decreased from $2.8 billion in 2019 to $2.6 billion in 2020. Electric revenue comprised 92% of the company's revenue.

Strategy

As metropolitan population is projected to add another one million community members over the next two decades CPS Energy expects interest in how its energy is generated to increase. The company is continuing its Flexible Path to explore ways that it can keep integrating and optimizing cleaner sources of energy. The company consistently balances the tried and true with the new as demonstrated by the addition of its solar and battery storage project that went online in 2019 at Southwest Research Institute. This unique project helps CPS Energy gain valuable experience with battery technology today and for the future.

Company Background

A venerable company CPS Energy traces its roots to the 1860s when its predecessor opened a manufactured gas plant on Houston Street.

EXECUTIVES

Vice President Of Customer Service And Solutions, Maria Koudouris
Evp And General Counsel, Carolyn E. Shellman
President And Ceo, Doyle N. Beneby
Executive Vice President And Chief Strategy And Technology Officer, Cris Eugster
Vp Finance, Justin Locke
Executive Vice President, Alfonso Lujan
Vice President Of People And Culture, Lisa Lewis
Senior Vice President Of Engineering Services, Joel — Jupe
Vice President Community Engagement, John Bonnin
Vice President Operations, Edward Escamilla
Vice President, Patsy Velez
Vice President Marketing, Donald Murray
Senior Vice President Marketing, Curt Powell
Vice President Community Engagement, Maria Garcia
Vice President Of Engineering, Ronald Schaefer
Senior Vice President Partner Solutions, Deborah Gunn
Vice President Of Information Technolo, Stan Torvick
Senior Vice President Power Generation, Tammy Priess
Executive Vice President And Chief Administrative Officer, Laura Jimenez
It Vice President, Dan Torvik
Vice President, Marisol Mari
Senior Secretary, Grace Robledo
Auditors: GARZA PREIS & CO LLC/BAKER

LOCATIONS

HQ: CITY PUBLIC SERVICES OF SAN ANTONIO
500 MCCULLOUGH AVE, SAN ANTONIO, TX 782152104
Phone: 210 353-2222
Web: WWW.CPSENERGY.COM

PRODUCTS/OPERATIONS

2015 Sales

	$ mil.	% of total
Electric	2,320	92
Gas	175	7
Other	36	1
Total	**2,531**	**100**

COMPETITORS

AEP
AES
Duke Energy
NextEra Energy
ONEOK

HISTORICAL FINANCIALS

Company Type: Private

Income Statement — FYE: January 31

	REVENUE ($ mil.)	NET INCOME ($ mil.)	NET PROFIT MARGIN	EMPLOYEES
01/12	2,258	21	0.9%	3,100
01/11	2,068	78	3.8%	—
01/10	1,930	107	5.6%	—
Annual Growth	8.1%	(55.5%)	—	—

2012 Year-End Financials

Return on assets: 0.2%
Return on equity: 0.6%
Current ratio: 1.30
Cash ($ mil.): 148

CITYSERVICEVALCON, LLC

You don't have to live in the city to get the services of CityServiceValcon which markets and distributes petroleum products throughout the Inland Northwest and Rocky Mountain regions of the US as well as in the adjacent Plains states. Its products include gasoline diesel aviation fuels lubricants propane and heating oil. The company has diesel gasoline and heating oils for delivery through its network of bulk plants. CityServiceValcon also operates cardlock fueling facilities under the Pacific Pride brand name. Regional independent petroleum marketers City Service and Valcon merged their operations in 2003 to form CityServiceValcon.

EXECUTIVES

Ng MBR, Dallas Herron
Mng MBR*, Clifford F Kunnary
Mng MBR*, Lary P Johnson
Prin*, Benjamen M Binger
Prin*, James M Binger
Information Technology Manager, Joel Robinson
Marketing Sales Manager, Bonnie Grande
Inside Sales, Bethany Robinson
Marketing Sales, Drew Pike
Administrator, Eric Wyman
Accounting Manager, Rob Johnston

LOCATIONS

HQ: CITYSERVICEVALCON, LLC
640 W MONTANA ST, KALISPELL, MT 599013834
Phone: 406 755-4321
Web: WWW.CITYSERVICEVALCON.COM

COMPETITORS

Farstad Oil
Redwood Coast Petroleum
SPF Energy
Wilson Oil

HISTORICAL FINANCIALS

Company Type: Private

Income Statement — FYE: September 30

	REVENUE ($ mil.)	NET INCOME ($ mil.)	NET PROFIT MARGIN	EMPLOYEES
09/08	625	4	0.6%	150
09/07	490	3	0.6%	—
09/06	459	4	1.0%	—
Annual Growth	16.6%	(8.0%)	—	—

2008 Year-End Financials

Return on assets: 9.3%
Return on equity: 19.2%
Current ratio: 1.30
Cash ($ mil.): 1

CLARCOR INC.

CLARCOR cleans up with filters. The company's industrial and environmental filtration unit makes air and antimicrobial filters for commercial industrial and residential buildings along with filters used in industrial processes. Brands include Airguard Facet ATI Transweb UAS Keddeg MKI TF-Sand Purolator. Companies in CLARCOR's engine and mobile filtration business make products under brands such as Baldwin Hastings Filters and Clark that filter the air oil fuel coolant and hydraulic fluids. In 2017 in order to expand its filtration portfolio Parker-Hannifin acquired CLARCOR for about $4.3 billion.

Operations

CLARCOR operates in two industry segments: Engine/Mobile Filtration and Industrial/Environmental Filtration.

The Engine/Mobile Filtration segment (about 60% of total revenue) makes and sells filtration products for engines used in stationary power generation and for engines in mobile equipment applications including trucks automobiles buses and locomotives and marine construction industrial mining and agricultural equipment. The company manufactures and sells both 'First-fit' filtration systems and replacement products such as oil air fuel coolant transmission and hydraulic filters.

The company's Industrial/Environmental Filtration segment (about 40%) centers around the manufacturing and marketing of filtration products used in industrial and commercial processes and in buildings and infrastructures of various types. Its liquid process filtration products include specialty industrial process liquid filters; filters for pharmaceutical processes and beverages; and filtration systems and filters for the oil and natural gas industry sewage treatment and water recycling and other industrial uses.

Its air filtration products represent air filters and systems including advanced medias and treatments and high efficiency first-fit systems used in gas turbine power generation systems heavy industrial manufacturing processes thermal power plants commercial buildings hospitals general factories residential buildings paint spray booths medical devices and facilities motor vehicle systems aircraft cabins clean rooms compressors and compressor stations.

Geographic Reach

CLARCOR makes and sells its products worldwide and more than 30% of the company's sales come from outside the US. The company has manufacturing distribution and service facilities in US Brazil China France Germany India Italy Malaysia Netherlands the UAE the UK Japan and Mexico.

Sales and Marketing

The company's filtration products are sold through independent distributors and dealers for OEMs as well as directly to end users.

The 10 largest customers of the Engine/Mobile Filtration segment accounted for 35% of 2016 fiscal year (November year end) segment sales.

The 10 largest customers of the Industrial/Environmental Filtration segment accounted for more than 15% of that segment's revenue.

Financial Performance

In fiscal 2016 CLARCOR's revenue declined by 6% ($91 million) due to a number of factors including the 2015 divestiture of J.L. Clark (the former Packaging Segment) which accounted for $40.9 million; decreased net sales volume (due to lower industrial demand) of $26.3 million in the Industrial/Environmental Filtration segment; and $25.1 from a negative currency exchange rate impact due to the strong dollar.

CLARCOR's net income grew by 3.4% to $139.3 million primarily due to Other net income of $20.7 million (flat in 2015) which primarily reflected $27.3 million from 3M to settle a patent litigation case.

Net cash provided by operating activities increased by $131.7 million in 2016 to $285.4 million. Some $18.1 million of this increase came from the 3M patent litigation award and the remainder primarily from cost cutting activities including lowering inventory levels by $36.4 million (resulting in a $58.5 million improvement in cash from operations). The company also reported a $26 million impact from lower cash taxes paid driven by the timing of tax payments in 2016 and 2015.

Strategy

Following the closing of its acquisition by Parker Hannifin in 2017 CLARCOR will be combined with Parker's Filtration Group to form a diverse global filtration business.

Restructuring to focus on two core business lines in 2015 CLARCOR sold its J.L. Clark business (the former Packaging Segment) to CC Industries.

Mergers and Acquisitions

In addition to organic growth CLARCOR has pursued a strategy of expanding its portfolio through acquisitions.

To support its global growth and innovation activities in 2016 the company acquired certain assets of US-based FibeRio Technology (a technology company focused on the research development and commercialization of performance fabric and filtration media) for $11.9 million. That year its CLARCOR Industrial Air division acquired TDC Filter Manufacturing a top US manufacturer and supplier of pleated filter bags dust collection cartridges and gas turbine air filters for $11 million.

In 2014 the company acquired Stanadyne's diesel fuel filtration business for $327.7 million and changed its name to CLARCOR Engine Mobile Solutions. That year it also bought Filter Resources Inc. Filtration Inc. and Fabrication Specialties Inc. for $21.9 million.

Company Background

In 2013 CLARCOR purchased the air filtration business of General Electric's power and water division for $260.3 million.

In 2013 CLARCOR announced plans to invest $40 million for subsidiary Baldwin Filters Inc. to build a new 400000 sq. ft. warehouse and distribution center adjacent to Baldwin's manufacturing facility in Kearney Nebraska.

In 2012 the company acquired Modular Engineering Pty Ltd. an Australian manufacturer of natural gas filtration products as well as a distributor of aftermarket elements. Modular a longtime supplier to CLARCOR's PECOFacet division became part of the division. PECOFacet is included in the company's Industrial/Environmental Filtration segment. Modular produces skid-mounted equipment for the natural gas industry in the Asia/Pacific region and expands CLARCOR's presence in that region in both manufacturing and aftermarket sales.

In 2011 the company purchased one of its suppliers of filtration media Transweb LLC. New Jersey-based Transweb manufactures and supplies media used in end-market applications including respirators and HVAC filters.

CLARCOR was founded in 1904 and reincorporated in 1969.

EXECUTIVES

Senior Business Development Officer, Sam Ferrise, $400,795 total compensation
Vp Finance And Cfo, David J. Fallon, $394,808 total compensation
Chairman President And Ceo, Christopher L. Conway, $689,615 total compensation
Group President Clarcor Industrial Air, Keith A. White
President Engine And Mobile Group, Jacob Thomas
Vice President Of Operations, John Reuss
Vice President Strategic Business Systems, Chris Schechter
Vice President Of Business Development, Naimesh Dave
Vice President Human Resources, Pam K Kile
Vice President Advanced Product And Process Engineering, Thomas B Green
Vice President Finance, Dennis M Haun
Vice President Innovation Product And Process Engineering, Monte A Crabtree
Vice President Strategic Accounts, David Amato
Vice President Research And Development, Johnson Buddayaplli
Auditors: PRICEWATERHOUSECOOPERS LLP NA

LOCATIONS

HQ: CLARCOR INC.
840 CRESCENT CENTRE DR # 600, FRANKLIN, TN 370674687
Phone: 615 771-3100
Web: WWW.CLARCORWATER.COM

Sales 2016

	$ mil.	% of total
United States	944	68
Europe	152	11
Asia	144	10
Other International	148	11
Total	**1,389**	**100**

PRODUCTS/OPERATIONS

sales 2016

	$ mil.	% of total
Industrial/Environmental Filtration	803	58
Engine/Mobile Filtration	586	42
Total	**1,389**	**100**

COMPETITORS

Crown Holdings
Cummins
Dana
Delphi Automotive Systems
Donaldson Company
EMD Millipore
ESCO Technologies
Pall Corporation
Parker-Hannifin
W rth Group

HISTORICAL FINANCIALS

Company Type: Private

Income Statement — FYE: November 30

	REVENUE ($ mil.)	NET INCOME ($ mil.)	NET PROFIT MARGIN	EMPLOYEES
11/16	1,389	139	10.0%	5,773
11/15	1,481	134	9.1%	—
11/14	1,512	144	9.5%	—
11/13	1,130	118	10.5%	—
Annual Growth	7.1%	5.6%	—	—

2016 Year-End Financials

Return on assets: 8.0%
Return on equity: 12.2%
Current ratio: 3.10
Cash ($ mil.): 134

CLARK COUNTY SCHOOL DISTRICT

EXECUTIVES

Supt, Patrick Skorkowsky
Coordinator, Monica Robles
Executive of Information Techn, Alisha Bragg
Coordinator, Ransom Terrell
Executive of Information Techn, Chris Ahrens
Executive Officer, Teresa Holden
Executive of Information Techn, Robin Thomas
Information Specialist, Jonathan Swaby
Food Maintenance Super, Bill Pridmore
Executive Assistant, Cindy Krohn
Assistant, Constantine Christopulos
Auditors: EIDE BAILLY LLP LAS VEGAS NE

LOCATIONS

HQ: CLARK COUNTY SCHOOL DISTRICT
5100 W SAHARA AVE, LAS VEGAS, NV 891463406
Phone: 702 799-5000
Web: WWW.CCSD.NET

HISTORICAL FINANCIALS

Company Type: Private

Income Statement — FYE: June 30

	REVENUE ($ mil.)	NET INCOME ($ mil.)	NET PROFIT MARGIN	EMPLOYEES
06/20	3,616	285	7.9%	37,361
06/19	3,519	274	7.8%	—
06/18	3,313	134	4.1%	—
06/17	3,178	(112)	—	—
Annual Growth	4.4%	—	—	—

CLARK EQUIPMENT COMPANY

EXECUTIVES

Ceo, Jong Min Kim
Vice-President, Joel Honeyman
Utility Vehicle Manage, Brad Claus
Training Manager, Ellie Nickel
Marketing Manager, Bryan Zent
Talent Management Specialist, Caren Loebs
Manager, Curt Kasper
Network Administrator, David Landsiedel
Engineer, Gerald Duppong
Vice President, James Flynn
General Accounting, Jasmine Rambousek
Auditors: DELOITTE & TOUCHE LLP

LOCATIONS

HQ: CLARK EQUIPMENT COMPANY
250 E BEATON DR, WEST FARGO, ND 580782656
Phone: 701 241-8700
Web: WWW.BOBCAT.COM

HISTORICAL FINANCIALS

Company Type: Private

Income Statement				FYE: December 31
	REVENUE ($ mil.)	NET INCOME ($ mil.)	NET PROFIT MARGIN	EMPLOYEES
12/17	2,543	174	6.9%	5,822
12/16	2,415	166	6.9%	—
12/15	0	0	—	—
12/14	2,539	492	19.4%	—
Annual Growth	0.1%	(29.3%)	—	—

2017 Year-End Financials

Return on assets: 6.1%
Return on equity: 24.8%
Current ratio: 1.40
Cash ($ mil.): 127

CLEVELAND MUNICIPAL SCHOOL DISTRICT

EXECUTIVES

Ceo, Eric Gordon
Coo*, Patrick Zohn
Chb*, Denise W Link
Cfo*, John Scanlan
Exec Dir*, Megan Obryan
Purchasing Specialist, Marilyn Landrum
Program Manager, Pamela Scott
Director of Special Education, Patricia Schulz
Secretary, Shanetta Harris
Data Analyst, Terence Bush
Computer Operator, Russell Monk
Auditors: DAVE YOST-AUDITOR OF STATE CL

LOCATIONS

HQ: CLEVELAND MUNICIPAL SCHOOL DISTRICT
1111 SUPERIOR AVE E # 1800, CLEVELAND, OH 441142500
Phone: 216 838-0000
Web: WWW.MC2STEMHIGHSCHOOL.ORG

HISTORICAL FINANCIALS

Company Type: Private

Income Statement				FYE: June 30
	REVENUE ($ mil.)	NET INCOME ($ mil.)	NET PROFIT MARGIN	EMPLOYEES
06/19	941	(119)	—	9,500
06/18	957	(49)	—	—
06/17	854	(71)	—	—
06/16	902	18	2.1%	—
Annual Growth	1.4%	—	—	—

2019 Year-End Financials

Return on assets: (-6.5%)
Return on equity: (-47.1%)
Current ratio: —
Cash ($ mil.): 144

CLIFTONLARSONALLEN LLP

CliftonLarsonAllen (CLA) is all about the CPAs. Boasting more than $7.5 billion in client assets under management CLA is on the list of top 10 largest accounting firm that serves privately-owned firms and the firm's principals along with not-for-profits and government agencies. Also serving as a financial advisory and business consultancy CLA is organized as a holding company with three main business segments: wealth advisory outsourcing and audit tax and consulting. It mostly serves clients in the agribusiness financial employee benefit plan healthcare manufacturing and government sectors. With more than 6200 professionals in approximately 120 US locations and a global affiliation the firm's annual revenues was about $955 million.

Operations

The company's service include audit accounting tax consulting outsourcing and wealth advisory. Its investment advisory services are conducted through CliftonLarsonAllen Wealth Advisors LLC.

Other services include cybersecurity and risk management data analytics employee benefits plans M&A advisory and investment banking talent solutions and tax educations for CPAs.

Geographic Reach

Minnesota-based CLA boasts with more than 120 locations across the US.

Sales and Marketing

CLA which counts more than 183450 clients serves privately-held businesses individuals not-for-profits and governmental entities. Its major client groups include agribusiness and cooperatives dealerships employee benefit plans federal government financial institutions healthcare manufacturing and distribution companies as well as state and local governments. CLA serves clients outside the US through its affiliations with Nexia International.

Financial Performance

In 2019 CLA eclipsed the $1 billion revenue milestone. CLA reported approximately $1.2 billion in revenues in 2019 a vast improvement from $954 million the year prior.

Strategy

CLA continues to expand into new geographic markets while bolstering its service offerings and client list. In early 2020 CLA opened a new office in Irvine California. The newest addition to the Southern California region will serve several industries including real estate construction private equity financial institutions and manufacturing and distribution.

CLA also welcomed Seattle CPA firm Watson McDonell in early 2019 expanding CLA's nonprofit and low-income housing industries ? two key industries that it has been focused on and looking to expand throughout Puget Sound.

In addition CLA launched an innovative tracking tool to help health care organizations record COVID-19 economic relief spending. Now organizations can arrange spending in accordance with the compliance and reporting initiatives coming soon.

Company Background

CLA was formed in 2011 by the merger of Clifton Gunderson and LarsonAllen. Prior to the pairing both companies had been active in expanding across the country by purchasing smaller firms and parts of other firms.

EXECUTIVES

Coo, David E. Bailey
Cfo, Sharon Ten Clay
Cio, Steve Noble
Ceo Cliftonlarsonallen Wealth Advisors Llc, Tony Hallada
Ceo And Chief Business Officer, Denny Schleper

LOCATIONS

HQ: CLIFTONLARSONALLEN LLP
220 S 6TH ST STE 300, MINNEAPOLIS, MN 554021418
Phone: 612 376-4500
Web: WWW.CLACONNECT.COM

Selected Locations

Arizona
California
Colorado
Florida
Idaho
Illinois
Indiana
Iowa
Maryland
Massachusetts
Michigan
Minnesota
Mississippi
Missouri
New Jersey
New Mexico
New York
North Carolina
Ohio
Pennsylvania
Texas
Virginia
Washington
Wisconsin

PRODUCTS/OPERATIONS

Selected Services:

Audit and assurance
Consulting
CLA Intuition financial modeling
Employee benefit plans
Executive search
Forensic
Information security
Intacct software
Litigation support
Risk management
Technology
Transaction support
Valuation

COMPETITORS

BDO
BKD LLP
Baker Tilly Virchow Krause
Crowe Horwath
Deloitte & Touche
Eide Bailly
Ernst & Young LLP
Grant Thornton
KPMG L.L.P.
Moore Stephens International
PricewaterhouseCoopers UK
RSM US
SVA

HISTORICAL FINANCIALS

Company Type: Private

Income Statement				FYE: December 4
	REVENUE ($ mil.)	NET INCOME ($ mil.)	NET PROFIT MARGIN	EMPLOYEES
12/15	650	170	26.3%	4,786
12/14	598	163	27.3%	—
12/13	563	154	27.5%	—
Annual Growth	7.5%	5.1%	—	—

2015 Year-End Financials

Return on assets: 68.4%
Return on equity: 95.9%
Current ratio: 3.50
Cash ($ mil.): 12

CLOUD PEAK ENERGY RESOURCES LLC

EXECUTIVES

Ceo, Colin Marshall
Treas, Oscar Martinez
Exec V Pres, Michael Barrett
Exec V Pres, Gary Rivenes
Sr V Pres, Bruce Jones
Sr V Pres, Cary W Martin
Executive Assistant, Karen Nelson
Auditors: PRICEWATERHOUSECOOPERS LLP DE

LOCATIONS

HQ: CLOUD PEAK ENERGY RESOURCES LLC
505 S GILLETTE AVE, GILLETTE, WY 827164203
Phone: 303 956-7596
Web: WWW.RIOTINTOKENNECOTT.COM

HISTORICAL FINANCIALS

Company Type: Private

Income Statement — FYE: December 31

	REVENUE ($ mil.)	NET INCOME ($ mil.)	NET PROFIT MARGIN	EMPLOYEES
12/13	1,396	58	4.2%	1,200
12/12	1,516	155	10.3%	—
12/11	1,553	201	13.0%	—
12/10	1,370	170	12.4%	—
Annual Growth	0.6%	(29.8%)	—	—

2013 Year-End Financials

Return on assets: 2.5%
Return on equity: 5.5%
Current ratio: 1.80
Cash ($ mil.): 231

COASTAL CHEMICAL CO., L.L.C.

EXECUTIVES

MBR-Pres, Randy King
Pres*, Jim Doyle
Administrative Assistant, Lana Rogers
Controller, Bonnie Broussard
Network Administrator, Bryant Angelle
Facility Manager, Dane Hutchings

LOCATIONS

HQ: COASTAL CHEMICAL CO., L.L.C.
3520 VETERANS MEMORIAL DR, ABBEVILLE, LA 705105708
Phone: 337 898-0001
Web: WWW.COASTALCHEM.COM

HISTORICAL FINANCIALS

Company Type: Private

Income Statement — FYE: December 31

	REVENUE ($ mil.)	NET INCOME ($ mil.)	NET PROFIT MARGIN	EMPLOYEES
12/14	736	33	4.6%	750
12/09	386	10	2.6%	—
12/08	635	16	2.6%	—
Annual Growth	2.5%	12.9%	—	—

2014 Year-End Financials

Return on assets: 10.3%
Return on equity: 88.0%
Current ratio: 0.90
Cash ($ mil.): 3

COASTAL PACIFIC FOOD DISTRIBUTORS, INC.

Coastal Pacific Food Distributors (CPF) fuels the military forces from facility to fork. The company is one of the top wholesale food distributors that primarily serves the US armed forces across the Western US and in the Far East. As part of its business CPF provides a full line of groceries to military bases run by the US Army Navy Air Force and Marines. It delivers a variety of products from distribution centers located in California Washington and Hawaii. CPF also offers information system programming services for its customers to track sales and shipping as well as procurement and logistics through partnerships in Iraq Kuwait and Saudi Arabia. The company was founded in 1986.

Operations

CPF has grown to become the second-largest worldwide military distributor of food and related products.

As part of its business CPF operates distribution centers in California Washington Hawaii and Canada. In California its largest Stockton facility spans more than 500000 sq. ft. while its Ontario center boasts 429000 sq. ft. Its distribution center in Fife Washington is 153000 sq. ft. A 45000-sq.-ft. facility in Hawaii delivers food to four military commissaries.

Geographic Reach

California-based CPF caters to the Western US as well as Alaska Hawaii Guam Japan Okinawa Korea Singapore Kwajalein Diego Garcia and the Philippines. Its business extends to the Middle East through partnerships for procurement and logistics with other companies. These additional areas include Iraq Kuwait and Saudi Arabia.

Sales and Marketing

Industry partners that keep CPF busy include the Defense Logistics Agency the Defense Commissary Agency Air Force NAF Purchasing Office Navy Exchange (NEXCOM) Army and Air Force Exchange Service (AAFES) and the American Logistics Association to name a few.

The company counts on food manufacturers to keep its customers happy. They include Kraft Foods Tyson Foods Procter & Gamble General Mills Nestle ConAgra Unilever Frito-Lay Campbell J.M. Smucker Global Military Marketing Mars S&K Sales Del Monte Corp. Georgia-Pacific Johnson & Johnson and Alder Foods.

Strategy

The company works to support its existing markets. In 2013 CPF opened a new prime vendor platform in Calamba Luguna Philippines as it looks to serve future growth there. The platform supports Naval ships with dry chill and frozen items.

EXECUTIVES

Vice President Prime Vendor, Brian Murdoch
Executive Vice President Finance And Administration, Monika Bertke
Auditors: DIXON HUGHES GOODMAN LLP NORF

LOCATIONS

HQ: COASTAL PACIFIC FOOD DISTRIBUTORS, INC.
1015 PERFORMANCE DR, STOCKTON, CA 952064925
Phone: 909 947-2066
Web: WWW.CPFD.COM

PRODUCTS/OPERATIONS

Selected Products

Bakery
Candy
Deli
Fresh & frozen meats
Frozen foods
Pet foods
Refrigerated items
Sushi

Selected Brokers

Acosta Sales & Marketing
Alder Foods Inc.
Bisek & Co. Inc.
Dixon Marketing Inc.
Dunham & Smith Agencies
Elite Brands
Finnegan International Sales
First Wave Sales
Gateway Military LLC
Global Office Building
HI-PAC Ltd
Mid Valley
Overseas Service Corporation
Otis McAllister
Parra Sales Inc
Reese Group
S&K
S. Schwartz Sales Inc.
Turnkey Management
WEBCO General Partnership

COMPETITORS

AdvancePierre
JTM Provisions
Richmond Wholesale Meat

HISTORICAL FINANCIALS

Company Type: Private

Income Statement — FYE: December 29

	REVENUE ($ mil.)	NET INCOME ($ mil.)	NET PROFIT MARGIN	EMPLOYEES
12/12	1,212	15	1.2%	459
12/11*	1,162	25	2.2%	—
01/11	1,113	17	1.6%	—
Annual Growth	4.4%	(7.6%)	—	—

*Fiscal year change

2012 Year-End Financials

Return on assets: 6.7%
Return on equity: 50.6%
Current ratio: 2.60
Cash ($ mil.): 5

COBANK, ACB

You could say CoBank is dependent on its rural customers and vice versa. A member of the Farm Credit System (which is regulated by the FCA) the $110 billion cooperative bank provides seasonal and wholesale loans to agribusinesses as well as to rural power water and communications cooperatives across the US. The bank also leases vehicles farming equipment and agricultural facilities through various Farm Credit System affiliates. Its core agribusiness customers range from local and regional farmers' cooperatives to multinational food companies. It has counted Land O' Lakes Blue Diamond Almonds and National Beef as among its larger customers. Formed in 1989 CoBank merged with US AgBank in early 2012.

Operations

CoBank operates three main business segments: Strategic Relationships Agribusiness and Rural Infrastructure. Its Strategic Relationships loans made up 50% of its $80 billion loan portfolio at the end of 2014 while Agribusiness and Rural Infrastructure made up another 30% and 20% respectively.

About 76% of CoBank's total revenue came from loan interest in 2014 while another 16% came from interest income on investment securities. The rest of its revenue came from fee income (5% of revenue) prepayment income (1%) and other miscellaneous sources.

Geographic Reach

Based in Colorado the bank operates 15 regional offices throughout the US including locations in Iowa Georgia Texas Connecticut Kansas Missouri and Kentucky. It also has an international office in Singapore.

Sales and Marketing

CoBank mainly serves clients in rural America in the agribusiness water communications and power sectors.

Financial Performance

CoBank's annual revenues and profits have been rising over the past several years thanks to steady loan asset growth across all three of its target loan types (Strategic Relationships Agribusiness and Rural Infrastructure).

The bank's revenue jumped 5% to $2.2 million during 2014 mostly thanks to higher average loan volume and increased earnings from a strengthened balance sheet. CoBank's lending business grew with food and agribusiness customers Farm Credit Association customers and rural energy and communications customers which all in turn contributed to its top-line growth.

Revenue growth in 2014 drove CoBank's net income up 6% to $904.3 million for the year. The bank's operating cash levels dipped 2% to $883.1 million during the year due to unfavorable working capital changes related to accrued interest balance changes.

EXECUTIVES

Cfo, David P. Burlage
Chief Risk Officer, Lori L. O'Flaherty
Coo, Ann Trakimas
Evp Banking Services Group, Antony M. Bahr
Svp And Cio, James R. Bernsten
Evp Regional Agribusiness Banking Group, Amy H. Gales
Central Region President Regional Agribusiness Banking Group, Mike Hechtner
Chief Credit Officer, Daniel Key
Evp Corporate Agribusiness Banking Group, Jonathan B. Logan
Southern Region President Regional Agribusiness Banking Group, Lynn Scherler
Svp And Manager Communications Division, Robert F. (Rob) West
Eastern Region President Regional Agribusiness Banking Group, David Sparks
Western Region President Regional Agribusiness Banking Group, Leili Ghazi
Ceo, Robert B. Engel, $880,000 total compensation
President, Mary E. McBride
Chief Banking Officer; Member Management Executive Committee, Thomas Halverson
Vp And Managing Counsel Legal And Loan Processing Division, Chris Clayton
President Farm Credit Leasing, Mike Romanowski
Svp Power Energy And Utilities Banking Division, Todd E. Telesz
Svp Electric Distribution Water And Community Facilities, Nivin Elgohary
Vice President Lead Relationship Manager, David James
Vice President, Bert Johnson
Regional Vice President Southern Region Electric Distribution Division, Tamra Reynolds
Sector Vice President And Relationship Manager, Michael Tousignant
Vice President, Marshall Essig
Vice President Policy And Public Affairs, Sarah Tyree
Vice President And Executive D, Matthew Brill
Senior Vice President Communications Banking Division, Ted Koerner
Second Vice Chair, Kevin A. Still
First Vice Chair, Daniel T. (Dan) Kelley
Chairman, Everett M. Dobrinski
Auditors: PRICEWATERHOUSECOOPERS LLP DE

LOCATIONS

HQ: COBANK, ACB
6340 S FIDDLERS GREEN CIR, GREENWOOD VILLAGE, CO 801114951
Phone: 303 740-6527
Web: WWW.COBANK.COM

Selected Regional Offices

Ames IA
Atlanta GA
Austin TX
Enfield CT
Fargo ND
Louisville KY
Lubbock TX
Minneapolis MN
Omaha NE
Roseville CA
Spokane WA
St. Louis MO
Washington D.C.
Wichita KS

COMPETITORS

AgFirst
AgStar
AgriBank
Bank of America
Farm Credit Services of Mid-America
Northwest Farm Credit
Rabo AgriFinance
Wells Fargo

HISTORICAL FINANCIALS

Company Type: Private

Income Statement — FYE: December 31

	ASSETS ($ mil.)	NET INCOME ($ mil.)	INCOME AS % OF ASSETS	EMPLOYEES
12/18	139,015	1,190	0.9%	500
12/17	129,210	1,125	0.9%	—
12/16	126	945	749.8%	—
12/15	117,470	936	0.8%	—
Annual Growth	5.8%	8.3%	—	—

2018 Year-End Financials

Return on assets: 0.9%
Return on equity: 12.5%
Sales ($ mil): 4,320

COBB COUNTY BOARD OF EDUCATION

EXECUTIVES

Chair, Randy Scamihorn
Cfo*, Cathy Adams
Staff, Cherry Herron
Staff, Danielle Jesko
Auditors: MAULDIN & JENKINS LLC ATLANT

LOCATIONS

HQ: COBB COUNTY BOARD OF EDUCATION
514 GLOVER ST SE, MARIETTA, GA 300602750
Phone: 770 426-3300
Web: WWW.COBBK12.ORG

HISTORICAL FINANCIALS

Company Type: Private

Income Statement — FYE: June 30

	REVENUE ($ mil.)	NET INCOME ($ mil.)	NET PROFIT MARGIN	EMPLOYEES
06/17	1,299	(13)	—	115
06/16	1,238	(1)	—	—
06/15	1,166	(29)	—	—
06/14	532	67	12.6%	—
Annual Growth	34.7%	—	—	—

2017 Year-End Financials

Return on assets: (-0.6%)
Return on equity: (-1.6%)
Current ratio: —
Cash ($ mil.): 247

COBB COUNTY PUBLIC SCHOOLS

EXECUTIVES

Principal, Dr Ashley Hosey
Treasurer, An Goh
Supervisor, Ana P Murphy
Assistant Dean For Finance, Anthony Roberts
Region Director, Chris Corzine
Dance Director, Denise Reeves
Professor, Jeff Qin
Secretary, Marla McKissack
Auditors: MAULDIN & JENKINS ATLANTA GE

LOCATIONS

HQ: COBB COUNTY PUBLIC SCHOOLS
4575 WADE GREEN RD NW, ACWORTH, GA 301023407
Phone: 678 594-8320
Web: WWW.COBBK12.ORG

HISTORICAL FINANCIALS

Company Type: Private

Income Statement — FYE: June 30

	REVENUE ($ mil.)	NET INCOME ($ mil.)	NET PROFIT MARGIN	EMPLOYEES
06/17	1,299	(13)	—	15,796
06/16	1,238	(1)	—	—
06/15	1,166	(29)	—	—
06/14	0	0	13.9%	—
Annual Growth	1017.7%	—	—	—

2017 Year-End Financials

Return on assets: (-0.6%)
Return on equity: (-1.6%)
Current ratio: —
Cash ($ mil.): 247

COBB COUNTY SCHOOL DISTRICT

EXECUTIVES

Spdt, Chris Ragsdale
Vice President, Jenifer Farmer

LOCATIONS

HQ: COBB COUNTY SCHOOL DISTRICT
514 GLOVER ST SE, MARIETTA, GA 300602706
Phone: 770 426-3300
Web: WWW.COBBK12.ORG

HISTORICAL FINANCIALS

Company Type: Private

Income Statement FYE: June 30

	REVENUE ($ mil.)	NET INCOME ($ mil.)	NET PROFIT MARGIN	EMPLOYEES
06/19	1,407	24	1.7%	11
06/17	0	0	—	—
06/16	0	(0)	—	—
06/15	0	(0)	—	—
Annual Growth	1296.5%	—	—	—

2019 Year-End Financials

Return on assets: 1.0%
Return on equity: 20.2%
Current ratio: —
Cash ($ mil.): 400

COBB ELECTRIC MEMBERSHIP CORPORATION

Cobb Electric Membership Corporation (Cobb EMC) makes sure that Cobb County Georgia residents can cook corn on the cob (and anything else) using either electric power or natural gas. The utility distributes electricity to more than 200000 meters (more than 177000 residential commercial and industrial members) in Cobb County and four other north metro Atlanta counties. Cobb EMC operates about 10000 miles of power lines. The company's Gas South unit markets natural gas to customers who receive their service on Atlanta Gas & Light's natural gas distribution pipelines in Georgia.

Operations

Its Cobb Energy Management provides administrative and labor support to Cobb EMC and offers phone and Internet services to Cobb EMC's customers primarily through subsidiaries. Cobb Energy Management provides call center training tree trimming and billing software services and other ancillary support to EMC's core activities.

Geographic Reach

One of the largest of Georgia's 41 EMCs Cobb EMC's distribution system covers approximately 1434 square miles (Cobb Bartow Cherokee Fulton and Paulding counties in the north metro Atlanta area and Randolph Calhoun Quitman and Clay counties in Southwest Georgia).

Financial Performance

In 2012 the company reported a 46% increase in revenues thanks to a 10% rise in natural gas sales which outpaced a 2% decline in electric revenues. Net income grew by 194% in 2012 as a result of higher net sales and lower operating costs.

Strategy

Cobb EMC is a partner in Power4Georgians a consortium of six Georgia EMCs that collectively is developing a comprehensive strategy to provide reliable and affordable energy to the EMC members.

In 2013 as part of its ongoing transition out of non-energy businesses Cobb EMC announced today plans to cut its workforce by up to 20% percent through a company-wide offer of voluntary separation packages.

In 2012 Smart Energy Capital LLC and Jacoby Development Inc. signed a power purchase deal with Cobb EMC to provide power from the Azalea Solar Facility the largest solar power plant (10MW) in Georgia and one of the largest in the Southeast.

Company Background

The cooperative has been embroiled in litigation in recent years and in 2011 a Cobb County grand jury indicted Cobb EMC Dwight Brown on 31 counts of theft and racketeering. Brown was replaced as CEO by W.T. "Chip" Nelson.

The gas and support companies were merged into EMC as wholly owned units in 2009 as a way to streamline EMC's overall operations. The company has also sold a number of former assets to raise cash including Cooperative Business Ventures in 2009 for $2 million and the health and welfare brokerage business of Cooperative Benefits and Financial Services for a gain of $470000 in 2010.

Formed in 1938 Cobb EMC began life as an electric utility with 489 residential members and 14 commercial customers.

EXECUTIVES

Associate Vice President, Jim Gantt
Vice President Of Marketing And Corporate Communications, Kevan Espy
Vice President Member Care, Tim Sosebee
Vp Internal Audit, Kristi Knight
Board Of Director District: 1, Edward Crowell
Auditors: MCNAIR MCLEMORE MIDDLEBROOKS &

LOCATIONS

HQ: COBB ELECTRIC MEMBERSHIP CORPORATION
1000 EMC PKWY NE, MARIETTA, GA 300607908
Phone: 770 429-2100
Web: WWW.COBBEMC.COM

HISTORICAL FINANCIALS

Company Type: Private

Income Statement FYE: April 30

	REVENUE ($ mil.)	NET INCOME ($ mil.)	NET PROFIT MARGIN	EMPLOYEES
04/18*	849	25	3.0%	548
12/13	416	(8)	—	—
04/09	641	3	0.6%	—
12/08	2,104	0	—	—
Annual Growth	—	236.5%	—	—

*Fiscal year change

2018 Year-End Financials

Return on assets: 2.6%
Return on equity: 7.6%
Current ratio: 0.80
Cash ($ mil.): 20

COBORN'S, INCORPORATED

Coborn's hopes you'll shop at your convenience. The company operates more than 120 stores across Midwest of United States under the Coborn's Cash Wise Foods and Save-A-Lot banners. Coborn's operates its own central bakery fuel and convenience division pharmacy division in-house grocery warehouse and distribution center and tops cleaners. Along with its grocery stores the firm owns and operates pharmacies and convenience liquor and gas stations. Coborn's is a fourth generation business managed by its CEO Chris Coborn.

Operations

As part of its business Coborn's operates under several banner names including Cash Wise Save-A-Lot Marketplace Foods Hornbacher's and namesake Coborn's. These supermarkets are supported by their own central bakery fuel and convenience division pharmacy division in-house grocery warehouse and distribution center and tops cleaners. The company also runs convenience gas stations pharmacy and 35 liquor stores under the brands Coborn's Liquor Cash Wise Liquor and Captain Jack's.

Geographic Reach

Based in Minnesota Coborn's operates two support center offices in North Dakota and Wisconsin.

Sales and Marketing

Coborn's distribution channel includes grocery stores and online. It also offers home delivery service for its customers.

Strategy

Coborn's aims to empower employee owners to create unique shopping experiences anticipate needs and exceed expectations for its guests. By investing in its employees their engagement naturally increases which then is projected to its guests. Anticipating needs ties back into the simple piece of the company's vision. By putting itself into its guests' shoes each day Coborn's can find ways to make the shopping experience smooth and comfortable.

Coborn's is now requiring its guests to wear masks in supermarket and liquor stores for their overall safety. Coborn's has also anticipated should guests may not have a mask available a mask may be provided at the store. Aside from ensuring its guests' safety in its establishments with masks Coborn's has also been utilizing the SmartSense solution an IoT connectivity service from Digi International for food safety pharmacy and fleet to help protect its customers. Coborn's is in the process of rolling out a health screening program for its employees and it has previewed the new Safetemps solution from Digi.

Company Background

Founded in 1921 when Chester Coborn started a single produce market the company opened its first Cash Wise Foods store in 1979 and its first convenience store in 1986.

EXECUTIVES

Vp Information Technology, Dale D. Monson
Cfo, Tom Velin
President And Ceo, Chris Coborn
Evp, Greg Sandeno
Vp Operations, Dave Meyer
Vice President Of Organizational Development, Becky Estby
Auditors: RSM US LLP MINNEAPOLIS MINNE

LOCATIONS

HQ: COBORN'S, INCORPORATED
1921 COBORN BLVD, SAINT CLOUD, MN 563012100
Phone: 320 252-4222
Web: WWW.COBORNSINC.COM

PRODUCTS/OPERATIONS

Selected Store Formats
Convenience stores (Little Dukes Holiday)
Hardware stores (Ace)
Liquor stores
Pharmacies
Restaurants (Subway)
Supermarkets (Coborn's Cash Wise Foods JK Markets Save-A-Lot)
Video stores

COMPETITORS

7-Eleven
ALDI
Couche-Tard
Cub Foods
Kowalski's Markets
Kroger
Lunds
Target Corporation
Wal-Mart

HISTORICAL FINANCIALS

Company Type: Private

Income Statement — FYE: December 28

	REVENUE ($ mil.)	NET INCOME ($ mil.)	NET PROFIT MARGIN	EMPLOYEES
12/13	1,246	30	2.5%	7,200
12/12	1,220	32	2.7%	—
Annual Growth	2.1%	(5.0%)	—	—

2013 Year-End Financials

Return on assets: 8.8%
Return on equity: 17.7%
Current ratio: 1.10
Cash ($ mil.): 21

COC PROPERTIES, INC.

EXECUTIVES

Chb, Harry D Stephenson
Pres, Don Stephenson
V Pres, Betty Phillips
V Pres, Mark Maddox
V Pres, Jim Bosworth
Vice President, Craig Stephenson
Territory Sales Manager, Don Richardson
Auditors: BATCHELOR TILLERY & ROBERTS

LOCATIONS

HQ: COC PROPERTIES, INC.
110 MACKENAN DR STE 300, CARY, NC 275117901
Phone: 919 462-1100
Web: WWW.CARYOIL.COM

HISTORICAL FINANCIALS

Company Type: Private

Income Statement — FYE: December 31

	ASSETS ($ mil.)	NET INCOME ($ mil.)	INCOME AS % OF ASSETS	EMPLOYEES
12/19	110	13	12.5%	100
12/18	102	8	8.8%	—
12/16	90	9	10.3%	—
12/15	77	4	6.1%	—
Annual Growth	9.3%	30.9%	—	—

2019 Year-End Financials

Return on assets: 12.5%
Return on equity: 26.2%
Sales ($ mil): 1,544

COLONIAL PIPELINE COMPANY

Colonial Pipeline delivers about 100 million gallons of gasoline diesel jet fuel home heating oil and military fuels per day to cities and businesses across the eastern and southern US. The more than 5500-mile Colonial Pipeline system transports the fuels from Houston Texas to Linden New Jersey to more than 270 marketing terminals near major urban centers in the Southeast and along the Eastern Seaboard. Colonial provides a portfolio of information and logistics management services to its customers. Colonial Pipeline is owned by a consortium of companies including Koch KKR-Keats Pipeline Investors L.P. Caisse de depot et placement du Quebec IFM (US) Colonial Pipeline 2 and Shell Midstream Operating. Colonial Pipeline was founded in 1962.

Operations

The company operates an underground pipeline system that originates in the Houston Texas area and terminates at Linden New Jersey New York harbor. The Colonial Pipeline system connects refineries in the Gulf Coast and other locations to more than 270 marketing terminals. The batches of oil shipments carried by the pipeline is 2.5 million barrels per day.

The Colonial Pipeline system services seven airports directly and provides fuel to the US military. It has a 28-million-barrel tank storage capacity that helps maintain a stable supply of energy along its delivery system. In addition the company's marine logistics division offers shippers on Colonial Pipeline an alternative to the Houston Ship Channel by providing water access in the Beaumont Port Arthur area. It also provides energy logistics and solutions its shippers and customers. It offers system storage (tank leasing services) Intra Harbor Transfer (IHT) service exchange title transfer and other support services.

The company has other affiliates such as Bengal Pipeline Colonial Terminal Logistics Energy Logistics Solutions and Powder Springs Logistics. The ventures aid the company in terms of shipping marine operations and truck offloading just to name a few.

Geographic Reach

Colonial Pipeline is headquartered in Atlanta. Colonial Pipeline's network of customer-operated pipelines and terminals serves communities across the Southeast and Eastern US. It has shipper terminals in almost 15 states.

In terms of its facilities The company is currently maintaining more than 280 facilities along the system and has solar farms at two facilities in New Jersey.

Sales and Marketing

Colonial Pipeline refers to its customers as Shippers Suppliers/Consignees and Terminals (Tankage Parties). The shippers vary and can include oil companies traders wholesalers retailers government independent refiners airlines and other entities that have a need to transport fuel to the market. Colonial Pipeline has developed a set of resources to familiarize the shippers supplier/consignees and terminals with pipeline procedures that promote the safe and efficient movement of its products through the company's system.

Strategy

An affiliate of Colonial Pipeline Company Colonial Terminals Operating Company LLC has acquired three refined product terminals from Lincoln Terminal Company Inc. (Lincoln) a Southeast products and biofuels marketing and logistics company. This acquisition provides an excellent opportunity for Colonial to move into the terminal business offers a complementary service to Colonial Pipeline Company's current customers and lays the groundwork for further strategic expansion. Terminals are a natural extension of Colonial's overall business providing the opportunity to serve customers in new ways while building and strengthening relationships.

As part of its digital strategy the company relaunched a contractor portal on its external website. The portal can be accessed at www.colpipe.com/contractors and provides Colonial contractors with streamlined access to safety information in a state-of-the-art mobile-friendly platform. The company is also launching a new contractor safety recognition program to identify and reward contractors who are leading the way as allies in its commitment to excellence in safety. As the operator of the nation's largest refined products pipeline system the company integrates best practices in safety into every element of operational and occupational processes.

Mergers and Acquisitions

In late 2020 Colonial Terminals Operating Company LLC an affiliate of Colonial Pipeline Company completed the acquisition of three refined product terminals from Lincoln Terminal Company Inc. (Lincoln) a Southeast products and biofuels marketing and logistics company.

The new business will operate under the brand name Colonial Premier Terminals. Two of the terminals acquired located in Charlotte NC and Chattanooga TN are presently connected to the Colonial Pipeline Company system and the other located in Fredericksburg VA is connected to Plantation Pipe Line.

Company Background

Colonial Pipeline Company was founded in 1962.

In 2015 Colonial announces the purchase of Shell Pipeline Company LP's interest in the Port Arthur Products Station and Shell Ex Facility known as PAPS.

In 2000 Colonial announces the Alliance Pipeline purchase of a 147-mile line from a refinery in New Orleans to a 2.2 million barrel tank farm in Collins MS. The purchase includes a ten-year throughput agreement.

Responding to increased customer demand in 2011 Colonial Pipeline expanded the northern part of its Houston-to-New York system adding 100000 barrels per day of capacity (increasing its capacity in the New York Harbor market by 14%). In 2011 and 2012 it also conducted a series of system upgrades including adding 55000 barrels of daily capacity for diesel fuel home heating oil jet fuel and fuels and other petroleum products for the US military.

Taking advantage of the Yorktown Virginia refinery shut down and the conversion of its storage tanks to a delivery facility serving the Tidewater area in 2011 the company announced a capacity expansion to increase deliveries to the Tidewater region by 24000 barrels a day.

In 2010 Chevron sold its 23% stake in Colonial Pipeline to a KKR affiliate as part of its plan to sell non-core assets. In 2014 KKR-Keats Pipeline Investors L.P. owned 28% of Colonial Pipeline.

EXECUTIVES

Interim Ceo, John W. Somerhalder
Vp; General Manager Operations, Doug Belden
Director Technical Services, Rob Barbeauld
Vp And Cfo, Dave Doudna
Vice President Human Resources, Wayne Claire
Vice President Of Human Resources, Eve Brooks
Treasurer, Reca Porter

LOCATIONS

HQ: COLONIAL PIPELINE COMPANY
1185 SANCTUARY PKWY # 100, ALPHARETTA, GA 300094765
Phone: 678 762-2200
Web: WWW.COLPIPE.COM

Colonial Pipeline operates a pipeline system that spans from Texas to New Jersey.

PRODUCTS/OPERATIONS

Selected Customers

American Airlines Inc
Apex Oil Company
Astra Oil Co. Inc.
Atlantic Trading & Marketing
BP Oil Company
Cargill Incorporated
Center Oil Company
Chalmette Refinery
Charter-Triad Terminals LLC
Chevron Corporation
CHS Inc
CITGO Petroleum Corp.
ConocoPhillips
Continental Airlines Fuel Mgmt.Inc
Cummins Terminal Inc.
Department Of Defense
Energy Merchant LLC
Epsilon Trading Inc.
Equiva Trading
ExxonMobil Oil Corporation
Flint Hills Resources
George E. Warren Corporation
Glencore Ltd
Global Companies LLC
Gulf Oil Limited Partnership
Hess Corporation
Hunt Refining Co.
J. Aron & Company
Kinder Morgan Energy
Koch Petroleum Group LP
Lion Oil Company
Louis Dreyfus Energy Services LP
Mabanaft
Maples Gas Company Inc.
Marathon Petroleum Co. LLC
Metroplex Energy Inc
Morgan Stanley Capital Group Inc.
Motiva
Murphy Oil USA Inc.
Musket Corporation
NIC Holding Corp
NWA Fuel Services Corp.
Petro Services
Petrocom Energy Group Ltd
Petroleum Traders Corporation
Phibro Inc.
Pilot Corporation
Placid Refining Company
Premcor Refining Group Inc
Quiktrip Corp.
Rwe Trading Americas Inc
Sheetz Inc
Shell Oil Products US
Shell Trading
Societe Generale Energie (USA) Corp
South Padre Energy LTD
Southwest Airlines
Sprague Energy Corporation
Sun Refining & Marketing
Tauber Oil Co.
Trafigura AG
Transmontaigne
Truman Arnold
United Parcel Service
US Airways Inc
Valero Marketing And Supply
Valley Oil Company LLC
Vitol S.A. Inc.
WAWA Incorporated
Williams Energy Marketing And Trading
World Fuel Services

COMPETITORS

Buckeye Partners
Enterprise Products
Gateway Energy
Kinder Morgan Energy Partners
Magellan Midstream
Sunoco Logistics
TransMontaigne

HISTORICAL FINANCIALS

Company Type: Private

Income Statement — FYE: December 31

	REVENUE ($ mil.)	NET INCOME ($ mil.)	NET PROFIT MARGIN	EMPLOYEES
12/19	1,385	404	29.2%	700
12/18	1,340	407	30.4%	—
12/17	1,231	509	41.4%	—
12/16	1,214	233	19.2%	—
Annual Growth	4.5%	20.2%	—	—

2019 Year-End Financials

Return on assets: 13.5%
Return on equity: —
Current ratio: 0.60
Cash ($ mil.): 87

COLORADO STATE UNIVERSITY

Colorado State University (CSU) got its start as an agricultural college in 1870 six years before Colorado was even a state. The school still has agricultural and forestry programs as well as a veterinary medicine school but it also offers degrees in liberal arts business engineering and the sciences. True to its roots as a land-grant college CSU engages the larger community in research and outreach through statewide Cooperative Extension programs and centers like the Colorado Agricultural Experiment Station. More than 30000 students are enrolled at CSU about 80% of whom are Colorado residents. It employs about 1500 faculty members and has a student-to-teacher ratio of 19:1.

Operations

The school's student body is largely composed of undergraduate students (more than 80%) but also includes some graduate and professional veterinary medicine students. CSU's most popular undergraduate majors are business health and exercise science psychology biological science construction management and human development and family studies. Overall the university offers about 150 undergraduate graduate and professional degree programs through eight colleges.

CSU has extensive research programs in fields including atmospheric science clean energy the environment biomedicine and infectious diseases. The university's research programs attract some $300 million in external funding each year.

Geographic Reach

CSU's main campus and its nearby foothills agricultural and mountain campuses are located on about 5000 acres in Fort Collins Colorado. The university has more than 1200 international students and scholars from about 90 countries on its campus. Additionally about 900 CSU students travel abroad every year to participate in educational programs.

Financial Performance

CSU's revenues increased 8% in 2012 to $827 million from higher earnings on student tuition and fees grants and contracts auxiliary enterprises and other education activity sales and service income. Net income increased by 63% to $67 million that year as a result of the university's revenue growth.

CSU has primarily experienced an increase in revenues over the last five years with the exception a slight dip during 2010 caused by decreased state capital contributions and grants and contracts.

Student tuition and fees run at about $9000 per year for Colorado residents and $24000 for out-of-state students.

EXECUTIVES

Senior Advisor To The Executive Vice President, Bill Farland
Vice President, James Heisel
Vice President Of Research, Emma Mannino
Graduate Secretary, Kathleen Chynoweth

LOCATIONS

HQ: COLORADO STATE UNIVERSITY
6003 CAMPUS DELIVERY, FORT COLLINS, CO 805236003
Phone: 970 491-1372
Web: WWW.COLOSTATE.EDU

PRODUCTS/OPERATIONS

Selected Colleges Schools and Programs

Colleges

College of Agricultural Sciences
College of Applied Human Sciences
College of Business
College of Engineering
College of Liberal Arts
College of Natural Sciences
College of Veterinary Medicine and Biomedical Sciences
Warner College of Natural Resources

Schools and Programs

Graduate School
International Programs
Online Degrees and Courses (Online Plus)
School of the Arts
School of Biomedical Engineering
School of Education
School of Global Environmental Sustainability
School of Social Work

HISTORICAL FINANCIALS

Company Type: Private

Income Statement — FYE: June 30

	REVENUE ($ mil.)	NET INCOME ($ mil.)	NET PROFIT MARGIN	EMPLOYEES
06/08	740	(44)	—	6,701
06/06	562	26	4.7%	—
Annual Growth	14.7%	—	—	—

2008 Year-End Financials

Return on assets: (-3.6%)
Return on equity: (-6.6%)
Current ratio: 4.20
Cash ($ mil.): 249

COLORADO STATE UNIVERSITY SYSTEM

EXECUTIVES

Chancellor, Joe Blake
Chancellor, Michael Martin
Cfo, Henry Sobanet
Pres-Colorado State Univ.-Glob, Becky Takeda

Deputy General Counsel, Johnna Doyle
Doctor, Larue Johnson
Special Assistant Professor, Copper Ferreira
Assistant Professor, Deborah Fidler
Director, Guadalupe Salazar
Associate Professor of Applied, Maite Correa
Director of Graduate Programs, Sharon Anderson
Auditors: BKD LLP DENVER CO

LOCATIONS

HQ: COLORADO STATE UNIVERSITY SYSTEM
555 17TH ST STE 1000, DENVER, CO 802023910
Phone: 303 534-6290
Web: WWW.CSUSYSTEM.EDU

HISTORICAL FINANCIALS

Company Type: Private

Income Statement — FYE: June 30

	REVENUE ($ mil.)	NET INCOME ($ mil.)	NET PROFIT MARGIN	EMPLOYEES
06/15	1,011	33	3.3%	6,701
06/14	938	(5)	—	—
06/13	884	22	2.6%	—
Annual Growth	6.9%	21.7%	—	—

2015 Year-End Financials

Return on assets: 1.5%
Return on equity: 7.5%
Current ratio: 2.40
Cash ($ mil.): 352

COLUMBIA GAS OF OHIO, INC.

Columbia Gas of Ohio takes pride in the fact that it can deliver gas first class en masse without impasse to the working class the middle class and the upper class. The utility is the largest natural gas utility in the state serving 1.4 million customers (including about 1.3 million residential 112000 commercial and 2600 industrial customers in more than 1030 communities in more than 60 of Ohio's 88 counties). The NiSource subsidiary offers a customer choice program which allows customers to choose their energy suppliers while Columbia Gas of Ohio continues to deliver the gas.

Operations

In addition to operating more than 19160 miles of distribution mains the company also provides other gas products services and programs across its 25400-sq.-mi. service area. Columbia Gas of Ohio is part of the NiSource's Gas Distribution segment which contributed about 54% of the total sales in fiscal 2013.

Geographic Reach

Columbia Gas of Ohio distributes natural gas to residential commercial and industrial customers in Columbus Mansfield Parma Springfield and Toledo. It is one of a handful of NiSource's distribution companies which collectively serve about 3.4 million gas and electric customers in seven states and operates about 58000 miles of pipeline.

Financial Performance

Columbia Gas of Ohio is part of the NiSource's Gas Distribution segment which reported an increase of 9% in 2013 due primarily to an increase for regulatory and service programs (including the impact from the rate cases at Columbia of Pennsylvania and Columbia of Massachusetts and the implementation of rates under Columbia of Ohio's approved infrastructure replacement program); the effects of colder weather which increased residential commercial and industrial usage; and an increase in the numbers of residential and commercial customers.

Strategy

The company's strategy includes spending about $2 billion over 25 years to improve its underground pipeline system.

In 2014 it asked state regulators for permission to replace a mile-long 12-inch diameter pipeline that crosses the Maumee River between Maumee and Perrysburg with a new 20-inch pipeline.

Upgrading its main offices in order to be more efficient in 2013 Columbia Gas of Ohio announced plans to relocated to the Arena District of Columbus taking about 208000 sq. ft. of a planned 288000-sq.-ft. office complex.

In 2012 Columbia Gas of Ohio has finished work on its $14 million Ackerman Road natural gas pipeline replacement project in Columbus.

That year it moved more than 722000 customers to independent suppliers as part of a decade-long deregulation plan by the state.

Company Background

In 2011 Columbia Gas of Ohio announced plans to secure permission from the Public Utilities Commission of Ohio for a five year extension of its energy efficiency programs (home energy audits weatherization and other initiatives) aimed at bringing down energy costs for individual customers.

In 2010 Columbia Gas of Ohio commenced a $1.3 million gas mains upgrade in two neighborhoods in Toledo.

EXECUTIVES

Vice President, Vince Parisi
Vice President And General Manager Operations, Lisa Carmean
Treasurer Area Director Central, Michael Loges

LOCATIONS

HQ: COLUMBIA GAS OF OHIO, INC.
290 W NATIONWIDE BLVD # 1, COLUMBUS, OH 432151082
Phone: 614 460-6000
Web: WWW.COLUMBIAGASOHIO.COM

COMPETITORS

Dominion East Ohio
Duke Energy Ohio
Ohio Edison
Ohio Power
Stand Energy
The Illuminating Company
Toledo Edison
Vectren Energy Delivery of Ohio

HISTORICAL FINANCIALS

Company Type: Private

Income Statement — FYE: December 31

	REVENUE ($ mil.)	NET INCOME ($ mil.)	NET PROFIT MARGIN	EMPLOYEES
12/17	908	96	10.7%	2,500
12/16	854	114	13.4%	—
12/15	872	113	13.0%	—
12/14	993	102	10.3%	—
Annual Growth	(3.0%)	(1.9%)	—	—

2017 Year-End Financials

Return on assets: 2.3%
Return on equity: 7.9%
Current ratio: 0.40
Cash ($ mil.): 7

COLUMBUS CITY SCHOOL DISTRICT

EXECUTIVES

Supt, Gene T Harris
Dpty Supt*, Marvenia Bosley
Treas*, Mike Kinneer
V Pres*, Terry Boyd
Executive Officer, Blain Waldron
Executive Officer, Carol Rood
Executive Officer, Craig Bickley
Executive Officer, David Nelson
Executive Officer, Lean Katterheinrich
Executive Officer, Roxanne Moses
IBM Certified Administr, Chris Francia
Auditors: DAVE YOST COLUMBUS OHIO

LOCATIONS

HQ: COLUMBUS CITY SCHOOL DISTRICT
270 E STATE ST FL 3, COLUMBUS, OH 432154312
Phone: 614 365-5000
Web: WWW.ARTSIMPACTMIDDLESCHOOL.COM

HISTORICAL FINANCIALS

Company Type: Private

Income Statement — FYE: June 30

	REVENUE ($ mil.)	NET INCOME ($ mil.)	NET PROFIT MARGIN	EMPLOYEES
06/18	1,087	66	6.2%	10,000
06/17	1,038	106	10.3%	—
06/16	972	(13)	—	—
06/06	667	(51)	—	—
Annual Growth	4.2%	—	—	—

2018 Year-End Financials

Return on assets: 3.3%
Return on equity: —
Current ratio: —
Cash ($ mil.): 450

COMENITY BANK

World Financial Network National Bank (WFNNB) will take credit for the credit it extends. The company is the private-label and co-branded credit card banking subsidiary of Alliance Data Systems. Along with affiliate World Financial Capital Bank the company underwrites cards on behalf of more than 85 businesses. The company's largest clients include apparel retailers L Brands and Redcats USA. WFNNB oversees about 120 million cardholder accounts and roughly $4 billion in receivables. Private equity giant Blackstone planned to acquire parent Alliance Data Systems for more than $6 billion but that deal was terminated in 2008.

EXECUTIVES

Pres, Timothy King
Computer Operations, Mike Schick
Project Manager, Connie Murphy
Information Technology, Paul Wroten
Client Sales Manager, Stacey Siak
Director Financial Planning, Don Borowy
Client Sales Manager, Jennifer Staten
Marketing Staff, Jeffrey Fasino
Administrative Assistant, Kurt Fraczkowski
Senior Vice President Chief Co, Michael F Swallow

LOCATIONS

HQ: COMENITY BANK
12921 S VISTA STATION BLV, DRAPER, UT 840202377
Phone: 614 729-4000
Web: WWW.COMENITY.COM

COMPETITORS

American Express
Bank of America
Barclays Bank Delaware
Citigroup
Target Receivables

HISTORICAL FINANCIALS

Company Type: Private

Income Statement FYE: December 31

	ASSETS ($ mil.)	NET INCOME ($ mil.)	INCOME AS % OF ASSETS	EMPLOYEES
12/14	9,149	389	4.3%	200
12/13	7,453	350	4.7%	—
12/05	332	10	3.2%	—
12/03	672	88	13.2%	—
Annual Growth	26.8%	14.4%	—	—

2014 Year-End Financials

Return on assets: 4.3%
Return on equity: 30.8%
Sales ($ mil): 1,976

COMFORT SYSTEMS USA (ARKANSAS), INC.

EXECUTIVES

Pres, Clyde A Jester
V Pres*, Trent McKenna
SEC*, Dawn McElyea
Auditors: ERNST & YOUNG LLP HOUSTON TE

LOCATIONS

HQ: COMFORT SYSTEMS USA (ARKANSAS), INC.
4806 RIXIE RD, NORTH LITTLE ROCK, AR 721171537
Phone: 501 834-3320
Web: WWW.COMFORTAR.COM

HISTORICAL FINANCIALS

Company Type: Private

Income Statement FYE: December 31

	REVENUE ($ mil.)	NET INCOME ($ mil.)	NET PROFIT MARGIN	EMPLOYEES
12/15	1,580	49	3.1%	102
12/14	1,410	28	2.0%	—
12/13	1,357	28	2.1%	—
Annual Growth	7.9%	31.5%	—	—

2015 Year-End Financials

Return on assets: 7.1%
Return on equity: 13.5%
Current ratio: 1.40
Cash ($ mil.): 56

COMMON GROUND HEALTHCARE COOPERATIVE

EXECUTIVES

Ceo, Cathy Mahaffey
Cfo, Tom Lawless
Manager, Scott Bergman
Team Infrastructure Manager, Scott Soto
Delegation Oversight Manager, Julie Flaugher
Chief Strategy Officer, Melissa Duffy
Claim Manager, Ann Schultz
Vice President, Heather Oliva
Accountant, Janet Strasser
Human Resources Coordinator, Sara Stieve
Director, Robert Connolly
Auditors: BAKER TILLY VIRCHOW KRAUSE LLP

LOCATIONS

HQ: COMMON GROUND HEALTHCARE COOPERATIVE
120 BISHOPS WAY STE 150, BROOKFIELD, WI 530056234
Phone: 414 455-0500
Web: WWW.COMMONGROUNDHEALTHCARE.ORG

HISTORICAL FINANCIALS

Company Type: Private

Income Statement FYE: December 31

	REVENUE ($ mil.)	NET INCOME ($ mil.)	NET PROFIT MARGIN	EMPLOYEES
12/18	566	135	23.9%	1
12/17	173	(11)	—	—
12/15	0	(0)	—	—
12/14	0	(0)	—	—
Annual Growth	507.5%	—	—	—

2018 Year-End Financials

Return on assets: 52.7%
Return on equity: 303.9%
Current ratio: —
Cash ($ mil.): 197

COMMONSPIRIT HEALTH

Formed in 2019 through the merger of Catholic hospital systems Catholic Health Initiatives and Dignity Health CommonSpirit Health is a $29 billion not-for-profit organization with more than 140 hospitals in 21 states. Its hospitals range from large urban medical centers (many with educational and research programs) to small hospitals in rural areas. The company also operates clinics long-term care assisted-living and senior residential facilities (totaling more than 700 health care facilities) and provides home-based care services. The system is sponsored by nearly 20 different congregations of nuns. CommonSpirit is the largest not-for-profit health system in the US.

Operations

CHI's network includes acute-care hospitals including academic and teaching facilities rural facilities with critical-care access nursing colleges home-health agencies community health services organizations long-term care facilities assisted-care and residential senior homes research and development programs and labs. The company has about 25000 physicians and advanced practice clinicians.

Geographic Reach

CHI operates in Arkansas California Colorado Indiana Iowa Kansas Kentucky Minnesota Nebraska Nevada New Jersey New Mexico North Dakota Ohio Oregon Pennsylvania South Dakota Tennessee Texas Washington and Wisconsin – 21 states in all.

Strategy

The 2019 merger of California-based Dignity Health and Colorado-based Catholic Health Initiatives that resulted in the creation of CommonSpirit Health was just one of several health system transactions in a time of rising M&A activity. The systems joined forces to strengthen their operations enabling them to provide better care for more people. The combined system's operating goals include expanding its clinical capabilities shifting to providing care outside of the hospital investing in technology addressing social determinants of health and maintaining an experienced workforce.

Mergers and Acquisitions

After years of discussions CHI and Dignity Health merged in early 2019. The combined health system CommonSpirit Health is the largest not-for-profit hospital system in the US. The size of the system allows for it to provide expanded care to patients through such methods as virtual appointments a broader range of clinical programs and advanced technologies. The new organization with 142 hospitals in 21 states is headquartered in Chicago. Individual hospitals continue to operate under their existing names.

HISTORY

In 1860 the Sisters of St. Francis established a hospital in Philadelphia laying the foundation for a larger health care organization. In 1981 Franciscan Health System was formally established to be a national holding company for Catholic hospitals and related organizations. By the mid-1990s the system consisted of 12 member and two affiliate hospitals and 11 long-term-care facilities located in the mid-Atlantic states and the Pacific Northwest.

Sisters of Charity of Cincinnati and the Sisters of St. Francis Perpetual Adoration of Colorado Springs co-sponsored The Sisters of Charity Health Care Systems incorporated in 1979 as a multi-institutional health care network. By the mid-1990s the system included 20 hospitals in Colorado Kentucky Nebraska New Mexico and Ohio.

Three congregations collaborated to form Catholic Health Corporation in 1980 one of the first such health care partnerships between religious communities within the Roman Catholic Church in the US. By 1996 this coalition operated 100 health care facilities in 12 states.

The development of modern managed care health care systems put pressure on the smaller Catholic hospital operations so the three systems established Catholic Health Initiatives (CHI) in 1996 as a national entity serving five geographic regions. Patricia Cahill a lay health care veteran who previously served the Archdiocese of New York was appointed president and CEO of CHI. The following year CHI absorbed the 10-hospital Sisters of Charity of Nazareth Health Care System based in Bardstown Kentucky (founded in a log cabin in 1812).

That year CHI continued to seek new partnerships to improve efficiency. With Alegent Health it formed provider network Midwest Select with nearly 200 hospitals marketing discounted rates to businesses. CHI allied with the Daughters of Charity to form for-profit joint venture Catholic Healthcare Audit Network to provide operational financial compliance and information systems audits as well as due diligence reviews. CHI also joined insurance joint venture NewCap Insurance with the Daughters of Charity and Catholic Health East; the firm allowed CHI to operate independently of commercial insurers.

CHI made a secular tie-in with the University of Pennsylvania Health System in 1998 whereby the university's system would offer care through five Catholic hospitals (CHI made plans to transfer these hospitals to Catholic Health East in 2001). The next year CHI announced its first loss due to lackluster performance in the Midwest. During 2000 the company responded by streamlining operations and changing management resulting in a positive bottom line. In 2001 it sold three hospitals in Pennsylvania one in Delaware and one in New Jersey to Catholic Health East.

EXECUTIVES

President Ceo And Trustee, Kevin E. Lofton, age 65
President Enterprise Business Lines And Cfo, J. Dean Swindle
Svp Divisional Operations (texas), Michael H. Covert
Svp Marketing And Communications, Joyce M. Ross
Executive Vice President Mission, Thomas R. Kopfensteiner
Svp Divisional Operations And Ceo Chi Memorial (tennessee), Larry Schumacher, age 62
Svp Legal Services And General Counsel, Mitch H. Melfi
Evp Growth And Business Acquisitions, Paul W. Edgett
Svp Human Resources And Chief Human Resources Officer, Patricia G. (Pat) Webb
Svp Divisional Operations And Ceo Chi Health (nebraska And Southwest Iowa), Cliff A. Robertson
Senior Vice President And Division Executive Officer, Jeffrey S. Drop
Svp And Chief Nursing Officer, Kathleen D. Sanford
Svp Divisional Operations And Ceo Mercy Health Network (iowa), David H. Vellinga
Svp Divisional Operations And Ceo Chi Franciscan Health (tacoma), Ketul J. Patel
Svp And President And Ceo Kentuckyone Health, Ruth W. Brinkley
Ceo Chi St. Alexius Health, Matt Grimshaw, age 45
Interim Evp Operations, Anthony Jones
Svp And Chief Medical Officer, Robert J. Weil
Vice President Operational Finance Mercy Medical Center, Joseph Ruark
Vp Finance, Brent Schmidt
Auditors: ERNST & YOUNG LLP IRVINE CA

LOCATIONS

HQ: COMMONSPIRIT HEALTH
444 W LAKE ST STE 2500, CHICAGO, IL 606060097
Phone: 312 741-7000
Web: WWW.COMMONSPIRIT.ORG

COMPETITORS

Adventist Health System Sunbelt Healthcare
Allina Hospitals
Ascension Health
Baptist Health
Baptist Health (Arkansas)
BryanLGH Medical Center
Denver Health and Hospital Authority
Exempla Healthcare
HCA
Life Care Centers
Memorial Health System (Colorado)
Methodist Health System
OhioHealth
Tenet Healthcare
Universal Health Services

HISTORICAL FINANCIALS

Company Type: Private

Income Statement — FYE: June 30

	REVENUE ($ mil.)	NET INCOME ($ mil.)	NET PROFIT MARGIN	EMPLOYEES
06/19	7,170	9,008	125.6%	72,500
06/18	14,982	222	1.5%	—
06/17	15,547	128	0.8%	—
06/16	15,942	(703)	—	—
Annual Growth	(23.4%)	—	—	—

2019 Year-End Financials

Return on assets: 22.2%
Return on equity: 57.0%
Current ratio: 1.40
Cash ($ mil.): 1,569

COMMONWEALTH OF KENTUCKY

EXECUTIVES

Governor, Matt Bevin
Lt Govenor, Jenean Hampton
Chief Information Security Off, Joe Manley
Staff, Donna Cordier
Coordinator, Joe Wolford
Coordinator, Laronda Davis
Project Coordinator, Teresa Bailey
First Supreme Court Judge, David C Buckingham
Government Affairs Manager, Amy Mefford
Aging Program Case Manager, Dorris Phillips
Lims Administrator, Gerry Morford

LOCATIONS

HQ: COMMONWEALTH OF KENTUCKY
700 CAPITAL AVE STE 100, FRANKFORT, KY 406013410
Phone: 502 564-2611
Web: WWW.KENTUCKY.GOV

HISTORICAL FINANCIALS

Company Type: Private

Income Statement — FYE: June 30

	REVENUE ($ mil.)	NET INCOME ($ mil.)	NET PROFIT MARGIN	EMPLOYEES
06/19	27,091	3	0.0%	34,000
06/18	25,692	338	1.3%	—
Annual Growth	5.4%	(99.0%)	—	—

2019 Year-End Financials

Return on assets: —
Return on equity: —
Current ratio: —
Cash ($ mil.): 3,851

COMMONWEALTH OF MASSACHUSETTS

EXECUTIVES

Governor, Charlie Baker
Lt Gov*, Karyn Polito
State Superior Court Judges, Kenneth V Desmond
State Superior Court Judges, James R Lemire
State Solicitor, Peter Sacks
Assistant Attorney General, Sookyoung Shin
MA Orange District Court Clerk, Joella E Fortier
Engagement Director, Deidre Travis-Brown
Deputy Director Office of Empl, John Langan
Superior Court Judge, Valerie A Yarashus
District Court Judge, Shelby M Smith
Auditors: KPMG LLP BOSTON MA

LOCATIONS

HQ: COMMONWEALTH OF MASSACHUSETTS
1 ASHBURTON PL FL 9, BOSTON, MA 021081518
Phone: 617 727-5000
Web: WWW.MASS.GOV

HISTORICAL FINANCIALS

Company Type: Private

Income Statement — FYE: June 30

	REVENUE ($ mil.)	NET INCOME ($ mil.)	NET PROFIT MARGIN	EMPLOYEES
06/17	53,391	323	0.6%	59,253
06/16	52,992	(31)	—	—
06/15	50,609	685	1.4%	—
06/14	47,709	(250)	—	—
Annual Growth	3.8%	—	—	—

2017 Year-End Financials

Return on assets: 0.4%
Return on equity: —
Current ratio: 1.40
Cash ($ mil.): 7,580

COMMONWEALTH OF PENNSYLVANIA

EXECUTIVES

Governor, Tom Wolf
Lt Governor*, John Fetterman
General*, Linda Kelly
Chief of Staff*, Stephen Aichele
Acting Attorney General*, Bruce L Castor Jr
Portfolio Manager, James Del Gaudio
Compliance Staff, Megan Porta
Co-Chair PA Inter-Agency Elect, Robert Torres
Co-Chair PA Inter-Agency Elect, John Macmillan
Chair-PA Sch Safety SEC Commit, Charles H Ramsey
Forensic Laboratory Manager, Bruce Tackett
Auditors: CLIFTONLARSONALLEN LLP BALTIM

LOCATIONS

HQ: COMMONWEALTH OF PENNSYLVANIA
238 MAIN CAPITOL BUILDING, HARRISBURG, PA 171200022
Phone: 717 787-5962
Web: WWW.STATE.PA.US

HISTORICAL FINANCIALS

Company Type: Private

Income Statement — FYE: June 30

	REVENUE ($ mil.)	NET INCOME ($ mil.)	NET PROFIT MARGIN	EMPLOYEES
06/19	78,418	(338)	—	89,207
06/18	73,689	2,198	3.0%	—
06/17	72,373	187	0.3%	—
06/16	67,822	(630)	—	—
Annual Growth	5.0%	—	—	—

2019 Year-End Financials

Return on assets: (-0.3%)
Return on equity: —
Current ratio: 1.70
Cash ($ mil.): 7,004

COMMONWEALTH OF VIRGINIA

EXECUTIVES

Gov, Ralph Northam
Lt Gov, Justin E Fairfax
Attorney Gen, Ronald F McDonnell
Press Secretary, Crystal Carson
SEC of Fin, Jody Wagner
Executive Director, Diana Cantor
Treasurer, Lee Andes
Treasurer, Manju Ganeriwala
Director, Tod Massa
Policy Director, Jennie O'Holleran
Special Asst For Constituent S, Rickee Jones
Auditors: MARTHA S MAVREDES CPA RICHMO

LOCATIONS

HQ: COMMONWEALTH OF VIRGINIA
101 N 14ST JAMES MONROE ST, RICHMOND, VA 23219
Phone: 804 225-3131
Web: WWW.VIRGINIA.GOV

HISTORICAL FINANCIALS

Company Type: Private

Income Statement — FYE: June 30

	REVENUE ($ mil.)	NET INCOME ($ mil.)	NET PROFIT MARGIN	EMPLOYEES
06/19	40,939	1,480	3.6%	100,000
06/18	38,725	1,353	3.5%	—
06/17	36,395	18	0.1%	—
06/16	35,094	(744)	—	—
Annual Growth	5.3%	—	—	—

2019 Year-End Financials

Return on assets: 1.2%
Return on equity: 2.6%
Current ratio: —
Cash ($ mil.): 10,554

COMMUNITY BEHAVIORAL HEALTH

EXECUTIVES

Director, Arthur C Evans Jr
Director*, Estelle Richmond
Director*, Nancy Luckas
Clinical Care Manager, Dana Carlomagno
Auditors: MITCHELL & TITUS LLP PHILADEL

LOCATIONS

HQ: COMMUNITY BEHAVIORAL HEALTH
801 MARKET ST STE 7000, PHILADELPHIA, PA 191073158
Phone: 215 413-3100
Web: WWW.DBHIDS.ORG

HISTORICAL FINANCIALS

Company Type: Private

Income Statement — FYE: December 31

	REVENUE ($ mil.)	NET INCOME ($ mil.)	NET PROFIT MARGIN	EMPLOYEES
12/17	935	0	—	270
12/16	919	0	—	—
12/15	811	0	—	—
12/02	453	(0)	—	—
Annual Growth	4.9%	—	—	—

2017 Year-End Financials

Return on assets: —
Return on equity: —
Current ratio: —
Cash ($ mil.): 42

COMMUNITY FOUNDATION OF NORTHWEST INDIANA, INC.

EXECUTIVES

Pres, Frankie Fesko
SEC*, James J Richards
Treas*, David E Wickland
Administrative Assistant To CN, Kathryn Johnson
Registered Nurse, David Gasper
Security Staff, Derek Gilliam
Registered Nurse, Lynda Koppen
Phlebotomy Supervisor, Dorothy Grisham
Security Officer Armed, Jeffery Malachowski
Information Technology Adminis, Brian Kuss
Supervisor of Speech Pathology, Jill Westerfield

LOCATIONS

HQ: COMMUNITY FOUNDATION OF NORTHWEST INDIANA, INC.
905 RIDGE RD, MUNSTER, IN 463211773
Phone: 219 836-0130
Web: WWW.COMHS.ORG

HISTORICAL FINANCIALS

Company Type: Private

Income Statement — FYE: June 30

	REVENUE ($ mil.)	NET INCOME ($ mil.)	NET PROFIT MARGIN	EMPLOYEES
06/20	1,133	87	7.7%	2,000
06/19	1,125	104	9.3%	—
06/18	1,150	137	12.0%	—
06/17	1,084	122	11.2%	—
Annual Growth	1.5%	(10.6%)	—	—

2020 Year-End Financials

Return on assets: 4.7%
Return on equity: 8.0%
Current ratio: 0.60
Cash ($ mil.): 27

COMMUNITY HEALTH CHOICE TEXAS, INC.

EXECUTIVES

Dir, Jose Garcia Jr
Dir, Vivian Ho
Dir, Vicki Keiser
Dir, Raymond Khoury
Dir, Elena Marks
Dir, Daisy Stiner
Dir, Stephen L McKernan

LOCATIONS

HQ: COMMUNITY HEALTH CHOICE TEXAS, INC.
2636 S LOOP W STE 125, HOUSTON, TX 770542696
Phone: 713 295-2222
Web: WWW.COMMUNITYHEALTHCHOICE.ORG

HISTORICAL FINANCIALS

Company Type: Private

Income Statement — FYE: February 29

	REVENUE ($ mil.)	NET INCOME ($ mil.)	NET PROFIT MARGIN	EMPLOYEES
02/20	976	(17)	—	7
02/19	959	2	0.2%	—
Annual Growth	1.7%	—	—	—

2020 Year-End Financials

Return on assets: (-8.5%)
Return on equity: (-19.5%)
Current ratio: 1.70
Cash ($ mil.): 138

COMMUNITY HEALTH CHOICE, INC.

EXECUTIVES

Coo, Karen Love
Cfo, Brian Maude
Associate Web Developer, Becky Cantu
Coordinator, Richard Hobbs
Director, John Coakley
Vice-President, John Petrosino
Sales Staff, Leticia Neri
Administrative Assistant, Delwin Beene
Vice President, Jeff Allen
Director of Claims, Mychelle Scott
Controller, Peter Grant
Auditors: I KPMG LLP OKLAHOMA CITY OK

LOCATIONS

HQ: COMMUNITY HEALTH CHOICE, INC.
2636 S LOOP W STE 700, HOUSTON, TX 770545630
Phone: 713 295-2200
Web: WWW.COMMUNITYHEALTHCHOICE.ORG

HISTORICAL FINANCIALS

Company Type: Private

Income Statement — FYE: December 31

	ASSETS ($ mil.)	NET INCOME ($ mil.)	INCOME AS % OF ASSETS	EMPLOYEES
12/15	239	1	0.5%	700
12/14	192	16	8.6%	—
12/13	166	(3)	—	—
12/12	172	(17)	—	—
Annual Growth	11.6%	—	—	—

2015 Year-End Financials

Return on assets: 0.5%
Return on equity: 1.2%
Sales ($ mil): 851

COMMUNITY HEALTH NETWORK, INC.

Community Hospitals of Indiana (aka Community Health Network) has Indianapolis surrounded. The health care system includes 10 acute care hospitals nine surgery centers seven imaging centers seven immediate care centers 40 ambulatory care centers two endoscopy centers and four long term care facilities. One of its acute care facilities Community Hospital Anderson is located outside the state capital. It also runs the Community Heart and Vascular Hospital. Community Health Network whose origin reaches back to the 1950s has a total of about 1200 staffed beds and 2000 physicians. Other operations include physician practices occupational health facilities a rehab center and home health practices.

Operations

Community Health Network's physician practice Community Physician Network has more than 600 providers and working out of over 80 locations.

Together with its clinics health pavilions surgery centers and physician affiliations Community Health Network's service area covers an eight-county area in central Indiana. Various specialty centers treat digestive and joint ailments wounds spinal problems and gastrointestinal disease and also provide imaging services. Community's MedCheck clinics offer routine checkups and screenings in stand-alone locations while its MedCheck Express locations inside area Wal-Mart stores serve customers where they shop. Four Wellspring pharmacies all but one of which are located inside hospitals cover prescriptions patient education and wellness programs.

Among the system's notable features the Community Heart and Vascular Hospital which opened its doors in 2003 is an all-digital facility with digital equipment and wireless communications systems linking all its operations. Additionally the 42-bed neonatal intensive care room at Community Hospital North is one of the nation's largest labor delivery recovery and postpartum units and Westview Hospital is the state's only such facility offering osteopathic services.

In 2014 the system had more than a million outpatient visits. It also conducted some 96000 surgeries facilitated 7300 infant births and had more than 243000 emergency department visits.

Sales and Marketing

In 2014 Medicare patients accounted for about 41% of gross patient charges while Medicaid patients accounted for another 14%.

Financial Performance

Revenue grew 10% in 2014 to $1.9 billion thanks largely to growth in net patient service earnings and other revenue. This was partially offset by a decline in incentive payments related to electronic health records as well as the absence of gains on contributions to a joint venture.

Also that year the company reported a net loss of $0.9 million (versus a $179 million profit in 2013) as pension assets underperformed and gains on investments declined. However cash flow from operations rose 84% to $208 million due to changes in accrued pensions accounts payable and estimated third-party payor settlements.

Strategy

The health network is expanding in and around Indianapolis. It is investing nearly $250 million on two large building projects including a new hospital on the Community Hospital East campus and a new cancer center at the Community Hospital North campus.

In 2015 Community Health Network opened a new cardio-oncology clinic in Indianapolis. The facility is dedicated to understanding the impact that cancer-fighting treatments have on the heart.

EXECUTIVES

President And Ceo Community Health Network, William E. (Bill) Corley
President And Ceo Community Hospital Anderson, William C. (Bill) VanNess
Ceo Visionary Enterprises Inc., Bryan A. Mills
President Community Hospital North, Barbara (Barb) Summers
Ceo, Timothy L. Hobbs
Ceo The Indiana Heart Hospital, Thomas A. Malasto
Ceo Community Home Health Services, Jessie Westlund
President Community Hospital East, Robin Ledyard
President Community Hospital South, Anthony Lennen
President And Ceo, Beth Tharp
Chief Information Officer, Ron Strachan
Cfo, Joe Kessler
Coo, Tony Javorka
Vice President Corporate Finance, Kelly George
Senior Vice President And Head Human Resources, Jeffrey Purkey
Vice President Real Estate Services At Vei, Linda Pendleton
Vice President Of Innovation, Pete Turner
Vice President Chief Financial Officer V, Bret Weitzel
Svp Physician Executive And Interim President North Region, Dee Moonesinghe
Auditors: PRICEWATERHOUSECOOPERS LLP I

LOCATIONS

HQ: COMMUNITY HEALTH NETWORK, INC.
1500 N RITTER AVE, INDIANAPOLIS, IN 462193027
Phone: 317 355-1411
Web: WWW.CHNINC.COM

PRODUCTS/OPERATIONS

2014 Sales

	$ mil.	% of total
Net patient service revenue less provision for bad debts	1,815	94
Service fee revenue	25	1
Other revenue	100	5
Total	**1,942**	**100**

Selected Services

Advanced Wound Center
Assisted Fertility Services
Bariatric Services
Behavioral Health
Breast Care Services
Cancer Care Services
Children's Health
Clinical Research Trials
Community Home Health
Diet and Nutrition Services
Digestive Health Services
Emergency Services
Heart and Vascular
Inpatient Rehabilitation
Interventional Radiology
Maternity Services
Mid America Clinical Labs
Neuroscience Services
Orthopedic Services
Physical Therapy and Rehab
Radiology/Imaging Services
Sleep Wake Services
Sports Medicine
Surgical Services
Symptom Management Group
Weight Loss and Wellness
Women's Services

Selected Facilities and Affiliates

Community Health Pavilions
Community Heart and Vascular Hospital
Community Hospital Anderson
Community Hospital East
Community Hospital North
Community Hospital South
Community Imaging Centers
Community Physicians of Indiana network
Community Spine Center
Community Westview Hospital
Hook Rehabilitation Center
Indiana Surgery Centers
Indianapolis Endoscopy Center
MedCheck walk-in clinics
MedCheck Express clinics
Wellspring Pharmacy chain

COMPETITORS

Ball Memorial Hospital
Henry County Memorial Hospital
IU Health
IU Health Bloomington Hospital
Memorial Hospital (Logansport)
Riverview Hospital
St. Elizabeth Regional Health
St. Vincent Health
Wabash County Hospital

HISTORICAL FINANCIALS

Company Type: Private

Income Statement — FYE: December 31

	REVENUE ($ mil.)	NET INCOME ($ mil.)	NET PROFIT MARGIN	EMPLOYEES
12/14	1,942	(0)	—	5,000
12/13	1,763	179	10.2%	—
12/12	384	44	11.7%	—
Annual Growth	124.7%	—	—	—

2014 Year-End Financials

Return on assets: —
Return on equity: (-0.1%)
Current ratio: 2.10
Cash ($ mil.): 230

COMMUNITY HOSPITAL OF THE MONTEREY PENINSULA

Community Hospital of the Monterey Peninsula has a sunny disposition when it comes to medical care. The not-for-profit health care facility provides general medical and surgical services to residents of Monterey California. It has about 235 acute care and skilled nursing beds and offers specialty services including cardiac and cancer care obstetrics orthopedics and rehabilitation. In addition to its main facility the hospital operates several ancillary centers including a mental health clinic an inpatient hospice medical laboratory branches and several outpatient centers offering diagnostic imaging diabetes care and other services.

Operations

Community Hospital offers a broad range of healthcare services at 15 locations including the main hospital outpatient facilities satellite laboratories a mental health clinic a short-term skilled nursing facility Hospice of the Central Coast and business offices.

In 2012 the hospital systems served 12130 inpatients in 2012. It also had 49565 emergency visits 283181 outpatient visits and assisted in 1193 births.

Geographic Reach

The company has facilities in Carmel Marina Monterey and Seaside counties in California.

Financial Performance

Medicare accounted for 53% of Community Hospital of the Monterey Peninsula's revenues in 2012; commercial insurance 23% and Medi-Cal 10%.

Strategy

To improve care in its service territory the hospital is working to increase best-practice sharing among physicians. It is also supporting information sharing by coordinating electronic health records (EHRs).

In 2014 the hospital received a $200000 contribution from the Auxiliary of Community Hospital of the Monterey Peninsula completing a five-year $1 million pledge by the service organization to support the hospital.

Company Background

As health care costs skyrocket in the US Community Hospital of the Monterey Peninsula has worked to lower its expenses. Between 2008 and 2011 the organization lowered annual costs by about $44 million.

Community Hospital of the Monterey Peninsula was founded in 1934.

EXECUTIVES

Pres-Ceo, Steven J Packer
V Pres*, Terrill Lowe
Cfo*, Laura Zehm
V Pres*, Cynthia Peck
V Pres*, Tim Nylen
SEC*, Shelley Post
Vp*, Steven X Cabrales
Chief of Medicine, Berry Gendelman
Health Professional, Christian Le
Security Staff, Garry Glaser
General Surgery, Jeffrey Hyde
Auditors: MOSS ADAMS LLP SAN FRANCISCO

LOCATIONS

HQ: COMMUNITY HOSPITAL OF THE MONTEREY PENINSULA
23625 HOLMAN HWY, MONTEREY, CA 939405902
Phone: 831 624-5311
Web: WWW.CHOMP.ORG

PRODUCTS/OPERATIONS

Selected Community Hospital Service Locations

Community Hospital of the Monterey Peninsula: Monterey
Carol Hatton Breast Care Center: Monterey
Development/Patient Business Services: Monterey
Hartnell Professional Center: Monterey Peninsula
Primary Care/Satellite Laboratory: Carmel
Peninsula Wellness Center: Marina
Ryan Ranch Outpatient Campus: Monterey
Seaside Satellite Laboratory: Seaside
Westland House: Monterey

Selected Services

Bariatric Surgery
Behavioral Health Services
Carol Hatton Breast Care Center
Comprehensive Cancer Center
Diabetes
Diagnostic and Interventional Radiology
Emergency
Family Birth Center
Hospice of the Central Coast
Intermediate Intensive Care Nursery
Laboratory Services
Nutrition Therapy Program
Orthopedics
Outpatient Immunology Services
Outpatient Surgery Center
Pulmonary Wellness Services
Radiation Oncology
Rehabilitation Services
Sleep disorders
Social Services
Stroke Program
Tyler Heart Institute (Cardiac Care)
Westland House Skilled Nursing Facility
Wound Care and Hyperbaric Healing

COMPETITORS

Dignity Health
John Muir Health
Queen of the Valley Medical Center
Salinas Valley Memorial
Sequoia Healthcare District
Stanford Health Care
Sutter Health
The Palo Alto Medical Foundation
UCSF Medical

HISTORICAL FINANCIALS

Company Type: Private

Income Statement — FYE: December 31

	REVENUE ($ mil.)	NET INCOME ($ mil.)	NET PROFIT MARGIN	EMPLOYEES
12/19	693	77	11.2%	1,947
12/16	526	71	13.7%	—
12/15	560	66	11.9%	—
12/12	442	81	18.4%	—
Annual Growth	6.6%	(0.7%)	—	—

2019 Year-End Financials

Return on assets: 11.7%
Return on equity: 41.0%
Current ratio: 1.70
Cash ($ mil.): 57

COMMUNITY HOSPITALS OF CENTRAL CALIFORNIA

Community Medical Centers helps California's San Joaquin Valley stay healthy. The not-for-profit system operates four hospitals — along with nursing homes and freestanding outpatient facilities — in the greater Fresno area. Its Community Regional Medical Center is a roughly 600-bed academic hospital that provides advanced care in areas such as trauma cardiac care neuroscience and orthopedics. Clovis Community Medical Center (some 200 beds) provides general medical-surgical care with expertise in women's health and bariatric surgery. Specialty hospitals Fresno Heart & Surgical Hospital and Community Behavioral Health Center (the largest psychiatric care facility in the area) each have about 60 beds.

Operations

Community Medical Centers employs some 3000 nurses and has about 1200 affiliated physicians on its staff. Community Regional Medical Center serves about 35000 inpatient visitors and 111000 emergency room patients each year while Clovis Community Medical Center has some 13000 admissions and 51000 emergency encounters. Fresno Heart & Surgical Hospital which conducts cardiac vascular and bariatric procedures handles more than 3500 inpatient visits each year. Meanwhile Community Behavioral Health Center sees some 4000 admissions annually.

The network operates central California's only Level I trauma center and comprehensive regional burn center. It is also home to the region's only high-risk pregnancy unit as well as the Central California Neuroscience Institute and a Level III neonatal intensive care unit. The hospital system has a physician residency program it operates in conjunction with the University of California San Francisco.

Community Medical Centers serves as the area's essential "safety-net" provider conducting some $140 million in community benefits each year including care for uninsured and under-insured patients. Along with its acute care hospitals the organization operates outpatient centers clinics home care services community education programs and physician groups.

Geographic Reach

Community Medical Centers serves a 15000-mile territory including the California counties of Fresno Kings Madera Mariposa and Tulare. All four of the organization's main hospital facilities are located in the city of Fresno.

Sales and Marketing

Patient service revenues account for most of Community Medical Centers' earnings. Payer groups for patient services include Medicare and Medicaid plans which account for about 70% of sales as well as commercial insurance and self-paying clients.

Strategy

The system's Clovis campus in 2014 completed its largest-ever expansion through a $300 million project — expanding its bed count from 110 to 205 — and making the medical center the first full-service hospital in the region to have all private rooms. The renovations added a five-story bed tower a dedicated women's pavilion a special care nursery a physician practice office building and a new parking structure. The emergency department is also expanding to accommodate a projected 50000 patient visits annually.

EXECUTIVES

Ceo Clovis Community, Craig S. Castro
Svp Managed Care, Abdul Kassir
Ceo Fresno Heart And Surgical Hospital, Wanda Holderman
President And Ceo, Tim A. Joslin
Evp And Cfo, Stephen R. Walter
Evp And Coo, Patrick Rafferty
Svp And Cio, George Vasquez
Svp And Chief Nursing Officer, Mary Contreras
Ceo Community Regional, Jack Chubb
Vp Community Medical Foundation, Rob Saroyan
Vp And Chief Nursing Informatics Officer, David Boyd
Vice President Strategic Development, Charles Hensley
Director Of Him, Janet Paul
Director Of Nursing, Richard Brescione
Pharmacy Manager, Melissa Reger
Vice President Finance Administration Co, Debbie Moffett
Vice President Of Medical Records, Janet Perry
Vice President Legal Services, Brianne Marriott

Vice President Learning And Training, Sheldon Cohen
Vice President Corporate Communications, Michelle Vontersch
Vice President Corporate Communications, Michelle Von
Vice President Cmio, Judi Binderman
Vice President Chief Information Security Officer, Eric Saff
Vp Operations, Devin Huntley
Senior Vice President Human Resources, Margaret Breen
Vice President Of Information Technology, Joe Yzaguirre
Vice President, Khalil Sheibani
Vice President, Rosie Flores
Vice President, Audrey Schwartz
Vice President Corporate Internal Audit And Enterprise Risk Management, David Richstone
Board Member, Mark Mathieson
Auditors: MOSS ADAMS LLP SAN FRANCISCO

LOCATIONS

HQ: COMMUNITY HOSPITALS OF CENTRAL CALIFORNIA
2823 FRESNO ST, FRESNO, CA 937211324
Phone: 559 459-6000
Web: WWW.COMMUNITYMEDICAL.ORG

PRODUCTS/OPERATIONS

Selected Locations

Hospitals
Clovis Community Medical Center (Fresno)
Community Regional Medical Center (Fresno)
Community behavioral Health Center (Fresno)
Fresno Heart & Surgical Care (Fresno)
Outpatient centers
Advanced Medical Imaging
California Cancer Center
Community Medical Center-SierraDeran Koligian Ambulatory Care Center

COMPETITORS

Adventist Health System West
Catholic Health Initiatives
Dignity Health
Good Samaritan Hospital (San Jose)
HCA
Saint Agnes Medical Center
Sierra View District Hospital
Stanford Health Care
Sutter Health
Tenet Healthcare
UCSF Medical
ValleyCare Health System

HISTORICAL FINANCIALS

Company Type: Private

Income Statement — FYE: August 31

	REVENUE ($ mil.)	NET INCOME ($ mil.)	NET PROFIT MARGIN	EMPLOYEES
08/19	1,813	117	6.5%	6,200
08/18*	1,667	108	6.5%	—
06/10	33	0	2.1%	—
Annual Growth	55.8%	76.4%	—	—

*Fiscal year change

2019 Year-End Financials

Return on assets: 5.0%
Return on equity: 8.8%
Current ratio: 1.30
Cash ($ mil.): 143

COMMUNITY HOSPITALS OF CENTRAL CALIFORNIA

EXECUTIVES

Pres, Tim Joslin
Nurse Coordinator, Kathy Norkunas
Pharmacy Residency Program Dir, Alice Ung-Robbins
Materials Manager, Don Moyer
Chief Information Officer, Craig Castro
Registered Nurse, Lee Vang
BSN, Lisa Dellone
Vice President, Matt Joslin
General Surgeon, Amy Kwok
Anesthesiologist, Christopher Young
Chief of Neurology, Jeffrey Rosenfeld
Auditors: MOSS ADAMS LLP STOCKTON CA

LOCATIONS

HQ: COMMUNITY HOSPITALS OF CENTRAL CALIFORNIA
2823 FRESNO ST, FRESNO, CA 937211324
Phone: 559 459-6000
Web: WWW.COMMUNITYMEDICAL.ORG

HISTORICAL FINANCIALS

Company Type: Private

Income Statement — FYE: August 31

	REVENUE ($ mil.)	NET INCOME ($ mil.)	NET PROFIT MARGIN	EMPLOYEES
08/17	1,529	48	3.1%	1,000
08/14	127	0	0.5%	—
Annual Growth	128.9%	320.6%	—	—

2017 Year-End Financials

Return on assets: 2.4%
Return on equity: 4.3%
Current ratio: 1.60
Cash ($ mil.): 64

COMPASSION INTERNATIONAL INC

EXECUTIVES

Pres-Ceo, Santiago Mellado
Gen Dir*, Ronald Mathieu
V Chm*, Laurent Mbanda
Chm*, Karen Wesolowski
Gen Dir*, Jean-Franois Bussy
Gen Director*, Robert Hawkins
Gen Dir*, Mike Jeffs
Gen Dir*, Francisco Batres
SEC*, Judy Briscoe Golz
Gen Mgr*, Kenneth Morgan
Gen Dir*, Chris Knepper
Auditors: CAPIN CROUSE LP COLORADO SPRI

LOCATIONS

HQ: COMPASSION INTERNATIONAL INC
12290 VOYAGER PKWY, COLORADO SPRINGS, CO 809213694
Phone: 719 487-7000
Web: WWW.COMPASSION.COM

HISTORICAL FINANCIALS

Company Type: Private

Income Statement — FYE: June 30

	REVENUE ($ mil.)	NET INCOME ($ mil.)	NET PROFIT MARGIN	EMPLOYEES
06/16	800	13	1.6%	2,002
06/15	768	(8)	—	—
06/14	719	8	1.2%	—
06/13	659	15	2.3%	—
Annual Growth	6.6%	(4.4%)	—	—

2016 Year-End Financials

Return on assets: 4.4%
Return on equity: 6.2%
Current ratio: 1.30
Cash ($ mil.): 95

COMPUTER SCIENCES CORPORATION

Computer Sciences Corporation (CSC) has been one of the world's leading providers of systems integration and other information technology services. It offers application development data center management communications and networking development IT systems management and business consulting. It also provides business process outsourcing (BPO) services in such areas as billing and payment processing customer relationship management (CRM) and human resources. CSC boasts 2500 clients in more than 70 countries. In 2017 CSC merged with the Enterprise Services segment of Hewlett-Packard Enterprise to form DXC Technology Co. This report is based on CSC's last year as an independent company.

Change in Company Type

DXC is the result of mixing and matching of downsizing and upsizing corporate units. Computer Sciences Corp. spun out its government service unit several years ago which reduced CSC's revenue. Hewlett Packard Enterprise Services was part of Hewlett Packard Enterprise one of two companies created with Hewlett-Packard split up. The combination of HP Enterprise Services and CSC began in 2016 and concluded in April 2017 when DXC formally began operations. The new company is expected to have annual revenue of about $26 billion. This report reflects the final year of CSC as an independent company.

Operations

Prior to the creation of DXC CSC conducted business in through Global Business Services (GBS) and Global Infrastructure Services (GIS). GBS (55% of revenue) addresses key business challenges such as consulting applications services and software. GIS (45% of revenue) provides IT infrastructure services such as managed and virtual desktop solutions unified communications and collaboration services data center management cyber security and cloud-based offerings.

Geographic Reach

CSC has major operations throughout North America Europe Asia and Australia. The company has clients in more than 70 countries. About 40% of sales are made in the US and about 20% are in the UK the second biggest market.

Sales and Marketing

CSC's clients have included AboveNet Communications Deutsche Telekom DirecTV Vodafone and Ryman Hospitality Properties (formerly Gaylord Entertainment).

Financial Performance

After seven straight years of revenue declines CSC's sales rebounded in 2017 (ended March) to $7.6 billion a 7% increase from 2016. The increase was driven by the Global Business Services unit's business processing services offerings and contributions from recent acquisitions in the Digital Applications business. The Global Infrastructure Services unit posted a small revenue increase from new business and sales from acquisitions.

CSC lost about $123 million in 2017 down from a $251 million profit in 2016 mainly due to large restructuring charges.

Cash flow from operating activities rose to $978 million in 2017 from $802 million in 2016. The increase flowed from an increase in trade payables and a decrease in net account receivables.

Strategy

After going through corporate breakups DXC Technology bets that bigger will be better and stronger in competing in the worldwide market for IT services. The companies have a wide footprint and with some $26 billion in annual revenue and will have some weight to throw around. A question will be if the company can effectively compete with companies that provide similar services such as Cognizant WiPro Accenture IBM Global Service and Dell Technologies.

DXC has bulked up to ride the wave of digital transformation that its customers and potential customers are going through. The company's range of services could lead customers from legacy systems to private or public or hybrid cloud systems.

Mergers and Acquisitions

In 2016 CSC acquired Xchanging plc provider of technology-enabled business services for $633 million. Xchanging brings its Xuber software which is used by commercial insurance companies around the world.

Also in 2016 CSC acquired Aspediens a European provider in the service-management sector and a preferred partner of ServiceNow. The deal extended CSC's reach in software-as-a-service in Europe.

EXECUTIVES

Vice President, Debbie Granberry
Vice President Finance And Administration, Frank Sossi
Vice President Of Global Human Resources And Trans, Mike Darcy
Division Director Deputy Vice President General Manager, Richard Morrow
Senior Vice President And General Manager Security, Art Wong
Vice President, Brad Canel
Vp Corporate Communications, Caryn Kboudi
Svp Of Leasing, Michelle Waak
Auditors: DELOITTE & TOUCHE LLP MCLEAN

LOCATIONS

HQ: COMPUTER SCIENCES CORPORATION
1775 TYSONS BLVD STE 1000, TYSONS, VA 221024284
Phone: 703 245-9675
Web: WWW.CSC.COM

2017 Sales

	$ mil.	% of total
United States	2,986	40
United Kingdom	1,482	19
Australia	921	12
Other Europe	1,594	21
Other International	624	8
Total	**7,607**	**100**

PRODUCTS/OPERATIONS

2017 Sales

	$ mil.	% of total
Global Business Services	4,173	55
Global Infrastructure Services	3,434	45
Total	**7,607**	**100**

Selected Service Areas

Application outsourcing
Business process outsourcing
Customer relationship management
Data hosting
Enterprise application integration
Knowledge management
Management consulting
Risk management
Security
Supply chain management

Selected Solutions

Application Services
Big Data & Analytics
Business & Technology Consulting
Cloud Solutions & Services
Cybersecurity
Industry Software & Solutions
Infrastructure Services
Managed Services & Outsourcing
Mobility Solutions

COMPETITORS

ADP
Accenture
Atos
Booz Allen
CACI International
CIBER
Capgemini
Cognizant Tech Solutions
Computacenter
Convergys
Dell
Deloitte Consulting
Dimension Data
General Dynamics Information Technology
Getronics
HCL Technologies
Honeywell International
IBM Global Services
Infosys
Leidos
ManTech
NTT Data
Northrop Grumman
Siemens AG
Tata Consultancy
Tech Mahindra
Unisys
Wipro
Wipro Technologies

HISTORICAL FINANCIALS

Company Type: Private

Income Statement — FYE: March 31

	REVENUE ($ mil.)	NET INCOME ($ mil.)	NET PROFIT MARGIN	EMPLOYEES
03/17*	7,607	(100)	—	66,000
04/16	7,106	263	3.7%	—
04/15	12,173	7	0.1%	—
03/14	12,998	690	5.3%	—
Annual Growth	(16.4%)	—	—	—

*Fiscal year change

2017 Year-End Financials

Return on assets: (-1.2%)
Return on equity: (-4.6%)
Current ratio: 1.10
Cash ($ mil.): 1,263

CONROE INDEPENDENT SCHOOL DISTRICT

EXECUTIVES

Supt, Don Stockton
Asst Supt For Elementary Schl, Cathy Gibson
Special Education Assistant, Marla Mong
Teacher Jhstudent Success Teac, Vonelle Clark
Teacher, Wendy Ward
Office Administrator Worship, Calah Smith

LOCATIONS

HQ: CONROE INDEPENDENT SCHOOL DISTRICT
3205 W DAVIS ST, CONROE, TX 773042039
Phone: 936 709-7751
Web: WWW.CONROEISD.NET

HISTORICAL FINANCIALS

Company Type: Private

Income Statement — FYE: August 31

	REVENUE ($ mil.)	NET INCOME ($ mil.)	NET PROFIT MARGIN	EMPLOYEES
08/19	683	(80)	—	6,223
08/18	637	57	9.0%	—
08/17	609	7	1.2%	—
08/16	590	81	13.9%	—
Annual Growth	5.0%	—	—	—

2019 Year-End Financials

Return on assets: (-4.4%)
Return on equity: —
Current ratio: 4.80
Cash ($ mil.): 7

CONSIGLI CONSTRUCTION CO INC.

EXECUTIVES

Ceo, Anthony M Consigli
V Pres*, Matthew D Consigli
V Pres-Cfo*, J Scott Lerner
Internal Medicine Practitioner, Harrison Bond
Coordinator, Morgan Buckley
Accounting Staff, Patrick McNamara
Internal Medicine Practitioner, Zach Pearce
Assistant Project Manager, Patrick Gildea
Project Executive, Chris Scarvalas
Mep Manager, Janice Narowski
Superintendent, Kyle Shea

LOCATIONS

HQ: CONSIGLI CONSTRUCTION CO INC.
72 SUMNER ST, MILFORD, MA 017571663
Phone: 508 473-2580
Web: WWW.CONSIGLI.COM

HISTORICAL FINANCIALS

Company Type: Private

Income Statement				FYE: December 31
	REVENUE ($ mil.)	NET INCOME ($ mil.)	NET PROFIT MARGIN	EMPLOYEES
12/12	616	34	5.6%	390
12/11	297	12	4.3%	—
12/10	0	0	—	—
12/09	297	12	4.3%	—
Annual Growth	27.5%	39.6%	—	—

2012 Year-End Financials

Return on assets: 21.7%
Return on equity: 120.7%
Current ratio: 1.20
Cash ($ mil.): 29

CONSOLIDATED GRAIN & BARGE COMPANY

EXECUTIVES

Ceo, Kevin D Adams
V Pres*, Gregory Beck
Treasurer, Connie Brubaker
CGB Fertilizer Accounting Mana, Keith Brown
Regional Supervisor, Darin Cole
Loan Underwriter, John Graves
Corporate Controller, Joseph Barnett
Accounting Manager, Larry Bauman
Plant Engineer, Louis Volz
Supervisor, Megan Barklow
Scale Operations, Tom Smith
Auditors: KPMG LLP NEW ORLEANS LA

LOCATIONS

HQ: CONSOLIDATED GRAIN & BARGE COMPANY
1127 HWY 190 E SERVICE RD, COVINGTON, LA 704334929
Phone: 985 867-3500
Web: WWW.CGBGRAIN.COM

HISTORICAL FINANCIALS

Company Type: Private

Income Statement				FYE: May 31
	REVENUE ($ mil.)	NET INCOME ($ mil.)	NET PROFIT MARGIN	EMPLOYEES
05/20	5,640	54	1.0%	2,000
05/19	6,160	57	0.9%	—
05/17	6,430	16	0.3%	—
05/16	5,759	21	0.4%	—
Annual Growth	(0.5%)	27.2%	—	—

2020 Year-End Financials

Return on assets: 3.9%
Return on equity: 11.2%
Current ratio: 1.10
Cash ($ mil.): —

CONSOLIDATED PIPE & SUPPLY COMPANY, INC.

Consolidated Pipe and Supply lives up to its name: Its nine divisions supply pipe and pipeline materials to a swath of industries from energy to water and waste treatment chemical mining nuclear oil and gas and pulp and paper. Its industrial unit specializes in carbon and stainless alloy pipe valves and fittings. Vulcan makes all types of PVC. Corrosion resistant coatings are offered by a Line Pipe and Tubular unit and liquid applied coatings by Specialty Coatings. Its Consolidated Power Supply is the largest in the business of safety related metallic materials for commercial nuclear generation. Another unit caters to utilities. Consolidated also provides engineering services and inventory systems.

Operations

Consolidated Pipe and Supply is one of nearly 20 US Steel distributors authorized to sell seamless and electric resistance welded products in North America. Not limited to its branch and sales centers Consolidated Pipe and Supply's fitted semi-trailers complete with area row and bin and bar coded shelving serve as mobile warehouses for construction customers requiring on-site materials management.

The company operates through nine divisions: Industrial Line Pipe Structural Pipeline Coatings Utility Products Specialty Coatings Consolidated Power Vulcan Plastics and Consolidated Controls.

Geographic Reach

The company's reach extends to 19 US states including Alabama Arkansas Florida Georgia Illinois Indiana Kentucky Missouri Mississippi North Carolina Pennsylvania South Carolina Tennessee Texas and Virginia. It has nearly 50 sales offices in 15 states.

EXECUTIVES

Executive Vice President, Robert Kerr
Auditors: WARREN AVERETT CPAS AND ADVISO

LOCATIONS

HQ: CONSOLIDATED PIPE & SUPPLY COMPANY, INC.
1205 HILLTOP PKWY, BIRMINGHAM, AL 352045002
Phone: 205 323-7261
Web: WWW.CONSOLIDATEDPIPE.COM

PRODUCTS/OPERATIONS

Selected Industries Served

Chemical
Energy
Mining
Nuclear Generation
Oil and Gas
Petro-Chemical
Pulp and Paper
Water and Waste Treatment

Selected Divisions

Consolidated Controls (valves)
Consolidated Power (provides materials to energy industries)
Industrial (provides materials construction commercial energy pulp and paper chemical petro-chemical mining and fabrication industries)
Line Pipe (line pipe and tubular products)
Pipeline Coatings
Specialty Coatings (specialty linings for use in jet fuel and military applications)
Structural (1/8" through 48" structural and prime grades of carbon steel pipe)
Utility Products (provides utilities with products such as steel ductile iron PVC polyethylene and brass fittings and valves and steel PVC and polyethylene pipe)
Vulcan Plastics (water and sewer pipe)

COMPETITORS

American Cast Iron Pipe
Bristol Metals
Bull Moose Tube
Chicago Tube & Iron
Kelly Pipe Co. LLC
Phoenix Tube
Seymour Tubing
Southland Tube
Steel Ventures
U.S. Pipe

HISTORICAL FINANCIALS

Company Type: Private

Income Statement				FYE: December 31
	REVENUE ($ mil.)	NET INCOME ($ mil.)	NET PROFIT MARGIN	EMPLOYEES
12/18	810	44	5.4%	900
12/16	550	17	3.3%	—
12/15	575	7	1.3%	—
12/14	667	23	3.5%	—
Annual Growth	5.0%	17.3%	—	—

2018 Year-End Financials

Return on assets: 11.2%
Return on equity: 22.0%
Current ratio: 1.90
Cash ($ mil.): 3

CONSUMER PRODUCT DISTRIBUTORS, LLC

Consumer Product Distributors helps convenience stores provide convenient services to their customers. The company which operates as J. Polep Distribution Services is a leading wholesale supplier serving more than 4000 convenience retailers in New York Pennsylvania and the New England states. J. Polep distributes a variety of products including cigarettes and other tobacco items candy dairy products frozen foods snack items and general merchandise as well as alcohol and other beverages. As part of its business J. Polep provides merchandising sales and marketing and technology services. The family-owned company was founded as Polep Tobacco in 1898 by Charles Polep.

EXECUTIVES

Vice President Of Sales, Steve Peterson
Vice President Trade Development And Sales Analytics, Joe Normand
Auditors: MEYERS BROTHERS KALICKA PC

LOCATIONS

HQ: CONSUMER PRODUCT DISTRIBUTORS, LLC
705 MEADOW ST, CHICOPEE, MA 010134820
Phone: 413 592-4141
Web: WWW.JPOLEP.COM

PRODUCTS/OPERATIONS

Selected Products

Alcohol
Spirits
Wine
Automotive
Branded Motor Oils
Mag 1
Additives
Cleaning Supplies
Bakery/Pastry
Rachael's Gourmet
Mrs. Freshley's
Dolly Madison
Bon Appetite

Bellow's House
Diana's
Table Talk
Beverages
Poland Springs (Nestle Waters)
Adirondack Soda
Arizona
Florida's Natural
Simply Juices
Sweet Leaf Tea
Trade Winds
Daily Juice

Selected Services
Credit & Return Policy
Management Information Systems
Merchandising Support
Sales and Marketing Support

COMPETITORS

Atlantic Dominion
C&S Wholesale
Core-Mark
Eby-Brown
H. T. Hackney
Harold Levinson
McLane
SUPERVALU
Tripifoods

HISTORICAL FINANCIALS
Company Type: Private

Income Statement — FYE: September 29

	REVENUE ($ mil.)	NET INCOME ($ mil.)	NET PROFIT MARGIN	EMPLOYEES
09/18	1,248	1	0.1%	400
09/17*	1,101	5	0.5%	—
10/16	1,005	5	0.6%	—
10/15	968	2	0.3%	—
Annual Growth	8.8%	(14.4%)	—	—

*Fiscal year change

2018 Year-End Financials
Return on assets: 0.9%
Return on equity: 5.0%
Current ratio: 3.20
Cash ($ mil.): 6

CONTINUUM ENERGY SERVICES, L.L.C.

EXECUTIVES

MBR-Exec V Pres-Cfo, Dan Hawk
MBR*, Robert Rosene Jr
MBR*, John Greene
Program Director, Rick Pemberton
Auditors: GRANT THORNTON LLP TULSA OKL

LOCATIONS

HQ: CONTINUUM ENERGY SERVICES, L.L.C.
1323 E 71ST ST STE 100, TULSA, OK 741365036
Phone: 918 492-2840
Web: WWW.CONTINUUMES.COM

HISTORICAL FINANCIALS
Company Type: Private

Income Statement — FYE: December 31

	REVENUE ($ mil.)	NET INCOME ($ mil.)	NET PROFIT MARGIN	EMPLOYEES
12/13	2,092	5	0.2%	159
12/12	1,558	16	1.0%	—
12/11	2,021	26	1.3%	—
Annual Growth	1.7%	(56.3%)	—	—

2013 Year-End Financials
Return on assets: 1.0%
Return on equity: 3.3%
Current ratio: 1.10
Cash ($ mil.): 11

CONTINUUM MIDSTREAM, L.L.C.

EXECUTIVES

Member, Kent Dunbar
Member*, Robert B Rosene Jr
Member*, Daniel Frey
Member*, John Greene
Member*, Bob Malapkowski
Vice-President Business Develo, Brian Cutter
Auditors: GRANT THORNTON LLP TULSA OKL

LOCATIONS

HQ: CONTINUUM MIDSTREAM, L.L.C.
1323 E 71ST ST STE 100, TULSA, OK 741365036
Phone: 918 492-2840
Web: WWW.SEMINOLEENERGY.COM

HISTORICAL FINANCIALS
Company Type: Private

Income Statement — FYE: December 31

	REVENUE ($ mil.)	NET INCOME ($ mil.)	NET PROFIT MARGIN	EMPLOYEES
12/14	1,153	(2)	—	75
12/13	296	0	0.2%	—
12/02	17	0	5.3%	—
12/01	13	1	11.9%	—
Annual Growth	40.8%	—	—	—

2014 Year-End Financials
Return on assets: (-1.7%)
Return on equity: (-2.2%)
Current ratio: 0.70
Cash ($ mil.): 3

COOK CHILDREN'S HEALTH PLAN

EXECUTIVES

Pres, Doris Hunt
Coordinator, Chase Robinson
Coordinator, Allyson Tate
Director Facilities Management, Nick Markham
Manager of Fleet Operations, Robert Hailey
Manager of Engineering, Robert Weber
Manager Mkt, Teresa Hebert
Procurement Coordinator, Willy Rensing
Deputy Chief Investment Office, Apurva Mehta
Librarian, Dena Hanson
Pn Manager, Christine Oehlert
Auditors: BKD LLP HOUSTON TX

LOCATIONS

HQ: COOK CHILDREN'S HEALTH PLAN
801 7TH AVE, FORT WORTH, TX 761042733
Phone: 817 334-2247
Web: WWW.COOKCHILDRENS.ORG

HISTORICAL FINANCIALS
Company Type: Private

Income Statement — FYE: September 30

	REVENUE ($ mil.)	NET INCOME ($ mil.)	NET PROFIT MARGIN	EMPLOYEES
09/18	547	5	0.9%	27
09/17	484	(8)	—	—
09/15	307	17	5.8%	—
09/14	284	11	3.9%	—
Annual Growth	17.8%	(17.9%)	—	—

2018 Year-End Financials
Return on assets: 3.3%
Return on equity: 6.2%
Current ratio: 6.00
Cash ($ mil.): 85

COOK CHILDREN'S MEDICAL CENTER

EXECUTIVES

Pres-Ceo, Rick W Merrill
Director of Infection Control, Lisa La Rue
Credentaling Coordinator, Sandy Martin
Director of Human Resources, Beth Schmidt
Coordinator Audio Visual/Media, Terry Wilder
Human Resources Information MA, Jill Wegman
Osteopathy, Orlando Chapa Do
Director, Gary B Strong
Administrator, Darrien Carter
Vice President of Marketing, Becky Southworth
Engineer, Judy Guidry

LOCATIONS

HQ: COOK CHILDREN'S MEDICAL CENTER
801 7TH AVE, FORT WORTH, TX 761042796
Phone: 682 885-4000
Web: WWW.COOKCHILDRENS.ORG

HISTORICAL FINANCIALS
Company Type: Private

Income Statement — FYE: September 30

	REVENUE ($ mil.)	NET INCOME ($ mil.)	NET PROFIT MARGIN	EMPLOYEES
09/15	753	159	21.1%	2,000
09/14	753	107	14.2%	—
09/13	828	160	19.4%	—
09/09	563	99	17.7%	—
Annual Growth	5.0%	8.1%	—	—

2015 Year-End Financials
Return on assets: 14.5%
Return on equity: 27.5%
Current ratio: 0.90
Cash ($ mil.): 255

COOPERATIVE ENERGY, A MISSISSIPPI ELECTRIC COOPERATIVE

EXECUTIVES

Pres-Ceo, Jeff Bowman
V Pres*, Harlan Rogers
V Pres*, Billy Harden
SEC*, W T Shows
Gen Mgr*, James M Compton
Planning Staff, Guthrie Doug
Wholesale Power Supply Coordin, Terry Wright
Senior Vice President, Brad Wolfe
Maintenance, Bryan Hall
Senior Vice President, Chris Rhodes
Vice President, Don Hinton

LOCATIONS

HQ: COOPERATIVE ENERGY, A MISSISSIPPI ELECTRIC COOPERATIVE
7037 U S HIGHWAY 49, HATTIESBURG, MS 394029128
Phone: 601 579-0215

HISTORICAL FINANCIALS

Company Type: Private

Income Statement — FYE: December 31

	REVENUE ($ mil.)	NET INCOME ($ mil.)	NET PROFIT MARGIN	EMPLOYEES
12/16	822	0	—	238
12/13	811	0	—	—
12/12	771	0	—	—
12/11	766	0	—	—
Annual Growth	1.4%	—	—	—

2016 Year-End Financials

Return on assets: — Cash ($ mil.): 41
Return on equity: —
Current ratio: 1.50

COOPERATIVE FOR ASSISTANCE AND RELIEF EVERYWHERE, INC. (CARE)

The Cooperative for Assistance and Relief Everywhere (CARE) strives to be the beginning of the end of poverty. The organization works to reduce poverty in about 85 countries by helping communities in areas such as health education economic development emergency relief and agriculture. CARE supports more than 1100 projects to combat poverty. It also operates a small economic activity development (SEAD) unit that supports moneymaking activities. Through SEAD CARE provides technical training and savings and loans programs to help people — particularly women — open or expand small businesses. CARE was founded in 1945 to give aid to WWII survivors.

Operations

In addition to its home office in Georgia CARE maintains field offices in about 10 US cities including Boston Chicago Miami New York and Washington DC. The group's international field offices are located in more than 55 countries.

CARE's 1100 projects reach 122 million people more than half of which are women. About 90% of the funds that CARE receives go toward its aid efforts. The organization helps people in the poorest communities of developing nations. (It does not provide assistance in the US.)

Geographic Reach

From its headquarters in Atlanta CARE serves poor communities in nearly 85 countries. It does not provide assistance in the US.

Financial Performance

CARE's revenue increased a modest 1% to $590 million in fiscal 2011 as compared to 2010. While it logged a drop in revenues from the US government the organization saw a boost in private contributions — totaling $310 million — from CARE international members.

Strategy

CARE is supported by donations from thousands of individuals and dozens of corporations foundations and other charitable organizations in the US. Some of the participating organizations include World Wildlife Fund Covance Merck Meredith Corporation and the Wal-Mart Foundation. The group also receives funding and supplies from government agencies including the United Nations and European Union. As a result of the economic downturn CARE has been working to raise contribution levels as governments businesses and individuals cut back their spending including charitable donations.

EXECUTIVES

Vice President Finance And Information Technology And Chief Financial Officer, Peter Buijs
Vice President, Phil Mazzara
Auditors: ERNST & YOUNG LLP ATLANTA GA

LOCATIONS

HQ: COOPERATIVE FOR ASSISTANCE AND RELIEF EVERYWHERE, INC. (CARE)
151 ELLIS ST NE, ATLANTA, GA 303032420
Phone: 404 681-2552
Web: WWW.CARE.ORG

PRODUCTS/OPERATIONS

Selected International Partner Organizations
Covance Inc.
Merck Foundation
Meredith Corporation
The Wal-mart Foundation
WWF

HISTORICAL FINANCIALS

Company Type: Private

Income Statement — FYE: June 30

	REVENUE ($ mil.)	NET INCOME ($ mil.)	NET PROFIT MARGIN	EMPLOYEES
06/18	604	15	2.6%	10,000
06/16	530	(21)	—	—
06/13	492	(18)	—	—
06/11	589	10	1.7%	—
Annual Growth	0.4%	6.3%	—	—

2018 Year-End Financials

Return on assets: 3.0% Cash ($ mil.): 64
Return on equity: 4.3%
Current ratio: —

COOPERATIVE REGIONS OF ORGANIC PRODUCER POOLS

Cooperative Regions of Organic Producers Pool (CROPP) is the largest organic farming cooperative in North America. The group's 1840-plus farmer/members produce the co-op's Organic Valley Family of Farms and Organic Prairie brands of fluid and shelf-stable milk along with cheese butter and soy milk. Beyond the dairy barn the cooperative also offers organic citrus juices produce eggs meats and poultry. Its Organic Valley products are sold by food retailers and its ingredients are marketed to other organic food processors. Wisconsin-headquartered CROPP's farmer/members are located throughout North America and Australia. The co-op was founded in 1988.

Geographic Reach

The Wisconsin-based cooperative's farmer members are located in 35 US states including California and Florida and three Canadian provinces. It also has members in Australia.

Financial Performance

The co-op's sales grew 8% in 2013 versus 2012 to $928 million after increasing by 20% in the previous annual comparison. Sales have risen sharply along with increasing demand for organic milk and other dairy foods. CROPP added 10 new members in 2013. The co-op struggled in 2013 as a result of a fire that burned down part of its headquarters building. The blaze occurred about a year after the co-op completed a $6.7 million addition to the structure.

Strategy

CROPP seeks to quench consumers' growing thirst for organic milk with new products including the 2012 launch of Organic Valley Grassmilk an organic specialty milk produced from cows that are 100% grass fed. Organic Valley Grassmilk attained nationwide distribution in mid-2013.

The co-op operates under a regional business model by which milk is produced bottled and distributed in the region where it's farmed to ensure fewer miles from farm to table and to support local economies. About 75% of the co-ops 1800-plus farmers are located in the "Heartland" region of the US which includes Iowa Illinois Kansas Minnesota North Dakota Nebraska South Dakota Wisconsin Indiana Ohio and Michigan.

EXECUTIVES

Ceo, George Siemon
Coo, Louise Hemstead
Cfo, Mike Bedessem
Vice President Of Brand Marketing, Lewis Goldstein

LOCATIONS

HQ: COOPERATIVE REGIONS OF ORGANIC PRODUCER POOLS
1 ORGANIC WAY, LA FARGE, WI 546396604
Phone: 608 625-2602
Web: WWW.ORGANICVALLEY.COOP

PRODUCTS/OPERATIONS

Selected Products

Butter

Cheese
Cottage cheese
Cream

Cream cheese
Eggs
Healthy snacks
Juice
Meat
Milk
Sour cream
Soy
Yogurt

COMPETITORS

Albert's Organics
Aurora Organic Dairy
Berkeley Farms
Chiquita Brands
Crowley Foods
Dairy Crest
Dairy Farmers of America
Dakota Beef
Dannon
Dean Foods
Dole Food
Egg Innovations
Foster Dairy Farms
Fresh Del Monte Produce
Friendship Dairies
Galaxy Nutritional Foods
Garelick Farms
Great Lakes Cheese
Jonathan Sprouts
Keller's Creamery
Land O'Lakes
Laura's Lean Beef Co.
Lifeway Foods
Niman Ranch
Oberweis Dairy
Odwalla
Organically Grown Company
Rachel's Organic Dairy
Rockview Dairies
Sargento
Springfield Creamery
Stonyfield Farm
Straus Family Creamery
Stremicks Heritage Foods
Tyson Foods
Tyson Fresh Meats
United Natural
Willow Wind Organic Farms

HISTORICAL FINANCIALS

Company Type: Private

Income Statement FYE: December 31

	REVENUE ($ mil.)	NET INCOME ($ mil.)	NET PROFIT MARGIN	EMPLOYEES
12/10	619	12	2.0%	764
12/08	527	3	0.7%	—
12/07	432	6	1.4%	—
Annual Growth	12.7%	24.6%	—	—

2010 Year-End Financials

Return on assets: 7.5%
Return on equity: 12.8%
Current ratio: 2.20
Cash ($ mil.): 29

CORE CONSTRUCTION GROUP, LTD.

EXECUTIVES

Pres, Mark A Steffen
Exec V Pres*, Dennis Barber
Treas*, Michael J Thomas
Manager, Tim Hickey

LOCATIONS

HQ: CORE CONSTRUCTION GROUP, LTD.
601 SW WATER ST, PEORIA, IL 616021531
Phone: 309 263-0808
Web: WWW.CORECONSTRUCTION.COM

HISTORICAL FINANCIALS

Company Type: Private

Income Statement FYE: December 31

	REVENUE ($ mil.)	NET INCOME ($ mil.)	NET PROFIT MARGIN	EMPLOYEES
12/17	1,007	0	—	450
12/15	782	0	—	—
12/12	624	0	—	—
12/06	620	0	—	—
Annual Growth	4.5%	—	—	—

2017 Year-End Financials

Return on assets: —
Return on equity: —
Current ratio: 1.20
Cash ($ mil.): 37

CORNELL UNIVERSITY

To excel at Cornell you'll need every one of your brain cells. The Ivy League school's some 23620 students can select undergraduate graduate and professional courses from around 15 colleges and schools. In addition to its Ithaca New York campus the university has medical and professional programs in New York City and Doha Qatar. Cornell's faculty includes some 50 of Nobel laureates and the university has a robust research component studying everything from animal health to space to waste management. It has a student-faculty ratio of about 8:1. Notable alumni include author E. B. White and US Supreme Court Justice Ruth Bader Ginsburg.

Operations

Cornell awarded the nation's first university degree in veterinary medicine and first doctorates in electrical engineering and industrial engineering. It awarded the world's first degree in journalism (and taught the first university course in that subject) and established the first four-year schools of hotel administration and industrial and labor relations. Its School of Hotel Administration is one of the top-ranking educational training grounds for the hospitality industry in the world.

Cornell is deeply involved in research with more than 100 interdisciplinary research organizations pursuing research teaching and outreach on broad topics like nanofabrication life sciences computing and information science environmental sustainability human development agriculture space research and international issues. Cornell has dozens of research centers such as the Cornell High Energy Synchrotron Source (CHESS) the Cornell Electroacoustic Music Center (CEMC) the Cornell Center for Wildlife Conservation (CCWC) the National Biomedical Center for Advanced ESR Technology (ACERT) and the Laboratory of Elementary-Particle Physics (LEPP).

The University generates about a quarter of sales from medical physicians organization. Some 20% of its sales from tuition and fees while Educational activities and other sales and services generates about 15% and Grants contracts and similar agreements accounts for some 20%.

Geographic Reach

Cornell's main campus in Ithaca New York is composed of endowed colleges and contract colleges (operated on behalf of the state) spanning a 2300-acre campus in New York State's Finger Lakes region. In New York City Cornell operates the Sanford I. Weill Medical College which has an extension campus in Doha Qatar and the Graduate School of Medical Sciences. Also in New York City is Cornell Tech a technology-focused graduate campus that combines research and education with entrepreneurship and real-world application. It is operated with Israel's Technion University.

Cornell has students from around the US and around the world. More than 25% come from New York State and more than 20% are international students.

Financial Performance

Total operating revenues and other support decreased by $3.9 million to $4.3 billion in fiscal year 2020. The decrease in revenues was primarily due to the global pandemic.

Cash held by the company at the end of 2020 (ended June) increased to $591.5 million compared to $234.5 million in the prior year. Cash used for operations and investing activities were $37.5 million and $298.3 million respectively. Cash provided by financing activities was $692.8 million.

Strategy

The University's investment strategy incorporates a diversified asset allocation approach and maintains within defined limits exposure to the movements of the world equity fixed income commodities real estate and private equity markets. Based on guidelines established by the Investment Committee the University's Investment Office directs the investment of endowment and trust assets certain working capital and temporarily invested expendable funds.

Company Background

The Ivy League university was founded in 1865 as a land grant university as set out in the Morrill Act passed by the US Congress in 1862.

EXECUTIVES

Evp And Cfo, Joanne M. DeStefano
Dean School Of Continuing Education And Summer Sessions, Glenn C. Altschuler
Provost, Michael I. Kotlikoff
Dean College Of Human Ecology, Alan D. Mathios
Dean And Provost Cornell Nyc Tech, Daniel P. Huttenlocher
President, Martha E. Pollack
Dean College Of Agriculture And Life Sciences, Kathryn J. Boor
Dean College Of Engineering, Lance R. Collins
Dean Of The Cornell Sc Johnson College Of Business, Soumitra Dutta
Dean College Of Architecture Art And Planning, Kent Kleinman
Dean Graduate School, Barbara A. Knuth
Dean Graduate School Of Medical Sciences And Senior Associate Dean For Research At Weill Cornell Medicine, Gary Koretzky
Dean College Of Arts And Sciences, Gretchen Ritter
Dean School Of Law, Eduardo M. Peñalver
Provost For Medical Affairs And Dean Of Weill Cornell Medicine, Augustine M.K. Choi
Vp Information Technology And Chief Information Office, David Lifka
Dean Of The School Of Industrial And Labor Relations (ilr), Kevin F. Hallock
Interim Dean School Of Applied Economics And Management, Edward W. McLaughlin
Dean Of The Faculty Of Computing And Information Science, J. Gregory Morrisett
Dean Of The Samuel Curtis Johnson Graduate School Of Management, Mark W. Nelson
Interim Dean Of The School Of Hotel Administration And E. M. Statler Professor Of Hotel Administration, Kate Walsh
Dean Of The College Of Veterinary Medicine, Lorin D. Warnick
Vice President University Relations, Joel Malina
Co Vice President, Kevin McGovern
Vice President Of Business Development And Marketing, Arthur Brent

Assistant Vice President Finance Administration, Edna Dugan
Vice President Human Resources, Irene Hendricks
Vice President, George Saridakis
Vice President Of Marketing, Jennifer Sherwood
Vice President Johnson Hospitality Industry Club Jhic, Andrew Nesbitt
Vice Chairman, David D. Croll
Chairman, Robert S. Harrison
Vice Chairman, Barton J. Winokur
Board Member, Andrea Schultz
Secretary, Charles Bucher
Auditors: PRICEWATERHOUSECOOPERS LLP R

LOCATIONS

HQ: CORNELL UNIVERSITY
308 DUFFIELD HALL, ITHACA, NY 148532700
Phone: 607 254-4636
Web: WWW.CORNELL.EDU

HISTORICAL FINANCIALS

Company Type: Private

Income Statement — FYE: June 30

	REVENUE ($ mil.)	NET INCOME ($ mil.)	NET PROFIT MARGIN	EMPLOYEES
06/17	4,013	985	24.6%	12,207
06/16	3,809	(442)	—	—
06/12	2,956	(341)	—	—
06/11	2,955	814	27.5%	—
Annual Growth	5.2%	3.2%	—	—

2017 Year-End Financials

Return on assets: 7.5%
Return on equity: 9.8%
Current ratio: —
Cash ($ mil.): 181

CORONA-NORCO UNIFIED SCHOOL DISTRICT

EXECUTIVES

Ceo, Cathy L Sciortino
Supt*, Kent Bechler
Prin*, Ted Rozzi
Pres*, John Z Zickefoose
V Pres*, Jose W Lalas
SEC*, Linda Hawkins
Supervisor, Amanda Ruiz
Vice-President, Tammy Baer
Data Integrity Supervisor, Patty Painter
Clerk, Mary Abeyta
High School Teacher, Kelly Bustany
Auditors: VAVRINEK TRINE DAY & CO LL

LOCATIONS

HQ: CORONA-NORCO UNIFIED SCHOOL DISTRICT
2820 CLARK AVE, NORCO, CA 928601903
Phone: 951 736-5000
Web: WWW.CNUSD.K12.CA.US

HISTORICAL FINANCIALS

Company Type: Private

Income Statement — FYE: June 30

	REVENUE ($ mil.)	NET INCOME ($ mil.)	NET PROFIT MARGIN	EMPLOYEES
06/19	717	(47)	—	614
06/18	658	42	6.5%	—
06/17	637	(8)	—	—
06/16	635	113	17.8%	—
Annual Growth	4.1%	—	—	—

COUNTRYMARK COOPERATIVE HOLDING CORPORATION

EXECUTIVES

Ceo, Matt Smorch
Cfo, Jo Biggers
Safety Manager, Aaron Willis
Director, Belinda Puetz
Customer Representativ, Brad Crutchman
Supervisor, Brad Parker
Lubricant Sales Specialist, David Bates
Corrosion Technician, David Wiggins
Admin Assistant, Emily Vanhaaften
Director, Glenn Keller
Terminal Supervisor, Jerry Smith

LOCATIONS

HQ: COUNTRYMARK COOPERATIVE HOLDING CORPORATION
225 S EAST ST STE 144, INDIANAPOLIS, IN 462024059
Phone: 800 808-3170
Web: WWW.COUNTRYMARK.COM

HISTORICAL FINANCIALS

Company Type: Private

Income Statement — FYE: December 31

	REVENUE ($ mil.)	NET INCOME ($ mil.)	NET PROFIT MARGIN	EMPLOYEES
12/08	1,325	26	2.0%	425
12/07	964	56	5.9%	—
12/05	774	40	5.2%	—
Annual Growth	19.6%	(12.7%)	—	—

2008 Year-End Financials

Return on assets: 7.7%
Return on equity: 13.5%
Current ratio: 1.60
Cash ($ mil.): 8

COUNTY OF ALAMEDA

Just east of San Francisco Bay lies Alameda County. Governed by a five-member board of supervisors it includes 14 cities among them Hayward Oakland and San Leandro. Nearly 60 departments handle services like behavioral health care emergency medical and human resources along with law enforcement property tax assessment and collection and community development for a population of more than 1.5 million. The county also serves as the keeper of birth death and marriage certificates and other public records. Its budget is more than $2.7 billion; most of it goes to public assistance public protection and health care. Alameda was incorporated in 1853 from parts of neighboring Contra Costa and Santa Clara counties.

EXECUTIVES

Legal Secretary, Kathy Rieves
Legal Secretary, Rene Hai
Medical Director, Stacee Brackens
Director Of Nursing, Judy Linn
Clinical Director, Tuere Anderson
Secretary, Janice Mitchell
Assistant Treasurer, Greg Lawson
Board Member, Elizabeth Rogers
Auditors: MACIAS GINI & O'CONNELL LLP O

LOCATIONS

HQ: COUNTY OF ALAMEDA
1221 OAK ST STE 555, OAKLAND, CA 946124224
Phone: 510 272-6691
Web: WWW.ACGOV.ORG

HISTORICAL FINANCIALS

Company Type: Private

Income Statement — FYE: June 30

	REVENUE ($ mil.)	NET INCOME ($ mil.)	NET PROFIT MARGIN	EMPLOYEES
06/15	2,714	(26)	—	8,000
06/14	2,579	203	7.9%	—
06/13	2,622	65	2.5%	—
06/12	2,403	(155)	—	—
Annual Growth	4.1%	—	—	—

COUNTY OF ALBANY

EXECUTIVES

County Exec, Daniel P McCoy
Director of Finance, Jeff Neal
Executive Deputy Comptroller, John Curran
Chief Information Officer Chie, Joseph Paratore
Chief Deputy, Kerry Thompson
Database Administrator, Qun Lu
Marketing Executive, Edward Dott
Director, John Marsolais
Director, Mark Horan
Director of Communications, Mary Rozak
Stormwater Program Coordinator, Nancy Heinzen
Auditors: BST & CO CPAS LLP ALBANY

LOCATIONS

HQ: COUNTY OF ALBANY
112 STATE ST RM 1200, ALBANY, NY 122072023
Phone: 518 447-7040
Web: WWW.ALBANYCOUNTY.COM

HISTORICAL FINANCIALS

Company Type: Private

Income Statement				FYE: December 31
	REVENUE ($ mil.)	NET INCOME ($ mil.)	NET PROFIT MARGIN	EMPLOYEES
12/19	588	14	2.4%	2,567
12/18	582	63	10.9%	—
12/17	563	(9)	—	—
12/16	631	4	0.8%	—
Annual Growth	(2.4%)	41.4%	—	—

2019 Year-End Financials

Return on assets: 1.1%
Return on equity: —
Current ratio: 2.50
Cash ($ mil.): 157

COUNTY OF ALLEGHENY

EXECUTIVES

County Mgr, William McKey
Cheif Deputy, Dennis Skosnik
Dpty Prothonota, Michael Lamb
Fiscal Offc, Joseph Gurcak
Staff, Dave Hamrock
Law Specialist, Celeste McGraw
Coordinator, Carol Veal
Purchasing Agent, Matthew Breitenbach
Document Manager, Carl Dettlinger
Lan Tech, Bill Snyder
Environmental Health Superviso, Donna Scharding
Auditors: ZELENKOFSKE AXELORD LLC PITT

LOCATIONS

HQ: COUNTY OF ALLEGHENY
436 GRANT ST STE 104, PITTSBURGH, PA 152195403
Phone: 412 350-5300

HISTORICAL FINANCIALS

Company Type: Private

Income Statement				FYE: December 31
	REVENUE ($ mil.)	NET INCOME ($ mil.)	NET PROFIT MARGIN	EMPLOYEES
12/19	1,768	(51)	—	7,013
12/18	1,722	53	3.1%	—
12/17	1,640	(40)	—	—
12/16	1,613	60	3.7%	—
Annual Growth	3.1%	—	—	—

COUNTY OF ANNE ARUNDEL

EXECUTIVES

County Exec, Steuart Pittman
Budget Offcr, John Hammond
Executive Officer, Janet Owens
Coordinator, Tyjuan Thompson
Financial Operations Superviso, Brian Schenck
Coordinator, Anne Shawkey
Deputy States Atty, Attorney's, David P Ash
Maryland Circuit Court Judge, Pamela K Alban
Maryland Circuit Court Judge, Elizabeth S Morris
Maryland Circuit Court Judge, Robert Jeffrey
Environmental Policy Specialis, Matt Johnston
Auditors: CLIFTONLARSONALLEN LLP BALTIM

LOCATIONS

HQ: COUNTY OF ANNE ARUNDEL
44 CALVERT ST STE 1, ANNAPOLIS, MD 214011930
Phone: 410 222-1166
Web: WWW.AACOUNTY.ORG

HISTORICAL FINANCIALS

Company Type: Private

Income Statement				FYE: June 30
	REVENUE ($ mil.)	NET INCOME ($ mil.)	NET PROFIT MARGIN	EMPLOYEES
06/19	1,700	(20)	—	4,600
06/18	1,635	3	0.2%	—
06/17	1,573	40	2.6%	—
Annual Growth	4.0%	—	—	—

COUNTY OF ARLINGTON

EXECUTIVES

Gen Mgr, Barbara Donnellan
County Clerk*, Hope Halleck
Liet*, Chuck Kramaric
Deputy County Manager*, James Schwartz
Auditor*, Chris Horton
HB*, Jay Fisette
Human Resources Information MA, Alycia Pippen
Acting Fire Chief, Joseph Reshetar
Fire Chief, David Povlitz
Communications Manager, Kurt Larrick
Management Analyst, Cathy Fritts
Auditors: CLIFTONLARSONALLEN LLP ARLIN

LOCATIONS

HQ: COUNTY OF ARLINGTON
2100 CLARENDON BLVD # 500, ARLINGTON, VA 222015447
Phone: 703 228-3130
Web: WWW.ARLINGTONECONOMICDEVELOPMENT.COM

HISTORICAL FINANCIALS

Company Type: Private

Income Statement				FYE: June 30
	REVENUE ($ mil.)	NET INCOME ($ mil.)	NET PROFIT MARGIN	EMPLOYEES
06/19	1,409	71	5.1%	4,000
06/18	1,349	(14)	—	—
06/17	1,321	99	7.5%	—
06/16	1,261	(10)	—	—
Annual Growth	3.8%	—	—	—

2019 Year-End Financials

Return on assets: 1.3%
Return on equity: 3.2%
Current ratio: —
Cash ($ mil.): —

COUNTY OF BERGEN

EXECUTIVES

County Exec, James Tedesco
Payroll Staff, Donna Pallatta
Coordinator, Linda Cross
Coordinator Tobacco Con, Al Ferrara
Administrative Assistant, Bernadette Losito
Coordinator of Scheduling, Pat Tort
Assistant Planner, Alan Camlet
Superintendent of Roads, Barry Costanza
Assistant County Counsel, Christina D'Aloia
Purchasing Assistant, Janice Harley
Inspector, John Delia

LOCATIONS

HQ: COUNTY OF BERGEN
1 BERGEN COUNTY PLZ RM 1 # 1, HACKENSACK, NJ 076017075
Phone: 201 336-6000
Web: WWW.CO.BERGEN.NJ.US

HISTORICAL FINANCIALS

Company Type: Private

Income Statement				FYE: December 31
	REVENUE ($ mil.)	NET INCOME ($ mil.)	NET PROFIT MARGIN	EMPLOYEES
12/17	565	26	4.7%	2,347
12/16	604	22	3.8%	—
12/02	369	19	5.1%	—
12/01	18	0	—	—
Annual Growth	23.9%	—	—	—

2017 Year-End Financials

Return on assets: 1.0%
Return on equity: 1.8%
Current ratio: —
Cash ($ mil.): 248

COUNTY OF BEXAR

EXECUTIVES

County Judge, Nelson W Wolff
County Clerk*, Gerry Rickhoff
District Attorney*, Susan Reed
Auditor*, Susan Yeatts
Clerk*, Donna Kay McKinney
Assistant Auditor*, Leo Caldera
Sergeant, Al Damiani
Coordinator, Art Herrera
Coordinator, Audrey Cavazos
Sergeant, Augustin Pruneda
Coordinator, Marisa Nunez
Auditors: GARZA/GONZALEZ & ASSOCIATES S

LOCATIONS

HQ: COUNTY OF BEXAR
101 W NUEVA STE 1019, SAN ANTONIO, TX 782053482
Phone: 210 335-2626
Web: WWW.ALAMOAREAMPO.ORG

HISTORICAL FINANCIALS

Company Type: Private

Income Statement — FYE: September 30

	REVENUE ($ mil.)	NET INCOME ($ mil.)	NET PROFIT MARGIN	EMPLOYEES
09/19	703	131	18.7%	4,200
09/18	672	(103)	—	—
09/16	619	(43)	—	—
09/15	566	35	6.3%	—
Annual Growth	5.6%	38.8%	—	—

COUNTY OF BROWARD

EXECUTIVES

ADM, Bertha Henry
Asst Cnty ADM, Monica Cepero
Assistant County Administrator, Alphonso Jefferson Jr
Property Appraiser, Sheriff Lori Parrish
Coordinator, Efrem Crenshaw
Information Specialist, Lina Kulikowski
Administrative Coordinator I, Ruth Massie
Sheriff, Gregory Tony
Librarian, Frank Pennetti
Facilities Management Division, Alexander Bass
Maintenance Manager, Ash Morgan
Auditors: CROWE HORWATH LLP FORT LAUDER

LOCATIONS

HQ: COUNTY OF BROWARD
115 S ANDREWS AVE STE 409, FORT LAUDERDALE, FL 333011817
Phone: 954 357-7050
Web: WWW.BROWARD.ORG

HISTORICAL FINANCIALS

Company Type: Private

Income Statement — FYE: September 30

	REVENUE ($ mil.)	NET INCOME ($ mil.)	NET PROFIT MARGIN	EMPLOYEES
09/11	1,525	(76)	—	40,500
09/09	1,693	(28)	—	—
09/06	1,799	116	6.5%	—
Annual Growth	(3.3%)	—	—	—

2011 Year-End Financials

Return on assets: (-1.0%)
Return on equity: (-1.6%)
Current ratio: 3.60
Cash ($ mil.): 593

COUNTY OF CHESTERFIELD

EXECUTIVES

Admin, James J L Stegmaier
Prin*, Steve Elswick
Acting Deputy Administrator*, Rebecca T Dickson
Human Resources Information MA, Carla Shust
Accounting Staff, Donna Loehr
Coordinator, Lorne Field
Officer, Stephanie Brown MBA
Customer Staff, Bonita China
Senior Accounting Technician, Drecilla Smith
Auditors: KPMG LLP RICHMOND VA

LOCATIONS

HQ: COUNTY OF CHESTERFIELD
9901 LORI RD, CHESTERFIELD, VA 238326626
Phone: 804 748-1000
Web: WWW.CHESTERFIELD.GOV

HISTORICAL FINANCIALS

Company Type: Private

Income Statement — FYE: June 30

	REVENUE ($ mil.)	NET INCOME ($ mil.)	NET PROFIT MARGIN	EMPLOYEES
06/19	841	80	9.6%	4,618
06/18	857	(30)	—	—
06/17	816	91	11.2%	—
06/16	786	110	14.0%	—
Annual Growth	2.2%	(9.9%)	—	—

2019 Year-End Financials

Return on assets: 2.1%
Return on equity: 5.2%
Current ratio: —
Cash ($ mil.): 561

COUNTY OF CLARK

EXECUTIVES

County Mgr, Don Burnette
County Manager*, Don Burnett
Cfo*, Yolanda King
Staff, Hanks Jeffrey
Information Specialist, Bill Bonner
Family Supervisor, Angela Ranck
Family Supervisor, Bree-Annette Seaton
Family Supervisor, Elizabeth Stumpf
Manager, Jim Nance
Rec, Kelly Salyer
Family Supervisor, Lauren Soskin
Auditors: CROWE LLP COSTA MESA CALIFOR

LOCATIONS

HQ: COUNTY OF CLARK
500 S GRAND CENTRAL PKWY # 6, LAS VEGAS, NV 891554502
Phone: 702 455-3530
Web: WWW.CO.CLARK.NV.US

HISTORICAL FINANCIALS

Company Type: Private

Income Statement — FYE: June 30

	REVENUE ($ mil.)	NET INCOME ($ mil.)	NET PROFIT MARGIN	EMPLOYEES
06/19	3,301	625	18.9%	8,528
06/18	3,021	89	3.0%	—
06/17	2,873	96	3.4%	—
06/16	2,768	74	2.7%	—
Annual Growth	6.0%	102.9%	—	—

COUNTY OF COBB

EXECUTIVES

Chb, Tim Lee
Commissioner*, George Woody Thompson Jr
Commissioner*, Joe L Thompson
Commissioner*, Helen Goron
County Mgr*, David Hanerkson
Dir of Fin-Comptroller*, Brad Bowser
Dir*, Tony Hagler
Public Services Dir, J Virgil Moon
Coordinator, Daryl Sawyer
Coordinator, Michael Sigman
Sergeant, Amie Herd
Auditors: MOORE & CUBBEDGE LLP MARIETT

LOCATIONS

HQ: COUNTY OF COBB
100 CHEROKEE ST STE 400, MARIETTA, GA 300907004
Phone: 770 528-3300
Web: WWW.COBBCOUNTY.ORG

HISTORICAL FINANCIALS

Company Type: Private

Income Statement — FYE: September 30

	REVENUE ($ mil.)	NET INCOME ($ mil.)	NET PROFIT MARGIN	EMPLOYEES
09/19	834	57	6.9%	5,000
09/18	793	4	0.6%	—
09/17	823	11	1.4%	—
09/16	740	(230)	—	—
Annual Growth	4.1%	—	—	—

2019 Year-End Financials

Return on assets: 0.9%
Return on equity: 1.2%
Current ratio: —
Cash ($ mil.): 93

COUNTY OF CONTRA COSTA

EXECUTIVES

Prin, David Twa
Cfo*, Robert Campbell
Treasurer, Russell V Watts
Database Administrator, Barry Schamach
Administrative Assistant, Cindy Ray
Education Specialist, Clayton Johnson
Health Director, William Walker
Manager, Silvano Marchesi
Program Manager, Courtney Riddle
Auditors: MACIAS GINI & O'CONNELL LLP W

LOCATIONS

HQ: COUNTY OF CONTRA COSTA
625 COURT ST STE 100, MARTINEZ, CA 945531231
Phone: 925 957-5280
Web: WWW.CC-COURTS.ORG

HISTORICAL FINANCIALS

Company Type: Private

Income Statement				FYE: June 30
	REVENUE ($ mil.)	NET INCOME ($ mil.)	NET PROFIT MARGIN	EMPLOYEES
06/19	2,438	98	4.0%	7,193
06/18	2,259	84	3.7%	—
06/17	2,182	215	9.9%	—
06/16	2,022	80	4.0%	—
Annual Growth	6.4%	6.6%	—	—

COUNTY OF CUYAHOGA

EXECUTIVES

Commissioner, Timothy F Hagan
Ceo*, Bob Reid
Executive Officer, Sandra Bizzell
Purchasing Agent, Kristen Kaspar
Executive Assistant, Laura Roche
Managing, Farah Emeka
Information Technology Manager, Nadine Annoor
Gis Analyst, Jordan Abbott
Commercialization Associate, Timothy Nevin
Fiscal Officer, Diane Kirchendorfer
Assistant Prosecuting, Edward Brydle
Auditors: DELOITTE & TOUCHE LLP CLEVELA

LOCATIONS

HQ: COUNTY OF CUYAHOGA
1215 W 3RD ST, CLEVELAND, OH 441131532
Phone: 216 443-7022
Web: WWW.CUYAHOGABDD.ORG

HISTORICAL FINANCIALS

Company Type: Private

Income Statement				FYE: December 31
	REVENUE ($ mil.)	NET INCOME ($ mil.)	NET PROFIT MARGIN	EMPLOYEES
12/18	1,371	(118)	—	9,800
12/17	1,325	64	4.9%	—
12/16	1,324	(78)	—	—
12/07	1,507	54	3.6%	—
Annual Growth	(0.9%)	—	—	—

2018 Year-End Financials

Return on assets: (-2.1%) Cash ($ mil.): 1,674
Return on equity: (-49.0%)
Current ratio: —

COUNTY OF DALLAS

EXECUTIVES

County Judge, Clay Jenkins
Commissioner Prec 1*, Jimmy L Jackson
Commissioner Prec 2*, Mike Cantrell
Commissioner Prec 3*, John Wiley Price
Auditor*, Virginia Porter
Senior Analyst, Karl Warren
Hr Analyst, Kelvin Alexander
Auditors: DELOITTE & TOUCHE LLP DALLAS

LOCATIONS

HQ: COUNTY OF DALLAS
900 JACKSON ST STE 680, DALLAS, TX 752024425
Phone: 214 653-7099
Web: WWW.DALLASCOUNTY.ORG

HISTORICAL FINANCIALS

Company Type: Private

Income Statement				FYE: September 30
	REVENUE ($ mil.)	NET INCOME ($ mil.)	NET PROFIT MARGIN	EMPLOYEES
09/19	931	(34)	—	6,600
09/18	871	4	0.5%	—
09/17	821	(7)	—	—
09/16	779	227	29.2%	—
Annual Growth	6.1%	—	—	—

COUNTY OF DEKALB

EXECUTIVES

Ceo, Vernon Jones
Interim Ceo*, Lee May
Cpo*, Talisa R Clark
Attorney, Jonathan Weintraub
Gis Specialist, Tony Hall
Acting Sheriff, Ruth M Stringer
Communications, Yvette Jones
Director, Raymond R White
Auditors: KPMG LLP ATLANTA GA

LOCATIONS

HQ: COUNTY OF DEKALB
1300 COMMERCE DR, DECATUR, GA 300303222
Phone: 404 371-2881
Web: WWW.DEKALBCOUNTYGA.GOV

HISTORICAL FINANCIALS

Company Type: Private

Income Statement				FYE: December 31
	REVENUE ($ mil.)	NET INCOME ($ mil.)	NET PROFIT MARGIN	EMPLOYEES
12/19	749	34	4.6%	7,300
12/18	698	49	7.1%	—
12/17	628	20	3.2%	—
12/16	577	15	2.7%	—
Annual Growth	9.1%	30.2%	—	—

2019 Year-End Financials

Return on assets: 0.8% Cash ($ mil.): 561
Return on equity: 2.7%
Current ratio: —

COUNTY OF DELAWARE

EXECUTIVES

Chm, Tom McGarrigle
Exec Dir*, Marianne Grace
Manager, Dennis De Rosa
Health, Ellen Williams
Regional Safety Manager, Michael Fluck
Supervisor of Hearing, Stefani Doyle
Ward Secretary, John Barton
Administrative Assistant, Kathryn Masishin
Director, Linda F Hill
Transportation Planning, Thomas Shaffer
Vp Operations, Tom Bockius
Auditors: BAKER TILLY VIRCHOW KRAUSE LL

LOCATIONS

HQ: COUNTY OF DELAWARE
201 W FRONT ST FRNT, MEDIA, PA 190632700
Phone: 610 891-4000
Web: WWW.DELAWARECOUNTYPA.COM

HISTORICAL FINANCIALS

Company Type: Private

Income Statement				FYE: December 31
	REVENUE ($ mil.)	NET INCOME ($ mil.)	NET PROFIT MARGIN	EMPLOYEES
12/19	583	(16)	—	3,100
12/18	584	40	7.0%	—
12/17	562	(8)	—	—
12/16	568	(6)	—	—
Annual Growth	0.9%	—	—	—

2019 Year-End Financials

Return on assets: (-1.9%) Cash ($ mil.): 132
Return on equity: —
Current ratio: —

COUNTY OF ERIE

EXECUTIVES

County Exec, Mark Poloncarz
County Clerk*, Michael Kearns
Assoc Depty, Peggy A Lagree
Coordinator, Kelly Asher
Coordinator, Jack O'Connor
Assistant, Jacques Desjardins
Coordinator, James McCullough
Coordinator, Jeff Hartman
Coordinator, John Ryan
Staff, Kevin Hosey
Coordinator, Thomas Hersey

LOCATIONS

HQ: COUNTY OF ERIE
95 FRANKLIN ST RM 1603, BUFFALO, NY 142023914
Phone: 716 858-8500
Web: WWW.ERIE.GOV

HISTORICAL FINANCIALS

Company Type: Private

Income Statement				FYE: December 31
	REVENUE ($ mil.)	NET INCOME ($ mil.)	NET PROFIT MARGIN	EMPLOYEES
12/19	1,693	23	1.4%	10,200
12/18	1,646	34	2.1%	—
12/17	1,630	48	3.0%	—
12/16	1,589	(11)	—	—
Annual Growth	2.1%	—	—	—

2019 Year-End Financials

Return on assets: 0.8% Cash ($ mil.): 131
Return on equity: —
Current ratio: —

COUNTY OF ESSEX

EXECUTIVES

Prin, Joseph N Divincenzo
Acting Cty Treas*, Ron Weitz
Cty Admin*, Vincent A Dimauro
Chief of Staff, Alan Steinberg
Deputy, William Narvaez
Registrar, Carole Graves
Sheriff, Armando Fontoura
Director, David Berkowitz
Districtwide Parent Coordinato, Delores Wallace
Captain, John Napolitano
Guidance Counselor, Patricia Parisi
Auditors: SAMUEL KLEIN AND COMPANY-JOSEP

LOCATIONS

HQ: COUNTY OF ESSEX
465 MARTIN LUTHER KING, NEWARK, NJ 071021735
Phone: 973 621-4454
Web: WWW.ECDPW.ORG

HISTORICAL FINANCIALS

Company Type: Private

Income Statement — FYE: December 31

	REVENUE ($ mil.)	NET INCOME ($ mil.)	NET PROFIT MARGIN	EMPLOYEES
12/16	862	31	3.6%	5,300
12/09	784	25	3.2%	—
12/97	478	7	1.6%	—
12/95	1,107	0	—	—
Annual Growth	(1.2%)	—	—	—

2016 Year-End Financials

Return on assets: 1.2%
Return on equity: 1.7%
Current ratio: —
Cash ($ mil.): 182

COUNTY OF FREDERICK

EXECUTIVES

Commissioner, Jan H Gardener
County Mgr, Lori Depies
Council Pres-Vp, Bud Otis
Director, Wayne Howard
Chief Administrative Officer, Rick Harcum
Dir, Erin White
Occupational Specia, Heidi Ach
Coordinator, Sandy Turner
Sergeant, Mark Landahl
Foreman Supervisor, Jason Jenkins
Marketing Manager, Shawn Dennison

LOCATIONS

HQ: COUNTY OF FREDERICK
12 E CHURCH ST, FREDERICK, MD 217015402
Phone: 301 600-9000
Web: WWW.DISCOVERFREDERICKMD.COM

HISTORICAL FINANCIALS

Company Type: Private

Income Statement — FYE: June 30

	REVENUE ($ mil.)	NET INCOME ($ mil.)	NET PROFIT MARGIN	EMPLOYEES
06/19	723	22	3.1%	1,800
06/18	662	21	3.2%	—
06/17	625	8	1.4%	—
06/16	604	73	12.1%	—
Annual Growth	6.2%	(32.4%)	—	—

2019 Year-End Financials

Return on assets: 0.8%
Return on equity: 2.2%
Current ratio: —
Cash ($ mil.): 411

COUNTY OF FRESNO

EXECUTIVES

Chb, Bob Waterston
Exec Dir*, Brad Maggy
Dir*, David Pomaville
Prin*, David Luchini
Architect, Richard Wood
Attorney, Don Penner
Attorney, Robert Freed
Engineer, Bao Xiong
Program Technician, Crystal Ybarra
Financial Analyst, Letha Hood
Finance Director, Emilia Reyes
Auditors: BROWN ARMSTRONG ACCOUNTANCY CO

LOCATIONS

HQ: COUNTY OF FRESNO
2420 MARIPOSA ST, FRESNO, CA 937212204
Phone: 559 600-1710
Web: WWW.CO.FRESNO.CA.US

HISTORICAL FINANCIALS

Company Type: Private

Income Statement — FYE: June 30

	REVENUE ($ mil.)	NET INCOME ($ mil.)	NET PROFIT MARGIN	EMPLOYEES
06/19	1,649	30	1.9%	971
06/18	1,538	5	0.3%	—
Annual Growth	7.2%	510.4%	—	—

COUNTY OF FULTON

EXECUTIVES

Dty Cty Mgr, Richard Anderson
Admin Coordinator, Ronda Sanchez
Coordinator, Melba Blount
Coordinator, Michelle Broussard
Coordinator, Sandra Johnson
Coordinator, Juree Hall
Procurement Specialist, Lisa McKine
Ems Administrator, Charles Perdomo
Contracting Officer, Jacqueline Davis
Assistant Commander, Mike Hughes
Paralegal, Terry Allen
Auditors: PJC GROUP LLC ATLANTA GEORG

LOCATIONS

HQ: COUNTY OF FULTON
141 PRYOR ST SW STE 7001, ATLANTA, GA 303033468
Phone: 404 612-4000
Web: WWW.FULTONCOUNTYGA.GOV

HISTORICAL FINANCIALS

Company Type: Private

Income Statement — FYE: December 31

	REVENUE ($ mil.)	NET INCOME ($ mil.)	NET PROFIT MARGIN	EMPLOYEES
12/19	816	3	0.5%	5,000
12/18	843	70	8.3%	—
12/15	760	1	0.3%	—
12/14	755	5	0.7%	—
Annual Growth	1.6%	(6.6%)	—	—

2019 Year-End Financials

Return on assets: 0.1%
Return on equity: 0.4%
Current ratio: —
Cash ($ mil.): 925

COUNTY OF GUILFORD

EXECUTIVES

Administrator, Marty Lawing
Superior Court Judge, Judicial, Lora Cubbage
Environmental Enforcement Offi, Lorelei Elkins
Member, Stephen Dew
Auditors: CHERRY BEKAERT & HOLLAND LLP

LOCATIONS

HQ: COUNTY OF GUILFORD
301 W MARKET ST, GREENSBORO, NC 274012514
Phone: 336 641-3836
Web: WWW.COUNTYWEB.CO.GUILFORD.NC.US

HISTORICAL FINANCIALS

Company Type: Private

Income Statement — FYE: June 30

	REVENUE ($ mil.)	NET INCOME ($ mil.)	NET PROFIT MARGIN	EMPLOYEES
06/16	596	3	0.6%	2,700
06/15	584	(21)	—	—
06/08	577	(70)	—	—
06/07	548	67	12.3%	—
Annual Growth	0.9%	(28.4%)	—	—

COUNTY OF HAMILTON

EXECUTIVES

Administrator, Jeff Aluotto
Administrator*, David Krings
Commissioner*, Tom Neyer
Treasurer*, Robert A Goering
Commissioner*, John Dowlin
C-Level Human Resources, Kim Pennekamp
C-Level Human Resources, Marcie McDonald
Program Manager, Boubacar Diallo
District Chief, Cedric Robinson
Building Manager, Darnell Edwards
Program Manager, David Spatholt
Auditors: DAVE YOST COLUMBUS OHIO

LOCATIONS

HQ: COUNTY OF HAMILTON
138 E COURT ST RM 607, CINCINNATI, OH 452021226
Phone: 513 946-4400
Web: WWW.HAMILTON-CO.ORG

HISTORICAL FINANCIALS

Company Type: Private

Income Statement — FYE: December 31

	REVENUE ($ mil.)	NET INCOME ($ mil.)	NET PROFIT MARGIN	EMPLOYEES
12/19	853	44	5.2%	6,000
12/18	770	(10)	—	—
12/17	741	69	9.4%	—
12/16	735	32	4.4%	—
Annual Growth	5.1%	11.5%	—	—

2019 Year-End Financials

Return on assets: 1.0%
Return on equity: 3.1%
Current ratio: —
Cash ($ mil.): 37

COUNTY OF HARFORD

EXECUTIVES

County Exec, David Craig
Council Pres*, William Boniface
Treas*, Kathryn Hewitt
Procurement Staff, James P Barker
Procurement Staff, Stacy R Appold
Procurement Staff, Peter D Wakefiel
Procurement Staff, Stephanie L Si
Procurement Staff, Walter Ballesteros
Information Specialist, Constance Hirsch
Deputy Treasurer, Rick Pernas
Senior Internal Auditor, Brad Delauder
Auditors: SB & COMPANY LLC HUNT VALLEY

LOCATIONS

HQ: COUNTY OF HARFORD
220 S MAIN ST, BEL AIR, MD 210143820
Phone: 410 638-3000
Web: WWW.HARFORDCOUNTYMD.GOV

HISTORICAL FINANCIALS

Company Type: Private

Income Statement — FYE: June 30

	REVENUE ($ mil.)	NET INCOME ($ mil.)	NET PROFIT MARGIN	EMPLOYEES
06/20	692	(5)	—	1,400
06/18	630	22	3.5%	—
06/17	603	47	7.9%	—
06/13	553	(7)	—	—
Annual Growth	3.2%	—	—	—

COUNTY OF HENRICO

EXECUTIVES

County Mgr, John A Vithoulkas
Superintendent*, Amy Cashwell
Sergeant, Robert Dillard
Recreation Coordinator, Elbert Grinnell
Administrative Assistant, Tammy Damon
Personnel Coordinator, Andrew Snead
Human Resources Analyst Depart, Bettyann Moriarty
Battalion Chief 1a, John Shaffer
Assistant Director, Rebecca Simulcik
Administerative Assistant, Regina Windsor
Wastewater Collection Engineer, Ricky Blunt
Auditors: KPMG LLP RICHMOND VA

LOCATIONS

HQ: COUNTY OF HENRICO
4301 E PARHAM RD, HENRICO, VA 232282745
Phone: 804 501-4000
Web: WWW.HENRICO.US

HISTORICAL FINANCIALS

Company Type: Private

Income Statement — FYE: June 30

	REVENUE ($ mil.)	NET INCOME ($ mil.)	NET PROFIT MARGIN	EMPLOYEES
06/19	906	72	8.0%	9,178
06/18	853	(13)	—	—
Annual Growth	6.1%	—	—	—

COUNTY OF HILLSBOROUGH

EXECUTIVES

County Admin, Mike Merrill
Dep County Admin, Gregory Horwedel
Chief Fin Admin, Bonnie Wise
Chief Development Svs, Lucia Garsys
Chief of Human Svs, Carl Harness
Grants Admin, Wayne Finley
Executive of Information Techn, Hammond R Powes
Program Inspector, Wayne New
Admin Splst, Catherine Achat
Information Specialist, Douglas Blythe
Sergeant, Rick Roebuck
Auditors: RSM US LLP TAMPA FLORIDA

LOCATIONS

HQ: COUNTY OF HILLSBOROUGH
601 E KENNEDY BLVD, TAMPA, FL 336024156
Phone: 813 276-2720
Web: WWW.HILLSBOROUGHCOUNTY.ORG

HISTORICAL FINANCIALS

Company Type: Private

Income Statement — FYE: September 30

	REVENUE ($ mil.)	NET INCOME ($ mil.)	NET PROFIT MARGIN	EMPLOYEES
09/19	1,933	421	21.8%	10,000
09/18	1,737	66	3.9%	—
09/17	1,613	83	5.2%	—
09/16	1,521	(9)	—	—
Annual Growth	8.3%	—	—	—

2019 Year-End Financials

Return on assets: 3.4%
Return on equity: 4.4%
Current ratio: 6.20
Cash ($ mil.): 340

COUNTY OF KING

EXECUTIVES

County Exec, Dow Constantine
Mgr-Treas Div, Garry Holmes
Captain, Douglas Justus
Captain, Michael Woodbury
Legislative Relations Manager, April Putney
Education Specialist, Claudia Sierra
Project Management, Donna Frisk
Manager, Matthew Sykora
Database Administrator, Michael Stewart
Communications Specialist, Annie Kolb-Nelson
Preservation Program Manager, Brandi Link
Auditors: PAT MCCARTHY OLYMPIA WA

LOCATIONS

HQ: COUNTY OF KING
401 5TH AVE STE 3, SEATTLE, WA 981041818
Phone: 206 296-4040
Web: WWW.KINGCOUNTY.GOV

HISTORICAL FINANCIALS

Company Type: Private

Income Statement — FYE: December 31

	REVENUE ($ mil.)	NET INCOME ($ mil.)	NET PROFIT MARGIN	EMPLOYEES
12/19	2,367	61	2.6%	13,300
12/18	2,295	16	0.7%	—
12/17	2,191	121	5.5%	—
12/16	2,181	141	6.5%	—
Annual Growth	2.8%	(24.2%)	—	—

2019 Year-End Financials

Return on assets: 0.4%
Return on equity: 0.8%
Current ratio: —
Cash ($ mil.): 3,517

COUNTY OF LEE

EXECUTIVES

Dir, Roger Desjarlais
Exec Dir*, Jeff Mulder
Staff, Beth Moff
Director Digital Marketing, Allison Paula
Senior Engineer, Vincent Miller
Engineer, Ryerson John
Supervisor, Shawn Fournier
Lead Operator, Cadd Balogh
Implementation Analyst, Castro Enrique
Administrative Specialist, George Lawyer
Administrative Specialist, Leslie Erschen
Auditors: CLIFTONLARSONALLEN LLP FORT M

LOCATIONS

HQ: COUNTY OF LEE
2115 SECOND ST, FORT MYERS, FL 339013012
Phone: 239 533-2236
Web: WWW.LEEGOV.COM

HISTORICAL FINANCIALS

Company Type: Private

Income Statement FYE: September 30

	REVENUE ($ mil.)	NET INCOME ($ mil.)	NET PROFIT MARGIN	EMPLOYEES
09/19	726	(4)	—	3,000
09/18	693	0	0.1%	—
09/17	638	17	2.7%	—
09/16	615	36	5.9%	—
Annual Growth	5.7%	—	—	—

COUNTY OF LOS ANGELES

The County of Los Angeles could easily be its own country; all it really needs is just an "r." It encompasses more than 4000 square miles 88 cities two islands and has a population of more than 10 million. The regional level of state government provides such services as law enforcement property assessment tax collection public health protection and other social services within its boundaries (sometimes sharing and often providing municipal services for unincorporated cities). The county's elected Board of Supervisors provide political direction filling executive legislative and judicial roles while the various departments manage daily operations. LA County has an annual budget of nearly $30 billion.

EXECUTIVES

Secretary Ii, Diana Maldonado
Treasurer And Tax Collector, Nune Yaghjyan
Auditors: MACIAS GINI & O'CONNELL LLP L

LOCATIONS

HQ: COUNTY OF LOS ANGELES
500 W TEMPLE ST STE 437, LOS ANGELES, CA 900122724
Phone: 213 974-1101
Web: WWW.LACOUNTY.GOV

HISTORICAL FINANCIALS

Company Type: Private

Income Statement FYE: June 30

	REVENUE ($ mil.)	NET INCOME ($ mil.)	NET PROFIT MARGIN	EMPLOYEES
06/18	21,191	403	1.9%	100,000
06/17	20,064	393	2.0%	—
06/16	18,922	307	1.6%	—
06/15	18,435	482	2.6%	—
Annual Growth	4.8%	(5.8%)	—	—

COUNTY OF LOUDOUN, VIRGINIA

EXECUTIVES

County Admin, Kirby M Bowers
Treas*, H Roger Zurn Jr
Cntrl, Janet Romancyk
Payroll Staff, Michelle McTier
Coordinator, Fred Firestone
Coordinator, Tim Dudek
Coordinator, Marcus Gill
Coordinator, Kevin Johnson
Executive Officer, Indira Dholakia
Sergeant, Andrew Apollony
Captain, Chuck Wyant
Auditors: CHERRY BEKAERT LLP TYSONS COR

LOCATIONS

HQ: COUNTY OF LOUDOUN, VIRGINIA
1 HARRISON ST SE FL 1 # 1, LEESBURG, VA 201753102
Phone: 703 777-0100
Web: WWW.LOUDOUN.GOV

HISTORICAL FINANCIALS

Company Type: Private

Income Statement FYE: June 30

	REVENUE ($ mil.)	NET INCOME ($ mil.)	NET PROFIT MARGIN	EMPLOYEES
06/19	1,797	133	7.4%	6,999
06/18	1,716	71	4.2%	—
06/17	1,638	126	7.7%	—
06/16	1,470	59	4.1%	—
Annual Growth	6.9%	30.8%	—	—

2019 Year-End Financials

Return on assets: 2.1%
Return on equity: 7.3%
Current ratio: —
Cash ($ mil.): 1,321

COUNTY OF MARICOPA

EXECUTIVES

Cfo, Shelby Scharbach
Coordinator, Michele Hamm
Manager, Jeannie Taylor
Analyst, David Bross
Supervisor, Connie Ballard
Nutritionist, Sally Bordeaux
Coordinator, Lisa TSO
Procurement Specialist, Michael Cora
Infrastructure Technology Cent, Roseann Osborn-Perez
Budget Administrator, Cindy Goelz
Human Resources Manager, Allen Zingg
Auditors: LINDSEY PERRY CPA CFE AUDIT

LOCATIONS

HQ: COUNTY OF MARICOPA
301 W JEFFERSON ST # 960, PHOENIX, AZ 850032143
Phone: 602 506-3011
Web: WWW.MARICOPA.GOV

HISTORICAL FINANCIALS

Company Type: Private

Income Statement FYE: June 30

	REVENUE ($ mil.)	NET INCOME ($ mil.)	NET PROFIT MARGIN	EMPLOYEES
06/19	2,266	21	1.0%	15,751
06/18	2,136	25	1.2%	—
06/17	2,063	(34)	—	—
06/16	1,952	(47)	—	—
Annual Growth	5.1%	—	—	—

2019 Year-End Financials

Return on assets: 0.4%
Return on equity: 0.6%
Current ratio: —
Cash ($ mil.): 60

COUNTY OF MARIN

EXECUTIVES

ADM, Matthew Hymel
Supervisor*, Susan Adams
Supervisor*, Katie Rice
Supervisor*, Kathrin Sears
Supervisor*, Stephen Kinsey
Supervisor*, Judy Arnold
Accounting Specialist, Wendy Collins
Executive Assistant, Amanda Hassler
Assistant Clerk, Diane Patterson
Accountant, Ebrahim Azarbakhsh
Probation Officer, Fred Blum
Auditors: CLIFTONLARSONALLEN LLP ROSEVI

LOCATIONS

HQ: COUNTY OF MARIN
3501 CIVIC CENTER DR # 258, SAN RAFAEL, CA 949034112
Phone: 415 473-6358
Web: WWW.CO.MARIN.CA.US

HISTORICAL FINANCIALS

Company Type: Private

Income Statement FYE: June 30

	REVENUE ($ mil.)	NET INCOME ($ mil.)	NET PROFIT MARGIN	EMPLOYEES
06/19	651	69	10.7%	2,122
06/18	608	32	5.4%	—
06/17	567	28	5.0%	—
06/16	523	24	4.7%	—
Annual Growth	7.6%	41.3%	—	—

COUNTY OF MECKLENBURG

EXECUTIVES

Dir, Dena Diorio
Grant Admin, Anna Marie Cutijar
Information Specialist, Stefahn Orr
Employee Relations Analyst, Teresa Curlin
His Supervisor, Angie Craig
Administrative Assistant, Latonya Brewer
Captain, Mark McLaughlin
Director, Nha Yang
Park Maintenance Supervisor, Richard Reed
Senior It Business Analyst, Sandy Goodwin
Human Resources Manager, Andrea Grier
Auditors: CHERRY BEKAERT LLP RALEIGH N

LOCATIONS

HQ: COUNTY OF MECKLENBURG
600 E 4TH ST, CHARLOTTE, NC 282022816
Phone: 704 336-2108
Web: WWW.CHARLOTTENC.GOV

HISTORICAL FINANCIALS

Company Type: Private

Income Statement				FYE: June 30
	REVENUE ($ mil.)	NET INCOME ($ mil.)	NET PROFIT MARGIN	EMPLOYEES
06/16	1,603	(46)	—	4,800
06/15	1,469	17	1.2%	—
06/14	1,485	41	2.8%	—
06/13	1,433	109	7.7%	—
Annual Growth	3.8%	—	—	—

COUNTY OF MONMOUTH

EXECUTIVES

Dir, John Curley
Admin*, Teri O'Connor
Fin Dir*, Craig Marshall
Chief Acct, Joseph M Morris
Dir, Charles Brown III
Vice-Chairman, William Potter
Assistant Engineer, Daniel Olivares
Director of Technology, Chris Widmer
Public Information Assistant, Tricia Ring
Human, Charlie Brown
Show Manager, Colts Neck
Auditors: HOLMAN FRENIA ALLISON PC F

LOCATIONS

HQ: COUNTY OF MONMOUTH
1 E MAIN ST, FREEHOLD, NJ 077282273
Phone: 732 431-7000
Web: WWW.CO.MONMOUTH.NJ.US

HISTORICAL FINANCIALS

Company Type: Private

Income Statement				FYE: December 31
	REVENUE ($ mil.)	NET INCOME ($ mil.)	NET PROFIT MARGIN	EMPLOYEES
12/19	589	38	6.6%	3,800
12/18	563	38	6.9%	—
12/17	563	41	7.3%	—
12/16	561	43	7.8%	—
Annual Growth	1.6%	(4.0%)	—	—

2019 Year-End Financials

Return on assets: 1.4%
Return on equity: 2.4%
Current ratio: —
Cash ($ mil.): 339

COUNTY OF MONROE

EXECUTIVES

Exec Dir, Maggie Brooks
Controller, Toni Feransi
Controller, Anthony Feroce
Executive Director, Timothy Murphy
Director, Hilary Tantillo
Information Technology Interne, Mike Burke
Senior Manager, Trish Vantucci
Community Coordinator, Amy Mills
Vice President For Release, Charlene Leistman
Probation Officer, Corey Carpino
Information Technology Interne, Elizabeth Prescod
Auditors: KPMG LLP ROCHESTER NY

LOCATIONS

HQ: COUNTY OF MONROE
39 W MAIN ST STE 110, ROCHESTER, NY 146141408
Phone: 585 753-1700
Web: WWW.MONROECOUNTY.GOV

HISTORICAL FINANCIALS

Company Type: Private

Income Statement				FYE: December 31
	REVENUE ($ mil.)	NET INCOME ($ mil.)	NET PROFIT MARGIN	EMPLOYEES
12/18	1,353	21	1.6%	4,800
12/15	1,299	39	3.0%	—
Annual Growth	1.4%	(18.2%)	—	—

2018 Year-End Financials

Return on assets: 0.8%
Return on equity: 10.6%
Current ratio: 1.30
Cash ($ mil.): 248

COUNTY OF MONTGOMERY

EXECUTIVES

Chb-Chm, Josh Shapiro
Comm*, Bruce L Castor Jr
Cfo*, Uri Z Monson
Coo*, Lauren M Lambrugo
Prin*, Leslie Richards
Dep Contrl, Kevin Hoke
Asst Contrl, Diane Morgan
Information Specialist, William Pergine
Information Specialist, Carolyn Mayinja
Coordinator, Claudine Schull
Information Specialist, Mark Houseal
Auditors: MAILLIE LLP OAKS PENNSYLVANI

LOCATIONS

HQ: COUNTY OF MONTGOMERY
530 PORT INDIAN RD, NORRISTOWN, PA 194033502
Phone: 610 278-3072
Web: WWW.MONTCOPA.ORG

HISTORICAL FINANCIALS

Company Type: Private

Income Statement				FYE: December 31
	REVENUE ($ mil.)	NET INCOME ($ mil.)	NET PROFIT MARGIN	EMPLOYEES
12/19	661	17	2.6%	3,278
12/17	635	5	0.8%	—
12/15	525	(27)	—	—
12/12	542	(16)	—	—
Annual Growth	2.9%	—	—	—

2019 Year-End Financials

Return on assets: 1.7%
Return on equity: 52.2%
Current ratio: —
Cash ($ mil.): 167

COUNTY OF MONTGOMERY

EXECUTIVES

Cnty Admin, Michael Colbert
Coms*, Deborah Lieberman
Coms*, Judy Dodge
Coms*, Dan Foley
Coordinator, Jim Lewis
Director, Timothy S Nolan
Coordinator, Lenza Smith
Fleet Supervisor, Dan Fritz
Senior Engineer, Gary Shoup
Senior Buyer, Jacqueline Bailey
Director, Tyler Small
Auditors: PLATTENBURG & ASSOCIATES INC

LOCATIONS

HQ: COUNTY OF MONTGOMERY
451 W 3RD ST FL 4, DAYTON, OH 454220001
Phone: 937 225-4000
Web: WWW.MCOHIO.ORG

HISTORICAL FINANCIALS

Company Type: Private

Income Statement				FYE: December 31
	REVENUE ($ mil.)	NET INCOME ($ mil.)	NET PROFIT MARGIN	EMPLOYEES
12/19	559	25	4.5%	5,000
12/18	528	12	2.3%	—
12/17	495	(5)	—	—
12/16	508	33	6.6%	—
Annual Growth	3.3%	(9.3%)	—	—

2019 Year-End Financials

Return on assets: 1.3%
Return on equity: 2.5%
Current ratio: —
Cash ($ mil.): 529

COUNTY OF MULTNOMAH

EXECUTIVES

County Chair, Jeff Cogen
Accounting Spelialist, Leslie Ryan
Coordinator, Tameka Brazile
Staff, Tara Bowen-Biggs
Project Coordinator, Kappes Courtney
Coordinator, Erin Fairchild
Acting Director, John Wasiutynski
Information Technology Manager, Rodney Chin
Director of Data Processing, Anita Whynot
Senior Business Analys, Jason Heilbrun
Senior Human Resources Analyst, James Opoka
Auditors: MOSS ADAMS LLP EUGENE OREGON

LOCATIONS

HQ: COUNTY OF MULTNOMAH
501 SE HAWTHORNE BLVD # 531, PORTLAND, OR 972143587
Phone: 503 988-3511
Web: WWW.MCDA.US

HISTORICAL FINANCIALS

Company Type: Private

Income Statement — FYE: June 30

	REVENUE ($ mil.)	NET INCOME ($ mil.)	NET PROFIT MARGIN	EMPLOYEES
06/19	1,469	(56)	—	5,000
06/18	1,273	93	7.3%	—
06/17	1,238	(19)	—	—
06/16	1,142	3	0.3%	—
Annual Growth	8.8%	—	—	—

COUNTY OF NASSAU

EXECUTIVES

County Exec, Laura Curran
County Comptrl*, Jack Schnirman
Art Director, Fat C Paperie
Probation Supervisor I, Bryan Verdone
Commissioner, Craig Craft
Rectn Leader I, James Cleary
Legal Assistant, Kathryn Rapp
Personnel Supervisor, Kristin Bonfanti
Istructional Technology Specia, Nicholas Sarandis
Traffic Safety Stop Dwi Coordi, Christopher Mistron
Assistant To Clerk, Crystal Albert

LOCATIONS

HQ: COUNTY OF NASSAU
1 WEST ST, MINEOLA, NY 115014813
Phone: 516 571-3131
Web: WWW.NASSAUCOUNTYNY.GOV

HISTORICAL FINANCIALS

Company Type: Private

Income Statement — FYE: December 31

	REVENUE ($ mil.)	NET INCOME ($ mil.)	NET PROFIT MARGIN	EMPLOYEES
12/19	3,522	150	4.3%	14,500
12/18	3,442	111	3.2%	—
12/17	3,401	(115)	—	—
Annual Growth	1.8%	—	—	—

2019 Year-End Financials

Return on assets: 2.2%
Return on equity: —
Current ratio: 1.10
Cash ($ mil.): 925

COUNTY OF ONONDAGA

EXECUTIVES

Prin, Joanne M Mahoney
County Exec*, Nicholas J Pirro
Coordinator, Madison Quinn
Account Clerk II, April Warrick
Deputy County Executive, Bill Fisher
Intergovernmental Affairs, Bob Andrews
Special Education Transportati, Jason Laroche
Secretary, Karen Doster
Financial Analyst, Lori Pietruniak
Director of Economic Developme, Mary Primo
Commissioner, Michele Sardo
Auditors: BONADIO & CO LLP SYRACUSE

LOCATIONS

HQ: COUNTY OF ONONDAGA
1000 ERIE BLVD W, SYRACUSE, NY 132042748
Phone: 315 435-8683
Web: WWW.ONGOV.NET

HISTORICAL FINANCIALS

Company Type: Private

Income Statement — FYE: December 31

	REVENUE ($ mil.)	NET INCOME ($ mil.)	NET PROFIT MARGIN	EMPLOYEES
12/19	981	26	2.7%	508
12/18	964	(0)	—	—
12/17	906	(42)	—	—
12/16	10	(3)	—	—
Annual Growth	353.4%	—	—	—

COUNTY OF ORANGE

EXECUTIVES

Ceo, Frank Kim
Ceo*, Michael Gincola
Cfo*, Bob Franz
Prin*, Mary Chin
Clerk For Judge Thomas Goethal, Brenda Raab
Information Technology Manager, Luis Najera
Accounting Specialist, Cynthia Vela
Tourism Manager, Lori Landes-Carter
Director, Martha Campbell
Program Manager, Quazi Hashmi
It Analyst, Carrie Dooling
Auditors: MACIAS GINI & O'CONNELL LLP N

LOCATIONS

HQ: COUNTY OF ORANGE
333 W SANTA ANA BLVD 3F, SANTA ANA, CA 927014084
Phone: 714 834-6200
Web: WWW.OCGOV.COM

HISTORICAL FINANCIALS

Company Type: Private

Income Statement — FYE: June 30

	REVENUE ($ mil.)	NET INCOME ($ mil.)	NET PROFIT MARGIN	EMPLOYEES
06/19	4,105	152	3.7%	21,000
06/18	4,045	(78)	—	—
06/17	3,884	220	5.7%	—
06/16	3,715	170	4.6%	—
Annual Growth	3.4%	(3.7%)	—	—

2019 Year-End Financials

Return on assets: 1.2%
Return on equity: 4.4%
Current ratio: 15.70
Cash ($ mil.): 3,684

COUNTY OF ORANGE

EXECUTIVES

Mayor, Teresa Jacobs
County Administrator*, Ajit Lalchandani
Clerk*, Lydia Gardner
Comptroller*, Andy Diloreto
Commissioner Dist 1*, Betsy Vanderley
Commissioner Dist 2*, Rod A Love
Commissioner Dist 3*, Pete Clarke
Commissioner Dist 4*, Jennifer Thompson
Commissioner Dist 5*, Emily Bonilla
Commissioner Dist 6*, Victoria P Siplin
Customer Representativ, Deja Wallace
Auditors: CHERRY BEKAERT LLP ORLANDO F

LOCATIONS

HQ: COUNTY OF ORANGE
201 S ROSALIND AVE FL 5, ORLANDO, FL 328013527
Phone: 407 836-7350
Web: WWW.OCCOMPT.COM

HISTORICAL FINANCIALS

Company Type: Private

Income Statement — FYE: September 30

	REVENUE ($ mil.)	NET INCOME ($ mil.)	NET PROFIT MARGIN	EMPLOYEES
09/19	1,822	205	11.3%	7,315
09/18	1,694	126	7.5%	—
09/17	1,564	91	5.9%	—
09/16	1,473	71	4.8%	—
Annual Growth	7.3%	42.4%	—	—

COUNTY OF ORANGE

EXECUTIVES

Cnty Exec, Edward A Diana
Comm-Fin*, Joel Kleiman
MBR*, Steven M Neuhaus
Cntrl, Joel Kileman
Accounting Assistant, Brenda Christie
Commissioner, Brendan Casey
Director of Account Strategy, Kelly Bradley
DBA, Mary Mirabella
Director Integratio, Ray Jagos
Information Technician, Luke Ercoline
Executive Secretary, Christine Rudy

LOCATIONS

HQ: COUNTY OF ORANGE
255 MAIN ST STE 1055, GOSHEN, NY 109241641
Phone: 845 291-2480

HISTORICAL FINANCIALS

Company Type: Private

Income Statement — FYE: December 31

	REVENUE ($ mil.)	NET INCOME ($ mil.)	NET PROFIT MARGIN	EMPLOYEES
12/19	724	12	1.7%	2,700
12/18	699	(33)	—	—
12/17	674	5	0.8%	—
12/16	664	20	3.1%	—
Annual Growth	2.9%	(16.1%)	—	—

2019 Year-End Financials

Return on assets: 1.0%
Return on equity: —
Current ratio: —
Cash ($ mil.): 124

COUNTY OF PALM BEACH

EXECUTIVES

Mayor, Dave Kerner
Clerk*, Sharon R Bock
Cfo*, Darlene Malaney
Information Technology Manager*, Elena Madonna
Grants Coordinator, Claudia Salazar
Accounting Staff, Nancy Welling
Captain, Wendy Wise
Coordinator, Lauren Kurth
Senior Analyst, Parik Chokshi
Coordinator, Tyrell Hall
Administrative Secretary, Elinor Broullon

LOCATIONS

HQ: COUNTY OF PALM BEACH
301 N OLIVE AVE FRNT, WEST PALM BEACH, FL 334014703
Phone: 561 355-4950
Web: WWW.DISCOVER.PBCGOV.ORG

HISTORICAL FINANCIALS

Company Type: Private

Income Statement — FYE: September 30

	REVENUE ($ mil.)	NET INCOME ($ mil.)	NET PROFIT MARGIN	EMPLOYEES
09/18	2,081	134	6.5%	5,500
09/17	1,960	28	1.5%	—
09/16	1,821	68	3.8%	—
09/15	1,726	18	1.1%	—
Annual Growth	6.4%	94.4%	—	—

COUNTY OF PASCO

EXECUTIVES

Dmin, Michele Baker
Admin*, John J Gallagher
Budget Anaylst, Linda Bullard
Sr. Clerk, Debra Cleveland
Project Coordinator, Chris Dewey
Customer Staff, Lisa Stinnett
Engineering Director, Margaret Smith
Assistant Facilities Managemen, Andrew Baxter
Human Resources Director, Barbara Hitzemann
Laboratory Manager, Candia Mulhern
Teacher, Frank Nichols
Auditors: KPMG LLP TAMPA FL

LOCATIONS

HQ: COUNTY OF PASCO
8731 CITIZENS DR, NEW PORT RICHEY, FL 346545572
Phone: 727 847-2411
Web: WWW.PASCOCOUNTYFL.NET

HISTORICAL FINANCIALS

Company Type: Private

Income Statement — FYE: September 30

	REVENUE ($ mil.)	NET INCOME ($ mil.)	NET PROFIT MARGIN	EMPLOYEES
09/18	577	41	7.1%	1,540
09/17	520	58	11.3%	—
09/16	475	48	10.2%	—
09/15	447	28	6.3%	—
Annual Growth	8.9%	13.7%	—	—

2018 Year-End Financials

Return on assets: 1.3%
Return on equity: 2.0%
Current ratio: 7.30
Cash ($ mil.): 501

COUNTY OF PIERCE

EXECUTIVES

Ceo, Patricia McCarthy
Software Engineer Developer, Chuck Buzzard
Prevention Specialist, Gregory Tanbara
Auditors: PAT MCCARTHY OLYMPIA WA

LOCATIONS

HQ: COUNTY OF PIERCE
950 FAWCETT AVE STE 100, TACOMA, WA 984025603
Phone: 253 798-7285
Web: WWW.CO.PIERCE.WA.US

HISTORICAL FINANCIALS

Company Type: Private

Income Statement — FYE: December 31

	REVENUE ($ mil.)	NET INCOME ($ mil.)	NET PROFIT MARGIN	EMPLOYEES
12/19	647	107	16.6%	2,270
12/18	606	34	5.7%	—
12/17	582	27	4.7%	—
12/16	552	26	4.8%	—
Annual Growth	5.4%	59.9%	—	—

2019 Year-End Financials

Return on assets: 3.9%
Return on equity: 5.5%
Current ratio: —
Cash ($ mil.): 199

COUNTY OF PLACER

EXECUTIVES

Ceo*, Andrew Health
Administrative Direct, Darlene King
Program Supervisor, Gina Geisler
Librarian, Sheri Callow
Executive Director, Tiffany Johnson
Educational Audiologist, Christina Barbao
Assistant Risk Manager, Joe Ney
Vice Chair, John Allard
Assistant Planner, Kathleen Hanley
Tahoe Field Representative, Lindsay Romack
Administrative Technician, Lynn Gullion
Auditors: VAVRINEK TRINE DAY & CO LL

LOCATIONS

HQ: COUNTY OF PLACER
2986 RICHARDSON DR, AUBURN, CA 956032640
Phone: 530 889-4200
Web: WWW.PLACER.CA.GOV

HISTORICAL FINANCIALS

Company Type: Private

Income Statement — FYE: June 30

	REVENUE ($ mil.)	NET INCOME ($ mil.)	NET PROFIT MARGIN	EMPLOYEES
06/19	638	18	3.0%	3,024
06/18	596	7	1.2%	—
06/17	557	(19)	—	—
06/16	551	(3)	—	—
Annual Growth	5.0%	—	—	—

COUNTY OF PRINCE WILLIAM

EXECUTIVES

County Exec, Melissa S Peacor
Dir*, Chris Martino
Admin Coordinator, Deborah R Eaton
Appraiser, Ken Baxter
Assistant Count, Melissa Peacor
Cite Inspector, Alan Roberts
Cite Inspector, Keith Harper
Cite Inspector, Greg Compton
Cite Inspector, Todd Sheppard
Specialist II, Eduardo Londres
Specialist III, Carolyn Garrity
Auditors: CHERRY BEKAERT LLP TYSONS COR

LOCATIONS

HQ: COUNTY OF PRINCE WILLIAM
1 COUNTY COMPLEX CT, WOODBRIDGE, VA 221929202
Phone: 703 792-4640
Web: WWW.PWCGOV.ORG

HISTORICAL FINANCIALS

Company Type: Private

Income Statement — FYE: June 30

	REVENUE ($ mil.)	NET INCOME ($ mil.)	NET PROFIT MARGIN	EMPLOYEES
06/19	1,366	10	0.7%	2,700
06/18	1,261	(42)	—	—
06/17	1,217	(43)	—	—
06/16	1,180	107	9.1%	—
Annual Growth	5.0%	(54.6%)	—	—

COUNTY OF RAMSEY

EXECUTIVES

Ceo, Julie Kleinschmidt
Hr*, Gail Blackstone
Cfo*, Lee Mehrkens
Attorney*, John Choi
Officer*, Matt Bostrom

Asst Mgr, Heather Worthington
Administrator, Dawn Siegling
Sergeant, Fred Gray
Commissioner, Mary J McGuire
Assistant Chief, Todd Axtell
Dpty County Manager, Informati, Karen Francois
Auditors: REBECCA OTTO SAINT PAUL MN

LOCATIONS

HQ: COUNTY OF RAMSEY
121 7TH PL E STE 4000, SAINT PAUL, MN 551012419
Phone: 651 266-8044
Web: WWW.RAMSEYCOUNTY.US

HISTORICAL FINANCIALS

Company Type: Private

Income Statement — FYE: December 31

	REVENUE ($ mil.)	NET INCOME ($ mil.)	NET PROFIT MARGIN	EMPLOYEES
12/18	725	91	12.5%	4,000
12/17	638	(5)	—	—
12/16	649	19	3.1%	—
12/15	629	20	3.2%	—
Annual Growth	4.9%	64.9%	—	—

2018 Year-End Financials

Return on assets: 5.7%
Return on equity: 12.5%
Current ratio: 6.50
Cash ($ mil.): —

COUNTY OF ROCKLAND

EXECUTIVES

County Exec, Edwin Day
SEC*, Melanie Smith
Assistant To Sheriff, Robert Winzinger
Vice President of Habitat, Alden Wolfe
Board Member, Aron Wieder
Majority Leader, Michael Grant
Auditors: MARKS PANETH LLP NEW YORK NY

LOCATIONS

HQ: COUNTY OF ROCKLAND
11 NEW HEMPSTEAD RD # 10, NEW CITY, NY 109563664
Phone: 845 638-5122
Web: WWW.ROCKLANDGOV.COM

HISTORICAL FINANCIALS

Company Type: Private

Income Statement — FYE: December 31

	REVENUE ($ mil.)	NET INCOME ($ mil.)	NET PROFIT MARGIN	EMPLOYEES
12/19	624	34	5.6%	3,100
12/18	616	61	10.0%	—
12/17	703	(5)	—	—
12/16	791	76	9.6%	—
Annual Growth	(7.6%)	(22.9%)	—	—

2019 Year-End Financials

Return on assets: 2.3%
Return on equity: —
Current ratio: —
Cash ($ mil.): 324

COUNTY OF SACRAMENTO

EXECUTIVES

Sup, Phil Serna
Sup*, Patrick Kennedy
Sup*, Susan Peters
Sup*, Sue Frost
Sup*, Don Nottoli
Inspector General, Rick Braziel
Information Specialist, Luyen Le
Public Defender, Steven M Garrett
Director, Dept of Health Servi, Peter Beilenson
Registrar of Voters, Courtney Bailey-Kanelos
Court Manager, Brenda Allen
Auditors: VAVRINEK TRINE DAY & CO LL

LOCATIONS

HQ: COUNTY OF SACRAMENTO
700 H ST STE 7650, SACRAMENTO, CA 958141280
Phone: 916 874-5544
Web: WWW.SACCOUNTY.NET

HISTORICAL FINANCIALS

Company Type: Private

Income Statement — FYE: June 30

	REVENUE ($ mil.)	NET INCOME ($ mil.)	NET PROFIT MARGIN	EMPLOYEES
06/20	3,114	98	3.2%	10,968
06/19	2,857	(17)	—	—
06/18	2,801	62	2.2%	—
06/17	2,700	77	2.9%	—
Annual Growth	4.9%	8.3%	—	—

COUNTY OF SAN BERNARDINO

EXECUTIVES

Chm, Janice Rutherford
Aud-Ctrl-Treas, Ensen Mason
Aud-Ctrl-Rec, Errol J Mackzum
Chf Dep Aud, Howard Ochi
Aud-Ctrl-Rec, Larry Walker
Staff, Allen Simmons
Secretary, Amy Edward
Buyer, Bob Page
Assistant, Gary McBride
Coordinator, Maggie Latimer
Assistant Chief, Mary O'Toole
Auditors: VAVRINEK TRINE DAY & CO LL

LOCATIONS

HQ: COUNTY OF SAN BERNARDINO
385 N ARROWHEAD AVE, SAN BERNARDINO, CA 924150103
Phone: 909 387-3841
Web: WWW.SANBAG.CA.GOV

HISTORICAL FINANCIALS

Company Type: Private

Income Statement — FYE: June 30

	REVENUE ($ mil.)	NET INCOME ($ mil.)	NET PROFIT MARGIN	EMPLOYEES
06/19	3,806	228	6.0%	6,094
06/16	3,186	165	5.2%	—
06/15	3,077	176	5.8%	—
06/14	2,986	137	4.6%	—
Annual Growth	5.0%	10.7%	—	—

2019 Year-End Financials

Return on assets: 2.9%
Return on equity: 6.9%
Current ratio: —
Cash ($ mil.): 3,303

COUNTY OF SAN DIEGO

EXECUTIVES

Chief Admin, H Robbins-Meyer
Sup 1st Dist*, Greg Cox
Sup 2nd Dist*, Dianne Jacob
Sup 3rd Dist*, Pam Slater
Sup 4th Dist*, Ron Roberts
Sup 5th Dist*, Bill Horn
Second Vice President, Enrico Ferro
Assistant Professor of Public, Getachew Redae
Public Health Nurse Supervisor, Jessica Gaylord
Director, Phillip Smith
Senior Departmental Personnel, Mark Mandel
Auditors: VAVRINEK TRINE DAY & CO LL

LOCATIONS

HQ: COUNTY OF SAN DIEGO
1600 PACIFIC HWY STE 209, SAN DIEGO, CA 921012422
Phone: 619 531-5880
Web: WWW.SANDIEGOCOUNTY.GOV

HISTORICAL FINANCIALS

Company Type: Private

Income Statement — FYE: June 30

	REVENUE ($ mil.)	NET INCOME ($ mil.)	NET PROFIT MARGIN	EMPLOYEES
06/19	4,657	172	3.7%	17,000
06/18	4,480	169	3.8%	—
06/17	4,163	138	3.3%	—
06/16	4,254	81	1.9%	—
Annual Growth	3.1%	28.3%	—	—

2019 Year-End Financials

Return on assets: 1.9%
Return on equity: 5.3%
Current ratio: —
Cash ($ mil.): —

COUNTY OF SAN JOAQUIN

EXECUTIVES

County ADM, Monica Nino
Chief Information Officer*, Chris Cruz

Executive Director, Lani Schiff-Ross
Facilities Specialist, Tom Bugarin
Assistant Planner San Joaquin, Alisa Goulart
San Joaquin County Capital Pro, Eduardo Ramirez
Information Analyst SA, Jeff Marcelo
Employee, Maria Montalvo
County Safety, Tanya Moreno
Solid Waste Site Manager, Bill Baier
City Manager, Cruz Ramos
Auditors: VAVRINEK TRINE DAY & CO LL

LOCATIONS

HQ: COUNTY OF SAN JOAQUIN
44 N SAN JOAQUIN ST # 640, STOCKTON, CA 952022924
Phone: 209 468-3203
Web: WWW.SJGOV.ORG

HISTORICAL FINANCIALS

Company Type: Private

Income Statement — FYE: June 30

	REVENUE ($ mil.)	NET INCOME ($ mil.)	NET PROFIT MARGIN	EMPLOYEES
06/19	1,169	64	5.5%	6,498
06/18	1,154	97	8.4%	—
06/17	1,081	54	5.0%	—
06/16	1,017	59	5.9%	—
Annual Growth	4.8%	2.8%	—	—

COUNTY OF SAN MATEO

EXECUTIVES

Manager, John L Maltbie
Payroll Manager, Juan Raigoza
Human Resources Information MA, Austine Quien
Human Resources Information MA, Conny TSE
Human Resources Information MA, Danna Bandoma
Human Resources Information MA, Kate Singleton
Information Specialist, Alex Buencamino
Executive Assistant, Bianca Fasuescu
Human Resources Information MA, Eliza Rodriguez
Coordinator, Filomena Viveiros
Information Technology Manager, Andrew Sedik
Auditors: MACIAS GINI & O'CONNELL LLP W

LOCATIONS

HQ: COUNTY OF SAN MATEO
555 COUNTY CTR FL 4, REDWOOD CITY, CA 940631665
Phone: 650 363-4123
Web: WWW.SMCGOV.ORG

HISTORICAL FINANCIALS

Company Type: Private

Income Statement — FYE: June 30

	REVENUE ($ mil.)	NET INCOME ($ mil.)	NET PROFIT MARGIN	EMPLOYEES
06/19	1,721	443	25.7%	5,800
06/18	1,475	84	5.7%	—
06/16	1,325	62	4.7%	—
06/15	1,335	117	8.8%	—
Annual Growth	6.6%	39.3%	—	—

COUNTY OF SANTA BARBARA

EXECUTIVES

Chb, Brooks Firestone
Cty ADM*, Michael Brown
Supervisor*, Joni Gray
Chairperson*, Joseph Centeno
Supervisor*, Salud Carbajal
Supervisor*, Janet Wolf
Principal, Ken Masuda
Principal, Shirley Moore
Programmer, Chris Rauzino
Senior Deputy District Attorne, Lee Carter
Director, Polly Baldwin
Auditors: BROWN ARMSTRONG BAKERSFIELD

LOCATIONS

HQ: COUNTY OF SANTA BARBARA
105 E ANAPAMU ST RM 406, SANTA BARBARA, CA 931012065
Phone: 805 568-3400
Web: WWW.CARPINTERIACEMETERY.COM

HISTORICAL FINANCIALS

Company Type: Private

Income Statement — FYE: June 30

	REVENUE ($ mil.)	NET INCOME ($ mil.)	NET PROFIT MARGIN	EMPLOYEES
06/20	1,007	44	4.4%	4,582
06/19	987	53	5.4%	—
06/18	930	15	1.7%	—
06/17	889	21	2.4%	—
Annual Growth	4.3%	27.5%	—	—

COUNTY OF SANTA CLARA

EXECUTIVES

County Exec, Jeffrey V Smith
Prin, Alan Minato
Health Professional, Bea Herrick
Information Specialist, Judith McWilliams
Executive Officer, Neelima Palacherla
Assistant District, Brian Welch
Assistant District, David Angel
Chief of Staff, Derrick Seaver
Assistant District, James Gibbons-Shapiro
Controller Treasurer Departmen, Lynette Feliciano
Manager Office of Lgtbq, Maribel Martinez
Auditors: MACIAS GINI & O'CONNELL LLP W

LOCATIONS

HQ: COUNTY OF SANTA CLARA
70 W HEDDING ST 2WING, SAN JOSE, CA 951101768
Phone: 408 299-5200
Web: WWW.SCCGOV.ORG

HISTORICAL FINANCIALS

Company Type: Private

Income Statement — FYE: June 30

	REVENUE ($ mil.)	NET INCOME ($ mil.)	NET PROFIT MARGIN	EMPLOYEES
06/15	2,866	183	6.4%	14,500
06/14	2,660	12	0.5%	—
06/13	2,395	147	6.2%	—
06/11	2,408	54	2.2%	—
Annual Growth	4.5%	35.7%	—	—

COUNTY OF SANTA CRUZ

EXECUTIVES

Coord, Susan Mauriello
District 1*, Janet K Beautz
District 2*, Ellen Pirie
District 3, Chb*, Mardi Wormoudt
District 4*, Tony Campos
District 5*, Jeff Almquist
Prop Tax Acct, Marianne Ellis
Acct Tech, Mary Lou Cross
Facility Management, Mary Chavez
Tribal Administrator, Melinda Meek
Dental Assistant, Felipe Fuentes
Auditors: BROWN ARMSTRONG ACCOUNTANCY CO

LOCATIONS

HQ: COUNTY OF SANTA CRUZ
701 OCEAN ST RM 520, SANTA CRUZ, CA 950604015
Phone: 831 454-2100
Web: WWW.CO.SANTA-CRUZ.CA.US

HISTORICAL FINANCIALS

Company Type: Private

Income Statement — FYE: June 30

	REVENUE ($ mil.)	NET INCOME ($ mil.)	NET PROFIT MARGIN	EMPLOYEES
06/19	583	18	3.2%	1,654
06/18	544	0	0.0%	—
06/17	508	(4)	—	—
06/16	475	11	2.3%	—
Annual Growth	7.1%	19.4%	—	—

COUNTY OF SARASOTA

EXECUTIVES

Ctny Admin, James Ley
Dir of Fin*, Peter Ramsden
Attorney, Steven Demarsh
Project Coordinator, Andrea King
Program Inspector, Bob Levan
Coordinator, Gigi Bates
Accounting Staff, Nicole Jovanovski
Assistant Chief, Rodney Vanorsdol
Fiscal Consultant, Doreen Buonpastore
Media Relations, Jason Bartolone
Sarasota County Public Utiliti, Mechaela Reed
Auditors: CLIFTONLARSONALLEN LLP TAMPA

LOCATIONS

HQ: COUNTY OF SARASOTA
1660 RINGLING BLVD, SARASOTA, FL 342366808
Phone: 941 861-5165
Web: WWW.SCGOV.NET

HISTORICAL FINANCIALS

Company Type: Private

Income Statement FYE: September 30

	REVENUE ($ mil.)	NET INCOME ($ mil.)	NET PROFIT MARGIN	EMPLOYEES
09/19	586	56	9.6%	3,600
09/18	547	12	2.3%	—
09/16	482	(43)	—	—
09/15	482	(23)	—	—
Annual Growth	5.0%	—	—	—

COUNTY OF SHELBY

EXECUTIVES

Mayor, Mark H Luttrell Jr
Dir of ADM & Fin*, James Huntzicker
ADM of Fin*, Micheal A Swift
Mobile Security Officer, Charlie Brown
Mobile Security Officer, Keno Belford
Senior Manager, Caleb Tinkle
Officer, Lasundra Price
Secretary Counselor, Diane Morrow
Public Safety Talent Manager, Fonda Fouche
Police Officer, Gary Meador
Paramedic Firefighter, Germaine Pringle
Auditors: WATKINS UIBERALL PLLC BANKS

LOCATIONS

HQ: COUNTY OF SHELBY
160 N MAIN ST FL 4, MEMPHIS, TN 381031866
Phone: 901 222-2050
Web: WWW.SHELBYCOUNTYTRUSTEE.COM

HISTORICAL FINANCIALS

Company Type: Private

Income Statement FYE: June 30

	REVENUE ($ mil.)	NET INCOME ($ mil.)	NET PROFIT MARGIN	EMPLOYEES
06/19	1,125	39	3.5%	7,990
06/18	1,113	(10)	—	—
Annual Growth	1.1%	—	—	—

2019 Year-End Financials

Return on assets: 1.0%
Return on equity: 412.3%
Current ratio: —
Cash ($ mil.): 406

COUNTY OF SOLANO

EXECUTIVES

Co Admin, Michael Johnson
Chief Officer*, Philis Taynton
Clerical Support Specialist, Myra Schriila
Coordinator, Jefferson Dorman
Staff, Daniel Tolvtvar
Vice-President Legal, Paula McDowell
Prin, Edna White
Senior Analyst, Laura San Nicolas Tag
Staff Trainer, Aisha Teal
Ems Coordinator, Keith Erickson
Identification Bureau Supervis, Lisa Wilcox
Auditors: MACIAS GINI & O'CONNELL LLP S

LOCATIONS

HQ: COUNTY OF SOLANO
675 TEXAS ST STE 2600, FAIRFIELD, CA 945336338
Phone: 707 784-6706
Web: WWW.SOLANOCOUNTY.COM

HISTORICAL FINANCIALS

Company Type: Private

Income Statement FYE: June 30

	REVENUE ($ mil.)	NET INCOME ($ mil.)	NET PROFIT MARGIN	EMPLOYEES
06/19	739	36	4.9%	2,600
06/18	726	39	5.4%	—
06/17	680	28	4.1%	—
06/16	659	41	6.3%	—
Annual Growth	3.9%	(4.5%)	—	—

COUNTY OF SONOMA

EXECUTIVES

Admin, Sheryl Bratton
Chm*, Margaret Killian
Treas-Collector*, Rodney Dole
Information Specialist, Robert S Lee
Customer Staff, Patrick Mullin
Health Professional, Reid Harper
Programmer, Vinh Gruenhagen
Administrative Analyst, Peter Bruland
Accountant Auditor, Vanessa Thomas
Software Developer, Cynthia Krzywicki
Office Administrator, Rosalind L Girard
Auditors: VAVRINEK TRINE DAY & CO LL

LOCATIONS

HQ: COUNTY OF SONOMA
585 FISCAL DR 100, SANTA ROSA, CA 954032824
Phone: 707 565-2431

HISTORICAL FINANCIALS

Company Type: Private

Income Statement FYE: June 30

	REVENUE ($ mil.)	NET INCOME ($ mil.)	NET PROFIT MARGIN	EMPLOYEES
06/19	1,019	77	7.6%	5,260
06/18	984	26	2.7%	—
06/17	905	(6)	—	—
06/16	897	17	2.0%	—
Annual Growth	4.3%	63.8%	—	—

COUNTY OF ST LOUIS

EXECUTIVES

Cnty Exec, Charles Dooley
Dir of Admin*, Glen Powers
Dir of Admin*, Pamela Reitz
Director of Personnel*, Kirk McCarley
Supervisor, Sergeant Wendling
Supervisor, Sergeant R Rizzuti
Sergeant, Craig Molden
Security Staff, Joe Strehl
Associate County Counselor, Carl Becker
Assistant Treasurer, Cindy Williams
Sergeant, Jim Molden
Auditors: HOCHCHILD BLOOM & COMPANY LL

LOCATIONS

HQ: COUNTY OF ST LOUIS
41 S CENTRAL AVE, SAINT LOUIS, MO 631051719
Phone: 314 615-7016
Web: WWW.STLOUISCO.COM

HISTORICAL FINANCIALS

Company Type: Private

Income Statement FYE: December 31

	REVENUE ($ mil.)	NET INCOME ($ mil.)	NET PROFIT MARGIN	EMPLOYEES
12/19	810	49	6.1%	4,100
12/18	804	49	6.2%	—
12/17	715	27	3.8%	—
12/16	707	16	2.3%	—
Annual Growth	4.7%	44.7%	—	—

COUNTY OF SUFFOLK

EXECUTIVES

County Exec, Steven Bellone
Comptroller*, John Kennedy Jr
Treasurer, Angie M Carpenter
Controller, Joseph Sawicki
Coordinator, David Rubin
Associate Public Health Sanita, Cynthia Campbell
Planning, Danielle Lingg
Detective, James Bebry
Deputy County Executive, Lisa Black
Office Assistant, Michelle Marter
Detective, Ronald Bertucci
Auditors: DELOITTE & TOUCHE LLP JERICHO

LOCATIONS

HQ: COUNTY OF SUFFOLK
100 VETERANS HWY, HAUPPAUGE, NY 117885402
Phone: 631 853-4000
Web: WWW.SUFFOLKCOUNTYNY.GOV

HISTORICAL FINANCIALS

Company Type: Private

Income Statement FYE: December 31

	REVENUE ($ mil.)	NET INCOME ($ mil.)	NET PROFIT MARGIN	EMPLOYEES
12/19	3,378	36	1.1%	12,814
12/18	3,257	(69)	—	—
12/17	3,174	(9)	—	—
12/16	3,069	(83)	—	—
Annual Growth	3.2%	—	—	—

2019 Year-End Financials

Return on assets: 0.5%
Return on equity: —
Current ratio: 1.20
Cash ($ mil.): 761

COUNTY OF TARRANT

EXECUTIVES

Judge, B Glen Whitely
County Judge, B Glen Whiitely
Commissioner, Roy Brooks
Comissioner, Andy H Nguyen
Commissioner, J D Johnson
Information Specialist, Hannelore Baker
Coordinator, Velina Willis
Coordinator, Donna Zavala
Coordinator, Joyce Kirk
Coordinator, Linda Blair
Coordinator, Mary Chaisson
Auditors: KPMG LLP DALLAS TX

LOCATIONS

HQ: COUNTY OF TARRANT
100 E WEATHERFORD ST, FORT WORTH, TX 761960206
Phone: 817 884-1205
Web: WWW.ACCESS.TARRANTCOUNTY.COM

HISTORICAL FINANCIALS

Company Type: Private

Income Statement FYE: September 30

	REVENUE ($ mil.)	NET INCOME ($ mil.)	NET PROFIT MARGIN	EMPLOYEES
09/16	597	5	1.0%	139
09/15	580	52	9.1%	—
09/14	0	0	—	—
09/13	537	20	3.8%	—
Annual Growth	3.6%	(33.8%)	—	—

COUNTY OF TRAVIS

EXECUTIVES

Clerk, Dana Debeauvoir
Treasurer*, Dolores Ortega-Carter
District Attorney, Margaret Moore
Information Specialist, Don Castiglioni
Information Technology Directo, Judy Pittsford
Facilities Management Departme, Aj Jalifi
Commissioner Precinct 1, Jeff Travillion
Facility Manager, Mark Buchanan
Executive Assistant, Norma Guerra
Director, Tina Morton
Program Manager, Tonya Watson
Auditors: ATCHLEY & ASSOCIATES LLP AUST

LOCATIONS

HQ: COUNTY OF TRAVIS
700 LAVACA ST FL 11, AUSTIN, TX 787013101
Phone: 512 854-9125
Web: WWW.TRAVISCOUNTYTX.GOV

HISTORICAL FINANCIALS

Company Type: Private

Income Statement FYE: September 30

	REVENUE ($ mil.)	NET INCOME ($ mil.)	NET PROFIT MARGIN	EMPLOYEES
09/19	846	384	45.4%	3,900
09/17	758	(41)	—	—
09/16	726	58	8.0%	—
09/15	701	46	6.6%	—
Annual Growth	4.8%	69.8%	—	—

2019 Year-End Financials

Return on assets: 12.7% Cash ($ mil.): 1,087
Return on equity: 82.4%
Current ratio: —

COUNTY OF TULARE

EXECUTIVES

Assistant, Jean M Rousseau
Chief Accountant Property Tax, Rita Woodard
Staff, Dennis Haines
Captain, Mike Boudreaux
Network Administrator, Daniel Ruiz
Network Administrator II, Ferdinand Dancil
Director, Jim Sullins
Grants, Darlene Tyndal
Director, Ramona Robertson
Accountant II, Rekah Gridley
Deputy County Counsel, Barbara Grunwald
Auditors: BROWN ARMSTRONG AC BAKERSFIEL

LOCATIONS

HQ: COUNTY OF TULARE
2800 W BURREL AVE, VISALIA, CA 932914517
Phone: 559 636-5005
Web: WWW.AGCOMM.CO.TULARE.CA.US

HISTORICAL FINANCIALS

Company Type: Private

Income Statement FYE: June 30

	REVENUE ($ mil.)	NET INCOME ($ mil.)	NET PROFIT MARGIN	EMPLOYEES
06/19	882	80	9.1%	4,485
06/18	814	30	3.7%	—
06/17	739	16	2.2%	—
06/16	740	20	2.7%	—
Annual Growth	6.0%	58.5%	—	—

2019 Year-End Financials

Return on assets: 3.0% Cash ($ mil.): 1
Return on equity: 4.5%
Current ratio: —

COUNTY OF UNION

EXECUTIVES

Exec Dir, George W Devanney
Prin*, Deborah P Scanlon
Prin*, Angel G Estrada
Prin*, Carolyn Sullivan
Exec Dir*, Alfred Faella
Sergeant, George Valladares
Acting Prosecutor, Thomas K Isenhour
Special Asst To The Pres, Dir, Steven Cheung
Purchasing Division Director, Saura Scutari
County Commissioner, Alexander Mirabella
County Commissioner, Bruce Bergen

LOCATIONS

HQ: COUNTY OF UNION
10 ELIZABETH AVE, ELIZABETH, NJ 07206
Phone: 908 659-7407
Web: WWW.UCNJ.ORG

HISTORICAL FINANCIALS

Company Type: Private

Income Statement FYE: December 31

	REVENUE ($ mil.)	NET INCOME ($ mil.)	NET PROFIT MARGIN	EMPLOYEES
12/18	561	36	6.5%	2,700
12/17	550	47	8.6%	—
12/16	577	32	5.6%	—
12/15	555	43	7.9%	—
Annual Growth	0.4%	(6.0%)	—	—

2018 Year-End Financials

Return on assets: 1.7% Cash ($ mil.): 433
Return on equity: 9.4%
Current ratio: —

COUNTY OF VENTURA

EXECUTIVES

County Exec Offc, Michael Powers
Health Professional, Simone Mongiello
Supervisor, Karen Barstow
Program Inspector, Bruce Tanner
Law Specialist, Dean Kiser
Coordinator, Matt Savard
Officer, Christy Madden
Coordinator, Katy Hadduck
Coordinator, Marcy Snider
Information, David Stuart
Child Welfare Supervisor, Elizabeth Watson

LOCATIONS

HQ: COUNTY OF VENTURA
800 S VICTORIA AVE, VENTURA, CA 930090003
Phone: 805 654-2644
Web: WWW.VENTURA.ORG

HISTORICAL FINANCIALS

Company Type: Private

Income Statement FYE: June 30

	REVENUE ($ mil.)	NET INCOME ($ mil.)	NET PROFIT MARGIN	EMPLOYEES
06/19	1,482	66	4.5%	7,433
06/18	1,463	64	4.4%	—
06/17	1,388	41	3.0%	—
06/16	1,302	(12)	—	—
Annual Growth	4.4%	—	—	—

COUNTY OF WAKE

EXECUTIVES

County Mgr, David Ellis
Commissioner*, Betty Lou Ward
Accountant*, William Phillips
Chairman*, Joe Bryan
Vice Chair*, Phil Matthews
Commissioner*, Tony Gurley
Commissioner*, Caroline Sullivan
Commissioner*, James West
Commissioner*, Paul Coble
Attorney, Stephen Sizemore
Customer Staff, Mike Bass
Auditors: ELLIOTT DAVIS PLLC RALEIGH

LOCATIONS

HQ: COUNTY OF WAKE
300 S SALISBURY ST # 4800, RALEIGH, NC 276011751
Phone: 919 856-6160
Web: WWW.WAKEGOV.COM

HISTORICAL FINANCIALS

Company Type: Private

Income Statement — FYE: June 30

	REVENUE ($ mil.)	NET INCOME ($ mil.)	NET PROFIT MARGIN	EMPLOYEES
06/19	1,537	(93)	—	3,700
06/18	1,377	67	4.9%	—
06/16	1,291	(297)	—	—
06/15	0	0	—	—
Annual Growth	—	—	—	—

2019 Year-End Financials

Return on assets: (-4.8%)
Return on equity: —
Current ratio: —
Cash ($ mil.): 654

COUNTY OF WASHINGTON

EXECUTIVES

Administrator, Robert Davis
Training Coordinator, Deb Dalenberg
Human Resources Manager, Stephanie Reitmajer
Senior Managment Analyst, Amanda Bewersdorff
Information Technology Manager, Chris Gensler
Senior Info Analyst, Don Hunt
Executive Assistant, Angie Aguilar
Senior Human Resources Busines, Brandi Murray
Chief Information Officer, Christopher Gensler
Benefits Supervisor, Cynthia Kodachi
Right of Way Agent, Jeff Nakken
Auditors: TALBOT KORVOLA & WARWICK LLP

LOCATIONS

HQ: COUNTY OF WASHINGTON
155 N 1ST AVE STE 300, HILLSBORO, OR 971243001
Phone: 503 846-8685
Web: WWW.CO.WASHINGTON.OR.US

HISTORICAL FINANCIALS

Company Type: Private

Income Statement — FYE: June 30

	REVENUE ($ mil.)	NET INCOME ($ mil.)	NET PROFIT MARGIN	EMPLOYEES
06/19	577	(7)	—	1,800
06/18	522	(35)	—	—
06/17	499	220	44.2%	—
06/16	488	13	2.7%	—
Annual Growth	5.8%	—	—	—

COUNTY OF WESTCHESTER

EXECUTIVES

Exec Dir, Kevin J Plunkett
Mayor, Timothy C Idoni
Senior Programmer, Maria Pereira
Clerk, John Allen
Scientist, John Junker
Law Specialist, Michael R Dispenza
Information Technology Manager, Sergio Sensi
Information Technology Manager, Larry Oisher
Environmental Planne, Robert Doscher
Software, Aji Palappillil
Chief Special Operations Divis, Paul Stasaitis

LOCATIONS

HQ: COUNTY OF WESTCHESTER
148 MARTINE AVE, WHITE PLAINS, NY 106013311
Phone: 914 995-2000
Web: WWW.WESTCHESTERGOV.COM

HISTORICAL FINANCIALS

Company Type: Private

Income Statement — FYE: December 31

	REVENUE ($ mil.)	NET INCOME ($ mil.)	NET PROFIT MARGIN	EMPLOYEES
12/19	2,412	5	0.2%	5,927
12/18	2,268	1	0.0%	—
12/17	2,146	28	1.3%	—
12/16	2,133	(136)	—	—
Annual Growth	4.2%	—	—	—

2019 Year-End Financials

Return on assets: 0.1%
Return on equity: —
Current ratio: 1.20
Cash ($ mil.): 277

COUNTY SANITATION DISTRICT NO. 2 OF LOS ANGELES COUNTY

EXECUTIVES

Gen Mgr, Stephen Maguin
Acctg, Sherry Rachman
Director, Debra Bogdanoff
Director of Information Techno, Daniel Lee
Scientist, Jennipher CU
Project Engineer, Ryan Hall
Fleet Engineering Technician I, Edward Gomez
Supervisor, Frank Prieto
Chemist, Jorge Garcia
Senior Engineer, Roya Phillips
Engineer, Scott Partridge
Auditors: MOSS LEVY & HARTZHEIM LLP CU

LOCATIONS

HQ: COUNTY SANITATION DISTRICT NO. 2 OF LOS ANGELES COUNTY
1955 WORKMAN MILL RD, WHITTIER, CA 906011415
Phone: 562 699-7411
Web: WWW.LACOUNTY.GOV

HISTORICAL FINANCIALS

Company Type: Private

Income Statement — FYE: June 30

	REVENUE ($ mil.)	NET INCOME ($ mil.)	NET PROFIT MARGIN	EMPLOYEES
06/19	627	211	33.8%	1,700
06/16	545	144	26.4%	—
06/15	555	92	16.7%	—
06/12	550	74	13.6%	—
Annual Growth	1.9%	16.0%	—	—

2019 Year-End Financials

Return on assets: 3.5%
Return on equity: 5.0%
Current ratio: 14.10
Cash ($ mil.): 519

COVENANT HEALTH

Covenant Health has made a pact to provide good health to the good people of Tennessee. The not-for-profit health care system established in 1996 provides a variety of medical services through seven acute care hospitals a psychiatric hospital and a number of specialty outpatient centers offering geriatrics pediatric care cancer services weight management and diagnostics. Covenant Health also operates home health and hospice agencies and a physician practice management company. Covenant Health provides staffing and medical management services to its affiliated facilities and to make itself a really well-rounded health care provider it operates the Covenant Health Federal Credit Union.

EXECUTIVES

Senior Vice President, Mark Browne
Medical Director, Richard Bremer

LOCATIONS

HQ: COVENANT HEALTH
100 FORT SANDERS W BLVD, KNOXVILLE, TN 379223353
Phone: 865 531-5555
Web: WWW.COVENANTHEALTH.COM

PRODUCTS/OPERATIONS

Selected Tennessee Facilities

Fort Loudon Medical Center (Lenoir City TN)
Fort Sanders Regional Medical Center (Knoxville TN)
LeConte Medical Center (formerly Fort Sanders Sevier Medical Center; Sevierville TN)
Methodist Medical Center of Oak Ridge (Oak Ridge TN)
Parkwest Medical Center (Knoxville TN)
Peninsula Hospital (behavioral health care Louisville TN)
Roane Medical Center (Harriman TN)

COMPETITORS

Blount Memorial Hospital
East Tennessee Children's Hospital
Kindred Healthcare
LifePoint Health
Parkridge Medical Center
Saint Thomas Midtown Hospital
Saint Thomas Rutherford Hospital
Tennova Healthcare
University Health System Inc.
Vanderbilt University Medical Center

HISTORICAL FINANCIALS

Company Type: Private

Income Statement FYE: December 31

	REVENUE ($ mil.)	NET INCOME ($ mil.)	NET PROFIT MARGIN	EMPLOYEES
12/19	1,407	183	13.1%	2,469
12/18	1,296	(49)	—	—
12/17	1,268	144	11.4%	—
12/16	1,246	57	4.6%	—
Annual Growth	4.1%	47.1%	—	—

2019 Year-End Financials

Return on assets: 6.7%
Return on equity: 11.9%
Current ratio: 1.50
Cash ($ mil.): 145

COVENANT HEALTH SYSTEM

Covenant Health System ties West Texas and Eastern New Mexico together with quality health care. The health services provider offers some 1100 beds in its five primary acute-care and specialty hospitals; it also manages about a dozen affiliated community hospitals. Covenant Health System part of Providence St. Joseph Health also maintains a network of family health care and medical clinics. Covenant Health System's major facilities are Covenant Medical Center Covenant Specialty Hospital and Covenant Women's and Children's Hospital. The health system also includes some 20 clinics and 50 physician practices and its extensive outreach programs target isolated rural communities with mobile services.

EXECUTIVES

Director Of Pharmacy Director Of Pharmacy Services, Bill Welch
Vice President, Sharon Prather
Director Of Health Information, Beverly Houk
Medical Director, Jack Dubose
Occupational Medicine, Mack Evans
Auditors: ERNST & YOUNG US LLP IRVINE

LOCATIONS

HQ: COVENANT HEALTH SYSTEM
3615 19TH ST, LUBBOCK, TX 794101209
Phone: 806 725-1011
Web: WWW.STJHS.ORG

COMPETITORS

Baptist St. Anthony's Health System
Del Sol Medical Center
Encompass Health
Hunt Memorial
NW Texas Healthcare
Parkland Health & Hospital System
Tenet Healthcare
Texas Health Resources
The Methodist Health System
University Medical Center of El Paso

HISTORICAL FINANCIALS

Company Type: Private

Income Statement FYE: June 30

	REVENUE ($ mil.)	NET INCOME ($ mil.)	NET PROFIT MARGIN	EMPLOYEES
06/15	703	76	10.9%	5,000
06/13	552	35	6.5%	—
06/09	1,185	(38)	—	—
Annual Growth	(8.3%)	—	—	—

2015 Year-End Financials

Return on assets: 10.5%
Return on equity: 14.7%
Current ratio: 3.20
Cash ($ mil.): 39

COVENANT HEALTH, INC.

EXECUTIVES

Pres-Ceo, David R Lincoln
SEC*, Patricia Karl
Treas*, Harold R Acres
Chm*, Dorothy Cooper
V Chb*, Richard J Hanley
Dir*, Margaret Mary Modde
Svp-Cfo*, Stephen Forney
Controller*, Donald Clark
Asst Cfo, Laural Haug
Assistant Controller, Becky Lehoux
Admin Associate, Linda Gorgone
Auditors: WILLIAM STEELE & ASSOCIATES PC

LOCATIONS

HQ: COVENANT HEALTH, INC.
100 AMES POND DR STE 102, TEWKSBURY, MA 018761240
Phone: 978 654-6363
Web: WWW.COVENANTHEALTH.NET

HISTORICAL FINANCIALS

Company Type: Private

Income Statement FYE: December 31

	REVENUE ($ mil.)	NET INCOME ($ mil.)	NET PROFIT MARGIN	EMPLOYEES
12/18	666	(74)	—	6,500
12/17	670	38	5.8%	—
12/16	645	18	2.9%	—
12/12	12	1	12.0%	—
Annual Growth	95.2%	—	—	—

2018 Year-End Financials

Return on assets: (-8.5%)
Return on equity: (-16.0%)
Current ratio: 1.70
Cash ($ mil.): 49

COVENANT MEDICAL CENTER, INC.

Covenant Medical Center (operating as Covenant HealthCare) has made a pact with Wolverine Staters to try to keep them in good health. The not-for-profit health care provider operates more than 20 inpatient and outpatient care facilities including its two main Covenant Medical Center campuses. It serves residents in a 20-county area of east-central Michigan with additional facilities in Bay City Frankenmuth and Midland. Specialized care services include cardiovascular health cancer treatment and obstetrics. The regional health care system has more about 650 beds.

Operations

Covenant HealthCare programs and services range from high-risk obstetrics and neonatal/pediatric intensive care to acute care. Its assets include cardiology oncology orthopedics robotic surgery and Level II Adult and Pediatric Trauma Center.

The health system has more than 20 inpatient and outpatient facilities and a trauma/emergency department that provides 85000 visits per year. The system employs more than 500 physicians from 52 medical specialties.

Sales and Marketing

Covenant HealthCare markets its services via social media.

Financial Performance

In 2014 the company's revenue increased 4% to $528 million as patient service revenue rose; this gain was partially offset by a decline in realized gain and other revenues. An increase in salaries and wages as well as higher supplies expenses led to a 12% decline in net income (to $57 million).

Cash flow from operations also fell slipping 20% to $48 million as accounts receivable increased.

Strategy

Expanding its infrastructure to keep up with demand in 2014 Covenant HealthCare added 11456 sq. ft. to its Emergency Department. The addition allows for more efficient triage enhanced patient waiting areas and additional space for current technology. It added 18 treatment bays to the existing 47 and also brought a dedicated CT scanner and mini-laboratory within the department.

Also that year it opened the assisted living community of Covenant Glen in Frankenmuth. The 35000 sq. ft. structure has 45 rooms (15 dedicated to memory care and 30 with assisted living beds).

Company Background

Covenant HealthCare was formed in 1998 through the merger of Saginaw General and St. Luke's Hospitals.

EXECUTIVES

Medical Director, Babu Nahata
Medical Director Clinical Utilization, Glenn Cipullo
Physical Therapy Director, Jeff Berger
Vice President Patient Services, Carol Stoll
Director Of Pharmacy, Terry Wernette

LOCATIONS

HQ: COVENANT MEDICAL CENTER, INC.
1447 N HARRISON ST, SAGINAW, MI 486024727
Phone: 989 583-0000
Web: WWW.COVENANTHEALTHCARE.COM

PRODUCTS/OPERATIONS

2014 Revenues

	% of total
Net patient service revenues	95
Other revenues	5
Total	**100**

Selected services

Bariatrics
Birth Center
Cancer Care
Cardiology - Center for the Heart
Childbirth Classes
da Vinci Robotic Surgery
Diabetes Self-Management Program
Emergency Care Center
Imaging and Diagnostics
Neonatal Intensive Care

Neurology
Osteoporosis
Orthopaedics
Pediatrics
Physical Medicine and Rehab.
Pulmonary/Respiratory Care
Sleep Center
Surgical Services
Trauma
Urologic Surgery
Women's Health
Wound Healing Center

COMPETITORS

Genesys Health System
Genesys Regional Medical Center
Hurley Medical Center
McLaren Bay
McLaren Health Care
Munson Healthcare
Sparrow Health System
University of Michigan Health System

HISTORICAL FINANCIALS

Company Type: Private

Income Statement — FYE: June 30

	REVENUE ($ mil.)	NET INCOME ($ mil.)	NET PROFIT MARGIN	EMPLOYEES
06/16	579	40	7.0%	4,000
06/15	535	31	5.8%	—
06/14	566	34	6.1%	—
06/10	508	28	5.5%	—
Annual Growth	2.2%	6.2%	—	—

2016 Year-End Financials

Return on assets: 6.4%
Return on equity: 12.9%
Current ratio: 1.80
Cash ($ mil.): 21

CRETE CARRIER CORPORATION

Holding company Crete Carrier Corporation's flagship business Crete Carrier provides dry van truckload freight transportation services in the 48 contiguous states. It operates from some two dozen terminals mainly in the mid-western and southeastern US. The company's Shaffer Trucking unit transports temperature-controlled cargo and Hunt Transportation (no relation to J.B. Hunt Transport Services) hauls heavy equipment and other cargo on flatbed trailers. Overall the companies operate more than 5400 tractors and 13000 trailers. Family-owned Crete Carrier was founded in 1966 by chairman Duane Acklie; president and CEO Tonn Ostergard is his son-in-law.

EXECUTIVES

Vice President National Accounts, Bill Boehler
National Account Manager, Tim Stakolich
Vice President And Corporate General Counsel, Curtis Ruwe
Vice President Of Maintenance And Equipment, Winston Ostergard

LOCATIONS

HQ: CRETE CARRIER CORPORATION
400 NW 56TH ST, LINCOLN, NE 685288843
Phone: 800 998-4095
Web: WWW.CRETECARRIER.COM

COMPETITORS

Boyd Bros. Transportation
C.R. England
Celadon
Comcar
Covenant Transportation
Heartland Express
J.B. Hunt
Landstar System
Prime Inc.
Schneider National
Swift Transportation
U.S. Xpress
Werner Enterprises

HISTORICAL FINANCIALS

Company Type: Private

Income Statement — FYE: September 30

	REVENUE ($ mil.)	NET INCOME ($ mil.)	NET PROFIT MARGIN	EMPLOYEES
09/18	1,150	139	12.1%	6,000
09/16	984	95	9.7%	—
09/15	0	0	—	—
09/14	1,034	127	12.3%	—
Annual Growth	2.7%	2.3%	—	—

2018 Year-End Financials

Return on assets: 13.3%
Return on equity: 15.8%
Current ratio: 2.20
Cash ($ mil.): 128

CROWE LLP

EXECUTIVES

Ceo, James Powers
Cfo-Ptnr, Todd Welu
Cro-Ptnr, Fred J Bauters
Cmo, Ann Lathrop
CIO, Yvonne Scott
Coo, Joseph P Santucci Jr
Chief Strategy & Innovation of, Derek Bang
Cdso, Justin Bass
Business Executive, Lisa Mazzanti
Sharepoint Manager, Luis Segura
Valuation Leader, Mary A Travers
Auditors: CROWE LLP

LOCATIONS

HQ: CROWE LLP
225 W WACKER DR STE 2600, CHICAGO, IL 606061228
Phone: 312 899-7000
Web: WWW.CROWE.COM

HISTORICAL FINANCIALS

Company Type: Private

Income Statement — FYE: March 31

	REVENUE ($ mil.)	NET INCOME ($ mil.)	NET PROFIT MARGIN	EMPLOYEES
03/15	700	204	29.2%	3,130
03/14	670	163	24.4%	—
03/13	0	0	—	—
Annual Growth	—	—	—	—

2015 Year-End Financials

Return on assets: 71.1%
Return on equity: 260.7%
Current ratio: 2.00
Cash ($ mil.): 6

CROWLEY MARITIME CORPORATION

Crowley Maritime has pushed and pulled its way into prominence as a tug and barge operator. The company's Liner Services unit provides scheduled transportation of containers trailers and other cargo mainly among ports in Latin and North America Puerto Rico and the Caribbean Basin. Other units transport oil and chemical products and oil field equipment and provide ship assist/escort marine salvage and emergency towing logistics ship management and fuel distribution services. Overall the company's fleet includes more than 200 vessels. Members of the founding Crowley family own the company.

Operations

The company functions through its six operating lines of business which include Puerto Rico Liner Services Caribbean and Latin America Liner Services Logistics Services Marine Services and Technical Services. Its sixth business line which is Petroleum Services provides transportation distribution and sales of petroleum products for the fuel industry in Alaska through its Service Oil and Gas Group. Crowley Maritime operates fuel terminals and a barge and truck fleet to transport fuel throughout Alaska.

Crowley operates RO/RO (roll-on-roll-off) and LO/LO (lift-on-lift-off) vessels as well as tankers tugs and barges. In less than 10 years Crowley Maritime has invested almost one-quarter of a billion dollars in cargo equipment for its Liner Shipping Services segment. While Liner Shipping Services handles more traditional cargo such as automobiles trucks buses construction equipment refrigerated cargo apparel and even hazardous materials its TITAN Salvage subsidiary occasionally contends with more nontraditional cargo. It has a salvage base in Australia (strategically located to respond to marine emergencies in the Great Barrier Reef and in other South-West Pacific regions) and three other facilities in that country.

Geographic Reach

Crowley has operations in Africa the Asia/Pacific Canada the Caribbean (including Puerto Rico and Cuba) Central America the Middle East Europe Russia and the US.

Sales and Marketing

Crowley targets 20 industries such as oil and gas retail consumer services government and military manufacturing and apparel. The company's major customers have included such big names as Sears Toyota Bacardi Coca-Cola Hanes Procter & Gamble BP Exxon Mobil Parker Drilling WorleyParsons and the US Government.

Strategy

One important growth market for Crowley is in Cuba. Although the company has been shipping cargo to Cuba since 2001 it made its first shipment from Cuba to the US in 2017 due to the Obama administration's easing of American/Cuban relations.

Mergers and Acquisitions

Crowley grows through acquisitions and joint ventures. In mid-2016 Crowley acquired the aviation fuels business of Ace Fuels LLC a fixed base operator (FBO) headquartered at Merrill Field Alaska in downtown Anchorage offering Jet A and AV 100LL fuels. The acquisition enhanced the company's footprint by adding additional aviation fuels service stations throughout Alaska and also gave Ace Fuels customers better access to high-quality fuels in the south central and western parts of the state.

In 2015 Crowley and Svitzer Salvage merged their salvage divisions and created a joint venture called Ardent to offer customers a broader range of capabilities and marine related services. Ardent is headquartered in Houston Texas with operational offices in the Netherlands the UK and Singapore along with supporting offices in Australia Brazil South Korea Greece South Africa and other regions.

Company Background

Crowley traces its historical roots back to 1892.

EXECUTIVES

Vice President, John Ara
Vice Chairman And Evp, William A. (Bill) Pennella
Chairman And Ceo, Thomas B. (Tom) Crowley
Svp And General Manager Logistics, John P. Hourihan
Svp And General Manager Technical Services, Todd Busch
Svp And General Manager Logistics, Frank Larkin
Svp And General Manager Latin America Liner Services, Steven M. (Steve) Collar
Svp And General Manager Petroleum Distribution And Marine Services, Rockwell E. (Rocky) Smith
Svp And General Manager Petroleum Services, Robert B. (Rob) Grune
Svp Treasurer, Dan Warner
Vice President Government Services, Mike Golonka
Vice President Of Labor Relations, Rudy Leming
Vice President, Nicholas Orfanidis
Vice President Business Development, Ned Lagoy
Vice President Of Government Services, Jay Brickman
Vice President Of Information Technology, Herman Reich
Vice President Of Finance, Reynaldo Rojas
Vice President Marine Operations, Cole Cosgrove
Senior Vice President And General Manager Latin America Liner Services, Steve Collar
Executive Vice President Purchasing And Technology, Kelly Conaty
Vice President Risk Management, Dwight Menard
Vp Finance And Planning, David Nickless
Vice Presidents, Tony Otero
Vice President Of Organizational Development And C, Susan Michel
Vice President Of Business Development, Greg Buffington
Vp Procurement Strategic Sourcing, Jean Matthews
Vice President Marine Operations, Coleman Cosgrove
Treasurer, Daniel Warner
Assistant Treasurer, Steve Himes

LOCATIONS

HQ: CROWLEY MARITIME CORPORATION
9487 REGENCY SQUARE BLVD, JACKSONVILLE, FL 322258183
Phone: 904 727-2200
Web: WWW.CROWLEY.COM

PRODUCTS/OPERATIONS

Selected Services

Energy industry support services

Fuel sales and distribution

Liner services
Logistics
Ocean towing and transportation
Petroleum and chemical transportation
Project management
Salvage and emergency response
Ship assist and escort
Ship management
Vessel construction and naval architecture
Alaska fuel sales and distribution
Arctic all-terrain transportation
Harbor ship assist and tanker escort
Marine salvage wreck removal and emergency response
Ocean towing and barge transportation
OPA 90 compliance
Petroleum and chemical transportation
Ship management
Shipping And Logistics
Vessel design and construction management

COMPETITORS

A.P. M ,ller - M ¦rsk
APL
Foss Maritime
Horizon Lines
Hornbeck Offshore
K-Sea Transportation
Lynden Incorporated
SEACOR
Sea Star Line
Tidewater Inc.
Trailer Bridge
U.S. Shipping
UPS Supply Chain Solutions
Washington Companies

HISTORICAL FINANCIALS

Company Type: Private

Income Statement — FYE: December 31

	REVENUE ($ mil.)	NET INCOME ($ mil.)	NET PROFIT MARGIN	EMPLOYEES
12/08	1,955	86	4.4%	4,329
12/07	1,622	122	7.5%	—
12/06	1,467	38	2.6%	—
12/05	1,190	38	3.3%	—
Annual Growth	18.0%	30.3%	—	—

2008 Year-End Financials

Return on assets: 6.2%
Return on equity: 18.2%
Current ratio: 1.40
Cash ($ mil.): 64

CRST INTERNATIONAL, INC.

CRST International promises f-a-s-t freight transportation through its operating units. CRST Expedited provides standard dry van truckload transportation primarily on long-haul routes along with dedicated and expedited transportation services. CRST Malone hauls steel and other freight requiring flatbed trailers or trailers with removable sides and CRST Logistics arranges freight transportation and provides other third-party logistics services. The family-owned business' other operations include CRST Dedicated Services and Specialized Transportation. Overall the companies operate a fleet of about 4500 tractors and 7300 van trailers.

Operations

CRST operates through seven distinct operations. CRST Expedited is a long-haul truckload carrier and CRST Malone is a flatbed carrier serving customers in North America. The company's CRST Dedicated Services unit offers tailor-made specialized transportation services while CRST Logistics helps customers reduce costs and optimize their performance.

CRST Specialized Transportation provides multi-modal logistics supported by distribution centers located throughout the US and Canada. Other operations include Temperature Controlled Team Service (TCTS) (expedited transcontinental transportation of perishable products) and BESL Transfer Company (provider of short haul flatbed services).

Geographic Reach

Based in Cedar Rapids Iowa CRST operates more than 50 distribution centers terminals and offices across North America.

Sales and Marketing

The company targets the business and retail industrial metals building products technology telecommunications automotive government tradeshows and events health care transportation and residential markets.

Strategy

In 2015 CRST broke ground on its new $37 million world headquarters in downtown Cedar Rapids Iowa.

In 2013 CRST Expedited opened a training and repair facility in Riverside California.

Mergers and Acquisitions

CRST also continues to grow through the use of acquisitions.

In 2015 the company bought privately-held Pegasus Transportation based in Louisville Kentucky. The acquisition allows CRST to expand its temperature controlled operations nationwide footprint through its expanded customer base.

In early 2014 CRST obtained a privately held short haul and flatbed services provider BESL Transfer Co. based in Cincinnati Ohio in a transaction that fortified its CRST Malone operations. The acquisition of BESL allowed CRST to expand its flatbed operations nationwide footprint through its short haul regional services and expanded agent base.

In 2013 it picked up the Allied Special Products Division of Allied Van Lines based in Fort Wayne Indiana. The deal enabled its Specialized Transportation operations to further develop its distribution center network and provide better service and faster transit to its customers. That year subsidiary CRST Logistics added Top Shelf Logistics LLC to its rapidly growing agency network.

Company Background

CRST was founded in 1955 by Herald Smith father of chairman John Smith.

EXECUTIVES

Vice President Dedicated Services, Chad Humphrey
National Sales Manager, Luke Chalmers
Vice President, Scott Moran
Vice President And General Manager, Chris Broussard
Vice President, Dan Lockard
Auditors: DELOITTE & TOUCHE LLP CEDAR R

LOCATIONS

HQ: CRST INTERNATIONAL, INC.
201 1ST ST SE STE 400, CEDAR RAPIDS, IA 524011423
Phone: 319 396-4400
Web: WWW.CRST.COM

PRODUCTS/OPERATIONS

Selected Services

Expedited Team Service
Dry Van
Flatbed
Dedicated
High Value/White Glove
Temperature Controlled
Transportation Management
Brokerage
Home Delivery/First & Final Mile
Warehousing/Inventory Solutions
LTL
Intermodal
Equipment Sales

COMPETITORS

Anderson Trucking Service
Boyd Bros. Transportation
C.H. Robinson Worldwide
Comcar
Crete Carrier
Forward Air
J.B. Hunt
Ruan Transportation Management Systems
Schneider National
Swift Transportation
UPS Supply Chain Solutions
Werner Enterprises

HISTORICAL FINANCIALS

Company Type: Private

Income Statement				FYE: December 31
	REVENUE ($ mil.)	NET INCOME ($ mil.)	NET PROFIT MARGIN	EMPLOYEES
12/12	1,258	75	6.0%	5,960
12/11	1,143	81	7.1%	—
Annual Growth	10.1%	(7.8%)	—	—

2012 Year-End Financials

Return on assets: 13.7%
Return on equity: 45.2%
Current ratio: 2.70
Cash ($ mil.): 71

CSC SUGAR, LLC

EXECUTIVES

MBR-Pres, Paul J Farmer
Cfo-Treas, Francis X Claps
Customer Representativ, Rhea Kirkland
Auditors: GRANT THORNTON LLP MINNEAPOLI

LOCATIONS

HQ: CSC SUGAR, LLC
36 GROVE ST STE 2, NEW CANAAN, CT 068405329
Phone: 203 846-5610
Web: WWW.CSCSUGAR.COM

HISTORICAL FINANCIALS

Company Type: Private

Income Statement				FYE: December 31
	REVENUE ($ mil.)	NET INCOME ($ mil.)	NET PROFIT MARGIN	EMPLOYEES
12/09	574	18	3.2%	40
12/08	790	5	0.7%	—
12/07	515	6	1.2%	—
Annual Growth	5.6%	74.5%	—	—

2009 Year-End Financials

Return on assets: 24.8%
Return on equity: 104.6%
Current ratio: 1.20
Cash ($ mil.): 4

CXLOYALTY

Through its partners and affiliations Affinion Group aims to make fans of its customers' customers. The company operates membership and loyalty programs on behalf of corporate clients seeking to strengthen their ties to consumers. It specializes in launching a variety of media services – through direct mail and the Internet – and packaging these benefits to its clients' customers. Programs overseen include AutoVantage Buyers Advantage and Travelers Advantage. Overall the group offers its programs to some 65 million members worldwide through more than 5700 partners.

Geographic Reach

The company has offices in Europe South Africa and the US. Most recently Affinion expanded its footprint into Brazil and into Turkey. However the company gets about 80% of its revenue from US.

Sales and Marketing

Affinion provides its customer engagement and loyalty solutions through retail and wholesale arrangements with its marketing partners in addition to its direct to consumer marketing efforts. Under a retail arrangement it usually markets products to a marketing partner's customers by using that marketing partner's brand name and customer contacts. Under a wholesale arrangement the marketing partner bears the expense to market products and services to its customers collects revenue from the customer and typically pays us a monthly fee per end-customer.

Marketing partners have included Citibank JPMorgan Chase Royal Bank of Scotland and Wells Fargo. Revenues generated from Wells Fargo accounted for 15.3% of total revenues in fiscal 2012.

Affinion also markets its products through direct efforts such direct mail online marketing point-of-sale marketing and telemarketing.

Financial Performance

In fiscal 2012 the company reported revenue of about $1.49 billion down by 2.6% compared to the $1.53 billion it reported in revenue for fiscal 2011. The decline in revenue was attributed to decreases in revenue from membership products along with declines in revenue from insurance and package products.

Strategy

The company intends to continue its growth in international markets through both organic initiatives including geographic expansion as well as the continued evaluation of strategic acquisitions that strengthen its customer engagement solutions grow its distribution capabilities or enhance its scale.

Affinion sees substantial opportunities to add new marketing partners in the retail financial travel Internet cable telecom and utilities industries in both North America and Europe.

Mergers and Acquisitions

In 2012 Affinion extended its geographic reach in Europe with the acquisition of a majority stake in Back-Up a leading concierge service. Affinion has accelerated its entry into that growing market through the formation of a partnership with Boyner Holding Company one of the most respected and successful brands currently serving Turkish consumers.

EXECUTIVES

Vice President Of Sales, Jim Daxner
Vice President Strategic Partnerships, Walker Adams
Vice President Service Delivery Operations Global Contact Center Operations, Laurie Dunn
Vice President Service Delivery Infrastructure And Reporting, Rajiv Patel
Senior Vice President Service Delivery And Contact Center Operations, Richard Pitrolo
Group Vp Sales And Business Development, Tom Kazar
Vice President Insurance Product Management, Elizabeth Sheehan
Svp And Chief Accounting Officer, Lori Tansley

LOCATIONS

HQ: CXLOYALTY
6 HIGH RIDGE PARK, STAMFORD, CT 069051327
Phone: 203 956-1000
Web: WWW.CXLOYALTY.COM

2012 Sales

	$ mil.	% of total
US	1,191	80
UK	117	8
Other countries	186	12
Total	**1,495**	**100**

PRODUCTS/OPERATIONS

Selected Membership Products and Services

AutoVantage
Buyers Advantage
CompleteHome
CardCops
Everyday Privileges Gold
Everyday Values
Great Fun
Great Options
HealthSaver
Hot-Line
ID Secure
IdentitySecure
Just For Me
PC SafetyPlus
Privacy Guard
Shoppers Advantage
Travelers Advantage

Selected Partners

American Express
Bank of America
Choice Hotels
HSBC
JPMorgan Chase
TransWorld Entertainment
Wells Fargo

COMPETITORS

AEGON Direct Marketing Services
AIG
Access Plans USA
Assurant
Hospitality Marketing Concepts
Intersections Inc.
Maritz Loyalty & Motivation
Provell
Q Interactive
Rewards Network
Student Advantage
Synapse Group

HISTORICAL FINANCIALS

Company Type: Private

Income Statement				FYE: December 31
	REVENUE ($ mil.)	NET INCOME ($ mil.)	NET PROFIT MARGIN	EMPLOYEES
12/18	699	303	43.3%	3,860
12/17	953	(24)	—	—
12/16	969	16	1.7%	—
Annual Growth	(15.0%)	331.4%	—	—

2018 Year-End Financials

Return on assets: 44.5%
Return on equity: —
Current ratio: 1.00
Cash ($ mil.): 84

CYPRESS-FAIRBANKS INDEPENDENT SCHOOL DISTRICT

EXECUTIVES

Supt, Mark Henry
Supt*, Richard E Berry
General, Mary Jadlowski

Maintenance Buyer, Greg Segura
Substitute Teacher, Chastity Perkins
Teacher Coach, Mitchell Doty
Information Technology Project, Andrew Bailey
Secretary Assistant Director H, Debora McNair
Human Resources, Elizabeth Ford
Information Technology Project, Leonard Chance
Human Resources Secretary, Lisa Young
Auditors: WEAVER AND TIDWELL LLP CONROE

LOCATIONS

HQ: CYPRESS-FAIRBANKS INDEPENDENT SCHOOL DISTRICT
10300 JONES RD, HOUSTON, TX 770654208
Phone: 281 897-4000
Web: WWW.CFISD.NET

HISTORICAL FINANCIALS

Company Type: Private

Income Statement — FYE: June 30

	REVENUE ($ mil.)	NET INCOME ($ mil.)	NET PROFIT MARGIN	EMPLOYEES
06/20	1,331	208	15.7%	13,000
06/19	1,342	32	2.4%	—
06/18	1,259	20	1.6%	—
06/17	1,208	(58)	—	—
Annual Growth	3.3%	—	—	—

2020 Year-End Financials

Return on assets: 5.3%
Return on equity: —
Current ratio: —
Cash ($ mil.): 24

D/L COOPERATIVE INC.

Yes the farmer takes a wife then hi-ho the dairy-o the farmer takes membership in milk-marketing organizations such as Dairylea Cooperative. Owned by some 2000 dairy farmers in the northeastern US Dairylea processes and markets 6.3 billion pounds of milk for its farmers annually to dairy-product customers including food manufacturers. Its Agri-Services holding company provides members with a full range of financial and farm-management services as well as insurance. Its Empire Livestock Marketing unit operates regional livestock auction locations. Dairylea which was established in 1907 by New York dairy farmers merged with the US's largest milk marketing coop Dairy Farmers of America in 2014.

Operations

Through its DMS partnership with Dairy Farmers of America Dairylea sells and distributes raw milk. DMS serves both organizations as well as independent producers and cooperatives that produce 16 billion pounds of milk each year.

Geographic Reach

Dairylea sells 6 billion pounds of raw milk annually through a milk-marketing network that stretches from Maine to Ohio to Maryland.

Services provided by holding company Agri-Services LLC include insurance coverage information management livestock marketing loan programs milk price risk management services business planning and consulting services purchasing programs and investment and retirement planning advice.

Financial Performance

Dairylea has annual sales of about $1 billion.

Auditors: HERBEIN COMPANY INC READING

LOCATIONS

HQ: D/L COOPERATIVE INC.
5001 BRITTONFIELD PKWY, EAST SYRACUSE, NY 130579201
Phone: 315 233-1000
Web: WWW.DAIRYLEA.COM

PRODUCTS/OPERATIONS

Selected Affiliates & Subsidiaries

Agri-Edge Development
Agri-Max Financial Services
Agri-Services Agency
Dairy Risk Management Services
Eagle Dairy Direct
Empire Livestock Marketing Services

COMPETITORS

Agri-Mark
Associated Milk Producers
Dean Foods
Foremost Farms
Garelick Farms
Keller's Creamery
Land O'Lakes
Maryland & Virginia Milk Producers
Quality Chekd

HISTORICAL FINANCIALS

Company Type: Private

Income Statement — FYE: March 31

	REVENUE ($ mil.)	NET INCOME ($ mil.)	NET PROFIT MARGIN	EMPLOYEES
03/11	1,333	1	0.1%	107
03/10	1,066	1	0.1%	—
Annual Growth	25.1%	7.6%	—	—

2011 Year-End Financials

Return on assets: 9.2%
Return on equity: 0.1%
Current ratio: 0.60
Cash ($ mil.): 14

DAIRY FARMERS OF AMERICA, INC.

Dairy Farmers of America (DFA) is one of the world's largest dairy cooperatives with more than 13000 member farmers across the US. Along with fresh and shelf-stable fluid milk the co-op produces cheese butter powders and sweetened condensed milk for industrial wholesale and retail customers. It also offers contract manufacturing services. The company's brands include Borden and Cache Valley for consumer cheese; Keller's Creamery Plugra Breakstone's Falfurrias and Oakhurst Dairy; and other dairy products under Sport Shake (sports beverage) La Vaquita (queso) Kemps Guida's Dairy and Cass Clay. The company owns more than 85 production plants nationwide.

Geographic Reach

DFA is based in Kansas City Missouri and divides the US into seven areas: Central (which shares the main headquarters) Mideast (Medina OH) Mountain (Salt Lake City UT) Northeast (East Syracuse NY) Southeast (Knoxville TN) Southwest (Grapevine TX) and Western (Corona CA).

Sales and Marketing

DFA's customers include food manufacturers school cafeterias large restaurant and retailers among others.

Mergers and Acquisitions

In mid-2020 DFA acquired Dean Foods a dairy processor in the country based in Texas for $433 million. Dean Foods is a leading food and beverage company and the largest processor and direct-to-store distributor of fresh fluid milk and other dairy and dairy case products in the United States. The acquisition helps DFA in expanding its milk market.

Company Background

DFA was established in 1998 by leaders of four of the nation's leading milk cooperatives: Associated Milk Producers Mid-America Dairymen Milk Marketing and Western Dairymen Cooperative.

HISTORY

Mid-America Dairymen (Mid-Am) the largest of the cooperatives that merged to form Dairy Farmers of America (DFA) was born in 1968. At that time several Midwestern dairy co-ops banded together to attack common economic problems such as reduced government subsidies price drops resulting from a rising milk surplus dealer consolidation and improvements in production processing and packaging. The merging organizations – representing 15000 dairy farmers – were Producers Creamery Company (Springfield Missouri) Sanitary Milk Producers (St. Louis) Square Deal Milk Producers (Highland Illinois) Mid-Am (Kansas City Missouri) and Producers Creamery Company of Chillicothe (north central Missouri).

During the early 1970s Mid-Am struggled with internal restructuring. Most dairy farmers and co-ops were hit hard by the energy crisis and the government's decision to allow increased dairy imports in 1973 the same year the US Justice Department filed an antitrust suit against Mid-Am. (A judge cleared the co-op 12 years later.)

In 1974 Mid-Am lost almost $8 million on revenues of $625 million chalked up to record-high feed prices a weakened economy a milk surplus and a massive inventory loss. Co-op veteran Gary Hanman was named CEO that year. Over the next two years Mid-Am cut costs sold corporate frills downsized management and began marketing more of its own products under the Mid-America Farms label thus reducing dependency on commodity sales.

Mid-Am expanded its research and development efforts throughout the 1980s. The co-op opened its services to farmers in California and New Mexico in 1993 and a series of mergers in 1994 and 1995 nearly doubled its size. In 1997 it purchased some of Borden's dairy operations including rights to the valuable Elsie the Cow and Borden's trademarks.

Wary of falling milk prices Mid-Am merged with Western Dairymen Cooperative Milk Marketing and the Southern Region of Associated Milk Producers at the end of 1997 to form DFA. Hanman moved into the seat of CEO at the new co-op. DFA began a series of joint ventures with the #1 US dairy processor Suiza Foods (now Dean Foods).

DFA added California Gold (more than 330 farmers 1998) and Independent Cooperative Milk Producers Association (730 dairy farmer members in Michigan and parts of Ohio and Indiana 1999). In another joint venture with Suiza in early 2000 DFA sold its 50% stake in the US's #3 fluid milk processor Southern Foods in exchange for 34% of a new company named Suiza Dairy Group.

After mollifying the government's antitrust fears DFA acquired the butter operations of Sodiaal North America in 2000. It then molded all its butter businesses into a new entity Keller's Creamery. However another acquisition did not fare as well. The same year DFA acquired controlling interest in Southern Belle Dairy only to have the merger challenged three years later by the Department of Justice. Arguing that the merger formed a monopoly in school milk sales in several states the Department of Justice filed suit which a federal judge later dismissed.

During 2001 the cooperative went in with Land O'Lakes 50/50 to purchase a cheese plant from Kraft. Later in the year as Suiza Foods acquired Dean Foods (and took on its name) DFA sold back its stake in Suiza Dairy Group to the new Dean Foods. DFA then teamed up with a group of dairy investors to form a new 50/50 joint venture National Dairy Holdings which received 11 processing plants from Dean Foods as part of the exchange for Suiza Dairy.

EXECUTIVES

Senior Adviser; President Affiliate Division, Alan J. Bernon, age 65
President Farm Services, Gregory I. (Greg) Wickham
Coo And Ceo Dairylea, Richard P. (Rick) Smith
Evp; President Global Dairy Products Group, Mark Korsmeyer
Svp Finance, David Meyer
Executive Vice President Of Commercial Operations, Doug Glade
Vice President Sales And Marketing Global Ingredients, Lavonne Dietrich
Vice President Operations Fluid, Ray Mccoy
Assistant Vice President Legal, Heather Grossman
Vice President Milk Logistics, Ernest Yates
Vice Chairman, Bill Siebenborn
Chairman, Randy Mooney
Vice Chairman, Wayne Palla
Vice Chairman, George Mertens
Treasurer, Danelle Bender
Auditors: KPMG LLP KANSAS CITY MO

LOCATIONS

HQ: DAIRY FARMERS OF AMERICA, INC.
1405 N 98TH ST, KANSAS CITY, KS 661111865
Phone: 816 801-6455
Web: WWW.DFAMILK.COM

PRODUCTS/OPERATIONS

Selected Products and Brands

Consumer brands
- Borden cheese
- Breakstone's butter
- Cache Valley cheese
- Keller's Creamery butter
- Plugrá; butter
- Sport Shake energy milk shake

Contract manufacturing
- Cheese dips
- Cheese powders & flavors
- Coffee-based flavored drinks
- Instant formula
- Sour cream
- Sports drinks

Dairy ingredients
- Cheeses (American & Italian)
- Nonfat dry milk powder
- Skim milk powder
- Sweetened condensed milk

COMPETITORS

Arla Foods
Associated Milk Producers
Berkeley Farms
California Dairies Inc.
ConAgra
Darigold Inc.
Dean Foods
Farmland Dairies
Foremost Farms
Friendship Dairies
Garelick Farms
Glanbia plc
Great Lakes Cheese
HP Hood
Humboldt Creamery
Lactalis
Land O'Lakes
Marathon Cheese
Mayfield Dairy Farms
Northwest Dairy
Prairie Farms Dairy
Quality Chekd
Sargento

HISTORICAL FINANCIALS

Company Type: Private

Income Statement — FYE: December 31

	REVENUE ($ mil.)	NET INCOME ($ mil.)	NET PROFIT MARGIN	EMPLOYEES
12/16	13,528	136	1.0%	21,000
12/15	13,803	98	0.7%	—
12/14	17,856	48	0.3%	—
Annual Growth	(13.0%)	67.6%	—	—

2016 Year-End Financials

Return on assets: 3.8%
Return on equity: 14.1%
Current ratio: 1.10
Cash ($ mil.): 85

DAIRYAMERICA, INC.

EXECUTIVES

Pres-Ceo, Patricia Smith
SEC, Bill Schreiber
Treas, Craig Alexander
Auditors: DELOITTE & TOUCHE LLP FRESNO

LOCATIONS

HQ: DAIRYAMERICA, INC.
7815 N PALM AVE STE 250, FRESNO, CA 937115528
Phone: 559 251-0992
Web: WWW.DAIRYAMERICA.COM

HISTORICAL FINANCIALS

Company Type: Private

Income Statement — FYE: December 31

	REVENUE ($ mil.)	NET INCOME ($ mil.)	NET PROFIT MARGIN	EMPLOYEES
12/12	1,222	21	1.8%	51
12/11	1,319	19	1.5%	—
12/10	1,514	19	1.3%	—
Annual Growth	(10.2%)	5.5%	—	—

2012 Year-End Financials

Return on assets: 12.8%
Return on equity: 108.5%
Current ratio: 1.80
Cash ($ mil.): 1

DALLAS COUNTY HOSPITAL DISTRICT

Many people know Dallas County Hospital District doing business as Parkland Health and Hospital System or PHHS as Parkland Memorial Hospital the hospital where JFK died. Parkland Memorial sits at the heart of the health system and is Dallas' only public hospital. PHHS also manages a network of about 20 community clinics as well as Parkland Community Health Plan a regional HMO for Medicaid and CHIP (Children's Health Insurance Program) members. Additionally the system offers Parkland Financial Assistance a program to help residents of Dallas County pay for health care services. Parkland Memorial Hospital has more than 700 beds and is the primary teaching institution of The University of Texas Southwestern Medical Center.

Operations

PHHS is one of the largest public hospital systems in the US. In addition to its community-based clinics it offers a number of outreach and education programs to improve wellness in its service area.

Parkland Memorial Hospital has 870 single-patient rooms and is a Level I trauma center. Each year the hospital has some 39000 inpatient discharges and some 260000 emergency department visits. Specialty community and women's clinic outpatient visits total more than 1 million.

The system also manages the health system for Lew Sterrett – Dallas County Jail one of the nation's largest jails.

Sales and Marketing

Medicare and Medicaid payments account for about 15% and 30% of PHHS's net patient service revenues respectively.

Strategy

PHHS's original hospital location was established in 1954; more recently the system replaced the aging facility with a new hospital. The expansion included an 870-bed hospital an outpatient center an office center and parking. PHHS also invested in new and replacement information systems and medical equipment.

Additionally the system is working to open more primary care health clinics and launch new programs to reach further into its community.For example in 2016 it introduced the Acute Integrated Mental Health Services (AIMS) program to assist underserved patients with complex behavioral health issues and diabetes. It combines health care and social work services to connect patients with valuable resources and help them manage their health in an integrated manner.

Similarly the Parkland Information Exchange Portal (IEP) launched by PHHS health IT think tank Parkland Center for Clinical Innovation services to connect underserved individuals with social services including homeless shelters and food banks.

In early 2017 the system completed construction of a new five-story clinic with 171 exam rooms MRI's CT scanners radiology and ultrasound rooms laboratories and a pharmacy.

EXECUTIVES

Coo, David S. Lopez
President And Ceo, Frederick P. (Fred) Cerise, age 57
Interim Coo Ambulatory Care & Behavioral Health Services, Sharon Phillips
Evp And General Counsel, Paul Leslie
Evp And Chief Nursing Officer, Karen Watts
Evp And Chief Medical Officer, Roberto de la Cruz
Evp And Chief Talent Officer, Jim Dunn
Evp And Chief Strategy And Integration Officer, Esmaeil Porsa
Evp And Cfo, Richard Humphrey
Svp And Chief Human Resource Officer, James Johnson
Medical Director Of Homeless Outreach Medical Services, Susan Spalding
Medical Director, Waseem Ahmed
Medical Director, Barry Lachman
Medical Director Of Pediatrics, Donna Persaud
Senior Vice President Quality Safety And Performance Improvement, Jacqueline Sullivan
Vice President Of Government Relations, Katherine Yoder
Operating Room Dir, SUZANNE SIMS
Vice President, Christina Mintner
Executive Vice President And Chief Talent Officer, Corey Jackson
Radiology Director, Terry Napper

Vice President Professional And Support Services, Saul Cordero
Sr Vice President Chief Information Officer, Matthew Kull
Operating Room Dir, Samantha Rowley
Senior Vice President, Marilyn Callies
Vice President Total Rewards, Lisa Dutton
Vice President Professional Medical Affairs, Maggie Palmer
Vice Chair, Michael D. (Mike) Williams
Chair Board Of Managers, Winfred Parnell
Auditors: BKD LLP DALLAS TEXAS

LOCATIONS

HQ: DALLAS COUNTY HOSPITAL DISTRICT
5200 HARRY HINES BLVD, DALLAS, TX 752357709
Phone: 214 590-8000
Web: WWW.PARKLANDHOSPITAL.COM

PRODUCTS/OPERATIONS

Selected Facilities
Bluitt Flowers Health Center
de Haro-Saldivar Health Center
East Dallas Health Center
Garland Health Center
Oak West Health Center
Pediatric Primary Care Center
Simmons Ambulatory Surgery Center
Southeast Dallas Health Center
Vickery Health Center

COMPETITORS

Baylor University Medical Center
CHRISTUS Health
Children's Medical Center of Dallas
Community Health Systems
HCA
Harris Methodist Fort Worth Hospital
JPS Health Network
Presbyterian Hospital of Dallas
Tenet Healthcare
Texas Health Resources
The Methodist Health System

HISTORICAL FINANCIALS

Company Type: Private

Income Statement — FYE: September 30

	REVENUE ($ mil.)	NET INCOME ($ mil.)	NET PROFIT MARGIN	EMPLOYEES
09/19	1,600	208	13.0%	11,000
09/18	1,456	17	1.2%	—
09/17	1,734	(17)	—	—
09/16	1,641	(71)	—	—
Annual Growth	(0.8%)	—	—	—

2019 Year-End Financials

Return on assets: 7.8%
Return on equity: 18.7%
Current ratio: 2.20
Cash ($ mil.): 353

DALLAS INDEPENDENT SCHOOL DISTRICT

EXECUTIVES

Supt, Michael Hinojosa
Treas*, Darlene Williams
Cfo*, Larry Throm
Principal, Bill Quinones
Ronald E. McNair E, Cheryl Williams
Alternative Programs Assistant, Joseph Brew
Human Resources Information MA, Eric Shu
Coordinator, Lawana Porter
Designer, Jeff Houle
Teacher, Ashton Martin
Dcp Coordinator, Gary Rees
Auditors: DELOITTE & TOUCHE LLP DALLAS

LOCATIONS

HQ: DALLAS INDEPENDENT SCHOOL DISTRICT
9400 N CNTL EXPY STE 1510, DALLAS, TX 75231
Phone: 972 925-3700
Web: WWW.DALLASISD.ORG

HISTORICAL FINANCIALS

Company Type: Private

Income Statement — FYE: June 30

	REVENUE ($ mil.)	NET INCOME ($ mil.)	NET PROFIT MARGIN	EMPLOYEES
06/20	2,248	240	10.7%	24,937
06/19	2,241	(17)	—	—
Annual Growth	0.3%	—	—	—

2020 Year-End Financials

Return on assets: 4.5%
Return on equity: 154.0%
Current ratio: —
Cash ($ mil.): 941

DALLAS/FORT WORTH INTERNATIONAL AIRPORT

Many things are bigger in Texas and Dallas/Fort Worth International Airport (DFW) is no exception. Covering some 30 square miles DFW is one of the world's largest airports by land mass. The facility includes seven runways two active control towers five terminals and 165 gates. Some 65 million passengers pass through DFW annually to destinations domestic and international. Aside from airport fare DFW provides private warehouse and distribution centers to tenants and features Grand Hyatt and Hyatt Regency hotels. Opened in 1974 DFW is owned by the cities of Dallas and Fort Worth; it is situated halfway between them and within about a four-hour flight time of most US destinations.

Operations

DFW's primary operating goal is the facilitation of movement of people cargo and airplanes. Beyond that it leases land to travel-related businesses (car rental agencies) provide parking coordinates concessions and permits hotels to operate within its confines. About 45% of revenue comes from airlines (landing fees terminal usage fees) and 55% comes from non-airline activities.

With about 1800 flights per day serving 65 million customers a year DFW is the world's fourth busiest airport. Airlines flying out of DFW provide nonstop service to 163 domestic and 55 international non-stop destinations through about 25 passenger carriers and nearly 20 cargo carriers.

DFW is the home airport for the world's largest carrier American Airlines (AA) which operates 745 flights per day to nearly 200 domestic destinations and some 50 international destinations. AA is constructing a new headquarters on a 300-acre campus on DFW property.

Financial Performance

In FY2016 (ended September 30 2016) Dallas Fort Worth International Airport generated revenue of $745 million a 10% increase from the prior year.

The airport's earnings in FY2016 had a hard landing losing almost $94 million. Although its operations incurred a relatively small $4.6 million loss the big contributor was massive interest expense on its revenue bonds. The interest is a recurring annual charge and the airport has recently been running at an annual loss.

Strategy

DFW is in the midst of a $2.34 billion terminal improvement project that's expected to be completed in late 2018. Improvements include new gates and a new concourse light rail connections to downtown Dallas and renovations to existing terminals. Improvements to Terminals A B and E completed in 2017 and work on Terminal C is on hold due to financing decisions. The physical airfield is also on tap to receive capital funding: runway 17C to get $250 million and end-around taxiways to get $430 million.

The airport has excellent connectivity to Latin & South America and to Asia and believes it is well positions to serve as a gateway between the two world regions. It is geographically situated in an advantageous place and already has an extensive network of destinations into Mexico and Latin & South America.

EXECUTIVES

Ceo, Sean P. Donohue
Evp Operations, James M. (Jim) Crites
Evp And Cfo, Christopher A. Poinsatte
Evp Administration, Linda Valdez Thompson
Vp Marketing, Sharon McCloskey
Evp Revenue Management, Kenneth (Ken) Buchanan
Evp Global Strategy And Development, John Ackerman
Evp Airport Development And Planning, Khaled Naja
Svp Information Technology Services, Stephen Shaffer
Assistant Vice President Energy And Utility Services, Brian Yancy
Vice President, Ollie Malone
Vice President Information Technology, Michael Youngs
Vp Airline Relations And Cargo Business Development, Milton De La Paz
Assistant Vice President Community Engagement, Jj Cawelti
Chairman, Sam Coats, age 79
Vice Chairman, William W. (Bill) Meadows

LOCATIONS

HQ: DALLAS/FORT WORTH INTERNATIONAL AIRPORT
2400 AVIATION DR, DFW AIRPORT, TX 75261
Phone: 972 973-5400
Web: WWW.DFWAIRPORT.COM

HISTORICAL FINANCIALS

Company Type: Private

Income Statement — FYE: September 30

	REVENUE ($ mil.)	NET INCOME ($ mil.)	NET PROFIT MARGIN	EMPLOYEES
09/18	929	54	5.9%	1,700
09/16	745	(88)	—	—
09/07	567	28	5.0%	—
09/06	388	140	36.2%	—
Annual Growth	7.5%	(7.6%)	—	—

2018 Year-End Financials

Return on assets: 0.7%
Return on equity: 16.1%
Current ratio: 1.70
Cash ($ mil.): 154

DANA-FARBER CANCER INSTITUTE, INC.

The Dana-Farber Cancer Institute fights cancer on two fronts: It provides treatment to cancer patients young and old and researches new cancer diagnostics treatments and preventions. The organization's scientists also research AIDS treatments and cures for a host of other deadly diseases. Patients receive treatment from Dana-Farber through its cancer centers operated in conjunction with Brigham and Women's Hospital Children's Hospital Boston and Massachusetts General Hospital. The institute is also a principal teaching affiliate of Harvard Medical School. Dana-Farber is funded by the National Cancer Institute the National Institute of Allergy and Infectious Diseases and private contributions.

Operations

Dana-Farber reports more than 38300 patient visits a year and is involved in some 700 clinical trials.

Dana-Farber provides care to children and adults with cancer while advancing the understanding diagnosis treatment cure and prevention of cancer and related diseases. As an affiliate of Harvard Medical School and a Comprehensive Cancer Center designated by the National Cancer Institute the Institute also provides training for new generations of physicians and scientists designs programs that promote public health particularly among high-risk and underserved populations and disseminates innovative patient therapies and scientific discoveries to target community across the US and around the world. In 2014 the hospital has a community benefit of $6.75 million.

Geographic Reach

The institute primarily serves patients in New England. Dana-Farber's main campus is in Boston's Longwood Medical Area and it also has facilities in Brighton Milford South Weymouth and Pittsfield (all in Massachussets); Londonderry New Hampshire; and Waterford Connecticut.

Dana-Farber Community Cancer Care physician practices are in seven communities throughout eastern Massachusetts.

Financial Performance

The institute reported a 7% rise in revenues in 2014 thanks to an increase in patient service revenues unrestricted contributions and bequests and other operating revenues. Revenues from the Medicare and Medicaid programs accounted for approximately 25% and 5% respectively of Dana-Farber's net patient service revenue in 2014

Net income decreased by 11% due to an increase in temporarily restricted net assets and contributions.

Strategy

When it comes to patient care Dana-Farber emphasizes the importance of forming research and treatment partnerships with other health care organizations. To that end the institute has opened a handful of treatment clinics on other medical campuses including one at Faulkner Hospital in southwest Boston and another at Milford Regional Medical Center in Massachusetts.

Along with expanding on other campuses Dana-Farber built a new cancer care center on its main campus in Boston.

Although Dana-Farber directs its research efforts toward saving lives from deadly diseases some of its discoveries also bring in a tidy income as the company and its research partners occasionally license out their drug discoveries to pharmaceutical companies.

In 2015 new research by Dana-Farber scientists raised the prospect of cancer therapy that works by converting a tumor's best friends in the immune system into its gravest enemies. In a study published in the journal Science an international collaboration of investigators from Dana-Farber Harvard Medical School Boston Children's Hospital and the University of Strasbourg uncovered a mechanism that allows key immune system cells to keep a steady rein on their more belligerent brother cells thereby protecting normal healthy tissue from assault. The discovery has powerful implications for cancer. By blocking the mechanism with a drug it may be possible to turn the attack-suppressing cells into tumor-attacking cells.

Company Background

In 2013 the institute and Lawrence + Memorial Cancer Center opened a $34.5 million 47000 sq.-ft. cancer facility in Waterford Connecticut.

The Yawkey Center for Cancer Care named in honor of long-time contributor The Yawkey Foundation opened in 2011 to serve a growing number of patients. The 275000-sq.-ft center's 14-stories house most of Dana-Farber's adult outpatient care. The building has more than 100 exam rooms about 140 infusion chairs and a number of consultation rooms for family and patients. It also connected Dana-Farber to other campus buildings and to its clinical partners Brigham and Women's Hospital and Children's Hospital Boston.

Dana-Farber Cancer Institute was founded as a children's cancer research foundation in 1947 by Dr. Sidney Farber. The institute later expanded its services to provide programs for adults as well as children.

EXECUTIVES

President And Ceo, Laurie H. Glimcher, age 68
Evp Cfo And Assistant Treasurer, Dorothy E. Puhy, age 68
Vp And Chief Marketing Officer, David A. Feinberg
Svp Patient Care Services And Chief Nursing Officer, Anne Gross
Chair Department Of Medical Oncology, James D. Griffin
Chief Scientific Officer, Barrett J. Rollins
Svp And Cfo, Michael L. Reney
Chief Department Of Imaging, Annick D. Van den Abbeele
Chief Surgical Officer, Scott J. Swanson
Chief Medical Officer, Craig A. Bunnell
Chief Clinical Research Officer, Bruce E. Johnson
Chair Department Of Pediatric Oncology, Scott A. Armstrong
Chief Medical Officer Dana-farber/boston Children's Cancer And Blood Disorders Center, Lisa R. Diller
Professor And Chair Department Of Radiation Oncology Dana-farber Cancer Institute/brigham And Women's Hospital/boston Children's Hospital, Daphne Haas-Kogan
Chair Executive Committee For Research (ecr), William C. Hahn
Chair Executive Committee For Clinical Programs (eccp), Robert J. Soiffer
Chair Executive Committee For Clinical Research (eccr), Mary-Ellen Taplin
Chair Department Of Psychosocial Oncology And Palliative Care, James Tulsky
President Dana-farber/boston Children's Cancer And Blood Disorders Center, David A. Williams
Vice President Pharmacy Services, Sylvia Bartel
Clinical Director Adult Leukemia, Martha Wadleigh
Vice President, Melissa Shore
Senior Vice President, Barbara Bierer
Director Of Nursing Outpatient Solid Tumor, Laura Ma
Senior Vice President, Lesley Solomon
Vice President, Kelly Steve
Senior Vice President Chief Philanthropy Officer, Melany Duval
Senior Vice President, Maria Megdal
Associate Medical Director Medical Oncologist Hematologist, Olga Kozyreva
Board Treasurer, Sarah Solomon

LOCATIONS

HQ: DANA-FARBER CANCER INSTITUTE, INC.
450 BROOKLINE AVE, BOSTON, MA 022155450
Phone: 617 632-3000
Web: WWW.DANA-FARBER.ORG

PRODUCTS/OPERATIONS

2014 Sales

	% of total
Patients Services	62
Research	30
Unrestricted Contributions and Bequests	6
Other revenue	2
Total	**100**

Selected Clinical Affiliations

Dana-Farber/Brigham and Women's Cancer Center (outpatient services for adult cancer patients provided by Dana-Farber; and inpatient care provided by Brigham and Women's Hospital)
Dana-Farber/Children's Hospital Cancer Center (Dana-Farber Cancer Institute and Children's Hospital Boston outpatient care for children provided at Dana-Farber's Jimmy Fund Clinic)
Dana-Farber/Harvard Cancer Center (Beth Israel Deaconess Medical Center Brigham and Women's Hospital Children's Hospital Boston and Massachusetts General Hospital collaborate on research cancer prevention and treatments and therapies for cancer patients)
Dana-Farber/Lawrence + Memorial Cancer Center (cancer facility Waterford Connecticut).
Dana-Farber/Partners Cancer Care (consolidated adult oncology programs and clinical research of Dana-Farber Cancer Institute Brigham and Women's Hospital and Massachusetts General Hospital)

Selected Satellite Centers

Dana-Farber/Brigham and Women's Cancer Center at Faulkner Hospital in Jamaica Plain (southwest Boston area)
Dana-Farber/Brigham and Women's Cancer Center at Milford Regional Medical Center (Massachusetts)
Dana-Farber/Brigham and Women's Cancer Center in clinical affiliation with South Shore Hospital (South Weymouth Massachusetts)
Dana-Farber/New Hampshire Oncology-Hematology (Londonderry)
Adult Treatment Centers and Clinical Services
Blood Cancers
Breast Cancer
Cancer Genetics and Prevention
Cutaneous (Skin) Cancer
Gastrointestinal Cancer
Genitourinary Cancer
Gynecologic Cancer
Head and Neck Cancer
Hematology
Melanoma
Neuro-Oncology
Sarcoma
Thoracic (Lung) Cancer
Pediatric Treatment Centers and Clinical Services
Blood Disorders Center
Brain Tumor Center
Hematologic Malignancies Center
Solid Tumors Center
Stem Cell Transplant Center

COMPETITORS

Baystate Health
Beth Israel Deaconess Medical Center
Boston Medical Center
Brigham and Women's Hospital
Care New England
CareGroup
Children's National Medical Center
Emory Healthcare
Fox Chase Cancer Center
Johns Hopkins Medicine
MD Anderson Cancer Center
Mayo Clinic
Memorial Sloan-Kettering
Partners HealthCare
Roswell Park Cancer Institute
St. Elizabeth's Medical Center
St. Jude Children's Research Hospital

HISTORICAL FINANCIALS

Company Type: Private

Income Statement FYE: September 30

	REVENUE ($ mil.)	NET INCOME ($ mil.)	NET PROFIT MARGIN	EMPLOYEES
09/15	739	4	0.6%	3,000
09/14	672	34	5.1%	—
09/13	635	56	8.8%	—
09/10	894	16	1.9%	—
Annual Growth	(3.7%)	(22.7%)	—	—

2015 Year-End Financials

Return on assets: 0.4%
Return on equity: 0.8%
Current ratio: 0.90
Cash ($ mil.): 28

DANFOSS POWER SOLUTIONS INC.

Danfoss Power Solutions (formerly Sauer-Danfoss) makes hydraulic electronic and mechanical systems and components for manufacturers of agricultural construction road-building turf care specialty vehicle and material-handling equipment. It operates from several segments: Hydrostatics (hydrostatic transmissions); Work Function (gear pumps steering motors); Controls (electrohydraulic valves); and Stand-Alone businesses (gear pumps and motors valves and inverters). Danfoss Power Solutions is a wholly-owned subsidiary of Denmark-based industrial company Danfoss A/S.

Operations

Danfoss has Markets to serve; Automotive Buildings ? commercial District energy Energy and natural resources Food and beverage Industry Marine and offshore Mobile hydraulics and Refrigeration and air conditioning.

Geographic Reach

Danfoss Power Solutions operates about 25 manufacturing facilities in the Americas Asia/Pacific and Europe.

Sales and Marketing

Customers include original equipment manufacturers (OEMs) primarily of off-road vehicles. Danfoss Power Solutions also fits its production to the specific needs of the customer thus minimizing inventory levels and it maintains its global operations in a decentralized fashion so that products can be adapted to local market needs.

EXECUTIVES

President Ceo, Niels B. Christiansen
Evp And Chief Marketing Officer, Marc A. Weston, $287,388 total compensation
Evp And Cfo, Jesper V. Christensen, $355,297 total compensation
Evp And Cto, C. Kells Hall, $319,056 total compensation
Evp Human Resources, Anne Wilkinson
Executive Vice President And President - Work Function Division, Helge Jorgensen
Executive Vice President And President - Hydrostatics Division, Thomas Kaiser
Executive Vice President President Work Function Division, Helge J rgensen
Chairman, J rgen M. Clausen
Auditors: KPMG LLP DES MOINES IOWA

LOCATIONS

HQ: DANFOSS POWER SOLUTIONS INC.
2800 E 13TH ST, AMES, IA 500108600
Phone: 515 239-6000
Web: WWW.DANFOSS.COM

PRODUCTS/OPERATIONS

Selected Products

Controls
Control valves
Mobile electronics
Propel
Hydrostatic transmissions
Open circuit piston pumps
Stand-Alone
Cartridge valves and HICs
Directional control valves
Investors
Light duty hydrostatic transmissions
Open circuit gear pumps and motors
Work Function
Low speed high torque motors
Open circuit gear pumps and motors
Steering units

Selected Markets
Agriculture and turf care
Construction and road building
Material handling
Specialty vehicles

COMPETITORS

Bosch Rexroth
Eaton Hydraulics
HUSCO International
Haldex
Parker-Hannifin
Shimadzu
Sun Hydraulics
TB Wood's
The Linde Group
Twin Disc

HISTORICAL FINANCIALS

Company Type: Private

Income Statement FYE: December 31

	REVENUE ($ mil.)	NET INCOME ($ mil.)	NET PROFIT MARGIN	EMPLOYEES
12/11	2,057	259	12.6%	6,400
12/10	1,640	246	15.0%	—
12/09	1,159	(332)	—	—
Annual Growth	33.2%	—	—	—

2011 Year-End Financials

Return on assets: 20.3%
Return on equity: 45.0%
Current ratio: 2.30
Cash ($ mil.): 251

DANONE US, INC.

WhiteWave Foods rides a wave of dietary changes as consumers seek alternatives to conventional foods. The company is best known for its refrigerated Silk soymilk in the US and Alpro brand soy products in Europe. WhiteWave also produces organic dairy products under the Horizon Organic label and dairy related foods including International Delight coffee creamers and LAND O'LAKES-branded creamers and dairy dessert toppings (licensed from dairy co-op Land O'Lakes). WhiteWave products are sold through natural food and grocery stores as well as mass merchandisers and restaurants and food service businesses in the US and Canada and parts of Europe. WhiteWave has been part of French dairy giant Danone since 2017.

Operations

WhiteWave's plant-based food and drinks include Silk (milk from soy almonds cashews and coconuts as well as dairy-free yogurt); So Delicious Dairy Free (drinks creamers ice-cream shredded cheese); Alpro (dairy alternatives); and Vega (plant-based sports nutrition).

Other brands include Horizon (organic milk-based products); International Delight (sweet drinks and iced coffee); Half & Half (creamer); Earthbound Farm (salads frozen and dried fruit and fresh fruit and vegetables).

Geographic Reach

WhiteWave is headquartered in Denver Colorado.

Financial Performance

WhiteWave has maintained healthy if not entirely organic revenue gains for the past ten years.

EXECUTIVES

Chairman And Ceo, Gregg L. Engles, $1,120,000 total compensation
Us Group President Americas Foods And Beverages, Kevin C. Yost, $550,000 total compensation
Coo, Blaine E. McPeak, $650,000 total compensation
Evp And General Counsel, Roger E. Theodoredis
Evp Human Resources, Thomas N. Zanetich, $445,000 total compensation
Evp Strategy And Corporate Development, Edward F. Fugger, $362,000 total compensation
President Europe Foods And Beverages, Bernard P. J. Deryckere, $504,076 total compensation
Evp And Cfo, Greg S. Christenson
Senior Vice President, Tommy Zanetich
Vice President Engineering And Extraction, Rick Wietharn
Auditors: DELOITTE & TOUCHE LLP DENVER

LOCATIONS

HQ: DANONE US, INC.
12002 AIRPORT WAY, BROOMFIELD, CO 800212546
Phone: 303 635-4500
Web: WWW.WHITEWAVE.COM

2016 Sales

	% of total
North America	86
Europe	14
Total	**100**

PRODUCTS/OPERATIONS

Selected Products and Brands

Europe
Plant-based foods and beverages (Alpro Provamel)
Almond
Hazelnut
Oat
Rice
Soy
North America
Coffee creamers and beverages (Land O Lakes International Delight)
Flavored coffee creamers
Half & Half
Iced coffee
Unflavored coffee creamers
Plant-based foods and beverages (Silk)
Almond
Coconut

Soy
Premium dairy (Horizon Organic)
Organic milk
Other organic dairy
Other premium milk

COMPETITORS

Aurora Organic Dairy
Eden Foods
Galaxy Nutritional Foods
HP Hood
Hain Celestial
Kraft Heinz
Lifeway Foods
Nestlé
Odwalla
Old Home Foods
Organic Valley
Rockview Dairies
Springfield Creamery

HISTORICAL FINANCIALS

Company Type: Private

Income Statement FYE: December 31

	REVENUE ($ mil.)	NET INCOME ($ mil.)	NET PROFIT MARGIN	EMPLOYEES
12/15	3,866	168	4.4%	5,800
12/14	3,436	140	4.1%	—
12/13	2,542	99	3.9%	—
Annual Growth	23.3%	30.4%	—	—

2015 Year-End Financials

Return on assets: 4.0%
Return on equity: 13.9%
Current ratio: 1.00
Cash ($ mil.): 38

DARTMOUTH COLLEGE

EXECUTIVES

Mgr, James Fries
Assistant Professor, Ethan M Berke
Assistant Professor, WEI Wang
Coordinator, Ben Myers
Associate Professor, Sean Smith
Project Director, Carole Meyers
Associate Vice President For C, Diana Lawrence
Director of Advancement Servic, Dominic Albanese
Vice President of Operations, Jackson Baur
Administration, John L Fellows
Database Administrator, Jonathan Crossett
Auditors: PRICEWATERHOUSECOOPERS LLP BO

LOCATIONS

HQ: DARTMOUTH COLLEGE
6193 HINMAN, HANOVER, NH 037554007
Phone: 603 646-2191
Web: WWW.DARTMOUTHCOOP.COM

HISTORICAL FINANCIALS

Company Type: Private

Income Statement FYE: June 30

	REVENUE ($ mil.)	NET INCOME ($ mil.)	NET PROFIT MARGIN	EMPLOYEES
06/19	927	314	34.0%	10
06/18	893	739	82.8%	—
06/17	887	691	77.9%	—
06/16	859	(301)	—	—
Annual Growth	2.6%	—	—	—

2019 Year-End Financials

Return on assets: 3.7%
Return on equity: 4.7%
Current ratio: 1.50
Cash ($ mil.): 293

DARTMOUTH-HITCHCOCK CLINIC

The New England Alliance for Health (NEAH) brings together health care facilities and professionals looking to improve health in the New England region. Members of the alliance include about 20 community hospitals home health care agencies and mental health centers in New Hampshire Vermont and Massachusetts. While the members collaborate on wellness quality and communication initiatives each member of the alliance is an independently owned and operated not-for-profit organization with its own board of directors. Collaborative services provided by NEAH include procurement staff training information technology quality control and finance as well as the coordination of facility policies and planning.

Operations

NEAH's core services are provided to and funded by all of its member organizations. In addition the alliance provides some voluntary services (such as licensing and insurance services) that are funded only by the participating members.

An affiliated organization the New England Pharmacy Collaborative (NEPC) handles drug purchases for the health care members.

Geographic Reach

New Hampshire holds the largest number of NEAH members (11) while the organization has seven participants in Vermont and one in Massachusetts.

Company Background

NEAH was formerly known as Dartmouth-Hitchcock Alliance; it changed its name in 2009.

EXECUTIVES

Coo, Stephen LeBlanc
Auditors: PRICEWATERHOUSECOOPERS LLC BO

LOCATIONS

HQ: DARTMOUTH-HITCHCOCK CLINIC
1 MEDICAL CENTER DR, LEBANON, NH 037560001
Phone: 603 650-5000
Web: WWW.DARTMOUTH-HITCHCOCK.ORG

PRODUCTS/OPERATIONS

Selected Services

Core Services
- Financial Planning and Benchmarking
- Information Services
- Materials Management and Pharmacy Services
- Professional Staff Education and Development
- Program Administration
- Quality Improvement/Loss Prevention

Other Services
- Licenses
- Property/Casualty Insurance Program

Selected Alliance Members

Massachusetts
- Cooley Dickinson Health Care (Northampton)

New Hampshire
- Alice Peck Day Memorial Hospital (Lebanon)
- Cheshire Medical Center (Keene)
- Cottage Hospital (Woodsville)
- Dartmouth-Hitchcock Medical Center (Lebanon includes Mary Hitchcock Memorial Hospital)
- Monadnock Community Hospital
- New London Hospital
- Upper Connecticut Valley Hospital (Colebrook)
- Valley Regional Hospital (Claremont)
- Weeks Medical Center (Lancaster)
- West Central Behavioral Health (Lebanon)

Vermont
- Brattleboro Memorial Hospital
- Grace Cottage Hospital (Townshend)
- Mt. Ascutney Hospital (Windsor)
- Northeastern Vermont Regional Hospital (St. Johnsbury)
- Southwestern Vermont Medical Center (Bennington)
- Springfield Hospital
- VNA and Hospice of VT and NH

COMPETITORS

AMN Healthcare
HealthTrust
MedAssets
Premier Inc.
Vizient Inc.
Winchester Healthcare

HISTORICAL FINANCIALS

Company Type: Private

Income Statement FYE: June 30

	REVENUE ($ mil.)	NET INCOME ($ mil.)	NET PROFIT MARGIN	EMPLOYEES
06/19	1,888	22	1.2%	7,999
06/15	6	0	—	—
Annual Growth	313.1%	—	—	—

2019 Year-End Financials

Return on assets: 1.3%
Return on equity: 4.9%
Current ratio: 1.50
Cash ($ mil.): 47

DARTMOUTH-HITCHCOCK HEALTH

EXECUTIVES

Ceo, James Weinstein
Cfo, Daniel Jantzen
General Counsel, John Kacavas
Cao, Stephen Leblanc
Coo, Patrick Jordan III
Electrical Supervisor, Will Moore
Auditors: PRICEWATERHOUSECOOPERS LLP

LOCATIONS

HQ: DARTMOUTH-HITCHCOCK HEALTH
1 MEDICAL CENTER DR, LEBANON, NH 037560001
Phone: 603 653-1118
Web: WWW.DARTMOUTH-HITCHCOCK.ORG

HISTORICAL FINANCIALS

Company Type: Private

Income Statement FYE: June 30

	REVENUE ($ mil.)	NET INCOME ($ mil.)	NET PROFIT MARGIN	EMPLOYEES
06/20	2,344	(119)	—	8,000
06/19	2,299	40	1.8%	—
06/18	2,069	87	4.2%	—
06/16	1,791	(44)	—	—
Annual Growth	7.0%	—	—	—

2020 Year-End Financials

Return on assets: (-4.1%)
Return on equity: (-20.4%)
Current ratio: 1.30
Cash ($ mil.): 453

DATASITE GLOBAL CORPORATION

Document services company Merrill is no relation to financial services giant Merrill Lynch but the companies do share an interest in SEC paperwork. Merrill Corporation is a provider of outsourced document management branded marketing services and other information management services. It helps clients gather organize and manage confidential and time-sensitive information for legal and financial transactions. In addition the company provides marketing and communication services such as document composition printing fulfillment and digital delivery as well as technology integration.

Operations

Merrill's Legal and Financial Transaction Services (LFTS) offers legal financial and corporate professionals a suite of advanced services and web-based tools to gather organize and manage transactional information. The company's Marketing and Communication Solutions (MCS) segment specializes in technology-enabled marketing and compliance communications.

Geographic Reach

Merrill operates through more than 40 offices in the US and about 20 international locations. It also has an IT Technology Center in Chennai India and another IT-focused facility in Coimbatore India.

Strategy

While Merrill continues to print individual annual reports brochures catalogs and other publications it has diversified beyond its traditional printing business through numerous acquisitions and strategic alliances to position itself as a business process outsourcing company. It sees growth opportunities in its legal solutions offerings which include managing electronic data discovery and in Merrill Datasite which provides online hosting of documents related to mergers and acquisitions.

In addition to acquisitions Merrill also divests assets from time to time to support its ongoing strategic repositioning efforts in the business process outsourcing marketplace. In 2016 it sold its language services subsidiary Merrill Brink International to United Language Group Inc. The same year it divested its real Estate and Franchise Business selling it to direct marketing technologies firm Xpressdocs Holdings.

HISTORY

Kenneth Merrill founded K. F. Merrill with his wife Lorraine in 1968 and grew the company into a major regional printer. He turned over the reins in 1984 to John Castro who had worked his way up from production manager. The company went public two years later.

EXECUTIVES

Managing Director Asia, Nancy Yu
Chief Product Officer, Thomas Fredell, age 50
Evp And Chief Administrative Officer, Brenda J. Vale
Coo Marketing And Communications Solutions, Roy Gross
Coo, Rodney D. Johnson
Regional Managing Director Europe Middle East Africa (emea), Alun Baker
Ceo, James (Rusty) Wiley
Cfo, Thomas Donnelly
Cio, Brad Smuland
Senior Vice President, James Garippa
Vice President Sales, Laura Lipani
Senior Vice President Of Sales, Elin Lawrence
Vice President Sales, Lori Frederick
Vice President Finance, John Gyurci
Vice President, Raul Varela
Senior Vice President, Nancy Skluth
Vice President Sales, Phillip Juett
Vice President Sales, Mark Stefonek
Senior Vice President, Mark Lederman
Senior Vice President, Eric Polans
Senior Vice President Sales, Jim Garippa
Senior Vice President Business Solutions, Cathleen Napoli
Vice President Regional Sales Manager, Christy Vierzba
Senior Vice President Sales, Chris Boehmcke
Vice President Sales, Colin Schopbach
Executive Vice President Client Services, Deven Lindemann
Senior Vice President Controller And Chief Accounting Officer, Cathy Miller
Vice President Product Marketing, Axel Kirstetter
Senior Vice President Product Management, Christian Idiodi
Senior Vice President, Neal Davies
Senior Vice President, Clark Graebner
Vp Global Head Of Sales Operations, Phil Rowlinson
Vice President Business Solutions, Jean Goodwin
Vice President Sales, Kevin Mcallister
Senior Vice President And Director Of Financial Printing, Mike Linskey
Chairman, James V. (Jim) Continenza, age 57
Assistant Treasurer, Bradley Carlson
Auditors: PRICE WATER HOUSE COOPER LLP

LOCATIONS

HQ: DATASITE GLOBAL CORPORATION
733 MARQUETTE AVE STE 600, MINNEAPOLIS, MN 554022357
Phone: 651 646-4501
Web: WWW.DATASITE.COM

PRODUCTS/OPERATIONS

SERVICES

Capital Transactions
Contract Management
Data Warehousing
Elections
Financial Services Marketing & Communications
Healthcare Member Communications
Intellectual Property Management
M&A Reorganizations & Exchange Offers
Merrill IFN
Portfolio Management
Regulatory Disclosure

COMPETITORS

Applied Discovery
Diebold
Harte-Hanks
IntraLinks
Kroll Ontrack
Lionbridge
Pitney Bowes
R.R. Donnelley
Ricoh USA
St Ives
Williams Lea
Xerox

HISTORICAL FINANCIALS

Company Type: Private

Income Statement — FYE: January 31

	REVENUE ($ mil.)	NET INCOME ($ mil.)	NET PROFIT MARGIN	EMPLOYEES
01/17	609	53	8.9%	5,418
01/16	579	78	13.5%	—
01/15	691	64	9.3%	—
Annual Growth	(6.1%)	(8.5%)	—	—

2017 Year-End Financials

Return on assets: 17.4%
Return on equity: —
Current ratio: 2.30
Cash ($ mil.): 62

DATS TRUCKING, INC.

DATS Trucking specializes in less-than-truckload (LTL) freight transportation in the western US but that's not all there is to the company's operations. In addition to its LTL operations in which freight from multiple shippers is combined into a single trailer DATS Trucking provides truckload transportation. The company's tanker division Overland Petroleum transports gasoline diesel fuel and other petroleum products. Overall DATS Trucking operates a fleet of about 500 tractors and 2500 trailers. It offers LTL service outside its home territory via The Reliance Network a group of regional carriers that covers the US and Canada. President and CEO Don Ipson founded DATS Trucking in 1988.

LOCATIONS

HQ: DATS TRUCKING, INC.
321 N OLD HIGHWAY 91, HURRICANE, UT 847373194
Phone: 435 673-1886
Web: WWW.DATSTRUCKING.COM

COMPETITORS

Bulkmatic
Central Freight Lines
FedEx Freight
J.B. Hunt
Kenan Advantage Group
Penn Tank Lines
Schneider National
Swift Transportation
UPS Freight
Werner Enterprises
YRC Worldwide

HISTORICAL FINANCIALS

Company Type: Private

Income Statement — FYE: December 31

	REVENUE ($ mil.)	NET INCOME ($ mil.)	NET PROFIT MARGIN	EMPLOYEES
12/07	717	1	0.3%	475
12/06	658	7	1.2%	—
12/05	600	1	0.2%	—
12/04	391	1	0.4%	—
Annual Growth	22.3%	4.6%	—	—

DAVIS SCHOOL DISTRICT

EXECUTIVES

Pres, Tamara Lowe
V Pres*, Burke Larsen
Supt*, W Bryan Bowles
Asst Supt*, Lynn V Trenbeath
Asst Supt*, Nancy Fleming
MBR*, Barbara A Smith
MBR*, Larry Smith
MBR*, Peter Cannon
Facilities Director, John Swain
Before/After School Coordinato, Susy Jenson
Business Administrator, Craig Carter
Auditors: SQUIRE & COMPANY PC OREM UT

LOCATIONS

HQ: DAVIS SCHOOL DISTRICT
45 E ST ST, FARMINGTON, UT 84025
Phone: 801 402-5261
Web: WWW.DAVIS.K12.UT.US

HISTORICAL FINANCIALS

Company Type: Private

Income Statement FYE: June 30

	REVENUE ($ mil.)	NET INCOME ($ mil.)	NET PROFIT MARGIN	EMPLOYEES
06/18	645	(15)	—	6,310
06/14	509	12	2.5%	—
06/13	500	(6)	—	—
06/11	482	1	0.4%	—
Annual Growth	4.2%	—	—	—

DB US HOLDING CORPORATION

EXECUTIVES

Pres-Ceo, Dr Josef Blank
Ex V Pres-Cfo, Joseph L Groneman
V Pres-SEC, Brian P Lynch
Office Manager, Andrea Hollandt
Vice President, Brian Lynch
Assistant General Counsel, Dennis St George
Executive Secretary, Rosemary Humphries
Assistant General Counsel, Vicki Hassman
Auditors: PRICEWATERHOUSECOOPERS LLP N

LOCATIONS

HQ: DB US HOLDING CORPORATION
120 WHITE PLAINS RD, TARRYTOWN, NY 105915526
Phone: 914 366-7200
Web: WWW.DBUSHOLDING.COM

HISTORICAL FINANCIALS

Company Type: Private

Income Statement FYE: December 31

	REVENUE ($ mil.)	NET INCOME ($ mil.)	NET PROFIT MARGIN	EMPLOYEES
12/16	914	(2)	—	6,300
12/15	1,766	(10)	—	—
/ 0	0	—	—	
Annual Growth	—	—	—	—

2016 Year-End Financials

Return on assets: (-2.2%) Cash ($ mil.): 122
Return on equity: (-2.3%)
Current ratio: 102.70

DBSI INC

EXECUTIVES

Pres, Douglas Swenson
V Pres-Sec-Treas*, Charles Hassard
V Pres*, John Mayeron
Contrl, Paris Cole
Representative, Bonni L White
Administration Manager, Jeremy Evans
Human Resources Manager, Richard Stonhill

LOCATIONS

HQ: DBSI INC
12426 W EXPLORER DR # 100, BOISE, ID 837131560
Phone: 208 955-9800
Web: WWW.DBSI.COM

HISTORICAL FINANCIALS

Company Type: Private

Income Statement FYE: December 31

	ASSETS ($ mil.)	NET INCOME ($ mil.)	INCOME AS % OF ASSETS	EMPLOYEES
12/07	244	15	6.4%	70
12/06	168	2	1.6%	—
12/05	150	25	17.0%	—
12/04	70	49	69.9%	—
Annual Growth	51.2%	(31.7%)	—	—

2007 Year-End Financials

Return on assets: 6.4% Sales ($ mil): 625
Return on equity: 14.9%

DC WATER AND SEWER AUTHORITY

EXECUTIVES

Ceo-Gen Mngr, David L Gadis
Cfo, Olo Adebo
Treas, Robert Hunt
CIO, Omer Siddiqui
Acting Manager, Maxine Buchanan
Designer, Walter Burnett
Coordinator, Nicole Kaiser
Design Manager, Moussa Wone
Design Engineer, Tariq Mohammad
Emergency Planning Coordinator, Dusti Lowndes
Program Manager, Gordon Evans
Auditors: KPMG LLP WASHINGTON DC

LOCATIONS

HQ: DC WATER AND SEWER AUTHORITY
5000 OVERLOOK AVE SW, WASHINGTON, DC 200325212
Phone: 202 787-2000
Web: WWW.DCWATER.COM

HISTORICAL FINANCIALS

Company Type: Private

Income Statement FYE: September 30

	REVENUE ($ mil.)	NET INCOME ($ mil.)	NET PROFIT MARGIN	EMPLOYEES
09/18	684	187	27.4%	1,000
09/06	0	0	18.4%	—
09/05	272	48	17.6%	—
Annual Growth	7.3%	11.0%	—	—

2018 Year-End Financials

Return on assets: 2.4% Cash ($ mil.): 123
Return on equity: 9.0%
Current ratio: 1.40

DCR WORKFORCE, INC.

EXECUTIVES

Prin, Naveen Dua
Pres*, Ammu Warrier
Cgo*, Daniel Weinfurter
Accountant, Elena Wilson
Program Manager, Shannon White
Human Resources Lead, Allen Alexander
Supervisor, Kathleen Belotto
Human Resources, Shayla Jackson
Director Business, Tracy White
Operations Analyst, Vishal Hotwani
On Site Program Manager, Chris Stevens
Auditors: JOHN KAMMERER BOCA RATON FLO

LOCATIONS

HQ: DCR WORKFORCE, INC.
7795 NW BCN SQ BLVD # 201, BOCA RATON, FL 334871394
Phone: 561 998-3737

HISTORICAL FINANCIALS

Company Type: Private

Income Statement FYE: December 31

	REVENUE ($ mil.)	NET INCOME ($ mil.)	NET PROFIT MARGIN	EMPLOYEES
12/12	548	2	0.5%	82
12/11	464	2	0.6%	—
12/01	12	0	6.3%	—
Annual Growth	41.0%	11.9%	—	—

2012 Year-End Financials

Return on assets: 16.9% Cash ($ mil.): —
Return on equity: 21.1%
Current ratio: 3.80

DE PAUL UNIVERSITY

In the land of da Bulls and da Bears there's DePaul. One of the largest private not-for-profit universities in the US DePaul has more than 21920 students attending classes at its Chicago-area campuses and its increasing offerings of online learning courses. The university offers more than 300 undergraduate and graduate programs through 10 colleges and schools including the Driehaus College of Business and the College of Communication. It has a student teacher ratio of 16 to 1. One of the country's largest Catholic institutions of higher learning DePaul was founded in 1898 by the Vincentian religious community and is named after 17th century French priest St. Vincent de Paul.

Operations

The university's more than 130 undergraduate majors include accountancy acting animation chemistry criminology data science history journalism and marketing. Its more than 175 graduate programs include Counseling: Clinical Mental Health Counseling (MEd) Creative Producing (MFA) Early Childhood Education (EdD) Healthcare Markets & Analytics (MBA) Information Systems (MS) and Marketing Strategy and Planning (MBA) among its graduate programs. These programs are offered in School and Colleges of Business Communication Education Law Liberal Arts and Social Sciences Science and Health Music Continuing and Professional Studies as well as in Driehaus College of Business and The Theatre School.

Geographic Reach

DePaul's Chicago-area campuses are located in Lincoln Park (which is home to five colleges/schools) the Loop (for another five DePaul colleges and schools). DePaul's student body hosts learners from about 50 US states and more than 135 countries. In addition it study abroad programs are offered in more than 30 countries.

EXECUTIVES

Vice President, Bonnie Frankel
Evp Financial Affairs, Robert L. (Bob) Kozoman
Vp Facilities, Robert (Bob) Janis
Dean Driehaus College Of Business And Kellstadt Graduate School Of Business, Ray Whittington
Dean School For New Learning, Marisa Alicea
Dean Theatre School, John Culbert
Dean College Of Computing And Digital Media, David Miller
President, A. Gabriel Esteban
Director Information Services, Bob McCormick
Dean College Of Communication, Salma Ghanem
Provost, Marten denBoer
Vp Planning And Presidential Administration, Jay Braatz
Svp Enrollment Management, David Kalsbeek
Dean College Of Science And Health, Gerald P. Koocher
Athletic Director, Jean Lenti-Ponsetto
Interim Dean College Of Liberal Arts And Social Sciences, Lucy Rinehart
Dean College Of Law, Jennifer Rosato Perea
Dean School Of Education, Paul Zionts
Vice President Institutional Advancement, Alyssa Kupka
Vice President And General Counsel, Jose Padilla
Clinical Director, Alexander Brown
Assistant Vice President, Lisa Cheers
Assistant Vice President Academic Affairs, Charles Strain
Director Of Admissions, Dennis Shea
Associate Vice President For Enrollment Management, Jon Boeckenstedt
Assistant Vice President For Marketing Communications, Gwyn Friend
Associate Vice President Of Financial, Paula Luff
Executive Vice President Academic Affairs, Richard Meister
Vice President Student Affairs, James Doyle
Vice President Student Affairs Lincoln Park Campus, Kathryn Ao'brien
Associate Vice President, Barbara Schaffer
Assistant Vice President Communication Strategies, Linda Blakley
Associate Vice President, Doris Brown
Executive Vice President For Academic Affairs, Michael Greene
Director Of Admissions, Jason Beck
Assistant Vice President For Academic Space, Ralph Erber
Vice President And Chief Human Resources Officer, Stephanie Smith
Vice President Enrollment Management, Maria Null Molina-frias
Vice President Public Relations, Donna Washington
Vice President, Gracie Covarrubias
Associate Vice President For Philanthropy, Ivan Adames
Vice President For Mission And Ministry, Rev Edward Udovic
Vice President, Emily Hoey
Executive Vice President, Lucy Norton
Executive Vice President, Gisselle Cervantes
Executive Vice President, Sophia Modzelewski
Treasurer, Bonnie Hirsch
Secretary, Edtra Flowers
Secretary, Mary Jo Polark
Secretary, Wilma Rodriguez
Auditors: KPMG LLP CHICAGO ILLINOIS

LOCATIONS

HQ: DE PAUL UNIVERSITY
1 E JACKSON BLVD, CHICAGO, IL 606042287
Phone: 312 362-6714
Web: WWW.DEPAUL.EDU

HISTORICAL FINANCIALS

Company Type: Private

Income Statement — FYE: June 30

	REVENUE ($ mil.)	NET INCOME ($ mil.)	NET PROFIT MARGIN	EMPLOYEES
06/20	595	67	11.3%	3,895
06/19	580	45	7.9%	—
06/18	575	67	11.7%	—
06/17	575	67	11.7%	—
Annual Growth	1.2%	0.2%	—	—

2020 Year-End Financials

Return on assets: 3.8%
Return on equity: 5.6%
Current ratio: —
Cash ($ mil.): 56

DEACONESS HEALTH SYSTEM, INC.

While it primarily presides over numerous health care facilities in the southwestern corner of Indiana Deaconess Health System also serves residents in parts of southeastern Illinois and western Kentucky. The system consists of two general acute-care hospitals as well as specialty hospitals for women's health mental health and medical rehabilitation. Its flagship Deaconess Hospital boasts 365 beds and serves as a regional referral center. Deaconess Health also operates a standalone cancer treatment center medical group practice Deaconess Clinic and about 20 outpatient and urgent care clinics. Its Deaconess Health Plans unit is a PPO network that contracts with various health insurers.

Operations

As part of its operations the health system comprises half a dozen facilities including Deaconess Hospital (365 beds) Deaconness Gateway Hospital (120 beds) The Women's Hospital (50 beds) Deaconess Cross Pointe (60 beds) HealthSouth Deaconess Rehabilitation Hospital (80 beds) and The Heart Hospital of Deaconess Gateway (24 beds). It also operates primary care locations such as Deaconess Clinic Deaconess Primary Care for Seniors and Deaconess Urgent Care.

The hospital treats 18000 inpatients 350000 outpatients 65000 emergency patients and 7500 surgical patients each year.

Geographic Reach

Deaconess Health System primarily serves those who reside in 26 counties in Southern Indiana Southeast Illinois and West Kentucky.

Financial Performance

In 2014 net sales increased by 13% due to higher revenues from net patient service.

Deaconess Health System's net patient service revenue increased due to increased contractual adjustments. Medicare and Medicaid together accounted 57% of total net sales in 2014. Commercial and managed care and Self pay and other accounted for 36% and 7% respectively

In 2014 net income increased by 40% compared to 2013. The primary reason was due to increased sales partially offset by decreased benefit related changes other than net periodic benefit cost.

Deaconess Health System's net cash provided by the operating activities increased by 28%.

Strategy

Deaconess Health System has been focused on improving information technology systems including the implementation of an electronic health record (EHR) system. It has increased efficiencies through IT initiatives by installing new automated medication dispensing and prescription management programs.

MyChart is available at Deaconess Hospital Main Deaconess Gateway Deaconess Riley Hospital for Children The Heart Hospital Cross Point all Deaconess Clinic locations Deaconess Critical Care Deaconess Family Practice and Residency and Deaconess Primary Care for Seniors physician offices. MyChart is a secure online health management tool that connects MyChart patients to their personalized health information. MyChart contains inpatient and outpatient test results and information.

In 2015 the company finalized a letter of intent to partner directly with Methodist Hospital on a not-for-profit joint venture to bring additional and enhanced healthcare services to Henderson. The joint venture will improve access to care providers and quality of care in Henderson. Deaconess Health System purchased 10-plus acres of land off Barret Boulevard near Walmart in Henderson in 2014.

Company Background

Founded in 1892 Deaconess Hospital is a teaching facility that offers residency and clinical education programs in addition to providing general and specialty inpatient care. It also conducts medical research programs.

EXECUTIVES

Vice President Business Development, Jared Florence
Medical Director Clinical Research, Majed Koleilat
Nursing Director, JILL BUTTRY
Senior Vice President And Chief Medical Officer, Mack Blanton
Medical Records Director, Tillie Christian
Secretary, Lu Weil
Auditors: BLUE & CO LLC INDIANAPOLIS

LOCATIONS

HQ: DEACONESS HEALTH SYSTEM, INC.
600 MARY ST, EVANSVILLE, IN 477101658
Phone: 812 450-5000
Web: WWW.DEACONESS.COM

PRODUCTS/OPERATIONS

Selected Services

Back & Spine
Behavioral Health
Cancer
Children's Health
Clinical Research
Diabetes
Emergency Care
Joint Replacement
Orthopedic
Pain Management
Physical Medicine
Radiology
Respiratory
Senior Health
Weight Loss
Women's Health
Wound Care

COMPETITORS

Ball Memorial Hospital
Baptist Health Madisonville
Commonwealth Health Corporation
Community Health Network
Daviess Community Hospital
Good Samaritan Hospital (IN)
Henry County Memorial Hospital
Kosciusko Community Hospital
Memorial Hospital (Logansport)
St. Mary's Medical Center of Evansville

HISTORICAL FINANCIALS

Company Type: Private

Income Statement FYE: September 30

	REVENUE ($ mil.)	NET INCOME ($ mil.)	NET PROFIT MARGIN	EMPLOYEES
09/18	1,058	170	16.1%	6,086
09/17	930	127	13.7%	—
09/16	2	(27)	—	—
09/15	2	(24)	—	—
Annual Growth	628.6%	—	—	—

2018 Year-End Financials

Return on assets: 10.3%
Return on equity: 15.4%
Current ratio: 1.90
Cash ($ mil.): 83

DEACONESS HOSPITAL INC

Deaconess Hospital provides benevolent medical assistance to residents of southern Indiana western Kentucky and southeastern Illinois. The not-for-profit hospital is a 365-bed acute care medical facility that is the flagship hospital of the Deaconess Health System. Specialized services include cardiovascular surgery cancer treatment orthopedics neurological and trauma care. The hospital also offers home health care hospice services and medical equipment rental and it operates outpatient family practice surgery wellness and community outreach centers. Founded in 1892 Deaconess Hospital is a teaching and research facility affiliated with the Indiana University School of Medicine.

Operations

Deaconess handles about 18000 inpatient visits per year. It also sees about 350000 outpatients and 65000 emergency room visitors and it handles about 7500 annual surgery procedures.

Geographic Reach

Deaconess Hospital is located in Evansville Indiana and provides services to about 26 surrounding counties.

Strategy

To improve services to area residents Deaconess Hospital is expanding its outpatient care facilities and enhancing its IT resources. For instance in 2013 it moved its urgent care center to a larger more efficient facility. The hospital is also pursuing recognition for specialist programs such as its stroke center which was certified as a level one facility in 2013.

EXECUTIVES

Pres & Ceo, Linda E White
Chb*, John Lipert
Cfo-Asst SEC*, Richard Stivers
Program Director, Kim Volz
Pharmacist, Mark Bauer
Staff Pharmacist, Grace Voight
Pharmacist, Tracy Herr
Neurologist, Bhargav Trivedi
Business Coordinat, Catherine Perkins
Hospitalist, Christina Bennett
Senior Engineer, Darrell Clary

LOCATIONS

HQ: DEACONESS HOSPITAL INC
600 MARY ST, EVANSVILLE, IN 477101674
Phone: 812 450-5000
Web: WWW.DEACONESS.COM

Selected Services

24-hour Emergency Center
Cancer Services
Corporate Wellness
Family Medicine Clinic
Heart Services
Home Medical Equipment
Home-based Medical Care
Hospice Care
Inpatient and Outpatient Surgery
Mental Health Services
Neuro Services
Orthopedics
Pediatrics
Physician Referral Service
Radiology Services
Residency Program
Support Groups and Programs
Women's Hospital

COMPETITORS

Ball Memorial Hospital
Baptist Health
Baptist Health Madisonville
Commonwealth Health Corporation
Community Health Network
Daviess Community Hospital
Good Samaritan Hospital (IN)
Henry County Memorial Hospital
Jewish Hospital & St. Mary's HealthCare
Kosciusko Community Hospital
Memorial Hospital (Logansport)
Norton Healthcare
St. Mary's Medical Center of Evansville

HISTORICAL FINANCIALS

Company Type: Private

Income Statement FYE: September 30

	REVENUE ($ mil.)	NET INCOME ($ mil.)	NET PROFIT MARGIN	EMPLOYEES
09/18	823	153	18.6%	5,300
09/17	725	94	13.0%	—
09/16	698	108	15.5%	—
09/15	680	138	20.3%	—
Annual Growth	6.5%	3.5%	—	—

2018 Year-End Financials

Return on assets: 9.7%
Return on equity: 14.5%
Current ratio: 2.10
Cash ($ mil.): 71

DEER PARK REFINING LIMITED PARTNERSHIP

EXECUTIVES

Prin, Bruce A Henderson
Auditors: ERNST & YOUNG LLP HOUSTON TX

LOCATIONS

HQ: DEER PARK REFINING LIMITED PARTNERSHIP
5900 HIGHWAY 225, DEER PARK, TX 775362434
Phone: 713 246-7280
Web: WWW.DEERPARKTX.GOV

HISTORICAL FINANCIALS

Company Type: Private

Income Statement FYE: December 31

	REVENUE ($ mil.)	NET INCOME ($ mil.)	NET PROFIT MARGIN	EMPLOYEES
12/17	867	97	11.2%	3
12/16	897	154	17.2%	—
Annual Growth	(3.3%)	(36.9%)	—	—

2017 Year-End Financials

Return on assets: 4.7%
Return on equity: 6.7%
Current ratio: 1.90
Cash ($ mil.): 77

DEKALB COUNTY BOARD OF EDUCATION

EXECUTIVES

Chm, Michael A Erwin
Vice Chm*, Marshall D Orson
Executive of Information Techn, Will Thomas
Auditors: RUSSELL W HINTON CPA CGFM

LOCATIONS

HQ: DEKALB COUNTY BOARD OF EDUCATION
1701 MOUNTAIN INDUS BLVD, STONE MOUNTAIN, GA 300831027
Phone: 678 676-1200
Web: WWW.DEKALB.K12.GA.US

HISTORICAL FINANCIALS

Company Type: Private

Income Statement FYE: June 30

	REVENUE ($ mil.)	NET INCOME ($ mil.)	NET PROFIT MARGIN	EMPLOYEES
06/07	1,128	350	31.1%	270
06/06	1,055	10	0.9%	—
Annual Growth	7.0%	3405.8%	—	—

2007 Year-End Financials

Return on assets: 22.9%
Return on equity: 33.3%
Current ratio: 3.60
Cash ($ mil.): 116

DEKALB COUNTY PUBLIC LIBRARY

EXECUTIVES

Exec Dir, Darro Willey
Asst Dir*, Mag Dasossa
Library Branch Supervisor, Myguail Chappel
Information Technology Manager, Chris Lee
Executive Director, Joe Davich

Coordinator, Gina Jenkins
Director, Allison Weissinger
Assistant Director, Nancy Wright
Senior Librarian Clarkston Lib, Effie Chisholm
Payroll Personnel Tech Senior, Myra Minor
Program Manager, Aaron Worthy
Auditors: KPMG LLP ATLANTA GA

LOCATIONS

HQ: DEKALB COUNTY PUBLIC LIBRARY
215 SYCAMORE ST FL 4, DECATUR, GA 300303413
Phone: 404 370-3070
Web: WWW.DEKALBLIBRARY.ORG

HISTORICAL FINANCIALS

Company Type: Private

Income Statement — FYE: December 31

	REVENUE ($ mil.)	NET INCOME ($ mil.)	NET PROFIT MARGIN	EMPLOYEES
12/07	622	(124)	—	228
12/06	622	186	30.0%	—
12/05	564	56	10.0%	—
Annual Growth	5.1%	—	—	—

2007 Year-End Financials

Return on assets: (-3.8%)
Return on equity: (-6.5%)
Current ratio: —
Cash ($ mil.): 536

DENNIS K. BURKE INC.

EXECUTIVES

Ceo, Edmund F Burke
Cfo*, Joe Cote
Director of Operations, Dan Hill
Customer, Jenifer Miller
Director, Paul Atkinson
Manager, Shawn Barboza
Auditors: TONNESON & COMPANY INC WAKE

LOCATIONS

HQ: DENNIS K. BURKE INC.
555 CONSTITUTION DR, TAUNTON, MA 027807365
Phone: 617 884-7800
Web: WWW.BURKEOIL.COM

HISTORICAL FINANCIALS

Company Type: Private

Income Statement — FYE: April 30

	REVENUE ($ mil.)	NET INCOME ($ mil.)	NET PROFIT MARGIN	EMPLOYEES
04/12	929	3	0.3%	110
04/11	807	0	0.1%	—
04/10	2,050	0	—	—
Annual Growth	—25724.5%	—	—	—

2012 Year-End Financials

Return on assets: 5.3%
Return on equity: 21.3%
Current ratio: 1.20
Cash ($ mil.): 1

DENVER HEALTH AND HOSPITALS AUTHORITY INC

When you live a mile high you sometimes need a safety net; that's where Denver Health and Hospital Authority comes in. Though it serves all the people of Colorado's capital annually attending to a fourth of the city's population and a third of its children Denver Health is also the "safety net" care provider for the city's indigent uninsured mentally ill and other high-risk patients. The medical system's primary facility is the Denver Health Medical Center a 525-bed hospital offering care in more than 50 medical specialties that also houses a regional trauma center. It also includes a network of family health and dental clinics; a poison and drug center; and a 911 response system for Denver County.

Operations

Denver Health's principal facility Denver Health Medical Center is a teaching hospital affiliated with the University of Colorado at Denver and is one of the busiest medical centers in the state. The trauma center (known as Rocky Mountain Regional Trauma Center) has Level I status and is known for having one of the highest survival rates in the nation. In addition the hospital operates an ambulance service a pediatric emergency center and a terrorism and catastrophe response center. Denver Health operates Denver's 911 medical emergency response system. Annually Denver Health paramedics respond to about 90000 calls for emergency medical assistance and transport more than 61000 patients to 11 area hospitals.

The health system provides medical care at 16 K-12 school-based health centers as well as eight family health centers located throughout the city. It also runs a number of public health clinics that offer immunizations infectious disease treatment detoxification and behavioral health consultation.

Denver Health cares for some 66000 children each year. In 2013 the system delivered 3175 babies and reported 55511 emergency department visits.

Financial Performance

Denver Health's revenue increased 7% to $793 million in 2013 due to an increase in net patient service revenue as well as safety net reimbursements and government grants. The number of uninsured patients has fallen dramatically under the Affordable Care Act which has helped the system improve its earnings. However the company reported a net loss of $15 million as non-operating revenue declined and fair value of investments fell.

Strategy

Denver Health integrates acute hospital and emergency care with public and community health offerings to deliver preventive primary and acute care services.

The health system's health plan covers 17000 city and hospital employees members of Medicaid's child plan and Medicare and another 53000 Medicaid patients. It expects to serve 40000 new Medicaid customers over the next few years as a result of the 2014 Affordable Care Act including about 15000 the hospital already sees without any payment.

In 2014 the company opened the Lowry Family Health Center adding new exam rooms to its operations. It also opened a new dental clinic and Women Infants and Children (WIC) office location.

Company Background

Denver Health traces its beginnings back to territorial days in 1860. As Denver General Hospital it operated as an agency of Denver's city and county governments until 1997 when it became a freestanding authority.

Denver Health's flagship medical center joined forces with Children's Hospital Colorado in late 2010 to share best practices and resources to expand and improve pediatric care throughout the region. Through the collaboration the two have increased access to pediatric mental health services; they also coordinate recruitment and sharing of highly specialized pediatric providers.

EXECUTIVES

Coo, Stephanie Thomas
Ceo, Arthur A. Gonzalez
Chief Nursing Officer, Kathy Boyle
Cfo, Peg Burnette
Director Rocky Mountain Poison And Drug Center, Richard C. Dart
Chief Medical Officer, Phillip S. Mehler
Executive Director Denver Health Foundation, Paula Herzmark
Director Of Nursing, Keith Moorhead
Nursing Director, Nicole Stafford
Medical Director, Jeanne Rozwadowski
Respiratory Therapy Director, Andrea Ellis
Vice President, Christy Allen
Pharmacy Manager, Renee Toner
Pharmacy Manager, Bob Wilson
Second Vice Chairman, Hubert A. Farbes
Chair, Caz Matthews
Vice Chair, Rus Heise

LOCATIONS

HQ: DENVER HEALTH AND HOSPITALS AUTHORITY INC
777 BANNOCK ST, DENVER, CO 802044597
Phone: 720 956-2580
Web: WWW.DENVERHEALTH.ORG

PRODUCTS/OPERATIONS

2013 Sales

	$ mil.	% of total
Net patient service	368	46
Captation earned net of reinsurance expense	129	16
Medicaid disproportionate share & other safety net reimbursements	125	16
Federal state & other grants	71	9
Others	98	13
Total	**793**	**100**

Selected Medical Centers Clinics and Affiliates

Denver Emergency Center for Children
Denver Health Dental Care Clinics
Denver Health Medical Center
Denver Health Medical Plan (for Denver Health employees)
Denver Health Primary Care Clinics
Denver Paramedics
Denver Public Health
Rocky Mountain Center for Medical Response to Terrorism Mass Casualties and Epidemics
Rocky Mountain Poison & Drug Center
Rocky Mountain Regional Trauma Center

COMPETITORS

Banner Health
Catholic Health Initiatives
Centura Health
Children's Hospital Colorado
Exempla Healthcare
HealthONE
Porter Adventist Hospital
Rose Medical Center
University of Colorado Hospital

HISTORICAL FINANCIALS

Company Type: Private

Income Statement — FYE: December 31

	REVENUE ($ mil.)	NET INCOME ($ mil.)	NET PROFIT MARGIN	EMPLOYEES
12/19	1,111	127	11.4%	3,541
12/18	1,119	62	5.6%	—
12/17	1,056	14	1.3%	—
12/16	505	(6)	—	—
Annual Growth	30.0%	—	—	—

2019 Year-End Financials

Return on assets: 10.1%
Cash ($ mil.): 63
Return on equity: 23.2%
Current ratio: 1.30

DESAROLLADORA DEL NORTE S E

EXECUTIVES

Pres, Gabriel Escarrer
V Pres of Devel, Edgar Motta
Buyer, Luis Molina

LOCATIONS

HQ: DESAROLLADORA DEL NORTE S E
200 COCO BCH BL HWY 955, RIO GRANDE, PR 00745
Phone: 787 657-1026

HISTORICAL FINANCIALS

Company Type: Private

Income Statement — FYE: December 31

	REVENUE ($ mil.)	NET INCOME ($ mil.)	NET PROFIT MARGIN	EMPLOYEES
12/16	1,801	102	5.7%	500
12/15	1,738	0	—	—
Annual Growth	3.7%	—	—	—

2016 Year-End Financials

Return on assets: 3.1%
Cash ($ mil.): 366
Return on equity: 6.6%
Current ratio: 0.90

DETROIT WAYNE MENTAL HEALTH AUTHORITY

EXECUTIVES

Ceo, Thomas Watkins
Trainer, Marsha Adams
MA Ba Customer Member, Michael Shaw
Paralegal, Ranae Collins
Assistant To Chief Operati, Sonya Davis
Business Analyst, Steve Jamison
Department Manager Quality Man, April Siebert
Sud Initiatives Prevention Man, Karra Thomas
Children's Initiatives Coordin, Monica Hampton
Deputy Chief Information Offic, Nasr Doss

LOCATIONS

HQ: DETROIT WAYNE MENTAL HEALTH AUTHORITY
707 W MILWAUKEE ST, DETROIT, MI 482022943
Phone: 313 833-2500
Web: WWW.DWMHA.COM

HISTORICAL FINANCIALS

Company Type: Private

Income Statement — FYE: September 30

	REVENUE ($ mil.)	NET INCOME ($ mil.)	NET PROFIT MARGIN	EMPLOYEES
09/16	736	4	0.6%	99
09/15	701	19	2.8%	—
Annual Growth	5.0%	(77.0%)	—	—

2016 Year-End Financials

Return on assets: 2.1%
Cash ($ mil.): 176
Return on equity: 4.7%
Current ratio: 1.70

DEVCON CONSTRUCTION INCORPORATED

Devcon Construction has built a sturdy business from building in the Bay Area. One of the area's top general building contractors Devcon has constructed more than 30 million sq. ft. of office industrial and commercial space. Its focus is on Northern California mainly in the San Francisco Bay Area and Silicon Valley. The company provides engineering design/build and interior design services. It specializes in high-tech projects including data centers and industrial research and development facilities. In addition to building company facilities and offices Devcon works on such projects as hotels restaurants parking structures retail stores sports facilities and schools.

Geographic Reach

Based in Milpitas California Devcon maintains several satellite offices in California in Petaluma Stockton and Santa Cruz as well as an office in Reno Nevada.

Strategy

Although most of Devcon's work is in California the company also has completed projects in Nevada Oregon Idaho Texas Massachusetts and Florida. Recent projects in the San Francisco Forty Niners Stadium in Santa Clara San Jose Sharks Ice Center in Pleasanton and the Stanford Research Computing Facility.

The company partnered with US-based Central Concrete in 2012 to supply its high-performing low-CO2 concrete for the new San Francisco 49er Stadium. The move showcases Devcon's focus on sustainability as part of its projects.

EXECUTIVES

Vice President, Andy Schatzman
Vice President Of Construction, Jonathan Harvey
Vice President Of Construction, Daisy Pereira
Auditors: JOHANSON & YAU ACCOUNTANCY COR

LOCATIONS

HQ: DEVCON CONSTRUCTION INCORPORATED
690 GIBRALTAR DR, MILPITAS, CA 950356317
Phone: 408 942-8200
Web: WWW.DEVCON-CONST.COM

PRODUCTS/OPERATIONS

Selected Projects

Anderson Collection At Stanford University Stanford
Barnes & Nobles Palo Alto
Cisco Parking Structure 1 San Jose
Cisco Parking Structure 2 San Jose
Downtown Sunnyvale Town Center Sunnyvale
El Camino Family Housing South San Francisco
Fresno Hyatt Place Hotel Fresno
Friedenrich Center For Translational Research At 800 Welch Road
Lawson Lane East - Buildings A & B Santa Clara
Oakland Air Traffic Control Tower (ATCT) Oakland
San Francisco 49ers Stadium Santa Clara
San Jose Earthquakes - MLS Soccer Stadium San Jose
SanDisk Milpitas
Santa Clara University Admissions & Enrollment Services Building Santa Clara
Sharks Ice Center Pleasanton
Stanford Research Computing Facility Stanford
The Plaza At Triton Park Foster City
University Plaza Palo Alto
Villa Siena Nursing Care Units Mountain View

COMPETITORS

Charles Pankow Builders
DPR Construction
Hathaway Dinwiddie Construction
Hensel Phelps Construction
KPRS Construction
Obayashi
Rudolph & Sletten
Structure Tone
Swinerton
Turner Corporation
Webcor Builders

HISTORICAL FINANCIALS

Company Type: Private

Income Statement — FYE: December 31

	REVENUE ($ mil.)	NET INCOME ($ mil.)	NET PROFIT MARGIN	EMPLOYEES
12/15	1,224	14	1.2%	350
12/14	1,181	20	1.7%	—
12/13	1,012	12	1.2%	—
12/12	779	3	0.5%	—
Annual Growth	16.3%	60.4%	—	—

2015 Year-End Financials

Return on assets: 4.7%
Cash ($ mil.): 7
Return on equity: 38.2%
Current ratio: 1.10

DHPC TECHNOLOGIES, INC.

EXECUTIVES

Ceo-Pres, John M Curtis
Director, Robert Lake
Engineer, Tom Tokash
Senior Consultant, Dan Glasel
Engineer, Kevin Sullivan
Associate, David Gandarillas
Chief Scientist, Frank Barone
Contracts Manager, Natalya Gnyp
Training Manager, Susan Missenheim
Electrical Engineer, Jenny Maung
Software Engineer, John Morgan

LOCATIONS

HQ: DHPC TECHNOLOGIES, INC.
10 WODBRDGE CTR DR STE 65, WOODBRIDGE, NJ 07095
Phone: 732 791-5400
Web: WWW.DHPCTECH.COM

HISTORICAL FINANCIALS

Company Type: Private

Income Statement FYE: May 11

	REVENUE ($ mil.)	NET INCOME ($ mil.)	NET PROFIT MARGIN	EMPLOYEES
05/17*	38,584	1,320	3.4%	150
12/09	11	1	9.0%	—
12/07	6	1	29.2%	—
06/06	1,726	0	0.0%	—
Annual Growth	32.6%	179.9%	—	—

*Fiscal year change

2017 Year-End Financials

Return on assets: 14.5%
Return on equity: 21.9%
Current ratio: 2.80
Cash ($ mil.): 2,039

DIALYSIS CLINIC, INC.

Dialysis Clinic Inc. or DCI is dedicated to caring for patients with end-stage renal disease (ESRD). The not-for-profit company which operates a network of more than 210 dialysis centers serving more than 14000 patients in 27 states also provides kidney transplant assistance services. Affiliate DCI Donor Services is an organ and tissue procurement agency. DCI also funds kidney-related research and educational programs and is affiliated with various universities and teaching hospitals throughout the US including Tufts University the University of Arizona and Tulane University.

Geographic Reach

The company has its locations in Alabama Arizona Arkansas California Colorado Connecticut Florida Georgia Indiana Iowa Kentucky Louisiana Maine Massachusetts Missouri Montana Nebraska Nevada New Jersey New Mexico New York North Carolina Ohio Pennsylvania South Carolina Tennessee and Texas.

Strategy

DCI grows its network of facilities by forming partnerships with health care providers and other organizations. The company provides funding for construction and operation of the facility and it provides clinic support services including supply procurement and central laboratory services (through its DCI Lab subsidiary).

In 2012 the company opened a dialysis clinic in Albuquerque its first dialysis clinic in the South Valley region of New Mexico.

Company Background

DCI was established in 1971 by nephrologist Keith Johnson.

EXECUTIVES

Chb, H Keith Johnson
Dir*, James Perry
Pres*, Ed Attrill
SEC-Treas*, William Wood
Attorney, Karin A Barrett
Nurse Manage, Debra Breault
Nurse Manage, Kimberly Kale
Director of Corporate, Hal Whetstone
Accounts Receivable Specialist, Allison Discello
Controller, Andy Parker
Care Coordinator, Angela Tillotson
Auditors: DELOITTE & TOUCHE LLP NASHVIL

LOCATIONS

HQ: DIALYSIS CLINIC, INC.
1633 CHURCH ST STE 500, NASHVILLE, TN 372032948
Phone: 615 327-3061
Web: WWW.DCIINC.ORG

COMPETITORS

DaVita
FMCNA
Fresenius
Renal Advantage
U.S. Renal Care

HISTORICAL FINANCIALS

Company Type: Private

Income Statement FYE: September 30

	REVENUE ($ mil.)	NET INCOME ($ mil.)	NET PROFIT MARGIN	EMPLOYEES
09/18	760	5	0.7%	5,000
09/17	736	23	3.3%	—
09/16	719	22	3.2%	—
09/15	712	29	4.1%	—
Annual Growth	2.2%	(42.5%)	—	—

2018 Year-End Financials

Return on assets: 0.7%
Return on equity: 0.9%
Current ratio: 3.40
Cash ($ mil.): 135

DIGNITY HEALTH

Dignity Health has steadily grown to become the hospital provider in the state of California and the fifth-largest health system in the US. The not-for-profit health care provider operates a network of more than 40 cute care hospitals and 400-plus care-centers including neighborhood hospitals urgent care surgery and imaging centers home health and primary care clinics located in California Arizona and Nevada. Dignity Health is the official health care provider of the San Francisco Giants. It has more than 10000 active physicians. In 2019 Dignity Health merged with Denver-based hospital group Catholic Health Initiatives to create CommonSpirit Health the largest not-for-profit health system in the US.

Operations

Dignity Health offers inpatient outpatient subacute and home health care services as well as physician services through affiliates including Dignity Health Medical Foundation. Through another affiliate U.S. HealthWorks Dignity Health provides occupational health and urgent care services in about 20 additional states.

Geographic Reach

Dignity Health operates some 40 hospitals urgent care centers clinics emergency rooms and specialty care centers in California Nevada and Arizona. It has more than 65 facilities in California approximately 15 in Arizona and less than 5 in Nevada. Its headquarters is located in San Francisco California.

Sales and Marketing

Dignity Health serves all communities with physical mental and spiritual needs.

Strategy

Although Dignity Health combined with Catholic Health Initiatives in 2019 to become part of the larger CommonSpirit Health system it continues to pursue its own strategic goals. Those include improving quality of care in a just work environment implementing clinical and administrative changes to cut costs and expanding operations in existing markets and new markets.

Mergers and Acquisitions

After years of discussions Dignity Health and Catholic Health Initiatives merged in early 2019. The combined health system named CommonSpirit Health and with more than 140 hospitals in nearly 20 states is the largest not-for-profit hospital system in the US. The size of the new system allows it to provide expanded care to patients through such methods as virtual appointments a broader range of clinical programs and advanced technologies. The new organization is headquartered in Chicago. The group's hospitals continue to operate under their existing names.

Company Background

Dignity Health traces its roots to 1857. The Sisters of Mercy Catholic order was established in Dublin in 1831. In the 1850s eight Sisters arrived in San Francisco and began caring for residents with cholera typhoid and influenza. They established St. Mary's Hospital now that city's oldest continuously operating hospital. The order merged operations with another community of Sisters of Mercy in 1986 to create Catholic Healthcare West. The combined system had one retirement home and 10 hospitals throughout California.

The system changed its name to Dignity Health in early 2012 as part of a governance restructuring program. While the firm remained a not-for-profit organization with Catholic roots and its Catholic hospitals continued to be sponsored by their founding congregations (and governed by the Catholic health care directives) the parent organization itself was no longer an official ministry of the Catholic church. In 2019 Dignity Health joined forces with Catholic Health Initiatives to create CommonSpirit Health the nation's largest not-for-profit health system.

HISTORY

Dignity Health formerly Catholic Healthcare West (CHW) traces its roots to 1857 when the Sisters of Mercy founded St. Mary's Hospital in San Francisco. The order expanded in that area and in 1986 two different communities of the Sisters of Mercy merged their hospitals into an organization with one retirement home and 10 hospitals from the Bay Area to San Diego. Declining membership in Roman Catholic religious orders combined with consolidation in the field led the orders to see merger as their only route to survival.

CHW continued to add facilities including AMI Community Hospital in Santa Cruz California in 1990. Since CHW already owned the area's only other acute care hospital Dominican Santa Cruz Hospital CHW in 1993 was ordered not to acquire any more acute care hospitals in Santa Cruz County without FTC approval.

As the trend to managed care became a stampede in the 1990s CHW moved more into preventive care and began reigning in costs through productivity improvement plans. It continued to add hospitals including tax-supported institutions trying to compete with national for-profit systems.

The network increased its medical clout in 1994 by allying with San Diego-based Scripps one of the state's largest HMO systems. In 1995 the Daughters of Charity Province of the West realigned its six-hospital operation with CHW. The next year the Dominican Sisters (California) the Dominican Sisters of St. Catherine of Siena (Wisconsin) and the Sisters of Charity of the Incarnate Word allied their California hospitals with CHW. New community hospitals included Bakersfield Memorial Sierra Nevada Memorial (Grass Valley) Sequoia Hospital (Redwood City) and Woodland Healthcare.

Charity and cost-consciousness clashed in 1996 when union members staged a walkout to protest nonunion outsourcing of vocational nursing housekeeping and kitchen jobs. This dispute was settled but CHW continued to be a target for union organizers with a bitter battle against the Service Employees International Union (SEIU) starting in 1998.

The year 2000 brought CHW more problems with labor relations: SEIU argued that the organization was resistant to unionization. Continued losses led the organization to implement major restructuring the following year as its 10 regional divisions were consolidated into four.

The company parted ways with one of its sponsoring organizations the Franciscan Sisters of the Sacred Heart of Frankfort Illinois in 2003. The sponsorship ended when CHW closed St. Francis Medical Center of Santa Barbara. However the hospital operator that fiscal year posted its first operating profit in seven years.

The company changed its name from Catholic Healthcare West (CHW) to Dignity Health in early 2012 as part of a governance restructuring program. While the firm remained a not-for-profit organization with Catholic roots and its Catholic hospitals continued to be sponsored by their founding congregations (and governed by the Catholic health care directives) the parent organization itself was no longer an official ministry of the Catholic church.

The company's rebranding and restructuring aimed to give it more flexibility to pursue its growth strategy of widening its presence into additional regions of the US while lowering the overall cost of care (a desire of most large hospital operators as the US government works to reform its ailing health system). At the time of the governance shift Dignity Health operated 25 Catholic hospitals and 15 non-Catholic hospitals.

EXECUTIVES

Evp Sponsorship Mission Integration And Philanthropy, Bernita McTernan
President And Ceo, Lloyd H. Dean
Evp And Chief Human Resources Officer, Darryl L. Robinson
Evp And Chief Administrative Officer, Elizabeth Shih
Sevp And Coo, Marvin O'Quinn
Sevp And Cfo, Daniel J. Morissette
Sevp And Chief Strategy Officer, Charles P. Francis
Evp And Cio, Deanna L. Wise
Evp And Chief Medical Officer, Robert L. Wiebe
Evp And General Counsel, Rick Grossman
Evp Sponsorship And Mission Integration, Elizabeth Keith
Medical Director Health Informatics, David Camitta
Director Of Him, Swaran Dwarka
Senior Vice President And Chief Strategy Officer, Charlie Francis
Vice President Human Resources Southern California West Service Area, Ed Gonzales
Vice President Ambulatory Services, Margie Roper
Senior Vice President Of Philanthropy, Fred Najjar
Director Of Radiology, Richard Siegel
Senior Vice President Of Operations For Greater Sacramento Area, Laurie Harting
Vice President Strategy And Business Development, Susan Macmillan
Director Of Pharmacy, Jason Glick
Vice President Employee And Labor Relations, Scott Fuller
Medical Director, Christina Kwasnica
Senior Vice President Of Operations For Bay Area Service Area, Todd Strumwasser
Medical Director, Javier Cardenas
Vice President Of Philanthropy, Jessa Brooks
Chairman, Caretha Coleman
Vice Chair, Judy Carle
Auditors: DELOITTE & TOUCHE LLP SAN FRA

LOCATIONS

HQ: DIGNITY HEALTH
185 BERRY ST STE 300, SAN FRANCISCO, CA 941071773
Phone: 415 438-5500
Web: WWW.DIGNITYHEALTH.ORG

Selected Facilities

Arizona
Barrow Neurological Institute (Phoenix)
Chandler Regional Medical Center
Mercy Gilbert Medical Center
St. Joseph's Hospital and Medical Center (Phoenix)
California
Arroyo Grande Community Hospital
Bakersfield Memorial Hospital
California Hospital Medical Center (Los Angeles)
Community Hospital of San Bernardino
Dominican Hospital (Santa Cruz)
French Hospital Medical Center (San Luis Obispo)
Glendale Memorial Hospital and Health Center
Marian Medical Center (Santa Maria)
Mark Twain St. Joseph's Hospital (San Andreas)
Mercy General Hospital (Sacramento)
Mercy Hospital of Bakersfield
Mercy Hospital of Folsom
Mercy Medical Center Merced Community Campus
Mercy Medical Center Merced Dominican Campus
Mercy Medical Center Mt. Shasta
Mercy Medical Center Redding
Mercy San Juan Medical Center (Carmichael)
Mercy Southwest Hospital (Bakersfield)
Methodist Hospital of Sacramento
Northridge Hospital Medical Center
Oak Valley Hospital (Oakdale)
Saint Francis Memorial Hospital (San Francisco)
Sequoia Hospital (Redwood City)
Sierra Nevada Memorial Hospital (Grass Valley)
St. Bernardine Medical Center (San Bernardino)
St. Elizabeth Community Hospital (Red Bluff)
St. John's Pleasant Valley Hospital (Camarillo)
St. John's Regional Medical Center (Oxnard)
St. Joseph's Behavioral Health Center (Stockton)
St. Joseph's Medical Center (Stockton)
St. Mary Medical Center (Long Beach)
St. Mary's Medical Center (San Francisco)
Woodland Healthcare
Nevada
St. Rose Dominican Hospital Rose de Lima Campus (Henderson)
St. Rose Dominican Hospital San Martí;n Campus (Las Vegas)
St. Rose Dominican Hospital Siena Campus (Henderson)

PRODUCTS/OPERATIONS

Sponsoring Organizations

Congregation of the Dominican Sisters of St. Catherine of Siena of Kenosha (Kenosha Wisconsin)
Congregation of the Sisters of Charity of the Incarnate Word (Houston Texas)
Sisters of Mercy of the Americas West Midwest Community (Omaha Nebraska; formerly Auburn Regional Community of the Sisters of Mercy and Burlingame Regional Community of the Sisters of Mercy in California)
Sisters of St. Dominic Congregation of the Most Holy Rosary (Adrian Michigan)
Sisters of St. Francis of Penance and Christian Charity St. Francis Province (Redwood City California)
Sisters of the Third Order of St. Dominic Congregation of the Most Holy Name (San Rafael California)

COMPETITORS

Adventist Health System West
Banner Health
Community Health Systems
Community Hospital of the Monterey Peninsula
Ensign Group
HCA
John C. Lincoln Health Network
John Muir Health
Loma Linda University Medical Center
Memorial Health Services
Prospect Medical
Providence St. Joseph Health
Salinas Valley Memorial
Shasta Regional Medical Center
Stanford Health Care
Sutter Health
Tenet Healthcare
UCSF Medical
Universal Health Services
VITAS Healthcare

HISTORICAL FINANCIALS

Company Type: Private

Income Statement — FYE: June 30

	REVENUE ($ mil.)	NET INCOME ($ mil.)	NET PROFIT MARGIN	EMPLOYEES
06/09	8,957	(799)	—	55,494
06/08	8,401	169	2.0%	—
Annual Growth	6.6%	—	—	—

2009 Year-End Financials

Return on assets: (-7.2%)
Return on equity: (-22.6%)
Current ratio: 1.50
Cash ($ mil.): 868

DIGNITY HEALTH MEDICAL FOUNDATION

EXECUTIVES

Pres, Laurie Schwarctz
Cfo*, Theresa Hylen
Coordinator, Leticia Mendoza
Clinic Manager, Isabel Reyes
Clinical Pharmacist Utilizatio, Jonathan Miano
Financial Analyst, Sonja Greene
Director, Steve Scharmann
Telehealth Coordinator, Harinder Buttar
Senior Counsel, Kelley Evans
Area Manager, Osa Aimufua
Senior Recruiter, Yvette Thompson
Auditors: KPMG LLP SAN FRANCISCO CA

LOCATIONS

HQ: DIGNITY HEALTH MEDICAL FOUNDATION
3400 DATA DR, RANCHO CORDOVA, CA 956707956
Phone: 916 379-2840

HISTORICAL FINANCIALS

Company Type: Private

Income Statement — FYE: June 30

	REVENUE ($ mil.)	NET INCOME ($ mil.)	NET PROFIT MARGIN	EMPLOYEES
06/14	570	17	3.1%	1,000
06/09	297	0	0.1%	—
Annual Growth	13.9%	120.7%	—	—

2014 Year-End Financials

Return on assets: 9.4%
Return on equity: 19.7%
Current ratio: 1.40
Cash ($ mil.): 31

DISTRICT OF COLUMBIA WATER & SEWER AUTHORITY

EXECUTIVES

Ceo, George Hawkins
Customer Manager, Donna Lewis
Senior Network Administrator, Joe Edwards
Director, Teresa Scott
Counsel, Meena Gowda
Executive Assistant, Deborah Cole
Assistant Facilities Manager, Quintin Wilkinson
Director Technical, Leonard Benson
Mechanical Manager, Carlos Almeida
Computer Specialist, Rhonda Green
Green Infrastructure Assistant, Seth Charde

LOCATIONS

HQ: DISTRICT OF COLUMBIA WATER & SEWER AUTHORITY
5000 OVERLOOK AVE SW, WASHINGTON, DC 200325212
Phone: 202 787-2000
Web: WWW.DCWATER.COM

HISTORICAL FINANCIALS

Company Type: Private

Income Statement — FYE: September 30

	REVENUE ($ mil.)	NET INCOME ($ mil.)	NET PROFIT MARGIN	EMPLOYEES
09/19	705	165	23.4%	1,100
09/17	643	194	30.2%	—
Annual Growth	4.7%	(7.8%)	—	—

2019 Year-End Financials

Return on assets: 2.1%
Return on equity: 7.3%
Current ratio: 1.40
Cash ($ mil.): 144

DITECH HOLDING CORPORATION

Walter Investment Management does its best to collect from the credit-challenged. The firm owns and services residential mortgages (particularly those of the subprime and nonconforming variety) for itself as well as for government sponsored entities government agencies third-party securitization trusts and other credit owners. Operating through subsidiaries Walter Mortgage Company; Hanover Capital; Marix Servicing; Ditech; and third-party credit servicer Green Tree Walter Investment Management services 2 million residential loan accounts with unpaid balances of $256 billion making it one of the 10 largest mortgage servicers in the US. The firm also originates residential loans including reverse loans.The firm filed for Chapter 11 bankruptcy in 2017 and is expected to emerged from it less $800 million in debt overhang in early 2018.

Operations

Walter Investment Management operates three main business segments. Its Servicing segment which generates more than 50% of Walter's revenue mostly services mortgage loans for third-party creditors and its own mortgage loan portfolio on a fee-for-service basis. Following the simplification of its business in 2015 the segment also consists of an insurance agency serving residential loan borrowers and credit owners and a collections agency that performs collections of post charge-off deficiency balances for third parties and Walter's own portfolio. It also holds the assets and mortgage-backed debt of the Residual Trusts.

As one of the US' top 20 largest mortgage loan originators Walter's Origination segment (32% of revenue) purchases and originates mortgage loans that are sold to third parties with servicing rights generally retained. The Reverse Mortgage segment (10% of revenue) purchases and originates securitized loans backed by secured borrowings services loans for third-party credit owners and its portfolio and also provides complementary reverse mortgage services like property management and dispositions.

Geographic Reach

The Tampa-based firm has offices across the US.

Sales and Marketing

Walter's origination business sells nearly all of its mortgage loans into the secondary market for securitization or private investors as whole loans. It sells conventional conforming and government-backed mortgage loans through agency-sponsored securitizations where mortgage-backed securities are made and sold to third-party investors. Its non-conforming mortgage loans are sold to private investors.

The firm's consumer direct retail channel originates reverse loans through call centers and purchases leads from lead purveyors or through advertising campaigns. The wholesale channel sources reverse loans from a broker network. The correspondent channel buys reverse loans from a correspondents network in the marketplace.

Financial Performance

Walter Investment Management's revenues and profits have mostly trended higher over the past few years thanks to regular loan portfolio acquisitions as well as acquisitions of other servicing companies and financial firms.

The firm's revenue reversed course in 2014 however diving 18% to $1.49 billion for the year. Most of the decline came from the Servicing division which suffered from a $278 million decrease in fair value of servicing rights due to market-driven changes. The Origination segment's income fell by 24% on lower loan sales due to a shift in volume from the higher-margin consumer retention channel to the lower-margin correspondent lending channel.

Revenue declines coupled with an $82.3 million- impairment charge caused Walter to suffer a net loss of $110.33 million in 2014. The impairment charge came after an evaluation found its reverse mortgage's goodwill was less than its carrying value. Walter's operations continued to use more cash than it produced — operations used $204 million — though its cash levels improved greatly from the year before as it sold a higher volume of loans in relation to originated loans given the ramp up of its mortgage loan originations business in 2013.

Strategy

Walter Investment hopes to tap into growing demand from big lenders looking to shift their debt servicing functions to outside firms. A rise in borrower delinquencies and foreclosures following the recession has forced traditional loan servicers and owners such as banks to look for third-party assistance. Accordingly part of Walters' growth strategy focuses on acquiring and servicing large loan portfolios that other banks and other financial companies haven't been able to successfully collect on.

The firm also hopes to grow its consumer-facing origination business seeking more cross-sell opportunities as well as opportunities to grow its consumer direct and consumer retail channels to meet demand for low-cost mortgage loans in the market. To this end in 2015 it planned to leverage its well known Ditech brand (while saving $75 million in annual costs) by consolidating its Ditech and Green Tree Servicing into a single company: Ditech a Walter company.

In early 2017 the company agreed to sell Green Tree Insurance Agency to Assurant for $125 million thereby focusing further on its core operations.

Mergers and Acquisitions

In early 2013 in taking advantage of the opportunity to further expand its servicing portfolio Walter closed on two separate purchases (from Bank of America and Residential Capital LLC) of Fannie Mae mortgage serving rights for loans totaling $132 billion in unpaid principal balance.

Also in 2013 Walter Investment Management acquired a $12 billion reverse mortgage servicing portfolio from Wells Fargo. The portfolio with $12.2 billion in unpaid balance houses more than 76000 loans. The portfolio transferred to Walter's wholly-owned subsidiary Reverse Mortgage Solutions and doubled the size of its serviced book.

Company Background

The company entered the reverse mortgage business in late 2012 with the purchase of Reverse Mortgage Solutions (RMS) for some $120 million. RMS provided servicing origination asset management and technology services to the fast-growing reverse mortgage industry.

In 2011 Walter Investment Management increased its loan portfolio and transformed into a fee-based service provider when it paid $1 billion for GTCS Holdings the parent of Green Tree Servicing. As a result Walter Investment Management no longer qualified as a real estate investment trust (REIT). The Green Tree acquisition represented a dramatic increase the size and scope of Walter Investment Management's business. The company's servicing portfolio grew by 50% and nearly 2000 employees were added. Green Tree also increased Walter Investment Management's geographic footprint by adding 27 offices in the US.

Walter Investment Management was created in 2009 when Hanover Capital Mortgage merged with the home financing business of Walter Industries (now Walter Energy). Walter Energy was spun off after the closure of troubled homebuilder Jim Walter Homes.

EXECUTIVES

Chief Legal Officer General Counsel And Secretary, Jonathan F. Pedersen, $444,231 total compensation
President And Ceo, Anthony (Tony) Renzi
Evp And Cfo, Gary L. Tillett, $500,000 total compensation
President Reverse Mortgage Solutions, Christopher J. Mullins
Chairman, George M. Awad

LOCATIONS

HQ: DITECH HOLDING CORPORATION
500 OFFICE CENTER DR # 400, FORT WASHINGTON, PA 190343219
Phone: 844 714-8603
Web: WWW.WALTERINVESTMENT.COM

PRODUCTS/OPERATIONS

2014 Sales

	$ mil.	% of total
Servicing	563	37
Originations	481	32
Reverse Mortage	157	10
ARM	58	4
Insurance	71	5
Loans & Residuals	134	9
Other	41	3
Eliminations	(20.2)	-
Total	**1,487**	**100**

COMPETITORS

Annaly Capital Management
CIFC
Capstead Mortgage
DVL
Drive Shack
FirstCity Financial
Nationstar Mortgage
Ocwen Financial
Redwood Trust
Resource Capital

HISTORICAL FINANCIALS

Company Type: Private

Income Statement FYE: December 31

	REVENUE ($ mil.)	NET INCOME ($ mil.)	NET PROFIT MARGIN	EMPLOYEES
12/18	658	(205)	—	3,800
12/17	831	(426)	—	—
12/16	995	(529)	—	—
12/15	1,274	(263)	—	—
Annual Growth	(19.7%)	—	—	—

2018 Year-End Financials

Return on assets: (-1.8%)
Return on equity: —
Current ratio: —
Cash ($ mil.): 187

DO IT BEST CORP.

Do it Best Corp. is one of the industry's largest hardware cooperatives boasting thousands of member-owned stores in 50-plus countries but primarily the US. Besides hardware and lumber and building materials merchandise includes products and tools needed to tap into the fragmented maintenance repair and operations. Customers also can have products specially shipped to their local stores through Do it Best's web and e-commerce site. From single stores to multiple locations neighborhood hardware stores to regional pro yards and INCOM to e-tailers Do it Best serves as the total solution for thousands of thriving businesses around the globe.

Operations

Do it Best offers a broad range of products (more than 35000 items are available online) across such categories as automotive electrical hardware housewares outdoor living plumbing and storage and organization. Do it Best supplies products and services ? from hardware and lumber and building materials to industrial/commercial supplies ? as efficiently and economically as possible. Its members have access to more than 160 programs and services including Signature Store Design Best Rewards ecommerce planograms sales training and much more. Approximately 125 new brands and about 15 new subcategories were added including quarantine-driven items ? all providing competitive advantages and profits for members. Do it Best had achieved incredible success with about 10% year-over-year increase in warehouse sales record-breaking net profitability and a shareholder rebate of nearly $128.5 million.

Geographic Reach

Based in Fort Wayne Indiana Do it Best has more than 450 international stores across the US as well as in some 50 countries throughout Central and South America the Caribbean and numerous countries in Southeast Asia.

Its warehouses (called Retail Service Centers) are located in Dixon Illinois; Lexington South Carolina; Medina Ohio; Mesquite Nevada; Montgomery New York; Sikeston Missouri; Waco Texas; and Woodburn Oregon.

Sales and Marketing

Do it Best's new Transportation Management System (TMS) enables the company to coordinate hundreds of additional drivers tractors trailers and routes. Serving customers in retail commercial hospitals schools hotels industrial and other small businesses the company's international team has extensive experience working with hundreds of business owners around the world.

Strategy

Do it Best's member-focused approach guides itself at a strategic level. It significantly realigned its field sales teams' roles and responsibilities making it possible to provide members more personal attention and more time to really understand the unique needs of their businesses.

The Do it Best merchandising team works tirelessly in sourcing new products for members especially through the supply chain challenges of 2020. The 125 new brands and 13 new subcategories were added including quarantine-driven items ? all providing competitive advantages and profits for members.

The company analyzes wholesales sales and the purchase of data to develop optimized solutions.

Company Background

Formerly named Hardware Wholesalers Do it Best was founded in 1945 in Fort Wayne Indiana by Arnold Gerberding. The company launched its doitbest.com e-commerce site in 1996.

EXECUTIVES

Vp Finance And Cfo, Doug Roth
Vp Information Technology, Michael J. (Mike) Altendorf
President And Ceo, Daniel B. (Dan) Starr
Vp Marketing, Timothy (Tim) Miller
Vp Merchandising, Steve Markley
Vp Lumber And Building Materials, Gary Nackers
Gm Vice President Business Unit Manager, Dori Meighan
Vice President Information Technology, John Mergy
Vp Of It, Mike Altendorf
National Sales Manager, Rob Schmiedel
Vice President Information Technology, Mike Altenborf
Vice President, Ben Wimsatt
Vice President, George Miller
Vice President Of Human Resources, Ronald Brown
Vice President, Robert Paulson
Vice President, Verlin Pfannenstiel
Vice President, Brian Wolfe
Vice President, Susan Marsh
Vice Chairman, Brad McDaniel
Chairman, John Holmes
Treasurer, Zach Higgins
Secretary, Chris Wolfe
Secretary, Charles Fitzgerald
Auditors: CROWE HORWATH LLP FORT WAYNE

LOCATIONS

HQ: DO IT BEST CORP.
6502 NELSON RD, FORT WAYNE, IN 468031947
Phone: 260 748-5300
Web: WWW.DOITBESTCORP.COM

COMPETITORS

84 Lumber
Ace Hardware
Home Depot
Lowe's
Menard
Northern Tool
Orgill
Sutherland Lumber
True Value
Wal-Mart

HISTORICAL FINANCIALS

Company Type: Private

Income Statement FYE: June 25

	REVENUE ($ mil.)	NET INCOME ($ mil.)	NET PROFIT MARGIN	EMPLOYEES
06/16	2,925	0	0.0%	1,519
06/11	2,328	0	0.0%	—
06/10	2,296	0	0.0%	—
Annual Growth	4.1%	(5.7%)	—	—

2016 Year-End Financials

Return on assets: 0.1%
Return on equity: 0.2%
Current ratio: 1.40
Cash ($ mil.): 20

DOCTOR'S ASSOCIATES INC.

Doctor's Associates owns the Subway chain of sandwich shops the world's largest quick-service restaurant chain by number of locations surpassing burger giant McDonald's. The company boasts more than 44000 restaurants in greater than 110 countries. Virtually all Subway restaurants are franchised and offer such fare as hot and cold sub sandwiches turkey wraps and salads. The widely recognized eateries are in freestanding buildings as well as in airports convenience stores sports facilities and other locations.

Strategy

The Subway chain has tapped into the health food and weight loss zeitgeist in the US prominently featuring in its advertising Jared Fogle a man who famously lost nearly 250 lbs. by switching to a Subway sandwich diet. The chain continues to tout the health benefits of its sandwiches over traditional burgers and fries by introducing new low-fat menu items.

Subway has been developing an upscale concept called Subway Café. The new format conceived for office buildings and other high-end locations is larger than the average Subway restaurant and features coffee espresso lattes and hot chocolate along with an expanded breakfast menu.

The company also seeks partnerships with other food brands to generate buzz around its products. In 2019 the company partnered with Halo Top Creamery to introduce Halo Top milkshakes at almost 1000 Subway restaurants. That year it also collaborated with Hubert's Lemonade to offer the company's drinks at its locations. The company also began testing a Kings Hawaiian-branded bread offering at three cities.

The company is investing in improving the look of its operations. It has remodeled nearly 1400 franchise locations and has around 900 remodels underway. In 2019 Subway announced a grant program that will cover 25% of remodeling costs for more than 10500 restaurants.

Company Background

Co-founders DeLuca and Buck opened the first Subway in 1965.

HISTORY

In 1965 17-year-old Fred DeLuca dreamed of becoming a doctor while working as a stock boy in a Bridgeport Connecticut hardware store to earn college tuition. It wasn't enough so he cornered family friend Peter Buck at a backyard barbecue and asked for advice. Buck a nuclear physicist suggested DeLuca open a submarine sandwich shop and put up $1000 to get him started.

As the summer of 1965 was coming to an end DeLuca rented a small location in a remote area of Bridgeport opened Pete's Super Submarines and there he sold foot-long sandwiches. On the first day the sandwiches were so popular that DeLuca hired his own customers to work behind the counter; by the end of the day he had sold out of all his supplies. The sandwiches continued to be popular for a while but within a few months the shop started losing money and DeLuca and Buck found that selling submarine sandwiches was a seasonal business. They decided they could create an illusion of success by opening a second location and then a third. The third store was finally successful partly because of its more visible location and increased marketing and partly because of a new name – Subway.

DeLuca and Buck had set a goal of 32 shops opened by 1975 but they had only 16 by 1974. They realized that the only way they could reach their goal in one year was to license the Subway name. The first franchise opened that year in Wallingford Connecticut and they opened 32 by the end of 1975. The partners hit 100 by 1978 then 200 by 1983 and DeLuca set a new goal: 5000 Subway shops by 1994. The first international Subway opened in Bahrain in 1984 and DeLuca achieved his goal of 5000 shops by 1990.

During the 1990s DeLuca experimented with several other franchise concepts including We Care Hair (budget styling salons) Cajun Joe's (spicy fried chicken) and Q Burgers. But none of these ventures fared as well as his sandwich empire. As Subway grew however controversy surrounding its treatment of franchisees began to surface. A Federal Trade Commission investigation of the company was dropped in 1993 but Subway continued to battle franchisees complaining about broken contracts market over-saturation (and therefore too much competition and self-cannibalization) and what the franchisees viewed as unreasonably high royalty fees.

In spite of its franchising troubles Subway kept growing. It expanded into Russia and China in the mid-1990s and opened its 11000th restaurant in 1995. In 1997 Subway inked deals with the Army Navy and Air Force exchange services to bring Subway units to military bases. Two years later the company opened its 14000th restaurant in Mount Gambier Australia an event that coincided with Subway's renewed push to expand internationally.

The company got some unexpected publicity in 1999 when 22-year-old Jared Fogle claimed that he dropped 245 pounds from his 425-pound frame by subsisting on a diet of Subway turkey sandwiches. Subway helped Fogle extend his 15 minutes of fame by featuring him and his oversized pants in a TV commercial. (The company has since built an entire campaign around Fogle that features other weight watchers attributing their success to Jared and Subway.) Subway introduced its largest menu initiative ever in 2000 when it unveiled its Subway Selects Gourmet Sandwiches adding 13 items to the menu. In April 2001 the company opened its 15000th store.

Also that year Buck retired as chairman but stayed on as a member of the board of directors. Becoming one of the fastest-growing franchises in the world Subway expanded from 16000 locations in 2002 to more than 22000 stores by the end of 2004.

All US Subway outlets switched from Pepsi to Coke products in 2005. Two years later the chain surpassed 21000 locations in the US.

EXECUTIVES

President, Suzanne Greco
Vice President, Joseph Hofmann
Executive Vice President, Cynthia M Eadie
Vice President, Ruben Ysasi
Vice President Of Human Resources, Doni Pitchford
Vice President, Melodie Rupp
Vice President Business Development, Alejandra Perez
Vice President, Kathy Egbert
Vice President Of Sales, Donald Mckeehan
Vice President, Diane Debiec
Vice President Treasurer, Marianne Hurley
Vice President, Douglas Donaldson
Finance Vice President, Janna Burt
Vice President, Lenore Amschlinger
Pharmacy Manager, Sandy Ritchie
Vice President, Sarah Wade
Vice President, Greg Ramp
Vice President, Carol Lee
Vice President Secretary Treasurer, Tracy Dugdale
Vice President, Glenda David
Vice President, Mohammed Null Abid
Vice President, MATT BARCEY
Vp Of It, Salah Shakir
Vice President, Steven Bates
Vice President, Gerald Bobier
Vice President, Tammy Knoup
Vice President, Bryan Sullivan
Executive Vice President, Ronda Casey
Vice President, Robert Levand
Senior Vice President, Larry Barnette
Secretary, Haydee Buck
Secretary, Connie Arndt
Secretary, Cathy Kroll
Treasurer, William Davidson
Secretary, Laurie Croymans
Secretary, Mary Soud
Secretary, Joy Cassell
Secretary, Mahyar Saii
Secretary Treasurer, Jerry Nelson
Treasurer, Kurt Rothman

LOCATIONS

HQ: DOCTOR'S ASSOCIATES INC.
325 SUB WAY, MILFORD, CT 064613081
Phone: 203 877-4281
Web: WWW.SUBWAY.COM

COMPETITORS

Burger King	Panera Bread
CKE Restaurants	Papa John's
Chick-fil-A	Popeyes
Chipotle	Potbelly Sandwich Shop
Church's Chicken	Quiznos
Dairy Queen	Sonic Corp.
Domino's	Starbucks
Jack in the Box	Tim Hortons
McDonald's	Wendy's
Panda Restaurant Group	YUM!

HISTORICAL FINANCIALS

Company Type: Private

Income Statement FYE: December 31

	REVENUE ($ mil.)	NET INCOME ($ mil.)	NET PROFIT MARGIN	EMPLOYEES
12/10	1,049	7	0.7%	650
12/08	926	6	0.7%	—
12/07	780	5	0.7%	—
Annual Growth	10.4%	9.8%	—	—

2010 Year-End Financials

Return on assets: 6.5%
Return on equity: 49.4%
Current ratio: 1.00
Cash ($ mil.): 43

DOCTORS HOSPITAL AT RENAISSANCE, LTD.

EXECUTIVES

Ceo, Lawrence Gelman
Pres*, Susan Turley
Accounting Staff, Joyce Lustgarten
Vice-President, Patrick Blackwell
Benefit Coordinator, Noel Flores
Clinical Coordinator For Pedia, Andrew Kosko
Chief Technology Officer, James Crouch
Director, Shahbaz Salehi
Rn Bed Board Coordinator, Jan Trevino
Senior Vice President, Bhatt Vadlamani
Director of Security, Frank Nunez

LOCATIONS

HQ: DOCTORS HOSPITAL AT RENAISSANCE, LTD.
5501 S MCCOLL RD, EDINBURG, TX 785395503
Phone: 956 362-8677
Web: WWW.DHR-RGV.COM

HISTORICAL FINANCIALS

Company Type: Private

Income Statement FYE: December 31

	REVENUE ($ mil.)	NET INCOME ($ mil.)	NET PROFIT MARGIN	EMPLOYEES
12/16	580	80	13.9%	176
12/14	436	63	14.4%	—
Annual Growth	15.3%	13.1%	—	—

2016 Year-End Financials

Return on assets: 17.7%
Return on equity: 44.6%
Current ratio: 2.00
Cash ($ mil.): 49

DOCTORS MEDICAL CENTER OF MODESTO, INC.

EXECUTIVES

Ceo, Warren J Kirk
Cfo*, Greg Berry
Manager, Cindy Vingerhoets
Internist, Veronica Ortiz
Clinical Operationws Manager P, Joseph Garcia
Nurse, Linda Hawkins
Chemistry Supervisor, Amandip Mahil
SPD Manager, Anthony Vasquez
Hospitalist, Arun Manoharan
Staff Pharmacist, Berna Hilgers
MD, Edward W Verde

LOCATIONS

HQ: DOCTORS MEDICAL CENTER OF MODESTO, INC.
14201 DALLAS PKWY, DALLAS, TX 752542916
Phone: 209 578-1211
Web: WWW.DMC-MODESTO.COM

HISTORICAL FINANCIALS

Company Type: Private

Income Statement FYE: May 31

	REVENUE ($ mil.)	NET INCOME ($ mil.)	NET PROFIT MARGIN	EMPLOYEES
05/16	587	86	14.6%	2,000
05/09	306	4	1.4%	—
Annual Growth	9.8%	52.8%	—	—

2016 Year-End Financials

Return on assets: 28.1%
Return on equity: 41.1%
Current ratio: 2.30
Cash ($ mil.): —

DON FORD SANDERSON INC

EXECUTIVES

Pres, David Kimmerle
Chb*, La Verne Sanderson
SEC-Treas*, Stephen C Wendt
Prin*, Sandra Sue Kimmerle
Parts Manager, Dave Beard
Sales Associate, Florin Nichitean
Sales Manager, John Pratt
Sales Associate, Scott Sharp
Sales Staff, Steve Haines
Sales Manager, Tony Komadina
Used Vehicle Sales Manager, Mario Fernandez

LOCATIONS

HQ: DON FORD SANDERSON INC
6400 N 51ST AVE, GLENDALE, AZ 853014600
Phone: 623 842-8600
Web: WWW.SANDERSONFORD.COM

HISTORICAL FINANCIALS

Company Type: Private

Income Statement FYE: December 31

	REVENUE ($ mil.)	NET INCOME ($ mil.)	NET PROFIT MARGIN	EMPLOYEES
12/15	679	3	0.5%	416
12/14	671	4	0.7%	—
12/13	692	5	0.8%	—
12/12	590	3	0.6%	—
Annual Growth	4.8%	(3.8%)	—	—

2015 Year-End Financials

Return on assets: 2.7%
Return on equity: 8.9%
Current ratio: 1.40
Cash ($ mil.): 1

DORMITORY AUTHORITY - STATE OF NEW YORK

EXECUTIVES

Pres-Ceo, Reuben McDaniel III
Exec V Pres-Cheif ADM*, Maryanne Gridley
Gen Counsel*, Jeffery Pohl
Cfo*, John G Pasicznyk
Mng Dir Public Fin*, Cheryl Ishmael
Mng Dir Construction*, Douglas Vanvleck
Mng Dir Policy & Prog Dev*, Thomas E Guiley
Deputy Exec Dir*, Micheal Coorigan
Chief of Staff*, Caroline Griffin
Cfo-Treasurer*, Kim Nadeau
Personnel Assistant, Gail Beerle
Auditors: KPMG LLP ALBANY NY

LOCATIONS

HQ: DORMITORY AUTHORITY - STATE OF NEW YORK
515 BROADWAY STE 100, ALBANY, NY 122072964
Phone: 518 257-3000
Web: WWW.DASNY.ORG

HISTORICAL FINANCIALS

Company Type: Private

Income Statement FYE: March 31

	REVENUE ($ mil.)	NET INCOME ($ mil.)	NET PROFIT MARGIN	EMPLOYEES
03/11	2,075	(115)	—	625
03/06	1,693	(40)	—	—
03/05	0	0	—	—
Annual Growth	—	—	—	—

2011 Year-End Financials

Return on assets: (-0.3%)
Return on equity: (-27.6%)
Current ratio: 1.10
Cash ($ mil.): 452

DOUGLAS COUNTY SCHOOL DISTRICT

EXECUTIVES

Pres, David Ray
Supt*, Thomas Tucker
Teacher, Jason Dunkle
Teacher, Jim Dollaghan
Teacher of Cougar Run Elementa, Julie Davidson
Principals Secretary, Liz Thompson
Teacher, Peg Collins
Accounting Specialist, Denise Ruthenbeck
Teacher, Inga McAllen
Teacher Mathematics, Janet Jackson
Art Teacher, Jill Caven

LOCATIONS

HQ: DOUGLAS COUNTY SCHOOL DISTRICT
620 WILCOX ST, CASTLE ROCK, CO 801041730
Phone: 303 387-0100
Web: WWW.COYOTECREEKELEM.COM

HISTORICAL FINANCIALS

Company Type: Private

Income Statement FYE: June 30

	REVENUE ($ mil.)	NET INCOME ($ mil.)	NET PROFIT MARGIN	EMPLOYEES
06/13	562	(0)	—	8,000
06/10	551	(11)	—	—
06/08	480	(48)	—	—
06/07	0	0	—	—
Annual Growth	—	—	—	—

DPR CONSTRUCTION, INC.

From bio labs to wafer fabs DPR Construction runs the gamut for its high-tech and health care clients. The employee-owned firm provides general contracting and construction management services for the advanced technology/mission-critical life sciences health care higher education and corporate office markets. The construction firm specializes in developing retail stores hospitals data centers clean rooms laboratories manufacturing facilities and green buildings. Altogether DPR Construction boasts more than 25 regional offices nationwide. Company head Doug Woods former CEO Peter Nosler and secretary/treasurer Ron Davidowski (the D P and R in DPR Construction) founded the firm in 1990.

Operations

Since its founding the company has completed more than 12000 projects. DPR Construction has expertise in collaborative virtual building and Building Information Modeling (BIM) Integrating Project Delivery (IPD) sustainability preconstruction prefabrication and other niche areas. DPR also has Special Services Group where it focuses on small- to mid-size projects including building core upgrades hospital renovations office reconfigurations roof replacements and site improvements among others.

Geographic Reach

To maintain a presence near customers DPR boasts more than 25 regional offices. Its operations span around 15 states including Arizona California Colorado North Carolina Florida Georgia Maryland Texas Virginia and Washington DC. DPR also includes three international offices located in Netherlands South Korea and Singapore.

Sales and Marketing

DPR serves several core markets including advanced technology corporate offices healthcare higher education and life sciences. Customers have includes Adobe Systems AT&T EVA Airways Baptist Health Medical Center CHRISTUS Health Clif Bar & Company Intuit Facebook and Kaiser Permanente.

Strategy

DPR Construction pushed the envelope of sustainable design in the construction of its new office in Sacramento California in late 2019. DPR transformed an existing building with a material never used in Sacramento for a building's structure. The new DPR office space will house approximately 48 full-time employees with the intention to grow.

Earlier in 2019 DPR also finished the move to a new space of its Austin Texas office. The new office which occupies the third floor of the Foundry at 310 Canal Street was built by DPR employees. Aside from East Austin's growth the thriving entertainment district the eclectic local business and diverse community the Foundry's location offers new proximity to many of its clients partners and projects.

Company Background

Company head Doug Woods former CEO Peter Nosler and secretary/treasurer Ron Davidowski (the D P and R in DPR Construction) founded the firm in 1990 with offices in Redwood City CA and Sacramento CA. In 1993 DPR ranks #1 on both San Francisco Business Times' and San Jose/Silicon Valley Business Journal's Fastest-Growing Private Companies in the bay Area lists.

EXECUTIVES

Management Committee, Jim Dolen
Management Committee, Peter A. Salvati
President, Douglas E. (Doug) Woods
Management Committee, Eric Lamb
Regional Manager Raleigh-durham Nc Office, Mark Whitson
Regional Manager Tampa Fl Office, Page W. McKee
Regional Manager Redwood City, Jody Quinton
Regional Manager Baltimore And Washington Dc, Greg Haldeman
Management Committee, George Pfeffer
Management Committee, Mike Ford
Regional Manager West Palm Beach, Deborah Beetson
Regional Manager Austin And Houston Tx Offices, Gary Nauert
Regional Manager Phoenix, David Elrod
Regional Manager San Diego, Jay Leopold
Regional Manager Sacramento, Mark Cirksena
Regional Manager San Jose, Scott Greubel
Cfo, Michele Leiva
Regional Manager San Francisco, Mike Humphrey
Regional Manager Richmond Va, Lisa Lingerfelt
Regional Manager Atlanta, Russ Brockelbank
Regional Manager Denver Office, Michael Devens
Regional Manager Newport Beach And Pasadena Ca Offices, Dave Seastrom
Regional Manager Orlando Fl Office, Scott Lyons
Vice President Of Operations, Carolyn Hunter
Auditors: PRICEWATERHOUSECOOPERS LLP LO

LOCATIONS

HQ: DPR CONSTRUCTION, INC.
1450 VETERANS BLVD, REDWOOD CITY, CA 940632617
Phone: 650 474-1450
Web: WWW.DPR.COM

Selected Offices

Atlanta
Austin TX
Baltimore
Denver
Houston
Newport Beach CA
Orlando Florida
Pasadena CA
Phoenix
Raleigh-Durham NC
Redwood City CA
Richmond VA
Sacramento CA
San Diego CA
San Francisco CA
San Jose CA
Tampa Florida
Washington DC
West Palm Beach FL

COMPETITORS

Austin Industries
Bechtel
Devcon Construction
Fluor
Hensel Phelps Construction
Hoffman Corporation
Jacobs Engineering
M. A. Mortenson
PC Construction
Skanska USA Building
Swinerton
Turner Corporation
Whiting-Turner

HISTORICAL FINANCIALS

Company Type: Private

Income Statement — FYE: December 31

	REVENUE ($ mil.)	NET INCOME ($ mil.)	NET PROFIT MARGIN	EMPLOYEES
12/08	1,836	68	3.7%	5,785
12/00	1,958	25	1.3%	—
Annual Growth	(0.8%)	13.0%	—	—

2008 Year-End Financials

Return on assets: 13.0%
Return on equity: 37.9%
Current ratio: 1.50
Cash ($ mil.): 162

DRIVETIME AUTOMOTIVE GROUP, INC.

In this story the ugly duckling changes into DriveTime Automotive Group. Formerly known as Ugly Duckling the company is a used-car dealership chain that primarily targets low-income customers and those with less-than-stellar credit. To cater to subprime clients it's a "buy here-pay here" dealer meaning it finances and services car loans rather than using outside lenders. DriveTime operates more than 125 dealerships in 50 US metropolitan areas in 24 mostly southern and western states. The company provides customers with a comprehensive end-to-end solution for their automotive needs including the sale financing and maintenance of their vehicle.

Change in Company Type

The company withdrew its SEC registration in 2014.

Operations

The company's activities includes vehicle acquisition vehicle reconditioning and distribution vehicle sales underwriting and finance loan servicing and after sale support. DriveTime has sold more than 750000 used cars to consumers of all credit types and services a $2 billion loan portfolio.

DriveTime's financing business operates under the name DT Acceptance Corporation. The unit generates about a quarter of the company's total revenues

The company also offers DriveCare a 36-month/36000 miled (5-Year/50000 miled in some states) vehicle protection plan and extended powertrain coverage.

Geographic Reach

Phoenix-based DriveTime operates dealerships in 47 US metro areas throughout 24 states. More than a third of the dealerships are located in Florida and Texas.

Sales and Marketing

DriveTime markets its automotive products and services through TV commercials.

Strategy

DriveTime's long-term strategic goal is to expand its network of dealerships throughout the US targeting metropolitan areas with populations of 500000 to 3 million residents. In 2015 the company opened its first New Jersey location in Williamstown. In 2014 it established its presence in the Chicago area with the opening of the Lombard location; it also opened first location in the Washington DC area.

The used car dealer is also expanding in Texas opening a dealership in Corpus Christi in late 2013 its 20th in the Lone Star State.

As part of its business model DriveTime acquires used vehicles at auction. In 2013 the company purchased more than 96000 vehicles nationwide primarily from used vehicle auctions.

That year DriveTime teamed up with fellow car dealer Manheim to form Go Auto Exchange a new separate and independent wholesale auction company focused on independent dealers and the low-end vehicle segment.

Company venture Carvana (launched in early 2013) allows customers to buy its used cars online. Carvana expands the company's customer base by targeting customers outside its traditional credit-impaired low-income cohort.

Company Background

Chairman Ernest Garcia III owns the company through his Verde Investments firm. In 2012 the company abandoned plans to split its finance and used vehicle retail operations by selling the financing arm to Santander Consumer USA and the used car dealerships to a group of third-party investors. Prior to that DriveTime in early 2010 filed to go public but withdrew the proposed offering seven months later. It with drew a second IPO attempt in 2014.

EXECUTIVES

Prin, Ernest C Garcia II
Exec V Pres*, Jon D Ehlinger
Cfo*, Kurt Wood
Cfo*, Matthew Peel
Dir*, Gregg Tryhuss
Director, William N Plamondon
Corp Liaison, Kimberly Moon
General Manager, Matthew Bergantzel
CIO Cto, Paul Kaplan
Sales Manager, Gary Fuller
Information Technology, Steve Hansman

LOCATIONS

HQ: DRIVETIME AUTOMOTIVE GROUP, INC.
1720 W RIO SALADO PKWY, TEMPE, AZ 852816590
Phone: 602 852-6600
Web: WWW.DRIVETIME.COM

2014 Stores

	No.
Alabama	5
Arkansas	1
Arizona	6
California	5
Colorado	2
Delware	1
Florida	21
Georgia	9
Illinois	2
Indiana	2
Kentucky	2
Maryland	2
Missouri	4
Mississippi	1
North Carolina	9
New Jersey	1
New Mexico	3
Nevada	2
Ohio	7
Oklahoma	3
South Carolina	4
Tennessee	6
Texas	22
Virginia	7
Total	**127**

COMPETITORS

AutoNation
CarMax
Gillman Auto
Gunn Automotive
McCombs Enterprises
Sonic Automotive

HISTORICAL FINANCIALS

Company Type: Private

Income Statement FYE: December 31

	REVENUE ($ mil.)	NET INCOME ($ mil.)	NET PROFIT MARGIN	EMPLOYEES
12/17	3,267	(16)	—	1,636
12/15	2,372	32	1.4%	—
/ 0	0	—	—	—
Annual Growth	—	—	—	—

2017 Year-End Financials

Return on assets: (-0.3%)
Return on equity: (-3.0%)
Current ratio: 1.20
Cash ($ mil.): 32

DST SYSTEMS, INC.

EXECUTIVES

Ceo, William C Stone
Pres-Coo, Normand A Boulanger
Sr V Pres-Cfo, Patrick J Pedonti
Sr V Pres-Gencounsel-Sec, Paul G Igoe
Director, Roger Stanley
Senior Vice President, Wayne Armstrong
Administrator Lan Administrato, Anthony Lombardo
Information Technology Manager, Debbie Brunk
Information Technology Directo, Mike Goodwin
Database Administrator, Rue Pham
Vice President, Bill Chisholm
Auditors: PRICEWATERHOUSECOOPERS LLP K

LOCATIONS

HQ: DST SYSTEMS, INC.
333 W 11TH ST FL 5, KANSAS CITY, MO 641051628
Phone: 816 435-1000
Web: WWW.DSTSYSTEMS.COM

COMPETITORS

ADP
Advent Software
Algorithmics
Alliance Data Systems
Assurant
Bank of New York Mellon
Broadridge
CSG Systems International
CVS Caremark
Cerner
Convergys
Emdeon
Express Scripts
Fidelity National Information Services
First Data
Fiserv
GE Healthcare
Greenway Medical Technologies
HP Enterprise Services
HealthPort
IBM
Iron Mountain Inc
McKesson
Misys
NCR
Paychex
Pegasystems
Progress Software
R.R. Donnelley
Recall Corporation
SEI Investments
SS&C
StatPro Group
State Street
SunGard
TIBCO Software
TMG Health
TeleTech
Total System Services
TriZetto

HISTORICAL FINANCIALS

Company Type: Private

Income Statement FYE: December 31

	REVENUE ($ mil.)	NET INCOME ($ mil.)	NET PROFIT MARGIN	EMPLOYEES
12/17	2,218	452	20.4%	15,700
12/16	1,556	426	27.4%	—
12/15	2,825	358	12.7%	—
12/14	2,749	593	21.6%	—
Annual Growth	(6.9%)	(8.7%)	—	—

2017 Year-End Financials

Return on assets: 15.4%
Return on equity: 36.4%
Current ratio: 1.10
Cash ($ mil.): 80

DUKE UNIVERSITY

Recognized as a top institution of higher learning in the US Duke University is home to some 15635 Blue Devils who attend undergraduate- and graduate-level classes in 10 schools and colleges. Trinity College of Art and Sciences the Fuqua School of Business and the Pratt School of Engineering are among the most well-known. Duke's law and medical schools are also highly regarded nationwide. The private institution which boasts some 3870 faculty members also operates the Duke University Health System (DUHS). Duke was founded in 1924 but traces its roots to 1838. Notable alumni include Richard Nixon Timothy Cook Judy Woodruff and Elizabeth Dole.

Operations

Undergraduates at Duke enter either the Trinity College of Arts and Sciences or the Pratt School of Engineering. Top majors for Duke undergraduates include computer science economics public policy biology and psychology. The university's eight graduate schools cover law divinity medicine nursing business public policy the environment and other fields. Academic sources of revenue include government and private grants and contracts investment returns tuition and fees auxiliary enterprises and contributions.

More than half of Duke's operating revenue comes from the Duke University Health System (DUHS) which consists of Duke University Hospital Duke Regional Hospital Duke Raleigh Hospital and related clinics physician practices and home health and hospice agencies. The health system is closely aligned with Duke's schools of medicine and nursing.

Other Duke programs include student athletics (27 NCAA Division I teams) about a dozen research institutes Duke Libraries (one of the top US private library systems) the Duke Marine Laboratory and Duke University Press (publishes some 120 new books annually).

Like most universities Duke is governed by a board of trustees which serves as the institution's fiduciary. The board manages and oversees long-term financial health strategic direction educational policy finances and operations.

Geographic Reach

Most of Duke's operations occur in the heart of Durham North Carolina. Its facilities make up more than 9000acres and include the East West Central and Medical campuses plus Duke Gardens Duke Forest a golf course and an inn in Durham as well as the Duke Marine Laboratory in Beaufort North Carolina.

The university cooperates with other US-based institutions to support student exchanges in New York Los Angeles Chicago Silicon Valley and Washington DC. It also boasts study abroad programs in 20 countries including courses in Berlin Paris Glasgow Madrid St. Petersburg and Venice.

The Duke Kunshan University is a partnership campus between Duke and China's Wuhan University. Duke also partners with the National University of Singapore to operate the Duke-NUS Medical School in Singapore. The university has an office in Bangalore known as Duke University India which supports Duke research and learning programs in India.

Financial Performance

The University's revenue increased to $6.9 billion in 2020 compared to $6.8 billion in 2019. The increase was due to higher grants contracts and similar agreements; and investment returns.

Cash held by the University at the end of 2020 decreased by $105.4 million to $581.5 million. Cash provided by operations and financing activities were $306.6 million and $771.8 million respectively. Cash used for investing activities was $1.2 billion mainly for purchases of investments.

Company Background

Duke traces its roots to the founding of Union Institute in Randolph County North Carolina in 1838. Union Institute later became Trinity College which in 1892 moved to Durham where the Duke family became a primary benefactor. In 1924 American Tobacco Co. magnate James B. Duke established the Duke Endowment which allowed Trinity College to expand into Duke University.

The original Durham campus became known as the East Campus and a new West Campus opened in 1930. The East Campus served as a women's college until 1972 when the undergraduate colleges merged. The East Campus was transformed into a home for first-year students in 1995.

EXECUTIVES

Chief Administrative Officer And Cfo, Tallman Trask
President, Richard H. (Dick) Brodhead
Vp Information Technology, Tracy Futhey
Dean Fuqua School Of Business, William F. Boulding
Dean School Of Medicine, Nancy C. Andrews
Dean Law School, David F. Levi
Provost, Sally Kornbluth
Chancellor Health Affairs; President And Ceo Health System, A. Eugene Washington
President And Ceo Duke Management Company, Neal Triplett
Interim Dean Divinity School, Ellen F. Davis
Dean Graduate School, Paula D. McClain
Dean Nicholas School Of The Environment, Alan Townsend
Dean Pratt School Of Engineering, George Truskey
Dean Sanford School Of Public Policy, Kelly D. Brownell
Dean Trinity College Of Arts And Sciences, Valerie S. Ashby
Dean School Of Nursing, Marion E. Broome
Chancellor Duke Kunshan University, Liu Jingnan
Dean Duke-nus Graduate Medical School, Thomas Coffman
Associate Vice President For Capital Assets, Scott Selig
Vice President Of Finance, Tim Walsh
Medical Director, Larry Goldstein
Vice President Manager Director, Karen Hicks
Vice President And Director Of Athletics, Kevin White
Assistant Vice President Office Of Information Technology, Angel Wingate
J. Lamar Callaway Professor And Chair Department Of Dermatology, Russell Hall

Associate Vice President Duhs, Paul Lindia
Medical Director, Joseph Moore
Vice President Duke University Hospital, Jeffrey Langdon
Associate Vice President, Kimberly Denty
Vice President, Dick White
Associate Vice President Compliance Privacy Security And Integrity, Brian Bonanno
Associate Vice President, Emma Duffin
Medical Director, Marisa Dowling
Asst Vice President Community Oncology, David Nalepinski
Medical Director, Randall Brewer
Vice President, Blaine Mckee
Vice Chairman, Jack O. Bovender
Vice Chairman, Robin A. Ferracone
Chairman, David M. Rubenstein
Board Member, Karin Shapiro
Chairman Emeritus Board Of Visitors, Ronald L Nicol
Auditors: KPMG LLP GREENSBORO NC

LOCATIONS

HQ: DUKE UNIVERSITY
2200 W MAIN ST STE 710, DURHAM, NC 277054677
Phone: 919 684-8111
Web: WWW.DUKE.EDU

PRODUCTS/OPERATIONS

Selected Institutes

Center for the Study of Aging and Human Development
Duke Cancer Institute
Duke Global Health Institute
Duke Institute for Brain Sciences
Duke Science & Society Initiative
Duke University Energy Initiative
Institute for Genomic & Computational Biology
Interdisciplinary Studies
John Hope Franklin Humanities Institute
Kenan Institute for Ethics
Nicholas Institute for Environmental Policy Solutions
Trent Center for Bioethics Humanities and History of Medicine
Social Science Research Institute

Selected Schools and Colleges

Divinity School (Since 1926)
Duke Kunshan University (Since 2014; China)
Duke-NUS Medical School (Since 2005)
Fuqua School of Business (Since 1969)
Graduate School (Since 1926)
Nicholas School of the Environment (Since 1938)
Pratt School of Engineering (Since 1939)
Sanford School of Public Policy (Since 1971)
School of Law (Since 1904)
School of Medicine (Since 1930)
School of Nursing (Since 1931)
Trinity College of Arts & Sciences (Since 1859)

HISTORICAL FINANCIALS

Company Type: Private

Income Statement — FYE: June 30

	REVENUE ($ mil.)	NET INCOME ($ mil.)	NET PROFIT MARGIN	EMPLOYEES
06/12	4,611	(507)	—	3,400
06/05	1,832	246	13.5%	—
06/04	2,806	679	24.2%	—
Annual Growth	6.4%	—	—	—

2012 Year-End Financials

Return on assets: (-3.6%)
Return on equity: (-5.2%)
Current ratio: —
Cash ($ mil.): 526

DUKE UNIVERSITY HEALTH SYSTEM, INC.

More than a campus infirmary the Duke University Health System operates the Duke University Hospital and other medical educational and research facilities on the Duke University grounds. Duke University Hospital has about 960 acute pediatric and psychiatric patient beds and specializes in trauma care diagnostics and cardiac and endoscopic surgeries. The health system also operates two community hospitals – Duke Regional Hospital (370 beds) and Duke Raleigh Hospital (186 beds) – as well as other area health clinics. Duke University Health System's facilities provide primary and specialty care home and hospice care clinical research physician and nurse training and public education programs.

Operations

The system was formed in 1998 to expand the core Medical Center operations and has since added the Durham and Raleigh community hospitals. The Duke University Health System is closely affiliated with the Duke University Medical School as well as with the Duke University School of Nursing. The three entities are all located within the Duke University Medical Center complex (consisting of research educational and clinical care facilities on the Duke campus) also known as Duke Medical. The medical complex also includes the health system's Duke Clinic which provides outpatient and non-emergency specialist care.

Duke University Health System and the university's medical schools train health care professionals in cutting-edge technologies and infrastructures. The entities also work together to advance biomedical and general medical research with the goal of discovering and improving methods of care. Funding for medical research comes from the National Institutes of Health and other government organizations as well as from partnerships with pharmaceutical and medical device companies.

Geographic Reach

While Duke University Health System focuses on medical educational and research work in the US (in the states of North Carolina and Virginia) as part of its business the health system operates a joint venture in India.

Financial Performance

In 2014 revenues increased 2% to $4.9 billion mainly as a result of increases in patient service revenues tuition and fees and investment earnings. The system's net income rose 14% to $1.8 billion led by higher investment returns.

Cash flow from operations fell 90% to $12 million in 2014 due to an increase of cash used for accounts and contributions receivable and changes in inventories.

Strategy

Duke University Health System is working to expand further in existing and new territories and is looking to widen its service offerings in cancer vascular orthopedic musculoskeletal women and children's care and outpatient ambulatory care. To this end the health system is expanding by adding new medical locations and boosting its expertise in technology. For example in 2015 the Duke Eye Center opened a new four-story clinical pavilion. The system also aims to improve efficiencies across all locations and to help community members access needed services.

The company's DLP Healthcare joint venture with LifePoint Health provides management and cost-control services to community hospitals in North Carolina. Maria Parham Medical Center its first client is a small hospital looking for operational support in the face of health reform changes and rising competition in the marketplace. DLP Healthcare holds an 80% stake in the Maria Parham facility through the management agreement. An investment of $15 million in nearby Person Memorial Hospital will go to capital improvements help eliminate its debt and pave the way for DLP Healthcare to acquire the hospital.

Duke Medicine has a partnership with Medanta – The Medicity – through which the pair has established the Medanta Duke Research Institute (MDRI) in India to research medical treatments (drugs and devices). Medanta a 1500-bed institute will fund the creation and operation of the facility as part of the agreement with Duke providing scientific clinical research and operational expertise. Medanta and Duke share joint oversight over implementation and management of the unit.

EXECUTIVES

Svp Cfo And Treasurer, Kenneth C. Morris
Evp, William J. Fulkerson
Vp Patient Care And System And Chief Nurse Executive, Mary Ann Fuchs
President Duke Regional Hospital, Katie Galbraith
President Private Diagnostic Clinic Pllc, Mark F. Newman
Chief Medical Officer, Thomas A. Owens
President Duke Raleigh Hospital, David Zaas
President And Ceo, A. Eugene Washington
Associate Vice President, Britt Crewse
Vice President, Philip Stern
Assistant Vice President Development And Alumni Affairs, Ellen Luken
Assistant Vice President Government Relations, Doug Heron
Vice President Business Development, Jennie Simpson
Vice President Of Internal Affairs, Kristel Black
Chair, Thomas M. Gorrie
Vice Chair, Peter Van Etten
Auditors: KPMG LLP GREENSBORO NC

LOCATIONS

HQ: DUKE UNIVERSITY HEALTH SYSTEM, INC.
2301 ERWIN RD, DURHAM, NC 277054699
Phone: 919 684-8111
Web: WWW.DUKEHEALTH.ORG

Selected Facilities

Duke Clinic (Durham North Carolina)
Duke Raleigh Hospital (Raleigh North Carolina)
Duke University Hospital (Durham North Carolina)
Duke Children's Hospital & Health Center
Durham Regional Hospital (Durham North Carolina)

PRODUCTS/OPERATIONS

2014 Sales

	$ mil.	% of total
Patient service	2,437	50
Grants & contracts	1,097	22
Tuition & fees	408	8
Investment return	384	8
Auxiliary enterprises	186	5
Contributions	92	4
Net assets released from restrictions	46	2
Other	228	1
Total	**4,882**	**100**

Selected Services

AIDS Research and Treatment Center (DART)
Anesthesiology
Aortic Disease
Asthma and Allergies
Attention Deficit Hyperactivity Disorder
Breast Cancer
Cardiac Rehabilitation
Children's Health
Coronary Artery Disease
Dermatology
Developmental and Behavioral Pediatrics

Diabetes
Diet & Fitness Center
Duke Heart Center
Duke Medicine
Ear Nose Throat Head & Neck Surgery
Eating Disorders
Endocrinology
Esophageal Cancer
Executive Health
Eye Center
Foot and Ankle
Gastroenterology
Gastrointestinal Cancer
General Orthopaedics
General and Consultative Heart Care
Geriatrics
Gynecologic Cancer
Gynecology
Health & Fitness Center
Health and Wellness
Healthy Lifestyles for Children
Heart Rhythm Services
Hematology
Hereditary Cancer
Hyperbaric Diving and Altitude Medicine
Infectious Diseases
Integrative Medicine
Knee Treatments
Leukemias Lymphomas and Myelomas
Lung Cancer
Men's Health
Neurological Disorders
Neuroscience
Obstetrics and Gynecology
Pain Disorders
Peripheral Vascular Disease
Prostate Cancer
Psychiatry
Pulmonology and Respiratory Medicine
Radiology
Research
Rheumatology and Immunology
Skin Cancer
Sleep Disorders
Smoking/Smoking Cessation
Speech and Audiology
Sports Medicine
Stroke Center
Transplants
Urologic Cancer
Valvular Heart Disease
Vascular Diseases
Women's Health
Women's Heart Care

COMPETITORS

Carolinas HealthCare System
Cone Health
Cumberland County Hospital System
Danville Regional Medical Center
FirstHealth of the Carolinas
Morehead Memorial Hospital
Novant Health
Rex Healthcare
Rowan Regional Medical Center
UNC Hospitals
Vidant Health
WakeMed
Wesley Long Community Hospital

HISTORICAL FINANCIALS

Company Type: Private

Income Statement — FYE: June 30

	REVENUE ($ mil.)	NET INCOME ($ mil.)	NET PROFIT MARGIN	EMPLOYEES
06/20	3,951	(296)	—	2,400
06/19	3,836	160	4.2%	—
06/18	3,597	688	19.1%	—
06/16	3,160	(787)	—	—
Annual Growth	5.7%	—	—	—

2020 Year-End Financials

Return on assets: (-4.0%)
Return on equity: (-8.5%)
Current ratio: 1.90
Cash ($ mil.): 157

DUKE UNIVERSITY HOSPITAL

LOCATIONS

HQ: DUKE UNIVERSITY HOSPITAL
1 DUKE MEDICAL CTR, DURHAM, NC 277100007
Phone: 919 684-8111
Web: WWW.DUKEHEALTH.ORG

HISTORICAL FINANCIALS

Company Type: Private

Income Statement — FYE: June 30

	REVENUE ($ mil.)	NET INCOME ($ mil.)	NET PROFIT MARGIN	EMPLOYEES
06/19	2,597	25	1.0%	25
06/18	2,467	(0)	—	—
Annual Growth	5.3%	—	—	—

DUQUESNE LIGHT COMPANY

Duquesne Light is the first and last resort for light for many residential customers in the Keystone State. The utility company provides electricity to more than 588000 customers (90% of which are residential) in southwestern Pennsylvania via an extensive transmission and distribution system. The utility a subsidiary of Duquesne Light Holdings (formerly DQE) acts as a generation Provider of Last Resort (POLR) for customers who do not choose an alternative supplier. A consortium led by Macquarie Infrastructure Partners controls the company's parent.

Operations

The company has 212000 utility poles 103000 transformers and more than 45000 miles of overhead [pwer lines.

Geographic Reach

Duquesne Light provides electric service to customers in southwestern Pennsylvania including the city of Pittsburg in a service area that covers 817 square miles in Allegheny and Beaver counties.

Strategy

Duquesne Light which has been hurt by declining margins provided by its POLR service due to unrecovered payments to PJM Interconnection generators implemented a 2011-2013 POLR plan to yield more reliable returns taking advantage of favorable changes in Pennsylvania law regarding POLR costs and surcharges.

In an effort to improve reliability and public safety Duquesne Light has replaced 205 network transformers across its service region since 2002. In 2012 it replaced 29 of these network transformers and was working on replacing 42 more in 2013.

Company Background

The company was founded in 1880.

EXECUTIVES

Vice President Human Resources, Todd Faulk
Vice President Information Technology And Chief Information Officer, Mark S Miko
Vice President Communications And Corporate Citizenship, Jessica J Rock
Vice President Customer Service, Campbell Hawkins

LOCATIONS

HQ: DUQUESNE LIGHT COMPANY
411 7TH AVE 6-1, PITTSBURGH, PA 152191942
Phone: 412 393-6000
Web: WWW.DUQUESNELIGHT.COM

COMPETITORS

Dominion Energy
Exelon
FirstEnergy
PPL Corporation

HISTORICAL FINANCIALS

Company Type: Private

Income Statement — FYE: December 31

	REVENUE ($ mil.)	NET INCOME ($ mil.)	NET PROFIT MARGIN	EMPLOYEES
12/19	963	184	19.2%	1,000
12/18	937	152	16.2%	—
12/17	911	130	14.3%	—
12/16	903	118	13.1%	—
Annual Growth	2.2%	15.9%	—	—

2019 Year-End Financials

Return on assets: 4.6%
Return on equity: 13.0%
Current ratio: 0.60
Cash ($ mil.): 2

DUTCHESS, COUNTY OF (INC)

EXECUTIVES

Cnty Exec, Marcus J Molinaro
Deputy Commissioner*, Corinna Wu
Exec SEC*, Sandra Strippoli
Cntrl, Diane Jablonsky
Accounting Staff, Diane E Brangan
Personnel Assistant, Deirdre Caamano
Instructor of Film, Stephen Lawson
Network Support Specialist, Andrew Marallo
Fire Coordinator, David Alfonso
Senior Human Resources Associa, Karl Menuau
Technical Manager Office of He, Patricia Mensler
Auditors: DRESCHER & MALECKI LLP BUFFAL

LOCATIONS

HQ: DUTCHESS, COUNTY OF (INC)
626 DUTCHESS TPKE, POUGHKEEPSIE, NY 126031906
Phone: 845 486-2000
Web: WWW.CO.DUTCHESS.NY.US

HISTORICAL FINANCIALS

Company Type: Private

Income Statement — FYE: December 31

	REVENUE ($ mil.)	NET INCOME ($ mil.)	NET PROFIT MARGIN	EMPLOYEES
12/19	590	13	2.3%	1,852
12/18	549	9	1.8%	—
12/17	467	(16)	—	—
12/16	468	(17)	—	—
Annual Growth	8.0%	—	—	—

2019 Year-End Financials

Return on assets: 1.2%
Return on equity: 8.7%
Current ratio: —
Cash ($ mil.): 105

DUVAL COUNTY PUBLIC SCHOOLS

EXECUTIVES

Supt, John C Fryer Jr
Payroll Staff, Bobbie Johns
Technical Manager, Cathy S Maycott
Instructor, Amy Guth
Buyer, Caleb Powell
Cashier, Anastasia Dixon
Supervisor, Beth Tramel
Teacher, Denisha Jordan
Assistant, Jonathan Brown
Education Specialist, Megan McCumber
Teacher, Rusty Mathews

LOCATIONS

HQ: DUVAL COUNTY PUBLIC SCHOOLS
1701 PRUDENTIAL DR, JACKSONVILLE, FL 322078152
Phone: 904 390-2000
Web: WWW.DUVALSCHOOLS.ORG

HISTORICAL FINANCIALS

Company Type: Private

Income Statement FYE: June 30

	REVENUE ($ mil.)	NET INCOME ($ mil.)	NET PROFIT MARGIN	EMPLOYEES
06/19	1,279	22	1.8%	13,000
06/18	1,231	(7)	—	—
06/17	1,207	(25)	—	—
06/16	1,184	(63)	—	—
Annual Growth	2.6%	—	—	—

2019 Year-End Financials

Return on assets: 1.3%
Return on equity: 5.8%
Current ratio: —
Cash ($ mil.): 186

DYNCORP INTERNATIONAL LLC

EXECUTIVES

Ceo, George Krivo
Coordinator, Jeff Angus
Director, Kathryn Van Vleck
Accounting Staff, Arthur Jordan
Management Vice-President, Richard Minor
Information Specialist, Jason Granger
Human Resource Specialist, Nazeer Khan
Manager, Bradley Salls
Fuels Manager, Claude Poole
Logistics Advisor, Eric Ogborn
Electrical Engineer, Erick McAfee
Auditors: FRYE & COMPANY CPAS MANASSAS

LOCATIONS

HQ: DYNCORP INTERNATIONAL LLC
1700 OLD MEADOW RD, MC LEAN, VA 221024302
Phone: 571 722-0210
Web: WWW.DYN-INTL.COM

HISTORICAL FINANCIALS

Company Type: Private

Income Statement FYE: April 3

	REVENUE ($ mil.)	NET INCOME ($ mil.)	NET PROFIT MARGIN	EMPLOYEES
04/09*	3,101	69	2.2%	100
03/08	2,139	47	2.2%	—
Annual Growth	44.9%	45.5%	—	—

*Fiscal year change

2009 Year-End Financials

Return on assets: 4.5%
Return on equity: 14.0%
Current ratio: 2.00
Cash ($ mil.): 200

EAST TEXAS MEDICAL CENTER REGIONAL HEALTHCARE SYSTEM

East Texas Medical Center (ETMC) Regional Healthcare System works to meet the health care needs of residents of the Piney Woods. The not-for-profit health system operates more than a dozen hospitals across eastern Texas along with behavioral rehabilitation and home health care businesses. Its flagship 450-bed Tyler location serves as the hub and referral center for satellite medical centers located in more rural locations. The system also runs numerous primary care and outpatient clinics throughout the region. Serving more than 300000 patients each year ETMC operates an emergency ambulance service subsidiary and a clinical laboratory which provide services to the ETMC Regional Healthcare System.

Operations

The flagship ETMC Tyler facility offers specialized care for cancer and cardiovascular and neurological conditions. It is a Level I regional trauma center and provides diagnostic and outpatient surgery services.

The system is organized so that primary care is provided in the rural health clinics. Secondary care is also provided locally in the ETMC affiliate hospitals. High-level secondary and tertiary care is provided at ETMC Tyler.

Geographic Reach

ETMC serves the more than 1 million people who reside in East Texas communities. It caters to nearly 20 Texas counties including Anderson Camp Cherokee Ellis Franklin Freestone Henderson Hopkins Houston Panola Red River Rusk Shelby Smith Trinity Upshur Van Zandt and Wood. These communities range in size from fewer than 500 residents to more than 50000.

Sales and Marketing

The Medicare program accounted for 50% of net patient revenues in 2012; Medicaid contributed 12% of the same. Some 16% of total net patient service revenue came from commercial insurance carriers and preferred provider organizations.

Financial Performance

Due to an increase in patient service revenue ETMC's revenue rose by 6% to $942 million in 2012 from $888 million in 2011. Net income for the same reporting period dropped some 92% to $1.1 million from $16 million due to rising salaries and wages and employee benefits expenses as well as from an increase in loss from defined benefit pension adjustment.

Strategy

To keep up with the needs of its residents the ETMC Regional Healthcare System works to expand its operations.

In 2013 ETMC Pittsburg broke ground on a 5000-sq.-ft. expansion of the hospital's surgery department. Its East Texas Medical Center Regional Healthcare System also added a pair of emergency transport helicopters valued at more than $9 million.

In 2012 the company completed $30-million expansion and renovation project at East Texas Medical Center Henderson including a new emergency department grand lobby and clinic space. It also wrapped up the second phase of an expansion project at ETMC Fairfield that involved adding a new entrance lobby clinic space cardiopulmonary rehabilitation facility and administrative suite.

Its 100-bed Henderson Memorial Hospital joined the network in 2009 as ETMC Henderson. Soon after becoming part of the network ETMC assisted its new affiliate with facility upgrades that included building new emergency department facilities renovating old rooms and installing new electrical and HVAC systems all completed in 2011. ETMC also expanded its Trinity facility with a 15-bed patient wing at the cost of $7.4 million and expanded its mammography services at ETMC Cedar Creek Lake. A $35 million ETMC Quitman facility is expected to be completed in 2013.

ETMC also concentrates on upgrading its information systems. The healthcare system's data exchange organization FirstNet Exchange received a grant from the state of Texas in 2011 to develop and operate a secure health information network to support hospitals and clinicians.

EXECUTIVES

Nursing Director, Maria Kulma
Medical Director, Richard Yates
Vice President Of Engineering, Robert Layton
Nursing Director, Kevin Jablonski
Radiology Director, Bill Tobin
Vice President Public Relations And Media Communications, Jo Curry
Treasurer, Brenda Brown

LOCATIONS

HQ: EAST TEXAS MEDICAL CENTER REGIONAL HEALTHCARE SYSTEM
1000 S BECKHAM AVE, TYLER, TX 757011908
Phone: 903 596-3267
Web: WWW.UTHEALTHEASTTEXAS.COM

PRODUCTS/OPERATIONS

Selected Health and Medical Services

Bariatric Surgery Center
Behavioral Health Center
Cancer Institute
Cardiovascular Institute
Digestive Disease Center
Emergency Services
Fitness Centers
Home Health
Neurological Institute
Orthopedic Institute
Plastic Surgery
Podiatry Care
Radiology and Imaging
Rehabilitation Center
Sleep Disorders Center
Specialty Hospital
Transplant Center
Urology Institute
Women's Health
Wound Healing Center

Selected East Texas Medical Center Hospitals

ETMC Athens
ETMC Carthage

ETMC Clarksville
ETMC Crockett
ETMC Fairfield
ETMC Gilmer
ETMC Henderson
ETMC Jacksonville
ETMC Lake Palestine
ETMC Mount Vernon
ETMC Pittsburg
ETMC Quitman
ETMC Rehabilitation Hospital (Tyler)
ETMC Specialty Hospital (Tyler)
ETMC Trinity
ETMC Tyler

COMPETITORS

Community Health Systems
Good Shepherd Health System
HCA
Hunt Memorial
Memorial Health System of East Texas
Tenet Healthcare
Trinity Mother Frances Hospital and Clinics
Wadley Regional Medical Center
Woodland Heights Medical Center

HISTORICAL FINANCIALS

Company Type: Private

Income Statement — FYE: October 31

	REVENUE ($ mil.)	NET INCOME ($ mil.)	NET PROFIT MARGIN	EMPLOYEES
10/08	876	30	3.4%	7,600
10/07	827	40	4.8%	—
10/06	837	0	—	—
10/05	837	17	2.1%	—
Annual Growth	1.5%	20.4%	—	—

2008 Year-End Financials

Return on assets: 4.0%
Return on equity: 11.1%
Current ratio: 3.20
Cash ($ mil.): 175

EASTERN MAINE HEALTHCARE SYSTEMS

Eastern Maine Healthcare Systems (EMHS) keeps the folks in the Pine Tree State feeling fine. With more than a dozen member hospitals and multiple medical practices and clinics the organization offers patients emergency primary mental-health laboratory and other specialty services. It primarily serves eastern central and northern portions of rural Maine. Some hospitals include Eastern Maine Medical Center (410 beds) Acadia Hospital (100 beds) Aroostook Medical Center (75 beds) and Inland Hospital (50 beds). The system also operates long-term care hospice and home health facilities as well as emergency transportation and administrative services businesses.

Operations

Besides its Acadia Hospital Aroostook Medical Center Eastern Maine Medical Center and Inland Hospital EMHS operates three smaller community hospitals with 15 to 30 beds each: Blue Hill Memorial Hospital Charles A. Dean Memorial Hospital and Sebasticook Valley Hospital. The system has affiliations with the Houlton Regional Hospital and Millinocket Regional Hospital.

Subsidiaries of EMHS include Affiliated Healthcare Systems (medical communications and retirement ventures) Affiliated Laboratory (pathology services) Affiliated Material Services (medical supplies distribution and pharmacies) and Affiliated Healthcare Management (transcription and employee services).

As part of its operations EMHS also runs the Eastern Maine Medical Center Clinical Research Center which performs clinical studies in several medical disciplines and diseases including cancer hospital-acquired infections heart disease and physician best practices.

In fiscal 2014 EMHS had 105629 emergency room visits; 32964 inpatient and outpatient surgeries; 3017 births; and 388920 primary care visits.

The company's total Community Benefit that year was about $200 million and its philanthropy giving was nearly $3 million.

Geographic Reach

Despite its name Eastern Maine Healthcare System serves those in eastern central and northern portions of rural Maine.

Strategy

EMHS continues to work collaboratively at the national level looking at not only making a difference in healthcare in Maine but to be a change leader throughout the country. The Northern New England Accountable Care Collaborative is creating resources necessary to propel the reinvention of care model. In addition their work in the High Value Healthcare Collaborative (co-owned with Dartmouth MaineHealth and the University of Vermont Medical Center) this past year has been focused on sepsis care and prevention patient engagement and shared decision-making pilot projects.

In fiscal 2015 Maine's largest health insurer teamed up with Eastern Maine Healthcare Systems under a new venture aimed at keeping patients healthier while reducing costs. The deal involves Anthem Blue Cross and Blue Shield in Maine EMHS and an EMHS-led coalition of hospitals and physician practices across the state. EMHS and its partners have agreed to avoid any cost increase for services they deliver to 40000 Anthem policyholders.

In mid-2014 EMHS completed a community health needs assessment of the northern two-thirds of Maine including the counties of Aroostook Cumberland Hancock Kennebec Penobscot Piscataquis Somerset and Washington. This report was seen as foundational to the company achieving its mission of improving the health and well-being of the communities it serves.

Company Background

The system was established in 1982.

EXECUTIVES

Vice President Network Development And Aco Activity, Michael Donahue
Vice President Of Organizational Effectiveness, Deborah Sanford
Vice President Of Finance Chief Finance, Elmer Doucette
Senior Vice President Chief Medical Officer And Home Office Chief Administrative Officer, Erik Steele
Vice President, Scott Oxley
Vice President Application Services, Teri Hohentanner
Medical Director, Jens Rueter
Department Head, Mikele Neal
Senior Vice President, Charles D Therrien
Vice President, Helen Mckinnon
Vice President, Jeff Doran
Nursing Director, Jean Lydon
Director Of Pharmacy, James Cattin
Director Of Pharmacy, John Merchant
Medical Secretary, Chris Shaw
Board Member, Karen Marsters
Auditors: BERRY DUNN MCNEIL & PARKER LL

LOCATIONS

HQ: EASTERN MAINE HEALTHCARE SYSTEMS
43 WHITING HILL RD # 500, BREWER, ME 044121005
Phone: 207 973-7050
Web: WWW.NORTHERNLIGHTHEALTH.ORG

PRODUCTS/OPERATIONS

Selected Strategic Affiliates
Houlton Regional Hospital
Millinocket Regional Hospital
Member Hospitals
Acadia Hospital
Affiliated Healthcare Systems
Aroostook Medical Center
Beacon Health
Blue Hill Memorial Hospital
Charles A. Dean Memorial Hospital and Nursing Home
Dirigo Pines Retirement Community
Eastern Maine HomeCare
Eastern Maine Medical Center
Healthcare Charities
Inland Hospital
Rosscare
Sebasticook Valley Hospital

COMPETITORS

Franklin Community Health Network
Maine Coast Memorial Hospital
MaineGeneral Health
MaineHealth
Mercy Health System of Maine
Miles Health Care
Millinocket Regional Hospital
St. Joseph Healthcare

HISTORICAL FINANCIALS

Company Type: Private

Income Statement — FYE: September 30

	REVENUE ($ mil.)	NET INCOME ($ mil.)	NET PROFIT MARGIN	EMPLOYEES
09/19	1,744	16	0.9%	8,175
09/18	1,672	8	0.5%	—
09/17	1,654	43	2.6%	—
09/16	1,523	21	1.4%	—
Annual Growth	4.6%	(8.9%)	—	—

2019 Year-End Financials

Return on assets: 0.9%
Return on equity: 2.1%
Current ratio: 2.20
Cash ($ mil.): 90

EASTERN MAINE MEDICAL CENTER

EXECUTIVES

Ceo, Deborah C Johnson
V Pres-Cfo*, Elmer Doucette
V Pres*, John Doyle
Coor, Melissa Cadieux
Business Analyst, Karen Egan
Manager, Michelle Mayo
Health Professional, Resmi Rajan
Internal Medicine Practitioner, Chheki Sherpa
Internal Medicine Practitioner, Gayathri Thampatty
Surgeon, John Baxter
Health Professional, Mamta Sherchan
Auditors: BERRY DUNN MCNEIL & PARKER LL

LOCATIONS

HQ: EASTERN MAINE MEDICAL CENTER
489 STATE ST, BANGOR, ME 044016674
Phone: 207 973-7000
Web: WWW.NORTHERNLIGHTHEALTH.ORG

HISTORICAL FINANCIALS

Company Type: Private

Income Statement — FYE: September 24

	REVENUE ($ mil.)	NET INCOME ($ mil.)	NET PROFIT MARGIN	EMPLOYEES
09/16	776	23	3.0%	1,119
09/15	720	41	5.8%	—
09/13	646	56	8.8%	—
09/12	669	67	10.1%	—
Annual Growth	3.8%	(23.2%)	—	—

2016 Year-End Financials

Return on assets: 2.4%
Return on equity: 5.6%
Current ratio: 2.20
Cash ($ mil.): 65

EATON CORPORATION

EXECUTIVES

Chair-Ceo, Craig Arnold
Cfo, Richard Fearon
Exec V Pres, Mark McGuire
Sr V Pres-SEC, Thomas Moran
Sr V Pres-Contrl, Billie Rawot
Sr V Pres Corp Devt & Treas, David Foster
Gen Counsel, April Boise
Business Operations Manager, Ryan Strong
Sales Manager, Tony Ciammaichella
Pres Corporate/Electrical Sect, Tim Darkes
Vp, Treasury, Kirsten Park
Auditors: ERNST & YOUNG LLP CLEVELAND

LOCATIONS

HQ: EATON CORPORATION
1000 EATON BLVD, CLEVELAND, OH 441226058
Phone: 440 523-5000
Web: WWW.EATONELECTRICAL.COM

HISTORICAL FINANCIALS

Company Type: Private

Income Statement — FYE: December 31

	REVENUE ($ mil.)	NET INCOME ($ mil.)	NET PROFIT MARGIN	EMPLOYEES
12/15	6,925	821	11.9%	736
12/14	6,990	170	2.4%	—
Annual Growth	(0.9%)	382.9%	—	—

EDUCATIONAL TESTING SERVICE

Please completely fill in each circle on the answer sheet as prepared by Educational Testing Service (ETS). ETS develops and administers the Graduate Record Examinations (GRE) and Test of English as a Foreign Language (TOEFL). The nonprofit group develops and administers more than 50 million achievement admissions academic and professional tests a year at more than 9000 locations in more than 180 countries. It also develops assessment programs for corporations professional associations and state entities. ETS' research unit conducts advancing educational measurement and policy studies; test-development firm Prometric is a for-profit subsidiary.

Operations

ETS' K-12 products include Criterion an online writing evaluation service that helps students plan write and revise essays. Teachers are not forgotten – the company also develops and administers the Praxis Series assessments for teacher licensing and certifications. For college-bound scholars ETS supports The College Board's Scholastic Assessment Test (SAT) and National Assessment of Educational Progress (NAEP) test.

ETS Global the international arm of ETS has more than 3200 employees work at ETS's offices worldwide. Of these more than 2300 of its professional staff have training and expertise in education psychology statistics psychometrics computer sciences sociology and the humanities. Almost 1000 have advanced degrees and 390 hold doctorates. Some 1150 employees support ETS's wholly owned subsidiary Prometric.

Its EdAgree subsidiary offers a free platform and services to help students identify universities for international students. Edusoft Ltd. a foreign subsidiary is a global leader in technology-based comprehensive English Language Learning solutions serving a range of educational government and corporate sectors worldwide.

Prometric a global leader in technology-enabled testing and assessment services provides test development test delivery and data management capabilities to clients in the academic professional and government markets via the web or by utilizing a robust test center network in more than 160 countries.

Geographic Reach

ETS serves US customers from offices in (San Antonio & Austin) Texas (Concord Sacramento and San Francisco) California Florida Kansas New Jersey (headquarters) and Washington DC. In addition ETS has direct operating subsidiaries in Canada China Korea and other countries in South America Asia Europe the Middle East and Africa; these offices provide services to customers in about 80 countries.

Sales and Marketing

The company serves students educators schools businesses and governments.

Company Background

In 2011 the company opened several new customer support centers to support international customers seeking to take the TOEFL test.

The company bulked up its testing technology in early 2011 with the acquisition of Computerized Assessments and Learning (CAL). Operating as a subsidiary of ETS CAL offers assessment products for K-12 education systems.

To move beyond assessment and into actual education ETS acquired Edusoft an English language learning firm in 2011. The 2011 acquisition brought in Edusoft's English Discoveries Online product used around the world. The online product is designed to accompany and support classroom instruction with courses for general and technical English language instruction. Edusoft operates as a for-profit subsidiary.

ETS was founded in 1947.

EXECUTIVES

Svp And President Institute For Student Achievement (isa), Gerry House
Svp And Chief Administrative Officer, Yvette Donado
President And Ceo, Walt MacDonald
Svp And Cfo, Jack Hayon
Svp Strategy Marketing And Growth And Chief Marketing Officer, Scott Nelson
Svp Global Education And Workforce, David Hunt
Vice President Of Education, William Seibert
Associate Vice President Research And Technology Transfer, Marissa Farnum
Vice President, Ida Lawrence
Vice President Administration, Bruce Gilbertson
Vice President Of Training, Jane Borden
Vice President, Anne Rockey
Vice President Of Research, Joanna Gorin
Senior Strategic Advisor To The Vice President And Chief Operating Officer Of Global Education, Alberto Acereda
Manager Government Relations, Polina Levit
Vice President And Chief Learning Officer, Tj Elliott
Manager Government Relations, Shannon Litton
Auditors: DELOITTE & TOUCHE LLP

LOCATIONS

HQ: EDUCATIONAL TESTING SERVICE
660 ROSEDALE RD, PRINCETON, NJ 085402218
Phone: 609 921-9000
Web: WWW.ETS.ORG

PRODUCTS/OPERATIONS

Selected Testing Programs

Advanced Placement (AP)
Algebra end of course assessment (EOC)
California High School Exit Examination (CAHSEE)
California State University Placement Test (EPT/ELM)
College-Level Examination Program (CLEP)
ETS Literacy
ETS Proficiency Profile
EXADEP
Graduate Record Examinations (GRE)
High Schools That Work Assessment
iSkills Assessment
Major Field Tests (MFT)
Middle Grades Assessment (MGA)
National Assessment of Educational Progress (NAEP)
ParaPro Assessment
The Praxis Series: Professional Assessments for Beginning Teachers
Preliminary SAT/National Merit Scholarship Qualifying Test (PSAT/NMSQT)
Scholastic Aptitude Test (SAT)
School Leaders Licensure Assessment (SLLA)
School Leadership Series (SLS)
School Superintendent Assessment (SSA)
Secondary Level English Proficiency Test (SLEP)
Test Link Test Collection
TFI Test
Test of English as a Foreign Language (TOEFL)
Test of English for International Communication (TOEIC)

Selected Acquisitions

COMPETITORS

ACT Inc.
Houghton Mifflin Harcourt
Kaplan
Questar Assessment
S&P Global
Scantron
The Princeton Review
University of Iowa

HISTORICAL FINANCIALS

Company Type: Private

Income Statement — FYE: September 30

	REVENUE ($ mil.)	NET INCOME ($ mil.)	NET PROFIT MARGIN	EMPLOYEES
09/19	1,358	(22)	—	2,756
09/18	1,392	686	49.3%	—
09/17	1,398	53	3.8%	—
09/16	1,592	73	4.6%	—
Annual Growth	(5.2%)	—	—	—

2019 Year-End Financials

Return on assets: (-1.1%)
Return on equity: (-1.5%)
Current ratio: 1.30
Cash ($ mil.): 168

EDWARD HOSPITAL

EXECUTIVES

System Ceo, Pamela Davis
System Evp-Cfo*, William Devoney
System Vp-Physician Ambulatory*, Bill Kottman
Vice Pres-Facilities*, Gary Mielak
System Evp-Gen Counsel*, Chris Mollet
Exec V Pres*, Vince Pryor
V Pres*, Barbara Byrne
V Pres*, Patti Ludwig-Beymer
System Evp-Hr*, Susan Mitchell
System Vp-CIO*, Bobbie Byrne
System Vp-Cmo*, Brian Davis

LOCATIONS

HQ: EDWARD HOSPITAL
801 S WASHINGTON ST, NAPERVILLE, IL 605407499
Phone: 630 355-0450
Web: WWW.EEHEALTH.ORG

HISTORICAL FINANCIALS

Company Type: Private

Income Statement — FYE: June 30

	REVENUE ($ mil.)	NET INCOME ($ mil.)	NET PROFIT MARGIN	EMPLOYEES
06/16	592	2	0.5%	4,700
06/15	567	39	7.0%	—
06/14	615	106	17.2%	—
06/13	517	52	10.1%	—
Annual Growth	4.6%	(62.8%)	—	—

EDWARD-ELMHURST HEALTHCARE

EXECUTIVES

Ceo, Lou Mastro
Pres*, Pamela Meyer-Davis
Exec V Pres*, Chris Mollet
Exec V Pres*, Susan Mitchell
V Pres*, Bobbie Byrne
Cfo*, Vince Pryor
Vice President-Facilities, Gary Mielak
Neurology, Henry C Echiverri
Information Technology Project, Laura Georges
Director, Glenn Nelson
BSN, Donna Preisler
Auditors: KPMG LLP CHICAGO IL

LOCATIONS

HQ: EDWARD-ELMHURST HEALTHCARE
4201 WINFIELD RD, WARRENVILLE, IL 605554025
Phone: 630 355-0450
Web: WWW.EEHEALTH.ORG

HISTORICAL FINANCIALS

Company Type: Private

Income Statement — FYE: June 30

	REVENUE ($ mil.)	NET INCOME ($ mil.)	NET PROFIT MARGIN	EMPLOYEES
06/20	1,487	(107)	—	6,500
06/19	1,514	76	5.1%	—
06/18	1,474	119	8.1%	—
06/17	1,372	105	7.7%	—
Annual Growth	2.7%	—	—	—

2020 Year-End Financials

Return on assets: (-4.1%)
Return on equity: (-10.0%)
Current ratio: 0.90
Cash ($ mil.): 285

EL PASO COUNTY HOSPITAL DISTRICT

University Medical Center is a community not-for-profit health care system serving West Texas and southern New Mexico. The network includes the 330-bed University Medical Center of El Paso (formerly also known as Thomason General Hospital) several neighborhood primary care clinics and the El Paso First Health Plans HMO. The hospital is an acute-care teaching hospital affiliated with Texas Tech. It specializes in emergency/trauma care obstetrics pediatric medicine and orthopedics. The hospital district through its affiliates provides a range of outpatient services including physical rehabilitation speech therapy family planning dental care cancer treatment diagnostics and pharmacy services.

Company Background

University Medical Center of El Paso opened in 1915. The hospital was rebranded under the University Medical Center name in 2009 when Texas Tech opened a full four-year medical school on the Thomason General campus.

EXECUTIVES

Medical Records Director, Monica Blancas
Director Of Radiology, David Matta
Secretary Of Medical Executive Committee, Pedro Serrato
Auditors: BKD LLP DALLAS TEXAS

LOCATIONS

HQ: EL PASO COUNTY HOSPITAL DISTRICT
4815 ALAMEDA AVE, EL PASO, TX 799052705
Phone: 915 544-1200
Web: WWW.UMCELPASO.ORG

PRODUCTS/OPERATIONS

Selected Services

After Hours Pediatrics
Aquatic Therapy
Cardiac Cath
CAT Scan
Case Management
Dental Clinic
Diabetes Management
Diagnostic Radiology
Echocardiograms
Electrocardiograms
Emergency Department
Endoscopy/Special Procedures
Family Planning
Infusion Center
Interventional Radiology
Laboratory Services
Labor and Delivery
Laparoscopic Surgery
Lithotripsy
Mammography
Medical Unit
Mother/Baby Unit
MRI
Neonatal Intensive Care
Neonatal Intermediate Care
Neonatal Continuing Care
Newborn Nursery
Neurosurgery
Nuclear Medicine
Nutritional Care
Occupational Health
Occupational Therapy
Patient Financial Services
Pediatric Unit
Pediatric Rehabilitation
Pharmacy
Physical Therapy
Poison Control Center
Prenatal Services
Primary Care Clinics
Public Affairs
Rehabilitative Services
Respiratory Services
Special Care Nurseries
Speech Therapy
Surgical Services
Surgical Unit
Telemetry Unit
Trauma - Level 1
Ultrasound
West Texas Regional Poison Control Center
Wound Care

COMPETITORS

Covenant Health System
Del Sol Medical Center
Encompass Health
Tenet Healthcare
Texas Health Resources

HISTORICAL FINANCIALS

Company Type: Private

Income Statement — FYE: September 30

	REVENUE ($ mil.)	NET INCOME ($ mil.)	NET PROFIT MARGIN	EMPLOYEES
09/19	679	(10)	—	1,898
09/18	599	(31)	—	—
09/16	578	0	0.1%	—
09/15	177	(2)	—	—
Annual Growth	39.9%	—	—	—

2019 Year-End Financials

Return on assets: (-1.6%)
Return on equity: (-11.5%)
Current ratio: 1.00
Cash ($ mil.): 44

EL PASO INDEPENDENT SCHOOL DISTRICT EDUCATION FOUNDATION

EXECUTIVES

Spdt, Juan Cabrera
Superintendent, Tippin Message
Network Infrastructure Manager, Stephen Crye
Auditors: GIBSON RUDDOCK PATTERSON LLC

LOCATIONS

HQ: EL PASO INDEPENDENT SCHOOL DISTRICT EDUCATION FOUNDATION
6531 BOEING DR, EL PASO, TX 799251008
Phone: 915 230-2000
Web: WWW.EPISD.ORG

HISTORICAL FINANCIALS

Company Type: Private

Income Statement FYE: June 30

	REVENUE ($ mil.)	NET INCOME ($ mil.)	NET PROFIT MARGIN	EMPLOYEES
06/19	648	196	30.3%	9,000
06/18	625	(34)	—	—
06/17	621	188	30.3%	—
06/16	651	2	0.4%	—
Annual Growth	(0.2%)	324.9%	—	—

2019 Year-End Financials

Return on assets: 13.2%
Return on equity: —
Current ratio: —
Cash ($ mil.): 574

EL PASO NATURAL GAS COMPANY, L.L.C.

EXECUTIVES

Pres-Ceo, James J Cleary
Exec V Pres-Cfo, John R Sult
V Pres-Controller-Cao, Rosa P Jackson
Tech, Jesse Watkins
Area Manager, Ted Meinhold
Engineer Senior, Sule Amadu

LOCATIONS

HQ: EL PASO NATURAL GAS COMPANY, L.L.C.
1001 LOUISIANA ST, HOUSTON, TX 770025089
Phone: 713 420-2600
Web: WWW.KINDERMORGAN.COM

HISTORICAL FINANCIALS

Company Type: Private

Income Statement FYE: December 31

	REVENUE ($ mil.)	NET INCOME ($ mil.)	NET PROFIT MARGIN	EMPLOYEES
12/17	648	141	21.8%	525
12/16	627	128	20.5%	—
/ 0	0	—	—	
Annual Growth	—	—	—	—

ELECTRIC POWER BOARD OF CHATTANOOGA

Pardon me .... is that the Electric Power Board (EPB) of Chattanoogó EPB keeps on choo-chooin' along by providing electricity to more than 167410 residents and businesses. The utility (a non-profit agency of the City of Chattanooga) distributes energy in a 600 sq.-ml. area that includes greater Chattanooga as well as parts of surrounding counties in Georgia and Tennessee. It gets its wholesale power supply from the Tennessee Valley Authority. EPB also provides telecommunications (telephone and Internet) services to area homes and businesses through its EPB Fiber Optics unit.

Operations

In addition to its electric distribution business the company's all-fiber Internet product gives 50000 businesses and residences access to up to 500 Mbps of bandwidth a capacity 300 times faster than standard DSL cable or T1 connections. This service gives all EFB customers internet bandwidth capacity and service on a par with or superior to that offered in Atlanta Chicago and Los Angeles.

Geographic Reach

EPB serves greater Chattanooga and parts of surrounding counties (Bledsoe Bradley Marion Rhea and Sequatchie) and North Georgia (parts of Catoosa Dade and Walker counties).

Financial Performance

The company saw its operating revenues rise by 1% in 2013 thanks to an increase of $12.4 million in Fiber Optics residential services sales.

Strategy

EFB is pushing technological innovation and the modernization of its systems as a way to increase value and efficiency.

To help reduce power outages in 2013 the company added 200 smart switches to its 46 Kv system (in addition to its 1200 smart swtiches on the 12kV system already in place.

Company Background

During 2009 the company received a $111 million federal stimulus grant to build and operate a Smart Grid (an automated electric system with communication capabilities to help improve response time reduce outages cut down on theft and help clients take charge of their own power use). In 2012 EFB completed the installation of the 1170 IntelliRupter® PulseCloser (smart switches) making EPB's Smart Grid the most automated system of its size in the US.

The utility was established in 1935 to provide electric power to the people of the greater Chattanooga area.

EXECUTIVES

Vice President Of Strategic Research, Jim Ingraham
Vice President Of Services, Aaron Webb
Vice President Human Resources, Marie Webb
Vice President Marketing, Jed Marston
Assistant Vice President And Ore Manager, James Eldridge
Vice President Finance And Controller, Michael Kaiser
Executive Board Member, Steve Dover
Board Of Directors, Jon Kinsey
Auditors: MAULDIN & JENKINS LLC CHATTA

LOCATIONS

HQ: ELECTRIC POWER BOARD OF CHATTANOOGA
10 W MARTIN LUTHER KING B, CHATTANOOGA, TN 374021832
Phone: 423 756-2706
Web: WWW.EPB.COM

PRODUCTS/OPERATIONS

2013 Sales

	% of total
Electric	86
Fiber Optics	12
Other	2
Total	**100**

COMPETITORS

AT&T
Constellation Energy Group
Southern Company Gas

HISTORICAL FINANCIALS

Company Type: Private

Income Statement FYE: June 30

	REVENUE ($ mil.)	NET INCOME ($ mil.)	NET PROFIT MARGIN	EMPLOYEES
06/19	741	36	5.0%	400
06/18	729	43	6.0%	—
06/17	716	35	4.9%	—
06/16	683	32	4.7%	—
Annual Growth	2.7%	4.8%	—	—

2019 Year-End Financials

Return on assets: 4.0%
Return on equity: 8.1%
Current ratio: 1.20
Cash ($ mil.): 104

ELECTRIC POWER BOARD OF THE METROPOLITAN GOVERNMENT OF NASHVILLE & DAVIDSON COUNTY

The Electric Power Board of the Metropolitan Government of Nashville and Davidson County is a mouthful. Its operating name Nashville Electric Service (NES) sounds much better. And talking of sound the legendary "Nashville Sound" would be hard to hear without the resources of this power distributor which serves more than 360000 customers in central Tennessee. NES is one of the largest government-owned utilities in the US. The company is required to purchase all its power from another government-owned operator the Tennessee Valley Authority (TVA).

EXECUTIVES

Vice President Of Information Technology, Erika Walker
Auditors: PRICEWATERHOUSECOOPERS LLP NA

LOCATIONS

HQ: ELECTRIC POWER BOARD OF THE METROPOLITAN GOVERNMENT OF NASHVILLE & DAVIDSON COUNTY
1214 CHURCH ST, NASHVILLE, TN 372460001
Phone: 615 747-3831
Web: WWW.NESPOWER.COM

COMPETITORS

AEP
Constellation Energy Group
MLGW
Piedmont Natural Gas
Public Service Enterprise Group
SCANA
Southern Company
Southern Company Gas

HISTORICAL FINANCIALS

Company Type: Private

Income Statement FYE: June 30

	REVENUE ($ mil.)	NET INCOME ($ mil.)	NET PROFIT MARGIN	EMPLOYEES
06/19	1,342	90	6.7%	950
06/18	380	94	24.7%	—
06/16	1,203	28	2.4%	—
06/15	1,246	55	4.5%	—
Annual Growth	1.9%	12.7%	—	—

2019 Year-End Financials

Return on assets: 4.8%
Return on equity: 14.7%
Current ratio: 2.50
Cash ($ mil.): 387

ELEMENT14 US HOLDINGS INC

EXECUTIVES

Pres, Ralf Buehler
Vp, Gen Counsel and Secretary, Joseph R Daprile
Treasurer and Assistant Secret, Paul M Barlak
Web Chat, Emily Winter
Business, Gregory Gaiter
Director of Supplier Operation, Jim Entwistle
Continuous Improvement Analyst, Mark Ellis
Vice President Value Added Ser, Neil Davies
Director of Sales, Paul Starr
Director Echannel Sales, Renee Mack
Director Western Sales, Rodney Sellers

LOCATIONS

HQ: ELEMENT14 US HOLDINGS INC
4180 HIGHLANDER PKWY, RICHFIELD, OH 442869352
Phone: 330 523-4280

HISTORICAL FINANCIALS

Company Type: Private

Income Statement FYE: February 1

	REVENUE ($ mil.)	NET INCOME ($ mil.)	NET PROFIT MARGIN	EMPLOYEES
02/16	598	9	1.6%	1,043
02/15	717	48	6.7%	—
02/14	698	35	5.1%	—
Annual Growth	(7.5%)	(48.4%)	—	—

2016 Year-End Financials

Return on assets: 3.0%
Return on equity: 4.2%
Current ratio: 6.40
Cash ($ mil.): 70

ELLIOT HEALTH SYSTEM

EXECUTIVES

Ceo, Doug Dean
Coo*, Joseph Tate Curti
Human Resources, Paul Carter
Physical Medicine Specialist, Jill Mack
Analyst, Bob Blanchette
Benefits Administrator, Joanna Block
Assistant Business Manager, Mary Guarino
Accounts Receivable Coordinato, Jenny Kane
Aers Partner, Robert Dow
Accounts Payable Supervisor, Irene Fairfield
Registered Nurse, Vittoria Spada

LOCATIONS

HQ: ELLIOT HEALTH SYSTEM
1 ELLIOT WAY, MANCHESTER, NH 031033502
Phone: 603 663-1600
Web: WWW.ELLIOTHOSPITAL.ORG

HISTORICAL FINANCIALS

Company Type: Private

Income Statement FYE: June 30

	REVENUE ($ mil.)	NET INCOME ($ mil.)	NET PROFIT MARGIN	EMPLOYEES
06/20	582	6	1.0%	3,400
06/19	592	0	0.1%	—
06/18	556	9	1.6%	—
06/17	544	20	3.7%	—
Annual Growth	2.3%	(33.0%)	—	—

2020 Year-End Financials

Return on assets: 0.9%
Return on equity: 3.0%
Current ratio: 1.30
Cash ($ mil.): 139

ELLIOT HOSPITAL OF THE CITY OF MANCHESTER

Elliot Health System provides medical care to southern New Hampshire. The health care organization operates Elliot Hospital an acute care hospital with nearly 300 beds that is home to a regional cancer center a designated regional trauma center and a level III neonatal intensive care unit (NICU). In addition to general and surgical care the hospital offers rehabilitation behavioral health obstetrics cardiology and lab services. The system also operates the Elliot Physician Network which operates primary care centers specialty clinics and surgery centers in various regional communities. Elliot Hospital was founded in 1890.

Operations

Elliot Hospital is Manchester's designated Regional Trauma Center. Additional facilities include the Elliot Breast Health Center Elliot Urgent Care Elliot Senior Health Center and New Hampshire's Hospital for Children.

Strategy

Elliot Health System has expanded throughout the region by constructing new outpatient care centers in nearby towns. Most recently Elliot Health completed construction of satellite facilities including an ambulatory care center and a senior health center. In 2015 it partnered with Northeast Rehabilitation Hospital to create a new rehabilitation floor within its Elliot Hospital.

EXECUTIVES

Vice President Of Services, Carla Braveman
Auditors: BAKER NEWMAN & NOYES LLC MANC

LOCATIONS

HQ: ELLIOT HOSPITAL OF THE CITY OF MANCHESTER
1 ELLIOT WAY, MANCHESTER, NH 031033502
Phone: 603 669-5300
Web: WWW.ELLIOTHOSPITAL.ORG

PRODUCTS/OPERATIONS

Selected Centers and Services

Aeronautics Medicine
Adult Day Programs
Bariatric Surgery
Behavioral Health
Breast Health Center
Cardiology Services
Center for Sleep Evaluation
Center for Wound Care & Hyberbaric Medicine
Childbirth And Family Education
Community Health and Wellness
Critical Care at The Elliot
Diabetes and Outpatient Nutrition Services
Diagnostic Imaging
Elliot 1-Day Surgery Center
The Elliot at Hooksett
Elliot Behavioral Health Services
Elliot Endocrinology Associates
Elliot Gastroenterology
Elliot General Surgical Specialists
Elliot Maternal Fetal Medicine
Elliot Medical Center at Londonderry
Elliot Neurology Associates
Elliot Obstetrics and Gynecology
Elliot Orthopaedic Surgical Specialists
Elliot Physician Network
Elliot Regional Cancer Center
Elliot Sports Medicine
Elliot Trauma Center
Elliot Wellness Center
Endoscopy Center
Health Education Library
Home Medical Equipment
Hospitalist Program
Infection Control Department
Inpatient Care/Nursing Units
Laboratory Services
Max K. Willscher Urology Center
Neurophysiology
New England EMS Institute
New Hampshire Arthritis Center
Nursing Units/Inpatient Care
Nutrition Services
Occupational Health & Wellness
Oral Maxillofacial Surgery Center
Oxygen Therapy
Pain Management Center
Pediatric Surgery
Pharmacy Services
Pulmonary Medicine
Pulmonary Rehabilitation
Physical Therapy
Rehabilitation
Respiratory Care
Senior Health Center
Sports Medicine
Surgery
Speech Therapy
Urgent Car
Urgent Car
Visiting Nurse Association of Manchester & So. NH Inc.
Weight Management
Wellness Center
Women's & Children's Services
Wound Center

COMPETITORS

Caritas Holy Family Hospital
Catholic Medical Center
Concord Hospital
Exeter Health Resources
Frisbie Memorial Hospital
HCA
Southern New Hampshire Medical Center

HISTORICAL FINANCIALS

Company Type: Private

Income Statement FYE: June 30

	REVENUE ($ mil.)	NET INCOME ($ mil.)	NET PROFIT MARGIN	EMPLOYEES
06/20	549	(27)	—	2,000
06/19	560	(4)	—	—
06/16	394	49	12.5%	—
06/15	421	43	10.4%	—
Annual Growth	5.4%	—	—	—

2020 Year-End Financials

Return on assets: (-4.6%)
Return on equity: (-24.1%)
Current ratio: 1.20
Cash ($ mil.): 113

EMANATE HEALTH MEDICAL GROUP

Citrus Valley Health Partners is a 660-bed hospital system that serves the residents of California's San Gabriel Valley region located between Los Angeles and San Bernardino. It operates through four health care facilities: Citrus Valley Medical Center (CVMC) Queen of the Valley Campus CVMC Inter-Community Campus Foothill Presbyterian Hospital and Citrus Valley Hospice. Citrus Valley Health Partners also operates a home health care provider that offers nursing and rehabilitation care. The hospital system boasts several areas of specialty including diabetes care cancer treatment palliative care wound care and cardiac therapy.

Operations

Representing the largest slice of the Citrus Valley Health Partners system the CVMC Queen of the Valley Campus manages 325 beds and handles more than 54000 emergency room visits each year. The campus includes the Geleris Family Cancer Center; it is also known for birthing services that include a Level III Newborn Intensive Care Unit and it boasts robotic surgery systems and rehabilitation programs such as speech occupational and physical therapy for both children and adults.

With 220 beds the CVMC Inter-Community Campus specializes in cancer treatment electrophysiology cardiac care and wound care. The health system's Foothill Presbyterian Hospital boasts 105 beds and focuses on general acute care and such specialty services as an outpatient diabetes education program and rehabilitation. The Citrus Valley Hospice is a 10-bed inpatient facility that is the first freestanding hospice of its kind in California. Citrus Valley Home Health provides nursing and rehabilitation care.

Altogether the system employs some 1000 physicians at its facilities.

Geographic Reach

Citrus Valley Health Partners serves about 1 million residents from Covina Glendora and other California communities located in the San Gabriel Valley region.

Strategy

As part of a renovation and modernization program in 2013 the organization launched a construction program at its CVMC Inter-Community Campus to increase emergency operating and diagnostic capabilities. Once completed (in 2015) the new emergency department will nearly double the capacity of the campus' current 12-bed department. New patient treatment stations will enable medical nursing and support professionals to provide improved urgent care and other diagnostic care and treatment to more than 40000 patients each year.

In 2013 the Speech Pathology Outpatient Program expanded to include a Voice Clinic at Citrus Valley Medical Center – Queen of the Valley Campus in West Covina.

To reduce operational expenses that year Citrus Valley Health Partners signed a five-year $4.5 million managed print services agreement with Auxilio. Through the deal Auxilio will help the network improve process efficiencies supply chain management volume reduction and other initiatives.

Company Background

Inter-Community Campus began as a seven-bed hospital founded in 1922 by sisters Melisse and Mary Wittler a nurse and a schoolteacher.

EXECUTIVES

Secretary, Janet Lowe
Auditors: ERNST & YOUNG LLP LOS ANGELE

LOCATIONS

HQ: EMANATE HEALTH MEDICAL GROUP
210 W SAN BERNARDINO RD, COVINA, CA 917231515
Phone: 626 331-7331
Web: WWW.EMANATEHEALTH.ORG

PRODUCTS/OPERATIONS

Selected Services

Cancer services
Diabetes care unit
Diabetes education program
Emergency room services
Home health
Hospice
Maternity services
Newborn intensive care
Palliative care
Pediatric services
Rehabilitation
Robotic surgery

COMPETITORS

Anaheim Regional Medical Center
City of Hope
Glendale Adventist Medical Center
Good Samaritan Hospital (Los Angeles)
Memorial Health Services
Methodist Hospital of Southern California
Newhall Memorial Hospital
Pasadena Hospital Association
St. Jude Medical Center
Western Medical Center - Santa Ana

HISTORICAL FINANCIALS

Company Type: Private

Income Statement FYE: December 31

	REVENUE ($ mil.)	NET INCOME ($ mil.)	NET PROFIT MARGIN	EMPLOYEES
12/18	606	21	3.5%	2,800
12/17	64	2	3.8%	—
12/16	61	0	1.4%	—
12/15	58	(2)	—	—
Annual Growth	118.5%	—	—	—

2018 Year-End Financials

Return on assets: 2.9%
Return on equity: 4.3%
Current ratio: 1.90
Cash ($ mil.): 24

EMJ CORPORATION

EMJ does it all for the mall. Founded in 1968 by namesake Edgar M. Jolley the company specializes in building and renovating retail outlets and shopping centers throughout the US. It is also known for other building projects such as offices warehouses churches hotels multifamily residences hospitals and wind farms. Working from five offices nationwide EMJ provides general construction and construction management. The company's pre-construction services include creating detailed budgets and construction schedules and coordinating permitting utility companies and municipal requirements. To track a project's progress and monitor costs EMJ offers quality control and safety and warranty management.

Operations

EMJ owns several operating divisions including Signal Energy which engineers and builds renewable energy projects such as wind farms and solar and biomass energy projects. Another division Accent Construction Management provides site selection budgeting scheduling and other services. Its RedStone Construction Services builds commercial retail hospitality healthcare government facilities and others. It is focused on fostering economic growth in Native American communities.

Geographic Reach

From its base in Chattanooga Tennessee EMJ serves clients through a handful of US offices in Massachusetts Tennessee Texas and California.

Sales and Marketing

EMJ has built more than 500 million sq. ft. of construction projects. Its client roster includes Academy Barnes & Noble Bed Bath & Beyond Blue Cross and Blue Shield Home Depot PetSmart and Winn-Dixie.

The company serves several sectors such as airports education entertainment government and civic grocery healthcare hospitality industrial and warehouse and Native American tribal communities office buildings parking lifestyle and mixed use development retail renewable energy renovations and worship centers.

Strategy

The company is working on projects for Whole Foods Market TownPlace Suites Silverdale Baptist student center and Dick's Sporting Goods. Inked in 2013 EMJ's $250-million deal with Native American Chris Samples operating under the name RedStone Construction Services is building a 500-room hotel and expanding a casino in Tulsa Oklahoma.

EXECUTIVES

Vice President, Christopher Hall
Executive Vice President, Ray Catlin
Senior Vice President Of Construction, Jack Bowen
Vice President, Lance Gopffarth
Senior Vice President Of Construction, Philip Augustino
Vice President Southwest Office, Drew Halsey
Senior Vice President, Chas Torrence
Vice President Of Construction, Howard Smith
Vice President Of Construction, George Heath

LOCATIONS

HQ: EMJ CORPORATION
2034 HAMILTON PLACE BLVD # 400, CHATTANOOGA, TN 374216102
Phone: 423 855-1550
Web: WWW.EMJCORP.COM

PRODUCTS/OPERATIONS

Selected Projects
Airports
Education
Entertainment
Government/civic
Grocery
Healthcare
Hospitality
Industrial/warehouse
Lifestyle/mixed use development and retail
Native American tribal communities
Office buildings
Parking
Renewable energy
Renovations
Worship centers

Selected Services

Construction
Construction management
General contracting
Pre-construction services
Quality control
Safety consultation
Site evaluation
Warranty

COMPETITORS

Case Contracting
Embree Construction
Fisher Development
Graycor
Hardaway Construction
Hardin Construction
Hayward Baker
Hoar Construction
JESCO
Rodgers Builders
S.D. Deacon
Skanska USA Building
Weis Builders
Workman Commercial

HISTORICAL FINANCIALS

Company Type: Private

Income Statement — FYE: March 7

	REVENUE ($ mil.)	NET INCOME ($ mil.)	NET PROFIT MARGIN	EMPLOYEES
03/17*	960	4	0.5%	210
12/11	437	0	0.1%	—
12/08	821	7	1.0%	—
12/07	959	10	1.1%	—
Annual Growth	0.0%	(7.9%)	—	—

*Fiscal year change

2017 Year-End Financials

Return on assets: 2.3%
Return on equity: 18.5%
Current ratio: 1.10
Cash ($ mil.): 29

EMORY UNIVERSITY HOSPITAL MIDTOWN

EXECUTIVES

Ceo, Robert J Bachman
Dir*, Rosalind K Lett
Pres*, John T Fox
Exec V Pres*, S Wright Caughman
Attorney, Lorraine Spencer
Chief of Medicine, Harold Ramos
Director, Jakob V Johansen
Assistant Professor, James Weisberg
Coordinator, Crystal Evans
Otolaryngologist, Sarah Wise
Cardiovascular Disease, Alexis G Cutchins

LOCATIONS

HQ: EMORY UNIVERSITY HOSPITAL MIDTOWN
550 PEACHTREE ST NE, ATLANTA, GA 303082212
Phone: 404 686-4411
Web: WWW.EMORYHEALTHCARE.ORG

HISTORICAL FINANCIALS

Company Type: Private

Income Statement — FYE: August 31

	REVENUE ($ mil.)	NET INCOME ($ mil.)	NET PROFIT MARGIN	EMPLOYEES
08/16	735	64	8.7%	2,500
08/15	641	(21)	—	—
Annual Growth	14.8%	—	—	—

2016 Year-End Financials

Return on assets: 9.9%
Return on equity: 38.5%
Current ratio: 2.50
Cash ($ mil.): 269

EMPIRE SOUTHWEST, LLC

With CAT-like tread Empire Southwest has created a heavy equipment sales rental and leasing empire in the US Southwest. One of the largest Caterpillar dealerships in the US Empire Southwest operates through five divisions: hydraulic service machinery power systems precision machining and transport. The company's equipment includes backhoes compactors dozers front shovels loaders pipelayers telehandlers and tractors. It also handles equipment used for mining and forestry projects. Empire Southwest also sells ARCO agricultural equipment carries batteries power generators engines and tools and has a service department.

Operations

Empire Southwest consists of five operating divisions. Empire Machinery sells rents and provides product support for Caterpillar equipment and other brands. Empire Power Systems sells rents and provides product support for the Caterpillar engines used to provide power for electricity generation water pumping and other industrial applications.

Empire Transport hauls heavy equipment and other oversize loads for customers and other Empire divisions while Empire Precision Machining is a large machining shop that can handle massive components. Empire Hydraulic Service specializes in repairing and refurbishing all brands of heavy equipment hydraulic systems.

Geographic Reach

Since moving to the Southwest Empire has carved out a territory that includes more than 30 communities in Arizona southeastern California and portions of northern Mexico.

Sales and Marketing

The company targets the agriculture mining demo and scrap oil and gas forestry on-highway truck general construction heavy construction railway power marine and waste management industries.

Company Background

The company was founded in 1950 when Jack Whiteman acquired Empire Machinery (which held the Caterpillar and John Deere dealerships in eastern Oregon). In 1959 he relocated to Arizona and took over a Caterpillar dealership there.

EXECUTIVES

Chairman And Ceo, Jeffrey S. (Jeff) Whiteman
Executive Vice President, Chris Zaharis
Vice President, Jim Smith

LOCATIONS

HQ: EMPIRE SOUTHWEST, LLC
1725 S COUNTRY CLUB DR, MESA, AZ 852106099
Phone: 480 633-4000
Web: WWW.EMPIRE-CAT.COM

PRODUCTS/OPERATIONS

Selected Industries Served

Agriculture
Demo and Scrap
Forestry
General Construction
Governmental
Heavy Construction
Landscaping
Marine
Mining
Oil and Gas
On-Highway Truck
Paving
Pipeline
Quarry and Aggregates
Waste

COMPETITORS

Arnold Machinery
Cashman Equipment
Cummins
Komatsu
Komatsu America
Multiquip
NES Rentals
Sunbelt Rentals
United Rentals

HISTORICAL FINANCIALS

Company Type: Private

Income Statement — FYE: October 31

	REVENUE ($ mil.)	NET INCOME ($ mil.)	NET PROFIT MARGIN	EMPLOYEES
10/11	683	38	5.6%	1,450
10/10	528	22	4.3%	—
10/09	448	7	1.6%	—
Annual Growth	23.5%	127.0%	—	—

ENERG1Y RESEARCH AND DEVELOPMENT AUTHORITY, NEW YORK STATE

The New York State Energy Research and Development Authority (NYSERDA) uses technological innovation to solve the state's energy and environmental problems. The public benefit corporation funds energy supply and conservation research and energy-related environmental issues. It also conducts research projects that help state and city groups solve their energy problems. Its Energy Efficiency Services group works helps more than 450 schools businesses and municipalities find ways to reduce their energy costs. Investor-owned electric and gas utilities grants and contributions from the New York Power Authority and the Long Island Power Authority fund NYSERDA which was created in 1975.

EXECUTIVES

Acting President And Acting Ceo, Robert (Bob) Callender
Manager Information Technology, D. Young
Coo, David Margalit
Chairman, Vincent A. Delorio
Auditors: KPMG LLP ALBANY NEW YORK

LOCATIONS

HQ: ENERGY RESEARCH AND DEVELOPMENT AUTHORITY, NEW YORK STATE
17 COLUMBIA CIR, ALBANY, NY 122035156
Phone: 518 862-1090
Web: WWW.NYSERDA.NY.GOV

HISTORICAL FINANCIALS

Company Type: Private

Income Statement — FYE: March 31

	REVENUE ($ mil.)	NET INCOME ($ mil.)	NET PROFIT MARGIN	EMPLOYEES
03/19	1,091	51	4.7%	345
03/17	0	(0)	—	—
Annual Growth	7215.0%	—	—	—

ENTERGY SERVICES, LLC

EXECUTIVES

Ceo, Leo P Denault
Cfo*, Andrew Marsh
Coo*, Mark T Savoff
Pres*, Theo Bunting Jr
Exec Pres*, Marcus V Brown
V Pres*, Kimberly H Despeaux
V Pres*, Jere M Ahrens
V Pres*, Kay K Arnold
V Pres*, Michael A Balduzzi
V Pres*, Kelle J Barfield
Director, Cory Gruntz

LOCATIONS

HQ: ENTERGY SERVICES, LLC
639 LOYOLA AVE STE 300, NEW ORLEANS, LA 701137106
Phone: 504 576-4000
Web: WWW.ENTERGY.COM

HISTORICAL FINANCIALS

Company Type: Private

Income Statement — FYE: December 31

	REVENUE ($ mil.)	NET INCOME ($ mil.)	NET PROFIT MARGIN	EMPLOYEES
12/16	1,112	10	0.9%	1,325
12/04	10,123	933	9.2%	—
Annual Growth	(16.8%)	(31.2%)	—	—

2016 Year-End Financials

Return on assets: 0.8%
Return on equity: —
Current ratio: 0.70
Cash ($ mil.): 51

ENTERPRISE CRUDE PIPELINE LLC

EXECUTIVES

Pres, W Randall Fowler
Technician, Jacob Kahanek
Technician Mechanical, Willie Stubbs

LOCATIONS

HQ: ENTERPRISE CRUDE PIPELINE LLC
1100 LOUISIANA ST # 1000, HOUSTON, TX 770025227
Phone: 713 381-6500
Web: WWW.ENTERPRISEPRODUCTS.COM

HISTORICAL FINANCIALS

Company Type: Private

Income Statement — FYE: December 31

	REVENUE ($ mil.)	NET INCOME ($ mil.)	NET PROFIT MARGIN	EMPLOYEES
12/17	596	378	63.5%	300
12/16	472	284	60.2%	—
Annual Growth	26.2%	33.1%	—	—

ENTERPRISE TE PRODUCTS PIPELINE COMPANY LLC

EXECUTIVES

Ceo-MBR, Jerry E Thompson
Cfo-MBR, William G Manias
Technician, Brian Hall
Technician Pipeline, Kenneston Hale
Technician, Destry Starkey
Technician Pipeline, Rusty Bengston
Operations, Tim Kistner
Operations, Juan Contreras
Operations, Lonnie Foust
Technician Pipeline, Paul Deken
Operations, Ross Corbett

LOCATIONS

HQ: ENTERPRISE TE PRODUCTS PIPELINE COMPANY LLC
1100 LOUISIANA ST # 1600, HOUSTON, TX 770025227
Phone: 713 381-6500
Web: WWW.ENTERPRISEPRODUCTS.COM

HISTORICAL FINANCIALS

Company Type: Private

Income Statement — FYE: December 31

	REVENUE ($ mil.)	NET INCOME ($ mil.)	NET PROFIT MARGIN	EMPLOYEES
12/17	659	337	51.1%	8
12/16	628	275	43.9%	—
Annual Growth	5.0%	22.3%	—	—

EQUINOR MARKETING & TRADING (US) INC.

Check the stats. Oil. Hundreds of thousands of barrels of oil gasoline and more. Statoil Marketing & Trading is a wholesaler of oil and petroleum products. The company is the US trading arm of Statoil the leading Scandinavian oil and gas enterprise. Statoil Marketing & Trading delivers about 600000 barrels a day in the form of crude oil gasoline liquefied petroleum gas (LPG) propane and butane to the North American market. In addition to supplying Norwegian crude the company trades crude oil from Africa South America and North America. Statoil Marketing & Trading sells it oil products primarily to customers in Northeastern Canada the US East Coast and Gulf Coast.

EXECUTIVES

Vice President Of Administration, Geir Bjornstad
Executive Vice President Development And Production International, Torgrim Reitan
Executive Vice President Development And Production Brazil, Margareth Ovrum
Vice President Human Resources Services, Siv Oftedal
Vice President Operations Subsea, Rune Aase
Vice President Legal, Paul Owen
Vice President Project Management, Erik Westad
Vice President Project Management, Johnny Wollberg
Vice President Quality, Magne Ottera
Vice President, Sverre Serck-hanssen
Vice President Of Supply Chain, Mauro Andrade
Vp Tax, Tom Geczik
Executive Vice President Technology Projects And Drilling, Anders Opedal
Vice President Communications, Nathaniel Teti
Auditors: KPMG LLP STAMFORD CONNECTICU

LOCATIONS

HQ: EQUINOR MARKETING & TRADING (US) INC.
120 LONG RIDGE RD 3EO1, STAMFORD, CT 069021839
Phone: 203 978-6900
Web: WWW.STATOIL.COM

COMPETITORS

Global Partners	Irving Oil Limited
Gulf Oil	Shell Oil
Hess Corporation	Tauber Oil

HISTORICAL FINANCIALS

Company Type: Private

Income Statement — FYE: December 31

	REVENUE ($ mil.)	NET INCOME ($ mil.)	NET PROFIT MARGIN	EMPLOYEES
12/17	9,874	(28)	—	5
12/16	5,984	(259)	—	—
12/15	6,947	(132)	—	—
12/14	12,075	(140)	—	—
Annual Growth	(6.5%)	—	—	—

2017 Year-End Financials

Return on assets: (-1.4%)
Return on equity: (-9.6%)
Current ratio: 1.30
Cash ($ mil.): 46

EQUINOR NATURAL GAS LLC

EXECUTIVES

Pres, Asbjrn Skretting
Sec-General Counsel, Charles T O'Brien
Controller, Neil Tarling
Leader Tax, Kathleen Parchinski
Assistant Secretary, Josh Kaplan
Cfo, Gary A Turiano
V Pres of Tax, Martin J Pastore
Originator, Hugh Gleason
Operator, Paula Ahern
Researcher, Yaping Zhu
Auditors: KPMG LLP STAMFORD CONNECTICU

LOCATIONS

HQ: EQUINOR NATURAL GAS LLC
120 LONG RIDGE RD, STAMFORD, CT 069021839
Phone: 203 978-6900
Web: WWW.STATOIL.COM

HISTORICAL FINANCIALS

Company Type: Private

Income Statement — FYE: December 31

	REVENUE ($ mil.)	NET INCOME ($ mil.)	NET PROFIT MARGIN	EMPLOYEES
12/15	1,967	722	36.7%	15
12/13	3,507	(127)	—	—
12/10	1,614	149	9.3%	—
12/08	1,640	168	10.3%	—
Annual Growth	2.6%	23.1%	—	—

2015 Year-End Financials

Return on assets: 46.0% — Cash ($ mil.): 20
Return on equity: 67.1%
Current ratio: 3.40

ERIE COUNTY MEDICAL CENTER CORP.

EXECUTIVES

Ceo, Jody L Lomeo
Cfo*, Jonathan T Swiatkowski
Coo*, Richard C Cleland
R V Pres*, Ronald Krawiec
R V Pres*, Karen Ziemianski
Cfo*, Steven Gary
Chro-General Counsel*, Joseph T Giglia II
Evp*, Anthony J Colucci III
Asst Ceo, Kathleen Gellart
Infectious Diseases, Chiu Bin Hsiao
Internal Medicine Practitioner, Nelda Lawler
Auditors: RSM US LLP

LOCATIONS

HQ: ERIE COUNTY MEDICAL CENTER CORP.
462 GRIDER ST, BUFFALO, NY 142153098
Phone: 716 898-3000
Web: WWW.ECMC.EDU

HISTORICAL FINANCIALS

Company Type: Private

Income Statement — FYE: December 31

	REVENUE ($ mil.)	NET INCOME ($ mil.)	NET PROFIT MARGIN	EMPLOYEES
12/19	750	12	1.7%	3,300
12/18	661	1	0.2%	—
12/16	616	1	0.3%	—
12/14	514	3	0.6%	—
Annual Growth	7.8%	33.8%	—	—

2019 Year-End Financials

Return on assets: 1.4% — Cash ($ mil.): 13
Return on equity: —
Current ratio: 1.60

ERM-NA HOLDINGS CORP.

EXECUTIVES

Pres-Dir, David James McArthur
V Pres*, Michael O'Shaughnessy
V Pres*, Mark Pearson
V Pres-Dir*, Susan Angyal
Treas-Dir*, John Stipa
Asst Treas*, Joanne Della Valle
SEC*, Roy A Burrows
Store Director, Mamie Brown
Senior Geologist, Chris Berg
Gis Program Manager NA, Keith Kendall
Administrative Assistant, Penny Villafarra
Auditors: DELOITTE & TOUCHE LLP PHILADE

LOCATIONS

HQ: ERM-NA HOLDINGS CORP.
75 VALLEY STREAM PKWY, MALVERN, PA 193551459
Phone: 484 913-0300
Web: WWW.ERM.COM

HISTORICAL FINANCIALS

Company Type: Private

Income Statement — FYE: March 31

	REVENUE ($ mil.)	NET INCOME ($ mil.)	NET PROFIT MARGIN	EMPLOYEES
03/20	599	39	6.6%	1,573
03/19	405	31	7.9%	—
03/18	358	14	4.1%	—
03/17	356	10	2.9%	—
Annual Growth	18.9%	56.6%	—	—

2020 Year-End Financials

Return on assets: 8.5% — Cash ($ mil.): 29
Return on equity: 13.5%
Current ratio: 1.40

ESTES EXPRESS LINES

Founded during the Depression with a Chevy truck Estes Express Lines has grown into a multiregional less-than-truckload (LTL) freight hauler. Its fleet of some 7100 tractors and 25700 trailers operates via a network of some 210 terminals dotting the US. Service in Canada is provided by TST Overland Express an ExpressLINK partner and in Mexico through affiliate Almex. Estes Express works with designated carriers to offer door-to-door delivery in the Caribbean and in Mexico. Subsidiary Estes Forwarding Worldwide services ocean/air freight forwarding. The company is owned and run by the family of founder W.W. Estes.

Operations

The company operates through several divisions and companies. Divisions include Estes Time-Critical (offering four levels of shipping) Level2 Logistics (business-to-business and business-to-consumer shipping) Estes Specialized Truckload and Delivery Services and Estes SureMove (customers load shipments themselves and Estes provides transportation). Companies include Estes Forwarding Worldwide Estes Brokerage Estes Leasing and Big E Transportation.

Geographic Reach

Estes Express offers regional service to all 50 US states. It also offers direct service to Canada Mexico and the Caribbean.

Strategy

Estes Express has continued to build out its LTL business by offering expedited delivery volume truckload transportation supply chain management nationwide brokerage services warehousing services and equipment leasing. The latter has provided such rental services as laundry trucks for the Department of Veterans Affairs. Its slate of services are supported by an upgraded wireless onboard pickup and delivery system featuring real-time data enabling terminals and drivers to process freight more efficiently. It has also formed a Mexico third-party logistics subsidiary Estes Logistica for managing freight consolidation and transportation to points south of the US border.

Estes Express over the years has opened new offices in San Francisco Los Angeles Dallas Chicago Miami and New York. To support the continuing market growth in the Midwest in 2015 it opened a new terminal in Oswego Illinois. The next year it opened an additional terminal in the Chicago area to replace a smaller facility. The new location is in Markham Illinois and is the seventh terminal the company owns in the state.

Company Background

The company was formed in 1931.

EXECUTIVES

Vice President Human Resources, Tom Donahue
President And Ceo, Rob W. Estes, age 68
V Pres Corp Comm, Patricia Garland
President And Ceo Estes Forwarding Worldwide, Scott Fisher
Coo, Billy Hupp
Vp And Chief Information Officer, Bob Fowler
Corporate Vice President Of Operations, Al Bucher
Vice President National Accounts, Morton Mustian
Vice President Information Technology, Hugh Canden
Vice President, Steve Adkins
Vice President Fleet Services, Mike Palmer
Vice President Corporate Sales, Chuck Parker
V.p.d.p., Hugh Camden
Vice President Of Pricing And Traffic, Paul Dugent
Vice President Compliance And Field Support, Wayne Young
Vice President Of Information Technology, Thomas Donahue
Vice President Human Resources, Thomas Donaue
Vice President Of Human Resources, Greg Richardson
Vp Integrated Solutions, Ken Niemaseck

LOCATIONS

HQ: ESTES EXPRESS LINES
3901 W BROAD ST, RICHMOND, VA 232303962
Phone: 804 353-1900
Web: WWW.ESTES-EXPRESS.COM

PRODUCTS/OPERATIONS

Selected Services

Global (airfreight ocean international consolidation/deconsolidation customs brokerage international freight forwarding)
Less-than-truckload (regional national international/offshore)
Time critical (expedited guaranteed time/date definite)
Volume & truckload (LTL full loads backhaul services truckload brokerage dedicated truckload)

COMPETITORS

AAA Cooper Transportation
ArcBest
Averitt Express
FedEx Freight
Old Dominion Freight
Penske Truck Leasing
R+L Carriers
Ryder System
Saia
UPS Freight
Vitran
YRC Worldwide

HISTORICAL FINANCIALS

Company Type: Private

Income Statement — FYE: December 31

	REVENUE ($ mil.)	NET INCOME ($ mil.)	NET PROFIT MARGIN	EMPLOYEES
12/19	3,259	251	7.7%	14,000
12/18	3,159	252	8.0%	—
12/17	2,731	231	8.5%	—
12/16	2,403	128	5.3%	—
Annual Growth	10.7%	25.2%	—	—

2019 Year-End Financials

Return on assets: 13.6%
Return on equity: 19.0%
Current ratio: 1.80
Cash ($ mil.): 146

EVERGY MISSOURI WEST, INC.

EXECUTIVES

Ceo, Terry D Bassham
Sr V Pres*, Paul Perkins
V Pres*, Maria Jenks
V Pres*, Marvin L Rollison
V Pres*, Chuck Tickles
V Pres*, Stephen T Easley
V Pres*, Scott Heidtbrink
V Pres*, Lori A Wright
V Pres*, Jim Alberts
V Pres*, Kevin E Bryant
V Pres*, Lora C Cheatman

LOCATIONS

HQ: EVERGY MISSOURI WEST, INC.
1200 MAIN ST FL 30, KANSAS CITY, MO 641052122
Phone: 816 556-2200
Web: WWW.EVERGY.COM

HISTORICAL FINANCIALS

Company Type: Private

Income Statement — FYE: December 31

	REVENUE ($ mil.)	NET INCOME ($ mil.)	NET PROFIT MARGIN	EMPLOYEES
12/18	833	27	3.3%	2,213
12/17	818	(40)	—	—
12/16	801	60	7.6%	—
Annual Growth	2.0%	(32.8%)	—	—

2018 Year-End Financials

Return on assets: 0.8%
Return on equity: 2.3%
Current ratio: 2.50
Cash ($ mil.): 1

EVERSOURCE ENERGY SERVICE COMPANY

Northeast Utilities Service Company (NUSCO) provides support and reports for its cohorts. The company was created in 1966 to centralize corporate activities for Northeast Utilities (renamed Eversource Energy). NUSCO acts as an agent and offers centralized administrative services not only for its parent company Northeast Utilities but all of its subsidiaries (Connecticut Light and Power Public Service Company of New Hampshire Western Massachusetts Electric and Yankee Gas Services Company) as well. NUSCO duties include accounting financial legal operational information technology engineering planning and purchasing services.

EXECUTIVES

Vice President Finance Treasurer And Secretary Select Energy Services, Linda A Jensen
Vice President Governmental Affairs Northeast Utilities, Margaret Morton
Vice President, Mary J Keating
Vice President Electric System Operations, Joseph Luchini
Vice President Network Support, Alan Landever
Vice President Transmission Operations, Dwayne Basler
Vice President Customer Operations, Robert Coates
Vice President Rates And Regulatory Requirements, Christine Vaughan
Vice President Finance, Michael J Ausere
Vice President Engineering, Ken Bowes
Vice President, Rod Kay

LOCATIONS

HQ: EVERSOURCE ENERGY SERVICE COMPANY
56 PROSPECT ST, HARTFORD, CT 061032818
Phone: 800 286-5000
Web: WWW.EVERSOURCE.COM

COMPETITORS

Connecticut Water Service
PSEG Fossil

HISTORICAL FINANCIALS

Company Type: Private

Income Statement — FYE: December 31

	REVENUE ($ mil.)	NET INCOME ($ mil.)	NET PROFIT MARGIN	EMPLOYEES
12/16	831	11	1.4%	4,550
12/08	5,800	260	4.5%	—
12/07	5,822	246	4.2%	—
12/05	0	0	—	—
Annual Growth	—	—	—	—

2016 Year-End Financials

Return on assets: 0.8%
Return on equity: 8.2%
Current ratio: 0.60
Cash ($ mil.): 11

FAIRFAX COUNTY VIRGINIA

EXECUTIVES

City Exec, Anthony H Griffin
Business Dir, Angela Shaw
Telecommunications Staff, Alton Drew
Information, Tanya Quinonez
Captain, Roger Arnn
Coordinator, Kelly Bachand
Assistant Chief, Daryl Louder
Information Specialist, Joseph Sorrentino
Information Specialist, Michael Liddle
Battalion Chief Fire, Andrew Duke
Director, Catherine Spage
Auditors: KPMG LLP WASHINGTON DC

LOCATIONS

HQ: FAIRFAX COUNTY VIRGINIA
12000 GVRNMENT CTR PKWY S, FAIRFAX, VA 220350002
Phone: 703 324-3126
Web: WWW.FAIRFAXCOUNTY.GOV

HISTORICAL FINANCIALS

Company Type: Private

Income Statement — FYE: June 30

	REVENUE ($ mil.)	NET INCOME ($ mil.)	NET PROFIT MARGIN	EMPLOYEES
06/18	4,806	71	1.5%	12,000
06/17	4,695	171	3.6%	—
06/16	4,469	49	1.1%	—
06/15	0	60	—	—
Annual Growth	—	5.8%	—	—

2018 Year-End Financials

Return on assets: 0.4%
Return on equity: 18.8%
Current ratio: —
Cash ($ mil.): 1,364

FAIRVIEW HEALTH SERVICES

It's fair to say that when it comes to health care Fairview Health Services takes the long view. The not-for-profit system serves Minnesota's Twin Cities and nearby communities. Fairview Health is affiliated with the medical school of the University of Minnesota and counts among its 10 hospitals the University of Minnesota Medical Center. The hospitals house more than 2500 beds and provide comprehensive medical and surgical services. The system also operates primary and specialty care clinics that provide preventive and wellness care. Additionally it operates retail pharmacies and nursing homes and provides home health care and rehabilitation. Merger talks with University of Minnesota Physicians have stalled.

EXECUTIVES

Vice President Chief Information Security Officer, Barry Caplin
Vice President And Treasurer, Kim Faust
Nursing Director, Debbie Tharp
Vp It Systems And Ciso, Judy Hatchett
Vice President Consumer Solutions And System Operations Center, Marlena Kane
Auditors: ERNST & YOUNG LLP MINNEAPOLI

LOCATIONS

HQ: FAIRVIEW HEALTH SERVICES
7505 METRO BLVD STE 100, EDINA, MN 554393017
Phone: 612 672-6300
Web: WWW.FAIRVIEW.ORG

COMPETITORS

Abbott Northwestern Hospital
Allina Hospitals
Bethesda Hospital
Catholic Health Initiatives
CentraCare Health
HealthEast Care System
Mayo Clinic
North Memorial Health Care
Park Nicollet Health Services
Regions Hospital
St. John's Hospital (Minnesota)

HISTORICAL FINANCIALS

Company Type: Private

Income Statement — FYE: December 31

	REVENUE ($ mil.)	NET INCOME ($ mil.)	NET PROFIT MARGIN	EMPLOYEES
12/19	6,049	13	0.2%	18,000
12/18	5,709	5	0.1%	—
12/17	5,275	511	9.7%	—
Annual Growth	7.1%	(83.8%)	—	—

2019 Year-End Financials

Return on assets: 0.3%
Return on equity: 0.5%
Current ratio: 1.70
Cash ($ mil.): 70

FAMILY HEALTH INTERNATIONAL INC

Known as FHI 360 Family Health International believes that health is wealth. From a handful of offices located in the US Asia-Pacific and South Africa FHI 360 funds and manages public health programs research education and other resources in more than 60 countries. Founded in 1971 as the International Fertility Research Program of the University of North Carolina at Chapel Hill FHI 360 primarily focuses on and supports HIV/AIDS prevention research reproductive health services and maternal and neonatal health programs. The organization works with governments private agencies and non-governmental organizations to develop the most appropriate programs for different areas.

EXECUTIVES

Acting Chief Financial Officer, Rasika Padmaperuma
Executive Vice President And General Counsel, Robert Price
Auditors: ERNST & YOUNG US LLP TAMPA F

LOCATIONS

HQ: FAMILY HEALTH INTERNATIONAL INC
359 BLACKWELL ST STE 200, DURHAM, NC 277012477
Phone: 919 544-7040
Web: WWW.FHI360.ORG

PRODUCTS/OPERATIONS

Selected Services
Behavior-change communication
Capacity-building
Clinical trials services
Creative services
Data analysis
Quality assurance
Research services
Social marketing
Training and technical assistance

HISTORICAL FINANCIALS

Company Type: Private

Income Statement — FYE: September 30

	REVENUE ($ mil.)	NET INCOME ($ mil.)	NET PROFIT MARGIN	EMPLOYEES
09/14	653	(3)	—	4,000
09/13	664	10	1.5%	—
09/09	327	2	0.9%	—
Annual Growth	14.8%	—	—	—

2014 Year-End Financials

Return on assets: (-1.4%)
Return on equity: (-4.3%)
Current ratio: 1.50
Cash ($ mil.): 130

FAMILY HEALTH NETWORK, INC.

EXECUTIVES

Ceo, Keith Kudla
Pres*, Philip C Bradley
Cfo*, Tom Tennison
Information Specialist, Linda Merchant
Information Specialist, Shawn Cull
Senior Financial Analyst, Elisa Chiu
Intake Coordinator, Karin Fields
Compliance Director, Camille Trunkett
Claims Supervisor, James Segatto
Marketing Coordinator, Lawrence Evans
Senior Manager Claims, Mark Tikalsky

LOCATIONS

HQ: FAMILY HEALTH NETWORK, INC.
222 MERCHANDISE MART PLZ # 960, CHICAGO, IL 606541236
Phone: 312 243-5235
Web: WWW.FHNCHICAGO.COM

HISTORICAL FINANCIALS

Company Type: Private

Income Statement — FYE: December 31

	REVENUE ($ mil.)	NET INCOME ($ mil.)	NET PROFIT MARGIN	EMPLOYEES
12/17	549	(23)	—	30
12/09	60	2	4.9%	—
12/08	56	0	—	—
Annual Growth	28.7%	—	—	—

2017 Year-End Financials

Return on assets: (-15.0%)
Return on equity: (-341.2%)
Current ratio: —
Cash ($ mil.): 59

FARM CREDIT BANK OF TEXAS

The largest member of the federal Farm Credit System the Farm Credit Bank of Texas provides loans and financial services to about 20 lending cooperatives and financial institutions in Alabama Louisiana Mississippi New Mexico and Texas. These include agricultural credit associations which provide agricultural production loans agribusiness financing and rural mortgage financing; and federal land credit associations which offer real estate loans on farms ranches and other rural property. Farm Credit Bank of Texas is owned by the lending cooperatives it serves.

EXECUTIVES

Senior Vice President Policy Compliance, Matthew Byerly
Senior Vice President, Rusty Lampman
Vice President, Steve Donnell
Vice President And Controller, Vicki Rodriguez
Vice President Business Development, Jeremy Lightfoot
Vice President, Paul Rudd
Vice President Product Development, Paul Barton
Vice President Business Systems Unit Manager, Ed Benson
Vice President, Darren Cannon
Senior Vice President And Cco, John Logsdon
Vice President Regional Manager, Chris Amend
Vice President Lending, Boyd J Chambers
Vice President, Heath Davis
Vice President Collateral Risk Management, Brad Swinney
Vice President, Amy Pala
Vice President Branch Manager, Angela Shannon
Assistant Vice President Operations, William Foley
Vice President, Ronnie Sellers
Assistant Vice President At The Clarksdale Branch Office, Bobby Spinks
Vp Of Compliance, Thomas Ringler
Vice President, Jason Gandy
Vp Of It Compliance, Igor Stojanovski
Vice President, Mike Tippit
Senior Vice President, Doug Reinart
Senior Vice President Relationship Manager, Brett Valentine
Board Of Directors, Buddy Cortese
Auditors: PRICEWATERHOUSECOOPERS LLP AU

LOCATIONS

HQ: FARM CREDIT BANK OF TEXAS
4801 PLAZA ON THE LK # 1200, AUSTIN, TX 787461081
Phone: 512 465-0400
Web: WWW.FARMCREDITBANK.COM

HISTORICAL FINANCIALS

Company Type: Private

Income Statement FYE: December 31

	ASSETS ($ mil.)	NET INCOME ($ mil.)	INCOME AS % OF ASSETS	EMPLOYEES
12/16	21,222	192	0.9%	200
12/13	16,212	179	1.1%	—
/ 0	0	—	—	
Annual Growth	—	—	—	—

2016 Year-End Financials

Return on assets: 0.9%
Return on equity: 11.9%
Sales ($ mil): 530

FARM CREDIT SERVICES OF AMERICA

EXECUTIVES

Pres-Ceo, Doug Stark
Exec V Pres*, Neil Olsen
Sr V Pres-Cfo*, Eugene College
Sr V Pres*, Michelle Mapes
Sr V Pres*, David Martin
Turner Youth Initiative Direct, Twila Phillips
Engineer, Dave Cook
Senior Vice President Agribusi, Marshall Hansen
Auditors: PRICEWATERHOUSECOOPERS LLP M

LOCATIONS

HQ: FARM CREDIT SERVICES OF AMERICA
5015 S 118TH ST, OMAHA, NE 681372210
Phone: 800 884-3276
Web: WWW.FCSAMERICA.COM

HISTORICAL FINANCIALS

Company Type: Private

Income Statement FYE: December 31

	ASSETS ($ mil.)	NET INCOME ($ mil.)	INCOME AS % OF ASSETS	EMPLOYEES
12/15	24,772	514	2.1%	10,000
12/04	8,475	294	3.5%	—
12/03	7,633	114	1.5%	—
12/02	0	132	—	—
Annual Growth	—	11.0%	—	—

2015 Year-End Financials

Return on assets: 2.1%
Return on equity: 11.9%
Sales ($ mil): 1,099

FARM CREDIT WEST

EXECUTIVES

Ceo-Pres, Mark D Littlefield
Sr V Pres, Chris N Brumfield
Exec V Pres, John C Boyes
Exe V Pres, William M Noland
Cfo, Chris Doherty
Exec V Pres-Fiscal ADM, Ernest M Hodges
Prin, K E Graff
Loan Officer, Danielle Vietti
Senior Vice President Chief, Denise Warkomski
Human Resources Generalist, Tanya Berry
Executive Vice President Chief, Dan Clawson
Auditors: PRICEWATERHOUSECOOPERS LLP SA

LOCATIONS

HQ: FARM CREDIT WEST
3755 ATHERTON RD, ROCKLIN, CA 957653701
Phone: 916 724-4800
Web: WWW.FARMCREDITWEST.COM

HISTORICAL FINANCIALS

Company Type: Private

Income Statement FYE: December 31

	ASSETS ($ mil.)	NET INCOME ($ mil.)	INCOME AS % OF ASSETS	EMPLOYEES
12/12	6,668	151	2.3%	165
12/11	6,282	176	2.8%	—
12/10	6,129	0	—	—
Annual Growth	4.3%	—	—	—

2012 Year-End Financials

Return on assets: 2.3%
Return on equity: 12.5%
Sales ($ mil): 295

FARMERS COOPERATIVE

EXECUTIVES

Pres, Ron Velver
SEC-Treas*, Glen Capek
Branch Manager, Terry King
Branch Manager, Bill Horton
General Manager, Desten Segrest
Operations Manager, Randi Webb
BR Mgr, Roger Jacobsma
Manager, Ronnie Truelock
Agronomy Sales, Angie Baker
Accounting Specialist, Jamie Sand
Beef Specialist, Linda McKay
Auditors: GARDINER THOMSEN LINCOLN NE

LOCATIONS

HQ: FARMERS COOPERATIVE
208 W DEPOT ST, DORCHESTER, NE 683432375
Phone: 402 946-4631
Web: WWW.FARMERSCO-OPERATIVE.COM

HISTORICAL FINANCIALS

Company Type: Private

Income Statement FYE: August 31

	REVENUE ($ mil.)	NET INCOME ($ mil.)	NET PROFIT MARGIN	EMPLOYEES
08/14	830	19	2.3%	470
08/12	918	22	2.5%	—
08/11	695	21	3.1%	—
08/10	636	0	0.0%	—
Annual Growth	6.9%	1803.9%	—	—

2014 Year-End Financials

Return on assets: 7.6%
Return on equity: 11.5%
Current ratio: 1.80
Cash ($ mil.): 28

FARMERS COOPERATIVE COMPANY

The importance of cooperation — it's one of life's most important lessons. Dating back to the early 1900s the Farmers Cooperative Company (FCC) learned that lesson early on. The 5500-member-plus co-op offers agronomy and grain marketing services to its members who oversee some 3 million acres of farmland in central and north central Iowa. The largest of its kind in Iowa FCC operates 40 grain elevators and provides soil testing and mapping services. It sells supplies including seed feed and fertilizer to its members. The coop merged with another Iowa coop West Central Cooperative in 2016 to form Landus Cooperative.

Operations

Farmers Cooperative (FCC) operates four departments: Agronomy Feed Grain and Seed. Agronomy serves customers at some 40 locations across central Iowa and is one of largest agronomy divisions in the state. The Feed department has six manufacturing locations across central north central and northwest Iowa. FCC's feed mills produce more than 900000 tons of complete feed annually. FCC has 40 grain elevators across its membership area. More than 118 million bushels of grain are handled annually. FCC also has grain storage capacity of 75 million bushels. The cooperative's Seed department works closely with the Agronomy division since both serve the same customers.

EXECUTIVES

Ceo, James Chism
Pres*, Rick Brand
V Pres*, Chuck Lindberg
Director, Jeff Mulder
Auditors: MERIWETHER WILSON & COMPANY

LOCATIONS

HQ: FARMERS COOPERATIVE COMPANY
105 GARFIELD AVE, FARNHAMVILLE, IA 505386712
Phone: 515 817-2100
Web: WWW.LANDUSCOOPERATIVE.COM

PRODUCTS/OPERATIONS

Selected Departments

Agronomy

Feed

Grain

Seed

COMPETITORS

ADM
Ag Processing Inc.
CHS
Cargill
DeBruce Grain
Farm Service Cooperative
Farmers Cooperative Society
Five Star Co-op
Gold-Eagle Cooperative
Heartland Co-op
Ingredion
Scoular
Swiss Valley Farms
West Central Co-op

HISTORICAL FINANCIALS

Company Type: Private

Income Statement				FYE: August 31
	REVENUE ($ mil.)	NET INCOME ($ mil.)	NET PROFIT MARGIN	EMPLOYEES
08/10	779	10	1.3%	450
08/09	894	13	1.5%	—
Annual Growth	(12.8%)	(19.9%)	—	—

2010 Year-End Financials

Return on assets: 5.6% Cash ($ mil.): —
Return on equity: 1.3%
Current ratio: —

FARMERS GRAIN TERMINAL, INC.

EXECUTIVES

Pres-Ceo, Steve Nail
Exec V Pres*, Harvey Parrish
V Pres*, C C Craig
V Pres*, John Oakes
Director, Herbert H Huddleston Jr
Assistant Manager, Robert Smith
Assistant Elevator Manager, Gary Ballard
Staff Accountant, Brian Strazi
Manager, Nash Knighton
Manager, Ronnie Ferrell
Auditors: HUDSON CISNE & CO LLP LITT

LOCATIONS

HQ: FARMERS GRAIN TERMINAL, INC.
1977 HARBOR FRONT RD, GREENVILLE, MS 387019588
Phone: 662 332-0987
Web: WWW.FGTCOOP.COM

HISTORICAL FINANCIALS

Company Type: Private

Income Statement				FYE: July 31
	REVENUE ($ mil.)	NET INCOME ($ mil.)	NET PROFIT MARGIN	EMPLOYEES
07/13	929	19	2.1%	102
07/12	615	12	2.1%	—
07/11	471	8	1.8%	—
Annual Growth	40.4%	53.0%	—	—

2013 Year-End Financials

Return on assets: 15.6% Cash ($ mil.): 64
Return on equity: 30.0%
Current ratio: 2.20

FATHER MURRAY NURSING CENTER

EXECUTIVES

Admin, Kim Harrell
Human Resources Manager, Brendon Weill
Auditors: DELOITTE TAX LLP DETROIT MI

LOCATIONS

HQ: FATHER MURRAY NURSING CENTER
8444 ENGLEMAN, CENTER LINE, MI 480151567
Phone: 586 755-2400
Web: WWW.FATHERMURRAYHCC.COM

HISTORICAL FINANCIALS

Company Type: Private

Income Statement				FYE: June 30
	REVENUE ($ mil.)	NET INCOME ($ mil.)	NET PROFIT MARGIN	EMPLOYEES
06/09	1,562	(1)	—	317
06/08	15	(0)	—	—
Annual Growth	9831.8%	—	—	—

2009 Year-End Financials

Return on assets: (-24.0%) Cash ($ mil.): —
Return on equity: (-293.2%)
Current ratio: 2.10

FCTG HOLDINGS, INC.

EXECUTIVES

Pres, Craig Johnston
Cfo, Derrick Coder
SEC, Carl Neil
Sales Specialty Wood Products, Jared Bjur
Information Technology Directo, Kris Breuing

LOCATIONS

HQ: FCTG HOLDINGS, INC.
10250 SW GREENBURG RD # 200, PORTLAND, OR 972235461
Phone: 503 246-8500
Web: WWW.FCTG.COM

HISTORICAL FINANCIALS

Company Type: Private

Income Statement				FYE: January 31
	REVENUE ($ mil.)	NET INCOME ($ mil.)	NET PROFIT MARGIN	EMPLOYEES
01/09	1,535	2	0.2%	406
01/08	2,055	1	0.1%	—
01/07	2,798	(0)	—	—
Annual Growth	(25.9%)	—	—	—

2009 Year-End Financials

Return on assets: 2.7% Cash ($ mil.): 3
Return on equity: 11.0%
Current ratio: 1.20

FEDERAL-MOGUL HOLDINGS LLC

Auditors: GRANT THORNTON LLP SOUTHFIELD

LOCATIONS

HQ: FEDERAL-MOGUL HOLDINGS LLC
27300 W 11 MILE RD # 101, SOUTHFIELD, MI 480346193
Phone: 248 354-7700
Web: WWW.FEDERALMOGUL.COM

HISTORICAL FINANCIALS

Company Type: Private

Income Statement				FYE: December 31
	REVENUE ($ mil.)	NET INCOME ($ mil.)	NET PROFIT MARGIN	EMPLOYEES
12/16	7,434	90	1.2%	53,700
12/15	7,419	(104)	—	—
12/14	7,317	(161)	—	—
Annual Growth	0.8%	—	—	—

2016 Year-End Financials

Return on assets: 1.3% Cash ($ mil.): 300
Return on equity: 10.2%
Current ratio: 1.70

FIDELITY INV CHARITABLE GIFT FUND

EXECUTIVES

Vice President, Amy Grossman

LOCATIONS

HQ: FIDELITY INV CHARITABLE GIFT FUND
200 SEAPORT BLVD STE 1, BOSTON, MA 022102000
Phone: 617 392-8679
Web: WWW.FUNINBOSTON.COM

HISTORICAL FINANCIALS

Company Type: Private

Income Statement				FYE: June 30
	REVENUE ($ mil.)	NET INCOME ($ mil.)	NET PROFIT MARGIN	EMPLOYEES
06/11	1,874	599	32.0%	1
06/10	1,274	147	11.6%	—
Annual Growth	47.1%	306.7%	—	—

2011 Year-End Financials

Return on assets: 10.7% Cash ($ mil.): 77
Return on equity: 10.8%
Current ratio: 1.90

FINANCIAL INDUSTRY REGULATORY AUTHORITY, INC.

FINRA is one of the long arms of the law for the securities industry. It is a non-governmental regulatory authority that oversees U.S. broker-dealers. In addition it is autorized by the congress to protect America's investors by making sure the broker-dealer industry operates fairly and honestly. FINRA oversee more than 624000 brokers across the country and analyze billion dollors of market events. . FINRA was formed in 2007 from the consolidation of the National Association of Securities Dealers and certain regulatory and enforcement elements of the NYSE.

Operations

FINRA regulates the Broker-Dealers Capital Acquisition Brokers and Funding Portals. In additions Broker Dealer is in the business of buying or selling securities on behalf of its customers or its own account or both. A Capital Acquisition Broker is a Broker Dealer subject to a narrower rule book. A Funding Portal is a crowd-funding intermediary. FINRA plays a critical role in ensuring the integrity of America's financial system. It writes and enforces rules governing the ethical activities of all registered broker-dealer firms and registered brokers in the U.S. examines firms for compliance with rules fosters market transparency and educates investors.

Geographic Reach

FINRA operates from Washington DC where it is headquartered and New York with about 20 regional offices around the US.

Sales and Marketing

FINRA markets its services through conference and events virtual conference Panels E Leaning courses and Webinars.

Company Background

FINRA was founded in 2007 by NASD and NYSE.

EXECUTIVES

Evp And Chief Technology Officer, Martin P. Colburn
Evp And Cio, Steven J. (Steve) Randich
Evp Transparency Services, Steven A. (Steve) Joachim
Evp Market Regulation, Thomas R. Gira
Evp Regulatory Policy And Legal Compliance Officer, Thomas M. (Tom) Selman
Evp Fraud Detection And Market Intelligence, Cameron K. Funkhouser
Evp And Head Of Member Regulation Sales Practice, Michael G. Rufino
Evp Member Regulation Risk Oversight And Operational Regulation (roor), William J. (Bill) Wollman
Evp And Cfo, Todd T. Diganci
Svp And Chief Economist, Jonathan S. Sokobin
Evp Regulatory Operations, Susan F. Axelrod
Evp Enforcement, J. Bradley Bennett
President Finra Foundation, Gerri Walsh
Evp Corporate Communications And Government Relations, F. Gregory Ahern
Chief Risk Officer And Head Of Strategy, Carlo V. di Florio
Evp And Director Dispute Resolution, Richard W. Berry
President And Ceo, Robert W. Cook
Executive Vice President Corporate Communications Government Relat, Gregory Ahern
Senior Vice President And Director Of Mediation Business Strategies And Dispute Resolution, Kenneth Andrichik
Associate Vice President And Associate General Cou, Gary Lipkin
Senior Vice President Of Exchange Solutions And Market Regulation, James Price
Director Media Relations, Michelle Ong
Vice President, Angela Goelzer
Associate Vice President And Associate General Cou, Kosha Dalal
Vice President Of Neutral Management, Barbara Brady
Vice President And Associate General Counsel Of Regulatory Group, Stephanie Dumont
Vice President, Michael Hourigan
Vice President, Joseph Price
Vice President, Katri Arcaro
Associate Vice President, Terri Reicher
Vice President, Geraldine Walsh
Senior Vice President And Investment Officer, James Allen
Associate Vice President, Ethan Lish
Vice President Corporate Governance, Jennifer Mitchell
Executive Vice President Regulatory Policy And Legal Compliance Officer, Tom Selman
Senior Vice President, Alton Jones
Senior Vice President Financial Planning And Analysis, Robert Wood
Svp Office Of Government Affairs, Gregory Dean
Senior Vice President Corporate Communication, Josh Drobnyk
Vice President, Ornella Bergeron
Vice President, Danny Mileto
Associate Vice President, Hollie Schwartz
Associate Vice President And Council, Phil Shaikun
Vice President, Nick Maslavets
Vice President, Justin Tubiolo
Senior Vice President, Jon Kroeper
Vice President And Director Advertising Regulation, Tom Pappas
Svp Market Regulation Enforcement, Elizabeth Hogan
Vice President Federal Affairs, Jonathan Renfrew
Assistant Secretary, Jennifer Piorko
Auditors: ERNST & YOUNG LLP MCLEAN VIR

LOCATIONS

HQ: FINANCIAL INDUSTRY REGULATORY AUTHORITY, INC.
1735 K ST NW, WASHINGTON, DC 200061506
Phone: 301 590-6500
Web: WWW.FINRA.ORG

PRODUCTS/OPERATIONS

2015 Sales

	$ mil.	% of total
Regulatory revenue	444	45
User revenue	218	22
Contract services revenue	125	13
Fines	93	6
Transparency services revenue	63	4
Dispute resolution revenue	41	1
Other revenue	5	9
Total	**992**	**100**

HISTORICAL FINANCIALS

Company Type: Private

Income Statement FYE: December 31

	REVENUE ($ mil.)	NET INCOME ($ mil.)	NET PROFIT MARGIN	EMPLOYEES
12/12	878	10	1.2%	3,400
12/11	880	(84)	—	—
12/10	849	54	6.4%	—
Annual Growth	1.7%	(56.1%)	—	—

2012 Year-End Financials

Return on assets: 0.5%
Return on equity: 0.8%
Current ratio: 2.10
Cash ($ mil.): 356

FINANCIAL TRADER CORPORATION

LOCATIONS

HQ: FINANCIAL TRADER CORPORATION
5743 LONGMONT LN, HOUSTON, TX 770572510
Phone: 713 206-4600

HISTORICAL FINANCIALS

Company Type: Private

Income Statement FYE: December 31

	ASSETS ($ mil.)	NET INCOME ($ mil.)	INCOME AS % OF ASSETS	EMPLOYEES
12/13	398	6	1.7%	1
12/11	10	0	5.6%	—
Annual Growth	525.1%	243.5%	—	—

2013 Year-End Financials

Return on assets: —
Return on equity: 0.7%
Sales ($ mil): 992

FIRSTHEALTH OF THE CAROLINAS, INC.

FirstHealth of the Carolinas maintains a health care network that extends to 15 counties across the mid-Carolinas. The health network includes four hospitals — Moore Regional Richmond Memorial Moore Regional - Hoke and Montgomery Memorial — that provide emergency surgical acute care and diagnostic services and have a combined capacity of more than 580 beds. Moore Regional its largest hospital includes an inpatient rehabilitation center and a heart hospital. FirstHealth of the Carolinas also operates satellite facilities including family practice clinics fitness centers and dental practices. The system's FirstCarolinaCare provides home health and hospice services emergency care medical transportation and health insurance.

Operations

In addition to its four hospitals the network includes the Reid Heart Center a rehabilitation center three sleep disorders centers three dental clinics a dozen family medicine clinics five fitness centers four charitable foundations a Hospice program home health services and EMS.

The health care network offers major medical and surgical specialties and subspecialties such as open-heart surgery bariatric weight-loss surgery neurosurgery and neonatology. To provide these specialties FirstHealth maintains an active medical staff of 320 of which 95% are board certified.

Geographic Reach

FirstHealth serves those who reside in a 15-county region of the mid-Carolinas. Altogether it operates nearly 62 locations across North Carolina.

Financial Performance

The not-for-profit took in about 8% more in revenue for 2013 when it rose to $565 from $524 the previous year.

Strategy

Despite the downturn in the economy in recent years the health system worked to maintain its expansion efforts to meet the demand of area residents. On the Moore Regional campus it opened the 60-bed Reid Heart Hospital a cardiology and neurology facility in 2011.

In Hoke County FirstHealth built a medical campus consisting of an urgent care center diagnostic facilities and physician offices along with a new 65-bed acute care hospital in the area. Moore Regional - Hoke the county's first hospital began serving patients in 2013.

FirstHealth had been participating in a 50/50 joint venture with the University of North Carolina Healthcare System to run Sanford Hematology and Oncology. In 2013 it purchased full ownership of the facility.

EXECUTIVES

Nursing Director, Cheryl Batchelor
Director Physician Recruitment, Teresa Sessoms
Vice President Finance, Mark Rush
Medical Records Director, Cassina Hunt
Vice President Quality, Cindy Mcdonald
Medical Director Hospitalist Service, Gary Gammon
Vice President, Anthony Dolce
Vice President Of Sales And Marketing, Colleen West
Secretary, Robin Bunting
Secretary, Kasey Batten
Auditors: CLIFTONLARSONALLEN LLP CHARLO

LOCATIONS

HQ: FIRSTHEALTH OF THE CAROLINAS, INC.
155 MEMORIAL DR, PINEHURST, NC 283748710
Phone: 910 715-1000
Web: WWW.FIRSTHEALTH.ORG

PRODUCTS/OPERATIONS

2013 Sales

	$ mil.	% of total
Net patient service revenue	459	81
Net assets released from restrictions used for operations	103	18
other	2	1
Total	**565**	**100**

Selected Facilities

Montgomery Memorial Hospital (Troy North Carolina)
Moore Regional Hospital (Pinehurst North Carolina)
Moore Regional Hospital (Hoke North Carolina)
Richmond Memorial Hospital (Rockingham North Carolina)

COMPETITORS

Alamance Regional Medical Center
Carolinas HealthCare System
Cone Health
Cumberland County Hospital System
Duke University Health System
Morehead Memorial Hospital
Novant Health
Rex Healthcare
Stanly Medical Center
UNC Hospitals
Vidant Health
WakeMed

HISTORICAL FINANCIALS

Company Type: Private

Income Statement — FYE: September 30

	REVENUE ($ mil.)	NET INCOME ($ mil.)	NET PROFIT MARGIN	EMPLOYEES
09/20	768	98	12.8%	3,897
09/19	793	35	4.5%	—
09/18	747	43	5.9%	—
09/17	744	81	11.0%	—
Annual Growth	1.1%	6.3%	—	—

FLATIRON CONSTRUCTORS, INC.

EXECUTIVES

Ceo, John Diciurcio
Exec V-Pres-Coo*, Robert W French
Cfo*, Paul Driscoll
Coo*, Dale Swanberg
Exec Asst*, Judy Schek
Coo*, Javier Sevilla
Cfo*, Lars Leitner
Accounting Staff, Donna Clardy
Alternative Delivery Manager, Denny Stoddard
Controller, Drew Phillips
Vice President, Brian Stieritz
Auditors: DELOITTE & TOUCHE LLP DENVER

LOCATIONS

HQ: FLATIRON CONSTRUCTORS, INC.
385 INTERLOCKEN, BROOMFIELD, CO 80021
Phone: 303 485-4050
Web: WWW.FLATIRONCORP.COM

HISTORICAL FINANCIALS

Company Type: Private

Income Statement — FYE: December 31

	REVENUE ($ mil.)	NET INCOME ($ mil.)	NET PROFIT MARGIN	EMPLOYEES
12/12	941	(96)	—	611
12/11	1,017	39	3.9%	—
Annual Growth	(7.5%)	—	—	—

2012 Year-End Financials

Return on assets: (-18.0%)
Return on equity: (-55.9%)
Current ratio: 1.60
Cash ($ mil.): 123

FLORIDA CLINICAL PRACTICE ASSOCIATION, INC.

EXECUTIVES

Pres, Anthony Mancuso
Exec V Pres, William W Tharp
Auditors: PYA PC TAMPA FL

LOCATIONS

HQ: FLORIDA CLINICAL PRACTICE ASSOCIATION, INC.
1329 SW 16TH ST STE 4250, GAINESVILLE, FL 326081128
Phone: 352 265-8017
Web: WWW.COMFS.UFL.EDU

HISTORICAL FINANCIALS

Company Type: Private

Income Statement — FYE: June 30

	REVENUE ($ mil.)	NET INCOME ($ mil.)	NET PROFIT MARGIN	EMPLOYEES
06/18	667	11	1.8%	2
06/17	642	(1)	—	—
06/15	598	19	3.3%	—
06/13	419	2	0.5%	—
Annual Growth	9.7%	42.3%	—	—

2018 Year-End Financials

Return on assets: 4.9%
Return on equity: 7.3%
Current ratio: 7.10
Cash ($ mil.): 94

FLORIDA DEPARTMENT OF LOTTERY

The State of Florida Department of the Lottery runs instant-play scratch tickets and lotto games including Florida Lotto Mega Money Fantasy 5 and Cash 3. In addition to its own games Florida is part of the Multi-State Lottery Association which operates the popular Powerball drawing. Proceeds from the games are contributed to Florida's Educational Enhancement Trust Fund which provides funding for a variety of education programs from pre-kindergarten up to the state university level. The lottery has returned more than $19 billion to the state since starting in 1988.

EXECUTIVES

Secretary, Jim Poppell

LOCATIONS

HQ: FLORIDA DEPARTMENT OF LOTTERY
250 MARRIOTT DR, TALLAHASSEE, FL 323012983
Phone: 850 487-7777
Web: WWW.FLALOTTERY.COM

COMPETITORS

Georgia Lottery
Seminole Tribe of Florida

HISTORICAL FINANCIALS

Company Type: Private

Income Statement — FYE: June 30

	REVENUE ($ mil.)	NET INCOME ($ mil.)	NET PROFIT MARGIN	EMPLOYEES
06/19	7,157	36	0.5%	400
06/03	2,872	117	4.1%	—
06/02	2	0	2.0%	—
06/01	2,284	981	43.0%	—
Annual Growth	6.6%	(16.7%)	—	—

2019 Year-End Financials

Return on assets: 5.5%
Return on equity: 43.0%
Current ratio: 0.90
Cash ($ mil.): 198

FLORIDA GAS TRANSMISSION COMPANY, LLC

Florida Gas Transmission gasses up the Gulf Coast. The company transports natural gas to cogeneration facilities electric utilities independent power producers municipal generators and local distribution companies through a 5400-mile natural gas pipeline extending from south Texas to south Florida. It delivers 3.1 billion cu. ft. of natural gas a day to more than 250 delivery points consisting of more than 50 natural gas-fired electric generation facilities. Florida Gas Transmission is operated by Citrus Corp. which is a joint venture of Energy Transfer Partners and Kinder Morgan.

Operations

Florida Gas Transmission is the primary transporter of natural gas to the Florida energy market delivering more than 64% of the natural gas consumed by Floridians. The pipeline system operates and maintains more than 70 interconnects with major interstate and intrastate natural gas pipelines.

Geographic Reach

Florida Gas Transmission's pipeline system receives natural gas from producing basins in Louisiana and along the Texas Gulf Coast Mobile Bay and offshore in the Gulf of Mexico and transports it to markets in Florida.

Strategy

In 2013 the Florida Public Service Commission approved Florida Power & Light's contracts for a $3.5 billion 600-mile pipeline system. The project due for completion in 2017 will connect Florida's two existing pipelines the larger one owned by Florida Gas Transmission and the other by Gulfstream Natural Gas System LLC.

Upping its pipeline investment in 2012 Kinder Morgan invested about $2 billion in Citrus Corp.

Company Background

In 2008 Florida Power & Light agreed to contract for half the capacity of a $2 billion expansion of a natural-gas pipeline.

EXECUTIVES

Vice President Marketing, Gregg Russell
Vice President Technical Services, Eric Amundsen
Vice President Accounting, Mary Simon
Vice President Market Services, Brad Holmes

LOCATIONS

HQ: FLORIDA GAS TRANSMISSION COMPANY, LLC
1300 MAIN ST, HOUSTON, TX 770026803
Phone: 713 989-7000

COMPETITORS

Columbia Gulf Transmission
Enable Oklahoma
Gulf South Pipeline
Texas Gas Transmission
Williams Gas Pipeline

HISTORICAL FINANCIALS

Company Type: Private

Income Statement — FYE: December 31

	REVENUE ($ mil.)	NET INCOME ($ mil.)	NET PROFIT MARGIN	EMPLOYEES
12/18	838	321	38.3%	450
12/17	839	247	29.5%	—
12/16	829	238	28.7%	—
Annual Growth	0.6%	16.1%	—	—

FLORIDA HEALTH SCIENCES CENTER, INC.

Florida Health Sciences Center which does business as Tampa General Hospital (TGH) provides health care services in west-central Florida. The medical center offers general medical and surgical care as well as tertiary offerings including a Level 1 trauma center a burn unit a pediatric ward women's and cardiovascular centers and an organ transplant unit. The not-for-profit hospital has more than 1000 acute-care beds as well as 60 beds in its rehabilitation unit which specializes in helping patients recover from stroke head or spine trauma and other neuromuscular conditions. TGH is the primary teaching hospital for The University of South Florida College of Medicine.

Operations

TGH division Tampa General Medical Group (TGMG) is a multispecialty physician group with locations in Florida's Hillsborough and Pasco counties. Specialties include family practice internal medicine transplant cardiology endocrinology hepatology nephrology and surgery.

Geographic Reach

One of the largest employers in the Tampa Bay region TGH employs about 6300 workers. It also conducts research and operates community care centers in the Tampa area.

Each year TGH treats more than 91000 patients in its emergency department. This includes pediatric chest pain minor emergency and trauma center patients. The hospital also operates a regional helicopter medical transport program.

Strategy

TGH has added new wing to the hospital to expand patient capacity. TGH has added a new emergency/trauma center as well as cardiovascular diagnostic neurology and women's health units.

The hospital also works to stay on top of the latest medical advances. For example in 2014 TGH acquired the ThermoCool SmartTouch catheter a recently launched high-tech device that helps physicians control the amount of contact force applied to the heart wall during treatments for atrial fibrillation.

EXECUTIVES

Vice President Professional Services, David K Robbins
Evp Finance And Cfo, Steve Short
Evp Patient Care Services, Deana L. Nelson
Svp And Chief Medical Officer, Sally H. Houston
Chief Technology Officer, Balaji Ramadoss
Ceo, James R. Burkhart
Executive Vice President Chief Academic Officer, Charles J. Lockwood
Senior Vice President Finance, Judith Ploszek
Vice President Physician Practice And President Tampa General Medical Group, Lucila Ramiro
Vice President, Kim Rallis
Vice President Service, Todd Godfrey
Vice President Executive Assistant To, Rosa Rodriguez
Chairman, David A. Straz
Pharmacy Secretary, Sonia Burgos
Secretary Unit Management, Linda Starkey
Secretary Unit Management, Markelle Hunt

LOCATIONS

HQ: FLORIDA HEALTH SCIENCES CENTER, INC.
1 TAMPA GENERAL CIR, TAMPA, FL 336063571
Phone: 813 844-7000
Web: WWW.TGH.ORG

COMPETITORS

All Children's Hospital
BayCare Health System
Bayfront Health
DeSoto Memorial
Florida Hospital Tampa Bay Division
HCA
Lakeland Regional Medical Center
Lee Memorial
Manatee Memorial Hospital
Sarasota Memorial Health Care
Winter Haven Hospital

HISTORICAL FINANCIALS

Company Type: Private

Income Statement — FYE: September 30

	REVENUE ($ mil.)	NET INCOME ($ mil.)	NET PROFIT MARGIN	EMPLOYEES
09/19	1,447	57	4.0%	8,000
09/18	1,325	79	6.0%	—
09/17	1,257	98	7.8%	—
09/16	1,055	80	7.6%	—
Annual Growth	11.1%	(10.3%)	—	—

2019 Year-End Financials

Return on assets: 3.2%
Return on equity: 5.5%
Current ratio: 1.10
Cash ($ mil.): 42

FLORIDA HOSPITAL MEDICAL GROUP, INC.

EXECUTIVES

Pres, Terry Owen
Pres*, Bryan Stiltz
Dir*, Lamvu Georgine
Dir*, Lay Kevin
Diagnostic Radiologist, Antonio Gonzalez

LOCATIONS

HQ: FLORIDA HOSPITAL MEDICAL GROUP, INC.
2600 WESTHALL LN STE 400, MAITLAND, FL 327517107
Phone: 407 200-2700
Web: WWW.ADVENTHEALTHMEDICALGROUP.COM

HISTORICAL FINANCIALS

Company Type: Private

Income Statement — FYE: December 31

	REVENUE ($ mil.)	NET INCOME ($ mil.)	NET PROFIT MARGIN	EMPLOYEES
12/18	562	2	0.4%	350
12/15	421	0	0.2%	—
12/14	363	(17)	—	—
12/08	177	0	—	—
Annual Growth	12.2%	—	—	—

2018 Year-End Financials

Return on assets: 1.5%
Return on equity: 2.5%
Current ratio: 1.80
Cash ($ mil.): 48

FLORIDA HOUSING FINANCE CORP

Owning a home in Florida is just a bit easier thanks to Florida Housing Finance Corporation. Established in 1997 by the Florida Legislature as a public corporation Florida Housing's mission is to help Floridians obtain safe decent housing that might otherwise be unavailable to them. Florida Housing pursues its mission through a number of programs that provide financial assistance for first time homebuyers and for developers of multifamily dwellings that serve elderly and low income Floridians. Florida Housing partners with various local state and federal agencies as well as developers and not-for-profit organizations to achieve its goals.

EXECUTIVES

Exec Dir, Stephen Auger
Exec Dir*, Harold Price
Executive Officer, Vicki Robinson
Director of Asset Management, Laura J Cox
Controller, Angie Sellers
Senior Financial Administrator, Melanie Weathers
Homeownership Programs Adminis, Charles White
CIO, David Hearn
Director of Homeownerhip Progr, David Westcott
Human Resources Administrator, Jessica Cherry
Program Administrator, Robert Dearduff
Auditors: ERNST & YOUNG LLP ORLANDO F

LOCATIONS

HQ: FLORIDA HOUSING FINANCE CORP
227 N BRONOUGH ST # 5000, TALLAHASSEE, FL 323011367
Phone: 850 488-4197
Web: WWW.FLORIDAHOUSING.ORG

PRODUCTS/OPERATIONS

Selected Programs
First Time Homebuyer Program
Down Payment Assistance
Homeownership Loan Program
Mortgage Credit Certificate
Multifamily Development Programs
Multifamily Mortgage Revenue Bonds
Florida Affordable Housing Guarantee Program
HOME Investment Partnerships
Elderly Housing Community Loan Program
Low Income Housing Tax Credits
State Apartment Incentive Loan
Predevelopment Loan Program
State Housing Initiative Partnerships
Demonstration Loans
Affordable Housing Catalyst Program

HISTORICAL FINANCIALS

Company Type: Private

Income Statement — FYE: December 31

	ASSETS ($ mil.)	NET INCOME ($ mil.)	INCOME AS % OF ASSETS	EMPLOYEES
12/19	5,373	224	4.2%	130
12/18	4,974	125	2.5%	—
12/17	4,764	206	4.3%	—
12/16	4,567	141	3.1%	—
Annual Growth	5.6%	16.6%	—	—

2019 Year-End Financials

Return on assets: 4.2%
Return on equity: 7.9%
Sales ($ mil): 259

FLORIDA INTERNATIONAL UNIVERSITY

Living up to its name Florida International University (FIU) boasts a student population representing more than 140 countries. With total enrollment of 54000 students it has one of the largest student populations of all US universities. FIU operates on two primary campuses in Miami-Dade County as well as a handful of research facilities and smaller academic centers in surrounding areas. Through some 10 colleges and schools FIU offers bachelor's master's and doctoral degree programs in more than 200 majors including engineering law business administration and music. FIU is a member of the State University System of Florida. It held its first classes in 1972.

Operations

Befitting its location in South Florida FIU has activities that educate and conduct research in tourism- and extreme weather. Its Chaplin School of Hospitality and Tourism Management stages the annual Food Network South Beach Wine & Food Festival. And FIU's research facility called the Wall of Wind can simulate the force of a Category 5 hurricane. The university also operates the Aquarius Reef Base an underwater research laboratory 63 feet below the surface in the Florida Keys National Marine Sanctuary.

Geographic Reach

FIU operates from its Modesto A. Maidique Campus in Miami (western Miami-Dade County) and the Biscayne Bay Campus in North Miami Beach. It also operates an engineering center (near the Maidique Campus) a business center (Brickell) the Broward Pines Center (Pembroke Pines) the Miami Beach Urban Studios and the Wolfsonian FIU museum (South Beach). It also operates a Chinese program in Tianjin.

Strategy

Florida International University published its strategic plan called BeyondPossible2020. It defines a few dozen performance indicators to attain by the year 2020 such as continuing to foster student success with world class faculty and experiential-based programs pursuing the Carnegie Very High Research Designation as a motivator of the school's push towards stronger research credentials and by fine-tuning its degree programs to address future needs of employers and students.

The company's strategic plan consists of:

Student Success - The company will offer students an intense rigorous learning experience in a supportive academic community;

Preeminent Programs - Building preeminent programs and teams will strengthen FIU's capacity to provide high-quality teaching engage in state-of-the-art research and creative activity and collaborate with our local and global communities;

Carnegie Very High Research Designation - FIU will continue to build its research reputation and develop an infrastructure to support its growing research enterprise; and

Financial Base/Efficiency - FIUBeyondPossible2020 is FIU's roadmap for the future. To truly realize its promise the university must be resilient in the way it responds to external challenges. The legislative funding gap will vary depending upon factors not in its control and FIU must be prepared to manage those fluctuations and adapt as necessary

EXECUTIVES

President, Mark B. Rosenberg
Svp University Advancement And President And Ceo Fiu Foundation Inc., Howard R. Lipman
Svp Medical Affairs And Dean Herbert Wertheim College Of Medicine, John A. Rock
Dean Honors College, Lesley Northup
Svp Finance And Administration And Cfo, Kenneth A. Jessell
Dean College Of Architecture And The Arts, Brian Schriner
Dean College Of Law, R. Alexander (Alex) Acosta
Dean Undergraduate Education, Douglas Robertson
Vp Information Technology And Cio, Robert Grillo
Dean College Of Education, Delia Garcia
Dean College Of Nursing And Health Sciences, Ora Strickland
Dean Chaplin School Of Hospitality And Tourism Management, Mike Hampton
Dean School Of Journalism And Mass Communication, Paul Reis
Dean University Graduate School, Lakshmi N. Reddi
Evp And Provost, Kenneth G. Furton
Dean College Of Arts And Sciences (cas), Michael R. Heithaus
Acting Dean College Of Business, Jose M. Aldrich
Interim Dean College Of Engineering And Computing, Ranu Jung
Dean Of Robert Stempel College Of Public Health And Social Work, Tomas Guilarte
Medical Director, Saara Schwartz
Vice President Human Resources, Michaelle Maranto
Associate Vice President, Juan Cueto
Assistant Vice President, Angelique G Hutchinson
Assistant Vice President Academic Budgets, Matilde Gramling
Associate Vice President Controller, Cecilia Hamilton
Assoc Vice President, Deborah Gallay
Assistant Vice President, El Hudson
Ite Vice President, Claudio Diaferia
Senior Vice President, Amber Hoffman
Assistant Vice President For Research Innovation And Economic Development, Emily Gresham
Vice President, Larry Lunsford
Associate Vice President Of Academic Affairs, Jeff Gonzalez
Student Assistant Student Affairs Vice President Off, Fabio Zucatto
Vice President Of Events, Madiha Merchant
Director Of Admissions, Jody Glassman
Clinical Director, Erika Coles
Associate Vice President For Research, Jonathan Tubman
Vice President, Pablo Ortiz
Vice President Government Relations, Michelle Lorenzo
Assistant Vice President For Research Initiatives, Rita Teutonico
Vice President, David Mccluskey
Vice President For Finance And Administration, Matthews Brad
Senior Executive Assistant Office Of The Provost And Executive Vice President, Atilda Alvarado
Assistant Vice President For Student Affairs, Anthony Desantis
Vice President Accounting Spring 2018 Alpfa Honors Society, Cristina Nunez
Vice President, Chantal Salbo
Vice President Of Finance, Rolando Barrios
Vice President, Stephanie Sepulveda
Vice President, Scott Pagano
Phoenician Investment Fund Vice President Of Communications, Valentina Franco
Vice President, Alexander Pardo
Vice President, Patricia Gomez
Chairman, Claudia Puig

Secretary, Pat Brammer
Secretary, Lourdes Alvarez
Secretary, Marta Lee
Senior Secretary, Pupi Tomassini
Secretary, Claudia Estrada
Secretary, Linda Spears-bunton
Senior Secretary, Patricia Brammer
Senior Secretary, Ana Saenz
Secretary College Of Nursing And Health Sciences, Qiao Chan
Board Member, Victor Uribe-Uran
Secretary, Nyoka Giles
Interim Assistant Treasurer, Milly Garcia
Senior Secretary Biology, Maria Forlong
Secretary, Melanie Ponce
Sva Treasurer, Jennifer Puentes
Secretary, Daniel Correa
Recording Secretary, Sarah Hadeed
Secretary, Lindsey Ramirez
Match Secretary, Alexandra Diaz
Treasurer, Julianne Valdes
Auditors: DAVID W MARTIN CPA TALLAHAS

LOCATIONS

HQ: FLORIDA INTERNATIONAL UNIVERSITY
11200 SW 8TH ST, MIAMI, FL 331992516
Phone: 305 348-2494
Web: WWW.BUSINESS.FIU.EDU

PRODUCTS/OPERATIONS

Selected Colleges and Schools
Chaplin School of Hospitality and Tourism Management
College of Communication Architecture and the Arts
College of Arts Sciences and Education
College of Business
College of Engineering and Computing
College of Law
Green School of International and Public Affairs
Honors College
Stempel College of Public Health and Social Work
Wertheim College of Nursing and Health Sciences
Wertheim College of Medicine

HISTORICAL FINANCIALS

Company Type: Private

Income Statement — FYE: June 30

	REVENUE ($ mil.)	NET INCOME ($ mil.)	NET PROFIT MARGIN	EMPLOYEES
06/19	548	8	1.5%	4,000
06/07	307	89	29.3%	—
06/06	238	50	21.3%	—
06/05	0	0	—	—
Annual Growth	—	—	—	—

2019 Year-End Financials

Return on assets: 0.5%
Return on equity: 1.1%
Current ratio: 6.80
Cash ($ mil.): 6

FLORIDA MUNICIPAL POWER AGENCY

Unlike some politicians Florida Municipal Power Agency (FMPA) doesn't believe in holding on to power. The non-profit public agency generates and supplies electric power to 31 county or municipally owned distribution utilities which in turn serve 2 million Florida residents and businesses. Each of the distribution utilities appoints one representative to FMPA's board of directors which governs the Agency's activities. The Agency is authorized to undertake joint power supply projects for its members and to issue tax-exempt bonds to finance the costs of such projects. It is also empowered to implement a pooled financing program for utility-related projects.

Operations

FMPA has five distinct power supply projects and has stakes in 15 operating power plants. Each of its members have the option of whether or not to participate in a power supply project. Some members receive all their power from FMPA some receive part of their power and others receive no power. Agency members may participate in more than one project although each project is independent from the others.

FMPA supplies all of the power needs for 13 of its members and some of the power supply needs of seven others. All together FMPA supplies more than 40% of its members' total power needs.

Strategy

The Agency is looking to diversify its fuel mix in the long term adding nuclear and renewable energy powered plants to reduce the carbon emission output from its generation activities.

Company Background

FMPA has also been modernizing its power plant fleet since 2003 and in 2011 it opened a new low-emission high efficiency generator known as Cane Island Unit 4. Plant modernization has led to lower power costs enabling Florida Municipal Power Agency to reduce its wholesale rates to a number of members' cities in 2011 by 20% over 2009 levels.

The Agency was formed in 1978 to support the activities of Florida's locally owned and operated municipal utilities in projects requiring joint action such as the development of large power plants to serve a number of municipalities.

EXECUTIVES

Ceo, Jacob Williams
Chm*, Howard McKinnon
Manager, Richard Montgomery
Asst Treas, Edwin Nunez
Paralegal, Karen Culpepper
Compliance Audit Mana, Liyuan Woerner
Controller, Danyel Sullivan-Marrer
Vice Chairman Board of Directo, Barbara Q Ones
Assist GM Finance, Mark Larson
Public Relations Specialist, Ryan Dumas
Cash Manager, Victoria Bidwell
Auditors: PURVIS GRAY & COMPANY LLP OC

LOCATIONS

HQ: FLORIDA MUNICIPAL POWER AGENCY
8553 COMMODITY CIR, ORLANDO, FL 328199002
Phone: 407 355-7767
Web: WWW.FMPA.COM

HISTORICAL FINANCIALS

Company Type: Private

Income Statement — FYE: September 30

	REVENUE ($ mil.)	NET INCOME ($ mil.)	NET PROFIT MARGIN	EMPLOYEES
09/19	620	0	0.1%	67
09/18	604	32	5.3%	—
Annual Growth	2.7%	(98.7%)	—	—

2019 Year-End Financials

Return on assets: —
Return on equity: 4.3%
Current ratio: 2.10
Cash ($ mil.): 75

FLORIDA STATE UNIVERSITY

Home to the Florida State Seminoles Florida State University offers more than 300 undergraduate graduate and professional programs including M.D. (medicine) and J.D. (law) programs. The educational institution has 16 colleges dedicated to academic fields ranging from liberal arts music visual arts and education to criminology engineering social work and information. A major research institution the university is home to the National High Magnetic Field Laboratory or "Mag Lab" the only national lab in Florida and the only such high-magnetic facility in the US. Florida State was founded in 1851 and is part of the 11-school State University System of Florida.

Operations

Florida State boasts more than 41000 students and has a student/faculty ratio of 26:1. The school's reputation as a top-notch research school stems from its extensive network of research facilities that cover areas such as biological medicine social sciences and energy. Its facilities also include the Center for Advanced Power Systems which is supported by the US Department of Defense and the Department of Energy. The Mag Lab is funded by the National Science Foundation. Florida State also operates the John and Mable Ringling Museum of Art in Sarasota Florida.

Geographic Reach

The main Florida State University campus in Tallahassee covers about 450 acres. The university also offers degree programs in Sarasota Florida and in the Republic of Panama. It boasts instructional programs in London Florence and Valencia as well as programs in research development and/or services in Costa Rica Croatia and Italy.

Sales and Marketing

The Florida university enrolls students from more than 120 foreign countries.

EXECUTIVES

Director Of Admissions, John Barnhill
Assistant Vice President Faculty Development And Advanced, Jennifer Buchanan
Department Chair Professor, Jeff James
Vice President For Development, Perry Fulkerson
Vice President Finance And Administration, Kyle Clark
Executive Vice President, John Riveras
Assistant Vice President For Academic Affairs, Paul Harlacher
Vice President, Vanesa Moreno
Vice President Of Human Resources, Dennis Tudor
Vice President, Stephanie Hurtado
Treasurer Mock Trial Team, Gennifer Powell
Secretary, Susan Gay
Secretary, Anne Lamarre
Msf Association Treasurer, Garrett Hilbelink
Board Member, Karen L Doscher
Treasurer, Yihua Wang
Auditors: SHERRILL F NORMAN CPA TALLA

LOCATIONS

HQ: FLORIDA STATE UNIVERSITY
600 W COLLEGE AVE, TALLAHASSEE, FL 323061096
Phone: 850 644-5482
Web: WWW.FSU.EDU

PRODUCTS/OPERATIONS

Selected Colleges
College of Applied Studies
College of Arts and Sciences
College of Business

College of Communication and Information
College of Criminology and Criminal Justice
College of Education
College of Engineering
College of Human Sciences
College of Law
College of Medicine
College of Motion Picture Arts
College of Music
College of Nursing
College of Social Sciences and Public Policy
College of Social Work
College of Visual Arts Theatre and Dance

HISTORICAL FINANCIALS

Company Type: Private

Income Statement FYE: June 30

	REVENUE ($ mil.)	NET INCOME ($ mil.)	NET PROFIT MARGIN	EMPLOYEES
06/12	654	40	6.1%	13,497
06/11	607	188	31.0%	—
06/10	567	121	21.4%	—
Annual Growth	7.4%	(42.4%)	—	—

2012 Year-End Financials

Return on assets: 1.2%
Return on equity: 1.4%
Current ratio: 6.00
Cash ($ mil.): 48

FLOWORKS INTERNATIONAL LLC

EXECUTIVES

Ceo, Scott Jackson
Cfo, Gary Haire
Pres, Fabrication & Distributi, John Higgins
Pres, Ipvf, Michael Stanwood
Evp, Corp Strategy & Bus Dev, Rob Broyles
Vp & Treas, Rick Hawthorne
SEC, Suzanne Mailes-Dineff
Sr Vp & Chro, Herbert Allen
Vp, Corp Contrl & Acctng Offic, Michael Goldberg
Evp, Ipvf, Jeff Legrand
Pres,valves & Automation, Keith Barnard
Auditors: PRICEWATERHOUSECOOPERS LLP HO

LOCATIONS

HQ: FLOWORKS INTERNATIONAL LLC
3750 HWY 225, PASADENA, TX 77503
Phone: 713 943-3544
Web: WWW.FLOWORKSPVF.COM

HISTORICAL FINANCIALS

Company Type: Private

Income Statement FYE: February 2

	REVENUE ($ mil.)	NET INCOME ($ mil.)	NET PROFIT MARGIN	EMPLOYEES
02/14*	805	(30)	—	785
06/12	222	(5)	—	—
Annual Growth	90.5%	—	—	—

*Fiscal year change

2014 Year-End Financials

Return on assets: (-5.2%)
Return on equity: (-12.6%)
Current ratio: 4.70
Cash ($ mil.): 12

FONTANA UNIFIED SCHOOL DISTRICT

EXECUTIVES

Supt, Leslie Boozer
Human Resources Technician, Molly Garza
Sergeant, Doug Imhof
Strategic Transportation Engin, Kevin Ryan
Administrative Technician, Anna Sinner
Administrative Aide, Theresa Gardea
Gis Analyst, Angel Gonzalez
Landscape Technician, Brian Clements
Administrative Technician, Steve McGuffey
Network Analyst, Dawn Ziegler
Library Media, Debbie Ellis
Auditors: NIGRO NIGRO & WHITE PC TEMEC

LOCATIONS

HQ: FONTANA UNIFIED SCHOOL DISTRICT
9680 CITRUS AVE, FONTANA, CA 923355571
Phone: 909 357-7600
Web: WWW.FUSD.NET

HISTORICAL FINANCIALS

Company Type: Private

Income Statement FYE: June 30

	REVENUE ($ mil.)	NET INCOME ($ mil.)	NET PROFIT MARGIN	EMPLOYEES
06/19	589	(0)	—	3,627
06/18	543	31	5.7%	—
06/17	531	27	5.1%	—
06/16	525	23	4.5%	—
Annual Growth	3.9%	—	—	—

2019 Year-End Financials

Return on assets: —
Return on equity: (-0.2%)
Current ratio: —
Cash ($ mil.): 293

FOOD FOR THE POOR, INC.

Food For The Poor feeds spiritual and physical hunger. The Christian charity provides health social economic and religious services for impoverished people in 17 countries in Latin America and the Caribbean. Food For The Poor believes its organization serves God by helping those most in need distributing requested goods through local churches and charities. The group works through Caritas the American-Nicaraguan Foundation and others to provide vocational training clinic and school construction educational materials feeding programs and medical supplies. Food For The Poor has distributed more than $3 billion in goods since its 1982 inception; the group uses 96% of its funds on programs.

EXECUTIVES

Executive Vice President, Alvaro Pereira
Vice President Of International Operations, Rachmani Domersant
Vice President Major Giving, Natalie Carlisle
Executive Vice President, Edward Raine
Auditors: MAYER HOFFMAN MCCANN PC BOCA

LOCATIONS

HQ: FOOD FOR THE POOR, INC.
6401 LYONS RD, COCONUT CREEK, FL 330733602
Phone: 954 427-2222
Web: WWW.FOODFORTHEPOOR.ORG

HISTORICAL FINANCIALS

Company Type: Private

Income Statement FYE: December 31

	REVENUE ($ mil.)	NET INCOME ($ mil.)	NET PROFIT MARGIN	EMPLOYEES
12/18	942	(10)	—	418
12/17	948	(1)	—	—
12/16	994	14	1.5%	—
12/15	1,158	(0)	—	—
Annual Growth	(6.7%)	—	—	—

2018 Year-End Financials

Return on assets: (-32.0%)
Return on equity: (-40.7%)
Current ratio: 2.70
Cash ($ mil.): 7

FOOD GIANT SUPERMARKETS, INC.

EXECUTIVES

Pres, Kevin Ladd
V Pres-Oprs*, Gary Duncan
Asst SEC-Treas*, Steve Malone
SEC*, Spencer Coates
Information Technology Manager, Brent Benton
Loan Officer, Dedra Clark
Area Supervisor, Bruce Broughton
Meat Supervisor, Kevin Stanford
Information Technology Special, Monica Beck
Store Manager, Keith Frederick
Site Manager, Kenny Counts

LOCATIONS

HQ: FOOD GIANT SUPERMARKETS, INC.
120 INDUSTRIAL DR, SIKESTON, MO 638015216
Phone: 573 471-3500
Web: WWW.FOODGIANT.COM

HISTORICAL FINANCIALS

Company Type: Private

Income Statement FYE: October 1

	REVENUE ($ mil.)	NET INCOME ($ mil.)	NET PROFIT MARGIN	EMPLOYEES
10/16	725	22	3.1%	4,500
10/15	757	25	3.4%	—
10/10*	616	22	3.6%	—
09/06	468	108	23.1%	—
Annual Growth	4.5%	(14.6%)	—	—

*Fiscal year change

2016 Year-End Financials

Return on assets: 12.8%
Return on equity: 14.0%
Current ratio: 1.70
Cash ($ mil.): 18

FORDHAM UNIVERSITY

A private Catholic university Fordham offers its more than 16000 students numerous degree programs through about 10 graduate and undergraduate schools. Called the Jesuit University of New York Fordham has multiple locations including the original Rose Hill campus in the Bronx (often the scene of location shooting for movies TV shows and commercials) the Westchester campus and the Lincoln Center campus in Manhattan. It also operates a biological field station in Armonk New York and international centers in China and the UK. Fordham was founded in 1841.

Operations

Fordham offers more than 50 majors in liberal arts sciences and business. It has an undergraduate student/faculty ratio of 15:1. The university has more than 750 full-time instructors (including more than 30 Jesuits). More than 90% of its faculty holds a Ph.D. or other terminal degree.

Some 70% of Fordham's revenue comes from tuition and fees. Auxiliary enterprises bring in more than 10% of revenue. The rest of its income comes from investments contributions and grants and net assets released from restrictions.

Geographic Reach

Fordham's Rose Hill campus is located on 85 acres in the Bronx and offers studies in business liberal arts science and religion. The Lincoln Center campus provides education business administration social services and legal training while the Westchester campus provides graduate programs in a variety of subjects. The Armonk field station is the headquarters for several university research programs.

Financial Performance

In fiscal 2017 (ended June) Fordham had $596.5 million in operating revenues and $738.9 million in endowments and other investments. Operating expenses totaled $592.3 million that year.

Undergraduate tuition in 2016-17 was $47850 per student.

Company Background

The school opened in 1841 as St. John's College. It officially changed its name to Fordham University in 1907.

EXECUTIVES

Vice President Government Relations And Urban Affairs, Thomas Dunne
President, Joseph M. McShane
Provost, Stephen Freedman
Vp Finance, Frank Simio
Vp Technology And Cio, Frank Sirianni
Dean Fordham College At Lincoln Center, Robert R. Grimes
Interim Dean Fordham College At Rose Hill, John Harrington
Dean Gabelli School Of Business, Donna Rapaccioli
Dean Fordham School Of Professional And Continuing Studies, Isabelle Frank
Dean Graduate School Of Arts And Sciences, Eva Badowska
Dean Graduate School Of Education, James J. Hennessy
Dean Graduate School Of Religion And Religious Education, C. Colt Anderson
Dean Graduate School Of Social Service, Debra M. McPhee
Dean School Of Law, Michael M. Martin
Associate Vice President For Development, Michael Boyd
Assistant Vice President Academic Affairs, Kevin Munnelly
Assistant Vice President University Marketing Communications, Kate Spencer
Director Of Admissions And Marketing, Glenn S Berman
Avp, Peter Bundock
Associate Vice President Information Technology, Fleur Eshghi
Vice President For Finance, Nicholas Milowski
Assistant Vice President For Development And University Events, Elizabeth Manigan
Associate Vice President, Z Hong
1st Vice President, Robert Meyer
Assistant Vice President Of External Affairs, Vera Bullock
Vice President For Lincoln Center, Ines Vano Garcia
Department Chair, Melkana Brakalova
Mba Candidate 18 Vice President Full Time Students, Joe Colandrea
Vice President For Enrollment Admissions, Laurence J Abraham
Assistant Vice President For Student Affairs, Greg Pappas
Assistant Vice President, Ariel Fishman
Assistant Vice President, Tracey Vranich
Former Vice President, Anthony P Carter
Senior Vice President And General Counsel Lockheed Martin Corporation, Maryanne R Lavan
Vice President, John Massarelli
Vice President, Alex Keaton
Assistant Vice President Office Of The Provost, Eileen Burchell
Chairman Board Of Trustees, Robert D. (Bob) Daleo, age 71
Vice Chairman Board Of Trustees, Edward M. Stroz
Board Member, Justin Yancey
Secretary, Carla M Parris
Secretary, Patricia Crea
Secretary, Alexandra Fisher
Treasurer, Viliam Litavec
Treasurer, Gilda Severiano
Senior Secretary, Labelle De La Rosa
Secretary, Nanette Michel
Secretary, Diana Patino
Secretary, Linda Perri
Secretary, Nelson Roman
Senior Secretary, Isaac Tercero
Senior Secretary, Sheleema Bacchus
Soccer Club Treasurer, Alexander Khom
Senior Secretary, Nelsy Rivera
Chairman Emeritus Espn Inc., Herbert A Granath
Secretary, Raj Ghayalod
Secretary, Francesco Ciuffo
Board Member, Carol Sneider
Board Member, Arm Miranda
Auditors: KPMG LLP NEW YORK NY

LOCATIONS

HQ: FORDHAM UNIVERSITY
441 E FORDHAM RD, BRONX, NY 104589993
Phone: 718 817-1000
Web: WWW.FORDHAM.EDU

PRODUCTS/OPERATIONS

2017 Sales

	$ mil.	% of total
Net tuition & fees	424	71
Net auxiliary enterprises	78	13
Investments	27	5
Contributions & private grants	27	4
Government grants	17	3
Net assets released from restrictions	4	1
Other	16	3
Total	**596**	**100**

Selected Colleges

Graduate and Professional
Graduate School of Arts and Sciences
Graduate School of Business
Graduate School of Education
Graduate School of Religion and Religious Education
Graduate School of Social Services
School of Law

Undergraduate
Fordham College at Lincoln Center
Fordham College at Rose Hill
Gabelli School of Business
School of Professional and Continuing Studies

HISTORICAL FINANCIALS

Company Type: Private

Income Statement — FYE: June 30

	REVENUE ($ mil.)	NET INCOME ($ mil.)	NET PROFIT MARGIN	EMPLOYEES
06/18	631	41	6.6%	4,070
06/16	588	(52)	—	—
06/14	566	100	17.7%	—
06/12	518	60	11.6%	—
Annual Growth	3.4%	(5.9%)	—	—

2018 Year-End Financials

Return on assets: 2.1%
Return on equity: 3.1%
Current ratio: —
Cash ($ mil.): 14

FORSYTH COUNTY BOARD OF EDUCATION

EXECUTIVES

Chairperson, Darla Light
Cfo*, Dan Jones
Executive, Amanda Studt
Media Specialist, Jean Lipscomb
Teacher, Karen Pierce
Auditors: MAULDIN & JENKINS LLC ATLANT

LOCATIONS

HQ: FORSYTH COUNTY BOARD OF EDUCATION
1120 DAHLONEGA HWY, CUMMING, GA 300404536
Phone: 770 887-2461
Web: WWW.FORSYTH.K12.GA.US

HISTORICAL FINANCIALS

Company Type: Private

Income Statement — FYE: June 30

	REVENUE ($ mil.)	NET INCOME ($ mil.)	NET PROFIT MARGIN	EMPLOYEES
06/19	582	127	21.9%	4,160
06/17	526	(16)	—	—
06/16	472	21	4.5%	—
06/12	354	(6)	—	—
Annual Growth	7.4%	—	—	—

2019 Year-End Financials

Return on assets: 9.3%
Return on equity: 242.0%
Current ratio: —
Cash ($ mil.): 217

FORT WORTH INDEPENDENT SCHOOL DISTRICT

EXECUTIVES

Sup, Kent Scribner
Executive Officer, Martin Yarobough
Executive Officer, Camille Rodriguez
Executive Officer, Judy Needham
Executive Officer, Blaine Buchenau
Executive Officer, Diana Vargas
Staff, Micheal Lee
Executive Officer, Steven Senevy
Accounting Staff, Deborah Cooper-Boone
Teacher, Regina Pitts
Technology, Carter Cook
Auditors: WEAVER AND TIDWELL LLP FO

LOCATIONS

HQ: FORT WORTH INDEPENDENT SCHOOL DISTRICT
100 N UNIVERSITY DR, FORT WORTH, TX 761071360
Phone: 817 871-2000
Web: WWW.FWISD.ORG

HISTORICAL FINANCIALS

Company Type: Private

Income Statement — FYE: June 30

	REVENUE ($ mil.)	NET INCOME ($ mil.)	NET PROFIT MARGIN	EMPLOYEES
06/17	924	133	14.4%	10,360
06/16	909	(101)	—	—
06/15	843	64	7.7%	—
06/12	777	(98)	—	—
Annual Growth	3.5%	—	—	—

FORTIS CONSTRUCTION, INC.

Fortis Construction isn't afraid to get its hands dirty. The fast-growing US construction company offers general contracting preconstruction construction management and environmentally-friendly green building services to customers primarily in Portland Oregon and others in the Pacific Northwest. It specializes in remodeling and upgrading corporate offices health care facilities retail complexes and schools; it also conducts seismic and structural upgrades. Customers have included Oregon State University Portland State University PPG Industries and StanCorp.

EXECUTIVES

Vp Of Construction, Tim Jones
Secretary And Treasurer, Rene Gonzalez
Auditors: ALDRICH CPAS AND ADVISORS LLP

LOCATIONS

HQ: FORTIS CONSTRUCTION, INC.
1705 SW TAYLOR ST STE 200, PORTLAND, OR 972051922
Phone: 503 459-4477
Web: WWW.FORTISCONSTRUCTION.COM

PRODUCTS/OPERATIONS

Selected Services
Construction management
General contracting
Green building
Preconstruction
Web-based collaboration and electronic document management

COMPETITORS

Andersen Construction
Hoffman Corporation
Jacobsen Construction
Panattoni Construction
R&H Construction
S.D. Deacon
Swinerton Builders

HISTORICAL FINANCIALS

Company Type: Private

Income Statement — FYE: December 31

	REVENUE ($ mil.)	NET INCOME ($ mil.)	NET PROFIT MARGIN	EMPLOYEES
12/16	782	30	3.9%	175
12/15	468	18	3.9%	—
12/14	282	14	5.0%	—
Annual Growth	66.6%	48.0%	—	—

2016 Year-End Financials

Return on assets: 20.5%
Return on equity: 75.8%
Current ratio: 1.40
Cash ($ mil.): 41

FRANCISCAN ALLIANCE, INC.

The Franciscan Alliance keeps watch over a family of hospitals. The not-for-profit organization operates more than a dozen hospitals in Indiana and south suburban Chicago. The hospitals house about 3500 beds and include specialist centers for cancer care heart and vascular care weight loss pediatrics and women's health. In addition to inpatient acute care services they operate numerous outpatient facilities and medical practices within their local service areas. Other subsidiaries and affiliates perform clinical laboratory tests offer home health services and provide support services to the system. Franciscan Alliance was founded and is sponsored by the Sisters of St. Francis of Perpetual Adoration.

Operations

Franciscan Alliance's hospitals handle about 100000 inpatient visits annually. The organization also handles about 3 million outpatient visits each year at its hospitals clinics and practice offices. Its physician practice organization includes about 700 doctors.

Along with providing a wide range of health care services Franciscan Alliance educates future health care providers through affiliations with area universities. The schools offer a variety of degree programs in fields including nursing medical technician and pharmacy residency.

Geographic Reach

Franciscan Alliance's hospitals are located in about ten communities in Indiana as well as in southern Chicago suburbs. The facilities serve patients in parts of Michigan as well. The organization also operates hundreds of outpatient clinics and physician offices in the area as well as a data center in Beech Grove Indiana.

Strategy

In 2011 the Sisters of St. Francis of Perpetual Adoration decided to change the name of the health system from Sisters of St. Francis Health Services to Franciscan Alliance to spread brand awareness and illustrate cohesiveness among the system's various facilities. The name change came after several months of consumer research and took about a year to be fully implemented across the entire system.

Franciscan Alliance also expanded through new construction in 2011 with the completion of the first phase of its Indianapolis Campus Expansion project. The health system moved a number of services into the new patient tower there including emergency services surgical suites and a wound care institute. In 2012 the company closed its Beech Grove hospital and consolidated services to the expanded Indianapolis center. It also opened a new short-stay hospital in Carmel that year.

In 2013 however the company announced that it would explore options to sell all or part of its two Franciscan St. James Health hospitals. The organization sought a partner to invest in capital improvements at the facilities. No buyer stepped forward but economic conditions improved enough by 2014 that the alliance said it was no longer searching for a buyer or investor. It also broke ground on a Hospice facility opened a specialized wound-care center and started a $10.2 million renovation at its St. Margaret facility.

Mergers and Acquisitions

In 2011 Franciscan Alliance grew its outpatient facilities by acquiring Surgical Hospital of Munster which serves as an outpatient surgery center of Franciscan Physicians Hospital.

EXECUTIVES

President Ceo, Kevin Leahy
President And Ceo Franciscan St. Margaret Health, Michael J. Stenger
Ceo Franciscan Health Dyer Franciscan Health Hammond Franciscan Health Munster, Patrick Maloney
Ceo Western Indiana Region, Terrance E. Wilson
Svp And Coo Inpatient Services, Gene Diamond
President And Ceo Crown Point, Barbara Anderson
President Franciscan St. Anthony Health Michigan City, James Callaghan
Corporate Svp Post-acute Services, Thomas Gryzbek
Auditors: I PNCEWATERHOUSECOOPERS LLP

LOCATIONS

HQ: FRANCISCAN ALLIANCE, INC.
1515 W DRAGOON TRL, MISHAWAKA, IN 465444710
Phone: 574 273-3867
Web: WWW.FRANCISCANHEALTH.ORG

PRODUCTS/OPERATIONS

Selected Operations
St. Anthony Health (Crown Point and Michigan City Indiana)
St. Elizabeth Health (Crawfordsville Lafayette Central Lafayette East Indiana)
St. Francis Health (Carmel Indianapolis and Mooresville Indiana)
St. James Health (Chicago Heights and Olympia Fields Illinois)
St. Margaret Health (Hammond and Dyer Indiana)
Franciscan Healthcare Munster (formerly Physicians Hospital; Munster Indiana)

Selected Services
Anticoagulation Clinics
Behavioral Health
Cancer Care
Colon and Rectal Surgery
Diabetes Care
Ear Nose and Throat
Emergency Medicine

Heart & Vascular
Home Health Care
Hospice
Imaging
Joint & Spine Care
Laboratory Services
Neurology
Neurosurgery
Occupational Health
Ophthalmology
Pain Management
Palliative Medicine
Pediatrics
Plastic Surgery
Primary Care Physicians
Pulmonary Medicine
Registered Dietitians
Rehabilitation Services
Robotic Surgery
Senior Services
Sleep Disorders
Sports Medicine
Surgical Services
Urgent Care
Weight Loss/Bariatrics
Women's Health/OBGYN
Wound Care

Selected Hospitals

Franciscan St. Anthony - Crown Point
Franciscan St. Anthony - Michigan City
Franciscan St. Elizabeth - Lafayette Central
Franciscan St. Elizabeth - Lafayette East
Franciscan St. Elizabeth - Crawfordsville
Franciscan St. Francis - Carmel
Franciscan St. Francis - Indianapolis
Franciscan St. Francis - Mooresville
Franciscan St. James - Chicago Heights
Franciscan St. James - Olympia Fields
Franciscan St. Margaret - Dyer
Franciscan St. Margaret - Hammond
Franciscan Healthcare - Munster

COMPETITORS

Advocate Health Care
Ascension Health
Community Health Network
Covenant Ministries
IU Health
Memorial Hospital & Health System
NorthShore University HealthSystem
Northwestern Memorial HealthCare
Porter Health Care System
Riverview Hospital
Rush System for Health
Sinai Health System
St. Bernard Hospital and Health Care Center
Union Hospital (Indiana)
University of Chicago Medical Center

HISTORICAL FINANCIALS

Company Type: Private

Income Statement — FYE: December 31

	REVENUE ($ mil.)	NET INCOME ($ mil.)	NET PROFIT MARGIN	EMPLOYEES
12/19	3,302	409	12.4%	19,000
12/18	3,144	14	0.5%	—
12/15	2,731	250	9.2%	—
12/14	2,661	274	10.3%	—
Annual Growth	4.4%	8.3%	—	—

2019 Year-End Financials

Return on assets: 7.0%
Return on equity: 11.6%
Current ratio: 1.40
Cash ($ mil.): 28

FRANCISCAN HEALTH SYSTEM

St. Francis himself may have hailed from Italy but his followers look after the health of the residents of the South Puget Sound area through the Franciscan Health System. The not-for-profit system includes five full-service hospitals. The oldest and largest hospital is St. Joseph Medical Center in Tacoma Washington a 320-bed facility. Its facilities include community hospitals St. Clare Hospital (in Lakewood) and St. Francis Hospital (in Federal Way) as well as a hospice program and numerous primary and specialty care clinics. Its St. Anthony Hospital is an 80-bed full service pharmacy and home medical equipment retail location at Gig Harbor.

Geographic Reach

Franciscan Health System serves patients in Tacoma Washington and surrounding areas.

Financial Performance

The company gets most of its revenues from patient services. Other sources of income includes foundation gifts and investment community benefit charity care and uncompensated care (unreimbursed costs of serving patients enrolled in Medicaid and other state-subsidized programs).

Strategy

Franciscan Health System and Harrison Medical Center are looking to join forces while Franciscan's parent continues in talks to combine its Northwest operations with PeaceHealth of Vancouver Washington. If both plans are approved by regulators Harrison will become part of the largest community hospital system in the Northwest with facilities in Alaska Washington and Oregon. Both the Harrison-Franciscan affiliation and that of Franciscan's parent Catholic Health Initiatives with PeaceHealth is slated to be approved in 2013.

In addition Franciscan Health System is collaborating with the MultiCare Health System and TRA Medical Imaging to build a women's imaging and breast cancer care center.

St. Elizabeth Hospital opened its doors in 2011 in Enumclaw replacing Enumclaw Regional Hospital as that community's acute-care facility.

Company Background

St. Joseph Medical Center in Tacoma (the health system's oldest facility) was founded by the Sisters of St. Francis in 1891.

EXECUTIVES

Pharmacy Manager, Michael Bonck
Medical Director, Arthur Maslow
Medical Director, Martin Cieri
Vice President Of Quality And Associate Chief Marketing Officer, Kimberly Moore
Physical Therapy Director, DAVID LUNDGREN
Medical Director, Paul Darby
Vice President Of Informatics And Operations, Dean A Field
Medical Director, Haroon P Anwar
Vice President Ambulatory Operations St. Joseph Region, Jane Root
Director Of Nursing, Sheila Ball
Nursing Director, Sherry Ransom
Nursing Director, Alisa Murchek
Nursing Director, Mari Ross

LOCATIONS

HQ: FRANCISCAN HEALTH SYSTEM
1717 S J ST, TACOMA, WA 984054933
Phone: 253 426-4101
Web: WWW.CHIFRANCISCAN.ORG

PRODUCTS/OPERATIONS

Key Facilities and Services

Carol Milgard Breast Center Tacoma
Franciscan Center for Weight Management Federal Way
Franciscan Dialysis Center Eastside Tacoma
Franciscan Medical Group primary-care and specialty-care clinics
Franciscan Hospice House University Place
Franciscan Port Clinic Tacoma
Gig Harbor Medical Pavilion Gig Harbor
Gig Harbor Ambulatory Surgery Clinic Gig Harbor
St. Anthony Hospital Gig Harbor
St. Clare Hospital Lakewood
St. Clare Specialty Center Lakewood
St. Clare Medical Pavilion Lakewood
St. Elizabeth Hospital Enumclaw
St. Francis Hospital Federal Way
St. Francis Outpatient Center Federal Way
St. Joseph Medical Center Tacoma
St. Joseph Outpatient Center Tacoma
St. Joseph Heart & Vascular Center Tacoma
St. Joseph Dialysis Center Tacoma
St. Joseph Dialysis Center Gig Harbor
St. Joseph Dialysis Center Puyallup
St. Joseph Medical Clinic Tacoma
St. Joseph Medical Pavilion Tacoma
Milgard Medical Pavilion at St. Anthony Gig Harbor
Women's Health & Breast Center Federal Way

COMPETITORS

Harrison Medical Center
MultiCare Health System
Overlake Hospital
PeaceHealth
Providence St. Joseph Health
Seattle Children's Hospital
Swedish Health Services
Yakima Valley Memorial

HISTORICAL FINANCIALS

Company Type: Private

Income Statement — FYE: June 30

	REVENUE ($ mil.)	NET INCOME ($ mil.)	NET PROFIT MARGIN	EMPLOYEES
06/16	637	51	8.0%	3,183
06/15	610	56	9.2%	—
06/14	1,190	(106)	—	—
06/10	1,093	71	6.5%	—
Annual Growth	(8.6%)	(5.4%)	—	—

2016 Year-End Financials

Return on assets: 11.2%
Return on equity: 13.8%
Current ratio: 3.10
Cash ($ mil.): 113

FRANCISCAN MISSIONARIES OF OUR LADY HEALTH SYSTEM, INC.

EXECUTIVES

Pres-Ceo, Richard R Vath
V Pres, Pete Guarisco
SEC-Treas, Sr Helen Cahill
Cfo, Howard Harvill
Information Specialist, Chris Jones
Information Specialist, Trisha A Tunis

It Security, Becky Davis
Member, Denicca Dorsey
Coordinator, Denise Broussard
Law Specialist, Diane Allen
Information Specialist, Elizabeth McCurdy
Auditors: KMG LLP BATON ROUGE LOUISIA

LOCATIONS

HQ: FRANCISCAN MISSIONARIES OF OUR LADY HEALTH SYSTEM, INC.
4200 ESSEN LN, BATON ROUGE, LA 708092158
Phone: 225 923-2701
Web: WWW.FMOLSISTERS.COM

HISTORICAL FINANCIALS

Company Type: Private

Income Statement — FYE: June 30

	REVENUE ($ mil.)	NET INCOME ($ mil.)	NET PROFIT MARGIN	EMPLOYEES
06/20	3,007	44	1.5%	9,000
06/19	2,296	27	1.2%	—
06/18	2,029	106	5.3%	—
06/17	1,911	112	5.9%	—
Annual Growth	16.3%	(26.8%)	—	—

2020 Year-End Financials

Return on assets: 1.0%
Return on equity: 2.5%
Current ratio: 1.70
Cash ($ mil.): 839

FRANKLIN COUNTY BOARD OF COMMISSIONERS

EXECUTIVES

Commissioner, Marilyn Brown
Staff, Jenell Williams
Coordinator, Cecilia Weirick
Coordinator, Kris McDaniel
Coordinator, Kysten Palmore
Coordinator, Patti Froehlich
Coordinator, Phyllis Roberts
Contractor, Catherine Richards
Admin SEC, Victoria C
Network Administrator, Sharon Evrard
Licensed Social Worker, Carolyn Pierce-Jones
Auditors: ROBERT HINKLE CPA CGFM COLU

LOCATIONS

HQ: FRANKLIN COUNTY BOARD OF COMMISSIONERS
373 S HIGH ST FL 26, COLUMBUS, OH 432154591
Phone: 614 525-3322
Web: WWW.FCBDD.ORG

HISTORICAL FINANCIALS

Company Type: Private

Income Statement — FYE: December 31

	REVENUE ($ mil.)	NET INCOME ($ mil.)	NET PROFIT MARGIN	EMPLOYEES
12/19	1,348	(48)	—	6,000
12/17	1,281	85	6.7%	—
12/16	1,226	48	3.9%	—
12/09	1,163	(25)	—	—
Annual Growth	1.5%	—	—	—

FREEMAN HEALTH SYSTEM

Freeman Health System (FHS) offers comprehensive health and behavioral health services to the residents of Arkansas Kansas Missouri and Oklahoma through three hospitals with a total of more than 500 beds. Specialty facilities include a full-service cardiothoracic and vascular program at the Freeman Heart Institute and behavioral health services through its Ozark Health Center. Community-owned not-for-profit FHS also operates two urgent care centers a separate sleep center several doctors' office buildings and serves as a teaching hospital with three residency programs (ear nose and throat; emergency medicine; and internal medicine). FHS employs more than 300 physicians in 60 specialties.

Operations

FHS operates three Missouri hospitals - Freeman Hospital West and Freeman Hospital East in Joplin and Freeman Neosho in Neosho. Its Ozark Center provides behavioral health services to patients from Missouri Arkansas Oklahoma and Kansas.

Strategy

Like most health care providers FHS has been working to update it facilities and expand it offerings. To that end in 2013 it opened a transitional living and life skills assistance center for homeless teens and teamed with an autism support group to design an autism treatment program for its Ozark Center. The prior year it christened Will's Place behavioral health center for children and opened a $2 million sports and rehabilitation center.

Company Background

Located in Joplin Missouri – the site of the deadly E5 tornado that killed 161 people in May 2011– Freeman Health System was the only fully functional hospital in the aftermath of the disaster. Rival St. John's Regional Medical Center just two miles away was destroyed. However Ozark Health Center FHS's behavioral health division lost nine buildings in the disaster.

EXECUTIVES

Pres- Ceo, Paula Baker
Cfo*, Steven Graddy
Exec V Pres*, Joseph Kirk
Cmo*, Richard D Schooler
Cro*, Kevin Gaudette
Specialist, Thomas Coy
Auditors: BKD LLP SPRINGFIELD MISSOUR

LOCATIONS

HQ: FREEMAN HEALTH SYSTEM
1102 W 32ND ST, JOPLIN, MO 648043503
Phone: 417 347-1111
Web: WWW.FREEMANHEALTH.COM

PRODUCTS/OPERATIONS

Selected Services

Autism Services
Behavioral/mental health
Bladder care
Cancer care
Children's Miracle Network Hospitals
Clinical trials
Cosmetic/reconstructive surgery
Critical Care (ICU)
Diabetes education
Digestive care
Emergency medicine
Family care
Family counseling
Geriatric medicine
Health screenings
Hearing services
Home care
Internal medicine
Internet Addiction Services
Kidney Care
Lung care
Maternity
Neonatal intensive care
Nephrology & dialysis
Neurology & neurosurgery
Occupational medicine
Orthopedics
Pain management
Palliative care
QuickMeds Pharmacy;
Radiology
Rehabilitation
Senior Services
Skilled nursing
Sleep disorders
Sports medicine
Substance abuse services
Surgery
Tobacco cessation
Transitional Care Unit (TCU)
Urgent care
Women's Services
Wound care

Selected Facilities

Freeman Hospital West - Joplin MO
Freeman Hospital East - Joplin MO
Freeman Neosho Hospital - Neosho MO
Freeman Business Center - Joplin MO
Ozark Center - Joplin Missouri

COMPETITORS

Catholic Health Initiatives
Children's Mercy Hospital
Heartland Regional Medical
Mercy Health

HISTORICAL FINANCIALS

Company Type: Private

Income Statement — FYE: March 31

	REVENUE ($ mil.)	NET INCOME ($ mil.)	NET PROFIT MARGIN	EMPLOYEES
03/20	562	16	3.0%	3,887
03/19	624	57	9.2%	—
03/18	588	51	8.7%	—
03/17	564	45	8.1%	—
Annual Growth	(0.2%)	(28.2%)	—	—

2020 Year-End Financials

Return on assets: 3.1%
Return on equity: 4.7%
Current ratio: 1.90
Cash ($ mil.): 49

FRESH MARK, INC.

Fresh Mark is a leading producer of smoked and processed pork products for the domestic and international retail and foodservice industries. From its four plants in Ohio the company makes and markets such products as bacon (raw par-cooked and cooked) deli sausage ham (natural and smoked) hot dogs and lunch meats under the Sugardale and Superior's brands. The company also produces private-label processed meat products for others and supplies the foodservice industry through its Sugardale Food Service business. Founded in 1920 Ohio-based Fresh Mark is owned and operated by the Genshaft family.

EXECUTIVES

Vice President Of Resource Management, Rick Hawley
Vice President, Monica Taylor
National Sales Manager, Bryan Newton
Auditors: ERNST & YOUNG LLP AKRON OH

LOCATIONS

HQ: FRESH MARK, INC.
1888 SOUTHWAY ST SE, MASSILLON, OH 44646
Phone: 330 832-7491
Web: WWW.FRESHMARK.COM

PRODUCTS/OPERATIONS

Selected Products

Bacon
Deli meats
Dry sausage
Ham
Luncheon meats
Specialty meat items
Weiners

COMPETITORS

Birchwood Meat & Provision
Boar's Head
Cargill Meat Solutions
Carl Buddig
Coleman Natural Foods
ConAgra
Farmland Foods
Hormel
Indiana Packers
JBS USA
Johnsonville Sausage
Smithfield Foods
Tyson Foods

HISTORICAL FINANCIALS

Company Type: Private

Income Statement — FYE: January 1

	REVENUE ($ mil.)	NET INCOME ($ mil.)	NET PROFIT MARGIN	EMPLOYEES
01/11*	795	59	7.5%	2,300
12/07	534	31	5.8%	—
12/06	481	21	4.5%	—
12/05	481	23	4.9%	—
Annual Growth	10.6%	20.4%	—	—

*Fiscal year change

2011 Year-End Financials

Return on assets: 3.9%
Return on equity: 7.5%
Current ratio: 0.90
Cash ($ mil.): 4

FRESNO COMMUNITY HOSPITAL AND MEDICAL CENTER

EXECUTIVES

Pres-Ceo, Phillip Hinton
Ceo*, Tim A Joslin
Cfo*, William Grigg
Treas*, Roger Fretwell
Sr V Pres*, Mike Kingbury
Sr V Pres*, Stephen Walter
V Pres*, Les Abercrombie
Network Administrator, Hadi Habib
Network Administrator, Ian Reith
Pacs Administrator, Jason Hulsey
Network Administrator, John Ounesavath
Auditors: MOSS ADAMS LLP STOCKTON CA

LOCATIONS

HQ: FRESNO COMMUNITY HOSPITAL AND MEDICAL CENTER
2823 FRESNO ST, FRESNO, CA 937211324
Phone: 559 459-3948
Web: WWW.COMMUNITYMEDICAL.ORG

HISTORICAL FINANCIALS

Company Type: Private

Income Statement — FYE: August 31

	REVENUE ($ mil.)	NET INCOME ($ mil.)	NET PROFIT MARGIN	EMPLOYEES
08/15	1,571	139	8.9%	5,045
08/10	1,027	9	0.9%	—
08/09	1,010	65	6.5%	—
Annual Growth	7.6%	13.3%	—	—

2015 Year-End Financials

Return on assets: 7.8%
Return on equity: 13.3%
Current ratio: 0.50
Cash ($ mil.): 62

FRESNO UNIFIED SCHOOL DISTRICT

EXECUTIVES

Supt, Michael Hanson
Asst Supt-Oprs*, Rick Hausman
Magnet School Coordinator, Tammy Townsend
Substitute Teacher, Jack Karraker
Teacher, Sarina De La Rosa
Science Teacher, Anna Demaree
Manager III, David Jansen
Chief Technology Officer, Kurt Madden
Auditors: PERRY SMITH SACRAMENTO CALIF

LOCATIONS

HQ: FRESNO UNIFIED SCHOOL DISTRICT
2309 TULARE ST, FRESNO, CA 937212287
Phone: 559 457-3000
Web: WWW.FRESNOUNIFIED.ORG

HISTORICAL FINANCIALS

Company Type: Private

Income Statement — FYE: June 30

	REVENUE ($ mil.)	NET INCOME ($ mil.)	NET PROFIT MARGIN	EMPLOYEES
06/10	692	(13)	—	8,400
06/09	757	0	0.1%	—
06/08	771	(40)	—	—
06/07	781	74	9.5%	—
Annual Growth	(3.9%)	—	—	—

2010 Year-End Financials

Return on assets: (-1.5%)
Return on equity: (-4.6%)
Current ratio: —
Cash ($ mil.): 221

FROEDTERT MEMORIAL LUTHERAN HOSPITAL, INC.

Patients in southeastern Wisconsin count on Froedtert Memorial Lutheran Hospital for a full range of health services including trauma transplant sports medicine and senior care. The 500-bed hospital also known as Froedtert & The Medical College of Wisconsin is part of the Froedtert (pronounced "fray-dert") Health system. Specialty units include cancer dermatology neuroscience birthing fertility urology and vein clinics. The hospital also serves as a teaching facility for the Medical College of Wisconsin and it partners with the Children's Hospital of Wisconsin to provide pediatric services. Froedtert Hospital which was founded in 1980 operates the only adult Level I trauma center in the region.

Operations

Froedtert Health offers medical practice care in roughly 25 specialties and sub-specialties. Beyond the hospital's walls it operates four diagnostic imaging centers as well as rehabilitation facilities and a handful of primary care clinics in the community. The Froedtert Health system also includes Community Memorial Hospital in Menomonee Falls Wisconsin; St. Joseph's Hospital in West Bend Wisconsin; and Froedtert Health Medical Group.

Altogether the system's hospitals have 781 beds and see nearly 40000 admissions annually. They also manage more than 900000 outpatient visits each year. In 2014 Froedtert Hospital alone had about 65000 emergency department visits more than 736000 outpatient visits and delivered more than 2000 babies.

Strategy

To help advance the health of its service communities Froedtert Health is investing some $12 million to establish a new 22000-sq.-ft. health clinic in Milwaukee. It is partnering with clinic operator Sixteenth Street Community Health Centers on the project which is intended to address the needs of medically underserved neighborhoods. The facility will provide specialty care cancer prevention and access to cancer clinical trials.

EXECUTIVES

President Froedtert Hospital, Catherine (Cathy) Buck
Svp Finance, Jeffrey Van De Kreeke
President And Ceo Froedtert Health, Catherine A. Jacobson
Chief Medical Officer Froedtert Hospital, Lee Biblo
Coo Froedtert Health And President Community Memorial Hospital, Dennis Pollard
Vp And Cio, Robert DeGrand
Vp Perioperative Services, Gary Colpaert
Vp Supply Chain And Pharmacy, James Klauck
Vp Ambulatory Services, Katherine Bagemihl
Vp Patient Care Services, Kathleen Bechtel
Vp Clinical Integration And Payer Strategies, Patricia Ruff
Evp, Peter Pruessing
Assistant Vice President Finance And Decision Support Services, Timothy Waldoch
Medical Director, Lois Connolly
Medical Director, Surendra Patel
Vice President, Julie Kerk
Vice President Chief Diversity Officer, Andres Gonzalez
Senior Vice President Chief Human Resources Officer, Eric Humphrey

Vice President Of Marketing And Communications, Kathi Perlewitz
Senior Vice President Service Line And Network Development, Dean Thomas
Senior Vice President Chief Experience Officer, Steve Basilotto
Vice President, Ed Hardin
Vice President, Janet Kummeth
Vice President, Jennie Johns
Emeritus Board Members Member, Philip Smith
Auditors: KPMG LLP COLUMBUS OH

LOCATIONS

HQ: FROEDTERT MEMORIAL LUTHERAN HOSPITAL, INC.
9200 W WISCONSIN AVE, MILWAUKEE, WI 532263522
Phone: 414 805-3000
Web: WWW.FROEDTERT.COM

PRODUCTS/OPERATIONS

Selected Departments Centers and Programs

Clinical Cancer Center
- Blood and Lymph Node Cancer Program
- Blood and Marrow Transplant Program
- Bone and Connective Tissue Cancer Program
- Brain and Spine Tumor Program
- Breast Cancer Program
- Cancer Genetics Screening Program
- Colorectal Cancer Program
- Endocrine Cancer Program
- Eye/Orbital Cancer Program
- Geriatric Oncology
- Gynecologic Cancer Program
- Head and Neck Cancer Program
- Liver Pancreas and Bile Duct Cancer Program
- Neuro-oncology Cognitive Clinic
- Palliative Care Program
- Plastic Surgery Center
- Prostate and Urologic Cancer Program
- Skin Cancer Center
- Thoracic Cancer Program (Lung and Esophageal Cancers)

Heart and Vascular Center
- Adult Congenital Heart Disease
- Advanced Heart Failure and Cardiac Transplantation
- Aortic Disease
- Arrhythmia and Atrial Fibrillation
- Coronary Artery Disease (CAD)
- Hereditary Hemorrhagic Telangiectasia (HHT)
- Hypertrophic Cardiomyopathy (HCM)
- Preventive Cardiology and Lipid Therapy
- Peripheral Arterial Disease (PAD)
- Pulmonary Hypertension
- Valvular Disease
- Venous Thrombotic Disease
- Venous and Vein Disease
- Women and Heart Disease

Neurosciences Center
- Brain Injury Program
- Brain and Spine Tumor Program
- Comprehensive Epilepsy Program
- Comprehensive Spasticity Management Program
- Memory Disorders Program
- Neuro-Oncology Cognitive Clinic
- Normal Pressure Hydrocephalus
- Parkinson's and Movement Disorders Program
- Sleep Disorders Program
- SpineCare Program
- Spinal Cord Injury Center
- Stroke and Neurovascular Program

COMPETITORS

Children's Hospital and Health System
Columbia St. Mary's
Ministry Health Care
ProHealth Care
Rockford Health System
Waukesha Memorial
Wheaton Franciscan Services

HISTORICAL FINANCIALS

Company Type: Private

Income Statement — FYE: June 30

	REVENUE ($ mil.)	NET INCOME ($ mil.)	NET PROFIT MARGIN	EMPLOYEES
06/14	1,164	92	7.9%	3,400
06/11	980	79	8.1%	—
06/10	894	59	6.7%	—
Annual Growth	6.8%	11.6%	—	—

2014 Year-End Financials

Return on assets: 12.3%
Return on equity: 14.1%
Current ratio: 3.00
Cash ($ mil.): 16

FRONTROW CALYPSO LLC

EXECUTIVES

Ceo-Pres, Jens Holstebro
V Pres*, John Merline
V Pres*, Leo Stearns
SEC*, Per Lund
Manager, Kris Hutchins
Vice President of Sales, Ed Kisman

LOCATIONS

HQ: FRONTROW CALYPSO LLC
1690 CORPORATE CIR, PETALUMA, CA 949546912
Phone: 707 769-1110
Web: WWW.GOFRONTROW.COM

HISTORICAL FINANCIALS

Company Type: Private

Income Statement — FYE: December 31

	REVENUE ($ mil.)	NET INCOME ($ mil.)	NET PROFIT MARGIN	EMPLOYEES
12/08	1,009	128	12.7%	40
12/07	1,083	214	19.8%	—
12/04	21	(1)	—	—
Annual Growth	162.1%	—	—	—

2008 Year-End Financials

Return on assets: 17.4%
Return on equity: 126.6%
Current ratio: 0.80
Cash ($ mil.): 26

FTD COMPANIES, INC.

Mercury the Roman god of speed and commerce with winged feet (and an icon for megaflorist FTD) comes bearing flowers. FTD Group is the holding company for operating subsidiaries FTD.COM and FTD Inc. established in 1910 as the Florists' Telegraph Delivery Association by a group of 15 florists. Besides flowers the company offers plants gourmet foods and gift baskets to a variety of customers including consumers retailers and more than 40000 florist shops in the US Canada and the UK and under the brand Interflora in Ireland. FTD was spun off into a publicly traded company in 2013; it owns online floral and gift company Provide Commerce.

Change in Company Type

United Online acquired FTD in a deal valued at about $441 million. In return FTD shareholders received about 15% of United Online the operator of the NetZero and Juno ISPs.

Because FTD comprises the bulk of United Online's revenue and represents its more promising operations the parent company in November 2013 spun off FTD including the domestic and international operations of the company while continuing to run its communications and content and media segments as a separate company. As part of the move United Online will explore strategic alternatives for its non-FTD segments and cash in on its portfolio of patents and patent applications.

Operations

Product revenue for FTD comes from selling floral gift and related items to consumers through its web sites and by phone as well as through its floral network members. Its services revenue is generated from membership fees order-related fees and services and subscription and other fees generated from independent members of both the FTD and Interflora floral networks.

Geographic Reach

Based in Downers Grove Illinois FTD serves consumers across the US Canada the UK and Ireland through its floral network members web sites and by phone.

Sales and Marketing

The company's primary focus is on generating orders from new and existing customers marketing its services to its floral network members while enlisting new members and marketing its services to alternative channels the likes of supermarkets and mass merchants.

For its consumer business FTD uses online advertising (search engine marketing and optimization social media social gaming and group-buying programs) co-marketing and affiliate partnerships loyalty programs with airlines credit card companies and hotel chains database marketing via email promotions direct mail and other print advertising email-based reminder services with personalized reminders and radio and TV advertising.

FTD's marketing efforts for its floral network include conducting member appreciation and training events sponsoring and participating in floral and retail industry trade shows and rolling out offline media campaigns. The company boasts a dedicated sales force to market its products and services to floral network members and encourage non-member floral retailers to join the network.

Worth noting because orders placed through FTD's consumer websites or telephone numbers are paid for using a credit debit or payment card or PayPal consumers typically pay for floral and gift orders before FTD pays the floral network members and third-party providers to fulfill and deliver them. Its floral network members are billed monthly for products and services and for net clearinghouse order activity.

In 2014 FTD spent $69.5 million on advertising and promotion.

Financial Performance

FTD's revenues rose in 2014 as it has for the last five years. It hit $640 million a 2% increase over the previous year based on 10% higher sales in the International segment. Net income has fluctuated over the years and it rose 83% to $22.8 million.

Strategy

Looking to diversify the flower industry heavyweight acquired the flowers and gifts businesses of Provide Commerce from owner Liberty Interactive for $430 million in stock and cash in late 2014. The deal included ProFlowers Shari's Berries and Personal Creations but did not cover RedEnvelope.

FTD expects to wring out $25 million in annual cost savings from the deal over the next three years by cutting purchasing and distribution costs for the combined operation. Liberty Interactive will own a 35% stake in the combined company which will be run by FTD's current management team.

While the US and UK markets are highly fragmented with thousands of floral industry participants FTD has noted some key market trends that are steering its strategic focus. A growing percentage of orders are placed through floral mass marketers rather than with traditional retail florists. Consumers purchase "cash and carry" bouquets from supermarkets and mass merchants as opposed to traditional florists which have grown to rely more on floral network services to make up for this lost business and for orders through the Internet. In response traditional retail florists – and their fellow mass marketers – have expanded their product selection to include gift items.

Soon after United Online's acquisition of FTD the company oversaw FTD.com's face-lift which included updating the online florist's branding marketing packaging and websites. Initiatives also included a partnership with funeral service provider Batesville Casket Company to provide customized co-branded floral websites to its funeral homes in the US and Canada.

EXECUTIVES

Interim President And Ceo, Christopher W. Shean
Interim Cfo Principal Financial Officer And Principal Accounting Officer, Brian S. Cooper
Evp And Cio, Jay Topper
Evp General Counsel And Secretary, Scott D. Levin, $356,000 total compensation
President Interflora, Rhys J. Hughes, $267,552 total compensation
Evp Florist Division, Tom D. Moeller, $393,919 total compensation
Evp Crm And Quality, Michael Dorion
Evp Us Consumer Floral, Helen Quinn
Evp Gifting, Eric J. Vratimos
Evp Supply Chain Operations, Dale Perrott
Evp And Coo, Simha Kumar
Evp Of Florist Division, Tom Moeller
Svp Of Hr, Patricia Carl
Senior Vice President Technology, Vamsi Muddada
Vice President Supply Chain Planning, Nishad Gadgil
Vice President Crm And Analytics, Sajid Patel
Vice President Marketing Partnerships, Andrea Newsom
Senior Vice President General Manager An Ftd Company, Lincoln Rodman
Chairman, Robert Berglass
Auditors: DELOITTE & TOUCHE LLP CHICAGO

LOCATIONS

HQ: FTD COMPANIES, INC.
3113 WOODCREEK DR, DOWNERS GROVE, IL 605155420
Phone: 630 719-7800
Web: WWW.FTDCOMPANIES.COM

2014 Sales

	% of total
US	72
International	28
Total	**100**

2014 Sales

Revenue by Segments (in million)		% Contribu
Product Revenues:		
Consumer	318	48
International	155	24
Florist	46	7
Service Revenues:		
Florist	116	18
International	22	3
Intersegment Elimination	(18)	
Total	**640**	**100**

PRODUCTS/OPERATIONS

Selected Businesses

Consumer
US
1-800-SEND-FTD
www.ftd.com
Canada
www.ftd.ca
Ireland
www.interflora.ie
UK
www.drakealgar.com
www.interflora.uk
www.flyingflowers.co.uk
www.flowersdirect.co.uk
Floral Network
US
Canada
Ireland
UK

COMPETITORS

1-800-FLOWERS
Costco Wholesale
Harry & David Holdings
John Lewis
KaBloom
Kroger
Marks & Spencer
NEXT plc
Organic Bouquet
Provide Commerce
Safeway
Teleflora

HISTORICAL FINANCIALS

Company Type: Private

Income Statement				FYE: December 31
	REVENUE ($ mil.)	NET INCOME ($ mil.)	NET PROFIT MARGIN	EMPLOYEES
12/18	1,014	(224)	—	1,501
12/17	1,084	(234)	—	—
12/16	1,122	(83)	—	—
12/15	1,219	(78)	—	—
Annual Growth	(6.0%)	—	—	—

2018 Year-End Financials

Return on assets: (-58.0%)
Return on equity: —
Current ratio: 0.20
Cash ($ mil.): 16

FULTON COUNTY BOARD OF EDUCATION

EXECUTIVES

Pres, Linda McCain
Cfo*, Michael Russell
Contrl, W Harold Grindle
Executive Officer, Linda Bryant
Coordinator, Ashley Garrison
Auditors: MAULDIN & JENKINS LLC ATLANT

LOCATIONS

HQ: FULTON COUNTY BOARD OF EDUCATION
6201 POWERS FERRY RD, ATLANTA, GA 303392926
Phone: 404 768-3600
Web: WWW.FULTONSCHOOLS.ORG

HISTORICAL FINANCIALS

Company Type: Private

Income Statement				FYE: June 30
	REVENUE ($ mil.)	NET INCOME ($ mil.)	NET PROFIT MARGIN	EMPLOYEES
06/19	1,351	32	2.4%	10,000
06/18	1,268	40	3.2%	—
06/17	1,252	14	1.2%	—
06/16	1,201	(32)	—	—
Annual Growth	4.0%	—	—	—

2019 Year-End Financials

Return on assets: 1.2%
Return on equity: 4.2%
Current ratio: 3.00
Cash ($ mil.): 472

GANNETT FLEMING AFFILIATES, INC.

Auditors: STAMBAUGH NESS PC HANOVER P

LOCATIONS

HQ: GANNETT FLEMING AFFILIATES, INC.
207 SENATE AVE, CAMP HILL, PA 170112316
Phone: 717 763-7211
Web: WWW.GANNETTFLEMING.COM

HISTORICAL FINANCIALS

Company Type: Private

Income Statement				FYE: December 31
	REVENUE ($ mil.)	NET INCOME ($ mil.)	NET PROFIT MARGIN	EMPLOYEES
12/19	550	12	2.3%	2,000
12/18	462	17	3.7%	—
12/17	423	11	2.6%	—
12/16	386	11	3.0%	—
Annual Growth	12.6%	2.8%	—	—

2019 Year-End Financials

Return on assets: 4.6%
Return on equity: 15.4%
Current ratio: 2.00
Cash ($ mil.): 5

GARDEN GROVE UNIFIED SCHOOL DISTRICT

EXECUTIVES

Supt, Gabriela Mafi
Supt*, Laura Schwalm
Prin*, Coleen Cross
SEC*, Joyan Spraus
Pres*, George West
V Pres*, Lan Quoc Nguyen
Information Technology Executi, Rick Rodriguez
Accounting Staff, Cathy Joseph
Accounting Staff, Roxanne Linss
Accounting Technician, Tracie Truong
Teacher, Anna Lopez

LOCATIONS

HQ: GARDEN GROVE UNIFIED SCHOOL DISTRICT
10331 STANFORD AVE, GARDEN GROVE, CA 928406351
Phone: 714 663-6000
Web: WWW.GGUSD.US

HISTORICAL FINANCIALS

Company Type: Private

Income Statement FYE: June 30

	REVENUE ($ mil.)	NET INCOME ($ mil.)	NET PROFIT MARGIN	EMPLOYEES
06/19	655	2	0.4%	5,000
06/18	613	(90)	—	—
06/17	602	7	1.2%	—
06/16	632	(46)	—	—
Annual Growth	1.2%	—	—	—

GARFF ENTERPRISES, INC.

EXECUTIVES

Chm, Robert Garff
Pres*, John Garff
SEC*, Matthew Garff
V Pres*, Rick Fulkerson
Vice-President Business Develo, Sam Bracken
Information Technology Special, Alex Tauer
Staff, Kathi Garff
Marketing Team Member, Kirk Koenen
F and I Director, Star Zorn
Finance, Colton Maxwell
Director of Brand Advocacy, Dana Geddes
Auditors: MAYER HOFFMAN MC CANN PC SAL

LOCATIONS

HQ: GARFF ENTERPRISES, INC.
111 E BROADWAY STE 900, SALT LAKE CITY, UT 841115235
Phone: 801 257-3400
Web: WWW.KENGARFF.COM

HISTORICAL FINANCIALS

Company Type: Private

Income Statement FYE: December 31

	REVENUE ($ mil.)	NET INCOME ($ mil.)	NET PROFIT MARGIN	EMPLOYEES
12/13	576	14	2.5%	855
12/03	481	10	2.1%	—
12/02	270	4	1.5%	—
12/01	189	0	—	—
Annual Growth	9.7%	—	—	—

2013 Year-End Financials

Return on assets: 1.4%
Return on equity: 2.5%
Current ratio: 0.20
Cash ($ mil.): 26

GCI, LLC

EXECUTIVES

Ceo, Ronald Duncan
Pres, David Morris
Vpres, Wilson Hughes
Vpres, Bruce L Broquet
Exec V Pres, Gregory F Chapados
SEC-Treas, John M Lowber
Sales Staff, Carl St George
Director, Russ Doig
Program Manager It, Kirsten Von Dolteren
Senior Financial Analyst, Blake Pierce
Chief Operating Officer, Greg Chapados
Auditors: KPMG LLP DENVER COLORADO

LOCATIONS

HQ: GCI, LLC
2550 DENALI ST STE 1000, ANCHORAGE, AK 995032751
Phone: 907 868-5400
Web: WWW.GCI.COM

HISTORICAL FINANCIALS

Company Type: Private

Income Statement FYE: December 31

	REVENUE ($ mil.)	NET INCOME ($ mil.)	NET PROFIT MARGIN	EMPLOYEES
12/18	739	(917)	—	7
12/17	919	31	3.4%	—
12/16	933	(1)	—	—
12/15	978	(10)	—	—
Annual Growth	(8.9%)	—	—	—

2018 Year-End Financials

Return on assets: (-11.0%)
Return on equity: (-20.5%)
Current ratio: 0.40
Cash ($ mil.): 170

GEISINGER HEALTH

Geisinger Health System provides health care to a large portion of the Keystone State. The health care system serves more than 3 million residents of nearly 50 counties spanning central and northeastern Pennsylvania. Founded in 1915 the organization's flagship facility is Geisinger Medical Center a 400-bed medical-surgical hospital located in Danville. It includes the Janet Weis Children's Hospital. With joint venture partner HealthSouth Geisinger also runs a rehabilitation hospital in Danville. As part of its operations the health system runs the 240-bed Geisinger Wyoming Valley Medical Center as well as numerous outpatient facilities and doctors' offices located throughout the region.

Geographic Reach

Geisinger Health System extends the reach of its health care system to millions of central and northeastern Pennsylvania residents across about 50 counties.

Financial Performance

In fiscal 2014 the hospital reported net revenue of $9.8 billion a $1 billion increase over the prior year.

Strategy

Geisinger Health System has been working to standardize its procedural operations to improve the quality of care at its facilities and cut costs. Initiatives include assigning care coordinators and providing home visits for high-risk patients to avoid repeat hospitalizations. The health network also implemented an electronic medical records system and began using networking technology to reach into rural markets. Known as "telemedicine" the system's networking technologies are used among other things to facilitate remote two-way consultations between system physicians and rural patients. Additionally Geisinger runs the Geisinger Health Plan a not-for-profit HMO with some 230000 members.

In addition to its clinical operations Geisinger Health System also pursues industry partnerships and licensing opportunities through Geisinger Ventures its business development unit. The unit works to commercialize (and sometimes spin off) medical and technology-related innovations.

Mergers and Acquisitions

Geisinger has grown through several strategic acquisitions as of late. The health care system purchased central Pennsylvania's Cancer Care Centers in late 2014 adding four facilities to its network.

EXECUTIVES

Evp And Coo, Frank Trembulak
Evp Finance And Cfo, Kevin F. Brennan
Evp And Chief Medical Officer, Albert Bothe
Evp And Managing Partner Geisinger Consulting Services, Bruce H. Hamory
Evp And System Chief Nursing Officer, Susan M. Robel
Evp Clinical Operations, Lynn Miller
Evp And Chief Scientific Officer, David H. Ledbetter
President And Ceo, David T. Feinberg
President And Ceo Geisinger Health Plans, Steven R. Youso
Chief Medical Executive Geisinger Northeast Region, Robert J. Weil
Vice President Supply Chain Services, Deborah Templeton
Senior Vice President Finance, Thomas Sokola
Assistant To Greg Snow Vice President Of Revenue Cycle, Denise Baylor
Vice President Human Resources, Rick Flynn
Vice President Clinical Informatics, Joan Topper
Director Of Pharmacy, David Klinger
Senior Vice President And Chief Inform, Thomas Barna
Vice President Of Sales, Chris Fanning
Medical Director Government Programs, Perry Meadows
Associate Medical Director, David Withers
Pharmacy Manager, Nannette Leganza
Assistant Vice President, Kristy Hine
Medical Director, Carrie L Delone
Associate Vice President Compensation, Kelly Moore
Auditors: KPMG LLP PHILADELPHIA PA

LOCATIONS

HQ: GEISINGER HEALTH
100 N ACADEMY AVE, DANVILLE, PA 178229800
Phone: 800 275-6401
Web: WWW.GEISINGER.ORG

PRODUCTS/OPERATIONS

Selected Services

Adolescent & Young Adult Medicine
Allergy
Anesthesia
Audiology
Bariatric Surgery
Cancer Institute
Cardiology
Colorectal Surgery
Cosmetics Program
Critical Care
Dental Medicine
Dermatology
Ear Nose & Throat
Emergency Medicine
Endocrinology & Metabolism

Fertility Center
Gastroenterology
Gynecology
Gynecologic Oncology
Heart Services
Hip & Knee Center
Imaging Services
Infectious Disease
Internal Medicine
Joint Replacement
Laboratory Medicine
LASIK Surgery
Mammography
Maternal Fetal Medicine
Mental Health
Minimally Invasive Surgery
Mohs Surgery
Neonatology
Nephrology
Neurodevelopmental Pediatrics
Neuroscience Institute
Neurology
Neurosurgery
Obstetrics
Ophthalmology
Orthopaedics
Osteoporosis
Pain Management
Palliative Medicine
Pediatrics (General)
Pediatric Allergy & Immunology
Pediatric Anesthesia & Sedation
Pediatric Cardiology
Pediatric Dental Surgery
Pediatric Dentistry
Pediatric Dermatology
Pediatric Endocrinology
Pediatric Gastroenterology
Pediatric General Surgery
Pediatric Genetics
Pediatric Hematology/Oncology
Pediatric Hospitalists
Pediatric Infectious Disease
Pediatric Intensive Care
Pediatric Interventional Radiology
Pediatric Nephrology
Pediatric Neurology
Pediatric Neuropsychology
Pediatric Neurosurgery
Pediatric Ophthalmology
Pediatric Orthopaedics
Pediatric Otolaryngology
Pediatric Plastic Surgery
Pediatric Psychology & Psychiatry
Pediatric Pulmonology
Pediatric Rehabilitation
Pediatric Rheumatology
Pediatric Transplant Surgery
Pediatric Trauma
Pediatric Urology
Pediatric Weight Management & Nutrition
Plastic & Reconstructive Surgery
Podiatry
Psychiatry
Pulmonary Medicine
Radiology
Rehabilitation
Rheumatology
Sleep Services
Spine Medicine
Sports Medicine
Surgery
Thoracic Surgery
Transplant Surgery
Trauma Center
Urogynecology
Urology
Vascular Surgery
Weight Management Clinic
Women's Health

Selected Facilities

Geisinger HealthSouth Rehabilitation Hospital (Danville)
Geisinger Medical Center (Danville)
The Janet Weis Children's Hospital
Geisinger Wyoming Valley Medical Center (Wilkes-Barre)
Pearsall Heart Hospital
Geisinger South Wilkes-Barre Outpatient Center
Shamokin Area Community Hospital

COMPETITORS

Ascension Health
Blue Cross of Northeastern Pennsylvania
Capital BlueCross
Community Health Systems
HealthAmerica
Highmark
PinnacleHealth System
UPMC
Universal Health Services
Wyoming Valley Health Care System

HISTORICAL FINANCIALS

Company Type: Private

Income Statement — FYE: June 30

	REVENUE ($ mil.)	NET INCOME ($ mil.)	NET PROFIT MARGIN	EMPLOYEES
06/20	7,121	(190)	—	13,030
06/19	7,145	174	2.4%	—
06/18	6,536	359	5.5%	—
06/17	6,337	552	8.7%	—
Annual Growth	4.0%	—	—	—

2020 Year-End Financials

Return on assets: (-2.1%)
Return on equity: (-4.5%)
Current ratio: 1.60
Cash ($ mil.): 1,125

GEISINGER HEALTH PLAN

EXECUTIVES

Pres, Kurt Wrobel
V Pres*, Frank J Trembulak
Cfo-Coo*, Mark McCullough
Coordinator, Kevin Boyles
Senior Analyst, Kim Hackenberg
Appeal Coordinator, Mitzie Kerstetter
Nurse Underwriter, Patrice Molesevich
Medicare Sales, Bobbi Utt
Customer Team Member, Christine Jaegers
Quality Assurance Manager, Dave Evans
Marketing Specialist, Lynn Harter

LOCATIONS

HQ: GEISINGER HEALTH PLAN
100 N ACADEMY AVE, DANVILLE, PA 178229800
Phone: 570 271-8778
Web: WWW.HEALTHPLAN.GEISINGER.ORG

HISTORICAL FINANCIALS

Company Type: Private

Income Statement — FYE: June 30

	REVENUE ($ mil.)	NET INCOME ($ mil.)	NET PROFIT MARGIN	EMPLOYEES
06/18	2,638	55	2.1%	900
06/17	2,337	79	3.4%	—
06/10	875	35	4.0%	—
06/09	827	45	5.5%	—
Annual Growth	13.7%	2.3%	—	—

2018 Year-End Financials

Return on assets: 7.8%
Return on equity: 15.0%
Current ratio: —
Cash ($ mil.): 121

GEISINGER MEDICAL CENTER

EXECUTIVES

Ceo, Glenn D Steele Jr
Exec V Pres*, Frank J Trembulak
Exec V Pres*, Joanne E Wade
Exec V Pres*, Albert Bothe Jr
Exec V Pres*, Lynn Miller
SEC*, Jessica Robertson
Chief Medical Officer*, Rosemary Leeming
Evp-CIO*, Karen Murphy
Evp-Cfo*, Kevin V Roberts
Health Manager, Denise Miller
Pediatrician, Eileen Tengco

LOCATIONS

HQ: GEISINGER MEDICAL CENTER
100 N ACADEMY AVE, DANVILLE, PA 178220001
Phone: 570 271-6211
Web: WWW.GEISINGER.ORG

HISTORICAL FINANCIALS

Company Type: Private

Income Statement — FYE: June 30

	REVENUE ($ mil.)	NET INCOME ($ mil.)	NET PROFIT MARGIN	EMPLOYEES
06/16	1,095	108	9.9%	8,000
06/15	1,058	120	11.4%	—
06/10	815	79	9.7%	—
06/09	735	46	6.3%	—
Annual Growth	5.8%	12.8%	—	—

2016 Year-End Financials

Return on assets: 14.7%
Return on equity: 130.1%
Current ratio: 1.50
Cash ($ mil.): 8

GENERAL ELECTRIC INTERNATIONAL OPERATIONS COMPANY, INC.

EXECUTIVES

Pres, Robert Smits
Secretary, Kristen Urso
Lead Acct, Kyle Furnish
Auditors: KPMG LLP CINCINNATI OHIO

LOCATIONS

HQ: GENERAL ELECTRIC INTERNATIONAL OPERATIONS COMPANY, INC.
191 ROSA PARKS ST, CINCINNATI, OH 452022573
Phone: 513 813-9133

HISTORICAL FINANCIALS

Company Type: Private

Income Statement				FYE: December 31
	REVENUE ($ mil.)	NET INCOME ($ mil.)	NET PROFIT MARGIN	EMPLOYEES
12/17	966	192	19.9%	63
12/16	925	(55)	—	—
12/15	925	(22)	—	—
12/14	760	(8)	—	—
Annual Growth	8.3%	—	—	—

2017 Year-End Financials

Return on assets: 1.9%
Return on equity: 2.1%
Current ratio: 0.60
Cash ($ mil.): 101

GENERAL ELECTRIC INTERNATIONAL, INC.

EXECUTIVES

Pres, Giuseppe Recchi
V Pres*, Candace F Carson
V Pres*, Daniel Janki
SEC*, Pierrot Christophe
SEC*, Kristen Urso-Rio
Treas*, Michael J Geary
Senior Specialist, A Carbone
Power Performance Mana, Jerry King
Fbw Integrator, Joseph Desormeaux
Leader, Tyler Zimmer
Fleet Manager, Carrie McConnell
Auditors: KPMG LLP CINCINNATI OHIO

LOCATIONS

HQ: GENERAL ELECTRIC INTERNATIONAL, INC.
191 ROSA PARKS ST, CINCINNATI, OH 452022573
Phone: 617 443-3000
Web: WWW.GE.COM

HISTORICAL FINANCIALS

Company Type: Private

Income Statement				FYE: December 31
	REVENUE ($ mil.)	NET INCOME ($ mil.)	NET PROFIT MARGIN	EMPLOYEES
12/17	14,100	685	4.9%	125
12/16	13,364	1,339	10.0%	—
12/15	13,288	82	0.6%	—
12/14	12,884	(304)	—	—
Annual Growth	3.1%	—	—	—

2017 Year-End Financials

Return on assets: 3.5%
Return on equity: 10.5%
Current ratio: 1.50
Cash ($ mil.): 961

GENESIS HEALTH SYSTEM

Genesis Health System operates three acute care hospitals in Iowa and Illinois that have more than 660 beds total and employ some 700 doctors. Genesis Medical Center in Davenport Iowa with more than 500 beds is the system's flagship facility; the hospital offers a range of general surgical and specialist health services. The system's Illini Campus in Silvis Illinois features an assisted-living center. The Genesis Medical Center Dewitt Campus serves that Iowa town and the surrounding area with its 13-bed hospital nursing home and related care facilities. Genesis Health System also operates physician practices outpatient centers and a home health agency.

Operations

Altogether Genesis Health System has more than 100 locations including hospitals convenient care locations Genesis Health Group sites physical rehabilitation clinics and outpatient service centers.

Strategy

In 2014 the system invested $15 million in the new Genesis HealthPlex in Bettendorf.

The following year Genesis Health System entered into a partnership with technology vendor Cerner Corporation to improve its patient care enterprise management systems.

Company Background

Genesis Health System had its genesis in 1869 with the establishment of Mercy Hospital (one of the first hospitals west of the Mississippi) and in the 1895 founding of St. Luke's Hospital. The two hospitals merged in 1994 to form the health system.

EXECUTIVES

Medical Director, Fritz Null Swearingen
Vice President Human Resources, Edwin Maxwell
Medical Records Director, Betsy Tibbitts
Physical Therapy Tech Ii, Katrina Mchugh
Vice President Support Services, Mike Sharp
Director Of Radiology, Denise White
Vp Human Resources, Heidi Kahly Mcmahon
Medical Director Of Emergency Department, Wayne Gallops
Vice President, Andy Andresen
Medical Director, Linda Delessio
Board Member, Deborah Stafford
Department Secretary, Dana Fox-andrews
Department Secretary, Jennifer Flynn
Secretary, Mary Jo McVey
House Secretary, Mary Lux
Unit Secretary, Leslie Palzkill
Department Secretary, Theresa Czarnetzki
Auditors: MCGLADREY LLP DAVENPORT IA

LOCATIONS

HQ: GENESIS HEALTH SYSTEM
1227 E RUSHOLME ST, DAVENPORT, IA 528032459
Phone: 563 421-1000
Web: WWW.GENESISHEALTH.COM

PRODUCTS/OPERATIONS

Selected Services

Bariatric Surgery
Behavioral Health
Birthing Services
Cancer
Cardiology
Home Health/Hospice
Neuroscience
Nursing Homes
Physical Medicine & Rehab
Senior Services

COMPETITORS

Blessing Hospital
Catholic Health Initiatives
McDonough District Hospital
Mercy Health Network
OSF Healthcare System
UnityPoint Health

HISTORICAL FINANCIALS

Company Type: Private

Income Statement				FYE: June 30
	REVENUE ($ mil.)	NET INCOME ($ mil.)	NET PROFIT MARGIN	EMPLOYEES
06/20	648	4	0.7%	5,000
06/19	646	13	2.1%	—
06/18	511	20	4.1%	—
06/16	509	32	6.3%	—
Annual Growth	6.2%	(37.7%)	—	—

2020 Year-End Financials

Return on assets: 0.4%
Return on equity: 0.7%
Current ratio: 2.50
Cash ($ mil.): 148

GENPACT LIMITED

LOCATIONS

HQ: GENPACT LIMITED
1155 AVENUE OF THE AMERIC, NEW YORK, NY 100362711
Phone: 212 896-6600
Web: WWW.GENPACT.COM

HISTORICAL FINANCIALS

Company Type: Private

Income Statement				FYE: December 31
	REVENUE ($ mil.)	NET INCOME ($ mil.)	NET PROFIT MARGIN	EMPLOYEES
12/11	1,600	191	11.9%	325
12/10	1,258	149	11.8%	—
12/09	1,120	134	12.0%	—
Annual Growth	19.5%	19.0%	—	—

2011 Year-End Financials

Return on assets: 1.3%
Return on equity: 11.9%
Current ratio: 1.20
Cash ($ mil.): 408

GEOKINETICS INC.

EXECUTIVES

Pres-Ceo, David J Crowley
Exec V Pres-Cfo*, Michael Muse
Exec V Pres of Operations*, Richard M Cieslewicz
Evp of Processing, Reservoir &*, James W Bogardus
Gen Counsel & Corp SEC*, Jessica Palomino
Chief Human Resource Officer-S*, James Tastard
Scientist, Zhihong Lin
Financial Manager, Laura Hassell
Human Resources Administrator, Lina Colon
Operations Staff, Parker Lee
Manager, Christina Buchanan

LOCATIONS

HQ: GEOKINETICS INC.
1500 CITYWEST BLVD # 800, HOUSTON, TX 770422300
Phone: 713 850-7600
Web: WWW.GEOKINETICSINC.COM

HISTORICAL FINANCIALS

Company Type: Private

Income Statement FYE: December 31

	REVENUE ($ mil.)	NET INCOME ($ mil.)	NET PROFIT MARGIN	EMPLOYEES
12/11	763	(222)	—	5,695
12/10	558	(138)	—	—
12/09	510	(5)	—	—
Annual Growth	22.3%	—	—	—

2011 Year-End Financials

Return on assets: (-43.0%)
Return on equity: —
Current ratio: 1.10
Cash ($ mil.): 44

GEORGIA CARESOURCE CO

EXECUTIVES

Ceo, Pamela Morris
Administrative Specialist, Juanita Copeland
Manager, Kimberly Fluellen
Manager, Pascale Cadet-Dantes

LOCATIONS

HQ: GEORGIA CARESOURCE CO
600 GALLERIA PKWY SE, ATLANTA, GA 303395994
Phone: 678 214-7500
Web: WWW.CARESOURCE.COM

HISTORICAL FINANCIALS

Company Type: Private

Income Statement FYE: December 31

	REVENUE ($ mil.)	NET INCOME ($ mil.)	NET PROFIT MARGIN	EMPLOYEES
12/18	669	(20)	—	1
12/17	307	15	5.0%	—
Annual Growth	117.6%	—	—	—

2018 Year-End Financials

Return on assets: (-15.0%)
Return on equity: (-81.1%)
Current ratio: —
Cash ($ mil.): 42

GEORGIA TECH APPLIED RESEARCH CORPORATION

EXECUTIVES

Ceo-Cfo, Stephen Cross
Chm, Leslie R Sibert
Pres, G Wayne Clough
SEC, Robert McGrath
Director of Sponsored Programs, G Duane Hutchison
Controller, Barbara J Alexander
Assistant SEC Treasurer, Barbara Alexander
Facilities, Nicolas F Perez
Associate, Eric Sadler
Accountant III, Julienne Gloster
Director, Kevin Wozniak
Auditors: CHERRY BEKAERT LLP ATLANTA G

LOCATIONS

HQ: GEORGIA TECH APPLIED RESEARCH CORPORATION
926 DALNEY ST NW, ATLANTA, GA 30318
Phone: 404 894-4819
Web: WWW.GATECH.EDU

HISTORICAL FINANCIALS

Company Type: Private

Income Statement FYE: June 30

	REVENUE ($ mil.)	NET INCOME ($ mil.)	NET PROFIT MARGIN	EMPLOYEES
06/20	567	8	1.4%	1,100
06/19	491	7	1.5%	—
06/16	358	(0)	—	—
06/15	340	0	0.1%	—
Annual Growth	10.7%	87.0%	—	—

2020 Year-End Financials

Return on assets: 5.0%
Return on equity: 19.6%
Current ratio: 2.40
Cash ($ mil.): 57

GERBER SCIENTIFIC PRODUCTS INC

LOCATIONS

HQ: GERBER SCIENTIFIC PRODUCTS INC
83 GERBER RD W, SOUTH WINDSOR, CT 060743230
Phone: 860 648-8300

HISTORICAL FINANCIALS

Company Type: Private

Income Statement FYE: April 30

	REVENUE ($ mil.)	NET INCOME ($ mil.)	NET PROFIT MARGIN	EMPLOYEES
04/07	574	13	2.4%	300
04/06	530	0	—	—
Annual Growth	8.4%	—	—	—

2007 Year-End Financials

Return on assets: 4.0%
Return on equity: 9.3%
Current ratio: 1.70
Cash ($ mil.): 8

GGP, INC.

Auditors: DELOITTE & TOUCHE LLP CHICAGO

LOCATIONS

HQ: GGP, INC.
350 N ORLEANS ST STE 300, CHICAGO, IL 606541607
Phone: 312 960-5000
Web: WWW.GGP.COM

COMPETITORS

CBL & Associates Properties
DDR
Glimcher Realty
JMB Realty
Kimco Realty
Lincoln Property
Macerich
Prime Retail
Simon Property Group
Tanger Factory Outlet
Taubman Centers
Trade Street Residential
Vornado Realty
Weingarten Realty

HISTORICAL FINANCIALS

Company Type: Private

Income Statement FYE: December 31

	ASSETS ($ mil.)	NET INCOME ($ mil.)	INCOME AS % OF ASSETS	EMPLOYEES
12/12	27,282	(471)	—	1,500
12/11	29,518	(306)	—	—
12/10	32,367	(256)	—	—
12/09	28,149	(1,304)	—	—
Annual Growth	(1.0%)	—	—	—

2012 Year-End Financials

Return on assets: (-1.7%)
Return on equity: (-6.1%)
Sales ($ mil): 2,511

GILBANE BUILDING COMPANY

Gilbane Building Company has built a big business constructing for equally large customers. The firm provides construction services consulting subcontracting and facilities management to commercial institutional and governmental markets. Operating as the construction arm of Gilbane the company builds schools hospitals laboratories and prisons serving both the public and private sectors. Its completed projects include the Stroh Center at Bowling Green State University and the National WWII Memorial in Washington DC. Founded in 1870 as a carpentry and general contracting shop the family-owned Gilbane Building Company operates from more than 45 offices around the world.

Operations

The company offers Building Information Modeling (BIM) and Virtual Design and Construction (VDC) construction design-build disaster recovery & reconstruction environmental services facilities management fueling facilities construction & repair interdisciplinary document coordination multimedia studio multi-site project delivery systems preconstruction schedule risk analysis and transition planning & management. Its delivery methods include construction management; Integrated Project Delivery (IPD) a delivery model based on lean construction that collaborates and involve the owner A/E builders trade contractors facility managers end users; lump sum contracting and program/project management.

Geographic Reach

Rhode Island-based the company has more than 45 offices and 1000 projects underway around the world some of its domestic location are in Arizona California Colorado Florida Georgia New York and South Carolina. Gilbane Building Company enjoys a geographic footprint that extends from the US to Japan the United Arab Emirates Guam Ireland Saudi Arabia South Korea and Afghanistan.

Sales and Marketing

Gilbane Building Company serves several sectors such as healthcare higher education K-12 schools federal and public entities mission critical corporate and sports and recreation. The company reported over 75% of its work comes from repeat clients.

Some of its clients have included: Cleveland Museum Discovery World Science & Technology Center Dunkin' Donuts Marathon Petroleum Corp Phillips 66 PricewaterhouseCoopers LLP Arizona State University and Duke University.

Strategy

Gilbane Building Company has been appointing leadership for different segments and locations of the company in order to expand client relationships as well as expand business development strategies.

Company Background

In 1870 William Gilbane founded a carpentry firm and in 1871 Thomas Gilbane apprenticed with his brother William. Together the brothers worked tirelessly to found Gilbane Building Company in 1870.

EXECUTIVES

President And Ceo, Michael C. (Mike) McKelvy, age 60
Vice President Business Development, Randy Lowrance
Vice President Of Construction Operations For The New England Region, Thomas Comella
Vice President And Regional Operations Manager, Stephen Oaconnor
Vice President, Jay Prybylski
Vice President, Shawn Zimny
Vice President, Emery Molnar
Vice President Senior Director Of Business Midwest Region, James Arends
Vice President, James Busam
Vice Chairman, William J. (Bill) Gilbane, age 73
Chairman, Thomas F. (Tom) Gilbane, age 72
Auditors: RSM US LLP BOSTON MASSACHUSE

LOCATIONS

HQ: GILBANE BUILDING COMPANY
7 JACKSON WALKWAY STE 2, PROVIDENCE, RI 029033694
Phone: 401 456-5800
Web: WWW.GILBANECO.COM

PRODUCTS/OPERATIONS

Selected Markets

Convention/cultural

Corporate
Criminal justice
Federal/public
Health care
- Children's hospitals
- Women's centers
- Cardiac-care centers
- Cancer centers
- Clinical and research facilities

Higher education
- Research laboratories
- Academic facilities
- Admissions buildings
- Residence halls
- Performing arts centers
- Sports and recreational centers
- Libraries and technology centers
- Student unions

K-12 schools
Life sciences
Mission critical
Sports/recreation
Transportation
Water/wastewater

Selected Services

Pre-construction
- Transition planning and management
- Building information modeling
- Conceptual cost modeling
- High-performance building & energy modeling
- Interdisciplinary document coordination

Consulting
- CAT-response
- Facilities management services
- Schedule & risk analysis
- Transition planning & management

Construction
- Construction management at risk
- Construction management as agent
- Lump sum general contracting
- Integrated project delivery

COMPETITORS

Barton Malow
Batson-Cook
Bechtel
Bernards Brothers
Clark Construction Group
Dimeo Construction
Fluor
KBR
L.F. Driscoll
MEDCO Construction
McCarthy Building
Peter Kiewit Sons'
Skanska USA Building
Swinerton
The Pike Company
Thos. S. Byrne
Turner Construction
Turner Corporation
Tutor Perini
Walbridge Aldinger
Whiting-Turner

HISTORICAL FINANCIALS

Company Type: Private

Income Statement — FYE: December 31

	REVENUE ($ mil.)	NET INCOME ($ mil.)	NET PROFIT MARGIN	EMPLOYEES
12/17	4,899	63	1.3%	2,500
12/14	3,840	0	—	—
12/13	4,100	0	—	—
Annual Growth	4.5%	—	—	—

2017 Year-End Financials

Return on assets: 3.9%
Return on equity: 22.6%
Current ratio: 1.20
Cash ($ mil.): 252

GLOBAL HEALTH SOLUTIONS INC

EXECUTIVES

Vice President, T Rosenberger
V Pres, Thomas Rosenberger

LOCATIONS

HQ: GLOBAL HEALTH SOLUTIONS INC
325 SWANTON WAY, DECATUR, GA 300303001
Phone: 404 592-1430
Web: WWW.TASKFORCE.ORG

HISTORICAL FINANCIALS

Company Type: Private

Income Statement — FYE: August 31

	REVENUE ($ mil.)	NET INCOME ($ mil.)	NET PROFIT MARGIN	EMPLOYEES
08/15	1,609	0	—	2
08/14	1,790	0	—	—
08/13	1,574	0	—	—
08/10	1,120	0	0.0%	—
Annual Growth	7.5%	—	—	—

GOOD SAMARITAN HOSPITAL OF CINCINNATI

EXECUTIVES

Ceo, Mark Clement
Pres*, John S Prout
Chm*, Robert L Walker
Sr V Pres*, John R Robinson
Cfo*, Craig Rucker
Coo*, Gerald Oliphant
Internal Medicine Practitioner, Aleksandr Yultyev
Internal Medicine Practitioner, Ashirf Al-Ghanoudi
Internal Medicine Practitioner, Hiro Kawata
Internal Medicine Practitioner, Irina Gagua
Health Professional, Jiang Wu
Auditors: ERNST & YOUNG LLP CINCINNATI

LOCATIONS

HQ: GOOD SAMARITAN HOSPITAL OF CINCINNATI
375 DIXMYTH AVE, CINCINNATI, OH 452202489
Phone: 513 569-6251
Web: WWW.TRIHEALTH.COM

HISTORICAL FINANCIALS

Company Type: Private

Income Statement — FYE: June 30

	REVENUE ($ mil.)	NET INCOME ($ mil.)	NET PROFIT MARGIN	EMPLOYEES
06/20	563	(60)	—	3,452
06/19	563	33	5.9%	—
06/18	579	48	8.3%	—
06/15	578	81	14.0%	—
Annual Growth	(0.5%)	—	—	—

2020 Year-End Financials

Return on assets: (-6.2%)
Return on equity: (-8.0%)
Current ratio: 0.80
Cash ($ mil.): —

GOOD SAMARITAN HOSPITAL, L.P.

Good Samaritan Hospital lends a hand to help Silicon Valley's techies and their neighbors stay healthy. The facility part of the HCA family of for-profit hospitals administers care through campuses in San Jose (the main campus) and Los Gatos California. Good Samaritan Hospital provides general acute care as well as a host of tertiary services that include cardiology and cardiovascular surgery; oncology; obstetrics and gynecology; and psychiatry (both inpatient and outpatient care). The main campus hospital has some 408 patient beds and 600 physicians and the Los Gatos outpatient and short-stay facility houses approximately 100 beds.

Operations

Each year Good Samaritan admits 17000 patients (excluding newborns) and handles more than 93500 outpatient visits. More than 4000 deliveries and 8000 surgeries are performed annually in 18 surgical suites.

Strategy

In addition to being a community hospital Good Samaritan is a world-class academic medical center affiliated with both USC and UCLA Schools of Medicine. To cater to the diverse urban population the hospital system serves Good Samaritan's medical staff and employees speak more than 54 languages/dialects.

Company Background

Good Samaritan Hospital opened its doors in 1965 as an acute care hospital with a staff of about 400.

EXECUTIVES

Vice President Of Operations, Jim Lamar

LOCATIONS

HQ: GOOD SAMARITAN HOSPITAL, L.P.
2425 SAMARITAN DR, SAN JOSE, CA 951243985
Phone: 408 559-2011
Web: WWW.GOODSAMSANJOSE.COM

PRODUCTS/OPERATIONS

Selected Services and Departments

Cardiology
Cardiac Surgery
Comprehensive Sleep Center
Diagnostic Imaging (Radiology)
ENT (Ear Nose & Throat)
Emergency Services
Gamma Knife
Gastroenterology
Laboratory
Neurosciences
Oncology (Cancer)
Opthalmology & Retinal Medicine
Orthopedics
Podiatry
Physical Medicine
Pulmonary Medicine & Respiratory Care
Radiation Oncology
Surgery
Women's Health & Newborn Services
Urology

COMPETITORS

Dignity Health
Mills-Peninsula Health Services
Sequoia Healthcare District
Stanford Health Care
The Palo Alto Medical Foundation
ValleyCare Health System

HISTORICAL FINANCIALS

Company Type: Private

Income Statement FYE: January 31

	REVENUE ($ mil.)	NET INCOME ($ mil.)	NET PROFIT MARGIN	EMPLOYEES
01/17	618	141	22.8%	1,800
01/09*	413	30	7.3%	—
05/05	170	0	—	—
12/03	0	0	—	—
Annual Growth	—	—	—	—

*Fiscal year change

2017 Year-End Financials

Return on assets: 53.2%
Return on equity: 37.7%
Current ratio: 2.10
Cash ($ mil.): —

GOVERNMENT OF DISTRICT OF COLUMBIA

Our nation's capital is its own jurisdiction – and the Government of the District of Columbia manages it. The government body manages ticket and tax payments housing and property issues children and youth services and motor vehicles registration among other duties for Washington DC. More than 658000 people live in Washington DC and many more commute to the city every day to work for the federal government. Washington DC is overseen by a mayor and a 13-member city council. It acquires contracts with more than 30 local government agencies. The Government of the District of Columbia was created in 1790 with donated land from Maryland and Virginia as part of the Residence Act.

EXECUTIVES

Cfo, Jeffrey S. DeWitt
City Administrator, Rashad M. Young
Mayor, Muriel Bowser
Cto, Archana Vemulapalli
Secretary, Mary Pelzer
Auditors: SB & COMPANY LLC WASHINGTON

LOCATIONS

HQ: GOVERNMENT OF DISTRICT OF COLUMBIA
441 4TH ST NW, WASHINGTON, DC 200012714
Phone: 202 727-0252
Web: WWW.DC.GOV

PRODUCTS/OPERATIONS

Selected Services

311 Service Request Online
Children and Youth Services
District Neighborhoods
Emergency Preparedness
Health and Human Services
Housing and Property
Pay a Ticket
Public Safety
Public Works Sanitation and Utilities
Taxpayer Service Center
Transportation and Motor Vehicles

HISTORICAL FINANCIALS

Company Type: Private

Income Statement FYE: September 30

	REVENUE ($ mil.)	NET INCOME ($ mil.)	NET PROFIT MARGIN	EMPLOYEES
09/16	12,095	(78)	—	34,600
09/15	11,637	583	5.0%	—
09/11	9,822	102	1.0%	—
09/05	0	0	—	—
Annual Growth	—	—	—	—

2016 Year-End Financials

Return on assets: (-0.4%)
Return on equity: (-1.4%)
Current ratio: —
Cash ($ mil.): 1,687

GPM INVESTMENTS, LLC

Convenience is key for GPM Investments which operates or supplies fuel to more than 1100 convenience stores in about 20 US states. The stores sell BP Exxon Marathon and Valero brand gas among others as well as the usual beer smokes and snacks. Some locations also offer fresh made-to-order salads sandwiches and other items or offer branded food from Subway Taco Bell and others. The company which primarily serves the Midwest and eastern US operates or supplies stores under a host of names including Fas Mart Shore Stop Jiffi Stop Young's and Roadrunner Markets.

EXECUTIVES

Senior Vice President Operati, Mike Welsh
Vice President Of Facilities And Construction, Mark Wilson
Southeast Dvp Of Operations, Mike Davis
Auditors: GRANT THORNTON LLP RALEIGH

LOCATIONS

HQ: GPM INVESTMENTS, LLC
8565 MAGELLAN PKWY # 400, RICHMOND, VA 232271167
Phone: 276 328-3669
Web: WWW.GPMINVESTMENTS.COM

Selected Locations
Connecticut
Delaware
Maryland
New Jersey
North Carolina
Pennsylvania
Rhode Island
South Carolina
Tennessee
Virginia

COMPETITORS

7-Eleven
Cumberland Farms
Exxon Mobil
Gate Petroleum
Racetrac Petroleum
Sheetz
Wawa Inc.

HISTORICAL FINANCIALS

Company Type: Private

Income Statement FYE: December 31

	REVENUE ($ mil.)	NET INCOME ($ mil.)	NET PROFIT MARGIN	EMPLOYEES
12/08	1,249	(1)	—	2,150
12/07	891	3	0.4%	—
Annual Growth	40.2%	—	—	—

2008 Year-End Financials

Return on assets: 1.7%
Return on equity: (-0.1%)
Current ratio: 0.40
Cash ($ mil.): 12

GRADY MEMORIAL HOSPITAL CORPORATION

EXECUTIVES

Pres-Ceo, John M Haupert
Cfo, Mark Meyer
Exec V Pres, Christopher R Mosley
Exec V Pres, Timothy Jefferson
Exec V Pres, Curtis Lewis
Vp of Fin, Ozzie Gilbert
Senior Vice-President, Calvin Thomas IV
Grants Manager, David Noble
Security Staff, Donise Musheno

Vice-Chairman, Thomas W Dortch
Information Specialist, Jesse Rosauer
Auditors: KPMG LLP ATLANTA GA

LOCATIONS

HQ: GRADY MEMORIAL HOSPITAL CORPORATION
80 JESSE HILL JR DR SE, ATLANTA, GA 303033050
Phone: 404 616-4360
Web: WWW.GRADYHEALTH.ORG

HISTORICAL FINANCIALS

Company Type: Private

Income Statement — FYE: December 31

	REVENUE ($ mil.)	NET INCOME ($ mil.)	NET PROFIT MARGIN	EMPLOYEES
12/17	1,494	42	2.9%	7
12/16	1,444	47	3.3%	—
12/15	1,230	47	3.9%	—
12/08	358	(56)	—	—
Annual Growth	17.2%	—	—	—

2017 Year-End Financials

Return on assets: 5.2%
Return on equity: 7.5%
Current ratio: 2.30
Cash ($ mil.): 219

GRAHAM ENTERPRISE, INC.

EXECUTIVES

Pres, John C Graham
V Pres, Eugene W Graham III
SEC, Matthew X Graham
Treas, Patrick T Graham
Administrator, Matthew Graham
Auditors: FGMK LLC BANNOCKBURN ILLINO

LOCATIONS

HQ: GRAHAM ENTERPRISE, INC.
750 BUNKER CT STE 100, VERNON HILLS, IL 600611864
Phone: 847 837-0777
Web: WWW.GRAHAMEI.COM

HISTORICAL FINANCIALS

Company Type: Private

Income Statement — FYE: December 31

	REVENUE ($ mil.)	NET INCOME ($ mil.)	NET PROFIT MARGIN	EMPLOYEES
12/17	638	12	2.0%	350
12/16	596	6	1.1%	—
12/15	662	11	1.7%	—
12/14	866	8	0.9%	—
Annual Growth	(9.7%)	16.5%	—	—

2017 Year-End Financials

Return on assets: 32.4%
Return on equity: 47.9%
Current ratio: 1.90
Cash ($ mil.): 6

GRANDVIEW HEALTH HOMES, INC.

EXECUTIVES

Pres, Jerry E Boone
Marketing Public Relations Dir, Ann McLaughlin

LOCATIONS

HQ: GRANDVIEW HEALTH HOMES, INC.
78 WOODBINE LN, DANVILLE, PA 178218020
Phone: 570 275-5240
Web: WWW.GRANDVIEWNR.COM

HISTORICAL FINANCIALS

Company Type: Private

Income Statement — FYE: June 30

	REVENUE ($ mil.)	NET INCOME ($ mil.)	NET PROFIT MARGIN	EMPLOYEES
06/09	1,262	4	0.4%	240
06/99	2	2	89.8%	—
06/98	3	0	11.0%	—
Annual Growth	71.5%	25.8%	—	—

2009 Year-End Financials

Return on assets: 92.2%
Return on equity: —
Current ratio: 1.20
Cash ($ mil.): —

GRANITE SCHOOL DISTRICT

EXECUTIVES

Supt, Martin W Bates
SEC*, Mary Lynn
SEC*, Kathy Goodfellow
Information, Anjanette Anderson
Coordinator, Cindy Dunn
Supervisor, Mark Peterson
Manager, Russell Stauffer
Officer, Cole McAfee
Network Engineer, Jason Winn
Advisor, Kim Brian
Administrative Secretary, Marilyn Hardman
Auditors: SQUIRE & COMPANY PC OREM UT

LOCATIONS

HQ: GRANITE SCHOOL DISTRICT
2500 S STATE ST STE 500, SALT LAKE CITY, UT 841153195
Phone: 385 646-5000
Web: WWW.GRANITESCHOOLS.ORG

HISTORICAL FINANCIALS

Company Type: Private

Income Statement — FYE: June 30

	REVENUE ($ mil.)	NET INCOME ($ mil.)	NET PROFIT MARGIN	EMPLOYEES
06/20	693	0	0.0%	8,000
06/19	678	52	7.7%	—
06/18	610	79	13.0%	—
06/17	571	9	1.7%	—
Annual Growth	6.6%	(74.9%)	—	—

GRANITE TELECOMMUNICATIONS LLC

Granite Telecommunications carves out an increasing block of telecommunications services to commercial clients in the US and Canada. The company is a wholesaler of local and long distance telephone service as well as broadband internet connections with more than 1.3 million lines provided by network operators. It serves corporate clients many of whom run offices in multiple states offering them no account transfer charges and no term or volume contracts on telephone service. Granite also designs and installs network cabling and security systems and provides loss prevention and risk management services.

Operations

The company serves more than 4800 corporate clients in more than a half a million locations. Its customers include most of the US Fortune 100 companies and its customer retention rate is more than five times higher than the industry average. It has about 1.4 million phone lines; about 1.3 billion lines are business lines and 65000 are data lines. The company uses copper wiring found in traditional telecommunication networks which provide reliable and cost-effective service. Granite's subsidiary Granite Guard is a leading provider of loss prevention and risk management services solely for businesses.

Geographic Reach

Granite serves clients across Canada and the US from offices in Florida Massachusetts Georgia Illinois New York Texas and Rhode Island. It is based in Quincy Massachusetts.

Sales and Marketing

Granite's customers include PepsiCo Toys R Us Quality Distribution Jenny Craig Cardinal Health Southwest Airlines Brookdale Senior Living and Agrium.

Financial Performance

The company reported in 2016 that is annual revenue was more than $1.25 billion and that its revenue increased by more than $100 million.

Strategy

Expanding beyond its role as a reseller of telecom services Granite has rolled out its own Granite Grid. It's a fiber-based network with voice and data services for hospitals shopping malls and other multi-tenant buildings. The Granite-installed and maintained network offers better internet service. Simon Property Group one of the US's biggest mall operators has wired its properties to Granite Grid.

Granite has added clients with expansions in Florida and Georgia where it has built new facilities. It also built a new building at its Quincy Massachusetts headquarters to accommodate more employees.

EXECUTIVES

Svp And Coo, Rand Currier
Founder And Ceo, Robert T. (Rob) Hale
Cfo, Richard Wurman
Vp Sales, Kevin Nichols
National Account Manager, Jonathan Gosian
National Account Manager, Michael Perrone
National Account Manager, William Drago
National Accounts Manager, Drew Mullert
Svp Client Management, Mark Cameron
Vice President, Sam Kline
Senior Vice President Finance, Susan Zahka

Vice President Channels, Charlie Pagliazzo
National Sales Manager, Serge Saint-val
National Sales Manager, Dan Pratt
National Account Manager, Michelle Murphy
National Account Manager, Michael Fricker
National Account Manager, Georgiana Thompson
National Account Manager, Rick Treadwell
Assistant Vice President Operations, Victoria King
Regional Vice President Of Sales, Bruce Hoffman
Vice President Talent Management, Kyle Swist
National Account Manager, Joe Flaherty
National Account Manager, Derek Jeppe
National Account Manager, Carlos Mendoza
National Accounts Manager, Paul Sullivan
Vice President Sales Operations Marketing And Granite University, Tony Kenneally
National Account Manager, Clark Miller
National Sales Manager, Michael Hewatt
National Account Manager, Paul Atwood
National Account Manager, Brent Nelson
Vice President Sales Operations Marketing And Granite University, Anthony Kenneally
National Account Manager, Selwyn Scott
Senior Vice President, Don Macarthur
Vice President Treasury And Financial Operations, Allen Bottomley
National Account Manager, Chris Oberg
Vp Technical Product And Solutions Leader, Otis Hendershott
National Account Manager, Andrew Beckelhymer
Vp And General Manager Of Wholesale, James Balestraci
National Accounts Manager, Patrick Mcrae
National Account Manager, Spencer Gadbois

LOCATIONS

HQ: GRANITE TELECOMMUNICATIONS LLC
100 NEWPORT AVENUE EXT # 1, QUINCY, MA 021712126
Phone: 617 933-5500
Web: WWW.GRANITENET.COM

PRODUCTS/OPERATIONS

Products and Services

Voice
Managed Solutions
Data
Network Integration
Granite Grid

COMPETITORS

5LINX
ACN Inc.
AT&T
BCE
EarthLink
Rogers Communications
Sprint Communications
Verizon
World Communications

HISTORICAL FINANCIALS

Company Type: Private

Income Statement — FYE: December 31

	REVENUE ($ mil.)	NET INCOME ($ mil.)	NET PROFIT MARGIN	EMPLOYEES
12/12	736	187	25.5%	1,854
12/11	609	143	23.5%	—
12/10	517	109	21.2%	—
Annual Growth	19.3%	31.0%	—	—

2012 Year-End Financials

Return on assets: 110.0%
Return on equity: 394.1%
Current ratio: 1.40
Cash ($ mil.): 45

GREAT RIVER ENERGY

Great River Energy powers up cooperatives along the Great River Road. The utility provides wholesale electricity to 1.7 million through 28 distribution cooperatives in Minnesota and Wisconsin. It operates nearly 4600 miles of transmission lines and has more than 3500 MW of generation capacity that consists of a diverse mix of baseload and peaking power plants including coal and natural gas as well as wind and solar generation facilities. The company also owns or partially owns more than 100 transmission substations. Great River Energy is the #2 electric utility in Minnesota in terms of generating capacity and one of the largest generation and transmission cooperatives in the US (based on assets).

Operations

Great River Energy serves members through a diverse portfolio of power supply resources and dependable transmission system all of which are part of the region's energy market. Most of the company's power comes from coal with hydro renewable and natural gas making up the rest.

As part of its efforts to increase its green energy output Great River owns Blue Flint Ethanol which includes of approximately 75-80 million-gallon ethanol refinery that uses process steam produced at Great River Energy Coal Creek Station.

Geographic Reach

The company provides power to cooperatives which in turn serve customers in Minnesota (headquarters) and Wisconsin.

Sales and Marketing

Great River Energy provides reliable affordable and environmentally responsible wholesale electricity to 28 member-owner cooperatives that serve more than 700000 members served (or around 1.7 million people).

Financial Performance

Utility operating revenues ended the year at $990.6 million which was down $49.2 million from 2018. While member sales remained strong the retirement of the Elk River Resource Recovery Project (Elk River) and fewer nonmember market sales were the primary drivers for the reduction in 2019.

Net margin attributable to GRE for 2019 was $24.8 million and includes the net income from Midwest AgEnergy Group (MAG) and other equity method investments of $1.8 million.

Cash held by the company at the end of 2019 decreased to $240.7 million compared to $279.5 million in 2018. Cash provided by operations was $141.7 million while cash used for investing and financing activities were $125.8 million and $54.7 million respectively. Main uses for cash were utility plant additions and repayments of long-term obligations.

Company Background

In 2013 the company signed a deal with Tangshan Shenzhou Manufacturing Company to make Great River Energy's DryFining technology (for more efficient coal use in power stations) available to utilities in China.

It is also cut costs and increasing efficiency at its own power plants. In 2012 these measures saved Great River Energy more than $8 million.

In 2012 Great River bought the remaining 51% of Blue Flint Ethanol it didn't already own. The move added to its production capabilities and helped push the company to record production that year.

The utility was formed in 1999 through the combination of two Minnesota utilities Cooperative Power and United Power Association.

EXECUTIVES

Vp Generation, Rick Lancaster
Ceo And President, David Saggau
Vp And Cfo, Larry Schmid
Vp Transmission, Will Kaul
Vp And Cio, Jim Jones
Vice Chairman, Sherman Liimatainen
Chairman, Michael Thorson
Board Of Directors, Margaret Schreiner
Board Of Directors, Scott Hughes
Auditors: DELOITTE & TOUCHE LLP MINNEA

LOCATIONS

HQ: GREAT RIVER ENERGY
12300 ELM CREEK BLVD N, MAPLE GROVE, MN 553694718
Phone: 763 445-5000
Web: WWW.GREATRIVERENERGY.COM

PRODUCTS/OPERATIONS

2014 Sales

	% of total
Member	83
Non-member	7
Other	7
Nonutility operations Excluding non-controlling Interest	3
Total	**100**

2014 Sales

	$ mil.	% of total
Electric revenue	952	93
Other operating revenue	68	7
Total	**1,020**	**100**

COMPETITORS

AEP
Basin Electric Power
Black Hills
DTE
Entergy
Southern Company
Xcel Energy

HISTORICAL FINANCIALS

Company Type: Private

Income Statement — FYE: December 31

	REVENUE ($ mil.)	NET INCOME ($ mil.)	NET PROFIT MARGIN	EMPLOYEES
12/18	1,295	8	0.7%	850
12/17	1,270	18	1.4%	—
12/16	1,022	21	2.1%	—
12/15	983	15	1.5%	—
Annual Growth	9.6%	(17.8%)	—	—

2018 Year-End Financials

Return on assets: 0.2%
Return on equity: 1.0%
Current ratio: 1.30
Cash ($ mil.): 276

GREEN MOUNTAIN POWER CORPORATION

Public utility Green Mountain Power (GMP) lights up the hills of Vermont supplying electricity to more than 250000 customers in the state. The utility also markets wholesale electricity in New England. The company operates several thousand miles of transmission and distribution lines and owns a minority stake in high-voltage transmission operator Vermont Electric Power (VELCO). About half of the generation capacity GMP taps is from hydroelectric and other renewable energy sources. GMP is an indirect subsidiary of Canada's

GazMetro. The company absorbed Central Vermont Public Service's assets in 2012.

Operations

GMP produces transmits distributes and sells electricity in Vermont and is a leader in the production of wind and solar energy in that state.

Strategy

In a move to boost its Vermont assets in 2012 parent company GazMetro bought Central Vermont Public Service (CVPS) and is merging it with its GMP operations. CVPS is Vermont's largest electric utility and provides power to more than 159000 customers in 163 communities across the state.

The company is also pursuing a long term initiative to generate power from renewable sources as a way to cut carbon emissions and comply with strict federal clean air requirements. GMP has a preliminary deal to boost green energy sources with Hydro-Quebec as well as plans to to build a wind farm in Lowell make investments in solar power and upgrade its hydroelectric facilities.

While wind and solar only accounted for about 1% of the company's fuel mix for its power stations in 2011 it plans to boost that amount to almost 10% by the end of 2013.

Company Background

GazMetro acquired the company in 2007. The deal boosted Gaz Metro's presence in the Vermont energy market where it has owned Vermont Gas Systems for more than 20 years.

EXECUTIVES

Svp Chief Operating Officer, Brian Otley
Vp Of Field Engineering, Greg White
Vp Engineering, Ken Couture
Auditors: MCSOLEY MCCOY & CO SOUTH BURL

LOCATIONS

HQ: GREEN MOUNTAIN POWER CORPORATION
163 ACORN LN, COLCHESTER, VT 054466611
Phone: 888 835-4672
Web: WWW.GREENMOUNTAINPOWER.COM

COMPETITORS

Avangrid
Bangor Hydro-Electric
Con Edison
DPL
Eversource Energy
Maine & Maritimes
NSTAR
Unitil
Vermont Gas

HISTORICAL FINANCIALS

Company Type: Private

Income Statement FYE: December 31

	REVENUE ($ mil.)	NET INCOME ($ mil.)	NET PROFIT MARGIN	EMPLOYEES
12/19	698	77	11.1%	190
12/18	713	80	11.3%	—
12/16	652	69	10.6%	—
Annual Growth	2.3%	3.8%	—	—

2019 Year-End Financials

Return on assets: 3.1%
Return on equity: 9.1%
Current ratio: 0.70
Cash ($ mil.): 3

GROSSMONT HOSPITAL FOUNDATION

EXECUTIVES

Ex Dir, Elizabeth Morgante
Director of Case Management, Mike Murphey
Rn, Michelle Lescault
Doctor, Roxanne Hon
Auditors: ERNST & YOUNG US LLP SAN DIEG

LOCATIONS

HQ: GROSSMONT HOSPITAL FOUNDATION
5555 GROSSMONT CENTER DR, LA MESA, CA 919423077
Phone: 619 740-4200
Web: WWW.SHARP.COM

HISTORICAL FINANCIALS

Company Type: Private

Income Statement FYE: September 30

	REVENUE ($ mil.)	NET INCOME ($ mil.)	NET PROFIT MARGIN	EMPLOYEES
09/16	738	65	8.9%	6
09/09	5	0	8.5%	—
09/08	5	0	16.8%	—
09/01	1	3	314.9%	—
Annual Growth	54.5%	21.8%	—	—

2016 Year-End Financials

Return on assets: 6.9%
Return on equity: 8.5%
Current ratio: 2.40
Cash ($ mil.): 43

GROUP O, INC.

The "O" in Group O stands for optimization. It also stands for Ontiveros the family that leads this company. Founded by chairman Robert Ontiveros Group O is one of the largest Hispanic-owned companies in the US. It helps big businesses improve their operations through three divisions: marketing packaging and supply chain. It offers everything from direct mail creation to shrink wrap procurement to warehousing and distribution and business intelligence. It has served clients from various industries including food and beverage (Kerry) consumer goods (P&G) manufacturing (Johnson Controls) pharmaceutical (Bristol-Myers Squibb) and telecommunications (AT&T).

Operations

Group O is a diversified business process outsourcing provider specializing in marketing supply chain packaging and business analytics products.

The company's supply chain division mainly serves heavy equipment and high technology OEMs while its packaging division targets manufacturers and distributors in need of streamlining their packaging processes. It procures and distributes bags stretch films tapes and other materials and also repairs calibrates and upgrades equipment to optimize performance.

Its SMART Audit reporting tool provides real-time reports that monitor production and spending across a plant network so that companies can take appropriate cost reduction actions. Meanwhile its marketing division offers a range of service offerings including marketing analytics customer rewards programs direct mail and e-mail marketing outsourced printing and a customer call center.

The company's Business Analytics unit has experts that can guide companies that seek to make sense out of unstructured and structured data - providing strategists and decision-makers with new insights into customer behavior while maximizing both new and existing channels. The team guides the creation implementation and management of tools in the latest applications and platforms across a comprehensive spectrum of existing systems.

Geographic Reach

Group O maintains a national network of more than 20 facilities mostly concentrated in the Midwest (Illinois Iowa and Minnesota) and Texas. Other sales offices and warehouses are located in California Nevada Pennsylvania and various southern states. It also works with more than 7000 suppliers in more than 30 countries.

Sales and Marketing

The company serves FORTUNE 500 clients across a broad range of industries including food and beverage telecommunications manufacturing consumer packaged goods retail financial services pharmaceutical healthcare technology energy and the public sector.

Strategy

In 2014 Group O launched a new website for its O-vations service offering which is aimed at helping companies optimize the design and operation of enterprise-scale reward programs. Key services range from program design and management technology integration operations and communications value-added services and reporting and analytics.

That year the company also opened its Business Analytics unit in Hyderabad India. The team helps generate customer acquisition and loyalty marketing insights that clients can then use to make better business decisions.

Company Background

Ontiveros established Group O in 1974 as Bi-State Packaging which sold packaging materials and equipment to manufacturers. Today it is one of the top 15 Hispanic-owned businesses in the nation.

EXECUTIVES

Senior Vice President Business Development, Mike De La Cruz
Vice President, Chris Ontiveros
Auditors: HONKAMP KRUEGER & CO PC MO

LOCATIONS

HQ: GROUP O, INC.
4905 77TH AVE E, MILAN, IL 612643250
Phone: 309 736-8100
Web: WWW.GROUPO.COM

PRODUCTS/OPERATIONS

Selected Services

Marketing
- Analytics
- Consumer and trade fulfillment
- Customer call center and workforce management
- Direct mail and e-mail optimization
- Print management outsourcing
- Rewards and loyalty programs

Packaging
- Equipment supply and repair (bagging case handling labeling shrinking and stretch wrapping systems)
- Materials supply (labels poly bags protective packaging sanitation products shrink and stretch films and tape)
- Stretch film equipment auditing

Supply chain
- Business process outsourcing
- Distribution
- Global sourcing
- Inventory management
- Order management
- Supplier management
- Warehousing

Selected Industries Served

Food and Beverage
Telecommunications
Manufacturing
Consumer Packaged Goods
Financial Services
Pharmaceutical
Health care
Technology

COMPETITORS

Brightstar Corp.
CEVA Logistics U.S.
Fedex Supply Chain
Jay Group
Kenco Logistics Services
Ozburn-Hessey Logistics
The Bernd Group
UPS Supply Chain Solutions
Weber Logistics

HISTORICAL FINANCIALS

Company Type: Private

Income Statement FYE: December 31

	REVENUE ($ mil.)	NET INCOME ($ mil.)	NET PROFIT MARGIN	EMPLOYEES
12/13	569	5	1.0%	1,066
12/05	240	5	2.2%	—
Annual Growth	11.4%	0.9%	—	—

2013 Year-End Financials

Return on assets: 87.9%
Return on equity: 1.0%
Current ratio: 0.90
Cash ($ mil.): 7

GROVE ELK UNIFIED SCHOOL DISTRICT

EXECUTIVES

Supt, Steven Ladd
Assc Supt, Richard Odegaard
Staff, Amy Besler
Administrator, Dorothy Stoppelman
School Counselor, Jerome Orgeron
Nurse, Alyson Gonda
Registrar, Amanda Conklin
Counselor, Amanda Wilson
Parent Volunteer Coordinator, Barbara Malana
K 12 Special Ed Director, Douglas Phillips
Campus Supervisor, Felicia Robbins
Auditors: CROWE HORWATH LLP SACRAMENTO

LOCATIONS

HQ: GROVE ELK UNIFIED SCHOOL DISTRICT
9510 ELK GROVE FLORIN RD, ELK GROVE, CA 956241801
Phone: 916 686-5085
Web: WWW.EGUSD.NET

HISTORICAL FINANCIALS

Company Type: Private

Income Statement FYE: June 30

	REVENUE ($ mil.)	NET INCOME ($ mil.)	NET PROFIT MARGIN	EMPLOYEES
06/17	741	65	8.8%	5,600
06/07	560	(30)	—	—
06/06	0	0	—	—
06/03	454	19	4.4%	—
Annual Growth	3.6%	8.9%	—	—

GROWMARK, INC.

Agricultural and energy cooperative GROWMARK serves farm commercial and residential customers across the US and in parts of Canada. Under the Growmark FS name it offers a host of plant food and crop protection products as well as biotechnology services and training and agricultural marketing and consulting. The company also operates a full-line seed company Seedway and provides grain facility planning and grain marketing services. Lastly GROWMARK's energy offers a complete line of refined and renewable fuels lubricants and propane to member cooperatives and retail energy distributors including winterized fuels diesel exhaust fluid (DEF) biodiesel and bioblends.

Operations

GROWMARK delivers high quality agronomy and energy products as well as premium services from expert advisors. Its long-term relationships with manufacturers and refiners coupled with the company's extensive terminal network means GROWMARK has access to a broad and reliable supply of fertilizers fuel and propane. The company also offers private label crop protection products and proprietary brands of corn and soybean seeds.

In addition GROWMARK also provides grain marketing services through its subsidiary MID-CO COMMODITIES and has partnership with COFCO International. Its commercial construction provides equipment facilities and services that improve the operating efficiency of the company's customers. It is equipped to provide system consultations through complete turnkey construction services such as consultation development planning construction and operation. GROWMARK logistics includes brokerage services specializing in transporting and storing liquid fuel propane anhydrous ammonia bulk and packaged motor oils and crop inputs including seed liquid and dry fertilizer and bulk and packaged crop protection products while its Electronic Payments Network currently processes and settles more than 9.7 million transactions and approximately $500 million annually. The company keeps pace with regulatory and market demands for bank cards fleet cards DEBIT cards gift cards ACH/electronic check conversion and PC/web-based payments. Lastly GROWMARK Agronomy Equipment has national account relationships with John Deere Case IH AGCO and Caterpillar to provide its customers with competitive pricing and service from local dealer on application equipment tractors loaders construction equipment and small equipment.

GROWMARK's high performing product lines include proprietary brands FS InVISION FS HiSOY FS Wheat FS Alfalfa as well as distribution agreements with DEKALB Asgrow and NK.

Geographic Reach

GROWMARK is headquartered in Bloomington Illinois and serves customers in more than 40 US states and Ontario Canada. Its Electronic Payments Network serves network merchants across more than 15 states.

Its Seedway business has about 25 office and warehouse locations in Vermont North and South Carolina Mexico New York Pennsylvania and Florida among others.

Sales and Marketing

GROWMARK is serving cooperatives retailers grain companies and other business customers of all industries including freight brokerage and credit card processing.

Strategy

GROWMARK Inc. and Southern States Cooperative announced in September 2020 plans to close on a transaction that aligns the organizations operationally to yield increased innovation growth and returns for the farmer-owners of both cooperative systems.

GROWMARK will assume the wholesale agronomy and energy (fuels and propane) assets of Southern States along with several retail locations serving farmers in Delaware and Maryland. GROWMARK will provide crop inputs fuels propane and a variety of customer support and marketing services to Southern States and its member cooperatives. They in turn will continue to deliver custom solutions with access to GROWMARK's product mix distribution expertise and drive for innovation.

GROWMARK's vision is to be the best agricultural cooperative system in North America and this partnership enables both organizations to further that goal together. It is committed to delivering an unsurpassed customer experience to the patrons it serves across North America. The cooperative model is uniquely positioned to deliver that so this combination of efforts is great news for farmers invested in the cooperative organizations.

Company Background

GROWMARK traces its history back to 1920 and the establishment of local cooperatives by Farm Bureau members. One of those cooperatives Farm Bureau Service Company of Iowa in the early 1960s merged with Illinois Farm Supply Company (founded in 1927) to form the foundation of what is today GROWMARK. The GROWMARK name started being used in 1980.

EXECUTIVES

Vice President Agronomy, Jim Spradlin
Vice Chairman, John Reifsteck
Ceo, Jeff Solberg
Vp And General Counsel, Brent Bostrom
Vp Eastern Retail Operations, Steve Buckalew
Vp And Cfo, Marshall Bohbrink
Vp Energy, Kevin Carroll
Vp Midwest Retail And Acquisitions, Shelly Kruse
Vp Grain, Brent Ericson
Vice President Human Resources & Compliance, Gary Swango
Vp Agronomy, Mark Orr
Vp Financial And Risk Management, Mike Woods
Vp Member Services, Denny Worth
Region Vice President, Barry Schmidt
Senior Vice President, Jeffrey M Solberg
Vice President Corporate Services, Stan Nielsen
Vice President Information Technology, Carla Makowski
Vice Chairman, Rick Nelson
Vice Chairman, Chet Esther
Assistant Treasurer, Karmy Kays
Treasurer, Jeffrey Lynch
Auditors: ERNST & YOUNG LLP CHICAGO IL

LOCATIONS

HQ: GROWMARK, INC.
1701 TOWANDA AVE, BLOOMINGTON, IL 617012057
Phone: 309 557-6000
Web: WWW.GROWMARK.COM

COMPETITORS

ADM
AGRI Industries
Ag Processing Inc.
BP
Barkley Seed
Bayer CropScience
CHS
Cargill
Chevron
Costco Wholesale
DeBruce Grain
Exxon Mobil
Marathon Oil
NC Hybrids
Orscheln Farm and Home
Pfister Hybrid Corn
Pioneer Hi-Bred
Rabo AgriFinance
Sakata Seed
Seed Enterprises
Southern States
Terra Nitrogen
Wal-Mart
Wilbur-Ellis

HISTORICAL FINANCIALS

Company Type: Private

Income Statement — FYE: August 31

	REVENUE ($ mil.)	NET INCOME ($ mil.)	NET PROFIT MARGIN	EMPLOYEES
08/19	8,745	75	0.9%	7,000
08/18	8,522	65	0.8%	—
08/17	7,291	115	1.6%	—
08/16	7,031	101	1.4%	—
Annual Growth	7.5%	(9.4%)	—	—

2019 Year-End Financials

Return on assets: 2.8%
Return on equity: 6.8%
Current ratio: 1.60
Cash ($ mil.): 67

GRUMA CORPORATION

Gruma is the American subsidiary of giant Mexican food company Gruma S.A.B. de C.V. and the leading tortilla and corn flower producer in the US. The company manufactures and distributes corn flour corn tortillas and related products such as wraps and corn chips through roughly 25 production plants. The company runs the world's largest tortilla plant in Los Angeles; that facility has a production capacity of 25 million tortillas per day. Its highly recognizable brand names include Mission Calidad and Guerrero tortillas and Maseca corn flour. Gruma is its parent company's largest revenue producer.

Strategy

Gruma historically has chased the expanding US Hispanic population which added 63% between 2000 and 2016 but growing general popularity of Mexican food and rising numbers of Mexican food restaurants have led the company to increasingly target non-Hispanic populations (which account for most Mexican food purchases). To that end the company has developed and produced several non-Mexican or Americanized tortilla-like products such as whole wheat and spinach herb wraps and street taco-style tortillas.

Gruma is capitalizing on its market-leading position in corn flour and tortillas and its successful growth by upping its production capacity. Its largest plant launched in 2018 in Dallas Texas; those operations increased its tortilla production capacity by 10% and created production transportation and logistical efficiencies through adoption of new technologies.

Furthermore the company is moving its product mix toward higher-margin items including health foods value-added products and small-count products. The company's health-conscious alternatives (such as its Mission Organics tortilla chips and gluten-free organic and low-carb Mission wraps) have ridden the wave of the rising popularity of healthy living in the states producing double-digit sales growth.

EXECUTIVES

President And Ceo, Javier Velez Bautista

LOCATIONS

HQ: GRUMA CORPORATION
5601 EXECUTIVE DR STE 800, IRVING, TX 750382508
Phone: 972 232-5000
Web: WWW.MISSIONFOODS.COM

PRODUCTS/OPERATIONS

Selected Brands and Products

Guerrero

Chicharron de Cerdo
Tortillas de Harina (Original and Butter)
Tortillas de Maí;z Blanco
Tostadas Norte as Clá;sicas
Tostadas Caseras Doraditas

Mission Foods

96% Fat Free Heart Healthy tortillas

All Natural Spicy Bean dip
Caramel Twists
Carb Balance tortillas
Cheddar Cheese dip
Chicharrones (Original BBQ Habanero and Picante)
Cinnamon Twists
Chunky Salsa Medium
Corn tortilla
Flour tortillas
Guacamole dip
Jumbo Taco shells
Life Balance tortillas
Multi-Grain Flour tortillas
Organic Stone-Ground tortilla chips
Pork Cracklins Plain Tenders
Restaurant Style Tortilla Triangles (Cilantro Lime Premium White Corn and Salsa Roja)
Restaurant Style Tortilla Rounds
Salsa Con Queso
Salsa Verde Medium
Sliced Nacho Jalape o Peppers
Taco and tostada shells
Wraps (Original Garden Spinach Jalapeno Cheddar Multi-Grain Sun-dried Tomato Basil and Zesty Garlic Herb)

COMPETITORS

Azteca Foods
Bimbo Bakeries
Bob's Red Mill Natural Foods
Bunge Milling
C.H. Guenther & Son
Casa de Oro Foods
Don Pancho Authentic Mexican Foods
Flowers Foods
Frito-Lay
General Mills
Grupo Bimbo
Hodgson Mill
Horizon Milling
La Gloria Foods
La Reina
La Tortilla Factory
Minsa
Ole' Mexican Foods
Organic Milling
Ruiz Mexican Foods
Star of the West
Taco Bell
Tumaro's Gourmet Tortillas
Tyson Foods

HISTORICAL FINANCIALS

Company Type: Private

Income Statement — FYE: December 31

	REVENUE ($ mil.)	NET INCOME ($ mil.)	NET PROFIT MARGIN	EMPLOYEES
12/19	2,202	224	10.2%	7,000
12/16	2,023	179	8.9%	—
12/15	2,086	152	7.3%	—
Annual Growth	1.4%	10.2%	—	—

2019 Year-End Financials

Return on assets: 13.6%
Return on equity: 19.7%
Current ratio: 2.80
Cash ($ mil.): 76

GUILDNET, INC.

EXECUTIVES

Ceo, Alan R Morse
Chairman, James M Dubin
Treasurer, Lawrence E Goldschmidt
Secretary, Robert B Okun
Administrative Assistant, Angela Rosario
Neurologist, Helen Chang
Technical Consultant, Lok Wong
Occupational Medicine Speciali, Inna Babaeva
Optometrist, Laura Sperazza
Auditors: KPMG LLP NEW YORK NY

LOCATIONS

HQ: GUILDNET, INC.
15 W 65TH ST, NEW YORK, NY 100236601
Phone: 212 769-6200
Web: WWW.LIGHTHOUSEGUILD.ORG

HISTORICAL FINANCIALS

Company Type: Private

Income Statement — FYE: December 31

	REVENUE ($ mil.)	NET INCOME ($ mil.)	NET PROFIT MARGIN	EMPLOYEES
12/15	950	(24)	—	377
12/14	826	1	0.1%	—
12/13	672	45	6.8%	—
12/12	433	42	9.8%	—
Annual Growth	29.9%	—	—	—

2015 Year-End Financials

Return on assets: (-8.5%)
Return on equity: (-19.4%)
Current ratio: 1.40
Cash ($ mil.): 12

GUILFORD COUNTY SCHOOL SYSTEM

EXECUTIVES

Supt, Sharon L Contreras
Co-Interim Supt*, Nora K Carr
CIO*, Terrance Young
Superintendent, Sharon Contreras
Coordinator, April Dixon
Executive of Information Techn, Eric Brown
Security Staff, Les Allison
Coordinator, Todd Baldwin
Library Media Specialist, Betty Denny
5th Grade Teacher, Emily Harris
Assistant, Enid Barnum

LOCATIONS

HQ: GUILFORD COUNTY SCHOOL SYSTEM
712 N EUGENE ST, GREENSBORO, NC 274011622
Phone: 336 370-8100
Web: WWW.GCSNC.COM

HISTORICAL FINANCIALS

Company Type: Private

Income Statement — FYE: June 30

	REVENUE ($ mil.)	NET INCOME ($ mil.)	NET PROFIT MARGIN	EMPLOYEES
06/11	692	(0)	—	10,000
06/09	0	(0)	—	—
06/03	0	0	—	—
06/02	546	69	12.8%	—
Annual Growth	2.7%	—	—	—

2011 Year-End Financials

Return on assets: —
Return on equity: (-0.1%)
Current ratio: 1.10
Cash ($ mil.): 28

GUNDERSEN LUTHERAN ADMINISTRATIVE SERVICES INC.

EXECUTIVES

Ceo, Jeff Thompson
V Pres*, Wendy Williams
V Pres*, Gregory Prairie
SEC*, Brian Rude
Tres*, Wendy Lommen
General Manager, Liz Larsen
Administrative Director, Randy Lubahn
Auditors: KPMG LLP OMAHA NE

LOCATIONS

HQ: GUNDERSEN LUTHERAN ADMINISTRATIVE SERVICES INC.
1900 SOUTH AVE, LA CROSSE, WI 546015467
Phone: 608 782-7300
Web: WWW.GUNDERSENHEALTH.ORG

HISTORICAL FINANCIALS

Company Type: Private

Income Statement — FYE: December 31

	REVENUE ($ mil.)	NET INCOME ($ mil.)	NET PROFIT MARGIN	EMPLOYEES
12/18	841	40	4.8%	6,000
12/17	716	(38)	—	—
Annual Growth	17.5%	—	—	—

2018 Year-End Financials

Return on assets: 4.4%
Return on equity: —
Current ratio: 0.40
Cash ($ mil.): 159

GUNDERSEN LUTHERAN MEDICAL CENTER, INC.

At the heart of the Gundersen Lutheran health system Gundersen Lutheran Medical Center serves residents of nearly 20 counties that stretch across the upper Midwest. The clinical campus for the University of Wisconsin's medical and nursing schools operates a 325-bed teaching hospital with a Level II Trauma and Emergency Center. Focused on caring for patients in western Wisconsin the hospital boasts several specialty services such as bariatrics behavioral health cancer care orthopedics palliative care pediatrics rehabilitation and women's health. The physician-led not-for-profit medical center is affiliated with a group of regional clinics and specialty centers.

Operations

Gundersen Lutheran Medical Center has a staff of some 800 doctors dentists and other professionals. As part of Gundersen Lutheran (also known as Gundersen Health System) the hospital's sister entities include the Gundersen Clinic and the Gundersen Lutheran Administrative Services entity.

In 2013 the Gundersen Health System reported 1437 births 17000 surgeries and 278000 outpatient hospital visits.

Geographic Reach

From its main campus in La Crosse Wisconsin as well as a satellite outpatient center in Onalaska the hospital serves communities located in 19 counties throughout western Wisconsin northeastern Iowa and southeastern Minnesota.

Strategy

The Gundersen Lutheran organization expands though partnerships such as an alliance with the Allen Hospital in Iowa to enhance regional cardiovascular services in 2013. The medical center is also working to upgrade its infrastructure to enable 100% energy independence in 2014.

To offer advanced training to residents and physicians Gundersen Lutheran Medical Center developed and opened a high-tech training center in 2012. The Cleary Kumm Simulation and Training Labs offer mock operating rooms and simulation labs for use by local doctors and nationwide medical professionals for training or conferences. Gundersen Lutheran Medical Center is banking on the simulation and training facility to draw interest talent and outside funds.

Company Background

Gundersen Lutheran Medical Center was founded in 1995 through the merger of Gunderson Clinic and Lutheran Hospital-La Crosse. The Lutheran Hospital opened in 1902.

EXECUTIVES

Senior Vice President, Kathy Klock
Vice President Of Nursing, Mary Gerke
Director Of Home Healthcare Services, Kurt Oettel
Senior Vice President, Gerald Arndt
Medical Director, Jackie Yaeger
Secretary, Stacy Vix
Auditors: KPMG LLP MINNEAPOLIS MN

LOCATIONS

HQ: GUNDERSEN LUTHERAN MEDICAL CENTER, INC.
1900 SOUTH AVE, LA CROSSE, WI 546015467
Phone: 608 782-7300
Web: WWW.GUNDERSENHEALTH.ORG

PRODUCTS/OPERATIONS

Selected Services

Advance care planning
Apnea
Audiology
Autism Spectrum Disorder
BioBank
Brain disorders
Cardiac services
Children's health
Cleft Lip & Palate Clinic
Endocrinology
Hospice
Eye care
Gynecology
Hand surgery
Heart Institute
LASIK eye surgery
Massage
Neck surgery
Neurosciences
Oral and maxillofacial surgery
Pediatrics
Radiation oncology
Rehabilitation
Urgent care
Urology
Weight management
Wound care

COMPETITORS

Dean Health Systems Inc.
Franciscan Skemp Healthcare
Luther Midelfort
Mayo Clinic
Meriter Health Services
Ministry Health Care
Olmsted Medical
Sacred Heart Hospital
Tomah Memorial Hospital
University of Wisconsin Hospital and Clinics

HISTORICAL FINANCIALS

Company Type: Private

Income Statement — FYE: December 31

	REVENUE ($ mil.)	NET INCOME ($ mil.)	NET PROFIT MARGIN	EMPLOYEES
12/18	1,073	117	10.9%	4,500
12/17	1,071	112	10.5%	—
12/15	980	60	6.1%	—
12/14	894	94	10.6%	—
Annual Growth	4.7%	5.4%	—	—

2018 Year-End Financials

Return on assets: 8.2%
Return on equity: 8.2%
Current ratio: 189.00
Cash ($ mil.): —

GWINNETT COUNTY BOARD OF EDUCATION

EXECUTIVES

Chairperson, Robert McClure
Accounting Staff, Kathy Stillwell
Teacher, Laurie Pitcock
School Psychologist, Larris Boston
Auditors: MAULDIN & JENKINS LLC ATLANT

LOCATIONS

HQ: GWINNETT COUNTY BOARD OF EDUCATION
437 OLD PEACHTREE RD NW, SUWANEE, GA 300242978
Phone: 678 301-6000
Web: WWW.GWINNETT.K12.GA.US

HISTORICAL FINANCIALS

Company Type: Private

Income Statement — FYE: June 30

	REVENUE ($ mil.)	NET INCOME ($ mil.)	NET PROFIT MARGIN	EMPLOYEES
06/19	2,071	118	5.7%	112
06/18	1,973	(55)	—	—
06/17	1,868	(2)	—	—
06/16	1,791	349	19.5%	—
Annual Growth	5.0%	(30.2%)	—	—

2019 Year-End Financials

Return on assets: 2.9%
Return on equity: —
Current ratio: 2.70
Cash ($ mil.): 118

GWINNETT COUNTY GOVERNMENT

EXECUTIVES

County Admin, Glenn Stephens
Project Coord*, Susan Paul
Dir*, Joe Sorenson
Assistant Chief, Charles Wells
Engineer V, Kristopher Campbell
Information Technology, Jana Peerson
Program Supervisor, Melissa Day
Recreation Program Supervisor, Monte Harpe
Case Manager, Alexis Pryor
Probation Supervisor, Amy Mike
Information Technology, Andrea Frasier
Auditors: MAULDIN & JENKINS ATLANTA GA

LOCATIONS

HQ: GWINNETT COUNTY GOVERNMENT
75 LANGLEY DR, LAWRENCEVILLE, GA 300466935
Phone: 770 822-8000
Web: WWW.GWINNETTCOUNTY.COM

HISTORICAL FINANCIALS

Company Type: Private

Income Statement — FYE: December 31

	REVENUE ($ mil.)	NET INCOME ($ mil.)	NET PROFIT MARGIN	EMPLOYEES
12/19	930	42	4.5%	4,000
12/18	861	87	10.2%	—
12/17	802	87	10.9%	—
12/16	765	37	4.8%	—
Annual Growth	6.7%	4.3%	—	—

2019 Year-End Financials

Return on assets: 0.5%
Return on equity: 0.6%
Current ratio: —
Cash ($ mil.): 874

GWINNETT HOSPITAL SYSTEM, INC.

Auditors: KPMG LLP ATLANTA GA

LOCATIONS

HQ: GWINNETT HOSPITAL SYSTEM, INC.
1000 MEDICAL CENTER BLVD, LAWRENCEVILLE, GA 300467694
Phone: 678 343-3428
Web: WWW.GWINNETTMEDICALCENTER.ORG

HISTORICAL FINANCIALS

Company Type: Private

Income Statement — FYE: June 30

	REVENUE ($ mil.)	NET INCOME ($ mil.)	NET PROFIT MARGIN	EMPLOYEES
06/18	731	12	1.7%	2,050
06/17	729	29	4.1%	—
06/16	735	(31)	—	—
06/15	698	15	2.2%	—
Annual Growth	1.5%	(6.3%)	—	—

2018 Year-End Financials

Return on assets: 1.4%
Return on equity: 2.6%
Current ratio: 2.60
Cash ($ mil.): 54

H. J. BAKER SULPHUR, LLC

EXECUTIVES

Pres, Mark Whittemore
Project Manager, Rick Bloom
Auditors: GRANT THORNTON LLP HOUSTON T

LOCATIONS

HQ: H. J. BAKER SULPHUR, LLC
1450 LAKE ROBBINS DR # 500, THE WOODLANDS, TX 773803258
Phone: 346 372-3455
Web: WWW.OXBOW.COM

HISTORICAL FINANCIALS

Company Type: Private

Income Statement — FYE: December 31

	REVENUE ($ mil.)	NET INCOME ($ mil.)	NET PROFIT MARGIN	EMPLOYEES
12/08	878	26	3.0%	27
12/07	273	4	1.5%	—
12/05	170	(0)	—	—
Annual Growth	72.8%	—	—	—

2008 Year-End Financials

Return on assets: 17.3%
Return on equity: 75.7%
Current ratio: 1.40
Cash ($ mil.): 19

H. LEE MOFFITT CANCER CENTER AND RESEARCH INSTITUTE HOSPITAL, INC.

The H. Lee Moffitt Cancer Center and Research Institute founded in 1986 is a National Cancer Institute-designated Comprehensive Cancer Center located on the Tampa campus of the University of South Florida. The institute carries it out its stated mission of "contributing to the prevention and cure of cancer" through patient care research and education. It operates a 210-bed medical and surgical facility as well as outpatient treatment programs and a blood and marrow transplant program. Its research programs include study in the areas of molecular oncology immunology risk assessment health outcomes and experimental therapeutics.

Operations

The Moffitt Cancer Center sees more than 9000 cancer inpatients each year; it also handles some 328000 outpatient visits annually. In addition to its 40-bed blood and marrow transplant center which performs 400 annual transplants the hospital includes more than a dozen operating rooms and extensive diagnostic radiology and radiation therapy labs. The Cancer Screening and Prevention Center offers genetic testing for certain kinds of hereditary cancers (breast ovarian colon and melanoma).

The Moffitt Research Institute conducts a wide range of cancer studies and some of its drug discovery research programs are managed through partnerships with pharmaceutical companies and other research laboratories. The research institute also relies on funding grants from organizations such as the National Institutes of Health. It has received more than $80 million in grant funding and participated in some 300 clinical trials.

The Moffitt Cancer Center likewise has educational and health care alliances with a number of Florida hospitals and colleges including a three-way cancer care and research partnership with Shands HealthCare and the University of Florida. Through its affiliated network program (the Moffitt Oncology Network) Moffitt works with community doctors and centers across Florida to provide enhanced cancer services throughout the state. It also operates a number of outpatient clinics in surrounding areas.

Geographic Reach

Through its main campus and numerous outpatient sites Moffitt Cancer Center primarily serves residents of seven Florida counties: Hernando Hillsborough Manatee Pasco Pinellas Polk and Sarasota. It also serves patients from other areas of Florida and neighboring states.

Sales and Marketing

HMO and PPO plans account for about 65% of patient service revenues while reimbursements from Medicare and Medicaid plans account for another 32% of sales.

Financial Performance

Revenue at Moffitt Cancer Center and Research Institute increased 1% to $779 million in 2013 from $772 the previous year due to higher patient service revenues. After a net loss in 2012 the institute reported net income of $26 million due to an increase in net assets and non-operating gains. Cash from operations also grew by $77 million due to the net income increase and cash generated from an estimated third-party settlement.

Strategy

Moffitt Cancer Center conducts expansion and facility improvement projects to enhance services for its cancer patients. For instance it launched construction of a new $74 million outpatient facility at the current McKinley office site in 2013; the location is near the main campus and will provide surgery infusion imaging research and other services. It also formed a partnership with Space Coast Cancer Center Boca Raton Regional Hospital Advinus Therapeutics and Lehigh Valley Health Network to improve cancer care for all the organizations.

EXECUTIVES

Pres, Jack Kolosky
Ex V Pres-Ctr Dir*, Thomas Sellers
Dir*, Willam S Dalton
Vp/Cfo*, Yvette Tremonti
Director Cell-Based Therapies, James J Mul
Stewardship Officer, Jessica Skinner
Project Coordinator Design, Mark Lyon
Public Relations Account Coord, Nicole Drone
Director, Rebecca Young
Auditors: ERNST & YOUNG LLP

LOCATIONS

HQ: H. LEE MOFFITT CANCER CENTER AND RESEARCH INSTITUTE HOSPITAL, INC.
12902 USF MAGNOLIA DR, TAMPA, FL 336129416
Phone: 813 745-4673
Web: WWW.MOFFITT.ORG

PRODUCTS/OPERATIONS

Selected Services

Chemotherapy
Diagnosis
Emotional Support
Integrative Medicine
Labwork Scans and Biopsy
Other Patient Services

Pain Management
Radiation
Screening and Genetics
Spiritual Support
Surgical Care
Well-Being

Selected Research Fields

Basic Science Division
Cancer Imaging and Metabolism
Drug Discovery
Immunology
Integrated Mathematical Oncology
Molecular Oncology
Tumor Biology
Population Science Division
Biostatistics and Bioinformatics
Cancer Epidemiology
Health Outcomes & Behavior

COMPETITORS

All Children's Hospital
Baptist Hospital of Miami
Bay Medical Center
Boca Raton Regional Hospital
Dana-Farber
Fox Chase Cancer Center
Jackson County Hospital of Florida
MD Anderson Cancer Center
Manatee Memorial Hospital
Mayo Clinic Jacksonville
Memorial Sloan-Kettering
Oak Hill Hospital
Roswell Park Cancer Institute
Sacred Heart Health System
South Georgia Medical Center
St. Vincent's Health System

HISTORICAL FINANCIALS

Company Type: Private

Income Statement — FYE: June 30

	REVENUE ($ mil.)	NET INCOME ($ mil.)	NET PROFIT MARGIN	EMPLOYEES
06/20	1,353	287	21.3%	4,200
06/18	1,020	167	16.4%	—
06/14	855	50	5.9%	—
Annual Growth	8.0%	33.8%	—	—

2020 Year-End Financials

Return on assets: 100.0%
Return on equity: 144.8%
Current ratio: 2.80
Cash ($ mil.): —

H. LEE MOFFITT CANCER CENTER AND RESEARCH INSTITUTE, INC.

EXECUTIVES

Pres, William Dalton
Svp-Cdio, Edmondo Robinson
Vp-CIO, Elizabeth Lindsay-Wood
Project Coordinator, Donna Cosenzo
Scientist, Thinh Cao
Assistant Professor, Alfredo A Santillan
Manager, Lee Anne Corbin
Health Professional, Amber Shrewsbury
Assistant Professor, Andrew W Carroll
Pathologist, Santo V Nicosia
Scientist, Shelten G Yuen
Auditors: GRANT THORNTON LLP TAMPA FLO

LOCATIONS

HQ: H. LEE MOFFITT CANCER CENTER AND RESEARCH INSTITUTE, INC.
12902 USF MAGNOLIA DR, TAMPA, FL 336129416
Phone: 813 745-4673
Web: WWW.MOFFITT.ORG

HISTORICAL FINANCIALS

Company Type: Private

Income Statement — FYE: June 30

	REVENUE ($ mil.)	NET INCOME ($ mil.)	NET PROFIT MARGIN	EMPLOYEES
06/20	1,655	121	7.3%	1,428
06/19	1,509	111	7.4%	—
06/18	1,310	178	13.6%	—
06/17	1,132	76	6.8%	—
Annual Growth	13.5%	16.6%	—	—

2020 Year-End Financials

Return on assets: 6.0%
Return on equity: 11.6%
Current ratio: 2.20
Cash ($ mil.): 300

HAGGEN, INC.

Haggen showers shoppers in the Pacific Northwest with salmon coffee and other essentials. Formerly one of the area's largest independent grocers Haggen operated some 130 supermarkets in Washington and Oregon as well as California Nevada and Arizona. Most of the stores were acquired from Albertsons in late 2014. In late 2015 Haggen filed for Chapter 11 bankruptcy protection to allow it to reorganize around a reduced number of locations and in 2016 the company agreed to sell its remaining core stores to Albertsons. The chain was founded in 1933 in Bellingham Washington.

EXECUTIVES

Vice President, Mike Lobaugh
Pharmacy Manager, David Muirhead
Vice President, Brad Haggen
Vice President Of Finance, Stephanie Allen
Auditors: MOSS ADAMS LLP

LOCATIONS

HQ: HAGGEN, INC.
2211 RIMLAND DR STE 300, BELLINGHAM, WA 982265699
Phone: 360 733-8720
Web: WWW.HAGGEN.COM

2014 Stores

	total
Washington	15
Oregon	2
Total	17

COMPETITORS

Costco Wholesale
Fred Meyer Stores
Grocery Outlet
Quality Food
SUPERVALU
Safeway
Smart & Final
Target Corporation
Trader Joe's
Wal-Mart
Walgreen
WinCo Foods

HISTORICAL FINANCIALS

Company Type: Private

Income Statement — FYE: December 31

	REVENUE ($ mil.)	NET INCOME ($ mil.)	NET PROFIT MARGIN	EMPLOYEES
12/07	787	8	1.1%	3,900
12/06	758	6	0.9%	—
12/05	164	0	—	—
Annual Growth	—20237.1%		—	—

2007 Year-End Financials

Return on assets: 4.9%
Return on equity: 1.1%
Current ratio: 0.30
Cash ($ mil.): 6

HAMILTON CHATTANOOGA COUNTY HOSPITAL AUTHORITY

The Chattanooga-Hamilton County Hospital Authority (dba Erlanger Health System) offers a broad range of health service operations including the T.C. Thompson Children's Hospital a cancer treatment facility and centers devoted to heart treatment trauma and eye care. The system comprises five hospital campuses in Tennessee with some 810 acute care beds as well as 50 long-term care beds. A teaching center for the University of Tennessee College of Medicine Erlanger provides tertiary care for a region that includes southeastern Tennessee northern Georgia northern Alabama and western North Carolina.

Operations

Erlanger is the tri-state region's only Level One Trauma Center providing the highest level of trauma care for adults. The Children's Hospital at Erlanger houses the region's only Level III Neonatal Intensive Care Unit as well as a pediatric trauma team Emergency Center and Pediatric Intensive Care Unit

The hospital system treats more than 300000 patients every year. In 2014 Erlanger had 30394 inpatient admissions 230765 outpatient visits to physician practices and 28810 surgical patients. Some 3067 children were admitted to Children's Hospital and 43192 received treatment in the Emergency Department and outpatient surgery.

The LIFE FORCE air ambulance service is is equipped with two EC-135 aircraft capable of single pilot IFR and two Bell 407 aircraft. LIFE FORCE transported 1419 patients in 2014.

Geographic Reach

The Erlanger Health System is a multi-hospital system with five hospitals based in Chattanooga: the University Hospital Children's Hospital at Erlanger Erlanger North Hospital Erlanger East Hospital and Erlanger Bledsoe Hospital located in Pikeville Tennessee. Its LIFE FORCE air ambulance service is stationed in Chattanooga and Sparta in Tennessee and in Calhoun and Blue Ridge in Georgia.

Financial Performance

Medicare accounted for 33% of Erlanger's net patient revenues in fiscal 2014; Commercial insurance 31%; and Medicaid 22%.

Company Background

To extend its patient reach Erlanger entered into a management contract with Hutcheson Hospital located in North Georgia in 2011.

Erlanger was founded in 1889 through the generosity of French nobleman Baron Frederic Emile d'Erlanger who held financial interests in a number of railroads in the region. He donated $5000 (more than $4 million in today's dollars) for a new hospital. It opened with 72 beds in 1899.

EXECUTIVES

Radiology Director, Byron Stutz
Senior Vice President Physician Services, Steven Burkett
Senior Vice President Planning And Business Development, Joseph Winick Fache
Vice President Human Resources, Floyd Chasse
Svp, Joseph Winick
Director Of Him, Jim Brown
Vice President, Bruce Komiske
Chief Executive Officer Vice President, Phillip Jackson
Medical Director Of Quality And Safety, Woods Blake
Medical Director, Waleed Mourad
Medical Director, Jenny Mahaffey
Medical Director Infection Prevention And Antimicrobial Stewardship, Jay Sizemore
Assistant Vice President Of Oncology, Tony Dotson
Medical Director Pediatric Critical Care, Gregory Talbott
Board Member, Brian Ceraolo

LOCATIONS

HQ: HAMILTON CHATTANOOGA COUNTY HOSPITAL AUTHORITY
975 E 3RD ST, CHATTANOOGA, TN 374032147
Phone: 423 778-7000
Web: WWW.ERLANGER.ORG

PRODUCTS/OPERATIONS

Selected Campuses

Dodson Avenue Community Health Center
Erlanger Bledsoe Campus
Erlanger East Campus
Erlanger Medical Center
Erlanger North Campus
Southside Community Health Center
T.C. Thompson Children's Hospital

Selected Medical Services

Breast Imaging
Cancer Services
Cardiology
Chattanooga Lifestyle Center
Community Health Centers
Craniofacial Center
Erlanger Metabolic and Bariatric Surgery Center
Erlanger Pharmacy
Gastroenterology
Heart
Home Health (ContinuCare)
HouseCalls
Hypertension Management Center
Imaging Services
LIFE FORCE
Neurobehavioral and Memory Services
Orthopedics
Radiology
Respiratory Services
Rheumatology
Robotic Surgery
Sleep Disorders Center
Stroke
The Weight Loss Program
Trauma Services
Urgent Care - Adult
Urology
UT Erlanger Kidney Transplant Center
Weight Management
Women's Services
WorkForce Corporate Health
Wound Care and Hyperbaric Oxygen center

COMPETITORS

Catholic Health Initiatives
Community Health Systems
Hutcheson Medical
Parkridge Medical Center
Saint Thomas Rutherford Hospital
Southern Hills
Vanderbilt University Medical Center

HISTORICAL FINANCIALS

Company Type: Private

Income Statement — FYE: June 30

	REVENUE ($ mil.)	NET INCOME ($ mil.)	NET PROFIT MARGIN	EMPLOYEES
06/20	1,021	29	2.9%	4,700
06/18	973	26	2.8%	—
06/17	888	13	1.6%	—
06/07	499	13	2.7%	—
Annual Growth	5.7%	6.0%	—	—

2020 Year-End Financials

Return on assets: 3.1%
Return on equity: 8.7%
Current ratio: 1.60
Cash ($ mil.): 268

HARBOR-UCLA MEDICAL CENTER

LOCATIONS

HQ: HARBOR-UCLA MEDICAL CENTER
1000 W CARSON ST, TORRANCE, CA 905022059
Phone: 310 222-2301
Web: WWW.EMEDHARBOR.EDU

HISTORICAL FINANCIALS

Company Type: Private

Income Statement — FYE: June 30

	REVENUE ($ mil.)	NET INCOME ($ mil.)	NET PROFIT MARGIN	EMPLOYEES
06/16	637	(268)	—	3,000
06/15	607	(287)	—	—
Annual Growth	5.0%	—	—	—

2016 Year-End Financials

Return on assets: (-33.0%)
Return on equity: —
Current ratio: 1.40
Cash ($ mil.): 9

HARLEE MANOR, INC.

EXECUTIVES

Pres, Hardie A Beloff
V Pres*, Leland Beloff
SEC*, Geraldine Barbeau-Leonard
Treasurer, Jean Beloff
Health Care Director, Jennifer Bail

LOCATIONS

HQ: HARLEE MANOR, INC.
218 N DIAMOND ST, CLIFTON HEIGHTS, PA 190181507
Phone: 610 544-2200
Web: WWW.HARLEEMANOR.COM

HISTORICAL FINANCIALS

Company Type: Private

Income Statement — FYE: June 30

	REVENUE ($ mil.)	NET INCOME ($ mil.)	NET PROFIT MARGIN	EMPLOYEES
06/09	1,164	62	5.4%	151
06/98	8	0	6.3%	—
Annual Growth	55.9%	53.6%	—	—

2009 Year-End Financials

Return on assets: 48.8%
Return on equity: 821.7%
Current ratio: 1.80
Cash ($ mil.): —

HARRIS COUNTY FIRE MARSHAL

EXECUTIVES

Exec Dir, Gary K Trietsch
Customer Staff, Jonnie Bryant
Executive Assistant, Penny Younker
Information Technology Project, Brad Urban
Revenue Manager, Regina Fain
Revenue, Nancy Chamroeun
Senior Staff Engineer, John Tyler
Iop Representative, Quintrell Gage
Engineer, Douglas Emery
Program Manager, Karen McKinnon
Plaza Clerk, Mahogany Ganey

LOCATIONS

HQ: HARRIS COUNTY FIRE MARSHAL
7701 WILSHIRE PLACE DR, HOUSTON, TX 770405326
Phone: 713 587-7800
Web: WWW.HCTRA.ORG

HISTORICAL FINANCIALS

Company Type: Private

Income Statement — FYE: February 28

	REVENUE ($ mil.)	NET INCOME ($ mil.)	NET PROFIT MARGIN	EMPLOYEES
02/19	829	310	37.4%	3
02/18	740	224	30.4%	—
Annual Growth	12.1%	38.1%	—	—

2019 Year-End Financials

Return on assets: 6.7%
Return on equity: 17.0%
Current ratio: 4.80
Cash ($ mil.): 325

HARTFORD HEALTHCARE CORPORATION

Hartford Health Care provides a variety of health services to the descendants of our founding fathers. Founded in 1854 the health care system operates a network of hospitals behavioral health centers nursing and rehabilitation facilities medical labs and numerous community programs for residents in northern Connecticut. Medical specialties range from orthopedics and women's health to cancer and heart care. Hartford Health Care's flagship facility is the Hartford Hospital an 870-bed teaching hospital affiliated with the University of Connecticut Medical School. Its network also includes MidState Medical Center (some 155 beds) Windham Hospital (145 beds) and The Hospital of Central Connecticut (415 beds).

Operations

Hartford Health Care provides primary and specialty care services through partnerships with several physician practice organizations and specialist facilities including diagnostic imaging centers and mental health facilities. The company provides medical laboratory services including pathology genetic testing and other diagnostic services through its Clinical Laboratory Partners affiliate. It also provides long-term care through Central Connecticut Senior Health Services as well as home health services through VNA HealthCare.

Financial Performance

In 2013 Hartford Health Care reported a 2% rise in revenue from $1.7 million to $2.1 million due to increased patient service revenue.

Strategy

As it becomes increasingly challenging for hospitals to remain independently profitable in an unstable economic climate especially as health reform changes take effect Hartford has been working to expand its footprint in the Connecticut health care market. In 2012 Hartford Health Care formed an alliance with Backus Corporation which operates the Backus Hospital and other medical care centers in eastern Connecticut. Backus gained access to Hartford's broader resources but continues to manage its own day-to-day operations.

In 2014 Hartford Health Care broke ground on a new 90000-square-foot cancer center at The Hospital of Central Connecticut.

EXECUTIVES

Vice President Medical Director, Kent Stahl
Senior Vice President Finance And Treasurer, Richard Stys
Senior Vice President, Karen Goyette
Senior Vice President Chief Information Officer, Richard T Shirey
Senior Vice President, Gerald Boisvert
Vice President Marketing And Branding, Keith Fontaine
Senior Vice President, Gerard Lupacchino
Senior Vice President, Patricia Rehmer
Senior Vice President Physician Services, Vincent Dibattista
Vice President Of Clinical Operations Natchaug Hospital, Justin Sleeper
Vice President Of Hospice And Palliative Care, Laurie St John
Vice President Quality And Patient Safety, Jamie Roche
Vice President Quality And Safety, Stephanie Calcasola
Medical Director, Teodora Andrei
Vice Chair Department Of Radiology, Barry Stein
Auditors: ERNST & YOUNG LLP HARTFORD C

LOCATIONS

HQ: HARTFORD HEALTHCARE CORPORATION
1 STATE ST FL 19, HARTFORD, CT 061033102
Phone: 860 696-6248
Web: WWW.HARTFORDHEALTHCARE.ORG

PRODUCTS/OPERATIONS

2013 Sales

	$ mil.	% of total
Net patient revenue	1,906	90
Other operating revenue	211	10
Net asets released from restrctions for operations	10	-
Total	**2,128**	**100**

Selected Facilities

Alliance Occupational Health
Central Connecticut Senior Health Services
Clinical Laboratory Partners
Eastern Rehabilitation Network
Hartford Hospital (acute care)
Hartford Medical Group (primary care)
The Hospital of Central Connecticut (acute care)
Institute of Living (research and psychiatric care)
MidState Medical Center (acute care)
Natchaug Hospital (mental health facility)
Rushford (mental health treatment centers)
VNA HealthCare (home health)
Windham Hospital (acute care)

COMPETITORS

Baystate Medical Center
Berkshire Health Systems
Bristol Hospital
Connecticut Children's Medical Center
Griffin Health
Lawrence & Memorial Hospital
Saint Francis Hospital and Medical Center
St. Vincent's Health Services
University of Connecticut Health Center
Waterbury Hospital
Western Connecticut Health Network
Yale New Haven Health System
Yale-New Haven Hospital Saint Raphael Campus

HISTORICAL FINANCIALS

Company Type: Private

Income Statement — FYE: September 30

	REVENUE ($ mil.)	NET INCOME ($ mil.)	NET PROFIT MARGIN	EMPLOYEES
09/19	3,541	(101)	—	12,500
09/18	3,072	410	13.4%	—
09/15	297	(37)	—	—
09/12	2,090	63	3.1%	—
Annual Growth	7.8%	—	—	—

2019 Year-End Financials

Return on assets: (-2.2%)
Return on equity: (-4.4%)
Current ratio: 1.40
Cash ($ mil.): 394

HARTFORD HOSPITAL

EXECUTIVES

Pres-Ceo, Jeffrey A Flaks
V Pres, Gerry J Boisvert
Sr V Pres, Luis Tavares
Cfo, Tom Marchozzi
Coordinator, Betsy Centeno
Scientist, Michal Assaf
Health Professional, Gada M Abdelhafiz
Scientist, Pamela Tessier
Regional Vice-President, Barry Kriesberg
Coordinator, David Bailey
Assistant Chief, David Chung

LOCATIONS

HQ: HARTFORD HOSPITAL
80 SEYMOUR ST, HARTFORD, CT 061028000
Phone: 860 545-5000
Web: WWW.HARTFORDHOSPITAL.ORG

HISTORICAL FINANCIALS

Company Type: Private

Income Statement — FYE: September 30

	REVENUE ($ mil.)	NET INCOME ($ mil.)	NET PROFIT MARGIN	EMPLOYEES
09/17	1,283	96	7.6%	7,500
09/16	1,031	76	7.5%	—
09/15	993	64	6.5%	—
09/14	986	62	6.3%	—
Annual Growth	9.2%	16.0%	—	—

2017 Year-End Financials

Return on assets: 5.8%
Return on equity: 12.6%
Current ratio: 1.50
Cash ($ mil.): 39

HARVARD BUSINESS SCHOOL PUBLISHING CORPORATION

EXECUTIVES

Pres-Ceo, David Wan
Evp-Coo*, Raymond Carvey
Cfo*, Paul Bills
Vice-President Engineering, Patrick McManus
Customer Support Specialist (i, Jason Gerdom
Senior Manager, Jennifer Long
Customer Manager, Maureen Betses
Delivery Operations Coordinato, Nick Jordan
Customer Support Speci, Evan Ginja
Marketing Manager, Lisa Glynn
Global Leadership, Lisa Lai
Auditors: LB PRICEWATERHOUSECOOPERS LLP

LOCATIONS

HQ: HARVARD BUSINESS SCHOOL PUBLISHING CORPORATION
20 GUEST ST STE 700, BRIGHTON, MA 021352063
Phone: 617 783-7400
Web: WWW.HARVARDBUSINESS.ORG

HISTORICAL FINANCIALS

Company Type: Private

Income Statement — FYE: June 30

	REVENUE ($ mil.)	NET INCOME ($ mil.)	NET PROFIT MARGIN	EMPLOYEES
06/19	925	11	1.2%	390
06/15	207	2	1.2%	—
06/10	139	1	1.0%	—
06/09	141	1	0.7%	—
Annual Growth	20.7%	26.5%	—	—

2019 Year-End Financials

Return on assets: 0.2%
Return on equity: 0.2%
Current ratio: —
Cash ($ mil.): 105

HARVARD MANAGEMENT PRIVATE EQUITY CORPORATION

EXECUTIVES

Pres, Jane L Mendillo
Treas, Robert A Ettl
Human Resources Senior Analyst, Emily Cummings
Human Resources Staff Assistan, Jonathan Mascia
Human Resources Senior, Patricia Lowe
Assistant Vice President, Charisma Madamba
Assistant Vice President, Drew Hussar
Associate Administrative Assis, Julie Notaro
Attending Physician Department, Katherine Janeway
Assistant Professor Department, Randolph Watnick
Manager III, Suzanna Tran
Auditors: RSM MCGLADREY INC CHICAGO IL

LOCATIONS

HQ: HARVARD MANAGEMENT PRIVATE EQUITY CORPORATION
600 ATLANTIC AVE STE 1500, BOSTON, MA 022102203
Phone: 617 523-4400
Web: WWW.FAS.HARVARD.EDU

HISTORICAL FINANCIALS

Company Type: Private

Income Statement — FYE: June 30

	REVENUE ($ mil.)	NET INCOME ($ mil.)	NET PROFIT MARGIN	EMPLOYEES
06/17	663	477	71.9%	6
06/10	1,661	(611)	—	—
Annual Growth	(12.3%)	—	—	—

HAWAI I PACIFIC HEALTH

Hawaii may be paradise but even in paradise's some residents get sick. That's when Hawai'i Pacific Health (HPH) surfs in to save the day. HPH is a not-for-profit health care system consisting of four hospitals (Kapi'olani Medical Center for Women & Children Pali Momi Medical Center Straub Clinic & Hospital and Wilcox Memorial Hospital) across the islands with a combined capacity of 550 beds. The system offers a full array of tertiary specialty and acute care services through its hospitals which also serve as teaching and research centers as well as about 50 outpatient centers. Specialized services offered by HPH include cardiac care maternity services oncology orthopedics and pediatric care.

Operations

HPH supplies a wide range of primary and specialty medical services through its physician organizations. The Kapi'olani Medical Specialists group for instance comprises more than 100 physicians and partners with Kapi'olani Medical Center for Women & Children to care for patients from infancy through adulthood. The center also functions as the women's health and pediatric teaching hospital for the University of Hawaii School of Medicine. Its Visiting Specialists group provides care to the islands where HPH doesn't have primary care facilities.

Strategy

The system has partnered with Surgical Care Affiliates to build an outpatient surgical center in Honolulu in an effort to meet growing demand there. The center dubbed Surgicare of Hawai'i offers an array of medical services including orthopedics pain management ophthalmology general surgery and podiatry.

In 2010 the hospital system embarked on a 6-year $580 million master facility plan to expand and improve some of its primary hospital locations. The first stage included new intensive care units and parking capacity at the Kapi'olani Medical Center.

Company Background

The organization was formed through the 2001 merger of three entities: Kapi'olani Health Straub Clinic & Hospital and Wilcox Health System. Committed to supporting Hawaiian culture and values HPH and its member hospitals honor the Hawaiian language and its use of diacritical marks the glottal stop and the macron (okina and kahako).

EXECUTIVES

Vice President Of General Services, Susan Nonaka
Executive Vice President Chief Financial Officer, David Okabe
Director Of Pharmacy Director Of Pharmacy Services Manager, Kent Kikuchi
Executive Vice President And Chief Information Officer, Steve Robertson
Vice President Operations, Melinda Ashton
Vice President, Warren Chaiko
Board Of Director, Keith Matsumoto
Auditors: ERNST & YOUNG LLP DENVER CO

LOCATIONS

HQ: HAWAI I PACIFIC HEALTH
55 MERCHANT ST STE 2500, HONOLULU, HI 968134306
Phone: 808 949-9355
Web: WWW.HAWAIIPACIFICHEALTH.ORG

PRODUCTS/OPERATIONS

Selected Facilities

Kapi'olani Medical Center for Women & Children (Honolulu)
Kaua'i Medical Clinics (Kaua'i)
Pali Momi Medical Center (Aiea)
Straub Clinic & Hospital (Honolulu)
Straub Family Health Centers (Honolulu)
Visiting Specialists (Hilo Kaua'i Lana'i Maui Moloka'i Walmea)
Wilcox Memorial Hospital (Lihue Kaua'i)

COMPETITORS

Adventist Health System West
Kuakini Health System
Queen's Medical Center
Rehabilitation Hospital of the Pacific

HISTORICAL FINANCIALS

Company Type: Private

Income Statement — FYE: June 30

	REVENUE ($ mil.)	NET INCOME ($ mil.)	NET PROFIT MARGIN	EMPLOYEES
06/18	1,351	130	9.7%	5,400
06/17	1,290	153	11.9%	—
06/15	159	0	0.3%	—
06/14	145	1	1.1%	—
Annual Growth	74.5%	200.8%	—	—

2018 Year-End Financials

Return on assets: 7.0%
Return on equity: 12.8%
Current ratio: 2.50
Cash ($ mil.): 235

HCL AMERICA INC.

EXECUTIVES

Dir, Shiv Nadar
Dir, Prateek Aggarwal
Dir, C Vijayakumar
Dir, Anoop Tiwari
Dir, Robin Abrams
Ceo, Manish Anand
Technical Manager, Lawrence Anand
Technical Lead, Pooja Manocha
Sales Director, Shankar Narayan
Associate General Manager, Anand Vidhani
Consultant, Anchal Singhal
Auditors: SR BATLIBOI & CO LLP CAMAC

LOCATIONS

HQ: HCL AMERICA INC.
330 POTRERO AVE, SUNNYVALE, CA 940854194
Phone: 408 733-0480
Web: WWW.HCL.COM

HISTORICAL FINANCIALS

Company Type: Private

Income Statement — FYE: March 31

	REVENUE ($ mil.)	NET INCOME ($ mil.)	NET PROFIT MARGIN	EMPLOYEES
03/17*	3,559	130	3.7%	11,993
06/15	2,815	53	1.9%	—
06/14	2,353	0	0.0%	—
06/13	2,075	35	1.7%	—
Annual Growth	14.4%	37.9%	—	—

*Fiscal year change

2017 Year-End Financials

Return on assets: 8.8%
Return on equity: 20.2%
Current ratio: 1.10
Cash ($ mil.): 4

HDR ENGINEERING, INC.

EXECUTIVES

Ceo, George A Little
Pres, Eric L Keen
Coo, George Little
Cfo, Terence C Cox
Exec V Pres, Terry Cox
Treas, Chad M Hartnett
SEC, Louis J Pachman
Gis Analyst, Jade Dean
Human Resources Manager, Kaitlyn Gonet
Auditors: ERNST & YOUNG LLP CHICAGO I

LOCATIONS

HQ: HDR ENGINEERING, INC.
1917 S 67TH ST, OMAHA, NE 681062973
Phone: 402 399-1000
Web: WWW.HDRINC.COM

HISTORICAL FINANCIALS

Company Type: Private

Income Statement				FYE: December 29
	REVENUE ($ mil.)	NET INCOME ($ mil.)	NET PROFIT MARGIN	EMPLOYEES
12/18	1,399	107	7.7%	6,111
12/17	1,707	73	4.3%	—
12/16	1,748	89	5.1%	—
12/15	1,218	100	8.2%	—
Annual Growth	4.7%	2.3%	—	—

2018 Year-End Financials

Return on assets: 9.7%
Return on equity: 13.1%
Current ratio: 3.90
Cash ($ mil.): 25

HDR, INC.

With projects ranging from restoring the Pentagon and the Everglades to working on the Hoover Dam Bypass project HDR has left its mark on the US. HDR is an architecture engineering and consulting firm that specializes in such projects as bridges water- and wastewater-treatment plants and hospitals. The company also provides mechanical and plumbing services construction and project management and utilities planning. It has operation in nearly 15 countries and has offices in more than 200 global locations. The employee-owned company was founded as Henningson Engineering in 1917 to build municipal plants in the rural Midwest.

Operations

HDR's offers architecture services such as branding infrastructure interior landscape & site as well as lighting designs. Its real estate services includes acquisition and relocation project and property management and site and alignment analysis. Other programs and services includes asset management facility management economics and finance services and environmental sciences services (which includes acoustics noise vibration and ecosystem restoration) among others.

Geographic Reach

Headquartered in Omaha Nebraska HDR has operations in the Americas (US and Canada) Asia Pacific (Australia China India and Singapore) Europe (Denmark Germany Netherlands and the UK) and the Middle East.

Sales and Marketing

HDR's markets include defense & intelligence education health industrial power justice power & energy tech transportation and urban community among others. It has performed design and engineering work for a number of clients including: Shirley Ryan AbilityLab Kitsap Transit Road 13 Winery iKure Tucson Water and Allina Health Systems.

Strategy

HDR strives to do things better and stretch further. From its internal processes to the work it delivers and from the projects it does to the careers it enables. It is also conscious of its environmental impact as evidenced by ranking ninth for top environmental firms by revenue. HDR also believes that sustainability and resiliency make fiscal sense as sustainable resilient projects last longer can save money in the long term and can withstand unique shocks and hazards.

The company also continues to design and engineer big infrastructure projects for city and state governments. In September 2020 HDR was selected by the Southern California Regional Rail Authority to provide program management services for Phase 1 of the transformative Southern California Optimizes Rail Expansion program.

Earlier that year HDR celebrated the opening of the photon science laboratory building fit-out project at SLAC National Accelerator Laboratory Arrillaga Science Center in Menlo Park California. HDR led the 65000-sf major interior and utility systems fit-out which expands SLAC's photon science program.

Not only is HDR expanding its facilities but also its philanthropic efforts through its HDR Foundation. In mid-2020 HDR Foundation announced its expansion to Canada which broadens the reach of the foundation and offers support to its Canadian employees.

EXECUTIVES

Chairman And Ceo, George A. Little
Cfo, Terence C. (Terry) Cox
Evp And Director Federal Energy And Resource Management, Elwin Larson
Evp And Director Water Program, Gary L. Bleeker
Vice Chairman; President Hdr Engineering Inc., Eric L. Keen
President Manager, Kevin Keller
President Hdr Architecture Inc., Doug S. Wignall
Cio, Michael Geppert
Evp And Director Transportation, Charles O'Reilly
President Manager Richmond Hill Traffic Practice, David Argue
Auditors: ERNST & YOUNG LLP CHICAGO IL

LOCATIONS

HQ: HDR, INC.
1917 S 67TH ST, OMAHA, NE 681062973
Phone: 402 399-1000
Web: WWW.HDRINC.COM

PRODUCTS/OPERATIONS

Selected Mergers and Acquisitions

FY2015
Brentwood Tennessee-based Infrastructure Corporation of America (ICA)
FY2103
Rice Daubney (Australia architecture design for healthcare retail defense markets)
FY2012
Stetson Engineering (Wyoming projects in water sewer storm water hydrology and transportation)
FY2011
Amnis Engineering (Canada)
Cooper Medical (Healthcare design/build specialist)
HydroQual (New Jersey water resource management)
Schiff Associates (California engineering)
FY2009
Devine Tarbell & Associates (Maine now named HDR|DTA)
iTrans Consulting (Toronto-based engineering firm)

Selected Markets

Architecture
Academic
Civic
Corporate
Healthcare
Justice
Science and Technology
Energy
Oil and Gas
Power Delivery
Power Generation
Renewable Energy
Federal
Federal Architecture
Federal Engineering
Federal Planning
Federal Environmental
Federal Energy
Federal Construction
HDR SeaPort-e
Private Land Development
Commercial
Industrial
Institutional
Residential
Resorts and Hotels
Resource Management
Community Planning & Consulting
Environmental Sciences & Permitting
Fisheries Science & Design
Mining
Natural Resource Management
Waste Management and Industrial
Transportation
Aviation
Freight Rail
Highways and Local Roads
Maritime
Transit
Water
Water
Wastewater
Water Planning
Industrial

Selected Services

Analytical consulting
Architectural design
Coastal engineering and restoration
Consulting
Design/build
Environmental monitoring
Finished water storage facility services
Interior design
Landscape architecture
Master planning
Power facility engineering
Pump stations and flow control
Security services
Utility master planning and modeling
Water resources
Water treatment systems

COMPETITORS

AECOM
Black & Veatch
Brown and Caldwell
Epstein
Fuscoe Engineering
Gensler
Geotechnics
HBE Corporation
HKS Inc.
Interior Architects
Jacobs Engineering
KPA Associates
Kimley-Horn and Associates
Lee Burkhart Liu
Leo A Daly
MCG Architects
MWH Global
Michael Baker
Nasland Engineering
Perkowitz + Ruth
RMJM
RTKL Associates
SAIC Energy Environment & Infrastructure
STV
Tetra Tech
The Austin Company
Western Summit Constructors
Willdan Group

HISTORICAL FINANCIALS

Company Type: Private

Income Statement				FYE: December 29
	REVENUE ($ mil.)	NET INCOME ($ mil.)	NET PROFIT MARGIN	EMPLOYEES
12/18	1,762	115	6.5%	10,000
12/17	2,362	82	3.5%	—
12/16	2,230	90	4.0%	—
12/15	2,132	74	3.5%	—
Annual Growth	(6.1%)	15.9%	—	—

2018 Year-End Financials

Return on assets: 7.8% | Cash ($ mil.): 283
Return on equity: 20.1%
Current ratio: 2.00

HEALTH FIRST, INC.

Health First works to keep Florida's Space Coast denizens in tip-top shape. The not-for-profit health system operates four hospitals in Brevard County. Health First's biggest hospital is Holmes Regional Medical Center in Melbourne with more than 500 beds. Its Cape Canaveral Hospital and Palm Bay Community Hospital have 150 and 60 beds respectively. Its Viera Hospital is a 100-bed acute-care hospital. The system also runs outpatient clinics a home health service and a physicians group. Its for-profit subsidiary Health First Health Plans is the county's largest insurer with about 60000 commercial members and 23000 Medicare members.

Operations

The company operates four hospitals (Holmes Regional Medical Center Palm Bay Hospital Cape Canaveral Hospital and Viera Hospital) and offers a wide variety of health insurance plan options for patients in Brevard and Indian River Counties. Health First is the largest multi-specialty physician group on Florida's Space Coast. It also operates to Brevard County's only trauma center and a number of outpatient and wellness services including four pro-health and fitness centers.

Geographic Reach

Health First operates four hospitals and a health insurance company in Brevard County Florida.

Strategy

To expand its capacity Health First makes complementary acquisitions and pursues organic growth.

In 2103 Health First opened of a new center for fracture care at Health First Holmes Regional Medical Center and the center for joint replacement at Health First Viera Hospital. That year it formed a new Small Group Preferred Provider Organization (PPO) Plan offering increased flexibility when it comes to out-of-network coverage and fulfilling the needs of employer groups in its service area.

Mergers and Acquisitions

In 2012 the company acquired Melbourne Internal Medicine Associates (250 physician providers based in Melbourne) to increase patient quality safety and the patient experience. The entity was renamed the Health First Medical Group in 2013.

Company Background

In 2011 Health First partnered with Nemours to expand pediatric care in Brevard County. That year Health First Health Plans opened a new Vero Beach office to serve residents of Indian River County and launch its Medicare Advantage plans to the rest of Indian River County.

Despite an ongoing lawsuit with Wuesthoff Health System (which claims that Health First has an unfair monopoly of hospital services in Brevard County) the company forged ahead with construction of its fourth hospital in the county the Viera hospital campus. The Medical Plaza at Viera Health Park which will includes offices for multi-specialty physicians and a diagnostic/imaging center opened in 2010. And the park's centerpiece Viera Hospital a 100-bed acute-care hospital opened in 2011.

Health First was founded in 1995 through a merger of regional hospitals. The Brevard Hospital (now Holmes Regional Medical Center) first opened in 1937.

EXECUTIVES

Chief Physician Executive, Jeffrey C. Stalnaker
Evp And Coo, J. Stuart Mitchell
Evp Chief Strategy Officer; Ceo Health First Health Plans, Drew Rector
Evp And Cfo, Joseph (Joe) Felkner
President Health First Medical Group, Travis L Douglass
President And Ceo, Steven P. Johnson
Ceo Community Hospitals, Aaron Robinson
Svp And Cio, Alex Popowycz
President Hospital Operations, Bill Calhoun
Chief Nursing Officer, Constance (Connie) Bradley
Vice President And Corporate Attorney, Grant Dearborn
Vice President Marketing And Communications, Matthew Gerrell
Pharmacy Manager, Marta Hamilton
Medical Director Cardiac Electrophysiology, Ken Lee
Physical Therapy Physical Therapy Assistant, Carol Harrington
Director Of Pharmacy, John Malek
Chairman, Pamela A. Gatto
Vice Chairman, Kevin B. Steele

LOCATIONS

HQ: HEALTH FIRST, INC.
6450 US HIGHWAY 1, ROCKLEDGE, FL 329555747
Phone: 321 434-4300
Web: WWW.HEALTH-FIRST.COM

Selected facilities

Cape Canaveral Hospital (Cocoa Beach)
Holmes Regional Medical Center (Melbourne)
Palm Bay Community Hospital (Palm Bay)
Viera Hospital (Viera)

COMPETITORS

Adventist Health System Sunbelt Healthcare
Aetna
CIGNA
Florida Blue
HCA
Orlando Health
Osceola Regional Medical Center
Tenet Healthcare
Wuesthoff Health System

HISTORICAL FINANCIALS

Company Type: Private

Income Statement — FYE: September 30

	REVENUE ($ mil.)	NET INCOME ($ mil.)	NET PROFIT MARGIN	EMPLOYEES
09/15	1,255	19	1.6%	6,900
09/14	1,136	90	7.9%	—
09/13	1,059	51	4.8%	—
09/11	129	(0)	—	—
Annual Growth	76.5%	—	—	—

2015 Year-End Financials

Return on assets: 1.2% | Cash ($ mil.): 152
Return on equity: 2.7%
Current ratio: 4.30

HEALTH PARTNERS PLANS, INC.

Health Partners wants to partner up with Pennsylvanians in need of health care. The company is a not-for-profit health plan that provides health benefits to some 210000 Medicaid recipients in the Philadelphia area. Its HealthChoices plans for Medicaid participants cover medical dental prescription and vision costs. Its KidzPartners program is provided in partnership with the state of Pennsylvania's Children's Health Insurance Program (CHIP). Its provider network includes about 6000 primary and specialty care doctors and 30 hospitals in the region. The company also provides community outreach and wellness programs. Health Partners was founded in 1985 by a group of hospitals in the Philadelphia area.

Geographic Reach

Health Partners' plans cover members in Philadelphia and in Chester Delaware Bucks and Montgomery counties outside the city.

Strategy

Health Partners signed a provider contract with the University of Pennsylvania Health System that will increase access to care in Philadelphia for Health Partners Medicare members.The agreement increases Health Partners' network to include more than 1300 additional physicians from the Health System's network of practices and four hospitals.

Health Partners has been working to enhance its community health programs in recent years. It launched its Computer Health Care Management Education program to provide free monthly computer lessons combined with tutorials about healthy lifestyle programs.

It also teamed up with the Norcom Community Center to offer HealthChoices and KidzPartners members fitness benefits at the facility; the company has a total of more than 20 fitness centers in its expanding provider network. The KidzPartners program provides free or affordable insurance coverage to children and teens who don't qualify for Medicaid.

Company Background

The area hospitals that own Health Partners are Albert Einstein Medical Center Aria Health Temple University Hospital Episcopal Hospital and two Tenet Healthcare facilities (Hahnemann University Hospital and St. Christopher's Hospital for Children).

EXECUTIVES

President And Ceo, William S. George
Svp Healthcare Management And Chief Medical Officer, Steven E. Szebenyi
Svp Operations And Coo, Lisa Getzfrid
Government Relations, Kearline Jones
Svp Of Healthcare Economics, Carol Potts
Vice President Of Marketing, Caroline Russell
Vice President Finance And Chief Financi, John Sehi
Vice President Information Technology Infrastructure And Operations, Anthony Marino
Vice President Government Relations And Compliance, Jones Kearline
Vice President Compliance Medicare Compliance Of, Andy Finkelstein
Executive Vice President Clinical And Provider Management, Denise Croce
Senior Vice President Of Medicare Sales And Actuarial Services, Mark Cary
Vice President Medical Management, Michelle Mattiace
Government Relations And Compliance Analyst, Shane Kovach
Vice President And Treasurer, Joe Dodi
Vice President Medicare Sales, Hicham Elanmati
Auditors: KPMG LLP PHILADELPHIA PENNSY

LOCATIONS

HQ: HEALTH PARTNERS PLANS, INC.
901 MARKET ST STE 500, PHILADELPHIA, PA 191074496
Phone: 215 849-9606
Web: WWW.HEALTHPARTNERSPLANS.COM

COMPETITORS

Aetna
CIGNA
Gateway Health Plan
Health Net
Highmark
Independence Blue Cross
Keystone Mercy
UnitedHealth Group

HISTORICAL FINANCIALS

Company Type: Private

Income Statement — FYE: December 31

	REVENUE ($ mil.)	NET INCOME ($ mil.)	NET PROFIT MARGIN	EMPLOYEES
12/14	910	(8)	—	620
12/13	1,000	(0)	—	—
12/12	1,034	(1)	—	—
Annual Growth	(6.2%)	—	—	—

2014 Year-End Financials

Return on assets: (-2.9%)
Return on equity: (-10.8%)
Current ratio: 0.90
Cash ($ mil.): 60

HEALTH QUEST SYSTEMS, INC.

EXECUTIVES

Ceo, Denise George
V Pres, Mary Ann Keppel
Sr V Pres, Ron Tatelbaumm
Sr V Pres, David Ping
Cfo, Yann Kepple
Sr V Pres, Ann Armater
Coordinator, Cheryl Mathieu
Information Specialist, Lew Hulse
Internal Medicine Practitioner, Christopher Panettieri
Coordinator, Carissa Sharp
Chief of Medicine, Imtiaz Mallick
Auditors: PRICEWATERHOUSECOOPERS LLP N

LOCATIONS

HQ: HEALTH QUEST SYSTEMS, INC.
1351 ROUTE 55 STE 200, LAGRANGEVILLE, NY 125405144
Phone: 845 475-9500
Web: WWW.HEALTHQUEST.ORG

HISTORICAL FINANCIALS

Company Type: Private

Income Statement — FYE: December 31

	REVENUE ($ mil.)	NET INCOME ($ mil.)	NET PROFIT MARGIN	EMPLOYEES
12/14	796	5	0.6%	2,000
12/13	706	103	14.6%	—
12/12	692	8	1.2%	—
Annual Growth	7.3%	(21.3%)	—	—

2014 Year-End Financials

Return on assets: 0.6%
Return on equity: 1.2%
Current ratio: 3.10
Cash ($ mil.): 75

HEALTH RESEARCH, INC.

Health Research Inc. (HRI) knows where the money is. The group is a not-for-profit organization that helps the New York State Department of Health and its affiliated Roswell Park Cancer Institute solicit evaluate and administer financial support. Sources of that support come from federal and state government sources other non-profits and businesses. HRI's Technology Transfer office also assists the Department of Health in sharing its research findings with other public and private institutions and finding ways to create biomedical technologies through private sector development. HRI was founded in 1953 and has administered $7 billion over its lifetime.

EXECUTIVES

Exec Dir, Cheryl A Mattox
Exec Dir*, Cheryl Mattox
Law Specialist, Nicole McMillin
Scientist, Vincent Escuyer
Administrative Assistant II, Catherine Janese
Graduate Research Assistant, Trisha Winchester
Senior Operations Clerk Accts, Domenica Terry
Research Scientist, Gene Shackmann
Director of Information Techno, John Bintz
Biostatistician, Lawrence Schoen
Microbiology Researcher, Maureen Shail
Auditors: BONADIO & CO LLP ALBANY NE

LOCATIONS

HQ: HEALTH RESEARCH, INC.
150 BROADWAY STE 560, MENANDS, NY 122042726
Phone: 518 431-1200
Web: WWW.HRINET.ORG

HISTORICAL FINANCIALS

Company Type: Private

Income Statement — FYE: March 31

	REVENUE ($ mil.)	NET INCOME ($ mil.)	NET PROFIT MARGIN	EMPLOYEES
03/15	677	22	3.3%	1,400
03/14	703	13	1.9%	—
03/13	665	25	3.9%	—
03/12	661	(10)	—	—
Annual Growth	0.8%	—	—	—

2015 Year-End Financials

Return on assets: 4.5%
Return on equity: 29.8%
Current ratio: —
Cash ($ mil.): 187

HEALTHPARTNERS, INC.

EXECUTIVES

Pres-Ceo, Mary Brainerd
Exec V Pres-Chief Mktg Offcr*, Andrea Walsh
Cfo*, David A Dziuk
Coordinator, Renee Hannan
Team Leader Appl, Chao Nguyen
Admin Asst, Kristi Brandt
Senior Director, Frank Muller
Business Analyst, Laurie Lorence
Project Coordinator, Lesley Pereira
Information Specialist, Milagros Ogania
Information Specialist, Pierre Gingerichboberg
Auditors: KPMG LLP MINNEAPOLIS MINNES

LOCATIONS

HQ: HEALTHPARTNERS, INC.
8170 33RD AVE S, BLOOMINGTON, MN 554254516
Phone: 952 883-6000
Web: WWW.HEALTHPARTNERS.COM

HISTORICAL FINANCIALS

Company Type: Private

Income Statement — FYE: December 31

	REVENUE ($ mil.)	NET INCOME ($ mil.)	NET PROFIT MARGIN	EMPLOYEES
12/19	7,251	278	3.8%	22,000
12/18	7,061	143	2.0%	—
12/97	1,247	(2)	—	—
12/96	1,178	9	0.8%	—
Annual Growth	8.2%	16.0%	—	—

2019 Year-End Financials

Return on assets: 5.0%
Return on equity: 8.6%
Current ratio: 2.00
Cash ($ mil.): 842

HEARTLAND CO-OP

Heartland Co-op has no need to go against the grain. The cooperative offers agricultural products and services for its central Iowa member/farmers. Heartland operates more than 50 grain elevators and service centers. It offers agronomy products and services such as seed treatments and alfalfa fertilization; grain drying storage and merchandising; petroleum products for farm vehicles and home heating; livestock and pet feed; and personal and crop credit and financing. Headquartered in West Des Moines Heartland was formed in 1987 when cooperatives in Dallas Center Minburn and Panora merged. Heartland which has grown to more than 5400-members merged with Farm Service Company of Council Bluffs in 2013.

Operations

Heartland Co-op operates more than 60 cooperatives in Iowa.

Geographic Reach

Iowa-based Heartland Co-op operates across its home state in the cities of Blairstown Luzerne Chelsea Elberon Conroy Hartwick Marengo Malcom and Montezuma.

Strategy

Heartland Co-op has grown through consolidation and mergers with many smaller cooperatives.

Mergers and Acquisitions

Heartland Co-op acquired Farm Service Company (FSC) in Council Bluffs Iowa in August 2013. The combination of the two extended Heartland's reach westward in Iowa. The corporate offices of the combined operation remains in West Des Moines in Central Iowa.

It sold its service station business in 2012 as it was deemed non-core.

EXECUTIVES

Vice President Sales And Marketing, Dave Coppess
Executive Vice President, Marc Melhus
Executive Vice President, Todd Phillips
Auditors: BERGAN PAULSEN & COMPANY PC

LOCATIONS

HQ: HEARTLAND CO-OP
2829 WESTOWN PKWY STE 350, WEST DES MOINES, IA 502661340
Phone: 515 225-1334
Web: WWW.HEARTLANDCOOP.COM

PRODUCTS/OPERATIONS

Selected Products & Services
Crop Nutrition
Seed Solutions
Precision Ag Services
Agronomy Services
Crop Protection Products

COMPETITORS

ADM
Ag Processing Inc.
CHS
Cargill
Farm Service Cooperative
Farmers Cooperative Company
Farmers Cooperative Society
Five Star Co-op
IVESCO
Orscheln Farm and Home
Pioneer Hi-Bred
Pro-Fac
West Central Co-op

HISTORICAL FINANCIALS

Company Type: Private

Income Statement — FYE: June 30

	REVENUE ($ mil.)	NET INCOME ($ mil.)	NET PROFIT MARGIN	EMPLOYEES
06/19	867	17	2.0%	678
06/18	901	20	2.2%	—
06/17	932	17	1.9%	—
06/16	854	15	1.9%	—
Annual Growth	0.5%	3.5%	—	—

HEARTLAND PAYMENT SYSTEMS, LLC

Heartland Payment Systems (HPS) a wholly owned subsidiary of Global Payments Inc. makes sure plastic-card transactions don't get lost along their way. The company performs credit debit and prepaid card processing services at some 300000 locations nationwide. Its client list includes restaurants retailers convenience stores and professional service providers. The Heartland Payroll Solutions segment provides payroll processing such as check printing and direct deposit for more than 10000 customers. Other markets for the firm include K-12 school nutrition programs and payment processing for colleges and universities. Global Payments bought Heartland for $4.3 billion in 2016.

Change in Company Type

Atlanta-based payment technology firm Global Payments acquired Heartland Payment Systems in its largest acquisition to-date in 2016. Through that purchase it expanded its presence in the US small and mid-sized commercial customer market and added new merchant customers. Operating results of HPS are now reported as part of the Global Payments? North American segment.

Operations

Heartland primarily offers card payment processing and related services to small and midsized merchants and network services merchants. Its Campus Solutions unit provides payment processing integrated commerce solutions higher education loan services and open/closed loop payment solutions. Heartland School Solutions provides school nutrition and point-of-sale and related payment services to K-12 schools while Heartland Payroll Solutions provides payroll processing and related tax filing services. Other activities include electronic check processing gift card marketing and processing online payments and the sale and rental of point-of-sale processing equipment.

Geographic Reach

Princeton NJ-based Heartland Payment Systems serves customers throughout the US. The largest centers of its small and medium-sized business merchants are in California Texas Florida New York and Pennsylvania which together represent more than 30% of card processing volume. Its network services merchants are predominantly gas stations located throughout the US.

Sales and Marketing

The company serves small and midsized customers in a variety of businesses including restaurant hospitality education parking and retail. The network service segment primarily serves gas station merchants.

The firm employs sales professionals and relationship managers to build and maintain direct customer relationships.

Strategy

HPS is addressing the fast growth of mobile payments launching a variety of mobile applications in recent years to take advantage of the opportunity. The firm continues to nurture its Heartland Mobile and Online Ordering platform which allows smaller restaurants to accept mobile orders and payments. It also tends to the growth of its OneCard Mobile application which serves as a ?one-for-all? card for university students. The card is issued by campus administrators and serves as a virtual ID card and payment system for all campus services and activities and for permission-based access to events buildings rooms libraries and other facilities.

EXECUTIVES

Ceo, Robert O Carr
Co-Pres*, Michael A Lawler
Co-Pres*, David Gilbert
Cfo*, Samir Zabaneh
Clo-Gen Counsel*, Charles Kallenbach
Coo*, Conan Lane
Cbo*, Michael McMillan
Cso*, Marty Moretti
Cso*, John R South
Cao*, Joseph E White
Cto*, Bryan Thompson
Auditors: DELOITTE & TOUCHE LLP PHILADE

LOCATIONS

HQ: HEARTLAND PAYMENT SYSTEMS, LLC
10 GLENLAKE PKWY STE 324, ATLANTA, GA 303283495
Phone: 609 683-3831
Web: WWW.HEARTLANDPAYMENTSYSTEMS.COM

PRODUCTS/OPERATIONS

Products:
Billing Solutions
E-Commerce
Gift Cards
Internet of Things
Lending
Loyalty Program
Mobile Ordering
Mobile Payment
Payroll Services
Point of Sale Processing
School Nutrition
School Payment

COMPETITORS

Banc of America Merchant Services
Cardtronics
Chase Paymentech Solutions
Comdata
Deluxe Corporation
ECHO Inc.
Elavon
Fidelity National Information Services
Fifth Third
First Data
Fiserv
Fujitsu America
Total System Services
Vantiv
Wells Fargo
iPayment

HISTORICAL FINANCIALS

Company Type: Private

Income Statement — FYE: December 31

	REVENUE ($ mil.)	NET INCOME ($ mil.)	NET PROFIT MARGIN	EMPLOYEES
12/15	2,682	84	3.2%	3,734
12/14	2,311	31	1.4%	—
12/13	2,135	78	3.7%	—
12/12	2,013	66	3.3%	—
Annual Growth	10.0%	8.4%	—	—

2015 Year-End Financials

Return on assets: 5.5%
Return on equity: 25.2%
Current ratio: 0.90
Cash ($ mil.): 56

HEARTLAND REGIONAL MEDICAL CENTER

Heartland Regional Medical Center strives for healthy hearts minds and bodies in the US heartland. The acute care hospital a subsidiary of Heartland Health provides medical services to residents of St. Joseph Missouri and some 20 surrounding counties in northwest Missouri southeast Nebraska and northeast Kansas. Heartland Regional Medical Center encompasses specialty centers for trauma and long-term care acute rehabilitation cancer heart disease and birthing. As part of the services provided by the medical center Heartland Regional Medical Center offers services such as arthritis pain and wound treatments as well as home health and hospice care.

Geographic Reach

Operating in Missouri Heartland Regional Medical Center serves the residents and visitors of its home state as well as those in Nebraska and Kansas. Altogether the medical center caters to a more than 20-county area.

Financial Performance

In fiscal 2012 as compared to 2011 Heartland Regional Medical Center's revenue rose some 8% and its net income saw a 31% boost.

Strategy

As part of its operations Heartland Regional Medical Center partners with several managed care organizations such as Aetna CCN Managed Care Coventry Healthcare and Blue Cross Blue Shield of Kansas City to give its patients payment options for its health services. In 2012 Heartland Regional Medical Center developed an accountable care organization. It's a participant in the Medicare Shared Savings Program and enters into other similar shared savings arrangements with commercial self-insured or other third-party payors.

In recent years the medical facility has been investing in growing its footprint. Heartland Regional Medical Center is funding a $55-million expansion project that includes adding a handful of new operating rooms and renovating 10 more.

EXECUTIVES

Chm, Alfred L Purcell
Ceo*, Mark Laney
SEC*, John Wilson
Data Warehouse Arch, Andrew Bramlage
Chief of Pediatrics, Carmen Ford
Chief of Radiology, David Mena
Physical Therapy Director, Elena Schultz
Utilization Review Director, Elizabeth Jalbert
Records Director, Ellen Ellis
Director of Home SE, James McMillen
Laboratory Director, Jennifer Sapp
Auditors: BLD LLP KANSAS CITY MISSOUR

LOCATIONS

HQ: HEARTLAND REGIONAL MEDICAL CENTER
5325 FARAON ST, SAINT JOSEPH, MO 645063488
Phone: 816 271-6000
Web: WWW.MYMLC.COM

PRODUCTS/OPERATIONS

Selected Services

Appendectomy

Cholecystectomy
Colon Resection
Hernia Repair
Nephrectomy
Assisted Vaginal Hysterectomy
Peritoneal Dialysis Catheter Placement
Pyloromyotomy
Tubal Ligation
Abdominal Perineal Resection
Adrenalectomy
Colostomy
Gastric Banding
Gastric Bypass
Gastric Sleeve
Gastrostomy Tube Placement
Laser Lysis of Adhesions/Endometriosis
Nissan Fundoplication
Salpingo-Oophorectomy
Prostatectomy

COMPETITORS

Ascension Health
BJC HealthCare
Catholic Health Initiatives
Children's Mercy Hospital
CoxHealth
Mercy Health
Saint Luke's Health System
Shawnee Mission Medical Center
Sisters of Charity of Leavenworth
Truman Medical Centers
University of Kansas Medical Center

HISTORICAL FINANCIALS

Company Type: Private

Income Statement — FYE: June 30

	REVENUE ($ mil.)	NET INCOME ($ mil.)	NET PROFIT MARGIN	EMPLOYEES
06/19	645	38	5.9%	4,000
06/18	639	64	10.1%	—
06/17	605	26	4.4%	—
06/16	562	(5)	—	—
Annual Growth	4.7%	—	—	—

2019 Year-End Financials

Return on assets: 3.6%
Return on equity: 6.1%
Current ratio: 6.00
Cash ($ mil.): 18

HELM FERTILIZER CORPORATION (FLORIDA)

EXECUTIVES

Pres, Dale Miller
Cfo, Chris Carollo
Dir, Hans Christian Sievers
Vice President, Dennis Albarus
Auditors: ISRAELOFF TRATTNER & CO PC

LOCATIONS

HQ: HELM FERTILIZER CORPORATION (FLORIDA)
401 E JACKSON ST STE 1400, TAMPA, FL 336025264
Phone: 813 621-8846
Web: WWW.HELMAGRO.COM

HISTORICAL FINANCIALS

Company Type: Private

Income Statement — FYE: December 31

	REVENUE ($ mil.)	NET INCOME ($ mil.)	NET PROFIT MARGIN	EMPLOYEES
12/13	611	5	0.9%	28
12/12	947	11	1.2%	—
12/11	1,056	10	1.0%	—
12/10	667	6	1.0%	—
Annual Growth	(2.9%)	(6.7%)	—	—

2013 Year-End Financials

Return on assets: 7.6%
Return on equity: 24.4%
Current ratio: 1.40
Cash ($ mil.): —

HENDRICKS COUNTY HOSPITAL

EXECUTIVES

Jd, Ceo, Kevin P Speer
Cfo, Isadore Rivas
Assistant, Anita Dieckmann
Coordinator, Stephanie Jones
Anesthesiologist, Clint Myers
Manager, Stacey Bulla
Therapist, Amy Barton
Director of Wellness and Popul, Jennifer Bates
Event Marketing Specialist, Julie Arnold
Director Support, Kevin McGovern
Team Leader Support, Linda McCammack
Auditors: BLUE & CO LLC INDIANAPOLIS

LOCATIONS

HQ: HENDRICKS COUNTY HOSPITAL
1000 E MAIN ST, DANVILLE, IN 461221991
Phone: 317 745-4451
Web: WWW.DANVILLEPEDS.COM

HISTORICAL FINANCIALS

Company Type: Private

Income Statement — FYE: December 31

	REVENUE ($ mil.)	NET INCOME ($ mil.)	NET PROFIT MARGIN	EMPLOYEES
12/19	747	13	1.8%	1,700
12/18	605	(25)	—	—
12/17	550	39	7.1%	—
12/16	530	43	8.2%	—
Annual Growth	12.1%	(32.5%)	—	—

2019 Year-End Financials

Return on assets: 1.9%
Return on equity: 3.1%
Current ratio: 1.30
Cash ($ mil.): 20

HENNEPIN HEALTHCARE SYSTEM, INC.

EXECUTIVES

Ceo, Jennifer Decubellis
Internal Medicine Practitioner, Rachel Sandler
Coordinator, Jennifer Kelley
Coordinator, Kris Hoplin
Gastroenterologist, Aaron Brosam
Internist, Danielle Haselby
Nephrologist, David Dahl
Pediatrician, Dawn Martin
Psychiatrist, Erica Mitchell
Otolaryngologist, George Goding
Chemistry, Jennifer Nicholson

LOCATIONS

HQ: HENNEPIN HEALTHCARE SYSTEM, INC.
701 PARK AVE, MINNEAPOLIS, MN 554151623
Phone: 612 873-3000
Web: WWW.HENNEPINHEALTHCARE.ORG

HISTORICAL FINANCIALS

Company Type: Private

Income Statement — FYE: December 31

	REVENUE ($ mil.)	NET INCOME ($ mil.)	NET PROFIT MARGIN	EMPLOYEES
12/18	950	13	1.4%	5,000
12/17	1,011	(19)	—	—
Annual Growth	(6.0%)	—	—	—

2018 Year-End Financials

Return on assets: 1.7%
Return on equity: 55.5%
Current ratio: 2.00
Cash ($ mil.): 38

HENRY FORD HEALTH SYSTEM

Not-for-profit Henry Ford Health System (HFHS) operates a network of medical facilities in Detroit and nearby communities. The system's half-dozen hospitals — including the flagship Henry Ford Hospital the Henry Ford Wyandotte Hospital and mental health facility Kingswood Hospital – are home to roughly 2400 beds. HFHS also operates a 1300-physician medical group (with more than 40 specialties) as well as nursing homes a hospice provider a home health care network and research and education centers. The system's Health Alliance Plan of Michigan provides managed care and health insurance to more than half a million members.

Strategy

HFHS is working to make health care more affordable for patients by improving efficiencies in both its care model and its business operations. Recent efforts to improve patient services include enacting new safety protocols and promoting virtual (telehealth) patient visits.

The company regularly upgrades or expands its facilities to provide state-of-the-art care and attract new patients and skilled health professionals. It invested $55 million to add a 66-bed patient tower and a medical education center to the Henry Ford Allegiance Health hospital campus in 2018. HFHS also partnered with the Detroit Pistons to construct a sports medicine facility (completed in 2019) and it is constructing a new Detroit cancer center the Brigitte Harris Cancer Pavilion (scheduled to open in 2020).

HFHS seeks to advance the medical profession by providing medical research and training programs. The Henry Ford Innovation Institute allows the network's specialists to engage in clinical research projects. The Henry Ford Hospital serves as an academic training center for the Wayne State University School of Medicine.

The company relies on payments from third parties for the majority of its income with reimbursements from Medicaid Medicare and commercial insurers making up the bulk of revenue. This can result in delayed payments if claims are denied. The company may also be vulnerable to reimbursement reduction decisions or non-payments from self-pay customers.

Company Background

Automaker Henry Ford founded Henry Ford Hospital in 1915.

The Health Alliance Plan became part of the Henry Ford Health System in 1986.

In 2016 Allegiance Health which operated a hospital and other health facilities in Jackson joined the Henry Ford Health System and began operating as Henry Ford Allegiance Health.

EXECUTIVES

Vice President, David Mazurkiewicz
Evp; President And Ceo Health Alliance Plan, James M. Connelly
Ceo, Nancy M. Schlichting
Svp And Coo Henry Ford Hospital And Health Network, Robert G. (Bob) Riney
President, Wright L. Lassiter, age 57
Chairman Department Of Medicine Henry Ford Hospital, John Popovich
President And Ceo Community Care Services, John J. Polanski
Evp And Cfo, Edward G. (Ed) Chadwick
Evp; Ceo Henry Ford Medical Group, William A. Conway
President And Ceo Henry Ford West Bloomfield Hospital, Lynn M. Torossian
President And Ceo Henry Ford Wyandotte Hospital, Denise Brooks-Williams
Chief Nursing Officer; Coo Henry Ford Hospital, Veronica M. Hall
President And Ceo Henry Ford Macomb Hospitals, Barbara W. Rossmann
Svp Community Health And Equity; Chief Wellness Officer, Kimberlydawn Wisdom
Svp And Cio, Mary Alice Annecharico
Medical Director, Nabil Khoury
Senior Vice President Is Clinical Integration And Transformation, Michelle Schreiber
Senior Vice President Strategic Business Development, William Schramm
Director Of Radiology, John W Bonnett
Director Of Radiology, Derrick Harper
Vice President, James O'connor
Senior Vice President And Chief Human Resources Officer, Kathy Oswald
Vice President Clinical Transformation And Information Technology Integration, Matt Walsh
Vice President, Mike Ellis
Director Of Radiology, Jay Pearlberg
Director Of Radiology, Mark I Burnstein
Director Of Radiology, Sabala R Mandava
Director Of Radiology, William P Sanders
Senior Vice President And Chief Development Officer, Mary Vogt
Medical Director Of Perioperative Services, Gaylord Alexander
Vice President Of Finance, Asad Malik
Vice President Of Information Technology Applications, Josephine Molle
Director Of Radiology, David Mcvinnie
Director Of Radiology, Daniel Croteau
Medical Records Director, SUSAN GLEASON
Vice President Physician Development, Timothy Ryan
Vice President Andamp; Medical Director, Usamah Mossallam
Vice President, Linda Gifford
Vice President Hospital And Clinic Services, Linda Fisher
Executive Vice President And Chief Strategy Officer, Seth Frazier
Medical Director, William O'neill
Svp And Cio, Paul Browne
Regional Vice President, Paul Szilagyi
Vice President Heart And Vascular Services, Ruth Fisher
Vice President Corporate Government Affairs, Marc Corriveau
Medical Director, Gwendolyn Graddy
Vice President Revenue Cycle, Kevin Oneill
Medical Director, Christopher Lewandowski
Vice President Associate General Counsel, Alice Macdermott
Executive Vice President, Munkarah Adnan
Vice President Human Resources, Aline Lafferty
Member Of The Board Of Directors Board Of Directors, Paul Edwards
Secretary, Jasmine Parks
Secretary, Stacey Johnson
Secretary Iii, Alicia Bias
Vice Chairman Department Of Surgery, Arthur Carlin
Secretary, Mary Cantu
Secretary, Barbara Paul
Secretary Ii, Paulette Wojcik
Secretary Iii, Marcia Hendrick
Medical Secretary, Diana Popp
Auditors: DELOITTE & TOUCHE LLP DETROI

LOCATIONS

HQ: HENRY FORD HEALTH SYSTEM
1 FORD PL, DETROIT, MI 482023450
Phone: 313 916-2600
Web: WWW.HENRYFORD.COM

HOSPITAL LOCATIONS

Henry Ford Allegiance Health
Henry Ford Hospital
Henry Ford Kingswood Hospital
Henry Ford Macomb Hospital - Clinton Township
Henry Ford West Bloomfield Hospital
Henry Ford Wyandotte Hospital

PRODUCTS/OPERATIONS

SELECTED SERVICES

Bariatric Surgery
Cancer
Heart & Vascular
Neurology & Neurosurgery
OptimEyes
Orthopedic Surgery
Primary Care
Transplant Services

COMPETITORS

Ascension Health
Beaumont Health System
Crittenton Hospital
Detroit Medical Center
Garden City Hospital
Harper-Hutzel Hospital
McLaren Health Care
Mount Clemens Regional Medical Center
OmniCare Health Plan
St. John Health
Total Health Care
Trinity Health (Novi)
University of Michigan Health System

HISTORICAL FINANCIALS

Company Type: Private

Income Statement — FYE: December 31

	REVENUE ($ mil.)	NET INCOME ($ mil.)	NET PROFIT MARGIN	EMPLOYEES
12/18	5,853	89	1.5%	23,000
12/17	5,977	203	3.4%	—
12/14	1,513	(13)	—	—
12/13	4,517	135	3.0%	—
Annual Growth	5.3%	(8.0%)	—	—

2018 Year-End Financials

Return on assets: 2.0%
Return on equity: 4.2%
Current ratio: 1.50
Cash ($ mil.): 556

HENRY MODELL & COMPANY, INC.

A model corporate citizen retailer Henry Modell & Company sells sporting goods fitness equipment apparel and brand-name athletic footwear as America's oldest family-owned and -operated sporting goods retailer. Established in 1889 it has over 150 stores throughout the Northeast. Its top brands are Asics Champion Adidas and Converse to name a few. It also offers fan gear such as jerseys for football. It also boasts an online presence at Modells.com. Additionally it has stores in New Hampshire Delaware and Maryland. The company was founded by Morris A. Modell.

Operations

The company offers various products including but not limited to: sporting goods athletic footwear active apparel and fan gear.

Geographic Reach

The company offers various products including but not limited to: sporting goods athletic footwear active apparel and fan gear.

Sales and Marketing

Modell's markets and sells its products through its stores and online.

Company Background

Hungarian immigrant Morris Modell first sold menswear from a Lower East Side pushcart in New York City before he founded Henry Modell & Company in 1889. Led by CEO Mitchell Modell the company is operated by the fourth generation of the Modell family.

EXECUTIVES

Ceo, Mitchell B. (Mitch) Modell
Vp Information Technology, Hans Kantor

Vp Finance Controller, Joe Paltenstein
Vp Of Planning, Rob Stein
Vice President, Willy Kaplan
Auditors: BDO USA LLP NEW YORK NY

LOCATIONS

HQ: HENRY MODELL & COMPANY, INC.
498 7TH AVE FL 20, NEW YORK, NY 100186738
Phone: 212 822-1000
Web: WWW.MODELLS.COM

2016 Locations

	No.
New York	71
New Jersey	38
Pennsylvania	18
Maryland	9
Connecticut	6
Massachusetts	7
Virginia	5
District of Columbia	2
New Hampshire	2
Delaware	1
Rhode Island	1
Total	**160**

PRODUCTS/OPERATIONS

Selected Product Categories

Accessories

Apparel

Baseball

Basketball
Boxing/martial arts
Camping/hiking
Cycling
Electronics/optics
Fan shop-pro/college
Field hockey
Fishing
Fitness
Football
Footwear
Games
Golf
Ice/roller hockey
In-Line/roller skating
Lacrosse
Optics/telescopes
Outdoor recreation
Paintball
Pilates
Racquetball/squash
Roller hockey
Rugby
Running
Scooters
Skateboarding
Snow sports
Soccer
Softball
Tennis
Water recreation
Winter recreation
Wrestling
Yoga

COMPETITORS

Athleta
Dick's Sporting Goods
Dunham's
Eastern Mountain Sports
Foot Locker
Hat World
Olympia Sports
Sports Authority
Target Corporation
Wal-Mart

HISTORICAL FINANCIALS

Company Type: Private

Income Statement — FYE: February 2

	REVENUE ($ mil.)	NET INCOME ($ mil.)	NET PROFIT MARGIN	EMPLOYEES
02/13*	607	0	0.1%	5,430
01/12	570	(3)	—	—
01/11	558	(7)	—	—
Annual Growth	4.3%	—	—	—

*Fiscal year change

2013 Year-End Financials

Return on assets: 0.3%
Return on equity: 1.7%
Current ratio: 1.10
Cash ($ mil.): 3

HENSEL PHELPS CONSTRUCTION CO.

Hensel Phelps Construction builds it all from the courthouse to the big house. The employee-owned general contractor provides a full range of development pre-construction construction and renovation services for commercial institutional and government projects throughout the US. Its project portfolio includes prisons airports arenas laboratories government complexes offices and more. Major public and private clients have included the US Intercontinental San Diego Masonic Temple Hotel NASA Samsung US Air Force and Cinépolis Luxury Cinema. Hensel Phelps founded the eponymous company as a homebuilder in 1937.

Operations

The company also offers virtual design and construction (VDC) life-cycle cost analysis prefabrication and modularization as well as specialized construction solutions for small projects including renovations and retrofitting of existing facilities. Its facility services include asset management and preservation integrated facility management (FM) and it offers mobile maintenance service that dispatched technicians perform thorough inspections preventative maintenance and repair of building systems.

Geographic Reach

Colorado-based Hensel Phelps Construction has nearly ten regional offices throughout the continental US including two in California. Its Honolulu branch oversees operations in Hawaii Guam as well as Asia and other Pacific Islands.

Sales and Marketing

Sectors served include aviation commercial education government health care hospitality industrial technology and justice. Its public and private clients have included the University of Texas Hotel Indigo United Airlines Los Angeles International Airport and Universal Studios.

Strategy

Hensel Phelps Construction is always looking to revamp its tools to create new efficiencies that translate into better value for its clients faster building schedules and real-time project reporting for progress and financials. Whether it is using Building Information Models (BIM) or MEO its real-time cloud-based integrated building and management technology solutions utilizing technology is a critical component of the Hensel Phelps Way.

Hensel Phelps also continues adding projects to its portfolio. In mid-2020 Hensel Phelps completed the construction of the new Concourse D at Nashville International Airport (BNA). The Concourse D and Terminal Wings Expansion Project is a major project of the aggressive seven-year plant set out by BNA to rapidly expand the airport's capacity.

Hensel Phelps was also recently awarded two projects the Operations Building 1 and Central Utility Plant (OPS1 & CUP) and the North Campus Commons and Technology Building at Redstone Arsenal in Huntsville Alabama. The buildings will reach substantial completion in April 2021 and Hensel Phelps is looking forward to the opportunity to grow its presence in Huntsville Alabama and build relationships with new trade partners in the region.

Company Background

Hensel Phelps founded the eponymous company as a homebuilder in 1937. Operations initially were limited to home building and remodeling after which competitive contract work was undertaken on a limited scale.

EXECUTIVES

President Phelps Development, Eric L. Wilson
Cfo, Stephen J. (Steve) Carrico
Evp, Wayne S. Lindholm
Evp, Jon W. Ball
President And Ceo, Jeffrey K. (Jeff) Wenaas
Evp, Michael J. Choutka
Evp, Richard G. Tucker
President Hensel Phelps Services, Edwin (Glen) Miller
Auditors: KPMG LLP DENVER CO

LOCATIONS

HQ: HENSEL PHELPS CONSTRUCTION CO.
420 6TH AVE, GREELEY, CO 806312332
Phone: 970 352-6565
Web: WWW.HENSELPHELPS.COM

PRODUCTS/OPERATIONS

Selected Projects

Hilton Hok
Aegis Asho
Regional 0

Guam NAVFAC Bachelor Enlisted Quarters (BEQ)
Mamizu Utilities and Site Improvements Phase I
Samaritan MOB and Parking Structure
Santa Clara Valley Medical Center Receiving and Support Center
Santa Clara Family Justice Center
Santa Clara Valley Medical Center Receiving and Support Center
Rotary PlayGarden
Norman Y. Mineta San José; International Airport Terminal Area Improvement Program (TAIP)
Vantage Data Center V2
Vantage Data Center V1

Selected Services

Construction
- Change management
- Construction waste management
- LEED project registration
- Quality control
- Safety management
- Scheduling
- Self-perfoming concrete
- Status reporting
- Subcontractor management
- Sustainability audits
- Quality control

Development
- Feasibility studies
- Financing
- Green building planning/education
- Land acquisition
- Leasing
- Pro forma review

Post-construction
- As-built documentation
- Building operations
- Certificate of occupancy

Commissioning and warranty programs
LEED project certification
Moving services
Preconstruction
Bid packaging
Budgeting/cost modeling
Design management
Estimating
Green building and planning/education
Phasing plans
Regulatory investigation
Scheduling
Status reporting
Subcontractor prequalification
Value engineering

Selected Markets

Commercial
Education
High technology
Industrial
International
Justice
Leisure
Medical
Multiresidence
Public
Transportation

COMPETITORS

Balfour Beatty Construction
C.F. Jordan
Clark Construction Group
Fluor
Gilbane
Hunt Construction
Jacobs Engineering
KBR
M. A. Mortenson
McCarthy Building
PCL Employees Holdings
Rooney Holdings
Skanska USA Building
Turner Corporation
Tutor Perini
Walbridge Aldinger
Walsh Group
Whiting-Turner

HISTORICAL FINANCIALS

Company Type: Private

Income Statement — FYE: December 31

	REVENUE ($ mil.)	NET INCOME ($ mil.)	NET PROFIT MARGIN	EMPLOYEES
12/19	5,676	177	3.1%	2,000
12/18	4,604	131	2.9%	—
12/17	3,360	80	2.4%	—
12/16	3,540	76	2.2%	—
Annual Growth	17.0%	32.4%	—	—

2019 Year-End Financials

Return on assets: 8.5%
Return on equity: 53.7%
Current ratio: 1.30
Cash ($ mil.): 561

HIGHER EDUCATION COORDINATING BOARD, TEXAS

EXECUTIVES

President, Raymund Paredes
Accounting Staff, Ai-Ching Reed
Accounting Staff, Charlie Cannon
Accounting Staff, Daniel Flores
Accounting Staff, Jannice Smith
Accounting Staff, Manuel Ortiz
Accounting Staff, Susan Schroeder
Accountant, Angela Burnett
Information Specialist, Heidi Langdon
Compliance Staff, Jamyen Robinson-Hall
Information Technology Manager, Linda Barrera

LOCATIONS

HQ: HIGHER EDUCATION COORDINATING BOARD, TEXAS
1200 E ANDERSON LN, AUSTIN, TX 787521706
Phone: 512 427-6100
Web: WWW.THECB.STATE.TX.US

HISTORICAL FINANCIALS

Company Type: Private

Income Statement — FYE: August 31

	REVENUE ($ mil.)	NET INCOME ($ mil.)	NET PROFIT MARGIN	EMPLOYEES
08/18	1,732	73	4.2%	290
08/03	1,116	(42)	—	—
08/02	0	0	—	—
08/01	0	36	—	—
Annual Growth	—	4.3%	—	—

HILAND DAIRY FOODS COMPANY., LLC

Hiland Dairy Foods is a processor and distributor of dairy foods and other beverages. It is a farmer-owned entity giving leverage to its members when negotiating prices and contract terms with buyers of their products. Its farmers' cows produce the raw ingredient for churning out butter ice cream fluid milk cheese yogurt and other dairy products free of artificial growth hormones. Hiland runs ten processing plants and has more than 40 distribution centers. It partners with a larger dairy co-operative Prairie Farms Dairy to market and sell product. Beyond dairy Hiland supplies juices bottled milk and coffee (cravélatté) as well as green tea water and other to-go drinks. It features limited-run specialty items such as peanut butter s'-mores ice cream. Founded in 1938 the farmer-owned venture operates manufacturing plants in the Midwest.

EXECUTIVES

President, Gary L. Aggus
General Manager, Woody Rogers
Auditors: BKD LLP SPRINGFIELD MO

LOCATIONS

HQ: HILAND DAIRY FOODS COMPANY., LLC
1133 E KEARNEY ST, SPRINGFIELD, MO 658033435
Phone: 417 862-9311
Web: WWW.HILANDDAIRY.COM

Selected Plant Locations

Chandler Oklahoma
Fayetteville Arkansas
Fort Smith Arkansas
Kansas City Missouri
Little Rock Arkansas
Norfolk Nebraska
Norman Oklahoma
Omaha Nebraska
Springfield Missouri
Tyler Texas
Wichita Kansas

PRODUCTS/OPERATIONS

Selected Products

Butter
Cheese
Cottage cheese
Cravé;latté; (milk and coffee)
Creams/Half-and-Half
Dips
Egg nog
Egg substitute
Fruit-flavored drinks
Ice cream
Juice
Lactose-free milk
Lemonade
Milk
Sour cream
Tea
To-go drinks
Water
Yogurt

COMPETITORS

Agri-Mark
Associated Milk Producers
Blue Bell
ConAgra
Dairylea
Dean Foods
Dreyer's
Fonterra
Great Lakes Cheese
Hornell Brewing
Land O'Lakes
MMPA
Nestlé
Oberweis Dairy
Organic Valley
Saputo
Sargento
Smith Dairy
Snapple
Wells' Dairy

HISTORICAL FINANCIALS

Company Type: Private

Income Statement — FYE: September 30

	REVENUE ($ mil.)	NET INCOME ($ mil.)	NET PROFIT MARGIN	EMPLOYEES
09/11	958	8	0.9%	1,350
09/10	588	24	4.2%	—
09/09	559	39	7.0%	—
Annual Growth	30.8%	(53.0%)	—	—

2011 Year-End Financials

Return on assets: 2.7%
Return on equity: 3.9%
Current ratio: 2.30
Cash ($ mil.): 19

HILL/AHERN FIRE PROTECTION, LLC

EXECUTIVES

MBR, Michelle Colyar
Sales Project Manager, Jim Lynch
Executive Adminstrative Assist, Julie Chapman
Project Manager, Matt Meyer
Sales Representative, Patricia Colar
Manager, Shannon Coomes

LOCATIONS

HQ: HILL/AHERN FIRE PROTECTION, LLC
11045 GAGE AVE, FRANKLIN PARK, IL 601311437
Phone: 847 288-5100
Web: WWW.HILLGRP.COM

HISTORICAL FINANCIALS

Company Type: Private

Income Statement — FYE: December 31

	REVENUE ($ mil.)	NET INCOME ($ mil.)	NET PROFIT MARGIN	EMPLOYEES
12/11	5,669	185	3.3%	100
12/10	2,568	80	3.1%	—
Annual Growth	120.7%	130.7%	—	—

2011 Year-End Financials

Return on assets: 7.3% Cash ($ mil.): 480
Return on equity: 11.4%
Current ratio: 2.60

HILLSBOROUGH COUNTY SCHOOL DISTRICT

EXECUTIVES

Chm, April Griffin
Superintendent*, Maryellen Elia
V Chm*, Cindy Stuart
MBR*, Susan L Valdes
MBR*, Sally Harris
MBR*, Melissa Snively
Building and Grounds Director, Chris Farkas
Principals Secretary, Lara Leto
Technology Specialist, Stephen Filingeri
Assistant Teacher Technology, Edna Z Colon
Teacher Math, Jean Wilson
Auditors: KPMG LLP TAMPA FL

LOCATIONS

HQ: HILLSBOROUGH COUNTY SCHOOL DISTRICT
901 E KENNEDY BLVD, TAMPA, FL 336023502
Phone: 813 272-4000
Web: WWW.SDHC.K12.FL.US

HISTORICAL FINANCIALS

Company Type: Private

Income Statement FYE: June 30

	REVENUE ($ mil.)	NET INCOME ($ mil.)	NET PROFIT MARGIN	EMPLOYEES
06/16	2,133	(59)	—	25,000
06/15	2,042	(110)	—	—
06/14	1,984	(45)	—	—
06/13	1,878	(44)	—	—
Annual Growth	4.3%	—	—	—

2016 Year-End Financials

Return on assets: (-1.8%) Cash ($ mil.): 113
Return on equity: (-7.6%)
Current ratio: —

HMH HOSPITALS CORPORATION

Hackensack University Medical Center (HUMC) is an acute care teaching and research hospital that serves northern New Jersey and parts of New York. The hospital has about 775 beds and staffs more than 2200 medical professionals. HUMC administers general medical surgical emergency and diagnostic care. The center also includes specialized treatment centers including a children's hospital a women's hospital a cancer center and a heart and vascular hospital. HUMC is part of the Hackensack University Health Network which also includes a physician practice group and a joint venture that operates two community hospitals. In 2016 the network merged with Meridian Health to create Hackensack Meridian Health.

Operations

HUMC helps train future dentists and doctors through its affiliation with the University of Medicine and Dentistry of New Jersey. It expanded its education programs in 2012 by partnering with the Stevens Institute of Technology to offer joint biomedical training programs.

The hospital also performs research through the David Joseph Jurist Research Center for Tomorrow's Children. The center has roughly 475 research programs in operation at any given time.

Financial Performance

Medicare accounts for 29.5% of HUMC's funding; HMOs 28%; and Blue Cross 28%.

Strategy

The company grows organically and through acquisitions partnerships and affiliations.

To expand its services HUMC broke ground on a $35 million project to expand and renovate its trauma and emergency facilities in 2012 (scheduled to open in 2015).

Hackensack University Health Network is increasing its partnerships and affiliations with other regional care providers following the trend of US hospitals seeking to improve and lower the cost of health care through shared services and resources. The network partnered up with Texas-based LPH Hospital Group in 2012 to reenovate the Pascack Valley Hospital (now HackensackUMC Pascack) in Westwood New Jersey. Hackensack took over the bankrupt facility's ER back in 2007 and in 2012 the joint venture launched a $90 million project to revamp the rest of the 130-bed acute-care community hospital. It reopened in 2013.

Hackensack University Health Network also formed a joint venture with an area physician group to open two ambulatory surgery centers in 2012 and it entered a collaboration with CVS Health's MinuteClinic to open new urgent care centers.

That year HUMC formed a joint venture partnership with community physicians and United Surgical Partners International to buy and operate ambulatory surgery centers in Bergen County: Hackensack Endoscopy Center and the Endoscopy Center of Bergen County.

Mergers and Acquisitions

In 2015 the Hackensack University Health Network agreed to merge with fellow New Jersey care provider Meridian Health. The combined system to be named Hackensack Meridian Health will have 11 hospitals and two children's hospitals. The deal which is one of a number of consolidation efforts by hospitals in the state is pending regulatory approval.

Company Background

To simplify its operations HUMC sold its hospice operations to Amedisys in 2011. The health provider previously sold its home health agency to Amedisys in 2009 to generate revenue and control costs after struggling with financial losses throughout the year due to declining admissions.

HUMC completed construction of its new John Theurer Cancer Center in late 2010 giving it one of the largest comprehensive cancer centers in the US. The center includes diagnostic and treatment units that focus on specific types of cancers.

HUMC was founded as a hospital in 1888 with 12 beds.

EXECUTIVES

Chairman Department Of Ophthamology, Michael Rosenberg
Auditors: PRICEWATERHOUSECOOPERS LLP NE

LOCATIONS

HQ: HMH HOSPITALS CORPORATION
343 THORNALL ST, EDISON, NJ 088372206
Phone: 201 996-2000
Web: WWW.HACKENSACKUMC.ORG

PRODUCTS/OPERATIONS

Selected Services

Donna A. Sanzari Women's Hospital
Emergency Services
Heart & Vascular Hospital
Hospital Services
John Theurer Cancer Center
Joseph M. Sanzari Children's Hospital
Medical
Specialized
Surgical
Tackle Kids Cancer

Selected Facilities

Donna A. Sanzari Women's Hospital
Hackensack University Medical Center Mountainside
Hackensack University Medical Center Pascack
Heart & Vascular Hospital
John Theurer Cancer Center
Joseph M. Sanzari Children's Hospital
Tomorrows Children's Institute for Cancer and Blood Disorders

COMPETITORS

Bergen Regional Medical
Bronx-Lebanon Hospital
Continuum Health Partners
Englewood Hospital and Medical Center
Hospital for Special Surgery
Lenox Hill Hospital
Montefiore Medical
NewYork-Presbyterian Healthcare
Newark Beth Israel Medical Center
St. Joseph's Healthcare System
Valley Health System

HISTORICAL FINANCIALS

Company Type: Private

Income Statement FYE: December 31

	REVENUE ($ mil.)	NET INCOME ($ mil.)	NET PROFIT MARGIN	EMPLOYEES
12/18	3,999	220	5.5%	1,100
12/16	1,707	41	2.4%	—
12/15	1,357	83	6.1%	—
12/14	1,309	106	8.1%	—
Annual Growth	32.2%	19.9%	—	—

2018 Year-End Financials

Return on assets: 5.7% Cash ($ mil.): 202
Return on equity: 8.6%
Current ratio: 1.50

HMO MINNESOTA

EXECUTIVES

Eo, Andrew Czajkowski
Chb*, Jonathon Killmer
Cfo*, Tim Peterson

LOCATIONS

HQ: HMO MINNESOTA
3535 BLUE CROSS RD, SAINT PAUL, MN 551221154
Phone: 952 456-8434

HISTORICAL FINANCIALS

Company Type: Private

Income Statement FYE: December 31

	REVENUE ($ mil.)	NET INCOME ($ mil.)	NET PROFIT MARGIN	EMPLOYEES
12/16	1,839	(156)	—	40
12/15	918	52	5.7%	—
12/14	850	85	10.1%	—
12/09	978	30	3.1%	—
Annual Growth	9.4%	—	—	—

2016 Year-End Financials

Return on assets: (-18.0%) Cash ($ mil.): 108
Return on equity: (-36.6%)
Current ratio: —

HOAG MEMORIAL HOSPITAL PRESBYTERIAN

Serving California's Orange County population Hoag Memorial Hospital Presbyterian boasts several hospitals and even more clinics to cater to area residents. The not-for-profit health care system is home to two acute care hospitals seven health centers five urgent care centers and a network of more than 1500 physicians. Its hospitals include Hoag Hospital Irvine and Hoag Hospital Newport Beach in Southern California. Combined the two hospitals have 617 beds and provide a comprehensive range of medical and surgical services with specialized expertise in a number of areas such as oncology cardiovascular disease neuroscience and orthopedics. Hoag is an affiliate of Providence St. Joseph Health.

EXECUTIVES

President And Ceo, Robert Braithwaite
Svp And Cfo, Jennifer Mitzner
Executive Vice President Chief Operating Officer, Michael Ricks
Medical Director, Richard Doering
Executive Medical Director, Burton Eisenberg
Vice President, Joanne Tucker
Assistant Vice President Speciality Business Development, Cathy Major
Pharm D, Nancy Yano
Director Of Him, Michele Morton
Senior Vice President Of Sales And Marketing, Bruce J Haupt
Board Member, Richard Taketa
Board Member, Kris Iyer
Vice Chairman, Robert Evans
Unit Secretary, Marissa Mastromatteo
Board Member, John Climaco
Board Member, Dimitrios Angelis
Board Member, John Sayward
Board Of Directors, Charles Gillman

LOCATIONS

HQ: HOAG MEMORIAL HOSPITAL PRESBYTERIAN
1 HOAG DR, NEWPORT BEACH, CA 926634162
Phone: 949 764-4624
Web: WWW.HOAG.ORG

COMPETITORS

Adventist Health System West
Anaheim Regional Medical Center
Children's Hospital of Orange County
Citrus Valley Health Partners
Dignity Health
Long Beach Memorial
Memorial Health Services
Pasadena Hospital Association
Saddleback Memorial Medical Center
St. Joseph Hospital of Orange
St. Jude Medical Center
Tenet Healthcare
Torrance Memorial Medical Center
Trinity Health (Novi)
Western Medical Center - Santa Ana

HISTORICAL FINANCIALS

Company Type: Private

Income Statement				FYE: June 30
	REVENUE ($ mil.)	NET INCOME ($ mil.)	NET PROFIT MARGIN	EMPLOYEES
06/16	894	100	11.2%	3,800
06/15	822	107	13.1%	—
/* 0	0	—	—	
Annual Growth	—	—	—	—

*Fiscal year change

2016 Year-End Financials

Return on assets: 3.0% Cash ($ mil.): 189
Return on equity: 5.1%
Current ratio: 1.20

HOBBY LOBBY STORES, INC.

If something wicker this way comes Hobby Lobby Stores may be the source. The craft-and-fabric retailer operates more than 850 stores in the US in more than 45 states selling arts and crafts supplies baskets beads candles frames home-decorating accessories and silk flowers. Hobby Lobby also owns stores in Canada and operates offices in China and Hong Kong. In addition Hobby Lobby operates Mardel Christian and Education Supply which sells Christian educational and homeschooling products. CEO David Green who owns the company founded Hobby Lobby in 1972 and operates it according to biblical principles including closing shop on Sunday.

Strategy

One of America's largest private companies fast-growing Hobby Lobby has been busy expanding its network of stores which average 55000 sq. ft. The company opened 54 stores in 2018 and relocated 20 store locations. In 2019 Hobby Lobby plans to open 65 new stores and relocate 16. The company has been lifted by renewed interest in crafting by younger generations.

Hobby Lobby often sets up shop in second-generation retail sites such as vacated supermarkets and superstores. In recent years the company has put new stores in previous Macy's Toys R Us and OfficeMax locations.

The company has announced the closure of its home furnishings chain Hemispheres admitting the competitive nature of the industry made profitability too difficult.

EXECUTIVES

Vice President Advertising, John Schumacher
Vice President Chief Legal Officer, Peter Dobelbower
Ceo, David Green
Cfo, Jon Cargill
President, Steve Green
Assistant Vice President Construction, Bob Mackey
Assistant Vice President, Deloris Miller
Vice President Information Technology, Teddy Amadou
Vice President Finance, Mandy Rodriguez
Vice President Store Operations, Randy Betts
Vice President Of Marketing, Timothy Mattingly
Assistant Vice President Of Accounting, Barbara Walke
Assistant Vice President Risk Manager, Rebecca Robinson
Department Head, JEAN STEPHENSON
Regional Vice President Region 9, Joe Guerra
Vice President International Relations, Allen Quine
Assistant Vice President Of Accounting, Barbara A Walke
Administrative Assitant To Vice President Of Information And Interactive Sys, Sherri R Fisher
Vice President, Jessica Mchart
Administrative Assitant To Vice President Of Information And Interactive Sys, Sherri Fisher
Senior Vice President Information Technology, Francine English
Department Head, Ian Leighly
Sec Treas, Mart Green

LOCATIONS

HQ: HOBBY LOBBY STORES, INC.
7707 SW 44TH ST, OKLAHOMA CITY, OK 731794899
Phone: 405 745-1100
Web: WWW.HOBBYLOBBY.COM

PRODUCTS/OPERATIONS

Selected Products

Arts and crafts supplies
Baskets
Candles
Cards
Furniture
Home accent pieces
Jewelry-making supplies
Needlework
Party supplies
Picture frames and framing
Scrapbooking supplies
Seasonal items
Sewing materials (fabric patterns notions)
Silk flowers
Toys
Wearable art

Selected Affiliates

Hemispheres (home furnishings and accessories stores)
Mardel Christian Office & Educational Supply (Christian materials office supplies and educational products)

COMPETITORS

A.C. Moore
Burnes Home Accents
Garden Ridge
Hancock Fabrics
Jo-Ann Stores
Kirkland's
Michaels Companies
Old Time Pottery
Target Corporation
Wal-Mart

HISTORICAL FINANCIALS

Company Type: Private

Income Statement				FYE: December 31
	REVENUE ($ mil.)	NET INCOME ($ mil.)	NET PROFIT MARGIN	EMPLOYEES
12/17	4,544	352	7.8%	23,000
12/06	196	58	29.5%	—
12/04	1,363	88	6.5%	—
12/03	150	58	39.0%	—
Annual Growth	27.5%	13.7%	—	—

2017 Year-End Financials

Return on assets: 11.2% Cash ($ mil.): —
Return on equity: 20.8%
Current ratio: 2.10

HOLY CROSS HEALTH, INC.

EXECUTIVES

Pres-Ceo, Kevin Sexton
Cfo*, Anne D Gillis
V Pres*, Eileen Cahill
V Pres*, Patrick Connely
Obstetrician, Ronald D Jacobs
Ophthalmology, Benjamin D Magno
Gynecology/Obstetrics, Angela D Thompson
Obstetrician, Oluyemisi O Famuyiwa
Home Health Care Director, Margaret Hadley Sr
Information Technology Manager, Patricia Okolie
Senior Manager, Liz Orr

LOCATIONS

HQ: HOLY CROSS HEALTH, INC.
1500 FOREST GLEN RD, SILVER SPRING, MD 209101460
Phone: 301 754-7000
Web: WWW.HOLYCROSSHEALTH.ORG

HISTORICAL FINANCIALS

Company Type: Private

Income Statement FYE: June 30

	REVENUE ($ mil.)	NET INCOME ($ mil.)	NET PROFIT MARGIN	EMPLOYEES
06/18	561	43	7.7%	3,270
06/16	434	28	6.6%	—
Annual Growth	13.7%	22.4%	—	—

2018 Year-End Financials

Return on assets: 4.8%
Return on equity: 10.4%
Current ratio: 4.20
Cash ($ mil.): 282

HONORHEALTH

EXECUTIVES

Ceo, Todd Laporte
Chb*, Robert C Johnson
V Chb*, Gary J Goodman
Pres*, Max Poll
SEC*, Julian L Fruhling
Exec V Pres*, Gary Baker
Sr V Pres*, James F Burke
Sr V Pres*, Alan B Kelly
Treas*, F Michael Geddes
Svp-Cfo*, Paul Briggs
Member*, Jennifer Miller
Auditors: ERNST & YOUNG US LLP PHOENIX

LOCATIONS

HQ: HONORHEALTH
8125 N HAYDEN RD, SCOTTSDALE, AZ 852582463
Phone: 480 324-7215
Web: WWW.HONORHEALTH.COM

HISTORICAL FINANCIALS

Company Type: Private

Income Statement FYE: December 31

	REVENUE ($ mil.)	NET INCOME ($ mil.)	NET PROFIT MARGIN	EMPLOYEES
12/17	1,817	44	2.5%	14,000
12/14*	900	25	2.9%	—
09/09	847	4	0.5%	—
09/08	812	(17)	—	—
Annual Growth	9.4%	—	—	—

*Fiscal year change

2017 Year-End Financials

Return on assets: 2.1%
Return on equity: 3.9%
Current ratio: —
Cash ($ mil.): 96

HOOSIER ENERGY RURAL ELECTRIC COOPERATIVE INC.

Who's yer daddy? In terms of providing electricity for many Indianans (and some residents of Illinois) that would be Hoosier Energy Rural Electric Cooperative which provides wholesale electric power to 18 member distribution cooperatives in 59 central and southern Indiana counties and 11 counties in southeastern Illinois. These electric cooperatives serve 300000 consumers (650000 residents businesses industries and farms) in a 18000 sq. mi. service area. Hoosier Energy operates six power plants and a 1720-mile transmission system and maintains the Tuttle Creek Reservoir in Southwest Indiana. Hoosier Energy is part of the Touchstone Energy network of electric cooperatives.

Operations

Hoosier Energy operates coal- natural gas- and renewable energy-generation plants. It delivers electricity via a 1720-mile transmission network including 21 major substations and more than 350 delivery points.

Geographic Reach

The company delivers power to member distribution cooperatives in central and southern Indiana and southeastern Illinois.

Financial Performance

In 2013 the power coop's revenues increased by 3% due to higher member revenues and increased sales of electricity. Net income grew by 1% as the result of higher revenues and slight decrease in maintenance costs.

Strategy

To advance its push for more renewable sources Hoosier Energy is pursuing cost-effective generating projects and supply contracts including the Clark-Floyd Landfill Methane Generation plant which has four landfill/coal bed methane projects and which has purchased power agreements for wind and hydropower. These measures are expected to provide 7% of member energy sales annually.

Its recent capital projects include a $400 million multi-year upgrade of the Merom Station investing $18 million in power delivery projects to support growth and reliability and continuing progress toward renewable energy goals with the commercial operation of the Osprey Point coalbed methane plant and the Livingston landfill-methane plant.

Company Background

In 2011 the coop was operating a 2.5 MW landfill methane generation facility in addition to buying 25 MW of wind energy.

Expanding its geographic coverage in 2011 Hoosier Energy began to supply power to the Wayne-White Counties Electric Cooperative when that coop's contract with an independent power supplier ended. The distribution coop serves 13500 residential farm and business consumers in 11 counties in southeastern Illinois.

Hoosier Energy was formed in 1948 as part of the nationwide rural electrification drive initiated by the Roosevelt administration in the 1930s.

EXECUTIVES

Vice President Strategic Business And Diversity Relations, Larry Cox
Auditors: DELOITTE & TOUCHE LLP INDIAN

LOCATIONS

HQ: HOOSIER ENERGY RURAL ELECTRIC COOPERATIVE INC.
2501 S COOPERATIVE WAY, BLOOMINGTON, IN 474035175
Phone: 812 876-2021
Web: WWW.HOOSIERENERGY.COM

PRODUCTS/OPERATIONS

2012 Sales

	$ mil.	% of total
Members	532	82
Nonmembers	115	18
Other	0	-
Total	**647**	**100**

Member Cooperatives

Member Cooperatives
Bartholomew County REMC
Clark County REMC
Decatur County REMC
Daviess-Martin County REMC
Dubois REC Inc.
Harrison REMC
Henry County REMC
Jackson County REMC
Johnson County REMC
Orange County REMC
RushShelby Energy
South Central Indiana REMC
Southeastern Indiana REMC
Southern Indiana Power
Utilities District of Western Indiana REMC
Wayne-White Counties Electric Cooperative
WIN Energy REMC
Whitewater Valley REMC

COMPETITORS

IPALCO Enterprises
Indiana Michigan Power
Indiana Municipal Power Agency

HISTORICAL FINANCIALS

Company Type: Private

Income Statement FYE: December 31

	REVENUE ($ mil.)	NET INCOME ($ mil.)	NET PROFIT MARGIN	EMPLOYEES
12/12	647	27	4.3%	475
12/11	649	30	4.7%	—
12/09	575	16	2.9%	—
Annual Growth	4.1%	18.9%	—	—

2012 Year-End Financials

Return on assets: 1.6%
Return on equity: 11.0%
Current ratio: 1.50
Cash ($ mil.): 50

HORRY COUNTY SCHOOL DISTRICT

EXECUTIVES

Supt, Dr Rick Maxey
Accounting Staff, Patsy Johnson
Health Professional, Marti Graves
Case Manager, Hope Lupo
Case Management Specialist, Josue Valentin
Nutrition Manager, Kimberly Johnson
Director, Kristin Wilson
School Resource Officer Horry, Lcpl Anderson
Director of Network, Peggy Vickery
Supervisor, Robin Vaughn
Clerk of Court Administrative, Tania Bellamy
Auditors: MCGREGOR & COMPANY LLP COLUM

LOCATIONS

HQ: HORRY COUNTY SCHOOL DISTRICT
335 FOUR MILE RD, CONWAY, SC 295264506
Phone: 843 488-6700
Web: WWW.CFHSPANTHERS.COM

HISTORICAL FINANCIALS

Company Type: Private

Income Statement — FYE: June 30

	REVENUE ($ mil.)	NET INCOME ($ mil.)	NET PROFIT MARGIN	EMPLOYEES
06/19	585	(8)	—	5,000
06/18	548	(42)	—	—
06/17	520	(140)	—	—
06/16	494	218	44.2%	—
Annual Growth	5.8%	—	—	—

2019 Year-End Financials

Return on assets: (-0.6%)
Return on equity: —
Current ratio: 2.30
Cash ($ mil.): 250

HOSPITAL OF THE UNIVERSITY OF PENNSYLVANIA

EXECUTIVES

Director, Pamela Mack-Brooks
Coordinator, Alvaro Talavera
Coordinator, Cherlyn Bynum
Coordinator, Denise Amaro
Coordinator, Pete Caldwell
Assistant Professor, Rajat Deo
Assistant Professor, Dennis Hadjiliadis
Nurse Practitioner, Diana Van Houten
Assistant Professor, Lachlan Smith
Coordinator, Barbara Lopez
Staff, Diane Frain

LOCATIONS

HQ: HOSPITAL OF THE UNIVERSITY OF PENNSYLVANIA
3400 SPRUCE ST OFC, PHILADELPHIA, PA 191044208
Phone: 215 301-3776
Web: WWW.PENNMEDICINE.ORG

HISTORICAL FINANCIALS

Company Type: Private

Income Statement — FYE: June 30

	REVENUE ($ mil.)	NET INCOME ($ mil.)	NET PROFIT MARGIN	EMPLOYEES
06/16	2,236	283	12.7%	25
06/15	2,164	320	14.8%	—
Annual Growth	3.3%	(11.5%)	—	—

2016 Year-End Financials

Return on assets: 9.3%
Return on equity: 13.2%
Current ratio: 9.90
Cash ($ mil.): 1,091

HOUCHENS INDUSTRIES, INC.

Houchens Industries is a supermarket of businesses as well as an operator of supermarkets. The diversified company runs some 400 retail grocery convenience and neighborhood markets across the US. That includes conventional supermarkets under the Houchens Food Giant IGA Van Meter Insurance Tampico and Pan-Oston banners. It has more than 800 Save-A-Lot discount grocery stores that offer approximately 1800 products. Outside the grocery store Houchens operates Cohen's Fashion Optical franchise stores and several Sheldon's Express Pharmacy stores. Other businesses include construction financial services real estate restaurants and recycling. Houchens is 100%-owned by its employees.

Operations

Houchens is the largest franchisee of limited-assortment Save-A-Lot stores in the US. The company's manufacturing businesses include Stephens Pipe & Steel a leading maker and distributor of fence materials. Southern Recycling collects and processes metals paper glass and plastics. The company also franchises Sonic and Subway quick-serve restaurants. Other franchises include Cinnabon Carvel Schlotzsky's Which Wich and Shell.

Geographic Reach

Based in Kentucky Houchens Industries operates more than 400 retail grocery convenience and neighborhood market stores across nearly 15 states.

Sales and Marketing

Beyond the grocery segment Houchens also serves customers in the construction insurance wealth management technology and healthcare industries.

Company Background

Founded by Ervin Houchens as BG Wholesale in rural Kentucky in 1917 Houchens has been owned by its employees since 1988.

EXECUTIVES

Chairman And Ceo, James (Jimmie) Gipson
President, Spencer A. Coates
Ceo Tampico Beverages, Scott Miller
Cfo, Gordon Minter
President Cohen's Fashion Optical, Bob Cohen
President Hitcents.com, Chris Mills
President And Ceo Food Giant Supermarkets, Ron Watkins
Head Pan Oston, Jim Vance
Head Save A Lot, David Burnett
Executive Vice President, Dion Houchins
Vice President Produce, John Mudd
Auditors: BKD LLP BOWLING GREN KENTUC

LOCATIONS

HQ: HOUCHENS INDUSTRIES, INC.
700 CHURCH ST, BOWLING GREEN, KY 421011816
Phone: 270 843-3252
Web: WWW.HOUCHENSINDUSTRIES.COM

PRODUCTS/OPERATIONS

Selected Operations

American Sun Systems (tanning salon supplier)
Blake Hart Taylor & Wiseman (insurance)
Buehler's Buy Low (grocery retail)
Cohen's Fashion Optical (optical stores)
Food Giant (grocery retail)
Hilliard Lyons (financial services)
Houchens Markets (grocery retail)
IGA (licensed grocery retail)
Insurance Specialists (insurance)
Jr. Food Stores (convenience stores)
Price Less Foods (grocery retail)
Save-A-Lot (licensed grocery retail)
Scotty's (asphalt paving)
Sheldon's Express Pharmacy (drugstores)
Southern Recycling Inc. (recycling)
Stewart-Richey Construction Inc. (construction management)
Taco Del Mar (fast-food)
Tampico (juice)
TS Trucking (hauling)
Van Meter Insurance (insurance benefits)
White's Fresh Foods (grocery retail)

COMPETITORS

7-Eleven
ALDI
Ameriprise
CVS
Charles Schwab
Citigroup
Citrus World
Cumberland Farms
Dole Food
Dr Pepper Snapple Group
E*TRADE Financial
E. W. James
Edward D. Jones
FMR
Faygo
Goya
John Hancock Financial Services
Jugos del Valle USA
K-VA-T Food Stores
Kroger
Luxottica Retail
Meijer
Mott's
Nestlé
Ocean Spray
Odwalla
Old Orchard
Raymond James Financial
Rite Aid
Sheetz
Southeastern Grocers
Sunkist
Sunny Delight
TD Ameritrade
Thorntons Inc.
Tree Top
Tropicana
Visionworks of America
Wal-Mart
Walgreen
Weis Markets
Welch's

HISTORICAL FINANCIALS

Company Type: Private

Income Statement — FYE: September 29

	REVENUE ($ mil.)	NET INCOME ($ mil.)	NET PROFIT MARGIN	EMPLOYEES
09/18*	2,613	29	1.1%	16,000
10/16	2,987	104	3.5%	—
10/15	3,212	99	3.1%	—
Annual Growth	(6.7%)	(33.4%)	—	—

*Fiscal year change

2018 Year-End Financials

Return on assets: 1.7%
Return on equity: 2.3%
Current ratio: 2.10
Cash ($ mil.): 117

HOUSING DEVELOPMENT AUTHORITY, MICHIGAN STATE

EXECUTIVES

Chairperson, Steven Arwood
V Chmn*, Bernard Glieberman
Coordinator, Jared Boll
Coordinator, Jeff Westra
Coordinator, Justin Logsdon
Coordinator, Linda Hegstrom
Coordinator, Randall McKinney
Budget Specialist, Mary Cupp
Director of Legal Affairs, Clarence Stone
Department Analyst, Dorinda Sparks-Boak
Grants Manager, Joelle Letts
Auditors: PLANTE & MORAN PLLC

LOCATIONS

HQ: HOUSING DEVELOPMENT AUTHORITY, MICHIGAN STATE
735 E MICHIGAN AVE, LANSING, MI 489121474
Phone: 517 373-8370
Web: WWW.MICHIGAN.GOV

HISTORICAL FINANCIALS

Company Type: Private

Income Statement — FYE: June 30

	REVENUE ($ mil.)	NET INCOME ($ mil.)	NET PROFIT MARGIN	EMPLOYEES
06/20	701	26	3.7%	320
06/19	684	25	3.7%	—
06/18	633	9	1.5%	—
Annual Growth	5.3%	66.5%	—	—

2020 Year-End Financials

Return on assets: 0.5%
Return on equity: 3.5%
Current ratio: —
Cash ($ mil.): 381

HOUSTON INDEPENDENT SCHOOL DISTRICT

EXECUTIVES

Supt, Grenita Lathan
Accounting Staff, Glenn Reed
SEC-Treas, Diana Davila
Int Cao, Yolanda Rodriguez
Accounting Staff, Stephanie Matlock
Executive Officer, Manuel Rodriguez
Accounting Staff, David Clardy
Special Education Teacher, Carol Franklin
Coach, Kathleen Suedel
Teacher Coach, Brian Fortenberry
Administrative Assistant, Sharon McBride
Auditors: WEAVER AND TIDWELL LLP HOUSTO

LOCATIONS

HQ: HOUSTON INDEPENDENT SCHOOL DISTRICT
4400 W 18TH ST, HOUSTON, TX 770928501
Phone: 713 556-6000
Web: WWW.HOUSTONISD.ORG

HISTORICAL FINANCIALS

Company Type: Private

Income Statement — FYE: June 30

	REVENUE ($ mil.)	NET INCOME ($ mil.)	NET PROFIT MARGIN	EMPLOYEES
06/18	2,695	(250)	—	22,440
06/17	2,329	(39)	—	—
06/16	2,333	266	11.4%	—
06/13	1,876	117	6.3%	—
Annual Growth	7.5%	—	—	—

2018 Year-End Financials

Return on assets: (-3.7%)
Return on equity: (-22.3%)
Current ratio: —
Cash ($ mil.): 7

HOUSTON METHODIST HOSPITAL

EXECUTIVES

Ceo, Marc L Boom
Chm*, Ewing Werlein Jr
Treas*, Carlton E Baucum
SEC*, Gregory V Nelson
Manager, Enrica De Rosa
Information Specialist, Larry Tomazinis
Director, Mariana Pope
Volunteer Coordinator, Gabrielle Montoya
Information Technology Field S, Billy Koch
Director of Health Information, John Stewart
Chief Information Offi, Nicholas Desai
Auditors: DELOITTE & TOUCHE LLP HOUSTON

LOCATIONS

HQ: HOUSTON METHODIST HOSPITAL
6565 FANNIN ST, HOUSTON, TX 770302703
Phone: 713 790-3311
Web: WWW.HOUSTONMETHODIST.ORG

HISTORICAL FINANCIALS

Company Type: Private

Income Statement — FYE: December 31

	REVENUE ($ mil.)	NET INCOME ($ mil.)	NET PROFIT MARGIN	EMPLOYEES
12/19	5,225	1,275	24.4%	773
12/17	3,887	681	17.5%	—
12/16	3,746	338	9.0%	—
Annual Growth	11.7%	55.7%	—	—

2019 Year-End Financials

Return on assets: 12.2%
Return on equity: 16.1%
Current ratio: 1.10
Cash ($ mil.): 198

HOWARD COUNTY OF MARYLAND (INC)

EXECUTIVES

County Executive, Calvin Ball
Chief Administrator Officer*, Raquel Sanodo
Dep Chief of Staff*, Candace Dodson-Reed
Attorney, Marna McLendon
Coordinator, Chris Eatough
Captain, Rick Leonard
Creative Manager, Beth Vessey
Director of Policy, Carl Delorenzo
Planning Specialist Recycling, Gemma Evans
Emergency Management Specialis, Michael Hinson
Chief Innovation Officer, Angela L Cabellon
Auditors: CLIFTONLARSONALLEN LLP BALTIM

LOCATIONS

HQ: HOWARD COUNTY OF MARYLAND (INC)
3430 COURT HOUSE DR, ELLICOTT CITY, MD 210434300
Phone: 410 313-2195
Web: WWW.HOWARDCOUNTYMD.GOV

HISTORICAL FINANCIALS

Company Type: Private

Income Statement — FYE: June 30

	REVENUE ($ mil.)	NET INCOME ($ mil.)	NET PROFIT MARGIN	EMPLOYEES
06/19	1,335	(25)	—	3,463
06/18	1,298	76	5.9%	—
06/17	1,274	6	0.5%	—
06/16	1,247	(24)	—	—
Annual Growth	2.3%	—	—	—

2019 Year-End Financials

Return on assets: (-0.5%)
Return on equity: (-2.0%)
Current ratio: —
Cash ($ mil.): 408

HPS LLC

EXECUTIVES

Mng MBR, Matt Thompson
Cfo-MBR*, Thomas J La Pres
Tres-MBR*, Joseph Schodde
Treas-MBR*, Dwith Gascho
Customer Representativ, Tracy Keeler
Regional Manager, Jami Markle
Regional Sales Manager, Brian Smith
Member Resources, David Gregory
Region Manager, Jackie Hepler
Regional Sales Manager, Bryan Brauer
Regional Sales Manager, Emley Navarro
Auditors: MEYNARD TOLMAN & VENLET PC

LOCATIONS

HQ: HPS LLC
3275 N M 37 HWY, MIDDLEVILLE, MI 493339126
Phone: 269 795-3308
Web: WWW.HPSGPO.COM

HISTORICAL FINANCIALS

Company Type: Private

Income Statement FYE: June 30

	REVENUE ($ mil.)	NET INCOME ($ mil.)	NET PROFIT MARGIN	EMPLOYEES
06/19	899	0	0.1%	38
06/18	782	0	0.1%	—
06/16	1,032	0	0.1%	—
06/15	960	0	0.1%	—
Annual Growth	(1.6%)	(4.7%)	—	—

2019 Year-End Financials

Return on assets: 4.0%
Return on equity: 5.3%
Current ratio: 2.00
Cash ($ mil.): 4

HUMBLE INDEPENDENT SCHOOL DISTRICT

EXECUTIVES

Supt, Guy M Sconzo
Nurse, Lorraine Cano
Psychologist, Carol Reiner
Public Relations Director, Robin McAdams
Coordinator, Sukari Stredit-Thomas
Coordinator of Affective Educa, Matt Smith
Accounts Payable Specialist, Renee Chewning
Information Director, Arthur Allen
Cte Director, Marley Morris
Benefits Specialist, Tammye Vaughn
Registrar, Selene Greff
Auditors: WHITLEY PENN LLP HOUSTON TEX

LOCATIONS

HQ: HUMBLE INDEPENDENT SCHOOL DISTRICT
10203 BIRCHRIDGE DR, HUMBLE, TX 773382200
Phone: 281 641-1000
Web: WWW.HUMBLEISD.NET

HISTORICAL FINANCIALS

Company Type: Private

Income Statement FYE: June 30

	REVENUE ($ mil.)	NET INCOME ($ mil.)	NET PROFIT MARGIN	EMPLOYEES
06/19	546	132	24.3%	5,000
06/18	490	(67)	—	—
06/17	462	(11)	—	—
06/16	458	11	2.4%	—
Annual Growth	6.0%	127.8%	—	—

HUNTER ROBERTS CONSTRUCTION GROUP LLC

EXECUTIVES

Mbr-Pres-Ceo, James C McKenna
Sr V Pres*, John Alicandri
Executive Vice President*, Kevin Barrett
V Pres*, Mark Lamble
V Pres*, Alex Craig
V Pres*, Dan Dirscherl
Vice President*, Brian Aronne
V Pres-Dir of Purchasing*, Tim Dillon
Exec V Pres-Gen Mgr NY*, Paul Andersen
Vp of Finance*, Robert Belitz
V Pres*, Chuck Petrusky
Auditors: GRASSI & CO JERICHO NEW YOR

LOCATIONS

HQ: HUNTER ROBERTS CONSTRUCTION GROUP LLC
55 WATER ST FL 51, NEW YORK, NY 100413201
Phone: 212 321-6800
Web: WWW.HRCG.COM

HISTORICAL FINANCIALS

Company Type: Private

Income Statement FYE: December 31

	REVENUE ($ mil.)	NET INCOME ($ mil.)	NET PROFIT MARGIN	EMPLOYEES
12/13	762	3	0.4%	260
12/12	706	1	0.2%	—
12/10	458	7	1.7%	—
Annual Growth	18.4%	(26.8%)	—	—

2013 Year-End Financials

Return on assets: 1.4%
Return on equity: 6.4%
Current ratio: 1.20
Cash ($ mil.): 61

HUNTINGTON HOSPITAL

LOCATIONS

HQ: HUNTINGTON HOSPITAL
100 W CALIFORNIA BLVD, PASADENA, CA 911053010
Phone: 626 397-5000
Web: WWW.HUNTINGTONHOSPITAL.ORG

HISTORICAL FINANCIALS

Company Type: Private

Income Statement FYE: December 31

	REVENUE ($ mil.)	NET INCOME ($ mil.)	NET PROFIT MARGIN	EMPLOYEES
12/17	654	15	2.3%	3,500
12/16	646	6	0.9%	—
12/15	551	3	0.7%	—
12/14	513	1	0.4%	—
Annual Growth	8.4%	102.0%	—	—

2017 Year-End Financials

Return on assets: 1.7%
Return on equity: 2.6%
Current ratio: 3.30
Cash ($ mil.): 11

HUNTSVILLE HOSPITAL HEALTH SYSTEM

EXECUTIVES

Ceo, David Spillers
Coo*, Jeff Samz

LOCATIONS

HQ: HUNTSVILLE HOSPITAL HEALTH SYSTEM
101 SIVLEY RD SW, HUNTSVILLE, AL 358014470
Phone: 256 265-1000
Web: WWW.HUNTSVILLEHOSPITAL.ORG

HISTORICAL FINANCIALS

Company Type: Private

Income Statement FYE: June 30

	REVENUE ($ mil.)	NET INCOME ($ mil.)	NET PROFIT MARGIN	EMPLOYEES
06/16	864	98	11.4%	34
06/15	799	100	12.6%	—
Annual Growth	8.1%	(2.4%)	—	—

2016 Year-End Financials

Return on assets: 7.0%
Return on equity: 9.7%
Current ratio: 2.10
Cash ($ mil.): 186

HUNTSVILLE UTILITIES

EXECUTIVES

Pres, William C Pippin
Staff, Mike Coranet
Executive Assistant, Beverly Wilson

LOCATIONS

HQ: HUNTSVILLE UTILITIES
112 SPRAGINS ST NW, HUNTSVILLE, AL 358014902
Phone: 256 535-1200
Web: WWW.HSVUTIL.ORG

HISTORICAL FINANCIALS

Company Type: Private

Income Statement FYE: September 30

	REVENUE ($ mil.)	NET INCOME ($ mil.)	NET PROFIT MARGIN	EMPLOYEES
09/19	629	32	5.1%	634
09/18	525	18	3.6%	—
09/11	493	10	2.1%	—
09/10	456	5	1.3%	—
Annual Growth	3.6%	20.9%	—	—

2019 Year-End Financials

Return on assets: 3.1%
Return on equity: 5.6%
Current ratio: 2.50
Cash ($ mil.): 6

HURON HEALTH CARE CENTER, INC

EXECUTIVES

Admin, Amy Donaldson
Minimum Data Set Coordinator, Shelly Shaffer

LOCATIONS

HQ: HURON HEALTH CARE CENTER, INC
1920 CLEVELAND RD W, HURON, OH 448391211
Phone: 419 433-4990
Web: WWW.ADMIRALS-POINTE.NET

HISTORICAL FINANCIALS

Company Type: Private

Income Statement FYE: December 31

	REVENUE ($ mil.)	NET INCOME ($ mil.)	NET PROFIT MARGIN	EMPLOYEES
12/09	584	58	10.0%	125
12/98	3	0	—	—
12/97	3	3	97.8%	—
12/96	3	0	—	—
Annual Growth	48.0%	—	—	—

2009 Year-End Financials

Return on assets: 999.0%
Return on equity: 999.9%
Current ratio: 2.20
Cash ($ mil.): —

HY-VEE, INC.

Give Hy-Vee a high five for being one of the largest privately owned US supermarket chains despite serving some modestly sized towns in the Midwest. The company runs more than 240 stores in eight Midwestern states. It distributes products to its stores through several subsidiaries including Amber Pharmacy D&D Foods Inc. Hy-Vee Construction and Midwest Heritage. Charles Hyde and David Vredenburg founded the employee-owned firm in 1930. It takes its name from a combination of its founders' names.

Operations

Hy-Vee Inc. offers groceries ready to go meals pastries and cakes. Through its subsidiaries Hy-Vee established a distribution system that secures the highest quality merchandise and transports its products quickly and efficiently to its customers.

Geographic Reach

Iowa-based Hy-Vee Inc. operates 240 retail stores in Illinois Iowa Kansas Minnesota Missouri Nebraska South Dakota and Wisconsin.

Sales and Marketing

Hy-Vee Inc. sell its products through online and its own groceries located in eight Midwestern states in the US.

Financial Performance

Hy-Vee Inc. is an employee-owned corporation operating retail stores across eight Midwestern states with sales of $11 billion annually.

Strategy

Hy-Vee Inc. announced recently the launch of its newest subsidiary Vivid Clear Rx. The new subsidiary will offer affordable pharmacy benefit management services to Hy-Vee's more than 88000 employees as well as other employers looking to maximize their employee benefits spending. With the launch of Vivid Clear Rx it is leveraging its experience in the pharmacy industry and the expertise it gained from serving millions of pharmacy patients to help other employers make the most of every health care dollar they're investing in their employees.

Vivid Clear Rx will offer a full range of flexible pharmacy benefit management services powered by RxSense's RxAgile enterprise technology which will provide clarity to those utilizing the company's services. RxSense is providing Vivid Clear Rx with a full-service suite of modules for pharmacy benefit management that will supplement assets that Hy-Vee already owns and operates. RxSense's analytics product RxIQ will provide Vivid Clear Rx with real-time health plan performance insights through customizable data dashboards; financial operational and clinical action alerts; and the ability to quickly evaluate data by claim type pharmacy or geography.

EXECUTIVES

Vp General Merchandise, Jon S. Wendel
Chairman President And Ceo, Randy Edeker
Evp And Chief Customer Officer, Sheila Laing
Evp Cfo And Treasurer, Mike Skokan
Vice Chairman Evp And Chief Administrative Officer, Andy McCann
Evp Western Region, Brett Bremser
Evp And Coo, Jay Marshall
Evp Eastern Region, Darren Baty
Vice President Retail Information Technology, Julie Proffitt
Assistant Vice President Operations, Jim Watters
Senior Vice President And Chief Health Officer, Kristin Williams
Assistant Vice President Employee Benefits, Kristine Hennings
Pharmacy Manager, Marrianne Ryno
Assistant Vice President Sec, Angie Rosenberger
Assistant Vice President Operations, Rob Eslick
Group Vice President, Jason Pride
Assistant Vice President Bakery Operations, Tony Byington
Group Vice President Equipment Purchasing, Mark Brauer
Assistant Vice President Meat Operations, Kenan Judge
Assistant Vice President Engineering, Adam Bishop
Assistant Vice President For Marketing Projects, Erin Bailey
Assistant Vice President Logistics, Jody Sandy
Vice President Sales, Katie Graham
Assistant Vice President, Tony Kaska
Assistant Vice President Auditing Services, Juli Egeland
Assistant Vice President Western Region, Pat Hensley
Vice President Special Projects, Gary Goodhall
Vice President Government Relations, Noreen Otto
Assistant Vice President Store Setup, Mark Millsap
Vice President Distribution, Tod Hockenson
Vice President Information Technology Operation, Cevin Anderson
Assisant Vice President, Chuck Seaman
Vice President Customer Care, Denise Broderick
Vice President, Karl Kruse
Assistant Vice President Information Technology Operations, Travis Hoover
Assistant Vice President Risk Management, Janet Crocker
Group Vice President Information Technology, Tom Settle
Assistant Vice President Of Produce Operations, Jason Sheridan
Assistant Vice President, Marshall Sanders
Avp Produce Operations, Mike Orf
Vice President Store Development, Jeff Markey
Assistant Vice President Risk Management, John Brummit
Assistant Vice President Information Technology Projects, Angie Dachenbach
Pharmacy Manager, Rick Awbrey
Pharmacy Manager, Jeff Jorgensen
Pharmacy Manager, Brad Moriarty
Pharmacy Manager, Heather Yennie
Vice President Business Development, Kevin Sherlock
Vice President Of Real Estate, Pete Hosch
Gvp Ecommerce, Brandon Williams
Vice President Of Human Resources, Karen Boriskey
Assisant Treasurer, Jeff Pierce
Secretary To Greg Frampton, Stacey Groff
Assistant Secretary, Michael Jurgens
Senior Vice President Secretary And General Counsel, Steve Meyer

LOCATIONS

HQ: HY-VEE, INC.
5820 WESTOWN PKWY, WEST DES MOINES, IA 502668223
Phone: 515 267-2800
Web: WWW.HY-VEE.COM

PRODUCTS/OPERATIONS

Selected Subsidiaries

D & D Foods Inc. (salads dips and meats)
Florist Distributing Inc. (flowers plants and florist supplies)
Hy-Vee Construction L.C. (construction)
Hy-Vee Pharmacy Solutions (specialty pharmacy services)
Hy-Vee Weitz Construction L.C. (construction)
Lomar Distributing Inc. (specialty foods)
Midwest Heritage Bank FSB (banking)
Perishable Distributors of Iowa Ltd. (meat fish seafood and ice cream)

COMPETITORS

ALDI
Associated Wholesale Grocers
Ball's Food
CVS
Casey's General Stores
Fareway Stores
Kmart
Kroger
Niemann Foods
Rite Aid
Roundy's
SUPERVALU
Save-A-Lot Food Stores
Target Corporation
Wal-Mart
Walgreen

HISTORICAL FINANCIALS

Company Type: Private

Income Statement FYE: September 30

	REVENUE ($ mil.)	NET INCOME ($ mil.)	NET PROFIT MARGIN	EMPLOYEES
09/19	10,672	0	—	83,000
09/18*	10,290	0	—	—
12/16	9,842	0	—	—
09/13	8,014	0	—	—
Annual Growth	4.9%	—	—	—

*Fiscal year change

2019 Year-End Financials

Return on assets: —
Return on equity: —
Current ratio: 1.00
Cash ($ mil.): 3

HYUNDAI TRANSYS GEORGIA POWERTRAIN, INC.

EXECUTIVES

Ceo, Sam Ho Cha
SEC*, Taeeuk Kim
Cfo*, Changyoung Kim
Purchasing Specialist, Darren Wiker
Fin & Acct Specialist, Do Hyun Lee
Machining Leader, Jason Aikens
Assistant Manager, Jin Kwak
Associate Professor, Carmello Chris

Senior Specialist J Gen Ral AF, Semin Chun
Senior It Specialist, Andrew Jacob Key
Leader Maintenance, Blake Willoughby
Auditors: PK LLP OPELIKA ALABAMA

LOCATIONS

HQ: HYUNDAI TRANSYS GEORGIA POWERTRAIN, INC.
6801 KIA PKWY, WEST POINT, GA 318334937
Phone: 706 902-6800

HISTORICAL FINANCIALS

Company Type: Private

Income Statement FYE: December 31

	REVENUE ($ mil.)	NET INCOME ($ mil.)	NET PROFIT MARGIN	EMPLOYEES
12/16	1,134	7	0.6%	500
12/15	1,230	12	1.0%	—
12/14	1,250	11	0.9%	—
12/13	1,220	11	0.9%	—
Annual Growth	(2.4%)	(14.3%)	—	—

2016 Year-End Financials

Return on assets: 2.5%
Return on equity: 6.0%
Current ratio: 1.70
Cash ($ mil.): 22

ICAHN SCHOOL OF MEDICINE AT MOUNT SINAI

EXECUTIVES

Ceo, Ken Davis
Dean*, Dennis Charney
Cfo*, Stephen Harvey
Director of Geriatric Srvs, Albert Siu
Nurse Practitioner, Cynthia Esrig
Anesthesiology, Daniel Gainsburg
Director of Breast, Laurie Margolies
Physician, Mark Lebwohl
Ob Gyn Surg Director, Michael Brodman
Professor, Michael Hausman
Doctor of Medicine, Nanci Pittman
Auditors: ERNST & YOUNG US LLP NEW YORK

LOCATIONS

HQ: ICAHN SCHOOL OF MEDICINE AT MOUNT SINAI
1 GUSTAVE L LEVY PL, NEW YORK, NY 100296504
Phone: 212 241-6500
Web: WWW.MOUNTSINAI.ORG

HISTORICAL FINANCIALS

Company Type: Private

Income Statement FYE: December 31

	REVENUE ($ mil.)	NET INCOME ($ mil.)	NET PROFIT MARGIN	EMPLOYEES
12/18	2,954	41	1.4%	7,000
12/17	2,843	272	9.6%	—
12/13	1,625	89	5.5%	—
12/12	1,577	119	7.6%	—
Annual Growth	11.0%	(16.3%)	—	—

2018 Year-End Financials

Return on assets: 1.7%
Return on equity: 3.9%
Current ratio: 0.60
Cash ($ mil.): 154

ICE DATA SERVICES, INC.

EXECUTIVES

Pres, Scott A Hill
Treasurer, Martin Hunter
Secretary, Octavia Spencer
Vice President, Chuck Adkins
Vice President Information TEC, Scott Caudell
Director Evaluated Op, Steve Miano
Oracle Database Administrator, Sudhir Patel
Senior Relationship Manager, Kevin Mulvey
Global Data Administration Man, Nick Benkovich
Director, Joseph Greiner
Manager, Lisa Dizenzo

LOCATIONS

HQ: ICE DATA SERVICES, INC.
32 CROSBY DR STE 100, BEDFORD, MA 017301448
Phone: 781 687-8500

HISTORICAL FINANCIALS

Company Type: Private

Income Statement FYE: December 31

	ASSETS ($ mil.)	NET INCOME ($ mil.)	INCOME AS % OF ASSETS	EMPLOYEES
12/13	3,968	33	0.8%	2,600
12/12	3,962	1	0.0%	—
12/11	4,093	(29)	—	—
Annual Growth	(1.5%)	—	—	—

2013 Year-End Financials

Return on assets: 0.8%
Return on equity: 2.8%
Sales ($ mil): 905

IDEMIA IDENTITY & SECURITY USA LLC

MorphoTrust USA builds trust with its credentials and biometrics-based recognition systems. MorphoTrust provides driver's licenses passports voter and other government and corporate-issued IDs as well as related data verification systems. Its biometrics products include face finger and iris recognition scanners. The company which operates in all 50 states serves US federal state and local governments and commercial entities; government contracts represent about 95% of revenues. In addition to its contract-based services MorphoTrust operates a network of more than 1200 ID service centers. It is a subsidiary of Paris-based aerospace components maker SAFRAN.

Geographic Reach

MorphoTrust has 1100 service centers located in Illinois Iowa Indiana Minnesota Massachusetts New Jersey Tennessee Virginia and the District of Columbia.

Sales and Marketing

MorphoTrust caters to more than 3 million customers each year including the Department of Defense the State Department and the Department of Homeland Security.

Financial Performance

The company claims to generate $400 million in annual revenue.

Strategy

MorphoTrust has enjoyed growth from its US federal government activities primarily its FBI products and services involving universal enrollment and weapons permits. However like most companies servicing the public sector it is at the mercy of its clients' budgetary cuts and restrictions.

In 2014 the company won new contracts to provide fingerprint-based background checks for the Massachusetts Executive Office of Public Safety and Security the New Jersey Department of Public Safety the Division of State Police and fingerprint channeling services in Nevada for the Department of Public Safety. It believes these agreements could yield up to $25 million in revenue over the next six years.

EXECUTIVES

President And Ceo, Robert A. (Bob) Eckel
Vice President, Ben Mallen

LOCATIONS

HQ: IDEMIA IDENTITY & SECURITY USA LLC
296 CONCORD RD STE 300, BILLERICA, MA 018213487
Phone: 978 215-2400
Web: WWW.IDEMIA.COM

PRODUCTS/OPERATIONS

Selected Products and Services

Biometric-based access control to buildings and restricted areas
Biometric recognition technologies that accurately identify individuals
Enrollment centers for processing pre-employment background checks
Secure credentials that serve as proof of identity
Solving critical issues facing US intelligence and national security

COMPETITORS

3M Cogent
Acsys Biometrics
Allied Security Innovations
CSSN
Cross Match Technologies
De La Rue
Edentify
Entrust DataCard
ImageWare Systems
SecuGen
Security First
Ultra-Scan
Verint Systems

HISTORICAL FINANCIALS

Company Type: Private

Income Statement FYE: December 31

	REVENUE ($ mil.)	NET INCOME ($ mil.)	NET PROFIT MARGIN	EMPLOYEES
12/16	708	(7)	—	1,000
12/15	604	0	—	—
Annual Growth	17.1%	—	—	—

2016 Year-End Financials

Return on assets: (-0.5%)
Return on equity: (-0.7%)
Current ratio: 1.70
Cash ($ mil.): 73

IHC HEALTH SERVICES, INC.

EXECUTIVES

Pres-Ceo, William Nelson
Svp-Cfo, Bert Zimmerli
V Pres-Pres, Charles Sorenson
Chief Staff, Steven Vannorman
Surgery Director, Brent Hardy

Food Manager, Brent Lamoreaux
Manager Plant Operations, George McGee
Biomedical Engineer, Bryan White
Womens Health Director, Kenzie Peterson
Emergency Medicine Specialist, Stanford Benson
Anesthesiologist, Todd Plumb
Auditors: KPMG LLP SALT LAKE CITY UT

LOCATIONS

HQ: IHC HEALTH SERVICES, INC.
1380 E MEDICAL CENTER DR, ST GEORGE, UT 847902123
Phone: 435 251-2992
Web: WWW.INTERMOUNTAINHEALTHCARE.ORG

HISTORICAL FINANCIALS

Company Type: Private

Income Statement FYE: December 31

	REVENUE ($ mil.)	NET INCOME ($ mil.)	NET PROFIT MARGIN	EMPLOYEES
12/19	6,947	888	12.8%	4,000
12/18	6,037	317	5.3%	—
12/17	5,483	884	16.1%	—
12/16	5,275	564	10.7%	—
Annual Growth	9.6%	16.3%	—	—

2019 Year-End Financials

Return on assets: 6.5%
Return on equity: 11.2%
Current ratio: 1.30
Cash ($ mil.): 290

ILLINOIS STATE OF TOLL HIGHWAY AUTHORITY

The Illinois State Toll Highway Authority (ISTHA) is trying to give Illinois drivers a little relief from congestion making their morning and afternoon commutes easier to swallow. The department maintains and operates about 275 miles of interstate tollways in 12 Northern Illinois counties. ISTHA is mid-way through its 10-year $6.3 billion Congestion-Relief Program which is conducting major improvements including rebuilding widening and extending tollway segments; converting toll plazas to provide non-stop toll collection for I-PASS users; opening additional tollway oases; and adding electronic over-the-road signs to improve communication with tollway users.

EXECUTIVES

Pres, John Mitola
Cfo*, Mike Colsch
Acting Exec Dir*, Michael King
Coordinator, Vicky Czuprynski
Chief of Information Technolog, Joseph Kambich
Information Technology Manager, Christine Benn
Communications Supervisor, Thomas Andruscavage
Information Technology Manager, Richard Howard
Administrator, Robert Godsil
Chief of Operations Officer, David Wilson
General Manager Performance ME, Michael Catolico
Auditors: MCGLADREY & PULLEN LLP SCHAU

LOCATIONS

HQ: ILLINOIS STATE OF TOLL HIGHWAY AUTHORITY
2700 OGDEN AVE, DOWNERS GROVE, IL 605151703
Phone: 630 241-6800
Web: WWW.ILLINOISTOLLWAY.COM

HISTORICAL FINANCIALS

Company Type: Private

Income Statement FYE: December 31

	REVENUE ($ mil.)	NET INCOME ($ mil.)	NET PROFIT MARGIN	EMPLOYEES
12/19	1,484	374	25.2%	1,750
12/18	1,436	353	24.6%	—
12/17	1,398	356	25.5%	—
12/16	1,303	319	24.5%	—
Annual Growth	4.4%	5.5%	—	—

2019 Year-End Financials

Return on assets: 3.1%
Return on equity: 10.9%
Current ratio: 2.10
Cash ($ mil.): 319

ILWU-PMA WELFARE TRUST

EXECUTIVES

Prin, Michael Ouchida
Auditors: PRICEWATERHOUSECOOPERS LLP SA

LOCATIONS

HQ: ILWU-PMA WELFARE TRUST
1188 FRANKLIN ST STE 101, SAN FRANCISCO, CA 941096852
Phone: 415 673-8500
Web: WWW.BENEFITPLANS.ORG

HISTORICAL FINANCIALS

Company Type: Private

Income Statement FYE: June 30

	REVENUE ($ mil.)	NET INCOME ($ mil.)	NET PROFIT MARGIN	EMPLOYEES
06/18	738	(4)	—	3
06/17	738	5	0.8%	—
06/15	676	27	4.1%	—
06/14	624	(21)	—	—
Annual Growth	4.3%	—	—	—

2018 Year-End Financials

Return on assets: (-2.4%)
Return on equity: (-4.6%)
Current ratio: 1.80
Cash ($ mil.): 5

IMPERIAL IRRIGATION DISTRICT

Imperial Irrigation District (IID) keeps the lights on and the water flowing. A public agency IID is the six largest public power utility in the state of California providing generation transmission and distribution services to more than 145000 residential commercial and industrial customers. It is also the largest irrigation district in the US with more than 3000 miles of canals and drains delivering water to active farmland and providing wholesale water to local municipalities primarily in the Southern California desert corridors of Imperial Valley and Coachella Valley. The district is governed by a five-member board of directors elected by district residents.

Financial Performance

IID saw its revenues increase 6% from $530 million in 2011 to $562 million in 2012. The growth was driven by a 12% surge in water revenue; this was due to a rise in water transfer rates and a volume increase in water transferred to the San Diego County Water Authority and the Coachella Valley Water District of about $5 million. Power revenues also climbed 4% in 2012 due to a spike in energy sales mainly from residential customers.

Strategy

In the area of renewable energy IID is part of a statewide effort to significantly increase solar energy development and production by the year 2017. In 2011 it announced a public-private partnership with renewable energy generators. The partnership involves the signing of interconnection and transmission service agreements among IID CalEnergy Generation 8minuteenergy Ormat Technologies and the Los Angeles Department of Water and Power. It's the first step in a renewable energy transmission expansion plan to increase capacity enough to support more than a dozen renewable energy construction projects.

In addition IID offers a variety of programs to assist its customers in reducing their personal energy consumption including rebates for buying select energy efficient products online home energy audits and funding for residential projects that involve installing solar technologies such as photovoltaic (PV) systems.

Company Background

Founded in 1911 IID acquired properties from the financially struggling California Development Company and its Mexican subsidiary. By 1922 it had purchased 13 mutual water companies each of which had developed and operated distribution canals in the Imperial Valley. Principal water customers today include farm operators and municipalities that treat the water and resell it to their residential and business customers. The district entered the power business in 1936 to utilize the hydroelectric generation of the All-American Canal. Since that time IID has added geothermal natural gas coal and solar to its energy generation portfolio. Its electric services account for majority of IID's annual revenues.

EXECUTIVES

Vice President, Alfonso Juarez
Vice President Customer, Efrain Macias
Board Member, Jim Hanks
Secretary Admin, Angelita Alvarado
Secretary Admin, Angelica Velasquez

LOCATIONS

HQ: IMPERIAL IRRIGATION DISTRICT
333 E BARIONI BLVD, IMPERIAL, CA 922511773
Phone: 800 303-7756
Web: WWW.IID.COM

HISTORICAL FINANCIALS

Company Type: Private

Income Statement FYE: December 31

	REVENUE ($ mil.)	NET INCOME ($ mil.)	NET PROFIT MARGIN	EMPLOYEES
12/19	642	51	8.0%	1,300
12/18	615	48	7.9%	—
12/17	634	3	0.5%	—
12/16	631	(16)	—	—
Annual Growth	0.6%	—	—	—

2019 Year-End Financials

Return on assets: 1.9%
Return on equity: 3.0%
Current ratio: 2.00
Cash ($ mil.): 109

INDEPENDENT PHARMACY COOPERATIVE

EXECUTIVES

Pres, Don Anderson
Director of Marketing/Sales, Linda Reedy Sr
Staff, Vickie Miller
Human Resources Executive, Michelle R Johnson
Sales Associate, Nicole Burbach
Sales Associate, Tammy Riley
Marketing Coordinator, Emily Gutgesell
Director Regional Sales, Stacy Hall
Administration Staff, Susan Oechsner
Vp of Finance, Devin Millard
Inside Sales Representative, Matt Meisenheimer
Auditors: GRANT THORNTON LLP APPLETON

LOCATIONS

HQ: INDEPENDENT PHARMACY COOPERATIVE
1550 COLUMBUS ST, SUN PRAIRIE, WI 535903901
Phone: 800 755-1531
Web: WWW.IPCRX.COM

HISTORICAL FINANCIALS

Company Type: Private

Income Statement — FYE: December 31

	REVENUE ($ mil.)	NET INCOME ($ mil.)	NET PROFIT MARGIN	EMPLOYEES
12/16	1,427	30	2.1%	160
12/14	1,052	2	0.2%	—
12/13	1,058	2	0.2%	—
12/11	806	1	0.2%	—
Annual Growth	12.1%	73.9%	—	—

2016 Year-End Financials

Return on assets: 12.5%
Return on equity: 60.7%
Current ratio: 1.20
Cash ($ mil.): 40

INDEPENDENT SCHOOL DIST 625

EXECUTIVES

Spdt, Joe Gothard
Mgmt Specialist, Andrew Mosca
Executive of Information Techn, Cathy Bloomquist
Executive of Information Techn, Jim Litwin
Accounting Staff, Shirley Davis
Accounting Staff, Patty Kelly
Accounting Staff, Gloria Thompson
Director, Traci Gauer
Bus/Finance/Purchasing Directo, Brad Miller
Athletic Director, Laura Ranum
Assistant Superintendent, Omoyefe Agbamu
Auditors: MALLOY MONTAGUE KARNOWSKI R

LOCATIONS

HQ: INDEPENDENT SCHOOL DIST 625
360 COLBORNE ST, SAINT PAUL, MN 551023228
Phone: 651 767-8100
Web: WWW.SPPS.ORG

HISTORICAL FINANCIALS

Company Type: Private

Income Statement — FYE: June 30

	REVENUE ($ mil.)	NET INCOME ($ mil.)	NET PROFIT MARGIN	EMPLOYEES
06/19	732	(83)	—	6,500
06/18	711	17	2.5%	—
06/17	706	49	7.0%	—
06/16	693	(37)	—	—
Annual Growth	1.8%	—	—	—

INDIANA UNIVERSITY

EXECUTIVES

Staff, Emily Tenney
Faculty, Timothy Keene
Director of Training, Andrew Shea
Director of Special Projects, Beth Feickert
Marketing Manager, Damen Morris
Director of Communications, Deborah Galyan
Office of Marketing, Joel Fosha
Assistant Director of Events, John Bower
General Manager, Jose Fajardo
Clinical Assistant Professor, Lesa Huber
Director, Anne Kibbler

LOCATIONS

HQ: INDIANA UNIVERSITY
1020 E KIRKWOOD AVE, BLOOMINGTON, IN 474057103
Phone: 812 855-7581
Web: WWW.IU.EDU

HISTORICAL FINANCIALS

Company Type: Private

Income Statement — FYE: June 30

	REVENUE ($ mil.)	NET INCOME ($ mil.)	NET PROFIT MARGIN	EMPLOYEES
06/14	2,195	201	9.2%	31
06/13	2,146	189	8.8%	—
Annual Growth	2.3%	6.3%	—	—

2014 Year-End Financials

Return on assets: 10.0%
Return on equity: 9.2%
Current ratio: 1.10
Cash ($ mil.): 313

INDIANA UNIVERSITY HEALTH, INC.

Indiana University Health (IU Health) is one of the largest health systems in Indiana. Not-for-profit IU Health owns or is affiliated with more than 20 hospitals throughout the state including three major facilities ? Methodist Hospital Indiana University Hospital and Riley Hospital for Children ? in downtown Indianapolis. The hospitals serve as teaching facilities for Indiana University's medical school. The largest Methodist Hospital features the Methodist Research Institute which conducts research and clinical trials. The 2700-bed IU Health system also includes primary and specialty care clinics surgery and urgent care centers a health insurance provider and a home health agency.

Financial Performance

IU Health reported relatively flat revenue in 2018. Sales increased a little over 1% to some $6.4 billion as a 7% increase in patient service revenue (accounting for most of sales) was offset by a 70% decline in member premium (health plan) revenue.

Excess of revenue over expenses was $296.2 million in 2018 down from $989.3 million in 2017 due to investment losses.

The company ended 2018 with $345 million in cash down $69.6 million from 2017. Operating activities contributed $178.2 million while investing activities used $265.8 million (on property and equipment) and financing activities contributed $18 million via issuance of long-term debt.

Strategy

The system's growth strategy includes expanding into Indianapolis' suburbs and other growing areas of Indiana through construction efforts acquisitions and affiliation agreements. It also regularly improves upon existing facilities to enhance services for area residents.

Current projects include the construction of the $344 million Bloomington Regional Academic Health Center which will replace and expand the existing Bloomington Hospital (opening in 2021) and the addition of a $104 million patient tower at the Ball Memorial Hospital (scheduled for completion in 2022). IU Health has announced plans to construct a new Academic Health Center to replace some aging assets in downtown Indianapolis. It is opening new urgent and ambulatory care centers to increase outpatient revenue as industry service models shift towards non-inpatient care.

IU Health also works to improve the health of Indiana residents through research education and community outreach programs. Recent initiatives include improving access to affordable care behavioral health care and obesity prevention services.

While it continues to expand the organization is also working to reduce expenses during a time when US health providers and regulatory agencies look to control medical spending.

Company Background

The organization was formed in 1997 as Clarian Health Partners through the merger of University Hospital and Riley Hospital (operated by the Trustees of Indiana University) with the Methodist Hospital (operated by Methodist Health Group).

The company changed its name from Clarian Health Partners to Indiana University Health (IU Health) in 2011 to reflect its relationship with the university.

EXECUTIVES

Evp And Coo, Al W. Gatmaitan
Evp And Chief Medical Executive, Jonathan E. Gottlieb
President And Ceo, Dennis M. Murphy
Svp And Cio, Mark Lantzy
President System Clinical Services, Ron Stiver
President And Ceo Iu Health Ball Memorial Hospital, Michael Haley
Chief Nurse Executive, Michelle Janney
Evp And Chief Administrative Officer, Ryan C. Kitchell
President And Ceo Iu Health North Hospital And Iu Health Saxony Hospital, Jonathan Goble
President Iu Health South Central Region, Matt Bailey

President And Ceo Iu Health Tipton Hospital, Michael Harlowe
Ceo Iu Health Paoli Hospital, Larry Bailey
President And Ceo Iu Health Bedford Hospital, Bradford W. Dykes
President Iu Health Arnett Hospital, Donald E. Clayton
President Iu Health West Hospital, Doug Puckett
President Riley Hospital For Children, Matthew Cook
President Iu Health East Central Region, Jeff Bird
Interim President And Chief Medical Officer Iu Health Methodist And University, Ryan Nagy
Vice President Latino Alumni Association, Adam Karcz
Vice President Of Clinical Excellence, Lisa Sparks
Vice President Quality And Patient Safety, James Bien
Vice President Revenue Cycle Services And Treasurer, Jennifer Alvey
Vice President Cno, Linda Chase
Vice President Revenue Cycle Services, Jonathan Vanator
Vice President Ambulatory Services, Scott Brenton
Radiology Director, Shelli Kordes
Vice President Physician Recruitment, Jenny Garver
Vice President Retail Health Services, David Kogan
Senior Vice President And Chief Health Information Officer, Joseph Hschneider
Vp Marketing And Community Relations, Teri Dematas
Evp Mission And Values And Chief Of Staff, Kevin R Armstrong
System Vice President Orthopedics, Lisa Brandt
Vp It And Innovation, Sulabh Srivastava
Vice President Clinical Strategy And Integration, Andrea Kessler
Vice President Supply Chain Operations, Dennis Mullins
Medical Director, Jeffrey Nace
Vice President Human Resources Total Rewards, Lauren Zink
Vice President Finance And Operations, Joseph Traeger
Vice President Operations, Terry Pence
Director Of Pharmacy, Pat Schneider
Chairman, Anne Nobles
Cpe Secretary, Lorie Vaughn
Department Secretary, Susan Dripps
Secretary Administrative, Valerie Craig
Auditors: ERNST & YOUNG LLP INDIANAPOLI

LOCATIONS

HQ: INDIANA UNIVERSITY HEALTH, INC.
340 W 10TH ST, INDIANAPOLIS, IN 462023082
Phone: 317 962-2000
Web: WWW.IUHEALTH.ORG

PRODUCTS/OPERATIONS

Selected Facilities
INDIANAPOLIS-AREA HOSPITALS
Indiana University Hospital (dba IU Health University Hospital Indianapolis)
Methodist Hospital (dba IU Health Methodist Hospital Indianapolis)
Riley Hospital for Children (dba Riley Hospital for Children at IU Health Indianapolis)
IU Simon Cancer Center
Clarian North Medical Center (dba IU Health North Hospital Carmel)
Clarian West Medical Center (dba IU Health West Hospital Avon)
STATEWIDE PARTNERS
Clarian Arnett Health (dba IU Health Arnett Hospital Lafayette)
Ball Memorial Hospital (dba IU Health Ball Memorial Hospital Muncie)
Bedford Regional Medical Center (dba IU Health Bedford Hospital Bedford)
Blackford Community Hospital (dba IU Health Blackford Hospital Hartford City)
Bloomington Hospital (dba IU Health Bloomington Hospital Bloomington)
Bloomington Hospital of Orange County (dba IU Health Paoli Hospital Paoli)
Goshen Health System (dba IU Health Goshen Hospital Goshen)
LaPorte Regional Health System (dba IU Health LaPorte Hospital La Porte)
Midwest Proton Radiotherapy Institute (dba IU Health Proton Therapy Center Bloomington)
Starke Memorial Hospital (dba IU Health Starke Hospital Knox)
Tipton Hospital (dba IU Health Tipton Hospital Tipton)
METHODIST MEDICAL PLAZAS (outpatient centers)
Georgetown Medical Plaza
Methodist Medical Plaza Eagle Highlands
Methodist Medical Plaza East
Methodist Medical Plaza North
Methodist Medical Plaza South

COMPETITORS

Ascension Health
Banner Health
Catholic Health Initiatives
Community Health Network
Community Hospital Anderson
Daviess Community Hospital
Franciscan Alliance
Good Samaritan Hospital (IN)
Henry County Memorial Hospital
MedStar Health
Riverview Hospital
St. Elizabeth Regional Health
St. Vincent Health
Tenet Healthcare
Union Hospital (Indiana)

HISTORICAL FINANCIALS

Company Type: Private

Income Statement — FYE: December 31

	REVENUE ($ mil.)	NET INCOME ($ mil.)	NET PROFIT MARGIN	EMPLOYEES
12/08	1,889	(23)	—	17,242
12/06	2,478	159	6.4%	—
12/05	2,281	68	3.0%	—
Annual Growth	(6.1%)	—	—	—

2008 Year-End Financials

Return on assets: (-1.3%)
Return on equity: (-1.8%)
Current ratio: 0.90
Cash ($ mil.): 237

INFIRMARY HEALTH SYSTEM, INC.

EXECUTIVES

Ceo, D Mark Nix
Pres*, E Chandler Bramlett
Human Resources Information MA, Stephanie Andrews
Controller, Becky Michels
Chief Strategy Officer, Alan Whaley
Director of Radiology, Anthony Mosley
Coordinator, Alex Oditt
Coordinator, Allan Farnum
Information Specialist, Anne Glesie
Vice-President, Susan Boudreau
Information Technology, Terry Rowe

LOCATIONS

HQ: INFIRMARY HEALTH SYSTEM, INC.
5 MOBILE INFIRMARY CIR, MOBILE, AL 366073513
Phone: 251 435-3030
Web: WWW.INFIRMARYHEALTH.ORG

HISTORICAL FINANCIALS

Company Type: Private

Income Statement — FYE: March 31

	REVENUE ($ mil.)	NET INCOME ($ mil.)	NET PROFIT MARGIN	EMPLOYEES
03/20	839	(65)	—	5,000
03/19	783	(4)	—	—
03/18	727	35	4.8%	—
03/17	696	70	10.2%	—
Annual Growth	6.4%	—	—	—

2020 Year-End Financials

Return on assets: (-7.9%)
Return on equity: (-19.4%)
Current ratio: 4.10
Cash ($ mil.): 41

INLAND COUNTIES REGIONAL CENTER, INC.

EXECUTIVES

Ceo, Carol A Fitzgibbons
Exec Dir*, Carol Fitzgibbons
Secretary, Sandra Fortino
Director, Denise Fanelli
Manager, Elizabeth Stroh
Manager, Mary Hernandez
Office Assistant, Stephen Hughes
Auditors: WINDES INC LONG BEACH CA

LOCATIONS

HQ: INLAND COUNTIES REGIONAL CENTER, INC.
1365 S WATERMAN AVE, SAN BERNARDINO, CA 924082804
Phone: 909 890-3000
Web: WWW.INLANDRC.ORG

HISTORICAL FINANCIALS

Company Type: Private

Income Statement — FYE: June 30

	REVENUE ($ mil.)	NET INCOME ($ mil.)	NET PROFIT MARGIN	EMPLOYEES
06/19	557	(0)	—	586
06/18	502	(0)	—	—
06/17	463	(39)	—	—
06/16	402	(7)	—	—
Annual Growth	11.5%	—	—	—

2019 Year-End Financials

Return on assets: (-0.6%)
Return on equity: —
Current ratio: 0.70
Cash ($ mil.): 31

INNOVATIVE AG SERVICES CO.

EXECUTIVES

Ceo, Rick Vaughan
Pres*, Randy Blake
1st Vp*, Paul Cook
Cfo*, Brenda Hoefler

Human Resources Staff, Marilyn E Ewing
Associate Director, Allen Jaspers
Vice President of Human Resour, Carla Elliott
Associate Director, Jeff Lindsay
Director, Ryan Collins
Vice President, Kevin Babcock
Location Manager, Gerald Severson
Auditors: MERIWETHER WILSON & COMPANY

LOCATIONS

HQ: INNOVATIVE AG SERVICES CO.
2010 S MAIN ST, MONTICELLO, IA 523107707
Phone: 319 465-3501
Web: WWW.INNOVATIVEAG.COM

HISTORICAL FINANCIALS

Company Type: Private

Income Statement — FYE: August 31

	REVENUE ($ mil.)	NET INCOME ($ mil.)	NET PROFIT MARGIN	EMPLOYEES
08/19	597	9	1.6%	500
08/18	649	11	1.8%	—
08/17	615	15	2.6%	—
08/16	682	10	1.6%	—
Annual Growth	(4.4%)	(4.6%)	—	—

2019 Year-End Financials

Return on assets: 3.2%
Return on equity: 6.0%
Current ratio: 1.80
Cash ($ mil.): 1

INOVA HEALTH CARE SERVICES

EXECUTIVES

Chm, Nicholas Carosi
Pres, John Knox Singleton
V Pres, Richard C Magenheimer
V Pres, James Hughes
V Pres, H Patrick Walters
SEC, Shannon Sinclair
Tres, Lydia Thomas
SEC, Tony Nader
Vice-President Information Ser, Maggie Cornett
Coordinator, Roxanne Wright
Chief of Emergency Room, Robert Cates

LOCATIONS

HQ: INOVA HEALTH CARE SERVICES
8110 GATEHOUSE RD 200E, FALLS CHURCH, VA 220421217
Phone: 703 289-2000
Web: WWW.INOVA.ORG

HISTORICAL FINANCIALS

Company Type: Private

Income Statement — FYE: December 31

	REVENUE ($ mil.)	NET INCOME ($ mil.)	NET PROFIT MARGIN	EMPLOYEES
12/13	2,134	145	6.8%	13,000
12/09	1,663	200	12.0%	—
12/03	1,012	46	4.6%	—
12/02	1	(0)	—	—
Annual Growth	96.8%	—	—	—

2013 Year-End Financials

Return on assets: 3.9%
Return on equity: 7.8%
Current ratio: 0.30
Cash ($ mil.): 203

INOVA HEALTH SYSTEM FOUNDATION

Inova Health Foundation provides financial support and assistance to the Inova Health System which operates a network of not-for-profit community hospitals in northern Virginia. It also supports home health services heart care programs clinical research and trials emergency and urgent care centers family practice locations and rehabilitation centers. To raise funds for the hospital system the foundation organizes fundraising monthly giving Inova visionaries gifts of stocks and corporate giving. Donors can also make contributions through the Inova website.

EXECUTIVES

Cfo, Richard Magenheimer
Ceo, John Niederhuber
Director Of Pharmacy, Gill Abernathy
Radiology Director, Deborah Berg
Chief People Officer, Terri Feely
Chairman, Terry D. McCallister
Executive Assistant To The Chair And Vice Chairs Department Of Medicine, Barbara Perry

LOCATIONS

HQ: INOVA HEALTH SYSTEM FOUNDATION
8110 GATEHOUSE RD 200E, FALLS CHURCH, VA 220421217
Phone: 703 289-2069
Web: WWW.FOUNDATION.INOVA.ORG

HISTORICAL FINANCIALS

Company Type: Private

Income Statement — FYE: December 31

	REVENUE ($ mil.)	NET INCOME ($ mil.)	NET PROFIT MARGIN	EMPLOYEES
12/17	765	717	93.6%	16,000
12/15	2,972	234	7.9%	—
Annual Growth	(49.2%)	74.8%	—	—

2017 Year-End Financials

Return on assets: 14.1%
Return on equity: 25.6%
Current ratio: 8.40
Cash ($ mil.): —

INTEGRIS BAPTIST MEDICAL CENTER, INC.

INTEGRIS Baptist Medical Center seeks integrity by caring for citizens from across the state of Oklahoma. The Oklahoma City-based medical center is the flagship hospital of the not-for-profit INTEGRIS Health system. With about 510 beds INTEGRIS Baptist is home to specialty care facilities for burns women's and children's health infertility stroke treatment cardiac care organ transplantation cancer treatment and more. The company also has centers for wellness hearing sleep disorders senior health and weight loss and it provides medical training and residency programs. INTEGRIS Baptist Medical Center opened its doors in 1959 with 200 beds.

EXECUTIVES

Nursing Director, Lewis Perkins
Secretary, Stacey Turner

LOCATIONS

HQ: INTEGRIS BAPTIST MEDICAL CENTER, INC.
3300 NW EXPRESSWAY, OKLAHOMA CITY, OK 731124418
Phone: 405 949-3011
Web: WWW.INTEGRISOK.COM

PRODUCTS/OPERATIONS

Selected Centers and Services

Advanced Cardiac Care
Anticoagulation Clinics
Bariatrics
Bennett Fertility Institute
Bones and Joints
Breast Care
Burn Center
Cancer Care
Cardiology
Case Management
Children's Health
Comprehensive Breast Center of Oklahoma
Continuing Medical Education
Corporate Assistance Program
Diabetes
Diagnostic Services
Digestive Health
Emergency Department
Fertility
General Heart Care
General Pediatrics
Home Care
Hospice
Hospitalist Program
Hough Ear Institute
Hyperbaric Medicine and Wound Care
James R. Daniel Cerebrovascular and Stroke Center
Jim Thorpe Rehabilitation Center
Labor and Delivery
Men's Health
Nazih Zuhdi Transplant Institute
Neonatal Intensive Care Unit (NICU)
Orthopedics
PACER Fitness Center
Pastoral Care
Pediatric Intensive Care Unit (PICU)
Pediatric Neurology
Pharmacy
Radiology Services
Senior Health
Sleep Disorders Center of Oklahoma
Stroke Center
Surgical Services
TeleHealth
Urogynecology
Weight Loss

COMPETITORS

Deaconess Health Care
Hillcrest Medical Center
Jackson County Memorial Hospital
Marian Health System
Mercy Health
Norman Regional Health
SSM Health Care
Saint Francis Health System
Texas Health Denton
Universal Health Services

HISTORICAL FINANCIALS

Company Type: Private

Income Statement — FYE: June 30

	REVENUE ($ mil.)	NET INCOME ($ mil.)	NET PROFIT MARGIN	EMPLOYEES
06/20	950	(14)	—	2,700
06/18	814	67	8.3%	—
06/16	701	6	1.0%	—
06/09	582	22	3.9%	—
Annual Growth	4.5%	—	—	—

2020 Year-End Financials

Return on assets: (-0.8%)
Return on equity: (-2.6%)
Current ratio: 1.90
Cash ($ mil.): 508

INTEGRIS HEALTH, INC.

INTEGRIS Health provides a range of health services to residents throughout the Sooner state. The company one of Oklahoma's largest not-for-profit health care organization operates 16 hospitals with some 1500 combined beds in both urban and rural communities. The hospitals provide services including primary diagnostic emergency surgical behavioral therapeutic and rehabilitative care. INTEGRIS also operates specialty facilities for the treatment of hearing disorders and neuromuscular ailments and for rehabilitation care. The company operates assisted living centers and a home health agency plus a network of physician clinics and ambulatory care centers.

Operations

Operations include INTEGRIS Baptist Medical Center (the system's largest with 629 beds) INTEGRIS South Oklahoma City (dba INTEGRIS Southwest Medical Center 389 beds) and INTEGRIS Rural Health facilities INTEGRIS Baptist Regional Health Center INTEGRIS Bass Baptist Health Center and INTEGRIS Grove Hospital.

INTEGRIS Health has approximately 1400 physicians in its system.

Sales and Marketing

Managed care payments account for more than half of net patient service revenue; Medicare and Medicaid combined account for around a third.

INTEGRIS Health offers community residents with more life experience such services as senior seminars and classes health screenings support groups and technology classes to help stay up-to-date on computer use. The idea is to help keep the elderly as independent as possible for as long as possible.

Financial Performance

The company's revenue increased slightly in fiscal 2015 rising 1% to $1.4 billion. This was due to growth in net patient service revenues. However INTEGRIS Health reported a net loss of $150 million (versus a net gain in 2014) due to factors that included higher operating expenses (salaries supplies) and higher pension liability adjustments. This in turn led to a 60% drop in cash flow from operations which totaled $49 million.

EXECUTIVES

President Integris Southwest Medical Center, James D. Moore
Chief Medical Officer, James White
Evp And Coo, Chris Hammes
President And Ceo, Bruce Lawrence
Cfo, David Hadley
President Integris Baptist Medical Center, Tim Johnsen
President Integris Bass Baptist Health Center Enid, Eddie Herrman
President Integris Baptist Regional Health Center Miami, Jordan Cash
President Integris Canadian Valley Hospital Yukon, Rex Van Meter
President Integris Cancer Institute Of Oklahoma, Phil Lance
President Integris Health Edmond, Avilla Williams
President Integris Health Partners, Carl Raczkowski
President Integris Heart Hospital, R. Mel Clark
President Integris Medical Group, Jeff Cruzan
President Lakeside Women's Hospital, Kelley Brewer
President And Coo Integris Mental Health And James L. Hall Jr. Center For Mind Body And Spirit, R. Murali Krishna
Vp Integris Nazih Zuhdi Transplant Insitute Integris Advanced Cardiac Care, Kathie Calbone
President Integris Grove Hospital, Tim Bowen, age 37
Clinical Director, Cindy Penland
Director Of Radiology, Amy Brown
Clinical Director, Elizabeth Davis
Vice President Integris Jim Thorpe Rehabilitation, Keith Wilton
Medical Director, Derek Irwin
Clinical Director, Nada Cain
Vice President, Paul Szymanski
Vice President Administrator Mental Health, Jim Igo
Assistant Vice President, Lynda Van Horn
Executive Vice President And Chief Financial Officer, Doug Smith
Pharmacy Manager, Jennifer Maune
Clinical Director, Lisa Aishman
Medical Director Paul Silverstein Burn Center, Christopher Lentz
Director Of Pharmacy, Larry Anderson
Assistant Vice President, Lynda Van
System Vp Finance, Jaquetta Clemons
Executive Vice President And Chief Physician Executive, Tommy Ibrahim
Medical Director, Jonathan Schwartz
Medical Records Director, Cheryl Luke
Auditors: KPMG LLP OKLAHOMA CITY OKLA

LOCATIONS

HQ: INTEGRIS HEALTH, INC.
3300 NW EXPRESSWAY, OKLAHOMA CITY, OK 731124418
Phone: 405 949-6066
Web: WWW.INTEGRISOK.COM

PRODUCTS/OPERATIONS

2015 Sales

	$ mil.	% of total
INTEGRIS Baptist Medical Center Inc.	635	39
INTEGRIS South Oklahoma City Hospital Corporation	244	15
INTEGRIS Rural Health Inc.	227	14
INTEGRIS Health Edmond	48	3
All others	459	29
Eliminations	(229.7)	-
Total	1,384	100

Selected Facilities

Baptist Medical Center
Baptist Regional Health Center
Bass Baptist Health Center
Blackwell Regional Hospital
Canadian Valley Regional Hospital
Cancer Institute of Oklahoma
Clinton Regional Hospital
Grove General Hospital
Health Edmond
Hospice House
Jim Thorpe Rehabilitation
Marshall County Medical Center
Mayes County Medical Center
Mental Health Spencer
Seminole Medical Center
Southwest Medical Center

COMPETITORS

Ardent Health Services
Deaconess Health Care
Fairview Health
HealthEast Care System
Hillcrest Medical Center
Marian Health System
Mercy Health
Norman Regional Health
Saint Francis Health System
St. John Health System

HISTORICAL FINANCIALS

Company Type: Private

Income Statement — FYE: June 30

	REVENUE ($ mil.)	NET INCOME ($ mil.)	NET PROFIT MARGIN	EMPLOYEES
06/20	2,077	(172)	—	9,500
06/19	1,950	11	0.6%	—
06/18	1,673	53	3.2%	—
06/17	1,558	111	7.2%	—
Annual Growth	10.1%	—	—	—

2020 Year-End Financials

Return on assets: (-5.7%)
Return on equity: (-16.1%)
Current ratio: 1.40
Cash ($ mil.): 555

INTERBOND CORPORATION OF AMERICA

Interbond Corporation of America (doing business as BrandsMart USA) boasts more than 500 brand names across its nearly 50000 electronics and entertainment products. It sells them in the US and internationally. It offers low-priced appliances computers TVs car stereos mobile phones personal care gadgets movie music games and more. The retailer runs about 10 electronics stores under the BrandsMart USA banner in the South Florida and Atlanta metropolitan areas. Each stocks more than $8 million in merchandise. BrandsMart USA also sells products online providing shipping for orders placed throughout the US Latin America and the Caribbean. Chairman Robert Perlman founded the company in 1977.

Operations

BrandsMart USA is one of the nation's largest volume-per-store retailers. With help from its low-price strategy the retailer has performed relatively well in the consumer electronics niche which once included bankrupt rivals such as Circuit City.

The company operates in Latin America and the Caribbean through a marketing agreement with shopping facilitator Punto Mio. Using Punto Mio's integration technology international customers accessing BrandsMart USA's website can browse products listed in their local currencies (purchase prices include applicable delivery fees and taxes).

Geographic Reach

Aside from its home office and warehouse facilities in Hollywood Florida BrandsMart USA operates stores in South Florida and in Georgia providing some 2600 jobs. Its clearance center is located in Florida's South Broward County.

Sales and Marketing

BrandsMart USA stores are known for their brightly lit interiors and neon price tags as well as their noisy bustling atmospheres. The simple presentation scheme helps to keep price tags low and to move crowds of customers. The retailer faces competition from the likes of Best Buy hhgregg and Wal-Mart.

To promote an eco-friendly message BrandsMart USA runs a Go Green Trade In Program a take-back initiative in partnership with the Consumer Electronics Exchange. The program issues BrandsMart USA gift cards to shoppers who trade in their unwanted electronics (including gaming consoles MP3 players and mobile phones) which are then recycled by the Consumer Electronics Exchange.

EXECUTIVES

Senior Vice President Chief Information Officer, Vincent Visco
Vice President Sales, Neil Anello
Vice President Customer Operations, Eydie Bowe
Auditors: KAUFMAN ROSSIN & CO PA MIAM

LOCATIONS

HQ: INTERBOND CORPORATION OF AMERICA
3200 SW 42ND ST, HOLLYWOOD, FL 33020
Phone: 954 797-4000
Web: WWW.BRANDSMARTUSA.COM

2013 Stores

	No.
Florida	5
Georgia	4
Total	**9**

PRODUCTS/OPERATIONS

Selected Products

Appliances
Blu-rays & DVDs
Headphones
Home audio
Car audio & GPS
Computers
Fitness
Games
Home security
Mobile phones
Office products
Personal care
Tablets
Toys
TVs
Wellness

Selected Brands
Bose
Dell
Electrolux
Epson
Frigidaire
iRobot
LG
Logitech
Samsung
Sharp
Sony

COMPETITORS

Best Buy
Costco Wholesale
Fry's Electronics
Home Depot
RadioShack
Wal-Mart

HISTORICAL FINANCIALS

Company Type: Private

Income Statement — FYE: September 24

	REVENUE ($ mil.)	NET INCOME ($ mil.)	NET PROFIT MARGIN	EMPLOYEES
09/11	743	3	0.5%	2,400
09/10	800	7	0.9%	—
09/08	936	19	2.1%	—
Annual Growth	(7.4%)	(43.3%)	—	—

2011 Year-End Financials

Return on assets: 1.3%
Return on equity: 2.2%
Current ratio: 1.00
Cash ($ mil.): 1

INTERMOUNTAIN HEALTH CARE INC

If you whoosh down the side of one of Idaho's majestic mountains and take a nasty spill Intermountain Health Care (dba Intermountain Healthcare) can pick you up and put you back together. From air ambulance services to urgent care clinics and general hospitals Intermountain has all the tools to mend skiers (and non-skiers alike) in Utah and southern Idaho. With about 1600 physicians the not-for-profit health system operates 22 hospitals and some 180 clinics as well as urgent care centers and rehabilitation centers. Intermountain also has an insurance arm named SelectHealth.

Operations

Intermountain Healthcare's hospitals range from general surgical to specialty care including orthopedic and pediatric facilities. Along with the full spectrum of physical health care services Intermountain also offers comprehensive mental health and substance abuse programs for patients of all ages. The organization's spectrum of care includes acute inpatient residential treatment day treatment chemical dependency inpatient/detoxification and intensive outpatient programs.

The system conducts cancer research through its partnership with Huntsman Cancer Institute at the University of Utah. The two share data best practices funding and co-conduct clinical trials. They also operate a number of cancer-specific treatment centers including multi-disciplinary tumor-specific clinics designed to provide one-stop service for cancer patients to meet with different cancer specialists on the same day for a more comprehensive treatment plan. Other areas of research include cardiovascular intensive medicine surgical care and behavioral health.

On the physician side the Intermountain Medical Group administers multi-specialty health care services in clinics located throughout the region. The group also operates urgent care clinics under the InstaCare and KidsCare banners.

Entering itself into the "what doesn't Intermountain do?" category the health system also provides health and dental insurance plans through its SelectHealth division.

Geographic Reach

Intermountain Healthcare serves the health care needs of Utah and Idaho residents.

Financial Performance

In 2016 Intermountain Healthcare's revenue grew 14% to $7.6 billion in fiscal 2016. This was due to increases in net patient services income non-patient activity income and investment income. Net patient services accounted for 63% of the system's total revenue that year.

The company used $7 billion of that revenue towards operating expenses including salaries and benefits medical supplies and facilities maintenance and other business services as well as towards funds dedicated to future needs.

Strategy

Intermountain Healthcare uses its dedicated supply chain organization to continuously improve system efficiency. In addition to delivering medical supplies the unit also oversees hospital vehicles.

The system partners with several leading IT companies (including Xi3 Intel Dell and NetApp) to operate its Healthcare Transformation Lab on the campus of its flagship hospital Intermountain Medical Center in Murray Utah. The lab researches develops and measures new ideas to improve patient care.

In 2016 the system launched Navican Genomics its genomics research and testing arm. Also that year it partnered with the Stanford Genome Technology Center to establish a collaborative research program.

Intermountain has a number of projects underway to add expand or replace existing facilities.

Company Background

Intermountain was formed in 1975 when the Church of Jesus Christ of Latter Day Saints donated 15 hospitals to local communities.

EXECUTIVES

Senior Vice President Community Health, Mikelle Moore
Senior Vice President, Greg Poulsen
Ceo Intermountain Medical Group And Vp Physician Division, Linda C. Leckman
President And Ceo Selecthealth, Patricia R. Richards
Evp And Cfo, Bert R. Zimmerli
Evp And Coo, Laura S. Kaiser
Regional Vp Central Region, Moody L. Chisholm
Vp And Cio, Marc Probst
President And Ceo, A. Marc Harrison, age 56
Regional Vp Soutwest Region, Terri Kane
Svp And Coo, Robert Allen
Vp Clinical Operations And Chief Nursing Officer, Kim Henrichsen
Ceo Urban North Region And Mckay-dee Hospital Center, Timothy T. Pehrson
Chief Medical Officer, Brent E. Wallace
Ceo Primary Children's Medical Center, Katherine A. (Katy) Welkie
Regional Vp South Region, Steve Smoot
Vp Supply Chain And Support Services, Joe Walsh
Assistant Vice President Of Risk Management Services, Harlan Hammond
Assistant Vice President Investments, Stacy Jennings
Assistant Vice President Communications, Tom Vitelli
Assistant Vice President Compensation And Benefits, David Adams
Vice President Marketing And Communication, Todd Frehse
Assistant Vice President, Katherina Holzhauser
Vice President Healthcare Transformation, Joe Mott
Vice President, George Null Hamilton
Director Of Pharmacy, Scott Yardley
Medical Director, Scott Whittle
Vice President Of Pharmacy Affairs, Eric Cannon
Vice President Human Resources, Dan Zuhlke
Vice President And General Counsel, Doug Hammer
Medical Director, Tamara Lewis
Avp Pharmacy Services, Nannette Berensen
Assistant Vice President Clinical Is Operations, Tammy Madsen
Medical Director Community Health And Prevention, Tamara Sheffield
Vice President Rural Region, Rob Allen
Medical Director Imaging Services, Keith White
Pharmacy Manager, Robb Dengg
Pharmacy Manager, Bevan Jensen
Director Of Him, Mary Staub
Pharmacy Manager, Heather Hansen
Assistant Vice President Telehealth Services, Brian Wayling
Medical Director Clinical Genetics Institute, Steven Bleyl
Clinical Director Primary Children's Pediatric Behavioral Health Clinic, Nancy Cantor
Nursing Director, David Hurst
Vice President Of Operational Finance, Mark Runyon
Medical Director Informatics, Farukh Usmani
Director Of Pharmacy, Tom Dockendorf

Pharmacy Director Vice President Of Pharmacy Services, Matt Mitchell
Vice President Marketing, Caralee Lyon
Operating Room Dir, Travis Fullmer
Director Of Radiology, Coby Knudsen
Operating Room Dir, Dorothy Evans
Medical Director, Masood Safaee
Vice Chairman, Bruce T. Reese
Chairman, A. Scott Anderson
Secretary, Nicole Houghton
Secretary, Jeri Lay
Secretary, Sheri Jones
Medical Secretary, Janet Staker
Medical Secretary, Renee Harston
Board Member, Kim Bennion
Scheduling Secretary, Jeanine Price
Secretary, JoAnn Fountain
Medical Secretary, Sherri Longhurst
Secretary, Stephanie Stromberg
Secretary, Jodi Simmons
Secretary, Heidi Null Leon
Auditors: KPMG LLP SALT LAKE CITY UTA

LOCATIONS

HQ: INTERMOUNTAIN HEALTH CARE INC
36 S STATE ST STE 1600, SALT LAKE CITY, UT 841111633
Phone: 801 442-2000
Web: WWW.INTERMOUNTAINHEALTHCARE.ORG

PRODUCTS/OPERATIONS

2016 Sales

	$ mil.	% of total
Net patient services	4,368	57
Non-patient activities	3,010	40
Non-operating income	237	3
Total	**7,617**	**100**

Selected Hospitals

Alta View Hospital (Sandy UT)
American Fork Hospital (Utah)
Bear River Valley Hospital (Tremonton UT)
Cassia Regional Medical Center (Burley ID)
Delta Community Medical Center (Utah)
Dixie Regional Medical Center (St. George UT)
Fillmore Community Medical Center (Utah)
Garfield Memorial Hospital (Panguitch UT)
Heber Valley Medical Center (Heber City UT)
Intermountain Medical Center (Murray UT)
LDS Hospital (Salt Lake City)
Logan Regional Hospital (Orem UT)
McKay-Dee Hospital Center (Ogden UT)
McKay-Dee Behavioral Health Institute
Orem Community Hospital (Utah)
Park City Medical Center (Park City UT)
Primary Children's Medical Center (Salt Lake City)
Riverton Hospital (Riverton UT)
Sanpete Valley Hospital (Mt. Pleasant UT)
Sevier Valley Hospital (Richfield UT)
TOSH - The Orthopedic Specialty Hospital (Murray UT)
Utah Valley Regional Medical Center (Provo UT)
Valley View Medical Center (Cedar City UT)

COMPETITORS

CHRISTUS Health
Encompass Health
HCA
LifePoint Health
Ogden Regional Medical Center
Regence BlueCross BlueShield of Utah
St. Mark's
University of Utah Hospitals & Clinics

HISTORICAL FINANCIALS

Company Type: Private

Income Statement — FYE: December 31

	REVENUE ($ mil.)	NET INCOME ($ mil.)	NET PROFIT MARGIN	EMPLOYEES
12/19	8,812	1,212	13.8%	35,000
12/18	7,724	420	5.4%	—
12/17	6,940	1,061	15.3%	—
12/16	6,716	606	9.0%	—
Annual Growth	9.5%	26.0%	—	—

2019 Year-End Financials

Return on assets: 8.0%
Return on equity: 13.3%
Current ratio: 1.20
Cash ($ mil.): 376

INTERNATIONAL RESCUE COMMITTEE, INC.

EXECUTIVES

Pres-Ceo, David Miliband
General Counsel*, Ricardo Castro
Cfo*, Danusia Dzierzbinski
Project Coordinator, Emelina Cesheshyan
Programmer Analyst, Adnan Suvalic
Human Resources Manager, Sead Eminovic
Procurement Staff, Sherif Blaku
Country Director, Jason Phillips
Senior Program Officer, Natalia Lopez
Senior Project Manager, Quentin Scott
Regional Resettlement Director, Suzy Cop
Auditors: KPMG LLP NEW YORK NY

LOCATIONS

HQ: INTERNATIONAL RESCUE COMMITTEE, INC.
122 E 42ND ST, NEW YORK, NY 101680002
Phone: 212 551-3000
Web: WWW.THEIRC.ORG

HISTORICAL FINANCIALS

Company Type: Private

Income Statement — FYE: September 30

	REVENUE ($ mil.)	NET INCOME ($ mil.)	NET PROFIT MARGIN	EMPLOYEES
09/18	744	2	0.3%	8,000
09/17	753	44	5.9%	—
09/14	562	9	1.7%	—
09/11	397	11	2.9%	—
Annual Growth	9.4%	(19.9%)	—	—

2018 Year-End Financials

Return on assets: 0.6%
Return on equity: 1.1%
Current ratio: 1.60
Cash ($ mil.): 99

INTERNATIONAL WIRE GROUP, INC.

International Wire Group (IWG) bares it all in the wire business. Through three divisions – Bare Wire Products Engineered Products - Europe and High Performance Conductors – IWG makes multi-gauge bare silver- nickel- and tin-plated copper wire as well as engineered wire products and performance conductors. The company's customers (General Cable is one of its largest) include suppliers and OEMs. IWG's wire products are used in industrial/energy consumer electronics aerospace and defense medical electronics automotive and appliance applications.

Operations

The company's Bare Wire Products (or conductors) are used to transmit digital video and audio signals or conduct electricity and are sold to more than 1000 insulated wire manufacturers and various industrial OEMs for use in computer and data communications products general industrial energy appliances automobiles and other applications.

IWG's Engineered Products - Europe makes bare copper wire products which are sold to a diverse customer base of various OEMs in Europe.

Its High Performance Conductors include tin nickel and silver plated copper and copper alloy conductors including standard and customized conductors as well as specialty film insulated conductors and miniature tubing products.

Subsidiaries include US-based Continental Cordage a leading maker of braided wire for a wide range of commercial military and industrial applications and Tresse Metallique J. Forissier SAS and Italtrecce leading European makerd of bare copper wire products.

Geographic Reach

The company maintains 18 manufacturing plants and two distribution facilities in the US and Europe (Belgium France Italy and Poland). IWG makes the majority of its sales in the US.

Sales and Marketing

IWG serves customers in the electrical appliances power supplies aircraft railway and automotive system sectors. The volatile pricing of raw materials especially copper is a lingering concern for IWG. The company depends on four leading suppliers for copper and does not have long-term supply contracts with any of them creating concern about the reliability of IWG's copper supply chain. Many of the company's customers have their own captive (in-house) wire production facilities and they could exclusively turn to those facilities reducing orders to IWG.

Mergers and Acquisitions

In late 2019 International Wire Group (IWG) bought New York-based Owl Wire & Cable (Owl) from Marmon Holdings. The deal expands IWG's copper wire manufacturing footprint.

EXECUTIVES

Chb, Rodney D Kent
Sr V Pres-Cfo-Sec*, Glenn J Holler
V Pres Fin*, Donald F Dekay
V Pres Purchasing & Logistics*, Geoff Kent
Customer Representativ, Brett Charbonneau
Customer Representativ, Briant Meagher
Process Engineer Manager, Chris Lyon
Engineer, David Sherwood
Customer Team Member, Jessica Carle
Executive Assistant, Lauren Badger
Human Resources Manager, Linda McKay

LOCATIONS

HQ: INTERNATIONAL WIRE GROUP, INC.
12 MASONIC AVE, CAMDEN, NY 133161202
Phone: 315 245-2000
Web: WWW.INTERNATIONALWIREGROUP.COM

PRODUCTS/OPERATIONS

Selected Products
Bare wire products
Bare and tin-plated copper wire (or conductors)
Engineered
Bare copper wire (to conduct electricity)
High performance conductors
Conductors

COMPETITORS

A.E. Petsche
Cerro Wire
Driver-Harris
Encore Wire
LEONI
LS Cable
Loos & Co.
Nexans
Okonite
Owl Wire & Cable
Prestolite Wire
Republic Wire
Southwire

HISTORICAL FINANCIALS

Company Type: Private

Income Statement — FYE: December 31

	REVENUE ($ mil.)	NET INCOME ($ mil.)	NET PROFIT MARGIN	EMPLOYEES
12/08	736	6	0.9%	1,600
12/07	730	15	2.2%	—
12/06	1,789	0	—	—
Annual Growth	—13597.3%		—	—

2008 Year-End Financials

Return on assets: 1.8%
Return on equity: 3.6%
Current ratio: 2.10
Cash ($ mil.): 7

INVACARE CORPORATION (TW)

LOCATIONS

HQ: INVACARE CORPORATION (TW)
39400 TAYLOR PKWY, NORTH RIDGEVILLE, OH 440356270
Phone: 440 329-6000
Web: WWW.INVACARE.COM

HISTORICAL FINANCIALS

Company Type: Private

Income Statement — FYE: December 31

	REVENUE ($ mil.)	NET INCOME ($ mil.)	NET PROFIT MARGIN	EMPLOYEES
12/11	1,801	(4)	—	45
12/10	1,722	25	1.5%	—
12/09	1,693	41	2.4%	—
Annual Growth	3.1%	—	—	—

2011 Year-End Financials

Return on assets: (-0.3%)
Return on equity: (-0.7%)
Current ratio: 1.80
Cash ($ mil.): 34

IOWA HEALTH SYSTEM

Iowa Health System (IHS) which does business as UnityPoint is an integrated health care system that operates more than 20 acute care hospitals in large communities throughout Iowa as well as parts of western Illinois and Madison Wisconsin. UnityPoint also supports more than 15 rural hospitals and it manages about 300 physician clinics located in rural and suburban areas. The system's hospitals provide general medical-surgical care as well as care in a number of medical specialties such as cardiovascular disease mental health and home health services.

Operations

In 2014 the system had about 155000 patient admissions facilitated 20000 births and saw a total of some 4.5 million patients.

Geographic Reach

UnityPoint Health includes a dozen hospitals in 10 Iowa cities four in Illinois and another in Wisconsin. Its largest geographic markets served are Anamosa Cedar Rapids Des Moines Dubuque Fort Dodge Sioux City and Waterloo Iowa; the Quad Cities/Muscatine region in Iowa and Illinois; Peoria Illinois; and Madison Wisconsin.

Strategy

The health system operates many of its member hospitals through affiliation agreements where it provides administration contracting billing legal recruitment information technology and other central services. The health system expands by adding new affiliation agreements and by building new health facilities.

UnityPoint Health struck a major merger agreement with South Dakota-based Sanford Health in 2019 but the deal was terminated later that year. The combination would have created a massive health network with more than 75 hospitals in 26 states.

Company Background

Iowa Health System (IHS) was founded in 1993. In 2013 the network rebranded itself UnityPoint to showcase its mission to be a point of unity for patient care and its expansion to include health care facilities in other states including Illinois and Wisconsin.

EXECUTIVES

President And Ceo Unitypoint Health -des Moines, Eric Crowell
Vp And Cio, Joy M. Grosser
Ceo, Kevin Vermeer
Vp Supply Chain Management, Katie Marchik
Svp And Cfo, Mark Johnson
Evp And Coo; President And Ceo Meriter-unitypoint Health Madison, Arthur Nizza
Vp Payor Innovation; Ceo Unitypoint At Work, Brian Jones
Ceo Unitypoint Health -st. Luke's -sioux City, Lynn Wold
Ceo Jones Regional Medical Center Anamosa, Eric Briesemeister
President And Ceo Unitypoint Health -dubuque, David Brandon
President And Ceo Unitypoint Health -peoria, Debbie Simon
President And Ceo Unitypoint Health -trinity (quad Cities Muscatine), Rick Seidler
President And Ceo Unitypoint Health -waterloo, Pam Delagardelle
President And Ceo St. Luke's -cedar Rapids, Ted Townsend
Ceo Unitypoint Health Partners, David Williams
Svp Insurance Division And Ceo Physicians Plus Insurance Corporation (ppic), Troy Caraway
Evp And Coo Unitypoint Health Des Moines And Interim Ceo Unitypoint Clinic, Steve Stephenson
Svp Integration And Optimization And Interim Ceo Unitypoint At Home, Susan K. Thompson
President And Ceo Unitypoint Health Fort Dodge, Mike Dewerff
Vice President People Excellence, Emily Porter
Vice President Of Behavioral Health, Kevin Carroll
Vice President Of Practice Operations, Matt Behrens
Associate Medical Director, Julia Jenkins
Vice President Patient And Community Advocacy, Pat Shouse
Vice President Operations, Joe Linn
Vice President Network Business Services Development, Lori Weih
Medical Director Finley Wound Care Center, David Arnold
Vice President, Tammy Duvendack
Vice President Of Operations And Homecare, Jane Arnold
Medical Director, Michael Oconnor
Vice President Secretary Administration, Debra Russell
Radiology Director, Vickie Rahe
Chairman, Mike Williams
Vice Chair, Mike Stone
Secretary, Lucinda Barnes
Department Secretary, Allison Kamerling
Department Secretary, Diane Hagan
Auditors: KPMG LLP MINNEAPOLIS MN

LOCATIONS

HQ: IOWA HEALTH SYSTEM
1776 WEST LAKES PKWY # 400, WEST DES MOINES, IA 502668377
Phone: 515 241-6161
Web: WWW.IHS.ORG

PRODUCTS/OPERATIONS

Selected Facilities
Metropolitan Hospitals
Allen Memorial Hospital Corporation (Waterloo Iowa)
Iowa Lutheran Hospital (Des Moines Iowa)
Iowa Methodist Medical Center (Des Moines Iowa)
Blank Children's Hospital (Des Moines Iowa)
Methodist Medical Center of Illinois (Peoria Illinois)
Methodist West Hospital (West Des Moines Iowa)
St. Luke's Hospital (Cedar Rapids Iowa)
St. Luke's Regional Medical Center (Sioux City Iowa)
Jones Regional Medical Center (Anamosa Iowa)
The Finley Hospital (Dubuque Iowa)
Trinity Bettendorf (Bettendorf Iowa)
Trinity Moline (Moline Illinois)
Trinity Muscatine (Muscatine Iowa)
Trinity Regional Medical Center (Fort Dodge Iowa)
Trinity Rock Island (Rock Island Illinois)
Rural Hospitals
Buena Vista Regional Medical Center (Storm Lake Iowa)
Clarke County Hospital (Osceola Iowa)
Community Memorial Hospital (Sumner Iowa)
Greater Regional Medical Center (Creston Iowa)
Greene County Medical Center (Jefferson Iowa)
Grundy County Memorial Hospital (Grundy Center Iowa)
Guthrie County Hospital (Guthrie Center Iowa)
Guttenberg Municipal Hospital (Guttenberg Iowa)
Humboldt County Memorial Hospital (Humboldt Iowa)
Loring Hospital (Sac City Iowa)
Pocahontas Community Hospital (Pocahantas Iowa)

COMPETITORS

Avera Health
Blessing Hospital
CHI Health
Genesis Health System
McDonough District Hospital
Mercy Health Network
Methodist Health System
OSF Healthcare System

HISTORICAL FINANCIALS

Company Type: Private

Income Statement				FYE: December 31
	REVENUE ($ mil.)	NET INCOME ($ mil.)	NET PROFIT MARGIN	EMPLOYEES
12/17	4,157	229	5.5%	18,923
12/16	4,054	148	3.7%	—
Annual Growth	2.5%	54.4%	—	—

2017 Year-End Financials

Return on assets: 4.1%
Return on equity: 6.8%
Current ratio: 1.50
Cash ($ mil.): 251

IOWA PHYSICIANS CLINIC MEDICAL FOUNDATION

EXECUTIVES

Pres-Ceo, Sanjeeb Khatua
Pres, Daniel P Allen
Cfo, Robin McNichols
SEC, Kenneth W Anderson

LOCATIONS

HQ: IOWA PHYSICIANS CLINIC MEDICAL FOUNDATION
8101 BIRCHWOOD CT UNIT N, JOHNSTON, IA 501312930
Phone: 515 471-9200
Web: WWW.UNITYPOINT.ORG

HISTORICAL FINANCIALS

Company Type: Private

Income Statement				FYE: December 31
	REVENUE ($ mil.)	NET INCOME ($ mil.)	NET PROFIT MARGIN	EMPLOYEES
12/17	600	17	3.0%	1,000
12/00	76	(13)	—	—
12/99	8	2	31.3%	—
12/98	61	(19)	—	—
Annual Growth	12.8%	—	—	—

2017 Year-End Financials

Return on assets: 8.6%
Return on equity: 26.0%
Current ratio: 2.30
Cash ($ mil.): 11

IOWA STATE UNIVERSITY OF SCIENCE AND TECHNOLOGY

Home to the Cyclones athletics teams Iowa State University of Science and Technology (ISU) can be a whirlwind experience for some. ISU is a public land-grant institution offering higher education courses and programs with an emphasis on science technology and related areas. ISU's eight colleges offer more than 100 undergraduate degrees and nearly 200 fields of study leading to graduate and professional degrees. The university has an enrollment of more than 31000 students and charges more than $7720 in tuition and fees for resident students for two semesters.

Operations

In fiscal 2012 Iowa State received $360.2 million in grants contracts co-operative agreements and gifts of which about 60% is utilized for research purpose. The university's research park has about 20000 square feet of incubators space including office and laboratories.

Geographic Reach

The university enrolls students from 50 states and more than 100 countries.

Financial Performance

The 6% increase in revenues in 2012 was due to higher tuition and fees sales and services of educational activities and auxiliary enterprise revenues. The tuition revenue increase was to a 5% hike in the resident tuition rate coupled with record enrollments. The increase in sales and services of educational activities was due to large one-time events ISU farms and the Vet Diagnostic Lab. ISU's auxiliary enterprises reported revenue growth thanks to new revenue sources and a record number of students in the residence system.

ISU's net income increased by 47% in 2012 thanks to higher operating expenses and a decline in non-operating revenues. Non-operating revenues decreased $24.4 million thanks to an $11 million decrease in funding from education appropriations. Investment income also dropped $16.3 million or 49% mainly due to an unrealized loss in the value of investments.

Company Background

Chartered as Iowa Agriculture College in 1858 the school first officially opened for classes in 1869. Among ISU's notable alumni is scientist and inventor George Washington Carver.

EXECUTIVES

Senior Vice President And Provost, Jonathan Wickert
Assistant Vice President Chief Of Police, Michael Newton
Vice President, Atalie Ruhnke
Vice President, Karen Bramow
Vice President Membership Development, Tyler Brodeur
Department Chair Lynn Gleason Professor Of Interdisciplinary Engineering, Caroline Hayes
Associate Vice President For Student Affairs, Vernon Hurte
Vice President, Aline Sartor-chicowski
Vice President, Parker Bibus
Vice President Community Service, Kate Stewart
Vice President Membership, Sam Britt
Vice President Finance, Emily Cory
Secretary, Kris Tigges
Secretary, Robin Gogerty
Secretary, Joyce Wray
Secretary, Traci Stewart
Secretary Department Of Agricultural And Biosystems Engineering, Kristine Bell
Secretary, Nancy Paris
Secretary, Paula Kokemiller
Secretary, Katherine Petersen
Secretary, Annmarie Butler
Secretary, Jessica Toliver
Auditors: MARLYS K GASTON CPA DES MOI

LOCATIONS

HQ: IOWA STATE UNIVERSITY OF SCIENCE AND TECHNOLOGY
515 MORRILL RD, AMES, IA 500112105
Phone: 515 294-6162
Web: WWW.IASTATE.EDU

PRODUCTS/OPERATIONS

Colleges

Agriculture and Life Sciences
Business
Design
Engineering
Graduate
Human Sciences
Liberal Arts and Sciences
Veterinary Medicine

HISTORICAL FINANCIALS

Company Type: Private

Income Statement				FYE: June 30
	REVENUE ($ mil.)	NET INCOME ($ mil.)	NET PROFIT MARGIN	EMPLOYEES
06/19	952	97	10.2%	5,800
06/18	948	58	6.2%	—
06/17	920	77	8.4%	—
06/16	902	67	7.5%	—
Annual Growth	1.8%	12.7%	—	—

2019 Year-End Financials

Return on assets: 3.6%
Return on equity: 5.7%
Current ratio: 1.20
Cash ($ mil.): 41

J M SMITH CORPORATION

J M Smith Corporation has gone from corner drugstore to supplying drugstores and more. The family-owned holding company's primary subsidiary is Smith Drug which provides purchasing and distribution services for more than 1000 independent pharmacies in more than 20 US states. It also operates through QS/1 Data Systems and Integral Solutions both of which offer data management software and services for pharmacies care providers and government agencies. Smith Premier provides prescription benefit management while other divisions offer automated dispensing systems for pharmacies and marketing services for drugmakers. Other units include Norgenix and RxMedic Systems.

Operations

The company operates through six business units: Smith Drug Company QS/1 Smith Premier Services Integral Solutions Group Norgenix and RxMedic Systems.

In addition to being its oldest subsidiary J M Smith's core Smith Drug unit is one of the top private wholesale drug distributors in the US. The company's Smith Premier unit also has a nationwide presence providing prescription management services through some 57000 contracted pharmacies.

Meanwhile the growing QS/1 division has installed more than 12000 health care and pharmacy automation systems and has more than 20 service offices across the US. The Integral Solutions unit which has about 15 offices scattered across the nation offers communication networking systems for universities banks and manufacturers in addition to health care customers.

J M Smith newest subsidiary Norgenix is a specialty pharmaceutical medical device and biotech company that engages in the development commercialization and sales of pharmaceutical products that serve the unmet needs within women's health. It acquires or licenses rights for select pharmaceuticals which it then markets through its direct sales force in North America. Norgenix is focused on the women's health markets and began marketing its first hormone replacement therapy in 2009.

RxMedic Systems provides leading-edge dispensing technology to pharmacies.

Geographic Reach

Smith Drug serves customers in 21 states primarily in the southern US as well as Washington DC and the Virgin Islands.

Sales and Marketing

The company supplies products services and technologies to pharmacies institutions local government agencies and businesses across the US.

Strategy

J M Smith's cornerstone Smith Drug subsidiary continues to be a key growth component doubling the number of states in which it operates over the last decade. However the company is also extolling its energies towards developing and introducing innovative data management and technology solutions through other subsidiaries to meet the rising demand for such solutions in the health care market.

Smith Premier is working to help customers go paperless by offering electronic prescription processing while RxMedic's dispensing systems allow pharmacies to increase productivity with its robotic counting and dispensing equipment.

The company's QS/1 subsidiary has experienced rapid growth in recent years as pharmacies and care providers increasingly look to automate processes and the Integral Solutions unit also benefits from recent trends in the health care market to improve electronic communication systems.

Partnerships are also key to J M Smith's growth. In 2014 Norgenix partnered with CrossBay Medical for the co-promotion of the SonoSure a device for use to access the uterine cavity for saline infusion sonohysterography and to obtain an endometrial biopsy if needed using the same device.

Mergers and Acquisitions

In late 2016 the company agreed to buy Vermont-based Burlington Drug Company which serves community pharmacies in New England and New York as well as certain assets of Pharmacy Health Services. The moves will broaden J M Smith's presence in the Northeast a target market for the company.

Company Background

In 2010 Smith expanded by acquiring health equipment manufacturing firm RxMedic. Through the purchase the company entered the automated dispensing system market.

J M Smith was founded in 1943 by drugstore proprietor James Smith and is run by the Smith family.

EXECUTIVES

President Integral Solutions Group (isg), Joe Strayer
President Smith Drug Company, Jeff Foreman
President Integra Ltc Solutions Llc, Kevin Welch
Chairman And Ceo, A. Alan Turfe
President Qs/1, Saul Factor
Cfo And Treasurer, Philip J. Ryan
Senior Vice President Business Development, Rick Simerly
Vice President General Counsel And Corporate Secretary, Robert Barrett

LOCATIONS

HQ: J M SMITH CORPORATION
101 W SAINT JOHN ST # 305, SPARTANBURG, SC 293065150
Phone: 864 542-9419
Web: WWW.JMSMITH.COM

Selected Office Locations

Altamonte Springs FL
Brandon MS
Columbia SC
Dallas TX
Fairmont WV
Gray ME
Hermitage PA
Houston TX
Indianapolis IN
Lexington KY
Mechanicsburg PA
Miami FL
Morrisville GA
Paragould AR
Perry GA
Pleasant Hill MO
Richmond VA
Seattle WA
Spartanburg SC
St. Paul MN
Sturbridge MA
Valdosta GA
Valencia CA
Wake Forest NC

PRODUCTS/OPERATIONS

Selected Divisions

Integral Solutions Group
Norgenix Pharmaceuticals
QS/1
RxMedic
Smith Drug Company
Smith Premier Services

COMPETITORS

AmerisourceBergen
CVS
Cardinal Health
Express Scripts
Fiserv
H. D. Smith Wholesale Drug
HP Enterprise Services
Kinray
McKesson
PharMerica

HISTORICAL FINANCIALS

Company Type: Private

Income Statement — FYE: February 28

	REVENUE ($ mil.)	NET INCOME ($ mil.)	NET PROFIT MARGIN	EMPLOYEES
02/15	2,566	47	1.8%	235
02/14	2,370	38	1.6%	—
02/13	2,362	26	1.1%	—
Annual Growth	4.2%	33.8%	—	—

2015 Year-End Financials

Return on assets: 8.1%
Return on equity: 16.0%
Current ratio: 1.60
Cash ($ mil.): 142

J.E. DUNN CONSTRUCTION COMPANY

From first building designs to the last brick J.E. Dunn Construction helps make building plans a done deal. The contractor offers general construction services construction management and design/build services nationwide. It's known for its work on campus health care and commercial projects including the BayCare Health System CHI Health - Creighton University Medical Center - Bergan Mercy Seaton Hall/Regnier Hall Decatur High School and Ron Clark Academy. Founded in 1924 the company is one of Kansas City's top commercial construction firms and has been listed as one of the nation's top 20 general building companies. It operates as a subsidiary of J.E. Dunn Construction Group.

Operations

JE Dunn has ranked as one of the top 20 largest general building companies in the US. It offers services such as virtual design & construction augmented reality smart building solutions robotics as well as wearable technology including tool assist personal safety access to data as job aids and visualization. JE Dunn also operates a real estate investment through its subsidiary JE Dunn Capital Partners.

It counts several noteworthy projects among its portfolio such as Cerner Innovations Campus Omaha Capitol District Restoration Hardware The Thompson Hotel Minnesota State Capitol Lenexa Civic Center and Minnesota Children's Museum Renovation and Addition.

Geographic Reach

Based in Kansas City Missouri JE Dunn operates nearly 25 offices throughout the US.

Sales and Marketing

JE Dunn works on projects for clients in several sectors including projects related to: science and technology corporate environments healthcare hospitality government and military energy and utility education and multifamily residential properties among others.

Financial Performance

While full financial information of the privately-held company were not available the company reported that it brings in annual revenue of $3.6 billion as of early 2019. Its revenues in 2019 rose to $4.3 billion representing the company's consistent revenue growth over the years.

Strategy

J.E. Dunn Construction Company has been busy working on a variety of different projects in recent years. In 2020 J.E. Dunn completed the seven-story 350000-square-foot new Johnson County Courthouse which replaced the aging overcrowded existing courthouse by consolidating the Tenth Judicial District Court District Attorney and supporting spaces into a distinctive civic building. The team plans to finish installing systems and ancillary furniture in November. Johnson County staff will begin occupying the courthouse by September and the building is intended to open to the public in the first quarter of 2021.

Earlier that year it started construction on the new General Leonard Wood Army Community Hospital a $295 million state-of-the-art 52-acre hospital complex that when completed in 2024 will replace the current hospital facility.

J.E. Dunn also worked on the $40 million Minnehaha County Jail expansion which added 329 beds and new administration space which will solve a long-standing space problem. J.E. Dunn worked with Henry Carlson Construction JLG Architects and BWBR Architects for this project.

Company Background

John Ernest Dunn (Ernie) founded JE Dunn Construction Company in Kansas City Missouri in 1924. In the past JE Dunn grew through acquisitions purchasing RJ Griffin & Co. (Atlanta) in 2000 Witcher Construction (Minneapolis) in 1990 and Drake Construction (Portland Oregon) in 1992.

EXECUTIVES

Executive Vice President, William Dunn
President & Chief Executive Officer, Gordon E. Lansford
Midwest Regional President, Dirk Schafer
Evp And Chief Risk Officer, Casey S. Halsey
Evp And Chief Legal Officer, Thomas F. (Tom) Whittaker
West Regional President, Steve Hamline
East Regional President, Dan Kaufman
Cio, John Jacobs
South Central Regional President, Greg Lorei
Cfo, Beth Soukup
Evp And Chief Marketing Officer, Greg Nook
Vice President Of Preconstruction For The Southwest Division, Curt Campbell
Vice President, Tom Heger
Vice President, David Slovikoski
Vice President, Mike Cloud
Vice President, Brent Ferguson
Assistant Vice President Field Operations, Bob Jacquinot
Senior Vice President, Bill Edwards
Vice President, Dave Ruf
Senior Vice President, Randall Bredar
Vice President, Kevin Rogert
Vice President Systems Quality Assurance, Michael Clippinger
Vice President Group Manager, Dustin Liljehorn
Senior Vice President, Jeff Fuller
Vice President, John Johnston
Vice President, Curtis Golba
Vice President Operations, Marc Hutson
Vice President, David Barber
Vice President Marketing, Diane Miller
Executive Vice President Field Operations, Dan Hotchkiss
Vice President, Jeff Blaesing
Senior Vice President Healthcare, Bruce Anderson
Assistant Vice President, Kyle McQuiston
Vice President Healthcare, Bill Igel
Vice President, Donnie Lindstrom
Vice President, Jim Ray
Vice President Group Manager, Jake Nellis
Vice President Industrial Group, Brent Strength
Vice President, Angela Talbot
Vice President Of Communications, Emily Gallagher
Vice President Of Operations, Matthew Braun
Vice President, Gene Mccarthy
Vice President East Region, Pat Arrington
Vice President, Patrick Oaks
Vice President Chc, Todd Freed
Vice President Preconstruction, Monty Everson
Vice President Nw Division, Darin Stegemoller
Senior Vice President, Jeff Hicks
Senior Vice President, Kevin O'gara
Vice President Group Manager, Sean Buck
Vice President, Jeff Camplwell
Vice President Of Operations, Matthew Braun Pe
Vp Diversity Inclusion And Compliance, Pete Burney
Vice President, Terry Dunn
Vice President Of Domestic Business Development, David Wells
Vice President, Justin Vanderbrink
Chairman, Steve Dunn
Secretary, Barbara Hachey
Secretary, Barb Hachey
Treasurer Vice President, Judith Martin
Auditors: KPMG LLP KANSAS CITY MO

LOCATIONS

HQ: J.E. DUNN CONSTRUCTION COMPANY
1001 LOCUST ST, KANSAS CITY, MO 641061904
Phone: 816 474-8600
Web: WWW.JEDUNN.COM

PRODUCTS/OPERATIONS

Selected Project Delivery Methods
Competitive Bid
Construction Management (Agency)
Design-Build
General Contracting/CM At Risk
Integrated Project Delivery
Project Management

COMPETITORS

Adolfson & Peterson Inc.
Barnhart
Boran Craig Barber Engel
C.F. Jordan
CORE Construction
Clarkson Construction
Flintco
H.J. Russell
Hensel Phelps Construction
Korte
M. A. Mortenson
MEDCO Construction
Skanska USA Building
Turner Corporation
Weitz

HISTORICAL FINANCIALS

Company Type: Private

Income Statement — FYE: December 31

	REVENUE ($ mil.)	NET INCOME ($ mil.)	NET PROFIT MARGIN	EMPLOYEES
12/17	2,945	0	—	1,635
12/16	2,909	0	—	—
12/15	2,909	0	—	—
12/14	2,242	0	—	—
Annual Growth	9.5%	—	—	—

2017 Year-End Financials

Return on assets: —
Return on equity: —
Current ratio: 1.10
Cash ($ mil.): 29

J.E. DUNN CONSTRUCTION GROUP, INC.

Owned by descendants of founder John Ernest Dunn J.E. Dunn Construction Group operates as the holding company for a group of construction firms that includes flagship J.E. Dunn Construction and Atlanta-based R.J. Griffin & Company. Founded in 1924 it builds institutional commercial and industrial structures nationwide. It also provides construction and program management and design/build services. J.E. Dunn Construction which is among the largest US general builders was one of the first contractors to offer the construction management delivery method. Some of its major projects have included an IRS facility and the world headquarters for H&R Block both located in Kansas City Missouri.

Operations

Besides its primary operations of J.E. Dunn Construction and R.J. Griffin & Company the construction company runs Dunn Project Solutions a construction services unit that tackles projects ranging in size from $50000 to $5 million. The business focuses on projects related to corporate interiors retail improvements historic rehabilitation additions fixtures and equipment building upgrades maintenance work and small office projects.

The company's ranked as the 10th largest general building company in the US in 2015.

Geographic Reach

Headquartered in Kansas City Missouri J.E. Dunn operates some 20 offices across the nation. It has offices in Georgia Texas North Carolina Colorado Iowa Missouri Minnesota Tennessee Oklahoma Nebraska Arizona Oregon Kansas and North Dakota.

Sales and Marketing

The company works on corporate environments mission critical correctional/justice and mixed use/retail projects among others.

Financial Performance

J.E. Dunn Construction last reported annual revenues of more than $2.6 billion in 2014.

Strategy

Some of the group's more recent projects projects include work on the North Dakota governor's residence and the new Bank of North Dakota Financial Center in Bismark (2016); the Harold Newman Arena in Jamestown (2016); the Trinity High School reconstruction and expansion project (2016); the building of the 378000 sq. ft. Cambridge North Tower at The University of Kansas Hospital (September 2017); the 92000 sq. ft. entertainment of the arts at the University of Colorado; the 151000 sq. ft. expansion project on an inpatient pavilion at the UCHealth University of Colorado Hospital (May 2015); the 92000 sq. ft. Fallen Fire Fighter Memorial in Colorado Springs (June 2015); and the 160000 sq. ft. CHI St. Joseph's Hospital and Health Center (October 2014).

Past projects include work on the Charles R. Drew Charter School Senior Academy the Kauffman Center for the Performing Arts the Topfer Theatre at ZACH the Energy Systems Integration Facility (ESIF) the Collaborative Life Sciences Building & Skourtes Tower and the Georgia Regents Health System Outpatient Cancer. Other past projects have included Baylor Scott & White Cancer Center Hotel Sorella GSA National Nuclear Security Administration City of Houston Bethel Park Renovation and the B.E. Smith Corporate Headquarters Renovation.

Company Background

A bigwig particularly in the Midwest the group regularly bids on federal government projects. J.E. Dunn won a major contract from the US Army Corps of Engineers to build a regional correctional facility at Fort Leavenworth Kansas that replaced smaller prisons in Texas Kentucky and Oklahoma.

In 2012 the company earned the designation of having the first ever LEED Gold Certified building in downtown Kansas City.

The descendants of John Ernest Dunn hold a majority stake in the company.

EXECUTIVES

President And Ceo, Gordon E. Lansford
President Midwest Region, Dirk Schafer
Evp, William H. (Bill) Dunn
Evp General Counsel And Secretary, Casey S. Halsey
President West Region, Steve Hamline
Evp Marketing, Gregory E. (Greg) Nook
President East Region, Dan Kaufman
Evp And Chief Legal Officer, Tom Whittaker
Cio, John Jacobs
President South Central, Greg Lorei
Cfo, Beth Soukup
Vice President, Dan West
Senior Vice President, Patrick Dennis
Assistant Vice President And Director Of Compensation And Benefits, Stephen Best
Senior Vice President Business Development, Thomas Raney
Vice Chairman & Treasurer, Stephen D. (Steve) Dunn
Auditors: KPMG LLP KANSAS CITY MISSOUR

LOCATIONS

HQ: J.E. DUNN CONSTRUCTION GROUP, INC.
1001 LOCUST ST, KANSAS CITY, MO 641061904
Phone: 816 474-8600
Web: WWW.JEDUNN.COM

PRODUCTS/OPERATIONS

Selected Group Companies
JE Dunn Midwest
JE Dunn North Central
JE Dunn Northwest
JE Dunn Rocky Mountain
JE Dunn South Central
R.J. Griffin & Company

Selected Services
Preconstruction
- Constructability review
- Feasibility studies
- Market analysis
- Mechanical electrical plumbing review
- Preconstruction estimating
- Quality control
- Risk management
- Scheduling

Construction
- Change order management
- Labor relations
- Progress monitoring
- Quality control and testing

Post Construction
- Commissioning
- Final closeout
- Lien releases
- One-year walkthrough
- Operations and maintenance manuals

COMPETITORS

Alberici
Clark Enterprises
Hensel Phelps Construction
Hunt Construction
McCarthy Building
Skanska USA Building
Sundt
Turner Corporation
Tutor Perini
Weitz
Whiting-Turner

HISTORICAL FINANCIALS

Company Type: Private

Income Statement — FYE: December 31

	REVENUE ($ mil.)	NET INCOME ($ mil.)	NET PROFIT MARGIN	EMPLOYEES
12/15	2,910	0	—	2,080
12/14	2,243	0	—	—
12/13	2,243	0	—	—
Annual Growth	13.9%	—	—	—

JACKSON ELECTRIC MEMBERSHIP CORPORATION

Jackson EMC distributes electricity to more than 197800 individual customers (more than 210200 meters) in 10 counties around Atlanta and in northeastern Georgia. The majority of customers are residential with commercial and industrial customers accounting for 42% of fiscal year 2013 revenues. One of the largest nonprofit power cooperatives in the US and the largest electric cooperative in Georgia Jackson EMC is owned by its members. The cooperative's generation and transmission partners include Oglethorpe Power Corp. Georgia Systems Operation and Georgia Transmission Corp.

Operations

Jackson EMC operates 86 substations and more than 13550 miles of power line.

Financial Performance

In fiscal 2013 the coop reported a revenue increased of 1%. Net income declined slightly by 0.3%. That year the non-profit coop returned $5.5 million in margin refunds to nearly 201000 members.

Strategy

Among other initiatives Jackson EMC is promoting conservation and green energy options as a way to slow energy growth and reduce greenhouse gas emissions. Initiatives include advocating the use of more efficient light bulbs and the widespread use of solar panels for power generation.

Company Background

Although the county of Jackson is named after a Georgia statesman from the Revolutionary War era Jackson Electric Membership Corporation (Jackson EMC) can trace its roots more directly to US president Franklin Roosevelt whose frequent trips to Warm Springs alerted him to the shortage of affordable electric power outside of major cities. Jackson EMC was founded in 1938 as part of the Roosevelt government's national rural electrification drive.

EXECUTIVES

Vp Of Marketing, Stefano Sandoval
Auditors: MCNAIR MCLEMORE MIDDLEBROOKS &

LOCATIONS

HQ: JACKSON ELECTRIC MEMBERSHIP CORPORATION
850 COMMERCE RD, JEFFERSON, GA 305493329
Phone: 706 367-5281
Web: WWW.JACKSONEMC.COM

HISTORICAL FINANCIALS

Company Type: Private

Income Statement — FYE: May 31

	REVENUE ($ mil.)	NET INCOME ($ mil.)	NET PROFIT MARGIN	EMPLOYEES
05/19	571	29	5.1%	445
05/18	548	37	6.8%	—
05/17*	518	28	5.5%	—
12/15	541	0	—	—
Annual Growth	1.8%	—	—	—

*Fiscal year change

2019 Year-End Financials

Return on assets: 2.7%
Return on equity: 6.4%
Current ratio: 1.40
Cash ($ mil.): 16

JACKSON HEALTHCARE, LLC

Jackson Healthcare can help find physicians to work at hospitals and help keep track of patients as they enter and leave hospitals. Its staffing businesses offer job search recruiting and placement services for physicians and other health care professionals; provide anesthesiologists; and coordinate the work of traveling nurses. Jackson Healthcare's physician job boards attract thousands of visitors per month giving it a reputation for filling openings quickly. Subsidiary Patient Placement Systems manages patient flow through the medical system and Care Logistics provides patient tracking software. Richard Jackson formed the company in 1978.

Operations

Jackson Healthcare operates more than a dozen subsidiaries and operations units and serves more than 7 million patients spread throughout 1300 health care facilities.

Subsidiaries and divisions include Premier Anesthesia Jackson Therapy Partners LucumTenens.com Jackson Nurse Professionals and Jackson & Coker. Other operations include AdvancedPractice.com Jackson Surgical Assistants Jackson Pharmacy Professionals Tyler & Company and Parker HealthcareIT.

Its health care software and technology portfolio is managed by Care Logistics and Patient Placement Systems.

Mergers and Acquisitions

Jackson Healthcare's growth strategy involves acquiring other staffing businesses to augment its geographical reach. In 2014 it purchased Sullivan Healthcare Consulting (SHC) a Michigan-based firm focused on improving the performance of the hospital's perioperative suite.

EXECUTIVES

Managing Director Jackson Healthcare, Paul D. Foster
President And Ceo Jackson Therapy Partners, Scott L'Heureux
Ceo, Richard L. Jackson
Vp Finance, R. Shane Jackson
Vp Human Resources, Michael Hiffa
Cto, Tim Aligheri
Cfo, Douglas B. Kline
President Care Logistics, Karl Straub
President Premier Anesthesia, Kerry Teel
President Advancedpractice.com, Susan Mesa
President Jackson & Coker Permanent Placement, Tony Stajduhar
President And Ceo Parker Health Care It, Debbie Crandall
President Healthit Project Managers, Jack Williams
Vp And General Manager Healthcare Staffing Technologies, Karyn Mullins
Vp Advancedpractice.com And Jackson Pharmacy Professionals, David McAnally
Vp And General Manager Patient Placement Systems, Doug Walker
Cio, Ryan Esparza
Vice President Property Management, Leslie Harrell
Vice President Corporate Development, Jonathan Ward
Vice President Human Resources, Matthew Harrison
National Accounts Manager, Julie Ianni
Vice Chairman, William H. Franklin

LOCATIONS

HQ: JACKSON HEALTHCARE, LLC
2655 NORTHWINDS PKWY, ALPHARETTA, GA 300092280
Phone: 770 643-5500
Web: WWW.JACKSONHEALTHCARE.COM

PRODUCTS/OPERATIONS

Selected Subsidiaries and Operating Units
Jackson Healthcare Staffing
- AdvancedPractice.com (a full-service locum tenens agency dedicated to physician assistants and nurse practitioners)
- Healthcare Staffing Technologies (provider of career concierge sites in the healthcare market)
- HealthIT Project Managers (provider of experienced IT project management contractors to hospitals)
- Jackson & Coker (locum tenens and permanent recruitment firm for physicians)

Jackson Nurse Professionals (specializes in the placement of registered nurses in healthcare settings nationwide)
Jackson Pharmacy Professionals (national pharmacy-only staffing and recruiting company)
Jackson Surgical Assistants (staffing of certified surgical assistants to surgeons and hospitals)
Jackson Therapy Partners (staffing of rehabilitation therapists and other allied healthcare professionals)
LocumTenens.com (locum tenens physician recruitment agency)
Parker HealthcareIT (provider of supplemental IT staffing)
Premier Anesthesia (anesthesia department management company)
Jackson Healthcare Technology
Care Logistics (firm that helps hospitals transform their operations to deliver hospital efficiency)
Patient Placement Systems (supplier of continuing care provider software)

COMPETITORS

AMN Healthcare
ATC Healthcare
Adecco
CHG Healthcare
CompHealth
Cross Country Healthcare
Gentiva
Kelly Services
ManpowerGroup
On Assignment
RehabCare
TeamStaff
inVentiv Health

HISTORICAL FINANCIALS

Company Type: Private

Income Statement — FYE: December 31

	REVENUE ($ mil.)	NET INCOME ($ mil.)	NET PROFIT MARGIN	EMPLOYEES
12/17	949	99	10.5%	949
12/16	838	93	11.1%	—
12/15	696	70	10.2%	—
12/07	384	18	4.8%	—
Annual Growth	9.5%	18.4%	—	—

2017 Year-End Financials

Return on assets: 25.6%
Return on equity: 132.6%
Current ratio: 3.60
Cash ($ mil.): 65

JACKSON-MADISON COUNTY GENERAL HOSPITAL DISTRICT

EXECUTIVES

Pres-Ceo, James Ross
Chm*, Phil Bryant
Cfo*, Jeffrey Blankenship
Coordinator, Trisha Ross
Director, Mary Bryant
Director, Angela Holmes
Information Technology Manager, Currie Higgs
Senior Vice President of Devel, Karl Misulis
Cme Coordinator, Cathy Brown
Director of Property Managemen, Lester Sands
Senior Human Resources General, Yvette Forrest

LOCATIONS

HQ: JACKSON-MADISON COUNTY GENERAL HOSPITAL DISTRICT
620 SKYLINE DR, JACKSON, TN 383013923
Phone: 731 541-5000
Web: WWW.WTH.ORG

HISTORICAL FINANCIALS

Company Type: Private

Income Statement — FYE: June 30

	REVENUE ($ mil.)	NET INCOME ($ mil.)	NET PROFIT MARGIN	EMPLOYEES
06/16	597	10	1.8%	6,000
06/15	554	20	3.7%	—
06/04	429	37	8.6%	—
06/03	307	247	80.4%	—
Annual Growth	5.3%	(21.4%)	—	—

2016 Year-End Financials

Return on assets: 1.2%
Return on equity: 2.3%
Current ratio: 3.70
Cash ($ mil.): 20

JACO OIL COMPANY

Jaco Oil Company is jockeying for its piece of the convenience store pie. The company's Fastrip Food Stores subsidiary operates more than 50 convenience stores and gas stations primarily in and around Bakersfield California but also in Arizona. Besides offering customers traditional convenience-store fare which includes coffee milk beer snacks tobacco and the like the Fastrip chain stocks a full range of grocery items and provides in-store financial service centers. Financial services include check cashing payday loans wire transfer services via The Western Union Company refund anticipation loans and other services at many locations. Jaco Oil Company was founded in 1970.

Operations

The company operates nearly 50 stores in Bakersfield and Kern counties as well as in Fresno Sacramento and the Chico area. It also has four stores in Arizona located in Bullhead Casa Grande and Nogales. As part of its business Jaco Oil offers food beverages and financial services such as payday loans wire transfer services and tax preparation services.

Geographic Reach

Jaco Oil owns and operates gasoline service stations and convenience stores in the Western US.

Strategy

Fastrip works to distinguish itself from other convenience store chains by stocking a complete assortment of grocery items including such staples as sugar flour salt cake mix and even green beans. The chain bills itself as a Mini Grocery Store a strategy that other retailers including Dollar General and drugstore-giant Walgreen have adopted. It's also always open (24/7/365).

EXECUTIVES

Ceo, T J Jamieson
V Pres*, Charles Mc Can
SEC-Treas*, Lee Jamieson
Cfo*, Brian Busacca
Auditors: MOSS ADAMS LLP LOS ANGELES

LOCATIONS

HQ: JACO OIL COMPANY
3101 STATE RD, BAKERSFIELD, CA 933084931
Phone: 661 393-7000
Web: WWW.FASTRIP.COM

2013 Stores

	No.
California	49
Arizona	4
Total	53

PRODUCTS/OPERATIONS

Selected Services

Check cashing
EBT
Ice
Liquior
Lottery
Money orders
Money transfers
Phone cards
Quick serve restaurant
Restrooms
WIC

Selected Products

Alcoholic beverages
Beverages
Coffee
Dairy
Food
Fountain drinks
Groceries
Snacks
Tobacco products

COMPETITORS

7-Eleven
Chevron
Couche-Tard
Dollar General
Exxon Mobil
Ralphs Grocery
Stater Bros.
Vons
Walgreen

HISTORICAL FINANCIALS

Company Type: Private

Income Statement — FYE: December 31

	REVENUE ($ mil.)	NET INCOME ($ mil.)	NET PROFIT MARGIN	EMPLOYEES
12/19	657	25	3.9%	350
12/18	636	19	3.1%	—
12/17	506	13	2.7%	—
12/16	429	17	4.0%	—
Annual Growth	15.3%	14.3%	—	—

2019 Year-End Financials

Return on assets: 14.6%
Return on equity: 17.5%
Current ratio: 2.80
Cash ($ mil.): 98

JARDEN LLC

EXECUTIVES

Chair, Patrick D Campbell
Ceo, Debra A Crew
Pres, Ravi Saligram
Vp Human Resources, Brian Stull
Bi Architecture Lead, Calvin Francart
Director Marketing, Fernando Pacheco
Senior Channel Marketing Manag, Sarah Chirillo
Data Analyst, Aileen Wall
It Procurement Specialist, Alicia Miastkowski
Amazon Sales Manager Technical, Allison Kennedy
Marketing Operations Manager, Amanda Gillis
Auditors: PRICEWATERHOUSECOOPERS LLP NE

LOCATIONS

HQ: JARDEN LLC
221 RIVER ST, HOBOKEN, NJ 070305989
Phone: 201 610-6600
Web: WWW.NEWELLBRANDS.COM

COMPETITORS

AZZ
Academy Sports
Amazon.com
Amer Sports
Andis
BWAY
Bass Pro Shops
Bauer Hockey
Bed Bath & Beyond
Burton
Cabela's
CalCedar
Canadian Tire
Carrefour
Church & Dwight
Conair Consumer Products
Costco Wholesale
Crayola
Daiwa
De'Longhi
Deswell
Dick's Sporting Goods
EBSCO
Easton-Bell Sports
Elmer's Products
Energizer Holdings
Evenflo
Female Health
Gaming Partners International
Gerber Products
Habasit America
Hamilton Beach
Hanesbrands
Head N.V.
Hillerich & Bradsby
HoMedics
Home Depot
Honeywell ACS
Igloo Products
Intex DIY
Invensys
Johnson & Johnson
Johnson Outdoors
Kaz
Kellwood
Lasko Products
Lifetime Brands
Lowe's
MEGA Brands
Mattel
Mayborn Group
Mizuno
NACCO Industries
NIKE
New Balance
Newell Rubbermaid
Owens-Illinois
Patch Products
Philips Avent
Procter & Gamble
Quiksilver
REI
Richco
Rollerblade
Rossignol
Russell Hobbs
SEB
Sealy
Simmons
Spectrum Brands
Suncast
Target Corporation
Tecnica
Tegrant
UTC Climate Controls & Security
Universal Security Instruments
VF Corporation
W.C. Bradley Co.
Wahl Clipper
West Pharmaceutical Services
Whirlpool
Worthington Industries
adidas

HISTORICAL FINANCIALS

Company Type: Private

Income Statement — FYE: December 31

	REVENUE ($ mil.)	NET INCOME ($ mil.)	NET PROFIT MARGIN	EMPLOYEES
12/15	8,603	146	1.7%	17,000
12/14	8,287	242	2.9%	—
12/13	7,355	203	2.8%	—
12/12	6,696	243	3.6%	—
Annual Growth	8.7%	(15.6%)	—	—

2015 Year-End Financials

Return on assets: 1.0%
Return on equity: 3.6%
Current ratio: 2.00
Cash ($ mil.): 1,298

JEA

As long as sparks are flying in Jacksonville everything is A-OK with JEA. The community-owned not-for-profit utility provides electricity to 438000 customers in Jacksonville and surrounding areas in northeastern Florida. Managing an electric system that dates back to 1895 JEA has a net generating capacity of 3747 MW. It owns an electric system with five primarily fossil-fueled generating plants. JEA also gets 12.8 MW of generating capacity from two methane-fueled landfill plants. The company resells electricity to other utilities including NextEra Energy. JEA also provides water and wastewater services; it serves 321600 water customers and 247500 wastewater customers.

Operations

JEA is the largest community-owned utility in Florida and the eighth largest in the US.

The company operates in four segments: the Electric System and Bulk Power Supply System; the St. Johns River Power Park System System; the Water and Sewer System; and the District Energy System.

The Electric System operates five generating plants in Florida (and holds a stake in a power plant in Georgia) and all transmission and distribution facilities including more than 745 miles of transmission lines and more than 6500 miles of distribution lines. It purchases power locally from a solar field and a landfill gas facility. This segment accounted for 77% of the company's 2014 revenues.

JEA's Water System consists of 134 artesian wells that tap into the Floridan aquifer. Water is distributed through 37 water treatment plants and more than 4300 miles of water lines. Wastewater is collected through more than 3800 miles of wastewater collection lines and treated at seven regional treatment plants.

The company's operations are funded by three enterprise funds: the Electric Enterprise Fund the Water and Sewer Fund and the District Energy System The Electric Enterprise Fund is comprised of the JEA Electric System Bulk Power Supply System and St. Johns River Power Park System.

Geographic Reach

The cooperative serves customers in Northeast Florida.

Financial Performance

In 2014 JEA's revenues increased by 3% due to a 3% growth in electric sales as the result of higher consumption (primarily 4.3% in residential sales). Water and sewer sales increased by 1% related to a rise in customers and District Energy System sales increased by 2%. Approximately 47% of JEA's electric 2014 revenues came from its 375000 residential customers 50% from 48000 commercial and industrial customers and 3% from one wholesale customer.

The company's net income increased by 97% due to higher investment returns and a decline in loss from interest on debt.

JEA's operating cash flow decreased by 4% due to higher payments to suppliers.

Strategy

To help meet state regulations for carbon emission control JEA plans to get 10% of its energy requirements from nuclear energy by 2018 and 30% by 2030. In this regard JEA has signed a purchase power agreement to get 206 MW from a nuclear plant beginning in 2016 and is pursuing additional purchased power contracts.

JEA is also building out more fossil fuel capacity.

Company Background

The electric utility grew from a department of city of Jacksonville into an independent authority created by city and county government consolidation in 1967. In 1997 the water and sewer systems (which had been operated by the city since 1880) were also placed under JEA management.

In 2011 it completed the Greenland Energy Center which included two 175-MW natural gas-fired combustion turbines.

EXECUTIVES

Ceo, Jay Stowe
V Pres*, Mike Brost
V Pres*, Brian Roche
Exec Pres*, James Chancellor
Exec V Pres*, James Dickenson
Mng Dir*, Walter Bussells
CIO*, Ron Baker
Cfo*, Melissa Dykes
Chief Legal Officer*, Jody Brooks
Vp*, Kurt Wilson
Int Chief Comp Officer*, Steve Tuten
Auditors: ERNST & YOUNG LLP JACKSONVILL

LOCATIONS

HQ: JEA
21 W CHURCH ST FL 1, JACKSONVILLE, FL 322023158
Phone: 904 665-6000
Web: WWW.JEA.COM

PRODUCTS/OPERATIONS

2014 Sales

	$ mil.	% of total
Electric	1,431	77
Water & wastewater	383	21
District Energy System	8	-
Other	38	2
Total	**1,861**	**100**

COMPETITORS

Chesapeake Utilities
Florida Power & Light
Florida Public Utilities
NextEra Energy
Progress Energy
Seminole Electric
Southern Company
TECO Energy
United Water Inc.
Utilities Inc.

HISTORICAL FINANCIALS

Company Type: Private

Income Statement — FYE: September 30

	REVENUE ($ mil.)	NET INCOME ($ mil.)	NET PROFIT MARGIN	EMPLOYEES
09/18	1,789	126	7.1%	2,356
09/17	1,875	254	13.6%	—
09/16*	1,782	210	11.8%	—
06/09	1,319	71	5.4%	—
Annual Growth	3.4%	6.5%	—	—

*Fiscal year change

2018 Year-End Financials

Return on assets: 1.5%
Return on equity: 4.6%
Current ratio: 4.20
Cash ($ mil.): 441

JEFFERSON COUNTY SCHOOL DISTRICT NO. R-1

EXECUTIVES

Supt, Dan McMinimee
Supt*, Cindy Stevenson
Office Aid, Grease Butte
Coordinator, Mary J Abbott
Secretary Director, Christine Thomas
Director Special Education, Dawn Loge Greer
Database Manager Da Database, Robert Sukiennicki
Director, Veronica Lee
Technical Education Coordinato, Shelley Brunjak
Assistant Director of Early Ch, Julie Osborne
Chief of Schools, Kristopher Schuh
Auditors: CLIFTONLARSONALLEN LLP BROOMF

LOCATIONS

HQ: JEFFERSON COUNTY SCHOOL DISTRICT NO. R-1
1829 DENVER WEST DR # 27, GOLDEN, CO 804013120
Phone: 303 982-6500
Web: WWW.JEFFCOPUBLICSCHOOLS.ORG

HISTORICAL FINANCIALS

Company Type: Private

Income Statement — FYE: June 30

	REVENUE ($ mil.)	NET INCOME ($ mil.)	NET PROFIT MARGIN	EMPLOYEES
06/19	960	368	38.4%	12,000
06/18	848	(4)	—	—
06/17	808	(40)	—	—
06/15	801	(18)	—	—
Annual Growth	4.6%	—	—	—

2019 Year-End Financials

Return on assets: 15.9%
Return on equity: —
Current ratio: —
Cash ($ mil.): 7

JEFFERSON PARISH SCHOOL BOARD INC

EXECUTIVES

Pres, Mark Morgan
Attorney, Jack Grant
Director of Transportation, Brandon Williams
Office Manager, Gwen Kerner
General Manager, Tiffany Kuhn
Auditors: MIKE B GILLESPIE CPA JENNIN

LOCATIONS

HQ: JEFFERSON PARISH SCHOOL BOARD INC
501 MANHATTAN BLVD, HARVEY, LA 700584443
Phone: 504 349-7803
Web: WWW.JPSCHOOLS.ORG

HISTORICAL FINANCIALS

Company Type: Private

Income Statement — FYE: June 30

	REVENUE ($ mil.)	NET INCOME ($ mil.)	NET PROFIT MARGIN	EMPLOYEES
06/11	556	3	0.7%	1,245
06/09	501	(70)	—	—
06/08	521	22	4.2%	—
Annual Growth	2.2%	(43.9%)	—	—

2011 Year-End Financials

Return on assets: 0.7%
Return on equity: 1.5%
Current ratio: —
Cash ($ mil.): 242

JERSEY CENTRAL POWER & LIGHT COMPANY

New Jersey native son Bruce Springsteen may be The Boss but Jersey Central Power & Light (JCP&L) electrifies more fans than he does every day. The company a subidiary of multi-utility holding company FirstEnergy transmits and distributes electricity to 1.1 million homes and businesses in 13 counties in central and northern New Jersey. JCP&L operates 22670 miles of distribution lines; its 2550-mile transmission system is overseen by regional transmission organization (RTO) PJM Interconnection. The utility also has some power plant interests.

Operations

The company provides regulated electric transmission and distribution services. JCP&L also has an ownership interest in a hydroelectric generating facility.

Geographic Reach

JCP&L conducts business in 3200 square miles of east central northern and western New Jersey. The area it serves has a population of approximately 2.7 million.

Financial Performance

Revenues decreased by 18% in 2011 due to a rate adjustment for all customer classes and lower power deliveries. The lower power delivery to residential customers was the result of decreased weather-related usage in 2011. Lower distribution deliveries to commercial and industrial customers that year reflected the impact of economic conditions in JCP&L's service territory. A decrease in retail generation revenues was due to lower generation power sales in all customer classes primarily due to an increase in customers shopping around for alternative providers. Wholesale generation revenues decreased due to a drop in PJM spot market energy sales.

JCP&L's net income decreased by 39% in 2011 due to lower revenues offset by reductions in purchased power costs and amortization of regulatory assets.

Company Background

The utility was organized under the laws of the State of New Jersey in 1925.

EXECUTIVES

Pres-Ceo, Donald M Lynch
Cfo-Cao-Controller*, Marlene A Barwood
Director, Ernest J Novak Jr
Director, Jesse T Williams Sr
Vp Corporate Risk and Chief R, William D Byrd
V Pres External Affairs, Mark A Jones
Customer Staff, Sandra Rudolph
Vp-Operations, Alex Patton
Manager Feu Process, Bret Ingram
General Manager, Chad Hampson
Assistant Business Analyst, Rachel Greer
Auditors: PRICEWATERHOUSECOOPERS LLP C

LOCATIONS

HQ: JERSEY CENTRAL POWER & LIGHT COMPANY
76 S MAIN ST, AKRON, OH 443081812
Phone: 800 736-3402
Web: WWW.FIRSTENERGYCORP.COM

PRODUCTS/OPERATIONS

Selected Services

Electrical services
Outdoor lighting
Professional tree services

COMPETITORS

Conectiv Power Delivery
New Jersey Natural Gas
Orange & Rockland Utilities
Public Service Electric and Gas
South Jersey Gas
Southern Company Gas

HISTORICAL FINANCIALS

Company Type: Private

Income Statement — FYE: December 31

	REVENUE ($ mil.)	NET INCOME ($ mil.)	NET PROFIT MARGIN	EMPLOYEES
12/17	1,801	115	6.4%	1,413
12/16	1,787	80	4.5%	—
12/11	2,495	144	5.8%	—
12/10	3,027	192	6.3%	—
Annual Growth	(7.1%)	(7.1%)	—	—

2017 Year-End Financials

Return on assets: 1.3%
Return on equity: 3.6%
Current ratio: 2.20
Cash ($ mil.): 251

JEWISH COMMUNAL FUND

EXECUTIVES

Pres, Zoya Raynes
V Pres, Susan F Dickman
Sr V Pres, Jose Virella
Coordinator, Claudia Pinto
Director of Grants, Karla Floris
Chief Operations Officer, Beth Wohlgelernter
Contribution Coordinator, Wanda Gutierrez
Senior Director of Grants Admi, Melanie Marchfeld
Business Senior Di, Michelle Lebowits
Director, Tamar Snyder
Auditors: EISNERAMPER LLP NEW YORK NY

LOCATIONS

HQ: JEWISH COMMUNAL FUND
575 MADISON AVE STE 703, NEW YORK, NY 100228591
Phone: 212 752-8277
Web: WWW.JCFNY.ORG

HISTORICAL FINANCIALS

Company Type: Private

Income Statement — FYE: June 30

	REVENUE ($ mil.)	NET INCOME ($ mil.)	NET PROFIT MARGIN	EMPLOYEES
06/19	822	355	43.3%	14
06/18	511	65	12.9%	—
06/17	461	55	12.0%	—
06/13	390	110	28.3%	—
Annual Growth	13.2%	21.6%	—	—

2019 Year-End Financials

Return on assets: 17.5%
Return on equity: 17.7%
Current ratio: 115.30
Cash ($ mil.): 101

JFK HEALTH SYSTEM, INC.

EXECUTIVES

Pres-Ceo, Raymond Fredericks
Chm*, Dr Michael Kleiman
Plant Manager, Mark Di Geronimno
Coordinator, John Schenk
Osteopathic Physician, Richard Malone
Media Relations Mgr, Mary Jo Layton
Neuroscience Supervisor, Zahra Jiwani
Interior Designer, Asid Persico
or Network Administrato, Bill Thorpe
Director Cardiac, Jim Lindquist
Project Director, Keith Cicerone

LOCATIONS

HQ: JFK HEALTH SYSTEM, INC.
80 JAMES ST, EDISON, NJ 088203938
Phone: 732 321-7000
Web: WWW.JFKHEALTHSYSTEM.ORG

COMPETITORS

Atlantic Health
Barnabas Health
Catholic Health East
CentraState Healthcare System
Continuum Health Partners
East Orange General Hospital
NewYork-Presbyterian Healthcare
Newark Beth Israel Medical Center
Raritan Bay Medical Center
Robert Wood Johnson University Hospital
Saint Peter's University Hospital
Somerset Medical Center
St. Joseph's Healthcare System
Staten Island University Hospital
Trinitas Regional Medical Center

HISTORICAL FINANCIALS

Company Type: Private

Income Statement — FYE: December 31

	REVENUE ($ mil.)	NET INCOME ($ mil.)	NET PROFIT MARGIN	EMPLOYEES
12/18	591	128	21.7%	6,735
12/17	0	(0)	—	—
12/15	0	0	—	—
12/14	0	0	—	—
Annual Growth	—	—	—	—

2018 Year-End Financials

Return on assets: 33.7%
Return on equity: 74.5%
Current ratio: 0.70
Cash ($ mil.): 35

JOBSOHIO BEVERAGE SYSTEM

LOCATIONS

HQ: JOBSOHIO BEVERAGE SYSTEM
41 S HIGH ST STE 150, COLUMBUS, OH 432156115
Phone: 614 224-6446
Web: WWW.JOBSOHIO.COM

HISTORICAL FINANCIALS

Company Type: Private

Income Statement — FYE: June 30

	REVENUE ($ mil.)	NET INCOME ($ mil.)	NET PROFIT MARGIN	EMPLOYEES
06/19	1,284	(126)	—	3
06/17	444	4	1.0%	—
Annual Growth	70.1%	—	—	—

2019 Year-End Financials

Return on assets: (-9.3%)
Return on equity: —
Current ratio: 1.80
Cash ($ mil.): 75

JOHN C. LINCOLN HEALTH NETWORK

John C. Lincoln Health Network takes care of the health of John Q. Public in Arizona. The not-for-profit health care network serves the northern Phoenix area and is home to two hospitals: John C. Lincoln Deer Valley Hospital with more than 200 beds and John C. Lincoln North Mountain Hospital with roughly 260 beds (the Valley's first Magnet nursing hospital an accredited Chest Pain Center and the host of a Level 1 Trauma Center). The system also features a children's care facility various physician and dental clinics a food bank and assisted living facilities for the elderly all operating under the Desert Mission moniker. John C. Lincoln Health Network is part of the Scottsdale Lincoln Health Network along with Scottsdale Healthcare.

Operations

John C. Lincoln Health Network has a staff of about 1100 physicians.

In addition to its hospital locations the network includes physician practices for primary and specialty care as well as medical imaging and research centers. John C. Lincoln's facilities serve about 750000 patients each year and provide specialty services in fields including cardiology pulmonary care neuroscience and women's health. The Deer Valley Hospital is also home to Mendy's Place the North Valley's only 24-hour hospital emergency center exclusively for children and an accredited Chest Pain Center.

In 2012 John C. Lincoln Health Network had 748019 patient visits to its hospitals and physicians and specialty practices; 26868 exams at the breast health and research center; and 8719 adult day health care visits.

Its specialized medical services includes heart care pulmonary care neurosciences emergency care and a Breast Health and Research Center. Community services include Desert Mission Food Bank a dental clinic for uninsured children a resource center for families in crisis and a child care center. The John C. Lincoln Health Foundation conducts philanthropic efforts.

The health system's Desert Mission Food Bank distributed roughly 41000 emergency food boxes to members of its community in 2012. Other locations providing community outreach services include the Community Health Center Children's Dental Clinic Lincoln Learning Center Adult Day Health Care and Neighborhood Renewal. The Marley House Behavioral Health Clinic provides mental health and related services for children and adults on a sliding scale basis in English and Spanish.

Strategy

In 2013 John C. Lincoln expanded its infrastructure opening the John C. Lincoln Sonoran Health and Emergency Center a new emergency center and outpatient clinic in Phoenix. The $18 million project includes an emergency department medical practice and diagnostic imaging facilities.

Upgrading its technology in 2012 John C. Lincoln Deer Valley Hospital added the da Vinci Si Robotic Surgical System. To help it improve its medical record keeping that year the health system's primary care offices launched JCL Connect electronic health records software.

Mergers and Acquisitions

To strengthen its footing in the Arizona marketplace in 2014 John C. Lincoln formed an affiliation with Scottsdale Healthcare. The combined networks operating under the moniker Scottsdale Lincoln Health Network include five hospitals with some 3700 affiliated physicians and an extensive outpatient services network.

Company Background

The hospital gained its first real funding in 1933 from millionaire entrepreneur John C. Lincoln the founder of Lincoln Electric.

LOCATIONS

HQ: JOHN C. LINCOLN HEALTH NETWORK
2500 E DUNLAP AVE, PHOENIX, AZ 85020
Phone: 602 870-6060

Hospitals

Deer Valley Hospital: Phoenix Arizona
North Mountain Hospital: Phoenix Arizona

PRODUCTS/OPERATIONS

Selected Centers and Services

Breast Health and Research Center
Cancer Treatment
Cardiac Care
Deep Vein Thrombosis Program
Emergency Care
Heartburn Program
Level I Trauma Center
Medical Imaging
Neurosciences
Orthopedics
Outpatient Surgery Centers
Pediatrics
Pulmonary Program
Reconstructive Plastic Surgery
Scarless Surgery
Uterine Fibroid Treatment
Varicose Vein Treatment

COMPETITORS

Banner Health
Community Health Systems
Dignity Health
Flagstaff Medical Center
Northern Arizona Healthcare
Phoenix Children's Hospital
Scottsdale Healthcare
Universal Health Services
University of Arizona Health Network
Yuma Regional Medical Center

HISTORICAL FINANCIALS

Company Type: Private

Income Statement — FYE: December 31

	REVENUE ($ mil.)	NET INCOME ($ mil.)	NET PROFIT MARGIN	EMPLOYEES
12/13	584	44	7.6%	3,500
12/12	509	32	6.4%	—
12/11	486	17	3.6%	—
12/10	551	19	3.5%	—
Annual Growth	2.0%	31.3%	—	—

2013 Year-End Financials

Return on assets: 4.7% Cash ($ mil.): 40
Return on equity: 7.6%
Current ratio: 1.30

JOHN MUIR HEALTH

Named after famed naturalist and champion of wilderness preservation John Muir John Muir Health provides health care throughout the scenic San Francisco Bay area. The not-for-profit system operates three hospitals eight outpatient and urgent care centers two surgery centers a physician practice organization and several community health foundations. The John Muir Medical Center Walnut Creek Campus has more than 570 beds and specializes in neurological and obstetrics care. The Concord Campus has about 315 beds and specializes in cardiac and cancer care. The John Muir Behavioral Health Center is a 70-bed psychiatric hospital. John Muir Health also offers home health rehabilitation and wellness programs.

Operations

John Muir Health's network of outpatient facilities include physical therapy and occupational therapy centers as well as specialty pediatric women's health and diabetes centers. The system also includes medical imaging centers and the MuirLab division which performs a full range of clinical and anatomic pathology laboratory testing at more than a dozen locations.

The system has 900 physicians associated with the John Muir Physician Network which owns and operates two dozen locations.

John Muir Health partners include Aetna Anthem Blue Cross Blue Shield of California and CIGNA.

Geographic Reach

The company's hospitals are located in California's Contra Costa County (Concord and Walnut Creek); outpatient centers are located in Brentwood Concord Walnut Creek and Walnut Creek gated community Rossmoor.

Financial Performance

John Muir Health reported $1.41 billion in revenues for 2012 a total that was slightly down from the $1.44 billion it reported in 2011.

Strategy

To better serve residents of the growing San Francisco Bay area John Muir Health has made additions to its existing facilities including increasing bed counts and upgrading its IT infrastructure. Other initiatives that aim to improve patient care – and ultimately to lower the overall cost of care and meet federal reform guidelines – include upgrading medical equipment coordinating regional care establishing joint ventures and attracting and retaining skilled physicians. In 2015 the system partnered with Stanford Children's Health to open a new pediatric intensive care unit at its Walnut Creek medical center.

Also that year John Muir Health joined together with Health Net of California to form an Accountable Care Organization (ACO) serving Health Net's members from the system's medical centers.

In 2013 John Muir Health established a joint venture with Tenet Healthcare Corporation that created a partnership with San Ramon Regional Medical Center. Through this partnership John Muir Health is spending $100 million to acquire a 49% ownership interest in San Ramon Regional Medical Center. Together the two organizations will expand and improve the efficiency and coordination of care in the TriValley area and nearby communities including San Ramon. The new partnership will also increase patient access to a stronger network of services and align outpatient and physician-focused health care in the region. In 2014 the partnership invested in a 92000 sq. ft. building slated to become a new outpatient center in Pleasanton California.

Company Background

John Muir Health was formed from the 1997 merger of the John Muir Medical Center (the Walnut Creek Campus which dates back to 1965) and the Mt. Diablo Medical Center (now the Concord Campus dating back to 1930 as the Concord Hospital).

EXECUTIVES

President And Ceo, Calvin (Cal) Knight
President And Chief Administrative Officer John Muir Medical Center Walnut Creek Campus, Jane A. Willemsen
President And Chief Administrative Officer John Muir Medical Center Concord Campus, Michael S. Thomas
President Cao Of John Muir, Lee Huskins
President John Muir Health Foundation, Patrick J. Carew
Interim Cfo, Chris Pass
Svp And Cio, Jon Russell
Respiratory Therapy Director, George Rice
Chairman, David L. Goldsmith
Vice Chairman, Thomas Rundall
Auditors: KPMG LLP SAN FRANCISCO CALIF

LOCATIONS

HQ: JOHN MUIR HEALTH
1601 YGNACIO VALLEY RD, WALNUT CREEK, CA 945983122
Phone: 925 947-4449
Web: WWW.JOHNMUIRHEALTH.COM

PRODUCTS/OPERATIONS

Selected California Locations

Behavioral Health Center (Concord)
Breast Health Center (Walnut Creek)
Caring Hands Volunteer Program (Walnut Creek)
Clinical Research Centers (Concord)
Diabetes Center (Walnut Creek)
Garret Thrift Shop (Walnut Creek)
John Muir Medical Center (Concord)
John Muir Medical Center (Walnut Creek)
John Muir Outpatient Center (Brentwood Tice Valley/Rossmoor)
Medical Imaging (Brentwood Concord San Ramon Walnut Creek)
MuirLab (Regional)
Occupational Medicine (Brentwood Concord Walnut Creek)
Physical Rehabilitation Center (Concord Pleasant Hill)
Urgent Care Centers (Brentwood Concord San Ramon Walnut Creek)
Women's Health Center (Walnut Creek)
Wound Care Center (Walnut Creek)

Selected Services

Behavioral Health
Cancer
Cardiovascular Services
Chemical Dependency
Children's Services
Emergency Services
Lab Services
Medical Imaging
Orthopedics
Neurosciences
Physical Rehabilitation
Pregnancy & New Parent
Primary Care
Urgent Care

COMPETITORS

Alta Bates Summit Medical Center
California Pacific Medical Center
Children's Hospital & Research Center at Oakland
Community Hospital of the Monterey Peninsula
Dignity Health
Healdsburg District Hospital
Hill Physicians Medical Group
Marin General Hospital
Mills-Peninsula Health Services
Sequoia Healthcare District
Stanford Health Care
Sutter Health
Tenet Healthcare
The Palo Alto Medical Foundation
UCSF Medical
ValleyCare Health System

HISTORICAL FINANCIALS

Company Type: Private

Income Statement FYE: December 31

	REVENUE ($ mil.)	NET INCOME ($ mil.)	NET PROFIT MARGIN	EMPLOYEES
12/17	1,831	92	5.0%	2,200
12/16	1,734	107	6.2%	—
Annual Growth	5.6%	(14.0%)	—	—

2017 Year-End Financials

Return on assets: 3.1% Cash ($ mil.): 72
Return on equity: 5.0%
Current ratio: 1.10

JOHNS HOPKINS BAYVIEW MEDICAL CENTER, INC.

If you've just been pulled from the bay like an old empty crab trap Johns Hopkins Bayview might be the first place you're taken. One of five member institutions in the Johns Hopkins Health System Johns Hopkins Bayview Medical Center is a community teaching hospital. Its Baltimore-based operations include a neonatal intensive care unit as well as centers devoted to trauma geriatrics sleep disorders and weight management. It also features the state's only regional burn center. The facility includes a meditation labyrinth for patients families and staff to walk. Established in 1773 the medical center has more than 560 beds.

Operations

As an academic teaching hospital all of the physicians at Johns Hopkins Bayview are also full-time faculty at the Johns Hopkins School of Medicine. Students from The Johns Hopkins University School of Nursing also come to the medical center for hospital-based instruction in acute and long term care.

EXECUTIVES

Vice President Support Services, Cheryl Koch
Auditors: PRICEWATERHOUSECOOPERS LLP BA

LOCATIONS

HQ: JOHNS HOPKINS BAYVIEW MEDICAL CENTER, INC.
4940 EASTERN AVE, BALTIMORE, MD 212242735
Phone: 410 550-0100
Web: WWW.HOPKINSMEDICINE.ORG

PRODUCTS/OPERATIONS

Selected services
Primary Care Services
- General Internal Medicine
- Obstetrics/Gynecology
- Pediatrics

Specialty Services
- Bariatrics
- Burn
- Cardiology
- Clinical Nutrition
- Dermatology
- Endocrinology
- Gastroenterology
- General Surgery
- Hematology/Oncology
- Imaging (X-ray mammography ultrasound etc)
- Minor Surgery
- Neurodiagnostic Lab
- Neurology
- Ophthalmology
- Otolaryngology (ear nose and throat)
- Orthopaedics
- Plastic Surgery
- Podiatry
- Urology
- Vascular Lab

COMPETITORS

Franklin Square Hospital Center
GBMC
Good Samaritan Hospital of Maryland
Harbor Hospital
Levindale Hospital
LifeBridge Health
Sinai Hospital of Baltimore
St. Agnes HealthCare
St. Joseph Medical Center
University of Maryland Medical System

HISTORICAL FINANCIALS

Company Type: Private

Income Statement — FYE: June 30

	REVENUE ($ mil.)	NET INCOME ($ mil.)	NET PROFIT MARGIN	EMPLOYEES
06/20	669	(41)	—	3,300
06/19	648	(39)	—	—
06/18	628	12	1.9%	—
06/16	544	11	2.1%	—
Annual Growth	5.3%	—	—	—

2020 Year-End Financials

Return on assets: (-9.3%)
Return on equity: —
Current ratio: 1.20
Cash ($ mil.): 39

JOHNS HOPKINS HEALTHCARE LLC

EXECUTIVES

Prin, Robert Neall
Human Resources, Linda Evans
Case Manager, Michael Braxton
Coordinator, Yvonne Bonner
Information Specialist, Sara McElligott
Executive Assistant, Terri Higgins
Director of Pharmacy, Hugh Fatodu
Administrative Assistant, Leah Adams
Senior Director Operations Sup, Peggy Smith
Lan Administrator Information, Tim Collins
Senior Director Usfhp Admin, Melissa Teves

LOCATIONS

HQ: JOHNS HOPKINS HEALTHCARE LLC
7231 PARKWAY DR STE 100, HANOVER, MD 210762331
Phone: 410 424-4400
Web: WWW.HOPKINSMEDICINE.ORG

HISTORICAL FINANCIALS

Company Type: Private

Income Statement — FYE: June 30

	REVENUE ($ mil.)	NET INCOME ($ mil.)	NET PROFIT MARGIN	EMPLOYEES
06/20	2,412	26	1.1%	520
06/19	2,248	(18)	—	—
06/18	2,125	6	0.3%	—
Annual Growth	6.6%	110.1%	—	—

2020 Year-End Financials

Return on assets: 4.4%
Return on equity: 18.2%
Current ratio: 0.50
Cash ($ mil.): 107

JOHNS HOPKINS HOSPITAL

EXECUTIVES

Pres, Ronald Peterson
Cfo, Ronald Werthman
Ophthalmologist, Albert Jun
Health Professional, Tonya Bradley
Physical Therapist, Perticone Greg
Director of Pharmacy, Rhiannon Fitzsimmons
MD, Daniel P Judge
General Surgeon, Jeffrey Lukish
Director, Leo Dorsey
Genetics Specialist, Tao Wang
Nursing Project Analyst, Catherine Garger
Auditors: PRICEWATERHOUSECOOPERS LLP BA

LOCATIONS

HQ: JOHNS HOPKINS HOSPITAL
1800 ORLEANS ST, BALTIMORE, MD 212870010
Phone: 410 550-0730
Web: WWW.HOPKINSMEDICINE.ORG

HISTORICAL FINANCIALS

Company Type: Private

Income Statement — FYE: June 30

	REVENUE ($ mil.)	NET INCOME ($ mil.)	NET PROFIT MARGIN	EMPLOYEES
06/20	2,617	(202)	—	12,000
06/19	2,527	(64)	—	—
06/18	2,422	98	4.1%	—
06/16	1,968	80	4.1%	—
Annual Growth	7.4%	—	—	—

2020 Year-End Financials

Return on assets: (-6.2%)
Return on equity: (-17.8%)
Current ratio: 1.10
Cash ($ mil.): 41

JOHNS HOPKINS UNIVERSITY

Founded in 1876 with a $7 million bequest from its namesake The Johns Hopkins University has established its reputation by molding itself in the image of a European research institution. While renowned for its School of Medicine the private university offers 260 academic programs spanning fields of study including arts and sciences business and international studies. The university enrolls more than 24000 full- and part-time students. Johns Hopkins has about a half-dozen campuses in Maryland and Washington DC as well as facilities in China and Italy. The student-teacher ratio is 13:1. The affiliated Johns Hopkins Health System provides health care from its three Baltimore-area hospitals.

Operations

Johns Hopkins University a private and non-profit institution with 1700 non-medical and 2800 medical faculty members offers education research and professional medical services. Its research and related services are offered through about 1800 government and private sponsors.

Keenly focused on research Johns Hopkins is engaged in a range of disciplines including health and medicine social sciences humanities the arts natural sciences engineering and technology. Projects include researching alternatives to animal testing disease treatments and chemical and biomolecular engineering topics among others.

The Johns Hopkins University offers graduate programs in business finance and real estate through its relatively new Carey Business School.

Notable alumni of the school include 28th US president Woodrow Wilson Michael Bloomberg and horror film director Wesley Craven.

Geographic Reach

Johns Hopkins University boasts three major campuses in Baltimore as well as single campus locations in (Montgomery County) Maryland and Washington DC. Johns Hopkins also operates facilities in the Baltimore-Washington area and abroad in Nanjiing China and Bologna Italy.

Strategy

Johns Hopkins is on the verge of completing its Ten By Twenty program – comprising 10 goals to achieve by 2020 – launched in 2013. The 10 goals are divided into four categories: One University (forging collaboration across disciplines); Individual Excellence (supporting faculty students and staff); Commitment to Our Communities (enriching ties to Baltimore the US and the world); and Institution Building (building a stronger university).

EXECUTIVES

Cio And Vice Provost Information Technology, Stephanie L. Reel
President, Ronald J. (Ron) Daniels
Svp Finance And Administration, Daniel G. Ennis
Svp Academic Affairs And Provost, Sunil Kumar
Vice President, Joseph Zolenas
Medical Director, Haig Kazazian
Senior Vice President Patient Care Services, Laura Wood
Medical Director Wilmer Eye Instructor At Columbia, Dean Glaros
Medical Director, Jeanette Nazarian
Clinical Director, Peter Hill
Pharmacy Manager, Charles Wells
Vice President, Keith Hill
Vice President For Quality, Renee Demski

Senior Vice President Human Resources (john Hopkins Health System), Inez Stewart
Vice President And Chief Administrator, Sowell Ashlyn
Vice President Human Resources, Marcos Deleon
Director Of Nursing, Laurie Saletnik
Director Of Nursing, Deborah Baker
Senior Vice President Health Care Transformation And Strategic Planning, John Colmers
Vice President For Finance, Sidd Patel
Secretary, Beth Six
Secretary Iii, Kristy Stewart
Medical Secretary, Samantha Boeshore
Medchi Vice Chair, Pranjal Gupta
Secretary, Keisha Guice
Auditors: KPMG LLP BALTIMORE MARYLAND

LOCATIONS

HQ: JOHNS HOPKINS UNIVERSITY
3400 N CHARLES ST, BALTIMORE, MD 212182680
Phone: 410 516-8000
Web: WWW.JHU.EDU

PRODUCTS/OPERATIONS

Selected Schools and Colleges
Bloomberg School of Public Health
Carey Business School
Krieger School of Arts and Sciences
Peabody Institute
School of Advanced International Studies
School of Education
School of Medicine
School of Nursing
Whiting School of Engineering

Selected Centers and Institutes
American Institute for Contemporary German Studies
Bloomberg School of Public Health Department of Health Policy and Management Fall Institute in Barcelona Spain
Bloomberg School of Public Health Research Centers
Center for Africana Studies
Center for Communication Programs
Center for Constitutional Studies and Democratic Development
Center for Clinical Global Health Education
Center for Global Health
Center for International Business and Public Policy
Center for Language Education
Center for Talented Youth
Center for Transatlantic Relations
Central Asia Caucasus Institute
Foreign Policy Institute
Hopkins Nanjing Center
Institute for Global Studies in Culture Power and History
Institute for Policy Studies
Johns Hopkins SAIS Bologna Center
Office of Global Nursing
SAIS Research Centers
Summer Language Institute
The Institute for Johns Hopkins Nursing
Yeung Center for Collaborative China Studies

Selected Campuses
Columbia Center - Columbia Maryland
East Baltimore Campus - Baltimore
Harbor East - Downtown Baltimore
Homewood Campus - Baltimore
Hopkins-Nanjing Center - Nanjing Jiangsu Province People's Republic of China
Johns Hopkins University Applied Physics Laboratory - Laurel MD; Baltimore and Washington
Johns Hopkins University Zanvyl Krieger School of Arts & Sciences Advanced Academic Programs - Washington DC
Montgomery County Center - Rockville Maryland
Nitze School of Advanced International Studies (SAIS) - Washington D.C
Peabody Campus - Baltimore
School of Advanced International Studies - Bologna Italy

HISTORICAL FINANCIALS

Company Type: Private

Income Statement — FYE: June 30

	REVENUE ($ mil.)	NET INCOME ($ mil.)	NET PROFIT MARGIN	EMPLOYEES
06/20	6,470	903	14.0%	37,600
06/19	6,410	2,017	31.5%	—
06/18	6,020	705	11.7%	—
06/13	4,793	526	11.0%	—
Annual Growth	4.4%	8.0%	—	—

2020 Year-End Financials

Return on assets: 6.2%
Return on equity: 8.9%
Current ratio: —
Cash ($ mil.): 531

JOHNSON & JOHNSON PATIENT ASSISTANCE FOUNDATION INC

EXECUTIVES

Prin, Nancy Moyer

LOCATIONS

HQ: JOHNSON & JOHNSON PATIENT ASSISTANCE FOUNDATION INC
1 JOHNSON AND JOHNSON PLZ, NEW BRUNSWICK, NJ 089330001
Phone: 732 524-1394
Web: WWW.JJPAF.ORG

HISTORICAL FINANCIALS

Company Type: Private

Income Statement — FYE: December 31

	REVENUE ($ mil.)	NET INCOME ($ mil.)	NET PROFIT MARGIN	EMPLOYEES
12/14	787	(16)	—	12
12/13	741	13	1.8%	—
12/10	425	(6)	—	—
12/09	355	(2)	—	—
Annual Growth	17.2%	—	—	—

2014 Year-End Financials

Return on assets: (-23.0%)
Return on equity: (-23.4%)
Current ratio: —
Cash ($ mil.): 31

JOHNSON CONTROLS FIRE PROTECTION LP

SimplexGrinnell handles emergencies well. The company provides integrated security alarm fire suppression healthcare communications and emergency lighting systems. SimplexGrinnell reaches some 1 million customers in the US and Canada through more than 150 district offices located in the Americas Europe Asia and other regions. In addition to providing security and fire related products SimplexGrinnell operates a service division devoted to test and inspection preventive maintenance central station monitoring and emergency services. The company's clients include members of local state and federal government agencies corporations oil and gas companies hospitals and educational facilities.

Operations

The company's communications segment provides mass notification and commercial paging as well as intercom and other sound systems. The company also provides healthcare communications such as infant security nurse call and emergency alert units.

Strategy

SimplexGrinnell launched a new website to give its customers a fast and convenient way to purchase many of its products that do not require installation support.

EXECUTIVES

Vp And Cfo, Robert F. (Bob) Chauvin
Ceo, George Oliver
Vice President, Scott Roberts

LOCATIONS

HQ: JOHNSON CONTROLS FIRE PROTECTION LP
6600 CONGRESS AVE, BOCA RATON, FL 334871213
Phone: 561 988-7200
Web: WWW.TYCOSIMPLEXGRINNELL.COM

PRODUCTS/OPERATIONS

Selected Products and Services
Fire Detection and Alarm
Control Panels
Notification
Network Solutions
Smoke Detector and Carbon Monoxide Detection
Sound and Communication
Healthcare Communications
Emergency Communications
Public Address and Intercom
Sound Reinforcement
Telephone Networks
Integrated Security
Access Control
Intrusion Detection
Property Surveillance
Mass Notification
Fire Sprinkler and Suppression
Fire Extinguisher
Special Hazards
Sprinkler

COMPETITORS

APi Group
Brink's
COSCO Fire Protection
Honeywell International
Ingersoll-Rand Security Technologies
Protection One

HISTORICAL FINANCIALS

Company Type: Private

Income Statement — FYE: September 30

	REVENUE ($ mil.)	NET INCOME ($ mil.)	NET PROFIT MARGIN	EMPLOYEES
09/16	1,871	182	9.7%	9,500
09/09	1,750	0	—	—
Annual Growth	1.0%	—	—	—

JOHNSON CONTROLS, INC.

EXECUTIVES

Ceo, Alberto Ventura
Chb-Ceo, George R Oliver
Exec V Pres-Cfo*, Brian Stief
V Pres-Gen Counsel-Sec*, Brian J Cadwallader
V Pres-Corp Contrl*, Suzanne M Vincent
Cpo-V Pres of Controls Operati*, Michael Bartschat
Central Region Sales, Joe Tieman
Project Manager, John Brumm
Project Manager, John Snell
Marketing Grant Research, Judith Mouton
Account Executive, Kevin Vercher
Auditors: PRICEWATERHOUSECOOPERS LLP MI

LOCATIONS

HQ: JOHNSON CONTROLS, INC.
5757 N GREEN BAY AVE, MILWAUKEE, WI 532094408
Phone: 800 382-2804
Web: WWW.JOHNSONCONTROLS.COM

COMPETITORS

3M
A123 Systems
Addison
Alcoa
Building Technologies
Caterpillar
Comfort Systems USA
DENSO
Deere
Delphi Automotive Systems
Dow Chemical
DuPont
Eagle-Picher
East Penn Manufacturing
Eaton
Emerson Electric
Exide
Faurecia
GS Yuasa
General Dynamics
General Motors
Goodman Global
Goodyear Tire & Rubber
Honeywell International
Illinois Tool Works
Inci Aku
International Paper
Invensys
Lear Corp
Lennox
Lockheed Martin
Magna International
Northrop Grumman
Paloma Group
Raytheon
Rieter Automotive North America
Robert Bosch
SPX
Trane Inc.
United Technologies
Valeo
Visteon
Whirlpool
Yazaki North America

HISTORICAL FINANCIALS

Company Type: Private

Income Statement — FYE: September 30

	REVENUE ($ mil.)	NET INCOME ($ mil.)	NET PROFIT MARGIN	EMPLOYEES
09/15	37,179	1,679	4.5%	105,000
09/14	42,828	1,335	3.1%	—
09/13	42,730	1,297	3.0%	—
Annual Growth	(6.7%)	13.8%	—	—

2015 Year-End Financials

Return on assets: 5.7%
Return on equity: 15.9%
Current ratio: 1.10
Cash ($ mil.): 597

JOINT SCHOOL DISTRICT NO. 28-J OF THE COUNTIES OF ADAMS AND ARAPAHOE

EXECUTIVES

Supt, Rico Munn
Contrl*, Gina Lanier
Chief Operating Officer, Anthony Sturges
Executive Officer, Matthew Eckert
Coordinator, Stephanie Gianneschi
Internal Auditor, Peter Doan
Dean of Students Athletics Dir, Casey Powell
Legal Counsel, Brandon Eyre
Literacy Coach Teacher Leader, Kayla Cook
Teacher, Janelle Flanscha
Assistant Executive Director, Shelia Siegert
Auditors: BKD LLP DENVER COLORADO

LOCATIONS

HQ: JOINT SCHOOL DISTRICT NO. 28-J OF THE COUNTIES OF ADAMS AND ARAPAHOE
15701 E 1ST AVE STE 106, AURORA, CO 800119037
Phone: 303 365-5810
Web: WWW.AURORAK12.ORG

HISTORICAL FINANCIALS

Company Type: Private

Income Statement — FYE: June 30

	REVENUE ($ mil.)	NET INCOME ($ mil.)	NET PROFIT MARGIN	EMPLOYEES
06/20	608	24	4.0%	6,000
06/19	555	6	1.2%	—
06/18	492	(8)	—	—
06/17	466	193	41.5%	—
Annual Growth	9.3%	(49.9%)	—	—

2020 Year-End Financials

Return on assets: 2.1%
Return on equity: —
Current ratio: 2.00
Cash ($ mil.): 234

KADLEC REGIONAL MEDICAL CENTER

Kadlec Regional Medical Center is an acute care hospital facility serving southeastern Washington and northeastern Oregon. In addition to providing comprehensive medical surgical and emergency services the hospital provides neonatal intensive care cardiopulmonary rehabilitation interventional cardiology neurology cancer care and other specialist services. Not-for-profit Kadlec Regional has some 270 inpatient beds including pediatric intensive intermediate and critical care capacity. It also operates outpatient physician offices and clinics in surrounding areas.

Operations

Kadlec Regional's cardiovascular programs include open heart surgery and interventional cardiology. The hospital also operates an all-digital outpatient imaging center and the region's only level III neonatal intensive care unit (NICU). Kadlec was is also designated as a Level 1 Cardiac Center and a Level 2 Stroke Center. Area specialist practices include centers for dermatology colorectal surgery nephrology pediatrics women's health ENT (ear nose and throat) and foot and ankle practices. Kadlec Regional also operates satellite urgent care and family practice clinics.

The Kadlec Neuroscience Center offers a wide range of services to treat and diagnose conditions related to the brain spine spinal cord & peripheral nervous system.

In 2013 the hospital reported more than 2700 births 66000 emergency department visits and about 15000 admissions.

That year Kadlec Regional provided $27 million in charity care.

Geographic Reach

Kadlec Regional has hospital and clinic locations in Hermiston Kennewick Pasco Pendleton Prosser and Richland.

Financial Performance

The hospital reported revenue of $312 million in 2012 consisting of $305 million in net patient service earnings and other revenue of some $7.5 million. Kadlec Regional brought in profits of some $29 million.

Strategy

The hospital has undergone aggressive expansion efforts adding a new patient tower with diagnostic outpatient and intermediate care and surgery rooms. Kadlec Regional is enhancing its specialty service units in fields to attract specialists and increase revenue.The organization launched a $10 million project to expand its NICU unit in 2013. It will add 27 private and semi-private rooms and new observation gathering and lactation areas.

It is also expanding outpatient service facilities such as a new $19 million three-story specialty physician practice office that opened in Richland in 2013. The new building increases collaboration between various surgical and medical specialists in the Kadlec Regional clinic network.

The year the company also expanded its emergency room offerings through the opening of the Kadlec ER in Kennewick. The new 15-bed ER is the first in the region to operate as a freestanding facility like traditional hospital-based ERs.

Mergers and Acquisitions

Kadlec Regional also absorbs other area providers. In 2013 Inland Cardiology Associates become part of the Kadlec Regional health system. The region's largest independent group of experienced cardiologists Inland provides comprehensive invasive noninvasive and interventional services throughout southeast Washington and northeast Oregon.

Company Background

In 2011 it partnered with the nearby PMH Medical Center to increase collaboration and specialist referrals between the two hospitals. The partnership extends the reach of Kadlec Regional's medical specialists to additional communities and brings PMH online with Kadlec Regional's electronic health record system. Both hospitals remained independently run.

The hospital system was founded in 1944.

EXECUTIVES

Vice President Finance Chief Financial Officer, Julie Meek
Secretary And Director, David Merkley

LOCATIONS

HQ: KADLEC REGIONAL MEDICAL CENTER
888 SWIFT BLVD, RICHLAND, WA 993523514
Phone: 509 946-4611
Web: WWW.KADLEC.ORG

PRODUCTS/OPERATIONS

Selected Services
The Birth Center
Bloodless Medicine and Surgery
Cancer Care
Cardiac Care
Cardiac Catheterization
CardioPulmonary Rehabilitation
Cardiovascular and Thoracic Surgery
CaringBridge
Clinical Decision Unit
Coumadin Clinic
Diabetes Learning Center
Diagnostic Imaging
Don and Lori Watts Pediatric Center
Emergency Department
Emergency Room-Kennewick
Home Health Care
Imaging
Inpatient Rehabilitation and Therapy
Intensive Care Unit
Joint Care Center
Kadlec Academy
Kadlec Healthy Ages
Kadlec Medical Associates
Neonatal Intensive Care Unit
Occupational Medicine
Occupational Therapy
Ostomy Support Group
Outpatient Imaging Center
Outpatient Procedures
Physical Therapy
Planetree
Rehabilitation and Therapy Services
Speech Therapy
Urgent Care
Water Therapy
Wound Healing Center

COMPETITORS

Adventist Health System West
Asante Health System
Legacy Health System
PeaceHealth
Providence Health & Services-Washington
Providence St. Joseph Health
Salem Hospital
Wenatchee Valley Medical Center
Yakima Valley Memorial

HISTORICAL FINANCIALS

Company Type: Private

Income Statement — FYE: December 31

	REVENUE ($ mil.)	NET INCOME ($ mil.)	NET PROFIT MARGIN	EMPLOYEES
12/18	640	51	8.0%	2,668
12/17	595	87	14.7%	—
12/16	534	9	1.9%	—
12/15	504	(7)	—	—
Annual Growth	8.3%	—	—	—

2018 Year-End Financials

Return on assets: 8.6%
Return on equity: 19.5%
Current ratio: 2.00
Cash ($ mil.): 18

KAISER FDN HEALTH PLAN OF COLORADO

Auditors: PRICEWATERHOUSECOOPERS LLP PH

LOCATIONS

HQ: KAISER FDN HEALTH PLAN OF COLORADO
1 KAISER PLZ STE 15L, OAKLAND, CA 946123610
Phone: 510 271-6611

HISTORICAL FINANCIALS

Company Type: Private

Income Statement — FYE: December 31

	REVENUE ($ mil.)	NET INCOME ($ mil.)	NET PROFIT MARGIN	EMPLOYEES
12/13	3,197	115	3.6%	14
12/09	2,374	32	1.4%	—
Annual Growth	7.7%	37.5%	—	—

2013 Year-End Financials

Return on assets: 7.2%
Return on equity: 14.7%
Current ratio: 0.50
Cash ($ mil.): 3

KAISER FOUNDATION HOSPITALS INC

Kaiser Foundation Hospitals is on a roll. The hospital group operates nearly 40 acute care hospitals and 680 medical offices in eight states (California Colorado Georgia Hawaii Maryland Oregon Virginia and Washington) and Washington D.C. The company's largest presence is in California where the majority of its hospitals are located. Kaiser Foundation Hospitals employs more than 21000 physicians representing all medical specialties. Kaiser Foundation Hospital's doctors group is controlled by Permanente Medical Groups and its HMO is offered through Kaiser Foundation Health Plan. Altogether the group provides care for about 11.7 million members.

Operations

Kaiser Foundation Hospitals works with other organizations to tackle such issues as obesity access to care and violence. It also works to promote health in the communities it serves through wellness programs.

In 2016 Kaiser Foundation Hospitals logged 44 million office visits. It facilitated 106000 births performed 129000 surgeries and filled 90 million prescriptions.

Company Background

Kaiser Foundation Hospitals was founded in 1945.

EXECUTIVES

Evp Kaiser Foundation Hospitals And Health Plan; Group President Kaiser Permanente Northern California And Mid-atlantic States; President Kaiser Permanente Northern California, Gregory A. Adams
Evp Kaiser Foundation Hospitals And Health Plan; Group President Kaiser Permanente Southern California And Hawaii; President Kaiser Permanente Southern California, Benjamin K. Chu
Chairman Southern California Permanente Medical Group And Executive Medical Director, Edward Ellison
Senior Management Senior Vice President General Manager Director, Anne Mcnealis
Secretary, Sandra Walker

LOCATIONS

HQ: KAISER FOUNDATION HOSPITALS INC
1 KAISER PLZ, OAKLAND, CA 946123610
Phone: 510 271-6611
Web: WWW.HEALTHY.KAISERPERMANENTE.ORG

PRODUCTS/OPERATIONS

Selected Hospitals
Antioch Medical Center
Fremont Medical Center
Fresno Medical Center
Hayward Medical Center
Manteca Medical Center
Modesto Medical Center
Oakland Medical Center
Redwood City Medical Center
Richmond Medical Center
Roseville Women and Children's Center
San Jose Medical Center
Santa Clara Medical Center
Sacramento Medical Center
South San Francisco Medical Center
South Sacramento Trauma Center
Santa Rosa Medical Center
San Francisco Medical Center
San Rafael Medical Center
Vacaville Medical Center
Vallejo Medical Center
Walnut Creek Medical Center
Baldwin Park Medical Center
Downey Medical Center
Fontana Medical Center
Los Angeles Medical Center
Moreno Valley Community Hospital
Orange County - Anaheim Medical Center
Orange County - Irvine Medical Center
Panorama City Medical Center
Riverside Medical Center
San Diego Medical Center
Harbor City (South Bay Medical Center)
Woodlands Hills Medical Center
West Los Angeles Medical Center
Sunnyside Medical Center (Portland Oregon area)
Moanalua Medical Center (Hawaii)

COMPETITORS

Adventist Health System West
Ascension Health
Banner Health
CHRISTUS Health
Catholic Health Initiatives
Community Health Systems
Dignity Health
HCA
LifePoint Health
Sutter Health
Tenet Healthcare
The Cleveland Clinic
Universal Health Services

HISTORICAL FINANCIALS

Company Type: Private

Income Statement — FYE: December 31

	REVENUE ($ mil.)	NET INCOME ($ mil.)	NET PROFIT MARGIN	EMPLOYEES
12/09	14,795	429	2.9%	175,668
12/08	0	0	99.0%	—
12/05	9,852	774	7.9%	—
Annual Growth	10.7%	(13.7%)	—	—

2009 Year-End Financials

Return on assets: —
Return on equity: 2.9%
Current ratio: —
Cash ($ mil.): 57

KALEIDA HEALTH

Kaleida Health provides a kaleidoscope of services to residents of western New York. The health system operates five acute care hospitals including Buffalo General Hospital and Gates Vascular Institute (combined with about 550 beds) The Women & Children's Hospital of Buffalo (200) DeGraff Memorial Hospital (70) and Millard Fillmore Suburban Hospital (260). Community health needs are met through a network of some 80 medical clinics. Kaleida Health also operates skilled nursing care facilities and provides home health care through its Visiting Nursing Association. To help train future medical professionals Buffalo General Hospital is a teaching affiliate of the State University of New York.

Operations

Kaleida Health is also home to the Deaconess Center and Waterfront long-term care facilities. Along with primary care the system's network of outpatient centers offers medical and surgical subspecialty care dental and oral surgery services and behavioral health and outpatient alcohol treatment services. Kaleida Health also operates the Pediatric Trauma Center and Pediatric HIV/AIDS Center for the Western New York (WNY).

In 2012 the health system had 55125 inpatient discharges 158902 emergency department visits and 2.3 million clinic and lab visits.

Financial Performance

The company's revenues grew by 3% to $1.2 billion in 2012 thanks to higher net patient service revenues and other revenues (including increases from a medical resident tax refund and HITECH incentive funds). It reported that 37% of net patient service revenues came from Medicare; 21% from New York State Medicaid; and 38% from commercial insurance plans.

Kaleida Health saw net income of $52 million in 2012 (compared to a net loss in 2011) as the result of higher revenues and an increase in investment returns (including a gain from a net change in unrealized gains and losses on investments).

Strategy

In an effort to draw in more patients to the eight communities in which it already operates in the US Kaleida Health has become one of a handful of US medical providers to market itself to patients north of the border in Canada. The organization launched a marketing campaign in Ontario over the years that included a website aimed at pulling in Canadian patients seeking bariatric care for obesity gastrointestinal services (such as colonoscopies) joint replacement or spinal surgery pediatric care and radiology services. Overall Kaleida is focused on attracting Canadian patients who can either pay out-of-pocket or patients seeking non-emergency services covered in the US by the Ontario Health Insurance Program.

Growing its operations in 2013 The Kaleida Health Laboratories (which performs more than 4 million tests a year) opened four new patient service centers in New York (Tonawanda Lancaster Buffalo and Cheektowaga).

Teaming up with Olean General Hospital (OGH) in 2013 Kaleida Health and OGH opened their new interventional cardiac catheterization lab joint-venture in the Southern Tier of New York.

Kaleida Health and The University at Buffalo opened a new 10-story vascular institute and research building in 2012. The $291 million Gates Vascular Institute and the University at Buffalo's Clinical and Translational Research Center integrates Kaleida Health's physicians and UB researchers in a collaborative effort to deliver clinical care investigate the causes of a wide range of human diseases and spin-off new biotechnology businesses and jobs.

In 2012 Kaleida Health's Visiting Nursing Association of Western New York received regulatory approval to expand into four additional counties.

To raise cash in 2013 Kaleida Health sold the former Millard Fillmore Gates Circle Hospital to TM Montante Development for commercial development.

Mergers and Acquisitions

In 2013 The Visiting Nursing Association of Western New York was selected as the provider of choice to buy the Livingston County Certified Home Health Agency. In 2012 it was selected as the provider of choice to purchase the Wyoming Certified Home Health Agency.

Company Background

Along with trying to grab a share of the Canadian market Kaleida is working to renovate and refurbish its current locations to draw in more patients. In late 2011 the system completed renovations of its maternity services at Women & Children's Hospital of Buffalo. The new Mother-Baby Unit offers 14 additional single rooms with private showers and enhanced amenities. The health system underwent another complete renovation that serves as an additional Mother-Baby Unit as well as inpatient beds for the Perinatal Center gynecology and other women's services.

EXECUTIVES

Senior Vice President Business Development, Michael P Hughes
Doctor Of Pharmacy, William Loeffler
Director Of Nursing, Sandra Boneberg
Medical Director, Edward Spangenthal
Medical Director, Michael Wilson
Executive Vice President Chief Human Resources Officer, Jerry Venable
Executive Vice President And Chief Financial Officer, Robert J Nesselbush
Clinical Director, Laurie Sadler
Operating Room Dir, Christina Leo
Vice President Physician Quality, Kenneth Snyder
Medical Secretary, Veronica Baker
Unit Secretary, Molly Beyer
Medical Secretary, Patti Carpino
Ed Medical Secretary, Deanna Partis

LOCATIONS

HQ: KALEIDA HEALTH
726 EXCHANGE ST, BUFFALO, NY 142101484
Phone: 716 859-5600
Web: WWW.KALEIDAHEALTH.ORG

PRODUCTS/OPERATIONS

Selected Facilities

Buffalo General Hospital (Buffalo)
Deaconess Center (Buffalo)
DeGraff Memorial Hospital (North Tonawanda)
Gates Vascular Institute (Buffalo)
Millard Fillmore Suburban Hospital (Williamsville)
VNA Home Care Services (Allegany County Chautauqua County Erie County Genesee County Niagara County)
Women and Children's Hospital of Buffalo (Buffalo)

Selected Services

Admissions
Adult Day Services
Allergy & Immunology Clinic
Anesthesia
Bariatric Program
Bereavement Services
Blood Draw Labs
Breast Reconstruction Surgery Information
Buffalo Niagara MRI Center
Cardiac Program
Center for Asthma & Environmental Exposure
Center for Wound Care
Chest Pain Center
Colorectal Surgery
Community Health
Department
DeGraff Skilled Nursing Facility
Diabetes-Endocrinology Center of Western New York
Dialysis Treatments
Diversity & Inclusion
Ear Nose and Throat Center/Otolaryngology
Easy Referrals
Emergency Department
Epilepsy Family Planning Center
Gastroenterology
Geriatric Center of Western New York
Hernia Center
Imaging Services
Immunology Laboratory
Laboratory and Pathology
Maternity Services
Minimally Invasive Surgery
Minor Surgery
Multiple Sclerosis
Neonatology
Neuropsychology
Neurosciences
Neurosurgery and Procedures
Obstetrics and Gynecology
Occupational Therapy
Orthopedics
Parkinson's Disease Comprehensive Movement Disorder Center
Pastoral Care
Personal Care Services
Personal Response System (Lifeline)
Pharmacy - High Street
Pharmacy Pharmacy - Suburban Family Pharmacy
Pharmacy Residency Program
Physical Therapy Prenatal Testing
Primary Care
Rehabilitation Medicine - Acute Medical
Rehabilitation Rehabilitation Services
Retinal
Surgical Services
Robotic Surgery
School Based Health Centers
Security
Speech Therapy - Outpatient
Spirit of Women
Stroke Program
Subacute Rehabilitation
Surgical Services
Telehealth Home Monitoring
The Greater Buffalo
United Accountable Healthcare
Urology Services
Vascular Lab
Vascular Services
Visiting Nursing Association of WNY
VNA Diabetes Program
Women's Services
Wound Care

COMPETITORS

Catholic Health System
Ellis Hospital
Hamot Medical Center
Kane Community Hospital
Lifetime Health
Oneida Healthcare Center
SUNY Upstate Medical University
St. Joseph's Hospital Health Center
St. Peter's Health Partners
St. Vincent Health System
Titusville
United Health Services Hospitals
Upstate University Hospital at Community General

HISTORICAL FINANCIALS

Company Type: Private

Income Statement FYE: December 31

	REVENUE ($ mil.)	NET INCOME ($ mil.)	NET PROFIT MARGIN	EMPLOYEES
12/17	1,331	60	4.5%	9,000
12/13	1,139	(14)	—	—
12/09	1,155	75	6.5%	—
Annual Growth	1.8%	(2.7%)	—	—

2017 Year-End Financials

Return on assets: 4.3% Cash ($ mil.): 16
Return on equity: 19.6%
Current ratio: 1.40

KALISPELL REGIONAL HEALTHCARE SYSTEM

EXECUTIVES

Pres-Ceo, Pamela Robertson
Chb, Doug Nelson
Pres, Velinda Stevens
Treas, Charles T Pearce
Cfo, Craig Boyer
Director of Materials Manager, Dave Brabham
Network Engineer, Aaron Turner
Phlebotomist, Doreen Hatcher
Technology Specialist, Lauren Krass
Urologist, Vassilis Siomos
Maintenance, Andrew Bastick
Auditors: JORDAHL & SLITER PLLC KALISPE

LOCATIONS

HQ: KALISPELL REGIONAL HEALTHCARE SYSTEM
310 SUNNYVIEW LN, KALISPELL, MT 599013129
Phone: 406 752-8991
Web: WWW.KRH.ORG

HISTORICAL FINANCIALS

Company Type: Private

Income Statement FYE: March 31

	REVENUE ($ mil.)	NET INCOME ($ mil.)	NET PROFIT MARGIN	EMPLOYEES
03/18	571	(21)	—	3,100
03/14	2	(2)	—	—
03/12	2	(1)	—	—
03/11	1	(1)	—	—
Annual Growth	126.9%	—	—	—

2018 Year-End Financials

Return on assets: (-3.7%) Cash ($ mil.): 50
Return on equity: (-8.2%)
Current ratio: 1.10

KANSAS DEPARTMENT OF TRANSPORTATION

The Kansas Department of Transportation (KDOT) helps connect the dots with residents who love to travel the 140000-plus miles across the Sunflower State. The agency focuses on providing a transportation system for citizens in the state by offering a wide range of services such as maintaining roads and bridges transportation planning and designing construction projects. The department also provides federal fund program administration as well as administrative support travel information and programs in traffic safety. KDOT traces its roots to the organization of interstate travel in 1917.

Strategy

The agency hopes to bring in additional revenue and preserve and expand its state's road bridge and highway infrastructure through its $7.8 billion T-WORKS program in effect from fiscal year end 2011 through 2020. It includes $2.7 billion in new revenues from registration fees for heavy trucks and a sales tax deposit that begins in 2014. KDOT will spend at least $8 million in each of Kansas' 105 counties during T-WORKS' administration. KDOT plans for the program to create 175000 jobs over the course of the next 10 years.

EXECUTIVES

Secretary, Richard Carlson
Coordinator, Scott Shields
Bridge Inspector Team Leader, Ed Burdiek
Director, Bob Brock
Gis Manager, Kyle Gonterwitz
Chief Global Strategist, Amanda Baxter
Transportation, Andrea Barnes
Chief Counsel, Barbara Rankin
Engineer, G Comstock
Public Affairs Manager, Kirk Hutchinson
Transportation, Michael Slief
Auditors: CLIFTONLARSONALLEN LLP BROOM

LOCATIONS

HQ: KANSAS DEPARTMENT OF TRANSPORTATION
700 SW HARRISON ST # 500, TOPEKA, KS 666033964
Phone: 785 296-3501
Web: WWW.KSDOT.ORG

HISTORICAL FINANCIALS

Company Type: Private

Income Statement FYE: June 30

	REVENUE ($ mil.)	NET INCOME ($ mil.)	NET PROFIT MARGIN	EMPLOYEES
06/19	1,583	312	19.7%	3,000
06/18	1,476	265	18.0%	—
06/17	1,476	(91)	—	—
06/15	1,430	190	13.3%	—
Annual Growth	2.6%	13.1%	—	—

2019 Year-End Financials

Return on assets: 2.2% Cash ($ mil.): 580
Return on equity: 2.7%
Current ratio: —

KANSAS STATE UNIVERSITY

K-State is a big deal in the Little Apple. Located in Manhattan Kansas (aka the Little Apple) Kansas State University (K-State) is a land grant institution that has an enrollment of some 24000 students. It offers more than 250 undergraduate majors 65 master's degrees 45 doctoral degrees and more than 20 graduate certificate programs. Major fields of study include agriculture technology and veterinary medicine. Notable alumni include former White House press secretary Marlin Fitzwater and actor Gordon Jump. Along with the University of Kansas and other universities technical schools and community colleges in the state K-State is governed by The Kansas Board of Regents.

Operations

With a student-to-faculty ratio of 20:1 K-State ranks among top US colleges and has one of the highest levels of prestigious scholarship winners (including Rhodes Marshall and Truman scholars) in the US. The university also has several notable research organizations in fields including agriculture and genetic science.

K-State is also big on sports and is part of the Big 12 Conference of collegiate athletics.

Geographic Reach

K-State has its main campus on 670-acres in Manhattan Kansas. It also has satellite campuses in Salina and Olathe. It also has agricultural and research centers at five Kansas locations. The university's students come from all 50 US states and more than 90 countries.

Financial Performance

K-State increased revenues by 9% to $541 million in 2012 due to higher income from student fees; government and non-government grants and contracts (for research and athletic activities); and auxiliary enterprises. Net income decreased 24% to $47 million due to higher operating expenses and lower non-operating revenues which was attributed to lower state appropriation levels and higher interest expenses.

Strategy

K-State is expanding its facilities and programs to meet the needs of its students. It completed the first $22 million phase of its National Bio and Agro-Defense Facility in 2012 as well as work on a new student recreational housing classroom and athletics facilities. In 2011 it added a new bachelor's degree program in social work. It also expanded its partnership with the Chinese scholarship council to allow additional students from China to study at K-State.

Company Background

K-State was established in 1858 as Bluemont Central College; five years later it was one of the first colleges in the US to be designated a land-grant school.

EXECUTIVES

Senior Vice President Of Business Develo, David Pacey
Vice President Marketing And Brand Development, Jackie Coletta
Chapter Treasurer Spring 2017, Dan Baker
Treasurer, Taylor Hegarty

LOCATIONS

HQ: KANSAS STATE UNIVERSITY
ANDERSON HALL 110 1301 MI, MANHATTAN, KS 66506
Phone: 785 532-6011
Web: WWW.K-STATE.EDU

PRODUCTS/OPERATIONS

Selected Colleges and Departments

College of Agriculture
- Agricultural Economics
- Agronomy
- Animal Sciences and Industry
- Entomology
- Food Science Institute
- Grain Science and Industry
- Plant Pathology

College of Architecture Planning and Design
- Architecture
- Interior Architecture and Product Design
- Landscape Architecture/Regional and Community Planning

College of Arts and Sciences
- Aerospace Studies
- American Ethnic Studies
- Art
- Biochemistry
- Chemistry
- Economics
- English
- Geography
- Geology
- History
- International and Area Studies

Journalism and Mass Communications
Kinesiology
Mathematics
Military Science
Modern Languages
Music
Philosophy
Physics
Political Science
Psychology
Statistics
Women's Studies
College of Business Administration
Accounting
Finance
Management
Marketing
College of Education
Educational Leadership
Elementary Education
Secondary Education
Special Education Counseling and Student Affairs
College of Engineering
Architectural Engineering and Construction Science
Biological and Agricultural Engineering
Chemical Engineering
Computing and Information Science
Electrical and Computer Engineering
Mechanical and Nuclear Engineering
College of Human Ecology
Apparel Textiles and Interior Design
Gerontology
Human Nutrition
College of Technology and Aviation
Arts Sciences and Business
Aviation Technology
College of Veterinary Medicine
Anatomy and Physiology
Clinical Sciences

COMPETITORS

Baylor University
Iowa State University
Oklahoma State
Texas A&M
Texas Tech
The University of Kansas
University of Colorado
University of Missouri
University of Nebraska
University of Oklahoma
University of Texas
Wichita State University

HISTORICAL FINANCIALS

Company Type: Private

Income Statement — FYE: June 30

	REVENUE ($ mil.)	NET INCOME ($ mil.)	NET PROFIT MARGIN	EMPLOYEES
06/19	637	51	8.1%	5,168
06/17	620	50	8.2%	—
06/10	459	50	11.0%	—
06/09	420	10	2.6%	—
Annual Growth	4.2%	17.0%	—	—

2019 Year-End Financials

Return on assets: 3.3%
Return on equity: 6.0%
Current ratio: 2.20
Cash ($ mil.): 206

KATY INDEPENDENT SCHOOL DISTRICT

EXECUTIVES

Pres, Bryan Michalsky
Pres-SEC*, Rebecca Fox
Katy Isd Board of Trustees Mem*, Henry Dibrell
V Pres*, Joe M Adams
Supt*, Alton Fraley
Treas*, Charles Griffin
Cfo*, William L Moore
Coordinator, Howard Grimet
Reading Specialist, Janet Sutherland
Teacher, Brandy Williams
Student Publications Advisor, Ed Larsen

LOCATIONS

HQ: KATY INDEPENDENT SCHOOL DISTRICT
6301 S STADIUM LN, KATY, TX 774941057
Phone: 281 396-6000
Web: WWW.KATYISD.ORG

HISTORICAL FINANCIALS

Company Type: Private

Income Statement — FYE: August 31

	REVENUE ($ mil.)	NET INCOME ($ mil.)	NET PROFIT MARGIN	EMPLOYEES
08/19	993	17	1.8%	6,631
08/18	922	0	0.1%	—
08/16	841	15	1.9%	—
08/11	601	123	20.5%	—
Annual Growth	6.5%	(21.5%)	—	—

2019 Year-End Financials

Return on assets: 0.6%
Return on equity: 31.9%
Current ratio: —
Cash ($ mil.): 522

KAWEAH DELTA HEALTH CARE DISTRICT

EXECUTIVES

Ceo, Donna Archer
Ceo*, Lindsay K Mann
V Pres-Cfo*, Gary Herbst
Vice-President Finance, Jennifer Stockton
Information Technology/Interne, Christine Muldoon
Human Resources Administrator, Jaime Thomason
Controller, Bill Blair
Health Care Director, Karen Bontekoe
Administrative Assistant, Valerie Lee
Auditing Manager, Suzy Plummer
Network Administrator, Christine Johns

LOCATIONS

HQ: KAWEAH DELTA HEALTH CARE DISTRICT
400 W MINERAL KING AVE, VISALIA, CA 932916237
Phone: 559 624-2000
Web: WWW.KDHCD.ORG

HISTORICAL FINANCIALS

Company Type: Private

Income Statement — FYE: June 30

	REVENUE ($ mil.)	NET INCOME ($ mil.)	NET PROFIT MARGIN	EMPLOYEES
06/20	734	(6)	—	3,200
06/19	751	28	3.8%	—
06/18	710	28	4.1%	—
06/16	537	52	9.8%	—
Annual Growth	8.1%	—	—	—

2020 Year-End Financials

Return on assets: (-0.7%)
Return on equity: (-1.4%)
Current ratio: 1.40
Cash ($ mil.): 11

KENNESTONE HOSPITAL AT WINDY HILL, INC.

Kennestone cures kidney stones and other ailments for residents of Cobb County Georgia. WellStar Kennestone Hospital has more than 630 beds and a full range of specialty services. The hospital's physicians provide cardiac care inpatient and outpatient surgery and rehabilitation trauma diabetes care oncology dialysis and home health care. The hospital also operates centers specializing in women's health senior living facilities diagnostic clinics and a wellness and fitness center. WellStar Kennestone Hospital is part of the not-for-profit WellStar Health System which operates hospitals and other medical facilities throughout Georgia.

Operations

WellStar Kennestone Hospital is the anchor of the group's WellStar Kennestone Regional Medical Center division. WellStar Kennestone Hospital handles about 37000 inpatient admissions each year as well as more than 400000 outpatient appointments and 120000 emergency room visits. It also conducts about 23000 inpatient and outpatient surgeries and 9000 births annually and operates a level II regional trauma center. The hospital has been recognized in a number of specialist fields such as orthopedics neurology and gastroenterology.

Geographic Reach

Located in Marietta Georgia WellStar Kennestone Hospital primary serves northern and central Cobb County.

Strategy

The hospital is undergoing renovation and expansion efforts including construction of a new hospital tower with all private patient rooms; the tower was completed and opened in early 2013. Two years later the hospital opened a new inpatient pediatric unit. It also began renovations of its cancer center.

WellStar Kennestone also regularly upgrades its medical technology systems and tools such as robotic surgery systems and data management programs.

EXECUTIVES

Director Of Him, Beth Kost
Assistant Vice President Hris, Todd Hamilton
Secretary Labor And Delivery, Miriam Murray

LOCATIONS

HQ: KENNESTONE HOSPITAL AT WINDY HILL, INC.
677 CHURCH ST NE, MARIETTA, GA 300601101
Phone: 770 793-5000
Web: WWW.WELLSTAR.ORG

COMPETITORS

Adventist Health System Sunbelt Healthcare
Children's Healthcare of Atlanta
DeKalb Medical
Emory Healthcare
Grady Health System
Northside Hospital
Piedmont Healthcare
Redmond Regional Medical Center
Regency Hospital
Shepherd Center
SunLink Health Systems
The Fulton-DeKalb Hospital Authority
West Georgia Health System

HISTORICAL FINANCIALS

Company Type: Private

Income Statement FYE: June 30

	REVENUE ($ mil.)	NET INCOME ($ mil.)	NET PROFIT MARGIN	EMPLOYEES
06/15	821	106	12.9%	2,950
06/05	481	54	11.2%	—
06/04	877	50	5.7%	—
06/03	792	24	3.1%	—
Annual Growth	0.3%	12.9%	—	—

2015 Year-End Financials

Return on assets: 20.5%
Cash ($ mil.): —
Return on equity: 38.2%
Current ratio: 8.90

KENNESTONE HOSPITAL INC

Auditors: PRICEWATERHOUSECOOPERS LLP PH

LOCATIONS

HQ: KENNESTONE HOSPITAL INC
805 SANDY PLAINS RD, MARIETTA, GA 300666340
Phone: 770 792-5023
Web: WWW.WELLSTAR.ORG

HISTORICAL FINANCIALS

Company Type: Private

Income Statement FYE: June 30

	REVENUE ($ mil.)	NET INCOME ($ mil.)	NET PROFIT MARGIN	EMPLOYEES
06/15	948	182	19.2%	15
06/14	836	113	13.5%	—
06/13	791	123	15.6%	—
06/10	800	123	15.5%	—
Annual Growth	3.5%	8.0%	—	—

2015 Year-End Financials

Return on assets: 29.0%
Cash ($ mil.): —
Return on equity: 48.5%
Current ratio: 8.60

KERN HIGH SCHOOL DST

EXECUTIVES

Supt, Donald E Carter
Principal, Robert Schneider
Principal, Jim Caswell
Payroll Staff, Gregory Vasquez
Superintendent, Don Carter
Substitute Teacher, Damien Lomack
Assistant Director of Food Ser, Randy Rico
Categorical Programs Administr, Krista Twist
Accounting Administrator, Bryan Campoy
Coordinator, Anthony Lopez
Administrator, Brian Mendiburu
Auditors: CROWE LLP SACRAMENTO CALIFO

LOCATIONS

HQ: KERN HIGH SCHOOL DST
5801 SUNDALE AVE, BAKERSFIELD, CA 933097908
Phone: 661 827-3100
Web: WWW.KERNHIGH.ORG

HISTORICAL FINANCIALS

Company Type: Private

Income Statement FYE: June 30

	REVENUE ($ mil.)	NET INCOME ($ mil.)	NET PROFIT MARGIN	EMPLOYEES
06/19	677	(43)	—	2,000
06/18	557	40	7.3%	—
06/17	518	40	7.8%	—
06/16	507	44	8.7%	—
Annual Growth	10.1%	—	—	—

KETTERING ADVENTIST HEALTHCARE

Kettering Adventist Healthcare dba Kettering Health Network and named for famed inventor Charles F. Kettering is an Ohio-based health care system. It comprises about 120 outpatient facilities including seven acute care hospitals: Kettering Medical Center Grandview Medical Center Sycamore Medical Center Southview Medical Center Fort Hamilton Hospital Greene Memorial Hospital and Soin Medical Center. Other facilities include Kettering Behavioral Hospital and multiple outpatient diagnostic senior care and urgent care clinics. Among its specialized services are heart care rehabilitation orthopedics women's health and emergency medicine.

Operations

Several times in recent years Kettering Health has been named by Thomson Reuters as one of the Top 10 US Healthcare Systems.

The system operates nine radiology centers 10 pharmacies eight outpatient rehab centers seven sleep centers 13 sports medicine centers and five wound centers.

Kettering Health provides community care benefits including health screenings education programs charity care for uninsured patients and coverage of Medicare/Medicaid shortfalls for under-insured patients.

Geographic Reach

Kettering Health's facilities are located in Dayton Ohio and the surrounding towns of Beavercreek Centerville Hamilton Kettering Miamisburg and Xenia.

Financial Performance

Revenue totaled $1.4 billion in 2014.

Strategy

Kettering makes capital investments in its medical centers to better serve its communities. It works to improve specialty units and equipment at its existing inpatient hospitals as well as technologically advanced hospitals tend to attract better physicians (and therefore patients). Kettering is adding new freestanding emergency room facilities in Franklin and in Eaton to the tune of $19 million. In 2015 it broke ground on a $49 million five-story cancer center at Kettering Medical Center.

The health network is also intent on expanding its outpatient facility network.

It's expanding in Ohio as well through a 2014 collaboration with Health Innovations of Ohio. To keep its database up to date Kettering in 2014 enlisted the help of ProVation Order Sets to oversee its clinical content management system.

EXECUTIVES

Vice President Of Clinical Integration And Innovation, Beverly Knapp
Vice President, Donald Ames
Clinical Director, Donna Arand
Vice President For Patient Car, Belinda Mallett
Medical Director, Rajinder Singh
Vice President Medical Affairs Chief Medical Officer, Robert Smith
Pharmacist Manager, Rachael Schlechty
Pharmacy Manager, Wayne Hoover
Pharmacy Manager, Don Groff
Medical Secretary, Sharon Stamas
Auditors: ERNST & YOUNG LLP CINCINNATI

LOCATIONS

HQ: KETTERING ADVENTIST HEALTHCARE
3535 SOUTHERN BLVD, DAYTON, OH 454291221
Phone: 937 298-4331
Web: WWW.KETTERINGHEALTH.ORG

PRODUCTS/OPERATIONS

Selected Ohio Facilities

Acute Care Hospitals
- Fort Hamilton Hospital (Hamilton)
- Grandview Medical Center (Dayton)
- Greene Memorial Hospital (Xenia)
- Kettering Medical Center (Kettering)
- Soin Medical Center (Beavercreek)
- Southview Medical Center (Dayton)
- Sycamore Medical Center (Miamisburg)

Other
- Adolescent Recovery Center of Hope
- Beavercreek Health Center
- Beavercreek Health Park
- Charles H. Huber Health Center
- Corwin M. Nixon Health Center
- Englewood Community Medical Center
- Kettering Behavioral Hospital (Dayton)
- Sugarcreek Health Center
- Sycamore Glen Health Center
- Sycamore Glen Retirement Center
- Sycamore Primary Care Center
- Urgent Care Centers (regional)

Selected Services

Assisted Living
Back Pain
Bariatric
Behavioral Health
Bladder Confidence
Breast Health
Cancer Care
Cardiovascular
Corporate Wellness
Community Outreach
Counseling
Diabetes
Emergency
Epilepsy
Executive Health
Fertility
Gamma Knife
Heart Care
Home Care
Hyperbaric Medicine
Imaging
Independent Living
Mammography
Maternity
Mental Health
Minimally Invasive Surgery
Neonatal Care
Neuroscience
NeuroRehab
Nutrition Counseling
Obstetrics
Oncology
Orthopedics
Pain Management
Palliative Care
Pastoral Care

Pelvic Control
Physical Therapy
Pulmonary Rehab
Radiology
Rehab Therapy
Reproductive
Robotic Surgery
Senior Living
Short-term Rehab
Skilled Nursing
Sleep
Spine
Spiritual Services
Sports Medicine
Stroke
Surgery
Urgent Care
Weight Loss
Wound Care

COMPETITORS

AdCare
Adena Health System
Cincinnati Children's Hospital
Fairfield Medical Center
Licking Memorial Health Systems
MetroHealth System
Mount Carmel Health
OhioHealth
Premier Health Partners
Regency Hospital
Select Medical
TriHealth
UC Health
University Hospitals Health System

HISTORICAL FINANCIALS

Company Type: Private

Income Statement — FYE: December 31

	REVENUE ($ mil.)	NET INCOME ($ mil.)	NET PROFIT MARGIN	EMPLOYEES
12/18	1,863	70	3.8%	6,800
12/17	1,753	171	9.8%	—
12/16	1,577	98	6.2%	—
Annual Growth	8.7%	(15.4%)	—	—

2018 Year-End Financials

Return on assets: 2.9%
Return on equity: 5.2%
Current ratio: 1.60
Cash ($ mil.): 63

KEY FOOD STORES CO-OPERATIVE, INC.

Key Food Stores Co-Operative is a friend to independent New York area grocers. The co-op provides retail support and other services to 150 independently owned food retailers in the New York City area. Key Food's member-owners run stores mainly in Brooklyn and Queens but also in the other boroughs and surrounding counties. It operates stores primarily under the Key Food banner but it also has Key Food Marketplace locations that feature expanded meat deli and produce departments. In addition the co-op supplies Key Foods-branded products to member stores. Among its members are Pick Quick Foods Dan's Supreme Super Markets Gemstone Supermarkets and Queens Supe rmarkets. Key Foods was founded in 1937.

Geographic Reach

Staten Island-based Key Food Stores Co-Operative operates supermarkets across the five boroughs and on Long Island in upstate New York and in New Jersey and Pennsylvania.

Financial Performance

Key Foods Stores has annual sales of about $1.5 billion.

Strategy

Key Food has been expanding in Queens and Brooklyn and on Long Island after scaling back in Manhattan – where many of its stores were converted to Duane Reade drugstores as the pharmacy chain expanded and took over individual locations. To that end in late 2013 the regional grocer launched a new banner called Urban Market in Brooklyn. The 16000-square foot store in Williamsburg was the co-op's 150th location. The cooperative is expanding aggressively adding more than 30 locations under the Key Food Key Fresh & Natural and Food Dynasty banners including stores in Harlem and the Bronx. It also recently reopened a store in Coney Island that was destroyed by Hurricane Sandy in 2012.

EXECUTIVES

Ceo, Dean Janeway
Chb*, Lawrence Mandel
Pres, Richard Grobman
V Pres, Salvatore Bonavita
SEC*, Sam Obeid
Treas, Anthony Bileddo
Asst SEC, Benjamin Levine
Coordinator, Marnique Ortiz
Information Technology Project, Michaele Domnisch
Vice President Finance, Sharon Konzelman
Vice President, George Knobloch
Auditors: ANCHIN BLOCK & ANCHIN LLP N

LOCATIONS

HQ: KEY FOOD STORES CO-OPERATIVE, INC.
100 MATAWAN RD STE 100 # 100, MATAWAN, NJ 077473913
Phone: 718 370-4200
Web: WWW.KEYFOOD.COM

PRODUCTS/OPERATIONS

Selected Banners

Food Dynasty
Food World
Holiday Farms
Key Food
Key Food Marketplace
Key Fresh & Natural
Locust Valley
Milford Farms
Urban Market
Vitelio's Marketplace

COMPETITORS

A&P
D'Agostino Supermarkets
Food Emporium
Fresh Direct
Gristede's Foods
King Kullen Grocery
Walgreen

HISTORICAL FINANCIALS

Company Type: Private

Income Statement — FYE: April 25

	REVENUE ($ mil.)	NET INCOME ($ mil.)	NET PROFIT MARGIN	EMPLOYEES
04/15	893	(0)	—	84
04/14	753	0	0.0%	—
04/11	537	(0)	—	—
04/10	0	0	—	—
Annual Growth	—	—	—	—

2015 Year-End Financials

Return on assets: (-0.6%)
Return on equity: (-2.7%)
Current ratio: 1.10
Cash ($ mil.): 4

KEYSTOPS, LLC

EXECUTIVES

Mmbr, Lester Key
Staff*, Rex Hazelip
MBR*, Richard Shepherd
MBR*, Kent Pyle
MBR*, Charles Key
Director of Safety, David Murphy
Auditors: BKD LLP BOWLING GREEN KENTUC

LOCATIONS

HQ: KEYSTOPS, LLC
376 REASONOVER AVE, FRANKLIN, KY 421344003
Phone: 270 586-8283
Web: WWW.KEYSTOPS.COM

HISTORICAL FINANCIALS

Company Type: Private

Income Statement — FYE: September 30

	REVENUE ($ mil.)	NET INCOME ($ mil.)	NET PROFIT MARGIN	EMPLOYEES
09/19	561	5	1.0%	200
09/18	578	0	0.1%	—
09/17	500	2	0.5%	—
09/16	430	4	1.0%	—
Annual Growth	9.3%	12.3%	—	—

2019 Year-End Financials

Return on assets: 5.1%
Return on equity: 9.7%
Current ratio: 2.60
Cash ($ mil.): 2

KFHP OF THE MID-ATLANTIC STATES INC.

Auditors: PRICEWATERHOUSECOOPERS LLP PH

LOCATIONS

HQ: KFHP OF THE MID-ATLANTIC STATES INC.
1 KAISER PLZ 15L, OAKLAND, CA 946123610
Phone: 510 271-6611

HISTORICAL FINANCIALS

Company Type: Private

Income Statement — FYE: December 31

	REVENUE ($ mil.)	NET INCOME ($ mil.)	NET PROFIT MARGIN	EMPLOYEES
12/13	2,511	(13)	—	2
12/09	2,089	(10)	—	—
Annual Growth	4.7%	—	—	—

2013 Year-End Financials

Return on assets: 7.1%
Return on equity: (-0.5%)
Current ratio: 0.60
Cash ($ mil.): 7

KGBO HOLDINGS, INC

Total Quality Logistics sets a high standard for moving merchandise. The third-party logistics (non-asset based) provider specializes in arranging freight transportation using reefers (refrigerated trucks) vans and flatbeds – moving in excess of 500000 loads each year. The trucking brokerage company serves more than 7000 clients across the US Canada and Mexico ranging from small businesses to Fortune 500 organizations. Founded in 1997 by company president Ken Oaks Total Quality Logistics (TQL) has contracts with carriers that include single owner operators and large fleets. Customers have included Kroger Dole Food and Laura's Lean Beef.

Operations

The company began as a produce shipper – not a popular item for most brokers because it is perishable – and expanded into flatbed shipments and other dry freight. As a non-asset-based business TQL does not own trucks or warehouses nor does it employ drivers. Rather it arranges for independent carrier companies and owner/operators to transport its customers' freight; TQL manages the shipment while it is on the road. Additionally the company has no expensive overhead and is not limited by fleet size equipment or shipping routes allowing more flexibility for its customers.

Geographic Reach

TQL largely caters to customers in the Greater Cincinnati Area where it has nearly five offices. It has about 25 satellite locations located in Chicago; Cleveland; Charlotte North Carolina; Charleston South Carolina; Detroit; Indianapolis; Denver; Columbus Ohio; Houston; Lexington Kentucky; Louisville; Nashville Tennessee; Orlando Florida; Dayton Ohio; Erlanger Kentucky; Pittsburgh; Tampa; and Austin Texas.

Sales and Marketing

The company serves more than 10000 customers and 50000 carriers across North America to move more than 800000 loads each year. Customers include Dole Food Wholesalers and Kroger.

Financial Performance

TOL posted $1.6 billion in annual sales for 2013 up from the $1.4 billion it posted the previous year. With no expense overhead to bog down its balance sheet the company has enjoyed three straight years of sizable growth.

Strategy

TQL grows its business by gradually launching additional locations and sales offices in key cities across the country. In 2013 it expanded its sales office in Charlotte North Carolina and moved its operations in Lexington Kentucky to a larger space. Also that year TQL launched a new sales office in Orlando Florida. In 2012 the company opened new offices in the key metropolitan areas of Cleveland Detroit and Pittsburgh. In 2014 it announced plans to launch a new office in Nashville Tennessee.

EXECUTIVES

Pres, Kenneth Oaks
Controller, Kate Lucas Stump
Distribution/Shipping/Transpor, Aaron Schaeffer
Logistics Consultant, Alex Danforth
Logistics Account Executive, Alexander Izsak
Logistics Account Executive, Brian Odioso
Account Executive, Chad Armel
National Sales Recruiter, Collin Saylor
Logistics Account Executive, Collin Wonderlic
Logistics Account Executive, Daniel McCarthy
Logistics Account Executive, Darrin Redus
Auditors: BARNES DENNIG & CO LTD CI

LOCATIONS

HQ: KGBO HOLDINGS, INC
4289 IVY POINTE BLVD, CINCINNATI, OH 452450002
Phone: 513 831-2600

COMPETITORS

Alliance Shippers
C.H. Robinson Worldwide
Echo Global
MIQ Logistics
Roadrunner Transportation Systems
Ryder System
Schneider Logistics
Transplace
UPS Supply Chain Solutions

HISTORICAL FINANCIALS

Company Type: Private

Income Statement — FYE: December 30

	REVENUE ($ mil.)	NET INCOME ($ mil.)	NET PROFIT MARGIN	EMPLOYEES
12/12	1,387	0	—	4,077
12/11	1,046	0	—	—
12/10	762	0	—	—
Annual Growth	34.9%	—	—	—

KIEWIT BUILDING GROUP INC.

EXECUTIVES

Pres-Ceo, Joseph R Lempka
Sr V Pres*, Michael J Colpack
Sr V Pres*, Ronald C Duce
Sr V Pres*, J D Vetter
Sr V Pres*, Kevin P Welker
Sr V Pres*, Lance K Wilhelm
V Pres*, Becky S Golden
V Pres*, Raymond D Hallquist
V Pres*, Michael J Piechoski
V Pres*, Herb J Reuss
V Pres*, Tobin A Schropp
Auditors: KPMG LLP OMAHA NE

LOCATIONS

HQ: KIEWIT BUILDING GROUP INC.
160 INVERNESS DR W # 110, ENGLEWOOD, CO 801125004
Phone: 402 977-4500
Web: WWW.KIEWIT.COM

HISTORICAL FINANCIALS

Company Type: Private

Income Statement — FYE: December 29

	REVENUE ($ mil.)	NET INCOME ($ mil.)	NET PROFIT MARGIN	EMPLOYEES
12/12	649	12	1.9%	1,047
12/11	860	85	10.0%	—
12/10	1,280	124	9.7%	—
Annual Growth	(28.8%)	(68.3%)	—	—

2012 Year-End Financials

Return on assets: 4.5%
Return on equity: 9.2%
Current ratio: 1.80
Cash ($ mil.): 47

KIEWIT CORPORATION

EXECUTIVES

Ceo, Bruce E Grewcock
Exec V Pres, Richard W Colf
Exec V Pres, Douglas E Patterson
Exec V Pres, Scott L Cassels
Sr V Pres, Steven Hansen
Treas, Stephen S Thomas
SEC, Michael F Norton
Major Project Mana, Joe Wingerter
Career, Heather Semple
Law Specialist, Simson Chan
Superintendent, Gary Dyer
Auditors: KPMG LLP OMAHA NE

LOCATIONS

HQ: KIEWIT CORPORATION
3555 FARNAM ST STE 1000, OMAHA, NE 681313302
Phone: 402 342-2052
Web: WWW.KIEWIT.COM

HISTORICAL FINANCIALS

Company Type: Private

Income Statement — FYE: December 28

	REVENUE ($ mil.)	NET INCOME ($ mil.)	NET PROFIT MARGIN	EMPLOYEES
12/13	11,826	796	6.7%	10,441
12/12	11,220	512	4.6%	—
12/11	10,381	796	7.7%	—
Annual Growth	6.7%	(0.0%)	—	—

KIEWIT INDUSTRIAL GROUP INC

EXECUTIVES

Pres, Douglas E Patterson
Ex V Pres, Richard A Lanoha
Auditors: KPMG LLP OMAHA NE

LOCATIONS

HQ: KIEWIT INDUSTRIAL GROUP INC
3555 FARNAM ST, OMAHA, NE 681313311
Phone: 402 342-2052
Web: WWW.KIEWIT.COM

HISTORICAL FINANCIALS

Company Type: Private

Income Statement — FYE: December 28

	REVENUE ($ mil.)	NET INCOME ($ mil.)	NET PROFIT MARGIN	EMPLOYEES
12/13	3,474	241	6.9%	20
12/12	3,397	110	3.2%	—
12/11	2,445	118	4.8%	—
12/10	2,546	173	6.8%	—
Annual Growth	10.9%	11.5%	—	—

2013 Year-End Financials

Return on assets: 13.8%
Return on equity: 26.4%
Current ratio: 1.80
Cash ($ mil.): 324

KIEWIT INFRASTRUCTURE CO.

EXECUTIVES

Pres, Bruce Grewcock
Prin, Scott L Cassels
Exec V Pres, H E Adams
Exec V Pres, David J Miles
Snr V Pres, Parke D Ball
Snr V Pres, Craig A Briggs
Cfo, Michael J Piechoski
V Pres, Stephen P Allen
V Pres, Michael K Breyer
Cntrl, Michael J Whetstine
Asst Cntrl, Jean Dulmaine

LOCATIONS

HQ: KIEWIT INFRASTRUCTURE CO.
KIEWIT PLZ, OMAHA, NE 68131
Phone: 402 342-2052
Web: WWW.KIEWIT.COM

HISTORICAL FINANCIALS

Company Type: Private

Income Statement — FYE: December 31

	REVENUE ($ mil.)	NET INCOME ($ mil.)	NET PROFIT MARGIN	EMPLOYEES
12/12	857	55	6.5%	9,000
12/11	1,127	74	6.6%	—
12/10	3,516	269	7.7%	—
Annual Growth	(50.6%)	(54.6%)	—	—

2012 Year-End Financials

Return on assets: 6.9%
Return on equity: 10.3%
Current ratio: 2.30
Cash ($ mil.): —

KIEWIT INFRASTRUCTURE SOUTH CO.

EXECUTIVES

Pres, David J Miles
V Pres, Jeffrey P Petersen
V Pres, Randall P Sanman
V Pres, Keith N Sasich
V Pres, S Van Groves
V Pres, Howard L Barton Jr
V Pres, Stephen Paul Carter Jr
V Pres, Timothy J Cleary
V Pres, Ricardo Cummings
V Pres, William D Glaser
V Pres, Mark D Langford
Auditors: KPMG LLP OMAHA NEBRASKA

LOCATIONS

HQ: KIEWIT INFRASTRUCTURE SOUTH CO.
KIEWIT PLZ NO 1044, OMAHA, NE 68131
Phone: 402 342-2052
Web: WWW.KIEWIT.COM

HISTORICAL FINANCIALS

Company Type: Private

Income Statement — FYE: December 29

	REVENUE ($ mil.)	NET INCOME ($ mil.)	NET PROFIT MARGIN	EMPLOYEES
12/12	549	85	15.6%	333
12/11	901	135	15.0%	—
12/10	1,009	126	12.6%	—
Annual Growth	(26.2%)	(17.8%)	—	—

2012 Year-End Financials

Return on assets: 21.0%
Return on equity: 39.7%
Current ratio: 2.00
Cash ($ mil.): 127

KIEWIT INFRASTRUCTURE WEST CO.

EXECUTIVES

Pres, Scott L Cassels
Exec V Pres, H E Adams
Exec V Pres, David J Miles
Exec V Pres, Alfredo E Sori
Sr V Pres, Jeffrey P Petersen
Sr V Pres, Eric M Scott
Sr V Pres, A T Skoro
Sr V Pres, Matt L Swinton
Sr V Pres, Eugene D Van Wagner III
Sr V Pres, J D Vetter
Sr V Pres, Jamie D Wisenbaker
Auditors: KPMG LLPOMAHA NEBRASKA

LOCATIONS

HQ: KIEWIT INFRASTRUCTURE WEST CO.
3555 FARNAM ST, OMAHA, NE 681313311
Phone: 402 342-2052
Web: WWW.KIEWIT.COM

HISTORICAL FINANCIALS

Company Type: Private

Income Statement — FYE: December 29

	REVENUE ($ mil.)	NET INCOME ($ mil.)	NET PROFIT MARGIN	EMPLOYEES
12/12	1,512	(126)	—	2,625
12/11	1,209	85	7.1%	—
12/10	945	31	3.3%	—
Annual Growth	26.5%	—	—	—

2012 Year-End Financials

Return on assets: (-13.0%)
Return on equity: (-47.1%)
Current ratio: 1.20
Cash ($ mil.): 152

KIMBALL HILL INC

LOCATIONS

HQ: KIMBALL HILL INC
5999 NEW WILKE RD STE 306, ROLLING MEADOWS, IL 600084503
Phone: 847 364-7300

HISTORICAL FINANCIALS

Company Type: Private

Income Statement — FYE: September 30

	REVENUE ($ mil.)	NET INCOME ($ mil.)	NET PROFIT MARGIN	EMPLOYEES
09/07	900	(220)	—	900
09/05	1,146	86	7.6%	—
09/04	927	55	6.0%	—
09/03	786	37	4.8%	—
Annual Growth	3.4%	—	—	—

2007 Year-End Financials

Return on assets: (-25.0%)
Return on equity: (-144.4%)
Current ratio: —
Cash ($ mil.): 31

KING COUNTY PUBLIC HOSPITAL DISTRICT 2

EXECUTIVES

Ceo, Bob Malte
Sr V Pres*, Neil Johnson
V Pres*, Jack Handley
Scientist, Deanne Gilbert
Chief of Medicine, James D Brown
Information Specialist, Dana Tran
Physician, Aileen Mickey
Director, Francis X Riedo
Senior Recruiter, Jon Rheinheimer
Pharmacy Tech, Kazue Kussmann
Health Education Coordinator, Lauren Bolen
Auditors: KPMG LLP SEATTLE WASHINGTON

LOCATIONS

HQ: KING COUNTY PUBLIC HOSPITAL DISTRICT 2
12040 NE 128TH ST, KIRKLAND, WA 980343013
Phone: 425 899-2769
Web: WWW.EVERGREENHEALTH.COM

HISTORICAL FINANCIALS

Company Type: Private

Income Statement — FYE: December 31

	REVENUE ($ mil.)	NET INCOME ($ mil.)	NET PROFIT MARGIN	EMPLOYEES
12/17	713	14	2.0%	2,400
12/16	597	(3)	—	—
12/15	565	3	0.7%	—
12/06	273	16	6.2%	—
Annual Growth	9.1%	(1.4%)	—	—

2017 Year-End Financials

Return on assets: 2.1%
Return on equity: 4.4%
Current ratio: 1.70
Cash ($ mil.): 44

KIRBY - SMITH MACHINERY, INC.

EXECUTIVES

Pres, Ed Kirby
Coordinator, Alan Soab
Tulsa Rental Manager, Brian Burris
General Manager, Brad Campbell
Executive Officer, Hoyt Kirby
Rental Manager, Michael Fuentes
Vice President, John Arapidis
Sales and Operations, Randy Bailey
Crane Division Territory Manag, Shane Schartau
Chief Information Officer, Dan Slusarchuk
Auditors: EIDE BAILLY OKLAHOMA CITY OK

LOCATIONS

HQ: KIRBY - SMITH MACHINERY, INC.
6715 W RENO AVE, OKLAHOMA CITY, OK 731276590
Phone: 888 861-0219
Web: WWW.KIRBY-SMITH.COM

HISTORICAL FINANCIALS

Company Type: Private

Income Statement FYE: December 31

	REVENUE ($ mil.)	NET INCOME ($ mil.)	NET PROFIT MARGIN	EMPLOYEES
12/19	575	47	8.3%	516
12/18	666	52	7.9%	—
12/17	421	36	8.6%	—
12/16	312	25	8.2%	—
Annual Growth	22.6%	23.5%	—	—

2019 Year-End Financials

Return on assets: 8.2%
Return on equity: 20.1%
Current ratio: 1.50
Cash ($ mil.): —

KLEIN INDEPENDENT SCHOOL DISTRICT

EXECUTIVES

Supt, Bret A Champion
Pres, Steven E Smith
V Pres, Ronnie K Anderson
SEC, Stephen J Szymczak
Building) Instructional Office, Pat Braunagel
Accounting Staff, Heather Cummings
Coordinator, Karri Clark
Coordinator, Kim Huseman
Auditors: HEREFORD LYNCH SELLARS & KIR

LOCATIONS

HQ: KLEIN INDEPENDENT SCHOOL DISTRICT
7200 SPRING CYPRESS RD, SPRING, TX 773793215
Phone: 832 249-4000
Web: WWW.KLEINISD.NET

HISTORICAL FINANCIALS

Company Type: Private

Income Statement FYE: August 31

	REVENUE ($ mil.)	NET INCOME ($ mil.)	NET PROFIT MARGIN	EMPLOYEES
08/19	622	39	6.3%	5,691
08/18	594	2	0.4%	—
08/17	548	8	1.5%	—
08/16	539	(135)	—	—
Annual Growth	4.9%	—	—	—

2019 Year-End Financials

Return on assets: 2.3%
Return on equity: —
Current ratio: —
Cash ($ mil.): 271

KMM TELECOMMUNICATIONS

EXECUTIVES

Ceo, Katherine McConvey
Cfo, Kofi Badu
Pres, Nick Shanker
Corporate Communications Staff, Sarah McNab
Accnt, Brad Van Kalsbeck
Auditors: DORFMAN ABRAMS MUSIC LLC SAD

LOCATIONS

HQ: KMM TELECOMMUNICATIONS
1900 LAKEWAY DR STE 100, LEWISVILLE, TX 750576012
Phone: 844 566-8488
Web: WWW.KMMCORP.NET

HISTORICAL FINANCIALS

Company Type: Private

Income Statement FYE: December 31

	REVENUE ($ mil.)	NET INCOME ($ mil.)	NET PROFIT MARGIN	EMPLOYEES
12/08	868	13	1.5%	190
12/07	789	17	2.2%	—
12/06	483	0	0.0%	—
Annual Growth	34.0%	70961.0%	—	—

2008 Year-End Financials

Return on assets: 13.3%
Return on equity: 57.5%
Current ratio: 1.30
Cash ($ mil.): 3

KNIGHTS OF COLUMBUS

Good Knight! The Knights of Columbus is a formidable volunteer group boasting about 15900 councils made up of 1.9 million Roman Catholic male members in the US Canada Mexico Cuba the Philippines Poland and several other countries. The fraternal organization is also a force to be reckoned with in the insurance world providing life insurance annuities and long-term care insurance to its members and their families. More than 1500 full-time insurance agents work across the United States and Canada. In addition the group manages the Knights of Columbus Museum in New Haven Connecticut featuring exhibits of religious art and history. The group was founded in 1882 by Father Michael J. McGivney.

Operations

The Knights of Columbus (KoC) was formed to render financial aid to members and their families. Mutual aid and assistance are offered to sick disabled and needy members and their families. Social and intellectual fellowship is promoted among members and their families through educational charitable religious social welfare war relief and public relief works. KoC is also engaged in religious education the support of public policy issues and charitable activities such as disaster relief.

The entity is a Catholic family fraternal service organization. This theme permeates the entire Service Program: all Church community council family culture of life and youth activities. The Service Program is designed to establish each council as an influential and important force within the community elevate the status of the programming personnel provide more meaningful and relevant programs of action establish direct areas of responsibility build leadership and ensure the success of council programs.

The group's supreme council has more than 75 state council organizations.

Geographic Reach

The Knights of Columbus is made up of local councils throughout the US Canada Mexico Puerto Rico Guam Saipan and the US Virgin Islands. It also has councils in the Bahamas Cuba the Dominican Republic Guatemala Lithuania Panama the Philippines Poland South Korea and Ukraine. The United States Canada and the Philippines have the largest membership numbers.

Financial Performance

In 2019 Knights of Columbus Insurance reported nearly $9 billion in annual sales and more than $26 billion in assets under its management.

Strategy

Known for its charitable giving the Knights of Columbus is also an insurance company providing insurance to its membership.

The organization has 1500 agents who are also members of the Knights. Knights of Columbus launched its new life insurance product in early 2020. This new product provides affordable guaranteed lifetime coverage flexible premium payment options and a low-cost guaranteed death benefit that will ensure future obligations are met.

To expand its reach Knights have led major charitable initiatives including Coats for Kids the Ultrasound Initiative and Christians at Risk and have also sponsored events and programs with organizations such as Special Olympics and the Global Wheelchair Mission.

Knights of Columbus also has various charity programs such as its Christian refugee fund disaster relief and its Leave No Neighbor Behind which supports communities affected by the COVID-19 pandemic.

Company Background

The Knights of Columbus was founded in New Haven by Father Michael J. McGivney in 1882 and has been selling insurance since its founding.

EXECUTIVES

Supreme Knight, Carl A. Anderson
Supreme Secretary, Michael J. (Mike) O'Connor
Supreme Chaplain, William E. Lori
Deputy Supreme Knight, Patrick E. Kelly
Supreme Treasurer, Ronald F. Schwarz
Assistant Vice President Of Application Development, Niki Kratzert
Vice President, Gary Nolan
Vice President Actuary, Marc Andre-Brunet

Senior Vice President Chief Communications Officer, Kevin Shinkle
Vice President Portfolio Manager, Gil Marchand
Treasurer, Logan Ludwig
Treasurer, Keith Ryan
Treasurer, Ron Schwarz

LOCATIONS

HQ: KNIGHTS OF COLUMBUS
1 COLUMBUS PLZ STE 1700, NEW HAVEN, CT 065103326
Phone: 203 752-4000
Web: WWW.KOFC.ORG

HISTORICAL FINANCIALS

Company Type: Private

Income Statement — FYE: December 31

	ASSETS ($ mil.)	NET INCOME ($ mil.)	INCOME AS % OF ASSETS	EMPLOYEES
12/13	20,534	113	0.6%	2,300
12/12	19,401	127	0.7%	—
12/11	18,026	81	0.4%	—
12/10	16,861	86	0.5%	—
Annual Growth	6.8%	9.5%	—	—

2013 Year-End Financials

Return on assets: 0.6%
Return on equity: 6.0%
Sales ($ mil): 2,115

KNOXVILLE UTILITIES BOARD

Providing utility services to residential and business customers has proven to be an excellent idea for Knoxville Utilities Board (KUB) an independent agency that serves the city of Knoxville and surrounding areas. The multi-utility provides services to 196500 electric 96920 gas 77600 water and 68740 wastewater customers. The company accesses electric power from the Tennessee Valley Authority. KUB's natural gas supply comes from the East Tennessee Natural Gas pipeline. It also maintains five treatment plants which provide water and wastewater services.

Operations

In 2013 the company was operating 1324 miles of wastewater mains 1407 miles of water mains 5265 miles of electric service lines and 69 substations and 2295 miles of natural gas mains.

Geographic Reach

The company serves 440000 customers in Knoxville and parts of seven surrounding counties.

Financial Performance

In 2013 KUB's operating revenues grew by 7%. Electric Division operating revenue increased $27.4 million thanks to a 1% rise in sales volumes and electric rate increases. Gas Division revenues grew 20% thanks to 14% rise in natural gas sales volumes. Water Divisionrevenue increased by 1.4% due tomwater rate increases. The Wastewater Division revenues were $4.1 million higher than in 2012 thanks to a rate increase.

Strategy

KUB is engaged in a long term plan to renovate its aging infrastructure. The push began the mid-1990s with a focus on upgrading Knoxville's water tanks distribution pipelines and the its water treatment plants.

Company Background

The agency was founded by the City of Knoxville in 1939. The utility's electric system is one of the nation's most dependable reporting a 99.9% uninterrupted service rating.

EXECUTIVES

Vice President Finance, Mark Walker
Vice President Of Operations, Paul Null Randolph
Vice President Customer Service, Mike Bolin
Vice President And Spokesperson, Susan Edwards
Board Member, Tyvi Small
Auditors: COULTER & JUSTUS PC KNOXVI

LOCATIONS

HQ: KNOXVILLE UTILITIES BOARD
445 S GAY ST, KNOXVILLE, TN 379021125
Phone: 865 594-7531
Web: WWW.KUB.ORG

HISTORICAL FINANCIALS

Company Type: Private

Income Statement — FYE: June 30

	REVENUE ($ mil.)	NET INCOME ($ mil.)	NET PROFIT MARGIN	EMPLOYEES
06/20	803	78	9.7%	500
06/19	815	65	8.0%	—
06/18	815	63	7.8%	—
Annual Growth	(0.7%)	10.8%	—	—

2020 Year-End Financials

Return on assets: 3.0%
Return on equity: 6.4%
Current ratio: 1.70
Cash ($ mil.): 99

KOOTENAI HOSPITAL DISTRICT

EXECUTIVES

Prin, Jon Ness
Cfo*, Kim Webb
V Pres*, Jeremy S Evans
Accounting Staff, Jenny Lea
Chief Staff, Thomas Nickol
Physician Recruitment Manager, Brian S Jerome
Phlebotomist, Daphne Kaiser
Coordinator, Megan Clevenger
Regional Information Technolog, Charles Andrews
Physician, Cody Reese
Server Administrator II, Daniel Gardner

LOCATIONS

HQ: KOOTENAI HOSPITAL DISTRICT
2003 KOOTENAI HEALTH WAY, COEUR D ALENE, ID 838146051
Phone: 208 625-4000
Web: WWW.KH.ORG

HISTORICAL FINANCIALS

Company Type: Private

Income Statement — FYE: December 31

	REVENUE ($ mil.)	NET INCOME ($ mil.)	NET PROFIT MARGIN	EMPLOYEES
12/18	550	17	3.1%	2,776
12/17	506	35	6.9%	—
12/16	467	15	3.4%	—
12/15	398	35	9.0%	—
Annual Growth	11.3%	(21.6%)	—	—

2018 Year-End Financials

Return on assets: 2.8%
Return on equity: 4.0%
Current ratio: 2.40
Cash ($ mil.): 55

KRAMM HEALTHCARE CENTER, INC

EXECUTIVES

Pres, Jeffrey Kramm
Activities Director, Mindy Bartholomew

LOCATIONS

HQ: KRAMM HEALTHCARE CENTER, INC
743 MAHONING ST, MILTON, PA 178472232
Phone: 570 742-2681
Web: WWW.KRAMMHEALTHCARE.ORG

HISTORICAL FINANCIALS

Company Type: Private

Income Statement — FYE: June 30

	REVENUE ($ mil.)	NET INCOME ($ mil.)	NET PROFIT MARGIN	EMPLOYEES
06/09	925	98	10.7%	330
06/00	5	0	3.8%	—
06/98	1	0	—	—
06/97	4	0	1.8%	—
Annual Growth	56.0%	80.8%	—	—

2009 Year-End Financials

Return on assets: 688.0%
Return on equity: 582.5%
Current ratio: 1.10
Cash ($ mil.): —

KRATON POLYMERS U.S. LLC

EXECUTIVES

Mng MBR, Kevin M Fogarty
MBR*, David A Bradley
MBR -Exec V Pres*, Stephen E Tremblay
MBR*, Stephen W Duffy
Vice-President*, Richard A Ott
MBR*, Lothar P Freund
MBR*, G Scott Lee
MBR*, Holger R Jung
Associate Director of Human RE, Joop Oranje
Chief Operating Officer, David Bradley
Director, Kevin O'Brien

LOCATIONS

HQ: KRATON POLYMERS U.S. LLC
15710 JOHN F KENNEDY BLVD # 300, HOUSTON, TX 770322347
Phone: 281 504-4700
Web: WWW.KRATON.COM

HISTORICAL FINANCIALS

Company Type: Private

Income Statement FYE: December 31

	REVENUE ($ mil.)	NET INCOME ($ mil.)	NET PROFIT MARGIN	EMPLOYEES
12/08	1,226	28	2.3%	520
12/07	1,089	(43)	—	—
12/06	0	0	—	—
12/05	975	166	17.1%	—
Annual Growth	7.9%	(44.6%)	—	—

2008 Year-End Financials

Return on assets: 6.1%
Return on equity: 2.3%
Current ratio: 1.10
Cash ($ mil.): 101

KRUEGER INTERNATIONAL, INC.

Krueger International can be found in classrooms cafeterias and college dorms. The company which does business as KI makes ergonomic seating cabinets and other furniture used by businesses healthcare organizations government agencies and educational institutions. The company offers everything from benches and beds to desks and tables not to mention shelving filing systems and movable walls. KI markets its products through sales representatives furniture dealers architects and interior designers worldwide. Founded in 1941 KI was purchased in the 1980s by its managers who later allowed employees to buy stock. Today KI is 100% employee owned.

Operations

KI operates a variety of subsidiaries including KI UK Ltd. KI East Asia Sdn. Bhd KI Nova Scotia KI Canada KI-Sebel and KI India. The company provides delivery and furniture installation services worldwide. Its service program includes space planning on-site project management furniture reconfiguration special inside delivery and coordination of product staging and a dedicated transportation fleet. KI also offers the option to purchase furniture according to what fits to its clients' ordering and fulfillment process whether direct or via a third party.

KI also owns Pallas Textiles and Spacesaver. Pallas Textiles which operates out of Wisconsin creates textile products for contract upholstery panel systems and wall-coverings healthcare environments and casements. Spacesaver Corporation also located in Wisconsin makes high-density mobile storage systems for office institutional and industrial applications and is a major supplier of steel shelving systems rotary storage systems and storage accessories.

Ki's products include seating tables desks architectural walls pods files and storage casegoods residence hall & dormitory furniture library furniture auditorium & lecture hall furniture and accessories among others.

Geographic Reach

Based in Wisconsin KI sells its products worldwide and operates manufacturing facilities showrooms and sales offices in the US Canada China and India as well as throughout Europe Middle East America and Asia. It has subsidiaries based in the UK Canada India Australia and China. Its showrooms are in several metropolitan areas across the US Toronto and London.

Sales and Marketing

KI sells its products globally through furniture dealers sales representatives architects and interior designers. It primarily serves the educational university healthcare business and government markets.

The company has direct sales offices around the world and also boasts showrooms in metropolitan areas to display its products to potential business and individual customers.

Company Background

The company has expanded its network of showrooms in the US and abroad over the years. KI added a showroom in Houston in 2010 to boost its US presence which includes about 10 locations in half a dozen states. To better serve its Asian and European customers the company operates through a showroom in Shanghai China. KI has international showrooms in London Malaysia Mexico Puerto Rico and Toronto. To support its growth KI completed a $3.3-million 100000-sq.-ft. plant expansion in 2012 to reduce costs and streamline its business. The move boosts its manufacturing shipping receiving and warehousing space.

As its showroom presence grew KI also formed new sales partnerships. The company tapped Heartland Furniture Group a contract furniture representative in 2011 to take care of existing customer accounts and broker sales in Kansas Missouri and southern Illinois.

It's also looked to acquisitions to extend the reach of its business. In 2011 KI purchased Sebel Furniture Limited from GWA Group Ltd. a top supplier of building fixtures in Australia. The $24 million deal has given KI a foothold in the commercial furniture business in Australia New Zealand the UK and Hong Kong.

EXECUTIVES

Chairman And Ceo, Richard J. (Dick) Resch
President, Brian Krenke
Vice President Oei Sales And Operations, Patrick Morris
Vice President Corporate Communications, Joe Burkard
Vice President Architectural Wall Operations, Ryan Usiak
Vice President Marketing, Tom Abrahamson
Vice President, Don Gust
Vice President Marketing And Distribution, Eric Schmidt
Assistant Secretary, Michael Pum
Auditors: BAKER TILLY VIRCHOW KRAUSE LL

LOCATIONS

HQ: KRUEGER INTERNATIONAL, INC.
1330 BELLEVUE ST, GREEN BAY, WI 543022197
Phone: 920 468-8100
Web: WWW.KI.COM

PRODUCTS/OPERATIONS

Selected Products

Auditorium seating
Beds
Benches
Bookcases
Carrels
Chairs
Desks
File cabinets
Lecterns
Movable walls
Planters
Power and data connections
Receptacles
Recliners
Residence hall furniture
Sleepers
Special events seating
Stools
Tables

COMPETITORS

ABCO Office Furniture
Allsteel
Bretford
CFGroup
Columbia Manufacturing
Edsal Manufacturing
Global Group
HNI
Haworth Inc.
Herman Miller
Inscape corp
Kewaunee Scientific
Kimball International
Knoll Inc.
La-Z-Boy
Norstar Office Products
Sagus
Steelcase
Trendway
Virco Mfg.

HISTORICAL FINANCIALS

Company Type: Private

Income Statement FYE: December 31

	REVENUE ($ mil.)	NET INCOME ($ mil.)	NET PROFIT MARGIN	EMPLOYEES
12/15	617	53	8.6%	2,300
12/11	649	56	8.8%	—
12/10	40	0	—	—
Annual Growth	—	1047.2%	—	—

2015 Year-End Financials

Return on assets: 19.5%
Return on equity: 92.6%
Current ratio: 1.10
Cash ($ mil.): 4

KWIK TRIP, INC.

Midwesterners who need to make a quick trip to get gas or groceries cigarettes or donuts race on over to Kwik Trip stores. Kwik Trip owns and operates more than 600 Kwik Trip and Kwik Star convenience stores in Iowa Minnesota and Wisconsin. Kwik Trip owns in-house dairy and bakery operations and makes many of its products in-house; popular products include Glazers donuts and Karuba Coffee. All Kwik Trip stores built since 1990 are owned by Convenience Store Investments a separate firm which leases the land and stores to Kwik Trip. Kwik Trip which opened its first store in 1965 in Eau Claire Wisconsin is owned by the family of CEO Don Zietlow.

Strategy

Kwik Trip's main route to growth is opening new stores. It's currently adding store at a rate of roughly 40 each year.

The company is always looking at ways to improve its food and drink offering. Initiatives have included a new line of take-home meals produced each day in house and a tie-up with delivery service EatStreet that allows customers near select locations to order up to 400 items.

Company Background

The John Hansen family founded Kwik Trip in Eau Claire Wisconsin in 1965. In 2000 the Hansens sold their interest in Kwik Trip to the Zietlow family for $120 million. The two families had jointly owned Kwik Trip since 1972.

EXECUTIVES

President And Ceo, Donald P. (Don) Zietlow
Vp And Director Petroleum Operations, Steve Zietlow
Vice President Retail Operations, Greg Olson
Vice President Of Operations Support, Steve Loehr
Auditors: MCGLADREY & PULLEN LLP MINNE

LOCATIONS

HQ: KWIK TRIP, INC.
1626 OAK ST, LA CROSSE, WI 546032308
Phone: 608 781-8988
Web: WWW.KWIKTRIP.COM

PRODUCTS/OPERATIONS

Selected Banners
Hearty Platter
Kwik Star
Kwik Trip
Tobacco Outlet Plus

COMPETITORS

7-Eleven
Brinker
Carlson Restaurants
Casey's General Stores
Chevron
Couche-Tard
Cub Foods
Denny's
Exxon Mobil
Hy-Vee
Krause Gentle
Northern Tier Energy
Roundy's

HISTORICAL FINANCIALS

Company Type: Private

Income Statement — FYE: September 27

	REVENUE ($ mil.)	NET INCOME ($ mil.)	NET PROFIT MARGIN	EMPLOYEES
09/08	3,640	23	0.7%	10,500
09/04	1,887	24	1.3%	—
09/03	1,651	24	1.5%	—
Annual Growth	17.1%	(0.2%)	—	—

2008 Year-End Financials

Return on assets: 3.6%
Return on equity: 20.3%
Current ratio: 0.70
Cash ($ mil.): 1

LADENBURG THALMANN FINANCIAL SERVICES INC.

Ladenburg Thalmann Financial Services provides brokerage asset management institutional sales and trading and investment research banking and wholesale life insurance and annuity brokerage services through its subsidiaries throughout the US. The company serves primarily retail clients through independent broker-dealer subsidiaries which together have some 4400 financial advisors and manage about $188 billion in assets. The company's investment bank provides investment research on small- to mid-cap companies and finance and strategic advisory services to middle-market companies. Its asset management unit offers mutual funds multi managed accounts and investment counseling. Ladenburg's insurance subsidiaries provide support services to life insurance advisors and institutions.

Operations

The clear majority of Ladenburg Thalmann's revenue (more than 80%) is generated by its independent advisory and brokerage services business. Through six subsidiaries employing about 4400 representatives Ladenburg provides financial advice primarily to retail investors especially individuals and households with $100000 to $1.5 million in net investible assets.

Ladenburg's insurance brokerage business also contributes about 15% of revenue. The company's Highland Capital Brokerage subsidiary provides life insurance and fixed and equity indexed annuities to investment and insurance providers. Highland division provide services including risk underwriting back office processing and point of sale support.

Ladenburg's investment banking practice which it calls its Ladenburg segment generates about 5% of revenue and includes Ladenburg Thalmann & Co. and Ladenburg Thalmann Asset Management (LTAM). The investment bank mostly finances companies with market caps about $15.4 billion through underwritten public registered direct and at-the-market offerings and private placements. LTAM manages about $3.4 billion in assets for approximately 17200 clients.

Nearly 50% of sales came from commissions while another about 35% came from advisory fees and the remaining accounts the rest.

Geographic Reach

Ladenburg Thalmann is stationed in Miami. Its branch offices are in Naples and Boca Raton Florida; Melville Westhampton Beach and New York New York; Boston Massachusetts; Stamford Connecticut; Minneapolis Minnesota; and San Rafael and Irvine California.

Sales and Marketing

Ladenburg Thalmann's independent advisory and brokerage services business provides financial advice primarily to retail investors especially what the company calls "mass affluent" customers – individuals and households with $100000 to $1.5 million in net investible assets.

Financial Performance

The company's revenue for 2019 was $1.5 billion a 6% increase from the previous year. The increase is attributable to higher sales volume in the company's independent advisory and brokerage services and insurance brokerage segments.

In 2019 the company had a net income attributable to $22.8 million as compared to a net income of $33.8 million in 2018. The decrease in net income was primarily due to an overall increase in total expenses including approximately $5.9 million attributable to the Merger.

The company's cash at the end of 2019 was $249.5 million. Operating activities generated $54.0 million while investing activities used $13.1 million primarily due to the purchase of furniture equipment and leasehold improvements. Financing activities generated another $19.3 million.

Strategy

The independent advisory and brokerage services industry has been one of the fastest growing segments of the financial services industry during the past decade. The company's plan has been to marry the more stable and recurring revenue and cash flows of the independent advisory and brokerage business with Ladenburg's traditional investment banking capital markets institutional sales and trading and related businesses.

Mergers and Acquisitions

In 2020 Ladenburg Thalmann Financial Services announced the successful completion of its merger with Advisor Group Inc. one of the nation's largest networks of independent wealth management firms. The expanded Advisor Group will be one of the industry's leading providers of a multi-custodial multi-clearing model that drives maximum choice and flexibility for financial advisors. The organization will continue to be led by Advisor Group's current CEO and President Jamie Price. Ladenburg's firms will not be merged with Advisor Group's firms reflecting both companies' commitment to a multi-brand network model. In connection with the closing of the transaction Ladenburg Thalmann common shares have been delisted from the New York Stock Exchange.

EXECUTIVES

President Ceo And Director, Richard J. (Dick) Lampen, age 66, $200,000 total compensation
Evp And Director, Mark Zeitchick, age 54, $375,000 total compensation
Svp And Cio, Doreen Griffith
Svp Wealth Management, Paul Lofties
Svp And Cfo, Brett H. Kaufman, age 48, $325,000 total compensation
Evp And Coo, Adam Malamed, age 48, $350,000 total compensation
Chief Risk Officer, Craig Timm
Senior Vice President Corporate And Regulatory Affairs, Joseph Giovanniello
Senior Vice President Enterprise Initiatives, Carly Maher
Vice President Regional Sales Consultant, Patrick Mckay
Vice President Head Of Sponsor Relations, Oksana Poznak
Vice President Investment Banking, Jeffrey Caliva
Vice President Equity Research Telecom Media And Technology, Glenn G Mattson
Vice President Retirement And Fiduciary Services, Doug Baxley
Executive Vice President Equity Research Yield Oriented Equities, Christopher Nolan
Chairman, Phillip Frost, age 84
Vice Chairman, Howard M. Lorber, age 71
Board Member, Saul Gilinski
Board Member, Richard Krasno
Auditors: EISNERAMPER LLP NEW YORK NEW

LOCATIONS

HQ: LADENBURG THALMANN FINANCIAL SERVICES INC.
4400 BISCAYNE BLVD FL 12, MIAMI, FL 331373212
Phone: 305 572-4100
Web: WWW.LADENBURG.COM

PRODUCTS/OPERATIONS

2017 Sales

	$ mil.	% of total
Commissions	536	42
Advisory fees	560	44
Investment banking	46	4
Interest & dividends	25	2
Principal transactions	0	-
Service fees & other	98	8
Total	**1,268**	**100**

2017 Sales

	$ mil.	% of total
Independent Advisory & Brokerage	1,140	90
Ladenburg	66	5
Insurance Brokerage	57	5
Corporate	4	-
Total	**1,268**	**100**

COMPETITORS

Citigroup Global Markets
Detwiler Fenton
Investors Capital Holdings
JPMorgan Chase
LPL Financial
Morgan Stanley
National Holdings
Sage Advisory Services
UBS Financial Services

HISTORICAL FINANCIALS

Company Type: Private

Income Statement — FYE: December 31

	REVENUE ($ mil.)	NET INCOME ($ mil.)	NET PROFIT MARGIN	EMPLOYEES
12/19	1,469	22	1.5%	1,512
12/18	1,391	33	2.4%	—
12/17	1,268	7	0.6%	—
12/16	1,106	(22)	—	—
Annual Growth	9.9%	—	—	—

2019 Year-End Financials

Return on assets: 2.7%
Return on equity: 9.4%
Current ratio: —
Cash ($ mil.): 248

LAFAYETTE GENERAL HEALTH SYSTEM, INC.

EXECUTIVES

Chb, Clay M Allen
Pres-Ceo*, David Callecod
Svp-Cmo*, Amanda Logue
Cmio*, Fallon Strother McManus
Svp and Chief Administrative O, Al Patin
Svp, Gordon Rountree
Svp, Marisa M Alack
Evp, Patrick W Gandy
Svp, Roger Mattke
MGT, Helen Jong
Strategic Analysis Coordinator, Brittany Deal

LOCATIONS

HQ: LAFAYETTE GENERAL HEALTH SYSTEM, INC.
1214 COOLIDGE BLVD, LAFAYETTE, LA 705032621
Phone: 337 289-8125
Web: WWW.LAFAYETTEGENERAL.COM

HISTORICAL FINANCIALS

Company Type: Private

Income Statement — FYE: September 30

	REVENUE ($ mil.)	NET INCOME ($ mil.)	NET PROFIT MARGIN	EMPLOYEES
09/18	758	14	1.9%	2,600
09/16	700	13	1.9%	—
09/15	585	18	3.2%	—
09/14	495	24	5.0%	—
Annual Growth	11.2%	(11.9%)	—	—

2018 Year-End Financials

Return on assets: 2.2%
Return on equity: 4.7%
Current ratio: 2.70
Cash ($ mil.): 79

LAHEY CLINIC HOSPITAL, INC.

EXECUTIVES

Ceo, Howard R Grant JD
Ceo, David Barrett
Chm, Bernard Gordon
V Chm, John Libertino
V Pres, Donna Cameron
Director of Comm & Mktg, Scott V Hartman
Internal Medicine Practitioner, Anu Diddee
Ophthalmologist, Paul R Cotran
Laboratory Director, Barbara Sacco
Director Education, Donna Ales
Information Technology Manager, Elizabeth Gardner

LOCATIONS

HQ: LAHEY CLINIC HOSPITAL, INC.
41 MALL RD, BURLINGTON, MA 018050002
Phone: 781 273-5100
Web: WWW.LAHEY.ORG

HISTORICAL FINANCIALS

Company Type: Private

Income Statement — FYE: September 30

	REVENUE ($ mil.)	NET INCOME ($ mil.)	NET PROFIT MARGIN	EMPLOYEES
09/15	816	(17)	—	1
09/14	800	(0)	—	—
09/13	774	228	29.5%	—
09/12	796	192	24.1%	—
Annual Growth	0.8%	—	—	—

2015 Year-End Financials

Return on assets: (-2.3%)
Return on equity: (-12.0%)
Current ratio: 2.40
Cash ($ mil.): 105

LAKELAND REGIONAL HEALTH SYSTEMS, INC.

EXECUTIVES

Pres & Ceo, Elaine Thompson
Vp-Coo, Sarah Bhagat
Exec Vp-Cfo, Evan C Jones
Vp & Chief Public Relations, Timothy J Boynton
Svp & Chief Hr, Scott W Dimmick
Evp & Coo, Danielle Drummond
Evp & Chief Nurse Executive, Janet Fansler
Vp & Chief Analytics Officer, Caroline Gay
Vp Finance, Lance Green
Exec Dir & Chief Academic Offi, Graham F Greene
Evp & Chief Legal Officer, Jonn D Hoppe
Auditors: KPMG LLP TAMPA FL

LOCATIONS

HQ: LAKELAND REGIONAL HEALTH SYSTEMS, INC.
1324 LAKELAND HILLS BLVD, LAKELAND, FL 338054543
Phone: 863 687-1100
Web: WWW.MYLRH.ORG

HISTORICAL FINANCIALS

Company Type: Private

Income Statement — FYE: September 30

	REVENUE ($ mil.)	NET INCOME ($ mil.)	NET PROFIT MARGIN	EMPLOYEES
09/14	685	67	9.9%	3,124
09/13	24	(13)	—	—
09/12	582	67	11.6%	—
Annual Growth	8.5%	0.4%	—	—

2014 Year-End Financials

Return on assets: 7.2%
Return on equity: 10.9%
Current ratio: 1.40
Cash ($ mil.): 22

LAKELAND REGIONAL MEDICAL CENTER, INC.

Lakeland Regional Medical Center (LRMC) serves Florida's Polk County (roughly between Kissimmee and Tampa) through an acute care hospital with approximately 850 beds. Among its specialty services are cardiac care cancer treatment senior care urology emergency medicine orthopedics women's and children's health care and surgery. LRMC also operates general care and specialty outpatient clinics. Additionally the hospital provides medical training programs for radiology specialists. Its LRMC Foundation offers financial support for indigent patients facing ongoing treatment.

Operations

LRMC is part of Lakeland Regional Health System a not-for-profit organization that also includes Lakeland Regional Cancer Center Lakeland Regional Family Health Center and Lakeland Regional Health Medical Group.

Annually LRMC has more than 41000 admissions and performs more than 15000 surgeries. Its emergency department treats more than 200000 patients each year.

Financial Performance

Revenue in 2014 totaled $633 million (representing 92% of Lakeland Regional Health System's revenue) while net income totaled $67 million.

LRMC funds its activities through charges to patients for inpatient and outpatient services as well as from non-hospital activities such as its cafeteria gift and uniform shops and physicians' answering service. Although the hospital also receives payment from federal agencies such as Medicaid and Medicare they along with other managed care entities have cut their reimbursement levels causing LRMC's charity care levels to increase.

Strategy

The hospital has been undergoing facility and data systems improvement efforts to enhance care and increase efficiencies. It recently expanded its intensive care department and upgraded technology in areas including radiology orthopedics and chemotherapy.

In 2014 Lakeland Regional Health System announced plans to build an eight-story women and children pavilion at LRMC. The $250 million addition will include 300000 sq. ft. of space including 32 private rooms for mothers and newborns a 30-bed neonatal intensive care unit 64 private rooms for women's surgical and medical care three surgical suites and 12 private suites for labor delivery and recovery. It will also have an education and conference center. The pavilion is expected to open in 2017.

EXECUTIVES

President And Chief Medical Officer, Mack Reavis
Director Of Radiology, Fakhir F Elmasri
Executive Medical Director, Natalie Adsuar
Secretary, Christine Johnston
Auditors: PERSHING YOAKLEY & ASSOCIATES

LOCATIONS

HQ: LAKELAND REGIONAL MEDICAL CENTER, INC.
1324 LAKELAND HILLS BLVD, LAKELAND, FL 338054500
Phone: 863 687-1100
Web: WWW.LRMC.COM

PRODUCTS/OPERATIONS

Selected Facilities

Lakeland Regional Cancer Center
Lakeland Regional Medical Center (LRMC) Foundation
Lakeland Regional Orthopedics Associates
Lakeland Regional Rehabilitation and Sports Medicine Clinic

Selected Services and Centers

Emergency
Family health center
Gastroenterology
Heart center
Mental health & addictions
Neurosurgery
Nursing
Oncology care
Orthopedic care
Palliative care
Pharmacy
Rehabilitation and sports medicine clinic
Robotic surgery
School of radiologic technology
Stroke center
Surgery
Trauma services
Women and children
Wound center

COMPETITORS

Adventist Health System Sunbelt Healthcare
All Children's Hospital
Baptist Health South Florida
BayCare Health System
Bayfront Health
DeSoto Memorial
Florida Hospital Tampa Bay Division
HCA
Manatee Memorial Hospital
Sarasota Memorial Health Care
Tampa General Hospital
Winter Haven Hospital

HISTORICAL FINANCIALS

Company Type: Private

Income Statement — FYE: September 30

	REVENUE ($ mil.)	NET INCOME ($ mil.)	NET PROFIT MARGIN	EMPLOYEES
09/16	790	84	10.7%	3,100
09/15	674	68	10.2%	—
09/14	618	66	10.8%	—
09/13	584	55	9.4%	—
Annual Growth	10.6%	15.3%	—	—

2016 Year-End Financials

Return on assets: 10.5%
Return on equity: 25.6%
Current ratio: —
Cash ($ mil.): 1

LAMEX FOODS INC.

EXECUTIVES

Ceo, Phillip O Wallace
Pres*, Steven Anderson
V Pres*, Mark Barrett
Sr Dir*, Mark Ryder
Accounting Manager, Lisa Henkel
Latin America Trade Manager, Robert Preska
Trading Manager, Robert Lucas
Import Logistics Manager, Samantha Zarske
Export Coordinator, Danielle Waterhouse
Head of Global Juice, Paul Wallace
Imports Team Lead, Danielle Behling

LOCATIONS

HQ: LAMEX FOODS INC.
8500 NORMANDALE LAKE BLVD, BLOOMINGTON, MN 554373813
Phone: 952 844-0585
Web: WWW.LAMEXFOODS.EU

HISTORICAL FINANCIALS

Company Type: Private

Income Statement — FYE: March 31

	REVENUE ($ mil.)	NET INCOME ($ mil.)	NET PROFIT MARGIN	EMPLOYEES
03/15	592	7	1.3%	80
03/05	103	1	1.0%	—
03/04	76	0	0.9%	—
Annual Growth	20.4%	24.8%	—	—

2015 Year-End Financials

Return on assets: 7.2%
Return on equity: 20.8%
Current ratio: 1.50
Cash ($ mil.): —

LANE INDUSTRIES INCORPORATED

EXECUTIVES

Pres-Dir, Mark Schiller
Pres-Dir, Robert Alger
Treas-Asst SEC, Vincent Caiola
Dir-SEC, Gianfranco Catrini
Exec V Pres, Kirk Junco
V Pres, David Benton
Exec V Pres, Mike Cote
SEC, Carol Gallagher
Treas, Mark Tomkalski
Auditors: KPMG LLP HARTFORD CT

LOCATIONS

HQ: LANE INDUSTRIES INCORPORATED
90 FIELDSTONE CT, CHESHIRE, CT 064101212
Phone: 203 235-3351
Web: WWW.LANECONSTRUCT.COM

HISTORICAL FINANCIALS

Company Type: Private

Income Statement — FYE: December 31

	REVENUE ($ mil.)	NET INCOME ($ mil.)	NET PROFIT MARGIN	EMPLOYEES
12/18	856	(68)	—	4,500
12/17	1,592	14	0.9%	—
12/16	1,292	36	2.8%	—
12/15	1,197	(13)	—	—
Annual Growth	(10.6%)	—	—	—

2018 Year-End Financials

Return on assets: (-6.9%)
Return on equity: (-13.8%)
Current ratio: 1.80
Cash ($ mil.): 137

LEE MEMORIAL HEALTH SYSTEM FOUNDATION, INC.

Not feeling so bright in the Sunshine State? Lee Memorial Health System can help. Serving residents of Fort Myers and surrounding areas in Southwestern Florida's Lee County the community-owned not-for-profit health care system is home to four acute care hospitals (with a total of more than 1400 beds) a home health agency a 112-bed nursing home and numerous outpatient treatment and diagnostic centers. The flagship Lee Memorial Hospital also houses a 60-bed inpatient rehabilitation hospital and the HealthPark Medical Center location includes a dedicated 100-bed children's hospital. Lee Memorial Health Systems' corporate services include pre-employment screenings drug screens and wellness programs.

Operations

The system's facilities include the flagship Lee Memorial Hospital (355 beds) HealthPark Medical Center (270 beds) Gulf Coast Medical Center (350 beds) and Cape Coral Hospital (290 beds). Lee Memorial Health System employs more than 1200 doctors including primary and specialty care practitioners that are members of the affiliated Lee Physician Group. Patient service revenues account for nearly all of the company's revenues.

Lee Memorial Hospital is the only level II trauma center between Tampa and Miami.

Altogether the system has more than 1 million patient contacts each year.

Geographic Reach

Three of the systems' hospitals are located in Fort Myers Florida. Its fourth hospital (Cape Coral Hospital) is located in Cape Coral Florida.

Sales and Marketing

Medicare payments accounted for a third of the system's net patient service revenues in fiscal 2014 while Medicaid accounted for 15%. Self-pay accounted for 26% followed by managed care (20%) and commercial insurance (6%).

Financial Performance

Revenue increased 8% to $1.4 billion in fiscal 2014 (ended September) as net patient service revenues grew. This in turn led to an increase in net income which grew 31% to $158 million. Decreased interest expenses also helped boost profits.

Cash flow from operations increased 49% to $225 million that year largely due to cash received from patient care services.

Strategy

Lee Memorial Health System is a not-for-profit organization that proclaims its fiscal mission is to reinvest its profits back into the community it serves through facility and equipment upgrades and other measures. The system has undertaken a number of expansion projects at its hospitals in recent years to add specialty services and private patient rooms and has also opened a number of new community outpatient centers. In addition it is enhancing existing facilities to improve quality safety and financial performance.

In 2015 the system approved a $315 million expansion plan that will add 275 patient beds to Gulf Coast Medical Center. Construction on the project is expected to begin in 2017.

Lee Memorial Health System is also upgrading its IT systems to provide coordinated and efficient care. It has installed electronic health record programs (using EHR software from Epic Systems) at most of its facilities and it is improving other tools to streamline business systems and improve health care delivery processes.

Company Background

Tracing its roots to 1916 Lee Memorial Health System is a public health care system created by special act of the Florida Legislature in 1963. Its governing board is composed of 10 members elected by the public.

EXECUTIVES

Nursing Director, Tomaso Vicki
Nursing Director, Kristina Desfosses
Assistant Vice President Of Operations, Sheila Dupuy
Treasurer, Pablo Veintimilla
Secretary, Jennifer Parisi
Secretary, Monica Andacht
Resource Secretary, Debra Walker
Secretary, Jaclyn Smith
Auditors: PRICEWATERHOUSECOOPERS LLP

LOCATIONS

HQ: LEE MEMORIAL HEALTH SYSTEM FOUNDATION, INC.
2776 CLEVELAND AVE, FORT MYERS, FL 339015864
Phone: 239 343-2000
Web: WWW.LEEHEALTH.ORG

PRODUCTS/OPERATIONS

2014 Sales by Segment

	$ mil.	% of total
Lee Memorial Hospital	682	50
Gulf Coast Memorial Center	302	22
Cape Memorial Hospital	206	15
Physicians	133	10
Health Park Care Center	13	1
Lee Memorial Home Health	8	1
Lee Memorial Health System Foundation	3	-
Lee County Trauma Services District	3	-
Lee Community Health Care	1	-
Other	9	1
Total	**1,363**	**100**

Selected Florida Hospitals

Blood Centers
Cardiac Care (Heart Services)
Community Health Centers/United Way Houses
Convenient Care
Emergency Services
Home Health Services
The Kidney Transplant Center
Lee Physician Group
Mental Health Services
Neuroscience Services
Nursing Home
Occupational Health Services
Orthopedic and Spine Services
Palliative Services
Patient Services
Pediatric Services
Pulmonary Services
Rehabilitation Services
Sleep Disorder Center
Surgical Services
Volunteer Services
Wellness and Nutrition Services
Women's Health Services
Wound Care and Hyperbaric Medicine

COMPETITORS

Adventist Health System Sunbelt Healthcare
All Children's Hospital
BayCare Health System
Bayfront Health
DeSoto Memorial
H. Lee Moffitt Cancer Center & Research Institute
HCA
NCH Healthcare
Sarasota Memorial Health Care
St. Joseph's-Baptist Health Care
Tampa General Hospital

HISTORICAL FINANCIALS

Company Type: Private

Income Statement — FYE: September 30

	REVENUE ($ mil.)	NET INCOME ($ mil.)	NET PROFIT MARGIN	EMPLOYEES
09/18	1,789	101	5.6%	7,870
09/04	585	46	8.0%	—
09/03	522	50	9.8%	—
09/02	477	7	1.6%	—
Annual Growth	8.6%	17.4%	—	—

2018 Year-End Financials

Return on assets: 4.1%
Return on equity: 6.6%
Current ratio: 5.40
Cash ($ mil.): 33

LEE MEMORIAL HOSPITAL, INC.

EXECUTIVES

President, Jim Nathan
Coordinator, Shari Trivett
Executive Officer, Ken Szymanski
Health Professional, Furhan Qureshi
Internal Medicine Practitioner, Iasmina Jivanov
Internal Medicine Practitioner, Nadia Parchment
Secretary, Nancy McGovern
Family Practitioner, Asif Azam
Assistant Property Management, Brock Billman
Information Technology Staff, Connie Bowles
Business Analyst, Karol Williams

LOCATIONS

HQ: LEE MEMORIAL HOSPITAL, INC.
2776 CLEVELAND AVE, FORT MYERS, FL 339015855
Phone: 239 343-2000
Web: WWW.LEEHEALTH.ORG

HISTORICAL FINANCIALS

Company Type: Private

Income Statement — FYE: September 30

	REVENUE ($ mil.)	NET INCOME ($ mil.)	NET PROFIT MARGIN	EMPLOYEES
09/14	688	163	23.8%	1,159
09/13	632	135	21.4%	—
09/12	613	105	17.3%	—
Annual Growth	6.0%	24.4%	—	—

2014 Year-End Financials

Return on assets: 10.8%
Return on equity: 21.1%
Current ratio: 7.30
Cash ($ mil.): 32

LEGACY EMANUEL HOSPITAL & HEALTH CENTER

Legacy Emanuel Hospital and Health Center part of the Legacy Health System provides acute and specialized health care to residents of Portland Oregon and surrounding communities. The 420-bed teaching hospital's operations include centers devoted to trauma treatment burn care oncology birthing neurosurgery orthopedics and cardiology. It also houses a pediatric hospital and operates the region's Life Flight Network service which is owned by a consortium of local hospitals. Legacy Emanuel's emergency department handles more than 15600 visits every year.

Operations

Legacy Emanuel's trauma and burn centers are level I designated facilities meaning they receive severe trauma and burn cases from other area hospitals. The hospital's burn center is the only one of its kind in an area stretching from Seattle to Sacramento and Salt Lake City. Other specialist facilities at Legacy Emanuel include its maternity center and its diagnostic imaging and screening units.

The medical center sees more than 18000 inpatients each year. Its staff includes about 140 full-time doctors and dentists as well as 700 full-time registered nurses. The Randall Children's Hospital located within Legacy Emanuel has about 600 affiliated pediatricians and specialists on its staff and handles about 100000 patient encounters each year including 20000 emergency room visits.

Strategy

The hospital has undergone massive expansion efforts. The hospital has completed construction of the new Randall Children's Hospital facilities making it one of the largest pediatric facilities in the state. The new pediatric center is four times as large as the past facilities. Other expansion efforts in recent years include new acute and intensive care capacity.

Company Background

To expand its medical transportation services Legacy Emanuel and other owners of LFN teamed up to purchase 15 new helicopters in 2012.

Legacy Emanuel Hospital was established in 1912 by the Lutheran Church.

EXECUTIVES

Ceo-Pres, George J Brown
Administrative Assistant, Mary Ann McNulty

Executive Director, Lisa Harris
Coordinator, Amy Lyons
Project Manager, Barri Stiber
Internist, Smitha Chadaga

LOCATIONS

HQ: LEGACY EMANUEL HOSPITAL & HEALTH CENTER
2801 N GANTENBEIN AVE, PORTLAND, OR 972271623
Phone: 503 413-2200
Web: WWW.LEGACYHEALTH.ORG

PRODUCTS/OPERATIONS

Selected Centers and Services
Burn care
Cancer care
Children's care
Diabetes and nutrition
Emergency services
Family birth center
Gardens
High-risk obstetrics
Imaging
Injury prevention
Intensive care
Interventional and diagnostic cardiology
Level I trauma center
Life flight network
Maternal-fetal medicine
Neurology and neurosurgery including spine surgery
Orthopedics
Pediatrics
Rehabilitation (inpatient and outpatient)
Radiation oncology
Stroke
Surgery (including minimally invasive surgery)
Vascular clinic
Wound and ostomy clinic
Wound care and outpatient burn clinic

COMPETITORS

Adventist Health System West
Asante Health System
Dignity Health
Kadlec Regional Medical Center
PeaceHealth
PeaceHealth Southwest Medical Center
Providence St. Joseph Health
Salem Hospital

HISTORICAL FINANCIALS

Company Type: Private

Income Statement FYE: March 31

	REVENUE ($ mil.)	NET INCOME ($ mil.)	NET PROFIT MARGIN	EMPLOYEES
03/15	705	29	4.2%	3,619
03/14	649	30	4.8%	—
03/13	566	6	1.1%	—
03/12	571	(6)	—	—
Annual Growth	7.3%	—	—	—

LEGACY HEALTH

Legacy Health strives to promote positive health in the Portland/Vancouver metropolitan area. A not-for-profit provider of health care services in Oregon and Washington the health system operates half a dozen hospitals including Legacy Emanuel Medical Center and Legacy Good Samaritan Medical Center as well as the Randall Children's Hospital at Legacy Emanuel. Legacy Health has more than 70 primary care and its facilities provide such services as acute and critical care behavioral health and outpatient and health education programs. It also operates home health hospice and research facilities; emergency transportation helicopters; and a number of regional clinics and labs.

Operations

Legacy Health's hospitals include Legacy Emanuel Medical Center Randall Children's Hospital Legacy Good Samaritan Medical Center Legacy Meridian Park Medical Center Legacy Mount Hood Medical Center Legacy Silverton Medical Center and Legacy Salmon Creek Medical Center in Washington.

Legacy Medical Group includes nearly 3000 affiliated physicians and providers operating nearly 70 primary care clinics in the region as well as a number of specialty care centers in fields such as obstetrics pediatrics cardiology neurology and orthopedics.

Geographic Reach

Portland Oregon-based Legacy Health System operates seven hospitals some 70 outpatient clinics and a number of hospice research and diagnostic facilities in the Portland/Vancouver metropolitan area. It has three hospitals located in Portland as well as one each in Gresham Oregon; Tualatin Oregon; and Vancouver Washington.

Strategy

Legacy Health invests in improving the community while striving to help everyone live healthier lives making it essential to the health of the region.

In early 2020 Legacy Health and innovators came together to protect workers and the community. Local innovators used their creativity to produce equipment to protect healthcare workers during the coronavirus outbreak. Portland State University Center for Entrepreneurship teamed with the Portland 3D Printing Lab to produce face shields for local hospitals and local manufacturer A-dec switched from making dental equipment to producing face shields for protective helmets. Local companies came together with area health care organizations to help Legacy Health get its supplies it needs for doctors nurses and patients.

In addition Legacy Health offered innovative surgery to lymphedema patients. The procedure called "vascularized lymph node transfer" involves taking lymph nodes from the groin and transplanting them back into the patient's armpit.

Company Background

Legacy Health was founded through the 1989 merger of HealthLink and Good Samaritan Hospital.

EXECUTIVES

Svp And Chief Nursing Officer, Carol Bradley
President And Ceo, George J. Brown
Chief Administrative Officer Legacy Meridian Park Medical Center, Allyson Anderson
Chief Administrative Officer Legacy Salmon Creek Medical Center, Jonathan Avery
Svp And Cio, John Kenagy
Chief Admnistrative Officer Randall Children's Hospital At Legacy Emanuel, Bronwyn Houston, age 51
Svp And Coo, Mike Newcomb
Svp And Chief Medical Officer, Lewis Low
Chief Administrative Officer Legacy Mount Hood Medical Center, Gretchen Nichols
Svp And Cfo, Linda Hoff
Chief Administrative Officer, Bryce Helgerson
Vice President Finance, Gordon Edwards
Clinical Vice President Womens Services And Surgical Services, Duncan Neilson
Senior Vice President And Chief Development Officer, Maureen Bradley
Vice President Human Resources, Sonja Steves
Vice President Quality And Patient Safety, Aisha Furbach
Auditors: KPMG LLP PORTLAND OREGON

LOCATIONS

HQ: LEGACY HEALTH
1919 NW LOVEJOY ST, PORTLAND, OR 972091503
Phone: 503 415-5600
Web: WWW.LEGACYHEALTH.ORG

PRODUCTS/OPERATIONS

Selected Facilities

Hospitals
Legacy Emanuel Medical Center (Portland Oregon)
Legacy Good Samaritan Medical Center (Portland Oregon)
Legacy Meridian Park Medical Center (Tualatin Oregon)
Legacy Mount Hood Medical Center (Gresham Oregon)
Legacy Salmon Creek Medical Center (Vancouver Washington)
Randall Children's Hospital At Legacy Emanuel (Portland Oregon)
Clinics
Legacy Med
Legacy Med
Legacy Med
Legacy Med
Legacy Med
Legacy Medical Group - Fisher's Landing
Legacy Medical Group - Good Samaritan
Legacy Medical Group - Lake Oswego
Legacy Med
Legacy Med
Legacy Medical Group - Salmon Creek Family Medicine (Vancouver Washington)
Legacy Medical Group - Salmon Creek Internal Medicine (Vancouver Washington)
Legacy Med
Legacy Medical Group - West Linn
Legacy Med

COMPETITORS

Adventist Health System West
Asante Health System
Kadlec Regional Medical Center
Kaiser Foundation Hospitals
Oregon Health & Science University
PeaceHealth
Providence St. Joseph Health
Salem Hospital

HISTORICAL FINANCIALS

Company Type: Private

Income Statement FYE: March 31

	REVENUE ($ mil.)	NET INCOME ($ mil.)	NET PROFIT MARGIN	EMPLOYEES
03/20	2,336	(42)	—	10,675
03/19	2,219	84	3.8%	—
03/18	2,117	100	4.7%	—
03/17	1,965	172	8.8%	—
Annual Growth	5.9%	—	—	—

2020 Year-End Financials

Return on assets: (-1.5%)
Return on equity: (-2.7%)
Current ratio: 1.60
Cash ($ mil.): 144

LEHIGH GAS CORPORATION

EXECUTIVES

Pres, David Hrinak
V Pres*, Lowell Brogan
SEC-Treas*, Howard J Krapf
Director of Marketing, Anne Boran
Senior Manager of Information, Wayne Maresch

LOCATIONS

HQ: LEHIGH GAS CORPORATION
702 HAMILTON ST STE 203, ALLENTOWN, PA 181012469
Phone: 610 791-3800

HISTORICAL FINANCIALS

Company Type: Private

Income Statement				FYE: December 31
	REVENUE ($ mil.)	NET INCOME ($ mil.)	NET PROFIT MARGIN	EMPLOYEES
12/07	1,034	4	0.5%	200
12/05*	53	(0)	—	—
06/04	116	1	1.2%	—
Annual Growth	72.5%	36.5%	—	—

*Fiscal year change

2007 Year-End Financials

Return on assets: 2.5%
Return on equity: 46.7%
Current ratio: 0.80
Cash ($ mil.): 1

LEHIGH VALLEY HEALTH NETWORK, INC.

Residents of the Lehigh Valley seeking medical care head uptown to facilities operated by the Lehigh Valley Health Network (LVHN). The not-for-profit health care provider operates through four full-service hospital campuses housing a total of about 1000 licensed beds. The medical center serves as a regional referral center for trauma and burn care and organ transplantation as well as specialty care in numerous areas such as cardiology women's health and pediatric surgery. LVHN also boasts a network of physician practices and community health centers as well as home health and hospice units.

Operations

The company's hospitals provide care in about 95 specialist fields including pediatric care burn treatment trauma care organ transplant cardiovascular care oncology and neurology. Its children's hospital includes inpatient emergency and specialist units. LVHN also conducts medical training programs and performs research in a range of different areas including cancer cardiovascular and infectious disease; a number of these programs are conducted through partnerships with entities including the H. Lee Moffitt Cancer Center and the University of South Florida's Morsani College of Medicine.

In addition to its core hospital operations the health organization has an alliance with the Sacred Heart Hospital of Allentown through which it provides Sacred Heart with certain services in the areas of cardiac care primary care telehealth services and mental health care. The two hospitals discussed but ultimately dismissed the possibility of a formal merger settling on being affiliated instead.

LVHN's 40 community clinics administer primary and specialty care for area residents including facilities for low-income patients. For patients (insured or not) who need care for minor ailments and routine tests LVHN operates a handful of retail health clinics under the Careworks brand. In addition the network includes a system of medical laboratories (Health Network Laboratories).

Geographic Reach

The LVHN system's main facilities are located in Allentown Bethlehem and Hazleton. With more than a dozen additional health centers the network provides services to residents of a five-county territory in Pennsylvania.

Financial Performance

Revenues increased 8% to $1.7 billion in 2014 on higher patient service and supporting operations revenues as well as higher investment earnings. Net income increased 59% to $95.5 million that year.

Strategy

LVHN opened the region's first pediatric emergency department at its Cedar Crest campus in 2011. The center houses about a dozen beds and is staffed by pediatric emergency physicians and nurses as well as a child life specialist. To further expand its emergency capabilities in 2013 the organization added emergency transportation services to its offerings.

In early 2014 LVHN merged with Greater Hazleton Health Alliance adding Hazleton General Hospital (now Lehigh Valley Hospital-Hazleton) to its network of facilities. The merger also added a physician group a hospital-based home health agency and a health and wellness center all in Hazleton

To promote care coordination and communication LVHN entered into a clinical affiliation with CVS Health in 2015. Through the partnership information on patient visits and prescriptions is accessible to care providers through secure electronic health record (EHR) systems.

EXECUTIVES

President And Ceo, Brian A. Nester
Coo, Terry Capuano
Evp And Chief Medical Officer, Thomas V. Whalen
Svp And Cfo, Edward O'Dea
Acting President Lehigh Valley Hospital Pocono, Elizabeth Wise
President Lehigh Valley Health Network Medical Staff And Trustee, Joseph Patruno
President Lehigh Valley Hospital-hazleton Medical Staff And Trustee, Anthony P. Veglia
Svp Patient Care Services And Chief Nursing Officer, Marie K. (Kim) Jordan
Vice President Supply Chain, Bill Matthews
Vice President Financial Services And Controller, Robert Thomas
Vice President Support Services, Craig Onori
Vice Chair, William F. Hecht, age 77
Chairman, John D. Stanley, age 63
Vice Chair, Jefferson K. (Jeff) Aiken
Secretary, Vicki Bush
Secretary, Sue Humza
Auditors: KPMG LLP PHILADELPHIA PENNS

LOCATIONS

HQ: LEHIGH VALLEY HEALTH NETWORK, INC.
1247 S CEDAR CREST BLVD # 105, ALLENTOWN, PA 181036298
Phone: 610 402-8000
Web: WWW.LVHN.ORG

PRODUCTS/OPERATIONS

Selected Facilities

Community Health Centers
- Hamburg Community Health Center
- Lehigh Valley Health Center at Bath
- Lehigh Valley Health Center at Bethlehem Township
- Lehigh Valley Health Center at Hellertown
- Lehigh Valley Health Center at Kutztown
- Lehigh Valley Health Center at Saucon Valley
- Lehigh Valley Health Center at Trexlertown
- Upper Bucks Health & Diagnostic Center (in partnership with Grand View Hospital Quakertown)

Hospitals
- Lehigh Valley Hospital - Cedar Crest (Allentown)
- Lehigh Valley Hospital - Muhlenberg (Bethlehem)

COMPETITORS

Abington Memorial Hospital
Ascension Health
Community Health Systems
Doylestown Hospital
Grand View
Main Line Health System
Mercy Health System
Moses Taylor Hospital
North Philadelphia Health System
Pennsylvania Hospital
Reading Hospital and Medical Center
Sacred Heart Hospital of Allentown
Shore Memorial Hospital
St. Luke's University Health Network
Tenet Healthcare
University of Pennsylvania Health System
Wyoming Valley Health Care System

HISTORICAL FINANCIALS

Company Type: Private

Income Statement				FYE: June 30
	REVENUE ($ mil.)	NET INCOME ($ mil.)	NET PROFIT MARGIN	EMPLOYEES
06/20	3,129	2	0.1%	12,000
06/19	2,978	118	4.0%	—
06/18	2,739	106	3.9%	—
06/17	2,432	409	16.8%	—
Annual Growth	8.8%	(82.7%)	—	—

2020 Year-End Financials

Return on assets: —
Return on equity: 0.1%
Current ratio: 1.20
Cash ($ mil.): 451

LELAND STANFORD JUNIOR UNIVERSITY

The Leland Stanford Junior University better known as simply Stanford University is one of the top universities in the US. It boasts respected programs across seven schools and 18 interdisciplinary institutes such as business engineering law and medicine among others. Stanford serves more than 16500 students (taught by 2240 faculty members) from all 50 US states and more than 90 other countries. Its student-teacher ratio sit at about 5:1. A private institution Stanford is supported through an endowment of some $27.7 billion one of the largest in the US. The university was established in 1885 by Leland Stanford Sr. who made his fortune selling provisions to California gold miners; it was named after his son Leland Stanford Jr.

Operations

Stanford University is widely recognized as one of the top US research universities and sports a host of laboratories and research centers including the Stanford Institute for Economic Policy Research and the Stanford Linear Accelerator Center. Its faculty members include around 17 Nobel Prize winners a handful of Pulitzer Prize winners and more than 30 MacArthur fellows.

The university also offers 35 varsity sports and 20 club sports; it boasts more than 110 NCAA team championships.

Geographic Reach

Stanford is located in the heart of California's Silicon Valley known worldwide as an epicenter for technology and research ventures. Google (headquartered in Silicon Valley) got its start at

Stanford when Sergey Brin and Larry Page developed the page-rank algorithm while they were still computer science graduate students.

The university is located on 8180 contiguous acres and has almost 700 major buildings.

Financial Performance

Stanford University reported total operating revenue of $12.3 billion in fiscal 2019 (ended August 31) an increase of 8%. The rise mainly came from higher patient services revenue from the Stanford Hospitals and Clinics organization. Student income sponsored support and investment income were broadly comparable with the prior year.

Net income rose 32% to $623 million due to comparatively lower expenses.

Stanford's cash balance grew $432.2 million to $1.6 billion during 2019. Operating activities generated $299.3 million and financing generated $628.9 million while investing activities used $496.0 million.

The university's sizable endowment grew 5% to $27.7 billion in fiscal 2019.

HISTORY

In 1885 Leland Stanford Sr. and his wife Jane established Leland Stanford Junior University in memory of their son Leland Jr. who had died of typhoid at age 15. Stanford made his fortune selling provisions to California gold miners and as a major investor in the Central Pacific Railroad one of the two companies that built the first transcontinental railway. It was Stanford who connected the tracks laid eastward by Central Pacific and westward by Union Pacific with a gold railway spike in 1869. He also served as California's governor and as a US senator.

The Stanfords donated more than 8000 acres of land from their own estate to establish an unconventional university one that was coeducational and nondenominational with a focus on preparing students for a profession. Stanford opened its doors in 1891 to a freshman class of 559 students. It awarded its first degrees four years later and among the graduates was future US president Herbert Hoover.

Leland Stanford Sr. died in 1893 and in 1903 Jane Stanford turned the university over to the board of trustees. After weathering significant damage in 1906 from the Great San Francisco Earthquake the university established a law school in 1908 and its medical school five years later.

During WWI the university mobilized half of its students into the Students' Army Training Corps. The School of Education was established in 1917 followed by the School of Engineering and Graduate School of Business eight years later. In 1933 a rule limiting the number of women admitted to Stanford was abolished.

Wallace Sterling who became president of the university after WWII initiated the transformation of Stanford into a world-class institution with a reputation for teaching and research. Under Sterling the university initiated development on the Stanford Research Park.

In 1958 Stanford opened its first overseas campus (near Stuttgart Germany) and the Stanford Medical Center was completed the following year. The university created a computer science department in 1965 and two years later opened the Stanford Linear Accelerator Center dedicated to physics research.

Donald Kennedy became president in 1980. The next year students voted to abandon the university's official mascot the "Indians" in response to concerns raised by Native American students. The nickname "Cardinal" was adopted in its place. The term refers to the school's color cardinal red.

Also during Kennedy's tenure it was revealed that Stanford had overcharged the Office of Naval Research for indirect costs associated with research. The scandal led to Kennedy's resignation in 1992 and in 1994 the Office of Naval Research and the university settled a related lawsuit for $1.2 million and a stipulation that Stanford had not committed any wrongdoing. Gerhard Casper succeeded Kennedy as president.

In 1997 Stanford and the University of California at San Francisco combined their teaching hospitals in a public/private merger. Two years later after the controversial experiment had harmed both hospitals' financial pictures the merger was terminated and the two hospitals agreed to go their separate ways.

In 1999 Casper announced his intention to resign as president. The school tapped provost John Hennessy as his replacement. Soon after his appointment in 2000 Hennessey launched a campaign to raise $1 billion. Former Stanford professor and Netscape co-founder Jim Clark donated $150 million later that year to support Stanford's biomedical engineering and sciences program. The school also launched a new company SKOLAR which developed an online search engine for the medical industry.

EXECUTIVES

President, John L. Hennessy
Provost, John W. Etchemendy
Dean School Of Humanities And Science, Richard P. Saller
Vp Business Affairs And Cfo, Randall S. (Randy) Livingston
Dean School Of Earth Energy And Environmental Sciences, Pamela Matson
Associate Vp It Services, Bill Clebsch
President And Ceo Stanford Health Care, Amir Dan Rubin
Vice Provost And Dean Of Research, Ann Margaret Arvin
Dean Graduate School Of Business, Garth Saloner
Dean Graduate School Of Education, Deborah Stipek
Dean School Of Engineering, Persis S. Drell
Dean Law School, M. Elizabeth Magill
Dean School Of Medicine, Lloyd Minor
President And Ceo Stanford Children's Health, Christopher Dawes
Vice President Human Resources, David Jones
Vice President, Britt Hedman
Vice President Slac National Accelerator Laboratory, William Madia
Associate Vice President Of Sponsored Research, Russell Brewer
Medical Director Performance Improvement, Terry Platchek
Medical Director, Kirsti Weng
Assocaite Vice President For University Affairs, Phil Taubman
Assoc. Vice President Of Human Resources Benefits, Leslie Schlaegel
Vice President, Carolyn Manning
Vp Finance, Wakuna Galega
Vice President Human Resources, Elizabeth Zacharias
Associate Vice President For The Arts, Matthew Tiews
Medical Director Emergency Medicine, Sam Shen
Medical Director, James Lau
Vpge, Rebecca Jantzen
Clinical Director Ibd, Sarah Streett
Medical Director Clinical Assistant Professor Of Medicine Division Of Primary Care And Population Health, Kurt Hafer
Associate Vice President Human Resources Communications, Melissa Mcvicker
Executive Vice President Technology, Ruth Ohara
Vice President, Anupam Singhal
Vpue Facilities Service Manager, Omar Ochoa
Assistant Vice President Of Development, Donna Lawrence
Director Of Pharmacy, Michael Brown
Senior Advisor To The Vice President F, Carol Dressler
Vice President Finance, David Connor
Vice President And Corporate Controller, James Martin
Vice President, Bill Madia
Vice President Ambulatory Care Services, Tim Engberg
Vice President Engineering, Douglas Gray
Co Vice President, Giselle Tran
Vice President And General Manager, Brian Freed
Vp Operations, Will Pfalzgraff
Vp Records, Andrew Doyle
Vice Chair, Mary Goldstein
Board Member, Udai Baisiwala
Auditors: PRICEWATERHOUSECOOPERS LLP SA

LOCATIONS

HQ: LELAND STANFORD JUNIOR UNIVERSITY
450 JANE STANFORD WAY, STANFORD, CA 943052004
Phone: 650 723-2300
Web: WWW.STANFORD.EDU

PRODUCTS/OPERATIONS

2014 Sales

	$ mil.	% of total
Healthcare services	3,942	50
Sponsored reseach support	1,266	16
Investment income	1,181	15
Student income	533	7
Special program fee and other income	641	7
Gifts	212	3
Net assets released from restrictions	146	2
Total	**7,924**	**100**

Selected Schools

Undergraduate
School of Earth Sciences
School of Engineering
School of Humanities and Sciences
Graduate
School of Business
School of Earth Sciences
School of Education
School of Engineering
School of Humanities and Sciences
School of Law
School of Medicine

Selected Interdisciplinary Research Centers

Alliance for Innovative Manufacturing at Stanford
Center for Computer Research in Music and Acoustics
Center for Integrated Facility Engineering
Center for Integrated Systems

Selected Laboratories Centers and Institutes

Center for Research on Information Storage Materials
Center for the Study of Language and Information
Edward L. Ginzton Laboratory
Institute for International Studies
Institute for Research on Women and Gender
John and Terry Levin Center for Public Service and Public Interest Law
Stanford Center for Buddhist Studies
Stanford Humanities Center
Stanford Institute for Economic Policy Research
W.W. Hansen Experimental Physics Laboratory

Selected Medical Research Facilities

Center for Biomedical Ethics
Center for Research in Disease Prevention
Human Genome Center
Richard M. Lucas Center for Magnetic Resonance Spectroscopy & Imaging
Sleep Disorders Center
Other Selected Research Facilities
Hoover Institution on War Revolution and Peace
Hopkins Marine Station
Martin Luther King Jr. Papers Project
Stanford Linear Accelerator Center

HISTORICAL FINANCIALS

Company Type: Private

Income Statement FYE: August 31

	REVENUE ($ mil.)	NET INCOME ($ mil.)	NET PROFIT MARGIN	EMPLOYEES
08/19	12,262	1,961	16.0%	15,000
08/18	11,311	2,653	23.5%	—
08/17	5,604	2,972	53.0%	—
08/06	4,511	3,007	66.7%	—
Annual Growth	8.0%	(3.2%)	—	—

2019 Year-End Financials

Return on assets: 3.4%
Return on equity: 4.3%
Current ratio: —
Cash ($ mil.): 1,631

LENOX HILL HOSPITAL

LOCATIONS

HQ: LENOX HILL HOSPITAL
210 E 64TH ST FL 4, NEW YORK, NY 100657471
Phone: 212 472-8872
Web: WWW.LENOXHILL.ORG

HISTORICAL FINANCIALS

Company Type: Private

Income Statement FYE: December 31

	REVENUE ($ mil.)	NET INCOME ($ mil.)	NET PROFIT MARGIN	EMPLOYEES
12/16	960	21	2.3%	41
12/15	885	6	0.7%	—
Annual Growth	8.5%	244.8%	—	—

2016 Year-End Financials

Return on assets: 1.8%
Return on equity: 4.7%
Current ratio: 0.80
Cash ($ mil.): —

LESTER E. COX MEDICAL CENTERS

Lester E. Cox Medical Centers (dba CoxHealth) provides a myriad of medical services to people in Missouri and Arkansas. CoxHealth's network includes six acute care hospitals (with more than 1000 beds) and more than 80 physician clinics. Centers for cardiac care cancer treatment orthopedics and women's health are among CoxHealth's specialized care options. Other operations include an ambulance service offering both ground and air transportation the Cox Health insurance and educational programs. The organization was named after its primary fundraiser in the 1940s.

Operations

Each year CoxHealth handles about 1.5 million outpatient visits; more than 280000 emergency urgent care and trauma visits; nearly 40000 ground ambulance transports; and more than 4000 births. Its hospitals include Cox Medical Center South Cox Medical Center Branson Cox North Hospital Cox Monett Hospital and the Meyer Orthopedic and Rehabilitation Hospital. Its specialty clinics include centers for cancer orthopedics cardiovascular care women's and children's health outpatient surgery and diagnostic imaging.

Geographic Reach

Springfield Missouri-based CoxHealth has primary and specialty care providers located in more than 80 clinics across the region. CoxHealth serves about 25 communities in approximately 25 counties in southwestern Missouri and northwestern Arkansas. Major facilities are in Branson Monett and Springfield Missouri.

Sales and Marketing

CoxHealth primarily serves families children women seniors and athletes.

Strategy

CoxHealth strives to improve its services and the health of its community. The system typically grows by adding or expanding facilities. CoxHealth is building a super clinic in 2020 bringing a new level of care to the Republic community with this addition. The super clinic will replace CoxHealth's current facility in Republic and is the health system's fourth super clinic.

CoxHealth also consolidated Crighton Olive Dunn Surgical Group in late 2020. The consolidated clinic which will be rebranded as CoxHealth Vein Center will offer a variety of outpatient procedures including vein ablations microphlebectomies and sclerotherapy as well as other general surgical services and diagnostic imaging.

CoxHealth and North Arkansas Regional Medical Center (NARMC) collaborated to expand health care access for residents of North Central Arkansas jointly opening a new medical facility in Harrison so residents can continue to receive exceptional primary care while increasing access to specialists close to home. CoxHealth also opened a new Cardiovascular Observation Unit at Cox South responding to the growing need for cardiovascular services.

Other initiatives include upgrading clinical processes and information technology systems. CoxHealth and Humana Inc. signed an agreement that provides in-network access for Humana commercial plan members in the Ozarks at all of CoxHealth's hospitals and outpatient locations and with its employed and affiliated technicians.

CoxHealth also partnered with Even in 2020 to help employees get paid early automatically budget and grow their savings and have full visibility into their earnings at all times. CoxHealth has had a number of programs in place to address employees' financial stress but wanted to find something more lasting and impactful hence its exploration of on-demand pay.

Company Background

CoxHealth was founded as Burge Deaconess Hospital in 1908. It became Lester E. Cox Medical Centers in 1968 following the death of Cox a St. Louis businessman who led a series of major fundraising campaigns in the 1940s critical to the survival and growth of the hospital.

EXECUTIVES

Vice President And Chief Medical Officer; And Medical Director Oxford Hospice, Dan Sontheimer
Senior Vice President Chief Hospital Officer, John Duff
Vice President And Chief Nursing Officer, Karen Kramer
Svp And Cfo, Jacob McWay
Vice President And Chief Information Officer, Bruce Robison
President Cox Healthplans, Jeffrey C. (Jeff) Bond
Vp And Chief Clinical Officer, Ron Prenger
Vice President; President Cox Monett, Genny Maroc
Vice President; President Oxford Healthcare, Karen Thomas
Chairman Joint Operations Committee And Chief Integrated Physicians, Kenneth Powell
Vice President President Home Parenteral Services, H. Lynn Kelley
President And Ceo; Director, Steven D. (Steve) Edwards
President Coxhealth Foundation, Lisa Alexander
President Cox College, Anne Liners Brett
Vice President Clinical Services, Amanda Hedgpeth
Director Of Respiratory Therapy, Martin Rohrer
Vice President Marketing, James Anderson
Medical Director, Sam Alexander
Vice President Clinical Services, Jeff Hawkins
Medical Director Of Cardiovascular Services, Jim Ceaser
Pharmacy Manager, Kirsten Dougherty
Cno Vice President Clinical Services Enterprise Nursing Informatics Coxhealth Branson, Lynne Yaggy
Pharmacy Manager, Steven Crain
Director Of Pharmacy, Rhonda Flannery
Director Of Radiology Services, Patrick Blamey
Medical Director, Christine Kaufman
Vice President Secretary, Carol Christiansen
Clinical Director, Sally Felton
Vice President, Kayla Mattingly
Unit Secretary, Donna Lee
Department Secretary I, Regina Barfield
Treasurer, Connie Smith

LOCATIONS

HQ: LESTER E. COX MEDICAL CENTERS
1423 N JEFFERSON AVE, SPRINGFIELD, MO 658021917
Phone: 417 269-3000
Web: WWW.COXHEALTH.COM

PRODUCTS/OPERATIONS

Selected Services

Air Care
Alzheimer's Disease
Behavioral Health
Brain and Spine Disorders
Breast Care
Cancer Services
Children's Health
Diabetes
Dialysis
Ear Nose and Throat (ENT)
Emergency Department
Fitness Centers
Food and Nutrition
Heart and Vascular
Home Health
Hyperbaric Medicine and Wound Care
Neuroscience
Occupational Medicine
Orthopedics
Parenting
Parkinson's Clinic
Pharmacy
Physical Medicine
Pregnancy
Radiology
Rehabilitation
Respiratory Care
Robotic Surgery
Sleep Disorders
Smoking Cessation
Specialty Services
Sports Medicine
Stroke
Trauma Services
Urgent Care
Weight Loss
Wellness Consultations
Women's Health
Workers' Compensation

COMPETITORS

Ascension Health
BJC HealthCare
Catholic Health Initiatives
Children's Mercy Hospital
HCA
Mercy Health
Mercy Hospital Springfield
Saint Luke's Health System
Shawnee Mission Medical Center
Sisters of Charity of Leavenworth
St. Anthony's Medical Center
Tenet Healthcare
Truman Medical Centers
Universal Health Services
University of Kansas Medical Center

HISTORICAL FINANCIALS

Company Type: Private

Income Statement FYE: September 30

	REVENUE ($ mil.)	NET INCOME ($ mil.)	NET PROFIT MARGIN	EMPLOYEES
09/14	898	50	5.6%	11,170
09/13	858	105	12.3%	—
09/12	843	66	7.9%	—
Annual Growth	3.2%	(13.0%)	—	—

2014 Year-End Financials

Return on assets: 3.6%
Return on equity: 7.3%
Current ratio: 2.00
Cash ($ mil.): 61

LEVI STRAUSS & CO.

Pioneering American apparel maker Levi Strauss & Co. has jeans in its genes. A global manufacturer of brand-name clothing Levi Strauss sells jeans and sportswear under the Levi's Dockers Signature by Levi Strauss and Denizen labels in more than 110 countries. The company distributes its brand products through more than 900 company-operated stores located in over 30 countries and through the third-party and first-party online stores. Levi Strauss makes some two-thirds of its revenue from Levi's branded men's pants. The company went public (again) in early 2019 although the Haas family (descendants of founder Levi Strauss) still controls it.

HISTORY

Levi Strauss arrived in New York City from Bavaria in 1847. In 1853 he joined his brother-in-law David Stern in San Francisco selling dry goods to the gold rushers. Shortly after a prospector told Strauss of miners' problems in finding sturdy pants. Strauss made a pair out of canvas for the prospector; word of the rugged pants spread quickly.

Strauss continued his dry-goods business in the 1860s. During this time he switched the pants' fabric to a durable French cloth called serge de Nimes soon known as denim. He colored the fabric with indigo dye and adopted the idea from Nevada tailor Jacob Davis of reinforcing the pants with copper rivets. In 1873 Strauss and Davis produced their first pair of waist-high overalls (later known as jeans). The pants soon became de rigueur for lumberjacks cowboys railroad workers oil drillers and farmers.

Strauss continued to build his pants and wholesaling business until he died in 1902. Levi Strauss & Co. passed to four Stern nephews who carried on their uncle's jeans business while maintaining the company's philanthropic reputation.

After WWII Walter Haas and Peter Haas (a fourth-generation Strauss family member) assumed leadership of LS&CO. In 1948 they ended the company's wholesaling business to concentrate on Levi's clothing. In the 1950s Levi's jeans ceased to be merely functional garments for workers; they became the uniform of American youth. In the 1960s LS&CO. added women's attire and expanded overseas.

The company went public in 1971. That year it added a women's career line and bought Koret sportswear (sold in 1984). By the mid-1980s profits declined. Peace Corps-veteran-turned-McKinsey-consultant Robert Haas (Walter's son) grabbed the reins of LS&CO. in 1984 and took the company private the next year (he became chairman in 1989). He also instilled a touchy-feely corporate culture often at odds with the bottom line.

In 1986 LS&CO. introduced Dockers casual pants. The company's sales began rising in 1991 as consumers forsook the designer duds of the 1980s for more practical clothes. LS&CO. says seven out of every 10 American men own a pair of Dockers. However LS&CO. missed out on the birth of another trend: the split between the fashion sense of US adolescents and their Levi's-loving baby boomer parents.

In 1996 the company introduced Slates dress slacks. That year LS&CO. bought back nearly one-third of its stock from family and employees for $4.3 billion. Grappling with slipping sales and debt from the buyout in 1997 LS&CO. closed 11 of its 37 North American plants laying off 6400 workers and 1000 salaried employees; it granted generous severance packages even to those earning minimum wage.

In 1998 citing improved labor conditions in China LS&CO. announced it would step up its use of Chinese subcontractors. Further restructuring added a third of its European plants to the closures list that year. LS&CO.'s sales fell 13% in fiscal 1998. Also that year Haas handed his CEO title to Pepsi executive Philip Marineau; Haas remained chairman.

LS&CO. closed 11 of 22 remaining North American plants in 1999. It also unleashed several new jeans brands that eschewed the company's one-style-fits-all approach of old.

In April 2002 LS&CO. announced it would close six of its last eight US plants and cut 20% of its worldwide staff (3300 workers). In September 2003 it cut another 5% of its global staff (650 workers). That month the company opened its first girls-only store located in Paris. In December LS&CO. replaced CFO Bill Chiasson with an outside turnaround specialist.

Pinpointing 2006 as the best time to step down as the company's chief executive Philip Marineau retired at the end of 2006. John Anderson president of LS&CO.'s Asia/Pacific division and head of the firm's global supply chain unit replaced Marineau as president and CEO.

Levi Strauss chairman Robert Haas retired in 2008 after 18 years in that role. His successor was Dryer's ice cream executive T. Gary Rogers who became the first leader in the company's history who was not a descendant of the founder. In August 2008 CFO Hans Ploos van Amstel left the company the and was replaced by Heidi Manes its corporate controller and principal accounting officer.

Looking to gain a more active role in its store business LS&CO. in July 2009 bought the operating rights for more than 70 Levi's and Dockers Outlet locations from store operator Anchor Blue Retail Group which had filed for bankruptcy for $72 million. Anchor Blue said the US recession and drop in consumer spending especially among teens severely affected its financial performance. LS&CO. said the acquisition will enable it to better manage its brands' positioning.

Rogers retired in late 2009 and Richard Kauffman became chairman.

EXECUTIVES

Evp; President The Dockers Brand, Seth M. Ellison, age 61, $609,808 total compensation
President & Ceo Director, Charles V. (Chip) Bergh, age 62, $1,343,077 total compensation
Evp And Cfo, Harmit J. Singh, age 56, $746,538 total compensation
Executive Vice President And General Counsel, Seth R. Jaffe
Chief Human Resources Officer, Elizabeth Wood
Executive Vice President And President Of Direct-to-consumer (dtc), Marc Rosen, age 51
Executive Vice President And President Of Levi Strauss Asia Middle East And Africa, David Love, age 57, $580,387 total compensation
Senior Vice President And Chief Communications Officer, Kelly McGinnis
Executive Vice President And President Levi Strauss Americas, Roy Bagattini, age 56, $690,433 total compensation
Executive Vice President And President Product Innovation And Supply Chain, Liz O'Neill
Senior Vice President & Chief Marketing Officer, Jennifer (Jen) Sey
Senior Vice President Global Brands Strategy And Finance, Paul Todgham
Vice President Global Mand D Plng And Operations, Barb Gollert
Vice President Sustainability, Michael Kobori
Vice President Global Creative Brand, Chad Hinson
Vice President Human Resources, Karthik Sarma
Vice President Sales, Donna Null Paulo
Senior Vice President Cio, Christopher Clark
Vice President Global Logistics, Doug Flores
Senior Vice President Global Demand And Supply Management, Malcolm Goonetileke
Vp Purchasing, Dean Edwards
Senior Vice President Global Distribution And Logistics, Stephen Berube
Vice President Managing Director South Europe, Diana Dimitian
Vice President Global Tax, Daniel Wenzel
Executive Vice President President, Levi Strauss Americas
Vice President Omni Channel Merchandising, Kiera Ganann
Chairman, Stephen C. Neal, age 70
Auditors: PRICEWATERHOUSECOOPERS LLP SA

LOCATIONS

HQ: LEVI STRAUSS & CO.
1155 BATTERY ST, SAN FRANCISCO, CA 941111264
Phone: 415 501-6000
Web: WWW.LEVISTRAUSS.COM

2018 Stores		#
Americas region		268
Europe region		300
Asia/Pacific region		256
Total	0	697

2018 Sales	$ mil.	% of total
Americas	3,042	55
Europe	1,646	29
Asia/Pacific region	886	17
Total	5,575	100

PRODUCTS/OPERATIONS

2018 Sales		% of total
Levi's brand		86
Dockers brand		7
Signature by Levi Strauss & Denizen brands		7
Total	0	100

Selected Brands

Denizen
Dockers
Dockers Alpha Khaki
Dockers for Men
Dockers for Women

Levi's
- Levi's 501 Original
- Levi's 505 Straight
- Levi's 511 Skinny
- Levi's 513 Slim
- Levi's 514 Slim Straight
- Levi's Curve ID

Signature by Levis Strauss & Co.
Intro
Waterless
Wellthread
Wasteless

COMPETITORS

Abercrombie & Fitch
American Eagle Outfitters
Benetton
Calvin Klein
Diesel SpA
FUBU
Fast Retailing
Fruit of the Loom
Guess?
Haggar
Hugo Boss
Inditex
J. Crew
Jockey International
Joe's Jeans
Kmart
Kohl's
Lands' End
Macy's
NIKE
Nautica Apparel
Nine West
OshKosh B'Gosh
Oxford Industries
PVH
Perry Ellis International
Ralph Lauren
Sean John
Target Corporation
The Gap
True Religion Apparel
Under Armour
VF Corporation
Victoria's Secret Stores
Wacoal
Wal-Mart
Warnaco Group
adidas

HISTORICAL FINANCIALS

Company Type: Private

Income Statement — FYE: November 25

	REVENUE ($ mil.)	NET INCOME ($ mil.)	NET PROFIT MARGIN	EMPLOYEES
11/18	5,575	285	5.1%	15,800
11/17	4,904	284	5.8%	—
11/16	4,552	291	6.4%	—
11/15	4,494	209	4.7%	—
Annual Growth	7.4%	10.8%	—	—

2018 Year-End Financials

Return on assets: 8.1%
Return on equity: 42.7%
Current ratio: 2.20
Cash ($ mil.): 713

LEXA INTERNATIONAL CORPORATION

EXECUTIVES

Chb-Pres, Antonia Axson Johnson
V Chb, P Goeran Ennerfelt
V Pres-Contrl, Charles W Seitz
V Pres, John Pascale
Dir, William I Turner
Asst Treas-Dir of Credit, Kory Arthur
Vice-Chairman, Goeran P Ennerfelt
Investment Manager, Frank Ingarra
General Manager, Nelson Weinstein
Auditors: CITRIN COOPERMAN & COMPANY LL

LOCATIONS

HQ: LEXA INTERNATIONAL CORPORATION
1 LANDMARK SQ STE 407, STAMFORD, CT 069012601
Phone: 203 326-5200
Web: WWW.AXELJOHNSON.COM

HISTORICAL FINANCIALS

Company Type: Private

Income Statement — FYE: December 31

	REVENUE ($ mil.)	NET INCOME ($ mil.)	NET PROFIT MARGIN	EMPLOYEES
12/09	2,598	6	0.2%	1,204
12/08	4,312	4	0.1%	—
12/07	4,003	(21)	—	—
Annual Growth	(19.4%)	—	—	—

2009 Year-End Financials

Return on assets: 0.6%
Return on equity: 3.1%
Current ratio: 1.80
Cash ($ mil.): 43

LEXINGTON COUNTY HEALTH SERVICES DISTRICT, INC.

EXECUTIVES

Pres, Michael Biediger
V Pres*, Melinda P Kruzner
Coo*, Tod Augsburger
Infection Control Manager, Janet Foster
Cardiovascular Disease, Brandon Drafts
Vp Marketing, Charles Wendt
Internal Audit, Jason McKinney
Critical Care Pharmacist, Amanda Guffey
Buyer, Sherry Mohundro
Auditors: KPMG LLP ATLANTA GA

LOCATIONS

HQ: LEXINGTON COUNTY HEALTH SERVICES DISTRICT, INC.
2720 SUNSET BLVD, WEST COLUMBIA, SC 291694810
Phone: 803 791-2000
Web: WWW.LEXFAMILYPRACTICENORTHEAST.COM

HISTORICAL FINANCIALS

Company Type: Private

Income Statement — FYE: September 30

	REVENUE ($ mil.)	NET INCOME ($ mil.)	NET PROFIT MARGIN	EMPLOYEES
09/10	576	59	10.4%	6,000
09/09	528	57	10.9%	—
09/08	491	35	7.2%	—
Annual Growth	8.3%	29.8%	—	—

2010 Year-End Financials

Return on assets: 7.3%
Return on equity: 11.6%
Current ratio: 4.70
Cash ($ mil.): 170

LEXINGTON MEDICAL CENTER

EXECUTIVES

Pres-Ceo, Tod Augsburger
Sr V Pres-Cfo*, Melinda Kruzner
Emergency Medicine Specialist, Patrick M O'Malley
Coordinator, Sarah Walker
Health Professional, Hope Wisniewski
Family Practitioner, Benjamin Askins
Outcomes Coordinator, Cathy Jashinsky
Director of Materials Manageme, Douglas McCullough
Sergeant Communications, Joshua Angle
Internist, Gilbert L Rogers
Purchasing Agent, Joanna Christifoli
Auditors: KPMG LLP ATLANTA GA

LOCATIONS

HQ: LEXINGTON MEDICAL CENTER
2720 SUNSET BLVD, WEST COLUMBIA, SC 291694810
Phone: 803 791-2000
Web: WWW.LEXMED.COM

PRODUCTS/OPERATIONS

Selected Services

Patient Care
Alzheimer's Care
Birth Center
Extended Care
Family Medicine
General Surgery
Imaging
Laboratory & Pathology
Occupational Health
Weight-Loss Surgery
Health & Wellness
Community Health Screenings
Health Directions Wellness Center
Nutrition Therapy
Sleep Solutions

Selected Facilities

Community Medical Centers
- LMC Batesburg-Leesville
- LMC Chapin
- LMC Gilbert
- LMC Irmo
- LMC Lexington
- LMC Swansea

Hospital Units
- Alzheimers Care Center
- Birth Center
- Cancer Center
- Emergency Care
- Extended Care
- Heart Center
- Obesity Surgery Center
- Urgent Care
- Women's Services

COMPETITORS

Carolinas HealthCare System
Carolinas Hospital System
Georgetown Hospital System
Grand Strand Regional Medical Center
Laurens County Hospital
McLeod Health
Palmetto Health
Upstate Affiliate

HISTORICAL FINANCIALS

Company Type: Private

Income Statement FYE: September 30

	REVENUE ($ mil.)	NET INCOME ($ mil.)	NET PROFIT MARGIN	EMPLOYEES
09/17	953	(9)	—	5,616
09/16	906	21	2.3%	—
09/15	863	86	10.0%	—
09/14	781	95	12.2%	—
Annual Growth	6.8%	—	—	—

2017 Year-End Financials

Return on assets: (-0.6%)
Return on equity: (-3.2%)
Current ratio: 2.80
Cash ($ mil.): 173

LHH CORPORATION

When Manhattanites are looking for health care many of them head for the hill: Lenox Hill Hospital to be exact. The 650-bed facility provides care to patients on Manhattan's Upper East Side – about 45% of its patient base is from Manhattan the rest from surrounding boroughs. Services include cardiac care high-risk obstetrics pediatrics and orthopedics and sports medicine. Lenox Hill serves as a teaching affiliate for NYU Medical Center and also owns Manhattan Eye Ear and Throat Hospital a provider of specialty care for vision hearing and speech disorders. Today it's part of North Shore-Long Island Jewish Health System.

Operations

As part of the North Shore-LIJ system Lenox Hill has access to the larger organization's resources. North Shore-LIJ one of the largest health care providers in New York State; Lenox Hill is its first hospital in the New York metropolitan area.

Lenox Hill Hospital operates a handful of outpatient locations that provide medical surgical and specialized services. Its center for mental health administers a wide range of inpatient and ambulatory psychiatric services for adults and children. To provide quality services to a diverse population Lenox Hill provides multi-lingual translators.

The hospital treats more than 325000 patients a year.

Geographic Reach

The hospital serves patients from Manhattan and surrounding neighborhoods from two campuses in New York City and one in Westchester County.

Financial Performance

In 2012 Lenox Hill reported revenues of $729 million and a net loss of $37 million.

Strategy

Lenox Hill Hospital has also expanded in recent years by opening primary care center and urgent care centers in Manhattan and upgrading and enhancing some of its existing facilities such as its emergency care center to accommodate a growing number of patients. In 2012 it opened a new pediatric inpatient care unit for general and surgical care as well as new head and neck and cranial base surgery centers. In 2013 it opened a new reproduction clinic for fertility services.

Expanding its medical services outside of North Shore-LIJ system's 16 hospitals and into community settings in 2013 Lenox Hill opened the 3200-sq.-ft. Heart and Vascular Institute in Yorktown Heights – the first facility for the hospital system in Westchester County.

In 2012 Lenox Hill became the first in the New York area to perform minimally invasive heart valve replacement.

Company Background

US News & World Report has ranked Lenox Hill as one the top 50 in Cardiology and Heart Surgery and Ear Nose and Throat facilities in the US and among the top 10 hospitals in New York state.

In 2010 the hospital expanded its service offerings by adding palliative care to its medical roster. The services are aimed at relieving pain symptoms and stress related to serious illness. In many cases palliative care specialists provide care to patients who are not eligible for or don't want hospice care when facing a fatal illness.

It performed the first coronary angioplasty in the US (in 1978) and the first angiocardiogram (in 1938).

The hospital was established in 1857 as the German Dispensary.

EXECUTIVES

Radiology Director, Fred Desarno

LOCATIONS

HQ: LHH CORPORATION
100 E 77TH ST, NEW YORK, NY 100751850
Phone: 212 434-2000
Web: WWW.LENOXHILL.NORTHWELL.EDU

PRODUCTS/OPERATIONS

Selected Services

Bariatric surgery
Cardiothoracic surgery
Cardiovascular care
Colorectal surgery
Critical care
Maternal and child health
Manhattan Ear Eye and Throat Institute
Mental health
Neurosurgery
Palliative care
Pathology
Plastic and reconstructive surgery
Primary care
Radiology
Rehabilitation
Robotic surgery

COMPETITORS

Beth Israel Medical Center
Bronx-Lebanon Hospital
Catholic Health Services of Long Island
Catholic Healthcare System
Lutheran HealthCare
Maimonides Medical Center
Memorial Sloan-Kettering
Montefiore Medical
New York City Health and Hospitals
NewYork-Presbyterian Hospital

HISTORICAL FINANCIALS

Company Type: Private

Income Statement FYE: December 31

	REVENUE ($ mil.)	NET INCOME ($ mil.)	NET PROFIT MARGIN	EMPLOYEES
12/18	1,064	73	6.9%	2,955
12/16	960	21	2.3%	—
12/14	790	3	0.4%	—
Annual Growth	7.7%	119.1%	—	—

2018 Year-End Financials

Return on assets: 5.8%
Return on equity: 12.9%
Current ratio: 1.10
Cash ($ mil.): 2

LIBERTY UNIVERSITY, INC.

EXECUTIVES

Cfo, Don Moon
Sr V Pres*, Mark Hine
Cao*, Ronald E Hawkins
Coo*, Randy Smith Randy Smith
SEC*, David M Corry
Project Coordinator, William Mailand
Assistant Professor, Bruce M Kirk
Assistant Professor, Danielle E Scholten
Assistant Professor, Michael R Mitchell
Accounting Staff, Michael Ohemeng-Dapaah
Assistant Professor, Neal Brasher
Auditors: DIXON HUGHES GOODMAN LLP RICH

LOCATIONS

HQ: LIBERTY UNIVERSITY, INC.
1971 UNIVERSITY BLVD, LYNCHBURG, VA 245150002
Phone: 434 582-2000
Web: WWW.LIBERTY.EDU

HISTORICAL FINANCIALS

Company Type: Private

Income Statement FYE: June 30

	REVENUE ($ mil.)	NET INCOME ($ mil.)	NET PROFIT MARGIN	EMPLOYEES
06/19	989	316	32.0%	7,200
06/18	896	276	30.8%	—
06/17	961	289	30.1%	—
06/15	1,001	223	22.3%	—
Annual Growth	(0.3%)	9.1%	—	—

2019 Year-End Financials

Return on assets: 10.1%
Return on equity: 11.7%
Current ratio: —
Cash ($ mil.): 272

LIFEBRIDGE HEALTH, INC.

LifeBridge Health links patients to healthcare. Serving the Baltimore region the not-for-profit company operates two general hospitals – Sinai Hospital of Baltimore and Northwest Hospital – with specialties including oncology neurology pediatrics and sports medicine. The LifeBridge Health network also provides long-term care at the Levindale Hebrew Geriatric Center and Hospital (nursing subacute and adult day care services) and the Courtland Gardens Nursing & Rehabilitation Center. Altogether the health system boasts some 1190 beds. LifeBridge's Health Wellness division includes a health and fitness program and community fitness center.

Operations

Sinai Hospital is a teaching hospital with residency programs for medical students training at Johns Hopkins University and University of Maryland. Levindale also serves as a teaching facility for medical dental nursing and social work students pursuing training to serve geriatric populations.

EXECUTIVES

Executive Vice President, Leslie Simmons
Board Of Directors, Sinai Price
Auditors: KPMG LLP BALTIMORE MD

LOCATIONS

HQ: LIFEBRIDGE HEALTH, INC.
2401 W BELVEDERE AVE, BALTIMORE, MD 212155216
Phone: 410 601-5653
Web: WWW.LIFEBRIDGEHEALTH.ORG

PRODUCTS/OPERATIONS

Selected Locations
Courtland Gardens Nursing & Rehabilitation Center
Levindale Hebrew Geriatric Center and Hospital
Northwest Hospital
Sinai Hospital

Selected Services
Bariatric and Minimally Invasive Surgery
Brain & Spine Institute
Cancer Institute
Hospitalist Program
Rubin Institute for Advanced Orthopedics
Vascular Institute

COMPETITORS

Anne Arundel Medical Center
Ascension Health
Bon Secours Health
Franklin Square Hospital Center
GBMC
Johns Hopkins Health System
MedStar Health
MedStar Union Memorial Hospital
University of Maryland Medical System

HISTORICAL FINANCIALS

Company Type: Private

Income Statement — FYE: June 30

	REVENUE ($ mil.)	NET INCOME ($ mil.)	NET PROFIT MARGIN	EMPLOYEES
06/20	1,662	54	3.3%	6,000
06/19	1,610	65	4.1%	—
06/17	1,527	111	7.3%	—
06/15	145	0	0.5%	—
Annual Growth	62.8%	134.1%	—	—

2020 Year-End Financials

Return on assets: 2.1%
Return on equity: 4.1%
Current ratio: 2.00
Cash ($ mil.): 251

LIMETREE BAY TERMINALS LLC

HOVENSA brings together US and Latin American know-how and operations to handle oil products in the US Virgin Islands. HOVENSA is a joint venture of Hess and Venezuelan oil giant PDVSA (its major crude oil supplier). Once the largest private employer in the US Virgin Islands the company operated a 500000-barrels-per-day crude oil refinery on St. Croix along with two specialized oil processing complexes a 150000-barrels-per-day fluid catalytic cracking unit and a 58000-barrels-per-day delayed coker unit. However the St. Croix refinery had run up losses for years; it was shut down in 2012 and was put up for sale in 2013.

Strategy

Citing high operating and maintenance costs (the refinery was fueled by oil not the cheaper natural gas) and the growth of lower-cost refineries in emerging markets HOVENSA has posted $1.3 billion in losses since 2009. As a result the company decided to cut its losses by converting the refinery into an oil storage terminal which can take advantage of St. Croix's strategic location. Its 55-ft. deep harbor enables it to receive crude oil tanker deliveries from Venezuela and around the world. The storage terminal employs about 100 workers. The shutdown of the refinery resulted in more than 2000 employes being laid off.

Company Background

In 2009 the global economic downturn depressed demand for oil caused a dip in production and prompted the company to lay off 270 employees (about 21% of its total contract workers).

Crude thoughput has declined steadily at HOVENSA due to weaker refining margins and planned and unplanned maintenance from 402000 barrels per day (bpd) in 2009 to 390000 bpd in 2010 to 284000 bpd in 2011.

Auditors: ERNST & YOUNG LLP NEW YORK N

LOCATIONS

HQ: LIMETREE BAY TERMINALS LLC
1 ESTATE HOPE, CHRISTIANSTED, VI 00820
Phone: 340 692-3000

COMPETITORS

Chevron
ConocoPhillips
Exxon Mobil
Marathon Oil
Royal Dutch Shell
Sunoco
Valero Energy

HISTORICAL FINANCIALS

Company Type: Private

Income Statement — FYE: December 31

	REVENUE ($ mil.)	NET INCOME ($ mil.)	NET PROFIT MARGIN	EMPLOYEES
12/09	10,048	(451)	—	1,300
12/08	17,479	94	0.5%	—
Annual Growth	(42.5%)	—	—	—

2009 Year-End Financials

Return on assets: 3.2%
Return on equity: (4.5%)
Current ratio: 0.20
Cash ($ mil.): 77

LINCOLN MEDICAL AND MENTAL HEALTH CENTER

EXECUTIVES

Exec Dir, Milton Nunez
Anesthesiologist, Jean R Maurice
Infectious Disease Specialist, Chung Kim
Doctor, Karen Hennessey
Emergency Medicine Specialist, Karlene Hosford
Emergency Medicine Specialist, Lee Donner
Obstetrician Gynecologist, Manisha Jain
Infection Control Director, Melba Talan
Emergency Medicine Specialist, Andaleeb H Raja
Psychiatrist, Christian R Gonzalez
Cardiovascular Disease, David P Akman

LOCATIONS

HQ: LINCOLN MEDICAL AND MENTAL HEALTH CENTER
234 E 149TH ST, BRONX, NY 104515504
Phone: 718 579-5000
Web: WWW.NYCHEALTHANDHOSPITALS.ORG

HISTORICAL FINANCIALS

Company Type: Private

Income Statement — FYE: June 30

	REVENUE ($ mil.)	NET INCOME ($ mil.)	NET PROFIT MARGIN	EMPLOYEES
06/16	616	120	19.6%	77
06/15	530	20	3.9%	—
Annual Growth	16.2%	488.5%	—	—

2016 Year-End Financials

Return on assets: 14.0%
Return on equity: 50.4%
Current ratio: 1.40
Cash ($ mil.): —

LOGISTICARE SOLUTIONS, LLC

LogistiCare is a go-between for getting from your house to the doctor's office and back. The company brokers non-emergency transportation services for commercial health plans government entities (such as state Medicaid agencies) and hospitals throughout the US. Using its nearly 20 call centers and a network of some 1500 independent contracted transportation providers the company coordinates the medical-related travel arrangements of its clients' members. In addition it contracts with local school boards to coordinate transportation for special needs students. The company provides more than 26 million trips each year for clients in some 40 states. LogistiCare is a subsidiary of Providence Service.

Operations

LogistiCare also known as Charter LCI has contracts with clients including metro transit authorities HMOs and commercial insurance firms. Other services include finance and consulting to help companies with billing management and claims adjudication customer reimbursement risk management and discount programs for patients requesting noncovered services. LogistiCare's eligibility and authorization services include call screening to determine client-provided benefit criteria as well as screening to determine type of transport needed.

The company operates more than a dozen regional call centers that match incoming requests with subcontracted transportation providers including local taxi and ambulance companies. Transportation customers often include the elderly or those with disabilities that prevent self-transportation.

Strategy

A major part of LogistiCare's growth strategy is to secure contracts with state and local authorities to become the sole Medicaid or Medicare transportation provider. It scored one such contract in late 2010 with Sussex County Delaware. Under terms of that agreement LogistiCare became the statewide broker for all Medicaid medical transportation.

EXECUTIVES

Vice President Human Resources, Jenny Southern
Vice President Finance, Ken Shepard
Vice President Information Technology, Matt Williams
Vice President Business Planning, Nicholas Luoma
Senior Vice President And Chief Commercial Officer, John Lauer

LOCATIONS

HQ: LOGISTICARE SOLUTIONS, LLC
1275 PEACHTREE ST NE FL 6, ATLANTA, GA 303093580
Phone: 404 888-5831
Web: WWW.LOGISTICARE.COM

PRODUCTS/OPERATIONS

Selected Services
Billing and claims management
Call center management
Credentialing
Data management and reporting
Eligibility and authorization services
Logistics
Non-emergency transportation management (ambulatory/livery vans wheel chair vans stretcher vans)
Provider payment
Quality assurance

COMPETITORS

AMR
Coach USA
FirstGroup America
MV Transportation
National Express Group
Safe Ride Services
Veolia Transportation

HISTORICAL FINANCIALS

Company Type: Private

Income Statement — FYE: December 31

	REVENUE ($ mil.)	NET INCOME ($ mil.)	NET PROFIT MARGIN	EMPLOYEES
12/17*	1,318	35	2.7%	2,000
04/17	1,234	44	3.6%	—
12/15	1,083	40	3.7%	—
12/14	884	71	8.1%	—
Annual Growth	14.2%	(21.0%)	—	—

*Fiscal year change

2017 Year-End Financials

Return on assets: 19.1%
Return on equity: 73.8%
Current ratio: 1.10
Cash ($ mil.): 26

LONG BEACH MEDICAL CENTER

Long Beach Memorial Medical Center (LBMMC) is an old-timer in the Long Beach health care market. A subsidiary of Memorial Health Services LBMMC provides a full range of health services to residents of the Long Beach California area. The medical center a 420-bed acute-care hospital was founded in 1907 and is one of the largest private hospitals on the West Coast. Services include primary emergency diagnostic surgical therapeutic and rehabilitative care. The hospital is home to centers for treatment of cancer heart stroke and women's and children's health concerns. It also provides home and hospice care programs as well as occupational health services.

Operations

LBMMC comprises a breast center cancer institute center for women heart and vascular institute imaging center joint replacement center rehabilitation institute and stroke center. The medical center is a 420-bed acute-care hospital.

Geographic Reach

Long Beach Memorial Medical Center (LBMMC) is one of the nation's largest private hospitals on the West Coast.

Strategy

LBMMC boasts an electronic medical record (EMR) system that connects the hospital and all of its affiliated physicians and pharmacies so that they can transfer patient information electronically between different care providers and locations. Hospitals that use an EMR are eligible for incentives and higher reimbursements from the federal government. Additionally EMRs help to reduce medical errors and increase patient safety by eliminating things like medication interactions and duplicate patient records.

LBMMC expanded its cancer services by building a new $31 million dedicated outpatient cancer facility. The MemorialCare Todd Cancer Institute at Long Beach Memorial which was completed in mid-2013 serves to supplement its current center which had reached capacity. With the new 65000-sq.-ft. MemorialCare Todd Cancer Institute pavilion LBMMC enhances its cancer care technology and capacity.

LBMMC has also expanded its robotics program beyond cardiology. The hospital recently established a new intensivist program in the Intensive Care Unit (ICU). The ICU program integrates teaching from the University of California Irvine residents and interns.

EXECUTIVES

Cio, Scott Joslyn
Cfo, Wendy Dorchester
President And Ceo, Barry Arbuckle
Executive Vice President And Chief Administrative Officer, Melvin Marks
Vice President, Rhoda Weiss
Vice President Of Quality, Donna Hartman
Vice President Of Technical Informatio, Kevin Torres
Vice President Material Resources, Gerald Olson
Medical Director Ed, Gary Moreau
Medical Director Imaging Services, Jagdish Patel
Operating Room Dir, Deborah Ebert
Vice President Of Sales, David Sax
Medical Director, Standiford Helm
Vice President Physician Integration, Laurie Sicaeros
Vice President, Mai Tran
Director Of Pharmacy, Alisa Groesch
Senior Vice President, Rajesh Govindaiah
Vice President, Seth Ellis
Executive Vice President Operations, Lon Ledwith
Secretary Executive, Donna Gorman
Secretary Department Medical, Maria Barajas
Secretary Executive, Donna Reyes
Secretary Executive, Kathleen Webster
Secretary Executive, Barbara Steinhauser
Secretary Executive, Kelly Ambrose
Secretary Department Medical, Heather Lawrence
Secretary Executive, Elayne Turner
Secretary Executive, Evelyn Satele
Secretary Admin, Carmencita De Jesus
Secretary Admin, Carol Fraser
Secretary Department Medical, Deborah Ruman
Unit Secretary, Gabrielle Ray
Secretary Executive, Jeanne Picard
Unit Secretary, Mary Fernandez
Secretary, Elizabeth Munoz
Treas, Darrel Brownell
Secretary, Suzanne Paolella

LOCATIONS

HQ: LONG BEACH MEDICAL CENTER
2801 ATLANTIC AVE FL 2, LONG BEACH, CA 908061701
Phone: 562 933-2000
Web: WWW.MEMORIALCARE.ORG

PRODUCTS/OPERATIONS

Selected Institutes and Centers
Certified Comprehensive Stroke Center
Long Beach Adult & Pediatric Sleep Center
MemorialCare Breast Center at Long Beach Medical Center
MemorialCare Heart & Vascular Institute
MemorialCare Imaging Center
MemorialCare Joint Replacement Center
MemorialCare Rehabilitation Institute
MemorialCare Todd Cancer Institute
Spine Center at Long Beach Memorial
Trauma Center at Long Beach Medical Center

Selected Services
Blood Donation Center
Diabetes Care
Digestive Care
Emergency Department
Gynecological Care at Long Beach Medical Center
Lung & Respiratory Care
Minimally Invasive Surgery at Long Beach Memorial
Palliative Care Program at Long Beach Medical Center
Pharmacy at Long Beach Medical Center
Robotic-Assisted Surgery at Long Beach Memorial
Surgical Care
Wound Healing & Hyperbaric Medicine at Long Beach Medical Center

COMPETITORS

Adventist Health System West
Aptium Oncology
Brotman Medical Center
Cedars-Sinai Medical Center
Dignity Health
Good Samaritan Hospital (Los Angeles)
HCA
Hoag Memorial Hospital
Hollywood Presbyterian Medical Center
Methodist Hospital of Southern California
Newhall Memorial Hospital
Pasadena Hospital Association
Providence Health System Southern California
Sutter Health
Tenet Healthcare
Torrance Memorial Medical Center
Trinity Health (Novi)
Western Medical Center - Santa Ana

HISTORICAL FINANCIALS

Company Type: Private

Income Statement — FYE: June 30

	REVENUE ($ mil.)	NET INCOME ($ mil.)	NET PROFIT MARGIN	EMPLOYEES
06/18	633	63	10.1%	6,000
06/16	618	88	14.4%	—
06/15	624	93	15.0%	—
06/11	1,083	63	5.9%	—
Annual Growth	(7.4%)	0.1%	—	—

2018 Year-End Financials

Return on assets: 4.8%
Return on equity: 5.3%
Current ratio: 11.70
Cash ($ mil.): —

LONG ISLAND JEWISH MEDICAL CENTER

Long Island Jewish Medical Center serves the western edge of Long Island and the eastern edge of the greater metropolitan New York area. The medical center campus includes Long Island Jewish Hospital a general acute care hospital; Cohen Children's Medical Center of New York Hospital which provides a full range of pediatric care services; and The Zucker Hillside Hospital a psychiatric hospital for patients of all ages. The medical center's staff includes 1200 physicians. Long Island Jewish Medical Center is the primary clinical and medical training facility of Northwell Health.

Operations

The Long Island Jewish Medical Center's main activities are centered at the Long Island Jewish Hospital which provides emergency diagnostic surgical inpatient and outpatient services. The hospital has centers for cancer treatment cardiac surgery and women's health as well as units specializing in hearing loss stroke recovery sleep disorders and hemophilia treatment. As an affiliate of Hofstra University the Long Island Jewish Hospital also provides graduate medical education programs.

Geographic Reach

Long Island Jewish Medical Center is located on a 48-acre campus on the border of New York's Queens and Nassau counties about 15 miles east of Manhattan.

EXECUTIVES

Medical Records Director, Patricia Hennelly

LOCATIONS

HQ: LONG ISLAND JEWISH MEDICAL CENTER
27005 76TH AVE, NEW HYDE PARK, NY 110401496
Phone: 516 465-2600
Web: WWW.LIJED.COM

PRODUCTS/OPERATIONS

Selected Facilities

Long Island Jewish Hospital (490 beds)
The Steven and Alexandra Cohen Children's Medical Center (160 beds)
The Zucker Hillside Hospital (240 beds)

Selected Services

Anesthesiology
Cardiac Services
Center for Maternal-Fetal Health
Dental Medicine
Emergency Medicine
Medicine
Neurosciences
Obstetrics
Ophthalmology
Orthopaedic Surgery
Otolaryngology
Pathology
Radiation Oncology
Radiology
Rehabilitation
Surgery
Thoracic Surgery
Urogynecology
Urology: The Arthur Smith Insitute for Urology

COMPETITORS

Catholic Health Services of Long Island
Mercy Medical Center (NY)
North Shore University Hospital
NuHealth
St. Francis Hospital Roslyn
Winthrop-University Hospital

HISTORICAL FINANCIALS

Company Type: Private

Income Statement — FYE: December 31

	REVENUE ($ mil.)	NET INCOME ($ mil.)	NET PROFIT MARGIN	EMPLOYEES
12/18	2,448	56	2.3%	1,214
12/17	2,222	154	6.9%	—
12/16	2,093	162	7.8%	—
12/15	1,524	44	2.9%	—
Annual Growth	17.1%	7.6%	—	—

2018 Year-End Financials

Return on assets: 2.0%
Return on equity: 8.4%
Current ratio: 2.00
Cash ($ mil.): 1

LONG ISLAND POWER AUTHORITY

The long and short of it is that Long Island Power Authority (LIPA) owns the electric transmission and distribution system on Long Island that delivers power to more than 1.1 million retail customers. The company's network which is managed and operated by the National Grid USA consists of nearly 14000 miles of overhead and underground lines. LIPA offers energy conservation products and services as well as incentive programs to encourage customers to purchase energy from "green" (environmentally friendly) power generation sources. LIPA is a municipally owned not-for-profit utility company.

EXECUTIVES

Ceo, Thomas Falcone
Gen Counsel-Sec*, Lynda Nicolino
V Pres-Envrnm Affrs*, Michael Deering
V Pres-Cfo*, Herbert L Hogue
V Pres*, Kenneth Kane
Procurement Director, Maria Gomes
Manager Customer Operations Ov, Timothy Lederer
Enterise Risk Manager, Jessica Swenson
Auditors: KPMG LLP NEW YORK NEW YORK

LOCATIONS

HQ: LONG ISLAND POWER AUTHORITY
333 EARLE OVINGTON BLVD # 403, UNIONDALE, NY 115533606
Phone: 516 222-7700
Web: WWW.LIPOWER.ORG

PRODUCTS/OPERATIONS

Energy Conservation Products and Services

Commercial energy analysis
Construction and renovation incentives
Energy Star labeled homes program
Geothermal rebates
HVAC upgrades
Lighting and appliance solutions
Peak demand reduction programs
Residential energy affordability program
Residential energy audit
Solar Pioneer program
Wind energy development initiatives

COMPETITORS

Avangrid
CH Energy
Con Edison
New York Power Authority

HISTORICAL FINANCIALS

Company Type: Private

Income Statement — FYE: December 31

	REVENUE ($ mil.)	NET INCOME ($ mil.)	NET PROFIT MARGIN	EMPLOYEES
12/19	3,516	24	0.7%	100
12/18	3,576	22	0.6%	—
12/16	3,399	(26)	—	—
12/09	3,312	40	1.2%	—
Annual Growth	0.6%	(5.1%)	—	—

2019 Year-End Financials

Return on assets: 0.2%
Return on equity: 4.6%
Current ratio: 1.90
Cash ($ mil.): 166

LOS ANGELES COUNTY OFFICE OF EDUCATION

EXECUTIVES

Ceo, Rudell S Freer
Pres*, Rebecca J Turrentine
V Pres*, Katie Braude
E-Business Point of Contact, Roberta Gerarde
Executive Officer, Ronald Reynolds
Coordinator, Matthew Jaffke
Consultant, Will Santos
Executive Assistant, Estela Marroquin
Director, Dotti Ysais
Secretary, Christine Cabrera
Faculty, Lucy Domingo
Auditors: VAVRINEK TRINE DAY & CO LL

LOCATIONS

HQ: LOS ANGELES COUNTY OFFICE OF EDUCATION
9300 IMPERIAL HWY, DOWNEY, CA 902422813
Phone: 562 922-6111
Web: WWW.BTPLACOE.COM

HISTORICAL FINANCIALS

Company Type: Private

Income Statement — FYE: June 30

	REVENUE ($ mil.)	NET INCOME ($ mil.)	NET PROFIT MARGIN	EMPLOYEES
06/19	621	38	6.2%	4,000
06/18	657	22	3.4%	—
06/17	646	17	2.6%	—
06/16	661	7	1.2%	—
Annual Growth	(2.1%)	71.2%	—	—

LOS ANGELES DEPARTMENT OF WATER AND POWER

The Los Angeles Department of Water and Power (LADWP) keeps the movie cameras running and the swimming pools full. The largest municipally owned utility in the US LADWP provides electricity to approximately 1.4 million residential and business customers and water to some 681000 customers. The company has net dependable capacity of about 8010 MW from a diverse mix of energy resources; it also buys and sells wholesale power. As a revenue-producing proprietary department the LADWP transfers a portion of its annual estimated electric revenues to the City of Los Angeles general fund.

Operations

LADWP's operations are financed solely by the sale of water and electric services. The department has about 125 tanks and reservoirs ranging in size from 10000 to 60 billion gallons and a storage capacity of approximately 323820 acre feet. Nine aqueduct reservoirs provide some 95% of the Water system's storage capacity while major and minor distribution reservoirs and tanks provide the remaining nearly 5%. It also has about 85 pump stations a distribution main of around 7335 miles of pipe.

The company has about 35 generation plants with some 1.6 MW of city-owned energy storage approximately 21.5 MW of utility-scale battery energy storage and some 1244 MW of pumped hydro storage. About 35% of power resources come from renewable energy over 25% from natural gas about 25% from nuclear around 20% from coal and nearly 5% from large hydroelectric.

Geographic Reach

The company is based in Los Angeles California.

Sales and Marketing

The company delivers reliable safe water and electricity to some 4 million residents and businesses in Los Angeles. LADWP also provides its around 681000 water customers and some 1.4 million electric customers with quality service at competitive prices.

Financial Performance

LADWP's operations are entirely financed by the sale of water and electric services. For fiscal 2020 the multi-utility transferred $230 million of its annual electric revenues to the City of Los Angeles general fund. Operating revenue decreased $264 million mainly due to a decrease of $203 million in total from retail customers a $50 million decrease in wholesale and other revenue and a $9.7 million increase of uncollectable accounts.

LADWP's operating revenue from its Water System in fiscal 2020 increased by $22 million or 2% from fiscal year 2019 primarily due to increase in pass-through rates as a result of higher capital expenditures and operating and maintenance expenses for Water Quality projects.

Strategy

LADWP continues to provide the city with reliable water and power service in a cost effective and environmentally responsible manner. In late 2020 LADWP teamed up with the California Air Resources Board (CARB) to offer the California Clean Fuel Reward (CCFR) a point-of-sale price reduction of up to $1500 for the purchase or lease of any eligible new battery electric or plug-in hybrid vehicle from a participating automotive retailer. In addition to accessing the CCFR LADWP residential customers could apply for EV incentives for used EVs and charging stations through the Department's "Charge Up L.A." rebate program.

LADWP also offered a new energy management program that allowed customers to save energy and support a cleaner more reliable power grid by enrolling their smart thermostats. LADWP Power Savers is the energy management program for residential and small business electric customers to help lower and manage their energy costs while reducing strain on the power grid during periods of high energy demand. At the same time the program supports LADWP's Clean Grid LA initiative by providing a clean energy alternative to using natural gas "peaker" plants to maintain reliability when energy use spikes.

Company Background

LADWP was founded in 1902.

EXECUTIVES

Chief Administrative Officer, David H. Wiggs
Senior Assistant General Manager Power System, David H. (Dave) Wright
General Manager, Marcie L. Edwards
Senior Assistant General Manager Water System, Martin L. Adams
Chief Sustainability And Economic Development Officer, Nancy Sutley
Cfo, Phil Leiber
Legal Secretary, Wendy Johnson
Fac Vice President, Kevin Brown
Vice President, Ann Unkcd Santilli
Legal Secretary, Patricia Stanard
Vice President, Brendon Owens
Legal Secretary, Yvette Furr
President Board Of Commissioners, Mel Levine
Vp Board Of Commissioners, William W. Funderburk
Secretary, Lisa Solomon
Secretary, Clariza Valdovinos
Secretary, Chris Reinhart
Secretary Legal, Caroletta Johnson
Auditors: KPMG LLP LOS ANGELES CA

LOCATIONS

HQ: LOS ANGELES DEPARTMENT OF WATER AND POWER
111 N HOPE ST, LOS ANGELES, CA 900122607
Phone: 213 367-1320
Web: WWW.LADWP.COM

COMPETITORS

AES
American States Water
Avista
California Water Service
Calpine
Duke Energy
Edison International
PG&E Corporation
Sacramento Municipal Utility
Sempra Energy
SouthWest Water

HISTORICAL FINANCIALS

Company Type: Private

Income Statement — FYE: June 30

	REVENUE ($ mil.)	NET INCOME ($ mil.)	NET PROFIT MARGIN	EMPLOYEES
06/17	1,118	140	12.6%	9,500
06/11	3,125	57	1.8%	—
06/10	812	67	8.3%	—
Annual Growth	4.7%	11.1%	—	—

2017 Year-End Financials

Return on assets: 1.4%
Return on equity: 4.5%
Current ratio: 1.20
Cash ($ mil.): 320

LOS ANGELES LOMOD CORPORATION

EXECUTIVES

Pres, Nancy Wesoff
Dir*, Lucelia Hooper
President*, Connie Loyola
Principal*, Ben Besley
Principal*, Erica Jacquez
Information Technology Manager, Robin Fox
Auditors: MACIAS GINI & O'CONNELL LLP L

LOCATIONS

HQ: LOS ANGELES LOMOD CORPORATION
2600 WILSHIRE BLVD, LOS ANGELES, CA 900573400
Phone: 213 252-2510
Web: WWW.LOMOD.ORG

HISTORICAL FINANCIALS

Company Type: Private

Income Statement — FYE: December 31

	REVENUE ($ mil.)	NET INCOME ($ mil.)	NET PROFIT MARGIN	EMPLOYEES
12/18	575	14	2.5%	44
12/17	534	12	2.4%	—
12/13	405	6	1.5%	—
12/09	356	5	1.4%	—
Annual Growth	5.5%	12.3%	—	—

2018 Year-End Financials

Return on assets: 34.9%
Return on equity: 35.2%
Current ratio: —
Cash ($ mil.): 37

LOUDOUN COUNTY PUBLIC SCHOOL DISTRICT

EXECUTIVES

Supt, Eric Williams
Coordinator, Mark Taylor
Assistant Superintendent, Mary V Kealy
Coordinator, Paige Neeley
Sergeant, Linda Cerniglia
Information Technology Manager, Andrew Leith
Auditors: CHERRY BEKAERT LLP TYSONS COR

LOCATIONS

HQ: LOUDOUN COUNTY PUBLIC SCHOOL DISTRICT
21000 EDUCATION CT, BROADLANDS, VA 201485526
Phone: 571 252-1000
Web: WWW.LCPS.ORG

HISTORICAL FINANCIALS

Company Type: Private

Income Statement — FYE: June 30

	REVENUE ($ mil.)	NET INCOME ($ mil.)	NET PROFIT MARGIN	EMPLOYEES
06/16	1,130	14	1.3%	6,900
06/15	1,080	19	1.8%	—
Annual Growth	4.7%	(28.6%)	—	—

LOUISIANA CHILDRENS MEDICAL CENTER, INC

EXECUTIVES

Pres-Ceo, Mary Perrin
Cfo*, Jenny Barnett-Sarpalius
Coordinator, Susan Wack MBA
Coordinator, Jennifer Turner
Chief Administrative Officer, Ayame Dinkler
Svphuman Resources, Chad Courrege
Vice President Marketing, Christine Albert
Vpsupply Chain Management, James Ludwig
Chief Legal Officer, Jody Martin
Vppopulation Health Network De, Meg Vitter
Director of Marketing, Nicole Marinello

LOCATIONS

HQ: LOUISIANA CHILDRENS MEDICAL CENTER, INC
200 HENRY CLAY AVE, NEW ORLEANS, LA 701185720
Phone: 504 896-9581
Web: WWW.LCMCHEALTH.ORG

HISTORICAL FINANCIALS

Company Type: Private

Income Statement — FYE: December 31

	REVENUE ($ mil.)	NET INCOME ($ mil.)	NET PROFIT MARGIN	EMPLOYEES
12/18	1,617	(34)	—	6,100
12/14	21	0	—	—
12/13*	926	285	30.8%	—
03/13	500	10	2.1%	—
Annual Growth	21.6%	—	—	—

*Fiscal year change

2018 Year-End Financials

Return on assets: (-1.3%)
Return on equity: (-2.3%)
Current ratio: 1.20
Cash ($ mil.): 104

LOUISVILLE-JEFFERSON COUNTY METRO GOVERNMENT

Louisville is so much more than bourbon baseball bats and horse races. The largest city in Kentucky Louisville counts about 600000 people in the urban area which has the same parameters as Jefferson County. Louisville is home to liquor company Brown-Forman; Hillerich & Bradsby maker of Louisville Slugger baseball bats; and Churchill Downs where the Kentucky Derby is held. In addition Louisville has a few Fortune 500 companies in the city - fast food operator YUM! Brands and health care companies Humana and Kindred.

EXECUTIVES

Secretary, Cecli M Bandy
Auditors: CROWE HORWATH LLP LOUISVILLE

LOCATIONS

HQ: LOUISVILLE-JEFFERSON COUNTY METRO GOVERNMENT
527 W JEFFERSON ST # 400, LOUISVILLE, KY 402022814
Phone: 502 574-2003
Web: WWW.JEFFERSONCOUNTYCLERK.ORG

HISTORICAL FINANCIALS

Company Type: Private

Income Statement — FYE: June 30

	REVENUE ($ mil.)	NET INCOME ($ mil.)	NET PROFIT MARGIN	EMPLOYEES
06/19	873	(38)	—	6,500
06/18	825	14	1.8%	—
06/17	797	11	1.5%	—
06/16	780	43	5.5%	—
Annual Growth	3.8%	—	—	—

2019 Year-End Financials

Return on assets: (-0.5%)
Return on equity: (-1.7%)
Current ratio: —
Cash ($ mil.): 308

LOWER COLORADO RIVER AUTHORITY

The stars at night may be big and bright but about 1.9 million people deep in the heart of Texas still need electricity from the Lower Colorado River Authority (LCRA). Serving more than 75 counties along the lower Colorado River between Central Texas and the Gulf of Mexico the not-for profit state-run entity supplies wholesale electricity to more than 30 retail utilities (primarily municipalities and cooperatives). It operates three fossil-fuel powered plants and six hydroelectric dams that give it a production capacity of about 3330 megawatts; it also purchases electricity from Texas wind farms. The LCRA supply for more than 1.4 million people and managing floodwaters that otherwise could devastate Austin and other communities.

Operations

The LCRA has pursued two complementary goals – providing reliable low-cost utility and public services and ensuring the protection of the area's natural resources. In the latter role the LCRA owns or operates more than 40 public recreation areas comprising more than 11000 acres; it also monitors the water quality and levels of the lakes formed by its dams.

Geographic Reach

The company was based Austin Texas.

Sales and Marketing

The company offers business opportunities Land development and Land parks concessionaires

Strategy

In 2020 The Lower Colorado River Authority has completed a nearly two-year project to replace each of the floodgates at Tom Miller Dam in Austin with new custom-made floodgates that meet today's engineering standards. The $10.8 million projects continue LCRA's long-standing commitment to public safety. Since the fiscal year 2010 LCRA has invested more than $110 million in capital projects along the Highland Lakes Lake Bastrop and Lake Fayette. LCRA plans to invest about $64 million more in dam rehabilitation and maintenance over the next five years.

Company Background

The company was founded in 1934 by State Legislature

EXECUTIVES

Deputy General Manager, Ross Phillips
General Manager And Ceo, Phil Wilson
Cfo, Brady Edwards
Manager Information Services And Strategy, Debbie Dunn-Krause
Chairman, Timothy T. Timmerman, age 59
Vice Chairman, John C. Dickerson
Auditors: BAKER TILLY VIRCHOW KRAUSE LLP

LOCATIONS

HQ: LOWER COLORADO RIVER AUTHORITY
3700 LAKE AUSTIN BLVD, AUSTIN, TX 787033504
Phone: 512 473-3200
Web: WWW.LCRA.ORG

PRODUCTS/OPERATIONS

Selected Subsidiaries and Affiliates

Fayette Power Project (coal-fired power generating units)
GenTex Power Corporation (power generation)
LCRA Transmission Services Corporation (power transmission services)

HISTORICAL FINANCIALS

Company Type: Private

Income Statement — FYE: June 30

	REVENUE ($ mil.)	NET INCOME ($ mil.)	NET PROFIT MARGIN	EMPLOYEES
06/15	1,021	15	1.5%	1,800
06/12	1,261	101	8.0%	—
06/11	1,185	48	4.1%	—
06/10	1,244	110	8.9%	—
Annual Growth	(3.9%)	(32.5%)	—	—

2015 Year-End Financials

Return on assets: 0.3%
Return on equity: 1.2%
Current ratio: 1.20
Cash ($ mil.): 182

LOYOLA UNIVERSITY MEDICAL CENTER

Auditors: PRICEWATERHOUSECOOPERS LLP WA

LOCATIONS

HQ: LOYOLA UNIVERSITY MEDICAL CENTER
2160 S 1ST AVE, MAYWOOD, IL 601533328
Phone: 708 216-9000
Web: WWW.LOYOLAHEALTH.ORG

HISTORICAL FINANCIALS

Company Type: Private

Income Statement — FYE: June 30

	REVENUE ($ mil.)	NET INCOME ($ mil.)	NET PROFIT MARGIN	EMPLOYEES
06/11	938	14	1.6%	4
06/10	917	8	0.9%	—
Annual Growth	2.3%	75.7%	—	—

2011 Year-End Financials

Return on assets: — Cash ($ mil.): 65
Return on equity: 1.6%
Current ratio: 0.30

LOYOLA UNIVERSITY OF CHICAGO INC

Loyola University is a Jesuit Catholic university with a reach that extends far beyond the Windy City. In addition to its three Chicago-area campuses the university also maintains an undergraduate campus in Italy and a study center in Beijing China. Loyola University's nearly 14765 students can choose from more than 80 undergraduate nearly 100 master's a dozen doctoral and more than 140 graduate professional and certificate programs. With nearly 1390 full-time faculty and staff members the not-for-profit school has a 15:1 student-teacher ratio. Notable alumni include actor Bob Newhart and writer Sandra Cisneros. Established in 1870 by a group of Jesuit priests the university turned its medical center into a separate subsidiary in 1995.

Operations

The university's undergraduate offers major and minor programs including accounting advertising and public relations biochemistry criminal justice and criminology economics film and digital media and theology among others. It also offers graduate and professional education such as arts and sciences biomedical sciences & medicine business continuing and professional studies (adult) education law nursing pastoral studies and social work.

Undergraduate students work with advisors in Academic Advising. Graduate students are advised differently depending on their school and program. These schools include The Graduate School Quinlan School of Business Institute of Pastoral Studies Marcella Niehoff School of Nursing School of Continuing and Professional Studies School of Education and School of Social Work.

Geographic Reach

Headquartered in Illinois Loyola University three Chicago campuses include Lake Shore Water Tower and Health Sciences as well as the John Felice Rome Center in Italy. It is home to a dozen schools and colleges that include arts and sciences business administration communication education graduate studies law medicine nursing continuing and professional studies and social work.

Loyola also features course locations in Beijing China and Saigon-Ho Chi Minh City Vietnam.

Sales and Marketing

Loyola University uses social media channels such as Facebook Twitter and YouTube to connect with the students faculty staff and Alumni.

Strategy

The Loyola University Chicago created Plan 2020. Plan 2020 is a framework to focus its energies on improving the quality of education so its students are prepared to be agents of change affecting their families careers and communities.

Plan 2020 has four institutional priorities: student access and success faculty development programs for societal needs and local and global partnerships.

For the first institutional priority strategies include recruitment of and retaining underserved students and making programs for student success.

For the second priority recruitment retaining and development of faculty for social justice will be of focus.

For the third priority strategies include collaboration for the reduction of health disparities the advancement of STEM and sustainability and addressing injustice and violence.

Lastly to promote local and global partnerships the university will develop community outreach programs and expand global engagement.

Company Background

Founded in 1870 by Arnold Damen S.J. as St. Ignatius College the college was originally located at West Twelfth Street next to Holy Family Church the current location of St. Ignatius College Prep. In 1909 St. Ignatius College was re-chartered by the State of Illinois as Loyola University and in 1922 the University moved operations from West Twelfth Street to Sheridan and Devon in the Rogers Park neighborhood. College classes had been offered at the Rogers Park campus since 1912 and Loyola Academy opened on the property in 1909.

EXECUTIVES

Svp Administrative Services And Chief Hr Officer, Thomas Kelly
Vice President Information Services And Cio, Susan Malisch
President And Ceo, Michael J. Garanzini
Provost, John Pelissero
Government Relations, Philip Hale
Vice President Spence And Elster, Nanette Elster
Vice President Of Professional Development, Lisa Marks
Senior Vice President For Academic Affairs, Larry Braskamp
Chairman, Robert L. Parkinson
Vice Chairman, Mary Ann Zollmann
Senior Vice President Finance Of Cfo And Treasurer, William Laird
Treasurer, Susan Bodin
Board Member, Carolyn Saari
Secretary, Carol Grimm
Auditors: DELOITTE & TOUCHE LLP CHICAG

LOCATIONS

HQ: LOYOLA UNIVERSITY OF CHICAGO INC
1032 W SHERIDAN RD, CHICAGO, IL 606601537
Phone: 773 274-3000
Web: WWW.LUC.EDU

PRODUCTS/OPERATIONS

Selected Schools & Colleges

College of Arts and Sciences
Graduate School of Business
Institute of Pastoral Studies
Marcella Niehoff School of Nursing
Quinlan School of Business
School of Communication
School of Continuing and Professional Studies
School of Education
School of Law
School of Social Work
Stritch School of Medicine
The Graduate School

HISTORICAL FINANCIALS

Company Type: Private

Income Statement — FYE: June 30

	REVENUE ($ mil.)	NET INCOME ($ mil.)	NET PROFIT MARGIN	EMPLOYEES
06/20	611	23	3.8%	10,500
06/19	614	78	12.8%	—
06/18	594	109	18.4%	—
06/17	582	109	18.7%	—
Annual Growth	1.6%	(40.2%)	—	—

2020 Year-End Financials

Return on assets: 1.0% Cash ($ mil.): 77
Return on equity: 1.4%
Current ratio: —

LUCILE SALTER PACKARD CHILDREN'S HOSPITAL AT STANFORD

EXECUTIVES

Pres-Ceo, Christopher Dawes
Cfo*, Timothy W Carmack
Coordinator, Arlene Sheehan
Coordinator, Sonja Avery
Chief Information Security Off, Auston Davis
Coordinator, Carrie Johnson
Coordinator, Erin Murphy
Coordinator, Jennifer Cctc
Occupational Specia, Quiara Smith
Senior Human Resources General, Alexis Silver
Is Applications Manager, Andrea Aurand
Auditors: PRICEWATERHOUSECOOPERS LLP BO

LOCATIONS

HQ: LUCILE SALTER PACKARD CHILDREN'S HOSPITAL AT STANFORD
725 WELCH RD, PALO ALTO, CA 943041601
Phone: 650 497-8000
Web: WWW.STANFORDCHILDRENS.ORG

HISTORICAL FINANCIALS

Company Type: Private

Income Statement — FYE: August 31

	REVENUE ($ mil.)	NET INCOME ($ mil.)	NET PROFIT MARGIN	EMPLOYEES
08/19	1,959	99	5.1%	1,100
08/18	1,637	22	1.4%	—
08/17	1,486	227	15.3%	—
08/16	1,402	157	11.2%	—
Annual Growth	11.8%	(14.2%)	—	—

2019 Year-End Financials

Return on assets: 2.6% Cash ($ mil.): 276
Return on equity: 3.9%
Current ratio: 2.00

LUKOIL PAN AMERICAS, LLC

EXECUTIVES

Ceo, Timothy Bullock
Managing Director*, Simon Fenner
Manager, Alexandra Krylova
Controller Risk Manager, Paul Carroll

LOCATIONS

HQ: LUKOIL PAN AMERICAS, LLC
1095 AVEUE OF THE AMRCAS, NEW YORK, NY 100366797
Phone: 646 562-3600
Web: WWW.LITASCO.COM

HISTORICAL FINANCIALS

Company Type: Private

Income Statement — FYE: December 31

	REVENUE ($ mil.)	NET INCOME ($ mil.)	NET PROFIT MARGIN	EMPLOYEES
12/08	4,745	5	0.1%	77
12/07	4,717	3	0.1%	—
12/06	3,021	23	0.8%	—
12/05	2,788	21	0.8%	—
Annual Growth	19.4%	(37.8%)	—	—

2008 Year-End Financials

Return on assets: — Cash ($ mil.): 1
Return on equity: 0.1%
Current ratio: 0.40

M. F. A. OIL COMPANY

Many farmers appreciate MFA Oil. The energy cooperative controlled by its 40000 farmer-members produces fuel and lubrication products and manages bulk petroleum and propane plants in the Central and Western US. Operating 140 propane plants the company sells more propane for farm use and home heating than any other company in Missouri. It also operates nearly 100 oil and lubricant bulk plants and serves customers in Arkansas Iowa Kansas and Oklahoma. Additionally the company operates 76 convenience stores under the Break Time brand (in Arkansas and Missouri) more than 160 Petro-Card 24 fueling locations and owns 10 Jiffy Lube and a dozen Big O Tire franchises.

Geographic Reach

MFA Oil serves customers in Arkansas Colorado Kansas Kentucky Indiana Iowa Missouri Nebraska Oklahoma Virginia and Wyoming.

Strategy

While not a pure vertically integrated enterprise over time the cooperative has developed multiple complementary business lines to enable it to respond to a wide range of its members' fuel transportation and food service needs. In this tradition in 2011 MFA Oil teamed up with biofuel developer Aloterra Energy to form MFA Oil Biomass LLC. The partnership aims to help farmers to produce a renewable energy crop that can be used as biomass for an alternative cleaner burning energy supply for use in power generation plants as well as a liquid fuel. In 2011 about 250 farmers had signed letters of intent to grow miscanthus (a perennial grass) on more than 21000 acres as part of this initiative.

Mergers and Acquisitions

Expanding its geographic network in 2013 MFA Oil acquired Kansas-based American Petroleum Marketers which distributes fuel to more than 60 Cenex branded sites along with unbranded fuel in six states.

Company Background

MFA Oil has grown well beyond its Missouri roots where it was founded by farmers in 1929. The company's first bulk plant was located at Wright City Missouri.

EXECUTIVES

Vice President Logistics, Larry Ehrman
Auditors: WILLIAMS-KEEPERS LLC COLUMBIA

LOCATIONS

HQ: M. F. A. OIL COMPANY
1 RAY YOUNG DR, COLUMBIA, MO 652013506
Phone: 573 442-0171
Web: WWW.MFAOIL.COM

COMPETITORS

Ag Processing Inc.
Green Brick Partners
Green Plains
Jordan Oil Company
Lykins
Shell Oil Products
Valero Energy
WilcoHess

HISTORICAL FINANCIALS

Company Type: Private

Income Statement — FYE: August 31

	REVENUE ($ mil.)	NET INCOME ($ mil.)	NET PROFIT MARGIN	EMPLOYEES
08/18	1,086	20	1.9%	1,500
08/17	900	8	0.9%	—
08/16	800	24	3.1%	—
08/15	1,045	48	4.6%	—
Annual Growth	1.3%	(24.7%)	—	—

2018 Year-End Financials

Return on assets: 4.7% Cash ($ mil.): 22
Return on equity: 6.5%
Current ratio: 2.30

MAGEE-WOMENS HOSPITAL OF UPMC

EXECUTIVES

Pres, Leslie C Davis
Chb*, William Pietragallo
Treas*, Peter Eisenbrandt
SEC*, Claire Williams
Oncology, Margaret V Ragni
Project Coordinator, Meredith Colaizzi
Information Specialist, Michele King
Director, Dan Pototo
Family Practitioner, Susan Hellier
Doctor, Jacob Larkin
Genetic Counselor, Maureen May

LOCATIONS

HQ: MAGEE-WOMENS HOSPITAL OF UPMC
300 HALKET ST, PITTSBURGH, PA 152133108
Phone: 412 641-1000
Web: WWW.UPMC.COM

HISTORICAL FINANCIALS

Company Type: Private

Income Statement — FYE: June 30

	REVENUE ($ mil.)	NET INCOME ($ mil.)	NET PROFIT MARGIN	EMPLOYEES
06/16	838	92	11.1%	2,300
06/15	823	62	7.6%	—
06/00	7	7	98.8%	—
Annual Growth	33.9%	16.8%	—	—

2016 Year-End Financials

Return on assets: 17.7% Cash ($ mil.): 1
Return on equity: 19.0%
Current ratio: 9.40

MAGELLAN PIPELINE COMPANY, L.P.

EXECUTIVES

Ptnr-Pres-Ceo, Don Wellendorf
Ptnr-V Pres-Tres,, Jeff Holman
Analyst, Tj Simmons
Facility Maintenance Superviso, Kevan Heil
Senior Technician, Chris Sullivan
Tech, Dan Sotelo
Analyst Senior, Glen Jackson
Area Supervisor, James Bacon
Technician Senior, Todd Huls
Real Estate Representative, Dustin Howerton
Corrosion Technician II, Jeff Saehler

LOCATIONS

HQ: MAGELLAN PIPELINE COMPANY, L.P.
1 WILLIAMS CTR, TULSA, OK 741720140
Phone: 918 574-7000
Web: WWW.MAGELLANLP.COM

HISTORICAL FINANCIALS

Company Type: Private

Income Statement — FYE: December 31

	REVENUE ($ mil.)	NET INCOME ($ mil.)	NET PROFIT MARGIN	EMPLOYEES
12/17	828	396	47.9%	435
12/16	911	339	37.2%	—
Annual Growth	(9.1%)	17.0%	—	—

2017 Year-End Financials

Return on assets: 18.5% Cash ($ mil.): 15
Return on equity: 20.9%
Current ratio: 0.60

MAIMONIDES MEDICAL CENTER

Maimonides Medical Center a not-for-profit hospital offers emergency medicine surgical procedures psychiatric treatment and other traditional hospital services to patients in Brooklyn New York. It has more than 710 beds and more than 70 subspecialty treatment programs for a range of conditions including cancer cardiac stroke neurological pediatric and women's health ailments. It also operates outpatient family health and specialty clinics. Maimonides Medical Center is an independent teaching hospital that serves as a training facility for SUNY-Brooklyn St. George's University and other schools.

Financial Performance

In fiscal 2015 revenue remained flat at $1.1 billion compared to 2014. Although net patient service revenue rose 1% the hospital saw a 23% decline in "other" revenue. Net income fell 78% to

$11 million that year as expenses rose; the center also reported accrued benefits liabilities to be recognized in future periods.

Despite the decline in profits operating cash flow increased 203% to $33 million primarily due to a change in receivables for patient fare.

Strategy

Maimonides Medical Center works to keep its utilization rates up (the number of patients it sees) and make itself attractive to doctors by making capital investments in its facilities and technology systems on a regular basis. In 2015 it established a partnership with North Shore-LIJ Health System (now Northwell) through which the systems will share services infrastructure and expertise; Northshore will also provide Maimonides with funding.

The hospital uses a fully-implemented electronic health record (EHR) system that includes a computerized physician order entry system (CPOE) that reduces prescription errors and a picture archival communications system (PACS) to store digital radiology images. The use of such technology is becoming increasingly tied to how the government reimburses hospitals for the services they provide especially in the new health care reform laws.

Company Background

Maimonides Medical Center traces its roots to the New Utrecht Dispensary which opened in 1911. The medical center later merged with Beth Moses and United Israel Zion hospitals in 1947. It is named after 12th-century philosopher Rabbi Moshe Ben Maimon.

EXECUTIVES

Evp And Cfo, Robert Naldi
Vp Management Information Systems And Cio, Walter J. Fahey
Executive Vice President Clinical Affairs & Affiliations, David I. Cohen
Evp And Coo, Dominick Stanzione
Chairman, Kenneth Gibbs
Senior Vice President, Karen Nelson
Senior Vice President, Thomas Doherty
Medical Director, Elie Hamaoui
Vice President, Elaine Gunn
Assistant Vice President Heart And Vascular Center, Lorraine Carroll
Avp Mis, Nancy Daurio
Assistant Vice President, William Howe
Vice President Physician Enterprise, Gail Simhon
Pharmacy Manager, Anne Monarch
Assistant Vice President Human Resources, Paul Stuart
Avp Health Information Services, Silviya Semenskaya
Vice President For Legal Affairs, Anthony Mancuso
Vice President Of Research And Development, Rich Casazza
Director Of Hospitalist Service, Ping Zhou
Director Of Pharmacy And Compliance, Neal Neumann
Medical Director, Robert Adler
Chairman, Eugene J. Keilin
Secretary, Rosalyn Levin
Secretary, Larisa Zmoyro
Vice Chair, Jasminka Balderacchi
Medical Secretary, Elizabeth Bowen
Secretary, Doris Zablidowsky

LOCATIONS

HQ: MAIMONIDES MEDICAL CENTER
4802 10TH AVE, BROOKLYN, NY 112192916
Phone: 718 581-0598
Web: WWW.MAIMONIDESMED.ORG

PRODUCTS/OPERATIONS

2014 Sales

	$ mil.	% of total
Net patient revenue less provision for bad debts	1,001	95
Net assets released from restrictions	0	-
Other revenue	48	5
Total	**1,051**	**100**

Selected Services

Adult Primary Care
Ambulatory Health Services
Bay Parkway Multi-Specialty
Manfredi Family Health Center
Newkirk Family Health Center
Outpatient Eye Clinic
Pediatric Primary Care
Primary Health Services
Sheepshead Bay
Women's Primary Care Services

COMPETITORS

Beth Israel Medical Center
Bronx-Lebanon Hospital
Brookdale University Hospital
Brooklyn Hospital Center
Catholic Healthcare System
Continuum Health Partners
Jamaica Hospital Medical Center
Kingsbrook Jewish Medical Center
Long Island College Hospital
Lutheran HealthCare
Montefiore Medical
New York City Health and Hospitals
New York Methodist Hospital
NewYork-Presbyterian Hospital
North Shore University Hospital
SUNY Downstate
Staten Island University Hospital
Wyckoff Heights Medical Center

HISTORICAL FINANCIALS

Company Type: Private

Income Statement — FYE: December 31

	REVENUE ($ mil.)	NET INCOME ($ mil.)	NET PROFIT MARGIN	EMPLOYEES
12/17	958	19	2.0%	6,382
12/16	940	20	2.2%	—
12/15	890	(2)	—	—
12/14	884	10	1.2%	—
Annual Growth	2.7%	23.2%	—	—

2017 Year-End Financials

Return on assets: 1.5%
Return on equity: 7.1%
Current ratio: 1.50
Cash ($ mil.): 16

MAIN LINE HEALTH SYSTEM

Main Line Health is a not-for-profit network that includes four acute care hospitals a drug and alcohol recovery treatment center home care outpatient centers a physician network and a biomedical research organization all serving the greater Philadelphia area. Its hospitals — Lankenau Medical Center Bryn Mawr Hospital Paoli Hospital and Riddle Hospital — are accredited as primary stroke care centers comprehensive breast centers and chest pain centers. Other specialties include diabetes and endocrinology orthopedics and cardiovascular care. Bryn Mawr Hospital offers residency programs in family practice radiology and surgical podiatry. Main Line Health was founded in 1985.

EXECUTIVES

Pres-Ceo, Jack Lynch
Sr V Pres*, Thomas Mendicino
Hris Analyst, Michelle Massaro
Event Marketing Specialist, Karen Rawlings

LOCATIONS

HQ: MAIN LINE HEALTH SYSTEM
240 N RADNOR CHESTER RD, RADNOR, PA 190875170
Phone: 610 225-6200
Web: WWW.MAINLINEHEALTH.ORG

COMPETITORS

Abington Memorial Hospital
Albert Einstein Healthcare Network
Crozer-Keystone Health System
LVHN
Lancaster General
Memorial Hospital (PA)
Mercy Health System
North Philadelphia Health System
TUHS
University of Pennsylvania Health System
Virtua Health

HISTORICAL FINANCIALS

Company Type: Private

Income Statement — FYE: June 30

	REVENUE ($ mil.)	NET INCOME ($ mil.)	NET PROFIT MARGIN	EMPLOYEES
06/20	1,781	(17)	—	17,485
06/19	1,769	21	1.2%	—
06/18	1,742	267	15.4%	—
06/17	1,695	51	3.0%	—
Annual Growth	1.7%	—	—	—

2020 Year-End Financials

Return on assets: (-0.4%)
Return on equity: (-0.7%)
Current ratio: 1.90
Cash ($ mil.): 150

MAIN LINE HOSPITALS, INC.

Bryn Mawr Hospital a member of the Main Line not-for-profit health network is an acute care facility providing a variety of inpatient and outpatient services in the western suburbs of Philadelphia. With some 320 beds Bryn Mawr Hospital is recognized nationally for its orthopedic program. Founded in 1893 by Dr. George Gerhard the teaching hospital also provides cancer cardiac surgical pediatric reproductive health diagnostic imaging psychiatric bariatric and wound care services. The hospital also operates the Main Line Health Center outpatient facility (which includes a comprehensive breast center) in Newtown Square.

EXECUTIVES

Medical Director Of The Main Line Health Stroke Program, Gary Friday
Vice President Of Operations, Jim Paradis
Vice President Of Finance And Treasurer, Michael Bouongiono
Vice President Planning And Business Development, Joel Port
Owner President Vice President, Aaron Shapiro
Vp Clinical Prog Devel, Rebecca O'shea

LOCATIONS

HQ: MAIN LINE HOSPITALS, INC.
130 S BRYN MAWR AVE, BRYN MAWR, PA 190103121
Phone: 610 526-3000
Web: WWW.MAINLINEHEALTH.ORG

COMPETITORS

Abington Memorial Hospital
Albert Einstein Healthcare Network
Christiana Care
Crozer-Keystone Health System
Doylestown Hospital
Memorial Hospital (PA)
Moses Taylor Hospital
North Philadelphia Health System
Tenet Healthcare
University of Pennsylvania Health System
Virtua Memorial

HISTORICAL FINANCIALS

Company Type: Private

Income Statement — FYE: June 30

	REVENUE ($ mil.)	NET INCOME ($ mil.)	NET PROFIT MARGIN	EMPLOYEES
06/20	1,345	11	0.8%	5,840
06/19	1,323	58	4.4%	—
06/18	1,193	100	8.4%	—
06/16	327	36	11.0%	—
Annual Growth	42.4%	(25.5%)	—	—

2020 Year-End Financials

Return on assets: 0.3%
Return on equity: 0.4%
Current ratio: 3.00
Cash ($ mil.): 115

MAINE MEDICAL CENTER

EXECUTIVES

Manager, Paul Ranucci
Psychiatrist, Edward Pontius
Occupational Specia, Katie Hazel

LOCATIONS

HQ: MAINE MEDICAL CENTER
576 SAINT JOHN ST, PORTLAND, ME 041022710
Phone: 207 780-0020
Web: WWW.MAINEHEALTH.ORG

HISTORICAL FINANCIALS

Company Type: Private

Income Statement — FYE: September 30

	REVENUE ($ mil.)	NET INCOME ($ mil.)	NET PROFIT MARGIN	EMPLOYEES
09/19	1,622	74	4.6%	11
09/18	1,564	164	10.5%	—
Annual Growth	3.7%	(55.0%)	—	—

2019 Year-End Financials

Return on assets: 6.0%
Return on equity: 24.8%
Current ratio: 1.70
Cash ($ mil.): 3

MAINEHEALTH

Maine Medical Center (MMC) makes healing happen for the residents of northern New England. Part of MaineHealth the not-for-profit medical center consists of a tertiary care community hospital The Barbara Bush Children's Hospital and outpatient clinics. Specialty services include cancer care geriatrics emergency medicine cardiovascular care rehabilitation neurology orthopedics and women's health. Through its partnership with the Tufts University School of Medicine the 640-bed teaching hospital provides a variety of medical education and training programs. MMC also conducts research through the Maine Medical Center Research Institute. The medical center was founded in 1874 with 40 beds.

Operations

MMC boasts a large ever-expanding outpatient segment that provides day surgery cardiac catheterization laboratory services and rehabilitation services. It also operates about three dozen outpatient clinics. MMC provides preventive and consultation services including the MMC Diabetes Center the AIDS Consultation Service and the Center for Lipids and Cardiovascular Health.

MMC is expanding the surgical facilities at its main campus. Due for completion in 2015 the medical center embarked on a $40-million expansion plan that will add five modern operating rooms including a cardiac hybrid operating room and 20 perioperative spaces for patient prep and recovery.

The medical center is one of the largest employers in its service territory with a workforce of some 6500. Its Maine Medical Partners physician organization maintains about 175 doctors who provide care at some 30 primary and specialty care centers. MMC also provides more than 20% of charity care for uninsured or underinsured patients in the state.

Geographic Reach

Located in Portland the MMC serves the northern New England area.

Strategy

In keeping with its reputation of being technologically forward the hospital operates a Telestroke Network that provides area residents with around-the-clock access to MMC's neurology and ER physicians. The Telestroke Network is a form of telemedicine an increasingly popular way of expanding access to care by allowing patients to "visit" physicians either telephonically or via streaming web and video. MMC is also one of a growing number of teaching hospitals to use high-tech simulation rooms to train medical students.

To improve the quality of care MMC is enacting evidence-based medicine programs. Through such programs hospitals seek to lower medical expenses and improve patient outcomes through data exchange systems that allow physicians to review best practices in specific medical fields. The hospital is also looking to expand its research programs by partnering with other area medical R&D firms.

EXECUTIVES

Assistant Vice President Benefits, Keith Kolodgie
President And Ceo, Richard W. (Rich) Petersen
Senior Vice President Chief Information Officer, Barry Blumenfeld
Svp Planning And Marketing Maine Medical Center And Mainehealth, Mark A. Harris
Vp Medical And Academic Affairs; Chief Medical Officer And Academic Dean Tufts University School Of Medicine Medical School Program, Peter W. Bates
Evp And Coo, Jeffrey D. (Jeff) Sanders
President Medical Staff, M. Parker Roberts
President And A Principal Of Cbre|boulos Property Management, Morris Fisher
President Mainehealth, William L. Caron
Medical Director, Kate Zimmerman
Vice President Of Strategy And Business Development, Edward Farrell
Senior Vice President Of Finance, Lugene Inzana
Vice President Finance, Jeffrey Kirby
Senior Vice President, Maureen Van Benthuysen
Nursing Director, Deborah Bachand
Vice President Revenue Cycle, Chausse Paul
Medical Director Language:spanish Gender:male, Michael Eng
Pharmd Bcps Aq Maine Medical Center, Minkey Wungwattana
Associate Vice President Of Nursing, Kathleen Hale
Vice President, Eric Tweedie
Nursing Director, Marguerite Anderson
Medical Director, Tammi Schaeffer
Medical Director, Mark Fulton
Vice President Revenue Cycle, Paul Chausse
Vice President Global Information Technology, Belinda Broome
Vice President, Melissa Norton
Senior Vice President Fiscal, Coyne Cynthia
Chairman, Christopher W. Emmons
Secretary, Kay Mullen
Department Secretary, Andrea Fletcher
Secretary, Chris Motyl
Secretary, Kate Kennedy
Auditors: KPMG LLP BOSTON MA

LOCATIONS

HQ: MAINEHEALTH
22 BRAMHALL ST, PORTLAND, ME 041023134
Phone: 207 662-0111
Web: WWW.MMC.ORG

PRODUCTS/OPERATIONS

Selected Specialty Centers

Cancer Institute
Cardiovascular Institute
Emergency Medicine
Family Birth Center
Joint Replacement Center
Neuroscience Institute
The Barbara Bush Children's Hospital

COMPETITORS

Eastern Maine Healthcare Systems
Franklin Community Health Network
Maine Coast Memorial Hospital
MaineGeneral Health
Mercy Health System of Maine
St. Joseph Healthcare

HISTORICAL FINANCIALS

Company Type: Private

Income Statement — FYE: September 30

	REVENUE ($ mil.)	NET INCOME ($ mil.)	NET PROFIT MARGIN	EMPLOYEES
09/19	2,717	5	0.2%	2,000
09/18	2,523	205	8.2%	—
09/17	1,236	152	12.4%	—
09/16	1,126	3	0.3%	—
Annual Growth	34.1%	21.6%	—	—

2019 Year-End Financials

Return on assets: 0.2%
Return on equity: 0.3%
Current ratio: 4.00
Cash ($ mil.): 292

MAINEHEALTH SERVICES

MaineHealth provides health care to residents of central southern and western Maine. The health system's facilities include Maine Medical Center Spring Harbor Hospital and Stephens Memorial Hospital (part of Western Maine Health). MaineHealth also operates long-term care facilities a home health care service physician practices medical laboratories and other health care service units. The company's Synernet subsidiary provides administrative and group purchasing services for MaineHealth's members and other health care organizations.

EXECUTIVES

Senior Vice President Payor Relations, Colin Mchugh
Executive Vice President And Treasurer, Albert Swallow
Sr. Vice Pres. General Counsel, Robert Frank
Vice President Human Resources, Andrew Forbes
Vice President Finance, Daniel Forgues
Vice President For Operations, Michael J Ryan
Senior Vice President Clinical Services, Maureen Van Benthuysen
Vice President Human Relations, Susan Pelletier
Auditors: KPMG LLP BOSTON MASSACHUSETT

LOCATIONS

HQ: MAINEHEALTH SERVICES
110 FREE ST, PORTLAND, ME 041013576
Phone: 207 661-7010
Web: WWW.MAINEHEALTH.ORG

PRODUCTS/OPERATIONS

Members and Affiliates
HomeHealth Visiting Nurses of Southern Maine
Intellicare (joint venture)
LincolnHealth Miles Campus (aka Miles Health Care/Miles Memorial Hospital affiliate)
LincolnHealth St. Andrews Campus (aka St. Andrews Hospital affiliate)
MaineGeneral Health (affiliate)
Maine Medical Center
Maine Physician Hospital Organization (MPHO)
MidCoast Health Services (affiliate)
New England Rehabilitation Hospital (joint venture)
NorDx
PenBay Healthcare (affiliate)
St. Andrews Hospital & Healthcare Center
Southern Maine Medical Center (affiliate)
Spring Harbor Hospital
Stephens Memorial Hospital/Western Maine Health Care
St. Mary's Regional Medical Center (affiliate)
Synernet

COMPETITORS

Eastern Maine Healthcare Systems
Franklin Community Health Network
Maine Coast Memorial Hospital
MaineGeneral Health
Mercy Health System of Maine
St. Joseph Healthcare

HISTORICAL FINANCIALS

Company Type: Private

Income Statement — FYE: September 30

	REVENUE ($ mil.)	NET INCOME ($ mil.)	NET PROFIT MARGIN	EMPLOYEES
09/19	2,717	5	0.2%	7,000
09/08	23	(0)	—	—
09/99	493	30	6.2%	—
09/98	1,001	0	—	—
Annual Growth	4.9%	—	—	—

2019 Year-End Financials

Return on assets: 0.2%
Return on equity: 0.3%
Current ratio: 4.00
Cash ($ mil.): 292

MANAGEMENT & TRAINING CORPORATION

Management & Training Corporation (MTC) prepares prison inmates for re-entry into society. It provides a variety of academic vocational and social-skills training in rehabilitation-oriented private prisons. Its holistic education model offers programs to help inmates avoid substance abuse as they also boost their engagement in community service find work and increase their cognitive skills. As part of its services MTC operates more than 20 correctional facilities in eight states as well as international corrections in Australia and the UK. The company also operates Job Corps centers and provides healthcare-related services to correctional facilities.

Operations

MTC operates through four divisions: Correctional Education & Training MTC Medical and Economic & Social Development. Its correctional division operates facilities that house more than 31000 inmates. The Education & Training division trains more than 20400 students in a variety of fields including healthcare construction technology and business.

The company's MTC Medical unit provides medical dental and mental-health services to over 14000 detainees at a dozen facilities. The Economic & Social Development division provides workforce training to people worldwide. It has provided training to citizen in: Jordan China Pakistan Tunisia Iraq Haiti South Sudan Mongolia and the West Bank.

Geographic Reach

The company's main offices are located in Centerville Utah and has regional office in Texas and Washington DC. MTC operates correctional facility contracts in Arizona California Florida Idaho Ohio New Mexico Mississippi and Texas. It also operates two international correction in Rainsbrook Secure Training Centre (in the UK) and Parklea Correctional Centre in Australia.

Sales and Marketing

MTC clients including the Federal Bureau of Prisons Immigration & Customs Enforcement US Marshals Service and state departments of corrections. It also provided workforce training to USAID the World Bank the United Nations regional development banks and national governments.

Strategy

In 2020 MTC has been awarded a contract to be the technical assistance provider for a newly created Moroccan public-private partnership (PPP) called the Institute of the National Federation of Construction and Public Works (IFNBTP). The principal partner in IFNBTP is the Federation of Construction and Public Works a collective of Moroccan construction companies.

Company Background

MRC was founded in 1981.

EXECUTIVES

President, R. Scott Marquardt
Vice President Corrections Marketing, Mike Murphy
Vice President, Greg Niblett
Vice President Human Resources, Teresa Aramaki
Vice President Information Systems And Chief Information Officer, Richard Skeen
Vice President, Lowder Korey
Chairman, Robert Marquardt
Auditors: KPMG LLP SALT LAKE CITY UTAH

LOCATIONS

HQ: MANAGEMENT & TRAINING CORPORATION
500 N MARKET PLACE DR # 100, CENTERVILLE, UT 840141711
Phone: 801 693-2600
Web: WWW.MTCTRAINS.COM

PRODUCTS/OPERATIONS

Selected Services
Communicate through formal and informal channels
Develop custom training for students clients & offenders
Manage facilities
Provide community connections
Provide data solutions

COMPETITORS

Avalon Correctional Services
Community Education Centers
Conmed Healthcare
Corizon
Corrections Corporation of America
G4S
GEO Group
MHM Services
Res-Care
Wexford Health

HISTORICAL FINANCIALS

Company Type: Private

Income Statement — FYE: December 31

	REVENUE ($ mil.)	NET INCOME ($ mil.)	NET PROFIT MARGIN	EMPLOYEES
12/15	753	30	4.0%	9,500
12/13	735	50	6.9%	—
12/12	704	45	6.5%	—
Annual Growth	2.3%	(13.0%)	—	—

2015 Year-End Financials

Return on assets: 14.9%
Return on equity: 27.7%
Current ratio: 1.70
Cash ($ mil.): 10

MANAGEMENT-ILA MANAGED HEALTH CARE TRUST FUND

EXECUTIVES

MGT, Jason Cury
Accounting Director, Robin Csabon
Auditors: DESENA & COMPANY CPAS EAST HA

LOCATIONS

HQ: MANAGEMENT-ILA MANAGED HEALTH CARE TRUST FUND
111 BROADWAY FL 5, NEW YORK, NY 100061901
Phone: 212 766-5700
Web: WWW.MILAMHCTF.COM

HISTORICAL FINANCIALS

Company Type: Private

Income Statement FYE: December 31

	REVENUE ($ mil.)	NET INCOME ($ mil.)	NET PROFIT MARGIN	EMPLOYEES
12/17	675	64	9.6%	3
12/14	492	(39)	—	—
12/13	491	24	5.0%	—
Annual Growth	8.3%	27.3%	—	—

2017 Year-End Financials

Return on assets: 6.9%
Return on equity: 7.5%
Current ratio: 1.90
Cash ($ mil.): 28

MANN+HUMMEL FILTRATION TECHNOLOGY INTERMEDIATE HOLDINGS INC.

EXECUTIVES

Pres-Ceo, Keith A Wilson
Chb, James S McElya
Sr V Pres-Cfo-Treas, Steven P Klueg
CIO, Karl J Westrick
Sr V Pres Hr, Kay Teixeira
Sr Vpres-General Counsel-Sec, David E Sturgess
Auditors: DELOITTE & TOUCHE LLP CHARLOT

LOCATIONS

HQ: MANN+HUMMEL FILTRATION TECHNOLOGY INTERMEDIATE HOLDINGS INC.
1 WIX WAY, GASTONIA, NC 280546142
Phone: 704 869-3300
Web: WWW.WIXFILTERS.COM

HISTORICAL FINANCIALS

Company Type: Private

Income Statement FYE: December 31

	REVENUE ($ mil.)	NET INCOME ($ mil.)	NET PROFIT MARGIN	EMPLOYEES
12/15	899	(72)	—	5,581
12/14	1,396	82	5.9%	—
12/13	1,361	10	0.7%	—
12/12	1,453	(102)	—	—
Annual Growth	(14.8%)	—	—	—

2015 Year-End Financials

Return on assets: (-12.0%)
Return on equity: —
Current ratio: 0.90
Cash ($ mil.): 28

MAP INTERNATIONAL (INC.)

EXECUTIVES

Pres/Ceo, Steve Stirling
Int Pres-Ceo*, Chok-Pin Foo
Cfo*, Daniel C Reed
Chm*, Immanuel Phangaraj
VCM*, Edwin G Corr
SEC*, Ingrid M Mail
Asst SEC*, Carrene G Rosser
Coordinator, Connie Reed
Executive Director, John Reid
Human Resources, Lindsey Holland
Executive, Steve Wang
Auditors: CAPIN CROUSE LLP LAWRENCEVILL

LOCATIONS

HQ: MAP INTERNATIONAL (INC.)
4700 GLYNCO PKWY, BRUNSWICK, GA 315256901
Phone: 912 265-6010
Web: WWW.MAP.ORG

HISTORICAL FINANCIALS

Company Type: Private

Income Statement FYE: September 30

	REVENUE ($ mil.)	NET INCOME ($ mil.)	NET PROFIT MARGIN	EMPLOYEES
09/18	575	11	2.1%	200
09/17	598	(40)	—	—
09/16	606	87	14.5%	—
09/15	547	60	11.1%	—
Annual Growth	1.7%	(41.7%)	—	—

2018 Year-End Financials

Return on assets: 6.0%
Return on equity: 6.0%
Current ratio: 189.10
Cash ($ mil.): 2

MARINA DISTRICT DEVELOPMENT COMPANY, LLC

EXECUTIVES

Pres-Coo, Tom Ballance
MBR, Bob Boughner
MBR, Auggie Cipollini
Pres-Coo, Melonie Johnson
V Pres of Fin, Hugh Turner
Executive Officer, Cassie Fireman
Vice-President, Signe Huff
Vice President, Jason Lyons
Marketing Staff, Dorothy Gregory-Jones
Assistant Executive Steward, Enrique Villanueva
Advertising Manager, Meg Elevich

LOCATIONS

HQ: MARINA DISTRICT DEVELOPMENT COMPANY, LLC
1 BORGATA WAY, ATLANTIC CITY, NJ 084011946
Phone: 609 317-1000
Web: WWW.THEBORGATA.COM

HISTORICAL FINANCIALS

Company Type: Private

Income Statement FYE: December 31

	REVENUE ($ mil.)	NET INCOME ($ mil.)	NET PROFIT MARGIN	EMPLOYEES
12/10	738	44	6.0%	7,000
12/09	777	108	13.9%	—
12/08	830	83	10.0%	—
Annual Growth	(5.7%)	(27.1%)	—	—

2010 Year-End Financials

Return on assets: 3.1%
Return on equity: 9.6%
Current ratio: 0.80
Cash ($ mil.): 42

MARITZ HOLDINGS INC.

Maritz Holdings designs employee incentive and reward programs including incentive travel rewards and customer loyalty programs. The company also plans corporate trade shows and events and offers traditional market research services such as the creation of product launch campaigns. Its programs are designed to help its clients improve workforce quality and customer satisfaction. The company operates through a number of subsidiaries including Maritz Motivation (services for marketing sales HR) Maritz Automotive (helping clients and partners' sales) Maritz Global Events (meeting and event industry professionals) and Maritz Travel (planners sales operations and procurement). The company is owned by Steve Maritz.

Operations

Maritz provide solutions such as meetings & events employee experience incentives & rewards customer loyalty and automotive solutions.

The company operates through its subsidiaries: Maritz Motivation; Maritz Automotive; Maritz Global Events; Maritz Travel; Experient; and Impact Dimensions.

Maritz Motivation works with marketing human resources and sales and channel marketing executives to provide consumer loyalty channel loyalty employee engagement and sales incentive solutions to Fortune 100 companies.

Maritz Automotive is dedicated to helping clients and its retail partners sell more vehicles parts and service.

Maritz Global Events partners with meeting and event industry professionals to help prove the value of face-to-face meetings.

Maritz Travel a Maritz Global Events company works with meeting planners sales operations and procurement teams to deliver business meetings and incentive travel programs for corporate Fortune 100 companies.

Experient a Maritz Global Events company works with meeting planners executive administrators and marketing professionals in the government association and tradeshow markets providing meeting and event services.

Impact Dimensions works with meeting planners sales and marketing managers and administrative professionals.

Geographic Reach

Maritz' headquarters is located in Fenton Missouri.

Sales and Marketing

The company's major customers are GM HSBC Purina Southwest and Konica Minolta. Maritz is supporting approximately 845 Nissan dealers (onsite and virtually).

Strategy

Maritz's strength is reinvention. The company pioneered the incentives industry revolutionized meeting planning and is transforming customer experiences. The scientific study of human behavior is a central component of Maritz's DNA and ingrained in the design of its solutions.

In 2019 Maritz partnered with Hireology to help dealers identify the best candidates for key dealership positions hire top talent with greater speed and confidence and manage onboarding by delivering training communications incentives recognition and other performance improvement tools. Maritz also partnered with Northwood University to help develop the next generation of leaders in the automotive industry.

In addition MaritzCX was sold in early 2020 to InMoment. The newly combined company offers an unprecedented combination of state-of-the-art technology and distinctive professional services alongside a unique agile-first' approach that offers extraordinary capabilities to drive results for the world's leading brands. The full transition to an InMoment company is expected to take 12-18 months.

Maritz Motivation also launched the Applied Behavioral Science Assessment in mid-2020 which helps incorporate behavioral science principles into its clients' sales or channel program to drive better results. The created assessment finds out if clients' loyalty employee experience sales or channel program is scientifically sound therefore finding out how their loyalty program stacks up.

EXECUTIVES

Chairman And Ceo, W. Stephen (Steve) Maritz, age 63
Vp Sales, Dennis Hummel
Cfo, Rick Ramos
President Of Maritz Travel Company, David Peckinpaugh
Senior Vice President Sales And Marketing, Charlie Ferbet
Vice President Human Resources, David Estes
Vice President Managing Director, Alfredo Legoretta
Vice President, Dick Oconnor
Senior Vice President And Corporate Controller, Holly Francois
Vice President, Mike Mcclernon
Vice President Of Sales And Marketing, Carrie Nolan
Division Vice President, Kari Mcgraw
Vice President Group Business Manager, Terry Erwin
Vice President Marketing, Tom Wilson
Vice President And Corporate Real Estate And Property Services, Mark Alspaw
Vice President Experience Design, Greg Bogue
Executive Vice President And Chief Financial Officer, Richard Ramos
Group Vice President Pharmaceutical Sector, David Caldwell
Vice President Financial Shared Services, Gwen Sommerville
Vice President Global Business Manager, Joel Barone
Vice President Corporate Controller, Greg Dunn
Vice President Major Account Sales, Bill Moulder
Vice President Corporate Infrastructure Team Solutions, Jason Hampton
Vice President Of Engagement Marketing, Jen Hunter
Senior Vice President Of Sales And Marketing, Mary Casey
Division Vice President, Kimberly Clark
Vp Of Business Development, Jason Mauser
Board Member, Karen Staten
Board Member, Debbie Juntti
Auditors: KPMG LLP ST LOUIS MISSOURI

LOCATIONS

HQ: MARITZ HOLDINGS INC.
1375 N HIGHWAY DR, FENTON, MO 630990001
Phone: 636 827-4000
Web: WWW.MARITZ.COM

PRODUCTS/OPERATIONS

Selected Services

Marketing Research
- Custom marketing research
- Customer satisfaction and customer value analysis
- Data collection (focus groups telephone interviews)
- Maritz Polls and Maritz Research Reports
- Syndicated buyer research
- Telecommunications research

Performance Improvement
- Communications
- e-Learning
- Fulfillment
- Internet consulting
- Loyalty marketing
- Measurement and feedback
- Rewards and recognition

Travel
- Consulting services
- Corporate travel management
- Group travel services
- Travel award programs

COMPETITORS

Franklin Covey
Gallup
GiftCertificates.com
Harris Interactive
IMS Health
Information Resources Inc.
J.D. Power
JTB Corp.
Kantar Group
Motivcom
Nielsen
ORC International

HISTORICAL FINANCIALS

Company Type: Private

Income Statement — FYE: March 31

	REVENUE ($ mil.)	NET INCOME ($ mil.)	NET PROFIT MARGIN	EMPLOYEES
03/19	1,326	2	0.2%	4,646
03/18	1,263	(9)	—	—
03/17	1,217	(30)	—	—
03/16	1,274	(16)	—	—
Annual Growth	1.3%	—	—	—

2019 Year-End Financials

Return on assets: 0.4%
Return on equity: 6.3%
Current ratio: 0.80
Cash ($ mil.): 153

MARSHFIELD CLINIC HEALTH SYSTEM, INC.

Marshfield Clinic Health System (MCHS) is a private group medical practice that operates more than 50 medical locations across Wisconsin. The network provides primary secondary and tertiary care through its more than 800 physicians who represent about 90 medical specialties. Through primary operations ? Marshfield Medical Center Flambeau Hospital and Marshfield Children's Hospital and clinics MCHS annually serves hundreds of thousands of patients and handles millions of patient encounters. Other parts of the network include Marshfield Labs and Security Health Plan of Wisconsin as well as medical education and research organizations.

Operations

MCHS has about 15 primary operations including Marshfield Clinic Flambeau Hospital Marshfield Children's Hospital Marshfield Clinic Research Institute Security Health Plan and Marshfield Clinic Health System Foundation. The integrated health system has more than 1200 providers comprising approximately 90 specialties a health plan and research and education programs. Among its specialties are neuro-oncology maternal-fetal medicine pediatric orthopedic surgery and electrophysiology. Over 1200 hospitals clinics and other sites participate in a variety of clinic outreach programs. Clinic physicians and staff provide off-site consultation in more than 50 specialties. Its dental clinics see more than 60000 unique patients per year.

Geographic Reach

MCHS has about 65 clinics and medical offices in over 50 locations throughout northern central and western Wisconsin. It also has operations in some 35 Wisconsin communities in northern central and western Wisconsin including hospitals in Marshfield Eau Claire Minocqua Neillsville Park Falls Rice Lake and Weston.

Mergers and Acquisitions

In 2020 Marshfield Clinic Health System completed its acquisition of Ascension St. Clare's Hospital in Weston and is renaming the hospital Marshfield Medical Center-Weston. The transaction also includes the transfer of Ascension Wisconsin's 50% interest in Flambeau Hospital in Park Falls Wisconsin and The Diagnostic & Treatment Center in Weston (DTC) which offers a broad range of advanced diagnostic therapeutic and surgical services to meet the needs of area physicians and their patients. Both will be transitioned into the Health System over the next couple of months including the renaming of Flambeau Hospital to Marshfield Medical Center-Park Falls. Terms of the sale are not being disclosed.

Company Background

Marshfield Clinic was founded in 1916.

EXECUTIVES

Executive Director, Narayana S. Murali
Ceo, Susan L. Turney
Coo, Daniel J. Ramsey
Cfo, Gordon T. Edwards
Pharmacy Manager, Adam Maguire
Vice Chairman, Mark J. Bradley
Chairman, Mark D. Bugher
Secretary Treasurer, Kevin McEwen
Auditors: KPMG LLP MILWAUKEE WI

LOCATIONS

HQ: MARSHFIELD CLINIC HEALTH SYSTEM, INC.
1000 N OAK AVE, MARSHFIELD, WI 544495702
Phone: 715 387-5511
Web: WWW.MARSHFIELDCLINIC.ORG

PRODUCTS/OPERATIONS

Selected Services
Allergy and Asthma
Ambulatory Surgery
Anesthesia
Athletic Training
Audiology
Bariatric Surgery
Cancer Care
Cardiology (Heart Care)
Center for Community Outreach
Child Development Center
Dental Care
Dermatology
Diabetes Education
Ear Nose and Throat (ENT)
Emergency Medicine
Endocrinology (Diabetes and Metabolism)
Family Medicine
Gastroenterology (Digestive Care)
General Surgery
Genetic Services
Hospitalists (Hospital Care)
Infectious Diseases
Internal Medicine
Nephrology (Kidney Care)
Neurosciences (Neurology)
Nutrition Services
Obstetrics and Gynecology (OB/GYN)
Occupational Health
Oncology (Cancer Care)
Ophthalmology and Optometry (Eye Care)
Optical
Oral and Maxillofacial Surgery
Orthopedics
Orthotics and Prosthetics
Pain Management
Palliative Medicine
Pediatrics
Pharmacy
Physical and Occupational Therapy
Physical Medicine and Rehabilitation
Plastic and Cosmetic Surgery
Podiatry
Primary Care
Psychiatry and Psychology
Pulmonary Medicine (Lung Care)
Radiology
Rheumatology and Arthritis Care
Sports Medicine
TeleHealth
Urgent Care
Urology
Wound Healing

COMPETITORS

Blue Cross Blue Shield of Wisconsin
Compcare Health Services Insurance Corporation
Dean Health Systems Inc.
Group Health Cooperative
Luther Midelfort
Meriter Health Services
Ministry Health Care
ThedaCare Inc.
University of Wisconsin Hospital and Clinics

HISTORICAL FINANCIALS

Company Type: Private

Income Statement FYE: September 30

	REVENUE ($ mil.)	NET INCOME ($ mil.)	NET PROFIT MARGIN	EMPLOYEES
09/19	2,613	107	4.1%	8,377
09/18	2,430	(3)	—	—
09/15	0	(3)	—	—
Annual Growth	834.3%	—	—	—

2019 Year-End Financials

Return on assets: 3.9%
Return on equity: 8.9%
Current ratio: 1.60
Cash ($ mil.): 209

MARSHFIELD CLINIC, INC.

EXECUTIVES

Pres, Brian H Ewert
V Pres, Douglas Reding
Cfo, Gary Jankowski
V Pres, C Todd Stewart
Treas, Mark A Lepage
Urology Specialist, Gregory A Anderson
Ophthalmologist, Richard B Patchett
Director Facilities and Proper, James D Colburn
Dir Buss Devlopment, Victoria L Strobel
Accounting Staff, Debra Brock
Ophthalmologist, James Holzberger
Auditors: KPMG LLP MINNEAPOLIS MN

LOCATIONS

HQ: MARSHFIELD CLINIC, INC.
1000 N OAK AVE, MARSHFIELD, WI 544495702
Phone: 715 387-5511
Web: WWW.MARSHFIELDCLINIC.ORG

HISTORICAL FINANCIALS

Company Type: Private

Income Statement FYE: September 30

	REVENUE ($ mil.)	NET INCOME ($ mil.)	NET PROFIT MARGIN	EMPLOYEES
09/15	1,211	24	2.0%	363
09/09	1,062	78	7.4%	—
09/08*	102	6	5.9%	—
06/06	813	23	2.9%	—
Annual Growth	4.5%	0.5%	—	—

*Fiscal year change

2015 Year-End Financials

Return on assets: 2.3%
Return on equity: 4.5%
Current ratio: 0.70
Cash ($ mil.): 96

MARTIN PRODUCT SALES LLC

EXECUTIVES

Pres, Ruben S Martin III
MBR-V Pres*, Chris Booth
Coo*, Randall L Tauscher
Exec V Pres*, Robert D Bondurant

LOCATIONS

HQ: MARTIN PRODUCT SALES LLC
4200 STONE RD, KILGORE, TX 756626935
Phone: 903 983-6200
Web: WWW.MARTINMIDSTREAM.COM

HISTORICAL FINANCIALS

Company Type: Private

Income Statement FYE: December 31

	REVENUE ($ mil.)	NET INCOME ($ mil.)	NET PROFIT MARGIN	EMPLOYEES
12/07	1,204	8	0.7%	206
12/02*	156	1	0.7%	—
06/01	260	3	1.4%	—
06/99	132	0	0.2%	—
Annual Growth	27.8%	46.7%	—	—

*Fiscal year change

2007 Year-End Financials

Return on assets: 2.0%
Return on equity: 21.2%
Current ratio: 1.80
Cash ($ mil.): 5

MARTIN RESOURCE MANAGEMENT CORPORATION

Martin Resource Management likes to push around petroleum products. The employee-owned company's flagship affiliate Martin Midstream Partners offers transportation storage marketing and logistics management services for petroleum products including sulfur sulfur derivatives fuel oil liquefied petroleum gas asphalt and other bulk tank liquids primarily in the southern US. Martin Resource also manufactures and markets fertilizer and other processed sulfur products. Through its Martin Energy Services unit the company offers inland marine fuel supply and offshore support services. Other units include The Brimrock Group (sulfur) Cross Oil Refining & Marketing and Martin Asphalt.

Operations

Each year the company markets more than 250 million gallons of diesel fuel and lubricants along the Gulf Coast and 1.5 million barrels of naphthenic lubricants and base oils across the US. In addition Martin Resource also provides surface transportation services for products such as molten sulfur sulfuric acid fuel oil natural gas liquids (NGLs) asphalt paper mill liquids and other bulk tank liquids.

The company's more than $550 million of assets include a fleet of truck trailers and tractors. Its Martin Transport subsidiary has about 25 terminals in the Southeast and Southern US with more than 850 trucks and 1200 trailers. Martin Product Sales LLC markets and distributes petroleum-based products including asphalt fuel oil and sulfuric acid.

Martin Resource owns a 28.0% limited partnership interest and a 2% general partnership interest in its flagship operating company Martin Midstream Partners. Its Martin Energy Services subsidiary offers marine fuel supply and offshore support services.

Sales and Marketing

The company's customers include agriculture petrochemical petroleum and utility companies.

Strategy

Martin Resource markets oil and gas and by-products through facilities located throughout the Gulf Coast region. It acquires other companies or forms joint ventures to develop its portfolio. It also redistributes operating assets to its major subsidiaries to improve their performance.

In 2013 Canadian subsidiary Brimrock signed an engineering service agreement with Keyera to act as the engineering management and technology provider for Keyera's planned sulphur forming and materials handling facilities upgrade.

That year Martin Resource sold a 49% voting interest in MMGP Holdings LLC a newly-formed sole member of Martin Midstream GP LLC the general partner of Martin Midstream Partners to Alinda Capital Partners.

In 2012 Martin Midstream Partners also sold its East Texas and Northwest Louisiana natural gas gathering and processing assets to CenterPoint Energy Field Services for $275 million.

Streamlining its businesses in 2012 the company formed Martin Energy Services LLC combining the entities of Midstream Fuel Service LLC L & L Oil and Gas Services L.L.C. and PEPCO into one entity for improved service and growth.

Mergers and Acquisitions

In 2013 Martin Midstream Partners' subsidiary Martin Operating Partnership L.P bought Kansas City Missouri-based NL Grease LLC a grease manufacturer that specializes in private-label packaging of commercial and industrial greases.

Boosting its NGL handling capabilities that year Martin Midstream Partners purchased six liquefied petroleum gas pressure barges and two commercial push boats from affiliates of Florida Marine Transporters for $51 million.

In 2012 Martin Midstream Partners acquired Gulf Coast fuels and lubricants provider Talen's Marine & Fuel LLC. The transactions boosted the company's marine terminal infrastructure adding ten marine terminals between Houston/Galveston and Port Fourchon in Louisiana with total tankage of 300000 barrels and an additional 4000 feet of water-accessible bulkhead.

In 2012 Martin Midstream Partners bought the remaining equity interests in Redbird Gas Storage LLC for $150 million. (In 2011 Martin Resource and Martin Midstream Partners formed the Redbird Gas Storage natural gas storage joint venture to invest in Cardinal Gas Storage Partners a joint venture between Redbird and Energy Capital Partners focused on the development of natural gas storage facilities across North America).

Company Background

The acquisition of L & L Oil and Gas L.L.C. by Midstream Fuel Service in 2011 increased Martin Resources' capability along the U.S. Gulf Coast to 31 facilities for offshore fuels lubricants and logistical services including land based commercial and industrial fuels and lubricants.

In 2011 Martin Resource and Martin Midstream Partners formed the Redbird Gas Storage natural gas storage joint venture to invest in Cardinal Gas Storage Partners. Cardinal is a joint venture between Redbird and Energy Capital Partners that is focused on the development construction operation and management of natural gas storage facilities across North America.

To raise cash and boost the Martin Midstream Partners' storage segment in 2011 Martin Resource sold 13 terminals to that unit for $36.5 million.

Founded in 1951 by R. S. Martin Jr. Martin Resource also holds a stake in Ican Energy an LPG distributor. To raise cash and increase its financial flexibility in 2002 the company spun off a portion of its assets.

EXECUTIVES

Vice President Of Human Resources, Melanie Mathews
Senior Vice President Of Surface Transportation, Johnnie Murry
Vice President, Mike Lawrence
Auditors: KPMG LLP DALLAS TEXAS

LOCATIONS

HQ: MARTIN RESOURCE MANAGEMENT CORPORATION
4200 STONE RD, KILGORE, TX 756626935
Phone: 903 983-6200
Web: WWW.THEMARTINCOMPANIES.COM

PRODUCTS/OPERATIONS

Selected Companies

Altec Environmental Consulting
Commercial & Industrial Fuels & Lubricants
Commercial & Industrial Tanks & Equipment
Cross Oil Refining & Marketing Inc.
Marine Lubricants & Specialty Products
Martin Crude Marketing Company
Martin Energy Services LLC
Martin Product Sales LLC
Martin Transport Inc
Roddey engineering services Inc.

COMPETITORS

Enterprise Products
George Warren
Global Partners
Gulf Oil
Penn Octane
Sun Coast Resources
Williams Companies

HISTORICAL FINANCIALS

Company Type: Private

Income Statement — FYE: December 31

	REVENUE ($ mil.)	NET INCOME ($ mil.)	NET PROFIT MARGIN	EMPLOYEES
12/15	2,493	27	1.1%	2,300
12/11	2,985	37	1.3%	—
12/09	1,537	23	1.5%	—
12/08	2,903	5	0.2%	—
Annual Growth	(2.1%)	24.9%	—	—

2015 Year-End Financials

Return on assets: 1.5%
Return on equity: 6.9%
Current ratio: 1.80
Cash ($ mil.): 13

MARTIN'S POINT HEALTH CARE, INC.

EXECUTIVES

Ceo-Pres, David Howes
Chb*, Robert Moore
Cfo*, Daniel Chojnowski
Coordinator, Elizabeth Chadbourne
Coordinator, INA Levasseur
Coordinator, Jeanne Richards
Coordinator, Sheryl Fossett
Vice-President, Jeffry Bland
Information Specialist, Brandon Bergman
Financial Business Partner, Benjamin Hayes
Administrative Project Coordin, Kacey Parquette
Auditors: BAKER NEWMAN & NOYES LLC POR

LOCATIONS

HQ: MARTIN'S POINT HEALTH CARE, INC.
331 VERANDA ST STE 1, PORTLAND, ME 041035544
Phone: 207 774-5801
Web: WWW.MARTINSPOINT.ORG

HISTORICAL FINANCIALS

Company Type: Private

Income Statement — FYE: December 31

	ASSETS ($ mil.)	NET INCOME ($ mil.)	INCOME AS % OF ASSETS	EMPLOYEES
12/16	386	17	4.6%	839
12/14	351	3	1.0%	—
12/13	345	10	3.0%	—
12/09	247	30	12.2%	—
Annual Growth	6.6%	(7.2%)	—	—

2016 Year-End Financials

Return on assets: 4.6%
Return on equity: 6.6%
Sales ($ mil): 704

MARYLAND AND VIRGINIA MILK PRODUCERS COOPERATIVE ASSOCIATION, INCORPORATED

Milk is "Mar-VA-lous" for the members of the Maryland & Virginia Milk Producers Cooperative Association. Known as Maryland & Virginia the co-op processes and sells milk for nearly 1500 member/farmers with dairy herds in the south-eastern US and mid-Atlantic region. Maryland & Virginia produces fluid milk ice cream and cultured dairy products for retail sale under the Marva Maid Maola and Valley Milk brands. Its butter condensed milk and milk-powder products are sold primarily to food manufacturers. As a co-op it also offers agricultural supplies to its members. Maryland & Virginia operates three fluid-milk processing plants a manufacturing plant and an equipment-supply warehouse.

Operations

Maryland & Virginia operates three fluid processing plants a single manufacturing plant and a farm supply equipment division. It also owns a majority stake in Valley Milk LLC. The co-op transports more than 300 tanker truckloads of milk daily to nearly 30 different plants. Member farms range in size from fewer than 100 cows to more than 2000. Combined Maryland & Virginia members produce three billion pounds of milk annually.

Geographic Reach

The co-op gets its milk from member farmers in Delaware Florida Georgia Kentucky Maryland North Carolina Ohio Pennsylvania South Carolina Tennessee Virginia and West Virginia. Its fluid processing plants are located in Newport News Virginia; Landover Maryland; and New Bern North Carolina. It has manufacturing facilities in Laurel Maryland and Strasburg Virginia and a warehouse in Frederick Maryland.

Sales and Marketing

In addition to supermarkets the co-op counts customers such as Walgreens Starbucks Sheetz convenience stores and Dairy Queen among its customers.

Financial Performance

The co-op's revenue decreased by 5% to $1.3 billion in 2012 versus $1.4 billion in 2011 due to a decline in milk dairy and other products as well as sales of equipment and supplies partially offset by an increase in sales of its members' and nonmembers' raw milk. Despite the decline in sales the Maryland & Virginia reported a profit of $5.5 million in 2012 versus a loss of $2.8 million the prior year. Like other milk producers Maryland & Virginia has been contending with sluggish milk sales due to decreasing milk consumption beginning in the 1970s.

EXECUTIVES

Secretary And Treasurer, Jay Bryant
Auditors: HERLIEM & COMPANY INC READING

LOCATIONS

HQ: MARYLAND AND VIRGINIA MILK PRODUCERS COOPERATIVE ASSOCIATION, INCORPORATED
1985 ISAAC NEWTON SQ W, RESTON, VA 201905031
Phone: 703 742-6800
Web: WWW.MDVAMILK.COM

COMPETITORS

Associated Milk Producers
Dairy Farmers of America
Dairy Manufacturers
Dairylea
Dean Foods
Foremost Farms
Land O'Lakes

HISTORICAL FINANCIALS

Company Type: Private

Income Statement — FYE: December 31

	REVENUE ($ mil.)	NET INCOME ($ mil.)	NET PROFIT MARGIN	EMPLOYEES
12/12	1,296	5	0.4%	550
12/11	1,362	(2)	—	—
12/10	1,219	8	0.7%	—
Annual Growth	3.1%	(20.4%)	—	—

2012 Year-End Financials

Return on assets: 3.4%
Return on equity: 14.9%
Current ratio: 0.80
Cash ($ mil.): —

MARYLAND DEPARTMENT OF TRANSPORTATION

Traveling in Maryland? You can thank (or curse) the Maryland Department of Transportation (MDOT). MDOT is responsible for building operating and maintaining a safe and seamless transportation network that includes highway transit maritime and aviation facilities. The Department of Transportation is organized along various administrative groups including the Maryland Motor Vehicle Administration Transit Administration Port Administration Aviation Administration and Highway Administration. MDOT annual budget of about $1.5 billion is funded through the state's Transportation Trust Fund and federal aid.

EXECUTIVES

SEC, Pete K Rahn
SEC, John Porcari
Prin, Donald A Halligan
Prin, Robert Ehrlich
Bay Bridge Facility Administra, Richard Jaramillo
Coordinator, Cathy Kahl
Coordinator, Colleen Johnson
Treasurer, Bill Oliver
Assistant Manager, Jane Shock-Osborn
Deputy Director, Sandy Hertz
Member, Steven Miles
Auditors: SB & COMPANY LLC HUNT VALLEY

LOCATIONS

HQ: MARYLAND DEPARTMENT OF TRANSPORTATION
7201 CORPORATE CENTER DR, HANOVER, MD 210761415
Phone: 410 865-1037
Web: WWW.MDOT.MARYLAND.GOV

HISTORICAL FINANCIALS

Company Type: Private

Income Statement — FYE: June 30

	REVENUE ($ mil.)	NET INCOME ($ mil.)	NET PROFIT MARGIN	EMPLOYEES
06/19	4,609	229	5.0%	1,000
06/18	4,407	(189)	—	—
06/17	4,490	85	1.9%	—
06/16	4,170	(232)	—	—
Annual Growth	3.4%	—	—	—

2019 Year-End Financials

Return on assets: 1.0%
Return on equity: 1.6%
Current ratio: —
Cash ($ mil.): 36

MARYLAND TRANSPORTATION AUTHORITY

EXECUTIVES

Governor, Larry Hogan
Senior Engineer, Alex Cobern
Field Compliance Officer, Angela Estes
Internal Audit Supervisor, Christina Thompson
Account Manager, David Ferrara
Chief of Audit, Jody McCurley
Information Technology Web Sys, Mario Mento
Procurement Administrator, Paul Becker
Senior Business Analyst, Vanessa Otway

LOCATIONS

HQ: MARYLAND TRANSPORTATION AUTHORITY
2310 BROENING HWY, BALTIMORE, MD 212246639
Phone: 410 537-7833
Web: WWW.MARYLAND.GOV

HISTORICAL FINANCIALS

Company Type: Private

Income Statement — FYE: June 30

	REVENUE ($ mil.)	NET INCOME ($ mil.)	NET PROFIT MARGIN	EMPLOYEES
06/19	862	321	37.2%	77
06/18	862	309	35.9%	—
06/17	869	332	38.3%	—
Annual Growth	(0.4%)	(1.7%)	—	—

2019 Year-End Financials

Return on assets: 4.2%
Return on equity: 6.6%
Current ratio: 1.90
Cash ($ mil.): 175

MASHANTUCKET PEQUOT GAMING ENTERPRISE INC

EXECUTIVES

Pres, John O' Brain
Staff, Michelle Jolly
Information Specialist, Ronald Guy
Senior Marketing Executive, Kenneth Reels
Executive, Mark Keenan
Engineer, Michael Grillo
Executive, Susan Goskowsky
Ticketing Manager, David Billing
Executive Director of Finance, Ed Marolda
Director, Joseph Macrino
Information, Mark Thornton
Auditors: DELOITTE & TOUCHE LLP HARTFO

LOCATIONS

HQ: MASHANTUCKET PEQUOT GAMING ENTERPRISE INC
350 TROLLEY LINE BLVD, MASHANTUCKET, CT 063383830
Phone: 860 312-3465
Web: WWW.FOXWOODS.COM

HISTORICAL FINANCIALS

Company Type: Private

Income Statement FYE: September 30

	REVENUE ($ mil.)	NET INCOME ($ mil.)	NET PROFIT MARGIN	EMPLOYEES
09/19	787	(40)	—	2
09/18	828	(46)	—	—
Annual Growth	(5.0%)	—	—	—

2019 Year-End Financials

Return on assets: (-5.8%)
Return on equity: (-7.1%)
Current ratio: 0.80
Cash ($ mil.): 47

MASS GENERAL BRIGHAM INCORPORATED

Partners HealthCare operates two large acute-care medical centers – Brigham and Women's Hospital and Massachusetts General Hospital – and about 15 community hospitals in Boston and surrounding communities. The not-for-profit system also provides primary and specialty care through clinics physician offices rehabilitation centers long-term care facilities and home health and hospice agencies. Subsidiary MassHealth provides medical insurance to state residents. Partners HealthCare also provides medical training and research through an affiliation with Harvard. The organization has additional partnerships with health research and educational organizations around the globe.

Financial Performance

Partners Healthcare reported $13.3 billion in revenue in 2018 a less than 1% decline from 2017 results. Patient service revenue which accounts for about 70% of sales increased 10% but insurance premium revenue (10% of sales) decreased 43% due to membership declines (related to the transition of customers from managed care to accountable care programs). Academic and research revenue (15% of sales) increased 4%.

Excess of revenue over expenses increased 25% to $826.6 million due to lower operating costs related to the insurance business.

The organization ended 2018 with $398.4 million in cash down $340.7 million from 2017. Operating activities contributed $899 million while investing activities used $1.4 billion (mostly for acquisitions property and equipment) and financing activities contributed $140.8 million via long-term debt proceeds and investment income.

Strategy

Partners HealthCare has expanded its operations through a stream of acquisitions and construction efforts. It completed construction of a replacement facility for the Nantucket Cottage Hospital in 2018. The company is also adding three new outpatient care buildings (containing primary women's cancer diagnostic orthopedic physical therapy and surgery care centers) to its Wentworth-Douglass Hospital campus.

Partners HealthCare is investing in new IT tools to improve efficiencies enhance quality and lower the cost of care. The company has installed an electronic health record (EHR) system across all of its facilities; it is also adding a digital imaging platform and a centralized credentialing system.

In addition the company regularly updates medical equipment at its facilities to keep pace with medical innovations. For instance it has added a minimally invasive spine surgery program at Brigham and Women's Faulkner Hospital and robotic surgery centers at two of its community hospitals in recent years.

Mergers and Acquisitions

Partners HealthCare has had two failed efforts to expand beyond Massachusetts. The company's agreement to acquire Care New England was canceled in 2019 after Rhode Island's governor objected to the deal. Partners and Care New England had approached Rhode Island-based Lifespan to also join forces in 2018 but that proposal was subsequently dropped. The organization did successfully acquire specialty hospital Massachusetts Eye and Ear in 2018.

Company Background

Partners HealthCare was founded in 1994 through the merger of Brigham and Women's Hospital and Massachusetts General Hospital.

EXECUTIVES

Vice President Public Affairs Partners Community Benefit Programs, Lee Chelminiak
Vice President Of Finance, David Mcguire
Evp Administration And Finance Cfo And Treasurer, Peter K. Markell, age 64
President And Ceo Massachusetts General Hospital, Peter L. Slavin
Cio, James W. (Jim) Noga
President And Ceo North Shore Medical Center, Robert G. (Bob) Norton, age 70
President And Ceo Neighborhood Health Plan, Deborah C. Enos
President And Ceo Partners Continuing Care, David E. Storto
President And Ceo Brigham And Women's Hospital, Elizabeth G. (Betsy) Nabel
President And Chief Executive Officer, David F. Torchiana
President Of Partners Community, Thomas H. Lee
President And Ceo Spaulding Rehabilitation Network, Maureen Banks
President Mclean Hospital, Scott L. Rauch
President And Ceo Brigham And Women's Physicians Organization, Allen L. Smith
President And Ceo Martha's Vineyard Hospital, Timothy J. Walsh
President And Ceo Mgh Institute Of Health Professions, Janis P. Bellack
President And Ceo, David Torchiana
President And Ceo Nantucket Cottage Hospital, Margot Hartmann
President And Ceo Partners Healthcare At Home, Rod Carnifax
Medical Director, Jane Erb
Medical Director Breast Care Center, Katherina Zabicki
Director Of Nursing, Deborah Morrissey
Avp Technical Services (dana Farber Cancer Institute), Rick Williams
Vice President Of Population Health Management, Timothy Ferris
Senior Medical Director, Elizabeth Mort
Nursing Director, Michelle Anastasi
Medical Director Of The Breast And Ovarian Cancer, Paula Ryan
Nursing Director, Elizabeth Mcgrath
Medical Director, David Chen
Vice President Of Partners Innovation, Christopher Coburn
Clinical Director, Karon Konner
Director Of Nursing, Deirdre Greene
Medical Director, William Holgerson
Senior Vice President Of Clinical Services, David Mccready
Medical Director, Richard Kaufman
Project Manager To Senior Vice President Research, Angela Vail
Senior Vice President Human Resources, Jeff Davis
Medical Director, Sharon Bober
Nursing Director, Michele Ohara
Clinical Director, Martha Kane
Clinical Director Department Of Pt Ot; Clinical Content Lead Partners Ecare, James Zachazewski
Vice President Of Operations, Hofmann Erika
Nursing Director, Peggy Settle
Director Of Medical Records, Doherty Linda
Nursing Director, Lisa Wichmann
Nursing Director, Dorothy Parker
Vice President, Anne Fitzgerald
Assistant Vice President Regional Consultant, Viscomi Rudy
Nursing Director, Jennifer Sargent
Director Of Radiology, Dave Marchione
Rsvp Team Leader, Jessica Grajeda
Vice President Of Information Technology, Karl Fitch
Medical Director, Renee Sorrentino
Medical Director, Angelo Volandes
Vice President, Shelly Anderson
Medical Director Emergency Medicine, Patricia Henwood
Senior Vice President Of Communication And Public Affairs, Erin Mcdonough
Senior Vice President Payer Solution Sales, Wilson Caryn
Vice President Of Operations, Ricci Elisabeth
Senior Vice President Research, Richard Bringhurst
Medical Director, Robert Gottlieb
Vice President, Terry Garfinkle
Nursing Director, Kathryn Hall
Senior Vice President, Estrela Rui
Senior Vice President Of Finance And Treasurer, Karen Lavoie
Vice President, Eileen Flaherty
Associate Medical Director, R Nicholas Nace Md
Physical Therapy, Tom Rossignoll
Vp Operations, Mary Jo Gagnon
Co Medical Director, Jaime Rivera
Medical Director, James Macon
Nursing Director, Diane Tsitos
Physical Therapy Notetaker, Jaclyn Pontell
Chairman, Edward P. Lawrence, age 78
Vice Chair Of Medicine, Jacob Karas
Secretary, Maria Sanchez
Secretary, Ruth Valdez
Board Member, Warren Foote
Treasurer, Xandra Breakefield
Board Member, Natalia Berry
Board Member, Martha Pitman
Department Secretary, Theresa Crotty
Secretary, Estimable Jerry
Department Secretary, Julie Baratta
Treasurer, Susanne Churchill
Secretary, Rosemary T Jaromin
Treasurer, Peggy Breneus
Board Member, Edgar Robertson

LOCATIONS

HQ: MASS GENERAL BRIGHAM INCORPORATED
800 BOYLSTON ST STE 1150, BOSTON, MA 021998123
Phone: 617 278-1000
Web: WWW.PARTNERS.ORG

PRODUCTS/OPERATIONS

2014 Sales

	$ mil.	% of total
Net patient service revenue	7,042	65
Premium revenue	1,622	15
Direct academic and research	1,225	11
Indirect academic and research	353	3
Other revenue	662	6
Total	**10,906**	**100**

COMPETITORS

Baystate Health
Boston Medical Center
Cambridge Health Alliance
Cape Cod Healthcare
Cape Cod Hospital
Care New England
CareGroup
Children's Hospital Boston
Milford Regional Medical Center
Northeast Health System
Southcoast Hospitals Group
Steward Health Care
Universal Health Services

HISTORICAL FINANCIALS

Company Type: Private

Income Statement — FYE: September 30

	REVENUE ($ mil.)	NET INCOME ($ mil.)	NET PROFIT MARGIN	EMPLOYEES
09/15	11,665	(916)	—	67,000
09/10	8	(0)	—	—
09/08	551	(44)	—	—
Annual Growth	54.7%	—	—	—

2015 Year-End Financials

Return on assets: (-6.1%)
Return on equity: (-15.1%)
Current ratio: 2.30
Cash ($ mil.): 621

MASSACHUSETTS BAY TRANSPORTATION AUTHORITY

EXECUTIVES

Chm, John R Jenkins
Ceo-Gen Mgr*, Luis M Ramirez
Treas-Contrl*, Paul Brandley
Exec Dir*, Alan G Macdonald
Coordinator, John Ford
Sergeant, Paul Carroll
Procurement Staff, Judi Kidd
Procurement Staff, Karen Love
Operation Control Center OCC S, Alex Yuen
Director of Environmental Comp, Janis Kearney
Software Quality Assurance Jun, Anthony Leoni
Auditors: KPMG LLP BOSTON MA

LOCATIONS

HQ: MASSACHUSETTS BAY TRANSPORTATION AUTHORITY
MBTA 10 PARK PLZ STE 3910, BOSTON, MA 02116
Phone: 617 222-3106
Web: WWW.MBTA.COM

HISTORICAL FINANCIALS

Company Type: Private

Income Statement — FYE: June 30

	REVENUE ($ mil.)	NET INCOME ($ mil.)	NET PROFIT MARGIN	EMPLOYEES
06/19	777	459	59.1%	6,100
06/18	764	408	53.4%	—
06/06*	379	(23)	—	—
12/05	0	0	—	—
Annual Growth	—	—	—	—

*Fiscal year change

2019 Year-End Financials

Return on assets: 3.5%
Return on equity: 18.6%
Current ratio: 0.80
Cash ($ mil.): 296

MASSACHUSETTS DEPARTMENT OF TRANSPORTATION

The Massachusetts Department of Transportation (MassDOT) oversees the operations essential for the massive job of moving people and goods throughout the Commonwealth. In 2009 the former Massachusetts Executive Office of Transportation merged with other state agencies to form MassDOT. The unified organization operates in four divisions: highway; transit; aeronautics; and the registry of motor vehicles. In addition to its regulatory responsibility MassDOT also provides research planning and information services relevant to the state's transportation system.

EXECUTIVES

Ceo, Stephanie Pollack
Technical Project Manager, David Chirokas
State Survey Engineer, John Anthony
Executive Assistant, Kathleen Quirk
Administrator, Kevin Lopez
Director, Lisa Strout
General Manager, Paul Garrity
Information Technology Manager, Paul Jay

LOCATIONS

HQ: MASSACHUSETTS DEPARTMENT OF TRANSPORTATION
10 PARK PLZ STE 4160, BOSTON, MA 021163979
Phone: 857 368-4636
Web: WWW.MASSDOT.STATE.MA.US

HISTORICAL FINANCIALS

Company Type: Private

Income Statement — FYE: June 30

	REVENUE ($ mil.)	NET INCOME ($ mil.)	NET PROFIT MARGIN	EMPLOYEES
06/18	2,957	1	0.1%	6,100
06/17	2,984	(107)	—	—
06/16	3,235	15	0.5%	—
Annual Growth	(4.4%)	(64.9%)	—	—

MASSACHUSETTS HOUSING FINANCE AGENCY PROPERTY ACQUISITION AND DISPOSITION CORPORATION

EXECUTIVES

Chb, Michael J Dirrane
Chm*, Ronald A Homer
Exec Dir*, Thomas R Gleason
Treas*, Andris J Silins
Prin*, Tom O'Brien
Cfo*, Michael Fitzmaurice
Staff, Tyrone Reed
Real Estate Conultant, Kristin Olsen
Vp-Homeownership Programs, Mounzer M Aylouche
Business Officer E, Angelo Nuby
Officer, Antonio Torres

LOCATIONS

HQ: MASSACHUSETTS HOUSING FINANCE AGENCY PROPERTY ACQUISITION AND DISPOSITION CORPORATION
1 BEACON ST, BOSTON, MA 021083107
Phone: 617 854-1000
Web: WWW.MASSHOUSING.COM

HISTORICAL FINANCIALS

Company Type: Private

Income Statement — FYE: June 30

	ASSETS ($ mil.)	NET INCOME ($ mil.)	INCOME AS % OF ASSETS	EMPLOYEES
06/20	5,948	149	2.5%	325
06/18	5,460	6	0.1%	—
Annual Growth	4.4%	395.9%	—	—

2020 Year-End Financials

Return on assets: 2.5%
Return on equity: 10.0%
Sales ($ mil): 380

MASSACHUSETTS INSTITUTE OF TECHNOLOGY

Massachusetts Institute of Technology (MIT) takes the prize for breeding ingenuity. A leading research institution the school is typically granted more patents annually than any other university and about 90 people associated with MIT are Nobel Prize recipients. Blending that science and engineering acumen with top business programs (including the Sloan School of Management) MIT graduates have started more than 30000 active companies. MIT has more than 11000 students more than 60% of whom attend graduate school. The faculty of the nearly three dozen academic departments includes more than 1000 professors. The school's student teacher ratio is 3:1 (undergraduates). Founded in 1865 MIT is privately endowed.

Operations

MIT's research is conducted both through its academic facilities which employ more than 3700 researchers and engage some 2500 graduate students and through its Lincoln Laboratory in Lexington Massachusetts. The Lincoln Laboratory has approximately 3200 workers focused on federally funded research programs in areas of national security such as information communication and decision making. Lincoln Laboratory specialized in sensors signal processing and embedded computer systems.

The university offers 46 major and 49 minor undergraduate programs. Its undergraduate tuition for academic year 2016-2017 was about $48000. MIT's libraries have more than 5 million items in print and digital formats.

MIT is one of a growing number of universities to begin offering OpenCourseWare which makes teaching materials used in MIT undergraduate and graduate courses available on the internet free of charge to any user anywhere in the world for uses ranging from curriculum development to self-learning.

Geographic Reach

MIT is located on 168 acres in Cambridge Massachusetts and includes 18 student residences and 26 acres of athletic fields.

MIT enrolled students from all 50 states and the District of Columbia three territories and about 100 foreign nations in the academic year ending 2017.

Financial Performance

MIT clearly has a strong emphasis on procuring funding for its technology research programs. The institute receives grants from a variety of commercial and non-commercial entities bringing in a total of $1.7 billion in sponsored funding each year. The Department of Defense and Department of Health and Human Services and the largest sponsors. Other sponsors include the Department of Energy National Science Foundation NASA local government agencies and not-for-profit entities. MIT also conducts $100 million in contracted general industry research each year.

Annual revenue for MIT in fiscal 2017 was $3.5 billion up from about $3.4 billion in 2016. About 50% of revenue comes from research funding. About 10% comes from tuition.

Strategy

MIT's primary goal is to advance science and technology both among its students and on a worldwide scale. It aims to make discoveries in areas including energy economics and medicine. To take its efforts to the broader population MIT licenses more technologies to startups than any other university. Its licensing office enters about 100 licensing and option agreements each year with about a quarter of those going to startup technology firms.

While MIT is well-known for students and graduates who create businesses the university has created a fund to help early stage enterprises along. The Engine as the fund is called invests in university-related startups in their early stages. It steps in where venture capital funds usually don't go technologies that require time to commercialize. Main areas of investment include robotics biotechnology manufacturing and materials and energy. The fund has about $200 billion for investment.

Company Background

MIT has some extraordinary alumni who include former chairman of the Federal Reserve Ben Bernanke former US Representative Pete Stark former National Economic Council chairman Lawrence H. Summers and former Council of Economic Advisors chairwoman Christina Romer. Outside of politics MIT alumni founded or co-founded several notable companies such as Intel Hewlett-Packard Texas Instruments Qualcomm Bose and Campbell Soup.

EXECUTIVES

Dean Digital Learning, Sanjay Sarma
President, L. Rafael Reif
Dean Sloan School Of Management, David C. Schmittlein
Evp And Treasurer, Israel Ruiz
Dean School Of Engineering, Ian A. Waitz
Dean Graduate Education, Christine Ortiz
Dean Undergraduate Education, Dennis M. Freeman
Dean Student Life, Costantino (Chris) Colombo
Chancellor, Cynthia Barnhart
Provost, Martin A. Schmidt
Dean School Of Architecture And Planning, Hashim Sarkis
Dean School Of Humanities Arts And Social Sciences, Melissa Nobles
Dean School Of Science, Michael Sipser
Vp Information Systems And Technology, John Charles
Associate Vice President For Communications, Nate Nickerson
Associate Vice President For Human Resources, Meg Regan
Vice President, Susan Hockfield
Vice President For Human Resources, Gregory Leonelli
Associate Vice President And Chief Operating Officer, David Woodruff
Vice President Marketing, Scott Hanna
Vice President Product, Nadav Aharony
Senior Vice President Of Information Technology, Ed Gazarian
Vice President For Open Learning, Laura White
Senior Advisor To The Senior Vice President, Kathryn Liede
Vice President, Ann Drumm
Department Head, Maria Zuber
Vice President Of Sales, Andrew Mcinnes
Vice President Of Products, Stefan Schmitz
Vice President For Institute Affairs And Secretary Of The Corporation, Jennifer Walsh
Executive Vice President, James Hodges
Vice President, Haizheng Zhang
Senior Advisor Office Of The Vice President For Research, Tom Kiley
Vice President Information Technology, Lisa Mandel
Vice President, Sreehari Rayavarapu
Medical Director, Cecilia Stuopis
Svp And Cio, Christopher Chang
Vice President, Sandro Salgueiro
Vice President Strategy And Analysis, Amanda Chiu
Vice President Sales, James Dunn
Vice President For Students Affairs, Allison Dolan-wilson
Senior Vice President Engineering Manufactuaring And Test Operations, Paul Estey
Vice President, William S Elkus
Vice President Administration, Gregory Sullivan
Vice President, Rami Habal
Vice President Of Finance, Larry Kernan
Vice President, John Kocher
Chairman, Robert B. Millard, age 70
Secretary, George Apostolakis
Vice Chair, Judy Pederson
Secretary, Richard Zhang
Treasurer Office, Michael Fahey
Deputy Treasurer And Director Of Investments, Allan Bufferd
Treasurer, Duane Dreger
Treasurer, Lauren Weiss
Treasurer, Kindrick Blais
Treasurer, Karen Hearn
Assistant Treasurer, Harry Foden
Auditors: PRICEWATERHOUSECOOPERS LLP BO

LOCATIONS

HQ: MASSACHUSETTS INSTITUTE OF TECHNOLOGY
77 MASSACHUSETTS AVE, CAMBRIDGE, MA 021394307
Phone: 617 253-1000
Web: WWW.WEB.MIT.EDU

PRODUCTS/OPERATIONS

2014 Sales

	$ mil.	% of total
Reseach revenue	1,528	49
Support from investment	625	20
Tuition and similar revenue	324	10
Fee and services	176	6
Gifts	162	5
Auxiliary enterprises	120	4
Other program	117	4
Net asset reclassification	69	2
Total	**3,124**	**100**

Schools and Areas of Study

Schools and Areas of Study
School of Architecture and Planning
Architecture
Media Arts and Sciences
Urban Studies and Planning
School of Engineering
Aeronautics and Astronautics
Biological Engineering
Chemical Engineering
Civil and Environmental Engineering
Electrical Engineering and Computer Science
Engineering Systems Division
Materials Science and Engineering
Mechanical Engineering
Nuclear Science and Engineering
School of Humanities Arts and Social Sciences
Anthropology
Comparative Media Studies
Economics
Foreign Languages and Literatures
History
Humanities
Linguistics and Philosophy
Literature
Music and Theater Arts
Political Science
Science Technology and Society
Writing and Humanistic Studies
Sloan School of Management
Management
School of Science
Biology
Brain and Cognitive Sciences
Chemistry
Earth Atmospheric and Planetary Sciences
Mathematics
Physics
Whitaker College of Health Sciences and Technology
Harvard-MIT Division of Health Sciences and Technology
MIT-WHOI Joint Program in Oceanography and Applied Ocean Science and Engineering
Degrees Offered
Bachelor of Science (SB)
Master of Architecture (MArch)
Master of Business Administration (MBA)
Master in City Planning (MCP)
Master of Engineering (MEng)
Master of Finance (MFin)
Master of Science (SM)
Engineer (degree designates the field)
Doctor of Philosophy (PhD)
Doctor of Science (ScD)

HISTORICAL FINANCIALS

Company Type: Private

Income Statement FYE: June 30

	REVENUE ($ mil.)	NET INCOME ($ mil.)	NET PROFIT MARGIN	EMPLOYEES
06/20	3,950	1,447	36.7%	12,000
06/19	3,931	1,252	31.8%	—
06/18	3,626	2,391	65.9%	—
06/17	3,551	2,195	61.8%	—
Annual Growth	3.6%	(13.0%)	—	—

2020 Year-End Financials

Return on assets: 4.7% Cash ($ mil.): 572
Return on equity: 6.0%
Current ratio: —

MASSACHUSETTS PORT AUTHORITY

Massachusetts Port Authority (Massport) operates three airports: Boston Logan International Hanscom Field and Worcester Regional. Logan is home to 50 airlines and is New England's largest airport and the first port of call for many international flights entering the US. (It accounts for the majority of Massport's revenues.) Hanscom Field operates as the region's main aviation airport and offers niche commercial services while Worcester Regional primarily supports commercial flight services. Massport also oversees various waterfront properties of the Port of Boston. The agency was created by the Commonwealth of Massachusetts in 1956. The governor of Massachusetts appoints the agency's board members.

Operations

Massport's business consists of two distinct operating departments: Aviation and the Port. Logan airport catered to 29.4 million aviation passengers and 369000 cruise passengers in 2013. Its shipping operations serviced more than 110000 containers of products at its port.

Financial Performance

Massport's net revenues have steadily climbed over the years. Revenues jumped 2% from $1.78 billion in 2012 to $1.83 billion in 2013 thanks mainly to parking concession ground services and other revenue from nearly 125000 more passengers at Logan. The overall revenue increase for 2013 was generated by operating revenues exceeding operating expenses by $2.4 million.

EXECUTIVES

Secretary, Rita Hannon

LOCATIONS

HQ: MASSACHUSETTS PORT AUTHORITY
1 HARBORSIDE DR STE 200S, BOSTON, MA 021282905
Phone: 617 561-1600
Web: WWW.MASSPORT.COM

HISTORICAL FINANCIALS

Company Type: Private

Income Statement FYE: June 30

	REVENUE ($ mil.)	NET INCOME ($ mil.)	NET PROFIT MARGIN	EMPLOYEES
06/16	699	105	15.1%	1,102
06/15	662	107	16.2%	—
Annual Growth	5.5%	(2.0%)	—	—

2016 Year-End Financials

Return on assets: 2.5% Cash ($ mil.): 63
Return on equity: 5.1%
Current ratio: 1.50

MASSACHUSETTS SCHOOL BUILDING AUTHORITY

EXECUTIVES

Exec Director, Katherine Craven
Accounting Staff, Audrey Cushman
Senior Project Manager, Gregory Brunell
Senior Project Manager, Richard Hudson
Assistant Project Manager, Rachel O'Brien

LOCATIONS

HQ: MASSACHUSETTS SCHOOL BUILDING AUTHORITY
40 BROAD ST STE 500, BOSTON, MA 021094371
Phone: 617 720-4466
Web: WWW.MASSSCHOOLBUILDINGS.ORG

HISTORICAL FINANCIALS

Company Type: Private

Income Statement FYE: June 30

	REVENUE ($ mil.)	NET INCOME ($ mil.)	NET PROFIT MARGIN	EMPLOYEES
06/19	998	270	27.0%	8
06/18	891	252	28.3%	—
06/17	828	148	17.9%	—
06/16	908	237	26.1%	—
Annual Growth	3.2%	4.4%	—	—

MASSACHUSETTS WATER RESOURCES AUTHORITY

EXECUTIVES

Chm, Richard K Sullivan Jr
Exec Dir*, Fred Laskey
Coo*, Michael Hornbrook
Cfo*, Rachel Madden
SEC*, Joseph C Foti
Senior Analyst, Michael Farmer
Senior Program Manager, Daniel Nvule
Manager It Security Architectu, Paula Weadick
Senior Administrator, Caren Sekenski
Project Leader, Kristen Hall
Supervisor, Lewis Boynton
Auditors: CLIFTONLARSONALLEN LLP BOSTON

LOCATIONS

HQ: MASSACHUSETTS WATER RESOURCES AUTHORITY
100 1ST AVE, BOSTON, MA 021292043
Phone: 617 242-6000
Web: WWW.MWRA.COM

HISTORICAL FINANCIALS

Company Type: Private

Income Statement FYE: June 30

	REVENUE ($ mil.)	NET INCOME ($ mil.)	NET PROFIT MARGIN	EMPLOYEES
06/20	778	(40)	—	1,200
06/18	738	(39)	—	—
06/17	716	(37)	—	—
06/16	696	(7)	—	—
Annual Growth	2.8%	—	—	—

2020 Year-End Financials

Return on assets: (-0.6%) Cash ($ mil.): 70
Return on equity: (-2.6%)
Current ratio: 0.30

MAXIFACIAL DENTAL SURGERY

Auditors: ERNST & YOUNG US LLP INDIAN

LOCATIONS

HQ: MAXIFACIAL DENTAL SURGERY
1 MEDICAL CENTER DR, LEBANON, NH 037561000
Phone: 603 650-5000
Web: WWW.HITCHCOCK.ORG

HISTORICAL FINANCIALS

Company Type: Private

Income Statement FYE: September 30

	REVENUE ($ mil.)	NET INCOME ($ mil.)	NET PROFIT MARGIN	EMPLOYEES
09/09	1,147	27	2.4%	7,500
09/06	913	15	1.7%	—
Annual Growth	7.9%	20.7%	—	—

2009 Year-End Financials

Return on assets: 2.3% Cash ($ mil.): 40
Return on equity: 10.6%
Current ratio: 1.30

MAXIM HEALTHCARE SERVICES, INC.

Maxim Healthcare Services aims to promote good health by offering medical staffing and home health care as well as immunizations and other wellness services to clients nationwide. The company provides medical and administrative personnel for hospitals school systems nursing homes and correctional facilities. The company's staffing division offers contract per diem and travel assignments. Maxim Healthcare's consultants are available 24 hours a day seven days a week to provide assistance for clients. The company which operates from approximately 215 locations nationwide was established in 1988.

Operations

Maxim Healthcare offers in-home skilled nursing physical rehabilitation companion care respite care and behavioral care for people with illnesses or disabilities. The company's team of nurses therapists and home health aides help patients of all ages maintain the highest quality of life.

The company offers care services such as behavioral care and personal caregiving. Care services include private duty nursing military and veterans home health care nursing and therapy. Behavioral care includes Applied Behavior Analysis and autism services habilitation services and intensive in-community services while personal caregiving includes personal care and companionship.

Geographic Reach

Maryland-based Maxim Healthcare has approximately 215 offices.

Sales and Marketing

Maxim Healthcare's compassionate patient care and staffing experienced healthcare professionals has made the company as an established resource in the healthcare industry. The company provides its services to elderly chronically ill disabled recuperating and pediatric patients.

EXECUTIVES

Cio, Kevin Apperson
Coo, Chris Powell
Ceo, W. Bradley (Brad) Bennett
Vp Chief Medical Officer And Chief Quality Officer, W. John Langley
Cfo, Raymond (Ray) Carbone
Area Vice President Regional Account Manager, Jimmy Nichols
Director Of Clinical Services, Denise Sutton
Vice President Of Compliance, Shane Campbell
Director Of Clinical Services, Ann Lopez
Vice President, Andrew Friedell
Director Of Clinical Services, Lisa Malone
Director Of Clinical Services, Jolinda Jackson
Area Vice President, John Smalley
Senior Vice President And Chief Medical Officer, John Langley
Director Of Clinical Services, Jean Jacks
Area Vice President, Mike Beams
Area Vice President, Haven Andrews
Area Vice President, Chris Bodmer
Area Vp Southeast, Matt Rozelle
Area Vice President, Jeremy Markewicz
Director Of Clinical Services, Andrea Chontos
Area Vice President Of Clinical Operations, Kathy Mandeville
Vice President Of Finance, Steve Walsh
Area Vice President Of Clinical Operations, Savannah Moose
Vice President Human Resources, Kelly Bart
Director Of Clinical Services, Diane Charboneau
Director Of Clinical Services, Jennifer Turner
Home Health Nursing Director, Anny Busick
Director Of Nursing Services, Ramona Ward
Auditors: PRICEWATERHOUSECOOPERS LLP BA

LOCATIONS

HQ: MAXIM HEALTHCARE SERVICES, INC.
7227 LEE DEFOREST DR, COLUMBIA, MD 210463236
Phone: 410 910-1500
Web: WWW.MAXIMHEALTHCARE.COM

PRODUCTS/OPERATIONS

Selected Services

Allied Health staffing
Facility nurse staffing
Flu and wellness services
Government services
Health information services
International nursing
Home healthcare
HME/pharmacy services
Habilitation services
Physician services
Travel nursing

Selected Divisions

CareFocus
CareFocus Companion Services
Centrus Premier Homecare
Logix Healthcare Search Partners
Maxim Coders
Maxim Government Services
Maxim Health Information Services
Maxim Health Systems
Maxim Healthcare Services (Homecare)
Maxim Home Health Resources
Maxim Pediatric Services
Maxim Physician Resources
Maxim Staffing Solutions - Administrative Staffing
Maxim Staffing Solutions - Allied Health
Maxim Staffing Solutions - Nurse Staffing
Orbis Clinical
Reflectx Services
StaffAssist
TimeLine Recruiting
TravelMax

COMPETITORS

American HomePatient
Apria Healthcare
Cross Country Healthcare
MedStaff
Medsearch Staffing Services
PHS Correctional Healthcare
Team Health
TeamStaff

HISTORICAL FINANCIALS

Company Type: Private

Income Statement — FYE: December 31

	REVENUE ($ mil.)	NET INCOME ($ mil.)	NET PROFIT MARGIN	EMPLOYEES
12/17	1,510	38	2.5%	35,000
12/15	1,382	11	0.8%	—
12/14	1,269	4	0.4%	—
12/13	1,226	(1)	—	—
Annual Growth	5.3%	—	—	—

2017 Year-End Financials

Return on assets: 14.2%
Return on equity: 71.1%
Current ratio: 1.40
Cash ($ mil.): 8

MAYER ELECTRIC SUPPLY COMPANY, INC.

Mayer Electric Supply helps to light up those southern nights. The company is one of the nation's largest distributors of electrical supplies with about 50 branch locations in the southeastern US. It offers some 40000 items made by leading manufacturers such as 3M GE Littelfuse and Schneider Electric. Products include conduit circuit breakers controls and switches fire and safety products LED and low-voltage lighting systems motors power tools transformers and wire and cable. Mayer Electric supplies customers in the construction datacomm government industrial and utility industries. The Collat family including CEO Nancy Collat Goedecke owns Mayer Electric.

Operations

Besides distributing electrical supplies Mayer Electric offers several services. Its Mayer Project Management group works to lower cost for construction contractors by providing on-site storage and inventory management. Other services include lamp and battery recycling conduit bending and threading and wire and cable cutting. The company also specializes in factory automation energy efficiency and datacomm systems.

Geographic Reach

Mayer Electric serves customers through locations in Alabama Florida Georgia Mississippi the Carolinas Texas Tennessee and Virginia.

Sales and Marketing

The electrical supplies distributor serves multiple customer segments including those in the construction government industrial datacomm and utility industries through about 51 branch locations across US Southeast.

Strategy

Growing its geographic presence in 2013 Mayer Electric opened a branch location in the Houston area.

Mergers and Acquisitions

Looking to expand further in the southeastern US Mayer Electric in 2012 acquired Mustang Electric Supply based outside Dallas in Lewisville Texas. Established in 1998 Mustang Electric serves commercial and residential contractors across the Dallas and Fort Worth area allowing Mayer Electric to expand to the dynamic and lucrative Dallas market. The purchase included Mustang Electric's 40000-sq.-ft. facility in Lewisville.

Company Background

The recession hit companies like Mayer Electric hard as residential and commercial construction efforts were backburnered. Sales for Mayer Electric dropped by about 21% in 2009 compared to the prior year. Rather than responding by laying off employees or shuttering branches the company planned for break-even results or a small loss for the year. Indeed the company made a small profit in 2009.

Mayer Electric was founded in 1930.

EXECUTIVES

Chb-Ceo, Nancy Collat Goedecke
Pres*, Wes Smith
Exec V Pres-Coo*, Charles A Collat Jr
Exec V Pres*, Glenn Goedecke
Executive Officer, Mike Dunaway
Staff, Steve Poremba
Commercial Outside Sales, Marcus Abdo
Counter Sales, Hank Mitchell
Outside Account Manager, James Corby
Inside Sales, Mike Sowers
Outside Sales, Brian Miller

LOCATIONS

HQ: MAYER ELECTRIC SUPPLY COMPANY, INC.
3405 4TH AVE S, BIRMINGHAM, AL 352222300
Phone: 205 583-3500
Web: WWW.MAYERELECTRIC.COM

PRODUCTS/OPERATIONS

Selected Services

Basic distributor services
Construction partner
Maintenance repair and operations

Selected Products

Ballasts
Batteries
Cable and wire

Circuit breakers
Conduit
Factory automation products
Fan boxes
Fasteners
Fuses
LED lighting systems
Lenses
Lighting fixtures
Locks
Low-voltage lighting systems
Meters
Motors
Panelboards
Power supplies
Relays
Switches
Surge protection devices
Terminal blocks
Tools
Transformers
Voltage regulators

COMPETITORS

Anixter International
Consolidated Electrical
Crescent Electric Supply
Gexpro
Graybar Electric
Independent Electric Supply
Rexel Inc.
W.W. Grainger
WESCO International
Wholesale Supply Group

HISTORICAL FINANCIALS

Company Type: Private

Income Statement FYE: December 28

	REVENUE ($ mil.)	NET INCOME ($ mil.)	NET PROFIT MARGIN	EMPLOYEES
12/19	1,138	14	1.2%	900
12/18	1,072	11	1.1%	—
12/17	911	11	1.2%	—
12/16	812	5	0.7%	—
Annual Growth	11.9%	33.6%	—	—

MAYO CLINIC HOSPITAL-ROCHESTER

Multidisciplinary teamwork with coordinated care is Mayo Clinic's secret sauce. The not-for-profit Mayo Clinic provides health care most notably for complex medical conditions through its clinics in Rochester Minnesota Arizona and Florida. The clinics' multidisciplinary approach to care attracts more than a million patients a year from around the globe. For less specialized care the Mayo Clinic Health System operates a regional network of affiliated community hospitals and clinics in Minnesota Iowa and Wisconsin. Mayo Clinic also conducts research and trains physicians nurses and other health professionals. The Mayo Clinic is named for Dr. William Worrall Mayo who settled in Rochester in 1863.

Operations

Mayo Clinic Health System's regional network operates more than a dozen hospitals that combined are home to about 1000 beds and 3800 staff physicians medical scientists and clinical and research associates. The system also includes roughly 70 clinics in northern Iowa western Wisconsin and southeastern Minnesota. To manage its patient load Mayo forms referral alliances with other hospital groups HMOs and other organizations.

The clinic's education programs include the Mayo Medical School Mayo Graduate School and the Mayo School of Health Sciences; some medical training programs are conducted through partnerships with universities including the University of Minnesota. It also provides continuing education programs to medical professionals.

Financial Performance

The Mayo Clinic's revenue increased by nearly 7% in 2011 vs. 2010 while net income declined 18% over the same period. Indeed revenue gains and other support has steadily increased in recent years to nearly $8.5 billion in 2011. Sales of medical services (which account for about 85% of the Mayo Clinic's total) grew by 6% vs. the prior year. The Mayo Clinic list more than $10 billion in total assets.

Strategy

Already a giant in health care in the Midwest the Mayo Clinic continues to grow in other regions. In 2018 it announced plans to invest some $648 million in its Phoenix campus over the next five years. The project will roughly double the size of the campus allowing the system to meet growing demand for complex health care services in the Southwest. Similarly Mayo Clinic is investing some $144 million in its Jacksonville Florida campus.

Mayo Clinic strives to accommodate patients who travel to get to its facilities and will schedule multiple appointments and tests tightly together to make the most of patient's time. Rather than paying physicians based upon the quantity of patients seen the clinic's doctors are paid salaries as an incentive to quality care. These and other innovations have drawn attention to the clinic's patient-centered model of care. It has created a Center for the Science of Health Care Delivery and collaborates with other innovators including Cleveland Clinic and Intermountain Healthcare.

To reach remote areas Mayo Clinic in Arizona pioneered a telemedicine program that places robots in rural hospitals allowing local doctors and hospital staff to communicate with Mayo doctors in real time as they treat patients with such conditions as stroke or collapsed lungs.

EXECUTIVES

Regional Vice President, Annie Sadosty
Vice President, Brian Arendt
Treasurer, Harry N Hoffman
Assistant Treasurer, Paul A Gorman
Medical Secretary, Judy Jerabek
Vice Chair Dermatology, Marian Mcevoy
Medical Secretary, Deborah Stark
Medical Secretary, Mark Wojahn
Medical Secretary, Gina Robertson
Auditors: ERNST & YOUNG LLP MINNEAPOLIS

LOCATIONS

HQ: MAYO CLINIC HOSPITAL-ROCHESTER
200 1ST ST SW, ROCHESTER, MN 559050002
Phone: 507 284-2511
Web: WWW.MAYOCLINIC.ORG

Selected Locations and Affiliates

Direct subsidiaries
Arizona
Mayo Clinic Hospital (Phoenix)
Mayo Clinic Scottsdale
Florida
Mayo Clinic Hospital (Jacksonville)
Mayo Clinic Jacksonville
Minnesota
Mayo Clinic Rochester
Rochester Methodist Hospital
Saint Marys Hospital (Rochester)
Mayo Eugenio Litta Children's Hospital
Mayo Health System affiliates
Iowa
Armstrong Clinic
Decorah Clinic
Lake Mills Clinic
Franciscan
Swea City Clinic
Minnesota
Fountain Centers in Fairmont
Fountain Centers in Waseca
FamilyHeal
FamilyHealth Medical Clinic - Northfield Hospital
Franciscan Healthcare in Caledonia
Franciscan Healthcare La Crescent Clinic
Mayo Clinic Health System - Albert Lea
Mayo Clini
Mayo Clini
Mayo Clini
Mayo Clini
Wisconsin
Chippewa Valley in Bloomer
Chippewa Valley in Chippewa Falls
Chippewa Valley in Colfax
Eau Claire Home Health & Hospice
Franciscan Healthcare Arcadia Campus
Franciscan Healthcare Holmen Clinic
Franciscan Healthcare Lake Tomah Clinic
Franciscan Healthcare Onalaska Clinic
Franciscan Healthcare Prairie du Chien Clinic
Franciscan Healthcare Sparta Campus
Northland in Barron
Red Cedar in Elmwood
Red Cedar in Glenwood
Red Cedar in Menomonie

PRODUCTS/OPERATIONS

2015 Revenues

	$ mil.	% of total
Medical services	8,620	84
Grants & contracts	386	4
Investment return	233	2
Contributions	211	2
Premiums	144	1
Other	721	6
Total	**8,476**	**100**

COMPETITORS

Allina Hospitals
Ascension Health
Beth Israel Deaconess Medical Center
CentraCare Health
Children's Hospitals and Clinics of Minnesota
Dana-Farber
Fairview Health
Fox Chase Cancer Center
Gundersen Lutheran
HCA
Henry Ford Health System
Intermountain Health Care
Johns Hopkins Medicine
MD Anderson Cancer Center
Memorial Sloan-Kettering
North Memorial Health Care
Olmsted Medical
Park Nicollet Health Services
Roswell Park Cancer Institute
Scottsdale Healthcare
Tenet Healthcare
The Cleveland Clinic
Wistar Institute

HISTORICAL FINANCIALS

Company Type: Private

Income Statement FYE: December 31

	REVENUE ($ mil.)	NET INCOME ($ mil.)	NET PROFIT MARGIN	EMPLOYEES
12/17	11,993	856	7.1%	32,271
12/16	10,998	(480)	—	—
Annual Growth	9.0%	—	—	—

2017 Year-End Financials

Return on assets: 5.2%
Return on equity: 10.7%
Current ratio: 1.00
Cash ($ mil.): 66

MAYO FOUNDATION FOR MEDICAL EDUCATION AND RESEARCH

EXECUTIVES

Pres-Ceo, William Litchy
Pres and Ceo*, John H Noseworthy
Operations Administrator, Adrienne Palmer Fache
Senior Analyst Programmer, Craig Robert Stancl
Information, Gerhardt Hartke
Information Technology/Telecom, Jeralyn Waller Smith
Information Project Sp, Joe Woodie
Information Unit Head, Karen Laures
Assistant To Chief Technology, Kristin Olson
Net, Neal Briest
Information, Calvin Beebe

LOCATIONS

HQ: MAYO FOUNDATION FOR MEDICAL EDUCATION AND RESEARCH
200 1ST ST SW, ROCHESTER, MN 559050001
Phone: 507 284-2511
Web: WWW.MAYO.EDU

HISTORICAL FINANCIALS

Company Type: Private

Income Statement — FYE: December 31

	REVENUE ($ mil.)	NET INCOME ($ mil.)	NET PROFIT MARGIN	EMPLOYEES
12/13	1,069	6	0.6%	60,000
12/05	5,802	505	8.7%	—
12/03	4,822	348	7.2%	—
12/02	0	0	—	—
Annual Growth	—	—	—	—

2013 Year-End Financials

Return on assets: 75.4%
Return on equity: 0.6%
Current ratio: 0.70
Cash ($ mil.): 496

MCCARRAN INTERNATIONAL AIRPORT

EXECUTIVES

Prin, Chris Anderson
Coordinator, Brian Davis
Customer Representativ, Laura Prather-Harold
Management Analyst II, Michael Alonzo
Administrative Assistant, Tucker Field
Technician II, Anna Chenier
Software Superviso, Ashraf Younis
Nurse, Erika Hanuscin
Call Center Manager, Freddie Kirtley
Programmer Software Applicatio, Hema Kumar
Airport Program Administrator, Jeff Jacquart

LOCATIONS

HQ: MCCARRAN INTERNATIONAL AIRPORT
5757 WAYNE NEWTON BLVD, LAS VEGAS, NV 891118037
Phone: 702 261-5100
Web: WWW.MCCARRAN.COM

HISTORICAL FINANCIALS

Company Type: Private

Income Statement — FYE: June 30

	REVENUE ($ mil.)	NET INCOME ($ mil.)	NET PROFIT MARGIN	EMPLOYEES
06/19	565	83	14.7%	4
06/18	559	75	13.5%	—
Annual Growth	1.2%	10.0%	—	—

2019 Year-End Financials

Return on assets: 1.4%
Return on equity: 5.8%
Current ratio: 2.60
Cash ($ mil.): 504

MCCARTHY BUILDING COMPANIES, INC.

A company that was in construction before Reconstruction McCarthy Building Companies is one of the oldest and largest privately-held builders in the US. The general contractor and construction manager ranks among the top builders of health care education and green building facilities in the country. Contracts include heavy construction projects (bridges and water- and waste-treatment plants) commercial projects (retail and office buildings) and institutional projects (airports schools and prisons). Subsidiary MC Industrial handles energy auto and other manufacturing projects. Founded by Timothy McCarthy in 1864 the company is 100% employee owned and generates $3 billion in annual revenues.

Operations

As of 2016 nearly half of the builder's project portfolio was made up of Construction Manager at Risk projects while around a quarter of the portfolio consisted of Hard Bid projects. The rest was made up of Design/Build Construction Manager Owner Agent and Negotiated General Contracting projects. About 70% of its work came from repeat clients.

That year the company reported that it had 1600 full-time salaried and 1200 weekly payroll employees.

Geographic Reach

Headquartered in Saint Louis McCarthy Building Companies has worked on projects in 44 US states. Its offices are in Newport Beach San Francisco Sacramento and San Diego California; Albuquerque New Mexico; Las Vegas; Phoenix; St. Louis; Atlanta; Dallas; Houston; and Illinois. It does business in about 45 states.

Sales and Marketing

The firm gets more than 70% of its work from repeat clients which have included Kaiser Permanente California State University and Bally's Casino Resort.

Financial Performance

Ranked among the Top 10 commercial builders in the US McCarthy generates about $3 billion in annual revenues (as of 2016).

Strategy

McCarthy Building Companies has been steadily building its presence with new office openings in strong building markets across the US over the past few years with one of its most recent being an office in Lakewood Colorado in mid 2015. The company has also been growing through acquisitions of smaller companies that complement its existing service lines.

Some of the company's more recent contracts (around early 2016) include: the Genome Lab for J. Craig Venter Institute; the Chino Valley Solar project for Arizona Public Service; the Dallas City Performance Hall for the City of Dallas; the McCarran International Airport for Clark County; the Sacramento Recreation & Wellness Center for California State University; the San Diego and Paramount Unified School Districts in California; and the Lake Pleasant Water Treatment Plant for the City of Phoenix among others.

Some of its past projects include The Platinum condominium/hotel tower in Las Vegas expansion at M.D. Anderson Cancer Center and renovation and expansion of the National Baseball Hall of Fame and Museum in Cooperstown New York.

Mergers and Acquisitions

In October 2014 McCarthy bought St. Louis-based Castle Contracting and its subsidiary CastleGPS. Castle provided turnkey civil services utilities earthwork and trenchless technology directly to owners general contractors and mechinncal electrical and plumbing contractors. Castle's GPS technology provides "industry-leading" subsurface 3-Dimensional utility mapping. The acquired company would continue using the Castle brand name.

EXECUTIVES

Chairman And Ceo, Michael D. (Mike) Bolen
President And Coo, Derek W. Glanvill
President Northern Pacific Division, Richard A. (Rich) Henry
President Southwest Region, Robert (Bo) Calbert
President Texas Division, Michael J. McWay
President Southeast Division, Kevin Kuntz
President Mc Industrial, Tom Felton
Corporate President And Coo, Scott Wittkop
Evp, Ray Sedey
Evp Operations, Robert Betz
Vp And Cio, Mike Oster
Cfo, Doug Audiffred
President Central Division, John Buescher
Vice President, Drew Jackson
Vice President, Mark Heit
Senior Vice President And General Counsel, Matt Lawson
Vice President Business Development Houston, Wendell Rychlik
Senior Vice President Atlanta, Bobby Campbell
Vice President Finance Southwest Region, Christine Mostaert
Vice President Chief Estimator, Joshua Lawrence
Auditors: RUBINBROWN LLP SAINT LOUIS M

LOCATIONS

HQ: MCCARTHY BUILDING COMPANIES, INC.
1341 N ROCK HILL RD, SAINT LOUIS, MO 631241441
Phone: 314 968-3300
Web: WWW.MCCARTHYBUILDINGCOMPANIES.COM

PRODUCTS/OPERATIONS

Selected Markets

Commercial
Education K-12
Health care
Heavy/civil/transportation
Higher education
High performance/green
Hospitality/entertainment

Industrial
Native American
Parking structures
Science and technology
Water/wastewater

Selected Services

Negotiated general contracting
Construction management
Hard bid (lump sum contract for services)
Design/build
Construction management/general contracting

COMPETITORS

Alberici
Barton Malow
Bechtel
Clayco
DPR Construction
Gilbane
HBE Corporation
Hensel Phelps Construction
Korte
Peter Kiewit Sons'
Primus Builders
S. M. Wilson
Skanska
Swinerton
Turner Corporation
Tutor Perini

HISTORICAL FINANCIALS

Company Type: Private

Income Statement — FYE: December 31

	REVENUE ($ mil.)	NET INCOME ($ mil.)	NET PROFIT MARGIN	EMPLOYEES
12/19	4,513	0	—	4,266
12/18	3,852	0	—	—
12/17	3,574	0	—	—
12/16	3,265	0	—	—
Annual Growth	11.4%	—	—	—

2019 Year-End Financials

Return on assets: —
Return on equity: —
Current ratio: 1.40
Cash ($ mil.): 514

MCCARTHY HOLDINGS, INC.

EXECUTIVES

Ceo, Raymond J Sedey
Chb, Michael D Bolen
Pres-Coo*, Scott Wittkop
Exec V Pres-Cfo-Sec*, J Douglas Audiffred
Sr V Pres-Gen Counsel*, Matthew Lawson
Treas-Asst SEC*, Danel Dillon
Project Engineer, Adam Lampe
Engineer, Amanda Morgan
Project Engineer, Austin Everett
Superintendent, Edward Meade
Assistant Superintendent, Eric Fletcher
Auditors: RUBINBROWN LLP SAINT LOUIS M

LOCATIONS

HQ: MCCARTHY HOLDINGS, INC.
1341 N ROCK HILL RD, SAINT LOUIS, MO 631241441
Phone: 314 968-3300
Web: WWW.MCCARTHY.COM

HISTORICAL FINANCIALS

Company Type: Private

Income Statement — FYE: December 31

	REVENUE ($ mil.)	NET INCOME ($ mil.)	NET PROFIT MARGIN	EMPLOYEES
12/19	4,591	0	—	4,835
12/18	3,925	0	—	—
12/17	3,666	0	—	—
12/16	3,481	0	—	—
Annual Growth	9.7%	—	—	—

2019 Year-End Financials

Return on assets: —
Return on equity: —
Current ratio: 1.30
Cash ($ mil.): 85

MCHS HOSPITALS INC

EXECUTIVES

Prin, Jerard J Jensen
Physical Therapy Director, Amy Pearson
Occupational Therapist, Vivienne F Neerdaels
Chief Financial Officer, James Braun
Security Manager, Robert Pflanz

LOCATIONS

HQ: MCHS HOSPITALS INC
1000 N OAK AVE, MARSHFIELD, WI 544495703
Phone: 715 389-3258

HISTORICAL FINANCIALS

Company Type: Private

Income Statement — FYE: September 30

	REVENUE ($ mil.)	NET INCOME ($ mil.)	NET PROFIT MARGIN	EMPLOYEES
09/18	629	17	2.8%	1
09/17	82	(4)	—	—
Annual Growth	665.0%	—	—	—

2018 Year-End Financials

Return on assets: 2.6%
Return on equity: 17.8%
Current ratio: —
Cash ($ mil.): 10

MCLANE COMPANY, INC.

McLane Company is one of the largest wholesale suppliers of grocery and food products in the US serving some 50000 retail locations and 35000 restaurants across all 50 states. It delivers more than 50000 different consumer products to customers such as convenience and discount stores mass merchandisers wholesale clubs drug stores military bases and quick-service and casual dining restaurants. The company also distributes alcoholic beverages in the southeastern US and Colorado through subsidiaries. McLane is owned by Warren Buffett's Berkshire Hathaway and accounts for about a fifth of its revenue.

Operations

McLane operates through three business units: grocery distribution foodservice distribution and beverage distribution.

Its grocery business which accounts for about two-thirds of sales serves convenience stores and other retailers nationwide. The company's foodservice business focuses on restaurants across the country while subsidiaries such as Empire Distributors and Baroness Small Estates provide spirits wine and beer to more than 25000 retail locations in the southeastern US and Colorado. Food and beverage distribution together generates about a third of sales.

Geographic Reach

McLane has an extensive distribution network of some 80 facilities across the country with reach in all 50 US states. Its headquarters and grocery operations are based in Temple Texas while its Foodservice operation is based in Carrollton Texas.

The company supplies alcoholic beverages throughout the southeastern US and in Colorado through distribution centers in Colorado Georgia North Carolina and Tennessee.

Sales and Marketing

McLane is a leading supplier to convenience stores; other customers include discount and drug stores mass merchants wholesale clubs military bases and quick-service and casual dining restaurants.

The company is heavily reliant on former parent Walmart which generates about 20% of its revenue; 7-Eleven and Yum! Brands each account for about 10% of revenue.

Financial Performance

McLane's revenue has grown slightly over the past several years up 4% since 2016 amid intense competition.

The company reported 2018 revenue of about $50 billion up less than a percent from the prior year. A slight rise in grocery sales was mostly offset by a decline in foodservice sales because of a net loss in customers.

Strategy

Although McLane is one of the leaders in grocery and food distribution the business is low-margin and intensely competitive. As the company continues to expand by opening new distribution centers it is focused on technology and automation that can improve service while reducing costs. In late 2017 it opened what was its most technologically advanced distribution center in Findlay Ohio. The facility makes use of automation robotics and artificial intelligence among other technologies. McLane has continued opening distribution centers since then including a 2018 opening in Fort Worth Texas and a 2019 opening in Ocala Florida.

In addition to distribution center technology the company has also introduced a new mobile app (Mobile Virtual Trade Show or Mobile VTS) to simplify the ordering process for convenience store retailers.

Company Background

Starting as a family-owned grocery store in 1894 McLane expanded into wholesale distribution in the early 1900s. The McLane family including former Houston Astros owner Drayton McLane sold the business to Wal-Mart Stores in the 1990s. Conglomerate Berkshire Hathaway acquired McLane Company in 2003 for about $1.5 billion.

EXECUTIVES

President Mclane Grocery, Mike Youngblood
Evp Administration, James L. (Jim) Kent
President And Ceo, W. Grady Rosier
President Southeast Southern And Dothan Divisions, Ron Clark
President Mclane Carolina And Mid-atlantic Divisions, George Bolts
President Southwest And High Plains Divisions, Scott Braden
Svp And Chief Marketing Officer, Tom Sicola

Vice President Of Information Technology, Mona Huffman
Second Vice President Customer Service, Margo Star
Vice President Of Sales, Jimmy Morales
Senior Vice President, Charles Freeman
Senior Vice President, Julie Norris
Vice President National Accounts, Jeff Hayes
Vice President Of Distribution, Jackie Palmer
Vice President Of Logistics, Robbie Wainwright
Division Vice President, John Havel
Region Vice President, Calvin Parker
Vice President, Chris Short
Senior Vice President Midwest Division, Tim Donahoe
Senior Vice President Midwest Division, Matt Bowen

LOCATIONS

HQ: MCLANE COMPANY, INC.
4747 MCLANE PKWY, TEMPLE, TX 765044854
Phone: 254 771-7500
Web: WWW.MCLANECO.COM

COMPETITORS

AMCON Distributing
Associated Wholesale Grocers
Ben E. Keith
C&S Wholesale
Core-Mark
Eby-Brown
GSC Enterprises
Golden State Foods
Gordon Food Service
H. T. Hackney
MAINES
Performance Food Group
Reinhart FoodService
SUPERVALU
Southern Glazer's Wine and Spirits
Sysco
US Foods
United Natural
Wakefern Food

HISTORICAL FINANCIALS

Company Type: Private

Income Statement FYE: December 30

	REVENUE ($ mil.)	NET INCOME ($ mil.)	NET PROFIT MARGIN	EMPLOYEES
12/16*	48,016	0	—	20,128
01/16	48,144	0	—	—
12/12	37,389	0	—	—
01/09	29,800	0	—	—
Annual Growth	6.1%	—	—	—

*Fiscal year change

2016 Year-End Financials

Return on assets: —
Return on equity: —
Current ratio: 1.40
Cash ($ mil.): 122

MCNAUGHTON-MCKAY ELECTRIC CO.

Getting connected at work has a completely different meaning at McNaughton-McKay and two offices in Germany and Brazil. One of the largest employee-owned companies in the US McNaughton-McKay distributes some 500 product lines from manufacturers such as Hubbell GE Brady Belden Coleman Cable Leviton Thomas & Betts Cognex Specter Instruments and Rockwell Automation. It sells to the construction commercial government and industrial automation markets.

Geographic Reach

McNaughton-McKay Electric Company is headquartered in Madison Heights Michigan with about 45 locations across seven states and two sales offices in Germany.

Sales and Marketing

The company sells its products from its sales offices and as well as eSales Centers. In addition to the industrial automation commercial and construction markets McNaughton-McKay supports government customers on a Federal State and Local level by providing hundreds of electrical products and MRO supplies with local support and inventory. McNaughton-McKay's customers include supplyFORCE Vanguard National Alliance and Vantage Group.

Company Background

Founded in 1910 the Bull and McNaughton families ran McNaughton-McKay until 2006. It established a sales office in Germany in 2004.

EXECUTIVES

Evp And, Donald D. (Don) Slominski
Evp Sales And Marketing, Richard (Rick) Dahlstrom
Vp Information Technology, Gregory H. (Greg) Chun
Vp Finance, John D. Kuczmanski
Corporate Purchasing Manager, Maridee Curry
Auditors: KPMG LLP

LOCATIONS

HQ: MCNAUGHTON-MCKAY ELECTRIC CO.
1357 E LINCOLN AVE, MADISON HEIGHTS, MI 480714126
Phone: 248 399-7500
Web: WWW.MC-MC.COM

PRODUCTS/OPERATIONS

Selected Products

Bar code scanners and systems
Communication input/output (I/O) networks
Computers and peripherals
Convenience panels (cables and equipment)
Cordsets
Data-collection terminals and software
Drives and motor controllers
Engineered products
I/O products (AC/DC modules)
Motion-control products
 CNC controls
 Servos
 Spindles
Motors (AC)
PLC processors
Radio-frequency identification (RFID) products
Safety products
 Gate switches
 Light curtains
 Mats
 Relays
Sensors
Software
Vision products (inspection equipment)

COMPETITORS

Anixter International
Border States Electric
Consolidated Electrical
Crescent Electric Supply
Dealers Electrical
Electrocomponents
Graybar Electric
Hite Company
Kendall Electric
Madison Electric
Medler Electric
OneSource Distributors
Rexel Inc.
SUMMIT Electric Supply
Steiner Electric
Stuart C. Irby
W.W. Grainger
WESCO International

HISTORICAL FINANCIALS

Company Type: Private

Income Statement FYE: December 31

	REVENUE ($ mil.)	NET INCOME ($ mil.)	NET PROFIT MARGIN	EMPLOYEES
12/19	1,515	0	—	854
12/16	724	0	—	—
12/15	702	0	—	—
12/14	835	0	—	—
Annual Growth	—	—	—	—

2019 Year-End Financials

Return on assets: —
Return on equity: —
Current ratio: 3.30
Cash ($ mil.): 5

MED AMERICA HEALTH SYSTEMS CORPORATION

EXECUTIVES

Pres, T G Breitenbach
SEC*, Dale Creech
Cfo*, Timothy Jackson
Coordinator, Evan Ichikawa
Coordinator, Kimiko Johnson

LOCATIONS

HQ: MED AMERICA HEALTH SYSTEMS CORPORATION
1 WYOMING ST, DAYTON, OH 454092722
Phone: 937 223-6192

HISTORICAL FINANCIALS

Company Type: Private

Income Statement FYE: December 31

	REVENUE ($ mil.)	NET INCOME ($ mil.)	NET PROFIT MARGIN	EMPLOYEES
12/11	919	24	2.7%	10,700
12/10	843	67	8.1%	—
12/08	790	(153)	—	—
Annual Growth	5.1%	—	—	—

2011 Year-End Financials

Return on assets: 1.7%
Return on equity: 3.5%
Current ratio: 1.90
Cash ($ mil.): 42

MEDCO, L.L.C.

EXECUTIVES

Admin, Archie J Chapman
Office Manager, Henry Williams

LOCATIONS

HQ: MEDCO, L.L.C.
3701 DADEVILLE RD, ALEXANDER CITY, AL 350109075
Phone: 256 215-3889
Web: WWW.CHAPMANHEALTHCARE.NET

HISTORICAL FINANCIALS

Company Type: Private

Income Statement				FYE: June 30
	REVENUE ($ mil.)	NET INCOME ($ mil.)	NET PROFIT MARGIN	EMPLOYEES
06/09*	854	(173)	—	225
09/02	4	0	13.6%	—
09/00	2	0	13.7%	—
12/99	0	0	—	—
Annual Growth	—	—	—	—

*Fiscal year change

2009 Year-End Financials

Return on assets: (-999.0%)
Return on equity: (-999.9%)
Current ratio: 1.40
Cash ($ mil.): —

MEDICAL UNIVERSITY HOSPITAL AUTHORITY

EXECUTIVES

Exec Dir, Patrick Pawley
Auditors: KPMG LLP ATLANTA GA

LOCATIONS

HQ: MEDICAL UNIVERSITY HOSPITAL AUTHORITY
169 ASHLEY AVE, CHARLESTON, SC 294258905
Phone: 843 792-1414
Web: WWW.MUSCHEALTH.ORG

HISTORICAL FINANCIALS

Company Type: Private

Income Statement				FYE: June 30
	REVENUE ($ mil.)	NET INCOME ($ mil.)	NET PROFIT MARGIN	EMPLOYEES
06/08	821	(19)	—	4,000
06/07	749	26	3.5%	—
06/06	0	0	—	—
Annual Growth	—	—	—	—

2008 Year-End Financials

Return on assets: (-2.2%)
Return on equity: (-8.3%)
Current ratio: 1.50
Cash ($ mil.): 14

MEDSTAR HEALTH, INC.

Whether you're seeing stars or are just plain sickly MedStar Health can cater to you. The not-for-profit organization runs 10 hospitals and about 20 other health-related businesses across Maryland and the Washington DC area including Union Memorial and Georgetown University Hospital. With more than 3000 beds and 6000 affiliated physicians MedStar has a comprehensive service offering including acute and long-term sub-acute care emergency services home health care and rehabilitation. It also operates emergency clinics and assisted living and nursing homes maintains a primary care and specialist physician network (MedStar Physician Partners) and conducts research and medical education activities.

Operations

Along with its 10 hospitals and a dizzying array of inpatient and outpatient services MedStar Health also operates a Medicaid managed care program called MedStar Family Choice.

Its Nascott Orthotics and Prosthetics division provides adult and pediatric prosthetic services and devices to patients in Washington DC and Baltimore. The company provides a continuum of care from initial measurement to fabrication of the device and maintenance through four locations scattered throughout the service areas.

MedStar Health's Visiting Nurse Association (VNA) administers home health care infusion services private duty nursing and hospice as well as immunizations. The VNA also uses telemonitoring services to keep tabs on home care patients without having to physically visit each patient's home.

In 2014 the system had 148685 inpatient admissions and nearly 4 million outpatient visits.

Financial Performance

In fiscal 2014 MedStar Health's net operating revenue totaled $4.6 billion.

Strategy

Despite its already hefty size MedStar Health is not adverse to getting bigger. It grows usually through acquisitions of existing facilities but also through alliances with other health care providers. MedStar Health has acquired several hospitals in recent years including St. Mary's Hospital with 100 beds in southern Maryland and Montgomery General Hospital a 150-bed general acute care facility located in Montgomery County Maryland.

The company also grows by establishing new facilities. In 2014 it opened an integrated multi-specialty care center in downtown Baltimore as well as four new PromptCare locations in Maryland and Virginia. That year it began work on a new ambulatory care center at the 16-acre MedStar Health Bel Air Medical Campus. MedStar is also developing a new ambulatory care center at Lafayette Centre in northwest Washington DC.

MedStar Health has also entered the growing quick-care and urgent care market by partnering with Rite Aid to establish walk-in health clinics in a number of Rite Aid pharmacies throughout the Baltimore and Washington DC markets.

In 2015 the system expanded its Medicare Choice plan into Baltimore City and Anne Arundel Baltimore Charles Prince George's and St. Mary's counties.

EXECUTIVES

Evp Insurance And Diversified Operations, Eric R. Wagner
Evp And Chief Administrative Officer, Michael J. Curran
Evp And Coo, M. Joy Drass
President Medstar Ambulatory Services, Bob Gilbert
Svp And President Medstar Good Samaritan Hospital And Medstar Union Memorial Hospital, Bradley S. Chambers
Svp And Chief Nursing Officer, Maureen P. McCausland
President Medstar Medical Group, Richard Goldberg
President Ceo And Director, Kenneth A. Samet
President Medstar Visiting Nurse Association, Traci K. Anderson
Evp Medical Affairs And Chief Medical Officer, Stephen R. T. Evans
Svp And President Medstar National Rehabilitation Network, John D. Rockwood
President Medstar Health Research Institute, Neil J. Weissman
Svp And President Medstar Southern Maryland Hospital Center And St. Mary's Hospital, Christine R. Wray
Svp And President Medstar Franklin Square Medical Center, Samuel E. Moskowitz
Evp And General Counsel, Oliver M. Johnson
Svp And President Medstar Washington Hospital Center, John Sullivan
Svp Marketing And Strategy, Kevin P. Kowalski
Evp And Cfo, Susan K. Nelson
Vp Applications And Interim Cio, Mark K. Schneider
Svp And President Medstar Georgetown University Hospital, Michael C. Sachtleben
Svp And President Medstar Montgomery Medical Center, T. J. Senker
Vice President Cnio, Barbara Frink
Vice President Digital Marketing, Sameer Kasargod
Chairman, William R. Roberts
Vice Chairman, William J. Oetgen
Auditors: KMPG LLP BALTIMORE MD

LOCATIONS

HQ: MEDSTAR HEALTH, INC.
10980 GRANTCHESTER WAY WA, COLUMBIA, MD 210446097
Phone: 410 772-6500
Web: WWW.MEDSTARHEALTH.ORG

Selected Facilities

Maryland
Franklin Square Hospital Center (Baltimore)
Good Samaritan Hospital (Baltimore)
Harbor Hospital (Baltimore)
Montgomery General Hospital (Olney)
St. Mary's Hospital (Leonardtown)
Union Memorial Hospital (Baltimore)
Washington DC
Georgetown University Hospital
National Rehabilitation Hospital
Washington Hospital Center

PRODUCTS/OPERATIONS

Selected Affiliates/Operations

Clinical Research
Georgetown University Medical Center (Washington DC)
MedStar Research Institute (Hyattsville Maryland)
Home Health Care
MedStar Health VNA (Washington DC)
MedStar Health Infusion (Elkridge Maryland)
MGH Community Health (Olney Maryland)
Managed Care
MedStar Family Choice (Baltimore Maryland)
Nursing Homes/Senior Living
Franklin Woods (Rosedale Maryland)
Good Samaritan Nursing Center (Baltimore Maryland)
Belvedere Green (Baltimore Maryland)
Woodbourne Woods (Baltimore Maryland)
Primary Care
MedStar Physician Partners (Washington DC)
Outpatient Surgery Centers
MedStar Surgery Center (Washington DC)
Harbor Hospital HealthPark (Pasadena Maryland)
SurgiCenter at Pasadena (Pasadena Maryland)

COMPETITORS

Adventist HealthCare
Anne Arundel Medical Center
Ascension Health
Bon Secours Health
Carilion Clinic
Children's National Medical Center
Christiana Care
Civista Health
Franklin Square Hospital Center
GBMC
Harbor Hospital
Inova
Johns Hopkins Health System
Johns Hopkins Medicine
Kaiser Foundation Health Plan of the Mid-Atlantic
Levindale Hospital
LifeBridge Health
MedStar Union Memorial Hospital
Sinai Hospital of Baltimore
Suburban Hospital
Trinity Health (Novi)
University of Maryland Medical System
Valley Health
Virginia Hospital Center

HISTORICAL FINANCIALS

Company Type: Private

Income Statement — FYE: June 30

	REVENUE ($ mil.)	NET INCOME ($ mil.)	NET PROFIT MARGIN	EMPLOYEES
06/20	5,788	136	2.4%	33,000
06/19	5,690	187	3.3%	—
06/18	5,604	324	5.8%	—
06/13	4,217	311	7.4%	—
Annual Growth	4.6%	(11.1%)	—	—

2020 Year-End Financials

Return on assets: 1.7%
Return on equity: 7.0%
Current ratio: 1.30
Cash ($ mil.): 2,064

MEDSTAR-GEORGETOWN MEDICAL CENTER, INC.

Medstar-Georgetown Medical Center (dba as Medstar Georgetown University Hospital as a part of MedStar Health) is a 609-bed acute care teaching hospital serving residents of the greater Washington DC area including Maryland and Virginia. The hospital's staff of more than 1100 physicians represents a wide range of medical specializations including cardiology oncology neurology/neurosurgery and surgical transplantation. Medstar Georgetown provides a comprehensive array of inpatient outpatient surgical and rehabilitative care services. The hospital is part of a local network of affiliated primary care providers.

Operations

Medstar Georgetown's Transplant Institute is one of a handful of centers in the US that offers living-donor liver transplants; it opened a new medical space in 2014. Also Georgetown Neurosciences is the sixth unit nationwide to provide CyberKnife stereotactic radiosurgery for the treatment of tumors and lesions of the brain neck and spine.

Strategy

In 2015 Medstar Georgetown submitted a letter of intent with the District of Columbia State Health Planning and Development Agency seeking approval to modernize its existing medical facility by constructing a new state-of-the-art medical surgical pavilion. The pavilion will house surgical critical care and emergency departments as well as related administrative functions.

In 2014 MedStar Georgetown became the first center in Washington DC to perform a two-level artificial disc replacement in a patient's neck.

Company Background

In 2011 Medstar Georgetown became the first health system in the area to offer bloodless surgery to patients who prefer not to receive someone else's blood usually for religious reasons. There are three primary approaches to performing bloodless surgeries: before during and after surgery. Before surgery the hospital gives the patient medications such as iron supplements or epoprotein to boost the blood's hemoglobin level. During surgery the hospital is precise as it can be with its surgical techniques to limit blood loss and there are anesthesia techniques to lower blood pressure so patients bleed less. There is also a machine called Cell Saver that is used during surgery that collects blood lost suctions it into a canister washes and filters it and then returns it directly into the patient as a product that is about 60-percent pure red blood cells. After surgery medications are used to raise blood levels and medical providers avoid taking multiple blood draws for blood tests.

The hospital was founded in 1898 to promote health through education research and patient care. The current hospital/medical center was opened in 1947.

EXECUTIVES

Assistant Vice President Safety, Seth Krevat
Medical Director, Maral Skelsey
Vice President Foundation, Aaron Piccirilli
Pharmacy Manager, Dina Wolfe
Vice President Enterprise Analytics And Business Development, Jennifer Maher
Assistant Vice President Financ Planning And Analysis, Thomas F Knight
Medical Director, Tia Medley
Vice President. Financial Planning And Analysis, Patricia Grubb
Assistant Vice President, Maureen Stuart

LOCATIONS

HQ: MEDSTAR-GEORGETOWN MEDICAL CENTER, INC.
3800 RESERVOIR RD NW, WASHINGTON, DC 200072113
Phone: 202 444-2000
Web: WWW.MEDSTARGEORGETOWN.ORG

PRODUCTS/OPERATIONS

Selected Services

Anesthesiology
Audiology
Bloodless Medicine and Surgery Program
Bone Marrow Transplant
Breast Cancer
Breast Health Program
Cancer Care
Cardiology
Cerebrovascular Center
Colon and Rectal Surgery
Ear Nose and Throat (ENT)
Emergency Urgent Care and Trauma
Endocrinology
Epilepsy
Family Medicine
Fracture Liaison
Head and Neck Cancer
Headache Center
Hematology
Hospital Medicine
Huntington Disease Center
Hyperbaric Oxygen Therapy
Ophthalmology
Orthopaedics
Ostomy Clinic
Otolaryngology
Pastoral Care
Pediatrics
Pharmacy
Physical Medicine
Plastic Surgery
Primary Care
Prostate Cancer

COMPETITORS

Adventist HealthCare
Bon Secours Health
Calvert Memorial Hospital
Children's National Medical Center
Chindex International
Dimensions Healthcare
Doctors Community Hospital
Inova Alexandria Hospital
Providence St. Joseph Health
Suburban Hospital
Upper Chesapeake Health

HISTORICAL FINANCIALS

Company Type: Private

Income Statement — FYE: June 30

	REVENUE ($ mil.)	NET INCOME ($ mil.)	NET PROFIT MARGIN	EMPLOYEES
06/16	801	104	13.1%	4,000
06/15	774	98	12.7%	—
06/11	809	43	5.4%	—
06/10	782	45	5.8%	—
Annual Growth	0.4%	15.0%	—	—

2016 Year-End Financials

Return on assets: 23.6%
Return on equity: 31.3%
Current ratio: 1.90
Cash ($ mil.): 5

MEGLOBAL AMERICAS INC.

EXECUTIVES

Pres, Ramesh Ramachandran
Cfo, Niklaus Meier
Treas, Sumit Pathak
Contrl, William Leikhim
Customer Staff, Nicole Hunt

LOCATIONS

HQ: MEGLOBAL AMERICAS INC.
2150 TOWN SQUARE PL # 750, SUGAR LAND, TX 774791465
Phone: 844 634-5622
Web: WWW.MEGLOBAL.BIZ

HISTORICAL FINANCIALS

Company Type: Private

Income Statement — FYE: December 31

	REVENUE ($ mil.)	NET INCOME ($ mil.)	NET PROFIT MARGIN	EMPLOYEES
12/13	596	10	1.7%	15
12/12	597	13	2.2%	—
12/11	743	20	2.7%	—
Annual Growth	(10.4%)	(29.9%)	—	—

2013 Year-End Financials

Return on assets: 13.6%
Return on equity: 107.6%
Current ratio: 1.10
Cash ($ mil.): 5

MELLANOX TECHNOLOGIES, INC.

EXECUTIVES

Chb-Pres-Ceo, Eyal Waldman
V Pres Engineering, Roni Ashuri
Coo, Shai Cohen
V Pres Architecture-Cto, Michael Kagan
Cfo, Michael Gray
V Pres Worldwide Sls, Marc Sultzbaugh
Vp-Quality & Reliability, Ayelet Margalit-Ilovich
Vice-President Business Develo, Chris Shea
Marketing Manager, Blade Meng
Customer Staff, Einav Ezra
Vice-President of Business, Alon Webman
Auditors: PRICEWATERHOUSECOOPERS LLP SA

LOCATIONS

HQ: MELLANOX TECHNOLOGIES, INC.
350 OAKMEAD PKWY, SUNNYVALE, CA 940855400
Phone: 408 970-3400
Web: WWW.MELLANOX.COM

HISTORICAL FINANCIALS

Company Type: Private

Income Statement — FYE: December 31

	REVENUE ($ mil.)	NET INCOME ($ mil.)	NET PROFIT MARGIN	EMPLOYEES
12/19	1,330	205	15.4%	876
12/18	1,088	134	12.3%	—
12/17	863	(19)	—	—
12/16	857	18	2.2%	—
Annual Growth	15.8%	122.9%	—	—

2019 Year-End Financials

Return on assets: 9.7%
Return on equity: 12.4%
Current ratio: 3.70
Cash ($ mil.): 77

MEMORIAL HEALTH CARE SYSTEM, INC.

EXECUTIVES

Pres, James M Hobson
Pres*, Shawn Morrow
Sr V Pres*, Debra L Moore
Cfo*, Cheryl A Sadro
V Pres*, Leigh Bertholf
V Pres*, Diona Brown
Auditors: CATHOLIC HEALTH INITIATIVES E

LOCATIONS

HQ: MEMORIAL HEALTH CARE SYSTEM, INC.
2525 DESALES AVE, CHATTANOOGA, TN 374041161
Phone: 423 495-2525
Web: WWW.MEMORIAL.ORG

HISTORICAL FINANCIALS

Company Type: Private

Income Statement — FYE: June 30

	REVENUE ($ mil.)	NET INCOME ($ mil.)	NET PROFIT MARGIN	EMPLOYEES
06/16	545	22	4.1%	8,800
06/15	527	34	6.6%	—
06/14	557	25	4.6%	—
Annual Growth	(1.1%)	(6.0%)	—	—

2016 Year-End Financials

Return on assets: 2.9%
Return on equity: 4.8%
Current ratio: 3.70
Cash ($ mil.): 238

MEMORIAL HEALTH SERVICES

Where do you go after you get sick riding the tea cups at Disneyland? Not-for-profit Memorial Health Services (known as MemorialCare) owns six hospitals in Southern California including Long Beach Memorial Medical Center Miller Children's Hospital Orange Coast Memorial Medical Center and Saddleback Memorial Medical Center. The facilities have a total of more than 1500 beds and offer a full spectrum of medical services including rehabilitation diagnostic/radiology and emergency services. MemorialCare also operates women's health facilities and other specialty and general practice clinics as well as home health and hospice programs. The organization was founded in 1907.

Operations

MemorialCare's outpatient facilities include the physician practices of the MemorialCare Medical Group the Memorial Prompt Care urgent care centers and the MemorialCare HealthExpress clinics. The network also includes the affiliated practices of the Greater Newport Physicians organization. In addition to inpatient outpatient and home medical care the organization provides clinical training and graduate medical education programs.

Altogether the system's facilities employ 2600 physicians and serve 70000 inpatients each year. They also handle some 35000 surgeries 10000 births 200000 emergency room visits and 40000 home health visits.

Geographic Reach

MemorialCare's facilities are located in Los Angeles County and Orange County in Southern California.

Financial Performance

MemorialCare reported $1.9 billion in revenues and $83 million in net income in 2012. Most of the organization's revenues come from patient services.

Strategy

MemorialCare is expanding to meet continued demand throughout its service area. It has several projects either going on or recently completed that have added operating rooms neonatal beds more advanced technology and centers of excellence in imaging cardiac cancer and obesity at several of its hospitals. In 2014 it opened the new Lung Nodule Center at The MemorialCare Todd Cancer Institute part of Long Beach Memorial.

The organization is also expanding its outpatient care facilities. For instance MemorialCare has joined the growing trend of hospitals partnering with retailers to open in-store retail clinics (under the HealthExpress brand) that offer basic after-hours medical care through physicians and nurse practitioners. It has recently opened four new outpatient surgery centers and launched a couple of new physician locations in affiliation with UC Irvine Health.

EXECUTIVES

Senior Vice President Chief Financial Officer, Cheryl Sadro
President Ceo, James Hobson
Medical Director, Adam Wass
Senior Vice President Decision Support, Wendy Dorchester
Nursing Director, Carol Pilote
Medical Director Of Breast Surgery, Jane Kakkis
Vice President, Lpugh Kristen
Chairman, Keith Nelson
Auditors: PRICEWATERHOUSECOOPERS LLP LO

LOCATIONS

HQ: MEMORIAL HEALTH SERVICES
17360 BROOKHURST ST # 160, FOUNTAIN VALLEY, CA 927083720
Phone: 714 377-6748
Web: WWW.MEMORIALCARE.ORG

Selected Facilities

Long Beach Memorial Medical Center (Long Beach California)
Miller Children's Hospital (Long Beach California)
Community Hospital (Long Beach California)
Orange Coast Memorial Medical Center (Fountain Valley California)
Saddleback Memorial Medical Center (San Clemente California)
Saddleback Memorial Medical Center (Laguna Hills California)
MemorialCare Medical Group (regional)
MemorialCare HealthExpress (regional)
MemorialCare Imaging Centers (regional)
Memorial Prompt Care (regional)

PRODUCTS/OPERATIONS

Selected Services

Blood Donation
Diabetes Care
Heart and Vascular Care
Joint Replacement
Neonatal Intensive Care
Rehabilitation and Therapy
Wellness Care
Cancer Care
Gynecological Care
Imaging and Radiology
Maternity Care
Orthopedic Care
Stroke Care
Wound Healing
Breast Care
Express Care
Hyperbaric Medicine
Laboratory Services
Pediatric Care
Surgical Care
Women's Care

COMPETITORS

Adventist Health System West
Cedars-Sinai Medical Center
Childrens Hospital Los Angeles
Community Health Systems
Dignity Health
Good Samaritan Hospital (IN)
Good Samaritan Hospital (Los Angeles)
HCA
HealthCare Partners
Hollywood Presbyterian Medical Center
LifePoint Health
Methodist Hospital of Southern California
Pasadena Hospital Association
Prospect Medical
Providence St. Joseph Health
St. Jude Medical Center
Sutter Health
Tenet Healthcare
Trinity Health (Novi)
Western Medical Center - Santa Ana

HISTORICAL FINANCIALS

Company Type: Private

Income Statement — FYE: June 30

	REVENUE ($ mil.)	NET INCOME ($ mil.)	NET PROFIT MARGIN	EMPLOYEES
06/19	2,438	208	8.6%	6,000
06/18	2,232	101	4.5%	—
06/15	215	26	12.3%	—
Annual Growth	83.3%	67.6%	—	—

2019 Year-End Financials

Return on assets: 5.6%
Return on equity: 8.0%
Current ratio: 0.90
Cash ($ mil.): 100

MEMORIAL HEALTH, INC.

Auditors: DIXON HUGHES GOODMAN LLP ASHE

LOCATIONS

HQ: MEMORIAL HEALTH, INC.
4700 WATERS AVE, SAVANNAH, GA 314046220
Phone: 912 350-8000
Web: WWW.MEMORIALHEALTH.COM

HISTORICAL FINANCIALS

Company Type: Private

Income Statement — FYE: December 31

	REVENUE ($ mil.)	NET INCOME ($ mil.)	NET PROFIT MARGIN	EMPLOYEES
12/16	581	(38)	—	4,500
12/14	42	(11)	—	—
12/13	24	0	—	—
Annual Growth	185.6%	—	—	—

2016 Year-End Financials

Return on assets: (-6.8%)
Return on equity: (-28.3%)
Current ratio: 1.50
Cash ($ mil.): 16

MEMORIAL HERMANN HEALTH SYSTEM

EXECUTIVES

Ceo-Pres, David Callender
Chb, Wh Easter III
Chief of Medicine, Todd M Price
Coordinator, Melissa Aing
Director of Radiology, Alla Vargo
Obstetrics, Jennifer Weber
Director of Business Developme, Amanda Spielman
Head of Cardiology, Byron Auzenne
Chief Operating Engineer, Dennis Fults
Chief Administrative Officer, Keith Alexander
Quality Assurance Director, David Stowers
Auditors: ERNST & YOUNG LLP HOUSTON TX

LOCATIONS

HQ: MEMORIAL HERMANN HEALTH SYSTEM
929 GESSNER RD STE 1900, HOUSTON, TX 770242317
Phone: 713 242-3000
Web: WWW.MEMORIALHERMANN.ORG

HISTORICAL FINANCIALS

Company Type: Private

Income Statement — FYE: June 30

	REVENUE ($ mil.)	NET INCOME ($ mil.)	NET PROFIT MARGIN	EMPLOYEES
06/20	5,792	248	4.3%	14,000
06/19	5,528	270	4.9%	—
06/18	5,258	318	6.1%	—
06/17	5,061	313	6.2%	—
Annual Growth	4.6%	(7.4%)	—	—

2020 Year-End Financials

Return on assets: 2.6%
Return on equity: 6.1%
Current ratio: 1.00
Cash ($ mil.): 1,138

MEMORIAL HOSPITAL CORPORATION

Memorial Hospital tries to keep good health more than a memory for the patients in its care. The hospital is a 520-bed general hospital which provides a range of children's and adult health-care services and specialties including cardiac care cancer treatment trauma care women's services pediatric medicine and rehabilitation. The hospital has about 700 physicians on its medical staff. Memorial Hospital also includes the 100-bed Memorial Hospital North and Children's Hospital Colorado as well as outpatient clinics throughout the Colorado Springs area. In 2012 it became an affiliate of University of Colorado Health.

EXECUTIVES

Vice President Sales And Marketing, Char Longwell
Vp Of Physician Services, Vivek Abhyankar
Vice President Finance, Michael Ryan

LOCATIONS

HQ: MEMORIAL HOSPITAL CORPORATION
1400 E BOULDER ST, COLORADO SPRINGS, CO 809095599
Phone: 719 365-5000
Web: WWW.UCHEALTH.ORG

COMPETITORS

Banner Health
Centura Health
Exempla Healthcare
HealthONE
Poudre Valley Health System
The Memorial Hospital
University of Colorado Hospital
Valley View Hospital

HISTORICAL FINANCIALS

Company Type: Private

Income Statement — FYE: June 30

	REVENUE ($ mil.)	NET INCOME ($ mil.)	NET PROFIT MARGIN	EMPLOYEES
06/20	1,037	49	4.8%	2,438
06/19	1,051	97	9.3%	—
06/16	693	25	3.7%	—
06/15	612	34	5.6%	—
Annual Growth	11.1%	7.7%	—	—

2020 Year-End Financials

Return on assets: 5.7%
Return on equity: 21.4%
Current ratio: 1.10
Cash ($ mil.): 39

MEMORIAL HOSPITAL FOR CANCER AND ALLIED DISEASES

EXECUTIVES

Ceo, Craig B Thompson
Finance Manager, Brendan Phalan

LOCATIONS

HQ: MEMORIAL HOSPITAL FOR CANCER AND ALLIED DISEASES
1275 YORK AVE, NEW YORK, NY 100656094
Phone: 212 639-2000
Web: WWW.MSKCC.ORG

HISTORICAL FINANCIALS

Company Type: Private

Income Statement — FYE: December 31

	REVENUE ($ mil.)	NET INCOME ($ mil.)	NET PROFIT MARGIN	EMPLOYEES
12/14	2,035	71	3.5%	5,000
12/08	1,236	(51)	—	—
Annual Growth	8.7%	—	—	—

2014 Year-End Financials

Return on assets: 3.5%
Return on equity: 7.4%
Current ratio: 0.90
Cash ($ mil.): —

MEMORIAL MEDICAL CENTER

If you've lost the spring in your step and need a little care Memorial Medical Center will be there. As the flagship facility for Memorial Health System in Springfield Illinois this acute care and teaching hospital provides a wide range of medical and surgical services as well as emergency medicine and outpatient care. Its myriad specialties include cardiovascular maternity cancer care behavioral health orthopedic rehabilitation and burn treatment services. The hospital which sees 25000 inpatients per year also has special surgical divisions for bariatric procedures and organ transplants. The 500-bed hospital is a teaching affiliate of the Southern Illinois University (SIU) School of Medicine.

EXECUTIVES

Vice President, Robert W Kay
Physical Therapy Director, Jason Beeler
Vice President, Kevin England
Medical Director, David Gelber
Respiratory Therapy Director, Debbie Ramlow
Treasurer, Calvin Bell
Auditors: ERNST & YOUNG LLP ST LOUIS

LOCATIONS

HQ: MEMORIAL MEDICAL CENTER
701 N 1ST ST, SPRINGFIELD, IL 627810001
Phone: 217 788-3000
Web: WWW.MEMORIALMEDICAL.COM

PRODUCTS/OPERATIONS

Selected Services
Bariatric Services
Behavioral Health
Regional Burn Center
Regional Cancer Center
Da Vinci Robotic Surgery
EEG
Emergency Department
Express Care
Family Maternity
Food Nutrition Counseling
Healthcare Psychology
Hearing Center
Heart and Vascular Services
Intensive Care Unit
Industrial Rehab
JointWorks
Lab Services
Medical Imaging Services
Neurosciences
Orthopedic Services
Palliative Care
Rehab Services
Sleep Disorder Center
SpineWorks
SportsCare
Stroke Center
Surgical Services
Transplant Services
Would Healing Center

COMPETITORS

Decatur Memorial Hospital
Hospital Sisters Health System
OSF Healthcare System
Sarah Bush Lincoln Health Center
St. John's Hospital (Illinois)

HISTORICAL FINANCIALS

Company Type: Private

Income Statement — FYE: September 30

	REVENUE ($ mil.)	NET INCOME ($ mil.)	NET PROFIT MARGIN	EMPLOYEES
09/19	734	(13)	—	2,849
09/18	711	58	8.3%	—
09/17	682	63	9.3%	—
09/16	699	12	1.8%	—
Annual Growth	1.7%	—	—	—

2019 Year-End Financials

Return on assets: (-1.4%)
Return on equity: (-2.3%)
Current ratio: 1.60
Cash ($ mil.): 27

MEMORIAL SLOAN-KETTERING CANCER CENTER

Memorial Sloan-Kettering Cancer Center (MSKCC) leads the way in cancer research and treatment. The center includes the 500-bed Memorial Hospital for Cancer and Allied Diseases providing pediatric and adult cancer care and the Sloan Kettering Institute for cancer research activities. Memorial Hospital specializes in bone-marrow transplants radiation therapy and chemotherapy. It also offers programs in cancer prevention diagnosis treatment research and education. The Sloan Kettering Institute conducts medical and clinical laboratory research on cancer genetics and therapeutics. In addition to the main cancer center and research facilities in New York City MSKCC operates clinics in New York New Jersey and Long Island.

Financial Performance

MSKCC has showed steadily increasing sales in recent years as it has expanded its care network. Revenue increased each year between 2014 and 2018 showing an overall gain of 46% over the period.

Revenue grew 11% in 2018 to some $4.9 billion. Patient care which accounts for about 80% of sales showed a 12% improvement. Grants and contracts revenue grew 13% while contributions declined 12%.

Strategy

MSKCC is the largest private cancer center worldwide and ranks among the top cancer centers in the US. It is one of 50 facilities designated as a Comprehensive Cancer Center by the National Cancer Institute. To maintain its position the company invests in cutting-edge cancer technologies and conducts extensive research into next-generation medical treatments.

MSKCC has expanded its network over the years by renovating existing centers and adding new outpatient facilities. The company opened the Memorial Sloan Kettering Bergen outpatient treatment center in Montvale New Jersey in 2018. The facility offers chemotherapy immunotherapy radiation and other treatments to cancer patients.

Sloan Kettering Institute researchers work with physicians to develop more comprehensive and effective cancer care techniques. The institute also conducts clinical trials to develop new cancer pharmaceuticals; it is typically engaged in hundreds of pediatric and adult clinical trials.

To keep its various projects and clinical trials funded MSKCC counts on grants from a number of biomedical research institutions including the National Institutes of Health and the National Cancer Institute. It also receives a good portion of its cash through fundraising efforts and philanthropic donations.

Company Background

Memorial Hospital was founded in 1884 as the New York Cancer Center by a group that included John and Charlotte Astor. Sloan Kettering Institute was founded in 1945 by Alfred Sloan and Charles Kettering to research new cancer cures; the institute was located adjacent to Memorial Hospital. The two entities formed a coordinating corporate entity (Memorial Sloan Kettering Cancer Center) in 1960 and officially merged in 1980.

EXECUTIVES

Svp Information Systems And Cio, Patricia C. Skarulis
Evp And Cfo, Michael P. Gutnick
Coo, Kathryn Martin
Vp Facilities Management, Edward J. Mahoney
Head Of Surgical Metabolism Laboratory; Chairman Department Of Surgery, Murray F. Brennan, age 79
President And Ceo, Craig B. Thompson, age 67
Vice President Research And Technology Management, Eric M. Cottington
Svp And Chief Investment Officer, Jason Klein
Physician-in-chief And Chief Medical Officer Memorial Hospital, José Baselga
Chairman Department Of Surgery, Jeffrey A. Drebin
Evp And Hospital Administrator, Ned Groves
Evp And General Counsel, Jorge Lopez
Radiology Director, Michelle Ginsberg
Vice President Human Resources, Kerry Bessey
Vice President Human Resources Operations And Information Systems, Bill Morgan
Respiratory Therapy Director, Carmela Cunneen
Vice President Director Of Other Admin Financial Depts, Melvin McLean
Senior Vice President Patient Revenues, Ruth Lande
Director Of Radiology, Chester Mah
Director Of Radiology, Stefanie Jacobs
Director Of Radiology, Linda Aboody
Senior Vice President And Chief Information Technology Officer, Anna A Spitzer
Pharm D, Nina Cohen
Vice President Marketing Insights And Branding, Andy Kantor
Vice President Environmental Health And Safety, Erik Talley
Vice President Finance, Anthony Diasio
Vice President Marketing, Ken Marians
Vice President And Chief Information Security Officer, Michael Czumak
Svp And Chief Development Officer, Kenneth Manotti
Reuters Secretary, Maureen Flaherty
Secretary Iii, Debra Alston
Secretary Iii, Pascale Presendor
Secretary Iii, Mahon Ledgister
Med Secretary Iv (g), Michel Barbagallo
Secretary Iv, Sorita Alvarez
Secretary V, Noila Johnson
Secretary Iv, Nanci Prefach
Secretary, Simone Joseph
Medical Secretary, Tashara Mason
Medical Secretary, Bonnie Correa
Board Member, J Stewart
Secretary, Maire Brennan
Secretary, Danielle Bridges
Auditors: ERNST & YOUNG US LLP INDIANAP

LOCATIONS

HQ: MEMORIAL SLOAN-KETTERING CANCER CENTER
1275 YORK AVE, NEW YORK, NY 100656007
Phone: 212 639-2000
Web: WWW.MSKCC.ORG

PRODUCTS/OPERATIONS

2013 Sales

	$ mil.	% of total
Patient care	2,367	78
Grants and contracts	202	7
Other	455	15
Total	**3,025**	**100**

COMPETITORS

Aptium Oncology
City of Hope
Columbia University
Continuum Health Partners
Dana-Farber
Fox Chase Cancer Center
Johns Hopkins Medicine
MD Anderson Cancer Center
Mayo Clinic
New York City Health and Hospitals
NewYork-Presbyterian Healthcare
Northwell Health
Partners HealthCare
Roswell Park Cancer Institute
Sandford Burnham Institute
St. Jude Children's Research Hospital
Wistar Institute

HISTORICAL FINANCIALS

Company Type: Private

Income Statement — FYE: December 31

	REVENUE ($ mil.)	NET INCOME ($ mil.)	NET PROFIT MARGIN	EMPLOYEES
12/17	4,499	314	7.0%	9,325
12/13	582	0	0.2%	—
12/09	2,105	(195)	—	—
12/06	1,622	320	19.8%	—
Annual Growth	9.7%	(0.2%)	—	—

2017 Year-End Financials

Return on assets: 3.0%
Return on equity: 5.2%
Current ratio: 1.00
Cash ($ mil.): 1,139

MENTOR GRAPHICS CORPORATION

Mentor Graphics lends a hand to guide engineers who design electronic components. The company is a leading global developer of electronic design automation (EDA) software and systems used by engineers to design simulate and test electronic components such as integrated circuits (IC's) wire harness systems and printed circuit boards (PCBs). Products include PADS (PCB design) Nucleus (operating system) and Calibre (IC design). Its software is used to design components for such products as computers and wireless handsets. Clients come from the aerospace IT telecommunications and increasingly transportation industries. Mentor Graphics was acquired by Siemens for $4.5 billion in 2017.

Change in Company Type

Mentor Graphics supplies a crucial set of software products to help Siemens fill out its portfolio. The companies agreed to the $4.5billion deal in 2016 and it was finalized in 2017. Mentor Graphics became part of the Siemens PLM Software business in the Siemens Digital Factory division. Mentor's system design product portfolio adds to Siemens' Digital Enterprise strategy bolstering model-driven design methodologies with Mentor's electronic system design expertise.

Operations

Mentor Graphics creates system and software products most of which are sold through term software license contracts. It also provides service and support including professional services consulting training and other services.

Geographic Reach

Based in Wilsonville Oregon Mentor Graphics has US research and development operations in Colorado Washington Alabama and Massachusetts. It also conducts R&D in Armenia Egypt France Germany Hungary India Israel Pakistan Poland Russia Taiwan and the UK.

Financial Performance

Mentor Graphics reported increases in revenue and profit in 2017 (ended January). The company's sales rose 9% to $1.3 billion in 2017 from 2016 and profit shot up 60% to $155 million for the year. The company had robust growth in all geographic markets except for the US its biggest market with about 40% of sales. Japan was particularly strong in 2017 with sales jumping more than 35% while sales rose about 15% each in the Pacific Rim and Europe. The company credited the overseas growth to the timing of contract renewals and blamed the North America decline of 3% on weaker sales of emulation hardware systems and a slower rate of contract renewals for the year.

The 60% rise in profit to $1.3 billion in 2017 resulted from higher sales combined with lower special charges in 2017 from 2016. The higher profit helped boost cash flow from operations to $322 million in 2017 from $228 million in 2016.

Strategy

Mentor Graphics is moving to apply its processes to new businesses. The automotive business is one example. It has grown to 20% of Mentor Graphics' revenue in several years. The company is keen on driving its products into other transportation areas such as the design of electronic components in airplanes and trains.

HISTORY

Mentor Graphics was founded in 1981 by a group from instrument maker Tektronix to market desktop computers to design engineers. Throughout the 1980s the company was a leader in electronic design automation (EDA) software but the early 1990s found it in trouble. Revenues fell because of delays in upgrade releases and a worldwide recession.

In 1992 Mentor Graphics began phasing out hardware sales further disrupting operations. Texas Instruments veteran Walden Rhines became CEO in 1993. That year the company acquired CheckLogic a maker of testing software for integrated circuit (IC) design. By 1994 cost-cutting and product line restructuring returned Mentor to profitability.

The company bought ANACAD which developed design software for analog and mixed-signal ICs and Model Technology a very-high-density logic simulation tool firm in 1994. It acquired 14 more companies in 1995 and 1996 including embedded software tool developer Microtec Research (1996) which moved Mentor into the market for software development tools.

EXECUTIVES

Vice President, Henry Potts
President, Gregory K. (Greg) Hinckley, $619,000 total compensation
Chairman And Ceo, Walden C. (Wally) Rhines, $761,000 total compensation
Vp And General Manager Deep Submicron Division, Robert Hum, $319,725 total compensation
Vp Corporate Marketing, Brian Derrick, $350,000 total compensation
Vp Europe And India, Hanns Windele
Vp And General Manager Design-to-silicon, Joseph D. (Joe) Sawicki, $345,000 total compensation
Vp And General Manager Mentor Emulation, Eric Selosse
General Manager System-level Engineering, Serge Leef
Vp And General Manager Embedded Software Division, Glenn Perry
Vp Pacrim, Danny Perng
Vp Worldwide Consulting, Paul Hofstadler
Vp And Cio, Ananthan Thandri
Vp Focus Products Organization, Erich Buergel
President And Managing Director Mentor Graphics Japan Co. Ltd., Yukio Tsuchida
Vp And General Manager Board Systems Division, A.J. Incorvaia
Vp And General Manager Integrated Electrical Systems Division, Martin O'Brien
Senior Vice President, John Sturtevant
Vice President Manager Diretor, Subba Somanchi
Vp Human Resources, Paul Sale
Senior Vice President World Trade, Don Maulsby
Vice President, Ethan Manuel
Vice President Of Engineering, Guy Insley
Vice President Engineering, Juan Rey
Vice President, Dean Freed
Vice President General Manager Design To Silicon Division, Joe Sawicki
Vice President Americas, Veronica Watson
Treasurer, Dennis Weldon
Board Member, Kurt Takara
Auditors: KPMG LLP PORTLAND OREGON

LOCATIONS

HQ: MENTOR GRAPHICS CORPORATION
8005 SW BOECKMAN RD, WILSONVILLE, OR 970707777
Phone: 503 685-7000
Web: WWW.NEW.SIEMENS.COM

2016 Sales

	$ mil.	% of total
United States	488	41
Europe	254	22
Japan	87	7
Pacific Rim	335	29
Other	15	1
Total	**1,181**	**100**

PRODUCTS/OPERATIONS

2017 Sales

	$ mil.	% of total
System and software	794	62
Service & support	488	38
Total	**1,282**	**100**

Selected Products

Embedded software development
- Compilers
- Debugger
- Real-time operating system

Integrated circuit (IC) design and verification
- Analog/mixed signal
- Custom design
- Design-for-test
- Field-programmable gate array/application-specific IC design
- Formal verification
- High-capacity circuit simulation
- Interconnect modeling
- Physical optimization
- Physical verification & manufacturability
- Resolution enhancement technologies
- Static timing
- Synthesis

Printed circuit board design and analysis
- Design tools
- Digital high-speed

Integration interfaces and viewers
Layout
Library management
Radio-frequency/mixed-signal
Simulation and analysis
System-level design and verification
Accelerated system verification
Cabling design and analysis
Design creation
Digital simulation
Hardware emulation and simulation
Intellectual property
Process management
System-on-a-chip
Web-based development system

COMPETITORS

ANSYS
AXIOM Design
Altium
Autodesk
Blue Ridge Numerics
Cadence Design
CollabNet
Green Hills Software
Interra Systems
Intrinsix
PDF Solutions
QNX Software Systems
Silvaco
Synopsys
Wind River Systems
Zuken

HISTORICAL FINANCIALS

Company Type: Private

Income Statement FYE: January 31

	REVENUE ($ mil.)	NET INCOME ($ mil.)	NET PROFIT MARGIN	EMPLOYEES
01/17	1,282	154	12.1%	5,700
01/16	1,180	94	8.0%	—
01/15	1,244	145	11.7%	—
01/14	1,156	153	13.3%	—
Annual Growth	3.5%	0.3%	—	—

2017 Year-End Financials

Return on assets: 6.8%
Return on equity: 11.3%
Current ratio: 1.30
Cash ($ mil.): 441

MERCY CARE

Mercy Care is a not-for-profit provider of managed health care services in Arizona. The Mercy Care Plan provides these services under a contract with the Arizona Health Care Cost Containment System the state of Arizona's Medicaid program. The plan provides health coverage and prescription drug benefits to some 300000 members. The company founded in 1985 is affiliated with St. Joseph's Hospital & Medical Center (which is part of Catholic Healthcare West) Dignity Health and Carondelet Health Network. The plan is administered by health care management firm Schaller Anderson.

Operations

Mercy Care provides coverage to families children the elderly and the developmentally disabled. In addition to traditional HMO coverage the company also offers disease management and preventative health care services.

Along with the Centers for Medicare & Medicaid Services (CMS) Mercy Care provides qualified members with medical and prescription drug benefits. Its Mercy Care Long Term Care (MCLTC) offers services to those covered by the AHCCCS Arizona Long Term Care System (ALTCS) which accounts for 22% of revenue.

The Division of Developmental Disabilities Long Term Care serves members who are enrolled through the Arizona Department of Economic Security/Division of Development Disabilities (DES/DDD) which generates approximately 2% of SCHN's revenue. Through a contract with the DES/DDD the company provides medical care to qualified members.

Geographic Reach

Mercy Care serves the Arizona counties of Maricopa Pima Graham Greenlee and Cochise providing covered services to enrolled members.

Sales and Marketing

As part of its business Mercy Care provides patients with prescriptions through retail pharmacies mail order pharmacies home infusion pharmacies long-term care pharmacies and Indian Health Service/Tribal/Urban Indian Health Program (I/T/U) pharmacies.

EXECUTIVES

Vice President Of Health Plan Operations, John Monte
Board Director, Leona Brown

LOCATIONS

HQ: MERCY CARE
4755 S 44TH PL, PHOENIX, AZ 850408895
Phone: 602 263-3000
Web: WWW.MERCYCAREAZ.ORG

COMPETITORS

Aetna
Blue Cross Blue Shield of Arizona
CIGNA HealthCare of Arizona
Health Net
UnitedHealth Group

HISTORICAL FINANCIALS

Company Type: Private

Income Statement FYE: June 30

	REVENUE ($ mil.)	NET INCOME ($ mil.)	NET PROFIT MARGIN	EMPLOYEES
06/14	1,808	41	2.3%	500
06/12	1,747	28	1.6%	—
06/11	1,939	58	3.0%	—
06/10	1,904	49	2.6%	—
Annual Growth	(1.3%)	(3.8%)	—	—

2014 Year-End Financials

Return on assets: 12.6%
Return on equity: 23.5%
Current ratio: 1.20
Cash ($ mil.): 46

MERCY CHILDREN'S HOSPITAL

Children's Mercy Kansas City is a not-for-profit health system providing care services for youngsters in and around Kansas City Missouri. The system has two hospitals three urgent care facilities and five campuses featuring primary care offices and more than 25 specialty clinics. Among its specialized services are diabetes and endocrinology genetics heart surgery neonatology and rehabilitation. Children's Mercy also offers medical training and research facilities. Founded in 1897 the system today has some 500000 patient visits annually.

Operations

Children's Mercy has a medical staff of roughly 750 pediatric specialists. Its main campus Children's Mercy Adele Hall has 355 beds; there are an additional 53 at the Children's Mercy Hospital Kansas suburban campus.

The system performs roughly 20000 surgeries annually; it has around 200000 emergency room visits each year.

Geographic Reach

Children's Mercy Adele Hall is the only Level I pediatric trauma center between St. Louis Missouri and Denver Colorado.

It is a teaching hospital affiliated with University of Missouri-Kansas City School of Medicine University of Kansas School of Medicine and the Kansas City University of Medicine and Biosciences among others.

Sales and Marketing

Children's Mercy has recently begun advertising for the first time. It uses its marketing campaign in part to solicit donations as it relies heavily on philanthropy to manage operating costs.

Financial Performance

In 2017 Children's Mercy had revenue of $1.3 billion about 95% of which came from patient care services.

Strategy

Children's Mercy is in the midst of a multi-year $800 million expansion plan designed to more than double the size of the main hospital increase the number of patient beds by 50% add a new emergency room six new operating rooms new heart catheterization labs new educational buildings clinics and doctors' offices. A nine-story research tower will also be built atop an existing parking garage at the hospital's campus.

A large part of the funding for the expansion comes from philanthropic donations. Since the project began growth at the health system has included new urgent and specialty care centers a Pediatric Research Center new primary care centers and additional patient units and beds. The hospital has also undergone remodeling and expansion of certain existing facilities.

Children's Mercy has been expanding its research activities. It recently launched the Children's Research Institute to manage its research portfolio which includes gene therapy trials for leukemia and a cancer research partnership.

The system is vulnerable to potential reimbursement cutbacks that could result from the termination or reduction of the federal Children's Health Insurance Program (CHIP). Funding for the program temporarily ran out in 2017 as Congress deliberated on CHIPs future. Other public health care programs could also be shut down which would impact the system's ability to provide services to low-income families.

Company Background

Children's Mercy is a not-for-profit free-standing pediatric health system that offers low-income families a low- or no-cost health plan through the Take CARE benefit plans.

EXECUTIVES

Vice President Audit And Compliance, Kimberly Brown
President Ceo And Director, Randall L. O'Donnell
Svp Patient Care Services, Karen Cox
Evp And Co-coo, Jo Stueve
Evp And Cfo, Sandra A. J. Lawrence
Vp And Chief Nursing Officer, Cheri Hunt
Vp Market Development And Outreach, Warren Dudley
Surgeon-in-chief, George W. Holcomb
Pediatrician-in-chief, Michael Artman
Medical Director, Mamta Reddy
Medical Director, Ashley Daly
Vice President General Counsel, Sally B Surridge
Medical Director Office Of Equity And, John Cowden
Vice President, Kim Brown
Medical Director, Jeanette Higgins
Pharmacy Manager, Ashley Duty

Medical Director Geriatric Programs, Krista Nelson
Director Of Nursing, Dustin Hahn
Vice President, Jenea L Oliver
Chairman, Jack Ovel
Board Member, Kristi Canty
Assistant Treasurer Honorary Directors, David White

LOCATIONS

HQ: MERCY CHILDREN'S HOSPITAL
2401 GILLHAM RD, KANSAS CITY, MO 641084619
Phone: 816 234-3000
Web: WWW.CHILDRENSMERCY.ORG

Selected locations

Children's Mercy Adele Hall Campus (Kansas City MO)
Children's Mercy Blue Valley (Overland Park KS)
Children's Mercy Broadway (Kansas City)
Children's Mercy College Boulevard (Overland Park KS)
Children's Mercy East (Independence MO)
Children's Mercy Hospital Kansas (Overland Park KS)
Children's Mercy Northland (Kansas City MO)
Children's Mercy Olathe (Olathe KS)
Children's Mercy West (Kansas City KS)
Children's Mercy Sports Medicine Center at Village West (Kansas City KS)

COMPETITORS

Ascension Health
CoxHealth
Liberty Hospital
Saint Luke's Health System
Shawnee Mission Medical Center
Shriners Hospitals For Children
Sisters of Charity of Leavenworth
Truman Medical Centers
University of Kansas Medical Center

HISTORICAL FINANCIALS

Company Type: Private

Income Statement — FYE: June 30

	REVENUE ($ mil.)	NET INCOME ($ mil.)	NET PROFIT MARGIN	EMPLOYEES
06/16	1,020	35	3.5%	7,000
06/15	978	79	8.1%	—
06/13	9	(0)	—	—
06/11	816	13	1.6%	—
Annual Growth	4.5%	22.3%	—	—

2016 Year-End Financials

Return on assets: 2.8%
Return on equity: 4.0%
Current ratio: 1.70
Cash ($ mil.): 63

MERCY HEALTH

Mercy Health formerly known as the Sisters of Mercy Health System provides a range of health care and social services through its network of facilities and service organizations. The organization operates some 35 acute care hospitals (including four specialty heart hospitals and two children's hospitals) with more than 4200 licensed beds as well as 700 clinics and outpatient facilities in four Midwestern states. Its hospital groups include facilities for nursing homes medical practices and outpatient centers. Mercy Health also operates Resource Optimization & Innovation (ROi) its industry-leading health care supply chain organization and health outreach organizations in Louisiana Mississippi and Texas.

Operations

Mercy Health also operates three rehabilitation hospitals and two orthopedic hospitals. The system has more than 2000 Mercy Clinic physicians.

In 2014 Mercy Health had 150696 acute inpatient discharges; 158911 inpatient and outpatient surgeries; 631444 emergency department visits; 23213 births; and nearly 8.4 million outpatient visits.

Geographic Reach

The system operates in Arkansas Kansas Missouri and Oklahoma.

Mercy Health's outreach efforts include Mercy Ministries of Laredo a group providing primary health care and social services to residents of Laredo Texas. In New Orleans Mercy Health sponsors Mercy Family Center which provides mental health services; in Mississippi it funds a health care advocacy group.

Sales and Marketing

Commercial and other third-party payments accounted for 44% of net patient service revenue while Medicare and Medicaid combined accounted for 51%.

Financial Performance

Mercy Health's operating revenue increased 14% to $4.5 billion in 2014 as net patient and other revenues grew. However the system reported a net loss of $6.5 million that year (versus net income in 2013) as a result of interest rate swap agreement losses and higher expenses as well as lower investment earnings.

Cash flow from operations fell 46% to $354 million in 2014.

Strategy

In 2013 Mercy Health opened new facilities in Missouri (St. Charles and Wentzville) as well as a new heart and vascular center that centralized its outpatient heart and vascular offerings. The following year it opened a new orthopedic hospital in Fort Smith and a 60-bed rehabilitation hospital.

The system acquired Lincoln County Medical Center (renamed Mercy Hospital Lincoln) and its eight affiliated clinics in 2015 expanding its presence in eastern Missouri.

Despite its various expansions the Mercy system experienced the same industry challenges as its health care brethren including escalating medical and pharmaceutical costs and increasing self-pay bad debts (uninsured patients who leave their medical bills unpaid). Several of the health system's facilities have seen a decline in discharges.

Company Background

The organization was founded by the Sisters of Mercy of the St. Louis Regional Community in 1986 and operated under that model until 2008 when its sponsorship was transferred from the Sisters of Mercy of the St. Louis Regional Community to a new entity Mercy Health Ministry. The shift to the new sponsorship organization was made to allow lay members to join the Sisters of Mercy in sponsoring the ministry. It also reflected the growing number of lay people holding executive positions at the system's hospitals and on the board of directors.

EXECUTIVES

Pres-Ceo, Lynn Britton
Evp-Coo*, Michael McCurry
Evp-Cfo*, Shannon Sock
Vp of Information, Mike Mc Creary
Vp of Operations, Mike Mc Curry
Health Professional, Lora Petty
Chief Information Security Off, David Westman
Chief of Medicine, Edson Carrel
Information, Jon Allen
Executive Director, Ann Rucker
Svp Mission, Brian O'Toole
Auditors: ERNST & YOUNG LLP ST LOUIS

LOCATIONS

HQ: MERCY HEALTH
615 S NEW BALLAS RD, SAINT LOUIS, MO 631418221
Phone: 314 579-6100
Web: WWW.MERCY.NET

Selected Locations

Arkansas
Berryville
Fort Smith
Hot Springs
Ozark
Paris
Rogers
Waldron
Kansas
Columbus
Fort Scott
Independence
Missouri
Aurora
Cassville
Joplin
Lebanon
Mountain View
St. Louis
Springfield
Washington
Oklahoma
Ada
Ardmore
El Reno
Guthrie
Healdton
Kingfisher
Marietta
Oklahoma City
Tishomingo
Watonga

PRODUCTS/OPERATIONS

2014 Sales

	$ mil.	% of total
Net patient service revenue less provision for bad debts	3,838	85
Member revenue	477	11
Other revenue	194	4
Total	**4,510**	**100**

Selected Facilities

Arkansas
Mercy Hospital Berryville
Mercy Hospital Fort Smith
Mercy Hospital Hot Springs
Mercy Hospital Northwest Arkansas
Mercy Hospital of Scott County
Mercy Hospital Ozark
Mercy Hospital Paris
Mercy Hospital Waldron
Kansas
Mercy Health Center
Mercy Hospital Fort Scott
Mercy Hospital Independence
Mercy Maude Norton Hospital Columbus
Missouri
Mercy Hospital Aurora
Mercy Hospital Cassville
Mercy Hospital Joplin
Mercy Hospital Lebanon
Mercy Hospital St. Louis
Mercy Children's Hospital St. Louis
Mercy Heart and Vascular Hospital St. Louis
Mercy Heart Hospital St. Louis
Mercy Rehabilitation Hospital St. Louis
Mercy Hospital Springfield
Mercy Children's Hospital Springfield
Mercy Hospital Washington
Mercy McCune-Brooks Hospital
Mercy St. Francis Hospital
Oklahoma
Arbuckle Memorial Hospital
Mercy Health Love County
Mercy Hospital Ardmore
Mercy Hospital El Reno
Mercy Hospital Healdton
Mercy Hospital Logan County
Mercy Hospital Oklahoma City
Mercy Hospital - Tishomingo
Valley View Regional Hospital
Watonga Municipal Hospital

COMPETITORS

Ascension Health
BJC HealthCare
Baptist Health (Arkansas)
Barnes-Jewish Hospital
CHRISTUS Health
Christian Hospital
Community Health Systems
CoxHealth
HCA
INTEGRIS Health
Memorial Hospital (Illinois)
RehabCare
SSM Health Care
Saint Luke's Health System
Shawnee Mission Medical Center
Sisters of Charity of Leavenworth
St. Anthony's Medical Center
St. Vincent Health System
Tenet Healthcare
Universal Health Services

HISTORICAL FINANCIALS

Company Type: Private

Income Statement — FYE: June 30

	REVENUE ($ mil.)	NET INCOME ($ mil.)	NET PROFIT MARGIN	EMPLOYEES
06/20	6,519	(325)	—	8,800
06/19	6,509	(32)	—	—
06/18	6,254	243	3.9%	—
06/17	5,527	558	10.1%	—
Annual Growth	5.7%	—	—	—

2020 Year-End Financials

Return on assets: (-3.8%)
Return on equity: (-8.8%)
Current ratio: 1.10
Cash ($ mil.): 1,007

MERCY HEALTH

Auditors: ERNST & YOUNG LLP CINCINNATI

LOCATIONS

HQ: MERCY HEALTH
1701 MERCY HEALTH PL, CINCINNATI, OH 452376147
Phone: 513 639-2800
Web: WWW.HEALTH-PARTNERS.ORG

HISTORICAL FINANCIALS

Company Type: Private

Income Statement — FYE: December 31

	REVENUE ($ mil.)	NET INCOME ($ mil.)	NET PROFIT MARGIN	EMPLOYEES
12/18	4,860	(978)	—	35,000
12/17	4,737	456	9.6%	—
Annual Growth	2.6%	—	—	—

MERCY HEALTH PARTNERS

EXECUTIVES

Pres, Gordon A Mudler
V Pres, David Gingras
Chb, Richard C Lague
Treas, H Richard Morgenstern
SEC, Patrick T Kirk
Staff Rn, Erica Cousins
Internal Medicine, Mary Rosel
Staff Physician, Saundra Blanchard
Billing Supervisor, Jennifer Knapp
Director, Jerry Evans
Donor Relations, Joan Kessler

LOCATIONS

HQ: MERCY HEALTH PARTNERS
1675 LEAHY ST STE 101, MUSKEGON, MI 494425538
Phone: 231 728-4032
Web: WWW.HACKLEY.ORG

HISTORICAL FINANCIALS

Company Type: Private

Income Statement — FYE: June 30

	REVENUE ($ mil.)	NET INCOME ($ mil.)	NET PROFIT MARGIN	EMPLOYEES
06/18	666	36	5.5%	1,500
06/08	0	0	81.1%	—
06/06	0	0	50.7%	—
06/04	0	(0)	—	—
Annual Growth	96.2%	—	—	—

MERCY HEALTH SERVICES, INC.

EXECUTIVES

Pres, Thomas Mullen
Senior Vice President, Scott Spier
Senior Vice President, Claudia Keenan
Executive Vice President, John Topper
Senior Vice President, Robert A Edwards
Auditors: DIXON HUGHES GOODMAN LLP TYSO

LOCATIONS

HQ: MERCY HEALTH SERVICES, INC.
301 SAINT PAUL ST, BALTIMORE, MD 212022102
Phone: 410 332-9000
Web: WWW.MDMERCY.COM

HISTORICAL FINANCIALS

Company Type: Private

Income Statement — FYE: June 30

	REVENUE ($ mil.)	NET INCOME ($ mil.)	NET PROFIT MARGIN	EMPLOYEES
06/20	774	8	1.0%	1
06/19	766	30	4.0%	—
06/18	737	31	4.2%	—
06/17	705	50	7.1%	—
Annual Growth	3.2%	(45.6%)	—	—

2020 Year-End Financials

Return on assets: 0.6%
Return on equity: 1.6%
Current ratio: 1.50
Cash ($ mil.): 266

MERCY HEALTH SERVICES-IOWA, CORP.

EXECUTIVES

Ceo, Jack Weiner
Pres-Ceo*, Joseph Swevish
Pres*, Daniel Varnum
Cfo*, James Peppiatt-Combes
Gen Counsel*, Daniel G Hale
Prin*, Scott Leighty
Executive Director, Anne Voeke
Employee, Cheri Bowman
Director, Mary West
Desktop Netwk Supervis, John Edington
Executive Officer, Pat McDermott

LOCATIONS

HQ: MERCY HEALTH SERVICES-IOWA, CORP.
20555 VICTOR PKWY, LIVONIA, MI 481527031
Phone: 734 343-1000
Web: WWW.TRINITY-HEALTH.ORG

HISTORICAL FINANCIALS

Company Type: Private

Income Statement — FYE: June 30

	REVENUE ($ mil.)	NET INCOME ($ mil.)	NET PROFIT MARGIN	EMPLOYEES
06/18	969	31	3.3%	2,471
06/14	665	2	0.4%	—
06/05	546	23	4.3%	—
Annual Growth	4.5%	2.3%	—	—

MERCY HEALTH SERVICES-IOWA, CORP.

EXECUTIVES

Prin, Robin Edgar
Internal Medicine Practitioner, Natalia F Gabilondo
Family Practitioner, Teresa A Mock
Physician, Mark Johnson
Vascular Surgeon, Ali Mardan
Finance Business Manager, Connie Morrison
Marketing Director, Jason Monarch
Internist, Patrick Dunlay
Internist, Andrew Murray
Director Adult Day Care, Carol Klocke
Regional Director Phys Rev Cyc, Michelle Lohman

LOCATIONS

HQ: MERCY HEALTH SERVICES-IOWA, CORP.
1000 4TH ST SW, MASON CITY, IA 504012800
Phone: 641 428-7000
Web: WWW.MERCYNORTHIOWA.COM

HISTORICAL FINANCIALS

Company Type: Private

Income Statement — FYE: June 30

	REVENUE ($ mil.)	NET INCOME ($ mil.)	NET PROFIT MARGIN	EMPLOYEES
06/11	649	17	2.7%	—
06/10	632	19	3.0%	—
Annual Growth	2.7%	(7.9%)	—	—

2011 Year-End Financials

Return on assets: 2.2% Cash ($ mil.): 10
Return on equity: 3.5%
Current ratio: 0.40

MERCY HEALTH SYSTEM CORPORATION

EXECUTIVES

Ceo, Javon R Bea
V Pres-Cfo*, Joseph Nemeth
Optometrists, Kevin Walter
Optometrists, Becky Trujillo
Public Relations Director, Ronald Del Ciello
Procurement Staff, Steve Walker
Training and Direc, Wynn Biedermann
Coordinator, Kristin Hansberry
Coordinator, Karen Ellis
Coordinator, Jennifer Bestland
Patient Account Supervisor, Paula Boyce
Auditors: WIPFLI LLP MILWAUKEE WISCONS

LOCATIONS

HQ: MERCY HEALTH SYSTEM CORPORATION
1000 MINERAL POINT AVE, JANESVILLE, WI 535482940
Phone: 608 741-6891
Web: WWW.MERCYHEALTHSYSTEM.ORG

HISTORICAL FINANCIALS

Company Type: Private

Income Statement FYE: June 30

	REVENUE ($ mil.)	NET INCOME ($ mil.)	NET PROFIT MARGIN	EMPLOYEES
06/16	559	19	3.5%	2,200
06/15	523	12	2.3%	—
06/14	478	39	8.2%	—
06/13	473	21	4.5%	—
Annual Growth	5.7%	(2.5%)	—	—

2016 Year-End Financials

Return on assets: 4.0% Cash ($ mil.): 66
Return on equity: 10.9%
Current ratio: 0.60

MERCY HEALTH SYSTEM OF SOUTHEASTERN PENNSYLVANIA

EXECUTIVES

Chb, Christine McCann
Ceo*, H Ray Welch
Cfo*, Joseph Bradley
Asst Acct, Lia Onell
Scientist, Patricia Daly
Compliance Staff, Maryann L Cannon
Director Info Technology, Charles Welsh
Assistant To President, Janet Borger
Vice President Information TEC, Michael McCreary
Vice President, Brian Hannah
Manager of Information Securit, Joe Milanese
Auditors: DELOITTE TAX LLP PHILADELPHIA

LOCATIONS

HQ: MERCY HEALTH SYSTEM OF SOUTHEASTERN PENNSYLVANIA
3805 WEST CHESTER PIKE # 10, NEWTOWN SQUARE, PA 190732329
Phone: 610 567-6000
Web: WWW.TRINITYHEALTHMA.ORG

HISTORICAL FINANCIALS

Company Type: Private

Income Statement FYE: June 30

	REVENUE ($ mil.)	NET INCOME ($ mil.)	NET PROFIT MARGIN	EMPLOYEES
06/18	745	64	8.7%	8,050
06/15	88	10	11.8%	—
Annual Growth	103.6%	83.7%	—	—

MERCY HOSPITAL SPRINGFIELD

Mercy Hospital Springfield is an 890-bed acute-care hospital in the Mercy Health system. The facility provides health care to southwestern Missouri and northwestern Arkansas and includes the Mercy Children's Hospital Springfield. Other hospital specialties include cardiology and stroke care as well as women's and seniors' health cancer emergency trauma burn neuroscience rehabilitation and sports medicine. In addition to its hospital in Springfield Mercy Hospital Springfield operates a number of community clinics and specialty care centers in the area.

Operations

Mercy Hospital Springfield has about 700 doctors on its medical staff. The center sees some 441000 outpatient visits per year as well as 94000 emergency room visits and 37000 surgeries. It also enables more than 3000 births Specialty units feature a level I trauma and burn center (the highest ranking in the US) a neonatal intensive care unit a nationally certified stroke center and high-tech surgery suites (including da Vinci robotic surgery and CyberKnife radiosurgery centers). It also operates an air ambulance service.

Geographic Reach

The hospital serves patients in southwest Missouri and northwest Arkansas.

Financial Performance

The hospital's revenues decreased by 1% in 2014 due to 1% drop in net patient service revenue (which contributed 98% of the revenue) and a 11% decrease in revenues from other sources.

In 2014 the company provided charity care of about $26 million along with unreimbursed Medicaid expenses of around $17 million.

Strategy

That year Mercy Hospital Springfield opened the 60-bed Mercy Rehabilitation Hospital Springfield which is spread across a 63000-square-feet facility. The new $28 million building allows for more options for patient rehabilitation and will also serve as the region's only burn unit.

In 2014 the company also opened Phase II of its Betty and Bobby Allison Neonatal Intensive Care Unit (NICU) which expands the number of beds under NICU to 46. With this final phase complete Mercy permanently closed its former NICU.

Company Background

Formerly St. John's Regional Health Center the hospital's name changed to Mercy Hospital Springfield in 2012; the move coincided with the parent organization's efforts to to unify its brand identity. (The parent group's named changed as well from Sisters of Mercy Health System to Mercy Health.)

The hospital was founded in 1891 by the Sisters of Mercy.

EXECUTIVES

Executive Vice President Operations, Donn Sorensen
Senior Vice President, Joseph J Kelly
Senior Vice President General Counsel, Philip Wheeler

LOCATIONS

HQ: MERCY HOSPITAL SPRINGFIELD
1235 E CHEROKEE ST, SPRINGFIELD, MO 658042203
Phone: 417 820-2000
Web: WWW.MERCY.NET

PRODUCTS/OPERATIONS

Selected Services

Bariatric Surgery
Cancer Care
Children's Care
Heart Care
Integrative Medicine
Mother and Baby Care
Neurosciences
Orthopedic and Sport Care
Palliative Care
Pastoral Care
Senior Care
Trauma and Burn Care
Women's Care

COMPETITORS

Ascension Health
BJC HealthCare
Boone Hospital Center
Catholic Health Initiatives
Christian Hospital
CoxHealth
HCA
Heartland Health
Liberty Hospital
Tenet Healthcare
Truman Medical Centers
University of Kansas Medical Center

HISTORICAL FINANCIALS

Company Type: Private

Income Statement FYE: June 30

	REVENUE ($ mil.)	NET INCOME ($ mil.)	NET PROFIT MARGIN	EMPLOYEES
06/16	1,024	104	10.2%	4,400
06/15	948	93	9.9%	—
06/14	964	42	4.4%	—
06/13	965	87	9.1%	—
Annual Growth	2.0%	6.1%	—	—

2016 Year-End Financials

Return on assets: 24.4% Cash ($ mil.): 25
Return on equity: 27.5%
Current ratio: 4.60

MERCY HOSPITALS EAST COMMUNITIES

EXECUTIVES

President, Jeffrey Johnston
Vice President*, Paul Hintze
Attorney, Melissa Jackson
Internist, Carolyn L Koenig
Dermatologist, Brooke Shadel
Director of Home SE, Carrie Harrison
Exec Director, Chris Carter
Obstetrics, Christina L Byron
Project Manager, David Spreen
Chief of Pediatrics, John Mantovani
Pediatrics, Joseph Kahn

LOCATIONS

HQ: MERCY HOSPITALS EAST COMMUNITIES
615 S NEW BALLAS RD, SAINT LOUIS, MO 631418221
Phone: 314 251-6000
Web: WWW.MERCY.NET

COMPETITORS

BJC HealthCare
Memorial Hospital (Illinois)
SSM Health Care
St. Anthony's Medical Center
St. Luke's Hospital (MO)

HISTORICAL FINANCIALS

Company Type: Private

Income Statement — FYE: June 30

	REVENUE ($ mil.)	NET INCOME ($ mil.)	NET PROFIT MARGIN	EMPLOYEES
06/16	1,023	184	18.0%	10,000
06/15	940	132	14.1%	—
06/14	1,177	118	10.1%	—
06/13	840	82	9.8%	—
Annual Growth	6.8%	30.9%	—	—

2016 Year-End Financials

Return on assets: 29.1%
Return on equity: 31.5%
Current ratio: 4.90
Cash ($ mil.): 22

MERCY SCRIPPS HOSPITAL

EXECUTIVES

Prin, Andrew C Ping
Coordinator, Callie Huza
General Surgery, Alan Wittgrove
Security Manager, Anthony Roman
Manager of Patient Access, Erlinda Medina
Chief Staff, Jerry Glassman
Risk Manager, Kathy Maroni
General Surgery, Kimberly Peck
General Surgery, Mayyas Isho
Registered Dietitian, Eileen Ackerman
General Surgery, Leo Murphy

LOCATIONS

HQ: MERCY SCRIPPS HOSPITAL
4077 5TH AVE MER35, SAN DIEGO, CA 921032105
Phone: 619 294-8111
Web: WWW.SCRIPPS.ORG

HISTORICAL FINANCIALS

Company Type: Private

Income Statement — FYE: September 30

	REVENUE ($ mil.)	NET INCOME ($ mil.)	NET PROFIT MARGIN	EMPLOYEES
09/15	750	44	5.9%	77
09/14	623	3	0.6%	—
09/13	700	41	5.9%	—
Annual Growth	3.5%	3.7%	—	—

MERCY WOODSTOCK MEDICAL CENTER

EXECUTIVES

Principal, Napoleon P Abando
Dermatologist, Jeffrey Altman
Orthopedics, Marko Krpan

LOCATIONS

HQ: MERCY WOODSTOCK MEDICAL CENTER
2000 LAKE AVE, WOODSTOCK, IL 600987401
Phone: 815 337-7100
Web: WWW.MERCYHEALTHSYSTEM.ORG

HISTORICAL FINANCIALS

Company Type: Private

Income Statement — FYE: June 30

	REVENUE ($ mil.)	NET INCOME ($ mil.)	NET PROFIT MARGIN	EMPLOYEES
06/19	592	23	3.9%	1
06/18	584	25	4.4%	—
Annual Growth	1.4%	(8.6%)	—	—

2019 Year-End Financials

Return on assets: 4.0%
Return on equity: 9.0%
Current ratio: 3.10
Cash ($ mil.): 84

MERIDIAN HOSPITALS CORPORATION

Auditors: PRICEWATERHOUSECOOPERS LLP NE

LOCATIONS

HQ: MERIDIAN HOSPITALS CORPORATION
1945 ROUTE 33, NEPTUNE, NJ 077534859
Phone: 732 751-7500

HISTORICAL FINANCIALS

Company Type: Private

Income Statement — FYE: December 31

	REVENUE ($ mil.)	NET INCOME ($ mil.)	NET PROFIT MARGIN	EMPLOYEES
12/16	1,667	244	14.7%	5,200
12/15	674	64	9.5%	—
12/09	929	94	10.2%	—
12/08	873	(140)	—	—
Annual Growth	8.4%	—	—	—

2016 Year-End Financials

Return on assets: 9.6%
Return on equity: 18.4%
Current ratio: 2.80
Cash ($ mil.): 257

MESA UNIFIED SCHOOL DISTRICT 4

EXECUTIVES

Supt, Amber Conley
Site Manager, Theresa Chucri
Exec Asst, Alice Swinehart
Department Head, Allison Miller
Risk Management Specialist, Carmen Rocha
Secretary, Cheryl Farney
Specialist, Christine Niven
Music Technology Director, Douglas Akey
Counselor, Gary Ingle
Specialist, Holly Benza
Teacher, Jay Cryder
Auditors: HEINFELD MEECH & CO PC P

LOCATIONS

HQ: MESA UNIFIED SCHOOL DISTRICT 4
63 E MAIN ST STE 101, MESA, AZ 852017422
Phone: 480 472-0200
Web: WWW.MPSAZ.ORG

HISTORICAL FINANCIALS

Company Type: Private

Income Statement — FYE: June 30

	REVENUE ($ mil.)	NET INCOME ($ mil.)	NET PROFIT MARGIN	EMPLOYEES
06/19	617	39	6.5%	9,621
06/18	580	8	1.4%	—
06/16	549	(22)	—	—
06/15	531	(19)	—	—
Annual Growth	3.8%	—	—	—

MESSER CONSTRUCTION CO.

From casinos and courthouses to laboratories and dormitories Messer Construction has built them all. The builder provides commercial construction services (including design/build and project management) for projects in Indiana Kentucky Ohio North Carolina and Tennessee. Messer has done more than $300 million worth of construction with Construction Management Agency. It has clients in the life sciences higher education senior living commercial manufacturing/industrial public and health care sectors among others. Its projects have included the renovation of Michaelman Inc. Advanced Materials Collboration Center & Corporate Campus and Cook Regentec Build-Out & Renovations. Founded in 1932 employee-owned Messer boasts nearly 20% of its annual revenue from design-build projects.

Operations

Messer offers a range of commercial construction services including building information modeling cost planning and estimating integrated project delivery lean construction and safety programs. It also offers prefabrication services such as mechanical/electrical/plumbing services bathroom pods and health care headwall assemblies.

Geographic Reach

Based in Cincinnati Ohio Messer operates regional offices in North Carolina (Charlotte and Raleigh) Ohio (Cincinnati Columbus and Dayton) Indiana (Indianapolis) Tennessee (Knoxville and Nashville) and Kentucky (Lexington and Louisville).

Sales and Marketing

Messer has served customers from a variety of industries including aviation federal/military education industrial science and technology and corporate that including clients such as: Charlotte Douglas International Airport (CDIA) Dayton Airport US Army Corps of Engineer Wright-Patterson Air Force Aisin Automotive Casting DHL Express the Connor Group and Valvoline.

Strategy

Messer continues to work on high-value projects across a wide range of industries in the Midwest particularly in secure industries such as healthcare government and education. One of the projects is the Andrew J Brady ICON Music Center which Messer along with GBBN Architects CMTA Engineers Inc. The Kleingers Group THP Limited Cini-Little Harvey Marshall Berling Associates Dynamix Engineering and WA Architects consulted in. The center is set to open in the fall of 2020.

Messer also acquired EGC Construction an industrial contractor based in Newport Kentucky. One part of Messer Construction's strategy for growth is to increase its industrial and manufacturing work across the Midwest. The purchase of EGC Construction is the first time Messer Construction has acquired another construction company.

Messer's Operations Technology Solutions (OTS) department has been developing virtual mock-ups: problem-solvers and cost-savers that help ensure work is done right the first time. These virtual mock-ups are being used on projects such as the CONRAC at Cincinnati/Northern Kentucky International Airport (CVG).

Mergers and Acquisitions

In mid-2019 Messer Construction completed its acquisition of Kentucky-based EGC Construction an industrial contractor that specializes in design-build services industrial manufacturing processes and manufacturing and medical equipment installation and rigging. With the acquisition Messer gains access to EGC's miscellaneous metal fabrication shop and team of approximately 75 skilled trade professionals with expertise as electrical and millwright workers ironworkers pipefitters carpenters and laborers. Details of the acquisition were not disclosed.

Company Background

Formerly known as Frank Messer & Sons Inc. the company changed its name to Messer Construction Co. in March 2002.

EXECUTIVES

Senior Vice President, Bernard Suer
Vice President, Robert Verst
Operations Vice President, Mark Hill
President And Ceo, Thomas M. (Tom) Keckeis
Svp And Cfo, E. Paul Hitter
Vp And Cio, Richard A. Hensley
Vice President Human Resources, Karen Pawsat
Finance Vice President, Brian Doyle
Vice President Leed Ap, Robert Williams
Operations Vice President, Richard Zoller
Vice President Of Sales Development, Mike Malone
Senior Vice President, Jim Hess
Assistant Treasurer, Thomas T Kmiecik
Auditors: DELOITTE & TOUCHE LLP CINCINN

LOCATIONS

HQ: MESSER CONSTRUCTION CO.
643 W COURT ST, CINCINNATI, OH 452031511
Phone: 513 242-1541
Web: WWW.MESSER.COM

PRODUCTS/OPERATIONS

Selected Projects

Health Care
- Norton Healthcare
- Knoxville Orthopedic Clinic

Life Sciences
- Indiana University
- University of Kentucky

Higher Education
- Xavier University
- Western Kentucky University

Senior Living
- Graceworks Lutheran Services
- Episcopal Retirement Homes

Commercial
- IGS Energy
- Penn National Gaming

Manufacturing & Industrial
- Aisin Automotive Casting Tennessee Inc.
- DHL Express Inc.

Public/Institutional
- The Ohio Building Authority
- Commonwealth of Kentucky

COMPETITORS

Albert M. Higley
Danis
F.A. Wilhelm
Gray Construction
Hunt Construction
Pepper Construction
Shook National
Skanska USA Building
The Austin Company
Turner Corporation
Tutor Perini

HISTORICAL FINANCIALS

Company Type: Private

Income Statement — FYE: September 30

	REVENUE ($ mil.)	NET INCOME ($ mil.)	NET PROFIT MARGIN	EMPLOYEES
09/17	1,092	0	—	1,390
09/15	1,167	0	—	—
09/14	1,029	0	—	—
09/13	831	0	—	—
Annual Growth	7.0%	—	—	—

2017 Year-End Financials

Return on assets: —
Return on equity: —
Current ratio: 1.20
Cash ($ mil.): 83

METALDYNE PERFORMANCE GROUP INC.

EXECUTIVES

Pres, Michael K Simonte
Chb, Kevin Penn
Coo, Douglas Grimm
Cfo, Mark Blaufuss
Exec V Pres-Gen Counsel-Sec, Thomas M Dono Jr
Exec V Pres Sls, Russell Bradley
V Pres-Cao-Controller, Gary Ford
Auditors: DELOITTE & TOUCHE LLP DETROIT

LOCATIONS

HQ: METALDYNE PERFORMANCE GROUP INC.
1 TOWNE SQ STE 550, SOUTHFIELD, MI 480763710
Phone: 248 727-1800
Web: WWW.AAM.COM

HISTORICAL FINANCIALS

Company Type: Private

Income Statement — FYE: December 31

	REVENUE ($ mil.)	NET INCOME ($ mil.)	NET PROFIT MARGIN	EMPLOYEES
12/16	2,790	96	3.5%	12,000
12/15	3,047	125	4.1%	—
12/14	2,717	73	2.7%	—
Annual Growth	1.3%	15.0%	—	—

2016 Year-End Financials

Return on assets: 3.0%
Return on equity: 14.3%
Current ratio: 2.00
Cash ($ mil.): 209

METHODIST HEALTH CARE SYSTEM

EXECUTIVES

Pres, Larry L Mathis
Pres*, Mauro Ferrari
V Pres*, S Jeffrey Atcherman
Operations Administrator, Laura Espinosa PHD Rn
Chief of Medicine, Bruce Kennedy
Staff, Korsh Jafarnia
Health Professional, Sherrie Alexander
Scientist, David Raskin
Clinic Manager, Dominique Bookman
Manager of Academic Developmen, Jessica Uriarte
Manager, Melita Howell
Auditors: GRANT THORNTON LLP DALLAS TX

LOCATIONS

HQ: METHODIST HEALTH CARE SYSTEM
6565 FANNIN ST D200, HOUSTON, TX 770302703
Phone: 713 793-1602

HISTORICAL FINANCIALS

Company Type: Private

Income Statement FYE: September 30

	REVENUE ($ mil.)	NET INCOME ($ mil.)	NET PROFIT MARGIN	EMPLOYEES
09/17	1,536	161	10.5%	30
09/14*	1,199	151	12.6%	—
06/05	17	0	1.9%	—
Annual Growth	45.4%	67.8%	—	—

*Fiscal year change

2017 Year-End Financials

Return on assets: 6.8%
Return on equity: 10.0%
Current ratio: 9.10
Cash ($ mil.): 58

METHODIST HEALTHCARE MEMPHIS HOSPITALS

EXECUTIVES

Ceo, David Baytos
Pres*, Meri Armour
Chief of Medicine, Karen Hopper
Executive Officer, Willeen Hasting
Co-Minimum Data Set Coordinato, Shelly Neal
Scientist, Keeba Hudson
Coordinator, Teresa Berkley
Executive Officer, Cato Johnson
Chief Financial Officer, Chuck Lane
Diagnostic Radiologist, Davis Moser
Director of Him, Dee White
Auditors: DIXON HUGHES GOODMAN LLP ASHE

LOCATIONS

HQ: METHODIST HEALTHCARE MEMPHIS HOSPITALS
1265 UNION AVE, MEMPHIS, TN 381043415
Phone: 901 516-7000
Web: WWW.METHODISTHEALTH.ORG

HISTORICAL FINANCIALS

Company Type: Private

Income Statement FYE: December 31

	REVENUE ($ mil.)	NET INCOME ($ mil.)	NET PROFIT MARGIN	EMPLOYEES
12/17	2,101	101	4.8%	7,000
12/02	784	(26)	—	—
12/01	717	(28)	—	—
Annual Growth	6.9%	—	—	—

METROHEALTH MEDICAL CENTER

LOCATIONS

HQ: METROHEALTH MEDICAL CENTER
2500 METROHEALTH DR, CLEVELAND, OH 441091900
Phone: 216 778-7800
Web: WWW.METROHEALTH.ORG

HISTORICAL FINANCIALS

Company Type: Private

Income Statement FYE: December 31

	REVENUE ($ mil.)	NET INCOME ($ mil.)	NET PROFIT MARGIN	EMPLOYEES
12/16	883	(8)	—	6,000
12/15	795	35	4.5%	—
12/14	782	32	4.2%	—
Annual Growth	6.3%	—	—	—

2016 Year-End Financials

Return on assets: (-0.8%)
Return on equity: (-4.9%)
Current ratio: 1.30
Cash ($ mil.): 11

METROPOLITAN EDISON COMPANY

Metropolitan Edison is an electric company and it knows a thing or two about serving cities and surrounding communities. The company a subsidiary of holding company FirstEnergy provides electric services to a population of 1.3 million in a 3300-sq. ml. service area in south central and eastern Pennsylvania. Metropolitan Edison or Met-Ed as it is sometimes referred to operates almost 16500 miles of power transmission and distribution lines. Although the company's primary source of electricity is derived from oil-and gas-fired units its York Haven Power Company generates hydroelectric power.

EXECUTIVES

Exec V Pres-Cfo, Mark T Clark
V Pres-Controller-Cao, Harvey L Wagner
Exec V Pres-Gen Counsel, Leila L Vespoli
V Pres-Treas, James F Pearson
Real Estate Consultant, Craig Correll
Clerk, Michelle Frey
Supervisor Engineering, Alfred Nerino
Customer Associate, Matthew Kemp
Manager Forestry, Doug Kinyo
Manager Regional Operations, James Frey
Clerk, Susan Youst
Auditors: PRICEWATERHOUSECOOPERS LLP CL

LOCATIONS

HQ: METROPOLITAN EDISON COMPANY
76 S MAIN ST, AKRON, OH 443081812
Phone: 800 736-3402
Web: WWW.FIRSTENERGYCORP.COM

COMPETITORS

Columbia Gas of Pennsylvania
Direct Energy
PECO Energy
PPL Electric

HISTORICAL FINANCIALS

Company Type: Private

Income Statement FYE: December 31

	REVENUE ($ mil.)	NET INCOME ($ mil.)	NET PROFIT MARGIN	EMPLOYEES
12/17	837	97	11.6%	678
12/16	865	87	10.1%	—
12/10	1,818	58	3.2%	—
12/09	1,688	55	3.3%	—
Annual Growth	(8.4%)	7.3%	—	—

2017 Year-End Financials

Return on assets: 2.7%
Return on equity: 10.4%
Current ratio: 1.50
Cash ($ mil.): —

METROPOLITAN GOVERNMENT OF NASHVILLE & DAVIDSON COUNTY

Memphis may have the blues but Nashville has that country sound. Tennessee's second-largest city (with about 600000 people) is home to many recording studios music labels and thousands of working musicians. The city also has a large health care community with two Fortune 500 companies - HCA and Community Health Systems- employing thousands of people.

EXECUTIVES

Mayor, John Cooper
Chief of Staff, Debby D Mason
Staff, Steve Glover
Information Specialist, Kale Lawson
Executive Director, Brenda Ramsey
Information Specialist, Matthew Keaton
Finance Officer II, Alan Enzo
Marketing Specialist, Amanda Clelland
Director of Corporate, Amanda Tate
Director Quality, Dan Freudberg
Human Resources Manager, Kent Minich

LOCATIONS

HQ: METROPOLITAN GOVERNMENT OF NASHVILLE & DAVIDSON COUNTY
100 METRO COURTHOUSE, NASHVILLE, TN 37201
Phone: 615 862-5000
Web: WWW.NASHVILLE.GOV

HISTORICAL FINANCIALS

Company Type: Private

Income Statement FYE: June 30

	REVENUE ($ mil.)	NET INCOME ($ mil.)	NET PROFIT MARGIN	EMPLOYEES
06/19	2,605	416	16.0%	18,000
06/18	2,462	(517)	—	—
06/17	2,367	130	5.5%	—
06/16	2,271	172	7.6%	—
Annual Growth	4.7%	34.3%	—	—

2019 Year-End Financials

Return on assets: 2.8%
Return on equity: 113.7%
Current ratio: —
Cash ($ mil.): 1,440

METROPOLITAN TRANSPORTATION AUTHORITY

The largest public transportation system in the US New York City's Metropolitan Transportation Authority (MTA) provides about 2.6 billion passenger trips and sees about 380 million vehicles travel its system annually. The MTA's largest agency the New York City Transit Authority operates about 8700 rail and subway cars that provide service across New York's five boroughs; it also runs a fleet of some 5900 buses. Other MTA units offer bus and rail service to Connecticut and Long Island and operate the Triborough system of toll bridges and tunnels.

Strategy

The government-owned MTA a public-benefit corporation chartered by the New York Legislature in 1965 operates with an annual budget of $12.6 billion. The system has been working to become more self-sufficient in recent years but it has battled persistent operating losses brought on by among other causes high operating costs and the struggling US economy. In an attempt to reduce its expenses the company in 2010 cut payroll by 20% at its headquarters and 15% at other agencies. The MTA has also bolstered its revenue through increased fares and tolls and freed up capital by restructuring its debt at lower interest rates.

While it is making cuts in some areas the MTA is investing in capital improvements to its system including extending the Long Island Rail Road to Grand Central Station and creating a direct link between John F. Kennedy Airport and downtown Manhattan. Other key projects have included the construction of the Second Avenue Subway and renovations at the Fulton Street Transit Center. The MTA also is looking at installing wireless Internet access on its Metro-North and Long Island rail lines' trains.

EXECUTIVES

Cfo, Robert E. (Bob) Foran
Executive Officer Corporate Communications Marketing And Branding, John McKay
Director Security, Raymond Diaz
Coo, Phil Eng
Interim Executive Director, Veronique Hakim
President Mta Bridges And Tunnels, Cedrick Fulton
Chairman, Joseph J. Lhota
Auditors: DELOITTE & TOUCHE LLP NEW YOR

LOCATIONS

HQ: METROPOLITAN TRANSPORTATION AUTHORITY
2 BROADWAY BSMT B, NEW YORK, NY 100043354
Phone: 212 878-7000
Web: WWW.MTA.INFO

PRODUCTS/OPERATIONS

Selected Operations

Bus

Long Island Bus
MTA Bus Company
New York City Transit

Commuter Rail

Long Island Rail Road
Metro-North Railroad
Staten Island Railway

HISTORICAL FINANCIALS

Company Type: Private

Income Statement — FYE: December 31

	REVENUE ($ mil.)	NET INCOME ($ mil.)	NET PROFIT MARGIN	EMPLOYEES
12/19	9,043	502	5.6%	67,457
12/18	8,736	(145)	—	—
12/17	8	(0)	—	—
12/16	8,527	(271)	—	—
Annual Growth	2.0%	—	—	—

2019 Year-End Financials

Return on assets: 0.5%
Return on equity: 11.3%
Current ratio: 0.80
Cash ($ mil.): 554

METROPOLITAN WATER RECLAMATION DISTRICT OF GREATER CHICAGO

EXECUTIVES

Exec Dir, Brian Perkovich
V Pres, Kathleen Meany
Chief of Mno, Thomas O Conner
Principal, Jeff Weber
Actng Public Info Coordinat, Mary Carroll
Accounting Staff, Marilyn Torres
Scientist, Weizhe An
Executive Officer, Joe Cannici
Scientist, Ali Oskouie
Program Inspector, Dwayne Logan
Administrator, Larry Williams
Auditors: RSM US LLP CHICAGO ILLINOIS

LOCATIONS

HQ: METROPOLITAN WATER RECLAMATION DISTRICT OF GREATER CHICAGO
100 E ERIE ST, CHICAGO, IL 606112829
Phone: 312 751-5600
Web: WWW.MWRD.ORG

HISTORICAL FINANCIALS

Company Type: Private

Income Statement — FYE: December 31

	REVENUE ($ mil.)	NET INCOME ($ mil.)	NET PROFIT MARGIN	EMPLOYEES
12/19	792	116	14.7%	2,259
12/18	755	107	14.2%	—
12/17	719	76	10.6%	—
12/16	703	10	1.5%	—
Annual Growth	4.0%	121.2%	—	—

2019 Year-End Financials

Return on assets: 1.2%
Return on equity: 2.5%
Current ratio: 0.20
Cash ($ mil.): 246

MFA INCORPORATED

Agricultural cooperative MFA brings together 45000 farmers in Missouri and adjacent states. One of the US' oldest regional co-ops supplying its member/owners with agronomy distribution financing and purchasing services it runs more than 145 retail farm supply centers and works with independent dealers. MFA supplies animal feeds seed fertilizer and crop protection products. The co-op also provides its members with agronomy services animal-health products and farm supplies. It also offers marketing services and is the publisher of Today's Farmer. The company's about 105 company-owned MFA Agri Services Centers combined with more than 25 locally owned MFA affiliates with about 25 branch locations contrast nicely with its approximately 400 independent dealers.

Operations

MFA's services include credit and finance crop insurance health track powercalf precision agronomy among others. MFA's Animal Health division provides its retail operations a good mix of over the counter (OTC) labeled medications and vaccines along with staff at the dealer locations. The crop protection division sells roughly 850 products from over 40 different vendors to meet the demand of producers. This division's products include but are not limited to pesticides - row crops aquatic range/pasture stored grain vineyards and lawn/garden foliar nutrition fertilizer stabilizers adjuvants and seed treatments and biological. Other product offerings include equine farm supply feed lawn and garden and pets among others.

With the combination of its core business subsidiaries and joint ventures the company delivers sales of about one billion dollars annually.

Geographic Reach

The company's corporate office is located in Columbia Missouri. The coop has fertilizer terminals on the Mississippi River as well as on the Missouri and Arkansas rivers.

Sales and Marketing

The coop sells through 400 independent dealers. MFA offers the best products and state-of-the-art services through its MFA Agri Services affiliates and partners. MFA also offers timely wholesale products to agricultural companies.

Company Background

Expanding its assets in 2013 MFA acquired Producers Grain Company's assets in El Dorado Springs Walker Bronaugh and Nevada in Missouri.

The co-op was established in 1914 when seven Missouri farmers got together to buy binder twine.

EXECUTIVES

Svp Corporate And Member Services, Janice Schuerman
Svp Corporate Operations, J. Brian Griffith
Svp Agri Services Division, Bill Streeter
Vp Feed Operations And Animal Health, Alan Wessler
Svp And Cfo, Ernie Verslues
Vp Plant Foods And Transportation, Bill Coen
Vp Crop Protection Seed And Farm Supply, Don Houston
Vp Agri Services, Craig Childs
Senior Vice President Corporate Operations, Brian Griffith
Second Vice President Finance, David Moore
Vice President And General Manager, Cassy Landewee
Vice Chairman, John Moffitt
Chairman, Don Mills
Treasurer, John Akridge
Recording Secretary, Allen Smith
Auditors: WILLIAMS KEEPERS LLC COLUMBIA

LOCATIONS

HQ: MFA INCORPORATED
201 RAY YOUNG DR, COLUMBIA, MO 652013599
Phone: 573 874-5111
Web: WWW.CENTRALIAMFA.COM

COMPETITORS

ADM
Andersons
Cargill
Farm Service Cooperative
Farmers Cooperative Company
GROWMARK
Heartland Co-op
Missouri Farm Bureau
Orscheln Farm and Home
Tennessee Farmers Co-op
United Producers

HISTORICAL FINANCIALS

Company Type: Private

Income Statement — FYE: August 31

	REVENUE ($ mil.)	NET INCOME ($ mil.)	NET PROFIT MARGIN	EMPLOYEES
08/19	1,160	(9)	—	1,393
08/18	1,367	6	0.5%	—
08/17	1,373	14	1.0%	—
08/16	1,192	4	0.3%	—
Annual Growth	(0.9%)	—	—	—

MGM HOLDINGS, INC.

EXECUTIVES

Ceo, Gary Barber
Pres, Mark Burnett
Is Acquisitions Coordinator, Elizabeth Brouillette
Computer Operations Administra, Keith Pennington
Executive Vice President, Kristin Cotich
Pres Orion Unscripted & Alt TV, Barry Poznick
Director Information Technolog, Todd Woods
Web Content Manager, Amir Noori
Senior Vice President, Kelly Campbell
Executive Vice President Globa, Robert Marick
Chief Marketing Officer, Stephen Bruno
Auditors: ERNST & YOUNG LLP LOS ANGELES

LOCATIONS

HQ: MGM HOLDINGS, INC.
245 N BEVERLY DR, BEVERLY HILLS, CA 902105319
Phone: 310 449-3000
Web: WWW.MGM.COM

HISTORICAL FINANCIALS

Company Type: Private

Income Statement — FYE: December 31

	REVENUE ($ mil.)	NET INCOME ($ mil.)	NET PROFIT MARGIN	EMPLOYEES
12/16	1,184	155	13.1%	4
12/15	1,158	252	21.8%	—
Annual Growth	2.2%	(38.5%)	—	—

MIAMI CHILDREN'S HEALTH SYSTEM MANAGEMENT SERVICES, LLC

EXECUTIVES

Chm, Mario Morgado
Chm, Mario Murgado
V Chm, Michael Fux
Treas-SEC, Tim Birkenstock
Svp-Gen Coun, Jodi B Laurence
Cfo, Arianna Urquia
Vp Clinical Affairs, Elizabeth Menocal

LOCATIONS

HQ: MIAMI CHILDREN'S HEALTH SYSTEM MANAGEMENT SERVICES, LLC
3100 SW 62ND AVE, MIAMI, FL 331553009
Phone: 305 666-6511
Web: WWW.NICKLAUSCHILDRENS.ORG

HISTORICAL FINANCIALS

Company Type: Private

Income Statement — FYE: December 31

	REVENUE ($ mil.)	NET INCOME ($ mil.)	NET PROFIT MARGIN	EMPLOYEES
12/19	754	(38)	—	11
12/16	688	72	10.5%	—
Annual Growth	3.1%	—	—	—

2019 Year-End Financials

Return on assets: (-2.9%)
Return on equity: (-5.8%)
Current ratio: 1.90
Cash ($ mil.): 153

MIAMI UNIVERSITY

Not that Miami the other one. Named for the Miami Indian Tribe that inhabited the area now known as the Miami Valley Region of Ohio Miami University emphasizes undergraduate study at its main campus in Oxford (35 miles north of Cincinnati) as well as at commuter campuses in Hamilton Middletown and West Chester Ohio and a European Center in Luxembourg. The school offers bachelors masters and doctoral programs in areas including business administration arts and sciences engineering and education. Its student body includes more than 15000 undergraduates on the Oxford campus; 2500 graduate students; and another 5700 students attending satellite campuses. Miami University was established in 1809.

Financial Performance

Miami University's 2011 revenue increased 3% vs. 2010 due to a corresponding increase in undergraduate tuition on its three campuses and a rising rates for room and board. Net income at the public university rose 25% over the same period on higher revenue and lower operating expenses due primarily to a reduction in the number of positions and no salary increases. The rise in tuition for Ohio residents in 2011 was the first in four years. Also investment income rose in 2011 for the second consecutive year.

Company Background

Miami University celebrated its bicentennial in 2009. The school was chartered in February of 1809 by the State of Ohio but the first classses were not held until 1824.

EXECUTIVES

Vice President, Beck Parker
Vice President, Brenden Clinton
Cio And Vice President Information Technology, Peter Natale
Assistant Vice President For End User Services, Annie Pagura
Vice President For Student Affairs, Barbara Jones
Senior Vice President, Michael Kabbaz
Program Associate Vice President Of Finance, Agnes A Shea
Assistant Vice President For Enrollment Management, Brent Shock
Assistant Vice President Enterprise Operations Information Technology Services, Troy Travis
Vice President Of Human Resource, Eric White
Vice President, Darryl Rice
Vice President Information Technology Technical Support, Carolyn Ledford
Executive Manager, Susan Clark
Interim Associate Vice President Human Resources, Dawn Fahner
Vice President Of Administration, Drew Unger
Vice President Recruitment, Liam Patton
Vice President Of Public Relations, Shannon Obrien
Student Aid Office Of The Vice President, Justin Hucke
Vice President, Nancy Heidtman
Assistant Vice President For Student Affairs, Lauren Delk
Vice President, John Mcdonnell
Vice President Of Facilities Management, Mason Busch
Vice President And Chief Marketing And Communications Officer, Michele Sparks
Finance Vice President, Natan Ostro
Israel Vice President, Lindsey Sellman
Vice President Of Public Relations, Blake Eve
Vice President Of Marketing, Bridget Sarr
Vice President Business Develo, Kathy Finney
Board Member, Phyllis Wykoff
Economics Major Entrepreneurship Minor Theta Chi Treasurer, Michael Beresford
Treasurer, Madison Ryan
Treasurer, Don Streit
Treasurer, Tyler Ko
Auditors: MCGLADREY LLP CLEVELAND OHIO

LOCATIONS

HQ: MIAMI UNIVERSITY
501 E HIGH ST, OXFORD, OH 450561846
Phone: 513 529-1809
Web: WWW.MIAMIOH.EDU

HISTORICAL FINANCIALS

Company Type: Private

Income Statement — FYE: June 30

	REVENUE ($ mil.)	NET INCOME ($ mil.)	NET PROFIT MARGIN	EMPLOYEES
06/18	551	184	33.5%	4,925
06/17	544	83	15.4%	—
06/16	522	65	12.5%	—
06/12	440	32	7.5%	—
Annual Growth	3.8%	33.3%	—	—

2018 Year-End Financials

Return on assets: 7.7%
Return on equity: 15.7%
Current ratio: 6.20
Cash ($ mil.): 85

MIAMI VALLEY HOSPITAL

Don't go to Florida looking for this hospital! Miami Valley Hospital (MVH) is an acute care facility serving the residents of Dayton Ohio and surrounding areas through two campuses. MVH and MVH South have roughly 950 beds and offer 50 primary and specialty care practices through its Regional Adult Burn Center the MVH Cancer Center MVH Sports Medicine Center and behavioral health units for outpatient and inpatient chemical dependency therapy and other psychiatric services. MVH also offers Level I trauma services Level III-B NICU adult burn center an air ambulance program and blood marrow and kidney transplant services. The hospital is part of the Premier Health Partners network.

Operations

In addition to MVH the Premier Health Partners network consists of Good Samaritan Hospital (also stationed in Dayton Ohio) Atrium Medical Center in nearby Middletown and Upper Valley Medical Center in Troy. Collectively the multi-hospital health system houses about 1800 inpatient beds and around 65 facilities.

MVH have more than 1100 physicians in more than 70 primary and specialty medical practice areas. It was a 2012 recipient of the HealthGrades Distinguished Hospital Award for Clinical Excellence placing it among the top 5% of hospitals in the US.

In 2012 it had 41555 inpatient admissions; 164140 outpatient visits; 125622 emergency department visits; and oversaw 4000 births.

Financial Performance

Medicare accounted for 40% of the company's 2012 revenues; Medicaid 20%.

Strategy

Over the past few years MVH has focused on upgrading its infrastructure. It has built a $135 million 440000-sq. ft. 11-story heart tower on the south side of the campus and spent $19 million on renovating and expanding its neonatal intensive care unit.

In 2013 it opened its new $6 million 24-hour Emergency Center in Jamestown Ohio to meet the growing demand for emergency care.

In 2013 MVH South opened a $20 million Comprehensive Cancer Center and (in 2012) a new maternity center which includes five labor and delivery suites two surgical suites for c-section deliveries and 16 private after-birthing suites.

Company Background

MVH was formed in 1890.

EXECUTIVES

Pres-Ceo, Jenny M Lewis
Pres*, Mark Shaker
V Pres*, Makkie Clancy
Cfo*, Lisa Bishop
V Pres-Coo*, Barbara Johnson
Health Professional, Jon D Girard
Human Resources, Gretchen Long MBA
Coordinator, Melissa Brook
Obstetrician Gynecologist, Janice Duke
Facilities Technician, Jeremy Greth
Laboratory Director, Lisa Berger

LOCATIONS

HQ: MIAMI VALLEY HOSPITAL
1 WYOMING ST, DAYTON, OH 454092711
Phone: 937 208-8000
Web: WWW.PREMIERHEALTH.COM

PRODUCTS/OPERATIONS

Campus Locations

Miami Valley Hospital - Dayton OH
Miami Valley Hospital South - Centerville Ohio

Selected Services and Specialties

Ablation (Cardiology)
Access and Transfer Center (physicians)
Alcoholism Drug Dependency and Addiction Treatment
Aneurysm (Neurosciences)
Ankle Surgery
Arterial Interventions
Audiology
Bariatrics/Weight Loss Surgery
Behavioral Services
Biotherapy/Targeted Therapy
Blood and Marrow Transplant Program
Brachytherapy
Brain Conditions and Treatments
Brain Injury Rehabilitation
Breast Cancer Navigators
Breast Center
Breast Center
Brethen Center for Surgical Advancement (physicians)
Bull Family Diabetes Center
Burn Center
Cancer Care
Cancer Care (Oncology)
Cardiac Electrophysiology Lab
Cardiac Rehabilitation
Cardiology
Cardiology
Cardiothoracic Surgery
CareFlight - Medical Transportation
Catheterization Lab Procedures
Center for Sleep and Wake Disorders
Chemoembolization
Chemotherapy and Infusion Therapy
Childbirth Education
Colon Cancer
Colorectal Cancer
Complementary Medicine (Cancer)
Comprehensive Outpatient Rehab Program (CORP)
Counseling/Pastoral Care
Craniectomy (Neuroscience)
Craniotomy (Neuroscience)
Cryoablation
CT scan (Imaging)
Dental Center
Depression/Anxiety Treatment
Diabetes
Dialysis Services
Discectomy
Drug Addiction Treatment
Elder Care
Emergency & Trauma Center (ETC)
Foot Surgery
Fractures (Athletes)
Fusion (spinal treatment)
Gastric Bypass
Genetic Testing
Gynecologic Cancer
Gynecology
Hand Therapy
Head and Neck Cancer
Heart Care
Heart Surgery
High Risk Breast Cancer Center
Hip Surgery
Hormone Therapy
Hospitalists/Medical Professionals
Hyperbaric Oxygen Therapy Center
Image Guided Radiation Therapy (IGRT)
Injury Prevention Center
Inpatient Rehabilitation
Intensity Modulated Radiation Therapy (IMRT)
Intensive Care Unit (ICU)
Interventional Radiology
Joint replacements
Kidney Transplant
Knee Surgery
Kyphoplasty
Leukemia
Lung Cancer
Lymphoma
Mammography Screenings
Maternal-Fetal Medicine
Maternity
Maternity
Medical Professionals/Hospitalists
Medical Transportation - CareFlight
Mental Health Services
Minimally Invasive Surgery
Mother and Baby Services
MRI (Imaging)
Nanoknife
Neonatal Intensive Care
Neuro Rehabilitation
NeuroInterventional Center
Neuroscience
Neurosciences
Nutrition Services
OB-GYN
Obstetrics
Occupational Rehabilitation
Occupational Therapy
Oncology
Organ Transplant
Orthopedics
Orthopedics
Outpatient Physical Therapy
Pain Management
Palliative Care
Pancreatic Cancer
Perinatal Intensive Care
PET Scan (Imaging)
Pharmacy
Physiatry
Physical Therapy
Pre-Admission Testing
Premier HeartWorks
Preventive Cardiology
Prostate Cancer
Pulmonary Services
Radiofrequency ablation
Radiology
Radionuclide scan
Rehabilitation
Rehabilitation Institute of Ohio
Respiratory Care
Robotic Surgery
Shoulder Surgery
Shunt (Neuroscience)
Skin Cancer
Sleep Center
Solitaire Revascularization Device (Neurosciences)
Speech-Language Pathology
Spinal decompression surgery
Spinal disc replacement
Spinal fracture treatment
Spinal tumor surgery
Spine and back injuries (Orthopedics)
Spine Conditions and Treatments (Neuroscience)
Sports Medicine
Sports Medicine
Stereotaxis
Stomach Cancer
Stroke Treatments
Surgery Center
Surgical Oncology
Thoracic Surgery
Throat Cancer
Trauma
Ultrasound (Imaging)
Urological Cancer
Urology
Vascular Services
Venous Interventions
Vertebroplasty
Weight Loss Surgery (Bariatrics)
Weight Loss Surgery/Bariatrics
Wheelchair Clinic
Women's Health
Women's Heart Services
Women's Services
Wound Therapy
X-rays (Imaging)
Y-90 Radioembolization

COMPETITORS

Cincinnati Children's Hospital
Deaconess Associations
Encompass Health
Good Samaritan Hospital (IN)
Kettering Health Network
OhioHealth
The Christ Hospital Corporation
TriHealth
UC Health

HISTORICAL FINANCIALS

Company Type: Private

Income Statement — FYE: December 31

	REVENUE ($ mil.)	NET INCOME ($ mil.)	NET PROFIT MARGIN	EMPLOYEES
12/16	809	35	4.4%	8,403
12/15	827	37	4.5%	—
12/14	785	37	4.8%	—
12/07	622	44	7.1%	—
Annual Growth	3.0%	(2.3%)	—	—

2016 Year-End Financials

Return on assets: 2.3%
Return on equity: 5.2%
Current ratio: 10.00
Cash ($ mil.): 42

MIAMI-DADE AVIATION DEPARTMENT

EXECUTIVES

Aviation Dir-Ceo, Lester Sola
Deputy Dir, Ken Pyatt
Chief of Staff, Arlyn Rull
Cfo, Sergio San Miguel
Senior Executive Assistant, Patricia Hernandez
Terminal Operations Agent, Alexandra Diaz-Zablah
Maintenance Supervisor, Juan Riera
Telephone Supervisor, Maria Perez
Senior Aviation Property Manag, Stephen Harold
Executive Secretary, Tc Cherenek
Personnel Technician, Dania Vidal
Auditors: CHERRY BEKAERT TAMPA FLORIDA

LOCATIONS

HQ: MIAMI-DADE AVIATION DEPARTMENT
13344 SW 108TH STREET CIR, MIAMI, FL 331863424
Phone: 305 876-7000

HISTORICAL FINANCIALS

Company Type: Private

Income Statement — FYE: September 30

	REVENUE ($ mil.)	NET INCOME ($ mil.)	NET PROFIT MARGIN	EMPLOYEES
09/16	830	(29)	—	40
09/15	794	(15)	—	—
Annual Growth	4.6%	—	—	—

2016 Year-End Financials

Return on assets: (-0.4%)
Return on equity: (-3.1%)
Current ratio: 2.00
Cash ($ mil.): 171

MICHIGAN MILK PRODUCERS ASSOCIATION

Ice cream and other dairy products might be missing a major ingredient without Michigan Milk Producers Association (MMPA). The dairy cooperative which serves more than 2100 farmers in Michigan Ohio Indiana and Wisconsin produces some 3.9 billion pounds of milk each year. Milk products include sweetened condensed milk instant nonfat milk and dried buttermilk as well as other items the likes of cream cheese butter and ice-cream mixes. With no consumer brands or products MMPA sells its products as ingredients to food makers who sell baby formulas candy ice cream and yogurt. Founded in 1916 the co-op operates a pair of Michigan plants and a merchandise facility.

Operations

As part of its business of serving member-farmers MMPA provides them with product quality incentives testing and customized blending as well as protection against loss from disaster.

Geographic Reach

From its headquarters in Novi Michigan MMPA operates solely in the state of Michigan where it has manufacturing plants in the villages of Ovid and Constantine and a merchandise facility in the Michigan city of Saint Louis. Its farmers are located in Michigan Ohio Indiana and Wisconsin.

EXECUTIVES

Treasurer, Eric Frahm
Auditors: CLIFTONLARSONALLEN LLP

LOCATIONS

HQ: MICHIGAN MILK PRODUCERS ASSOCIATION
41310 BRIDGE ST, NOVI, MI 483751302
Phone: 248 474-6672
Web: WWW.MIMILK.COM

PRODUCTS/OPERATIONS

Selected Products

Condensed skim milk
Condensed whole milk
Dried buttermilk
Dried whole milk
Ice cream mixes
Instant nonfat dry milk
Nonfat dry milk
Standardized cream
Standardized milk
Sweet condensed milk
Sweet cream butter

COMPETITORS

Associated Milk Producers
Dairy Farmers of America
Dean Foods
Foremost Farms
Land O'Lakes
Main Street Ingredients
Quality Chekd
Saputo

HISTORICAL FINANCIALS

Company Type: Private

Income Statement — FYE: September 30

	REVENUE ($ mil.)	NET INCOME ($ mil.)	NET PROFIT MARGIN	EMPLOYEES
09/11	870	6	0.7%	200
09/10	698	6	1.0%	—
09/09	556	6	1.1%	—
Annual Growth	25.1%	3.2%	—	—

2011 Year-End Financials

Return on assets: 3.8%
Return on equity: 13.4%
Current ratio: 1.50
Cash ($ mil.): 5

MICHIGAN STATE UNIVERSITY

Remember the Spartans? You should if you graduated from a land-grant university in the US. Founded in 1855 Michigan State University (MSU) was the model of a land-grant institution made into law in 1862. Today MSU and its 49700 students cover a lot of land in East Lansing. The university offers more than 200 programs of study through 17 colleges. It has extensive programs in core fields including education physics psychology medicine and communications. It is also a leading research university with top-ranked international studies programs. As a highly ranked research university MSU is awarded millions of dollars in research grants each year from public and private entities.

Operations

Michigan State University has nearly 100 active research centers and institutes on campus as well as field research sites throughout the state of Michigan. Most are interdisciplinary and several are joint initiatives between Michigan State University and other universities around the world.

With more than 5700 faculty and academic staff members and a student-teacher ratio of about 16:1 MSU is noted by U.S. News & World Report for its programs in graduate-level elementary and secondary education nuclear physics and industrial and organizational psychology. It is the only university in the country with three on-campus medical schools graduating allopathic (MD) and osteopathic (DO) physicians as well as veterinarians (DVMs).

Geographic Reach

MSU's 5300-acre main campus is in East Lansing three miles east of Lansing (the capital city of Michigan). The university also has another 17500 acres-some used for animal agricultural and forestry research.

MSU's students hail from all 50 US states as well as 130 other countries. MSU also offers an extensive study abroad program which includes 275 programs in 60 different countries and all seven continents.

Financial Performance

For the year ended 2020 the University's revenues totaled $2 billion.

The University's cash for the year ended 2020 was $205.8 million. Operating activities used $495.1 million primarily for payments to employees as well as suppliers while non-capital financing activities generated $488.5 million. Investing activities generated another $364.9 million.

Strategy

The 2019 novel Coronavirus (COVID-19) has had a significant impact on the University the state the nation and the world. By adhering to its basic financial principles including funding recurring operations with recurring revenues the University has made and will continue to make necessary fiscal adjustments with the objective of maintaining quality. The University continues to focus on cost controls pursue a long-term investment strategy to maximize risk-adjusted total returns and appropriately utilize debt and other resources to meet programmatic needs including the maintenance and replacement of the University's infrastructure.

Company Background

MSU was founded in 1855 a forerunner of the land-grant college concept under the name Agricultural College of the State of Michigan. The Morrill Act which codified land-grant institutions became law in 1862. MSU became a full university in 1955 as Michigan State University of Agriculture and Applied Science. It changed its name to Michigan State University in 1964.

EXECUTIVES

Provost And Vp Academic Affairs, Lou Anna K. Simon
Assistant Provost And Dean Of Undergraduate Studies, June Youatt
Dean College Of Engineering, Satish Udpa
Dean James Madison College, Sherman W. Garnett
Dean Lyman Briggs College, Elizabeth H. Simmons
Dean College Of Law, Joan W. Howarth
Dean College Of Music, James (Jim) Forger
Dean College Of Natural Science, R. James Kirkpatrick
Dean College Of Osteopathic Medicine, William D. Strampel
Dean Residential College In The Arts And Humanities, Stephen L. (Steve) Esquith
Dean Honors College, Cynthia Jackson-Elmoore
Vp Information Technology And Cio, Joanna Young
Dean College Of Education, Donald E. Heller
Vp Finance And Treasurer, Mark P. Haas
Dean College Of Veterinary Medicine, John Baker
Dean College Of Communication Arts And Sciences, Prabu David
Vice President For Auxiliary Enterprises, Vennie Gore
Assistant Vice President For Human Resources, Chris Hanna
Assistant Vice President For Regulatory Affairs, Jr Haywood
Department Chair, Steven Rust
Military Science Department Chair, Jason Degeorge
Assistant Vice President Research And Grad Stds Office Of Sponsored Programs, Twila Reighley
Vice President Of Programming, Lisa Thompson
Vice President, Patrick Gallagher
Vice President, Kate Peabody
Vice President, Jake Beachum
Vice President, Robert Pell
Vice President, James Pickard
Vice President, Holly Crowther
Vice Chairperson, Joel I. Ferguson, age 81
Vice Chairman, Mitch Lyons
Secretary, Tammy Endsley
Wrac Secretary, Diana Shank
Secretary, Nikki Bindschatel
Secretary, Shawna Prater
Graduate Secretary, Tammy Spangler
Secretary, Raven Richardson
Treasurer, Michele Beltran
Secretary, Tanner Schudlich
Middlebury Township Treasurer, Carolyn Stevens
Graduate Secretary, Logan O'Neil
Secretary, Joni Tucker
Treasurer, Ray Jussaume
Board Member, Fadel Alyaqoub
Auditors: PLANTE & MORAN PLLC EAST LAN

LOCATIONS

HQ: MICHIGAN STATE UNIVERSITY
426 AUDITORIUM RD, EAST LANSING, MI 488242600
Phone: 517 355-1855
Web: WWW.MSU.EDU

PRODUCTS/OPERATIONS

Selected Colleges and Divisions
College of Agriculture and Natural Resources
College of Arts and Letters
College of Communication Arts and Sciences
College of Education
College of Engineering
College of Human Medicine
College of Law (affiliated)
College of Music
College of Natural Science
College of Nursing
College of Osteopathic Medicine
College of Social Science
College of Veterinary Medicine
Eli Broad College of Business and Eli Broad Graduate School of Management
Honors College
James Madison College
Lyman Briggs College
Residential College in the Arts and Humanities
Undergraduate University Division

HISTORICAL FINANCIALS

Company Type: Private

Income Statement — FYE: June 30

	REVENUE ($ mil.)	NET INCOME ($ mil.)	NET PROFIT MARGIN	EMPLOYEES
06/19	2,046	146	7.2%	11,100
06/18	1,986	(246)	—	—
06/17	1,931	481	25.0%	—
06/16	1,811	71	3.9%	—
Annual Growth	4.2%	27.3%	—	—

2019 Year-End Financials

Return on assets: 2.0%
Return on equity: 5.9%
Current ratio: 1.00
Cash ($ mil.): 91

MID-AMERICA PIPELINE COMPANY, LLC

EXECUTIVES

Mng MBR-Pres, J M Collingsworth
MBR, W Randall Fowler
MBR-Sr V Pres, Michael J Knesek
MBR-Treas, Bryan F Bulawa
MBR-SEC, Raymond P Albrecht
Managing Member, James Collingsworth

LOCATIONS

HQ: MID-AMERICA PIPELINE COMPANY, LLC
1100 LA ST STE 1000, HOUSTON, TX 77002
Phone: 713 880-6500
Web: WWW.ENTERPRISEPRODUCTS.COM

HISTORICAL FINANCIALS

Company Type: Private

Income Statement — FYE: December 31

	REVENUE ($ mil.)	NET INCOME ($ mil.)	NET PROFIT MARGIN	EMPLOYEES
12/17	591	361	61.1%	250
12/16	591	366	62.0%	—
Annual Growth	0.0%	(1.4%)	—	—

MIDCOAST ENERGY PARTNERS, L.P.

Midcoast Energy Partners was formed by Enbridge Energy Partners in 2013 as an investment vehicle to own and grow its natural gas and NGL midstream business. It has minority stakes in Enbridge's network of natural gas and natural gas liquids (NGLs) gathering and transportation systems natural gas processing and treating facilities and NGL fractionation plants in Texas and Oklahoma. Organized as a limited partnership Midcoast Energy Partners is exempt from paying income tax as long as it distributes quarterly dividends to shareholders. It went public in 2013 raising $333 million. In 2017 Enbridge Energy Partners agreed to acquire control of Midcoast Energy Partners.

EXECUTIVES

Pres, Laura Sayavedra
Sr V Pres, Mark A Maki
L.L.C., Gen Ptnr, Midcoast Holdings
Vice President, Stephen J Neyland
Auditors: PRICEWATERHOUSECOOPERS LLP HO

LOCATIONS

HQ: MIDCOAST ENERGY PARTNERS, L.P.
1100 LA ST STE 3300, HOUSTON, TX 77002
Phone: 713 821-2000
Web: WWW.MIDCOASTPARTNERS.COM

COMPETITORS

Buckeye Partners
DCP Midstream Partners
Duke Energy
Koch Industries Inc.
Magellan Midstream
Martin Midstream Partners
ONEOK
Sunoco Logistics
TransCanada
Williams Companies

HISTORICAL FINANCIALS

Company Type: Private

Income Statement — FYE: December 31

	REVENUE ($ mil.)	NET INCOME ($ mil.)	NET PROFIT MARGIN	EMPLOYEES
12/16	1,966	(157)	—	11
12/15	2,842	(284)	—	—
12/14	5,894	144	2.4%	—
12/13	5,593	53	1.0%	—
Annual Growth	(29.4%)	—	—	—

2016 Year-End Financials

Return on assets: (-3.2%)
Return on equity: (-4.2%)
Current ratio: 0.50
Cash ($ mil.): 7

MILES HEALTH CARE, INC

Miles Health Care provides acute and specialty health care service to the residents of Maine's Lincoln County. The not-for-profit company operates Miles Memorial Hospital – known as LincolnHealth Miles Campus – a rural medical center with about 40 beds and has emergency intensive care surgery and birthing departments. In addition Miles Health Care operates outpatient and specialty practice clinics physician practice offices and home health rehabilitation and hospice programs. It also provides long-term senior care through its nursing assisted and independent living facilities. Miles Health Care is a member of Lincoln County Healthcare (LincolnHealth) which is part of the MaineHealth network.

Change in Company Type

In 2013 parent MaineHealth combined two of its hospitals – Miles Memorial Hospital and St. Andrews Hospital – to form the two-campus LincolnHealth organization. The merger aimed to reduce operating expenses by more than $6 million annually as well as a more than $5 million increase revenue due to the combined organization's new status as a critical access hospital (which leads to higher reimbursements from Medicare and Medicaid plans). The increased earnings will allow the LincolnHealth campuses to reduce the price of services including x-rays laboratory tests and minor surgeries and procedures.

Operations

In addition to the two main hospital campuses LincolnHealth includes physician practices operated by the Lincoln Medical Partners as well as family care and urgent care centers. It also continues to operate nursing home health hospice and assisted-living organizations.

Geographic Reach

The LincolnHealth Miles Campus is located in Lincoln County Maine in the town of Damariscotta (which is north of Portland). The LincolnHealth St. Andrews Campus is located in Boothbay Harbor.

Strategy

Both the Miles and St. Andrews medical centers began using electronic health record (EHR) systems in 2010 which allows doctors to access a patient's past medical and diagnostic experiences to make the best decisions on current treatment plans and avoid duplication. Such EHR systems are part of an initiative to lower the cost of medical care in the US.

Company Background

Miles Health Care was established in 1941. Miles has historically been governed by a board of trustees (the Lincoln County Healthcare Board of Trustees) that also oversee the nearby St. Andrews Hospital; as an independently governed member of MaineHealth Miles has received planning consulting capital and group purchasing benefits. In 2013 St. Andrews Hospital and Miles Memorial Hospital were officially merged to serve as dual campuses of the single LincolnHealth hospital.

EXECUTIVES

Senior Vice President Of Hospital Operations, Cynthia Wade

LOCATIONS

HQ: MILES HEALTH CARE, INC
35 MILES ST, DAMARISCOTTA, ME 045434047
Phone: 207 563-1234
Web: WWW.MAINEHEALTH.ORG

PRODUCTS/OPERATIONS

Selected Centers and Services

Chase Point Adult Day Services
Chase Point Assisted Living
Cove's Edge
Emergency Services
Family Support Services
General Surgery
Internal Medicine
Mammography
Miles & St. Andrews Home Health & Hospice
Miles Family Medicine
MMH BabyNet
Obstetrics
Orthopedic Services
Pediatric Services
Schooner Cove
Senior Services
Waldoboro Family Medicine
Wellness and Rehabilitation
Wiscasset Family Medicine
Women's Services

COMPETITORS

Eastern Maine Healthcare Systems
MaineGeneral Health
Mercy Health System of Maine
St. Joseph Healthcare

HISTORICAL FINANCIALS

Company Type: Private

Income Statement — FYE: September 30

	REVENUE ($ mil.)	NET INCOME ($ mil.)	NET PROFIT MARGIN	EMPLOYEES
09/09	1,042	12	1.2%	800
09/08	14	0	3.9%	—
09/06	58	3	5.9%	—
09/05	52	(0)	—	—
Annual Growth	111.6%	—	—	—

2009 Year-End Financials

Return on assets: 112.0%
Return on equity: 494.4%
Current ratio: 1.30
Cash ($ mil.): —

MILLS-PENINSULA HEALTH SERVICES

With health facilities south of San Francisco Mills-Peninsula Health Services provides care to communities in and around Burlingame California. The not-for-profit health care group includes the 240-bed Mills-Peninsula Medical Center an acute-care hospital in Burlingame; Mills Health Center an outpatient diagnostic surgery and rehabilitation facility in San Mateo; and physician practice offices in surrounding areas. The facilities provide specialty services such as cancer care cardiovascular therapy behavioral health radiology respiratory care and senior services. Mills-Peninsula Health Services is part of the Sutter Health network.

Operations

Along with sister company Palo Alto Medical Foundation Mills-Peninsula forms the Peninsula Coastal Region division of Sutter Health. Together the organizations operate collaborative medical clinic and physician practice locations.

Geographic Reach

Mills-Peninsula Health Services operates facilities in Burlingame and San Mateo in California.

Financial Performance

Mills-Peninsula Health Services reported revenues of $611 million (7% of the parent company's net revenues) in 2013.

Its net income in 2013 was $53 million.

Strategy

Through the contribution of donors in 2014 the Mills-Peninsula Women's Center replaced all its digital mammography units with digital breast tomosynthesis allowing it to provide 3D mammography for breast cancer screenings at no extra cost to patients.

The hospital enhanced its surgical capabilities in 2013 with the addition of a da Vinci Si robotic system for surgical procedures.

That year Mills-Peninsula's Dorothy E. Schneider Cancer Center introduced a new cancer treatment Xofigo (Radium-223 dichloride) for patients with advanced-stage prostate cancer that has metastasized to the bones but not other organs.

Company Background

The organization opened the doors on its newly constructed Mills-Peninsula Medical Center in Burlingame in 2011. The $618 million project added a new 240-bed main hospital facility (to replace the aging Peninsula Medical Center facility) with all private patient rooms as well as a 180000 sq. ft. medical office building and a parking garage. The new hospital is compliant with California's new earthquake safety requirements.

The Peninsula facility was founded as a public hospital district in 1954. The two hospitals merged in 1985 and became part of Sutter Health the following year.

Founded in 1908 the Mills hospital was named for philanthropist Elizabeth Mills Reid who helped to fund the medical facility.

Auditors: ERNST & YOUNG US LLP SAN DIEG

LOCATIONS

HQ: MILLS-PENINSULA HEALTH SERVICES
1501 TROUSDALE DR, BURLINGAME, CA 940104506
Phone: 650 696-5400
Web: WWW.MILLS-PENINSULA.ORG

PRODUCTS/OPERATIONS

Selected Services

Arthritis & Osteoporosis
Behavioral Health
Birth Center
Cancer Center
Cardiovascular
Children's Services
Psychiatric Emergency
Senior Services
Obesity Surgery
Orthopedic Surgery
Women's Center

COMPETITORS

Alta Bates Summit Medical Center
California Pacific Medical Center
Dignity Health
Good Samaritan Hospital (San Jose)
John Muir Health
Marin General Hospital
Sequoia Healthcare District
The Palo Alto Medical Foundation
UCSF Medical

HISTORICAL FINANCIALS

Company Type: Private

Income Statement — FYE: December 31

	REVENUE ($ mil.)	NET INCOME ($ mil.)	NET PROFIT MARGIN	EMPLOYEES
12/13	609	54	8.9%	2,200
12/09	533	56	10.6%	—
12/02	274	18	6.6%	—
12/01	398	0	0.0%	—
Annual Growth	3.6%	172.8%	—	—

2013 Year-End Financials

Return on assets: 12.6%
Return on equity: 8.9%
Current ratio: 0.10
Cash ($ mil.): 20

MILTON HERSHEY SCHOOL & SCHOOL TRUST

EXECUTIVES

Owner, Milton Hershey
Auditors: PRICEWATERHOUSECOOPERS LLP PH

LOCATIONS

HQ: MILTON HERSHEY SCHOOL & SCHOOL TRUST
711 CREST LN, HERSHEY, PA 170338903
Phone: 717 520-1100
Web: WWW.HERSHEYTRUST.COM

HISTORICAL FINANCIALS

Company Type: Private

Income Statement — FYE: July 31

	REVENUE ($ mil.)	NET INCOME ($ mil.)	NET PROFIT MARGIN	EMPLOYEES
07/18	1,069	784	73.4%	14
07/17	469	198	42.2%	—
07/12	386	180	46.7%	—
07/10	211	3	1.6%	—
Annual Growth	22.4%	97.8%	—	—

2018 Year-End Financials

Return on assets: 5.6%
Return on equity: 5.7%
Current ratio: —
Cash ($ mil.): 72

MILWAUKEE PUBLIC SCHOOLS (INC)

EXECUTIVES

Supt, Darienne Driver
Cfo*, Gerald Pace
Personnel Dir*, Daniel Chanen
Comptroller*, Lawanda Baldwin
Principal, Deborah Bell
Principal, Martha Wheeler-Fair
Principal, Jewell Riano
Principal, Daniel J Donder
Social Worker, Cathy Klein
Staff, Carmen M Rahming
Lobbyist, Ceasar Stinson
Auditors: BAKER TILLY VIRCHOW KRAUSE LL

LOCATIONS

HQ: MILWAUKEE PUBLIC SCHOOLS (INC)
5225 W VLIET ST, MILWAUKEE, WI 532082698
Phone: 414 475-8393
Web: WWW.MPS.MILWAUKEE.K12.WI.US

HISTORICAL FINANCIALS

Company Type: Private

Income Statement — FYE: June 30

	REVENUE ($ mil.)	NET INCOME ($ mil.)	NET PROFIT MARGIN	EMPLOYEES
06/19	1,199	(22)	—	14,154
06/18	1,196	2	0.2%	—
06/17	1,182	9	0.8%	—
06/16	1,178	(0)	—	—
Annual Growth	0.6%	—	—	—

MINERS INCORPORATED

Miner's is a family-owned chain of about 30 grocery stores in Michigan North Dakota northern Minnesota and Wisconsin. Most of the company's stores fly the Super One Foods banner but there are a few under the U-Save Foods and Marketplace Foods names. Following the acquisition of seven Jubilee and Festival Foods stores in Minnesota from Plaza Holding Co. Miner's converted the stores to its Super One Foods banner most of which are located in Minnesota. Miner's also has a wholesale grocery operation in Duluth. Miner's was founded by Anton and Ida Miner who started out selling groceries out of their tavern in Grand Rapids Michigan in the 1930s. In 1943 they built the family's first store Miner's Market.

Geographic Reach

Minnesota is the regional grocery chain's largest market home to 21 of its 31 stores. Wisconsin and Michigan are each home to about five locations. The grocery chain has a single store North Dakota.

Financial Performance

Miner's rang up an estimated $437 million in sales in fiscal 2013 (ended June).

Strategy

Miner's takes a measured approach to growth combining occasional acquisitions with organic growth. Its newest location is a 59000-square-foot Super One Foods store slated to open in 2014 in Superior Wisconsin.

Mergers and Acquisitions

In May 2011 Miner's upped its store count with the acquisition of four family-owned Paulson's Super Valu grocery stores in northern Minnesota and Wisconsin.

Prevented by Minnesota law from selling alcohol in grocery stores the company recently bought two liquor stores in Cloquet and Duluth.

EXECUTIVES

Ceo-Pres, James A Miner Sr
Treas*, Theresa Lorentz
Information Specialist, Jason Kearney
General Counsel, Bruce Anderson
Director of Finance, Scott Paulson
Manager District, Michael Peterson
Director Loss Prevention, Mike Utecht
Manager District, Patrick Miner
Director, Joe Fournier
Information Technology Directo, Bill Rulla
Vice President Operations, Bob Halvorson
Auditors: RSM US LLP DULUTH MINNESOTA

LOCATIONS

HQ: MINERS INCORPORATED
5065 MILLER TRUNK HWY, HERMANTOWN, MN 558111442
Phone: 218 729-5882
Web: WWW.SUPERONEFOODS.COM

2014 Stores

	No.
Minnesota	21
Michigan	5
Wisconsin	4
North Dakota	1
Total	31

PRODUCTS/OPERATIONS

2014 Stores

	No.
Super One Foods	27
U-Save Foods	2
Country Market	1
Marketplace Foods	1
Total	31

COMPETITORS

Cub Foods
IGA
Kroger
Meijer
Roundy's
SpartanNash
Target Corporation
Wal-Mart

HISTORICAL FINANCIALS

Company Type: Private

Income Statement — FYE: June 24

	REVENUE ($ mil.)	NET INCOME ($ mil.)	NET PROFIT MARGIN	EMPLOYEES
06/17	548	26	4.8%	2,300
06/12	501	31	6.3%	—
06/11	475	30	6.4%	—
06/10	463	27	5.8%	—
Annual Growth	2.4%	(0.5%)	—	—

2017 Year-End Financials

Return on assets: 10.7%
Return on equity: 15.4%
Current ratio: 1.80
Cash ($ mil.): 7

MINNEAPOLIS PUBLIC SCHOOL DISTRICT

EXECUTIVES

Suptd, Michael Goar
Supt*, Bernadeia Johnson
Payroll Staff, Diane Woolridge
Occupational Specia, Laura Wilcox
Payroll Staff, Stacy Swain
Coordinator, Ben Mulhern
Research Assistant, Eric V Berk
Coordinator, Matthew Branch
Occupational Specia, Nancy Bradehoft
Information Specialist, Jeremiah Bohn
Coordinator, Max Athorn
Auditors: BERGAN KDV LTD MINNEAPOLIS

LOCATIONS

HQ: MINNEAPOLIS PUBLIC SCHOOL DISTRICT
1250 W BROADWAY AVE, MINNEAPOLIS, MN 554112533
Phone: 612 668-0200
Web: WWW.MPLS.K12.MN.US

HISTORICAL FINANCIALS

Company Type: Private

Income Statement — FYE: June 30

	REVENUE ($ mil.)	NET INCOME ($ mil.)	NET PROFIT MARGIN	EMPLOYEES
06/16	709	(25)	—	9,000
06/15	685	116	17.1%	—
06/05	441	18	4.2%	—
06/04	632	(42)	—	—
Annual Growth	1.0%	—	—	—

MISSION HEALTH SYSTEM, INC.

EXECUTIVES

Ceo-Pres, Ronald A Paulus
Cmo-Mission Hospital, William R Hathaway
Innovation, Marc B Westle
Operations, Sonya B Greck
Auditors: KPMG LLP CHARLOTTE NORTH CAR

LOCATIONS

HQ: MISSION HEALTH SYSTEM, INC.
425 W NEW ENG AVE STE 300, WINTER PARK, FL 327894228
Phone: 828 213-1111
Web: WWW.MISSIONHEALTH.ORG

HISTORICAL FINANCIALS

Company Type: Private

Income Statement — FYE: September 30

	REVENUE ($ mil.)	NET INCOME ($ mil.)	NET PROFIT MARGIN	EMPLOYEES
09/18	1,799	120	6.7%	12,000
09/17	1,753	161	9.2%	—
09/16	1,632	90	5.5%	—
09/08	17	7	42.3%	—
Annual Growth	59.1%	32.3%	—	—

2018 Year-End Financials

Return on assets: 4.5%
Return on equity: 6.7%
Current ratio: 2.00
Cash ($ mil.): 149

MISSION HOSPITAL REGIONAL MEDICAL CENTER INC

EXECUTIVES

Ceo, Seth Peigen
Financial Executive, Kenn Mc Farland
Coordinator, Maryann Hubbard
Emergency Medicine, Kenneth Kwon
Gastroenterology, Habib Rahman
Cardiology, Michael Gault
Cardiovascular Disease, David T Kawanishi
Emergency Medicine, James Keany
MD, Lauren Dwinell
Vice President, Mark Jablonski
MD, Elwyn Rexinger
Auditors: ERNST & YOUNG US LLP SAN DIEG

LOCATIONS

HQ: MISSION HOSPITAL REGIONAL MEDICAL CENTER INC
27700 MEDICAL CENTER RD, MISSION VIEJO, CA 926916426
Phone: 949 364-1400
Web: WWW.MISSION4HEALTH.COM

HISTORICAL FINANCIALS

Company Type: Private

Income Statement — FYE: June 30

	REVENUE ($ mil.)	NET INCOME ($ mil.)	NET PROFIT MARGIN	EMPLOYEES
06/16	547	28	5.3%	2,600
06/15	516	23	4.5%	—
06/10	500	50	10.1%	—
06/09	355	12	3.5%	—
Annual Growth	6.4%	13.0%	—	—

2016 Year-End Financials

Return on assets: 4.9%
Return on equity: 10.5%
Current ratio: 1.40
Cash ($ mil.): 38

MISSION HOSPITAL, INC.

Its mission is clear and bold: Improve the health of all in western North Carolina. Mission Hospital is a 760-bed regional referral center serving the western quarter of North Carolina and portions of adjoining states. A not-for-profit community hospital system Mission is located in Asheville on two adjoining campuses: Memorial and St. Joseph's. It provides tertiary-level services in neurosciences cardiac care trauma care surgery pediatric medicine and women's services and has a medical staff of more than 540. It also includes the Mission Children's Hospital. Mission Hospital is the flagship hospital of Mission Health System which is being acquired by HCA Healthcare for $1.5 billion.

Change in Company Type

In 2018 hospital operator HCA Healthcare agreed to buy Mission Health System which includes Mission Hospital and six smaller hospitals in Asheville North Carolina for $1.5 billion. As part of the deal HCA will keep all rehab and acute-care hospitals open for at least 10 years. It will also invest several hundreds of millions of dollars in various expenditures.

Geographic Reach

Mission Health System serves patients in western North Carolina.

Strategy

Mission Hospital has been actively expanding and modernizing its facilities in recent years. It built a surgery registration and waiting area to ease patient comfort as they wait to be seen at the Memorial Campus. It also opened a four-story facility to provide more surgery suites and patient beds for Mission Hospital. In order to increase patient satisfaction the hospital opened a new surgery registration and waiting area at its Memorial Campus.

Mission Hospital places great focus on genetic medicine. It has an entire department dedicated to the study of genetics genetic therapy and the study of fetal alcohol spectrum disorders.

Mission Health partnered with Western Carolina University to provide a graduate certification program in Healthcare Innovation Management. The program which began in 2013 is a component of Mission Health's budding Center for Innovation established to foster a spirit of advancement in healthcare throughout western North Carolina. The program consists of four courses over a period of 21 months and is open to all Mission Health employees. Students who complete the program which is fully funded by Mission Health will earn credit towards bachelor's and master's degrees.

Company Background

Mission Hospital was formed in 1996 from the partnership (and eventual merger) of Memorial and St. Joseph's hospitals.

EXECUTIVES

Ceo, Chad Patrick
Pres*, Joseph Damore
Ceo*, Ronald A Paulus
Sr V Pres*, Charles F Ayscue
Human Resources Representative, Teresa McCarthy
Human Resources Representative, Dan McFatter
Chief Staff, Alan S Baumgarten
Allergy and Immunology, John Van Wye
Business Manager Senior, Cora McPherson

LOCATIONS

HQ: MISSION HOSPITAL, INC.
509 BILTMORE AVE, ASHEVILLE, NC 288014601
Phone: 828 213-1111
Web: WWW.MISSIONHEALTH.ORG

PRODUCTS/OPERATIONS

Surgical Services
General Surgery
Minimally Invasive Surgery
Outpatient Surgery
Prepare for Surgery
Robotic Surgery
Surgery at Mission Hospital
Surgery Guide
Programs of Service
Endoscopy
Genetics
Integrative Healthcare
Mother and Baby
Outpatient Care Centers
Sleep Center
Urology
Weight Management Center
Wound Healing and Hyperbarics
Support Services
Chronic Medical Conditions
Long-Term Acute Care
Laboratory
Pastoral Care Services
Pharmacy
Psychiatric Services
Radiology (Imaging) Services
Rehabilitation Services
Research Institute
Respiratory Therapy
Senior Services and Geriatrics

COMPETITORS

Blue Ridge HealthCare
CaroMont
Carolinas HealthCare System
Duke University Health System
Haywood Regional
Presbyterian Healthcare
UNC Hospitals

HISTORICAL FINANCIALS

Company Type: Private

Income Statement — FYE: September 30

	REVENUE ($ mil.)	NET INCOME ($ mil.)	NET PROFIT MARGIN	EMPLOYEES
09/15	1,019	91	9.0%	10,000
09/14	936	64	6.9%	—
09/13	942	71	7.6%	—
09/12	861	86	10.0%	—
Annual Growth	5.8%	2.0%	—	—

MISSOURI BAPTIST MEDICAL CENTER

EXECUTIVES

Pres, Joan Magruder
V Pres-Cfo*, Gary McLaughlin
Vpres*, Timothy Ranney
Vpres*, Douglas Black
Vpres*, Sandra Young
Vpres*, Tim Mislan
Pricipal*, John Antes
Health Professional, Anshu Jain
Director of Mis/Is, Rosa Davila
Food Director, Terri Powell
Pastoral Care Director, Alan Runge

LOCATIONS

HQ: MISSOURI BAPTIST MEDICAL CENTER
3015 N BALLAS RD, SAINT LOUIS, MO 631312329
Phone: 314 996-5155
Web: WWW.MISSOURIBAPTIST.ORG

HISTORICAL FINANCIALS

Company Type: Private

Income Statement FYE: December 31

	REVENUE ($ mil.)	NET INCOME ($ mil.)	NET PROFIT MARGIN	EMPLOYEES
12/18	584	15	2.6%	1,670
12/17	600	18	3.0%	—
12/16	570	25	4.5%	—
12/15	511	15	3.0%	—
Annual Growth	4.6%	(0.1%)	—	—

2018 Year-End Financials

Return on assets: 4.4%
Return on equity: 4.8%
Current ratio: 4.20
Cash ($ mil.): —

MISSOURI CITY OF KANSAS CITY

You may not be in Kansas anymore but you could still be in Kansas City . Situated opposite Kansas City Kansas is the city of Kansas City Missouri the state's largest city with a population of about 460000. Its council-manager form of government is made up of 12 members presided over by the mayor. The city manager serves and advises the council and prepares the annual budget for council consideration as well as enforces municipal laws and ordinances and manages city operations. With more than 200 fountains within 320 square miles its official nickname is the "City of Fountains." Incorporated in 1850 it is home to the Chiefs and Royals and is famous for barbeque.

EXECUTIVES

Senior Vice President Enterprise Information Technology, James Poindexter
Auditors: BKD LLP KANSAS CITY MISSOUR

LOCATIONS

HQ: MISSOURI CITY OF KANSAS CITY
414 E 12TH ST STE 105, KANSAS CITY, MO 641062705
Phone: 816 513-1313
Web: WWW.HELLOKANSASCITY.COM

HISTORICAL FINANCIALS

Company Type: Private

Income Statement FYE: April 30

	REVENUE ($ mil.)	NET INCOME ($ mil.)	NET PROFIT MARGIN	EMPLOYEES
04/19	1,150	(22)	—	8,000
04/18	1,085	13	1.2%	—
04/17	1,058	(9)	—	—
04/16	1,055	67	6.4%	—
Annual Growth	2.9%	—	—	—

MISSOURI DEPARTMENT OF TRANSPORTATION

Missouri has come a long way since its first byway Three Notch Road was built in 1735 and MoDOT has had a lot to do with the progress. The Missouri Department of Transportation (MoDOT) overseas one of the nation's largest state highway systems. Specifically it designs builds and maintains the 32000-plus miles of highway and some 10000 bridges and administers federal and state programs that affect public transit and air water and rail transportation throughout the state. MoDOT is governed by the six-member Missouri Highways and Transportation Commission. The agency that became MoDOT got its start when the Missouri Legislature established a job for a state highway engineer in 1907.

EXECUTIVES

Dir, Dave Nichols
Transportation Planner*, Machelle Watkins
SEC*, Sharon Monroe
Compensation Manager, Paul Imhoff
Program Manager, Amy Wilson
Program Manager, Denise Fennewald
Program Manager, Eileen Rackers
Program Manager, Harry Gilmore
Assistant Const, Jay Bestgen
Program Manager, Melissa Wilbers
General Manager Purch, Rebecca Jackson
Auditors: BKD LLP SPRINGFIELD MO

LOCATIONS

HQ: MISSOURI DEPARTMENT OF TRANSPORTATION
105 W CAPITOL AVE, JEFFERSON CITY, MO 651016811
Phone: 573 751-2551
Web: WWW.MODOT.ORG

PRODUCTS/OPERATIONS

Selected Services and Operations

Commnity Services
- Adopt-A-Highway
- Being Green
- Economic Impact Analysis
- Local Programs
- Memorial Designation Programs
- Partnership Development
- Planning and Policy Group
- Request a Speaker
- Roadside Vegetation Management
- Scenic Byways
- Sponsor-A-Highway
- Stormwater Pollution Reporting
- Transportation Enhancements
- Work-Zone Safety Awareness

Engineering Services
- Bridge Engineering Assistance Program
- Traffic Engineering Assistance Program

Travel Services
- Carpool Connections
- Commuter Lots
- Gateway Guide
- Intelligent Transportation Systems
- Kansas City Scout
- Missouri Rest Area Guide
- Motorist Assist
- Online Traveler Information Map
- Ozark Traffic Information
- Snow Plowing info — priorities driving tips and more

HISTORICAL FINANCIALS

Company Type: Private

Income Statement FYE: June 30

	REVENUE ($ mil.)	NET INCOME ($ mil.)	NET PROFIT MARGIN	EMPLOYEES
06/17	2,213	(107)	—	6,295
06/09	2,142	(357)	—	—
06/05	0	0	—	—
Annual Growth	—	—	—	—

2017 Year-End Financials

Return on assets: (-0.3%)
Return on equity: (-0.4%)
Current ratio: 2.60
Cash ($ mil.): 735

MMR CONSTRUCTORS, INC.

EXECUTIVES

Pres, James B Rutland
V Pres*, Tom Welborn
SEC-Treas*, Donald Fairbanks
Manager, John Salisbury
Notary Legal Assistant, Sharon Odom
Superintendant, Barry Lewis
Accounts Payable, Brandi Dauthier
Project Manager, Brett Jacob
Hsande Coordinator, Furnell Hankton
Site Manager, Herbie Bordelon
Office Manager, Irina Lee
Auditors: MADDOX & ASSOCIATES APC BATO

LOCATIONS

HQ: MMR CONSTRUCTORS, INC.
15961 AIRLINE HWY, BATON ROUGE, LA 708177412
Phone: 225 756-5090
Web: WWW.MMRGRP.COM

HISTORICAL FINANCIALS

Company Type: Private

Income Statement FYE: December 31

	REVENUE ($ mil.)	NET INCOME ($ mil.)	NET PROFIT MARGIN	EMPLOYEES
12/18	775	25	3.3%	4,000
12/17	581	16	2.9%	—
12/16	531	14	2.7%	—
12/15	513	16	3.1%	—
Annual Growth	14.8%	16.5%	—	—

2018 Year-End Financials

Return on assets: 5.5%
Return on equity: 12.3%
Current ratio: 3.50
Cash ($ mil.): 1

MMR GROUP, INC.

That murmur you hear could be the gentle hum of a properly functioning power system. MMG Group provides electrical and instrumentation construction maintenance management and technical services for clients in the oil and gas manufacturing chemical and power generation industries around the world. It also offers services in offshore marine and platform environments. Its Power Solutions division constructs onsite power-generation systems in industrial plants and other facilities. The group primarily operates in the Gulf of New Mexico. Founded in 1990 MMG is 100% management owned and has served such clients as Chevron Shell BP Merck Air Liquide DuPont and 3M.

Operations

MMR Group's provides four main services: electrical and instrumentation contracting safety services panel fabrication and communications.

MMR's electrical and instrumentation contractors work on projects throughout the US and overseas. To ensure its projects are completed on time and within budget its personnel has support and management control systems and emphasizes planning scheduling progress tracking and labor analysis.

The MMR Offshore Safety Services division specializes in disaster prevention and safety helping with navigation fire and gas detection suppression products paging and alarm systems level one cathodic protection inspections and other related services.

For panel fabrication services MMR stages tests and designs control systems that best fit client needs.

The MMR ProCom division is in charge of precommissioning commissioning and start-Up activities for both MMR Group construction projects and for outside clients interested in turning their facilities construction into a safe and reliable operation seamlessly.

Geographic Reach

MMR operates out of some 20 offices spread across North and South America with most of its offices in Texas Louisiana and California. The company works on projects all over the world with foreign affiliate offices in Calgary Canada; Cartagena Colombia; Puerto la Cruz Venezuela; and Port of Spain Trinidad & Tobago.

Sales and Marketing

MMR serves a variety of markets including: alternative energy exploration and production chemical and petrochemical industrial and manufacturing oil and gas power generation and waste and water treatment among others.

Some of the company's panel fabrication clients have included Shell Pipeline Chevron Pipeline Enbridge Pipeline AGI Services Cimitation Engineering ExxonMobil Keystone Engineering W.S. Nelson Engineering and Entergy among others.

Depending on the project and client's preference MMR operates on all types of fixed-price and cost-plus contracts.

Strategy

The company continues to expand its operations to accommodate more projects. In 2014 the company built a 19-office administration building along with a 6000 square-foot warehouse facility to support the influx of new projects going on in the Golden Triangle area between Beaumont TX and Lake Charles LA.

EXECUTIVES

Vice President Marketing, Grady Saucier
Auditors: MADDOX & ASSOCIATES APC BATO

LOCATIONS

HQ: MMR GROUP, INC.
15961 AIRLINE HWY, BATON ROUGE, LA 708177412
Phone: 225 756-5090
Web: WWW.MMRGRP.COM

PRODUCTS/OPERATIONS

Selected Services

Instrumentation
- Air supply installation
- Control room equipment installation
- Instrument installation
- Process leads
- Panel fabrication
- Signal wiring

Electrical
- Controls
- Electrical equipment setting
- Grounding
- Lighting
- Power distribution

Technical
- Calibration
- Commissioning
- Detail design
- High voltage testing
- Instrument procurement
- Loop check
- Maintenance
- Start up assistance
- System analysis

Selected Divisions

MMR Constructors
MMR International
MMR Power Solutions
MMR Offshore Services
MMR Technical Services
Southwestern Power Group

COMPETITORS

Alberici
EMCOR
Fisk Electric
Industrial Specialty Contractors
MYR Group
Matrix Service
Turner Industries

HISTORICAL FINANCIALS

Company Type: Private

Income Statement — FYE: December 31

	REVENUE ($ mil.)	NET INCOME ($ mil.)	NET PROFIT MARGIN	EMPLOYEES
12/19	783	23	3.0%	4,000
12/18	786	17	2.2%	—
12/17	618	9	1.5%	—
12/16	608	14	2.5%	—
Annual Growth	8.8%	16.6%	—	—

2019 Year-End Financials

Return on assets: 5.0%
Return on equity: 10.5%
Current ratio: 2.10
Cash ($ mil.): 11

MODERN WOODMEN OF AMERICA

No need to pitch a tent to have Modern Woodmen in your camp. One of the largest fraternal benefit societies in the US Modern Woodmen of America provides annuities life insurance and other financial savings products to more than 740000 members through some 1000 agents. The group founded in 1883 is organized into "camps" (or chapters) that provide financial social recreational and service benefits to members. Founder Joseph Cullen Root chose the society's name to compare pioneering woodmen clearing forests to men using life insurance to remove the financial burdens their families could face upon their deaths.

Operations

The organization claims some approximately 2500 chapters nationwide provide opportunities for members to take part in educational social and volunteer activities; nearly 300 summit chapters offer activities for members age 55 and over; and more than 800 youth service clubs which are led by adult member volunteers.

In addition to financial services the organization offers life insurance for member families include term life insurance plans specifically designed for children and young adults and permanent life insurance plans with a minimum insurance amount of $50000. Its annuities services include Max-Provider for retirement savings variable annuity for multiple investment options and single premium immediate annuity. In addition to life insurance and annuities the company offers retirement accounts including IRAs college savings plans investment assistance and other insurance products. Modern Woodmen has $20.4 million in life insurance in force.

Subsidiary MWA Financial Services offers securities and advisory products. The MWABank (dba Modern Woodmen Bank) division provides retail banking services.

Geographic Reach

Based in Rock Island Illinois the organization has nearly 500 home offices and operates throughout the US. It has agents in more than 45 regions throughout 45 states.

Financial Performance

In 2019 Modern Woodmen had $17.34 billion in assets. This was higher than the $16.5 billion reported in 2018 as bonds and stocks both increased.

Net income for the same year was $89.5 million which was lower than the $109.9 million reported the year prior. The decrease was mainly due to lower realized capital gains.

Cash at the end of the year for the company was $363.4 million. Net cash provided by operating activities was $189.2 million while cash used for investments was $299.9 million.

Strategy

Modern Woodmen manages its assets so that changes in the financial markets ? recessions depressions or periods of inflation ? have minimal effect. Modern Woodmen is also careful not to follow investment fads. To build its investment portfolio its financial management team follows these principles: High-quality investments; Diversified investments; and Competitive rates of return.

Assets are invested primarily in high-quality low-risk investments. As of December 31 2019 approximately 99.7 percent of bonds were of high or medium quality.

Company Background

Although Modern Woodmen's roots are tangled with Woodmen of the World Life Insurance Society the two fraternal benefit societies are not related. Modern Woodmen of America was founded in 1883.

EXECUTIVES

Vice President, Rob Sevilla
Vice President Of It, Becky Hansen
Vice Pres, Alan Blackmon
Board Of Directors, Gary Medd

LOCATIONS

HQ: MODERN WOODMEN OF AMERICA
1701 1ST AVE, ROCK ISLAND, IL 612018779
Phone: 309 793-5537
Web: WWW.MODERNWOODMEN.ORG

PRODUCTS/OPERATIONS

Selected Products

Annuities (fixed immediate and variable; through MWA Financial Services)
Banking (MWABank)
- Certificates of Deposit
- Checking and savings accounts
- Credit cards and gift cards
- First mortgage and refinancing home loans
- Home equity loans

Insurance (through MWAGIA)
- Dental and vision insurance
- Disability income insurance
- Group employee benefits
- Group voluntary benefits
- Impaired risk life insurance
- International life and health insurance
- Long-term care insurance
- Major medical insurance
- Medicare supplement insurance

Investment (through MWA Financial Services)
- Brokerage services
- College savings plans
- Mutual funds
- Retirement plans

Life Insurance
- Term life insurance
- Term life insurance for children
- Universal life insurance
- Whole life insurance

COMPETITORS

Allstate
MassMutual
MetLife
Nationwide Financial
New York Life
Northwestern Mutual
Prudential
Reliance Standard
Royal Neighbors Of America
State Farm
Thrivent Financial
Woodmen of the World Life Insurance

HISTORICAL FINANCIALS

Company Type: Private

Income Statement	ASSETS ($ mil.)	NET INCOME ($ mil.)	INCOME AS % OF ASSETS	EMPLOYEES
				FYE: December 31
12/07	8,318	96	1.2%	480
12/06	7,928	99	1.3%	—
Annual Growth	4.9%	(2.6%)	—	—

2007 Year-End Financials

Return on assets: 1.2%
Return on equity: 8.2%
Sales ($ mil): 1,065

MONMOUTH MEDICAL CENTER INC.

Monmouth Medical Center is a 530-bed tertiary care teaching hospital providing comprehensive health care to residents of central New Jersey. The not-for-profit medical center offers services ranging from orthopedics diagnostics and obstetric care to surgery dentistry and geriatric services. The medical center campus also includes a children's hospital a cancer center a neuroscience institute an outpatient care clinic and hospice and home health facilities. Monmouth Medical Center is a teaching affiliate of the Rutgers-Robert Wood Johnson Medical School. The hospital is part of the RWJBarnabas Health network.

Company Background

Monmouth Medical Center was founded in 1887. It has expanded over the years to provide a number of specialist services including high-tech offerings such as robotic surgery. Parent Barnabas Health merged with Robert Wood Johnson Health in 2016 to form RWJBarnabas.

EXECUTIVES

Medical Records Director, Dianna Jankos
Vice President Of Supply Chain, Robert Carretta
Vice President Of Patient Care Services, Sari Kaplon
Auditors: KPMG LLP NEW YORK NY

LOCATIONS

HQ: MONMOUTH MEDICAL CENTER INC.
300 2ND AVE, LONG BRANCH, NJ 077406395
Phone: 732 222-5200
Web: WWW.RWJBH.ORG

PRODUCTS/OPERATIONS

Selected Centers and Services

Anesthesiology Services
Behavioral Health Network
Brain Tumor Center (David S. Zocchi)
The Breast Center (Jacqueline M. Wilentz Comprehensive)
Burn Center
Cancer Services
Cardiac Services
Cardiac Surgery
Children's Hospital at Monmouth (Pediatrics)
Cleft Palate Center
Cord Blood Banking Program
Cosmetic Surgery
Cranmer Ambulatory Surgery Center
Critical Care Services
Diabetes Education - Center for Diabetes Education
Dental Medicine
Diagnostic Imaging Services
The Eisenberg Family Center
Emergency Services
Epilepsy Monitoring Program
Extracorporeal Membrane Oxygenation Program (ECMO)
The Gamma Knife Center
Geriatric Emergency Medicine (GEM) Unit
Geriatric Health Center
Head & Neck Surgery
Hernias Repair Institute for the Treatment of Complex
HIV/AIDS Program
Home Health Care
Home Infusion Care
Hospice
Hyperbaric Oxygen Therapy
Integrative Medicine (Center for)
Joint Replacement and Spine Center
Medical Records
Medical Alert/Lifeline
Medicine (Department of)
Minimally Invasive Surgery
Monmouth Family Health Center
Neonatal Intensive Care Unit (Regional Newborn Center)
Neuroscience Institute
Nutritional Counseling
Obstetrics/Gynecological Services
Occupational Medicine
Orthopaedic Services
Outpatient Services Location
Pain Management Program
Palliative Care
Pastoral Care
Pathology & Laboratory Services
Pediatric Services
Pediatric Subspecialty Center at Toms River The
Pediatric Surgery
Pharmacy Department
Plastic Surgery
Podiatry Services
Pre-Admission Testing Services
Psychiatric Services
Pulmonary Services
Radiation Oncology
Rehabilitation Services
Renal Services
Renal Transplantation
Respiratory Services
Robotic Surgery
Senior Services Program
Sleep Disorders Center
Spine Center
Surgical Services
Total Joint Replacement
Urogynecology
Urology
Valerie Fund Cancer Center (Pediatrics)
Vascular Surgery
The Weight Loss Institute of New Jersey
Wound Treatment Center

COMPETITORS

Atlantic Health
Bergen Regional Medical
Capital Health System
CentraState Healthcare System
Hackensack Meridian Health
Princeton HealthCare
Saint Peter's University Hospital
Shore Memorial Hospital
St. Joseph's Healthcare System
Trinitas Regional Medical Center
Valley Health System

HISTORICAL FINANCIALS

Company Type: Private

Income Statement	REVENUE ($ mil.)	NET INCOME ($ mil.)	NET PROFIT MARGIN	EMPLOYEES
				FYE: December 31
12/19	556	5	1.0%	2,400
12/18	546	43	8.0%	—
12/17	529	52	10.0%	—
12/16	399	46	11.5%	—
Annual Growth	11.7%	(50.5%)	—	—

2019 Year-End Financials

Return on assets: 0.7%
Return on equity: 1.6%
Current ratio: 2.90
Cash ($ mil.): —

MONOGRAM FOOD SOLUTIONS, LLC

Monogram Food Solutions is focused on M E A and T. As a manufacturer of meat and meat snack products the company produces beef jerky sausage hot dogs bacon and other processed food items. Its brands include Circle B King Cotton and Trail's Best Meat Snacks. Through several special licensing agreements Monogram Food Solutions also sells Jeff Foxworthy Jerky Products NASCAR Jerky and Steak Strips and Bass Pro Uncle Buck's Licensed Products. The company which distributes its products nationwide operates facilities in Minnesota Indiana and Virginia. Founded in 2004 Monogram Food Solutions was formed through the merger of assets (King Cotton and Circle B) previously owned by Sara Lee Corp.

Geographic Reach

From its headquarters in Memphis Tennessee Monogram Food Solutions directs the operation of additional facilities in (Chandler) Minnesota (Muncie and Bristol) Indiana and (Martinsville) Virginia. The company distributes its products nationwide.

Strategy

Licensing agreements have helped Monogram Food Solutions build a firm foundation for its business. Aside from its deal with Bass Pro Shops and Jeff Foxworthy the company enjoys licensing partnerships with Johnsonville Sausage and Glory Foods. Its alliance with Johnsonville Sausage inked in 2012 gave Monogram Food Solutions the go-ahead to produce and market Johnsonville Deli

Bites Bacon Jerky and other meat snacks innovations.

Beginning in 2010 the company began manufacturing and selling meat snacks for the energy drink maker DNA Beverages Corporation under the DNA brand. Geared toward a younger consumer the DNA beef products gives Monogram a larger demographic for its products.

Mergers and Acquisitions

Since its founding the company has quickly built itself up by buying established meat product manufacturers and processing plants. In 2009 it acquired three companies including beef jerky maker Wild Bill's Foods and Al Pete's Meats (and the Pete's Pride brand name). It also acquired the Hannah's Bull's O'Brien's and Dakota meat snack brands from meat processing company American Foods Group.

In late 2012 Monogram Food Solutions purchased Hinsdale Farms of Bristol Indiana. As one of the nation's largest makers of corn dogs Hinsdale also has a hand in serving retail private label customers and co-packing for other manufacturers. The deal added a fourth manufacturing plant for processing meat. As part of the acquisition Monogram Food Solutions is working to integrate the Hinsdale business into its manufacturing and sales systems.

EXECUTIVES

Vice President Operations Fina, George Roden
Senior Vice President Information Technology, Joan Vanness
Management Vice President, Brett Elliott
Corporate Vice President And Controller, Matt Arinder
Vice President And General Manager, Richard Foster
Vice President And Product Development, Bill Southard
Vice President Sales Business Development, Corey Williamson
Vice President Of Sales And Marketing, Scott Torrey
Vice President Of Operations, Kent Kring
Auditors: MAYER HOFFMAN MCCANN PC MEM

LOCATIONS

HQ: MONOGRAM FOOD SOLUTIONS, LLC
530 OAK COURT DR STE 400, MEMPHIS, TN 381173735
Phone: 901 685-7167
Web: WWW.MONOGRAMFOODS.COM

PRODUCTS/OPERATIONS

Selected Brands

Circle B
Hannah's
King Cotton
O'Brien's Meat Snacks/Sausages
Wild Bill's

COMPETITORS

Bridgford Foods
Carl Buddig
Clemens Family Corporation
ConAgra
Hormel
Jerky Snack Brands
Link Snacks
Oberto Sausage Company
Weaver Meats

HISTORICAL FINANCIALS

Company Type: Private

Income Statement — FYE: December 28

	REVENUE ($ mil.)	NET INCOME ($ mil.)	NET PROFIT MARGIN	EMPLOYEES
12/19	747	(4)	—	790
12/18	647	11	1.7%	—
12/17	640	2	0.4%	—
12/16	565	12	2.2%	—
Annual Growth	9.8%	—	—	—

2019 Year-End Financials

Return on assets: (-1.0%)
Return on equity: (-3.5%)
Current ratio: 1.60
Cash ($ mil.): —

MONONGAHELA POWER COMPANY

Electricity flows from Monongahela Power (Mon Power) just like the river the utility was named after. The company services approximately 388000 residential and commercial customers in a service area of 13000 sq. mi. in West Virginia. Mon Power along with West Penn Power and Potomac Edison comprise the Allegheny Power arm of Allegheny Energy which is now part of FirstEnergy. In 2013 Mon Power owned or controlled 3580 MW of generating capacity. The company is contractually obligated to supply Potomac Edison with sufficient power to meet that company's power load obligations in West Virginia.

Operations

Mon Power provides generation transmission and distribution services. Its infrastructure includes 25390 miles of distribution lines and more than 2125 miles of transmission lines.

Geographic Reach

The utility's service area includes Northern Central and Southeastern West Virginia.

Strategy

In 2013 the parent company invested about $131 million in Mon Power and planned to invest about $233 million more in 2014 to help Mon Power expand its operations.

In a transfer of assets within FirstEnergy's West Virginia-based operations to improve efficiencies in 2013 Mon Power sold its 8% share of the Pleasants power plant at its fair market value of $73 million to Allegheny Energy Supply. In return Allegheny Energy Supply sold its 80% stake in the Harrison plant to Mon Power at its book value of $1.2 billion.

To lower carbon emissions in 2012 Mon Power shut down three aging coal-fired power plants in West Virginia: Albright Willow Island and Rivesville.

Company Background

The company is a subsidiary of Allegheny Energy which is owned by FirstEnergy.

Mon Power was incorporated in Ohio in 1924.

EXECUTIVES

Chb-Ceo, Paul J Evanson
V Pres*, Philip L Goulding
Pres*, David E Flitman
Contrl*, Thomas R Gardner
V Pres-SEC*, Hyun Park
Cfo*, Jeffrey David Serkes
Associate Business Analyst, Jane Campbell
Auditors: PRICEWATERHOUSECOOPERS LLP CL

LOCATIONS

HQ: MONONGAHELA POWER COMPANY
5001 NASA BLVD, FAIRMONT, WV 265548248
Phone: 800 686-0022
Web: WWW.FIRSTENERGYCORP.COM

COMPETITORS

Appalachian Power
Buckeye Power
Dominion Hope
Dominion Transmission
Ohio Edison
Ohio Valley Electric

HISTORICAL FINANCIALS

Company Type: Private

Income Statement — FYE: December 31

	REVENUE ($ mil.)	NET INCOME ($ mil.)	NET PROFIT MARGIN	EMPLOYEES
12/17	1,619	69	4.3%	4,000
12/16	1,613	66	4.1%	—
Annual Growth	0.3%	4.5%	—	—

2017 Year-End Financials

Return on assets: 1.6%
Return on equity: 5.4%
Current ratio: 1.80
Cash ($ mil.): 76

MONSTER BEVERAGE 1990 CORPORATION

LOCATIONS

HQ: MONSTER BEVERAGE 1990 CORPORATION
1 MONSTER WAY, CORONA, CA 928797101
Phone: 951 739-6200
Web: WWW.MONSTERBEVCORP.COM

COMPETITORS

5-hour ENERGY
Bazi
Campbell Soup
Caribou Coffee
Celsius Holdings
Chiquita Brands
Cinnabon
Clearly Canadian
Coca-Cola
Cott
Del Monte Foods
Dole Food
Dr Pepper Snapple Group
Energy Brands
Gatorade
Godiva Chocolatier
Goya
Hornell Brewing
IZZE
Impulse Energy USA
Jones Soda
Mondelez International
Mott's
Naked Juice
National Beverage
National Grape Cooperative
Nestle
Ocean Spray
Odwalla
PepsiCo
Red Bull
Reed's
Smucker
South Beach Beverage
Starbucks
Sunny Delight
Suntory Holdings
Tree Top
Tropicana
Unilever
Welch's
Wet Planet Beverages
illy

HISTORICAL FINANCIALS

Company Type: Private

Income Statement — FYE: December 31

	REVENUE ($ mil.)	NET INCOME ($ mil.)	NET PROFIT MARGIN	EMPLOYEES
12/17	3,369	820	24.4%	2,001
12/16	3,049	712	23.4%	—
12/15	2,722	546	20.1%	—
12/14	2,464	483	19.6%	—
Annual Growth	11.0%	19.3%	—	—

2017 Year-End Financials

Return on assets: 17.1% Cash ($ mil.): 528
Return on equity: 21.1%
Current ratio: 3.70

MONTAGE HEALTH

EXECUTIVES

Pres-Ceo, Steven Packer
V Pres*, Terril Lowe
V Pres-Fin*, Laura Zehm
V Pres*, Cynthia Peck
V Pres*, Tim Nylen
Dentist, Diane Day DDS
Doctor, George H Penn
Radiologist, Kristine W Leatherberry
Urologist, Craig Stauffer
Family Practice, Deborah Biller
Director of Lipid Serv, Diane Sobkowicz
Auditors: MOSS ADAMS LLP SAN FRANCISCO

LOCATIONS

HQ: MONTAGE HEALTH
23625 HOLMAN HWY, MONTEREY, CA 939405902
Phone: 831 625-4830
Web: WWW.CHOMP.ORG

HISTORICAL FINANCIALS

Company Type: Private

Income Statement FYE: December 31

	REVENUE ($ mil.)	NET INCOME ($ mil.)	NET PROFIT MARGIN	EMPLOYEES
12/19	784	143	18.3%	2,003
12/17*	145	139	95.9%	—
11/11	450	23	5.2%	—
Annual Growth	7.2%	25.4%	—	—

*Fiscal year change

2019 Year-End Financials

Return on assets: 8.4% Cash ($ mil.): 76
Return on equity: 11.8%
Current ratio: 1.60

MONTEFIORE MEDICAL CENTER

The primary teaching hospital of the Albert Einstein College of Medicine Montefiore Medical Center attends to the health care needs of residents of the Bronx and nearby Westchester County. The health system operates four main hospitals with about 1500 beds (and 93000 annual admissions) more than 100 ambulatory care offices a children's hospital and Centers of Excellence in cancer care cardiovascular services transplantation and neurosciences. Additionally it operates a home health care agency as well as outpatient facilities that provide ambulatory and diagnostic services. Montefiore also offers medical education programs in partnership with the Albert Einstein College of Medicine.

Operations

Montefiore provides medical services to more than 2.6 million people in the Bronx and Westchester County. With nearly 300000 visits per year Montefiore's emergency department is one of the busiest in the nation while the home health program provides over 500000 visits annually. As the teaching hospital for Albert Einstein College of Medicine Montefiore provides postgraduate training for nearly 100 accredited residency and fellowship programs at the Children's Hospital at Montefiore Moses Division and Weiler Division and eight residency and fellowship programs sponsored by New York Medical College.

Through Montefiore Care Management the company uses a global prepayment or similar strategies to manage care for 200000 individuals for hospital care rehabilitation outpatient care professional services home care mental health counseling community-based services remote patient monitoring and other programs.

Montefiore and Einstein are among about three dozen academic medical centers nationwide to be awarded the Clinical and Translational Science Award (CTSA) by the National Institutes of Health.

Geographic Reach

Montefiore is made up of four hospitals within three main campuses in the Bronx and more than 100 ambulatory care offices throughout the Bronx and Westchester County (and a total of 140 locations across its entire service area). It has nearly 50 primary care locations throughout the New York metropolitan area.

Strategy

The health center's strategy is to advance its partnership with the Einstein College of Medicine and to improve the health of the communities it serves. Montefiore has grown in scale through acquisitions and mergers in order to diversify its earning potential and increase its bargaining power with drug wholesalers. The system which treats a relatively high percentage of Medicaid patients also stands to benefit by serving a larger volume of patients. Medicaid is shifting to the managed care model which pays a set amount per patient or service. Therefore Montefiore and other providers are seeking growth by caring for more patients in a more efficient manner thereby reducing losses from providing patient care above the government payor's set payment. Additionally the system launched its own insurance coverage for small businesses in early 2015.

The health system is largely involved in the community and is one of the region's hospitals to participate in the Bronx Regional Health Information Organization (Bronx RHIO) a not-for-profit organization established to help the borough's vast number of health care providers share patient information. Participants include hospitals health systems ambulatory care centers individual physician offices long-term care and home care services. Collectively they deliver care to more than 1 million residents including more than 95% of the borough's annual hospital discharges.

Company Background

Founded in 1884 to treat tuberculosis patients Montefiore has a long history of responding to community health crises including lead poisoning and AIDS. In response to rising needs in the community Montefiore opened a community clinic with the aim of vaccinating young women for HPV a sexually transmitted disease that can cause cervical cancer.

EXECUTIVES

Evp Finance And Cfo, Joel A. Perlman
President And Ceo, Steven M. Safyer, age 72
Evp And Coo, Philip O. Ozuah
Svp And Chief Medical Officer, Andrew D. Racine
Executive Vice President Chief Strategy Officer, Lynn Richmond
Chief Development Officer And Vice President, Rachelle Sanders
Vp Of It, Kirk Rodgers
Vp Of It, Ohannes Doghramadjian
Vp Of It, Justin Arriaga
Director Of Nursing, Maureen Vachna
Medical Director Aids Ctr, Barry Zingman
Md Professor And University Chair Department Of Radiology, Judy Yee
Vp Of It, Francisco Melo
Vp Of It, Gilberto Dixon
Vp Of It, Kevin Sanchoo
Vp Of It, Mark Kim
Assoc. Vp Patient Access Transformation Officer, Adrin Mammen
Secretary, Evette Francis
Secretary, Vilma Crespo
Secretary, Hilda Marchany
Auditors: ERNST & YOUNG LLP NEW YORK

LOCATIONS

HQ: MONTEFIORE MEDICAL CENTER
111 E 210TH ST, BRONX, NY 104672401
Phone: 718 920-4321
Web: WWW.MONTEFIORE.ORG

PRODUCTS/OPERATIONS

Selected Services

Allergy & Immunology
Arthritis & Joint Disease (Rheumatology)
Blood (Hematology)
Bones Muscles & Joints Orthopaedics)
Brain (Neurology)
Centers of Excellence
Dentistry & Oral Surgery
Dermatology
Diabetes Hormones Metabolism (Endocrinology)
Diagnostics & Testing (Pathology)
Digestive & Liver Dieases (Gastroenterology)
Elder Care (Geriatrics)
Emergency Medicine
Eyes (Opthalmology and Visual Sciences)
Family and Social Medicine
General Internal Medicine
Headache Center
HIV/AIDS
Home Care
ICU (Critical Care Medicine)
Infectious Diseases
Internal Medicine
Kidney Disease (Nephrology)
Lungs (Pulmonary Medicine)
Neurosurgery
OB/GYN & Women's Health
Otorhinolaryngology - Head and Neck Surgery
Pain Management & Anesthesiology
Pediatrics
Pharmacy Services
Primary Care
Psychiatry and Behavioral Sciences
Radiology
Rehabilitation Medicine
Sleep-Wake Disorders Center
Surgery
Surgical Services (All)
Urology
Wound Care (Hyperbaric Medicine)

Selected Facilities

Greene Medical Arts Pavilion (outpatient care)
Mercy Community Care (outpatient care)
Montefiore Medical Group (23 Bronx and Westchester locations)
Montefiore Medical Park (outpatient care)
Moses Division Hospital (or Henry and Lucy Moses Division)
The Children's Hospital at Montefiore
North Division (formerly Our Lady of Mercy Medical Center)
Weiler Division Hospital (or Jack D. Weiler Hospital)

COMPETITORS

Beth Israel Medical Center
Bronx-Lebanon Hospital Center
Brookdale University Hospital
Brooklyn Hospital Center
Catholic Healthcare System
Jamaica Hospital Medical Center
Kingsbrook Jewish Medical Center
Lenox Hill Hospital
Maimonides Medical Center
New York City Health and Hospitals
NewYork-Presbyterian Healthcare
Northwell Health
Phelps Memorial Hospital Center
SUNY Downstate
Winthrop-University Hospital

HISTORICAL FINANCIALS

Company Type: Private

Income Statement FYE: December 31

	REVENUE ($ mil.)	NET INCOME ($ mil.)	NET PROFIT MARGIN	EMPLOYEES
12/17	3,762	43	1.2%	11,000
12/16	2,690	42	1.6%	—
Annual Growth	39.9%	2.7%	—	—

2017 Year-End Financials

Return on assets: 1.2%
Return on equity: 5.1%
Current ratio: 1.70
Cash ($ mil.): 253

MONTGOMERY COUNTY, MARYLAND

EXECUTIVES

County Executive, Marc Elrich
Pres, Hans Riemer
Exec Dir, Linda Herman
Prin, Amy Moskowitz
Captain, Dan Ogren
Captain, Gary Rebsch
Captain, Mike Green
Program Inspector, Brian Keeler
Program Inspector, Kevin Embry
Coordinator, Michael Brown
Coordinator, Paulina Alvarado
Auditors: CLIFTONLARSONALLEN LLP BALTIM

LOCATIONS

HQ: MONTGOMERY COUNTY, MARYLAND
101 MONROE ST FL 15, ROCKVILLE, MD 208502503
Phone: 240 777-8220
Web: WWW.MONTGOMERYCOUNTYMD.GOV

HISTORICAL FINANCIALS

Company Type: Private

Income Statement FYE: June 30

	REVENUE ($ mil.)	NET INCOME ($ mil.)	NET PROFIT MARGIN	EMPLOYEES
06/18	4,203	217	5.2%	7,400
06/17	4,191	52	1.3%	—
06/16	3,874	(89)	—	—
06/15	0	0	—	—
Annual Growth	—	—	—	—

2018 Year-End Financials

Return on assets: 1.6%
Return on equity: 20.7%
Current ratio: —
Cash ($ mil.): 337

MONUMENT HEALTH RAPID CITY HOSPITAL, INC.

EXECUTIVES

Chm, Tom Morrison
Ceo, Charles E Hart
Exec V Pres, Joseph Sluka
Treas, Roy Dishman
Coo, Timothy Sughrue
Information, Bill Stockmann
Staff, Clinton Oyler
Staff, Teresa Lemmer
Compliance Staff, Sabine Colton
Applications Supervisor, Christopher Brandner
Trainer, Jennifer Archambeau
Auditors: EIDE BAILLY LLP MINNEAPOLIS

LOCATIONS

HQ: MONUMENT HEALTH RAPID CITY HOSPITAL, INC.
353 FAIRMONT BLVD, RAPID CITY, SD 577017375
Phone: 605 755-1000
Web: WWW.MONUMENT.HEALTH

HISTORICAL FINANCIALS

Company Type: Private

Income Statement FYE: June 30

	REVENUE ($ mil.)	NET INCOME ($ mil.)	NET PROFIT MARGIN	EMPLOYEES
06/18	689	22	3.2%	4,258
06/09	0	0	—	—
Annual Growth	114.9%	—	—	—

2018 Year-End Financials

Return on assets: 1.9%
Return on equity: 2.9%
Current ratio: 3.30
Cash ($ mil.): 26

MORSE OPERATIONS, INC.

Morse Operations (dba Ed Morse Automotive Group) has been selling cars and trucks long enough to know the code of the road. It owns about a dozen new car dealerships across Florida most of them operating under the Ed Morse name. Dealerships house more than 15 franchises and 10 domestic and import car brands including Cadillac Fiat Chevrolet Buick GMC Scion Honda Mazda and Toyota. The company's Bayview Cadillac in Fort Lauderdale is one of the world's largest volume sellers of Cadillacs. Morse Operations also sells used cars provides parts and service and operates a fleet sales division. Founder and auto magnate the late Ed Morse entered the automobile business in 1946 with a 20-car rental fleet.

Operations

Ed Morse Fleet Sales offers vehicles from about 10 different brands including Honda Cadillac Fiat Chevrolet Buick GMC Scion Mazda and Toyota. To date annual fleet sales have reached 100000 vehicles.

Fleet customers include daily rental companies such as National Car Rental Avis and Alamo Rent A Car.

Geographic Reach

The dealership network serves customers throughout Florida along the East and West coasts and in Central Florida.

EXECUTIVES

Pres, Edward J Morse III
V Pres-Cfo*, Carmine Colella
Ceo-Coo*, Dennis M Macinnes
V Pres*, Rany Hoffman
Manager, Mike Byrne
Auditors: CROWE HORWATH LLP FORT LAUDER

LOCATIONS

HQ: MORSE OPERATIONS, INC.
2850 S FEDERAL HWY, DELRAY BEACH, FL 334833216
Phone: 561 276-5000
Web: WWW.EDMORSESAWGRASS.COM

PRODUCTS/OPERATIONS

Selected Dealerships

Brandon Auto Mall
Ed Morse Auto Plaza - Port Richey
Ed Morse Bayview Cadillac
Ed Morse Cadillac - Delray Beach
Ed Morse C
Ed Morse C
Ed Morse Delray Toyota/Scion
Ed Morse Honda Blue Heron
Ed Morse M
Ed Morse Sawgrass

COMPETITORS

AutoNation
Braman Management
Buchanan Automotive
Ferman Automotive
Holman Enterprises
Island Lincoln-Mercury
JM Family Enterprises
March/Hodge
Penske Automotive Group
Scott-McRae

HISTORICAL FINANCIALS

Company Type: Private

Income Statement FYE: December 31

	REVENUE ($ mil.)	NET INCOME ($ mil.)	NET PROFIT MARGIN	EMPLOYEES
12/18	1,125	(0)	—	925
12/17	1,019	4	0.4%	—
12/16	1,334	9	0.7%	—
12/15	1,095	14	1.3%	—
Annual Growth	0.9%	—	—	—

2018 Year-End Financials

Return on assets: (-0.2%)
Return on equity: (-1.1%)
Current ratio: 1.50
Cash ($ mil.): 11

MORTON PLANT HOSPITAL ASSOCIATION, INC.

EXECUTIVES

Pres, Brandon May
V Pres-Oprs-Adm*, Hal Ziecheck
Doctor, Margaret Ann Kelleher

Doctor, Michael Starsiak
Obstetrician Gynecologist, David D Desper Jr
Internist, Tommie Betancourt
Registrar 1, Dianna Biscoglia
Rn, Michelle Mdevivo

LOCATIONS

HQ: MORTON PLANT HOSPITAL ASSOCIATION, INC.
300 PINELLAS ST, CLEARWATER, FL 337563892
Phone: 727 462-7000
Web: WWW.BAYCARE.ORG

HISTORICAL FINANCIALS

Company Type: Private

Income Statement FYE: December 31

	REVENUE ($ mil.)	NET INCOME ($ mil.)	NET PROFIT MARGIN	EMPLOYEES
12/16	555	83	14.9%	3,000
12/15	107	(8)	—	—
12/13	598	49	8.3%	—
12/09	517	33	6.5%	—
Annual Growth	1.0%	13.8%	—	—

2016 Year-End Financials

Return on assets: 8.2%
Return on equity: 8.5%
Current ratio: 21.40
Cash ($ mil.): —

MOSAIC HEALTH SYSTEM

Heartland Health provides medical care in the heart of the Midwest. The integrated health care system serves residents of northwest Missouri as well as bordering areas of Kansas and Nebraska. Its flagship facility is Heartland Regional Medical Center a 350-bed acute-care hospital that features an emergency room and Level II trauma center as well as specialty care programs in heart disease cancer and obstetrics. Heartland Health also provides primary care through a multi-specialty medical practice (Heartland Clinic) and it offers home health hospice and long-term care services from the primary medical center facility. The company's Community Health Improvement Solutions unit is an HMO health insurer.

Strategy

In 2012 Heartland Health joined the Mayo Clinic Care Network which will enable to it to tap the knowledge and expertise of Mayo Clinic physicians to better serve its patients.

Company Background

Heartland Health was formed in 1984 through the merger of two St. Joseph Missouri hospital: Methodist Medical Center and St. Joseph's Hospital. The two facilities trace their roots back to 1924 and 1861 respectively.

EXECUTIVES

Ceo, Mark Laney
Pres*, Lowell Kruse
V Pres-Cfo*, John Wilson
Chairman*, Alfred L Purcell
Asst SEC*, Karen Dittemore
Asst Treas-Contrl*, Douglas Brandt
Cmo*, Robert Permet
Chm*, David Solanski
Coo*, Cut Kretzinger
Staff, C R Shumann III
Staff, Monica Ray
Auditors: RSM US LLP DAVENPORT IOWA

LOCATIONS

HQ: MOSAIC HEALTH SYSTEM
5325 FARAON ST, SAINT JOSEPH, MO 645063488
Phone: 816 271-6000
Web: WWW.HEARTLAND-HEALTH.COM

PRODUCTS/OPERATIONS

Selected Affiliates

Atchison Hospital (Atchison KS)
Community Hospital (Fairfax MO)
Community Medical Center (Falls City NE)
Dental Clinic (St. Joseph MO)
Laser Cosmedic Center (Platte City MO)
North Kansas City Hospital (North Kansas City MO)
The Surgery Center (St. Joseph MO)

COMPETITORS

Ascension Health
BJC HealthCare
Blue Cross and Blue Shield of Kansas City
Catholic Health Initiatives
Children's Mercy Hospital
CoxHealth
HCA
Mercy Health
Mercy Hospital Springfield
Saint Luke's Health System
Shawnee Mission Medical Center
Sisters of Charity of Leavenworth
Truman Medical Centers
University of Kansas Medical Center

HISTORICAL FINANCIALS

Company Type: Private

Income Statement FYE: June 30

	REVENUE ($ mil.)	NET INCOME ($ mil.)	NET PROFIT MARGIN	EMPLOYEES
06/20	778	75	9.6%	32,000
06/19	688	85	12.4%	—
06/18	667	64	9.6%	—
06/16	584	(6)	—	—
Annual Growth	7.4%	—	—	—

2020 Year-End Financials

Return on assets: 6.0%
Return on equity: 9.5%
Current ratio: 7.30
Cash ($ mil.): 23

MOTION PICTURE INDUSTRY HEALTH PLAN

EXECUTIVES

Prin, David Wescoe
Chief Human Resources Officer, Rita Van Vranken
Auditors: MILLER KAPLAN ARASE LLP NORTH

LOCATIONS

HQ: MOTION PICTURE INDUSTRY HEALTH PLAN
11365 VENTURA BLVD, STUDIO CITY, CA 916043148
Phone: 818 769-0007
Web: WWW.MPIPHP.ORG

HISTORICAL FINANCIALS

Company Type: Private

Income Statement FYE: December 31

	ASSETS ($ mil.)	NET INCOME ($ mil.)	INCOME AS % OF ASSETS	EMPLOYEES
12/13	856	60	7.1%	17
12/09	543	(75)	—	—
Annual Growth	12.0%	—	—	—

2013 Year-End Financials

Return on assets: 7.1%
Return on equity: 18.7%
Sales ($ mil): 732

MOUNT CARMEL HEALTH PLAN MEDIG

LOCATIONS

HQ: MOUNT CARMEL HEALTH PLAN MEDIG
6150 E BROAD ST, COLUMBUS, OH 432131574
Phone: 614 546-3138
Web: WWW.MEDIGOLD.COM

HISTORICAL FINANCIALS

Company Type: Private

Income Statement FYE: December 31

	REVENUE ($ mil.)	NET INCOME ($ mil.)	NET PROFIT MARGIN	EMPLOYEES
12/16	571	(20)	—	4
12/13	423	37	8.8%	—
Annual Growth	10.5%	—	—	—

2016 Year-End Financials

Return on assets: (-7.1%)
Return on equity: (-14.2%)
Current ratio: 3.40
Cash ($ mil.): 55

MOUNT CARMEL HEALTH PLAN, INC.

EXECUTIVES

Prin, Ginny Gale

LOCATIONS

HQ: MOUNT CARMEL HEALTH PLAN, INC.
6150 E BROAD ST, COLUMBUS, OH 432131574
Phone: 614 546-4300
Web: WWW.MEDIGOLD.COM

HISTORICAL FINANCIALS

Company Type: Private

Income Statement FYE: December 31

	REVENUE ($ mil.)	NET INCOME ($ mil.)	NET PROFIT MARGIN	EMPLOYEES
12/18	582	47	8.1%	8
12/17	614	32	5.3%	—
Annual Growth	(5.3%)	44.2%	—	—

2018 Year-End Financials

Return on assets: 14.0%
Return on equity: 21.8%
Current ratio: 2.30
Cash ($ mil.): 99

MOUNT CARMEL HEALTH SYSTEM

Mount Carmel Health System cares for the sick in the greater Columbus area and central Ohio. The health care system boasts 1500 physicians at three general hospitals and a specialty surgical hospital offering a comprehensive range of medical and surgical services including cardiovascular care. Mount Carmel Health also operates outpatient centers including primary care and specialty physicians' practices and it offers home health care services. The hospital group is part of Trinity Health one of the largest Catholic health care systems in the US.

Operations

Mount Carmel's facilities include the acute care Mount Carmel East Mount Carmel West and Mount Carmel St. Ann's hospitals as well as the Mount Carmel New Albany a surgical hospital specializing in orthopedic neurological and musculoskeletal treatments. The system also operates several freestanding emergency and surgery centers and other outpatient and community care centers. Its HealthProviders subsidiary manages about two dozen primary care and specialty practices with more than 100 physicians in central Ohio.

In the realm of education Mount Carmel Health operates six medical residency programs for physicians and its Mount Carmel College of Nursing is one of the largest in the state.

Strategy

In 2015 Mount Carmel announced that it was investing more than $700 million in a major expansion. The investment includes big projects at three Mount Carmel campuses: Mount Carmel East Mount Carmel Grove City and Mount Carmel West. Mount Carmel East will begin a $310 million modernization in 2015 to be completed in phases through 2019.

That year the company signed an agreement with HealthSouth to begin construction on a new inpatient rehabilitation hospital in Westerville Ohio. The 60-bed hospital will be a joint venture between HealthSouth and Mount Carmel and will provide specialized rehabilitative care to patients who have experienced stroke trauma brain and orthopedic injuries or other major illnesses or injuries. Construction on the 60000-square-foot hospital is expected to be completed in early 2017. When the new hospital opens Mount Carmel will relocate its existing 24-bed unit at Mount Carmel West to the new facility.

Company Background

In 2012 the company launched a $110 million facilities improvement project (Project GRACE) which includes the renovation of the St. Ann's hospital. Mount Carmel Health plans for the upgraded St. Ann's facility to serve as a regional medical center.

In 2010 Mount Carmel completed construction of a new freestanding emergency center in the town of Canal Winchester through a partnership with Fairfield Medical Center. The center features both general emergency and pediatric urgent care facilities. In time the center might expand into a larger hospital facility.

Mother M. Angela and Sister M. Rufina Dunn of the Congregation of the Sisters of the Holy Cross of Notre Dame founded Mount Carmel in 1886.

EXECUTIVES

Senior Vice President Human Resources, John Heisler
Vice President Pfs, Karen Geisler
Vice President Patient Care Services And, Rachel Wright
Vice President, Mark D'aloisio
Chair Department Of Medicine, Amit Chatterjee
Vice President Of Sales, Jean Waddell
Medical Director, Wes Hard
Secretary, James Arnold

LOCATIONS

HQ: MOUNT CARMEL HEALTH SYSTEM
6150 E BROAD ST, COLUMBUS, OH 432131574
Phone: 614 234-6000
Web: WWW.MOUNTCARMELHEALTH.COM

PRODUCTS/OPERATIONS

Selected Facilities

Hospitals
- Mount Carmel East
- Mount Carmel New Albany
- Mount Carmel St. Ann's
- Mount Carmel West

Other Facilities
- Anticoagulation Centers
- Atrial Fibrillation Center
- Cardiac Rehabilitation
- Diley Ridge Medical Center
- Mount Carmel Grove City Medical Center
- Geriatrics Center
- Health Centers
- Heart Failure Centers
- Home Medical Equipment
- Imaging Centers
- Mount Carmel Medical Group
- Occupational Health Centers
- Outpatient Cancer Treatment
- Outpatient Labs
- Physician Offices
- Rehab and Sports Medicine Services
- Sleep Medicine
- Surgery Centers
- Urgent Care Centers
- Women's Health Centers
- Wound Centers

COMPETITORS

Adena Health System
Fairfield Medical Center
Genesis HealthCare System (Ohio)
Licking Memorial Health Systems
Nationwide Children's Hospital
OhioHealth
Regency Hospital

HISTORICAL FINANCIALS

Company Type: Private

Income Statement — FYE: June 30

	REVENUE ($ mil.)	NET INCOME ($ mil.)	NET PROFIT MARGIN	EMPLOYEES
06/18	1,911	157	8.2%	8,000
06/15	1,267	131	10.4%	—
06/14	1,223	94	7.7%	—
06/13	1,195	89	7.5%	—
Annual Growth	9.8%	11.9%	—	—

MOUNT CARMEL HEALTH SYSTEM

EXECUTIVES

Ceo, Jay Kasey
Vice-President, Bruce Lucas
Information Specialist, Mike Croyle
Internal Medicine Practitioner, John Weiss
Executive Assistant, Shawn Young
Information Specialist, Terri Theibert
Information Specialist, Tanya Hartshorn
Hematologist, Timothy Moore
Information Specialist, Anthony Lee
Information Specialist, Jaime Capestany
Administrative Assistant, Linda Barkhurst

LOCATIONS

HQ: MOUNT CARMEL HEALTH SYSTEM
5300 N MEADOWS DR, GROVE CITY, OH 431232546
Phone: 614 234-5000
Web: WWW.MOUNTCARMELHEALTH.COM

HISTORICAL FINANCIALS

Company Type: Private

Income Statement — FYE: June 30

	REVENUE ($ mil.)	NET INCOME ($ mil.)	NET PROFIT MARGIN	EMPLOYEES
06/16	743	33	4.5%	1
06/15	707	47	6.7%	—
Annual Growth	5.1%	(29.5%)	—	—

2016 Year-End Financials

Return on assets: 6.6%
Return on equity: 7.6%
Current ratio: 3.00
Cash ($ mil.): 39

MOUNT SINAI MEDICAL CENTER OF FLORIDA, INC.

Mount Sinai Medical Center of Florida is a not-for-profit acute care teaching hospital providing a wide range of health services to residents of South Florida. The medical center which boasts more than 670 beds provides general medical and surgical care as well as specialty care in cardiology (Mount Sinai Heart Institute) neuroscience oncology orthopedics pulmonology radiology and other fields. It also participates in clinical research studies and drug trials with an emphasis on cancer heart and lung conditions It maintains an inpatient behavioral health unit and houses the Wien Center for Alzheimer's disease and memory disorders diagnosis and research the largest such facility in the region.

Operations

Mount Sinai Medical Center of Florida has 26 operating suites and more than 700 physicians. In 2012 it reported more than 63000 emergency visits 22000 patients admissions and 12000 surgeries.

Geographic Reach

Reaching beyond its main South Florida campus the Mount Sinai Medical Center of Florida also operates a multi-specialty physicians' clinic emergency care and diagnostic center in nearby Aventura. It also operates physicians' clinics in Key Biscayne and Hialeah and an outpatient center in Coral Gables.

Sales and Marketing

The Center markets its services through TV and radio commercials and via print media.

Financial Performance

The company's revenues grew by 3% to $497 million in 2012 due to higher patient service revenues (net of contractual allowances discounts and other revenue). Medicare accounted for 36% of patient service revenues; Medicaid 7%.

Mount Sinai Medical Center of Florida reported net income of $34 million in 2012 (compared to a net loss in 2011) thanks to the absence of impairment of long-lived assets partially offset by a loss on extinguishment of debt. Net income also improved due to change in the beneficial interest in the net assets of Mount Sinai Medical Center Foundation Inc.

Strategy

The company teams up with larger institutions to expand its reach and skill set. Its medical education programs include a cardiology partnership with Columbia University and resident programs for medical students from the University of Miami Florida International University and Nova Southeastern University. The center's partnership with Columbia University has created the Mount Sinai Heart Institute and the Columbia University Division of Urology at Mount Sinai the only Ivy League affiliated programs in South Florida.

Other programs support students entering such health care professions as nursing pharmacy and therapy.

Enhancing its standing in 2014 Mount Sinai Medical Center of Florida received full accreditation for percutaneous coronary intervention from the Society of Cardiovascular Patient Care an international body dedicated to preventing and treating heart disease.

Company Background

Mount Sinai Medical Center of Florida was founded in 1949 by a group of philanthropists and concerned citizens.

EXECUTIVES

Senior Vice President And Chief Information Officer, Tom Gillette
President And Ceo, Steven D. Sonenreich
Evp Operations And Cfo, Alex Mendez
Chief Medical Officer, Robert C. Goldszer
President Medical Staff, Peter Segall
Vice President Patient Services, Karen Hermanson
Senior Vice President Operations, Angel Pallin
Senior Vice President And Chief Development Officer, Michael Milberg
Assistant Vice President Physician Practice Administration, Donna Owens
Vice President Facilities And Resource Management, Ben Davis
Head Nurse, Emelyn Salamorin
Vice President Finance, Wayne Chutkan
Vice President (region 14, Emily Forcke
Vice President Human Resources, Jennifer Foreman
Assistant Vice President Network Development, Jim Gaton Gomez
Chairman, Michael M. Adler
Medical Secretary, Zocima Gonzalez
Unit Secretary, Ethel Dandy
Unit Secretary, Allyson Shervington

LOCATIONS

HQ: MOUNT SINAI MEDICAL CENTER OF FLORIDA, INC.
4300 ALTON RD, MIAMI BEACH, FL 331402948
Phone: 305 674-2121
Web: WWW.MSMC.COM

PRODUCTS/OPERATIONS

Florida Locations

MOUNT SINAI MEDICAL CENTER (MAIN CAMPUS): Miami Beach
MOUNT SINAI AVENTURA EMERGENCY ROOM PHYSICIAN OFFICES CANCER CENTER AND DIAGNOSTIC CENTER: Aventura
MOUNT SINAI KEY BISCAYNE PHYSICIAN OFFICES: Key Biscayne
MOUNT SINAI CORAL GABLES DIAGNOSTIC CATHETERIZATION LAB: Coral Gables
MOUNT SINAI PRIMARY & SPECIALTY CARE CORAL GABLES: Coral Gables
MOUNT SINAI HIALEAH: Hialeah

COMPETITORS

Baptist Health South Florida
Broward Health
HCA
Jackson Health System
Miami Children's Hospital
Tenet Healthcare
University of Miami Hospital

HISTORICAL FINANCIALS

Company Type: Private

Income Statement — FYE: December 31

	REVENUE ($ mil.)	NET INCOME ($ mil.)	NET PROFIT MARGIN	EMPLOYEES
12/16	560	19	3.5%	3,225
12/15	533	38	7.2%	—
12/14	530	17	3.2%	—
12/13	584	42	7.3%	—
Annual Growth	(1.4%)	(22.9%)	—	—

2016 Year-End Financials

Return on assets: 2.8%
Return on equity: 8.7%
Current ratio: 3.30
Cash ($ mil.): 255

MOUNT SINAI ST. LUKE'S.

EXECUTIVES

Pres, Frank Cracolici
Sr V Pres*, Robert Catalano
Research Manager*, Anthony Grillo
Scientist, Emilia Sordillo
Manager, Jeff Horvath
Administrator, Sheila Monroe
Editor, Carolyn Waldron
Coordinator, Christella Watts
Social Worker, Yvette Washington
Assistant Professor, Preetika Mukherjee
Lab Manager, Mary Ellen Nusbaum
Auditors: ERNST & YOUNG US LLP INDIANAP

LOCATIONS

HQ: MOUNT SINAI ST. LUKE'S.
1111 AMSTERDAM AVE, NEW YORK, NY 100251716
Phone: 212 523-4000
Web: WWW.CHPNET.ORG

HISTORICAL FINANCIALS

Company Type: Private

Income Statement — FYE: December 31

	REVENUE ($ mil.)	NET INCOME ($ mil.)	NET PROFIT MARGIN	EMPLOYEES
12/16	901	53	5.9%	6,000
12/15	859	61	7.1%	—
12/14	1,160	(17)	—	—
Annual Growth	(11.9%)	—	—	—

2016 Year-End Financials

Return on assets: 6.0%
Return on equity: —
Current ratio: 0.80
Cash ($ mil.): 39

MULTI-COLOR CORPORATION

Multi-Color Corporation is a global label solutions supporting a number of the world's most prominent brands including leading producers of home & personal care wine & spirits food & beverage healthcare and specialty consumer products. The company serves international brand owners in the North American Latin American EMEA and Asia Pacific regions with a comprehensive range of the latest label technologies in Pressure Sensitive Cut and Stack In-Mold Shrink Sleeve Heat Transfer Roll Fed and Aluminum Labels. Multi-Color also provides a full complement of print methods including rotogravure lithographic flexographic digital and a combination of flexographic and screen printing plus in-house pre-press services.

Change in Company Type

In 2019 Multi-Color was acquired by an affiliate of Platinum Equity a leading private equity firm. At closing Multi-Color merged with a subsidiary of WS Packaging another label solutions leader within Platinum Equity's portfolio of companies.

Operations

Multi-Color provides a wide range of products for the packaging needs of customers and is one of the world's largest producers of high quality pressure sensitive in-mold and heat transfer labels and a major manufacturer of cut and stack roll fed aluminum and shrink sleeve labels.

Pressure sensitive labels adhere to a surface with pressure. The label typically consists of four elements ? a substrate which may include paper foil or plastic; an adhesive which may be permanent or removable; a release coating; and a backing material to protect the adhesive against premature contact with other surfaces.

The in-mold label process applies a label to a plastic container as the container is being formed in the mold cavity. The finished IML product is a finely detailed label that performs consistently well for plastic container manufacturers and adds marketing value and product security for consumer product companies.

HTL are reverse printed and transferred from a special release liner onto the container using heat and pressure. These labels are printed and then shipped to blow molders and contract decorators who transfer the labels to the containers

Cut and stack labels are adhered to containers using an adhesive applied during the labelling process. These labels can be produced on a wide variety of substrates and accommodate a comprehensive range of embellishments including foil stamping embossing metallic and unique varnish finishes. Roll fed labels can be applied to any type of container and offer customers optimum space for brand presentation at a competitive price. Shrink sleeve labels are produced in colorful cutting edge styles and materials. The labels are manufactured as sleeves slid over glass or plastic bottles and then heated to conform precisely to the contours of the container.

Geographic Reach

Headquartered in Ohio Multi-Color also has more than 70 manufacturing facilities located in North America Latin America EMEA and Asia Pacific.

Sales and Marketing

Multi-Color sells to a broad range of home & personal care wine & spirits food & beverage healthcare and specialty consumer product companies located in the North American Latin American EMEA (Europe Middle East and Africa) and Asia Pacific regions. During 2019 2018 and 2017 sales to major customers approximated 10% 14% and 17% respectively of the company's consolidated net revenues.

Financial Performance

The 2019 combination of Multi-Color and W/S Packaging created a business with $2.2 billion in annual revenue. Before the combination Multi-Color had reported steady year-over-year increases in revenues during the five-year-period from 2015 to 2019. Net income grew most years during this time except for 2019 when Multi-Color reported a loss.

Net revenues increased 33% in fiscal 2019 compared to 2018. While the company reported growth the increase was less than the 41% revenue growth Multi-Color reported from 2017 to 2018. As a result of a recent procurement savings initiative major customer Proctor & Gamble (P&G) diversified its supply of certain label products in North America in 2019. Multi-Color expects volume from P&G will be reduced and has stated that the loss or continued reduction of business from P&G could have a material adverse impact on its financial results.

Multi-Color recorded a loss of $29 million in 2019 when it made goodwill impairment charges related to its In-Mold Labels Food & Beverage and Europe Food & Beverage reporting units. Results also include costs related to the closure of manufacturing facilities in France and Canada as well as acquisition and integration expenses primarily related to the Constantia Labels acquisition and strategic review expenses.

Cash at the end of 2019 was $57.8 million. Cash from operations was $159.4 million while investing activities used $78.6 million. Financing activities used $83.3 million. Main cash uses for the year were for capital expenditures payment under revolving line credits and repayments of long-term debts.

Strategy

The company's strategy focuses on expanding its customer base and portfolio of products prepress activities and manufacturing locations throughout the world. In fiscal 2018 Multi-Color entered the German label market with the acquisition of GEWA Etiketten a manufacturer specializing in producing pressure sensitive labels for the wine and spirits market. Also in fiscal 2018 it purchased Constantia Labels growing its presence in the Germany Belgium Romania and Vietnam label markets. It entered the Tanzanian label market in fiscal 2018 with the acquisition of TP Label primarily a pressure sensitive and cut and stack business serving customers in the food and beverage market. It entered the New Zealand wine and spirits market in fiscal 2018 with the purchase of a start-up operating in Auckland.

The company sustainability strategy is based on CARE: Collaborate Act Resolve and Engage. To embark on this voyage the company engages with multiple stakeholder partners throughout the value chain who are aiming for a sustainable future. Only through open and constructive collaboration issues can be solved that the company are facing as an industry. The company also act to optimize its supply chain and production process. Multi-Color do this by maintaining a continuous improvement approach in each facility globally where it aim is to reduce energy and water usage as well as implementing waste reduction strategies. Research & Development team is constantly searching for label upgrades that meet today's sustainability needs. Each label upgrade starts with a dialogue with the customer - to fully understand which goal it trying to reach ? and the reclaimers ? to ensure the end of life. And at the core of its business are the people that it encounter every day. Multi-Color works hard to be the best possible employer to its workforce and a valued partner to its communities. The company fosters an inclusive safe and giving environment so its employees are fully engaged in ensuring a brighter tomorrow.

EXECUTIVES

Vp Finance International, Sharon E. Birkett, $387,500 total compensation

President Wine And Spirits Group North America, David G. Buse

President Ceo And Director, Vadis A. Rodato, $500,000 total compensation

President North America Consumer Products, Floyd E. Needham, $500,000 total compensation

National Account Manager, Bryant Hagen

Vice President Sales And Marketing, Bill Knopka

National Account Manager, Jeff Lozen

National Account Manager, Hal Hunt

National Account Manager, Warren Mckinney

Chairman, Nigel A. Vinecombe

Board Of Directors, Simon Roberts

Board Member, Jessie Baumgartner

Auditors: GRANT THORNTON LLP DETROIT M

LOCATIONS

HQ: MULTI-COLOR CORPORATION
4053 CLOUGH WOODS DR, BATAVIA, OH 451032587

Phone: 513 381-1480

Web: WWW.MCCLABEL.COM

2015 Sales

	$ mil.	% of total
US	512	58
Australia	63	7
Italy	57	5
Other International	177	30
Total	**810**	**100**

PRODUCTS/OPERATIONS

Selected Products and Services

Labels
- Heat transfer
- In-mold
- Neck bands
- Peel-away
- Pressure sensitive
- Re-sealable
- Shrink sleeve

COMPETITORS

Fort Dearborn
H. S. Crocker
Outlook Group
WS Packaging Group

HISTORICAL FINANCIALS

Company Type: Private

Income Statement — FYE: March 31

	REVENUE ($ mil.)	NET INCOME ($ mil.)	NET PROFIT MARGIN	EMPLOYEES
03/19	1,725	(28)	—	8,300
03/18	1,300	71	5.5%	—
03/17	923	61	6.6%	—
03/16	870	47	5.5%	—
Annual Growth	25.6%	—	—	—

2019 Year-End Financials

Return on assets: (-1.1%)
Return on equity: (-4.6%)
Current ratio: 1.90
Cash ($ mil.): 57

MULTICARE HEALTH SYSTEM

MultiCare Health System is a not-for-profit health system that serves the residents of four counties in the southern Puget Sound region and southwestern Washington. Altogether the system's five hospitals have more than 1100 beds. The largest facility Tacoma General boasts about 440 beds and provides specialized cancer cardiac orthopedic and trauma care in addition to general medical and surgical care. Other medical centers include Good Samaritan Hospital (with 286 beds) Allenmore Hospital (130 beds) Auburn Regional Medical Center (195 beds) and Mary Bridge Children's Hospital (82 beds).

Operations

MultiCare has more than 1000 staff physician specialists. In addition to its five hospitals the health system also operates dozens of primary care specialty care and urgent care clinics in the region as well as home health and hospice care agencies. Tacoma General Hospital operates the MultiCare Regional Cancer Center an obstetrics and neonatal intensive care unit the MultiCare Neuroscience Center of Washington orthopedics the MultiCare Surgical Care Center and the MultiCare Regional Heart & Vascular Center. Tacoma General also offers Level II Adult Trauma Center and Level IIIB neonatal intensive care unit. Mary Bridge Children's Hospital & Health Center operates a pediatric intensive care unit a pediatric heart center a Center for Childhood Safety child abuse intervention programs and outpatient specialty clinics.

In 2013 alone the company provided free and subsidized health care services at an estimated cost of $185 million.

In 2013 MultiCare reported 217590 emergency department visits; 47138 admissions; 9616 inpatient surgeries 23502 outpatient surgeries and 5817 live births.

Geographic Reach

MultiCare serves patients in more than 130 locations in Washington's Pierce South King Thurston and Kitsap counties.

Strategy

The company is expanding its infrastructure to keep up with demand.

In 2014 MultiCare opened the 115929-sq.-ft. Rainier Pavilion as part of a $192 million project to expand services for women newborns and children at Tacoma General Hospital and Mary Bridge Children's Hospital. When the final phase is completed in 2015 the project will add 133919 sq. ft.

of new space and 144835 sq. ft. of renovated space.

Also that year MultiCare broke ground on a new hospital in Covington improving access to health care services in South King County. The new 24-bed three-story hospital (with the potential to expand to 58 beds) will open in 2016. Other new facilities that broke ground in 2013 and 2014 are a 120-bed psychiatric hospital in Tacoma (for which MultiCare is partnering up with CHI Franciscan Health to build) and a birth center at Tacoma General Hospital.

On the technology front MultiCare uses technologies such as digital mammography CyberKnife Radiosurgery technology and Da Vinci Robotic Surgery to provide better service to the patients. In 2013 MultiCare Auburn Medical Center upgraded its billing processes to an electronic health record system.

EXECUTIVES

Vice President Information Technology, Harold Moscho
Medical Director Sleep Center, Kimberly Mebust
President And Ceo, William G. (Bill) Robertson, age 60
Evp, Florence Chang
President East Pierce Region, Glenn Kasman
President West Pierce Region, Shelly Mullin
Chief Physician Officer, Claire Spain-Remy
Vp Finance And Interim Cfo, Anna Loomis
President South King Region, Hugh Kodama
Cio, Robert Biernbaum
Respiratory Therapy Director, Clark Needham
Vice President, Dori Young
Medical Director, John Rieke
Senior Vice President And Cfo, Jim Mcmanus
Vice President Revenue Cycle, Sheri Beekman
Clinical Director, Jodi Gragg
Secretary, Debbie Day
Secretary, Cheryl Wamsley
Auditors: KPMG LLP SEATTLE WA

LOCATIONS

HQ: MULTICARE HEALTH SYSTEM
316 MRTIN LTHER KING JR W, TACOMA, WA 984054252
Phone: 253 403-1000
Web: WWW.MULTICARE.ORG

PRODUCTS/OPERATIONS

Selected Facilities

Hospitals

Allenmore Hospital (Tacoma)
Auburn Medical Center (Auburn)
Good Samaritan Hospital (Puyallup)
Mary Bridge Children's Hospital and Health Center (Tacoma)
Tacoma General Hospital (Tacoma)

Other facilities

Allenmore Medical Center
Auburn MultiCare Clinic
Covington MultiCare Clinic
Lakewood Urgent Care Clinic
Kent MultiCare Clinic
MultiCare Home Services
Spanaway MultiCare Clinic
Tacoma Family Medicine
University Place Urgent Care Clinic
Westgate Urgent Care Clinic

Selected Services

Adult Day Health
Behavioral Health
Boutique
Breast Health
Cancer Center
Center for Healthy Living
Children's Therapy Unit
Community Programs
CyberKnife Radiosurgery
Diabetes Services
Ear Nose and Throat
Emergency and Urgent Care
Family Birth Centers
Geriatric Psychiatric Center
Health Care Resource Center
Heart Care
Home Health and Hospice
Immunization Clinic
Infusion Center
Institute for Research & Innovation
Laboratories Northwest
Maternal-Fetal Medicine
Medical Imaging
Nephrology
Neonatal Intensive Care Unit
Neurosciences
Nutrition
OB/GYN
Occupational Medicine
Orthopedics
Pain Management
Palliative Medicine
Perinatal Outreach Program
Pharmacy
Physical Therapy
Podiatry
Primary Care Clinics
Pulmonary Care
Pulmonary Rehabilitation
Rehabilitation
Robotic Technology
Senior Services
Sexual Assault Services
Spa
Sports Medicine
Surgical Services
Tobacco Cessation
Transfusion Free Medical and Surgical Program
Urology
Weight Loss and Wellness
Wound Healing Center

COMPETITORS

Catholic Health Initiatives
Franciscan Health System
Harrison Medical Center
Overlake Hospital
PeaceHealth
Providence St. Joseph Health
Seattle Children's Hospital
Swedish Health Services
Yakima Valley Memorial

HISTORICAL FINANCIALS

Company Type: Private

Income Statement — FYE: December 31

	REVENUE ($ mil.)	NET INCOME ($ mil.)	NET PROFIT MARGIN	EMPLOYEES
12/19	3,234	336	10.4%	6,510
12/18	2,922	34	1.2%	—
12/17	2,416	347	14.4%	—
12/16	1,927	180	9.4%	—
Annual Growth	18.8%	23.0%	—	—

2019 Year-End Financials

Return on assets: 6.6%
Return on equity: 11.4%
Current ratio: 1.80
Cash ($ mil.): 434

MUNICIPAL ELECTRIC AUTHORITY OF GEORGIA

With more juice than a ripe Georgia peach the Municipal Electric Authority of Georgia (MEAG Power) supplies wholesale electric power. The authority has a generating capacity of 2069 MW through its interests in nuclear and fossil-fueled plants. Some 49% of the energy MEAG Power delivered in 2012 came from its nuclear plants. MEAG Power transmits electricity to 48 municipal and one county distribution systems across Georgia that in turn serve some 600000 consumers. It utilizes a transmission network that is co-owned by all the power suppliers in Georgia although it is considering joining a regional transmission organization (RTO) to further defray costs.

Operations

MEAG Power owns more than 1300 miles of high-voltage transmission lines and almost 200 substations. It also provides value-added services including management infrastructure and marketing support to its member municipalities energy marketers and other utilities.

The company generates most of its revenues from Project One (ownership stakes in nine generating units other owned transmission plants and working capital). Higher member billings for operating expenses related to fuel and nuclear operations lifted MEAG Power's revenues and net income in 2010.

Geographic Reach

The company serves 49 communities across Georgia.

Financial Performance

In 2012 MEAG Power's revenues increased by 8% thanks to higher participant billings related to a planned reduction in trust transfers as well as an increase in debt service related to environmental improvements to the coal operations and higher contract energy sales. These gains were partially offset by lower participant billings for maintenance and fuel expenses.

That year the company's net income increased by 351% as the result of higher net sales and decreased operating costs.

Strategy

With Georgia restricted in its natural potential for solar and wind power development MEAG Power is pushing hard for the expansion of nuclear power as a clean energy alternative to coal.

In a major breakthrough in 2012 the Nuclear Regulatory Commission approved a Combined Construction and Operating License for units 3 and 4 of the Vogtle plant (near Waynesboro Georgia) the first such license ever approved for a US nuclear plant and the first federal go-ahead for nuclear plant construction since 1978.

In 2013 MEAG Power completed a basemat of structural concrete for the nuclear island at the Vogtle Unit 4 nuclear expansion site the second of two units under construction at Plant Vogtle.

Company Background

In 2009 the Georgia Public Service Commission gave the go ahead for the expansion of the nuclear-powered Vogtle Electric Generating Plant which is co-owned by MEAG Power and in 2010 MEAP Power sold $2.7 billion in bonds to fund this expansion.

EXECUTIVES

Vice President Finance, Jim Fuller
Treasurer And Senior Portfolio Director, David Coss
Treasurer, Patrick Bowie
Auditors: PRICEWATERHOUSECOOPERS LLP AT

LOCATIONS

HQ: MUNICIPAL ELECTRIC AUTHORITY OF GEORGIA
1470 RIVEREDGE PKWY, ATLANTA, GA 303284640
Phone: 770 563-0300
Web: WWW.MEAGPOWER.ORG

COMPETITORS

AEP
Dominion Energy
Duke Energy
North Carolina Electric Membership
Oglethorpe Power
Progress Energy
Santee Cooper
Southern Company
Southern Company Gas
TVA

HISTORICAL FINANCIALS

Company Type: Private

Income Statement — FYE: December 31

	REVENUE ($ mil.)	NET INCOME ($ mil.)	NET PROFIT MARGIN	EMPLOYEES
12/19	648	17	2.7%	150
12/18	681	(4)	—	—
12/17	623	0	—	—
12/16	661	(110)	—	—
Annual Growth	(0.6%)	—	—	—

2019 Year-End Financials

Return on assets: 0.2%
Return on equity: —
Current ratio: 0.90
Cash ($ mil.): 703

MUNSON HEALTHCARE

Munson Healthcare is a not-for-profit health care system serving residents in northern Michigan. Its flagship facility is Munson Medical Center in Traverse City a regional referral hospital with about 390 beds offering specialty services including cancer treatment behavioral health cardiac care and orthopedics. Munson Healthcare also has management agreements and other types of affiliations with about a dozen other hospitals in the region. In addition Munson Healthcare operates urgent care and community clinics home health care and hospice agencies an ambulance service and the Northern Michigan Supply Alliance a supply chain management group co-owned with Trinity Health.

Operations

Munson Healthcare is composed of eight hospitals located throughout northern Michigan - Charlevoix Area Hospital (Charlevoix) Kalkaska Memorial Health Center (Kalkaska) Mercy Hospital Cadillac (Cadillac) Mercy Hospital Grayling (Grayling) Munson Medical Center (Traverse City) Otsego Memorial Hospital (Gaylord) Paul Oliver Memorial Hospital (Frankfort) and West Shore Medical Center (Manistee). Services are also available at Munson Community Health Center (Traverse City) and Mercy Community Health Center (Prudenville). Munson Healthcare also works closely with Alpena General Hospital in Alpena and War Memorial Hospital in Sault St. Marie.

In addition to its hospital operations Munson Healthcare also offers in-home care through Munson Home Health and Munson Hospice and Palliative Care. Other specialty services and resources include speech and hearing clinics physical rehabilitation CAT scans magnetic resonance imaging and cardiac catheterization.

Munson Healthcare provides direct access to nearly 800 physicians representing more than 50 specialties.

Eah year the system sees some 22500 admissions performs some 8000 inpatient and 7000 outpatient surgeries and has some 51000 emergency department visits.

Geographic Reach

The health care system offers a continuum of health care services to people in 24 Michigan counties.

Strategy

To better provide services to region residents Munson Healthcare partnered with critical access hospital Mackinac Straits Health System in 2015. The affiliation is focused on improving health care services in rural northern Michigan.

Munson Healthcare is also forming an air ambulance joint venture between its North Flight EMS Air Division and Spectrum Health's Aero Med. The venture to be named North Flight Aero Med will provide critical care air emergency transport services in northern Michigan. It will begin operating in 2016.

Company Background

Munson Healthcare was founded in 1915.

EXECUTIVES

Vice President Facilities And Plant Engineering, Steve Tongue
Director Of Nursing, Renee Cunningham
Medical Director, Ahmet Sevimli
Medical Director, Don Caraccio
Vice President Of Finance, Rob Wilcox
Vice President View Biography, Lorraine Franklightfoot
Vice President Marketing And Corporate Communications, Dianne Michalek
Medical Records Director, Joy White
Secretary, Jodi Radtke
Department Secretary, Carol Saxton
Department Secretary, Melissa Cholger
Vice Chair Kathy Ervin Secretary, Sonja Ganger
Department Secretary, Sue Winowiecki

LOCATIONS

HQ: MUNSON HEALTHCARE
1105 SIXTH ST, TRAVERSE CITY, MI 496842345
Phone: 800 252-2065
Web: WWW.MUNSONHEALTHCARE.ORG

PRODUCTS/OPERATIONS

Selected Michigan Facilities

Charlevoix
Kalkaska M
Mercy Hosp
Mercy Hosp
Munson Community Health Center - Traverse City
Munson Hospice House - Traverse City
Munson Manor Hospitality House - Traverse City
Munson Medical Center - Traverse City
Northwest Michigan Surgery Center - Traverse City
Otsego Mem
Paul Olive
Smith Family Breast Health Center - Traverse City
West Shore

Medical Specialties
Bariatric Surgery
Behavioral Health
Bleeding Disorders Center
Cancer Services
Diabetes
Dialysis
Emergency Services
Hearing Clinic
Heart and Vascular Services
Hospice and Palliative Care
Occupational Health and Medicine
Orthopedics
Senior's Health
Sleep Disorders Center
Stroke Care
Teen's Health
Urgent Care
Urology
Women and Children

COMPETITORS

Borgess Health
Covenant HealthCare
Genesys Regional Medical Center
Hurley Medical Center
McLaren Health Care
Spectrum Health
Trinity Health (Novi)
Zeeland Community Hospital

HISTORICAL FINANCIALS

Company Type: Private

Income Statement — FYE: June 30

	REVENUE ($ mil.)	NET INCOME ($ mil.)	NET PROFIT MARGIN	EMPLOYEES
06/18	1,039	142	13.7%	4,000
06/17	940	160	17.1%	—
06/15	8	(7)	—	—
06/13	6	(3)	—	—
Annual Growth	175.3%	—	—	—

2018 Year-End Financials

Return on assets: 10.5%
Return on equity: 16.0%
Current ratio: 2.90
Cash ($ mil.): 106

MUNSTER MEDICAL RESEARCH FOUNDATION, INC

EXECUTIVES

Pres-Ceo, Donald S Powers
Treas*, George E Watson
Admin*, Edward Robinson
SEC*, Palmer C Singleton
V Pres*, Joseph Morrow
Chm*, Frankie L Fesko
Prin*, James J Richards
SEC*, William A Hasse III
Treas*, David E Wickland
Coordinator, Carol Hernandez
Law Specialist, Cathy Reese
Auditors: ERNST & YOUNG LLP

LOCATIONS

HQ: MUNSTER MEDICAL RESEARCH FOUNDATION, INC
901 MACARTHUR BLVD, MUNSTER, IN 463212901
Phone: 219 836-1600
Web: WWW.COMHS.ORG

HISTORICAL FINANCIALS

Company Type: Private

Income Statement — FYE: June 30

	REVENUE ($ mil.)	NET INCOME ($ mil.)	NET PROFIT MARGIN	EMPLOYEES
06/20	541	(104)	—	2,000
06/19	537	1	0.2%	—
06/18	548	74	13.5%	—
06/16	508	50	9.9%	—
Annual Growth	1.6%	—	—	—

2020 Year-End Financials

Return on assets: (-34.0%)
Return on equity: (-59.3%)
Current ratio: 0.80
Cash ($ mil.): —

MV TRANSPORTATION, INC.

Need to supply transportation by bus? MV Transportation will run your bus system so you don't have to. The company operates more than 200 contracts to offer fixed-route and shuttle bus services as well as paratransit (transportation of people with disabilities) and transportation of Medicaid beneficiaries. Its customers consist primarily of transit authorities and other state and local government agencies responsible for public transportation. MV Transportation operates in more than 130 locations spanning 28 US states and in British Columbia Canada and Saudi Arabia; overall the company maintains a fleet of about 7000 vehicles. MV Transportation was founded in 1975.

Geographic Reach

MV Transportation and its subsidiaries joint ventures partnerships and affiliates operate more than 130 locations in 28 states the District of Columbia two Canadian Provinces and Saudi Arabia.

Sales and Marketing

The company provides its transportation services to cities counties municipalities and other jurisdictional entities as well as for private corporations non-profit agencies and community organizations. Some of its customers include Corpus Christi Regional Transportation Authority (B-Line paratransit and shuttle services) Ashland Public Transit (the curb-to-curb demand response transit service) Capital Area Transit System and Ashtabula County Transportation System (paratransit services).

Strategy

The company relies on the signing of year-long contracts and joint ventures for growth. In 2013 MV Transportation received a four-year contract to continue operation of the City of Irvine's iShuttle service; Irvine's iShuttle provides morning and evening peak-hour service along four routes connecting the Irvine Metrolink Station the Tustin Metrolink Station John Wayne Airport Irvine Spectrum and the Irvine Business Complex (IBC).

To expand its presence and experience in Qatar MV Transportation in 2013 opened its newest business venture in Doha Qatar: MV Global Transport Logistics WLL (MVGTL). In addition MVGTL signed an agreement with passenger transportation provider Mowasalat to provide planning scheduling and event management for the numerous events in Doha.

In early 2012 MV Transportation signed its first contract to manage a bus system outside North America when it made a two-year agreement to coordinate an operation of more than 400 buses carrying Saudi Arabian Oil employees in the Middle Eastern kingdom. Striving to extend its international reach even further the company purchased Transportation Management Services UK Limited (TMSUK) a few months later. The deal allowed MV Transportation to enter a niche market as TMSUK designs and operates transportation systems for special events worldwide.

EXECUTIVES

It Vice President, Mike Kopaczewski
Svp Operations Technology, Larry Biggers
Regional Vice President, Scott Germann
Vice President, Chris Burls
Vice President People, Julie Weber
Vice President Of Customer Service And Operations, Janey Appia
Vice President, Sandra Cunningham
Board Member, John Rogers
Board Member, Carolyn Flowers
Board Member, Scott Letier

LOCATIONS

HQ: MV TRANSPORTATION, INC.
2711 N HASKELL AVE # 1500, DALLAS, TX 752045903
Phone: 972 391-4600
Web: WWW.MVTRANSIT.COM

PRODUCTS/OPERATIONS

Selected Services

Bid committee consultation
Emergency evacuation planning
Global mobility and unique technology assets
International transport and logistics solutions
Logistics and security staffing
Paratransit and multimodal transport
Parking management and valet services
Sustainability transport initiatives
Traffic control planning staffing and consultation
Transport planning and operations
VIP fleet services

COMPETITORS

Coach USA
FirstGroup America
LogistiCare
National Express Group
Veolia Transportation

HISTORICAL FINANCIALS

Company Type: Private

Income Statement				FYE: December 31
	REVENUE ($ mil.)	NET INCOME ($ mil.)	NET PROFIT MARGIN	EMPLOYEES
12/09	706	23	3.3%	224
12/08	645	(2)	—	—
12/07	422	0	—	—
Annual Growth	29.3%	—	—	—

2009 Year-End Financials

Return on assets: 12.3%
Return on equity: 94.1%
Current ratio: 1.50
Cash ($ mil.): 6

MVP HEALTH PLAN, INC.

MVP Health Plan also know as MVP Health Care provides health insurance and employee benefits to its more than 700000 members in upstate New York New Hampshire and Vermont. MVP a not-for-profit organization offers a variety of plans including HMO PPO and indemnity coverage as well as dental plans health accounts and Medicare Advantage plans. Subsidiary MVP Select Care provides third-party administration (TPA) services for self-insured employers. MVP Health Care was founded in 1983 as Mohawk Valley Physicians' Health Plan.

Geographic Reach

MVP Health Care operates regional service and support offices across New York Vermont and New Hampshire. New York State is its largest service area. The firm has offices in Binghamton Fishkill Schenectady Syracuse Rochester and Utica New York as well as in Manchester New Hampshire; and Williston Vermont.

The company's provider network includes 19000 doctors in its three-state service territory; the firm also provides its members with access to about 500000 providers in other states through a partnership with CIGNA.

Sales and Marketing

The company uses a direct sales force as well as brokerages and call centers to sell its products. Its customers include individuals Medicare and Medicaid participants and employer groups.

Financial Performance

MVP Health Care revenue increased 18% to $2.9 billion in 2014; that growth was bolstered by the integration of Hudson Health Plan (acquired in 2013) as well as commercial and government membership growth. Medicaid Managed Care membership grew 21% that year.

Despite that growth the company lost a net $13.6 million.

Strategy

In addition to acquiring other area providers MVP Health Care widens its product offerings to attract a diversified customer base adding new non-employer group options (individual and high-deductible plans) and new small employer group products. It is has also launched new financial and preventative care tools including flexible spending accounts and disease management programs. Cutting policy prices has helped boost membership numbers as well.

The company also partners with health care providers to provide better care for its members as well as developing programs to target specific segments of the population.

MVP Health Care utilizes new technologies to cut its own operating costs. Recent initiatives include launching an e-commerce/plan administration platform creating virtual medical records with area health information organizations and supporting the Taconic Health Information Network and Community (an independent physician practice association).

EXECUTIVES

Evp And Medical Affairs Officer, Allen J. Hinkle
Evp Government Programs, Patrick Glavey
President And Ceo, Denise V. Gonick
Evp Networks And Contracting, Karla Austen
Evp And Cfo, Mark Fish
Associate Medical Director, Clifford Elson
Vice President Of Market Innovation, Augusta Martin
Medical Director, David Phelps
Vice President Human Resources, Lynn Manning
Vice President Legal Affairs And Deputy General Counsel, Dawn Jablonski
Licensed Mvp Medicare Products Advisor, Pamela Kennedy
Vice President Network Operations, Matt Mackinnon
Mvp, Vijaya Saduvu
Vice President And Chief Actuary, Kathleen Fish
Medical Director, Marvin Lederman
Vice President Medicaid Special Services, Julie Levin
Vice President Of Data, Patrick Roohan
Vice President Behavioral Health, Judith Feld
Vp Medicaid Operations And Regulatory Affairs, Sue Montgomery
Vice Chairwoman, Karen Johnson
Auditors: PRICEWATERHOUSECOOPERS LLP HA

LOCATIONS

HQ: MVP HEALTH PLAN, INC.
625 STATE ST, SCHENECTADY, NY 123052260
Phone: 518 370-4793
Web: WWW.MVPHEALTHCARE.COM

PRODUCTS/OPERATIONS

Selected Products

Alternative Funding Arrangements
Deferred Deductible Plans
Defined Contribution Plans
EPOs and PPOs

Health Spending Accounts
High-Deductible Health Plans
HMOs
Medicare Advantage Plans
Regional Plan Options

COMPETITORS

Affinity Health
Blue Cross and Blue Shield of Vermont
CIGNA
Capital District Physicians' Health Plan
EmblemHealth
Excellus BlueCross BlueShield
Fallon Community Health Plan
Fidelis Care New York
HealthPlus Amerigroup
Healthfirst
Independent Health
Lifetime Healthcare
UnitedHealth Group
healthnow new york inc

HISTORICAL FINANCIALS

Company Type: Private

Income Statement — FYE: December 31

	ASSETS ($ mil.)	NET INCOME ($ mil.)	INCOME AS % OF ASSETS	EMPLOYEES
12/15	589	11	1.9%	1,500
12/14	540	(26)	—	—
Annual Growth	9.2%	—	—	—

2015 Year-End Financials

Return on assets: 1.9%
Return on equity: 2.7%
Sales ($ mil): 1,573

MWH GLOBAL, INC.

MWH Global is an environmental engineering construction and management firm that specializes in water-related projects or "wet infrastructure." The company's typical projects include building water treatment or desalination plants water transmission systems or storage facilitates. MWH also provides general building services for transportation energy mining ports and waterways and industrial projects. The company is active in some 35 countries and serves governments public utilities and private sector clients. Affiliates of the employee-owned company include software provider Innovyze and business and government relations firm mCapitol. Canadian Engineering firm Stantec acquired MWH Global for $795 million in May 2016.

Geographic Reach

When it comes to projects MWH Global lives up to its name. The Colorado-based firm operates from 180 offices in 35 countries on six continents in the Americas the Asia/Pacific region the Middle East Africa and Europe.

Sales and Marketing

MWH Global seeks projects in five main markets including: the energy and power; water and wastewater; natural resources and mining; ports waterways and coastal; industrial and commercial transportation; and oil and gas markets.

It also does work for local regional and federal governments; US federal clients; public and private utilities; financial institutions; and insurance companies.

Strategy

MWH Global has kept busy in recent years working on a series of high-profile design and construction projects around the globe.

In 2015 the company continued its design-build work on the $7 billion Panama Canal Third Set of Locks project which will double the canal's capacity by the time its completed at the end of the year. The company also continued working with international electricity and gas company National Grid on the largest energy infrastructure program in the UK.

In late-2014 through a joint venture with Costain MWH Global signed on to a 200 million ($325 million) contract to provide design and build services for Southern Water's water and wastewater infrastructure and non-infrastructure assets program in Southeast England; part of Southern Waters' 3 billion ($5 billion) business plan for 2015-2020. Around the same time MWH Global completed its nearly two-decade-long Huanza Hydroelectric project in the Andes Mountains which now provides 92 Megawatts of electricity to some 90000 households in Peru.

In mid-2014 the South Florida Water Management District awarded MWH Global with a master services agreement to help implement the $880 million Restoration Strategies Regional Water Quality Plan which is part of the state's long-term strategy to restore the Everglades. In 2012 the Qatar Public Works Authority appointed MWH to design a drainage master plan in Qatar which will provide a road map for future investment into water and wastewater treatment and other water-related infrastructure programs over the next 50 years.

EXECUTIVES

Cfo, David G. Barnes, age 57
President Mwh Constructors Mwh Americas, Joseph (Joe) Adams
Chairman And Ceo, Alan J. Krause, age 66
President And Coo Mwh Soft Inc., Paul F. Boulos
President Business Solutions, Dan McConville
President Mwh Constructors, Blair Lavoie
President Europe Africa Government And Infrastructure, Wim Drossaert
President Government And Infrastructure Americas And Asia Pacific, Marshall Davert
Cio, Claire Rutkowski
Managing Director United Kingdom, Catherine Schefer
Chief Strategy Officer, David A. Smith
Vice President Finance, David Harper
Executive Vice President, Donald Smith
Vice President Of Information Technology, Greg Clark
Vice President Client Service Manager, Jonathan Hersey
Vice President Chief Accounting Officer And Corporate Controller, Chad Scherer
Vice President And Business Development Director, Sandra L Shuster
Principal Engineer Vice President, Bill Taplin
Vice President And Regional Marketing Manager, Dean Bell
Vice President Global Human Resources Operations, Shannon Aguilar
Vice President, Geoffrey Carthew
Vice President, Donald A Erpenbeck
Vice President, Jim Stahl
Vice President, Bob Parent
Vice President Location Manager Principal Geotechnical Engineer, Greg Rollins
Vice President And Senior Project Manager, Gary M Wantland
Vice President, Vincent Zipparro
Vice President Corporate Communications, Meg Vanderlaan
Vice President, Stephen Taylor
Senior Vice President, Donal J Bassett
Vice President, Philip Croessmann
Vice President, Kimberly Kesler-Arnold
Senior Vice President, Mario Finis
Vice President, Jim Brennan
Vice President, Tauseef Choudry
Vice President, Gary Hoornaert
Senior Vice President And Director Of Global Business Development, Paul Dekeyser
Vice President, Roger Stephenson
Vice President, Jason Hedien
Senior Vice President, James Lindell
Senior Vice President, Don Bassett
Executive Vice President, P Smith
Senior Vice President, Chip Labonte
Auditors: DELOITTE & TOUCHE LLP DENVER

LOCATIONS

HQ: MWH GLOBAL, INC.
370 INTERLOCKEN BLVD # 300, BROOMFIELD, CO 800218009
Phone: 303 533-1900
Web: WWW.STANTEC.COM

PRODUCTS/OPERATIONS

Selected Services

Construction
Airports
General building
Industrial
Highways bridges roads
Marine and port facilities
Engineering and technical services
Facilities development
Government relations
Program management and management consulting
Research and testing
Renewable energy and sustainability
Chemical and soil remediation
Hazardous waste
Hydroelectric power
Non-hydro renewable energy
Power distribution and transmission lines
Thermal power
Risk assessment
Specialized consulting services
Water and environment
Dams and reservoirs
Landfills biosolids
Sanitary/storm sewers conveyance pumping stations
Water resources planning management
Water treatment and desalination plants
Water transmission lines aqueducts
Waste water planning and management

COMPETITORS

AECOM
Bechtel
Black & Veatch
Camp Dresser McKee
EA Engineering
Engie
Fluor
Jacobs Engineering
KBR
Peter Kiewit Sons'
Severn Trent
Siemens Water Technologies
Tetra Tech
Veolia Environnement
WS Atkins
Zachry Inc.

HISTORICAL FINANCIALS

Company Type: Private

Income Statement — FYE: January 1

	REVENUE ($ mil.)	NET INCOME ($ mil.)	NET PROFIT MARGIN	EMPLOYEES
01/16*	1,318	35	2.7%	6,700
12/05	946	0	—	—
01/03	975	942	96.6%	—
12/01	774	19	2.6%	—
Annual Growth	3.9%	4.3%	—	—

*Fiscal year change

2016 Year-End Financials

Return on assets: 5.4%
Return on equity: 19.1%
Current ratio: 1.40
Cash ($ mil.): 68

NANA DEVELOPMENT CORPORATION

EXECUTIVES

Pres, Helvi Sandvik
Chairman*, Luke Sampson
Chairperson*, Lester Hadley
President*, Sandvik Helvi K
Sr V Pres*, Stan Fleming
V Pres*, Thomas Kevin E
Sr Vice President*, Jacquelyn R Luke
Secretary*, Dood Lincoln
Treasurer*, Henry Horner
Vice President*, Selina Moose
Vice President*, Charles J Greene
Auditors: KPMG LLP ANCHORAGE AK

LOCATIONS

HQ: NANA DEVELOPMENT CORPORATION
909 W 9TH AVE, ANCHORAGE, AK 995013322
Phone: 907 265-4100
Web: WWW.NANA.COM

HISTORICAL FINANCIALS

Company Type: Private

Income Statement — FYE: September 30

	REVENUE ($ mil.)	NET INCOME ($ mil.)	NET PROFIT MARGIN	EMPLOYEES
09/08	1,018	1	0.2%	3,000
09/07	833	7	0.8%	—
09/06	30	31	104.1%	—
09/00	119	0	0.6%	—
Annual Growth	30.7%	11.4%	—	—

2008 Year-End Financials

Return on assets: 0.3%
Return on equity: 4.0%
Current ratio: 2.10
Cash ($ mil.): 37

NANA REGIONAL CORPORATION, INC.,

EXECUTIVES

Prin, Wayne Westlake
Ceo*, Marie Green
Prin*, Kevin Thomas
Coo*, Lori Henry
Information Specialist, Justin Yeoman
Helpdesk Technician Manager, Eyler Santos
Vice President Shareholder Rel, Gia Hanna

LOCATIONS

HQ: NANA REGIONAL CORPORATION, INC.,
3150 C ST STE 150, KOTZEBUE, AK 99752
Phone: 907 442-3301
Web: WWW.NANA.COM

HISTORICAL FINANCIALS

Company Type: Private

Income Statement — FYE: September 30

	REVENUE ($ mil.)	NET INCOME ($ mil.)	NET PROFIT MARGIN	EMPLOYEES
09/09	1,257	17	1.4%	4,650
09/08	1,175	29	2.5%	—
09/07	975	37	3.8%	—
Annual Growth	13.6%	(32.4%)	—	—

2009 Year-End Financials

Return on assets: 2.3%
Return on equity: 7.0%
Current ratio: 1.60
Cash ($ mil.): 23

NAPLES COMMUNITY HOSPITAL INC

EXECUTIVES

Pres-Ceo, Phillip C Dutcher
Cfo*, Rick Wyles
Cso*, Mike Riley
M.D., Cmo*, Frank Astor
Interim Coo*, Jonathan Kling
Coordinator, Jeanie McCree
Coordinator, Lawrence Lasky
Chief Operating Officer, Phillip Dutcher
Administrative Director, Sheila Phillips
Physician, Gary A Bergen
Chief Strategy Officer, Michael Riley

LOCATIONS

HQ: NAPLES COMMUNITY HOSPITAL INC
350 7TH ST N, NAPLES, FL 341025754
Phone: 239 436-5000
Web: WWW.NCHMD.ORG

HISTORICAL FINANCIALS

Company Type: Private

Income Statement — FYE: September 30

	REVENUE ($ mil.)	NET INCOME ($ mil.)	NET PROFIT MARGIN	EMPLOYEES
09/19	656	9	1.5%	3,300
09/18	472	38	8.2%	—
09/17	472	38	8.2%	—
09/15	443	38	8.6%	—
Annual Growth	10.3%	(29.0%)	—	—

2019 Year-End Financials

Return on assets: 1.1%
Return on equity: 1.4%
Current ratio: 1.70
Cash ($ mil.): 13

NARRAGANSETT ELECTRIC COMP

LOCATIONS

HQ: NARRAGANSETT ELECTRIC COMP
642 GEORGE WASHINGTON HWY, LINCOLN, RI 028654244
Phone: 401 335-6238

HISTORICAL FINANCIALS

Company Type: Private

Income Statement — FYE: December 31

	REVENUE ($ mil.)	NET INCOME ($ mil.)	NET PROFIT MARGIN	EMPLOYEES
12/17	1,387	121	8.8%	2
12/16	1,269	84	6.7%	—
Annual Growth	9.3%	43.0%	—	—

2017 Year-End Financials

Return on assets: 2.6%
Return on equity: 6.1%
Current ratio: 0.70
Cash ($ mil.): 8

NASSAU HEALTH CARE CORPORATION

Nassau Health Care (NuHealth) keeps residents healthy in the suburbs of the Big Apple. The health system operates Nassau University Medical Center which has some 530 beds as well as the A. Holly Patterson Extended Care Facility a skilled nursing center with 590 beds. Other operations include about a half-dozen community family health centers and a home health care agency serving the people of Long Island. Nassau University Medical Center's specialized services include trauma burn care orthopedics psychiatry and obstetrics. NuHealth is a public benefit company governed by a representative board appointed by state and county officials.

Operations

The Nassau University Medical Center is a teaching center affiliated with the SUNY-Stony Brook Health Sciences Center. It also provides some services in affiliation with the North Shore-Long Island Jewish Health System. NuHealth's Nassau Medical Associates affiliate has an interest in primary care and selected specialty practices in central to southern Nassau County.

In 2012 NuHealth reported 283172 outpatient visits; 75240 emergency visits; 22347 discharges and 1576 births.

Sales and Marketing

In 2012 NuHealth launched the Talking Well social media campaign on Facebook and Twitter in an attempt to more effectively communicate with the public.

Financial Performance

The company's revenues grew by 5% to $518 million in 2012 due to an 8% increase in net patient service revenues thanks to an acceleration of intergovernmental transfers and higher contractual rates with third-party insurance companies. Other operating revenues declined in 2012 due to the reduction of services provided to the Nassau County Correctional Facility. Revenues from Medicaid and Medicare accounted for 77% of 2012 net revenues for services provided to patients.

NuHealth's net loss decreased by 69% to $45 million in 2012 due to a decline in salaries and wages primarily as the result of a reduction in full-time employees; a decline in a loss from employee benefits expenses; and changes to Medicaid eligibility estimates.

Strategy

NuHealth is conducting a $240 million multi-year modernization program. Efforts completed or in progress include the rebuilding of the Patterson Extended Care Facility reconstruction and renovation efforts at the Nassau University Medical Center (including the completion of a new emergency room in 2010 and the remodeling of its maternity wing in 2012) improvements to community health centers and equipment and technology investments. In 2014 NuHealth opened new labor and delivery suites and a new catheterization laboratory.

NuHealth is also working to promote community care wellness initiatives access to specialists and integrated delivery methods. In 2013 Nassau University Medical Center teamed up with Advocates for Community Health on Project DOCC which will deliver chronic care and the Center for Civic Engagement at Hofstra University to improve the health of underserved Long Island families particularly those whose children have developmental disabilities and serious chronic conditions.

Towards this goal NuHealth also collaborates with other area providers such as North Shore-LIJ. It is also expanding its physician education programs; it launched a new osteopathic family medicine residency program to train doctors at its inpatient and outpatient facilities in 2012. It also introduced a hematology and oncology fellowship program that year.

Fxpanding its products in 2012 Nassau University Medical Center began to offer personalized travel medicine services to meet the needs of travelers going abroad for both business and pleasure.

Company Background

The Nassau University Medical Center opened in 1935 as Meadowbrook Hospital and joined the NuHealth organization in 1997. It was renamed Nassau University Medical Center in 2001.

EXECUTIVES

Vice President Human Resources, Maureen Roarty
Senior Vice President Revenue Cycle, Vincent DiSanti
Director Of Health Information Management, Teresa Silversmith
Secretary, Ernestine Moore

LOCATIONS

HQ: NASSAU HEALTH CARE CORPORATION
2201 HEMPSTEAD TPKE, EAST MEADOW, NY 115541859
Phone: 516 572-0123
Web: WWW.NUMC.EDU

PRODUCTS/OPERATIONS

Selected Services

Anesthesiology
Blood Bank
Brain & Nerves
Burn Center
Cardiac Care
Community Services
Dental Medicine
Diagnostic Imaging
Emergency Medicine
Eye Care
Family Medicine
Hypertension Diabetes & Vascular Disease
Internal Medicine
Mental Health & Addiction
Orthopedics & Rehabilitation
Pathology
Pediatrics
Primary & Preventive Care
Primary Care & Wellness
Radiology
Radiology & Laboratory
Senior Services
Shared Laboratory Services
Specialized Medicine
Specialty Services
Surgery
Surgical & Emergency Care
Trauma Center
Women's Health

COMPETITORS

Catholic Health Services of Long Island
Catholic Healthcare System
Continuum Health Partners
Lutheran HealthCare
MediSys Health Network
New York City Health and Hospitals
Northwell Health
Queens-Long Island Medical Group

HISTORICAL FINANCIALS

Company Type: Private

Income Statement — FYE: December 31

	REVENUE ($ mil.)	NET INCOME ($ mil.)	NET PROFIT MARGIN	EMPLOYEES
12/18	587	(53)	—	3,500
12/17	425	15	3.7%	—
12/16	375	(62)	—	—
12/15	363	(80)	—	—
Annual Growth	17.4%	—	—	—

2018 Year-End Financials

Return on assets: (-10.0%)
Cash ($ mil.): 5
Return on equity: —
Current ratio: 1.30

NASSUA COUNTY INTERIM FINANCE AUTHORITY

EXECUTIVES

Exec Dir, Richard Luke
Executive Director, Evan Cohen
Auditors: RSM US LLP NEW YORK NEW YORK

LOCATIONS

HQ: NASSUA COUNTY INTERIM FINANCE AUTHORITY
170 OLD COUNTRY RD # 205, MINEOLA, NY 115014322
Phone: 516 248-2828
Web: WWW.NIFA.NY.GOV

HISTORICAL FINANCIALS

Company Type: Private

Income Statement — FYE: December 31

	REVENUE ($ mil.)	NET INCOME ($ mil.)	NET PROFIT MARGIN	EMPLOYEES
12/19	1,173	(2)	—	6
12/18	1,133	(0)	—	—
12/17	1,095	(5)	—	—
12/16	1	140	12831.1%	—
Annual Growth	924.2%	—	—	—

2019 Year-End Financials

Return on assets: (-1.3%)
Cash ($ mil.): —
Return on equity: —
Current ratio: —

NATIONAL ASSOCIATION OF LETTER CARRIERS

EXECUTIVES

Pres, Fredric V Rolando
SEC*, Maria Licalzi
Treas*, Jane E Broendell
Director of Finance, Debra Price
Executive Vice President, Brian Renfroe
Director, Brian Hellman
Chief of Staff, Jim Sauber
Administrative Assistant, Cindy Chaney
Human Resource Manager, Lynda Sist
Secretary, Nina Kunkel
Director of Governmental Affai, Paul Swartz
Auditors: BOND BEEBE PC BETHESDA MD

LOCATIONS

HQ: NATIONAL ASSOCIATION OF LETTER CARRIERS
100 INDANA AVE NW STE 709, WASHINGTON, DC 20001
Phone: 202 393-4695
Web: WWW.NALC.ORG

HISTORICAL FINANCIALS

Company Type: Private

Income Statement — FYE: March 31

	REVENUE ($ mil.)	NET INCOME ($ mil.)	NET PROFIT MARGIN	EMPLOYEES
03/14*	1,406	97	6.9%	533
12/13	0	0	17.9%	—
12/11	0	0	67.4%	—
03/10	1	0	28.8%	—
Annual Growth	436.7%	275.8%	—	—

*Fiscal year change

2014 Year-End Financials

Return on assets: 10.5%
Cash ($ mil.): 245
Return on equity: 20.1%
Current ratio: —

NATIONAL CHRISTIAN CHARITABLE FOUNDATION, INC.

EXECUTIVES

Prin, Terra Parker
Treasurer, David D Johnson
Vice President, George Cox
Chief Information Officer., Amy Garrett
Vice President., Marsha Walker
Gift Planning Team, Don Etheridge
Director of Giver, Bev Beppler
Chief Information Officer, Dan Brown
Information Technology Support, Matthew Schulz
Director, Maureen Starr
Vice President, Paul Forbes
Auditors: NATIONAL CHRISTIAN CHARITABLE

LOCATIONS

HQ: NATIONAL CHRISTIAN CHARITABLE FOUNDATION, INC.
11625 RAINWATER DR # 500, ALPHARETTA, GA 300098674
Phone: 404 252-0100
Web: WWW.NCFGIVING.COM

HISTORICAL FINANCIALS

Company Type: Private

Income Statement FYE: December 31

	REVENUE ($ mil.)	NET INCOME ($ mil.)	NET PROFIT MARGIN	EMPLOYEES
12/16	1,413	306	21.7%	2
12/11	665	141	21.3%	—
12/09	396	50	12.7%	—
Annual Growth	19.9%	29.4%	—	—

2016 Year-End Financials

Return on assets: 14.9%
Return on equity: 15.1%
Current ratio: —
Cash ($ mil.): 457

NATIONAL COLLEGIATE ATHLETIC ASSOCIATION

The National Collegiate Athletic Association (NCAA) supports the intercollegiate sports activities of around 1000 member colleges and universities. A not-for-profit organization the NCAA administers scholarship and grant programs enforces conduct and eligibility rules and works to support and promote the needs of student athletes. The association is known for its lucrative branding and television deals such as those surrounding the popular "March Madness" tournament for Division I men's basketball. Seeking reform of athletics rules and regulations officials from 13 schools formed the Intercollegiate Athletic Association of the United States in 1906. The organization took its current name in 1910.

Financial Performance

NCAA revenue in fiscal 2013 (ended August) was $913 million up 5% versus the prior year most of which came from the rights agreement with CBS Sports and Turner Broadcasting. Indeed about 80% of the NCAA's revenue come from television and marketing rights fees generated primarily from the Division I men's basketball championship. Another 12% comes from championships and NIT tournaments including ticket and merchandise sales.

About 96% of NCAA revenue is distributed directly to the Division I membership or to support championships or programs that benefit student-athletes. The remaining 4% goes for central services such as building operations and salaries not related to particular programs.

Strategy

In a major shift the NCAA in 2019 allowed student-athletes to receive compensation when their names images or likenesses are used for commercial purposes. The organization changed its rules on student-athletes aftere California passed a law allowing compensation (effective in 2023) following a lawsuit. The NCAA has long adamantly prohibited any payment of college athletes (other than scholarships) to preserve their amateur status. The NCAA's three major divisions were left to set rules governing compensation.

EXECUTIVES

Vice President, Kevin Lennon
Vp Of Academic And Membership Affairs, Dave Schnase
Vice President For Div. Iii, Dan Dutcher
Vice President Of Enforcement, Jonathan Duncan
Vice President, Bob Williams
Vice President For Men's Basketball, Dan Gavitt
Board Member, Tom Hosty
Auditors: DELOITTE & TOUCHE LLP INDIANA

LOCATIONS

HQ: NATIONAL COLLEGIATE ATHLETIC ASSOCIATION
700 W WASHINGTON ST, INDIANAPOLIS, IN 462042710
Phone: 317 917-6222
Web: WWW.NCAA.ORG

PRODUCTS/OPERATIONS

2013 Revenues

	% of total
Television & marketing rights fees	80
Championships & NIT tournaments	12
Investments	4
Sales & services	3
Contributions facilities & other	1
Total	**100**

HISTORICAL FINANCIALS

Company Type: Private

Income Statement FYE: August 31

	REVENUE ($ mil.)	NET INCOME ($ mil.)	NET PROFIT MARGIN	EMPLOYEES
08/19	1,118	70	6.3%	508
08/18	1,064	27	2.5%	—
08/17	1,061	104	9.9%	—
08/16	995	(403)	—	—
Annual Growth	3.9%	—	—	—

2019 Year-End Financials

Return on assets: 11.5%
Return on equity: 15.7%
Current ratio: 0.50
Cash ($ mil.): 15

NATIONAL GRAPE CO-OPERATIVE ASSOCIATION, INC.

Well of course grape growers want to hang out in a bunch! The more than 1090 grower/owner-members of the National Grape Cooperative harvest Concord and Niagara grapes from almost 50000 acres of vineyards. The plucked produce supplies the coop's wholly owned subsidiary Welch Foods. Welch Foods makes and sells fruit-based juices jams jellies and spreads under the Welch's and Bama brands in the US and nearly 50 other countries. Offerings include fresh eating grapes distributed by C.H. Robinson Worldwide as well as dried fruit and frozen juice pops. The grape growers own vineyards in Pennsylvania Michigan New York Ohio Washington and Ontario Canada which produce some 300000 tons of grapes annually.

EXECUTIVES

Pres, Randolph Graham
V Pres, Joseph C Falcone
Asst SEC, Vivian S Y Tseng
V Pres, Harold Smith
Dir, Jerry A Czebotar
Dir, Jon Hinkleman
Executive Administrative Assis, Ivis Edgerton
General Manager, Brent Roggie
Auditors: KPMG LLP BOSTON MA

LOCATIONS

HQ: NATIONAL GRAPE CO-OPERATIVE ASSOCIATION, INC.
80 STATE ST, WESTFIELD, NY 14787
Phone: 716 326-5200
Web: WWW.WELCHS.COM

COMPETITORS

B&G Foods
Big Heart Pet Brands
Chiquita Brands
Coca-Cola
Constellation Brands
Cranberries Limited
Dole Food
Dr Pepper Snapple Group
Fresh Del Monte Produce
Goya
Hornell Brewing
IZZE
Mondelez International
Monster Beverage
Nestlé USA
Ocean Spray
PepsiCo
Procter & Gamble
Smucker
Snapple
Tropicana

HISTORICAL FINANCIALS

Company Type: Private

Income Statement FYE: August 31

	REVENUE ($ mil.)	NET INCOME ($ mil.)	NET PROFIT MARGIN	EMPLOYEES
08/12	649	74	11.5%	1,325
08/11	640	74	11.6%	—
08/10	658	82	12.6%	—
Annual Growth	(0.7%)	(5.1%)	—	—

2012 Year-End Financials

Return on assets: 19.8%
Return on equity: 999.9%
Current ratio: 1.50
Cash ($ mil.): 4

NATIONAL RAILROAD PASSENGER CORPORATION

National Railroad Passenger Corporation better known as Amtrak has been riding the rails for more than 40 years. Amtrak is the US' intercity passenger rail provider and its only high-speed rail operator. More than 30 million passengers travel on Amtrak every year on more than 300 daily trains. It connects 46 states Washington DC and three provinces in Canada. Its network consists of about 21000 route miles of track most of which is owned by freight railroads. Amtrak also operates commuter rail systems on behalf of several states and transit agencies. Owned by the US government through the US Department of Transportation Amtrak depends on subsidies from the federal government to operate.

HISTORY

US passenger train travel peaked in 1929 with 20000 trains in operation. But the spread of automobiles bus service and air travel cut into business and by the late 1960s only about 500 passenger trains remained running in the country. In 1970 the combined losses of all private train operations exceeded $1.8 billion in today's dollars. That year Congress passed the Rail Passenger Service Act which created Amtrak to preserve America's passenger rail system. Although railroads were offered stock in the corporation for their passenger equipment most just wrote off the loss.

Amtrak began operating in 1971 with 1200 cars most built in the 1950s. Although the company lost money from the outset ($153 million in 1972) it continued to be bankrolled by Uncle Sam despite much criticism. Amtrak ordered its first new equipment in 1973 the year it also began taking over stations yards and service staff. The company didn't own any track until 1976 when it purchased hundreds of miles of right-of-way track from Boston to Washington DC.

After a 1979 study showed Amtrak passengers to be by far the most heavily subsidized travelers in the US Congress ordered the company to better utilize its resources. The 1980s saw Amtrak leasing its rights-of-way along its tracks in the Northeast corridor to telecommunications companies which installed fiber-optic cables and beginning mail and freight services for extra revenue.

In the early 1990s Amtrak faced a number of challenges: Midwest flooding falling airfares and safety concerns over a number of rail accidents particularly the 1993 wreck of the Sunset Limited near Mobile Alabama in which 47 people were killed (the worst accident in Amtrak's history). In 1994 Amtrak's board of directors (at Congress' behest) adopted a plan to be free of federal support by 2002. In 1995 the company began planning high-speed trains for its heavily traveled East Coast routes.

In 1997 Amtrak finalized agreements to buy the high-speed cars and locomotives central to its self-sufficiency plan. It also began increasing its freight hauling and had its first profitable offering: the Metroliner route between New York and Washington DC.

Amtrak's board of directors was replaced by Congress in 1997 with a seven-member Reform Board appointed by President Clinton. Chairman and president Thomas Downs resigned that year and Tommy Thompson then governor of Wisconsin took over as chairman. Former Massachusetts governor Michael Dukakis was named vice chairman and George Warrington stepped in as Amtrak's president and CEO.

Technical problems in 1999 delayed Amtrak's introduction of the Acela high-speed train in the Northeast until late 2000 when service began in the Boston-Washington corridor. In 2001 Amtrak pitched a 20-year plan involving an annual outlay of $1.5 billion in federal funds for expanding and modernizing its passenger service to help alleviate highway and airport congestion nationwide.

Thompson left the Amtrak board in 2001 after he was named US secretary of health and human services.

Realizing Amtrak would not meet its end-of-the-year deadline to be self-sufficient in 2002 the Amtrak Reform Council sent a proposal to Congress that Amtrak be divided into three groups: one to oversee operations and funding a second to maintain certain Amtrak-owned tracks and properties and a third to operate trains. It also called for competition to be allowed on some passenger routes within two to three years.

Also in 2002 Warrington resigned and was replaced by David Gunn who formerly headed the metropolitan transit systems in New York and Toronto. Gunn began moving to cut costs and he worked to secure new federal money to avert a threatened shutdown of rail service in July 2002. In 2004 the company exited the mail-carrying business which had not been profitable.

Gunn was fired in November 2005 however and chief engineer David Hughes was named interim president and CEO. He left the company after Alexander Kummant was made president and CEO in September 2006.

The Passenger Rail Investment and Improvement Act of 2008 gives five annual grants to Amtrak amounting to $9.8 billion for fiscal years 2009 through 2013. Another boon came in the form of $1.3 billion of stimulus money earmarked for Amtrak by the American Recovery and Reinvestment Act (ARRA) of 2009 which authorizes the Federal Railroad Administration to make the funds available to Amtrak by grant agreement. About $446.8 million will be used for capital security grants including life safety improvements. Another $884 million will go toward the repair rehabilitation or upgrade of railroad assets and infrastructure and toward capital projects that expand rail capacity including the rehabilitation of rolling stock. The Obama administration promised an ongoing investment of about $1 billion annually for high-speed rail projects.

A record 28.7 million passengers rode on Amtrak in fiscal 2010. While impressive the company also had a history of recurring operating losses. Although total revenues increased about 7% in 2010 compared to 2009 Amtrak reported fairly comparable net losses in both years.

EXECUTIVES

Pres-Ceo, Richard H Anderson
Exec V Pres-Gen Counsel-Corp S, Eleanor D Acheson
Sr Exec V Pres, Stephen J Gardner
Exec V Pres-Chief Mktg and Com, J Timothy Griffin
Exec V Pres-Chief Safety Offce, Kenneth Hylander
Exec V Pres- Coo, Scot Naparstek
Exec V Pres-Cao, Dj Stadtler
Exec V Pres-CIO, Christian Zacariassen
Evp-Chief Mktg & Comml Officer, Roger Harris
Acting Director, Frank Gallello
Procurement Staff, Marylin Jamisom
Auditors: ERNST & YOUNG LLP TYSONS VA

LOCATIONS

HQ: NATIONAL RAILROAD PASSENGER CORPORATION
1 MASSACHUSETTS AVE NW, WASHINGTON, DC 200011401
Phone: 202 906-3000
Web: WWW.AMTRAKOIG.GOV

PRODUCTS/OPERATIONS

2014 Sales

	% of total
Passenger related	78
Commuter	4
Other	18
Total	**100**

2014 Sales

	% of total
Ticket	69
State Contribution	7
Food Beverage	4
Others	20
Total	**100**

COMPETITORS

AirTran Airways
American Airlines Group
Delta Air Lines
Frontier Airlines
Greyhound
JetBlue
Port Imperial Ferry Corp.
Southwest Airlines
Trailways Transportation System
United Continental

HISTORICAL FINANCIALS

Company Type: Private

Income Statement FYE: September 30

	REVENUE ($ mil.)	NET INCOME ($ mil.)	NET PROFIT MARGIN	EMPLOYEES
09/19	3,503	(880)	—	18,650
09/18	3,386	(817)	—	—
Annual Growth	3.4%	—	—	—

2019 Year-End Financials

Return on assets: (-4.9%)
Return on equity: (-7.6%)
Current ratio: 1.80
Cash ($ mil.): 366

NATIONWIDE CHILDREN'S HOSPITAL

Buckeye babies toddlers and teens don't have to travel the country to find pediatric care with Nationwide Children's Hospital at their disposal. The Columbus Ohio health care provider is one of the largest pediatric care centers in the US. The hospital has some 430 licensed beds and offers services in areas such as behavioral health cardiology hospice orthopedics and surgery. It has roughly 1100 health care providers on its medical staff and its emergency department treats more than 83000 patients each year. The hospital also operates outpatient and specialty clinics in the area and a research institute which is investigating gene therapy.

Operations

The hospital provides more than $122 million in charity care and community benefit services annually. It had more than 1 million patient visits and had more than 25000 surgery cases in 2014.

Geographic Reach

Nationwide Children's Hospital serves patients from 50 US states and 32 countries. The company is 68 facilities extending out across Ohio and beyond. The company's top ten outpatient visits counties are Franklin Delaware Fairfield Licking Clark Pickaway Madison Union Muskingum and Knox.

Sales and Marketing

Nationwide Children's Hospital payor mix in 2014 included commercial 43%; Medicaid managed care Cap 33%; and Medicaid 13%.

Strategy

In 2015 Nationwide Children's Hospital announced plans to adopt and integrate GenomeNext's genomic sequencing analysis platform for both clinical laboratory services and clinical research initiatives

In 2014 the company outlined numerous details of its $130 million campus expansion project. Its plans include an $85 million outpatient care building and a $45 million building to house faculty offices. The outpatient building called the Livingston Ambulatory Center will house primary care services dental services behavioral health dermatology adolescent medicine sports rehabilitation and various clinics. Both buildings will be six stories tall.

The hospital added helicopter medical transport service in 2013.

Company Background

The health system in 2012 completed a $740 million project to build a new main hospital and add 2 million sq. ft. of clinical research and support space. The expansion added about 100 new beds.

Also in 2012 it opened an ambulatory surgery center in Westerville Ohio and a Close To Home lab and clinic in Springfield. In 2014 it opened the Sharon Woods Primary Care Center in north Columbus.

Nationwide Children's Hospital opened its doors in 1892.

EXECUTIVES

Vice President And Controller, Luke Brown
Chairman The Center For Family Safety And Healing, Abigail S. Wexner
Evp And Cfo, Timothy C. Robinson
President And Coo, Rick Miller
Svp And Chief Nursing Officer, Linda Stoverock
Ceo, Steve Allen
President The Research Institute, John Barnard
President The Center For Family Safety And Healing, Karen Days
Chief Medical Officer, Richard J. Brilli
Surgeon-in-chief, R. Lawrence Moss
Physician-in-chief, J. Philip Saul
Chairman Nationwide Children's Hospital Foundation, Cheryl W. Lucks
Chairman The Research Institute, Donald P. McConnell
Medical Director, Garey Noritz
Vice President Of Perioperative Services, Janet Berry
Vice President, Jeff Ziegler
Pharmd, Kevin Drewes
Medical Director, Desalegn Yacob
Vice President, Pam Edson
Vice President Development Services, Kevin Welch
Vice President, Karen Heiser
Senior Vice President Of Planning And Dvlpmt, Patty McClimon
Pharmacy Manager, Kim Novak
Vice President Regional Development, Darrell Mosby
Apheresis Medical Director, Erin Meyer
Vice President Neonatal Services, Lee Ann Wallace
Medical Director, Leena Nahata
Nursing Director Critical Care And Heart Services, Kelly Dials
Chairman, Alex Fischer
Secretary, Lacey Ashenfelter
Secretary, Dawn Friebis
Secretary 2, Trisha Strader
Secretary Ii, Melissa Gallas
Secretary Ii, Marianne starr-Howard
Secretary, Carla Winfrey
Auditors: ERNST & YOUNG LLP CINCINNATI

LOCATIONS

HQ: NATIONWIDE CHILDREN'S HOSPITAL
700 CHILDRENS DR, COLUMBUS, OH 432052639
Phone: 614 722-2000
Web: WWW.NATIONWIDECHILDRENS.ORG

PRODUCTS/OPERATIONS

Selected Subsidiaries

Nationwide Children's Hospital
Nationwide Children's Behavioral Health
Nationwide Children's Educational Institute
Nationwide Children's Hospital Inc
Nationwide Children's Hospital Homecare
Children's Anesthesia Associates
Nationwide Children's Hospital Foundation
Pediatric Academic Associates
Children's Orthopedic Medical Center
Children's Radiological Institute
Children's Surgical Associates Corp.
The Research Institute at Nationwide Children's Hospital
Pediatric Pathology Associates of Columbus
The Center for Family Safety and Healing at Nationwide Children's Hospital

Selected Departments and Services

Adolescent Congenital Heart Disease
Adolescent Medicine
Adult Congenital Heart Disease
Adult Medicine and Hospital Pediatrics
Allergy/Immunology
Ambulatory Pediatrics
Anatomic Pathology
Anesthesiology & Pain Medicine
Asthma Program
Audiology
Bariatric Surgery
Battelle Center for Mathematical Medicine
Behavioral Health
Blood Conservation Program
Burn Program
Cancer
CAP4Kids
Cardiology
Cardiopulmonary Rehabilitation
Cardiothoracic Surgery
Center for Biobehavioral Health (Research)
Center for Cardiovascular and Pulmonary Research
Center for Childhood Cancer (Research)
Center for Clinical and Translational Research
Center for Colorectal and Pelvic Reconstruction
Center for Gene Therapy (Research)
Center for Healthy Weight and Nutrition
Center for Injury Research and Policy
Center for Innovation in Pediatric Practice
Center for Microbial Pathogenesis (Research)
Center for Molecular and Human Genetics (Research)
Center for Perinatal Research
Center for Vaccines and Immunity (Research)
Central Ohio Poison Center
Cerebral Palsy Program
Chest Wall Clinic
Child Development/Psychology
Child Life Specialists
ChildLab
Cleft Lip and Palate Center
Clinical Nutrition and Lactation
Clinical Services and Care Coordination
Clinical Studies
Clinical Therapies
Close To Home Centers
Community Relations
Congenital Heart Disease
Connecting Families
Critical Care
Cystic Fibrosis
Dentistry
Dermatology
Developmental/ Behavioral Pediatrics
Diabetes Clinic
Disorders of Sexual Development (DSD)
Ear Nose & Throat Services (Otolaryngology)
Early Childhood Development Program
Education Classes
Emergency Services
Endocrinology Metabolism & Diabetes
Family Advisory Council
Family AIDS Clinic and Educational Services (FACES)
Family Health Information Center
Family Practice
Family Resource Center
Fetal Diagnostics
Financial Matters
Gastroenterology Hepatology and Nutrition
Gender Concerns
General Pediatric Surgery
Genetics (Molecular and Human)
Gift Cards
Gift Shop
Government Relations
Health Info Library
Health Information Management (HIM)
Hearing Program
Heart Center
Hemangioma Vascular Anomalies
Hematology Oncology & BMT
HIV Program
Homecare
Hospice
Immunology
Infectious Diseases
Interdisciplinary Feeding Clinic
International Adoption Clinic
Interventional Radiology
Jeune's Syndrome
Laboratory Medicine/Reference Lab
Massage Therapy
Medical Records
Melanoma & Pigmented Lesion Clinic
Music Therapy
myChildren's
Neonatology
Nephrology
Neurodiagnostics/EEG
Neurology
Neuromuscular Disorders
Neurosciences Center
Neurosurgery
Nuclear Medicine
Nurse-Family Partnership
Occupational Therapy
Ophthalmology/Eye Clinic
Orthopedics
Outpatient Surgery
Pain Service Clinic
Palliative Care
Pastoral Care
Patient and Family Relations
Patient and Visitor Guide
Patient Financial Services
PediaCast: a pediatric podcast for parents
Pediatric and Adolescent Gynecology
Pediatric Psychiatry
Pediatric Psychology
Pharmacy Services (Outpatient)
Physical Medicine & Rehabilitation
Physical Therapy
Physical Therapy - Sports and Orthopedic
Plastic and Reconstructive Surgery
Prader-Willi Syndrome Clinic
Primary Care Centers
Pulmonary Medicine
Radiology
Reach Out and Read
Rehabilitation
Request an Appointment
Research at Children's
Resonance Disorders Program
Rheumatology
Robot-Assisted Surgery
Ronald McDonald House
School Program
Sibling Support (Children's Clubhouse)
Sleep Disorder Center
Social Work
Speech and Language Pathology
Spina Bifida Program
Sports Medicine
Surgical Services

Telehealth
The Center for Family Safety and Healing
Therapeutic Recreation
THRIVE Program (DSD & Complex Urological & Gender Concerns)
Toxicology
Transplant Program
Transport
Trauma
Urgent Care Services
Urology
Velopharyngeal Dysfunction Program
Weight Loss Surgery

COMPETITORS

Akron Children's Hospital
Cincinnati Children's Hospital
Fairfield Medical Center
Genesis HealthCare System (Ohio)
Licking Memorial Health Systems
Mount Carmel Health
OhioHealth
Select Medical
Shriners Hospitals For Children

HISTORICAL FINANCIALS

Company Type: Private

Income Statement — FYE: September 30

	REVENUE ($ mil.)	NET INCOME ($ mil.)	NET PROFIT MARGIN	EMPLOYEES
09/20*	2,020	211	10.5%	12,000
12/19	2,696	724	26.9%	—
12/18	2,504	117	4.7%	—
12/17	2,317	647	27.9%	—
Annual Growth	(4.5%)	(31.1%)	—	—

*Fiscal year change

2020 Year-End Financials

Return on assets: 3.7%
Return on equity: 4.8%
Current ratio: 2.70
Cash ($ mil.): 400

NATURAL GAS PIPELINE COMPANY OF AMERICA LLC

EXECUTIVES

MBR-Pres, David Devine
Mng MBR*, Richard D Kinder
MBR*, Scott Parker
MBR-Cfo*, Jim Saunders
MBR-Exec V Pres*, Steve Kean
MBR*, Charles Schwager
MBR*, Joseph Listengart
Engineer Pipeline Senior, Fredrik Sultan
Senior Administrator, Robert L Gamble

LOCATIONS

HQ: NATURAL GAS PIPELINE COMPANY OF AMERICA LLC
1001 LOUISIANA ST, HOUSTON, TX 770025089
Phone: 713 369-9000
Web: WWW.KINDERMORGAN.COM

HISTORICAL FINANCIALS

Company Type: Private

Income Statement — FYE: December 31

	REVENUE ($ mil.)	NET INCOME ($ mil.)	NET PROFIT MARGIN	EMPLOYEES
12/17	679	130	19.2%	1,747
12/16	613	121	19.7%	—
Annual Growth	10.8%	8.0%	—	—

2017 Year-End Financials

Return on assets: 6.7%
Return on equity: 9.7%
Current ratio: 1.50
Cash ($ mil.): 15

NAVY EXCHANGE SERVICE COMMAND

Before Old Navy there was the Navy Exchange Service Command (NEXCOM). Active-duty military personnel reservists retirees and their family members can shop and gas up at more than 100 Navy Exchange (NEX) retail stores (brand-name and private-label merchandise ranging from apparel to home electronics) more than 150 NEXCOM Ships Stores (basic necessities) and its 100-plus Uniform Support Centers (the sole source of authorized uniforms). NEXCOM also runs about 40 Navy Lodges (motels) in the US and about half a dozen foreign countries. NEXCOM receives tax dollars for its shipboard stores but it is otherwise self-supporting. Most of the profits fund morale welfare and recreational programs (MWR) for sailors.

Geographic Reach

Navy Exchange Service Command has more than 100 NEX stores on land in the US Cuba Africa Europe the Middle East Japan and China.

Strategy

Since the government lifted restrictions on the types of items sold at the stores allowing more expensive furniture jewelry and televisions sales have been on the rise at NEX stores. NEXCOM has also been adding stores at home and abroad. In fall 2013 it opened a Fleet Store in Jebel Ali Dubai to serve sailors stationed in and around Dubai as well as military personnel passing through the area aboard ship.

To better compete with online rivals Walmart.com Target.com Amazon.com BestBuy.com and others in 2013 NEX expanded its Price Match Policy to match their prices.

EXECUTIVES

Ceo, Robert J Bianchi
Coo*, Michael P Good
Cfo*, Laurie P Hasten
Treas*, Thomas McDonald
Controllor*, Gerald Outar
Law Specialist, Nancy Haas
Staff, Cleveland Rogers
Network Manager, Tim Anthony
Coordinator, Charles Early
Law Specialist, Kia Coleman
Law Specialist, Kim Sherman

LOCATIONS

HQ: NAVY EXCHANGE SERVICE COMMAND
3280 VIRGINIA BEACH BLVD, VIRGINIA BEACH, VA 234525799
Phone: 757 631-3696
Web: WWW.MYNAVYEXCHANGE.COM

PRODUCTS/OPERATIONS

2014 Sales

	% of total
Total Sales	95
Income from Concessions net	2
Contributed Services	3
Other Revenue	0
Total	**100**

PRODUCT DEPARTMENTS

PRODUCT DEPARTMENTS
For The Home
Electronics
Shoes
Beauty
Women
Men
Kids
Navy pride
Handbags and accessories

COMPETITORS

7-Eleven
Amazon.com
Best Buy
Kmart
Target Corporation
Value City Furniture
Wal-Mart

HISTORICAL FINANCIALS

Company Type: Private

Income Statement — FYE: February 3

	REVENUE ($ mil.)	NET INCOME ($ mil.)	NET PROFIT MARGIN	EMPLOYEES
02/18*	2,617	32	1.2%	14,000
01/17	2,574	45	1.8%	—
01/16	2,635	73	2.8%	—
01/11	2,749	68	2.5%	—
Annual Growth	(0.7%)	(10.3%)	—	—

*Fiscal year change

NCH CORPORATION

NCH has been cleaning up for years and like everyone else it's been using soaps and detergents to do so. The company makes and sells chemical maintenance repair and supply products including all kinds of cleaners for customers in more than 50 countries throughout the world. NCH markets its products through a direct sales force to companies in industrial commercial and infrastructure markets. Other products include pet care supplies plumbing parts.

Operations

The company's major areas of focus include producing products for the industrial cleaning and maintenance pet care plumbing specialty industries supply and water treatment and remediation markets.

NCH's cleaning products include hand cleaners industrial cleaners and housekeeping supplies. Specialty chemical products including cleaning and water treatment chemicals degreasers grounds care and lubricants.

The company's divisions include: water treatment solutions plumbing industrial and institutional maintenance parts washing lubrication and biologicals.

Subsidiary Supply Line Direct offers safety and maintenance products such as janitorial supplies safety supplies and shop and warehouse equipment. Its plumbing products group provides plumbing supplies. Other subsidiaries include Pure Solve a parts washing service.

NCH sells its products directly through a number of wholly owned subsidiaries many of which are engaged in the maintenance products business. It include Certified Chemsearch Chem-Aqua Danco and Ecobionics.

Geographic Reach

NCH has operations throughout the world. The company has representatives in six continents It sales and service teams serve customers in North America Latin America Europe Asia Australia and India. NCH also has wholly owned subsidiaries in more than 50 countries. The company is headquartered in Irving Texas.

Sales and Marketing

NCH sells to industrial commercial and institutional customers. Its products are distributed nationally through home centers and hardware stores. The Plumbing Products group provides supplies for the do-it-yourself consumer and the OEM market.

Company Background

Founded in 1919 NCH Corporation is a global leader in industrial commercial and institutional maintenance products and services and one of the largest companies in the world to sell such products through direct marketing.

EXECUTIVES

President Nch Asia, Dong Eun Kim
Senior Vice President Sales And Marketing, Mark Ayers
Vice President Corporate Real Estate, Don Moulton
Senior Vice President Sales, Brenda Sanders
Senior Vice President, Roy Levin
Assistant Vice President, Donna Cagler
Vice President, Randy Marsh
Vice President, Ann Levy
Vice President Finance And Global Controller, John Currie
Vice President Of Global Logistics, Shayne Mai
Vice President Of Finance, Pete Bocian
Vice President Organizational Development And Learning, Jed Davis
Senior Vice President Of Sales, Frank Pellegrini
Medical Director, Julie Allison
Vice President Information Systems, Bruce Wineberger
Senior Vice President Domestic Sales Mantek Division, Joel Derketsch
Vice President Marketing Information Technology And Csd, James Marshall
Senior Vice President, John Larsson
Vice President Research And Development, John Roheim
Vice President Supply Chain, Walter Adams
Executive Vice President, Joe O'sullivan
Vice President Information Technology, Leonard Brown
Vice President, Charles E Anderson
Senior Vice President, Allen Irons
Vice President Strategy And Business Development, Mike Howdeshell
Vice President, Andy Leslie
V.p Of Sales, Ron Rashell
Vice President, Tasos Kolios
National Account Manager, Sally French
Senior Vice President Innovation And Product Development, Michael Schuster
Vice President Sales, Henrik Ingvardsen
Vice President, Garland Edgell
Group Senior Vp Strategy And Planning, Christina Wright
Board Member, Marga Tubb
Treasurer, Mark Hoesten
Treasurer, Joe Farrier
Auditors: PRICEWATERHOUSECOOPERS LLP DA

LOCATIONS

HQ: NCH CORPORATION
2727 CHEMSEARCH BLVD, IRVING, TX 750626454
Phone: 972 438-0211
Web: WWW.HEATINGREPAIRSGRANDPRAIRIE.COM

PRODUCTS/OPERATIONS

Selected Operations and Products

Chemical Specialties
- Cleaning chemicals
- Deodorizers
- Floor and carpet care products
- HVAC products
- Lubricants
- Oil production facility chemicals
- Paint
- Paint removers
- Water-treatment chemicals

Landmark Direct
- First-aid supplies
- Workplace signage and productivity products

Pet Care

Partsmaster Group
- Cutting tools
- Electrical products
- Fasteners
- Welding alloys

Plumbing Products Group
- Plumbing products for new construction
- Plumbing repair and replacement parts

Industrial and Institutional Maintenance
Industrial and commercial cleaning
Industrial Repair and maintenance
Drains Grease Traps and lift stations
Lubrication and coolants
Equipment and supplies
Parts washing
Grounds Care
Personal hygiene
Pet Care
Training pads
Stain and Odor Removers
Cleaners and Disinfectants
Allergy Relief and shed Control
Grooming products
Plumbing
Sinks
Faucets
Tub & Showers
Toilets
Drains
Specialty Industrial Supply
High Performance Cutting Tools
Welding
Abrasives
Compounds
Fasteners
Electrical and Automotive
Shop Supplies
Storage Hardware
Tools
Water Treatment Solutions
Boiler
Cooling Towers
Colsed Recirculation Systems
Biocides and Algaecides
Cleaner/Descalers
Equipment
Wastewater and Bio Remediation

COMPETITORS

Church & Dwight
Cintas
Clariant
Danaher
Detrex
Ecolab
H.B. Fuller
Illinois Tool Works
Pioneer Corporation
Quaker Chemical
Safety-Kleen
WD-40

HISTORICAL FINANCIALS

Company Type: Private

Income Statement — FYE: April 30

	REVENUE ($ mil.)	NET INCOME ($ mil.)	NET PROFIT MARGIN	EMPLOYEES
04/19	1,005	26	2.6%	8,500
04/12	1,045	6	0.6%	—
04/11	952	6	0.7%	—
Annual Growth	0.7%	18.5%	—	—

2019 Year-End Financials

Return on assets: 4.3%
Return on equity: 13.5%
Current ratio: 2.20
Cash ($ mil.): 26

NEBRASKA MEDICINE GUILD

EXECUTIVES

Pres, Bradley E Britigan
SEC*, James Linder
Treas*, Bruce Grewcock
Drug Policy Coordinator, Jenel Proksel
Drug Policy Coordinator, Jenny Van Moorleghem
Utilization Management Lead, Karie Eberhardt
Administrative Assistant, Mary Stenzel
Nurse Practitioner, Rachael Schmidt
Clinical Education Coordinator, Shaylene Michaels
Database Analyst, Andrew Novak
Registered Nurse, Jill Petersen

LOCATIONS

HQ: NEBRASKA MEDICINE GUILD
987400 NEBRASKA MED CTR, OMAHA, NE 681980001
Phone: 402 559-8650
Web: WWW.NEBRASKAMED.COM

HISTORICAL FINANCIALS

Company Type: Private

Income Statement — FYE: June 30

	REVENUE ($ mil.)	NET INCOME ($ mil.)	NET PROFIT MARGIN	EMPLOYEES
06/19	1,662	80	4.8%	15,200
06/18	1,514	58	3.9%	—
Annual Growth	9.8%	37.3%	—	—

2019 Year-End Financials

Return on assets: 5.1%
Return on equity: 8.3%
Current ratio: 2.50
Cash ($ mil.): 168

NEBRASKA PUBLIC POWER DISTRICT

Nebraska Public Power District (NPPD) electrifies the Cornhusker State. The government-owned electric utility the largest in the state provides power in 86 of the state's 93 counties. The firm has a generating capacity of about 3130 MW and operates more than 5200 miles of transmission lines. NPPD distributes electricity to about 89000 retail customers in 81 cities and towns; it also provides power to about 1 million customers through wholesale power contracts with more than 50 towns and 25 public power districts. In addition NPPD purchases electricity from the federally owned Western Area Power Administration and operates a surface water irrigation system.

Operations

The company uses multiple sources including nuclear steam mixed wind hydro and diesel to generate power.

NPPD's revenues comes from wholesale power supply agreements with 50 towns and 25 rural public power districts and rural cooperatives who rely totally or partially on NPPD's electrical system. NPPD also serves about 81 communities at the retail level.

Financial Performance

Revenues for 2013 increased by 2% due mostly to rate increases and sales to other utilities. Net income jumped 30% on the revenue increase and reduced costs. Cash from operations followed suit and rose nearly $100 million.

Strategy

Faced with growing long-term demand for electricity along with pressure to keep prices low NPPD has implemented plans to increase transmission capacity. With a goal of getting of 15% it energy from renewable sources by 2025 the company is exploring alternative fuel sources for future plants. With 45% of NPPD's energy supply coming from coal in 2011 the company was looking to cleaner alternatives such as wind power and biomass in order to meet stricter environmental regulations. In 2014 it signed a deal to purchase wind power from Sempra a move that put it within sight of its goal to have 10% of its power generation come from renewable sources.

Company Background

NPPD was formed in 1970 through the merger of three public utilities: Consumers Public Power District Platte Valley Public Power and Irrigation District and Nebraska Public Power System.

EXECUTIVES

Vice President, Theresa Shank
Vice President And Chief Nuclear Officer, John Dent
Vice President, John Wolfe
Deputy Assistant Treasurer, Christine Pillen
Vice Chairman, Barry Dekay
Auditors: PRICEWATERHOUSECOOPER LLP ST

LOCATIONS

HQ: NEBRASKA PUBLIC POWER DISTRICT
1414 15TH ST, COLUMBUS, NE 686015226
Phone: 877 275-6773
Web: WWW.NPPD.COM

PRODUCTS/OPERATIONS

2013 Sales

	$ mil.	% of total
Wholesale	584	53
Retail	294	27
Other	227	20
Total	**1,106**	**100**

COMPETITORS

Basin Electric Power
Berkshire Hathaway Energy
NorthWestern
Omaha Public Power
Tri-State Generation and Transmission

HISTORICAL FINANCIALS

Company Type: Private

Income Statement — FYE: December 31

	REVENUE ($ mil.)	NET INCOME ($ mil.)	NET PROFIT MARGIN	EMPLOYEES
12/19	1,074	89	8.3%	1,900
12/18	1,144	82	7.2%	—
12/17	1,101	71	6.5%	—
12/16	1,154	82	7.2%	—
Annual Growth	(2.4%)	2.5%	—	—

2019 Year-End Financials

Return on assets: 1.8%
Return on equity: 5.4%
Current ratio: 3.40
Cash ($ mil.): 16

NEVADA SYSTEM OF HIGHER EDUCATION

You can gamble on a solid academic foundation with The Nevada System of Higher Education (NSHE). The system oversees Nevada's public colleges and institutions. NSHE encompasses eight institutions: the University of Nevada Las Vegas; the University of Nevada Reno; Nevada State College; community colleges Truckee Meadows Great Basin College College of Southern Nevada and Western Nevada College; and environmental research arm Desert Research Institute (DRI). The system which enrolls some 106000 students is governed by the Nevada Board of Regents consisting of 13 members elected for six-year terms.

Financial Performance

Total operating revenue fell 4% in 2012 as an increase in NSHE's largest segment (student tuition and fees) was not enough to offset double-digit declines in federal state and local grants and contracts. The rise in tuition and fees resulted from an increase in tuition rates to offset an enrollment decrease.

Strategy

In late 2013 NSHE announced a partnership to establish medical schools at the University of Nevada Las Vegas and Reno campuses.

EXECUTIVES

Ceo, Daniel Klaich
Administrative Assistant II, Dennis Thieme
Associate Professor English, Jeffrey Jablonski
Assistant Professor, Natalie Berman
Acting Pres Wstrnnevadacollege, P Mark Ghan
Editor, Doug Smith
Executive, Emily Dyer
Internal Medicine Practitioner, Jihye Park
Graduate Student Teaching Assi, Armin Saraei
Unlvino Student Manager, Jackie Watson
Network Manager, Chris Gaub
Auditors: GRANT THORNTON LLP RENO NV

LOCATIONS

HQ: NEVADA SYSTEM OF HIGHER EDUCATION
2601 ENTERPRISE RD, RENO, NV 895121666
Phone: 775 784-4901
Web: WWW.NEVADA.EDU

HISTORICAL FINANCIALS

Company Type: Private

Income Statement — FYE: June 30

	REVENUE ($ mil.)	NET INCOME ($ mil.)	NET PROFIT MARGIN	EMPLOYEES
06/19	982	(6)	—	8,000
06/18	953	116	12.2%	—
06/17	1,115	140	12.6%	—
06/16	1,055	48	4.6%	—
Annual Growth	(2.4%)	—	—	—

2019 Year-End Financials

Return on assets: (-0.2%)
Return on equity: (-0.4%)
Current ratio: 2.90
Cash ($ mil.): 175

NEW ENGLAND PETROLEUM LIMITED PARTNERSHIP

EXECUTIVES

Ptnr, Gary Kaneb
Auditors: PRICEWATERHOUSECOOPERS LLP B

LOCATIONS

HQ: NEW ENGLAND PETROLEUM LIMITED PARTNERSHIP
6 KIMBALL LN STE 400, LYNNFIELD, MA 019402685
Phone: 617 660-7400

HISTORICAL FINANCIALS

Company Type: Private

Income Statement — FYE: December 31

	REVENUE ($ mil.)	NET INCOME ($ mil.)	NET PROFIT MARGIN	EMPLOYEES
12/12	1,081	4	0.4%	25
12/11	998	3	0.3%	—
12/10	568	2	0.5%	—
Annual Growth	37.9%	32.5%	—	—

2012 Year-End Financials

Return on assets: 7.7%
Return on equity: 13.5%
Current ratio: 2.40
Cash ($ mil.): 2

NEW JERSEY TRANSPORTATION TRUST FUND AUTHORITY

EXECUTIVES

Commissioner, James Weinstein
Scientist, Katie Lynch
Auditors: MERCADIEN PC PRINCETON NJ

LOCATIONS

HQ: NEW JERSEY TRANSPORTATION TRUST FUND AUTHORITY
1035 PARKWAY AVE, EWING, NJ 086182309
Phone: 609 530-2035

HISTORICAL FINANCIALS

Company Type: Private

Income Statement				FYE: June 30
	REVENUE ($ mil.)	NET INCOME ($ mil.)	NET PROFIT MARGIN	EMPLOYEES
06/19	2,272	(364)	—	1
06/18	1,676	(859)	—	—
06/17	1,338	(532)	—	—
06/16	1,261	(412)	—	—
Annual Growth	21.7%	—	—	—

2019 Year-End Financials

Return on assets: (-1.8%)
Return on equity: (-126.2%)
Current ratio: —
Cash ($ mil.): 904

NEW JERSEY TURNPIKE AUTHORITY INC

The New Jersey Turnpike Authority operates two toll-supported highways the New Jersey Turnpike and the Garden State Parkway. The New Jersey Turnpike runs for 148 miles from the Delaware River Bridge at the southern end of the state to the George Washington Bridge that connects New Jersey with New York. The turnpike includes about 10 rest stops or service areas named for former New Jersey residents such as Alexander Hamilton Vince Lombardi and Walt Whitman. The Garden State Parkway runs for 173 miles and spans the length of New Jersey's Atlantic coastline.

EXECUTIVES

Vice Chairman, Ronald Gravino
Treasurer, Michael R Dupont
Secretary To The Authority, Kim Schurman
Auditors: KPMG LLP SHORT HILLS NJ

LOCATIONS

HQ: NEW JERSEY TURNPIKE AUTHORITY INC
1 TURNPIKE PLZ, WOODBRIDGE, NJ 070955195
Phone: 732 750-5300
Web: WWW.NJTA.COM

HISTORICAL FINANCIALS

Company Type: Private

Income Statement				FYE: December 31
	REVENUE ($ mil.)	NET INCOME ($ mil.)	NET PROFIT MARGIN	EMPLOYEES
12/19	1,743	191	11.0%	2,400
12/18	1,753	209	12.0%	—
12/17	1,698	329	19.4%	—
12/16	1,689	260	15.4%	—
Annual Growth	1.1%	(9.8%)	—	—

2019 Year-End Financials

Return on assets: 1.2%
Return on equity: 32.4%
Current ratio: 2.20
Cash ($ mil.): 152

NEW PRIME, INC.

Specialized carrier New Prime (which does business simply as Prime) provides refrigerated flatbed tanker and intermodal trucking services throughout North America through over 11700 remotely monitored temperature-controlled trailers. The company operates through arrangements with other carriers. A subsidiary Prime Floral uses the parent company's refrigerated equipment and facilities to serve the flower industry. In addition to its freight-hauling operations Prime provides logistics services including freight brokerage. The company was founded in 1970.

Operations

Prime with a fleet of over 6500 trucks operates through four divisions.

Prime's liquid bulk fleet (Tanker Division) consists of over 300 trucks and over 500 6800 7000 or 7250 gallons. The company's Refrigerated Division has over 6500 trucks and over 11700 remotely monitored temperature-controlled trailers. It is a carrier that can ship fresh produce fresh cut floral pharmaceuticals fresh or frozen meats or any other dry or temperature-controlled freight. Flatbed division is focused on hauling freight from pipe and steel to drywall and roofing materials and more. Prime's Intermodal fleet is a direct link to virtually every market across the continent.

The company also offers two leasing options lease and lease purchase.

Geographic Reach

The company serves customers in North America. Based in Springfield Missouri Prime operates two US terminals in Pennsylvania and Utah. Additionally it has facilities in Colorado Texas Indiana Georgia Florida Oregon and California.

Sales and Marketing

Prime has hauled goods for cconsumer goods makers ConAgra Foods Kraft Foods FedEx Coca-Cola and General Mills among others.

Company Background

Prime was founded in 1970 by Robert Low who continues to serve as Prime's president.

EXECUTIVES

President And Ceo, Robert E. Low
Manager Of Success Leasing Program, Fred Ege
Director Of Logistics, Rick Gallagher
Director Of Operations, Pat Leonard
Director Of Flatbed And Tanker Operations, Jim Wilkins
Vp Sales And Marketing, Steve Wutke
Director Of Finance, Dean Hoedl
Director Of Technology, Rodney Rader
Manager Of Tanker Division, Brett Vonwiller

LOCATIONS

HQ: NEW PRIME, INC.
2740 N MAYFAIR AVE, SPRINGFIELD, MO 658035084
Phone: 800 321-4552
Web: WWW.PRIMEINC.COM

COMPETITORS

Boyd Bros. Transportation
C.H. Robinson Worldwide
C.R. England
Central Refrigerated Service
Comcar
Frozen Food Express
KLLM Transport Services
Marten Transport
Quality Distribution
Stevens Transport

HISTORICAL FINANCIALS

Company Type: Private

Income Statement				FYE: March 31
	REVENUE ($ mil.)	NET INCOME ($ mil.)	NET PROFIT MARGIN	EMPLOYEES
03/17*	1,653	116	7.1%	5,000
04/16	1,598	133	8.3%	—
03/12	1,022	60	6.0%	—
04/11	941	47	5.0%	—
Annual Growth	9.8%	16.2%	—	—

*Fiscal year change

2017 Year-End Financials

Return on assets: 12.7%
Return on equity: 32.2%
Current ratio: 0.40
Cash ($ mil.): —

NEW WORLD FUND

EXECUTIVES

Admn, Michael W Stockton

LOCATIONS

HQ: NEW WORLD FUND
333 S HOPE ST FL 53, LOS ANGELES, CA 900711418
Phone: 213 486-9200

HISTORICAL FINANCIALS

Company Type: Private

Income Statement				FYE: October 31
	REVENUE ($ mil.)	NET INCOME ($ mil.)	NET PROFIT MARGIN	EMPLOYEES
10/19	792	8,314	1049.1%	2
10/18	404	(94)	—	—
Annual Growth	95.8%	—	—	—

2019 Year-End Financials

Return on assets: 19.7%
Return on equity: 19.9%
Current ratio: —
Cash ($ mil.): 196

NEW YORK CITY ECONOMIC DEVELOPMENT CORPORATION

EXECUTIVES

Pres-Ceo, Maria Torres-Springer
Chb*, Michael Schlein
Cfo*, Kim Vaccari
Coo*, Euan Robertson
Evp*, Seth Myers
Treas*, Spencer Hobson
Asst Treas*, Fred D'Ascoli
Project Coordinator, Indira Ori
Vice-President, Harry Singh

Assistant Vice President of Le, Richard Tom
Administration Manager, Rosemary Scaduto
Auditors: ERNST & YOUNG LLP NEW YORK

LOCATIONS

HQ: NEW YORK CITY ECONOMIC DEVELOPMENT CORPORATION
1 LIBERTY PLZ, NEW YORK, NY 100061404
Phone: 212 312-3657
Web: WWW.EDC.NYC

HISTORICAL FINANCIALS

Company Type: Private

Income Statement FYE: June 30

	REVENUE ($ mil.)	NET INCOME ($ mil.)	NET PROFIT MARGIN	EMPLOYEES
06/18	761	14	1.9%	438
06/16	908	100	11.1%	—
Annual Growth	(8.5%)	(62.1%)	—	—

2018 Year-End Financials

Return on assets: 1.3%
Return on equity: 3.2%
Current ratio: 2.60
Cash ($ mil.): 92

NEW YORK CITY HEALTH AND HOSPITALS CORPORATION

New York City Health and Hospitals Corporation (NYC H+H) operates health care facilities in all five boroughs of New York City. As one of the largest municipal health service systems in the US HHC serves 1 million New Yorkers including more than 500000 who are uninsured. It operates a network of around 10 acute care hospitals (including Bellevue the nation's oldest public hospital) large diagnostic and treatment centers skilled nursing centers long-term care facilities and a home health care agency. NYC H+H also operates more than 70 community-based clinics and provides medical services to New York City's correctional facilities. In addition it operates MetroPlus a managed health care plan.

Operations

NYC H+H provides health care services including primary and preventive care emergency care long-term care plant-based nutrition guidance school-based health care and services for victims of domestic violence.

Geographic Reach

NYC H+H operates health care facilities in New York's Manhattan Brooklyn Queens Bronx and Staten Island boroughs.

Sales and Marketing

NYC H+H's MetroPlus health plan provides low to no-cost insurance to more than 500000 customers in New York. It insures many New York City government employees.

Financial Performance

NYC H+H's operating revenue fell in fiscal 2017 (ended June) but recovered the following year surpassing that of fiscal 2016. Operating revenue increased 6% to $7.8 billion in 2018 as net patient service revenue and net appropriations from New York City increased. Those gains were partially offset by a decline in grants revenue.

The company has been losing money for years. In fiscal 2018 it had an operating loss of $57.5 million an improvement over the 2017 operating loss of $272.7 million. That improvement was driven by the higher operating revenue plus certain cost-control measures such as lower other-than-personal services and pension expenses. NYC H+H ended fiscal 2018 with a net deficit of $5.5 billion.

Strategy

NYC H+H has been struggling financially facing a projected $1.8 billion budget gap by 2020. In mid-2017 the system cut 476 positions including nearly 400 management positions. It has closed certain clinics and shuttered its Goldwater specialty care hospital and nursing facility. And although the system has received positive care quality reviews from external organizations it is challenged to attract patients with commercial insurance. To further exacerbate matters the health system has a number of older facilities that would benefit from improvements but it has few resources to allocate to those types of projects.

HISTORY

The City of New York in 1929 created a department to manage its hospitals for the poor. During the Depression more than half of the city's residents were eligible for subsidized care and its public hospitals operated at full capacity.

Four new hospitals opened in the 1950s but the city was already having trouble maintaining existing facilities and attracting staff (young doctors preferred private insurance-supported hospitals catering to the middle class). Meanwhile technological advances and increased demand for skilled nurses made hospitals more expensive to operate. The advent of Medicaid in 1965 was a boon for the system because it brought in federal money.

In 1969 the city created the New York City Health and Hospitals Corporation (HHC) to manage its public health care system — and it was hoped to distance it from the political arena. But HHC was still dependent on the city for funds arousing criticism from those who had hoped for more autonomy. A 1973 state report claimed "the people of New York City are not materially better served by the Health and Hospitals Corporation than by its predecessor agencies."

City budget shortfalls in the mid-1970s led to cutbacks at HHC including nearly 20% of staff. Later in the decade several hospitals closed and some services were discontinued. Ed Koch became mayor in 1978 and gained more control over HHC's operations. Struggles between his administration and the system led three HHC presidents to resign by 1981. That year Koch crony Stanley Brezenoff assumed the post and helped transform HHC into a city pseudo-department.

The early 1980s brought greater prosperity to the system. Reimbursement rates and collections procedures improved allowing HHC to upgrade its record-keeping and its ambulatory and psychiatric care programs. In the late 1980s sharp increases in AIDS and crack addiction cases strained the system and a sluggish economy decreased city funding. Criticism mounted in the early 1990s with allegations of wrongful deaths dangerous facilities and lack of Medicaid payment controls. HHC lost patients to managed care providers and revenues plummeted. In 1995 a city panel recommended radically revamping the system.

Faced with declining revenues and criticism from Mayor Rudolph Giuliani that HHC was "a jobs program" the company began cutting jobs and consolidating facilities in 1996. Under Giuliani's direction HHC made plans to sell its Coney Island Elmhurst and Queens hospital centers. In 1997 the New York State Supreme Court struck down Giuliani's privatization efforts saying the city council had a right to review and approve each sale. In 1998 Giuliani continued to seek to restructure HHC and the agency itself contended it was making progress toward its restructuring goals which were aimed at giving HHC more autonomy as well as more fiscal responsibility. In anticipation of a budget shortfall that year the system laid off some 900 support staff employees. In 1999 the state court of appeals ruled HHC could not legally lease or sell its hospitals.

In 2000 HHC launched an effort to improve its physical infrastructure by beginning the rebuilding and renovation of facilities in Brooklyn Manhattan and Queens. The organization also began converting to an electronic (and thus more efficient) clinical information system. In 2001 HHC forged ahead with further restructuring initiatives. It introduced the Open Access plan a cost-cutting measure designed to expedite the processes involved in outpatient visits.

In 2006 Mayor Michael Bloomberg committed $16 million in funds toward the treatment of those affected by exposure to toxic fumes and dust from the 2001 attacks on the World Trade Center. Together with the city HHC established the WTC Environmental Health Center at Bellevue Hospital; treatment was made available at little or no charge to the patient.

EXECUTIVES

Svp And General Counsel, Alan D. Aviles
Svp South Manhattan Health Network; Executive Director Bellevue Hospital Center, Lynda D. Curtis
Svp North Bronx Healthcare Network; Executive Director Jacobi Medical Center, William P. Walsh
Svp Finance And Cfo, Marlene Zurack
Evp And Coo, Antonio Martin
Executive Director Metropolitan Hospital Center, Meryl Weinberg
Executive Director Elmhurst Hospital Center, Chris Constantino
Executive Director And Cfo Gouverneur Healthcare Services, Mendel Hagler
Executive Director And President Metroplus Health Plan, Arnold Saperstein
Executive Director Sea View Hospital Rehabilitation Center And Home, Angelo Mascia
Svp Queens Healthcare Network, Anne Marie Sullivan
Executive Director Hhc Health And Home Care, Ann Frisch
Svp Information Technology And Cio, Norberto (Bert) Robles
Executive Director Dr. Susan Smith Mckinney Nursing And Rehabilitation Center, Michael Tartaglia
Executive Director Coler-goldwater Specialty Hospital And Nursing Facility, Robert K. Hughes
Svp Quality And Corporate Chief Medical Officer, Ross Wilson
Acting Svp Generations Plus Northern Manhattan Healthcare Network; Executive Director Lincoln Medical And Mental Health Center, Denise C. Soares
Executive Director Kings County Hospital Center, Ernest J. Baptiste
Executive Director Queens Hospital Center, Julius Wool
Assistant Vice President Information Technology Services, Michael Keil
Senior Assistant Vice President, Roslyn Weinstein
Senior Assistant Vice President, Caroline Jacobs
Senior Assistant Vice President, Paul Albertson
Senior Vice President, Arthur Wagner
Senior Assistant Vice President, Maxine Katz
Director Of Admissions, Alex Toro
Assistant Vice President Data Science, Vijay Saradhi
Director Of Pharmacy, Danielle Petrocelli
Vice President Of Finance And Chief Fina, Tim Buit
Senior Vice President Of Hospitals, William Foley

Senior Assistant Vice President Onecity Health, Ishmael Carter
Assistant Vice President, Nichola Davis
Head Nurse, Carmentina Silvestre-tan
Senior Assistant Vice President, Kaushal Challa
Assistant Vice President Operations, Grace-ann Weick
Program Medical Director, Natalya Kozlov
Vice President Business Development, Ken Sundaresan
Chairman, Michael A. Stocker
Vice Chair, Diane E. Lacey
Auditors: KPMG LLP NEW YORK NY

LOCATIONS

HQ: NEW YORK CITY HEALTH AND HOSPITALS CORPORATION
125 WORTH ST RM 514, NEW YORK, NY 100134006
Phone: 212 788-3321
Web: WWW.NYCHEALTHANDHOSPITALS.ORG

HHC Networks

Central Brooklyn Family Health Network
Dr. Susan Smith McKinney Nursing and Rehabilitation Center
East New York Diagnostic & Treatment Center
Kings County Hospital Center
Generations Plus Northern Manhattan Health Network
Harlem Hospital Center
Lincoln Medical and Mental Health Center
Metropolitan Hospital Center
Morrisania Diagnostic & Treatment Center
Renaissance Health Care Network Diagnostic & Treatment Center
Segundo Ruiz Belvis Diagnostic & Treatment Center
North Bronx Healthcare Network
Jacobi Medical Center
North Central Bronx Hospital
North Brooklyn Health Network
Cumberland Diagnostic & Treatment Center
Woodhull Medical and Mental Health Center
Queens Health Network
Elmhurst Hospital Center
Queens Hospital Center
South Brooklyn and Staten Island Health Network
Coney Island Hospital
Sea View Hospital Rehabilitation Center & Home
South Manhattan Healthcare Network
Bellevue Hospital Center
Gouverneur Healthcare Services

PRODUCTS/OPERATIONS

2018 Sales

	$ mil.	% of total
Net patient services	6,216	80
Net appropriations from City of New York	787	10
Grants	652	9
Other	105	1
Total	**7,761**	**100**

Selected Services

Alcohol and Opioid Use Disorder
Asthma Care
Bariatric Services
Breast Health
Burn Care
Cancer Care
Cardiology
Child Health and Pediatrics
Colon Cancer Screening
Deaf and Hard-of-Hearing
Dental Care
Depression
Diabetes Care
Farmers Market
Flu Vaccination
Geriatric Services
HIV/AIDS Care
HPV Vaccine
Hyptertension
Language/Translation Services
LGBTQ Services
Men's Health
Mental Health
Neonatal Intensive Care
Obstetrics & Gynecology
Palliative Care
Parkinson's Disease
Pediatrics
Quit Smoking
Rehab Services
Victims of Domestic Violence
Sexual Response Assault Teams
Sickle Cell Disease
Sleep Disorder Labs
Stroke Prevention and Care
Telehealth Initiatives
Trauma Centers
Vision Care
Women's Health
WTC Environmental Health Center
Youth Health

COMPETITORS

Beth Israel Medical Center
Catholic Healthcare System
Columbia University
Continuum Health Partners
Cornell University
Lenox Hill Hospital
Memorial Sloan-Kettering
Montefiore Medical
NYU
NewYork-Presbyterian Healthcare
Northwell Health

HISTORICAL FINANCIALS

Company Type: Private

Income Statement — FYE: June 30

	REVENUE ($ mil.)	NET INCOME ($ mil.)	NET PROFIT MARGIN	EMPLOYEES
06/17	9,550	(193)	—	35,700
06/02	4,285	(118)	—	—
06/01	4,287	(71)	—	—
06/00	4,083	9	0.2%	—
Annual Growth	5.1%	—	—	—

2017 Year-End Financials

Return on assets: (-2.8%)
Return on equity: —
Current ratio: 1.00
Cash ($ mil.): 1,184

NEW YORK CITY SCHOOL CONSTRUCTION AUTHORITY

EXECUTIVES

Pres-Ceo, Loraine Grillo
Exec V Pres*, Ross J Holden
Sr V Pres*, Samir Eid
Manager, Samir Patel
Manager, Carmen Mateo
Senior Manager, Zita Devivo
Officer, Eric Tiedemann
Information Specialist, Scott Lindeman
Law Specialist, Jacqlin Narain
Contractor, Martina Davis
Officer, Mikhail Furman
Auditors: PRICEWATERHOUSECOOPER LLP NE

LOCATIONS

HQ: NEW YORK CITY SCHOOL CONSTRUCTION AUTHORITY
3030 THOMSON AVE FL 3, LONG ISLAND CITY, NY 111013019
Phone: 718 472-8000
Web: WWW.NYCSCA.ORG

HISTORICAL FINANCIALS

Company Type: Private

Income Statement — FYE: June 30

	REVENUE ($ mil.)	NET INCOME ($ mil.)	NET PROFIT MARGIN	EMPLOYEES
06/14	2,190	(410)	—	600
06/13	1,840	(494)	—	—
Annual Growth	19.0%	—	—	—

2014 Year-End Financials

Return on assets: (-16.0%)
Return on equity: (-24.4%)
Current ratio: —
Cash ($ mil.): 74

NEW YORK CITY TRANSIT AUTHORITY

New York City Transit Authority has your ticket to ride in the Big Apple. Known as MTA New York City Transit it provides subway and bus transportation throughout New York City's five boroughs. It is the primary agency of the MTA and the largest public transportation system in North America. Its subway system – which includes more than 6300 subway cars 468 stations and 660 miles of track – serves more than 5.5 million passengers a day day on 238 local six select bus service and 61 express routes in the five boroughs. Its more than 5700 buses transport some 2.6 million riders each day. The agency also operates the Staten Island Railway system.

Operations

New York City Subways and Buses is comprised of two agencies of the MTA regional transportation network - MTA New York City Transit Transit and MTA Bus. The regional network also includes MTA Staten Island Railway (part of NYC Transit's Department of Subways) MTA Long Island Rail Road MTA Metro-North Railroad MTA Bridges and Tunnels and MTA Capital Construction.

MTA New York City Transit and its subsidiary Manhattan and Bronx Surface Transit Operating Authority provide subway and public bus service within New York City's five boroughs.

In 2013 MTA New York City Transit's total ridership was 2.4 billion up 62 million or 2.7% from 2012. After including 44 million of lost ridership from Superstorm Sandy in 2012 the company's 2013 ridership increased by 0.8% with a subway ridership increase of 19 million or 1.1% and no change in bus ridership.

Geographic Reach

The company serves customers in Brooklyn the Bronx Manhattan and Queens and Staten Island

Financial Performance

Rebounding from the effects of Superstorm Sandy on ridership (which resulted in lost revenues of $52 million) in 2013 MTA New York City Transit's revenues from fares increased by 9%. In 2014 its operating budget was $10.1 billion.

Strategy

MTA New York City Transit's parent company the MTA has been plagued by operating losses. To mitigate its losses the MTA has in recent years raised fares cut jobs and decreased service on its buses and subway lines. It has also sought to raise its non-operating revenues by seeking increased government funding.

With the help of federal stimulus and other funding MTA New York City Transit has been making capital improvements to its systems. Projects have included the construction of the Second Avenue Subway and renovations at the Fulton Street Transit Center and other stations throughout the system.

In 2013 the company broke ground on a new MTA Staten Island Railway station. The 27-month construction project the first such project to include a parking lot will replace the existing Atlantic and Nassau Stations in the Tottenville section of the borough.

Company Background

New York City Transit Authority was formed in the 1950s by New York's legislature; the city's transit system dates back to the early 1900s.

EXECUTIVES

Secretary, Mary Cerrone
Confidential Secretary Ii, Yolanda Gambrell
Auditors: PRICEWATERHOUSECOOPERS LLP ST

LOCATIONS

HQ: NEW YORK CITY TRANSIT AUTHORITY
2 BROADWAY FL 18, NEW YORK, NY 100043357
Phone: 718 330-1234
Web: WWW.NEW.MTA.INFO

HISTORICAL FINANCIALS

Company Type: Private

Income Statement FYE: December 31

	REVENUE ($ mil.)	NET INCOME ($ mil.)	NET PROFIT MARGIN	EMPLOYEES
12/19	5,060	1,049	20.7%	47,956
12/18	4,892	985	20.1%	—
12/17	4,911	(287)	—	—
Annual Growth	1.5%	—	—	—

2019 Year-End Financials

Return on assets: 2.1%
Return on equity: 4.4%
Current ratio: 0.80
Cash ($ mil.): 48

NEW YORK POWER AUTHORITY

The hydropower generated by the mighty Niagara Falls is the real authority behind the New York Power Authority (NYPA). More than 70% of the power that NYPA produces is from hydropower resources. The company generates and transmits more than 20% of New York's electricity making it the largest state-owned public power provider in the US. It is also New York's only statewide electricity supplier. NYPA owns hydroelectric and fossil-fueled generating facilities (16 in total) that produce about 5700 MW of electricity and it operates more than 1400 circuit-miles of transmission lines. NYPA is owned by the State of New York.

Geographic Reach

The company serves customers throughout New York State various public corporations in Southeastern New York within the metropolitan area of New York City (SENY Governmental Customers) and certain out-of-state customers.

Sales and Marketing

NYPA services more than 500 businesses and industrial customers including manufacturing companies such as Anchor Glass of Elmira and General Motors of Tonawanda and non-manufacturing companies like GEICO of Amherst and Yahoo! of Lockport and 114 government entities in New York City and Westchester County including New York City government the Metropolitan Transportation Authority The Port Authority of New York and New Jersey the New York City Housing Authority Westchester County government and most Westchester municipalities school districts and other public entities.

The company provides electricity to 51 municipal and cooperative electric systems to sell to their customers.

Financial Performance

In 2014 the company's net revenues increased by 5% to $3.18 billion due to a higher volume of market energy and capacity sales and higher prices on those sales.

Net income grew by 9% due to higher net revenues and an increase in investment income.

In 2014 NYPA's operating cash inflow slightly decreased by 0.2% due to changes in working capital.

Strategy

NYPA receives no state funds or tax credits. Instead it finances new projects through bond sales.

Following its shift from a regulated monopoly to a competitor in an open power market NYPA is aiming to grow by reducing the cost of the energy it provides and by developing electric transportation (such as electric cars) and other energy-efficiency projects including installing emergency power generators in metropolitan buildings. It is also working to improve the state's transmission grid increase its generating capacity and help support the state's directive to get 45% of its power from clean energy sources (including 100 MW of power from solar arrays at buildings across the state). NYPA has been tagged as the lead agency to reduce energy use at state facilities by 20% by 2020.

In 2014 NYPA completed the installation of solar thermal hot water systems at five New York City firehouses in the Rockaways section of Queens. The $550000 investment will reduce operating costs and could lead to the wider use of the clean energy-transfer technology in other city government facilities. The company's energy efficiency projects have saved New Yorkers more than $148 million a year cutting annual oil use by more than 2.7 million barrels and offsetting the release of approximately 890000 tons of greenhouse gases. Its clean transportation program has placed more than 1300 electric-drive vehicles into service.

To improve its delivery of power the company is pursuing the development of a new cross-Hudson transmission line that will connect New York City customers to the PJM Interconnection power grid.

HISTORY

The Power Authority of the State of New York (aka New York Power Authority or NYPA) was established in 1931 by Gov. Franklin Roosevelt to gain public control of New York's hydropower resources. The utility's major power plants came on line with the opening of the St. Lawrence-Franklin D. Roosevelt Power Project (1958) and the Niagara Power Project (1961). The Blenheim-Gilboa Pumped Storage Power Project opened in 1973.

In the mid-1970s NYPA shifted to nuclear power when it opened the James A. FitzPatrick Nuclear Power Plant (1975) and the Indian Point 3 Nuclear Power Plant (1976). The company then opened gas- and oil-powered plants: the Charles Poletti Power Project (1977) and the Richard M. Flynn Power Plant (1994).

In 1998 the authority allocated low-cost electricity to five companies that planned to invest $104 million in business expansions in western New York. The company suffered a loss in 1999 in part from reduced hydro generation and a drop in investment earnings. In 2000 NYPA sold its two nuclear plants (1800 MW of capacity) to utility holding company Entergy for $967 million.

The company completed the installation of 11 gas-powered turbines at various locations in New York City and on Long Island in 2001; the program was initiated to prevent expected energy shortages that summer but it also helped maintain power in areas of the city during the September 11 terrorist attacks.

In 2013 The Village of Lake Placid unveiled a new hybrid-electric shuttle bus that will make commuting on public transportation quieter and cleaner. Financing for the bus was made possible through NYPA's Municipal Electric-Drive Vehicle Program which provides financial assistance to New York municipal utilities to facilitate the replacement of less fuel-efficient vehicles in order to advance the state's clean energy goals. That year NYPA added seven more hybrids and one more EV to its fleet bringing the total number of electric drive vehicles to 79. It also purchased just over 40000 gallons of B20 biodiesel which earned the Power Authority 17 Alternative Fuel Vehicle credits under the Department of Energy's Energy Policy Act that will be used to purchase additional hybrid and plug-in hybrid vehicles.

EXECUTIVES

Coo, Edward A. (Ed) Welz
President And Ceo, Gil C. Quiniones
Evp And Cfo, Robert F. Lurie
Vice President Technical Compliance, Saul Rojas
Vice President Finance, Scott Tetenman
Vice President Shared Services, Ruth Colon
Senior Vice President Chief Auditor, Jennifer Faulkner
Svp And Chief Risk Officer, Soubhagya Parija
Vp Of It, Gina Jackson
Vp Of It, Robert Piascik
Chairman Board Of Trustees, John R. Koelmel
Vice Chair Board Of Trustees, Joanne M. Mahoney
Secretary To Procurement Office, Susan Vertone
Auditors: KPMG LLP NEW YORK NY

LOCATIONS

HQ: NEW YORK POWER AUTHORITY
250 MARTINE AVE APT 2E, WHITE PLAINS, NY 106013410
Phone: 914 681-6200
Web: WWW.NYPA.GOV

PRODUCTS/OPERATIONS

2014 Sales

	$ mil.	% of total
Power sales	2,396	76
Wheeling charges	614	19
Transmission charges	165	5
Total	**3,175**	**100**

Selected Operations

Transmission Control Facility
- Frederick R. Clark Energy Center (Oneida County)

Fossil-Fueled Plants
- Charles Poletti Power Project (New York City)
- Richard M. Flynn Power Plant (Suffolk County)
- PowerNow! Turbines (11 units in New York City and Long Island)

Hydropower Plants
- Blenheim-Gilboa Pumped Storage Power Project (Schoharie County)
- Niagara Power Project (Niagara County)
- St. Lawrence-Franklin D. Roosevelt Power Project (St. Lawrence County)

Small Hydropower Plants
- Ashokan Project (Ulster County)
- Crescent Plant (Albany and Saratoga Counties)
- Gregory B. Jarvis Plant (Oneida County)
- Kensico Project (Westchester County)
- Vischer Ferry Plant (Saratoga and Schenectady counties)

COMPETITORS

Avangrid
CH Energy
Con Edison
Enbridge
Entergy
National Grid USA
Rochester Gas and Electric
TransCanada

HISTORICAL FINANCIALS

Company Type: Private

Income Statement				FYE: December 31
	REVENUE ($ mil.)	NET INCOME ($ mil.)	NET PROFIT MARGIN	EMPLOYEES
12/19	2,370	26	1.1%	2,237
12/18	2,689	102	3.8%	—
12/17	2,573	119	4.6%	—
12/16	2,421	22	0.9%	—
Annual Growth	(0.7%)	5.7%	—	—

2019 Year-End Financials

Return on assets: 0.3%
Return on equity: 0.5%
Current ratio: 1.00
Cash ($ mil.): 66

NEW YORK PRESBYTERIAN HOSPITAL WEILL CORNELL UNIVERSITY MEDICAL CENTER

EXECUTIVES

Prin, Lewis Drusin
Branch/Division/Department Hea, Janet Parisi
Administrator, David Weir
Administrator, Suzan Toro
Research Scientist, Catherine Liu
Vice President, Jolie Singer
MD, Brian Apatoff
MD, Bruce Lerman
Coordinator Finance Pss, Cheryl Ross
Practice Administrator, Christine C Hatola
MD, Daniel Lahm

LOCATIONS

HQ: NEW YORK PRESBYTERIAN HOSPITAL WEILL CORNELL UNIVERSITY MEDICAL CENTER
525 E 68TH ST, NEW YORK, NY 100654870
Phone: 212 746-1754
Web: WWW.NYP.ORG

HISTORICAL FINANCIALS

Company Type: Private

Income Statement				FYE: December 31
	REVENUE ($ mil.)	NET INCOME ($ mil.)	NET PROFIT MARGIN	EMPLOYEES
12/15	4,505	265	5.9%	5
12/12	75	21	28.2%	—
Annual Growth	290.4%	131.8%	—	—

2015 Year-End Financials

Return on assets: 3.9%
Return on equity: 7.6%
Current ratio: 2.20
Cash ($ mil.): 227

NEW YORK SOCIETY FOR THE RELIEF OF THE RUPTURED AND CRIPPLED, MAINTAINING THE HOSPITAL FOR

EXECUTIVES

Ceo, Louis Shapiro
Exec V Pres*, Lisa A Goldstein
Exec V Pres*, Stacey L Malakof
Cso*, Lionel B Ivashkiv
Cdo*, Catherine Callagy
Nurse Technician, Lilia Gargasz
Human Resources Manager, Lilliana Torres
Secretary, Luisa Mora
Pediatric Physical Therapist, Magdalena Oledzka
Senior Venipuncture Technician, Marie Franck
Senior Buyer, Melinda Smith

LOCATIONS

HQ: NEW YORK SOCIETY FOR THE RELIEF OF THE RUPTURED AND CRIPPLED, MAINTAINING THE HOSPITAL FOR
535 E 70TH ST, NEW YORK, NY 100214823
Phone: 212 606-1000
Web: WWW.HSS.EDU

HISTORICAL FINANCIALS

Company Type: Private

Income Statement				FYE: December 31
	REVENUE ($ mil.)	NET INCOME ($ mil.)	NET PROFIT MARGIN	EMPLOYEES
12/19	1,335	117	8.8%	3,350
12/18	1,219	119	9.8%	—
12/16	1,038	51	5.0%	—
12/15	811	79	9.8%	—
Annual Growth	13.2%	10.0%	—	—

2019 Year-End Financials

Return on assets: 4.9%
Return on equity: 9.9%
Current ratio: 3.70
Cash ($ mil.): 123

NEW YORK STATE CATHOLIC HEALTH PLAN, INC.

Fidelis Care hopes for always faithful health plan members. The New York State Catholic Health Plan which does business as Fidelis Care serves more than 921000 residents in some 60 counties across the state including the New York City area. The church-sponsored plan's provider network includes more than 63000 physicians hospitals and other health care professionals and facilities. Fidelis Care provides managed Medicaid Medicare and state-sponsored family and children's Health Plus plans as well as long-term care and behavioral health coverage.

Operations

The company boasts an overall statewide member retention rate of more than 78% with a s Child Health Plus retention rate of more than 85%.

Geographic Reach

Fidelis Care's regional offices are located in Rego Park Queens (Greater Metropolitan); Albany (Northeast); Syracuse (Central); and Buffalo (Western) with satellite offices in Poughkeepsie Rochester and Suffern.

Sales and Marketing

The health plan has expanded its membership by seeking new low-income patients who lack coverage. In addition to direct sales efforts Fidelis Care tries to maintain a presence at health centers frequented by its target audience partnering with neighborhood clinics to hold free health screenings and Health Plus enrollment information sessions.

Enroll NY a new website sponsored by not-for-profit organization Hudson Center for Health Equity & Quality is also connecting Fidelis Care and other Medicaid providers with potential customers. In 2013 Fidelis Care began selling through the New York State of Health insurance exchange marketplace.

To bosst membership in 2013 the company ran the "I Want Fidelis Care' campaign (which promoted Fidelis Care as a health care resource) in English and Spanish. TV was added to the media buy in the New York City and Buffalo regions. It also established a social media presence on Facebook Twitter YouTube and Google+.

Financial Performance

Fidelis Care reported gross revenues of $4.1 billion in 2013 up from $3.3 billion in 2012.

Strategy

The company is expanding its office to keep up with demand. In 2014 it opened Ridgewood Community Office; in 2013 it completed of?ce expansion projects in the Albany and Syracuse regional of?ces and the satellite of?ce in Suffern and opened new community of?ces in Flushing (Queens) the Bronx and Bath (Steuben County).

Forecasting substantial growth in 2014 with the enrollment of more than 120000 new members the company announced plans to add more than 75 new information technology jobs at its Buffalo regional office.

In 2013 Fidelis Care moved into 12 new counties with the Medicare Advantage program highlighted by the opportunity to serve residents of western New York for the ?rst time. It also made plans to expand into Seneca Yates and Jefferson counties in 2014 and served additional Managed Long Term Care members as part of the State's phased-in expansion of mandatory enrollment in counties beyond New York City.

Fidelis Care has grown by expanding rapidly into new counties in New York including a number of growth measures in the Medicare marketplace during 2012 and 2013. The health plan's recent activity includes completing construction of Fidelis Care's new operations center and offices in Getzville (Erie County) and the launch of its new provider portal (Provider Access Online). Other growth measures include a 2012 partnership with DentaQuest to promote dental checkups; it also launched a new member portal for members to access benefit information. In 2013 the company gained approval to be a qualified health plan provider on the official New York State of Health marketplace.

Fidelis Care regularly evaluates and broadens its plan offerings. Recent additions include its Fidelis Care at Home managed long-term care offering; the behavioral health and developmental disabilities coverage options; and its fully integrated dual advantage plans (for consumers with both Medicare and Medicaid coverage).

Company Background

The church-sponsored plan was founded in 1993 by the bishops of New York's Roman Catholic dioceses and the Catholic Medical Center of Brooklyn and Queens.

EXECUTIVES

Vice President, Carey Shoemaker
Vice President Finance, Dina Soroka
Senior Vice President And Chief Admini, David Thomas
Director Of Government Relations, Colleen Wilson
Senior Vice President, Brian Cummings
Medical Director, Ponle Durojaye
Vice President Strategic Planning, James Burnosky
Nursing Director, Margaret Leonard
Vice President Of Information Technology, David Szabad
Vice President Information Technology, Julie Ralph
Medical Director, Camille Pearte
Vice President Product Development And Corporate Innovation Fidelis Care New, Jason Reiser
Assistant Vice President Contract Management, John Place
Senior Medical Secretary, Osvaldo Aquino
Auditors: LB DELOITTE TAX LLP JERICHO

LOCATIONS

HQ: NEW YORK STATE CATHOLIC HEALTH PLAN, INC.
9525 QUEENS BLVD, REGO PARK, NY 113744510
Phone: 888 343-3547
Web: WWW.FIDELISCARE.ORG

PRODUCTS/OPERATIONS

Selected Plans
Child Health Plus
Dual Advantage
Family Health Plus
Fidelis Care at Home (managed long-term care)
Medicaid Advantage Plus (managed long-term care)
Medicaid Managed Care
Medicare Advantage
New York State of Health

COMPETITORS

Aetna
Affinity Health
Anthem
CIGNA
Capital District Physicians' Health Plan
EmblemHealth
Health Net
HealthPlus Amerigroup
Healthfirst
Healthplex
Humana
Independent Health
Lifetime Healthcare
MVP Health Plan
UnitedHealth Group
Vytra Healthcare
healthnow new york inc

HISTORICAL FINANCIALS

Company Type: Private

Income Statement — FYE: December 31

	REVENUE ($ mil.)	NET INCOME ($ mil.)	NET PROFIT MARGIN	EMPLOYEES
12/14	5,304	271	5.1%	1,625
12/10	1,920	51	2.7%	—
12/09	1,435	27	1.9%	—
12/08	1,068	3	0.4%	—
Annual Growth	30.6%	103.1%	—	—

2014 Year-End Financials

Return on assets: 12.4%
Return on equity: 22.3%
Current ratio: 9.10
Cash ($ mil.): 948

NEW YORK STATE HOUSING FINANCE AGENCY

EXECUTIVES

Pres-Ceo, Stephen J Hunt
Chb*, Judd S Levy
Sr V Pres*, Ralph J Madalena
Sr V Pres*, Bernard H Abramowitz
Sr V Pres*, Robert M Drillings
Sr V Pres*, James Angley
Account Executive, Faith Brenner
Senior Channel Sales Manager, Akello Ragwar
Vp of Engineering, Craig Walkinshaw
Vice President, Mark Flescher
Executive Assistant To Pre, Angela Hitlall
Auditors: ERNST & YOUNG LLP NEW YORK

LOCATIONS

HQ: NEW YORK STATE HOUSING FINANCE AGENCY
641 LEXINGTON AVE FL 4, NEW YORK, NY 100224503
Phone: 212 688-4069
Web: WWW.HCR.NY.GOV

HISTORICAL FINANCIALS

Company Type: Private

Income Statement — FYE: October 31

	REVENUE ($ mil.)	NET INCOME ($ mil.)	NET PROFIT MARGIN	EMPLOYEES
10/18	553	187	33.9%	131
10/17	400	112	28.0%	—
10/16	279	77	27.7%	—
10/09	182	(31)	—	—
Annual Growth	13.1%	—	—	—

2018 Year-End Financials

Return on assets: 1.0%
Return on equity: 17.5%
Current ratio: 1.70
Cash ($ mil.): 36

NEW YORK UNIVERSITY

Higher education is at the core of this Big Apple institution. The setting and heritage of New York University (NYU) make it one of the nation's most popular educational institutions. With more than 50000 students attending its 18 schools and colleges NYU is among the largest private schools in the US. Its Tisch School of the Arts is well-regarded and its law school and Leonard N. Stern School of Business are among the foremost in the country. NYU occupies five major centers in Manhattan; its Washington Square campus is in the heart of Greenwich Village. The school was founded in 1831. Notable alumni include former Federal Reserve Chairman Alan Greenspan and film producer Oliver Stone.

Operations

NYU reports its financials in two segments – University and NYU Langone Health. The latter segment is composed of the NYU Langone Health System and NYU School of Medicine.

The University includes nearly 20 colleges and divisions including schools of art and sciences law dentistry business mathematical sciences fine arts professional studies public services social work and engineering. NYU also operates NYU Abu Dhabi and NYU Shanghai a joint venture with East China Normal University. The University segment accounts for some 30% of NYU's total revenue.

NYU Langone Health operates two hospitals Kimmel Pavilion and Tisch Hospital which together have some 850 beds. It also operates the 225-bed NYU Langone Orthopedic Hospital the 450-bed NYU Langone Hospital in Brooklyn and several ambulatory care facilities. The segment brings in some 70% of NYU's total revenue.

NYU alumni and faculty boast several prestigious awards including more than a dozen Nobel and Crafoord prizes and another four Pulitzer prizes.

Geographic Reach

Along with its campuses in New York NYU operates degree-granting campuses in Abu Dhabi and Shanghai. It also has more than 10 global academic centers in Africa Asia Europe and the Americas and research programs in more than 25 countries.

Financial Performance

In fiscal 2018 (ended August) NYU's operating revenue increased 17% to $11.6 billion. Driving that gain was an increase in patient care revenue which rose from $5.6 billion to $7 billion that year.

However the university's excess of operating revenue over expenses fell dramatically from $196.8 million to $11.2 million in fiscal 2018. Salaries and medical and pharmaceutical costs rose as did facilities expenses professional services expenses and all other expenses.

NYU ended fiscal 2018 with $1.5 billion in net cash some $217 million more than what it had at the end of 2017. Operating activities provided $941.1 million in net cash financing activities provided another $580.4 million while investing activities used $1.3 billion.

Strategy

In 2018 NYU School of Medicine offered all students full tuition scholarships regardless of merit or financial need. The move was largely designed to promote the training of primary care physicians which is an area of great need in the US. By removing the heavy debt load that medical students typically face the school hopes to encourage students to pursue careers in lower-paying areas such as primary care.

Later that year NYU announced plans to establish a new medical school on Long Island. That campus will also provide full tuition scholarships to students.

HISTORY

New York University was founded by several prominent New Yorkers in 1831. The school held its first classes the following year in rented rooms on the corner of Beekman and Nassau streets then moved to a building in Washington Square in 1835. It established its law school that year. NYU started its school of medicine in 1841 followed by the school of engineering and science (1854). Post-graduate studies in arts and science (its first coeducational program) began in 1886.

NYU's enrollment jumped from fewer than 2000 in 1900 to 28000 in 1930. After a lull during the Depression and WWII the campus boomed again in the postwar years. During the 1950s the university began focusing on improving academics rather than on increasing enrollment. It created a school of the arts in 1965 and in the early 1970s it completed the Elmer Holmes Bobst Library. However a cash crunch during that decade almost forced the school into bankruptcy.

President Jay Oliva took the reins in 1981 and focused on transforming NYU from a largely commuter college into a global university. The school began a campaign to raise $1 billion in 1984 but earmarked the funds for campus improvements rather than swelling its endowment. During the late 1980s NYU opened several new dormitories and conference spaces. In 1994 British historian and collector Sir Harold Acton bequeathed to the school his Tuscany estate — five art-filled villas overlooking Florence Italy.

In 1996 NYU's Medical Center began talks with Mount Sinai Medical Center aimed at merging their hospitals and medical schools. The talks fell apart in early 1997 but the following year the two sides agreed to merge hospitals and keep their medical schools distinct. Also in 1998 NYU formed NYU On-Line Inc. a for-profit subsidiary to develop and sell specialized Internet courses to other schools training centers and students; the venture was subsequently folded in late 2001. During 1999 contributions to the school approached $250 million. That year however two upper-level school officials were fired following allegations of improper use of university money.

Oliva retired as president in 2002 and was replaced by John Sexton former School of Law dean. In 2004 Sexton announced that NYU would give $1 million to New York City towards renovation of Washington Square Park (the school annually gives some $200000 for the park's ongoing maintenance).

EXECUTIVES

Vp Academic And Health Affairs, Robert (Bob) Berne
Vp Information Technology And Chief Information Technology Officer, Marilyn A. McMillan
Provost, David W. McLaughlin
Evp Finance And Information Technology, Martin S. Dorph
Director Global Institute Of Public Health; Dean Of Global Public Health, Cheryl G. Healton
Dean Libraries, Carol A. Mandel
Herman Robert Fox Dean College Of Dentistry, Charles N. Bertolami
Evp Operations, Alison Leary
Director Institute For The Study Of The Ancient World, Roger Bagnall
Director Courant Institute Of Mathematical Sciences, Gérard Ben Arous
Saul J. Farber Dean Nyu School Of Medicine; Ceo Nyu Hospitals Center, Robert I. Grossman
Dean Gallatin School Of Individualized Study, Susanne L. Wofford
Dean Polytechnic School Of Engineering, Katepalli R. (Sreeni) Sreenivasan
Dean Silver School Of Social Work, Lynn Videka
Dean Liberal Studies, Fred Schwarzbach
Judy And Michael Steinhardt Director Institute Of Fine Arts, Patricia Lee Rubin
Dean Leonard N. Stern School Of Business, Peter B. Henry, age 50
Vice Chancellor New York University Abu Dhabi, Alfred H. Bloom
Vp Global Technology And Chief Global Technology Officer, Thomas A. (Tom) Delaney
Dean For Science Faculty Of Arts And Science, Michael D. Purugganan
President, Andrew Hamilton
Gale And Ira Drukier Dean Steinhardt School For Culture Education And Human Development, Dominic Brewer
Anne And Joel Ehrenkranz Dean Faculty Of Arts And Sciences, Thomas J. Carew
Dean For Humanities Faculty Of Arts And Sciences, Joy Connolly
Harvey J. Stedman Dean School Of Professional Studies, Dennis DiLorenzo
Dean Robert F. Wagner Graduate School Of Public Service, Sherry A. Glied
Dean Tisch School Of The Arts, Allyson Green
Dean For Social Sciences Faculty Of Arts And Science, Michael Laver
Vice Chancellor Nyu Shanghai, Jeffrey S. Lehman
Dean Undergraduate College Leonard N. Stern School Of Business, Geeta Menon
Dean School Of Law, Trevor Morrison
Director Marron Institute Of Urban Management, Paul Romer
Seryl Kushner Dean College Of Arts And Science, G. Gabrielle Starr
Dean College Of Nursing, Eileen Sullivan-Marx
Chancellor Nyu Shanghai, Yu Lizhong
Interim Dean Graduate School Of Arts And Science, Anna L. Harvey
Assistant Vice President, Zoe Ragouzeos
Vice President, Marc Wais
Vice Provost, Carol Morrow
Associate Vice President Student Health, Carlo Ciotoli
Vice President Financial Operations And Treasurer, Stephanie Pianka
Assistant Vice President Employee Relations, Barbara Cardeli-Arroyo
Vice President Finance, Harold T Read
Associate Vice President, Deborah Broderick
Assistant Vice President, Allen Mcfarlane
Assistant Vice President, John Beckman
Vice President, Andrew Gordon
Vice President Of Public Relations, Carolynn Choi
Associate Vice President Campus Planning And Design, Lori Mazor
Vice President Chief Information Security Officer, Mehdi Idrissi
Assistant Vice President, Janet Alperstein
Nursing Director, Mary Gribbin
Director Of Government Relations, Steve Heuer
Associate Medical Director, Nathan Bertelsen
Vice President For Enrollment Management, Mj Knoll-finn
Vice President For, Robert Campbell
Associate Vice President For Global Technologies, Heather Stewart
Administrative Aide To The Associate Vice President Of Alumni Relations, Danielle Ohrenberger
Vice President Finance, Pamela Morris
Vice President, Robert Levine
Executive Vice President, Tom Jordan
Vice President General Manager, Laurence F Maslon
Executive Vice President Research And Innovation Cross Platform, Lisa Sokolov
Vice President And Special Counsel, Leo L Goldsmith
Vice President, Victoria M Mccoy-cosentino
Vice President For Student Affairs, Susan B Neuman
Vice President Director Engineering, Chris Pak
Vice President Global Security And Crisis Management, Jules Martin
Assistant Vice President External Affairs And Protective Services, Carl Barchus
Senior Vice President Manager International Banking, Vonetta Moses
Director Of Admissions, Williams Cassandra
Vice President Finance And Administration, Charice Washington-warner
Vice President Sales, Joe Harris
Vice President And Manager Raines Perspectives Raines International, Jessica Deoliveira
Senior Vice President Deputy General Counsel Chief Compliance And Ethics Officer, Genie Gavenchak
Vice President For Operations Capital Projects, Andy Buonpastore
Executive Vice President, Mandy Hu
Vice President Facilities Management, Debra Berger
Vice President Global Campus Safety, Marlon Lynch
Medical Director, John Wang
Director Of Pharmacy Director Of Pharmacy Services, Jeanie Kantrowitz
Vice President Of Event Planning, Kristyn M Curran
Executive Vice President, Linda Tempel
Senior Vice President, Evelyn Alvarez
Executive Vice President, Mia Higgins
Assistant Vice President, De Toro Yadira
Vice President, Laura Schattschneider
Chairman Board Of Trustees, William R. (Bill) Berkley, age 74
Board Director, Christine Trump
Honorary Board Member, John Tintori
Treasurer, Peter Rajsingh
Treasurer, Simon Mun
Assistant Treasurer, Elisa Cohen
Medical Secretary, Latia Davis
Secretary, Candice Jarvis
Secretary, Jennifer Neuman
Ward Secretary, Mark Brennan
Ms Global Affairs Candidate Treasurer Energy Policy International Club, Jude Buenaseda
Secretary, Lara Maraziti
Treasurer, Daphne Tso
Secretary, Lewis R Steinberg
Secretary Athletic Development, Raffaela Ianniciello
Secretary And Marketing, August Morar
Secretary, Beverly Wideman
Cab Treasurer, Erin Adams
Secretary, Iris Lam
Secretary, John Milito
Vice Chairman, Allan Feldman
Secretary To The Authority, Thomas Donohue
Auditors: PRICEWATERHOUSECOOPERS LLP NE

LOCATIONS

HQ: NEW YORK UNIVERSITY
70 WASHINGTON SQ S, NEW YORK, NY 100121019
Phone: 212 998-1212
Web: WWW.NYU.EDU

PRODUCTS/OPERATIONS

2018 Sales

	$ mil.	% of total
Patient care	6,981	60
Tuition & fees	1,852	16
Grants & contracts	1,011	9
Auxiliary enterprises	505	4
Hospital affiliations	342	3
Endowment distribution	169	2
Contributions	168	2
Net assets from restrictions	121	1

Insurance premiums earned	115	1
Return on short-term investments	16	-
Programs & other	272	2
Total	**11,556**	**100**

2018 Sales

	$ mil.	% of total
NYU Langone Health	8,298	72
University	3,267	28
Adjustments	(10.3)	-
Total	**11,556**	**100**

Selected Schools and Colleges

College of Arts and Science (founded 1832)
College of Dentistry (1865)
Courant Institute of Mathematical Sciences (1934)
Gallatin School of Individualized Study (1972)
Graduate School of Arts and Science (1886)
Leonard N. Stern School of Business (1900)
Robert F. Wagner Graduate School of Public Service (1938)
School of Continuing and Professional Studies (1934)
School of Law (1835)
School of Medicine (1841)
School of Social Work (1960)
Steinhardt School of Culture Education and Human Development (1890)
Tisch School of the Arts (1965)

HISTORICAL FINANCIALS

Company Type: Private

Income Statement — FYE: August 31

	REVENUE ($ mil.)	NET INCOME ($ mil.)	NET PROFIT MARGIN	EMPLOYEES
08/16	8,500	177	2.1%	21,000
08/11	5,172	563	10.9%	—
08/06	2,148	195	9.1%	—
Annual Growth	14.7%	(1.0%)	—	—

2016 Year-End Financials

Return on assets: 1.1%
Return on equity: 2.4%
Current ratio: —
Cash ($ mil.): 1,033

NEW YORK UNIVERSITY

EXECUTIVES

Pres, John Sexton
Proj Dir*, Yamilee Bazile
Assistant Professor, Satarupa Dasgupta
Assistant Professor, Cristina Vatulescu
General Practitioner, Emanuela Corielli
General Practitioner, Steven David
Adjunct Instructor, William Hewitt
Assistant Professor of Marketi, Raluca Ursu
Professor of Social Work, Gary Holden
Professor of Social Work, Jeffrey Seinfeld
Clinical Placement Nurse Manag, Marigold Martinez
Auditors: PRICEWATERHOUSECOOPERS LLP NE

LOCATIONS

HQ: NEW YORK UNIVERSITY
433 1ST AVE RM 619, NEW YORK, NY 100104067
Phone: 212 998-5813
Web: WWW.HEARTBREAKDREAMS.COM

HISTORICAL FINANCIALS

Company Type: Private

Income Statement — FYE: August 31

	REVENUE ($ mil.)	NET INCOME ($ mil.)	NET PROFIT MARGIN	EMPLOYEES
08/12	4,016	53	1.3%	30
08/10	3,376	149	4.4%	—
08/09	2,970	(172)	—	—
Annual Growth	10.6%	—	—	—

2012 Year-End Financials

Return on assets: 0.7%
Return on equity: 1.4%
Current ratio: 0.70
Cash ($ mil.): 982

NEWARK BETH ISRAEL MEDICAL CENTER INC.

Part of the RWJBarnabas network Newark Beth Israel Medical Center is a 670-bed acute-care regional referral hospital. The facility serves residents of Newark and surrounding areas in northern New Jersey. The hospital offers services including primary diagnostic emergency surgical and rehabilitative care. It is home to specialized programs such as kidney transplantation cancer care dentistry sleep disorders geriatrics and women's health services. Newark Beth Israel Medical Center also houses the Children's Hospital of New Jersey and the Saint Barnabas Heart Center. The research and teaching hospital has a medical staff of more than 800 physicians.

Operations

Newark Beth Israel Medical Center along with sister hospital Saint Barnabas Medical Center has a teaching and research affiliation with the New Jersey Medical School (part of the University of Medicine and Dentistry of New Jersey). The hospital also has training programs with other regional schools.

Parent Barnabas Health merged with Robert Wood Johnson Health in 2016 to form RWJBarnabas.

EXECUTIVES

Medical Director Center For Asian Health, Su Wang
Vice President For Development, Richard J Pallamary
Senior Vice President Internal Audit, Anthony Palmerio
Senior Vice President Financial Advisor Ubs Financial Services, Gil Blitz
Executive Vice President Chief Development Officer, Glenn Miller
Executive Vice President Chief Medical And Quality Officer, John F Bonamoe
Executive Vice President Office Of Health Care Transformation, Joseph Scott
Senior Vice President Strategic Marketing And Communications, Michael E Knecht
Senior Vice President Facilities Management And Construction, William Cuthill
Secretary President Imperial Consultants Inc., Lee Livingston
Auditors: WITHUMSMITHBROWN PC MORRISTOW

LOCATIONS

HQ: NEWARK BETH ISRAEL MEDICAL CENTER INC.
201 LYONS AVE, NEWARK, NJ 071122027
Phone: 973 926-7000
Web: WWW.RWJBH.ORG

PRODUCTS/OPERATIONS

Selected Departments and Centers

Barnabas Health Heart Center
Center for Geriatric Health Care
Center for Women's Health
Children's Hospital of New Jersey
Cohen Comprehensive Cancer and Blood Disorder Center
Lung Center
Pacemaker and Defibrillator Center
Palliative Care Program
Regional Perinatal Center
Radiology
Robotic Surgery Center
Renal Transplantation
Sleep Disorders Center

COMPETITORS

AtlantiCare
Atlantic Health
Bergen Regional Medical
CentraState Healthcare System
Children's Specialized Hospital
Chilton Medical Center
East Orange General Hospital
Englewood Hospital and Medical Center
Hackensack Meridian Health
Hackensack University Medical Center
Newton Medical Center
Robert Wood Johnson University Hospital
Robert Wood Johnson University Hospital at Rahway
St. Joseph's Healthcare System
The Valley Hospital
Virtua Health
Winthrop-University Hospital

HISTORICAL FINANCIALS

Company Type: Private

Income Statement — FYE: December 31

	REVENUE ($ mil.)	NET INCOME ($ mil.)	NET PROFIT MARGIN	EMPLOYEES
12/19	660	(33)	—	3,000
12/18	645	19	3.1%	—
12/17	545	35	6.5%	—
12/16	539	27	5.2%	—
Annual Growth	7.0%	—	—	—

2019 Year-End Financials

Return on assets: (-6.1%)
Return on equity: (-19.2%)
Current ratio: 3.80
Cash ($ mil.): 1

NEWARK CORPORATION

Newark offers all sorts of electronic goods in one place and in places all across the Americas. The company doing business as Newark element14 distributes some 4.4 million electronic components and supplies including semiconductors passive devices electrical equipment connectors wire and cable optoelectronics test and measurement instruments and tools. It is also a source for companies needing parts compliant with the Restrictions of Hazardous Substances order in the European Union. Customers are electronics design engineers maintenance technicians and other electronics buyers. Newark element14 is a subsidiary of Premier Farnell a top UK electronic and industrial parts supplier.

Operations

Newark element14 also offers such services as re-calibration custom panel meters and cable assemblies and re-reeling as well as procurement and stockroom services.

The company stocks more than 500 brands from companies the likes of Analog Devices AVX Cypress Semiconductor Freescale Microchip and Texas Instruments.

Geographic Reach

The company operates in North America.

Sales and Marketing

Like its parent Newark element14 maximizes the Internet for selling and customer service purposes with a growing emphasis on electronics design engineering (EDE). Newark element14's EDE customers can access a website that offers collaborative design tools; the company also maintains a dedicated website just for US federal government customers. In addition to its websites Newark element14 operates a customer contact center has a dedicated sales force and offers a print catalog of its products.

Strategy

As part of its business Newark element14 regularly rolls out new products through partnerships with other companies. In 2014 for instance it launched the MagniV S12ZVML-MINIBRD variable-speed motor-control development kit alongside Freescale as well as the Tektronix TBS1000B Series digital storage oscilloscopes. Newark element14 also introduced three new Fluke Thermal Image cameras to its test and measurement portfolio to help boost a technician's productivity while in the field.

Expanding its distribution agreements also keeps Newark element14 growing. In 2014 the company became an authorized distributor of Wurth Electronics items. Wurth specializes in components circuit boards and intelligent systems.

Company Background

Newark was originally established in 1934 as Newark Electric Company a supplier of radio parts – the name of the Chicago-based company's way of recognizing Newark New Jersey as the home of the the first radio station in the US. Newark Electric first published a catalog of parts in 1948. The company went public in 1960 on the American Stock Exchange (now NYSE MKT) changing its name to Newark Electronics Corporation. In 1968 the company was acquired by Premier Industrial Corporation a Cleveland-based distributor. Premier Industrial merged in 1996 with Farnell Electronics plc to become Premier Farnell. Newark and element14 (another Premier Farnell company) combined in 2011 to create Newark element14.

EXECUTIVES

Vice President Of Marketing Services, David Macaluso

LOCATIONS

HQ: NEWARK CORPORATION
300 S RIVERSIDE PLZ # 220, CHICAGO, IL 606066613
Phone: 773 784-5100
Web: WWW.NEWARK.COM

PRODUCTS/OPERATIONS

Selected Product Categories

Automation and process control
Batteries and chargers
Cable wire and assemblies
Chemicals and adhesives
Circuit protection
Connectors
Crystals and oscillators
Electrical
Enclosures racks and cabinets
Fans heat sinks and HVAC
Fasteners and mechanical
LED technologies
Office and computer
Optoelectronics and displays
Passive components
Power and line protection
Security and audio visual
Semiconductors
Sensors and transducers
Static control and site safety
Switches and relays
Test measurement and inspection
Tools and production supplies
Transformers

COMPETITORS

Arrow Electronics
Avnet
Davis Instruments
EACO
Future Electronics
Rexel Inc.
Trek Equipment

HISTORICAL FINANCIALS

Company Type: Private

Income Statement — FYE: February 1

	REVENUE ($ mil.)	NET INCOME ($ mil.)	NET PROFIT MARGIN	EMPLOYEES
02/15	543	24	4.5%	834
02/14	541	23	4.4%	—
02/13	580	20	3.5%	—
Annual Growth	(3.2%)	9.6%	—	—

NEWMARK & COMPANY REAL ESTATE, INC.

Whether you're talking cubicle cities or corner offices Newmark & Company Real Estate (dba Newmark Knight Frank or NKF) makes its mark on commercial real estate. As one of the world's top commercial real estate advisory firms it provides property brokerage development and management services to investors corporations and property owners. Newmark also offers facility management services overseeing a portfolio of properties across the globe. Together with its London-based partner Knight Frank NKF operates more than 370 offices across six continents. NKF comprises parent company BGC Partners' Real Estate Services segment which made up 40% of the parent company's total revenue in 2014.

Operations

NKF manages a broad range of properties including headquarters facilities and office space for a wide range of companies. It manages the day-to-day operations and maintenance for urban and suburban commercial properties of most types including office industrial data centers healthcare retail call centers urban towers suburban campuses and landmark buildings.

Property management services include building operations and maintenance leasing vendor and contract negotiation project oversight and value engineering labor relations property inspection/quality control property accounting and financial reporting cash flow analysis financial modeling lease administration due diligence and exit strategies. Newmark's facilities management services also include facility audits and reviews energy management services janitorial services mechanical services bill payment maintenance project management and moving management.

Its affiliates include Cantor Fitzgerald CCRE-Cantor Commercial Real Estate and Cantor Gaming.

Sales and Marketing

NKF serves clients across more than half a dozen sectors including advertising and marketing education healthcare media and entertainment financial services law firms real estate retail and food services and technology and telecom sectors. It counts several big names among its list of clients including AEG Live Apollo Global Management Deutsch CBS Corporation Cornell University and AmTrust Realty Corporation.

Financial Performance

As the Real Estate Services segment of BGC Partners Newmark Knight Frank's revenue jumped 23% to $708.8 million during 2014 thanks to its acquisition of Cornish & Carey stronger broker productivity and favorable trends in sales and leasing in the US commercial real estate market.

Strategy

The company is growing its business by adding new brokers making technological improvements and cultivating the company's relationships with clients in the US and abroad. It has also been growing its geographic reach and business lines by acquiring smaller real estate firms.

Mergers and Acquisitions

In January 2016 NKF bought Memphis-based Steffner Commercial Real Estate which was the "cornerstone" in NKF's plan to grow across the Mid-South region of Tennessee Kentucky Mississippi Alabama Arkansas and Louisiana.

December 2015 the real estate firm boosted its presence in the Midwest after it purchased Cincinnati Commercial Real Estate (CCR) which leases and invests in offices industrial facilities and retail space. The acquisition also added CCR's diversified client base of top Fortune 500 companies institutions and privately owned firms while also supporting growth opportunities for NKF's existing Ohio business in Cleveland and Columbus.

In August 2014 the company bought bought Cornish & Carey Commercial Inc. the leading full-service commercial real estate services company in the San Francisco Bay area and Silicon Valley. The company believes that this is a key strategic addition for Newmark in the key Northern California market.

In early 2013 it acquired commercial real estate developer Frederick Ross and brokerage Smith Mack.

EXECUTIVES

Managing Principal San Francisco, Michael Brown
Executive Vice President, Jeffrey Roseman
Vice President Director Of Operations, Bart McDade
First Vice President, Paul Graham
Senior Vice President Global Management Services, Joseph Murtha
Vice President And National Director Of, Pat Langdon
Sr Vp Newmark Grubb, Doug Schuster
Senior Vice President, Sara Payne
Executive Vice President, Sherry Watkins
Senior Vice President, Philip Thomas

LOCATIONS

HQ: NEWMARK & COMPANY REAL ESTATE, INC.
125 PARK AVE, NEW YORK, NY 100175529
Phone: 212 372-2000
Web: WWW.NGKF.COM

Selected Locations

North America
US
Canada
Mexico
Europe
Asia-Pacific
Africa
Middle East

PRODUCTS/OPERATIONS

Selected Services
Leasing Advisory
Global Corporate Services
Investment Sales and Capital Markets
Retail
Industrial
Consulting
Program and Project Management
Facilities Management
Property Management
Landauer Valuation & Advisory
Residential Construction Services
Specialty Practice Groups
 Data Center Consulting
 Global Gaming Group
 Global Healthcare
 Government
 Hotels
 Law Firm Advisory
 Loan Sale Advisory
 Multi-Housing Group
 Not-For-Profit Advisory
 Retail Occupier Services
 Self Storage Group

COMPETITORS

Breslin Realty Development Corp.
CBRE Group
Colliers International
Cushman & Wakefield
Eastdil Secured
Greiner-Maltz
Jones Lang LaSalle
Lend Lease
Lincoln Property

HISTORICAL FINANCIALS

Company Type: Private

Income Statement — FYE: December 31

	ASSETS ($ mil.)	NET INCOME ($ mil.)	INCOME AS % OF ASSETS	EMPLOYEES
12/16	860	53	6.3%	2,250
12/15	694	139	20.1%	—
12/14	234	0	—	—
Annual Growth	91.7%	—	—	—

2016 Year-End Financials

Return on assets: 6.3%
Return on equity: 10.2%
Sales ($ mil): 1,058

NEWPORT CORPORATION

Newport helps all sorts of customers take a measured approach. The company makes lasers photonics instrumentation sub-micron positioning systems vibration isolation and optical components and subsystems. It makes products that are used around the world in such fields as scientific research microelectronics life and health sciences industrial manufacturing and defense/security. In addition Newport has built a strong history of partnering with OEM customers delivering solutions from subassemblies to full solutions including design testing and manufacturing. Established in 1969 as Newport Research Corporation the company is a wholly owned subsidiary of MKS Instruments Inc.

Operations

Newport offers products under leading brands such as Corion ILX Lightwave New Focus Oriel Instruments Ophir Optimet Richardson Gratings Spiricon and Spectra-Physics.

Geographic Reach

Newport operates manufacturing plants stateside and abroad. US plants are located in California Massachusetts Montana New York and Utah. Internationally its plants are located in developed and emerging markets in Austria China France Germany Israel and Romania. In addition The company has direct sales offices located in the US Austria China France Germany Japan Israel Singapore South Korea Taiwan and the UK.

Sales and Marketing

Newport uses a direct sales force as well as an international network of independent distributors and sales representatives.

EXECUTIVES

President Ceo And Director, Robert J. Phillippy, $529,000 total compensation
Svp Cfo And Treasurer, Charles F. (Chuck) Cargile, $377,577 total compensation
Svp And General Manager Lasers Group, David J. Allen, $300,192 total compensation
Vp Precision Components And Systems Business Photonics And Precision Technologies Division, Dennis L. Werth, $310,192 total compensation
Vp Asia Pacific, Wilson W. Lin
Evp General Counsel Corporate Secretary, Andrew Powell
Vice President Nasso Sales, Jeff Parker
Chairman, Kenneth F. Potashner
Auditors: DELOITTE & TOUCHE LLP COSTA M

LOCATIONS

HQ: NEWPORT CORPORATION
1791 DEERE AVE, IRVINE, CA 926064814
Phone: 949 863-3144
Web: WWW.NEWPORT.COM

2016 Sales

	$ mil.	% of total
US	231	38
Asia	170	28
Europe	157	26
Other regions	44	8
Total	**602**	**100**

PRODUCTS/OPERATIONS

2016 Sales

	$ mil.	% of total
Photonics & precision technologies	249	41
Lasers	192	32
Optics	160	27
Total	**602**	**100**

COMPETITORS

Adept Technology
Agilent Technologies
Allied Motion Technologies
Anritsu
Carl Zeiss
Coherent Inc.
Corning
Danaher
EXFO
HORIBA
II-VI
IPG Photonics
Jenoptik
Kinetic Systems
Manz
Nikon
Nordson
Oclaro
Palomar Technologies
Parker-Hannifin
Renishaw
Rockwell Automation
Roper Technologies
Spectris
TRUMPF
Thermo Fisher Scientific
Viavi Solutions
Zygo

HISTORICAL FINANCIALS

Company Type: Private

Income Statement — FYE: January 3

	REVENUE ($ mil.)	NET INCOME ($ mil.)	NET PROFIT MARGIN	EMPLOYEES
01/15*	605	35	5.8%	2,480
12/13	560	15	2.8%	—
12/12	595	(89)	—	—
Annual Growth	0.8%	—	—	—

*Fiscal year change

2015 Year-End Financials

Return on assets: 6.1%
Return on equity: 9.9%
Current ratio: 2.90
Cash ($ mil.): 46

NEWYORK-PRESBYTERIAN/BROOKLYN METHODIST

New York Methodist Hospital is a not-for-profit acute-care teaching hospital serving Brooklyn residents. Established in 1881 as the Methodist Episcopal Hospital the facility has more than 650 licensed beds. It offers a full range of medical services including primary and emergency care as well as specialty services such as women's health cancer cardiovascular pediatric geriatric and behavioral health. The hospital also operates satellite clinics in surrounding areas. A member of New York-Presbyterian Healthcare System New York Methodist is a teaching hospital affiliated with Cornell University's Weill Medical College.

Operations

New York Methodist Hospital handles about 40000 inpatient admissions and 100000 emergency department visits each year as well as 24000 surgeries and 5000 births. It also processes about 200000 laboratory sample processes annually.

New York Methodist Hospital includes specialty institutes in about 10 fields including pulmonary medicine cancer care and vascular health. In addition to providing inpatient care the organization operates some 10 primary and specialty outpatient centers. It also runs a number of graduate medical programs including programs affiliated with professional training schools in the areas of radiography medical technology radiation therapy and paramedics.

Geographic Reach

New York Methodist Hospital's main campus is in the Park Slope neighborhood of Brooklyn. It has several outpatient centers in other parts of Brooklyn as well.

Strategy

To expand care for area residents New York Methodist is adding new specialist programs and equipment. For instance in 2012 the hospital added a robotic-assisted surgery program for bariatric procedures. It also opened a new wound care and hyperbaric oxygen therapy center for hard-to-heal wounds. In addition in 2013 the hospital moved its sleep disorder center into a new facility.

EXECUTIVES

Senior Vice President, Una Morrissey
Auditors: ERNST & YOUNG LLP NEW YORK N

LOCATIONS

HQ: NEWYORK-PRESBYTERIAN/BROOKLYN METHODIST
506 6TH ST, BROOKLYN, NY 112153609
Phone: 718 780-3000
Web: WWW.NYP.ORG

COMPETITORS

Beth Israel Medical Center
Bronx-Lebanon Hospital
Brookdale University Hospital
Catholic Healthcare System
Kingsbrook Jewish Medical Center
Lutheran HealthCare
Maimonides Medical Center
New York City Health and Hospitals
Northwell Health
SUNY Downstate
Winthrop-University Hospital

HISTORICAL FINANCIALS

Company Type: Private

Income Statement — FYE: December 31

	REVENUE ($ mil.)	NET INCOME ($ mil.)	NET PROFIT MARGIN	EMPLOYEES
12/16	788	145	18.5%	4,929
12/15	732	88	12.1%	—
12/14	687	68	10.0%	—
Annual Growth	7.0%	45.4%	—	—

2016 Year-End Financials

Return on assets: 12.7%
Return on equity: 22.9%
Current ratio: 4.20
Cash ($ mil.): 135

NEWYORK-PRESBYTERIAN/QUEENS

EXECUTIVES

Pres-Ceo, Stephen S Mills
Sr V Pres-Cfo*, Kevin Ward
Exec V Pres*, John E Sciortino
Exec V Pres*, Stephen Rimar
Sr V Pres*, Kevin J Ward
Sr V Pres*, Michaelle Williams
Procurement Staff, Jed Golden
Chief Engineer, David Harris
Office Manager, Nancy Garcia
Anesthesiologist, Alizabeth Acevedo
Internist, Brigit Palathra
Auditors: ERNST & YOUNG LLP NEW YORK N

LOCATIONS

HQ: NEWYORK-PRESBYTERIAN/QUEENS
5645 MAIN ST, FLUSHING, NY 113555045
Phone: 718 670-2000
Web: WWW.NYHQ.ORG

PRODUCTS/OPERATIONS

Selected Services and Centers
Ambulatory Patient Care Facilities
Anesthesiology
Cancer Center
Cardiothoracic Surgery
Center for Dental and Oral Medicine
Children's Health (Pediatrics)
Emergency Medicine
Heart and Vascular Center
Neuroscience Institute
Obstetrics and Gynecology
Orthopaedics and Rehabilitation
Pathology and Laboratories
Primary Care and Specialties
Radiation Oncology
Radiology
Surgery
Women's Health

COMPETITORS

Catholic Healthcare System
Continuum Health Partners
Jamaica Hospital Medical Center
NewYork-Presbyterian Hospital
Nyack Hospital
Southside Hospital
Winthrop-University Hospital

HISTORICAL FINANCIALS

Company Type: Private

Income Statement — FYE: December 31

	REVENUE ($ mil.)	NET INCOME ($ mil.)	NET PROFIT MARGIN	EMPLOYEES
12/17	846	5	0.6%	2,380
12/14	669	14	2.1%	—
12/05	457	10	2.3%	—
12/03	389	7	1.9%	—
Annual Growth	5.7%	(2.5%)	—	—

2017 Year-End Financials

Return on assets: 0.8%
Return on equity: 5.8%
Current ratio: 1.80
Cash ($ mil.): 16

NFP CORP.

Through a network of subsidiaries and affiliates NFP provides commercial and personal insurance corporate benefits products and wealth management services to businesses and individuals in the US Canada and the UK. The consultancy and brokerage runs three professional advisor organizations: corporate benefits arm Benefits Partners; Partners Financial a network of independent life insurance and financial professionals; and the Retirement Plan Advisory Group (RPAG) which provides due diligence fiduciary compliance business consulting and other services through 2000 retirement plan advisors. NFP a Madison Dearborn Partners portfolio company is one of the largest retirement plan aggregators and privately owned brokers in the US.

Operations

NFP is organized along three business segments. Its Commercial Insurance business covers a range of areas including business income exposure casualty cyber liability domestic and foreign transit and workers' compensation; the company addresses diverse industries including communications chemical construction pharmaceutical and real estate. Corporate Benefits offers employee executive and retirement benefits products and HR consulting services to commercial clients. In addition to life and long-term care insurance Private Client Resources provides estate planning and wealth management to private customers.

Geographic Reach

New York-headquartered NFP has offices throughout the US and Puerto Rico Canada and the UK.

Strategy

NFP's growth strategy is focused heavily on expanding its geographic reach by acquiring regional insurance brokers and consultancies. In early 2019 and late 2018 the company's acquisitions included Ontario-based property and casualty brokers Mass Insurance Brokers and Easyway Insurance Brokers. In Florida the company purchased retirement plan and fiduciary risk firm Fiduciary First property and casualty broker Annette Willis Insurance Agency and financial education company The Participant Effect. The company also bought Louisianan employee benefits brokers Benefit Administration Group and HM Benefits.

Additionally NFP is partnering with and investing in complementary businesses through its NFP Ventures early-stage investment division. In December 2018 the company took minority stakes in Vivante Health and Indio Technologies. Vivante's digestive health management digital platform reduces emergency room and pharmacy costs by expanding digestive health services for clients of NFP's employee benefits offerings. Indio's automated property and casualty insurance data collection software streamlines NFP's underwriting process.

Mergers and Acquisitions

In 2019 NFP acquired Mass Insurance Brokers and Easyway Insurance Brokers. With operations in Ontario and Montreal the companies expand NFP's Canadian property and casualty insurance brokerage business. That year it also bought Independent Bankers Insurance Services a management liability coverage provider for community banks. The deal allows NFP to better serve its financial institution clients by expanding its product and service lineup including default protection and security products.

In late 2018 and early 2019 NFP extended its reach in the southeastern US with its purchases of Florida-headquartered Annette Willis Insurance Agency and Louisiana-based Benefit Administration Group and HM Benefits. Annette Willis is a property and casualty brokerage for businesses and individuals; Benefit Administration and HM Benefits are benefits brokerages with presences in New Orleans.

NFP acquired specialty managing general underwriter group Lenders Risk Services and Lenders Risk Management in November 2018. The Maryland company markets lender's single interest and mortgage impairment products to credit unions and community banks.

Company Background

In 2013 Chicago-based private equity investment firm Madison Dearborn Partners took NFP private in a $1.4 billion deal.

EXECUTIVES

Chairman And Ceo, Jessica M. Bibliowicz, $700,000 total compensation
Evp And Coo, Michael N. Goldman, $325,000 total compensation
Evp General Counsel And Corporate Secretary, Stancil E. (Stan) Barton, $300,000 total compensation
Senior Vice President President Advisor Services Group, James L. Poer
Svp; President Corporate Client Group, Edward O'Malley
Executive Vice President Mergers & Acquisitions, Carl Nelson
Senior Vice President Chief Technology Officer, Mark Grosvenor
Evp And General Counsel, Timothy M. Robb
Executive Vice President Chief Financial Officer, Brett Schneider
Cisr Assistant Vice President, Kim Holmes
Senior Vice President, Mei Au
Vice President, Elan Sharoni
Vice President Of Sales, Ronald Spencer
Regional Vice President, Sal Lundy
Vice President And Corporate Controller, Simon Hoyle
Vice President Financial Services, Ed Kroell
Vice President, Ford STANFORD Darger
Assistant Vice President, Gale Hamilton
Vice President, Chase Cannon

Assistant Vice President, Ron Cubicciotti
Vice President, Kim Harvill
Vice President Business Development, Matthew Douglas
Regional Vice President, Joe Kristovich
Assistant Vice President Business Development, Bob Peckham
Vice President Of Sales, Chris Phillips
Assistant Vice President Product Intelligence, Jeff Driscoll
Senior Vice President, Lara Nichols
Executive Vice President, Charlie Nelson
Vice President Of Agency Services, Stacey Scott
Vp Advanced Sales, Timothy Mcfarland
Vice President, Beth M Loubet
Vice President Pandc Business, Eric Wright
Assistant Vice President Corporate Benefits, Aleyne Secor
Senior Vice President Retirement, Andrew Prevost
Assistant Vice President, Blake Goldie

LOCATIONS

HQ: NFP CORP.
340 MADISON AVE FL 21, NEW YORK, NY 101730401
Phone: 212 301-4000
Web: WWW.NFP.COM

COMPETITORS

Aon	Marsh & McLennan
BlackRock	Northwestern Mutual
Brown & Brown	Old Mutual (US)
First Commonwealth Financial	Raymond James Financial
Gallagher	Securities America
Hub International	The Lockton Companies
LPL Financial	USI
M Financial Group	Willis Towers Watson

HISTORICAL FINANCIALS

Company Type: Private

Income Statement — FYE: December 31

	ASSETS ($ mil.)	NET INCOME ($ mil.)	INCOME AS % OF ASSETS	EMPLOYEES
12/11	894	36	4.1%	4,700
12/10	893	42	4.8%	—
12/09	970	(493)	—	—
12/08	1,543	14	1.0%	—
Annual Growth	(16.6%)	35.5%	—	—

2011 Year-End Financials

Return on assets: 4.1% — Sales ($ mil): 1,013
Return on equity: 9.1%

NHK INTERNATIONAL CORPORATION

EXECUTIVES

Ceo, Hideto Enomoto
Senior Engineer, Jason Oyler
Sales Associate, Mark Sakata
Information Technology Manager, James Green
Sales Account Manager, Yayoi Akamatsu
Administrative Assistant, Cheryl Mason
Project Manager, Jeff Schaad
Seating Sales Director, Takeshi Ozawa
Auditors: ERNST & YOUNG LLP LOUISVILLE

LOCATIONS

HQ: NHK INTERNATIONAL CORPORATION
46855 MAGELLAN DR, NOVI, MI 483772451
Phone: 248 926-0111
Web: WWW.NHKINTERNATIONAL.COM

HISTORICAL FINANCIALS

Company Type: Private

Income Statement — FYE: March 31

	REVENUE ($ mil.)	NET INCOME ($ mil.)	NET PROFIT MARGIN	EMPLOYEES
03/16	894	12	1.4%	200
03/15	842	(13)	—	—
03/14	739	17	2.4%	—
03/13	688	14	2.1%	—
Annual Growth	9.1%	(4.4%)	—	—

2016 Year-End Financials

Return on assets: 2.8% — Cash ($ mil.): 3
Return on equity: 6.1%
Current ratio: 1.00

NIELSEN HOLDINGS PLC

EXECUTIVES

Ceo, Mitch Barns
Senior Vice President Human Resources, Michael Alicea

LOCATIONS

HQ: NIELSEN HOLDINGS PLC
85 BROAD ST, NEW YORK, NY 100042434
Phone: 646 654-5000

HISTORICAL FINANCIALS

Company Type: Private

Income Statement — FYE: December 31

	REVENUE ($ mil.)	NET INCOME ($ mil.)	NET PROFIT MARGIN	EMPLOYEES
12/15	6,172	575	9.3%	43,061
12/14	6,288	381	6.1%	—
12/13	5,703	736	12.9%	—
12/12	5,612	273	4.9%	—
Annual Growth	3.2%	28.2%	—	—

2015 Year-End Financials

Return on assets: 16.4% — Cash ($ mil.): 357
Return on equity: 9.3%
Current ratio: 0.90

NOBLE HOLDING (U.S.) CORPORATION

EXECUTIVES

Prin, David W Williams
Assistant Subsea Engineer, Tim Matal
Global Head of Energy, Jermaine Gibbs
Operations Excellence Manager, Milton Watson
Auditors: PRICEWATERHOUSECOOPERS LLP H

LOCATIONS

HQ: NOBLE HOLDING (U.S.) CORPORATION
3135 S DAIRY ASHFORD, SUGAR LAND, TX 77478
Phone: 281 276-6100
Web: WWW.NOBLECORP.COM

HISTORICAL FINANCIALS

Company Type: Private

Income Statement — FYE: December 31

	REVENUE ($ mil.)	NET INCOME ($ mil.)	NET PROFIT MARGIN	EMPLOYEES
12/15	3,352	607	18.1%	3,744
12/14	3,232	83	2.6%	—
12/13	4,234	935	22.1%	—
Annual Growth	(11.0%)	(19.4%)	—	—

2015 Year-End Financials

Return on assets: 4.7% — Cash ($ mil.): 511
Return on equity: 8.2%
Current ratio: 1.40

NORTH AMERICAN LIGHTING, INC.

North American Lighting offers travelers a beacon of safety through the fog. The company is an independent manufacturer of vehicle lighting products in North America. Operating through four assembly plants and one technology center the company produces a line-up of headlamps signal lamps and fog lamps. Its forward-lighting products include mercury-free high intensity discharge (HID) headlamps and the Adaptive Front Lighting System (AFS). Among its signal lamps are rear-combo and license plate lamps. Its products are tailored to the designs of large auto makers and local Japanese automakers. Founded in 1983 North American Lighting is a subsidiary of Japan-based KOITO MANUFACTURING.

Geographic Reach

North American Lighting is stationed in Paris Illinois and has four manufacturing plants in Illinois and one in Alabama. Its technology research center resides in Michigan while a tool plan is located in Indiana.

Sales and Marketing

North American Lighting sells its products primarily to vehicle manufacturers in North America. It provides headlights and taillights to Toyota Nissan General Motors and Honda.

Financial Performance

The company generated 16% of its parent's revenue total in 2014. Revenues for the North American segment also skyrocketed by almost 20% in 2014 due to higher demand in the auto sector which resulted in increased automobile production.

Strategy

Like most players in the manufacturing sector North American Lighting's strategy for growth involves the expansion of its manufacturing capacity. It also attracts additional clients through new product launches. In 2013 the company invested $50 million to expand its plant in Edgar County Illinois by building a 200000 sq. ft. addition and purchasing new equipment for added production lines.

In 2014 the company also began production at its North American Lighting Mexico S.A. de C.V. (Mexican manufacturing plant) which was established in 2012 to expand automobile production throughout Mexico.

EXECUTIVES

Ceo, Takashi Ohtake
Pres*, Jun Toyota
V Pres*, Naoshi Misawa
SEC-Treas*, Kirk Gadberry
V Pres*, Kem Cooley
V Pres*, Kishore Ahuja
Asst SEC*, Theodore Cornell
Program Manager, Keith Blain
Engineer, Kyle Dasch
Maintenance Supervisor, Dave Sullens
Supplier Quality Engineer, Jeff Akeman

LOCATIONS

HQ: NORTH AMERICAN LIGHTING, INC.
2275 S MAIN ST, PARIS, IL 619442963
Phone: 217 465-6600
Web: WWW.NAL.COM

COMPETITORS

Delphi Automotive Systems
Hella
Robert Bosch
Valeo
Visteon

HISTORICAL FINANCIALS

Company Type: Private

Income Statement — FYE: December 31

	REVENUE ($ mil.)	NET INCOME ($ mil.)	NET PROFIT MARGIN	EMPLOYEES
12/17	1,466	111	7.6%	2,200
12/11	297	13	4.4%	—
12/10	297	13	4.4%	—
Annual Growth	25.6%	35.6%	—	—

2017 Year-End Financials

Return on assets: 16.2%
Return on equity: 22.9%
Current ratio: 2.10
Cash ($ mil.): 77

NORTH BROWARD HOSPITAL DISTRICT

North Broward Hospital District which operates as Broward Health takes care of shark bites and more. The taxpayer-supported not-for-profit health system serves the coastal city of Fort Lauderdale and the northern two-thirds of Broward County Florida with four acute care hospitals and a host of community-based centers. Flagship hospital Broward General Medical Center has more than 700 beds and features the Chris Evert Children's Hospital; all of the hospitals together have more than 1500 beds. Broward Health boasts about 30 additional facilities including family health and surgery centers and home health and hospice programs.

Operations

The Broward Health system also includes teaching hospital Broward Health Medical Center facilities such as Broward Health North and Broward Health Imperial Point Broward Health Community Services and Broward Health Physician Group. The company also operates urgent care clinics.

With more than 1200 physicians Broward Health typically sees some 62500 admissions 283000 emergency department visits 267000 outpatient visits and 17000 outpatient clinic visits each year. It also delivers some 6000 babies annually.

Broward Health is controlled by a seven-member board of commissioners appointed by Florida's governor. As a safety-net health provider in its service territory the system's hospitals receive property tax-based funding for the charity care they provide. The rest of Broward County is served by a second public hospital system South Broward Hospital District. (The county's dual structure goes back to the 1950s.)

Geographic Reach

The company has more than 50 locations across Broward County.

Sales and Marketing

Managed care accounts for more than half of Broward Health's net patient revenues; Medicare and Medicaid combined make up more than 20%.

Financial Performance

In fiscal 2014 revenue grew 2% to $971 million due to growth in net patient service revenues. Net income rose 20% that year on higher investment gains and a decline in interest expenses. The system reported an operating cash outflow to $80 million (versus $27 million in 2013) as less cash was generated from third-party payers and patients.

Strategy

Broward Health looks to improve services by adding new or renovating existing facilities in its system. For example in 2014 it opened a new Adult Cancer Infusion Center at Broward Health Medical Center (featuring an outdoor healing garden); it also opened AJ Acker Virtual Hospital with interactive patient simulators at Broward Health North for training purposes. It broke ground on a $70 million renovation of Broward Health North that will add more operating rooms and expand the emergency department. In 2015 it was given approval to expand Broward Health Coral Springs.

EXECUTIVES

Medical Director And Chief Pathologist, William D Williams
Senior Vice President Chief Human Resources Officer, Melanie Hatcher
Director Of Radiology Services, Carlos Duran
Director Of Pharmacy, Natalie Trach
Physical Therapy Director, Genevive Cuaboucher
Vp Hr, Tory Drakeford
Vice President Of Human Resources Corporate, Xx Wong
Vice President Corporate Communications And Marketing, Denise Moore
Medical Director, Caren Singer
Medical Director, Mark Saltzman
Medical Director, Craig Brodsky
Medical Director, Martin Edep
Associate Vice President Clinical Pharmacist Operations, Kelly Adler Schueler
Board Member, Ma James-Francis
Vice Chairman, Christopher Ure
Auditors: WARREN AVERETT LLC BIRMINGHA

LOCATIONS

HQ: NORTH BROWARD HOSPITAL DISTRICT
1800 NW 49TH ST, FORT LAUDERDALE, FL 333093092
Phone: 954 473-7010
Web: WWW.BROWARDHEALTH.ORG

PRODUCTS/OPERATIONS

2014 Sales

	$ mil.	% of total
Patient care		
Broward Health Medical Center	432	44
Broward Health North	207	21
Broward Health Imperial Point	100	10
Broward Health Coral Springs	140	15
Other	96	10
Eliminations	(5.9)	7
Total	**971**	**100**

Selected Services

Bariatric Surgery
Barrett's Esophagus
Behavioral Health
Broward Health Complete
Cancer Services
Cardiac Services
Children's Diagnostic & Treatment Center
Clinical Trials
Colorectal Services
Concussion Care
Diabetes
Digestive Health
Dysphagia
Emergency Services
Endoscopic Sinus Surgery
Home Health & Hospice Services
International Services
Liver Transplant
Maternity Place
Men's Health
Neurology
Orthopedic Services
Ostomy
Outpatient Services
Pediatric Services
Pharmacy
Primary Care
Senior Services
Sickle Cell Day Unit
Single Incision Laparoscopic Surgery (SILS)

Selected Facilities

Hospitals
- Broward General Medical Center (Fort Lauderdale)
- Coral Springs Medical Center (Coral Springs)
- Imperial Point Medical Center (Fort Lauderdale)
- North Broward Medical Center (Deerfield Beach)

Other Facilities
- Chris Evert Children's Hospital (Fort Lauderdale)
- Broward Health Physician Group (Fort Lauderdale)
- Broward Health Weston (Weston)
- Gold Coast Home Health & Hospice Services (Fort Lauderdale)
- Seventh Avenue Family Health Center (Fort Lauderdale)

COMPETITORS

Baptist Health South Florida
Boca Raton Regional Hospital
Continucare
HCA
Holy Cross Hospital Fort Lauderdale
Jackson Health System
Jupiter Medical Center
Larkin Community Hospital
Mount Sinai Medical Center of Florida
South Broward Hospital District
University of Miami Hospital

HISTORICAL FINANCIALS

Company Type: Private

Income Statement — FYE: June 30

	REVENUE ($ mil.)	NET INCOME ($ mil.)	NET PROFIT MARGIN	EMPLOYEES
06/18	1,035	120	11.6%	7,000
06/17	1,025	33	3.3%	—
06/16	1,014	(12)	—	—
06/08	1,335	67	5.0%	—
Annual Growth	(2.5%)	6.0%	—	—

2018 Year-End Financials

Return on assets: 7.1%
Return on equity: 13.3%
Current ratio: 3.60
Cash ($ mil.): 121

NORTH CAROLINA BAPTIST HOSPITAL

EXECUTIVES

Ceo-Pres, Eugene A Woods
Instructor, Carlos Rodriguez
Assistant Professor, Carol Anne Albright
Instructor, Clifford Howard
Magnet Program Director, Debbie Krueger
Instructor, Derek Parsonage
Associate Chair of Research, Edward Ip
Hospitalist, Elizabeth Halvorson
Director Center UI, Frederick Kremkau
Associate Professor, Iris Leng
Instructor, Kathleen McManus
Auditors: KPMG LLP GREENSBORO NORTH CA

LOCATIONS

HQ: NORTH CAROLINA BAPTIST HOSPITAL
MEDICAL CENTER BLVD, WINSTON SALEM, NC 271570001
Phone: 336 716-2011
Web: WWW.WAKEHEALTH.EDU

HISTORICAL FINANCIALS

Company Type: Private

Income Statement — FYE: June 30

	REVENUE ($ mil.)	NET INCOME ($ mil.)	NET PROFIT MARGIN	EMPLOYEES
06/20	1,887	8	0.5%	12,563
06/19	1,762	8	0.5%	—
06/18	1,633	60	3.7%	—
06/11	1,084	195	18.1%	—
Annual Growth	6.3%	(29.2%)	—	—

2020 Year-End Financials

Return on assets: 0.4%
Return on equity: 0.7%
Current ratio: 1.50
Cash ($ mil.): 271

NORTH CAROLINA BAPTIST HOSPITAL FDN

Auditors: DIXON HUGHES GOODMAN LLP ASHE

LOCATIONS

HQ: NORTH CAROLINA BAPTIST HOSPITAL FDN
MEDICAL CTR BLVD, WINSTON SALEM, NC 271570001
Phone: 336 716-4445
Web: WWW.WAKEHEALTH.EDU

HISTORICAL FINANCIALS

Company Type: Private

Income Statement — FYE: June 30

	REVENUE ($ mil.)	NET INCOME ($ mil.)	NET PROFIT MARGIN	EMPLOYEES
06/18	1,795	(6)	—	2
06/17	0	(0)	—	—
06/15	1	0	33.5%	—
06/11	1	0	32.2%	—
Annual Growth	170.8%	—	—	—

2018 Year-End Financials

Return on assets: (-0.4%)
Return on equity: (-0.6%)
Current ratio: —
Cash ($ mil.): 35

NORTH CAROLINA EASTERN MUNICIPAL POWER AGENCY

EXECUTIVES

Ceo, Jesse C Tilton III
Cfo*, Al Conyers
Energy Management Eng, Marcus Freeman
Manager Marketing, Robert Tugwell
Engineer, Stuart Britt
CPA, Susan R Ingram
Traffic Manager, James Bono
Controller, Tom Collins
Manager Economic, Brenda Daniels
Programmer, George Veney
General, Kathy Moyer
Auditors: CHERRY BEKAERT LLP RALEIGH

LOCATIONS

HQ: NORTH CAROLINA EASTERN MUNICIPAL POWER AGENCY
1427 MEADOW WOOD BLVD, RALEIGH, NC 276041532
Phone: 919 760-6000
Web: WWW.ELECTRICITIES.COM

HISTORICAL FINANCIALS

Company Type: Private

Income Statement — FYE: December 31

	REVENUE ($ mil.)	NET INCOME ($ mil.)	NET PROFIT MARGIN	EMPLOYEES
12/19	555	(19)	—	100
12/18	547	(16)	—	—
12/17	531	(13)	—	—
12/16	552	52	9.4%	—
Annual Growth	0.2%	—	—	—

NORTH CAROLINA ELECTRIC MEMBERSHIP CORPORATION

It's a cooperative effort: North Carolina Electric Membership Corporation (NCEMC) generates and transmits electricity to the state's 26 electric cooperatives (more than 2.5 million people) in 93 of 100 North Carolina counties. The co-op owns more than 600 MW of generating capacity through four primarily natural gas peak load generators plus a 61.5% stake in Catawba Nuclear Station Unit 1 and a 31% stake in the Catawba Nuclear Station in South Carolina. It also buys power from Progress Energy American Electric Power and other for-profit utilities. NCEMC's member cooperatives serve more than 950000 metered businesses and homes in North Carolina. The wholesale co-op also operates an energy operations center.

EXECUTIVES

Vice President, Tom Laing
Vice President Manager Director, Joy Hart
Auditors: ERNST & YOUNG LLP RALEIGH NC

LOCATIONS

HQ: NORTH CAROLINA ELECTRIC MEMBERSHIP CORPORATION
3400 SUMNER BLVD, RALEIGH, NC 276162950
Phone: 919 872-0800
Web: WWW.NCELECTRICCOOPERATIVES.COM

PRODUCTS/OPERATIONS

Subsidiaries

North Carolina Association of Electric Cooperatives (NCAEC training programs)
The Tarheel Electric Membership Association Inc. (TEMA purchasing and materials supply)
North Carolina Cooperatives
Albemarle Electric Membership Corporation
Blue Ridge Electric Membership Corporation
Brunswick Electric Membership Corporation
Cape Hatteras Electric Cooperative
Carteret-Craven Electric Cooperative
Central Electric Membership Corporation
Edgecombe-Martin County Electric Membership Corporation
EnergyUnited
Four County Electric Membership Corporation
French Broad Electric Membership Corporation
Halifax Electric Membership Corporation
Haywood Electric Membership Corporation
Jones-Onslow Electric Membership Corporation
Lumbee River Electric Membership Corporation
Pee Dee Electric Membership Corporation
Piedmont Electric Membership Corporation
Pitt & Greene Electric Membership Corporation
Randolph Electric Membership Corporation
Roanoke Electric Cooperative
Rutherford Electric Membership Corporation
South River Electric Membership Corporation
Surry-Yadkin Electric Membership Corporation
Tideland Electric Membership Corporation
Tri-County Electric Membership Corporation
Union Power Cooperative
Wake Electric Membership Corporation

COMPETITORS

AEP
Dominion Energy
Duke Energy
MEAG Power
Progress Energy
SCANA
Santee Cooper
TVA

HISTORICAL FINANCIALS

Company Type: Private

Income Statement FYE: December 31

	REVENUE ($ mil.)	NET INCOME ($ mil.)	NET PROFIT MARGIN	EMPLOYEES
12/18	1,188	30	2.5%	150
12/17	1,017	23	2.3%	—
12/16	1,022	25	2.5%	—
12/08	1,006	6	0.6%	—
Annual Growth	1.7%	17.2%	—	—

2018 Year-End Financials

Return on assets: 1.4%
Return on equity: 11.4%
Current ratio: 2.90
Cash ($ mil.): 163

NORTH DAKOTA UNIVERSITY SYSTEM

EXECUTIVES

Information, Jerry Olson
Residence Hall Director, Chelsee Rohmiller
Director of Event Operations, Colin Bailey
Faculty Lecturer, Riaz Aziz
Auditors: ROBERT R PETERSON STATE AUDI

LOCATIONS

HQ: NORTH DAKOTA UNIVERSITY SYSTEM
2000 44TH ST S STE 301, FARGO, ND 581037434
Phone: 701 231-6326
Web: WWW.NDUS.EDU

HISTORICAL FINANCIALS

Company Type: Private

Income Statement FYE: June 30

	REVENUE ($ mil.)	NET INCOME ($ mil.)	NET PROFIT MARGIN	EMPLOYEES
06/19	709	8	1.2%	14
06/18	713	19	2.8%	—
06/17	702	66	9.5%	—
06/16	695	116	16.8%	—
Annual Growth	0.7%	(58.4%)	—	—

2019 Year-End Financials

Return on assets: 0.4%
Return on equity: 0.6%
Current ratio: 3.50
Cash ($ mil.): 212

NORTH DAKOTA UNIVERSITY SYSTEM FOUNDATION

EXECUTIVES

Princ, Hamid Augustine Shirvani
Chancellor, William Goetz
Presi, Kirsten Diederich
V Pres, Terry Hjelmstad
Gis Coordinator, Subhro Mitra
Information Profession, Carol Tschakert
Scientist, Erin Koval
Scientist, Thomas Glass
Assistant Professor, Annie X Tangpong
Coordinator, David Dodds
Assistant Professor, David Newman
Auditors: ROBERT R PETERSON FARGO NORT

LOCATIONS

HQ: NORTH DAKOTA UNIVERSITY SYSTEM FOUNDATION
600 E BOULEVARD AVE # 215, BISMARCK, ND 585050601
Phone: 701 328-2960
Web: WWW.NDCHOOSE.COM

HISTORICAL FINANCIALS

Company Type: Private

Income Statement FYE: June 30

	REVENUE ($ mil.)	NET INCOME ($ mil.)	NET PROFIT MARGIN	EMPLOYEES
06/19*	709	8	1.2%	252
12/17	78	59	76.1%	—
06/17	1,252	66	5.3%	—
06/16	695	116	16.8%	—
Annual Growth	0.7%	(58.4%)	—	—

*Fiscal year change

2019 Year-End Financials

Return on assets: 0.4%
Return on equity: 0.6%
Current ratio: 3.50
Cash ($ mil.): 212

NORTH EAST INDEPENDENT SCHOOL DISTRICT

EXECUTIVES

Supt, Brian G Gottardy
Board Pres, Beth Plummer
Board V Pres, Susan Galindo
Board SEC, Sandy Hughey
Occupational Specia, Gayla Aguilar
Corrections Officer, Andres De Leon
Occupational Specia, Katherine Farrimond
Executive of Information Techn, Betsy Williams
Executive of Information Techn, Dawn Gembler
Director of Operations, Juan De Losntos
Accounting Staff, Lori Garrison
Auditors: ABIP PC SAN ANTONIO TEXAS

LOCATIONS

HQ: NORTH EAST INDEPENDENT SCHOOL DISTRICT
8961 TESORO DR, SAN ANTONIO, TX 782176209
Phone: 210 407-0359
Web: WWW.NEISD.NET

HISTORICAL FINANCIALS

Company Type: Private

Income Statement FYE: June 30

	REVENUE ($ mil.)	NET INCOME ($ mil.)	NET PROFIT MARGIN	EMPLOYEES
06/19	744	(41)	—	10,000
06/18	759	23	3.0%	—
06/17	747	(2)	—	—
06/16	737	(53)	—	—
Annual Growth	0.3%	—	—	—

2019 Year-End Financials

Return on assets: (-2.0%)
Return on equity: —
Current ratio: —
Cash ($ mil.): 282

NORTH KANSAS CITY HOSPITAL

EXECUTIVES

Ceo, Peggy Schmitt
Cfo*, Henry Seybold
Coo*, Kerri Jenkins
Director, Jana Longwith
Director of Manufacturing, Tim Ford
Vice President, Dawn Bryant
Member To Board of Trustee, James Hake
Vice President, Kristen Guillaume
Nus Coordinator, Andrea Phillips
Purchasing Supervisor, Barbara Wolfgeher
Database Administrator, Brenda Pratt
Auditors: BKD LLP KANSAS CITY MISSOUR

LOCATIONS

HQ: NORTH KANSAS CITY HOSPITAL
2800 CLAY EDWARDS DR, NORTH KANSAS CITY, MO 641163220
Phone: 816 691-2000
Web: WWW.NKCH.ORG

HISTORICAL FINANCIALS

Company Type: Private

Income Statement FYE: June 30

	REVENUE ($ mil.)	NET INCOME ($ mil.)	NET PROFIT MARGIN	EMPLOYEES
06/18	586	6	1.1%	3,100
06/16	484	31	6.6%	—
06/15	462	35	7.6%	—
06/11	419	22	5.3%	—
Annual Growth	4.9%	(16.7%)	—	—

2018 Year-End Financials

Return on assets: 0.8%
Return on equity: 1.0%
Current ratio: 1.50
Cash ($ mil.): 24

NORTH MEMORIAL HEALTH CARE

North Memorial Health Care fights illness in the Twin Cities. Established in 1939 as Victory Hospital the health care network is home to North Memorial Medical Center a 520-bed hospital that features a Level I trauma center and the Humphrey Cancer Center. The hospital also operates specialty centers for cardiovascular care orthopedics pediatrics and women's health as well as an emergency vehicle fleet of more than 125 ambulances and nearly 10 helicopters. The adjacent outpatient center provides oncology radiation and imaging services. North Memorial Health Care also has a network of primary and specialty care clinics in the Twin Cities region and it provides home health and hospice services.

Operations

As a regional trauma center North Memorial Medical Center must maintain a high level of technology resources and recruit skilled emergency room specialists. North Memorial's emergency fleet also adds to the facilities' capabilities as it is one of the largest hospital-based ambulance services in the country with eight helicopters and about 125 ground ambulances. Outpatient facilities include rehabilitation centers sleep diagnostic labs family practice offices imaging centers and mental health facilities.

The system's provider network includes more than 900 physicians including specialists and primary care providers.

Geographic Reach

North Memorial Health Care's primary facility (North Memorial Medical Center) is located in Robbinsdale Minnesota. In partnership with Fairview Health Services the company operates the 130-bed Maple Grove Hospital in nearby Maple Grove Minnesota. Its ambulance division serves the northwestern Twin Cities area as well other portions of Minnesota and Wisconsin.

Strategy

The health network is expanding its facilities to improve services for area residents. In 2015 it opened walk-in clinics in grocery stores located in the Minnesota cities of New Hope and Oakdale. The clinics offer primary health care services provided by North Memorial physician assistants and nurses.

North Memorial works to stay on top of the latest technological advances to enhance its care offerings. In 2015 North Memorial Medical Center became the first community hospital in Minnesota to use the da Vinci Xi robotic surgical system which provides more precision for minimally invasive procedures. The following year the system provided electronic tablets loaded with software designed to help caregivers calculate appropriate medication dosages for children. The tablets which are used by the company's ambulance EMTs and paramedics allow for first responders to adjust care while out in the field.

EXECUTIVES

Vp Emergency And Enterprise Operations, Mike Parrish
President North Memorial Medical Center, Gayle Mattson
Ceo Maple Grove Hospital, Andy Cochrane
Ceo, J. Kevin Croston
Vp Patient Care, Tracy Kirby
Chief Information Officer, Pat Taffe
Vp Operations, Jeff Wicklander
Chief Financial Officer, Todd Ostendorf
Medical Director And Physician, Peter Tanghe
Treasurer, Ryan Johnson

LOCATIONS

HQ: NORTH MEMORIAL HEALTH CARE
3300 OAKDALE AVE N, MINNEAPOLIS, MN 554222900
Phone: 763 520-5200
Web: WWW.NORTHMEMORIAL.COM

PRODUCTS/OPERATIONS

Selected Locations

Heart & Vascular Center - Maple Grove - Maple Grove Minnesota
Heart & Vascular Clinic - Buffalo - Buffalo Minnesota
Heart & Vascular Clinic - Monticello - Monticello Minnesota
Hope Chest Breast Center - Robbinsdale Minnesota
Humphrey Cancer Center - Robbinsdale Minnesota
Maple Grove Hospital - Maple Grove Minnesota
Maternal Fetal Medicine - Maple Grove - Maple Grove Minnesota
North Memorial Clinic Brooklyn Center - Brooklyn Center Minnesota
North Memorial Clinic Brooklyn Park - Brooklyn Park Minnesota
North Memorial Clinic Camden - Maple Grove - Maple Grove Minnesota
North Memorial Clinic Camden - Minneapolis - Minneapolis Minnesota
North Memorial Clinic Camden - Plymouth - Plymouth Minnesota
North Memorial Clinic Elk River - Elk River Minnesota
North Memorial Clinic Golden Valley - Golden Valley Minnesota
North Memorial Clinic Maple Grove - Maple Grove Minnesota
North Memorial Clinic Minnetonka - Minnetonka Minnesota
North Memorial Clinic Northeast - Minneapolis Minnesota
North Memorial Clinic Plymouth City Center - Plymouth Minnesota
North Memorial Clinic Silver Lake Clinic - St. Anthony - St. Anthony Minnesota
North Memorial Clinic Silver Lake Clinic - Blaine - Blaine Minnesota
North Memorial Medical Center - Robbinsdale Minnesota
North Memorial Urgent Care - Maple Grove - Maple Grove Minnesota
North Memorial Urgent Care - Roseville - Roseville Minnesota
Outpatient Imaging Center - Robbinsdale Minnesota
Outpatient Psychiatric Clinic - Robbinsdale Minnesota
Rehabilitation Services - Robbinsdale Minnesota
Rehabilitation Services - Maple Grove Minnesota
Rehabilitation Services - Elk River Minnesota
Residential Hospice - Brooklyn Center Minnesota
Sleep Health Center - Maple Grove Minnesota
Sleep Health Center - Robbinsdale Minnesota
Urgent Care - Blaine Minnesota

Selected Services

Acupuncture
Acute Concussion Clinic
Acute Inpatient Rehabilitation
Air Care
Ambulance Services
Anterior Hip Replacement
Balance Center
Breast Health
Breast Milk Depot
CACE Unit
Cancer Education & Support
Cancer Treatment
Cardiac Rehabilitation
Cardiology
Cardiology Clinic Services
Complex Heart Procedures and Interventional Services
Computed Tomography - CT
Dermatology
Diabetes Education
Domestic Abuse Victim Advocacy - SafeJourney
Emergency Department
EMS Education
Endovenous Laser Treatment (EVLT) for Varicose Veins
Family Birth Center
Family Medicine
Gastroenterology
General Radiology
Genetics Program
Geriatric Care
Gift Shop
Grief and Loss Support
Group Physical Therapy
Gynecology

COMPETITORS

Allina Hospitals
Bethesda Hospital
Catholic Health Initiatives
CentraCare Health
Children's Hospitals and Clinics of Minnesota
Fairview Health
First Care
HealthEast Care System
Mayo Clinic
Methodist Hospital (MN)
Park Nicollet Health Services
Regions Hospital
SCMC
St. John's Hospital (Minnesota)
St. Luke's Hospital (MN)
University of Minnesota Medical Center

HISTORICAL FINANCIALS

Company Type: Private

Income Statement — FYE: December 31

	REVENUE ($ mil.)	NET INCOME ($ mil.)	NET PROFIT MARGIN	EMPLOYEES
12/18	720	(16)	—	5,180
12/17	651	(28)	—	—
12/16	721	(0)	—	—
12/13	735	51	7.0%	—
Annual Growth	(0.4%)	—	—	—

NORTH MISSISSIPPI HEALTH SERVICES, INC.

North Mississippi Health Services (NMHS) isn't contained by its name: The health system also provides health care to residents of northwestern Alabama. NMHS includes half a dozen community hospitals including its flagship North Mississippi Medical Center in Tupelo. North Mississippi Medical Clinics a regional network of more than 30 primary and specialty clinics; and nursing homes. Combined the facilities have nearly 1000 beds designated for acute long term and nursing care. Specialty services include home health and long-term care inpatient and outpatient behavioral health and treatment centers for cancer and digestive disorders. NMHS also operates outpatient care and wellness clinics in the region.

Operations

During 2014 NMHS handled about 30000 inpatient visits as well as more than 128000 emergency room visits and some 345000 outpatient care visits. It also conducted about 24000 surgeries at its various facilities. Its outpatient centers include more than 30 primary and specialty care clinics in Mississippi and Alabama operated through the North Mississippi Medical Clinics division as well as more than half a dozen wellness centers.

Geographic Reach

In all NMHS serves two dozen counties across the two states. In addition to its main hospital in Tupelo NMHS operates health centers in communities including Eupora Iuka Pontotoc and West Point Mississippi and in Hamilton Alabama. It also manages a center in Calhoun City Mississippi. Its

Baldwyn Nursing Facility is located in Baldwyn Mississippi.

Financial Performance

Flagship North Mississippi Medical Center (NNMC)'s revenues increased by 6% due to a growth in net patient revenues. Medicare and Medicaid together accounted for about 50% of net patient revenues; managed care and commercial 25%; Blue Cross 14%; self-pay 10%; and Health Link 1%.

NNMC reported net loss of $14 million in 2014 over net income in 2013 due to pension-related changes.

NNMC's operating cash flow increased by 256% that year.

Mergers and Acquisitions

In 2018 North Mississippi Health Services agreed to buy Gilmore Memorial Hospital out of bankruptcy. It will pay $10.5 million for the Armory Mississippi hospital including the assumption of liabilities and financial commitments.

EXECUTIVES

Medical Director, Ken Harvey
Vice President Of Human Resources, Mark Pittman

LOCATIONS

HQ: NORTH MISSISSIPPI HEALTH SERVICES, INC.
830 S GLOSTER ST, TUPELO, MS 388014934
Phone: 662 377-3000
Web: WWW.NMHS.NET

Selected Locations

Baldwyn Nursing Facility (Baldwyn Mississippi)
Calhoun County Medical Clinic (managed facility; Calhoun Mississippi)
NMMC-Eupora (Eupora Mississippi)
NMMC-Hamilton (Hamilton Alabama)
NMMC-Iuka (Iuka Mississippi)
NMMC-Pontotoc (Pontotoc Mississippi)
NMMC-Tupelo (Tupelo Mississippi)
NMMC-West Point (West Point Mississippi)
North Mississippi Medical Clinics (NMMCI regional)

PRODUCTS/OPERATIONS

Selected Facilities and Services

Acute Stroke Unit
Advanced Wound Center and Hyperbarics
Bariatric Center
Behavioral Health Center
Breast Care Center
Cancer Center
Center for Digestive Health
Community Health
Critical Care Unit
CRNA Program
Diabetes Treatment Center
Emergency Services
Family Medicine Residency Center
Heart Institute
Home Health and Hospice
Hospitalists
Joint Replacement Center
Le Bonheur Specialty Clinics
Medical Imaging
North Mississippi Surgery Center
Outpatient Infusion
Pain Management Center
Pastoral Care
Physician Specialties
Radiology
Rehabilitation Services
Respiratory Therapy
Skilled Nursing Facility
Sleep Disorders Center
Surgical Services
Tupelo Wellness Center
Vein Center
Volunteer Services
Women's Hospital
Women's and Children Services

COMPETITORS

Baptist Memorial Health Care
Community Health Systems
Delta Regional Medical Center
Forrest General Hospital
HCA
Memorial Hospital at Gulfport
Methodist Healthcare
Natchez Regional Medical Center
North Mississippi Medical
Shelby County Health Care
Southwest Mississippi Regional Medical Center

HISTORICAL FINANCIALS

Company Type: Private

Income Statement — FYE: September 30

	REVENUE ($ mil.)	NET INCOME ($ mil.)	NET PROFIT MARGIN	EMPLOYEES
09/17	898	26	3.0%	6,000
09/16	893	30	3.4%	—
09/15	860	19	2.2%	—
09/14	779	(14)	—	—
Annual Growth	4.9%	—	—	—

2017 Year-End Financials

Return on assets: 2.2%
Return on equity: 3.4%
Current ratio: 4.00
Cash ($ mil.): 36

NORTH MISSISSIPPI MEDICAL CENTER, INC.

At North Mississippi Medical Center you might get some Mississippi Mud ice cream after your tonsils are removed. The full-service 650-bed regional referral hospital in Tupelo Mississippi is part of the North Mississippi Health Services system an affiliation of hospitals and clinics serving northern Mississippi northwestern Alabama and parts of Tennessee. It's the largest private not-for-profit hospital in Mississippi and the largest non-metropolitan hospital in America. Specialty services at the medical center include cancer treatment women's health care cardiology and behavioral health care. The hospital also operates a skilled-nursing facility and home health and hospice organizations.

Operations

Besides being a Mississippi State Department of Health-designated Level II trauma center North Mississippi Medical Center offers more than 40 specialties as well as centers for excellence in cardiac surgery cardiology research neurology neurosurgery pulmonology rehabilitation cancer treatment chemical dependency and neonatal programs.

The medical center's Home Health Agency canvases 17 counties in north Mississippi and provides complex and extremely high-tech procedures that can be performed in the home setting. It also operates Baldwyn Nursing Facility.

Geographic Reach

North Mississippi Medical Center serves more than 700000 people across 24 counties in north Mississippi northwestern Alabama and portions of Tennessee.

Strategy

In 2012 North Mississippi Medical Center - Hamilton opened a new pulmonary rehabilitation unit. Also the medical center's Outpatient Rehabilitation Center in 2012 became the first outpatient rehabilitation center in Mississippi to offer Fiberoptic Endoscopic Evaluation of Swallowing (FEES) to assess swallowing function. Awards and Recognition

North Mississippi Medical Center's hospitalist program has been recognized by The American Journal of Medicine for providing cost-effective care to patients in the hospital. The program begun in 1997 serves hospitalized patients who do not have a primary care physician or whose primary care physicians do not have hospital practices.

EXECUTIVES

Director Of Radiology, Helen Copeland
Secretary, Margaret Lofton

LOCATIONS

HQ: NORTH MISSISSIPPI MEDICAL CENTER, INC.
830 S GLOSTER ST, TUPELO, MS 388014934
Phone: 662 377-3000
Web: WWW.NMHS.NET

Selected Locations

Baldwyn Nursing Facility - Baldwyn Mississippi
NMMC - Eup
NMMC - Ham
NMMC - Iuk
NMMC - Pontotoc - Pontotoc Mississippi
NMMC - Tupelo - Tupelo Mississippi
NMMC - West Point - West Point Mississippi

PRODUCTS/OPERATIONS

Selected Programs & Services

Acute Stroke Unit
Advanced Wound Center and Hyperbarics
Bariatric Center
Behavioral Health Center
Breast Care Center
Cancer Center
Center for Digestive Health
Community Health
Critical Care Unit
CRNA Program
Diabetes Treatment Center
Emergency Services
Family Medicine Residency Center
Gift & Floral Shop
Heart Institute
Home Health and Hospice
Hospitalists
Joint Replacement Center
Le Bonheur Specialty Clinics
Medical Imaging
North Mississippi Surgery Center
Outpatient Infusion
Pain Management Center
Pastoral Care
Physician Specialties
Radiology
Rehabilitation Services
Respiratory Therapy
Skilled Nursing Facility
Sleep Disorders Center
Surgical Services
Tupelo Wellness Center
Vein Center
Volunteer Services
West Bedtower Project
Women's Hospital
Women's and Children Services

COMPETITORS

Community Health Systems
Delta Regional Medical Center
Forrest General Hospital
HCA
Memorial Hospital at Gulfport
Natchez Regional Medical Center
Southwest Mississippi Regional Medical Center

HISTORICAL FINANCIALS

Company Type: Private

Income Statement FYE: September 30

	REVENUE ($ mil.)	NET INCOME ($ mil.)	NET PROFIT MARGIN	EMPLOYEES
09/14	633	52	8.3%	6,000
09/13	537	2	0.5%	—
09/12	620	(6)	—	—
Annual Growth	1.0%	—	—	—

2014 Year-End Financials

Return on assets: 5.2%
Return on equity: 7.6%
Current ratio: 2.10
Cash ($ mil.): 12

NORTH SHORE UNIVERSITY HEALTH SYSTEM

LOCATIONS

HQ: NORTH SHORE UNIVERSITY HEALTH SYSTEM
2650 RIDGE AVE, EVANSTON, IL 602011700
Phone: 847 570-2640
Web: WWW.NORTHSHORE.ORG

HISTORICAL FINANCIALS

Company Type: Private

Income Statement FYE: September 30

	REVENUE ($ mil.)	NET INCOME ($ mil.)	NET PROFIT MARGIN	EMPLOYEES
09/15	1,419	55	3.9%	3
09/14	1,397	148	10.6%	—
09/13	1,815	238	13.1%	—
Annual Growth	(11.6%)	(51.7%)	—	—

2015 Year-End Financials

Return on assets: 1.7%
Return on equity: 3.0%
Current ratio: 0.60
Cash ($ mil.): 62

NORTH SHORE UNIVERSITY HOSPITAL

North Shore University Hospital (NSUH) knows you shouldn't have to leave the island for quality health care. The Long Island hospital has more than 800 beds devoted to adult and pediatric medicine rehabilitation stroke care women's health orthopedics urology wound healing dentistry and trauma emergency services among other areas. The hospital is home to specialist institutes for cancer care and cardiology. It also serves as a campus for the Hofstra Northwell Shool of Medicine. NSUH is part of Northwell Health.

Operations

The not-for-profit NSUH operates numerous satellite community health centers that provide primary surgery psychiatric dental and specialty care including the Schwartz Ambulatory Surgery Center. Its Stern Family Center for Extend Care and Rehabilitation has about 250 beds; NSUH also includes a Katz Women's Hospital (one of two in the system). The hospital provides comprehensive care in all health care specialties including organ transplant services. In addition the hospital operates mobile health vehicles and conducts educational and wellness programs for area residents.

NSUH has a staff of more than 6000 specialist and subspecialist physicians nurses and other medical workers. It handles about 50000 inpatient visits 90000 emergency room visits 20000 surgeries and 6000 births each year.

NSUH has medical health professional and nursing school affiliations with about 15 colleges and universities. Programs include residencies postgraduate training and fellowships.

Geographic Reach

Strategy

NSUH and the larger Northwell Health system tend to grow through the acquisitions of smaller campuses and mergers with other systems. This allows the hospital to gain operating efficiency through vertical integration bargaining power with vendors and a more diversified revenue stream.

In 2017 NSUH opened the Sandra Atlas Bass Heart Hospital for advanced cardiac care. The facility will be the first on Long Island to offer heart transplants and the sixth in New York State (which has a very high number of transplant candidates on its waiting list).

As part of its efforts to bring cutting-edge health care to the community it serves the hospital began offering 3D-printed titanium spinal implants in 2017.These synthetic implants approved in the US in 2016 are made with titanium powder rather than from a donor or from the patient's own body and manufactured using a 3D-printing process.

EXECUTIVES

Executive Vice President Chief Financial Officer, Robert S. (Bob) Shapiro
President North Shore-long Island Jewish Health System, Ralph A. Nappi
Senior Vice President Strategy And Business Informatics, Jeffrey A. Kraut
Executive Vice President Chief Operating Officer, Mark J. Solazzo
Regional Executive Director, Dennis Dowling
Executive Vice President And Physician-in-chief, Lawrence G. Smith
Executive Director, Susan Somerville
Vice President Chief Corporate Compliance Officer, Greg S Radinsky
Vice President Business Development, Robert Scoskie
Director Of Radiology, Edward S Wind
Vice President, Dorothy Feldman
Senior Vice President Consolidated Business Services, Donna Drummond
Director Of Him, Elizabeth Heller
Vice President Of Marketing, Don Simon
Vice President And Chief Talent Officer, Elaine Page
Medical Director, Rita Molina
Assistant Vice President Infrastructure And Technology Management, Randy Cleghorne
Ambulatory Services Dir, ELLEN SCHANTZ
Senior Vice President Strategy And Business Informatics, Kambhampaty Krishnasastry
Assistant Vice President Clinical Applications, Chris Petillo
Senior Vice President Behavioral Health Services; Chair Of Psychiatry Zucker Hillside Hospital A, John Kane
Svp, Andrew Yacht
Medical Director, Steven Rosen
Vice President Women's Strategic, Brian McKenna
Medical Director Blood Bank, Lennart Logdberg
Vice President Human Resources, Lisa Khavkin
Vice Chairman, Gary Giangola
Secretary Department, Linda Muscarella

LOCATIONS

HQ: NORTH SHORE UNIVERSITY HOSPITAL
300 COMMUNITY DR, MANHASSET, NY 110303876
Phone: 516 562-0100
Web: WWW.NORTHWELL.EDU

PRODUCTS/OPERATIONS

Selected Centers and Services

Bariatric Services
Cancer Institute
Cardiovascular and Thoracic Services
Colorectal Surgery
Emergency Department / Trauma Services
Fertility and Reproductive Services
Geriatric and Palliative Medicine
Infectious Diseases / AIDS Research
Kidney Transplantation
Laparoendoscopic Single-Site Surgery
Military/Veterans Services
Minimally Invasive Robotic Surgery
Neuroscience
Obstetrics and Gynecology
Orthopaedics
Pain Management
Pediatric Services
Radiation Medicine
Travel Immunization
Urology Services
Wound Care

COMPETITORS

Brookhaven Memorial Hospital Medical Center
Catholic Health Services of Long Island
Catholic Healthcare System
Long Island College Hospital
Maimonides Medical Center
New York City Health and Hospitals
NewYork-Presbyterian Healthcare
Winthrop-University Hospital

HISTORICAL FINANCIALS

Company Type: Private

Income Statement FYE: December 31

	REVENUE ($ mil.)	NET INCOME ($ mil.)	NET PROFIT MARGIN	EMPLOYEES
12/18	1,883	38	2.1%	5,000
12/17	1,826	191	10.5%	—
12/16	1,795	171	9.6%	—
12/15	1,617	37	2.3%	—
Annual Growth	5.2%	1.3%	—	—

2018 Year-End Financials

Return on assets: 1.9%
Return on equity: 3.8%
Current ratio: 3.00
Cash ($ mil.): 31

NORTH SHORE-LONG ISLAND JEWISH HEALTH CARE

EXECUTIVES

Prin, Filippo Petti
Information Technology/Interne, Phil Leonardi
Project Manager, Cathlyn Fagan
Director Research, Michael Ryan

LOCATIONS

HQ: NORTH SHORE-LONG ISLAND JEWISH HEALTH CARE
972 BRUSH HOLLOW RD 5TH, WESTBURY, NY 115901740
Phone: 516 876-6611
Web: WWW.NORTHSHORECHILDGUIDANCE.ORG

HISTORICAL FINANCIALS

Company Type: Private

Income Statement — FYE: December 31

	REVENUE ($ mil.)	NET INCOME ($ mil.)	NET PROFIT MARGIN	EMPLOYEES
12/14	719	(34)	—	2
12/13	633	(33)	—	—
12/09	351	(2)	—	—
Annual Growth	15.4%	—	—	—

2014 Year-End Financials

Return on assets: (-1.9%)
Return on equity: (-7.7%)
Current ratio: 0.50
Cash ($ mil.): 74

NORTH TEXAS TOLLWAY AUTHORITY

The North Texas Tollway Authority (NTTA) operates a toll system consisting of about 90 miles of roadway. Facilities include the Dallas North Tollway the President George Bush Turnpike the Addison Airport Toll Tunnel the Mountain Creek Lake Bridge and the Sam Rayburn Tollway. The authority serves four counties in the Dallas-Fort Worth area. A predecessor agency the Texas Turnpike Authority was created by the Texas Legislature in 1953; the NTTA was created by the Legislature in 1997 to take over for the turnpike authority in Collin Dallas Denton and Tarrant counties.

EXECUTIVES

Vice President, Keith Jackson
Vice Chairman, Victor Vandergriff
Secretary To The Board Of Directors, Lorelei Griffith
Board Of Directors, Kathy Dress
Auditors: CROWE HORWATH LLP DALLAS TEX

LOCATIONS

HQ: NORTH TEXAS TOLLWAY AUTHORITY
5900 W PLANO PKWY STE 100, PLANO, TX 750934695
Phone: 214 461-2000
Web: WWW.NTTA.ORG

HISTORICAL FINANCIALS

Company Type: Private

Income Statement — FYE: December 31

	REVENUE ($ mil.)	NET INCOME ($ mil.)	NET PROFIT MARGIN	EMPLOYEES
12/16	741	93	12.6%	733
12/13	551	(99)	—	—
12/12	0	(126)	—	—
Annual Growth	—	—	—	—

2016 Year-End Financials

Return on assets: 1.2%
Return on equity: —
Current ratio: 2.80
Cash ($ mil.): 54

NORTHEAST GEORGIA MEDICAL CENTER, INC.

EXECUTIVES

Ceo, Carol Burrell
V Pres*, Tracy Vardeman
V Pres*, Anthony Williamson
V Pres*, Paul Vervalin
Cfo*, Anthony M Herdener
Oncology, Jack T Griffeth
Internal Medicine Practitioner, Ernest T Kamara
Coordinator, Jason Grady
Internal Medicine Practitioner, Getachew Iyasu
Internal Medicine Practitioner, Pavani Pandiri
Internal Medicine Practitioner, Erine Raybon

LOCATIONS

HQ: NORTHEAST GEORGIA MEDICAL CENTER, INC.
743 SPRING ST NE, GAINESVILLE, GA 305013715
Phone: 770 219-9000
Web: WWW.NGHSCAREERS.COM

HISTORICAL FINANCIALS

Company Type: Private

Income Statement — FYE: September 30

	REVENUE ($ mil.)	NET INCOME ($ mil.)	NET PROFIT MARGIN	EMPLOYEES
09/18	1,266	113	9.0%	3,053
09/17	1,152	7	0.7%	—
09/16	1,024	45	4.5%	—
09/15	892	51	5.8%	—
Annual Growth	12.4%	30.4%	—	—

2018 Year-End Financials

Return on assets: 5.4%
Return on equity: 12.6%
Current ratio: 1.70
Cash ($ mil.): 50

NORTHEASTERN UNIVERSITY

Since 1898 Northeastern University has been educating students in Boston and beyond. The school enrolls about 17380 students and employs more than 3090 faculty members. Its nine colleges offer 195 undergraduate programs and 265 professional doctorate master's and certificate programs in areas such as the arts business engineering and law. Northeastern has a student-to-teacher ratio of about 14:1. Its highly-regarded experiential education program integrates classroom learning with real-world experience; students typically alternate between school and paid full-time work and leave with up to two years of professional experience. Northeastern started out as a night school housed in a YMCA facility.

Operations

Northeastern's students participate in its cooperative learning program which is conducted over four or five years and can include overseas study programs. The idea behind the teaching strategy is to give students some professional experience before graduation putting them a step ahead of peers. Sectors include the arts and humanities (think Boston Symphony Orchestra) finance and insurance (Goldman Sachs in the UK) and communications (the White House offers a co-op opportunity in its media affairs office).

The school also boasts extensive research centers and institutes. Northeastern receives research funding from a number of outside sources that include the National Institutes of Health the Department of Energy and the Department of Defense. Funded research areas include heart disease the link between preterm births and environmental contaminants new ways to detect explosives and renewable energy sources.

Geographic Reach

Northeastern's students hail from about 140 countries. The university has study abroad programs in locations including Argentina Costa Rica France China Germany and the UK (among many others).

In addition to its main campus in Boston Northeastern has satellite graduate schools in Charlotte North Carolina Seattle California and Toronto.

Financial Performance

Northeastern University's revenue rose 8% to $1.5 billion from $1.4 billion in 2019. Tuition and fees which accounted for 69% of the company's revenue increased from $998.1 million in 2019 to $1 billion in 2020.

Cash and cash equivalents at the end of the year were $481.3 million 42% higher than in the previous year. Cash provided by operations was $162.0 million. Investing activities provided $2.4 million primarily from acquisition of property plant and equipment while financing activities used $21.3 million primarily for debt refinancing.

Strategy

Northeastern University has adopted endowment investment and spending policies that attempt to provide a predictable stream of funding to programs supported by its endowment while seeking to maintain the purchasing power of endowment assets. To achieve its long-term rate of return objectives the university relies on a total return strategy in which investment returns are achieved through both capital appreciation (realized and unrealized gains) and current yield (interest and dividends).

EXECUTIVES

Senior Vice President Administration And Finance, John McCarthy
Svp And Ceo Northeastern University Global Network, Philomena V. Mantella
Senior Vice President For External Affairs External Affairs, Michael Armini
President, Joseph E. Aoun
Svp Academinc Affairs And Provost, James C. Bean
Vp And Chief Marketing Officer, Brian Sullivan
Senior Vice President For University Advancement, Diane Macgillivray
Vice President, Kathy Spiegelman
Vice President Enrollment Management, Jane Brown
Vice President Facilities, Nancy May
Assistant Vice President Student Affairs, Madeleine Estabrook
Vp Of Media And Marketing, Brenna Eagan
Vice President Student Affairs, Edward Klotzbier
Assistant Vice President For Academic Technologies, Stephanie Trowbridge
Vice Provost Undergraduate Education, Malcolm Hill
Assistant Vice President Student Affairs Residential Life, Marina Macomber
Vice President Academic Affairs, John Griffith
Vice President Cio, Bob Weir
Medical Director, Gairy Hall
Vice President For Enrollment Management, Sundar Kumarasamy
Associate Vice President Corporate And Foundation Rela, Robert Silk

Vice President Of External Affairs Bmes, Rachel Shaffer
Vice President Of Media And Membership, Vijayeta Singh
Vice President Online Experiential Learning, Chris Mallett
Associate Vice President, Robert Dietrich
Vice President Of Marketing And Outreach, Isha Srivastava
Vp Finance, Abhishek Garg
First Vice President, Heather L Seligman
Director Of Admissions, Jackson Dan
Vice President, Norton Julie
Executive Vice President, Angela Antoniello
Vice President, Harry Brodsky
Vice President Of Alumnae Relations, Sarah Nesti
Associate Vice President University Advancement, Bob Dietrich
Director Of Clinical Services, Sievert Jules Rochiell
Associate Vice President, Mallik Sundharam
Vice President For Facilities, Maria Cimilluca
Vice President, Doug Landry
Vice President For Government Relations, Michael Sarno
Vice President, Lester Noah
Secretary Receptionist Health Services, Debra Smith
Board Member, Mary Florentine
Secretary To Facilities Manager, Siobhan Fanning
Assistant Treasurer, Alysa Gerlach
Board Member, Eric Evje
Auditors: PRICEWATERHOUSECOOPERS LLP B

LOCATIONS

HQ: NORTHEASTERN UNIVERSITY
360 HUNTINGTON AVE, BOSTON, MA 021155000
Phone: 617 373-2000
Web: WWW.NORTHEASTERN.EDU

PRODUCTS/OPERATIONS

Selected Schools & Colleges
Bouvé; College of Health Sciences
College of Arts Media and Design
College of Computer and Information Science
College of Engineering
College of Professional Studies
College of Science
College of Social Sciences and Humanities
D'Amore-McKim School of Business
School of Law

HISTORICAL FINANCIALS

Company Type: Private

Income Statement FYE: June 30

	REVENUE ($ mil.)	NET INCOME ($ mil.)	NET PROFIT MARGIN	EMPLOYEES
06/20	1,523	193	12.7%	4,175
06/19	1,405	229	16.4%	—
06/18	1,306	163	12.5%	—
06/17	1,161	169	14.6%	—
Annual Growth	9.5%	4.7%	—	—

2020 Year-End Financials

Return on assets: 5.4%
Return on equity: 8.7%
Current ratio: —
Cash ($ mil.): 481

NORTHERN BORDER PIPELINE COMPANY

EXECUTIVES

V Pres-GM, Dean Ferguson
Director, Sorana Linder
Member of Management Committee, William Cordes
Associate, Denny Lee
Associate, Diane Myers
Member of Management Committee, John Gibson
Member of Management Committee, Mark Zimmerman
Associate, Viddy Harris
Accounts Payable Specialist, Anil Salim
Account Representative, Arlin Ball
Accounting Supervisor, Derek Richard
Auditors: KPMG LLP

LOCATIONS

HQ: NORTHERN BORDER PIPELINE COMPANY
700 LOUISIANA ST STE 700 # 700, HOUSTON, TX 770022873
Phone: 832 320-5000
Web: WWW.NORTHERNBORDER.COM

HISTORICAL FINANCIALS

Company Type: Private

Income Statement FYE: December 31

	REVENUE ($ mil.)	NET INCOME ($ mil.)	NET PROFIT MARGIN	EMPLOYEES
12/19	1,334	765	57.4%	135
12/18	289	135	46.9%	—
12/17	291	80	27.8%	—
12/16	291	86	29.6%	—
Annual Growth	66.0%	107.0%	—	—

2019 Year-End Financials

Return on assets: 10.0%
Return on equity: 11.8%
Current ratio: 0.50
Cash ($ mil.): 9

NORTHERN INDIANA PUBLIC SERVICE COMPANY

Northern Indiana Public Service Company (NIPSCO) can shine a little light on the topic of Hoosiers. The largest subsidiary of utility holding company NiSource NIPSCO has more than 457000 electricity customers and more than 786000 natural gas customers. The utility has three coal-fired power plants with 2540 MW of generating capacity. On the power side of the business NIPSCO generates transmits and distributes electricity to the northern part of Indiana and engages in electric wholesale and transmission transactions. The company operates approximately 13000 miles of electric transmission and distribution lines and 16000 miles of gas mains.

Operations

NIPSCO's three operating power facilities have a net capability of 2540 MW. It also owns and operates Sugar Creek a combined cycle gas turbine plant with a 535 MW capacity four gas-fired generating units with a net capability of 206 MW and two hydroelectric generating plants with a net capability of 10 MW. During 2012 NIPSCO generated 74.1% and purchased 25.9% of its electric requirements.

Geographic Reach

NIPSCO Gas is the largest natural gas distribution company in Indiana and NIPSCO Electric which serves customers in 20 counties is the state's #2 power distribution company behind Duke Energy Indiana.

Strategy

NIPSCO is promoting incentive plans to help customers save money through energy efficiency programs including appliance rebates for the installation of more energy efficient water heaters and other electric appliances and for automated air-conditioning cycling (cutting use for limited periods during peak loads). Other incentives are available for weatherizing energy audits and green construction projects.

In 2011 the company increased residential customer rates by 5%. The rate increase was in part a way to compensate for a decline in usage and revenues as a result of the global recession.

In 2011 NiSource companies Northern Indiana Fuel & Light and Kokomo Gas were consolidated with and into NIPSCO in order to improve operating efficiencies.

EXECUTIVES

Senior Vice President, Dan Douglas
Vice President, Dave Walter
Vice President, Paul Kelly
Vice President, Jim Zucal
Senior Vice President, Mike Hooper
Vice President And Chief Accounting Officer, Jeffrey Grossman

LOCATIONS

HQ: NORTHERN INDIANA PUBLIC SERVICE COMPANY
801 E 86TH AVE, MERRILLVILLE, IN 464106271
Phone: 800 464-7726
Web: WWW.NIPSCO.COM

PRODUCTS/OPERATIONS

Selected Services
Call 811 Before You Dig
Commercial and Industrial Services
DependaBill
Dusk to Dawn Streetlights
Extra Service Protection
Green Power
IN-Charge Electric Vehicle Program
Meter Reading
NIPSCO Choice Program
NIPSCO Connect
Price Protection Service
Residential Builder and Developer Services
Selling Your Clean Energy
Smart Grid Technology
Start or Stop Gas and Electric Services
Trees and Power Lines
Wood Stove Changeout Program

COMPETITORS

AEP
Citizens Energy
Dominion Energy
Duke Energy Indiana
IPALCO Enterprises
Indiana Michigan Power
Vectren

HISTORICAL FINANCIALS

Company Type: Private

Income Statement FYE: December 31

	REVENUE ($ mil.)	NET INCOME ($ mil.)	NET PROFIT MARGIN	EMPLOYEES
12/17	2,418	226	9.3%	3,096
12/16	2,252	178	7.9%	—
/ 0	0	—	—	
Annual Growth	—	—	—	—

2017 Year-End Financials

Return on assets: 3.2%
Return on equity: 9.0%
Current ratio: 0.50
Cash ($ mil.): 7

NORTHERN NATURAL GAS COMPANY

Northern Natural Gas (NNG) keeps the pipes gassed up. The company operates 14600 miles of natural gas pipeline stretching from the Permian Basin in Texas to Michigan's Upper Peninsula. It also provides transportation and storage services to more than 80 utilities and a number of other customers. The company has 6.3 billion cu. ft. per day market area peak capacity and its three natural gas storage facilities have a total capacity of 75 billion cu. ft. including 4 billion cu. ft. of liquefied natural gas (LNG). NNG which was formed in 1930 is an indirect subsidiary of Berkshire Hathaway Energy.

Operations

The company provides cross-haul and grid transportation between other interstate and intrastate pipelines in the Permian Anadarko Hugoton and Midwest areas.

NNG offers firm and interruptible transportation services storage services as well as other transportation related services that are available to customers as a reliable and flexible supply source to meet short-and long-term market demands.

Geographic Reach

Omaha Nebraska-bsed NNG accesses natural gas supply in the Mid-Continent Rocky Mountain and Western Canadian basins. Its northern service unit (Market Area) delivers gas supply to customers in Illinois Iowa Kansas Michigan Minnesota Nebraska South Dakota and Wisconsin.

The company's pipeline system stretches across over 10 states from the Permian Basin in Texas to Michigan's Upper Peninsula providing access to five of the major natural gas supply regions in North America.

Sales and Marketing

NNG offers its products for utilities and numerous producers energy marketing companies and industrial end-users.

Company Background

NNG was established in 1930 in Omaha to serve 44 communities in Iowa Kansas and Nebraska. Its more recent history includes a takeover by Dynegy in 2002 from the pipeline unit's former parent bankrupt energy giant Enron. The deal was part of Dynegy's proposed acquisition of Enron which was subsequently called off. To strengthen its own balance sheet Dynegy ended up selling NNG to MidAmerican Energy (which later became Berkshire Hathaway Energy) that year.

In 2011 NNG brought in 13 billion cu. ft. of new gas supply to its northern system from tight sand formations in Oklahoma and Texas.

EXECUTIVES

President Ceo, Mark A. Hewett
Vp Operations, Royce Ramsay
Vp Information Technology, Paul Maakestad
Vp Marketing, Adam Wright

LOCATIONS

HQ: NORTHERN NATURAL GAS COMPANY
1111 S 103RD ST, OMAHA, NE 681241072
Phone: 877 654-0646
Web: WWW.NORTHERNNATURALGAS.COM

COMPETITORS

Enbridge
Kinder Morgan Energy Partners
ONEOK Partners
TransCanada
Williams Companies

HISTORICAL FINANCIALS

Company Type: Private

Income Statement FYE: December 31

	REVENUE ($ mil.)	NET INCOME ($ mil.)	NET PROFIT MARGIN	EMPLOYEES
12/17	693	170	24.6%	1,055
12/16	636	159	25.0%	—
12/07	663	161	24.3%	—
12/06	633	142	22.5%	—
Annual Growth	0.8%	1.7%	—	—

2017 Year-End Financials

Return on assets: 4.6%
Return on equity: 10.8%
Current ratio: 1.00
Cash ($ mil.): 20

NORTHSHORE UNIVERSITY HEALTHSYSTEM

NorthShore University HealthSystem provides care to residents of Chicago's north side and its suburbs. The health system operates four hospitals a home care organization and a Medical Group with some 970 primary and specialty care physicians. With about 355 beds the organization's flagship Evanston Hospital has teaching and research programs as well as capabilities for trauma cancer and cardiology. The system also includes Glenbrook Hospital (about 175 beds) Highland Park Hospital (140 beds) and Skokie Hospital (more than 120 beds). The health care system is affiliated with the University of Chicago Pritzker School of Medicine.

Operations

Each of NorthShore's hospitals is known for a certain specialty. Evanston for example specializes in cancer and cardiac care; Glenbrook Hospital is known for advanced technology for the treatment of gastrointestinal disorders; Highland Park Hospital is the site of the first open heart surgery in the region; and Skokie Hospital is known for its expertise in cardiac care and orthopedics.Each year the hospitals see some 128000 emergency room visits and some 63000 hospital admissions.

The Center for Personalized Medicine at NorthShore is a comprehensive precision medicine organization utilizing genetic testing to help inform patients' care including disease prevention and treatment.

The system also operates a not-for-profit home and hospice services agency.

Geographic Reach

Based in Evanston Illinois NorthShore has some 130 medical offices across the region.

Financial Performance

NorthShore has annual revenues of approximately $2.1 billion.

Strategy

NorthShore's health facility network has grown over the years through acquisitions and through organic measures. The system regularly conducts expansion and remodeling projects at its facilities and it has stepped up recruiting efforts to attract high-skill doctors. In 2018 it announced plans to spend between $50 million and $60 million to open 50 immediate care centers by late 2020. (At the time of the announcement it operated six immediate care centers.) That strategy should bring more patients to the system overall as some 20% of its immediate care center patients are new to NorthShore.

The organization has also been working to expand its medical group to broaden its offering of specialized health care services. In 2017 it began offering genetic testing as part of patients' annual checkups through its Center for Personalized Medicine.

Fortunately for NorthShore it thrives in an area where the population is young and poverty is limited. While the health system receives a good amount of revenue from Medicare and Medicaid it also receives income from commercial insurance payers with a low level of charity care despite economic turmoil in the US. This patient mix has allowed the company to maintain revenue and income growth as well as plenty of cash on hand to fund its expansion initiatives.

In 2017 Northshore scrapped plans to merge with Advocate Health Care to create Advocate NorthShore Health Partners (ANHP). The combination would have created the largest integrated health care delivery system in Illinois (serving 3 million patients a year) and the 11th largest not-for-profit health care system in the US. The merger was blocked by the FTC which claimed that the deal would harm consumers by raising prices and lowering health care quality.

EXECUTIVES

President Northshore University Healthsystem Medical Group, Joseph Golbus
President Glenbrook Hospital, Douglas M. Silverstein
President Northshore Skokie Hospital, Kristen Murtos
Chief Investment Officer, Thomas H. Hodges
Chief Nursing Officer, Nancy Semerdjian
Cio, Steven Smith
President Northshore Highland Park Hospital, Jesse Peterson Hall
Evp Finance And Cfo, Gary E. Weiss
Chief Scientific Officer Northshore Research Institute, Michael S. Caplan
President Northshore Glenbrook Hospital, Sean O'Grady
President And Ceo, Gerald (J.P.) Gallagher
Executive Director Northshore Foundation, Murray T. Ancell
Avp Application Services Health Information Technology, Kate Steele
Medical Director, Harry J Jaffe
Assistant Vice President, Kevin Katz
Vice President Perioperative Services, Beverly Beine

Svp Marketing And Corporate Communications, Carol Franczek
Chairman, Mark R. Neaman
Unit Secretary, Sumbul Tahir
Vice Chairman Northshore Orthopaedic Institute And Division Head Of Hand And Upper Extremity Department Of Orthopaedic Surgery, Leon Benson
Secretary, Dorraine Russin
Auditors: ERNST & YOUNG LLP CHICAGO IL

LOCATIONS

HQ: NORTHSHORE UNIVERSITY HEALTHSYSTEM
1301 CENTRAL ST, EVANSTON, IL 602011613
Phone: 847 570-2000
Web: WWW.NORTHSHORE.ORG

COMPETITORS

Advocate Health Care
Central DuPage Hospital
Children's Hopsital of Chicago
Community Health Systems
Mercy Hospital and Medical Center
MetroSouth Medical
Northwest Community Healthcare
Northwestern Memorial HealthCare
Rockford Health System
Rush System for Health
University of Chicago Medical Center

HISTORICAL FINANCIALS

Company Type: Private

Income Statement — FYE: September 30

	REVENUE ($ mil.)	NET INCOME ($ mil.)	NET PROFIT MARGIN	EMPLOYEES
09/18	2,153	197	9.2%	9,000
09/09	1,085	(71)	—	—
09/08	26	0	0.4%	—
09/05	1,061	64	6.0%	—
Annual Growth	5.6%	9.1%	—	—

2018 Year-End Financials

Return on assets: 5.0%
Return on equity: 7.0%
Current ratio: 1.00
Cash ($ mil.): 52

NORTHSIDE HOSPITAL, INC.

Northside Hospital is no one-trick pony — it actually operates three hospitals serving Atlanta and surrounding areas. Also known as the Northside Healthcare Delivery System the Northside Hospital network includes some 840 licensed beds and more than 2500 physicians on multiple campuses with a host of outpatient health facilities including physician office parks and specialized cancer centers. All of Northside's hospitals are full-service acute-care facilities that provide specialty care including cancer care surgery radiology and women's health. Northside Hospital which opened in 1970 is merging with Gwinnett Health System.

Operations

In addition to its 537-bed hospital in Sandy Springs Northside has hospitals in Cherokee and Forsyth counties as well as more than 120 outpatient centers across Georgia.

Northside Hospital handles about 700000 patient visits annually at its facilities. The organization's cancer treatment division partners with the Cancer Support Community of Atlanta to provide mental health social and educational services to cancer patients and survivors as well as family members and friends.

Geographic Reach

Northside Hospital's three campuses are located in Atlanta Forsyth and Cherokee Georgia. It also operate about 40 outpatient clinics and physician practices scattered across the northern Atlanta metropolitan area.

Strategy

Northside Hospital is conducting expansion and renovation efforts to meet the needs of area residents. It recently completed an expansion and relocation of its Cherokee County Spine & Pain Center (near the Cherokee hospital campus). In 2015 it expanded its radiology offerings with a new outpatient imaging center in Jasper.

After two years of talks with fellow Georgia-based hospital system Gwinnett Health Northside and Gwinnett have agreed to merge operations. The combined system will have nearly 3500 physicians and 1480 beds.

EXECUTIVES

Cfo, Peggy Gatliff
Vp Administration And Ceo Northside Hospital-forsyth, Robert Putnam
Ceo Northside Hospital-cherokee, William (Billy) Hayes
Chair Department Of Obstetrics And Gynecology, Ceana Nezhat
Ceo Northside Hospital-forsyth, Skip Putnam
Coo, Peter Kennedy
Medical Director Flow Cytometry And Molecular Diagnostics Lab, Irina Grigorieva
Director Of Pharmacy Supervisor, Mike Tate
Director Of Radiology Services, Mary Shepherd
Radiology Director, DIEDRA DIXON
Director Of Pharmacy, Rae Benton
Senior Vice President, Stephanie Hamner
Physical Therapy Director, Connie Winkler
Medical Director, Steven Lobel
Secretary, Sandra Black
Secretary, Valarie Richardson
Secretary, Kristen Ryan
Unit Secretary, Renita Hicks

LOCATIONS

HQ: NORTHSIDE HOSPITAL, INC.
1000 JOHNSON FERRY RD, ATLANTA, GA 303421611
Phone: 404 851-8000
Web: WWW.NORTHSIDE.COM

Selected Locations

Alpharetta Medical Campus
Dunwoody Cancer Center
Imaging at Peachtree Dunwoody
Medlock Bridge Imaging
Meridian Park Plaza
Northside Hospital Doctors Center
Northside Hospital-Atlanta
Northside Hospital-Cherokee
Northside Hospital-Forsyth
Northside-Forsyth Outpatient Surgery Center
Northside Sugar Hill Imaging (Buford)
Pediatric Center at Northside/Alpharetta
Roswell Cancer Center
Townelake Medical Office/Riverstone Imaging

COMPETITORS

Children's Healthcare of Atlanta
DeKalb Medical
Emory Healthcare
Grady Health System
Gwinnett Health System
Northeast Georgia Health System
Piedmont Healthcare
Regency Hospital
Shepherd Center
SunLink Health Systems
The Fulton-DeKalb Hospital Authority
WellStar Health System

HISTORICAL FINANCIALS

Company Type: Private

Income Statement — FYE: September 30

	REVENUE ($ mil.)	NET INCOME ($ mil.)	NET PROFIT MARGIN	EMPLOYEES
09/18	2,081	265	12.8%	8,000
09/17	2,002	301	15.0%	—
09/16	1,897	157	8.3%	—
09/15	1,733	223	12.9%	—
Annual Growth	6.3%	6.0%	—	—

2018 Year-End Financials

Return on assets: 10.6%
Return on equity: 14.8%
Current ratio: 4.40
Cash ($ mil.): 448

NORTHSIDE INDEPENDENT SCHOOL DISTRICT

EXECUTIVES

Supt, John Folks
Supt*, Brian T Woods
Pres*, Robert Blount Jr
V Pres*, Katie N Reed
SEC*, Bennie L Cole
Principal, Ellen Sutton
General, Lora Mathison
Manager, Joe Delgadillo
Coordinator, Derek Howorth
Assistant Director of Integrat, Julie Martinez
Secretary, Alma Lira
Auditors: RSM US LLP SAN ANTONIO TEXAS

LOCATIONS

HQ: NORTHSIDE INDEPENDENT SCHOOL DISTRICT
5900 EVERS RD, SAN ANTONIO, TX 782381606
Phone: 210 397-8770
Web: WWW.NISD.NET

HISTORICAL FINANCIALS

Company Type: Private

Income Statement — FYE: August 31

	REVENUE ($ mil.)	NET INCOME ($ mil.)	NET PROFIT MARGIN	EMPLOYEES
08/19	1,223	4	0.3%	13,698
08/18	1,203	57	4.8%	—
08/17	1,152	75	6.5%	—
08/16	1,119	16	1.5%	—
Annual Growth	3.0%	(36.8%)	—	—

2019 Year-End Financials

Return on assets: 0.1%
Return on equity: —
Current ratio: —
Cash ($ mil.): 685

NORTHWEST DAIRY ASSOCIATION

Northwest Dairy Association (NDA) members milk a lot of cows. The dairy cooperative's 550-plus member/farmers ship 7.2 billion pounds of milk annually which is processed by the co-op's subsidiary Darigold and packaged and sold under the Darigold label. NDA produces fluid and cultured dairy products including milk butter cottage cheese sour cream and yogurt that altogether generate some $2 billion in sales. It also makes bulk butter and cheese milk powder and whey products. The co-op caters to several sectors nationwide. Its customers include food retailers and wholesalers as well as foodservice and food-manufacturing companies. The association's membership spans half a dozen US states.

EXECUTIVES

Ceo, Jim Werkhoven
Pres, James Wegner
V Pres, Steve Rowe
SEC-Treas, Randy Lindley
Corporate Health, Erin Allen
Corporate Counsel, Kristi Keene
Sr Environmental, Scott Algate
Leader of Supply Chain, Chris Stockwell
Chief Operating Officer, Grant Kadavy
Chief Financial Officer, Mark Garth

LOCATIONS

HQ: NORTHWEST DAIRY ASSOCIATION
5601 6TH AVE S STE 300, SEATTLE, WA 981082545
Phone: 206 284-7220
Web: WWW.DARIGOLD.COM

PRODUCTS/OPERATIONS

Selected Products

Consumer
Butter
Buttermilk
Cottage cheese
Cream
Half and half
Milk
Sour cream
Whipping cream
Yogurt
Ingredients
Bleached sweet dry whey
Colored cheddar cheese
Cultured skim milk powder
Milk protein concentrate
Monterey Jack cheese
Nonfat dry milk
Salted sweet cream butter
Skim milk powder
Sweet cream buttermilk powder
Unsalted butter
Whey protein concentrate

COMPETITORS

Associated Milk Producers
Berkeley Farms
California Dairies Inc.
Dairy Farmers of America
Dean Foods
Humboldt Creamery
Land O'Lakes
Straus Family Creamery
Tillamook County Creamery Association

HISTORICAL FINANCIALS

Company Type: Private

Income Statement — FYE: March 31

	REVENUE ($ mil.)	NET INCOME ($ mil.)	NET PROFIT MARGIN	EMPLOYEES
03/08	2,207	87	4.0%	1,300
03/07	1,450	12	0.9%	—
03/04	1,297	(6)	—	—
03/03	1,140	2	0.2%	—
Annual Growth	14.1%	107.0%	—	—

2008 Year-End Financials

Return on assets: 17.7%
Return on equity: 41.5%
Current ratio: 1.80
Cash ($ mil.): 10

NORTHWEST FARM CREDIT SERVICES

Customer-owned financial cooperative Northwest Farm Credit Services is an agricultural lender that provides financial services to farmers ranchers agribusinesses commercial fishermen timber producers and rural home owners in Alaska Idaho Montana Oregon and Washington. The company has a network of around 45 branches and offers a broad range of flexible loan programs to meet the needs of people in the agriculture business. Northwest Farm Credit also provides leasing services appraisal services and life mortgage disability and crop insurance as well as legal advocacy and assistance to customers in need. It is part of the Farm Credit System a network of lenders serving the US agriculture industry.

Operations

The credit union provides financing and related services to farmers ranchers agribusinesses commercial fishermen timber producers rural homeowners and crop insurance customers. Northwest Farm Credit provides $10.3 billion in loans. Farm Credit System a nationwide network of borrower-owned lending institutions of which it is part provides $205 billion in loans to rural America.

Geographic Reach

Northwest Farm Credit serves customers through 45 offices located in Idaho Alaska Montana Oregon and Washington.

Sales and Marketing

Northwest Farm Credit finances farmers ranchers agribusinesses commercial fishermen timber producers and rural homeowners as well as farm-related businesses agricultural cooperatives and rural utilities.

Financial Performance

In 2015 the company's net revenue increased by 5% due to higher net interest income driven by increased loan volume.

Northwest Farm Credit's net income rose by 12% due to higher net revenues and a decrease in income tax expense.

In 2015 the company's operating cash inflow increased by 19%.

Strategy

The company plans to continue to fund lending operations primarily through its borrowing relationship with CoBank (a fellow Farm Credit System member) and from retained earnings.

Mergers and Acquisitions

In 2014 the company expanded its operations in Montana by buying Culbertson State Agency's crop insurance portfolio.

Company Background

The US Congress created the Farm Credit System in 1916 to meet the financial needs of farmers ranchers and cooperatives who invest as well as borrow from the institutions within the system. All Farm Credit System members are regulated by the Farm Credit Administration.

EXECUTIVES

Evp Financial Services, Fred (Fred) DePell
Evp And General Counsel, Thomas (Tom) Tracy
Evp Corporate Administration And Secretary, Joan E. Haynes
Evp Cfo And Cio, Tom Nakano
Vice President Internal Controls, Don Bellamy
Vice President Market Research And Development, Michael Stolp
Vice President, Carol L Sobson
Vice President Appraisal Services, Joe Moore
Vice President Relationship Manager Iii, Sean Kolb
Svp Policy And Collateral Risk Management, Paul Nelson
Chairman, Drew Eggers
Vice Chairman, Kevin Riel
Auditors: PRICEWATERHOUSECOOPERS LLP S

LOCATIONS

HQ: NORTHWEST FARM CREDIT SERVICES
2001 S FLINT RD, SPOKANE, WA 992249198
Phone: 509 838-2429
Web: WWW.NORTHWESTFCS.COM

PRODUCTS/OPERATIONS

2015 Sales

	$ mil.	% of total
Interest Income	412	82
Patronage income	52	11
Financially Related Services	19	4
loans and other fee	6	1
Other non-interest income	11	2
Total	**502**	**100**

COMPETITORS

Bank of America
First Interstate
Idaho Independent Bank
KeyCorp
Northwest Bancorporation
U.S. Bancorp
Wells Fargo
Zions Bancorporation

HISTORICAL FINANCIALS

Company Type: Private

Income Statement — FYE: December 31

	ASSETS ($ mil.)	NET INCOME ($ mil.)	INCOME AS % OF ASSETS	EMPLOYEES
12/13	9,604	236	2.5%	500
12/12	9,471	187	2.0%	—
12/11	8,696	159	1.8%	—
Annual Growth	5.1%	22.0%	—	—

2013 Year-End Financials

Return on assets: 2.5%
Return on equity: 13.5%
Sales ($ mil): 460

NORTHWESTERN MEMORIAL HOSPITAL

EXECUTIVES

Ceo, Dean Harrison
Pres, Richard J Gannotta
Cfo, Peter McCanna
Chb, William J Brodsky
Health Consultant, Hattie Johnson
Neurosurgeon, Lisa Krammer
Call Center Supervisor, John Robinson
Pediatric Nurse Practitioner, Cathrine Angle
Doctor, Melissa Batenic
Vice President, Alfred Torrence
Director, Cindy A Parker

LOCATIONS

HQ: NORTHWESTERN MEMORIAL HOSPITAL
251 E HURON ST, CHICAGO, IL 606113055
Phone: 312 926-2000
Web: WWW.NM.ORG

HISTORICAL FINANCIALS

Company Type: Private

Income Statement FYE: August 31

	REVENUE ($ mil.)	NET INCOME ($ mil.)	NET PROFIT MARGIN	EMPLOYEES
08/16	1,499	237	15.8%	5,800
08/15	1,337	198	14.8%	—
08/10	1,380	64	4.7%	—
08/09	1,304	4	0.3%	—
Annual Growth	2.0%	76.0%	—	—

NORTHWESTERN UNIVERSITY

With its main campus in the Chicago suburb of Evanston Northwestern University (NU) serves its approximately 21000 students through about a dozen schools and colleges such as the Medill School of Journalism and the McCormick School of Engineering and Applied Sciences. Its Chicago campus houses the schools of law and medicine as well as several hospitals of the McGaw Medical Center. With a faculty of more than 3300 the school has a student-to-teacher ratio of about 6:1. NU is home to several research centers and community outreach programs; it also has a branch in Qatar. It is the only private member of the Big 10 conference; varsity sports include soccer football basketball and fencing.

Operations

Among NU's top-ranked programs are its law school medical school and its engineering program. Its Kellogg Graduate School of Management consistently ranks among the nation's top five business schools by Business Week and U.S. News & World Report. Its journalism and drama programs produced such alumni as Charlton Heston Gary Marshall and Julia Louis-Dreyfus. The late US Supreme Court Justice John Paul Stevens is also a former Wildcat.

NU spends nearly $886 million in annual sponsored research funds (and $388 million National Institute of health funding) conducting research at more than 40 university research institutes and centers (and 90 school-based research centers) in areas such as materials science biomedical engineering African studies performance studies and marketing. The school has earned recognition for its research in mesostructures neonatal biotechnology nanotechnology biomedical and materials sciences. NU partners have included the Argonne National Laboratory Fermilab and local universities.

Geographic Reach

NU's main campus encompasses about 240 acres in Evanston. The university operates another 25-acre campus in Chicago as well as its education center in Qatar.

Company Background

Northwestern University's Methodist founders met in 1850 to create an institution of higher learning serving the original Northwest Territory. The university was chartered in 1851 and two years later it acquired 379 acres of property north of Chicago on Lake Michigan. The town of Evanston was later named after John Evans one of the school's founders.

HISTORY

Northwestern University's Methodist founders met in 1850 to create an institution of higher learning serving the original Northwest Territory. The university was chartered in 1851 and two years later it acquired 379 acres of property north of Chicago on Lake Michigan. The town of Evanston was later named after John Evans one of the school's founders.

Classes began in the fall of 1855 with two professors and 10 students. By 1869 Northwestern had more than 100 students and began to admit women. In 1870 Northwestern signed an affiliation agreement with the Chicago Medical College (founded 1859) and three years later it joined with the original University of Chicago (no relation to the current institution) to create the Union College of Law. When the University of Chicago closed in 1886 due to financial difficulties Northwestern took control of the law school. The university reorganized in 1891 consolidating its affiliated professional schools (dentistry law medicine and pharmacy) into the university.

By 1900 Northwestern had become the third-largest university in the US (after Harvard and Michigan) with an enrollment of 2700. During the 1920s the university created the Medill School of Journalism named for Joseph Medill founder of the Chicago Tribune. In 1924 the school's athletic teams adopted the nickname Wildcats and two years later the university completed the primary buildings that form its Chicago campus. Northwestern suffered a drop in enrollment during the Depression but after WWII it saw student numbers swell as veterans took advantage of the GI Bill. Expansion continued throughout the 1960s and 1970s.

In 1985 the school and the City of Evanston began developing a research center to attract more high-tech industries to the area. The university's graduate school of business achieved national prominence in 1988 after it was ranked #1 in the US by Business Week. In 1995 Northwestern's football team forever the doormat of the Big 10 achieved national fame when it won the conference championship.

In 1998 faculty member Professor John Pople won the Nobel Prize in Chemistry the first Nobel Prize awarded to a faculty member while teaching at the university.

Northwestern won a significant legal battle in 1998 when a judge ruled that the university was not obligated to pay a faculty member simply because he had been granted tenure.

The university's dental school closed its doors in 2001 citing the difficulties posed for private schools in providing a competitive dental education.

EXECUTIVES

Vp Finance Operations And Treasurer, Ingrid S. Stafford, age 67
Vp Information Technology And Cio, Sean B. Reynolds
Dean Kellogg School Of Management, Sally E. Blount
Vp And Chief Investment Officer, William H. (Will) McLean
Dean School Of Communication, Barbara J. O'Keefe
Evp, Nim Chinniah
Provost, Daniel I. Linzer, age 67
Dean Libraries, Sarah M. Pritchard
President, Morton O. Shapiro
Vp Global Marketing And Cfhief Marketing Officer, Mary L. Baglivo
Dean Northwestern University In Qatar, Everette E. Dennis
Dean School Of Professional Studies, Thomas F. Gibbons
Dean Medill School Of Journalism Media And Integrated Marketing Communications, Bradley Hamm
Dean Graduate School, Dwight A. McBride
Dean Bienen School Of Music, Toni-Marie Montgomery
Dean Feinberg School Of Medicine, Eric G. Neilson
Dean School Of Education And Social Policy, Penelope L. Peterson
Dean Weinberg College Of Arts And Sciences, Adrian W. B. Randolph
Dean Mccormick School Of Engineering And Applied Science, Julio M. Ottino
Dean Pritzker School Of Law, Daniel B. Rodriguez
Vice President, Morteza Null Rahimi
Physical Therapy And Human Movement Sc, Julius Dewald
Vp Of It, Mylowe Wooley
Associate Vice President For Research, Fruma Yehiely
Assistant Vice President Marketing And Communications, Natasha DiPrima
Associate Vice President Alumni Relations And Development, David Lively
Associate Vice President And Executive Director, Alicia Loffler
Medical Director, Linda Guthrie
Vice President For International Relations, Devora Grynspan
Vice President Of Marketing And Product Management, Mark Crandon
Vice President, Jeffrey Kopin
Vice President For Research Professor Of Biomedical Engineering, Jay Walsh
Senior Vice President Global Human Resources Executive, Mikenzie Steffens
Associate Vice President And Dean Of Students, Todd Adams
Associate Vice President Administrative Systems, Kristine O'Brien
Clinical Director, Maureen Smith
Director Of Health Safety Security And Environment, Michael McDonough
Assistant Vice President Of Program Review, Megan Blackwelder
Director Of Admissions Evening And Weekend Mba Program Kellogg School Of Management, Emily Haydon
Vice President Information Technology, Jane Erb
Associate Vice President Human Resources, Dana Bradley
Director Of Clinical Services, David Shor

Executive Vice President Executive Director Senior Vice President Managing Director General Manager Vice President, Mike Null Monahan
Assistant Vice President Risk Management And Safety, Luke Figora
Medical Director, Matthew Kippenhan
Vice President Information Technology, Meghan Monaghan
Vice President, Earnest Sweat
Assistant Vice President Facilities Services, Angela Williams
Vice President, Marvin Siegel
Senior Vice President, Jay Anderson
Chairman, William A. Osborn, age 72
Assistant Treasurer, Richard Emrich
Secretary, Debbie Robert
Vice Chair For Research Department Of Medical Social Sciences, Richard Gershon
Secretary 1, Sheila Hodges
Board Member, Virginia Delancey
Board Member, Angela Y Lee
Treasurer, Mary Poole
Treasurer, Spencer Carlson
Division Secretary, Kelly Thompson
Treasurer And Membership, Jack Snarr
Board Member, Eitan Schwarz
Secretary, Clare Willis
Auditors: PRICEWATERHOUSECOOPERS LLP

LOCATIONS

HQ: NORTHWESTERN UNIVERSITY
633 CLARK ST, EVANSTON, IL 602080001
Phone: 847 491-3741
Web: WWW.NORTHWESTERN.EDU

PRODUCTS/OPERATIONS

Selected Programs

Continuing and Professional Programs
Graduate Programs
Pre-Collegiate Programs
Undergraduate Programs

Selected Schools and Colleges

Bienen School of Music
Feinberg School of Medicine
The Graduate School
Kellogg School of Management
McCormick School of Engineering and Applied Science
Medill School of Journalism Media Integrated Marketing Communications
Northwestern in Qatar
School of Communication
School of Continuing Studies
School of Education and Social Policy
School of Law
Weinberg College of Arts and Science

HISTORICAL FINANCIALS

Company Type: Private

Income Statement — FYE: August 31

	REVENUE ($ mil.)	NET INCOME ($ mil.)	NET PROFIT MARGIN	EMPLOYEES
08/19	2,579	(216)	—	5,954
08/18	2,464	560	22.7%	—
08/17	2,309	668	29.0%	—
Annual Growth	5.7%	—	—	—

2019 Year-End Financials

Return on assets: (-1.4%)
Return on equity: (-1.8%)
Current ratio: —
Cash ($ mil.): 155

NORTON HOSPITALS, INC

EXECUTIVES

Pres, Steven A Williams
SEC*, Robert B Azar
Treas*, Michael W Gough
V Pres*, Russell F Cox
SEC*, Theodore T Myre Jr
Internal Medicine Practitioner, Deep Ajmani
Manager of Management Informat, Joy Karrer
Human Resources Director, Judy Settle
Human Resources Director, Kevin Guthrie
Internal Medicine Practitioner, Sergio Cardinali
Chaplain, Kerry Wentworth

LOCATIONS

HQ: NORTON HOSPITALS, INC
200 E CHESTNUT ST, LOUISVILLE, KY 402021831
Phone: 502 629-8000
Web: WWW.NORTONHEALTHCARE.COM

HISTORICAL FINANCIALS

Company Type: Private

Income Statement — FYE: December 31

	REVENUE ($ mil.)	NET INCOME ($ mil.)	NET PROFIT MARGIN	EMPLOYEES
12/15	1,712	137	8.0%	1,500
12/14	1,577	187	11.9%	—
Annual Growth	8.6%	(26.7%)	—	—

2015 Year-End Financials

Return on assets: 8.0%
Return on equity: 8.6%
Current ratio: 2.20
Cash ($ mil.): —

NOVA SOUTHEASTERN UNIVERSITY, INC.

Nova Southeastern University (NSU) gives a whole new meaning to "school of sharks." NSU whose mascot is the deep sea predator has an enrollment of approximately 20435 students and offers a variety of undergraduate graduate and professional academic programs. NSU offers degrees in several medical disciplines (osteopathic medicine pharmacy optometry and pediatrics) marine biology business law education and computer science. The not-for-profit independent school operates seven campuses in the Miami-Fort Lauderdale area several health centers and an oceanographic center. Founded in 1964 Nova University merged with Southeastern University of the Health Sciences in 1994 to become Nova Southeastern University.

Operations

In addition to its more than 150 undergraduate and graduate programs NSU also operates The University School a pre-K through 12th grade college preparatory day school. The university's Mailman Segal Institute for Early Childhood Studies is a multidisciplinary demonstration and professional training center for education research and the advancement of knowledge in early childhood parenting and autism across the life span. Located at the Jim & Jan Moran Family Center Village the center offers educational programs clinical services and academic programs in collaboration with other NSU divisions.

Geographic Reach

NSU is a distance education pioneer (it was the one of the first US university to offer graduate programs online) offering classes on the Internet as well as at seven regional campuses in Florida and Puerto Rico.

Strategy

As universities do NSU regularly invests in facility upgrades to meet the growing needs of its students. In 2020 the university constructed the Alan B. Levan | NSU Broward Center of Innovation scheduled to open its doors in July 2021. The Levan Center of Innovation is the continuation of a long-standing public-private partnership with NSU and Broward County and will occupy the entire fifth floor of NSU's Alvin Sherman Library making it one of the largest of its kind in the nation occupying 54000-square-feet of space.

Company Background

Founded in 1964 Nova University merged with Southeastern University of the Health Sciences in 1994 to become Nova Southeastern University.

EXECUTIVES

Intrm Vice President Information Technology, Greg Horne
Vice President Community And Government Affairs Professor, Larry Calderon
Executive Vice Chancellor And Provost, Frederick Lippman
Evp And Coo, George L. Hanbury
Vp Finance, W. David Heron
Dean Student Affairs, Brad Williams
Director Alvin Sherman Library Research And Information Technology Center, Harriett MacDougall
Dean Shepard Broad Law Center, Athornia Steele
University Provost And Evp Academic Affairs, Frank DePiano
Dean University School, Jerome Chermak
Dean College Of Health Care Sciences, Richard E. Davis
Dean Oceanographic Center, Richard E. Dodge
Dean Center For Psychological Studies, Karen Grosby
Dean College Of Medical Sciences, Harold E. Laubach
Dean Mailman Segal Institute For Early Childhood Studies, Roni Leiderman
Dean College Of Optometry, David S. Loshin
Dean College Of Pharmacy, Andrés Malavé
Dean Farquhar College Of Arts And Sciences, Don Rosenblum
Dean College Of Osteopathic Medicine, Anthony J. Silvagni
Dean Fischler School Of Education, H. Wells Singleton
Dean College Of Dental Medicine, Robert A. Uchin
Dean Graduate School Of Humanities And Social Sciences, Honggang Yang
Evp And Coo, Jacqueline A. Travisano
Senior Executive Assistant President Manager, Shirley Naidoo
Ceo Health Clinics, Robert S. Oller
Vp Information Technology And Cio, Tom West
Executive Assistant Vice President, Katharine Perren
Pharmacy Manager, Todd Schmidt
Vice President Human Resources, Robert Pietrykowski
Vp Clinical Operations, Kelly Gregg
Vice President For Legal Affairs, Joel Berman
Executive Vice President, Catalina Gonzalez
Vice President, Heather Ruff
Vice President Finance, Noel Oliveras
Clinical Director Restorative, Amir Farhangpour
Director Of Admissions, Bridget Varisco
Vice President Marketing, Kyle Fisher

Department Chair, Wilma Robles
Phi Lambda Sigma Vice President, Meredith Brook
Evp And Coo, Harry Moon
Online Vice President, Carly Paro
Medical Director, Darren Hoffberger
Chair, Ronald G. Assaf
Vice Chair, Barry J. Silverman
Board Of Directors, Travis Nelson
Auditors: LB KPMG LLP GREENSBORO NC

LOCATIONS

HQ: NOVA SOUTHEASTERN UNIVERSITY, INC.
3301 COLLEGE AVE, DAVIE, FL 333147796
Phone: 954 262-7300
Web: WWW.NOVA.EDU

COMPETITORS

Florida Atlantic University
Florida International University
University of Florida

HISTORICAL FINANCIALS

Company Type: Private

Income Statement — FYE: June 30

	REVENUE ($ mil.)	NET INCOME ($ mil.)	NET PROFIT MARGIN	EMPLOYEES
06/15	678	45	6.7%	2,500
06/12	689	48	7.1%	—
06/10	612	22	3.7%	—
Annual Growth	2.1%	15.2%	—	—

2015 Year-End Financials

Return on assets: 3.5%
Return on equity: 6.6%
Current ratio: 0.20
Cash ($ mil.): 35

NOVANT HEALTH, INC.

With 14 hospitals and about 2600 beds Novant Health certainly has what it takes to keep denizens along the Eastern Seaboard in tip-top condition. The not-for-profit health system provides medical care to residents in more than 30 counties throughout North and South Carolina Georgia and Virginia. Its largest facilities include the 920-bed Forsyth Medical Center in Winston-Salem North Carolina and the 600-bed Presbyterian Hospital in Charlotte North Carolina. It also operates about 340 physician clinics outpatient surgery and diagnostic imaging centers. Additionally Novant is home to nursing homes rehabilitation and community outreach programs and philanthropic foundations.

Operations

In addition to owning and operating an array of health care facilities Novant provides management services for hospitals including information technology and managed care efficiency. The health care network has been expanding its services in the region through partnerships and acquisitions.

The system performs some 120000 surgeries each year.

Geographic Reach

Novant Health has dual headquarters in Winston-Salem and Charlotte North Carolina; it provides health care services to more than 500 locations.

Financial Performance

Novant reported a 7% increase in revenue for 2014 from $3.5 billion to $3.8 billion due largely to a 5% increase in patient revenue. Net income dropped from $395 million in 2013 to $106 million in 2014. This was primarily driven by a drop in investment earnings and charges related to defined benefit plans.

Cash flow from operations rose 6% to $319 million that year.

Strategy

Novant's five foundations — Presbyterian Hospital Foundation Forsyth Medical Center Foundation Thomasville Medical Center Foundation Rowan Regional Medical Center Foundation and Prince William Health System Foundation — help the organization fund its various methods of growth be they acquisitions or organic growth. They also aid the medical provider in establishing and running its various community outreach programs. Novant provides community education and screenings and supports health clinics that care for the uninsured.

In 2014 the system continued to expand its services and it geographic footprint. It opened a new medical center in Clemmons North Carolina and added a new $19 million geriatric psychiatric facility to its Franklin Medical Center. Novant also began the process of converting all its facilities to electronic health records per a government requirement and opening clinics inside some Charlotte Target store locations.

Company Background

Novant Health was formed in 1997 by a merger of Carolina Medicorp Presbyterian Healthcare and Thomasville Medical Center.

EXECUTIVES

President Novant, Paul M. Wiles
Evp And Chief Clinical Officer, Sallye A. Liner
President And Ceo, Carl S. Armato
Evp And Chief Medical Officer, Stephen L. Wallenhaupt
President Forsyth Medical Center, Denise Mihal
Evp And Cfo, Fred M. Hargett
President And Ceo Rowan Regional Medical Center, Jeff Lindsay
Evp And Chief Administrative Officer, Jacqueline R. Daniels
Evp And Chief Consumer Officer, Jesse Cureton
President Tml Copiers Xerox Company, Michael Hoover
Coo, Richard Belden
Chairman Department Of Ob/gyn At The Novant Health Matthews Medical Center, Gregory Reynolds
Vice President Business Development And, Derek Goldin
Vice President Human Resources, Karen Power
Executive Vice President And Chief Human Resources Officer, Janet Smith-Hill
Pharmacy Manager, Ron Lyerly
Vice President Finance, Melanie Shipek
Vice President And Reimbursement Services, Judy Morris
Director Of Radiology, Rhuona Saxon
Pharmacy Manager, Carla Kennedy
Vice President, Heather Bogan
Svp And Chief Human Experience Officer, Thomas Jenike
Vice President Of Human Resources, Jillian Huston
Senior Vice President {sv, Vincent Pompili
Chairman, Michael B. Baughan
Vice Chairman, Robert H. Stolz
Board Member, Melissa Ward
Advisory Board Member, Neil Desmond
Auditors: PRICEWATERHOUSECOOPERS LLP GR

LOCATIONS

HQ: NOVANT HEALTH, INC.
2085 FRONTIS PLAZA BLVD, WINSTON SALEM, NC 271035614
Phone: 336 277-1120
Web: WWW.NOVANTHEALTH.ORG

PRODUCTS/OPERATIONS

Selected Health Facilities

Brunswick Community Hospital (Supply North Carolina)
Forsyth Medical Center (Winston-Salem North Carolina)
Franklin Regional Medical Center (Louisburg North Carolina)
Kerner's Medical Center (Kernersville North Carolina)
Medical Park Hospital (Winston-Salem North Carolina)
The Oaks at Forsyth (residental long-term care; Winston-Salem North Carolina)
Presbyterian Hospital (Charlotte North Carolina)
Presbyterian Hemby Children's Hospital
Presbyterian Hospital Huntersville (Huntersville North Carolina)
Presbyterian Hospital Matthews (Charlotte North Carolina)
Presbyterian Orthopaedic Hospital (Charlotte North Carolina)
Rowan Regional Medical Center (Salisbury North Carolina)
Springwood Care Center (residental long-term care; Winston-Salem North Carolina)
Thomasville Medical Center (Thomasville North Carolina)
Upstate Carolina Medical Center (Gaffney South Carolina)

Selected Services

Assisted living
Behavioral health
Blood services
Breast health
Cancer
Children's services
Clinical research
Corporate health & wellness
Critical care
Diabetes
Emergency
Employer services
Heart & vascular
Hospice
Imaging
Infusion services
Inpatient services
Laboratory services
Orthopedics
Pain management
Pastoral care
Pharmacy
Rehabilitation
Respiratory services
Sickle cell
Sleep health
Sports medicine
Stroke & neurosciences
Supportive care
Surgery
Urgent and express care
Weight loss services
Wellness programs and services
Women's health
Women's heart health
Wound care

COMPETITORS

Alamance Regional Medical Center
Bon Secours Health
Carilion Clinic
CaroMont
Carolinas HealthCare System
Carolinas Medical Center-NorthEast
Cone Health
Davis Regional Medical Center
Duke University Health System
HCA
High Point Regional Health System
New Hanover Regional Medical Center
Rex Healthcare
Riverside Health System (Virginia)
Rowan Regional Medical Center
Sentara Healthcare
UNC Hospitals
Upstate Affiliate
Vidant Health
WakeMed

HISTORICAL FINANCIALS

Company Type: Private

Income Statement — FYE: December 31

	REVENUE ($ mil.)	NET INCOME ($ mil.)	NET PROFIT MARGIN	EMPLOYEES
12/19	5,434	547	10.1%	13,800
12/18	4,985	109	2.2%	—
12/17	167	(142)	—	—
12/16	4,340	559	12.9%	—
Annual Growth	7.8%	(0.7%)	—	—

2019 Year-End Financials

Return on assets: 7.2%
Return on equity: 11.9%
Current ratio: 1.70
Cash ($ mil.): 402

NOVARTIS PHARMACEUTICALS CORPORATION

EXECUTIVES

Pres, Marie-France Tschudin
Sr V-Pres-Cmo*, Nancy Lurker
Pres*, Andre Wyss
V Pres*, Yves Teirlynck
V Pres*, Julie Kane
Coo*, Alex Gorsky
V-Pres-Cfo*, Gary E Rosenthal
Cfo*, Helen Boudreau
US Country Head, Information T, Ruth Thorpe
Director, Kenneth Wong
Executive Director, Tom Jones
Auditors: PRICEWATERHOUSECOOPERS LLP-BR

LOCATIONS

HQ: NOVARTIS PHARMACEUTICALS CORPORATION
1 HEALTH PLZ, EAST HANOVER, NJ 079361016
Phone: 862 778-8300
Web: WWW.NOVARTIS.COM

HISTORICAL FINANCIALS

Company Type: Private

Income Statement — FYE: December 31

	REVENUE ($ mil.)	NET INCOME ($ mil.)	NET PROFIT MARGIN	EMPLOYEES
12/16	49,436	6,698	13.5%	7,000
12/15	49,440	17,794	36.0%	—
12/13	58,831	9,292	15.8%	—
Annual Growth	(5.6%)	(10.3%)	—	—

2016 Year-End Financials

Return on assets: 5.1%
Return on equity: 8.9%
Current ratio: 1.10
Cash ($ mil.): 7,007

NOVO CONSTRUCTION, INC.

EXECUTIVES

Ceo, James C Fowler
Pres*, Jim Fowler
SEC*, Robert Williamson
Superintendent, Dave Fournier
Superintendent, Todd Freeman
Director, Brian Cronin
Project Executive, Doug Ballou
Superintendent, Bruce Costa
Admin, Abigail Hernandez
Superintendent, Bill Young
Project Accountant, Pilar Bonilla

LOCATIONS

HQ: NOVO CONSTRUCTION, INC.
1460 OBRIEN DR, MENLO PARK, CA 940251432
Phone: 650 701-1500
Web: WWW.NOVOCONSTRUCTION.COM

HISTORICAL FINANCIALS

Company Type: Private

Income Statement — FYE: October 31

	REVENUE ($ mil.)	NET INCOME ($ mil.)	NET PROFIT MARGIN	EMPLOYEES
10/19	872	8	1.0%	133
10/18	684	7	1.1%	—
10/17	603	5	0.9%	—
10/16	577	6	1.1%	—
Annual Growth	14.8%	11.4%	—	—

2019 Year-End Financials

Return on assets: 2.4%
Return on equity: 95.0%
Current ratio: 1.00
Cash ($ mil.): 93

NPC RESTAURANT HOLDINGS, LLC

NPC International is the prince of pepperoni in a pizza empire. The world's largest franchisee of Pizza Hut restaurants NPC owns and operates more than 1275 pizza restaurants and delivery kitchens in about 30 states. The quick-service eateries located mostly in such southern states as Alabama Florida Georgia and Tennessee serve a variety of pizza styles as well as such items as buffalo wings and pasta. The pizza parlors are franchised from YUM! Brands the world's largest fast-food restaurant company. NPC was founded in 1962 by former chairman Gene Bicknell who was one of the first Pizza Hut franchisees. The company was acquired by private equity group NPC International Holdings in late 2011.

Operations

NPC runs more than 20 Wendys restaurants in addition to its large stable of pizza places. As a franchisee NPC gets the benefit of operating restaurants under a popular and well known name. It pays YUM! Brands royalties and fees in exchange for the right to use the Pizza Hut brand and other intellectual property. Typically local operators are also held to certain standards regarding food and service quality.

Strategy

NPC has grown to such a large size primarily through a series of acquisitions mostly corporate-run locations. In 2012 it snapped up 36 Pizza Hut units located primarily in Florida for roughly $19 million from Pizza Hut Inc. The deal enabled NPC to strengthen its position in its largest geographical market.

While NPC doesn't own the Pizza Hut chain as its largest franchisee the company can exert a certain amount of influence in how the fast-food business operates. It called upon YUM! Brands to improve its Pizza Hut marketing strategy while sales were slumping amid the economic downturn. The company spends 6% of its revenue on national and local advertising demonstrating its commitment to Pizza Hut operations and advertising strategy.

NPC's revenue improved in 2010 and 2011 partly as a result of promoting its value-priced menu items as a way to gain market share from competing chains including Domino's and Papa John's. (Within its local markets NPC competes against #1 Domino's franchisee RPM Pizza and Papa John's operator PJ United.)

EXECUTIVES

Chb-Pres-Ceo, James K Schwartz
V Pres Fin-Cfo, Troy D Cook
Sr V Pres-Head of Oprs, D Blayne Vaughn
Sr V Pres Mktg, Linda L Sheedy
Cao, Jason P Poenitske
Auditors: KPMG LLP KANSAS CITY MISSOUR

LOCATIONS

HQ: NPC RESTAURANT HOLDINGS, LLC
7300 W 129TH ST, OVERLAND PARK, KS 662132631
Phone: 913 327-5555
Web: WWW.NPCINTERNATIONAL.COM

COMPETITORS

Boddie-Noell
Burger King
Captain D's
Carrols
Chick-fil-A
Domino's
Hardee's
Interfoods
K-MAC
Krystal
Little Caesar's
McDonald's
PJ United
Papa John's
RPM Pizza
Sbarro
Sonic Corp.
Subway
Tacala
United States Beef
Valenti Management
Wendy's
West Quality Foods

HISTORICAL FINANCIALS

Company Type: Private

Income Statement — FYE: December 27

	REVENUE ($ mil.)	NET INCOME ($ mil.)	NET PROFIT MARGIN	EMPLOYEES
12/16	1,236	8	0.7%	29,000
12/15	1,223	6	0.5%	—
12/14	1,179	1	0.1%	—
12/13	1,094	29	2.7%	—
Annual Growth	4.2%	(33.5%)	—	—

2016 Year-End Financials

Return on assets: 0.7%
Return on equity: 3.1%
Current ratio: 0.40
Cash ($ mil.): 13

OAKLAND UNIFIED SCHOOL DISTRICT

EXECUTIVES

Coordinator, Marcus Silvi
Analysis, Byron Huey
Coordinator, Adimu Madyun
Teacher, Barbara Cone
Project Coordinator, Neena Bawa
Special Education Aide, Nola Taylor
Facilities Field Manager, Angela Lloyd
Vice, Donnell Mayberry
Community School Program Manag, Glendy Cordero
Educator, Tara Austin
Administrative Assistant, Ana Navarro

LOCATIONS

HQ: OAKLAND UNIFIED SCHOOL DISTRICT
1000 BROADWAY STE 300, OAKLAND, CA 946074099
Phone: 510 434-7790
Web: WWW.OUSD.ORG

HISTORICAL FINANCIALS

Company Type: Private

Income Statement FYE: June 30

	REVENUE ($ mil.)	NET INCOME ($ mil.)	NET PROFIT MARGIN	EMPLOYEES
06/19	731	(69)	—	7,200
06/18	677	(45)	—	—
06/17	658	(2)	—	—
06/06	0	0	—	—
Annual Growth	—	—	—	—

OCEAN SPRAY CRANBERRIES, INC.

Ocean Spray Cranberries has transformed that ubiquitous Thanksgiving side dish into a big business with beverages cereals and snacks. Known for its blue-and-white wave logo Ocean Spray is a top US maker of canned bottled and shelf-stable juice drinks. Structured as a cooperative Ocean Spray is owned by more than 700 cranberry and grapefruit growers in North America. It produces juice drinks by blending cranberries with other fruits typically ranging from apples to blueberries at around 20 processing facilities. Its other products include fresh and dried cranberries sauces and trail mixes along with fresh citrus fruits. Ocean Spray sells its products through food retailers foodservice providers and food makers worldwide.

Geographic Reach

Headquartered in Massachusetts Ocean Spray boasts a global business. It supplies cranberry products to food and beverage manufacturers worldwide. The company serves customers in North America the Caribbean Central America South America Africa Asia/Pacific Europe and the Middle East.

It has juice bottling facilities in Nevada Wisconsin Pennsylvania and Texas and dried cranberries and concentrate facilities in Washington Massachusetts and Wisconsin as well as Chile and Canada. All cranberry sauce is produced in Kenosha Wisconsin which Ocean Spray touts as The Home of Cranberry Sauce.

Mergers and Acquisitions

In 2018 Ocean Spray acquired Atoka Cranberries a Quebec based cranberry grower from The Bieler Group. Ocean Spray will invest in Atoka's operations to increase efficiency and improve yield.

HISTORY

Ocean Spray Cranberries traces its roots to Marcus Urann president of the Cape Cod Cranberry Company. In 1912 Urann who became known as the "Cranberry King" began marketing a cranberry sauce that was packaged in tins and could be served year-round. Inspired by the sea spray that drifted off the Atlantic and over his cranberry bogs Urann dubbed his concoction Ocean Spray Cape Cod Cranberry Sauce.

It didn't take long for other cranberry growers to make their own sauces and rather than compete the Cranberry King consolidated. In 1930 Urann merged his company with A.D. Makepeace Company and with Cranberry Products forming a national cooperative called Cranberry Canners. During the 1940s it added growers in Wisconsin Oregon and Washington and to reflect its new scope changed its name to National Cranberry Association.

Canadian growers were added to the fold in 1950. Urann retired in 1955 and two years later the co-op introduced its first frozen products. To take advantage of the popular Ocean Spray brand name in 1959 the company changed its name to Ocean Spray Cranberries.

EXECUTIVES

Assistant Vice President Internal Audit, Phil Parks
Vice President, Earl Larson
Vice President, Jane Borkowski
Svp Cooperative Dev't., Peter Wyman
Senior Vice President North America, Larry Martin
Senior Vice President Chief Operating Officer, Brian Schiegg
Vice President Cooperative Development General Counsel And Secretary, Rich Stamm
Vice President Marketing Services, Yash Sikand
Treas, Richard A Lees
Auditors: PRICEWATERHOUSECOOPERS LLP BO

LOCATIONS

HQ: OCEAN SPRAY CRANBERRIES, INC.
1 OCEAN SPRAY DR, MIDDLEBORO, MA 023490001
Phone: 508 946-1000
Web: WWW.OCEANSPRAY.COM

PRODUCTS/OPERATIONS

Selected Brands & Products

Dried fruit
- Craisins Blueberry Juice Infused Dried Cranberries
- Craisins Cherry Juice Infused Dried Cranberries
- Craisins Original Dried Cranberries
- Craisins Pomegranate Juice Infused Dried Cranberries
- Craisins Snack Packs
- Craisins Trail Mix - Cranberry & Chocolate
- Craisins Trail Mix - Cranberry Fruit & Nut

Fresh Produce
- Clementines
- Cranberries
- Grapefruit
- Lemons
- Limes
- Oranges
- Tangerines

Instant oatmeal
- Cranberry
- Cranberry Honey Multigrain
- Cranberry Orange Muffin
- Cranberry Pomegranate

Juice

100% Juice Blends
- Blueberry Juice Drinks
- Cran;Energy Energy Juice Drinks
- Cranberry Juice Cocktails
- Cranberry Juice Drink Blends
- Diet Juice Drinks
- Fruit & Veggie Juice
- Fruit & Veggie Juice Drinks
- Grapefruit Juice
- Grapefruit Juice Drinks
- Juice Drinks
- Light Juice Drinks
- On the Go Juice
- On the Go Juice Drinks
- Sugar-Free Drink Mixes
- White Cranberry Juice Drinks

Sauces
- Jellied cranberry sauce
- Whole berry cranberry sauce

COMPETITORS

A. Duda & Sons
Arcade Industries
Cherry Central Cooperative Inc.
Chiquita Brands
Citrus World
Coca-Cola
Coloma Frozen Foods
Cranberries Limited
Dole Food
Dundee Citrus Growers
Edinburg Citrus
Fresh Del Monte Produce
Freshco
Jugos del Valle USA
Mariani Packing
Meridian Nut Growers
Naked Juice
National Grape Cooperative
Nestlé USA
Odwalla
Shoreline Fruit
Sunsweet Growers
Tampico Beverages
Tropicana
Wonderful Company

HISTORICAL FINANCIALS

Company Type: Private

Income Statement FYE: August 31

	REVENUE ($ mil.)	NET INCOME ($ mil.)	NET PROFIT MARGIN	EMPLOYEES
08/17	1,660	272	16.4%	2,000
08/16	1,706	334	19.6%	—
08/15	1,719	317	18.5%	—
Annual Growth	(1.7%)	(7.4%)	—	—

2017 Year-End Financials

Return on assets: 16.1%
Return on equity: 81.6%
Current ratio: 2.30
Cash ($ mil.): 11

OCHSNER CLINIC FOUNDATION

EXECUTIVES

Ceo-Pres, Patrick J Quinlan
Exec V Pres-Dir of Fin, B C Brannon
Project Consultant, Sandy Warren
Endocrinology, Anita Richard
Executive Vice President, Bobby Brannon
Pulmonary Critical Care, Stephen Kantrow
Nurse, Bonnie Foto
Director of Supply Chain, Clifford C Harlan
Referral Coordinator, Denise Usand
Rn, Dennis Pfefferle
Coordinator, Natalie Rodriguez
Auditors: ERNST & YOUNG US LLP FORT WOR

LOCATIONS

HQ: OCHSNER CLINIC FOUNDATION
2614 JEFFERSON HWY, JEFFERSON, LA 701213828
Phone: 504 842-3000
Web: WWW.OCHSNER.ORG

HISTORICAL FINANCIALS

Company Type: Private

Income Statement — FYE: December 31

	REVENUE ($ mil.)	NET INCOME ($ mil.)	NET PROFIT MARGIN	EMPLOYEES
12/17	8,405	128	1.5%	10,500
12/14	2,196	(16)	—	—
12/13	5,550	52	0.9%	—
12/12	4,829	12	0.3%	—
Annual Growth	11.7%	60.1%	—	—

2017 Year-End Financials

Return on assets: 4.9%
Return on equity: 13.3%
Current ratio: 0.60
Cash ($ mil.): 306

OCHSNER HEALTH SYSTEM

Auditors: ERNST & YOUNG LLP NEW ORLEANS

LOCATIONS

HQ: OCHSNER HEALTH SYSTEM
1516 JEFFERSON HWY, NEW ORLEANS, LA 701212429
Phone: 504 842-3483
Web: WWW.OCHSNER.ORG

HISTORICAL FINANCIALS

Company Type: Private

Income Statement — FYE: December 31

	REVENUE ($ mil.)	NET INCOME ($ mil.)	NET PROFIT MARGIN	EMPLOYEES
12/16	2,812	55	2.0%	19,000
12/15	2,592	63	2.5%	—
Annual Growth	8.5%	(13.2%)	—	—

2016 Year-End Financials

Return on assets: 2.4%
Return on equity: 7.8%
Current ratio: 1.40
Cash ($ mil.): 121

OHIO EDISON COMPANY

Ohio Edison has taken a shine to the folks in the Buckeye state. The company distributes electricity to a population of about 2.3 million (more than 1 million customers) in a 7000 sq. ml. area of central and northeastern Ohio. Ohio Edison a unit of FirstEnergy also has 5955 MW of generating capacity from interests in primarily fossil-fueled and nuclear generation facilities and it sells excess power to wholesale customers. The utility's power plants are operated by sister companies FirstEnergy Nuclear and FirstEnergy Generation. Subsidiary Pennsylvania Power Company provides electric service to communities in a 1100 sq. ml. area of western Pennsylvania which has a population of approximately 400000.

Operations

Ohio Edison and Pennsylvania Power provide regulated electric distribution services and procure of generation services. Ohio Edison operates more than 30460 miles of distribution lines and 500 miles of transmission lines.

Geographic Reach

Ohio Edison and Pennsylvania Power conduct business in portions of Ohio and Pennsylvania.

Financial Performance

Revenues decreased by 11% in 2011 due to lower retail generation revenues partially offset by higher distribution and wholesale generation revenues. Retail generation revenues decreased primarily due to a drop in energy sales caused from an increase in customers shopping for alternative power providers and lower average prices across all customer classes.

Ohio Edison's net income decreased by 17% in 2011 due to lower revenues partially offset by lower purchased power costs.

Strategy

In 2011 parent FirstEnergy acquired Allegheny Energy in a $8.5 billion deal that grew FirstEnergy's generation capacity and dramatically boosted the company's position as a leading regional energy provider.

Company Background

FirstEnergy and Ohio Edison reached a settlement in 2005 with the federal government to reduce harmful emissions from its Ohio power generating plants; in addition to fines Ohio Edison has been mandated to pledge $25 million for wind power biomass and other alternative energy sources. In 2009 Ohio Edison began retrofitting two units at its Shadyside Ohio power plant to burn wood and other biomass materials in order to lower its greenhouse gas output.

EXECUTIVES

Sr V Pres-Cfo, James F Pearson
V Pres-Controller*, Harvey L Wagner
Supervisor Reg Operations Line, Darren Puffinburger
Adv Administrative Assistant, Tina Martin
Engineering Supervisor, Chris Hixon
Supervisor Reg Operations West, Damian Wess
Board Member, Ernest Novak
Adv Customer Specialis, Eric Weisenberger
Supervisor Reg Operations Line, Jeffery Akers
Human Resources, R Spiker
Auditors: PRICEWATERHOUSECOOPES LP CLEV

LOCATIONS

HQ: OHIO EDISON COMPANY
76 S MAIN ST BSMT, AKRON, OH 443081817
Phone: 800 736-3402
Web: WWW.FIRSTENERGYCORP.COM

COMPETITORS

Columbia Gas of Ohio
DPL
Dominion East Ohio
Duke Energy Ohio
Ohio Power
Vectren Energy Delivery of Ohio

HISTORICAL FINANCIALS

Company Type: Private

Income Statement — FYE: December 31

	REVENUE ($ mil.)	NET INCOME ($ mil.)	NET PROFIT MARGIN	EMPLOYEES
12/16	1,394	150	10.8%	1,190
12/11	1,633	128	7.8%	—
12/10	1,836	157	8.6%	—
12/09	2,516	122	4.9%	—
Annual Growth	(8.1%)	3.0%	—	—

OHIOHEALTH CORPORATION

Operating throughout the central part of the state OhioHealth aims to keep Buckeyes healthy. The not-for-profit system runs eight acute care hospitals and is affiliated with another 11 community hospitals and area health systems. All told OhioHealth has about 2000 staffed beds in and around Columbus. Additional facilities offer urgent care physical rehabilitation diagnostic imaging and sleep diagnostics services. Subsidiary HomeReach provides home health care and hospice care. Its WorkHealth program offers workers' compensation care management and occupational rehabilitation services. OhioHealth Group OhioHealth's joint venture with The Medical Group of Ohio operates the HealthReach PPO.

Operations

In addition to offering patient care OhioHealth also operates the The OhioHealth Research & Innovation Institute which coordinates research throughout the health system including conducting clinical trials of new drugs and medical devices. The system also operates The Center for Medical Education and Innovation a medical training facility that among other technologies offers human patient simulators on which medical professionals can practice new procedures in various clinical situations.

OhioHealth has some 28000 associates physicians and volunteers. Every year it facilitates approximately 2 million outpatient visits 95000 admissions 346000 emergency department visits 60000 surgeries and 13000 births.

Geographic Reach

OhioHealth operates in the Ohio communities of Athens Columbus Delaware Dublin Kenton Mansfield and Shelby.

Strategy

The company is focused on expanding geographically and capitalizing on opportunities due to population growth in the area. In 2013 it completed the construction of a new patient tower at its Riverside Methodist Hospital; the tower houses much of the company's Neuroscience Institute.

OhioHealth is now building an outpatient facility in Nelsonville which is expected to open sometime in 2017.

The system struck up a partnership with Berger Health System another Ohio-based health care network in 2014. The partners will explore ways to improve health care for the communities they serve.

Mergers and Acquisitions

In 2014 OhioHealth acquired O'Bleness Health System expanding its presence in southeastern Ohio. It also acquired MedCentral Health System.

Company Background

The health system traces its roots back to 1892 when Protestant Hospital (now known as Riverside Methodist Hospital) opened. The system initially organized as U.S. Health Corporation in 1984 later took on the OhioHealth name in 1997.

EXECUTIVES

Senior Vice President And Chief Communications Officer, Sue Jablonski
President And Ceo, David P. Blom, age 66
Evp And Coo, Michael W. (Mike) Louge
President Marion General Hospital, Bruce Hagen
President Riverside Methodist Hospital, Brian D. Jepson
Chief Medical Officer, Bruce Vanderhoff
Svp And Cio, Michael Krouse

Svp External Affairs; President Ohiohealth Foundation, Karen Morrison
President Doctors Hospital, Mike Reichfield
President Ohiohealth Physician Group, Hugh Thornhill
President Ohiohealth Home Care, James P. Newbrough
President O'bleness Hospital, Mark Seckinger
President Mansfield Hospital And Shelby Hospital, Jean Halpin
President Ohiohealth Grant Medical Center, Vinson M. Yates
President Grant Medical Center, Michael Lawson
Svp And Chief Nursing Executive, Donna Hanly
President Dublin Methodist Hospital And Grady Memorial Hospital, Steve Bunyard
Medical Director Trauma And Acute Care Surgery, Shay O'mara
Medical Director Of Hospital Medicine Services, Laura Burelli
Vice President System Service Line Support, Casey Liddy
Vice Chairman, John P. McConnell, age 66
Chairman, Steve Rasmussen
Auditors: PLANTE & MORAN PLLC COLUMBUS

LOCATIONS

HQ: OHIOHEALTH CORPORATION
3430 OHHALTH PKWY FL 5 FLR 5, COLUMBUS, OH 43202
Phone: 614 788-8860
Web: WWW.OHIOHEALTH.COM

PRODUCTS/OPERATIONS

Selected Facilities

Owned
Doctors Hospital (Columbus)
Doctors Hospital Nelsonville (Nelsonville)
Dublin Methodist Hospital (Dublin)
Grady Memorial Hospital (Delaware)
Grant Medical Center (Columbus)
Hardin Memorial Hospital (Kenton)
Marion General Hospital (Marion)
O'Bleness Memorial Hospital (Athens)
Riverside Methodist Hospital (Columbus)
Affiliated
Blanchard Valley Medical Center
Galion Community Hospital (Galion)
Genesis Healthcare System (Zanesville)
Knox Community Hospital
Morrow County Hospital (Mt. Gilead)
Samaritan Regional Health System (Ashland)
Southern Ohio Medical Center (Portsmouth)

COMPETITORS

Adena Health System
Fairfield Medical Center
Licking Memorial Health Systems
Mount Carmel Health
Nationwide Children's Hospital
Regency Hospital
Select Medical

HISTORICAL FINANCIALS

Company Type: Private

Income Statement — FYE: June 30

	REVENUE ($ mil.)	NET INCOME ($ mil.)	NET PROFIT MARGIN	EMPLOYEES
06/19	3,388	542	16.0%	15,000
06/18	4,045	519	12.8%	—
06/17	3,792	631	16.6%	—
06/14	2,179	354	16.3%	—
Annual Growth	9.2%	8.9%	—	—

2019 Year-End Financials

Return on assets: 7.8%
Return on equity: 11.5%
Current ratio: 0.40
Cash ($ mil.): 132

OHIOHEALTH RIVERSIDE METHODIST HOSPITAL

EXECUTIVES

Pres-Ceo, Brian D Jepson
Sr V Pres*, Steve Markovitch
Director of Information Techno, Vandhana V Veerni
Information Specialist, Anne Rhodes
Information Specialist, Elizabeth Queen
Information Specialist, Jeanne Walker
Chief of Medicine, Mark Davis
Technical Manager, James Lowder
Physician, Peter George
Registered Nurse, Ashley Schroeder
Director of Radiology, Dennis Horn

LOCATIONS

HQ: OHIOHEALTH RIVERSIDE METHODIST HOSPITAL
3535 OLENTANGY RIVER RD, COLUMBUS, OH 432143908
Phone: 614 566-5000
Web: WWW.OHIOHEALTH.COM

HISTORICAL FINANCIALS

Company Type: Private

Income Statement — FYE: June 30

	REVENUE ($ mil.)	NET INCOME ($ mil.)	NET PROFIT MARGIN	EMPLOYEES
06/16	1,207	190	15.8%	944
06/15*	19	0	2.3%	—
12/01	49	(1)	—	—
12/00	0	0	—	—
Annual Growth	—	—	—	—

*Fiscal year change

2016 Year-End Financials

Return on assets: 28.3%
Return on equity: —
Current ratio: 0.50
Cash ($ mil.): —

OKLAHOMA STATE UNIVERSITY

Oooooklahoma where the... students come to learn! Oklahoma State University is the flagship campus of its namesake (OSU) system which also includes OSU-Tulsa OSU-Oklahoma City OSU-Okmulgee the OSU Center for Health Sciences in Tulsa the OSU College of Veterinary Medicine and the Oklahoma Agricultural Experiment Station. OSU offers courses in a variety of disciplines and confers undergraduate graduate doctoral and professional degrees in everything from agriculture and the arts to business and engineering. Altogether the system boasts an enrollment of about 36000 students across its five campuses; its student-teacher ratio is about 17:1.

EXECUTIVES

Assoc Vice President Academic Affairs, Gail Gates
Vice President For Univ Relations, Gary C Clark
Vice President For Rsch Technology, Stephen W Mckeever
Vice President, Dana Brunson
Vice President For Research And Technology, Linda Goodwin
Vice President Administration And Finance, David Bosserman
Associate Vice President Chief Budget And Planning Officer, Joseph Weaver
Vice President For Institutional Diversity, Jason Kirksey
Vice President, Cem Diniz
Vice President, Tony Johnson
Managing Director Anethesia Or, Brad White
Vice President Of Fiscal Services, Jim Smith
Vice President, Autumn James
Avp For Research Compliance, Dawn Underwood
Vice President, Breana Houston
Treasurer, Tian Lin
Board Member, Kerry Morton
Treasurer, Matthew Jones
Auditors: GRANT THORNTON LLP OKLAHOMA

LOCATIONS

HQ: OKLAHOMA STATE UNIVERSITY
401 WHITEHURST HALL, STILLWATER, OK 740781030
Phone: 405 744-5000
Web: WWW.CDE.OKSTATE.EDU

PRODUCTS/OPERATIONS

Selected Colleges
Agricultural Sciences and Natural Resources
Arts and Sciences
Education
Engineering Architecture and Technology
Human Sciences
Spears School of Business
Center for Veterinary Health Sciences
Graduate College
Honors College

HISTORICAL FINANCIALS

Company Type: Private

Income Statement — FYE: June 30

	REVENUE ($ mil.)	NET INCOME ($ mil.)	NET PROFIT MARGIN	EMPLOYEES
06/19	904	95	10.6%	8,882
06/18	802	8	1.1%	—
06/17	815	40	5.0%	—
Annual Growth	5.3%	54.2%	—	—

2019 Year-End Financials

Return on assets: 3.9%
Return on equity: 9.8%
Current ratio: 2.70
Cash ($ mil.): 159

OMAHA PUBLIC SCHOOLS

EXECUTIVES

Supt, Cheryl Logan
Controller, Dr Liz Standish
Assist Superintendent, Dr Dennis Pool
Coordinator, Suann Witt
Assistant, Jennifer Schlapia
Health Professional, Kari Caddell
Project Coordinator, Lesley Dean
Coordinator, Lisa Thompson
Special Education, Aaron Brooker
School Nurse, Andrea Lostaglia-Hosko
Computer Technology Teacher, Angela Reick
Auditors: SEIM JOHNSON LLP OMAHA NEBR

LOCATIONS

HQ: OMAHA PUBLIC SCHOOLS
3215 CUMING ST, OMAHA, NE 681312000
Phone: 402 557-2120
Web: WWW.OPS.ORG

HISTORICAL FINANCIALS

Company Type: Private

Income Statement FYE: August 31

	REVENUE ($ mil.)	NET INCOME ($ mil.)	NET PROFIT MARGIN	EMPLOYEES
08/18	763	20	2.7%	8,000
08/17	720	33	4.7%	—
08/16	693	(41)	—	—
08/15	626	126	20.3%	—
Annual Growth	6.9%	(45.4%)	—	—

2018 Year-End Financials

Return on assets: 1.4%
Return on equity: —
Current ratio: —
Cash ($ mil.): 305

ONEOK PARTNERS, L.P.

For ONEOK Partners it's OK to have three businesses: natural gas pipelines; gas gathering and processing; and natural gas liquids (NGLs). Its pipelines include Midwestern Gas Transmission Guardian Pipeline Viking Gas Transmission and OkTex Pipeline. The ONEOK affiliate operates 17100 miles of gas-gathering pipeline and 7600 miles of transportation pipeline as well as gas processing plants and storage facilities (with 52 billion cu. ft. of capacity). It also owns one of the US's top natural NGL systems (more than 7200 miles of pipeline). In 2017 41%-owner ONEOK agreed to buy the stock of ONEOK Partners that it did not already own for $9.3 billion in a stock deal. Operations ONEOK Partners operates in three business segments: natural gas gathering and processing; natural gas pipelines; and natural gas liquids. Geographic Reach The company gathers and processes natural gas in the Mid-Continent region which includes the NGL-rich Cana-Woodford Shale and Granite Wash formations the Mississippian Lime formation of Oklahoma and Kansas and the Hugoton and Central Kansas Uplift Basins of Kansas. The Natural Gas Pipelines segment owns and operates regulated natural gas transmission pipelines natural gas storage facilities and natural gas gathering systems for nonprocessed gas. It also provide interstate natural gas transportation and storage service. The company's interstate natural gas pipeline assets transport natural gas through pipelines in North Dakota Minnesota Wisconsin Illinois Indiana Kentucky Tennessee Oklahoma Texas and New Mexico. Its Natural gas liquids assets provide nondiscretionary services to producers that consist of facilities that gather fractionate and treat NGLs and store NGL products primarily in Oklahoma Kansas and Texas. It also owns or has stakes in natural gas liquids gathering and distribution pipelines in Oklahoma Kansas Texas Wyoming and Colorado and terminal and storage facilities in Missouri Nebraska Iowa and Illinois. In addition it owns natural gas liquids distribution and refined petroleum products pipelines in Kansas Missouri Nebraska Iowa Illinois and Indiana that connect the company's Mid-Continent assets with Midwest markets including Chicago.

Financial Performance

Revenues decreased by 10% in 2012 due to lower net realized natural gas and NGL product prices offset partially by higher natural gas and NGL sales volumes from completed capital projects. The increase in natural gas supply resulting from the development of nonconventional resource areas in North America and a warmer than normal winter caused natural gas prices to drop. NGL prices particularly ethane and propane also decreased in 2012 due primarily to increased NGL production and an increase in available supply. Propane prices also were affected by a warmer than normal winter.

ONEOK Partners' net income grew by 7% in 2012 thanks to lower costs of sales and fuels and lower interest expenses.

Strategy

The company pursues a strategy of building up its fee-based earnings coupled with organic growth and complementary acquisitions in both conventional oil and gas and unconventional (shale plays).

It is looking to increase NGL volumes gathered and fractionated in its NGL segment and natural gas volumes processed in its natural gas gathering and processing segment as producers continue to develop NGL-rich resource plays in the Mid-Continent and Rocky Mountain areas.

In 2012 ONEOK Partners announced plans to invest up to $360 million to grow its projects in the Woodford Shale formation.

Company Background

ONEOK Partners was formed in 2006 when ONEOK spun off its gathering and processing NGLs pipelines and storage businesses for $3 billion following that company's acquisition of Northern Border Partners (which was founded in 1993). Building out its assets in 2007 the company acquired an interstate pipeline system from Kinder Morgan Energy Partners for $300 million.

EXECUTIVES

Pres-Ceo, Terry K Spencer
Evp-Cfo, Walter S Hulse III
Svp,naturalgasgathering&procce, Michael A Fitzgibbons
Executive Vice President Opera, Robert F Martinovich

LOCATIONS

HQ: ONEOK PARTNERS, L.P.
100 W 5TH ST STE LL, TULSA, OK 741034298
Phone: 918 588-7000
Web: WWW.ONEOK.COM

PRODUCTS/OPERATIONS

Natural Gas Pipelines

Midwestern Gas Transmission Company
Viking Gas Transmission Company
Guardian Pipeline
OkTex Pipeline Company
ONEOK Gas Transportation
ONEOK Gas Gathering
ONEOK Gas Storage
ONEOK WesTex Transmission
ONEOK Texas Gas Storage
Mid Continent Market Center
ONEOK Transmission Company
Natural Gas Gathering & Processing
Crestone Energy Ventures
ONEOK Field Services
ONEOK Rockies Midstream

COMPETITORS

Enbridge
Kinder Morgan Energy Partners
Panhandle Eastern Pipe Line
TransCanada

HISTORICAL FINANCIALS

Company Type: Private

Income Statement FYE: December 31

	REVENUE ($ mil.)	NET INCOME ($ mil.)	NET PROFIT MARGIN	EMPLOYEES
12/16	8,918	1,072	12.0%	2,364
12/15	7,761	597	7.7%	—
12/14	12,191	911	7.5%	—
Annual Growth	(14.5%)	8.5%	—	—

2016 Year-End Financials

Return on assets: 6.9%
Return on equity: 17.4%
Current ratio: 0.40
Cash ($ mil.): —

ORANGE AND ROCKLAND UTILITIES INC

Orange and Rockland Utilities (O&R) operates under the auspices of its big city cousin holding company Consolidated Edison (Con Edison). O&R's subsidiaries Rockland Electric and Pike County Power & Light operate in southeastern New York and adjacent portions of New Jersey and Pennsylvania. The utilities distribute electricity to more than 301800 customers in about 100 communities in those three states and deliver natural gas more than to 128000 customers in New York and Pennsylvania. O&R's transmission and distribution facilities include 5550 miles of overhead and underground power distribution lines 560 miles of transmission lines and more than 1850 miles of gas pipeline.

EXECUTIVES

Pres, John McAvoy
Pres*, William G Longhi
V Pres*, Francis Peverly

LOCATIONS

HQ: ORANGE AND ROCKLAND UTILITIES INC
1 BLUE HILL PLZ STE 20, PEARL RIVER, NY 109653100
Phone: 845 352-6000
Web: WWW.ORU.COM

PRODUCTS/OPERATIONS

2011 Sales

	$ mil.	% of total
Electric	641	75
Gas	214	25
Total	**855**	**100**

Subsidiaries

Subsidiaries
Pike County Light & Power Company
Rockland Electric Company

COMPETITORS

Avangrid
Delmarva Power
Enbridge
National Fuel Gas
New Jersey Resources
Niagara Mohawk
PPL Corporation
Public Service Enterprise Group

HISTORICAL FINANCIALS

Company Type: Private

Income Statement				FYE: December 31
	REVENUE ($ mil.)	NET INCOME ($ mil.)	NET PROFIT MARGIN	EMPLOYEES
12/16	653	59	9.1%	1,060
12/05	824	50	6.1%	—
12/04	703	46	6.5%	—
12/03	727	45	6.2%	—
Annual Growth	(0.8%)	2.1%	—	—

2016 Year-End Financials

Return on assets: 2.1%
Return on equity: 9.2%
Current ratio: 0.50
Cash ($ mil.): —

ORANGE COUNTY HEALTH AUTHORITY, A PUBLIC AGENCY

EXECUTIVES

Ceo, Richard Chambers
Ceo, Michael Schrader
Chief Medical Officer, Richard Helmer
Chief Operating Officer, Ladan Khamseh
Chief Counsel, Gary Crockett
Chief Administrative Officer, Kim Cunningham
General Counsel, George L Root
Telecommunications Admi, Chris Williams
Coordinator, Barbara Collins
Information Specialist, Faye Heidari
Information Specialist, Patrick Maez

LOCATIONS

HQ: ORANGE COUNTY HEALTH AUTHORITY, A PUBLIC AGENCY
505 CITY PKWY W, ORANGE, CA 928682924
Phone: 714 246-8500
Web: WWW.CALOPTIMA.ORG

HISTORICAL FINANCIALS

Company Type: Private

Income Statement				FYE: June 30
	REVENUE ($ mil.)	NET INCOME ($ mil.)	NET PROFIT MARGIN	EMPLOYEES
06/09	1,078	(17)	—	432
06/05	812	(24)	—	—
06/04	0	0	—	—
06/03	756	1	0.2%	—
Annual Growth	6.1%	—	—	—

2009 Year-End Financials

Return on assets: (-5.2%)
Return on equity: (-13.3%)
Current ratio: 1.00
Cash ($ mil.): 81

ORANGE COUNTY TRANSPORTATION AUTHORITY

Public transportation in sunny Orange County California is overseen by the Orange County Transportation Authority (OCTA). The OCTA is the main provider of bus services in its 800-sq.-mi. territory which is home to more than 3 million people. In cooperation with the Southern California Regional Rail Authority the OCTA oversees Metrolink commuter rail service in Orange County. The agency also operates a 10-mile toll road and issues permits to taxi operators. Revenue from a half-cent local sales tax allows the agency to pay for road improvement and mass transit projects.

Operations

OCTA builds designs operates plans maintains and regulates the robust transportation network within Orange County. In addition to the four modes of transportation (transit driving bicycling and walking) OCTA oversees paratransit services taxi services light rail commuter rail and high?occupancy managed lanes.

It operates rail service for OCTA centers on Metrolink Southern California's commuter rail system linking residential communities to employment and activity centers. Metrolink is operated by the Southern California Regional Rail Authority- a joint powers authority of five member agencies representing the counties of Los Angeles Orange Riverside San Bernardino and Ventura. OCTA is one of the five member agencies that administers Orange County Metrolink activities.

The 91 Express Lanes is a four-lane 10-mile toll road built in the median of California's Riverside Freeway (SR-91) between the Orange/Riverside County line and the SR-55.

Geographic Reach

The company is located in Southern California - south of Los Angeles County north of San Diego County and west of Riverside and San Bernardino counties.

Financial Performance

OCTA's rail budget for fiscal year 2015-16 consists of both operating and capital expenses. Operating expenses in FY 2015-16 are budgeted at $31.6 million while capital expenditures are anticipated to reach $100.4 million. The FY 2015-16 rail capital projects. The organization saw a decline in its budget for FY 2015-16 due to drop in passenger fares and state assistance federal capital assistance grants.

(OCTA uses its revenue primarily in salaries and benefits professional services and capital expenditure).

Strategy

The 2014 - 2019 OCTA Strategic Plan takes a comprehensive forward-looking approach to address Orange County's transportation needs during the next five years.(OCTA maintains a Long-Range Transportation Plan updated every four years to account for new planning efforts as well as changes in demographics economic conditions and available sources of transportation funding).

In the FY 2015-16 budget $6.9 million of Measure M funds deposited in the General Fund are being used to fund the final work on the West County Connectors project.

After four years in the making OCTA marked the completion of the $297 million West County Connector project in 2014 which will bring congestion relief where three major freeways (Interstate 405 Interstate 605 and State Route 22) converge.

In 2014 OCTA purchased 400 new buses for fixed-route and ACCESS services. This purchase combined with the in-process repainting of the existing fleet presents a cost-effective opportunity to explore new branding concepts for Orange County bus services.

Company Background

OCTA was formed in 1991 in a consolidation of seven transportation agencies.

EXECUTIVES

Ceo, Darrell Johnson
Dir*, Don Hansen
Director, Charles V Smith
Digital Marketing Specialist, Jacqueline Moon
Office Specialist Assistant, Leslie Tuiteleleapaga
Vanpool Administrator, Tracy McConnell
Coach Operator, Anthony McCollough
Supervisor, Abel Enriquez
Auditors: VAVRINEK TRINE DAY & CO LL

LOCATIONS

HQ: ORANGE COUNTY TRANSPORTATION AUTHORITY
550 S MAIN ST, ORANGE, CA 928684506
Phone: 714 636-7433
Web: WWW.OCTA.NET

PRODUCTS/OPERATIONS

2014 Sales

	$ mil.	% of total
Sales taxes	451	93
Unrestricted investment earning	18	4
Property taxes	12	3
Other	0	-
Total	482	100

Selected Services

91 Express Lanes toll facility
Bus transit service
Freeway improvements funding
Freeway Service Patrol
Long-range planning
Measure M2 administration
Metrolink rail service
Rideshare options
Street and road improvements grants
Taxi administration program
Vanpool subsidies

HISTORICAL FINANCIALS

Company Type: Private

Income Statement				FYE: June 30
	REVENUE ($ mil.)	NET INCOME ($ mil.)	NET PROFIT MARGIN	EMPLOYEES
06/18	634	(53)	—	1,050
06/17	611	54	9.0%	—
06/16	600	67	11.2%	—
06/15	607	43	7.2%	—
Annual Growth	1.5%	—	—	—

OREGON DEPARTMENT OF TRANSPORTATION

The Oregon Department of Transportation (ODOT) helps move people and goods across the state. The agency strives to provide a safe and efficient transportation system – including highway rail and public transit – for its residents. The department is responsible for construction and maintenance of highways and bridges improving public transportation services reducing traffic crashes and ensuring equal access for low-income and elderly citizens as well as people with disabilities. Its division of driver and motor vehicles (DMV) provides vehicle registration driver licenses and ID cards. The agency also tries to decrease the impact that its transportation system has on air and water quality.

EXECUTIVES

Dir, Mathew Garrett
Coordinator, Basil Christopher
Chief Procurement Officer, Kathy Booher
Chief Human Resources Officer, Madilyn Zike
Manager, Randy Gengler
Manager, Anna Giddens-Reed
Assistant Project Manager, Jennifer Pearce

LOCATIONS

HQ: OREGON DEPARTMENT OF TRANSPORTATION
355 CAPITOL ST NE MS21, SALEM, OR 973013871
Phone: 503 378-5849
Web: WWW.OREGON.GOV

HISTORICAL FINANCIALS

Company Type: Private

Income Statement — FYE: June 30

	REVENUE ($ mil.)	NET INCOME ($ mil.)	NET PROFIT MARGIN	EMPLOYEES
06/19	2,260	56	2.5%	4,800
06/18	2,017	23	1.2%	—
06/05	0	0	—	—
06/03	461	(198)	—	—
Annual Growth	10.4%	—	—	—

2019 Year-End Financials

Return on assets: 3.6%
Return on equity: 5.7%
Current ratio: 2.40
Cash ($ mil.): 958

OREGON HEALTH & SCIENCE UNIVERSITY

Oregon Health & Science University (OHSU) is the state's sole institution providing doctoral degrees in medicine dentistry and nursing. Its other two schools are science and engineering and in partnership with Oregon State University pharmacy. OHSU has about 2900 students. The university is also home to two hospitals (one a children's hospital) as well as specialty and primary care clinics research and interdisciplinary centers and community service programs. OHSU traces its roots to 1867 when members of the medical department at Willamette University began the first formal medical education program in Oregon.

Operations

OHSU's medical school has a small student-teacher ratio at just 4:1. The organization is renowned for its research initiatives. It has about 3000 active research projects and produced about 130 inventions in 2014. OHSU receives about $370 million in research funding each year. The school engages in an array of multidisciplinary research projects including diseases of the central nervous system weight regulation cancer rare genetic disorders and infectious disease.

Much of the university's medical research is performed at or in concert with clinical care operations at the University Hospital the Doernbecher Children's Hospital and other family care and specialty centers. The medical centers care for some 260000 patients each year.

Researchers at OHSU's Stem Cell Center worked with the Oregon National Primate Research Center to pioneer the first successful cloned nonhuman primate embryonic stem cells. Such cells could help stem cell research gain acceptance as the human element that causes such controversy has been removed.

Geographic Reach

OHSU's main campus includes about 40 buildings on 120 acres on Marquam Hill (overlooking downtown Portland). OHSU also operates two smaller research locations: The Schnitzer Campus in Portland and the West Campus in Hillsboro.

Financial Performance

The university's revenue totaled $2.5 billion in 2015 (versus less than $2 billion in 2012). The earnings primarily came from patient service revenue gifts grants and contracts. Net income increased 49% that year to $320 million thanks to the growing revenues.

OHSU has an operating budget of some $2.4 billion.

Strategy

OHSU completed construction of its collaborative life sciences building on the Schnitzer Campus in 2014. The 650000-sq.-ft. building features lecture halls classrooms specialty research centers offices simulation centers and serves as home to the School of Dentistry; it was built on land donated by the Schnitzer family in 2004. OHSU has purchased additional parcels of land in the area for future expansion efforts.

Also in 2014 OHSU partnered with the small hospital Mid-Columbia Medical Center (MCMC) to recruit medical professionals. Recruits will be employees of OHSU and their services will be leased to MCMC.

The system is working with Adventist Health Kaiser Permanente and Legacy Health to open up the Portland area's first comprehensive behavioral health center (to be named the Unity Center for Behavioral Health). It is expected to open in late 2016.

EXECUTIVES

Executive Vice President Chief Financial Officer, Lawrence J. Furnstahl
Evp And Executive Director Ohsu Hospitals And Clinics, Peter F. Rapp
President And Director, Joseph (Joe) Robertson
Dean School Of Medicine, Mark Richardson
Executive Vice President And Provost, Jeanette Mladenovic
Medical Director Pediatric Bone Marrow Transplantation Program, Eneida Nemecek
Senior Vice President, Constance French
Regional Vice President, Tom Wang
Senior Vice President Technology, Jackie Wirz
Director Of Admissions, Debbie Melton
Associate Vice President, Donald Lollar
Vice President Technology And Services, Nancy Goldschmidt
Medical Director, Zane Horowitz
Vice President Technology Transfer And Business Development, Brendan Rauw
Medical Director, Jim Chesnutt
Vice President Of Medical Affairs, Mariah Null Mason
Executive Vice President, Elena Andresen
Medical Director, Scott Naugler
Medical Director, Don Spight
Senior Vice President Of Human Resources, E F Keeling
Vice President Ohsu Asda, Alexa Brightman
Chairman, Charles A. Wilhoite
Vice Chairman, Jay Waldron
Treasurer, Thomas Hilton
Secretary, Diana Gernhart
Diplomate American Board Of Orthodontics, Ross Kaplan
Treasurer, Diane Price
Auditors: KPMG LLP PORTLAND OR

LOCATIONS

HQ: OREGON HEALTH & SCIENCE UNIVERSITY
3181 SW SAM JACKSON PK RD, PORTLAND, OR 972393011
Phone: 503 494-8311
Web: WWW.OHSU.EDU

PRODUCTS/OPERATIONS

Selected schools

School of Dentistry
School of Medicine
School of Nursing
School of Pharmacy (with Oregon State University)
School of Science & Engineering

HISTORICAL FINANCIALS

Company Type: Private

Income Statement — FYE: June 30

	REVENUE ($ mil.)	NET INCOME ($ mil.)	NET PROFIT MARGIN	EMPLOYEES
06/20	3,313	(13)	—	19,500
06/19	3,178	251	7.9%	—
06/18	3,050	259	8.5%	—
06/17	2,846	222	7.8%	—
Annual Growth	5.2%	—	—	—

2020 Year-End Financials

Return on assets: (-0.2%)
Return on equity: (-0.4%)
Current ratio: 2.30
Cash ($ mil.): 422

OREGON STATE LOTTERY

The Oregon State Lottery operates the Beaver State's lottery and other state-run games of chance. It offers traditional lotto numbers games and instant-win tickets and it operates video lottery and video poker machines. Oregon also takes part in the multistate Powerball drawing. About 65% of the lottery's profits are channeled into public education programs while the rest is used to fund economic development projects state parks and other government programs. Oregon created its lottery in 1984.

EXECUTIVES

Comm, Chris Telfer
Comm*, Elisa Dozono
Comm*, Mary Wheat
Comm*, Raul Valdivia
Comm*, Liz Carle
Dir*, Barry Pack
Coordinator, Sharon Ingram
Coordinator, James B Scheppke
Manager, Eric White
Senior Quality Assurance Analy, Gavin Araki
Video Support Manager, Chris Bagger

LOCATIONS

HQ: OREGON STATE LOTTERY
500 AIRPORT RD SE, SALEM, OR 973015068
Phone: 503 540-1000
Web: WWW.OREGONLOTTERY.ORG

COMPETITORS

California State Lottery
Multi-State Lottery
Washington State Lottery

HISTORICAL FINANCIALS

Company Type: Private

Income Statement — FYE: June 30

	REVENUE ($ mil.)	NET INCOME ($ mil.)	NET PROFIT MARGIN	EMPLOYEES
06/19	1,347	7	0.5%	420
06/18	1,302	(14)	—	—
06/16	1,230	61	5.0%	—
Annual Growth	3.1%	(51.0%)	—	—

2019 Year-End Financials

Return on assets: 1.0%
Return on equity: 2.6%
Current ratio: 1.50
Cash ($ mil.): 317

OREGON UNIVERSITY SYSTEM

Auditors: CLIFTONLARSONALLEN LLP GREENW

LOCATIONS

HQ: OREGON UNIVERSITY SYSTEM
, EUGENE, OR 97403
Phone: 541 737-0827
Web: WWW.OUS.EDU

HISTORICAL FINANCIALS

Company Type: Private

Income Statement — FYE: June 30

	REVENUE ($ mil.)	NET INCOME ($ mil.)	NET PROFIT MARGIN	EMPLOYEES
06/14	1,782	83	4.7%	26,000
06/13	1,701	14	0.8%	—
06/12	1,657	10	0.6%	—
06/08	1,251	80	6.4%	—
Annual Growth	6.1%	0.6%	—	—

2014 Year-End Financials

Return on assets: 9.8%
Return on equity: 4.7%
Current ratio: 1.30
Cash ($ mil.): 456

ORLANDO HEALTH, INC.

It's not Disney World but for Floridians needing health care it is a prime destination. Orlando Health is a not-for-profit organization with a network of community and specialty hospitals with nearly 2300 beds in Central Florida. Its flagship facility the Orlando Regional Medical Center features a Level 1 trauma center and provides comprehensive acute care services in a range of specialties. Orlando Health also operates several community hospitals. Its specialty hospitals include the Arnold Palmer Hospital for Children and the Winnie Palmer Hospital for Women and Babies. It also operates the renowned M. D. Anderson Cancer Center Orlando (the first affiliate of Houston-based M. D. Anderson center).

Operations

In addition to the Orlando Regional Medical Center and three fully owned community hospitals the company operates two medical centers through partnerships. It holds a 50% stake in the South Lake Hospital and a 20% stake in the St. Cloud Regional Medical Center. It also operates physician practice associations and an emergency air transport service (Air Care).

Across its facilities Orlando Health has about 2000 affiliated physicians who provide a full spectrum of health care services. Areas of clinical excellence include heart and vascular care cancer care obstetrics and gynecology neonatology neurosciences surgery pediatric orthopedics and sports medicine. Annually Orlando Health serves more than 2 million residents of central Florida and 4500 international patients. The organization also provides between $250 and $300 million in community health programs each year.

As a statutory teaching hospital system Orlando Health also engages in medical training programs through affiliation agreements with the University of Central Florida College of Medicine and other institutions. Orlando Health offers a number of medical residency and fellowship programs; its seven residencies are offered to 250 participants and include programs in emergency medicine internal medicine OB-GYN orthopedic surgery pathology and pediatrics. The organization also conducts research studies and clinical trials through partnerships with educational and commercial organizations.

Geographic Reach

Orlando Health operates throughout Orlando and in neighboring Clermont Longwood Ocoee and St. Cloud Florida.

Financial Performance

The company's revenues increased by 9% in 2014 due to higher net patient service revenues and other revenues. Medicare accounted for 23% of the net patient revenues; Medicaid 19%.

Orlando Health's net income grew by 349% due to higher revenues and investment income.

Operating cash flow increased by 235% in 2014.

Strategy

Orlando Health is working to improve its operating model by improving the quality of patient outcomes; enhancing collaboration between physicians medical professionals hospitals research centers and other institutions; and increasing clinical integration of various disciplines to share resources and skills.

As an example of its collaborative and quality enhancement efforts Orlando Health is involved in the formation of a regional health information exchange to connect its electronic health record (EHR) systems with other Central Florida health providers and the public health department. The program aims to improve quality of care by eliminating redundant tests and other repeated efforts as well as by providing hospitals swift access to patient data.

Orlando Health is also focused on making improvements to its Orlando Regional Medical Center through a multi-year $297-million renovation project. In 2015 the company opened its new 245-bed 10-story 345000-square-foot North Tower's front entrance and its existing Orlando Regional Medical Center building now will be referred to as Orlando Regional Medical Center South Tower. The North Tower is part of the hospital's redesign and renovation project and includes an expanded emergency department cardiovascular service areas operating suites and other ancillary services located inside Orlando Regional Medical CenterSouth Tower. The South Tower expansion is expected to was completed in 2015. That year the Orlando Regional Medical Center redesign and renovation project continued with its Surgical Services expansion and renovation. The 28000-square-foot addition includes 10 new operating rooms a new Post Anesthesia Care Unit area with 24 patient bays.

Other planned projects include the expansion of the neonatal intensive care unit at Winnie Palmer Hospital for Women and Babies.

In 2015 Orlando Health Physician Associates officially opened its doors in the Lake Nona area.

That year the West Orange Healthcare District awarded a $13.8 million grant to Health Central Hospital to expand. The grant was the second largest in the history of the district and funded 75 percent of the total expansion costs. Orlando Health funded the remaining 25 percent. Upon completion the expansion project will add 40 rooms to Health Central Hospital increasing its bed count from 171 to 211 and enabling the further development of specialized care.

Mergers and Acquisitions

In 2015 Orlando Health Physician Associates acquired Pediatric Associates of Orlando. Founded in 1939 it was one of the first pediatric practices in Central Florida.

Company Background

In 2012 Arnold Palmer Hospital added an outpatient rehabilitation center.

The health system expanded its network in 2012 by acquiring the 170-bed Health Central Hospital and its associated facilities in Ocoee Florida for $181 million. Orlando Health further expanded through the purchase of Physician Associates a professional practice organization in 2013.

Orlando Health was founded in 1918.

EXECUTIVES

Vp Information Services And Cio, Rick Schooler
President And Ceo, David W. Strong
Svp; President Arnold Palmer Medical Center And Orlando Health Foundation, John Bozard
Senior Vice President President Adult Hospitals Group, Shannon Elswick
President South Seminole Hospital, Steve Glazier
Cfo, Bernadette Spong
Vp; Executive Director Orlando Health Foundation, Karen Jensen
President Dr. P. Phillips Hospital, Mark A. Jones
Coo, Jessica Wertman
Medical Director, Muhammad Jawad
Medical Director, Alix Casler
Vice President And Senior Development Officer, Lee Ann Fleming
Director, Dianna Morgan
Department Secretary, Julie Bishop
Auditors: GRANT THORNTON LLP ORLANDO F

LOCATIONS

HQ: ORLANDO HEALTH, INC.
52 W UNDERWOOD ST, ORLANDO, FL 328061110
Phone: 407 841-5111
Web: WWW.ORLANDOHEALTH.COM

PRODUCTS/OPERATIONS

2014 Sales

	$ mil.	% of total
Net patient service revenue less provision for bad debts	2,010	95
Other revenue	103	5
Net assets released from restrictions	4	-
Total	2,118	100

Selected Facilities

Arnold Palmer Hospital for Children (Orlando)
Dr. P. Phillips Hospital (formerly Orlando Regional Sand Lake Hospital Orlando)
Health Central Hospital (Ocoee)
Lucerne Pavilion (Orlando)
M. D. Anderson Cancer Center Orlando
Orlando Health Heart Institute
Orlando Health Rehabilitation Institute

Orlando Regional Medical Center
South Lake Hospital (50% affiliate Clermont)
South Seminole Hospital (Longwood)
St. Cloud Regional Medical Center (20% affiliate)
Winnie Palmer Hospital for Women & Babies (Orlando)

Selected Specialties

Cancer care (at M. D. Anderson Cancer Center Orlando)
Emergency and trauma care
Heart and vascular
Neurosciences
Oncology/hematology
Orthopedic and sports medicine
Surgery
Women's services

Selected Services

Anesthesiology
Brain Injury Rehabilitation Center (BIRC)
Endocrinology (diabetes)
Endoscopy
Epilepsy care
Home health care
Infectious diseases
Internal medicine
Laboratory and pathology Services
Mammography
Memory Disorder Center
MRI
Multiple sclerosis treatment
Nephrology
Nuclear medicine
Ophthalmology
Otolaryngology (Ears Nose Throat)
Pain management
Patient and family counseling
Pediatric outpatient surgery
Pulmonary medicine
Radiology and diagnostic imaging
Rehabilitation and physical therapy

COMPETITORS

Adventist Health System Sunbelt Healthcare
All Children's Hospital
Baptist Health South Florida
Baptist Health System
Community Health Systems
Florida Hospital Heartland
Florida Hospital Waterman
HCA
Health First
Holmes Regional Medical Center
Mayo Clinic Jacksonville
Mount Sinai Medical Center of Florida
Munroe Regional Health System
Nemours Foundation
Ocala Regional Medical Center
Osceola Regional Medical Center
St. Vincent's Health System
UF&Shands

HISTORICAL FINANCIALS

Company Type: Private

Income Statement — FYE: September 30

	REVENUE ($ mil.)	NET INCOME ($ mil.)	NET PROFIT MARGIN	EMPLOYEES
09/14	1,663	231	13.9%	23,000
09/13	1,576	115	7.3%	—
09/10	1,700	91	5.4%	—
Annual Growth	(0.6%)	26.1%	—	—

2014 Year-End Financials

Return on assets: 9.8%
Return on equity: 20.5%
Current ratio: 2.30
Cash ($ mil.): 65

ORLEANS PARISH SCHOOL DISTRICT

EXECUTIVES

Supt, Stanley Smith
Ceo-Supt*, Alphonse G Davis
Coo*, Roger Reese
Principal, Victor Gordon
Security Officer, Jade Fisher
Assistant Director of Ecs, Kathryn Elichman
Director of Facility Maintenan, Paul Lucius
Auditors: LA PORTE METAIRIE LA

LOCATIONS

HQ: ORLEANS PARISH SCHOOL DISTRICT
3520 GEN DE GAULLE STE 5, NEW ORLEANS, LA 70114
Phone: 504 304-3520
Web: WWW.FCWCS.ORG

HISTORICAL FINANCIALS

Company Type: Private

Income Statement — FYE: June 30

	REVENUE ($ mil.)	NET INCOME ($ mil.)	NET PROFIT MARGIN	EMPLOYEES
06/19	626	10	1.6%	7,062
06/17	433	(0)	—	—
06/16	473	46	9.8%	—
06/05	419	19	4.7%	—
Annual Growth	2.9%	(4.7%)	—	—

2019 Year-End Financials

Return on assets: 0.5%
Return on equity: 0.6%
Current ratio: —
Cash ($ mil.): 33

OSF HEALTHCARE SYSTEM

OSF Healthcare helps patients who are feeling oh-so-frail in northern Illinois and southwestern Michigan. OSF Healthcare system includes 11 acute care hospitals and one long-term care facility that combined are home to more than 1500 beds and offer a full spectrum of inpatient and outpatient medical and surgical services. The system's primary care physician network consists of about 650 physicians at more than 105 locations throughout its service area. Subsidiary OSF Home Care provides hospice home visit and equipment services and OSF Saint Francis provides ambulance pharmacy and health care management services. The not-for-profit system is a subsidiary of the Sisters of The Third Order of St. Francis.

Operations

Along with its various acute care hospitals OSF Healthcare provides urgent care through its OSF PromptCare locations. PromptCare administers a range of services including labs MRI ultrasound and primary and specialty care.

The company also has two colleges of nursing – Saint Francis Medical Center College of Nursing in Peoria Illinois; and the Saint Anthony College of Nursing in Rockford Illinois.

The system had some 58000 inpatient admissions; 1.3 million outpatient visits; and 254000 emergency department visits in 2014.

Financial Performance

In 2014 gross patient services revenue totaled $6.9 billion.

Strategy

OSF Healthcare has an incubation collaboration with the University of Illinois College of Medicine at Peoria. The venture dubbed Jump Trading Simulation and Education Center was established in 2013 to focus on advances in education research and innovation. It has been involved in such activities as funding 3-D printing for surgical procedures and exposing high school students to medical training experiences.

EXECUTIVES

Ceo, Robert Sehring
Cmo*, Harley Brooks
Ceo Northern Region, Carol Friesen
Consultant, Dick Brooks
Executive Officer, Judith Duva
Staff, Marc Matulis
Corporate Office Site Director, Mike Redd
Executive Officer, Ruth Clift
Senior Vice President, Robert Sawicki
Auditors: KPMG LLP CHICAGO ILLINOIS

LOCATIONS

HQ: OSF HEALTHCARE SYSTEM
800 NE GLEN OAK AVE, PEORIA, IL 616033200
Phone: 309 655-2850
Web: WWW.OSFHEALTHCARE.ORG

PRODUCTS/OPERATIONS

Selected Clinical Services

Cancer Care
Diabetes & Endocrinology
Emergency Services
Heart & Vascular
Home Health
Hospice
Neurosciences
Pediatrics
Primary Care
Rehabilitation
Surgery
Transplant Services
Weight Loss Management
Women's Health

Selected Support Services

Advance Care Planning
Clinical Research
Equipment Technology Services
Home Infusion Pharmacy
Home Medical Equipment
Mobile Medical Systems
OSF Life Flight
Retail Services
Skilled Nursing Network
System Laboratory
Telehealth

Selected Facilities

OSF Holy Family Medical Center (Monmouth IL)
OSF Saint Anthony Medical Center (Rockford IL)
OSF Saint Clare Home (Peoria Heights IL)
OSF Saint Elizabeth Medical Center (formerly Ottowa Regional Hospital Ottowa IL)
OSF Saint Francis Medical Center (Peoria IL)
OSF Saint James - John W. Albrecht Medical Center (Pontiac IL)
OSF St. Mary Medical Center (Galesburg IL)
OSF St. Francis Hospital (Escanaba MI)
OSF St. Joseph Medical Center (Bloomington IL)

COMPETITORS

Advocate BroMenn
Centegra Health System
Central DuPage Hospital
Covenant HealthCare
Genesis Health System
McDonough District Hospital
Memorial Health System
Northwestern Memorial HealthCare
Rush-Copley Medical Center
SwedishAmerican Health System
University of Chicago Medical Center
University of Michigan Health System
Wheaton Franciscan Services

HISTORICAL FINANCIALS

Company Type: Private

Income Statement FYE: September 30

	REVENUE ($ mil.)	NET INCOME ($ mil.)	NET PROFIT MARGIN	EMPLOYEES
09/18	2,826	155	5.5%	4,000
09/17	2,561	144	5.7%	—
09/16	2,422	99	4.1%	—
09/15	86	19	22.3%	—
Annual Growth	220.1%	100.6%	—	—

2018 Year-End Financials

Return on assets: 3.9%
Return on equity: 9.9%
Current ratio: 1.60
Cash ($ mil.): 233

OU MEDICINE, INC.

EXECUTIVES

Prin, Steven Davis
Prin, Amy Sine
Prin, Armand Paliota
Vice President, Renee Landry
Project Manager, Brandi Wolff
Manager, Chris Wallace
Administrator, Joel Peebles
Manager, Kristian Brown
Vice President, Toni Steele
Surgical Pathology Supervisor, Ashley Hunzie

LOCATIONS

HQ: OU MEDICINE, INC.
700 NE 13TH ST, OKLAHOMA CITY, OK 731045004
Phone: 405 271-6035
Web: WWW.OUMEDICINE.COM

HISTORICAL FINANCIALS

Company Type: Private

Income Statement FYE: June 30

	REVENUE ($ mil.)	NET INCOME ($ mil.)	NET PROFIT MARGIN	EMPLOYEES
06/20	1,298	48	3.7%	2,900
06/19	1,213	12	1.0%	—
Annual Growth	6.9%	297.2%	—	—

2020 Year-End Financials

Return on assets: 2.4%
Return on equity: 20.3%
Current ratio: 2.40
Cash ($ mil.): 442

OUR LADY OF THE LAKE HOSPITAL, INC.

Our Lady of the Lake Regional Medical Center reaches out to Baton Rouge residents with a helping hand. Participating in teaching programs for LSU and Tulane medical schools the medical center has some 800 inpatient beds and includes trauma emergency surgery general medical and specialty care centers for conditions including heart disease cancer orthopedics and ENT (ear nose and throat) disorders. Our Lady of the Lake also includes a Children's Hospital two nursing homes and an independent-living facility and it offers outpatient services at its main campus and at satellite facilities throughout the greater Baton Rouge area.

Operations

The hospital's family of services include an 800-bed Regional Medical Center; a dedicated Children's Hospital; a 350-provider Physician Group primary care network free-standing emergency room in Livingston Parish; an outpatient imaging and surgery centers; Assumption Community Hospital; a network of urgent care clinics; and Our Lady of the Lake College.

Our Lady of the Lake is a primary teaching site for graduate medical education programs and serves 45000 inpatients and 350000 outpatients a year.

The company has more than 850 doctors. Some 70% of its physicians and other professional medical staff members are board certified and in nearly one-third of the hospital system's medical specialty areas 100% of the physicians and other professionals are board certified.

Strategy

As a major facility in the Baton Rouge area Our Lady of the Lake has been expanding its services in the region in recent years. In 2015 Our Lady of the Lake Children's Hospital opened its first pediatric specialty clinic outside of the Baton Rouge area offering specialized outpatient care for pediatric gastroenterology patients.

In 2014 the company opened a new children's emergency room and expanded its adult emergency department.

Company Background

In 2012 the hospital constructed a freestanding emergency room facility in the suburban community of Livingston Louisiana. It is also building a new nine-story patient tower to the main hospital campus; the tower will house the heart and vascular center as well as an expanded ER and a new level 1 regional trauma center and will be completed in late 2013.

Our Lady of the Lake has also expanded its education programs. For instance it added a pediatric residency program in 2010. The hospital also moved to extend its relationship with LSU that year by agreeing to become the primary clinical site for the LSU medical school. The agreement came as LSU considered whether to build a replacement hospital for its aging teaching facility and coincides with the Our Lady of the Lake expansion projects. The partnership launched a new psychiatric residency program in 2012.

Our Lady of the Lake was founded in 1923 by the Franciscan Missionaries of Our Lady.

EXECUTIVES

Vice Chair, William E Balhoff
Secretary, Yolanda Dixon

LOCATIONS

HQ: OUR LADY OF THE LAKE HOSPITAL, INC.
7777 HENNESSY BLVD, BATON ROUGE, LA 708084300
Phone: 225 765-6565
Web: WWW.OLOLRMC.COM

PRODUCTS/OPERATIONS

Selected Services

Advanced Wound and Ostomy Clinic
Cancer
Children's Hospital
Critical Care
Diabetes & Nutrition Center
Emergency Services
Endoscopy Center
Hearing and Balance Center
Heart & Vascular Institute
Imaging Services
Laboratory and Diagnostics
Lake Express Check-In
LSU Health Baton Rouge
Mental and Behavioral Health
Neurology Neurosurgery and Stroke
Orthopedics
Palliative Care
Pharmacy
Rehabilitation Center
Respiratory Care
Senior Services
St. Anthony's Home
Surgery
Trauma Center
Urgent Care
Voice Center
Weight Loss

COMPETITORS

CHRISTUS St. Frances Cabrini Hospital
Dynacq Healthcare
General Health System
Lane Regional Medical Center
Our Lady of Lourdes
River Parishes Hospital
Woman's Hospital

HISTORICAL FINANCIALS

Company Type: Private

Income Statement FYE: June 30

	REVENUE ($ mil.)	NET INCOME ($ mil.)	NET PROFIT MARGIN	EMPLOYEES
06/20	1,526	(18)	—	1,800
06/19	1,467	33	2.3%	—
06/18	1,254	103	8.2%	—
06/16	895	(89)	—	—
Annual Growth	14.3%	—	—	—

2020 Year-End Financials

Return on assets: (-0.7%)
Return on equity: (-1.6%)
Current ratio: 1.90
Cash ($ mil.): 383

OVERLAKE HOSPITAL ASSOCIATION

EXECUTIVES

Prin, Diane Sperry
Coordinator, Lisa Sato
Nurse Manager, Jody Burnell
Coordinator, Jennifer Fischer
Registered Nurse, Nancy Corbridge
Registered Nurse, Anastasia Samsonov
Admitting Manager, Jill Salsbury

Therapist, Svetlana Young
Senior Analyst, Caroline Curtis
Nurse Manager, Carolyn Holmes
Director, Edward Chun
Auditors: KPMG LLP SEATTLE WA

LOCATIONS

HQ: OVERLAKE HOSPITAL ASSOCIATION
1035 116TH AVE NE, BELLEVUE, WA 980044604
Phone: 425 688-5000
Web: WWW.OVERLAKEHOSPITAL.ORG

HISTORICAL FINANCIALS

Company Type: Private

Income Statement FYE: June 30

	REVENUE ($ mil.)	NET INCOME ($ mil.)	NET PROFIT MARGIN	EMPLOYEES
06/20	579	(0)	—	178
06/19	574	48	8.4%	—
06/18	559	41	7.4%	—
06/17	513	58	11.3%	—
Annual Growth	4.1%	—	—	—

2020 Year-End Financials

Return on assets: —
Return on equity: (-0.1%)
Current ratio: 1.00
Cash ($ mil.): 38

OVERLAKE HOSPITAL MEDICAL CENTER

Over the lake and through the sound to Overlake Hospital Medical Center we go! The not-for-profit hospital provides health care services to residents of Bellevue Washington in the Puget Sound region. The nearly 350-bed facility provides comprehensive inpatient and outpatient services ranging from cancer care and surgery to specialized senior care. Overlake also operates a number of outpatient clinics providing primary care urgent care and specialty care such as weight loss surgery. The organization also provides patients with health and wellness programs addressing issues like women's and children's health.

Operations

The medical center has more than 1000 physicians on staff and runs Centers of Excellence in cardiac care cancer care surgical services women's and infants' care and emergency and Level III trauma care. The facility is home to a 24-hour urgent care clinic an anticoagulation clinic and a breast screening center. Overlake also operates numerous outpatient clinics providing primary care urgent care and specialty care.

Geographic Reach

Overlake provides health care services to residents of Bellevue Washington and the entire Puget Sound region. It operates clinics on its main campus in Bellevue as well as in Redmond and in Issaquah and on Mercer Island.

Sales and Marketing

In 2014 Medicare payments accounted for 27% of net patient revenues followed by group health organizations (17%) Premera (13%) and Regence (12%).

Financial Performance

Overlake's revenues increased by 2% to $433 million in 2014 as the result of higher net patient revenues and contribution revenues.

Net income rose 50% to $60 million that year primarily due to income from change in net unrealized gains on investments. Cash flow from operations fell 3% to $47 million as more cash was used in net clinic accounts receivable pledges receivable prepaid expenses and other long-term receivables.

Strategy

Increasing demand in the region has led the hospital to invest in expansions and equipment upgrades that include more emergency treatment capabilities and an on-campus helistop for trauma patients being airlifted to the area.

Along with its expansion and construction projects Overlake is investing in new technology to keep the health system in line with its competitors and to improve patient care. It is adding endoscopic video towers to its operating rooms to facilitate improved views of surgical procedures and is also moving to digitize all of its facilities with electronic health records.

In 2013 it opened the new $17.4 million David and Shelley Hovind Heart & Vascular center. The new 19200-sq.-ft. facility brings cardiac and vascular services together in one location.

Overlake has also focused on adding new primary care clinics and expanding its physician network to serve patients in locations closer to where they live and work.

Company Background

Overlake founded in 1960 is led by CEO Craig Hendrickson a veteran health care executive.

EXECUTIVES

Vice President Human Resources, Lisa Brock
Managing Director, Peter Kures
Vice President Of It, Jolene Lim
Medical Director, Eiji Minami
Treasurer, Julie Sun
Auditors: KPMG LLP SEATTLE WA

LOCATIONS

HQ: OVERLAKE HOSPITAL MEDICAL CENTER
1035 116TH AVE NE, BELLEVUE, WA 980044687
Phone: 425 688-5000
Web: WWW.OVERLAKEHOSPITAL.ORG

Selected Locations

Outpatient Rehabilitation Services
Outpatient Surgery (park in the West Garage; Outpatient Surgery is located on the first floor of the West Garage.)
Overlake Bellevue Campus and Overlake Medical Clinics Medical Tower
Overlake Medical Clinics Downtown Bellevue
Overlake Medical Clinics Issaquah
Overlake Medical Clinics Kirkland
Overlake Medical Clinics Redmond
Urgent Care Clinic in Issaquah
Urgent Care Clinic in Redmond

PRODUCTS/OPERATIONS

2014 Sales

	$ mil.	% of total
Net patient service revenue	419	97
Other operating revenue	11	3
Contribution revenue	2	-
Total	**433**	**100**

Selected Medical Services

Breast Health Services
Cancer Center at Overlake
Cardiac Center at Overlake
Clinical Trials
Emergency & Trauma Center
Medical Imaging
Overlake Medical Clinics
Surgical Services
Weight Loss Surgery
Women's & Infants' Center

COMPETITORS

Catholic Health Initiatives
Franciscan Health System
Harrison Medical Center
Kaiser Permanente WA
MultiCare Health System
PeaceHealth
Providence St. Joseph Health
Seattle Children's Hospital
Swedish Health Services
University of Washington
Yakima Valley Memorial

HISTORICAL FINANCIALS

Company Type: Private

Income Statement FYE: June 30

	REVENUE ($ mil.)	NET INCOME ($ mil.)	NET PROFIT MARGIN	EMPLOYEES
06/20	574	(3)	—	2,450
06/19	570	45	8.0%	—
06/18	555	39	7.1%	—
06/16	502	21	4.3%	—
Annual Growth	3.4%	—	—	—

2020 Year-End Financials

Return on assets: (-0.3%)
Return on equity: (-0.6%)
Current ratio: 1.10
Cash ($ mil.): 36

PACIFIC COAST PRODUCERS

Fruits seafood sauces and organic tomato puree – rather than movies – are the creative output of this particular group of Pacific Coast Producers. The cooperative markets the apricots grapes peaches pears and tomatoes grown by its approximately 160 California-based members. It turns the produce into private-label canned fruit sauces and juices and sells them to the retail and foodservice industries. Pacific Coast Producers typically serves retailers the likes of Albertson's Aldi Kroger Safeway SUPERVALU Whole Foods and Wal-Mart as well as the US Department of Agriculture. The company founded in 1971 operates three production sites and one distribution center in California.

Operations

The cooperative boasts three food-processing facilities in California as well as distribution centers in California and Washington.

Geographic Reach

From its base in Lodi California Pacific Coast Producers grows its fruits in California and sells them nationwide.

Sales and Marketing

Pacific Coast Producers sells the products it grows and processes to retailers and foodservice operators nationwide as well as to the US Department of Agriculture.

Financial Performance

As one of California's premier private label packers Pacific Coast Producers has logged annual sales in excess of $535 million plus $100 million in alliance income.

Strategy

Pacific Coast Producers has expanded its warehouse space in Lodi to improve efficiency and boost capacity. The move cost the company $23 million. It expanded its distribution center by 50% to meet rising demand for canned food.

The cooperative serves tomato processor Morning Star through a sales and marketing alliance it formed with the company in 2009. As part of the collaboration Pacific Coast Producers provides canned tomatoes to the retail and foodservice industries.

EXECUTIVES

Ceo, Daniel L Vincent
V Pres*, Peter C Wtulich
V Pres*, Andrew K Russick
V Pres*, Mona Shulman
Treas*, Zeb Rocha
Cfo*, Matthew Strong
Retail Sales Manager, Tami Gross
Human Resources Manager, Tara Bahtka
Information Security M, Jeannette Anderson
Administrative Assistant, Jean Roberts
Assistant Sales Manager, Ashley Ganas
Auditors: KPMG LLP SACRAMENTO CALIFORN

LOCATIONS

HQ: PACIFIC COAST PRODUCERS
631 N CLUFF AVE, LODI, CA 952400756
Phone: 209 367-8800
Web: WWW.PACIFICCOASTPRODUCERS.COM

PRODUCTS/OPERATIONS

Selected Products

Apricots

Catsup
Chili Sauces
Chunky Mixed Fruit
Concentrated Crushed Tomatoes
Diced Style Tomatoes
Extra Heavy Concentrated Crushed Round Tomato Puree
Formulated Pizza Sauces
Fruit Cocktail
Fruit for Salad
Fruit Mix
Ground Tomatoes
Marinara Sauces
Non-Formulated Pizza Sauce
Organic Tomatoes
Peaches
Pears
Random Cut / Strip Style Tomatoes
Seafood Sauces
Stewed Style Tomatoes
Tomato Juice
Whole Peeled Tomatoes

COMPETITORS

Big Heart Pet Brands
Campbell Soup
Cento
ConAgra
Dole Food
General Mills
Glory Foods
Hain Celestial
Hanover Foods
Heinz
NORPAC
Pictsweet
Seneca Foods

HISTORICAL FINANCIALS

Company Type: Private

Income Statement — FYE: May 31

	REVENUE ($ mil.)	NET INCOME ($ mil.)	NET PROFIT MARGIN	EMPLOYEES
05/20	911	27	3.0%	1,000
05/19	806	14	1.8%	—
05/18	668	22	3.4%	—
05/17	607	26	4.4%	—
Annual Growth	14.4%	0.9%	—	—

2020 Year-End Financials

Return on assets: 5.1%
Return on equity: 12.0%
Current ratio: 1.70
Cash ($ mil.): 2

PACIFIC PREMIER BANK

EXECUTIVES

Pres-Ceo, Steven R Gardner
Chb*, Jeff C Jones
Sr V Pres-Cfo*, Kent Smith
Sr Exec Vpres-Cfo*, Ronald J Nicolas Jr
Cro*, Michael Karr
Evp-Cco*, Donn Jakosky
Evp-Chief Acctg Officer*, Lori Wright
Senior Vice President Director, Thomas Galindo
Desk Manager, Robert Prater
Vp Information Technology, Dinorah Roggero
Credit Analyst, Carol Hiegl

LOCATIONS

HQ: PACIFIC PREMIER BANK
17901 VON KARMAN AVE # 1, IRVINE, CA 926146297
Phone: 714 431-4000
Web: WWW.PPBI.COM

HISTORICAL FINANCIALS

Company Type: Private

Income Statement — FYE: December 31

	ASSETS ($ mil.)	NET INCOME ($ mil.)	INCOME AS % OF ASSETS	EMPLOYEES
12/17	8,022	68	0.9%	104
12/16	4,035	44	1.1%	—
12/15	2,782	29	1.1%	—
12/14	2,033	18	0.9%	—
Annual Growth	58.0%	54.0%	—	—

2017 Year-End Financials

Return on assets: 0.9%
Return on equity: 5.1%
Sales ($ mil): 298

PAN AMERICAN HEALTH ORGANIZATION INC

EXECUTIVES

Dir, Carissa Etienne
Pres, Mirta Periago
Cfo, Esteban Alzamora
Information Specialist, Claudia Ortiz
Information Specialist, Douglas Alvarado
Coordinator, Farida Kerouani
Human Resources, Paul De La
Coordinator, Alessandra Senisse
Coordinator, Fatima W Marinho
Information Specialist, Manuel A Mijango
Marketing Manager, Eleana Villanueva

LOCATIONS

HQ: PAN AMERICAN HEALTH ORGANIZATION INC
525 23RD ST NW, WASHINGTON, DC 200372825
Phone: 202 974-3000
Web: WWW.PAHO.ORG

HISTORICAL FINANCIALS

Company Type: Private

Income Statement — FYE: December 31

	REVENUE ($ mil.)	NET INCOME ($ mil.)	NET PROFIT MARGIN	EMPLOYEES
12/09	1,268	101	8.0%	1,500
12/06	541	84	15.7%	—
Annual Growth	32.9%	6.2%	—	—

2009 Year-End Financials

Return on assets: 0.9%
Return on equity: 8.0%
Current ratio: 14.00
Cash ($ mil.): 351

PANDUIT CORP.

Panduit's got your cables covered connected and enclosed. The company's electrical components tie together the communications computing power and security systems of a building or physical location. Products include cabling connectors copper wire fiber-optic components cabinets and racks grounding systems outlets terminals and other electrical components. It also offers software used to integrate and manage separate building functions. Panduit's products are used in data centers office buildings industrial plants processing lines and other settings. The privately held company has customers in more than 100 countries. Among its customers are Noosa Yogurt Iveco and Purdue University.

Financial Performance

Panduit claims to generate more than $1 billion in annual revenue.

Strategy

As companies have built out data centers Panduit has been in the thick of it supplying cables cabinets and rack enclosures. Most of the new products the company has introduced in recent years have concerned infrastructure that routes and connects miles of cable in data centers.

Panduit runs a robust research arm employing more than 200 R&D personnel working in about 20 laboratories. The company's research has netted about 2000 global patents. Panduit works with partners like Cisco Systems and Rockwell Automation and in 2019 the three companies opened a manufacturing technology center in Mexico City to showcase their products.

The company expanded its capability to provide audio/visual technologies with its acquisition of Atlona in 2019. With Atlona's networked AV signal distribution wireless collaboration and AV system automation offerings Panduit provides products for the increasing convergence of AV onto the network.

Some of Panduit's rivals have more revenue and resources to develop and market new products. Competitors include Amphenol TE Connectivity Molex and Corning all of which generate 10-times more annual revenue than Panduit.

Mergers and Acquisitions

Panduit makes acquisitions to expand its product line and reach new customers.

In 2019 Panduit acquired Atlona a maker of audio-visual equipment based in San Jose California. The deal helps Panduit round out its offerings with Atlona's networked AV signal distribution wireless collaboration and AV system automation technologies. Atlona became part of Atlona's enterprise group.

Company Background

Panduit was established in 1955 by Jack Caveney Sr.Its first product was the Panduct Wiring Duct.

EXECUTIVES

Ceo, John E. (Jack) Caveney
Vp Global Sales And Marketing, Ronald K. (Ron) Partridge
Cto, Jack Tison
President, Thomas C. (Tom) Donovan
Senior Vice President Global Supply Chain, William Ernest
Vice President Oem Business, Bob Krisel
Vice President, Neil Corradine
Vice President Sls And Marketing, Bernard Westapher
Vp Of Information Technology, Joanne Tyree
Vice President Global Human Resources, Timothy Dee
Vice President Marketing, Chad Reynolds
Vice President, Rina Lim
Group Vice President, Mark Acklin
Vp Quality, Glenn Henning
National Account Manager, Michael Taylor
Vice President, Vincent Walsh
Vice President Of International Sales And Marketing, Tom Donovan
Regional Vice President, Hank Smith
Senior Vice President Customer Experience, Philip Taylor
Vice President Business Operations, Joergen Schuetze
Svp Strategic Programs, Randall Woods
Vice President Contractor Development, Jeff Miller
Vp Global Supply Chain Centers Of Excellence, Deb Magee
Senior Vice President Human Resources, Tim Dee
Group Vp Of It, Jim Hall
Vice President Of Finance, Gerald Lange
Vice President Business Development, Dave Mack
Auditors: GRANT THORNTON

LOCATIONS

HQ: PANDUIT CORP.
18900 PANDUIT DR, TINLEY PARK, IL 604873600
Phone: 708 532-1800
Web: WWW.PANDUIT.COM

PRODUCTS/OPERATIONS

PRODUCTS

Cabinets Thermal Management Racks and Enclosures
Cable and Wire Bundling
Cable Routing and Pathways
Copper Systems
Fiber Systems
Grounding
Identification
Japan Market Only Products
Power Distribution and Environmental Monitoring
Product Promotions
Safety and Security
Software and Hardware
Tools
Wire Routing Protection and Insulation
Wire Termination
SOFTWARE/INTELLIGENCE
DCIM
6 Zone; Methodology
Data Center Management
Enterprise Management
Intelligent Hardware
Intelligent Software
SmartZone Overview
PROFESSIONAL SERVICES
Case Studies
Industrial Automation Services
Safety Services

COMPETITORS

Amphenol
Avaya
CommScope
Corning
Molex
Optical Cable
Ortronics
RiT Technologies
Schneider Electric
Siemens AG
TE Connectivity

HISTORICAL FINANCIALS

Company Type: Private

Income Statement — FYE: December 31

	REVENUE ($ mil.)	NET INCOME ($ mil.)	NET PROFIT MARGIN	EMPLOYEES
12/16	937	0	—	5,110
12/15	924	0	—	—
12/14	973	0	—	—
Annual Growth	(1.9%)	—	—	—

PAREXEL INTERNATIONAL CORPORATION

PAREXEL International is in the business of improving the world's health. From clinical trials to regulatory consulting and market access its therapeutic technical and functional ability is underpinned by a deep conviction in what it does. It is done through a suite of services that help life science and biopharmaceutical customers across the globe transform scientific discoveries into new treatments for patients. In 2021 PAREXEL completes separation of Parexel Informatics and Medical Imaging Business. As part of the separation Parexel Informatics will become Calyx.

Operations

Through its Clinical Development solutions Parexel offers a variety of clinical research services that bring together its global clinical and regulatory expertise with proprietary technologies.

Parexel's Regulatory & Access consulting organization includes around 100 former regulators and HTA assessors.

Parexel will continue to leverage Calyx's (formerly Integrated Technologies) Medical Imaging Clinical Trial Management Systems (CTMS) Electronic Data Capture (EDC) Interactive Response Technology (IRT) and Regulatory Information Management (RIM) solutions moving forward as part of the company's clinical development offerings.

Its outsourcing services includes Parexel Functional Service Provider (FSP) Model and Strategic Partnerships.

Parexel's other solutions are Medical and Scientific Services; and Real-World Evidence.

Geographic Reach

Headquartered near Boston Massachusetts and in Durham North Carolina Parexel has offices that support clients in over 100 countries around the world. It also has global study locations in Baltimore and Los Angeles as well as London and Berlin.

Strategy

In early 2021 Parexel completed the separation of its Parexel Informatics and Medical Imaging business. The strategic move is designed to simplify and streamline Parexel's business strategy and customer relationships while best positioning both organizations for continued long-term growth and success. As part of the separation Parexel Informatics will become Calyx. Parexel will continue to leverage Calyx's Medical Imaging Clinical Trial Management Systems (CTMS) Electronic Data Capture (EDC) Interactive Response Technology (IRT) and Regulatory Information Management (RIM) solutions moving forward as part of the company's clinical development offerings. Calyx will be privately held by the same ownership group that has owned Parexel since 2017.

Mergers and Acquisitions

In early 2020 Model Answers a consultancy firm based in Brisbane Queensland Australia. The company's expertise and proven approach will enhance the operational scale and global footprint of Parexel's Clinical Pharmacology Modeling and Simulation offering to drive more informed and efficient drug development.

Company Background

Founders Josef von Rickenbach a health care and international products specialist and Anne Sayigh a chemist and regulatory affairs specialist started PAREXEL in 1982 to provide regulatory consulting services to pharmaceutical firms. Its name referred to 16th-century Swiss physician Theophrastus Bombastus von Hohenheim – better known as Paracelsus the father of empirical chemistry.

Through a series of acquisitions PAREXEL entered new markets including biostatistics and data management medical marketing and health consulting.

The company went public in 1995 and was taken private again in 2017.

HISTORY

Founders Josef von Rickenbach a health care and international products specialist and Anne Sayigh a chemist and regulatory affairs specialist started PAREXEL in 1982 to provide regulatory consulting services to pharmaceutical firms. Its name referred to 16th-century Swiss physician Theophrastus Bombastus von Hohenheim – better known as Paracelsus the father of empirical chemistry.

In 1988 PAREXEL bought Consulting Statisticians and moved into the biostatistics and data management market. The next year it went international with the purchase of the biostatistics and data management division of McDonnell Douglas Information Systems. In 1991 PAREXEL augmented its European operations with the acquisition of German contract researcher AFB Arzneimittelforschung – a move that paid off in rising sales.

PAREXEL went public in 1995. In the following two years it bought six health consulting firms including State and Federal Associates and medical marketing firm Rescon with the intention of boosting its ability to get its clients' products on the market. The company continued its acquisition spree in 1998; this time European marketing and research companies were on the shopping list. Competitor Covance was set to buy PAREXEL in 1999 then called off the deal when investors balked.

The company announced in 2000 that it would lay off more than 400 workers after Novartis cancelled a major contract. That year the company formed new alliances with such companies as NeuroRecovery Research Phenome Sciences and Prevention Concepts. PAREXEL also bought a full-service clinical pharmacology unit in the UK from GlaxoWellcome (now GlaxoSmithKline) as well as a majority stake in FARMOVS a clinical pharmacology research business and laboratory in South Africa.

In 2001 the company formed Perceptive Informatics a subsidiary focused on developing Internet-based information management systems. To strengthen its clinical trial management services PAREXEL bought software developer FW Pharma Systems in 2003. In 2006 it purchased US-based Behavioral and Medical Research LLC for $69 million to expand its research services.

EXECUTIVES

Chairman And Ceo, Josef H. von Rickenbach, $966,874 total compensation
President And Coo, Mark A. Goldberg, $622,263 total compensation
President Perceptive Informatics, Xavier Flinois
Svp And Cfo, Simon N. R. Harford
Svp And Worldwide Head Parexel Access, Joshua Schultz
Svp General Counsel And Secretary, Douglas A. Batt, $415,860 total compensation
Svp Clinical Research Services, Gadi Saarony, $455,051 total compensation
Vp And Worldwide Head Early Phase, Sy Pretorius
Vice President, Paul Bridges
Vice President Of Human Resources, Michael Brandt
Senior Medical Director, Karla Kanis
Vp Clinical Science, Roland Andersson
Senior Vice President Global Business Development, David Godwin
Vice President, Conal Burgess
Vice President Worldwide Head Of Medcom, Susan Kammerman
Medical Director, Regina Sohn
Medical Director, Ronald Goldwater
Vice President Worldwide Head Business Development Clinical Pharmacology, Yves Grenon
Corporate Vice President, Janet Edwards
Vice President, Frank Panaccio
Medical Director, Lynn McRoy
Vice President Human Resources, Carl Weaver
Medical Director, Wayne Dankner
Vice President Human Resource Operations, Guy Schiller
Senior Vice President, Mary Bareilles
Vice President Technical, Tony Warchut
It Vice President Process Qm, Deborah Wade
Vice President Marketing, Ronald Kraus
Associate Medical Director, Claire Chehrazi
Medical Director, Marina Bussel
Corporate Vice President Strategic Account Leader, Jim Anthony
Corporate Vp Compensation Benefits And Hr Mergers And Acquisitions, Michele Fournier
Vice President Corporate Communications, Mark Stephenson
Corporate Vice President Head Global Medical Services, Dana Washburn
Vice President And Chief Scientific Officer For Medical Imaging, Peter Steiger
Vice President, Ubavka Denoble
Vice President Global Monitoring Operations, Dennis Joseph
Vice President Of Tax, John Benoit
Evp And Cfo, Greg Rush
Associate Medical Director, Anthony Bohnert
Corporate Vp Commercial Growth, Frederick Lemoine
Corporate Vice President Global Safety Services And Pharmacovigilance, Jamie Sidore
Corporate Vice President Parexel Quality, John Bell
Senior Medical Director, Rohit Sood
Vp Production Services Studio Operations, Shana Zarcufsky
Vp Access Consulting, Thom Schoenwaelder
Vice President Executive And Strategic Communications, Lori Dorer
Associate Medical Director, Dana Reddy
Auditors: ERNST & YOUNG LLP BOSTON MAS

LOCATIONS

HQ: PAREXEL INTERNATIONAL CORPORATION
195 WEST ST, WALTHAM, MA 024511146
Phone: 781 487-9900
Web: WWW.PAREXEL.COM

COMPETITORS

Albany Molecular Research
BioClinica
Charles River Laboratories
Covance
DATATRAK International
ICON
INC Research
IQVIA
PharmaNet Development Group
Pharmaceutical Product Development
ReSearch Pharmaceutical Services
WuXi PharmaTech
eResearchTechnology
inVentiv Health

HISTORICAL FINANCIALS

Company Type: Private

Income Statement — FYE: June 30

	REVENUE ($ mil.)	NET INCOME ($ mil.)	NET PROFIT MARGIN	EMPLOYEES
06/16	2,426	154	6.4%	18,900
06/15	2,330	147	6.3%	—
06/14	2,266	129	5.7%	—
Annual Growth	3.5%	9.5%	—	—

2016 Year-End Financials

Return on assets: 7.6%
Return on equity: 24.5%
Current ratio: 1.50
Cash ($ mil.): 248

PARISH OF JEFFERSON

EXECUTIVES

Pres, Michael Yenni
Accounting Staff, Donna Richoux
Information Technology Manager, Cynthia Austin
Information Technology Divisio, Danielle Shirk
Network Administrator, Hen Ly
Acct Mgr, Clifford Smith Jr
Council Member District 5, Jennifer Van Vrancken
Fins Administrative Assistant, Kathleen Fradella
Personell Director, Kathy Frey
Account Officer, Robin Angelica
Assistant Finance Director, Kerry Schrieffer
Auditors: CARR RIGGS & INGRAM LLC MET

LOCATIONS

HQ: PARISH OF JEFFERSON
200 DERBIGNY ST, GRETNA, LA 700535850
Phone: 504 364-2600
Web: WWW.JEFFPARISH.NET

HISTORICAL FINANCIALS

Company Type: Private

Income Statement — FYE: December 31

	REVENUE ($ mil.)	NET INCOME ($ mil.)	NET PROFIT MARGIN	EMPLOYEES
12/19	588	281	47.8%	3,217
12/18	561	(4)	—	—
12/17	561	146	26.1%	—
12/16	576	6	1.1%	—
Annual Growth	0.7%	252.6%	—	—

2019 Year-End Financials

Return on assets: 6.6%
Return on equity: 11.7%
Current ratio: 6.30
Cash ($ mil.): 97

PARKLAND COMMUNITY HEALTH PLAN, INC., A PROGRAM OF DALLAS COUNTY HOSPITAL

EXECUTIVES

Ceo, Rob Smith
Director of Provider Relations, Patricia Carney
Administrative Assistant, Camille Myers
Auditors: BRUCE E BERNSTEIN & ASSOC PC

LOCATIONS

HQ: PARKLAND COMMUNITY HEALTH PLAN, INC., A PROGRAM OF DALLAS COUNTY HOSPITAL
1341 W MOCKINGBIRD LN 1150E, DALLAS, TX 752474974
Phone: 214 266-2100
Web: WWW.PARKLANDHOSPITAL.COM

HISTORICAL FINANCIALS

Company Type: Private

Income Statement — FYE: December 31

	REVENUE ($ mil.)	NET INCOME ($ mil.)	NET PROFIT MARGIN	EMPLOYEES
12/18	577	(9)	—	2
12/17	541	17	3.3%	—
12/15	527	(32)	—	—
12/13	519	27	5.2%	—
Annual Growth	2.1%	—	—	—

2018 Year-End Financials

Return on assets: (-6.4%)
Return on equity: (-10.7%)
Current ratio: 2.50
Cash ($ mil.): 138

PARSONS ENVIRONMENT & INFRASTRUCTURE GROUP INC.

A unit of Parsons Corporation Parsons Commercial Technology Group (PARCOMM) provides project management engineering construction design maintenance and related services for industrial and commercial projects. The company's clients include firms in the telecommunications health care manufacturing defense petroleum and chemical industries. PARCOMM also completes projects for schools colleges and government entities. Specialized services include industrial environmental remediation factory modernization and developing state vehicle inspection and compliance programs. PARCOMM operates throughout the US and the world.

EXECUTIVES

Vice President Human Resources, Debra Fiori

LOCATIONS

HQ: PARSONS ENVIRONMENT & INFRASTRUCTURE GROUP INC.
4701 HEDGEMORE DR, CHARLOTTE, NC 282093281
Phone: 704 529-6246
Web: WWW.PARSONS.COM

COMPETITORS

Bechtel
Fluor
Halliburton
Jacobs Engineering

HISTORICAL FINANCIALS

Company Type: Private

Income Statement — FYE: July 29

	REVENUE ($ mil.)	NET INCOME ($ mil.)	NET PROFIT MARGIN	EMPLOYEES
07/14*	684	(12)	—	1,205
12/12	684	(12)	—	—
12/11	443	(57)	—	—
Annual Growth	15.6%	—	—	—

*Fiscal year change

2014 Year-End Financials

Return on assets: (-1.9%)
Return on equity: (-3.1%)
Current ratio: 1.30
Cash ($ mil.): 24

PASADENA HOSPITAL ASSOCIATION, LTD.

No need to hunt for medical care if you're near Huntington Hospital. The not-for-profit Pasadena Hospital Association which does business as Huntington Hospital provides health care to residents of the San Gabriel Valley in Southern California. The hospital boasts some 625 beds and offers acute medical and surgical care and community services in a number of specialties including cardiology gastroenterology women's and children's health orthopedics and neurology. It engages in clinical cancer research (as well as diagnosis and treatment) through the Huntington Cancer Center. The hospital is also a teaching facility for the University of Southern California (USC) Keck School of Medicine.

Operations

As part of its operations the California hospital runs The Stroke Center Heart and Vascular Center Huntington Hospital Cancer Center Regional Neonatal Intensive Care Unit Prenatal High Risk Unit and Pediatric Intensive Care Unit. The hospital is the only level II trauma center and level III NICU in the San Gabriel Valley.

Through its partnership with USC Huntington Hospital offers graduate medical education in areas such as general surgery and internal medicine. Its Huntington Cancer Center partners with area physicians (including some affiliated with USC and UCLA) and the City of Hope medical center to provide comprehensive oncology services and research potential new cancer treatments.

The hospital has 900 physicians and more than 1200 nurses. In 2013 it had about 26000 inpatient admissions more than 216000 outpatient visits and helped deliver more than 3300 babies. Huntington Hospital provided a $92.9 million in community benefits that year.

Geographic Reach

Huntington Hospital serves the health care needs of those who reside in and around Southern California's San Gabriel Valley.

Sales and Marketing

The medical center is working to upgrade its information technology systems including the addition of an electronic health record (EHR) system.

Financial Performance

Huntington Hospital's revenues rose by 3% in 2013 thanks to an increase in patient services and revenues.

The hospital recorded a net loss of $10 million that year due to higher expenses (including salaries employees benefits and other costs).

Strategy

The company is pursuing infrastructure and services expansion and innovation to keep up with demand.

In 2014 Huntington Hospital collaborated with Anthem Blue Cross and six of its fellow leading hospitals in Los Angeles and Orange counties to form Anthem Blue Cross Vivity a new insurance entity.

In 2013 the hospital signed a deal with Shriners Hospitals for Children- Southern California to provide inpatient surgical services for its pediatric patients.

Huntington Hospital completed renovating its existing emergency facility in 2013. The project to increase patient capacity up to 80000 and increase diagnostic facilities came about in response to growing levels of ER visits.

Company Background

Huntington Hospital broke ground several years ago on an $80-million expansion effort to double the size of its emergency department. The project has included building a new portion that was completed in 2012.

Upgrading its technology to increase efficiency in 2012 Huntington Hospital launched a multi-year project to replace and upgrade its computer information system with new system (Huntington Access Network Knowledge) to manage the hospital's clinical and financial software.

In a medical innovation in 2012 the hospital became the first hospital in Southern California to offer an Ekso Bionics' technology enabling patients with lower-extremity paralysis or weakness to stand and walk.

Huntington Hospital was founded in 1892.

EXECUTIVES

Medical Director Of Electrophysiology, Mayer Rashtian
Medical Director Of Radiology, Christopher G Hedley
Vice President Chief Nurse Executive, Gloria Sanchez
Auditors: ERNST & YOUNG US LLP IRVINE

LOCATIONS

HQ: PASADENA HOSPITAL ASSOCIATION, LTD.
100 W CALIFORNIA BLVD, PASADENA, CA 911053010
Phone: 626 397-5000
Web: WWW.HUNTINGTONHOSPITAL.COM

PRODUCTS/OPERATIONS

Selected Services

Ambulatory Care/Dispensary
Angiography
Anticoagulation Clinic
Asthma Education and Management
Bariatric Surgery
Breast Cancer Program
Cardiac Catheterization Lab
Cardiac Electrophysiology (EP)
Cardiac Rehabilitation
Cardiac Screening and Diagnostics
Cardiothoracic Surgery
Community Outreach
CT Scanning (Type 2) Diabetes Prevention and Management
Epilepsy and Brain Mapping
Gastroenterology
Genetic Counseling
Geriatric Assessment Clinic
Gynecological Cancer Program
Heart and Vascular Services
Neurophysiology
Neuroradiology
Neurosciences
Neurosurgery
Obstetrics
Orthopedics
Ostomy Clinic
Pediatric Obesity Prevention
Prenatal High Risk Unit
Prostate Cancer Program
Radiation Oncology
Urology
Uterine Artery Embolization (UAE)

COMPETITORS

Adventist Health System West
Cedars-Sinai Medical Center
Citrus Valley Health Partners
Dignity Health
Glendale Adventist Medical Center
Memorial Health Services
Tenet Healthcare

HISTORICAL FINANCIALS

Company Type: Private

Income Statement — FYE: December 31

	REVENUE ($ mil.)	NET INCOME ($ mil.)	NET PROFIT MARGIN	EMPLOYEES
12/17	654	15	2.3%	2,800
12/16	695	8	1.2%	—
12/15	593	0	0.0%	—
Annual Growth	5.0%	678.3%	—	—

2017 Year-End Financials

Return on assets: 1.7%
Return on equity: 2.6%
Current ratio: 3.30
Cash ($ mil.): 11

PASADENA INDEPENDENT SCHOOL DISTRICT

EXECUTIVES

Pres, Mariselle Quijano-Lerma
Supt*, Dr Kirk Lewis
V Pres*, Vickie Morgan
SEC*, Fred Roberts
Program Assistant, Sara Bergman
Cte Director, Sarah Wrobleski
Director of Professional Devel, Scott Harrell
Assistant, Stacey Barber
Transplant Social Worker, Stacy Fontenot
Assistant, Steve Fleming
Chief Technology Officer, Steve Wentz
Auditors: WHITLEY PENN LLP TEXAS CITY

LOCATIONS

HQ: PASADENA INDEPENDENT SCHOOL DISTRICT
1515 CHERRYBROOK LN, PASADENA, TX 775024099
Phone: 713 740-0000
Web: WWW.PASADENAISD.ORG

HISTORICAL FINANCIALS

Company Type: Private

Income Statement — FYE: August 31

	REVENUE ($ mil.)	NET INCOME ($ mil.)	NET PROFIT MARGIN	EMPLOYEES
08/19	696	30	4.3%	5,000
08/18	680	99	14.7%	—
08/17	606	(93)	—	—
08/16	611	(32)	—	—
Annual Growth	4.4%	—	—	—

PATERSON PUBLIC SCHOOL DISTRICT

EXECUTIVES

Supt, Jacqueline Jones
Supt*, Donnie W Evans
Acting Supervisor, Stephanie Wright
Purchasing Analyst, Maria Choy
Programmer, Alexander Victoria
Vice Paterson Public, Cosmo Braico
Secretary Confidential To, Esther Boone
Supervisor, Karen Bernard
Accounting, Kennia Fulgencio
Teacher Nurse, Marie Simeus
Assistant, Ronnie Estrict
Auditors: LERCH VINCI & HIGGINS LLP F

LOCATIONS

HQ: PATERSON PUBLIC SCHOOL DISTRICT
90 DELAWARE AVE, PATERSON, NJ 075031804
Phone: 973 321-0980
Web: WWW.PATERSON.K12.NJ.US

HISTORICAL FINANCIALS

Company Type: Private

Income Statement — FYE: June 30

	REVENUE ($ mil.)	NET INCOME ($ mil.)	NET PROFIT MARGIN	EMPLOYEES
06/19	642	(6)	—	3,055
06/18	602	(4)	—	—
06/17	601	1	0.3%	—
06/11	541	7	1.3%	—
Annual Growth	2.2%	—	—	—

2019 Year-End Financials

Return on assets: (-1.4%) — Cash ($ mil.): 14
Return on equity: (-4.9%)
Current ratio: —

PATIENT ACCESS NETWORK FOUNDATION

EXECUTIVES

Dir of Ops, Svelana Durkovic
Prin, Julia E Reynes
Director of Patient Advocacy, Amy Niles
Business Consultant, Ali Chegini
Human Resources Manager, Barbara Barb
Chief Financial Officer, Joel Straus
Marketing and Communications, Liz Eckert
Marketing Associate, Megan Crout
Auditors: CHERRY BEKAERT LLP CHARLOTTE

LOCATIONS

HQ: PATIENT ACCESS NETWORK FOUNDATION
805 15TH ST NW STE 500, WASHINGTON, DC 200052207
Phone: 202 347-9274
Web: WWW.PANFOUNDATION.ORG

HISTORICAL FINANCIALS

Company Type: Private

Income Statement — FYE: December 31

	REVENUE ($ mil.)	NET INCOME ($ mil.)	NET PROFIT MARGIN	EMPLOYEES
12/18	540	175	32.5%	3
12/17	532	171	32.2%	—
12/16	577	(243)	—	—
12/14	673	161	24.0%	—
Annual Growth	(5.3%)	2.1%	—	—

2018 Year-End Financials

Return on assets: 31.5% — Cash ($ mil.): 214
Return on equity: 41.4%
Current ratio: 27.30

PATIENT-CENTERED OUTCOMES RESEARCH INSTITUTE

EXECUTIVES

Ceo, Nakela Cook
Coo-Treas, Regina Yan
SEC-Gen Counsel, Mary Hennessey
Director of Technology, Mazen Atta-Allah
Senior Administrative Assistan, Tomica Singleton
Assistant Director Financial O, Aline Nario
Senior Program Manager, Donna Gentry
Recruiter, Leslie Garrett
Staff, Michael Rochelle
MPA Program Officer Special PR, Rachel Mosbacher
Program Officer Improving Heal, Andrea Brandau
Auditors: RSM US LLP WASHINGTON DC

LOCATIONS

HQ: PATIENT-CENTERED OUTCOMES RESEARCH INSTITUTE
1828 L ST NW STE 900, WASHINGTON, DC 200365114
Phone: 202 827-7700
Web: WWW.PCORI.ORG

HISTORICAL FINANCIALS

Company Type: Private

Income Statement — FYE: September 30

	REVENUE ($ mil.)	NET INCOME ($ mil.)	NET PROFIT MARGIN	EMPLOYEES
09/19	615	227	37.0%	272
09/18	506	121	24.0%	—
Annual Growth	21.5%	87.4%	—	—

2019 Year-End Financials

Return on assets: 16.5% — Cash ($ mil.): 28
Return on equity: 17.7%
Current ratio: —

PATTERN ENERGY GROUP INC.

Pattern Energy wants to be the wind power beneath customer's energy wings. The company has eight wind power projects (six operating two under construction) in the US Canada and Chile with a generation capacity of more than 1000MW. Nearly all of the company's capacity is contracted to be sold under long-term agreements. Pattern Energy named for the patterns the company says it uses to maximize both production and profits was formed in late 2012 by Pattern Energy Group (PEG) to take over that company's power operations while it focuses on development. Pattern went public in 2013; it intends to use its $352 million in IPO proceeds to repay PEG which still controls it and for general corporate purposes. Over 70% of the company's total sales were generated in US.

EXECUTIVES

President And Ceo, Michael M. Garland, $420,250 total compensation
Evp Business Development, Hunter H. Armistead, $341,453 total compensation
Evp And General Counsel, Daniel M. Elkort, $304,681 total compensation
Cfo, Michael J. Lyon, $242,300 total compensation
Svp Operations, Christopher M. Shugart
Vice President Engineering And, Kevin Deters
Chairman, Alan R. Batkin, age 75
Auditors: PRICEWATERHOUSECOOPERS LLP SA

LOCATIONS

HQ: PATTERN ENERGY GROUP INC.
1088 SANSOME ST, SAN FRANCISCO, CA 941111308
Phone: 415 283-4000
Web: WWW.PATTERNENERGY.COM

2016 sales

	$ mil.	% of total
United States	285	81
Canada	39	11
Chile	29	8
Total	**354**	**100**

PRODUCTS/OPERATIONS

2016 sales

	$ mil.	% of total
Electricity sales	346	97
Related party revenue	5	1
other revenue	2	1
Total	**354**	**100**

COMPETITORS

AES Wind Generation
Algonquin
Berkshire Hathaway Energy
Brookfield Renewable Energy
EDP Renewables North America LLC
First Wind Holdings
Green Mountain Energy
NRG Yield
Navitas Energy
NextEra Energy
Sea Breeze Power

HISTORICAL FINANCIALS

Company Type: Private

Income Statement — FYE: December 31

	REVENUE ($ mil.)	NET INCOME ($ mil.)	NET PROFIT MARGIN	EMPLOYEES
12/19	541	(107)	—	228
12/18	483	(69)	—	—
12/17	411	(82)	—	—
12/16	354	(52)	—	—
Annual Growth	15.2%	—	—	—

2019 Year-End Financials

Return on assets: (-1.5%)
Return on equity: (-4.6%)
Current ratio: 0.40
Cash ($ mil.): 156

PCL CONSTRUCTION ENTERPRISES, INC.

PCL Construction Enterprises is the contractor to call on for commercial and civil construction concerns. The company serves as the parent to half a dozen US construction companies: PCL Construction Services PCL Civil Constructors PCL Construction PCL Industrial Services PCL Industrial Construction and Nordic PCL Construction. The companies serve as the operating entities for PCL one of Canada's largest general contracting groups. Having completed projects in nearly every US state PCL Construction Enterprises is active in the commercial institutional multi-family residential heavy industrial and civil construction sectors. PCL first entered the US construction market in 1975.

Operations

PCL Construction Enterprises and its subsidiaries work on a variety of projects. PCL Construction Enterprises has completed bridges water and wastewater systems manufacturing plants office buildings and restaurants nationwide.

Like many construction companies PCL was hit by the economic recession. Backlogs were lacking and new projects became tougher to win due to an increase in competition. Contracts with water wastewater and renewable energy projects and universities have helped PCL Construction Enterprises through the downturn.

Geographic Reach

Denver-based PCL Construction Enterprises through its half a dozen operating units concentrates on commercial civil and industrial construction projects located in the US.

Its parent's work spans the US Canada the Caribbean and Australia.

Sales and Marketing

PCL caters to customers in three primary sectors: commercial buildings civil infrastructure and heavy industrial construction. Clients have included the Alaska Railroad Corporation US Army Corps of Engineers Shaw Constructors and OUC-The Reliable One.

Its markets span big cities in Alaska Georgia California North Carolina Texas Colorado Hawaii Minnesota Florida Arizona and Washington.

EXECUTIVES

Vice President And District Manager, Dave Yount
Vice President, Keith Sandlin
Vice President Of Health Safety And Environment, Jim Barry
Vice President, Gregory Saha

LOCATIONS

HQ: PCL CONSTRUCTION ENTERPRISES, INC.
2000 S COLO BLVD STE 2-50, DENVER, CO 80222
Phone: 303 365-6500
Web: WWW.PCL.COM

PRODUCTS/OPERATIONS

Selected Operating Companies

Nordic PCL Construction Inc.
PCL Civil Constructors Inc.
PCL Construction Inc.
PCL Construction Services Inc.
PCL Industrial Construction Co.
PCL Industrial Services Inc.

COMPETITORS

Adolfson & Peterson Inc.
Andersen Construction
Brasfield & Gorrie
C.W. Driver
Dimeo Construction
FCI Constructors
Fluor
Gilbane Building Company
M. B. Kahn
Skanska USA Civil
Suffolk Construction
TIC Holdings
Torix General Contractors
Turner Corporation

HISTORICAL FINANCIALS

Company Type: Private

Income Statement — FYE: October 31

	REVENUE ($ mil.)	NET INCOME ($ mil.)	NET PROFIT MARGIN	EMPLOYEES
10/10	1,616	23	1.5%	3,300
10/09	2,182	52	2.4%	—
10/08	2,315	84	3.7%	—
Annual Growth	(16.4%)	(47.2%)	—	—

2010 Year-End Financials

Return on assets: 4.2%
Return on equity: 17.6%
Current ratio: 1.20
Cash ($ mil.): 95

PEACEHEALTH

PeaceHealth provides patients with a tranquil place to recover. Make that several tranquil places to recover. PeaceHealth serves residents in southeastern Alaska coastal regions of Washington and central portions of Oregon. Its medical centers include PeaceHealth Ketchikan Medical Center PeaceHealth St. Joseph Medical Center PeaceHealth St. John Medical Center Sacred Heart Medical Center (two campuses) Cottage Grove Community Hospital Peace Harbor Hospital PeaceHealth Peace Island Medical Center and PeaceHealth Southwest Medical Center. Other operations include physician practices community clinics hospices chemical dependency rehabilitation clinics and other outpatient facilities and services.

Operations

In all PeaceHealth has about 16000 acute beds and 30 nursing home beds. It has some 16000 caregivers and a multi-specialty medical group practice with more than 800 physicians. It also has 10 medical centers in both rural and urban communities throughout the Northwest.

In 2014 the system reported more than 72000 inpatient admissions and nearly 746000 outpatient registrations as well as 1.2 million patient encounters with its medical group. It had more than 8000 infant births and more than 302000 emergency department visits that year.

Sales and Marketing

Commercial and other payers accounted for about half of Peacehealth's net patient revenue while Medicare accounts for about a third%.

Mergers and Acquisitions

In late 2018 Peacehealth agreed to buy telemedicine specialist ZOOM+Care. Formed in 2006 ZOOM+Care provides urgent care primary care specialty care and mental health care services. The purchase will further broaden the services Peacehealth provides in its communities.

Company Background

PeaceHealth was formed in 1923 by the Sisters of St. Joseph of Peace who opened the Little Flower Hospital in Ketchikan named after Saint Teresa. The Sisters of St. Joseph of Peace had previously opened St. Joseph Hospital in Bellingham in 1891.

PeaceHealth and Southwest Washington Health System merged in early 2011 boosting PeaceHealth's hospital holdings from six to eight with the addition of the two-campus Southwest Washington Medical Center in Vancouver Washington.

Under terms of the affiliation Southwest Washington Health System became part of PeaceHealth allowing Southwest to benefit from its larger peer's medical and financial resources. The move allows both health systems to increase the scope of services they offer in Washington State where Southwest Washington Health System also operates clinics a medical group and a foundation through which it conducts fundraising efforts.

EXECUTIVES

Ceo, Liz Dunne
President Peacehealth Medical Group, Michael Metcalf
Evp And Chief Administrative Officer, Carol Aaron
Chief Executive Columbia Network, Sean J. Gregory
Chief Executive Northwest Network, Dale Zender
Svp And Chief Nursing Officer, Victoria King
Svp And Cio, Dan Hein
President Hospital Services Oregon, Rand O'Leary
Evp Strategy And Community Health, Michael Dwyer
Evp And Cfo, Kimberly Hodgkinson
Evp And General Counsel, Ron Saxton
System Vice President Supply Chain, Eddie Sharp
Director Of Clinical Services, Merry Keane
Senior Vice President, Mark Hallett
Chairman, Andrea Nenzel

LOCATIONS

HQ: PEACEHEALTH
1115 SE 164TH AVE, VANCOUVER, WA 986839324
Phone: 360 788-6841
Web: WWW.PEACEHEALTH.ORG

PRODUCTS/OPERATIONS

2013 Sales

	$ mil.	% of total
Patient service revenue	1,984	92
Premium revenue	93	4
Other operating revenue	94	4
Total	**2,171**	**100**

Selected Hospitals

PeaceHealth Ketchikan Medical Center (Ketchikan Alaska)
Cottage Grove Community Hospital (Cottage Grove Oregon)
Peace Harbor Hospital (Florence Oregon)
PeaceHealth Peace Island Medical Center (Friday Harbor Washington)
PeaceHealth Southwest Medical Center (Vancouver Washington)
PeaceHealth St. John Medical Center (Longview Washington)
PeaceHealth St. Joseph Medical Center (Bellingham Washington)
Sacred Heart Medical Center at RiverBend (Springfield Oregon)
Sacred Heart Medical Center University District (Eugene Oregon)
Other Operations
PeaceHealth Laboratories (locations throughout Oregon and Washington)
PeaceHealth Medical Group (operates in Alaska Oregon and Washington)

COMPETITORS

Alaska Native Tribal Health Consortium
Franciscan Health System
HCA
Harrison Medical Center
Immediate Care
MultiCare Health System
Overlake Hospital
Providence St. Joseph Health
Seattle Children's Hospital
South Peninsula Hospital
Swedish Health Services
Tenet Healthcare
Yakima Valley Memorial

HISTORICAL FINANCIALS

Company Type: Private

Income Statement — FYE: June 30

	REVENUE ($ mil.)	NET INCOME ($ mil.)	NET PROFIT MARGIN	EMPLOYEES
06/14	2,249	114	5.1%	6,690
06/09	1,372	(88)	—	—
06/06	1,048	103	9.8%	—
Annual Growth	10.0%	1.3%	—	—

2014 Year-End Financials

Return on assets: 3.3%
Return on equity: 6.5%
Current ratio: 0.70
Cash ($ mil.): 549

PEDERNALES ELECTRIC COOPERATIVE, INC.

Created by Texas ranchers and business owners Pedernales Electric Cooperative provides electricity services in the Texas Hill Country. The company the largest electric cooperative in the US purchases its electricity from wholesale providers primarily the Lower Colorado River Authority (LCRA) and transmits and distributes it to about 209350 cooperative members (or more than 247810 individual customer meters). Pedernales Electric Cooperative operates more than 17450 miles of power line and maintains 290000 wooden utility poles in its service area.

Geographic Reach

The cooperative serves a customer base spread across 24 counties in Central Texas (8100 sq. miles an area larger than the state of Massachusetts).

Financial Performance

In 2012 the company's revenues decreased by 3% as the result of unfavorable weather conditions weakening demand for power (despite an increase of 5500 new customers). Net income decreased 24% driven by lower net sales.

Strategy

A member of the American Wind Energy Association Pedernales Electric Cooperative is committed to move toward conservation and cleaner energy (to meet clean air standards) and has a renewable energy goal of 30% of energy from renewable sources by 2020. The coop contracts with AEP Energy Partners to buy wind power produced at the South Trent Wind Farm near Sweetwater Texas. In all the wind-power purchase is expected to power up 22000 to 27000 homes.

In 2013 company upgraded the electric system in the Canyon Lake area manually converting more than 1900 transformers to accept higher voltage to better serve the growing energy needs of nearly 2600 coop members in the Clear Water Estates Tamarack Shores Scenic Terrace Linda Ledges Hancock Oak Hills and Rocky Creek Ranch subdivisions.

Company Background

As part of reforming its operations following a financial scandal in 2009 Pedernales Electric Cooperative became one of the first electric distribution cooperatives in the US to broadcast its Board meetings live on the Internet. In 2009 the cooperative ratified the first member advisory panel (on energy conservation and renewable energy use) in Pedernales Electric Cooperative's history.

Pedernales Electric Cooperative was founded in 1938 with the help of local landowner (and later US president) Lyndon Johnson.

EXECUTIVES

Vice President Sales Andamp; Marketing, Larry Landaker
Seinor Vice President And General Manager, Frank Chavez
Vice President, Richard Arellano
Vice President Power Supply And Energy Services, Ingmar Sterzing
Vice President Markets, David Thompson
Board Secretary, Renee Oelschleger
Auditors: BKD LLP HOUSTON TX

LOCATIONS

HQ: PEDERNALES ELECTRIC COOPERATIVE, INC.
201 S AVENUE F, JOHNSON CITY, TX 786364827
Phone: 830 868-7155
Web: WWW.PEC.COOP

HISTORICAL FINANCIALS

Company Type: Private

Income Statement — FYE: December 31

	REVENUE ($ mil.)	NET INCOME ($ mil.)	NET PROFIT MARGIN	EMPLOYEES
12/11	589	6	1.1%	741
12/10	550	53	9.8%	—
12/09	578	57	10.0%	—
Annual Growth	0.9%	(66.5%)	—	—

2011 Year-End Financials

Return on assets: 0.5%
Return on equity: 1.6%
Current ratio: 0.20
Cash ($ mil.): 27

PENNSYLVANIA - AMERICAN WATER COMPANY

Pennsylvania-American Water distributes water and provides wastewater services to a population of more than 2 million people in some 390 communities across Pennsylvania. The company serves 635000 water customers and 17500 wastewater customers. It operates about 35 water treatment plants six wastewater facilities and 9800 miles of pipeline. Pennsylvania-American Water's service territory covers some three dozen Pennsylvania counties. The utility the largest regulated water and wastewater service provider in Pennsylvania is a subsidiary of New Jersey-based American Water Works.

Operations

Pennsylvania-American Water also has 85 well stations and treats and delivers about 216 millions of gallons of water each day. In addition it operates 70 groundwater treatment facilities which process water sourced from more than 100 groundwater wells and maintains 250 treated water storage facilities 280 pumping stations and 60 dams.

Geographic Reach

The utility's primarily service areas include Mechanicsburg Mon Valley Norristown Pittsburgh Scranton Washington and Wilkes-Barre.

Financial Performance

Pennsylvania-American Water represents about a fifth of its parent company's sales; in 2011 it reported $516 million in revenue from Pennsylvania.

Mergers and Acquisitions

The utility expands its reach in Pennsylvania by picking up smaller water systems; in 2012 it completed six such acquisitions including a Monroe County system serving the Fernwood Resort and a Pike County system serving about 100 residents.

EXECUTIVES

Pres, Kathy Pape
V Pres, William C Kelvinton
SEC, Velma A Redmond
Treas, Stephen F Analdo
Information Technology Support, James P Oehling
Director of Mis/Is, David Jerpe
Domino Administrator, Jill Breneman
Senior Developer, Richard Watts
Counsel, Susan Simms
Senior Financial Analyst, Jim Alexander
Operations Upervisor, Brian Boal

LOCATIONS

HQ: PENNSYLVANIA - AMERICAN WATER COMPANY
800 W HERSHEY PARK DR, HERSHEY, PA 170332400
Phone: 717 533-5000
Web: WWW.AMWATER.COM

COMPETITORS

Aqua America
United Water Inc.
Utilities Inc.

HISTORICAL FINANCIALS

Company Type: Private

Income Statement				FYE: December 31
	REVENUE ($ mil.)	NET INCOME ($ mil.)	NET PROFIT MARGIN	EMPLOYEES
12/17*	661	160	24.3%	1,007
06/14	589	127	21.7%	—
03/14	584	128	22.0%	—
12/13	571	122	21.4%	—
Annual Growth	3.7%	7.1%	—	—

*Fiscal year change

2017 Year-End Financials

Return on assets: 3.5%
Cash ($ mil.): 3
Return on equity: 5.6%
Current ratio: 0.20

PENNSYLVANIA ELECTRIC COMPANY

Pennsylvania Electric (Penelec) has elected to provide power to the people of the Keystone State. The company distributes power to a population of 1.6 million in a 17600-square-mile portion of northern western and south-central Pennsylvania. The utility operates more than 20170 miles of distribution and more than 2700 transmission lines. The Waverly Electric Light & Power Company a subsidiary of Penelec provides electric services to a population of about 8400 in Waverly New York. Penelec is an operating subsidiary of regional utility power player FirstEnergy.

EXECUTIVES

Exec V Pres-Cfo, Mark T Clark
Exec V Pres-Gen Counsel, Leila L Vespoli
V Pres-Controller-Cao, Harvey L Wagner
V Pres-Treas, James F Pearson
Auditors: PRICEWATERHOUSECOOPERS LLP CL

LOCATIONS

HQ: PENNSYLVANIA ELECTRIC COMPANY
2800 POTTSVILLE PIKE, AKRON, OH 44308
Phone: 800 545-7741
Web: WWW.FIRSTENERGYCORP.COM

COMPETITORS

Columbia Gas of Pennsylvania
Direct Energy
PECO Energy
PPL Electric
Peoples Natural Gas

HISTORICAL FINANCIALS

Company Type: Private

Income Statement				FYE: December 31
	REVENUE ($ mil.)	NET INCOME ($ mil.)	NET PROFIT MARGIN	EMPLOYEES
12/17	893	95	10.7%	896
12/16	904	88	9.8%	—
12/10	1,539	59	3.9%	—
12/09	1,448	65	4.5%	—
Annual Growth	(5.9%)	4.9%	—	—

2017 Year-End Financials

Return on assets: 2.2%
Cash ($ mil.): —
Return on equity: 7.8%
Current ratio: 1.20

PENNSYLVANIA HIGHER EDUCATION ASSISTANCE AGENCY

Pennsylvania Higher Education Assistance Agency (PHEAA) mission is to make higher education more accessible for Pennsylvanians. The government-related financial aid agency does business under the names American Education Services and FedLoan Servicing. It's one of the nation's top guarantors of the US Department of Education's Federal Family Education Loan Program as well as one of the largest student loan servicers and one of the largest student loan holders. PHEAA uses the funds it generates to improve higher education opportunities lower the cost of financial assistance and streamline the financial aid process.

Operations

The Agency's primary operations involve servicing activities student loan holdings and guaranty activities.

Servicing Activities provides student loans (and also through third parties) through Commercial Servicing FedLoan Servicing and Remote Servicing lines of business.

Commercial Servicing services alternative and Federal Family Education Loan program loans.

FedLoan Servicing handles federally owned Federal Family Education Loan and William D. Ford (Direct Loan) program loans.

Remote Servicing provides system to guarantors other servicers and not-for-profit servicers to use in their internal servicing operations.

Student Loan Holdings handles all new Stafford PLUS and Consolidation student loans are originated under the Direct Loan program. It earns interest subsidies and special allowance payments on certain Federal Family Education Loan program student loans within our student loan portfolio.

Guaranty Activities manages the Federal Student Loan Reserve Fund for the Department of Education.

Sales and Marketing

PHEAA provides student financial aid services to millions of students and thousands of schools through its loan guaranty loan servicing financial aid processing outreach and other student aid programs.

Financial Performance

PHEAA's revenues decreased by 12% in 2015 due to a drop in non-interest revenues as a result of a decrease in the retention of collections on defaulted loans net and lower gains on debt retirement.

Revenues from the retention of collections on defaulted loans decreased due to the change in the retention of collections pricing under the 2013 Budget a decline in the total collections on direct consolidation loans and an increase in the discount offered to eligible lenders for purchasing rehabilitation loans.

PHEAA's net income decreased by 67% in 2015 due to lower net revenues an increase in personnel and benefits costs (related to higher compensation costs) pension expense and an increase in information technology costs.

In 2015 the company's operating cash inflows decreased by 41%.

Strategy

The organization's mandate is a public service one to reduce the financial burden of higher education. It carries out the mission by updating its outreach and education efforts regarding student loans and other financial aid and by guaranteeing loans. The company mainly focuses on finding ways to improve higher education opportunities for students families schools and taxpayers in Pennsylvanians.

Company Background

In 2013 PHEAA launched online tool MySmartBorrowing to help potential borrowers understand the long-term implications of debt.

EXECUTIVES

President Ceo Ceo, James L. Preston
Cio, Brian Lecher
Cfo, Timothy A. Guenther
Senior Vice President, Todd E Mosko
Senior Vice President Public Affairs, Nathan Hench
Assistant Vice President, Vicky Roganish
Senior Vice President, Mubashar Hameed
Senior Vice President Of Internal Audit, Judith S Bines
Senior Vice President, Stephanie Martella
Chairman, William F. Adolph
Vice Chairman, Wayne D. Fontana
Legislative Secretary, Tim Olsen
Auditors: ERNST & YOUNG LLP MCLEAN VA

LOCATIONS

HQ: PENNSYLVANIA HIGHER EDUCATION ASSISTANCE AGENCY
1200 N 7TH ST, HARRISBURG, PA 171021419
Phone: 717 720-2700
Web: WWW.PHEAA.ORG

PRODUCTS/OPERATIONS

2015 sales

	$ mil.	% of total
Non-interest		
Servicing fees	308	50
Retention of collections on defaulted loans net	130	21
Federal fees	20	3
Other	(1.2)	-
Interest		
Loans	155	25
Investments	5	1
Total	**619**	**100**

COMPETITORS

Bank of America
Discover
Educational Funding of The South
First Marblehead
KeyCorp
Sallie Mae
SunTrust

HISTORICAL FINANCIALS

Company Type: Private

Income Statement				FYE: June 30
	REVENUE ($ mil.)	NET INCOME ($ mil.)	NET PROFIT MARGIN	EMPLOYEES
06/13*	671	155	23.2%	2,700
03/12	436	68	15.7%	—
Annual Growth	53.8%	127.6%	—	—

*Fiscal year change

2013 Year-End Financials

Return on assets: 1.7%
Cash ($ mil.): 88
Return on equity: 16.4%
Current ratio: 5.60

PENNSYLVANIA HOUSING FINANCE AGENCY

Pennsylvania Housing Finance Agency (PHFA) helps residents of the Keystone State obtain keys to their dream homes. The government-owned agency provides financing for low-income home-buyers including the elderly and disabled and participates in rental housing development initiatives. It generates funding from state and federal grants interest earned on investments and loans and the sale of its own securities to private investors. The agency is run by a board which includes Pennsylvania's secretary of banking secretary of community and economic development secretary of public welfare and the state treasurer. The PHFA has funded more than 130000 houses and 54000 apartment units since its founding in 1972.

EXECUTIVES

Chm, Robin Wiessmann
V Pres*, Thomas B Hagen
Exec Dir*, Craig H Alexander
Human Resources Representative, Arlene Frontz
Finance Manager, John Zapotocky
Financial Officer, Kelly Wilson
Manager, Kevin Wike
Accountant, Laura Wildman
Senior Special Programs Office, Roberta Schwalm
Officer, Theodore Jackson
Engineer, Kris Clymans

LOCATIONS

HQ: PENNSYLVANIA HOUSING FINANCE AGENCY
211 N FRONT ST, HARRISBURG, PA 171011406
Phone: 717 780-3800
Web: WWW.PHFA.ORG

HISTORICAL FINANCIALS

Company Type: Private

Income Statement — FYE: June 30

	ASSETS ($ mil.)	NET INCOME ($ mil.)	INCOME AS % OF ASSETS	EMPLOYEES
06/20	4,542	14	0.3%	250
06/19	4,366	22	0.5%	—
06/18	4,366	20	0.5%	—
06/12	5,593	10	0.2%	—
Annual Growth	(2.6%)	4.3%	—	—

2020 Year-End Financials

Return on assets: 0.3%
Return on equity: 1.9%
Sales ($ mil): 240

PEPPER CONSTRUCTION COMPANY

EXECUTIVES

Ceo, J David Pepper
President, Kenneth Egidi
Exec Pres, James A Nissen
Cfo, Chris Averill
Manager, Atul Raj
Safety Coordinator, Danny Torres
Assistant Superintendent, Joe Mildice
Assistant To Atul Raj, Lori Brown
Coordinator of Marketing, Rebecca Wagner
Project Accounting Assistant, Janice Alvarado
Senior Vice President Director, Jay Jacobsmeyer
Auditors: BDD LLP OAKBROOK TERRACE IL

LOCATIONS

HQ: PEPPER CONSTRUCTION COMPANY
643 N ORLEANS ST, CHICAGO, IL 606543690
Phone: 312 266-4700
Web: WWW.PEPPERCONSTRUCTION.COM

HISTORICAL FINANCIALS

Company Type: Private

Income Statement — FYE: September 30

	REVENUE ($ mil.)	NET INCOME ($ mil.)	NET PROFIT MARGIN	EMPLOYEES
09/17	704	14	2.1%	900
09/16	805	20	2.5%	—
09/15	709	10	1.5%	—
09/11	668	4	0.6%	—
Annual Growth	0.9%	23.3%	—	—

2017 Year-End Financials

Return on assets: 6.7%
Return on equity: 37.7%
Current ratio: 1.20
Cash ($ mil.): 21

PEPPER CONSTRUCTION GROUP, LLC

Pepper Construction Group spices up the construction business with a little of this and a pinch of that. The company provides general contracting and construction management services for commercial office education entertainment health care and institutional clients as well as waterworks projects. (Health care projects account for about 50% of Pepper's revenue.) Its client list includes UBS Northwestern University University of Notre Dame Texas Heart Institute Loyola University Medical Center and NASA. Pepper Construction Group has divisions in Illinois Indiana Ohio and Texas. Stanley F. Pepper founded the company in Chicago in 1927. The group is owned by his family and employees of the firm.

Operations

The company's Pepper Environmental Technologies unit provides environmental services. Green building has become a large part of Pepper Construction's operations. Its Green Team of certified professionals have helped construct more than 2.9 million sq. ft. of eco-friendly space. The Green Team has built the Apple Computer flagship store HSBC Chicago North and Kohl's Children's Museum.

The firm's Pepper-Lawson Waterworks group constructs water purification plants for municipal clients including Houston and Missouri City Texas.

Geographic Reach

Chicago-based Pepper Construction comprises four geographic divisions: Illinois; Indiana; Ohio; and Texas. Overall the company is active in about 20 states mostly in the central and northeastern states.

EXECUTIVES

Chm, Dave Pepper
V Pres-Assist SEC*, Stephanie Vitner
Sr V Pres-Gen Counselor-Sec*, Timothy F Sullivan
Evp-Cfo*, Chris Averill
Senior Business Unit Accountan, Kelly Hampton
Senior Administrative, Kate Holstein
Director of Business Developme, Scott Nemshick
Marketing Generalist, Abby Baldocchi
Assistant Project Engineer, Clay Langebartels
Senior Project Manager, Daniel Titus
Project Engineer, Kathleen Landers
Auditors: BKD LLP OAKBROOK TERRACE IL

LOCATIONS

HQ: PEPPER CONSTRUCTION GROUP, LLC
643 N ORLEANS ST, CHICAGO, IL 606543690
Phone: 312 266-4700
Web: WWW.PEPPERCONSTRUCTION.COM

PRODUCTS/OPERATIONS

Selected Operations

Pepper Construction Group LLC (Chicago Illinois)
Pepper Construction Co. (Chicago Illinois)
Pepper Construction Co. of Indiana (Indianapolis Indiana)
Pepper Construction Co. of Ohio LLC (Dublin Ohio)
Pepper Environmental Technologies Inc. (Barrington Illinois)
Pepper-Lawson Construction LP (Houston Texas)
Pepper-Lawson Waterworks LLC (Houston Texas)

COMPETITORS

Barton Malow
Bulley & Andrews
C. G. Schmidt
Charles Pankow Builders
Clark Enterprises
Gilbane
Graycor
M. A. Mortenson
McCarthy Building
Power Construction
Turner Corporation
Walbridge Aldinger
Walsh Group

HISTORICAL FINANCIALS

Company Type: Private

Income Statement — FYE: September 30

	REVENUE ($ mil.)	NET INCOME ($ mil.)	NET PROFIT MARGIN	EMPLOYEES
09/16	1,179	23	2.0%	1,100
09/15	1,110	9	0.9%	—
09/11	911	15	1.7%	—
Annual Growth	5.3%	8.2%	—	—

2016 Year-End Financials

Return on assets: 8.0%
Return on equity: 47.7%
Current ratio: 1.20
Cash ($ mil.): 39

PERISHABLE DISTRIBUTORS OF IOWA, LTD.

EXECUTIVES

Pres, Dan Wampler
Exec V Pres*, Linda Sharp
Director, Ronald Pearson
Commodity Buyer, Claudia Dial
Logistics Coordinator, Cory Breese
Director, Dustin Moeller

Maintenance Supervisor, Glen Sievers
Human Resources Executive, Janel Jones
Senior Vice President of Wareh, Jim Brandt
Operations Manager, Joe McConnell
Tran Manager, Keith Lyman

LOCATIONS

HQ: PERISHABLE DISTRIBUTORS OF IOWA, LTD.
2741 SE PDI PL, ANKENY, IA 500213958
Phone: 515 965-6300
Web: WWW.CONTACTPDI.COM

HISTORICAL FINANCIALS

Company Type: Private

Income Statement — FYE: September 30

	REVENUE ($ mil.)	NET INCOME ($ mil.)	NET PROFIT MARGIN	EMPLOYEES
09/18*	1,346	38	2.9%	687
10/17	1,343	35	2.6%	—
10/16	1,307	33	2.6%	—
09/15	1,248	31	2.5%	—
Annual Growth	2.5%	7.3%	—	—

*Fiscal year change

2018 Year-End Financials

Return on assets: 25.9%
Return on equity: 55.2%
Current ratio: 1.30
Cash ($ mil.): 15

PERMANENT UNIVERSITY FUND

LOCATIONS

HQ: PERMANENT UNIVERSITY FUND
221 W 6TH ST STE 1700, AUSTIN, TX 787013451
Phone: 512 225-1600

HISTORICAL FINANCIALS

Company Type: Private

Income Statement — FYE: August 31

	REVENUE ($ mil.)	NET INCOME ($ mil.)	NET PROFIT MARGIN	EMPLOYEES
08/20	2,215	1,550	70.0%	2
08/19	1,035	953	92.1%	—
08/18	1,906	1,964	103.0%	—
08/17	2,888	2,032	70.4%	—
Annual Growth	(8.5%)	(8.6%)	—	—

2020 Year-End Financials

Return on assets: 6.2%
Return on equity: 6.4%
Current ratio: —
Cash ($ mil.): 776

PERMIAN EXPRESS PARTNERS LLC

LOCATIONS

HQ: PERMIAN EXPRESS PARTNERS LLC
1300 MAIN ST, HOUSTON, TX 770026803
Phone: 713 989-7000

HISTORICAL FINANCIALS

Company Type: Private

Income Statement — FYE: December 31

	REVENUE ($ mil.)	NET INCOME ($ mil.)	NET PROFIT MARGIN	EMPLOYEES
12/19	897	879	98.0%	1
12/18	643	626	97.5%	—
Annual Growth	39.6%	40.4%	—	—

2019 Year-End Financials

Return on assets: 57.8%
Return on equity: 60.7%
Current ratio: 1.10
Cash ($ mil.): 1

PETER KIEWIT SONS', INC.

A heavyweight in the heavy construction industry Kiewit is one of North America's largest construction and engineering firms. The company is active in building industrial mining oil gas chemicals power transportation water and wastewater. It builds everything from roads and dams to high-rise office towers and power plants. The company focuses on projects located throughout the US Canada and Mexico. Affiliate Kiewit Mining owns or manages coal mines in Texas and Wyoming and manages a phosphate operation in southeast Idaho. Founded in 1884 Kiewit is owned by employees and Kiewit family members.

Operations

Kiewit's operations are diversified across seven segments: Building; Industrial; Mining; Oil Gas & Chemical; Power; Transportation; and Water/Wastewater.

Kiewit's Transportation segment constructs airport runways bridges marine and port projects rail lines mass transit roads and tunnels. Transportation has completed about 1000 projects which provided nearly $30 billion in revenue over the last 10 years. Kiewit's Power unit is active in gas coal retrofit power delivery renewables nuclear energy and engineering. Over the last 10 years Power has generated almost $20 billion.

Generating $7.5 billion through more than 1100 projects in the last 10 years the company's Building segment builds offices; industrial complexes; education and sports facilities; hotels; hospitals; transportation terminals; science and technology facilities; manufacturing retail and special-use facilities; interior construction; and tenant improvements. Kiewit conducts general construction construction management design-build and -assist and turnkey project development.

The Mining segment (which has generated nearly $3 billion over more than 100 mining projects in the last 10 years) carries out contract mining mine infrastructure ore processing and owned operations. Kiewit's Oil Gas & Chemical business (which completed more than 1200 projects that provides nearly $22 billion in revenue over the last 10 years) includes offshore construction oil sands gas processing compressor and pump stations pipelines and terminals liquefied natural gas and refining.

Through its Industrial division the company processes minerals; builds cement plants; treats water; provides engineering procurement and construction; installs paper production and packaging machines; and constructs food plants and related structures. Water/Wastewater manages dam water supply and wastewater projects.

Kiewit operates a number of subsidiaries. Kiewit Offshore Services fabricates complex offshore oil production platforms at a facility in Texas. Another subsidiary Kiewit Energy US refines petroleum. Kiewit's TIC subsidiary is an industrial construction firm based in Colorado.

Geographic Reach

Based in Omaha Nebraska Kiewit operates across the US (approximately 85 locations) Canada (more than 10 locations) and Mexico (1 location).

Sales and Marketing

Kiewit's clients include various public and private entities.

Strategy

Data strategy and technology are becoming increasingly important in companies ? and Kiewit is no exception. As these practices develop Kiewit is looking to hire individuals who are excited about working for a company that values their skills and challenges them to learn more in these fields.

The Data Strategy and Transformation team; Danielle Maddux Manager of Strategy and Analytics works on aims to deliver data-driven solutions and augment various business processes to save Kiewit valuable time and money. She hopes for Kiewit to become "an industry leader in data strategy and technology and to promote data literacy across the company."

Company Background

The sons of Dutch immigrants Peter and Andrew Kiewit founded masonry contractor Kiewit Brothers in 1884 in Omaha Nebraska. Following the dissolution of the partnership in 1904 Peter continued as the company's sole proprietor. In 1931 ? 17 years after Peter's death ? his son Peter reorganized the business as Peter Kiewit Sons'.

HISTORY

Born to Dutch immigrants Peter Kiewit and brother Andrew founded Kiewit Brothers a brickyard in 1884 in Omaha Nebraska. By 1912 two of Peter's sons worked at the yard which was named Peter Kiewit & Sons. When Peter Kiewit died in 1914 his son Ralph took over and the firm took the name Peter Kiewit Sons'. Another son Peter joined Ralph at the helm in 1924 after dropping out of Dartmouth and later took over.

During the Depression Kiewit managed huge federal public works projects and in the 1940s it focused on war-related emergency construction projects.

One of the firm's most difficult projects was top-secret Thule Air Force Base in Greenland above the Arctic Circle. For more than two years 5000 men worked around the clock beginning in 1951; the site was in development for 15 years. In 1952 the company won a contract to build a $1.2 billion gas diffusion plant in Portsmouth Ohio. It also became a contractor for the US interstate highway system (begun in 1956).

Peter Kiewit died in 1979 after stipulating that the largely employee-owned company should remain under employee control and that no one employee could own more than 10%. His 40% stake when returned to the company transformed many employees into millionaires. Walter Scott Jr. whose father had been the first graduate engineer to work for Kiewit took charge. Scott made his mark by parlaying money from construction into successful investments.

When the construction industry slumped Kiewit began looking for other investment opportunities and in 1984 it acquired packaging company Continental Can Co. (selling off noncore insurance energy and timber assets). Continental was saddled with a 1983 class action lawsuit alleging that it had plotted to close plants and lay off workers before they were qualified for pensions. In 1991 Kiewit agreed to pay $415 million to settle the lawsuit. In the face of a consolidating packaging industry the company sold Continental in the early 1990s.

In 1986 Kiewit loaned money to a business group to build a fiber-optic loop in Chicago; by 1987 it had launched MFS Communications to build local fiber loops in downtown districts. In 1992 Kiewit split its business into two pieces: the construction group which was strictly employee-owned; and a diversified group to which it added a controlling stake in phone and cable TV company C-TEC in 1993. That year Kiewit took MFS public; by 1995 it had sold all its shares and the next year MFS was bought by telecom giant WorldCom.

In 1996 Kiewit assisted CalEnergy (now MidAmerican Energy) in a hostile $1.3 billion takeover of the UK's Northern Electric. Kiewit got stock in CalEnergy and a 30% stake in the UK electric company all of which it sold to CalEnergy in 1998.

That year Kiewit spun off its telecom and computer services holdings into Level 3 Communications. Scott who had been hospitalized the year before for a blood clot in his lung stepped down as CEO and Ken Stinson CEO of Kiewit Construction Group took over Peter Kiewit Sons'.

In 1999 Kiewit acquired a majority interest in Pacific Rock Products a construction materials firm in Canada. Kiewit spun off its asphalt concrete and aggregates operations in 2000 as Kiewit Materials. Also that year the company created Kiewit Offshore Services to focus on construction for the offshore drilling industry. In 2001 the company acquired marine construction firm General Construction Company (GCC). The next year it expanded its offshore business further by buying a Canadian subsidiary from oil and gas equipment services company Friede Goldman Halter which was trying to emerge from bankruptcy.

Kiewit made history in 2002 for the fastest completion of a project of its type when it completed the rebuilding of Webbers Falls I-40 Bridge in Oklahoma at the end of July. (The bridge had collapsed in May after being hit by a pair of barges resulting in 14 fatalities.)

In 2004 Kiewit greatly increased its coal sales and reserves with the acquisition of the Buckskin Mine in Wyoming from Arch Coal.

Kiewit underwent a changing of the guard at the end of 2004 when 22-year veteran Bruce Grewcock took the reins as the company's fourth CEO since its founding. Stinson stayed on as the company's chairman.

In 2008 the group acquired TIC Holdings a heavy industrial construction and engineering firm.

Through its Kiewit Power Engineers Co. the company was contracted by Plutonic Energy Corporation and GE Energy Financial Services to work on the 235 MW hydroelectric Toba Montrose project one of British Columbia's largest renewable energy projects (completed around 2011).

In 2013 Kiewit entered the Australian market through a joint venture agreement that involves as $247 million engineer-procure-construct contract for a wet front end and ore wash plant situated at the Cloudbreak Mine in Northwest Australia. Fortescue Metals Group is the previous owner of Cloudbreak prior to the handover in early 2013.

EXECUTIVES

Svp And Cfo, Michael J. Piechoski, $236,600 total compensation

Chairman President And Ceo, Bruce E. Grewcock, $750,000 total compensation

Evp Energy, Thomas S. Shelby

Cio, Kris Lappala

Vice President For Development, Gerald Pfeffer

Vp Healthcare Services, Aj Klebba

Senior Vice President District Manager, Matt Swinton

Vice President Finance Canada, Leonardo Morabito

Executive Vice President Operations, Jay Steinmetz

Treasurer, Stephen Thomas

Secretary, Matthew Michler

Auditors: KPMG LLP OMAHA NEBRASKA

LOCATIONS

HQ: PETER KIEWIT SONS', INC.
1550 MIKE FAHEY ST, OMAHA, NE 681024722

Phone: 402 342-2052

Web: WWW.KIEWIT.COM

Selected Locations

US

Alaska
Arizona
Arkansas
California
Colorado
Florida
Georgia
Hawaii
Idaho
Illinois
Iowa
Kansas
Louisiana
Maryland
Massachusetts
Minnesota
Nebraska
Nevada
New Jersey
New York
North Carolina
Oregon
Tennessee
Texas
Utah
Virginia
Washington
Wyoming

Australia
Western Australia

Canada
Alberta
British Columbia
Manitoba
Newfoundland
New Brunswick
Ontario
Quebec
Saskatchewan

PRODUCTS/OPERATIONS

Selected Locations

US
Alaska
Arizona
California
Colorado
Florida
Georgia
Hawaii
Illinois
Iowa
Kansas
Maryland
Massachusetts
Minnesota
Nebraska
Nevada
New Jersey
New York
North Carolina
Oregon
Texas
Utah
Virginia
Washington
Wyoming
Canada
Alberta
British Columbia
Newfoundland
Ontario
Quebec
Mexico
Mexico City

Selected Subsidiaries and Affiliates

Aero Automatic Sprinkler
Cherne Contracting Corporation
Continental Fire Sprinkler Company
Kiewit Australia
Kiewit Bridge & Marine
Kiewit Building Group
Kiewit Energy Company.
Kiewit Engineering Group Inc.
Kiewit Infrastructure Co.
Kiewit Infrastructure South Co.
Kiewit Infrastructure West Co.
Kiewit Mining Group
Dry Valley/No. Rassmussen Ridge Mines
Buckskin Mining Company
San Miguel Mine
Walnut Creek Mining Company
Kiewit Offshore Services Ltd..
Kiewit Power Constructors Co.
Kiewit Power Engineers
Kiewit Texas Construction L.P.

COMPETITORS

ABB
Ames Construction
Balfour Beatty Infrastructure
Bechtel
Black & Veatch
Fluor
Granite Construction
Halliburton
Hubbard Group
Jacobs Engineering
KBR
Lane Construction
PCL Constructors
Parsons Corporation
Raytheon
Rio Tinto plc
Skanska USA Civil
Turner Corporation
Tutor Perini
Walsh Group
Whiting-Turner
Williams Companies

HISTORICAL FINANCIALS

Company Type: Private

Income Statement FYE: December 29

	REVENUE ($ mil.)	NET INCOME ($ mil.)	NET PROFIT MARGIN	EMPLOYEES
12/12	11,220	515	4.6%	14,700
12/11	10,381	790	7.6%	—
12/10	9,938	789	7.9%	—
Annual Growth	6.3%	(19.2%)	—	—

2012 Year-End Financials

Return on assets: 7.6%
Return on equity: 13.2%
Current ratio: 1.90
Cash ($ mil.): 1,447

PETRO STAR INC.

Petro Star is an oil refining and fuel marketing shining star that brings heating fuel and energy (heating oil diesel and aviation and marine fuels) to the citizens of the communities in the vast cold and lonely expanses of the US' largest state Alaska. It operates refineries at North Pole and Valdez and distributes fuels and lubricants throughout Interior Alaska Dutch Harbor Kodiak and Valdez. Started in 1984 by a group of petroleum industry veterans the company built its first refinery operations along the Trans-Alaska Pipeline at North Pole Alaska. Petro Star is a subsidiary of Arctic Slope Regional Corp.

Operations

The company's divisions are Refining; Retail; Lubricants; Marine Fuel; Heating Fuel; Aviation; and Port of Alaska.

Refining operates two refineries: the 60000 barrel-per-day Petro Star Valdez refinery which produces jet fuel JP-8 JP-5 marine diesel heating fuel and turbine fuel; and the North Pole refinery approximately 22000-barrel-per-day facility producing heating fuel kerosene diesel jet fuels and asphalt base oil.

Its retail division is engaged in retail stores selling its products (North Pacific Fuel and Sourdough Fuel). It operates several gas stations and convenience stores throughout the state offering fuel food groceries and propane sales for customer's convenience.

Petro Star Lubricants is a bulk lube repackaging company offering several product lines and provide technical services for all of the company's product lines.

Marine offers marine fueling as well as supplies such as pumps hoses and nozzles.

Heating Fuel distributes locally produced heating and diesel fuel directly from the company's refineries in North Pole and Valdez to locations throughout Alaska.

Aviation is a supplier of jet fuel for the Ted Stevens International Airport for both commercial and corporate aircraft.

Petro Star distributes ultra low sulfur diesel jet fuel and gasoline at Terminal 1 at the Port of Alaska.

Geographic Reach

Headquartered in Alaska Petro Star operates in Kodiak Dutch Harbor Valdez St Paul Fairbanks Anchorage and an additional offices in Seattle.

Sales and Marketing

The company's customers include aviation residential commercial industrial marine and military.

Company Background

The company has expanded through acquisitions including fuel distribution firm Sourdough Fuel (in 1986) as well as the 1991 purchase of Alaska Lube and Fuel (now Petro Star Lubricants). Kodiak Sales (in 1997) and North Pacific Fuel (in 1998).

In 2008 Petro Star secured a $158.7 million aviation fuel contract from the Defense Logistics Agency.

EXECUTIVES

Vp Heating Fuel And Marine, Don Castle
Director North Pacific Fuel Operations, Mark Hughes

LOCATIONS

HQ: PETRO STAR INC.
3900 C ST STE 802, ANCHORAGE, AK 995035963
Phone: 907 339-6600
Web: WWW.PETROSTAR.COM

COMPETITORS

Exxon Mobil
Tesoro
Valero Energy

HISTORICAL FINANCIALS

Company Type: Private

Income Statement — FYE: December 31

	REVENUE ($ mil.)	NET INCOME ($ mil.)	NET PROFIT MARGIN	EMPLOYEES
12/08	992	0	—	300
12/03	291	3	1.2%	—
12/02	267	1	0.7%	—
12/01	279	3	1.1%	—
Annual Growth	19.9%	—	—	—

2008 Year-End Financials

Return on assets: —
Return on equity: —
Current ratio: 1.90
Cash ($ mil.): 106

PETROCARD, INC.

EXECUTIVES

Ceo-Pres, Laura Yellig
Chm*, Joseph Chythlook
V Pres*, Jack Mowreader
Treas*, Andrew Rewolinski
Senior Financial Analyst, Rebecca Benson
Chief Information Officer, Roger Hall
Branch Manager, David Harris
Fuel Consultant, Ryan McShane
Vice President Fuels, Samuel Steoger
Fuel Consultant, Leif Johnston
Fuel Consultant, Colleen Vogel

LOCATIONS

HQ: PETROCARD, INC.
730 CENTRAL AVE S, KENT, WA 980326109
Phone: 253 852-7801
Web: WWW.PETROCARD.COM

HISTORICAL FINANCIALS

Company Type: Private

Income Statement — FYE: March 31

	REVENUE ($ mil.)	NET INCOME ($ mil.)	NET PROFIT MARGIN	EMPLOYEES
03/12	1,173	0	0.1%	190
03/11	948	3	0.4%	—
03/10	791	3	0.4%	—
Annual Growth	21.7%	(50.7%)	—	—

2012 Year-End Financials

Return on assets: 0.6%
Return on equity: 1.7%
Current ratio: 1.00
Cash ($ mil.): 1

PETROLEUM TRADERS CORPORATION

Petroleum Traders Corporation barters with fuel. The company provides wholesale gasoline diesel fuel and heating oil to fuel distributors government agencies and other large consumers of fuel such as businesses with vehicle fleets. The largest pure wholesale fuel distributor in the country Petroleum Traders operates and trades in 44 US states. It supplies #1 and #2 low sulfur diesel fuels biodiesel high sulfur heating oil and kerosene and conventional ethanol and reformulated blends of gasoline in regular midgrade and premium octane ratings.

Operations

Petroleum Traders focuses on supplying wholesale diesel and gasoline exclusively in the US offering a range of turnkey wholesale diesel fuel and wholesale gasoline fuel services.

Sales and Marketing

The company provides discount fuel to commercial government and wholesale customers. In the commercial space it services the trucking construction railroad mining and manufacturing industries as well as utilities and private fleets.

Strategy

Petroleum Traders parlays its hedging experience into fuel cost management for its customers via firm pricing cap programs collars and fuel swaps.

Company Background

The company was founded in 1979.

EXECUTIVES

Vice President, Vicki Himes
Vice President, L Himesvicki
Auditors: BADEN GAGE & SCHROEDER LLC

LOCATIONS

HQ: PETROLEUM TRADERS CORPORATION
7120 POINTE INVERNESS WAY, FORT WAYNE, IN 468047928
Phone: 260 432-6622
Web: WWW.PETROLEUMTRADERS.COM

COMPETITORS

George Warren
Gulf Oil
Martin Resource Management
Petro Holdings
Sun Coast Resources

HISTORICAL FINANCIALS

Company Type: Private

Income Statement — FYE: June 30

	REVENUE ($ mil.)	NET INCOME ($ mil.)	NET PROFIT MARGIN	EMPLOYEES
06/19	2,030	39	1.9%	150
06/18	1,815	11	0.6%	—
06/17	1,606	19	1.2%	—
06/16	1,667	38	2.3%	—
Annual Growth	6.8%	1.0%	—	—

2019 Year-End Financials

Return on assets: 19.3%
Return on equity: 27.2%
Current ratio: 3.10
Cash ($ mil.): 40

PGA TOUR, INC.

It takes the ferocity of a Tiger to get to the top of this membership organization. The PGA TOUR which includes Tiger Woods and golf's other top players puts on more than 130 official events per year that offer more than $360 million in prize money. Its major championships are the Masters Open Championship and PGA Championship. The PGA TOUR is separate from the PGA of America which consists mostly of club pros although most tour players maintain membership in both groups. Some of its marketing partners are Rolex FedEx and Avis. The PGA TOUR was formed in 1968 by a splinter faction of the PGA of America.

Operations

The PGA TOUR is the world's premier membership organization for touring professional golfers co-sanctioning more than 130 tournaments on the PGA TOUR PGA TOUR Champions Korn Ferry Tour PGA TOUR Latinoamérica Mackenzie Tour-PGA TOUR Canada and PGA TOUR Series-China.

Geographic Reach

Headquartered in Florida the PGA TOUR holds events in the US Latin America and China among others. Its sponsors and players hail from around the world.

Sales and Marketing

Like other sporting organizations and leagues the TOUR depends heavily on sponsorships and fees from broadcasters to generate revenue. Partners include Morgan Stanley USA Today Konica Minolta and BHSports among others.

EXECUTIVES

Senior Vice President Human Resources, Tom Perry
Executive Vice President And Chief Legal Officer, Richard Anderson
Commissioner, Timothy W. (Tim) Finchem
Commissioner, Jay Monahan
Vp And Managing Director Pga Tour Japan, Masashi Ishii
Senior Vice President Treasury, Andrea King
Senior Vice President Customer Relations, Sheila Mclenaghan
Vice President, Ronald E Price
Vice President Of Business Development, Jim Wasson
Vice President, Peter Kent
Vice President Of Field Operations, Roger Stevenson
Vice President Of Information, Steven Evans
Vice President Of Competition, Tyler Dennis
Vice President Of Tournament Business Affairs, Tom Alter
Senior Vice President Of Human Resources, Thomas Perry
Vice President And Treasurer, Andrew Feldmann
Vice President Marketing, Tom Kuhn
Vice President Client Management, Mcmanu Christin
Vice President Data Analytics, Michael Vitti
Vice President Human Resources, Michelle Corse
Vp Consumer Marketing And Business Dev, John Mayeron
Treasurer, Bodney Alex
Treasurer, Bobelis Vita
Board Of Directors, Glenda Buchanan
Auditors: PRICEWATERHOUSECOOPERS LLP JA

LOCATIONS

HQ: PGA TOUR, INC.
100 PGA TOUR BLVD, PONTE VEDRA BEACH, FL 320823046
Phone: 904 285-3700
Web: WWW.PGATOUR.COM

COMPETITORS

FIFA
LPGA
Major League Baseball
Major League Soccer
NBA
NFL
PGA
Professional Bowlers Association
USTA
WTA Tour

HISTORICAL FINANCIALS

Company Type: Private

Income Statement — FYE: December 31

	REVENUE ($ mil.)	NET INCOME ($ mil.)	NET PROFIT MARGIN	EMPLOYEES
12/13	1,075	34	3.2%	3,563
12/06	894	3	0.3%	—
12/05	875	4	0.5%	—
12/04	802	3	0.4%	—
Annual Growth	3.3%	29.4%	—	—

2013 Year-End Financials

Return on assets: 1.6%
Return on equity: 3.7%
Current ratio: —
Cash ($ mil.): 149

PHILADELPHIA CONSOLIDATED HOLDING CORP.

Because each industry has its own unique set of risks Philadelphia Insurance Companies and its subsidiaries specialize in designing and underwriting commercial property/casualty insurance. Its niche clients include rental car companies (for that insurance they always want to sell you at the counter) not-for-profits health and fitness centers and day-care facilities. Its specialty lines include loss-control policies and liability coverage for such professionals as lawyers doctors accountants dog groomers and even insurance claims adjusters. Philadelphia Insurance Companies is a subsidiary of Tokio Marine Holdings.

Geographic Reach

Philadelphia Insurance Companies' operating subsidiaries Philadelphia Insurance and Philadelphia Indemnity Insurance sell and service policies through a network of independent agents and about 50 regional offices that stretch across the US. With its new-found backing from Tokio Marine the insurer has access to broader distribution avenues in the US and overseas.

Sales and Marketing

In addition to commercial property and casualty insurance the company also sells personal coverage for collectible cars and homeowners flood insurance.

Strategy

Philadelphia Insurance Companies has been enhancing its information technology systems. The firm is working to upgrade its back-office infrastructure for more efficient handling of billing claims accounting and data management functions.

EXECUTIVES

Regional Vice President, Brent Kruse
Vice President Metro Region, Brian O'reilly
Assistant Vice President, Michael Henk
Vp Marketing, Mike Ricca
Senior Vice President, John Doyle
Regional Vice President, Bill Misita
Assistant Vice President, Liney Kevin
Vice President Commerical Underwriting, Mark Plousis
Avp Contract Surety, Rick Morgan
Vice President, Robert Morgan
Regional Vice President, Daniel Shea
Assistant Vice President Chief Information Security Officer (ciso), Mark Viola
Vice President, Jon Peeples

LOCATIONS

HQ: PHILADELPHIA CONSOLIDATED HOLDING CORP.
1 BALA PLZ STE 100, BALA CYNWYD, PA 190041401
Phone: 610 617-7900
Web: WWW.PHLY.COM

PRODUCTS/OPERATIONS

Selected Products

Commercial and Personal Property/Casualty Insurance
- Adoption agencies
- Adult day care
- Amateur sports
- Antique collector car
- Apartments
- Auto leasing/rental program
- Boat dealers
- Bowling centers
- Builder's exchange
- Builders' risk
- Business auto fleet
- Camp operators
- Child care centers
- Consulting foresters
- Contractor environmental coverage
- Crime protection plus
- Entertainment
- Environmental
- Fairs and fairgrounds
- Festivals
- Film production
- Flood
- Golf and country clubs
- Health fitness and wellness
- Home health care
- Homeowners association
- Hospice
- Hotels
- Life and business coaches
- Loss control
- Medical facilities and hospitals
- Motorsports
- Museums
- Non-profit and social service organizations
- Nursing homes
- Office parks
- Outdoor recreation
- Performing arts
- Pest control services
- Professional sports
- Public entities
- Real rstate dchedules
- Religious organizations
- RV parks and campgrounds
- Schools
- Security services (The Guardian)
- Shopping centers
- Special events
- Substance abuse rehabilitation facilities
- Temporary staffing agencies
- Volunteer fire department
- Zoos

Liability
- Accountants professional liability
- Allied Health professional liability
- Business owners
- Cyber security liability
- Employed lawyers professional liability
- Employment practices stand alone
- Excess liability
- Miscellaneous professional liability (Affinity Pro)

COMPETITORS

AIG
American Financial Group
CNA Financial
Hagerty Insurance
Hanover Insurance
Liberty Mutual
Markel
North Pointe
RLI
State Farm
Travelers Companies

HISTORICAL FINANCIALS

Company Type: Private

Income Statement — FYE: December 31

	ASSETS ($ mil.)	NET INCOME ($ mil.)	INCOME AS % OF ASSETS	EMPLOYEES
12/16	9,719	347	3.6%	1,374
12/15	9,047	323	3.6%	—
Annual Growth	7.4%	7.5%	—	—

PHOENIX CHILDREN'S HOSPITAL, INC.

Phoenix Children's Hospital (PCH) invests in the health of the next generation. Founded in 1983 the hospital provides a comprehensive range of medical services specifically for children and adolescents in the greater Phoenix area. The hospital has about 385 beds and provides care in a number of pediatric sub-specialties including childhood cancers hematology neuroscience heart disease trauma and orthopedics. It also operates a newborn intensive care unit (NICU) at its main campus. PCH has several pediatric outpatient care centers in surrounding Phoenix suburbs.

Operations

The hospital has nearly 1000 pediatric specialists providing inpatient outpatient emergency and trauma care across more than 75 pediatric subspecialties. Each year PCH has some 18800 inpatient admissions 81000 emergency department visits 238000 outpatient visits and 16000 surgical cases.

PCH has clinical and non-clinical research collaborations with other institutions to make advances in pediatric care such as Mayo Clinic Translational Genomics Institute and the Children's Oncology Group.

Subsidiary Cambridge Arizona Insurance Company provides captive insurance coverage to the hospital and its affiliates.

Geographic Reach

The system operates satellites in Mesa Scottsdale the Northwest Valley Avondale Yuma and

Sales and Marketing

State Medicaid payments account for more than half of net patient revenues followed by contracted health care agreements (38%). The remainder comes from patients and other payors.

Financial Performance

The hospital's revenue increased by 11% to $724 million in fiscal 2014 on 10% higher net patient service earnings and a 74% jump in other operating income. However net income decreased 59% to $39 million on lower non-operating income more employee compensation paid and more cash used towards supplies and professional services. Operating cash flow totaled $66 million that year.

Strategy

To meet population growth levels in the region PCH is working to expand its medical center facilities. In 2015 it broke ground on a $40 million project to build a new emergency department and pediatric trauma center tripling the number of exam rooms at the hospital. This and other expansion efforts allow PCH to accommodate patients from other areas of Arizona and surrounding states in the Southwest.

In 2014 the hospital invested in a partnership with Obstetrix Medical Group of Phoenix to establish Arizona Pediatric Cardiology and Phoenix Children's Cardiology Diagnostics (which manages the PCH's cardiology product lines). PCH owns 25% of the pediatric cardiology unit and 63% of the diagnostics unit.

Also that year PCH opened a 22-bed pediatric inpatient unit on the campus of Dignity Health Mercy Gilbert Medical Center.

EXECUTIVES

President And Ceo, Robert L. Meyer
Vp And Chief Medical Officer, Murray M. Pollack
Evp And Cfo, Douglas T. Myers
Evp Phoenix Children's Medical Group And Surgeon-in-chief, Dennis P. Lund
Evp And Coo, Betsy Kuzas
Svp And Chief Information Officer, David Higginson
Svp Patient Care And Chief Nursing Officer, Pamela J. Carlson
Vp And Chief Medical Information Officer, Vinay Vaidya
Svp And Chief Administrative Officer Phoenix Children's Medical Group, Roger Logan
President Phoenix Children's Medical Staff, Jeffrey P. Morray
Chairman Phoenix Children's Hospital Foundation Board Of Directors, Brian Swartz
Medical Director, Janice Piatt
Senior Vice President Chief Sales Officer, Bob Campbell
Vice President Finance, James Champlin
Medical Director, Karen Gerber-Vecsey
Vice President Perioperative Services, Barbara Pankratz
Vice President Professional Practice, Connie Ford
Vice President, Chad Johnson
Vice President Individual Giving, Terri Burkel
Medical Director Antimicrobial Stewardship Program, Wassim Ballan
Senior Vice President Strategic Planning, Rich Lehmuth
Senior Vice President Of Research And Chief Research Officer, Terrence L Stull
Senior Vice President Human Resources, Page Bachman
Executive Vice President, Nenad Robert
Chairman, Mark B. Bonsall
Vice Chairman, Jon Hulburd
Board Member, ELIZABETH ZORN
Board Member, Joseph Mascari
Treasurer, Tuan Raphael

LOCATIONS

HQ: PHOENIX CHILDREN'S HOSPITAL, INC.
1919 E THOMAS RD, PHOENIX, AZ 850167710
Phone: 602 546-1000
Web: WWW.PHOENIXCHILDRENS.ORG

PRODUCTS/OPERATIONS

2014 Sales

	$ mil.	% of total
Net patient service revenue	691	95
Net assets released from restrictions used for operations	10	2
Donations gifts & contributions	8	1
Other operating revenue	15	2
Total	**725**	**100**

Selected Center of Excellence

Barrow Neurological Institute at Phoenix Children's Hospital
Center for Cancer and Blood Disorders
Center for Pediatric Orthopaedics
Level One Pediatric Trauma Center
Neonatal Intensive Care
Phoenix Children's Heart Center

COMPETITORS

Banner Health
Dignity Health
Flagstaff Medical Center
John C. Lincoln Health Network
Northern Arizona Healthcare
Scottsdale Healthcare
Shriners Hospitals For Children
University of Arizona Health Network

HISTORICAL FINANCIALS

Company Type: Private

Income Statement — FYE: December 31

	REVENUE ($ mil.)	NET INCOME ($ mil.)	NET PROFIT MARGIN	EMPLOYEES
12/14	661	26	4.1%	3,000
12/13	655	31	4.9%	—
12/11	498	(5)	—	—
12/09	408	106	26.1%	—
Annual Growth	10.1%	(24.1%)	—	—

2014 Year-End Financials

Return on assets: 2.4%
Return on equity: 8.8%
Current ratio: 4.50
Cash ($ mil.): 130

PIEDMONT HOSPITAL, INC.

Those feeling ill in Atlanta can count on Piedmont Healthcare for help. Founded in 1905 the not-for-profit organization's flagship facility is Piedmont Atlanta an acute care hospital with more than 485 beds. Piedmont Atlanta provides general and advanced medical-surgical care including open-heart surgery organ transplantation and neurosurgery. Also part of the Piedmont family are Piedmont Fayette Hospital with more than 170 beds; Piedmont Mountainside Hospital a 52-bed community hospital north of Atlanta; and the Piedmont Physicians Group a network of more than 150 primary care physicians operating in dozens of offices throughout metropolitan Atlanta.

Operations

Piedmont Healthcare also operates Piedmont Newnan Hospital a community hospital in Coweta County Georgia and the acute care community hospital Piedmont Henry Hospital.

Each year the system serves around 2 million patients performing some 44000 surgeries completing more than 200 organ transplants and handling more than 250000 emergency department visits. It also sees some 472000 outpatients and around 8000 infant deliveries annually.

Sales and Marketing

Medicare and Medicaid payments combined account for more than 40% of Piedmont's total net patient service revenue.

Financial Performance

Revenue increased 4% to $1.7 billion in fiscal 2014 (ended June) on higher net patient service revenues and other revenues. However net income fell 27% to $104.2 million as operating expenses and pension adjustments increased.

Cash flow from operations rose 66% to $150.1 million that year due primarily to a change in working capital.

Strategy

The health care system expands its offerings through investment and renovation as well as partnerships and acquisitions. In 2014 it partnered with WellStreet to launch Piedmont Urgent Care by WellStreet a network of urgent care centers offering extended-hour walk-in treatment for non-life threatening illnesses and injuries.

EXECUTIVES

Radiology Director, Louis H Jacobs
Ceo Piedmont Physicians, Sid Kirschner
Chief Medical Officer, Leigh S. Hamby
Vice Chair, Harry M. McFarling
Coo, Gregory A. (Greg) Hurst
Chief Nurse Executive, Denise Ray
President And Ceo, Kevin Brown
Chief Strategy & Performance Improvement Officer, Michelle Fisher
Chief Consumer Officer, Matt Gove
Cfo, Michael McAnder
Cio, Geoff Brown
Director Of Health Information Management, Pamela Marshall
Executive Assistant To Mark Cohen Medical Director Vpma, Kathie Alhadeff
Vice President Of Supply Chain, Joe Colonna
Medical Director Radiation Oncology, Fred Schwaibold
Vp Of Government And External Affairs, Thomas Worthy
Executive Vice President, Ed Lovern
Vp Corporate Finance Treasurer, Marie Gaffney
Medical Director, Thomas Wells

Executive Vice President, Edward Lovern
Vice President Cardiology, Ray Georgeson
Executive Vice President And President Natural Gas Business, Franklin Yoho
Vice President Sales, Jim Rice
Vice President, Douglas Oglesby
Assistant Vice President State Affairs, Ron Jackson
Nursing Director, Sharon Queen
Chair, Janine Brown
Medical Secretary, Karin Jackson
Medical Secretary, Susan Scott

LOCATIONS

HQ: PIEDMONT HOSPITAL, INC.
1968 PEACHTREE RD NW, ATLANTA, GA 303091285
Phone: 404 605-5000
Web: WWW.PIEDMONT.ORG

PRODUCTS/OPERATIONS

2014 Sales

	$ mil.	% of total
Net patient service revenue	1,595	96
Other revenue	62	4
Total	**1,657**	**100**

Selected Operations
Piedmont Atlanta
Piedmont Fayette Hospital (Fayetteville)
Piedmont Henry Hospital (Stockbridge)
Piedmont Mountainside Hospital (Jasper)
Piedmont Newnan Hospital (Newnan)
Piedmont Physicians Group (metropolitan Atlanta)

COMPETITORS

Children's Healthcare of Atlanta
DeKalb Medical
Emory Healthcare
Grady Health System
Northside Hospital
Shepherd Center
Tenet Healthcare
Universal Health Services

HISTORICAL FINANCIALS

Company Type: Private

Income Statement — FYE: June 30

	REVENUE ($ mil.)	NET INCOME ($ mil.)	NET PROFIT MARGIN	EMPLOYEES
06/16	918	60	6.5%	6,419
06/15	857	66	7.8%	—
06/10*	689	75	11.0%	—
12/09	1	(0)	—	—
Annual Growth	199.4%	—	—	—

*Fiscal year change

2016 Year-End Financials

Return on assets: 6.1%
Return on equity: 17.0%
Current ratio: 2.40
Cash ($ mil.): 25

PIGGLY WIGGLY ALABAMA DISTRIBUTING CO., INC.

EXECUTIVES

Ceo-Pres, David Bullard
Auditors: DENT BAKER & COMPANY LLP BI

LOCATIONS

HQ: PIGGLY WIGGLY ALABAMA DISTRIBUTING CO., INC.
2400 J TERRELL WOOTEN DR, BESSEMER, AL 350202272
Phone: 205 481-2300
Web: WWW.PWADC.NET

HISTORICAL FINANCIALS

Company Type: Private

Income Statement — FYE: July 29

	REVENUE ($ mil.)	NET INCOME ($ mil.)	NET PROFIT MARGIN	EMPLOYEES
07/11	772	0	0.1%	500
07/10	837	0	0.0%	—
07/09	830	0	0.0%	—
Annual Growth	(3.5%)	85.6%	—	—

2011 Year-End Financials

Return on assets: 0.5%
Return on equity: 1.7%
Current ratio: 1.70
Cash ($ mil.): 4

PIKEVILLE MEDICAL CENTER, INC.

Taking a nasty fall while hiking the rugged Appalachians will likely land you at Pikeville Medical Center (PMC). Serving patients in eastern Kentucky the hospital boasts more than 260 beds and provides a full range of inpatient outpatient and surgical services. PMC's centers and departments handle a number of specialties such as diagnostic imaging echocardiogram neurosurgery cancer care and bariatric surgery. Employing some 350 physicians PMC also operates a rehabilitation hospital a home health agency and outpatient family practice and specialty clinics as well as a physician residency program. PMC first opened on Christmas Day in 1924.

Operations

Pikeville Kentucky-based PMC offers more than 400 services.

Strategy

PMC is rapidly expanding its services and facilities to keep pace with the needs of area residents. In recent years it has added such new services as pulmonary rehabilitation plastic surgery and orthopedic trauma. In addition the hospital launched a $150 million expansion project that will add an 11-story outpatient center (including physician practices and surgery suites) and a 10-story parking garage. Additional expansion efforts have included opening new outpatient cancer diagnostic pain management and primary care clinics.

An active participant in clinical trials and studies PMC works to expand its research opportunities for patients and physicians. In 2013 the hospital began new treatment for patients with Paroxysmal Atrial Fibrillation (Afib) using Medtronic's Arctic Front Advance Cardiac Cryoballoon System.

Since 2012 when it inked a Medicaid contract with Coventry PMC has contracts with all three providers: Coventry Wellcare and Kentucky Spirit. PMC become member of the Mayo Clinic Care Network in 2013. The agreement gives PMC providers access to Mayo Clinic resources including its online point-of-care information system and its electronic consulting process that connects physicians with Mayo Clinic specialists on questions of diagnosis therapy or care management.

EXECUTIVES

Ceo-Pres, Walter E May
V Pres*, Ronald Burchett
SEC-Treas*, Joe Dean Anderson
Vp*, Michelle Hagy
Chief Operating Officer*, Debbie Puckett
Vp*, Peggy Rasnick Justice
Coo*, Juanita Deskins
Cfo*, Michelle Hagey
Occupational Specia, Alisa Bowers
Scientist, Sharon Weddington
Chief of Medicine, Ihari Malempati
Auditors: PERSHING YOAKLEY & ASSOCIATES

LOCATIONS

HQ: PIKEVILLE MEDICAL CENTER, INC.
911 BYPASS RD, PIKEVILLE, KY 415011689
Phone: 606 218-3500
Web: WWW.PIKEVILLEHOSPITAL.ORG

PRODUCTS/OPERATIONS

Selected Services
Bariatric Surgery
Breast Care Center
Critical Care
Diagnostics
Diabetes Education
Ear Nose & Throat (Otolaryngology)
Emergency
Endocrinology
Family Practice
Gastroenterology
Gynecology/Obstetrics
Family Practice Clinic
Heart Institute
Heart Failure/Coumadin Clinic
Home Health
Home Medical Equipment
Inpatient
Infectious Disease
Laboratory Services
Leonard Lawson Cancer Center
Neonatology
Nephrology
Neurosurgery
Ophthalmology
Other Patient Services
Orthopedic Surgery
Palliative Care
Pediatrics
Pharmacy
Plastic & Reconstructive Surgery
Pulmonary Clinic
Radiology
Rehabilitation
Residency Program
Rheumatology
Sleep
Urology
Women and Childrens' Services
Wound Care Center

COMPETITORS

Appalachian Regional Healthcare
Clinch Valley Medical Center
Community Health Systems
Highlands Health
Norton Community Hospital
Norton Healthcare
Russell County Medical Center
University of Kentucky Chandler Hospital

HISTORICAL FINANCIALS

Company Type: Private

Income Statement — FYE: September 30

	REVENUE ($ mil.)	NET INCOME ($ mil.)	NET PROFIT MARGIN	EMPLOYEES
09/19	547	5	1.1%	2,527
09/18	524	(14)	—	—
09/16	489	29	5.9%	—
09/15	381	9	2.5%	—
Annual Growth	9.5%	(12.2%)	—	—

2019 Year-End Financials

Return on assets: 1.0%
Cash ($ mil.): 145
Return on equity: 2.1%
Current ratio: 3.30

PILKINGTON NORTH AMERICA, INC.

Pilkington North America has a clear view of the US glass market.The company manufactures and markets glass and glazing products primarily for the automotive and building industries. Benefits of its glass include fire protection noise control solar heat control and thermal insulation. A majority of its sales come from automotive glass sold to the original equipment and replacement markets. More than a quarter of sales are made from building glass geared at homeowners and architects. A small but growing part of its business focuses on specialty glass used in solar energy conversion. Pilkington North America is a subsidiary of Pilkington plc which operates as part of Japanese glass giant Nippon Sheet Glass.

Geographic Reach

Pilkington North America manages six float glass lines in the US (where molten glass is poured on a bed of molten tin to ensure flat surface and uniform thickness) more than half a dozen automotive glass fabrication facilities in the US Canada and Mexico and a network of more than 100 US wholesale centers that distribute automotive replacement glass products.

Its six float glass lines including Rossford Ohio (2); Laurinburg North Carolina (2); Ottawa Illinois (1); Lathrop California (1). Products are shipped from its distribution centers in Columbus Ohio and Phoenix Arizona to external retailers and wholesale customers.

Sales and Marketing

The company provides glass products and glazing systems to automotive original equipment manufacturers of light vehicles buses trucks and specialized and utility vehicles; and glass products and accessories for replacing and repairing windshields and other glass parts to automotive glass replacement aftermarket sectors. Pilkington North America also serves homeowners architects and other window manufacturers and offers its products to retailers and wholesalers.

Automotive products (57% OEMs and 43% for automotive glass replacement) account for 70% of total sales; architectural products account for the remaining 30%. Products are shipped from its distribution centers in Phoenix and Columbus Ohio to external retailers and wholesale customers.

Strategy

In line with its parent's strategy a key focus for Pilkington North America's future is expanding its solar energy portfolio within its building products segment. The company anticipates an increase in volumes and that sales of solar energy glass will contribute a significant portion of those higher volumes. Although some of its float glass production lines were suspended during the economic crisis some have since been converted into solar energy lines and are coming back on stream to support its expansion particularly in photovoltaics.

Product introductions are also a key part of Pilkington North America's growth strategy. In 2014 it introduced Pilkington MirroView 50/50 which enhances the standard MirroView's visual performance for a brightly lit environment such as a store or showroom and Pilkington OptiView Pro a non-conductive anti-reflection coating especially designed for touch screen applications. In 2013 the company introduced Optiwhite which widens the color choice.

EXECUTIVES

Vp Human Resources, Spencer Harris

LOCATIONS

HQ: PILKINGTON NORTH AMERICA, INC.
811 MADISON AVE FL 3, TOLEDO, OH 436045688
Phone: 419 247-3731
Web: WWW.PILKINGTON.COM

PRODUCTS/OPERATIONS

Selected Products and Brands

Decoration
- Texture glass (18 pattern designs)

Fire protection
- Pyrodur (fire-resistant and radiant heat-protected glass)
- Pyrostop (fire-resistant insulating glass)

Glass systems
- Planar (structural glass system for architects)
- Profilit (exterior glazing glass)

Noise control
- Optiphon (laminated glass with high sound insulation)

Self-cleaning
- Activ Clear (clear float glass with self-cleaning properties)

Solar control
- Arctic Blue (tinted glass)
- Eclipse Advantage (solar control and thermal insulation glass)
- EverGreen (tinted glass)
- Solar-E (solar control and thermal insulation glass)
- SuperGrey (gray-colored solar control float glass)

Solar energy
- NSG TEC (coated glass for photovoltaic technologies)
- Sunplus (extra clear patterned glass for solar energy conversion)
- Optiwhite (extra clear float glass for solar energy conversion)

Special applications
- Mirropane (interior glass to create "infinity" mirror effects)
- TEC Glass (electrically conductive glass for flat panel displays heated glass and oven doors)

Thermal insulation
- Energy Advantage (energy-efficient window glass)
- OptiFloat (float glass)
- Spacia (medium thermal insulation glass)

COMPETITORS

Apogee Enterprises
Asahi Glass
Cardinal Glass
Guardian Glass
PPG Industries
Saint-Gobain
Schott Corporation
Taylor Made Group
Viracon

HISTORICAL FINANCIALS

Company Type: Private

Income Statement — FYE: March 31

	REVENUE ($ mil.)	NET INCOME ($ mil.)	NET PROFIT MARGIN	EMPLOYEES
03/08	967	(11)	—	3,747
03/07	913	(17)	—	—
03/04	931	31	3.4%	—
Annual Growth	1.0%	—	—	—

2008 Year-End Financials

Return on assets: 12.3%
Cash ($ mil.): —
Return on equity: (-1.2%)
Current ratio: 0.50

PIMA COUNTY

EXECUTIVES

Admin, Chuck Huckelberry
Information Specialist, Ed Sander
Customer Staff, Dana Moore
Coordinator, Monica Dennis
Librarian I, Maureen Kearney
Environmental Officer, Jim Faas
Admin Specialist, Mark Boyce
Supervisor District 5, Richard Elias
County, Barbara Lawall
Special Staff Assistant, Lisa Matthews
Energy Manager, Marc Lynn
Auditors: STATE OF ARIZONA-DEBBIE DAVENP

LOCATIONS

HQ: PIMA COUNTY
130 W CONGRESS ST FL 6, TUCSON, AZ 857011332
Phone: 520 724-9999
Web: WWW.WEBCMS.PIMA.GOV

HISTORICAL FINANCIALS

Company Type: Private

Income Statement — FYE: June 30

	REVENUE ($ mil.)	NET INCOME ($ mil.)	NET PROFIT MARGIN	EMPLOYEES
06/17	873	17	2.0%	7,500
06/16	863	2	0.3%	—
06/13	789	(13)	—	—
Annual Growth	2.6%	—	—	—

2017 Year-End Financials

Return on assets: 0.4%
Cash ($ mil.): 521
Return on equity: 0.9%
Current ratio: —

PINNACLE HEALTH HOSPITAL

EXECUTIVES

Ceo, Roger Longenderfer
Sr V Pres-Treas-Cfo*, William Pugh
Administrator*, Philip Guarneschelli
Law Specialist, John Warner
Coordinator, Andrea Flowers
Assistant Practice Manager, Michael Briner
Pain Management Specialist, Robert S Rankin
Family Practitioner, David Metzger
Internist, Julie Worthington
Podiatrist, Lauren Pruner
Director of Operations Lebanon, Oneida Deluca
Auditors: BAKER TILLY VIRCHOW KRAUSE LLP

LOCATIONS

HQ: PINNACLE HEALTH HOSPITAL
4300 LONDONDERRY RD, HARRISBURG, PA 171095317
Phone: 717 782-3131
Web: WWW.PINNACLEHEALTH.ORG

HISTORICAL FINANCIALS

Company Type: Private

Income Statement FYE: June 30

	REVENUE ($ mil.)	NET INCOME ($ mil.)	NET PROFIT MARGIN	EMPLOYEES
06/14	759	94	12.5%	4,800
06/13	733	105	14.4%	—
06/08	0	0	14.6%	—
06/05	0	0	—	—
Annual Growth	—	—	—	—

2014 Year-End Financials

Return on assets: 10.0%
Return on equity: 25.5%
Current ratio: 0.30
Cash ($ mil.): 1

PITT COUNTY MEMORIAL HOSPITAL, INCORPORATED

Vidant Medical Center is an acute health services facility that serves the vibrant community of Greenville North Carolina and surrounding areas. The 909-bed regional referral hospital's specialty divisions include Vidant Children's Hospital East Carolina Heart Institute a rehabilitation center and the outpatient Vidant SurgiCenter. Other services include oncology transplant women's health orthopedic behavioral care and home health and hospice care units. The center also serves as a teaching facility for East Carolina University's Brody School of Medicine. Vidant Medical Center (formerly Pitt County Memorial Hospital) is a member of University Health Systems of Eastern Carolina (dba Vidant Health).

Operations

In addition to serving as a primary teaching facility for the Brody School of Medicine Vidant Medical Center provides clinical training for East Carolina University's allied health and nursing programs. About 2000 students complete clinical programs at the medical center and its affiliated Vidant Health facilities each year.

Its subsidiary PMI Inc. offers property management services.

Altogether Vidant Medical Center serves more than 1.4 million people across its 29-county service area. Boasting a clinical staff of more than 500 physicians and 1200 nurses the medical center in 2013 tended to more than 46000 inpatients and more than 275000 outpatients. Its emergency department visits reached 121000-plus in 2013.

Geographic Reach

Vidant Medical Center provides care to patients in a 29-county service territory in eastern North Carolina. It operates as a regional referral center for smaller community hospitals in the area taking on complex care cases in its specialized fields of medicine.

Strategy

To enhance its service offerings to area residents the Vidant Health organization regularly updates its facilities through capital improvement projects. In addition to basic equipment and infrastructure upgrades in 2011 the hospital completed phase one of an expansion project at the Vidant Medical Center that aims to improve the hospital's pediatric and cancer care capabilities.

To signify its mission to enhance the quality of life in its service territories in 2012 University Health Systems of Eastern Carolina began operating as Vidant Health and the Pitt County Memorial Hospital was renamed as Vidant Memorial Hospital.

EXECUTIVES

Svp, Van Smith
Vice President Financial Services Supply Chain Management, Preston Comeaux
Senior Vice President Operations Vmg, Daniel Drake
Vice President Strategic Marketing, Daniel Stevens
Vice President Human Resources, Charlene Wilson
Vice President Director Of Information Technology Risk Management, Robin Watson
Materials Management Vice President Supply Chain, Steven Huckabaa
Auditors: RSM US LLP MINNEAPOLIS MINNE

LOCATIONS

HQ: PITT COUNTY MEMORIAL HOSPITAL, INCORPORATED
2100 STANTONSBURG RD, GREENVILLE, NC 278342832
Phone: 252 847-4100
Web: WWW.VIDANTHEALTH.COM

PRODUCTS/OPERATIONS

Selected Services

Asthma Program (Pediatric)
Audiology
Behavioral & Mental Health
Cancer Care
Child Life
Children's Care
Children's Emergency Department
Children's Hospital
Community Health Programs
CyberKnife
Diagnostic Imaging
Diabetes
Emergency Services
Endoscopy Services
Gamma Knife

COMPETITORS

Adventist Health System Sunbelt Healthcare
Bon Secours Health
Carolinas HealthCare System
Duke University Health System
Novant Health
Sentara Healthcare
Tenet Healthcare
UNC Hospitals
Upstate Affiliate

HISTORICAL FINANCIALS

Company Type: Private

Income Statement FYE: September 30

	REVENUE ($ mil.)	NET INCOME ($ mil.)	NET PROFIT MARGIN	EMPLOYEES
09/18	1,201	131	10.9%	15,000
09/15	1,066	79	7.5%	—
09/14	1,025	79	7.8%	—
09/13	1,031	91	8.9%	—
Annual Growth	3.1%	7.4%	—	—

2018 Year-End Financials

Return on assets: 8.3%
Return on equity: 10.7%
Current ratio: 2.70
Cash ($ mil.): 10

PITTSBURGH SCHOOL DISTRICT

EXECUTIVES

Supt, Linda Lane
Auditors: MAHER DUESSEL PITTSBURGH PEN

LOCATIONS

HQ: PITTSBURGH SCHOOL DISTRICT
341 S BELLEFIELD AVE, PITTSBURGH, PA 152133552
Phone: 412 622-3500
Web: WWW.PGHSCHOOLS.ORG

HISTORICAL FINANCIALS

Company Type: Private

Income Statement FYE: December 31

	REVENUE ($ mil.)	NET INCOME ($ mil.)	NET PROFIT MARGIN	EMPLOYEES
12/19	707	(21)	—	5,419
12/18	690	(19)	—	—
12/17	674	(4)	—	—
12/16	735	(2)	—	—
Annual Growth	(1.3%)	—	—	—

2019 Year-End Financials

Return on assets: (-2.4%)
Return on equity: —
Current ratio: 2.60
Cash ($ mil.): 60

PLACID HOLDING COMPANY

EXECUTIVES

Pres, Dan Robinson
V Pres, Larry Doty
V Pres, Ron Hurst
Manager, Eric Belvaux
Auditors: HEIN & ASSOCIATES LLP DALLAS

LOCATIONS

HQ: PLACID HOLDING COMPANY
1601 ELM ST STE 3900, DALLAS, TX 752014708
Phone: 214 880-8479

HISTORICAL FINANCIALS

Company Type: Private

Income Statement FYE: December 31

	REVENUE ($ mil.)	NET INCOME ($ mil.)	NET PROFIT MARGIN	EMPLOYEES
12/13	4,929	47	1.0%	2
12/02	532	3	0.6%	—
12/01	579	18	3.1%	—
12/00	564	5	1.0%	—
Annual Growth	18.1%	17.5%	—	—

2013 Year-End Financials

Return on assets: 7.5%
Return on equity: 12.8%
Current ratio: 1.40
Cash ($ mil.): 51

PLACID REFINING COMPANY LLC

A calm presence in the volatile oil and gas industry Placid Refining owns and operates the Port Allen refinery in Louisiana which converts crude oil into a number of petroleum products including diesel ethanol gasoline liquid petroleum gas jet fuel and fuel oils. Placid Refining's refinery has the capacity to process 80000 barrels of crude oil per day. The company is one of the largest employers and taxpayers in West Baton Rouge Parish. Placid Refining which is controlled by Petro-Hunt distribute fuels across a dozen states in the southeastern US from Texas to Virginia and is a major supplier of jet fuel to the US military.

EXECUTIVES

Pres, Daniel Robinson
V Pres, Ron Hurst
Treasurer, Barry Joffrion
Accounts Payable, Leeann Maze
Auditors: HEIN & ASSOCIATES LLP DALLAS

LOCATIONS

HQ: PLACID REFINING COMPANY LLC
2101 CEDAR SPRINGS RD, DALLAS, TX 752012104
Phone: 214 880-8479
Web: WWW.PLACIDREFINING.COM

COMPETITORS

CITGO Refining and Chemicals
NuStar Energy
United Refining
Valero Energy

HISTORICAL FINANCIALS

Company Type: Private

Income Statement — FYE: December 31

	REVENUE ($ mil.)	NET INCOME ($ mil.)	NET PROFIT MARGIN	EMPLOYEES
12/13	4,929	47	1.0%	200
12/11	4,699	4	0.1%	—
12/10	3,686	39	1.1%	—
12/06	2,925	128	4.4%	—
Annual Growth	7.7%	(13.1%)	—	—

2013 Year-End Financials

Return on assets: 4.2%
Return on equity: 1.0%
Current ratio: 1.10
Cash ($ mil.): 42

PLAINS COTTON COOPERATIVE ASSOCIATION

Plainly speaking most of the US cotton used by textile mills worldwide starts with the Plains Cotton Cooperative Association (PCCA). The farmer-owned co-op markets millions of bales annually for members in Oklahoma Kansas and Texas. To obtain a competitive price for their cotton PCCA takes advantage of Telmark LP's access to The Seam an online cotton marketplace that continually updates cotton prices buyer data and more. The co-op operates cotton warehouses in Texas Oklahoma and Kansas. PCCA sold its textile and apparel operations in 2014 to focus exclusively on cotton marketing and warehousing. Formed in 1953 PCCA's customers include Replay Urban Outfitters and Abercrombie & Fitch.

EXECUTIVES

Pres-Ceo, Kevin Brinkley
Chm*, Eddie Smith
Exec V Pres-Fin & Treas*, Sam Hill
Auditors: CROWE LLP DALLAS TEXAS

LOCATIONS

HQ: PLAINS COTTON COOPERATIVE ASSOCIATION
3301 E 50TH ST, LUBBOCK, TX 794044331
Phone: 806 763-8011
Web: WWW.PCCA.COM

PRODUCTS/OPERATIONS

Selected Sales and Services

Buying cotton
Cotton gins
- Gin bookkeeping
- Gin patronage
- Marketing and invoicing
- Scale ticket software
- Support and training
- Technology solutions

Cotton producers
- Agent gins
- Cash marketing
- marketing contracts
- Pool marketing

Warehousing

COMPETITORS

Alabama Farmers Cooperative
Calcot
Dunavant Enterprises
Greenwood Mills
International Cotton Marketing
J.G. Boswell Co.
Parkdale Mills
Staplcotn
Weil Brothers Cotton

HISTORICAL FINANCIALS

Company Type: Private

Income Statement — FYE: June 30

	REVENUE ($ mil.)	NET INCOME ($ mil.)	NET PROFIT MARGIN	EMPLOYEES
06/19	1,057	29	2.8%	170
06/16	892	23	2.7%	—
06/15	975	25	2.6%	—
Annual Growth	2.0%	3.4%	—	—

PLAINS PIPELINE, L.P.

EXECUTIVES

Ceo, Greg L Armstrong
V Pres, Harry N Pefanis
Exec V Pres, Al Swanson
Manager, Charles Manis
PIP L Operating General Partn, Aaron Cantrelle
Board Member, Taft Symonds
Assistant, Billy Rollins
Terminal Manager, Brad Dooley
Board Member, Everardo Goyanes
District Manager, James Mount

LOCATIONS

HQ: PLAINS PIPELINE, L.P.
333 CLAY ST STE 1600, HOUSTON, TX 770024101
Phone: 713 646-4100
Web: WWW.PLAINSALLAMERICAN.COM

HISTORICAL FINANCIALS

Company Type: Private

Income Statement — FYE: December 31

	REVENUE ($ mil.)	NET INCOME ($ mil.)	NET PROFIT MARGIN	EMPLOYEES
12/17	935	783	83.7%	200
12/16	780	621	79.6%	—
Annual Growth	19.9%	26.1%	—	—

2017 Year-End Financials

Return on assets: 8.9%
Return on equity: 17.4%
Current ratio: 0.40
Cash ($ mil.): 8

PLAN INTERNATIONAL, INC.

EXECUTIVES

Ceo, Rose Caldwell
Director, Brittney Rocourt
IMC Team Coordinator, Cathie Cabral
Country Wash Advisor, Edgar Viterbo
Director Institutional Funding, James Beale
Creative Director, Jennifer Teichman
Marketing and Acquisition, Jennifer Trainor
Senior Director, Jill Nosach
Complaince Manager, Laurent Kabore
Capacity Manager, Liz Carter
Manager Global Applications, Max Charman
Auditors: DYL & PERILLO INC PROVIDENCE

LOCATIONS

HQ: PLAN INTERNATIONAL, INC.
155 PLAN WAY STE A, WARWICK, RI 028861099
Phone: 401 294-3693
Web: WWW.PLAN-INTERNATIONAL.ORG

HISTORICAL FINANCIALS

Company Type: Private

Income Statement — FYE: June 30

	REVENUE ($ mil.)	NET INCOME ($ mil.)	NET PROFIT MARGIN	EMPLOYEES
06/15	684	(5)	—	7
06/14	657	(5)	—	—
06/12	601	29	4.9%	—
06/10	531	93	17.6%	—
Annual Growth	5.2%	—	—	—

2015 Year-End Financials

Return on assets: (-2.2%)
Return on equity: (-3.1%)
Current ratio: 6.60
Cash ($ mil.): 185

PLANO INDEPENDENT SCHOOL DISTRICT

EXECUTIVES

Exec Dir, Mark Allen
Spdt, Richard Matkin
Deputy Supt, Jeff Bailey
Assoc Supt, Jim Hirsch
Assistant, Mark De Hertogh
Coordinator, Suzana Spina
Assistant, Airica Kelly
Registered Nurse, Amy Cimino
Nurse, Ashly Taylor
Assistant, Brittany Drake
Pace Teacher, David Edmondson
Auditors: WEAVER AND TIDWELL LLP DA

LOCATIONS

HQ: PLANO INDEPENDENT SCHOOL DISTRICT
2700 W 15TH ST, PLANO, TX 750757524
Phone: 469 752-8100
Web: WWW.PISD.EDU

HISTORICAL FINANCIALS

Company Type: Private

Income Statement FYE: June 30

	REVENUE ($ mil.)	NET INCOME ($ mil.)	NET PROFIT MARGIN	EMPLOYEES
06/19	928	(74)	—	5,610
06/18	840	34	4.1%	—
06/17	775	288	37.2%	—
06/16	712	19	2.8%	—
Annual Growth	9.3%	—	—	—

PLY GEM HOLDINGS, INC.

Ply Gem brings out a new side of homes. The company makes and supplies exterior building materials used in home construction and renovation primarily in the US. Its products — vinyl siding aluminum windows and doors stone veneer and fencing — are supplied to home center retailers distributors construction companies and contractors in North America. Subsidiaries include Variform (vinyl siding) Napco (vinyl and metal exterior siding and trim) Kroy Building Products (vinyl fencing) and Great Lakes Window (energy-efficient vinyl windows and patio doors). Ply Gem Holdings was founded in 2004; it was acquired by Clayton Dubilier & Rice in 2018.

Change in Company Type

In April 2018 building products manufacturer Clayton Dubilier & Rice (CD&R) completed the acquisition of Ply Gem for $2.4 billion along with another company Atrium Windows & Doors. The combined Ply Gem and Atrium companies are now a privately-held exterior products subsidiary of CD&R under the Ply Gem name. The new Ply Gem will continue to be headquartered in Cary NC.

Operations

Ply Gem divides its business into two segments: windows and doors; and siding fencing and stone.

The windows and doors segment which generates nearly 55% of the company's revenue sells its products under the Ply Gem Windows Simonton Windows Great Lakes Window and Ply Gem Canada brands.

The siding fencing and stone segment which accounts for more than 45% of total revenue sells siding and accessories (under brands such as Variform Napco and Mastic) vinyl fencing and railing and stone veneer products. The company also sells cellular PVC trim engineered slate and shake roofing and gutter protection products.

Geographic Reach

North Carolina-based Ply Gem maintains manufacturing operations in the US and Canada. The company operates about 90 facilities across both countries. The US accounts for nearly 90% of revenue with Canada and other foreign countries accounting for the remaining 10%.

Sales and Marketing

Ply Gem has a multi-channel distribution network that serves both the new construction and the home repair and remodeling sectors. The company sells its products to specialty and wholesale distributors and directly to independent building material dealers regional and national lumberyard chains retail home centers independent home improvement dealers and big box retail outlets. Its top ten customers account for more than 45% of the company's net sales. ABC Supply Co. Inc. the company's largest customer accounts for more than 10%.

Financial Performance

Ply Gem's net revenues have seen a steady increase in the past five years. Sales increased more than 7% to $2.0 billion in 2017 compared with the previous year. In the windows and doors segment a 6% increase was the result of improved market conditions in the US and Canada especially in the new construction business. Net sales for the siding fencing and stone segment saw a 9% increase with contributing factors being— higher demand for its products new business wins and higher average selling prices.

Net income fell by 9% to $68.3 million in 2017 mainly as a result of increased product costs and higher operating expenses. A 30% decrease in operating cash ($102 million compared with $145 million in 2016) was driven by higher working capital levels rising commodity costs and the company's early pay discount practices.

Strategy

Going forward Ply Gem aims to capitalize on the continued improvement in the new construction and home repair and remodeling markets. Current strategic initiatives include increasing brand equity with digital marketing initiatives and improving profitability.

With housing starts recovering and the current underinvestment in homes in the US Ply Gem believes there is significant opportunity for growth. It will focus on products targeting energy efficiency and potential cost savings for the customer.

The company has invested recently in digital marketing capabilities such as improved search engine optimization lead generation and website user experience in order to build brand equity and increase market penetration.

To boost profits Ply Gem launched a new profitability initiative entitled "2x20" during 2017 aimed at increasing net sales by at least $40 million by 2020. 2x20 activities include lean manufacturing vertical integration in its manufacturing facilities and consolidating purchases of key raw materials supplies and services. It has also centralized many back-office functions into its corporate office in Cary NC and has implemented more automation in its manufacturing processes.

EXECUTIVES

Chairman President And Ceo, Gary E. Robinette, age 71, $825,000 total compensation
Evp And Coo, John C. Wayne, age 58, $527,875 total compensation
Evp And Cfo, Shawn K. Poe, age 58, $420,000 total compensation
Svp Human Resources, David N. Schmoll, age 61, $285,700 total compensation
President U.s. Window And Door Group, Arthur W. (Art) Steinhafel, age 51
President Siding Fencing And Stone Group, John L. Buckley, age 55, $337,840 total compensation
National Sales Manager, Rick Rinshed
Vice President Sales (window Group), Steve Gore
Vice President Corporate Controller, Brian Boyle
Vice President Financial Planning And Analysis, Jennifer Ward
National Accounts Manager, Jim Ross
Senior Vice President Human Resources, Dave Schmoll
National Account Manager, Jack Anderson
National Account Manager, John Wolma
Vice President National Accounts, Tom Winters
Vice President Finance, Chris Schaefer
Auditors: KPMG LLP RALEIGH NORTH CAROL

LOCATIONS

HQ: PLY GEM HOLDINGS, INC.
5020 WESTON PKWY STE 400, CARY, NC 275132322
Phone: 919 677-3900
Web: WWW.PLYGEM.COM

2017 Sales

	$ mil.	% of total
United States	1,849	90
Canada	202	10
Other foreign countries	3	-
Total	**2,056**	**100**

PRODUCTS/OPERATIONS

2017 Sales

	$ mil.	% of total
Windows & Doors	1,086	53
Sliding Fencing & Stone	970	47
Total	**2,056**	**100**

Selected Brands

Variform Siding
Napco Siding
Mastic Siding
Mitten Siding
Performance Siding
Georgia-Pacific
Canyon Stone
Simonton Windows
Great Lakes Window
Durabuilt
Leaf Relief
Leaf Relief Snap Tight
Leaf Smart
Leaf Logic
Ply Gem Shutters & Accents
Ply Gem Fence & Rail
Ply Gem Gutters
Ply Gem Roofing
Ply Gem Stone
Ply Gem Trim & Moulding
Ply Gem Windows & Doors

Selected Products

Fence & Rail
Gutters
Siding
Steel Siding
Stone Veneer
Trim
Windows and Doors

COMPETITORS

Alsco
Andersen Corporation
Arconic
Armstrong World Industries
Associated Materials
Atrium
CertainTeed
Harvey Industries
JELD-WEN
Louisiana-Pacific
MI Windows and Doors
Masco
Owens Corning
Pella
Royal Group
Simonton Windows Inc.
Therma-Tru
Trex Company

HISTORICAL FINANCIALS

Company Type: Private

Income Statement — FYE: December 31

	REVENUE ($ mil.)	NET INCOME ($ mil.)	NET PROFIT MARGIN	EMPLOYEES
12/17	2,056	68	3.3%	9,000
12/16	1,911	75	3.9%	—
12/15	1,839	32	1.8%	—
12/14	1,566	(31)	—	—
Annual Growth	9.5%	—	—	—

2017 Year-End Financials

Return on assets: 5.2%
Return on equity: 83.4%
Current ratio: 1.70
Cash ($ mil.): 71

POLK COUNTY

EXECUTIVES

Chm, Todd Dantdler
Commissioner*, Sam Johnson
Commissioner*, Jack Myers
Commissioner*, Bob English
Commissioner*, Wandy Wilkinson
Commissioner*, Jane Reed
Comptroller*, Stacy M Butterfield
Tax Collector, Joe Tetter
Property Appraiser, Marsha Faux
Commissioner, Bob Gernert Jr
Attorney, Mark Carpanini

LOCATIONS

HQ: POLK COUNTY
330 W CHURCH ST, BARTOW, FL 338303760
Phone: 863 534-6000
Web: WWW.POLK-COUNTY.COM

HISTORICAL FINANCIALS

Company Type: Private

Income Statement — FYE: September 30

	REVENUE ($ mil.)	NET INCOME ($ mil.)	NET PROFIT MARGIN	EMPLOYEES
09/18	602	48	8.0%	3,600
09/15	508	1	0.3%	—
09/12	593	(39)	—	—
09/09	589	(68)	—	—
Annual Growth	0.2%	—	—	—

2018 Year-End Financials

Return on assets: 1.0%
Return on equity: 1.3%
Current ratio: —
Cash ($ mil.): —

POLK COUNTY SCHOOL DISTRICT

EXECUTIVES

Spdt, Jacqueline Byrd
Occupational Specia, Amy Radano
Teacher Personnel Director, Brian Warren
Assistant Superintendent, Michael Perrone Jr
Administrative Secretary, Yvette Vega
Teacher, Jane Martinez
Director of Charter Schools, Melissa Brady
Teacher, Sarah Sojos
Mathematics Teacher, Deborah Craig
Teacher, Brooke Devane
Developer, Drury Roy
Auditors: CHERRY BEKAERT LLP ORLANDO F

LOCATIONS

HQ: POLK COUNTY SCHOOL DISTRICT
1915 S FLORAL AVE, BARTOW, FL 338307124
Phone: 863 534-0500
Web: WWW.POLKSCHOOLSFL.COM

HISTORICAL FINANCIALS

Company Type: Private

Income Statement — FYE: June 30

	REVENUE ($ mil.)	NET INCOME ($ mil.)	NET PROFIT MARGIN	EMPLOYEES
06/14	871	(5)	—	2,971
06/13	827	(40)	—	—
06/12	821	(42)	—	—
Annual Growth	3.0%	—	—	—

2014 Year-End Financials

Return on assets: (-0.4%)
Return on equity: (-0.6%)
Current ratio: —
Cash ($ mil.): 69

POPULATION SERVICES INTERNATIONAL

Population Services International (PSI) goes far beyond the scope of its name. Founded in 1970 to promote global family planning PSI has established social programs that use local networks in low-income regions to distribute such lifelines as insecticide-treated mosquito nets iodized salt snake boots and insect repellent along with condoms contraceptives and pregnancy test kits. The group prides itself on using business principals to confront health issues in more than 65 countries worldwide. It reportedly has averted 4.2 million unintended pregnancies some 29 million malaria cases and provided 1.8-plus million clients with of HIV testing and counseling. PSI is also active ensuring safe water supplies.

EXECUTIVES

Vice President, Douglas Call
Vice President, Krishna Jafa
Vice President Of Finance, Marusya Lazo
Executive Vice President, Peter Clancy
Svp Chief Strategy And Resources Officer, Michael Holscher

LOCATIONS

HQ: POPULATION SERVICES INTERNATIONAL
1120 19TH ST NW STE 600, WASHINGTON, DC 200363605
Phone: 202 785-0072
Web: WWW.PSI.ORG

HISTORICAL FINANCIALS

Company Type: Private

Income Statement — FYE: December 31

	REVENUE ($ mil.)	NET INCOME ($ mil.)	NET PROFIT MARGIN	EMPLOYEES
12/13	584	4	0.8%	455
12/01	121	(0)	—	—
12/00	96	3	3.4%	—
Annual Growth	14.8%	2.9%	—	—

2013 Year-End Financials

Return on assets: 10.1%
Return on equity: 0.8%
Current ratio: 0.60
Cash ($ mil.): 210

PORT OF SEATTLE

The Port of Seattle oversees both an airport (Seattle-Tacoma International also known as Sea-Tac) and a seaport. The agency's aviation division sees more than 33.2 million passengers a year. The seaport division serves more than 18 container steamship lines that import and export containerized and bulk cargo. It also handles calls from cruise ships. In addition the seaport division oversees commercial fishing marinas and portside commercial properties. Most of the agency's revenue comes from airport operations. The Port of Seattle is run by a five-member commission elected by King County voters.

Operations

One of the top landholders in King County the Port owns parks and public access areas cargo and container terminals and Sea-Tac airport. It also owns conference facilities at the airport and on the waterfront recreational boating marinas piers office space and storage and warehouse facilities.

Financial Performance

Operating revenues for fiscal 2013 were budgeted at $550.6 million 6% up on 2012 . Aeronautical revenues were $249.3 million (up 6%). Other operating revenues were budget for $301.3 million (7% higher than the 2012 budget) mainly due to Terminal 18 special bond refunding and higher concessions.

Strategy

Going forward the Port's projects are broadly aimed at preserving traffic to the Midwest via Seattle which other global gateways (the Panama and Suez canals and Prince Rupert's port British Columbia) threaten to divert. To this end it is pursuing cooperative opportunities between rail and highway infrastructure agencies. Concurrently the Port of Seattle is evaluating Sea-Tac airport's capacity needs. Its subsidy of Fisherman's Terminal which sustains jobs as well as the seaport's history and culture is on the table too given the cost to renovate and terminal's declining fish life. Most significant the Port is determined to continue to distinguish itself as the Green Gateway with the goal of minimizing the environmental consequences of its activities.

Company Background

In 2011 the Port marked its centennial year for moving people and cargo in and out of the Pacific Northwest.

EXECUTIVES

Cfo And Administrative Officer, Dan Thomas
Interim Ceo, Dave Soike
Managing Director Aviation Division, Lance Lyttle
Managing Director Economic Development Division, David McFadden
Managing Director Maritime Division, Lindsay Pulsifer
Vice President Of Internal Audit, Debbie Browning
Government Relations Director, Pearse Edwards
Auditors: MOSS ADAMS LLP SEATTLE WASHI

LOCATIONS

HQ: PORT OF SEATTLE
2711 ALASKAN WAY PIER 69, SEATTLE, WA 981211107
Phone: 206 728-3000
Web: WWW.PORTSEATTLE.ORG

HISTORICAL FINANCIALS

Company Type: Private

Income Statement FYE: December 31

	REVENUE ($ mil.)	NET INCOME ($ mil.)	NET PROFIT MARGIN	EMPLOYEES
12/19	764	267	34.9%	1,515
12/18	689	221	32.1%	—
12/17	632	199	31.6%	—
12/16	598	41	6.9%	—
Annual Growth	8.5%	86.1%	—	—

2019 Year-End Financials

Return on assets: 3.1%
Return on equity: 7.0%
Current ratio: 1.90
Cash ($ mil.): 157

PORTLAND GENERAL ELECTRIC COMP

LOCATIONS

HQ: PORTLAND GENERAL ELECTRIC COMP
33831 SE FARADAY RD, ESTACADA, OR 970238432
Phone: 503 630-6821

HISTORICAL FINANCIALS

Company Type: Private

Income Statement FYE: December 31

	REVENUE ($ mil.)	NET INCOME ($ mil.)	NET PROFIT MARGIN	EMPLOYEES
12/19	2,147	213	10.0%	4
12/17	2,009	187	9.3%	—
12/16	1,923	193	10.0%	—
Annual Growth	3.8%	3.5%	—	—

2019 Year-End Financials

Return on assets: 2.7%
Return on equity: 8.3%
Current ratio: 1.00
Cash ($ mil.): 20

PORTLAND PUBLIC SCHOOLS

EXECUTIVES

Superintendent, Carole Smith
Interim Chief of Staff, Alexander Perrins
Financial Analyst, Kathleen Hiigel
Facilities, Adam Napier
Teacher, Allen Lauraine
Art Teacher, Amy Hargrave
Assistant Director, Ben Dandeneau
Board Clerk, Caren Huson
Third Grade, Chris Meeker
Fourth Grade, Connie Spieler-Compton
School Psychologist, Diane Lewis
Auditors: TALBOT KORVOLA & WARWICK LLP

LOCATIONS

HQ: PORTLAND PUBLIC SCHOOLS
501 N DIXON ST, PORTLAND, OR 972271876
Phone: 503 916-2000
Web: WWW.PPS.NET

HISTORICAL FINANCIALS

Company Type: Private

Income Statement FYE: June 30

	REVENUE ($ mil.)	NET INCOME ($ mil.)	NET PROFIT MARGIN	EMPLOYEES
06/19	922	(133)	—	5,244
06/18	882	336	38.1%	—
06/17	770	(127)	—	—
06/16	744	(109)	—	—
Annual Growth	7.4%	—	—	—

2019 Year-End Financials

Return on assets: (-8.7%)
Return on equity: —
Current ratio: 1.50
Cash ($ mil.): 179

POUDRE VALLEY HEALTH CARE, INC.

Providing health care is what this Poudre Valley is all about. The not-for-profit Poudre Valley Health System (PVHS) cares for residents of Colorado western Nebraska and southern Wyoming through the Poudre Valley Hospital and the Medical Center of the Rockies. With a total of about 440 beds the two hospitals offer general medical and surgical services and trauma care. They also offer treatment centers for specialties including cancer heart brain and spine disorders. PVHS is home to the Mountain Crest Behavioral Healthcare Center which administers mental health and substance abuse treatment. PVHS is part of the Health District of Northern Larimer County; it is also part of University of Colorado Health.

Operations

The Poudre Valley Hospital features 270 patient beds while the Medical Center of the Rockies has a capacity of about 170 beds. Beyond its primary hospital campuses the health system also operates several outpatient clinics and a family medicine center that hosts a rural medicine residency program. Altogether PVHS has more than 550 physicians practicing in more than 40 specialty fields.

In addition to its joint operating agreement with the University of Colorado Hospital PVHS has formed collaborative care partnerships with local organizations including a local laser eye surgery center numerous outpatient centers for rehabilitation surgery and infusion therapy as well as home health care and home supply companies.

Geographic Reach

PVHS serves residents of Estes Park Fort Collins Greeley and Loveland Colorado as well as Larimer and Weld Counties. The system also serves customers from Cheyenne and Laramie Wyoming and Scottsbluff Nebraska.

Strategy

The organization has held a long tradition of partnering with numerous local organizations to expand its service offerings. To create a broader health organization for the Rocky Mountain region PVHS formed a joint operating agreement with University of Colorado Hospital in 2012. Together the systems are known as University of Colorado Health and are governed by a single board of directors. The hospitals continue to operate under their existing names.

Other growth efforts include the construction of a new $14.5 million emergency care center in 2012 and the opening of a new 12-bed women's and children's unit at Medical Center of the Rockies in 2013.

In 2013 it also opened the 36000-sq.-ft. Indian Peaks Medical Center in Frederick at an estimated cost of $20 million to $30 million. It includes cardiology and diagnostics departments.

Company Background

The organization was founded in 1925. Since 1995 when PVHS reorganized as a private not-for-profit health care organization local property taxes that used to go straight to PVHS have been paid to the Health District of Northern Larimer County which then uses them to fund PVHS' various activities.

EXECUTIVES

Dpt Ocs Faaompt Physical Therapy Specialist, Anthony Kinney
Vpoperations, David Leslie
Director Of Him, Kendra Adams
Vice President, Robert Homburg
Treasurer, Daniel Wilson
Auditors: PLANTE & MORAN PLLC DENVER

LOCATIONS

HQ: POUDRE VALLEY HEALTH CARE, INC.
12401 E 17TH AVE STE B132, AURORA, CO 800452589
Phone: 970 495-7000
Web: WWW.UCHEALTH.ORG

PRODUCTS/OPERATIONS

Selected Services

Back Neck and Spine Care
Cancer Care
Diabetes and Endocrinology
Hyperbaric Medicine
Imaging and Radiology
Laboratory Services
Orthopedics
Pain Care and Management
Seniors' Health
Weight and Metabolism
Women's Health
Wound Care

COMPETITORS

Catholic Health Initiatives
Centura Health
Denver Health and Hospital Authority
Exempla Healthcare
HealthONE
Memorial Health System (Colorado)
North Colorado Medical Center
University of Colorado Hospital
Valley View Hospital
Wyoming Medical Center

HISTORICAL FINANCIALS

Company Type: Private

Income Statement — FYE: June 30

	REVENUE ($ mil.)	NET INCOME ($ mil.)	NET PROFIT MARGIN	EMPLOYEES
06/20	1,266	209	16.5%	2,800
06/19	1,412	340	24.1%	—
06/16	523	92	17.7%	—
06/15	480	98	20.6%	—
Annual Growth	21.4%	16.2%	—	—

2020 Year-End Financials

Return on assets: 6.7%
Return on equity: 8.7%
Current ratio: 3.10
Cash ($ mil.): 381

POWERSOUTH ENERGY COOPERATIVE

Several hundred thousand Alabamans and Floridians get their electric power courtesy of the work of PowerSouth Energy Cooperative which provides wholesale power to its member-owners (16 electric cooperatives and four municipal distribution utilities). Its distribution members provide electric services to almost 417200 customer meters in central and southern Alabama and western Florida. PowerSouth operates a more than 2200-mile power transmission system and has more than 2000 MW of generating capacity from interests in six fossil-fueled and hydroelectric power plants.

Geographic Reach

PowerSouth serves customers in Alabama (39 counties) and Florida (10 counties).

Operations

The company owns and operates six generation facilities and holds ownership interest in an additional facility. Its diverse generating fuel mix includes natural gas coal and water (hydro). It also has compressed air energy storage technology and a disciplined fuel supply hedging program that minimizes the impact of fuel cost increases. In addition PowerSouth maintains long-term purchased power agreements to ensure economic and reliable power supply for its members.

PowerSouth serves the wholesale energy needs of electric cooperatives and municipal electric systems in Alabama and northwest Florida who in turn serve more than a million consumers. PowerSouth is dedicated to providing reliable energy at the lowest possible cost to its members.

Financial Performance

The company's revenues increased by 3% in 2013 primarily due to an increase in member revenues as a result of an increase in energy sales. The remaining increase was due to the surcharges added to the excess demand rate during 2013.

That year PowerSouth's net income decreased by 6% as the result of increased operating costs caused by higher distribution costs and administration and general expenses.

Its operating cash inflow increased to $63.5 million in 2013 (compared to $38.3 million in 2012) due to a rise in account receivables and inventories.

Strategy

To meet future demand and tightening environmental regulations the company is looking to diversify and expand its power production assets with an emphasis on cleaner energy plants. PowerSouth's long-term energy plans include a 20-year contract for 125 MW of nuclear power from two Vogtle Units being built by the Municipal Energy Authority of Georgia near Augusta and due to come onstream in 2016 and 2017. The company is also investing in wind power and biomass-to-energy initiatives.

Company Background

PowersSouth is owned and managed by it 20 distribution members.

The company once provided propane but sold its Cooperative Propane unit in 2011 to focus on its core power businesses.

In 2008 Alabama Electric Cooperative changed its name to PowerSouth Energy Cooperative to better reflect its service territory (Alabama and Florida) and its opportunities for future growth.

Founded in 1941 as Alabama Electric Cooperative the coop promotes a strong economic development program aimed at bringing industry into both Alabama and Florida.

EXECUTIVES

Vice President Corporate Affairs, Beth Woodard
Vice President Information Technology, Lewis Jeffers
Vice President Administration, Elizabeth Woodard
Procurement Secretary, Angela Kelly
Department Secretary, Lisa Wiggins
Auditors: BKD LLP OKLAHOMA CITY OKLAH

LOCATIONS

HQ: POWERSOUTH ENERGY COOPERATIVE
2027 E THREE NOTCH ST, ANDALUSIA, AL 364212427
Phone: 334 427-3000
Web: WWW.POWERSOUTH.COM

PRODUCTS/OPERATIONS

View Archived What Charts | Edit 2013 Sales

	% of total
Electric	
Cooperatives	93
Municipalities	6
Other	1
Total	100

HISTORICAL FINANCIALS

Company Type: Private

Income Statement — FYE: December 31

	REVENUE ($ mil.)	NET INCOME ($ mil.)	NET PROFIT MARGIN	EMPLOYEES
12/19	602	13	2.3%	640
12/18	612	12	2.0%	—
12/17	588	9	1.6%	—
12/16	596	13	2.2%	—
Annual Growth	0.3%	0.9%	—	—

2019 Year-End Financials

Return on assets: 0.7%
Return on equity: 3.8%
Current ratio: 1.20
Cash ($ mil.): 29

PRAIRIE FARMS DAIRY, INC.

Prairie Farms Dairy is very cooperative. With some 700 dairy farmer/members the cooperative offers a full line of retail and food service dairy products. It turns raw milk into fresh fluid cultured and frozen dairy products under the Prairie Farms label. It also makes juices and ice cream novelties. The company's customers include food drug and convenience stores mass merchandisers schools restaurants and other food service operators. Located in Carlinville Illinois it is the managing partner for joint ventures with smaller regional dairies. It makes its products at 24 Prairie Farms-owned plants and 13 joint-venture plants which are located throughout the midwestern and southern areas of the US.

Operations

From its 700 member farms Prairie Farms sources milk products for its array of food products. It produces all varieties of milk butter cottage cheese cream ice cream yogurt and other diary-based products. It also goes outside its core to produce and sell teas juices and iced coffee

To get its dairy products to market the co-op relies on subsidiaries Hawthorne-Mellody Distributors in Chicago and Tom David & Sons in Detroit.

In addition to manufacturing diary foods co-packing is a big part of Prairie Farms' operation. Approximately 50% of the co-operative's sales come from packing non-Prairie Farm brands. The co-op's PFD Supply and GMS Transportation non-dairy subsidiaries distribute products for fast-food chains including McDonald's Dairy Queen and Church's Chicken.

Geographic Reach

Prairie Farms and its subsidiaries manufacture dairy products at 24 co-op-owned plants as 13 joint venture plants in Arkansas Illinois Indiana Iowa Kansas Kentucky Michigan Mississippi Missouri Nebraska Oklahoma Ohio Tennessee and Wisconsin.

Sales and Marketing

Prairie Farms' products are for sale through a variety of retail grocery store foodservice drug store mass merchandiser and school locations in the same states in which it has production facilities. It sells about half of its product under the Prairie Farms brand name and the co-op also sells products through partners Central Hiland Dairy Foods Ice Cream Specialties Turner and Muller.

Company Background

The cooperative dates back to 1932 when Illinois farmers formed a statewide organization Illinois Producers Creameries to market and sell cream. In 1938 it became Prairie Farms Dairy.

EXECUTIVES

Director Information Services, Mark Harris
Ceo, Fletcher Gourley
Vice President Human Resources Labor Relations, Ray Silvey
National Accounts Manager, Chad Moss
Vice President Procurement, Lee Gary
Auditors: BKD LLP ST LOUIS MO

LOCATIONS

HQ: PRAIRIE FARMS DAIRY, INC.
3744 STAUNTON RD, EDWARDSVILLE, IL 620256936
Phone: 618 659-5700
Web: WWW.PRAIRIEFARMSDAIRY.COM

Selected Areas of Distribution

Arkansas

Illinois
Indiana
Iowa
Kansas
Kentucky
Michigan
Mississippi
Missouri
Nebraska
Ohio
Oklahoma
Tennessee
Wisconsin

PRODUCTS/OPERATIONS

Branded Partners
Hiland Dairy Foods Company
Ice Cream Specialties
Madison Farms Butter
Muller-Pinehurst Dairy
Turner Dairy

Selected Products
Butter
Cultured dairy products
  Cottage cheese (regular low fat and fat-free; small and large curd)
  Dips
  Sour cream
  Yogurt (regular low fat and fat-free)
Fluid milk products
  Buttermilk
  Cream
  Egg nog (seasonal)
  Milk (regular low fat and fat-free)
  Flavored milk
Frozen desserts
  Frozen yogurt
  Ice cream (regular low fat and fat-free)
  Novelties
  Sherbet
Juices drinks and iced tea

COMPETITORS

Associated Milk Producers
Dairy Farmers of America
Darigold Inc.
Dean Foods
Dreyer's
Farmland Dairies
Foremost Farms
Friendly's Ice Cream
HP Hood
Land O'Lakes
Quality Chekd
Rockview Dairies
Wells' Dairy

HISTORICAL FINANCIALS

Company Type: Private

Income Statement FYE: September 30

	REVENUE ($ mil.)	NET INCOME ($ mil.)	NET PROFIT MARGIN	EMPLOYEES
09/13	1,721	14	0.8%	1,965
09/12	1,649	38	2.4%	—
09/11	1,607	28	1.7%	—
Annual Growth	3.5%	(28.9%)	—	—

2013 Year-End Financials

Return on assets: 1.9%
Return on equity: 3.4%
Current ratio: 1.20
Cash ($ mil.): 12

PRATT CORRUGATED HOLDINGS, INC.

LOCATIONS

HQ: PRATT CORRUGATED HOLDINGS, INC.
1800 SARASOT BUS PKWY NE C, CONYERS, GA 300135775
Phone: 770 918-5678
Web: WWW.PRATTINDUSTRIES.COM

HISTORICAL FINANCIALS

Company Type: Private

Income Statement FYE: June 30

	REVENUE ($ mil.)	NET INCOME ($ mil.)	NET PROFIT MARGIN	EMPLOYEES
06/20	2,649	75	2.9%	116
06/18	2,518	87	3.5%	—
06/17	2,360	65	2.8%	—
Annual Growth	3.9%	4.9%	—	—

2020 Year-End Financials

Return on assets: 5.9%
Return on equity: 11.8%
Current ratio: 1.40
Cash ($ mil.): 128

PRATT INDUSTRIES, INC.

Pratt Industries (USA) doesn't mill around when it comes to recycling and caring for the environment. The company rivals the world's largest manufacturers of recycled paper and packaging and claims to be the 5th largest box manufacturer in the US and the world's largest privately-held 100% recycled paper and packaging company. Pratt has a handful of operating divisions: recycling mills corrugating converting displays packaging systems and national accounts. Its products which include container board and corrugated sheets are sold to clients such as Rubbermaid and Pringles.

Operations

The company operates 32 sheet plants 18 recycling centers 16 corrugating plants seven distribution centers seven displaying facilities four recycled paper mills and one clean energy plant. It operates through the main divisions of Clean Energy Converting Corrugating Display Paper Mills Recycling Logistics Specialty and Strategic Services.

Geographic Reach

Pratt operates some 50 plants in more than 20 US states and Mexico.

Strategy

Pratt has strategically located its manufacturing facilities to reduce freight time and cost and to provide regional design and account management support. The locations enable it to react quickly and decisively to meet the needs of customers.

In 2015 Pratt Industries broke ground on its new $52 million corrugated box factory in Beloit Wisconsin. The 350000 sq. ft. facility due for start-up in early 2016 will sit on a 56-acre site and produce 600 tons of recycled boxes a day at capacity.

Mergers and Acquisitions

In 2015 the company improved its footprint through the purchase of California-based food and agricultural packaging company Robert Mann Packaging (RMP). Pratt paid $60 million for the privately-owned RMP group which has $150 million in annual sales and more than a dozen facilities in the western US and Mexico including a 350000 square-foot box-making plant in Salinas California. The deal gave the company a nationwide footprint throughout the US with manufacturing sites stretching from New York to the West Coast.

Company Background

The company was founded in 1948 by Leon Pratt grandfather of Anthony Pratt.

EXECUTIVES

Executive Vice President, John Day
Vice President Corporate Controller, Dj Kyles
Vice President Purchasing And Logistics, Danielle Roszko
Regional Vice President, Jeff Turner
Vp Industry Relations And Supply Chain, Cathy Foley
Vice President Field Engineer (us And Canada), John Berggren
Vice President Sales And Marketing, Thomas Priest
Vice President Of Operations, Dar Nelson
Treasurer, Tom Stoskopf
Auditors: GRANT THORNTON LLP ATLANTA G

LOCATIONS

HQ: PRATT INDUSTRIES, INC.
1800 SARASOT BUS PKWY NE S, CONYERS, GA 300135775
Phone: 770 918-5678
Web: WWW.PRATTINDUSTRIES.COM

PRODUCTS/OPERATIONS

Selected Divisions

Converting

Corrugating

Displays

Mills
National Accounts
Packaging Systems
Recycling

Selected Products and Services
Bagging
  Merchandise bags
  Polypropylene bags
  Poly-tubing
  Seal-top bags
  Static shielded bags
Carton Closure/Sealing
  Adhesives
  Double coated tape
  Duct tape
  Filament tape
  Foam tape
  Foil tape
  Masking tape
  Poly-strapping
  Pressure sensitive carton sealing tape
  Staples
  Steel Strapping
  Teflon tape
  Water activate carton sealing tape
Cushioning/Void Fill
  Air dunnage bags
  Bubble wrap
  Cellulose wadding
  Foam-N-Place
  Honeycomb
  Kraft wrap
  Loose fill foam
  Newsprint
  Polyethylene foam
  Polypropylene foam
Edge/Corner Protection
  Angleboard
  Anglewrap
  Cornerboard
  Form-A-Board
  Protect-A-Board
  Protect-A-Wrap
  Stackmaster
  Strap protectors

Labeling and Coding
- Cleaners
- Inks
- Labels
- Ribbons

Mailing and Shipping
- Mailers
- Packing list envelopes
- Shipping tubes and tags

Unitization
- Poly pallet covers
- Poly pallet shrink bags
- Poly top sheets
- Poly-strapping
- Shrink bundling
- Steel strapping
- Stretch film

Visual Packaging
- Blister packaging
- Clamshells
- Polyolefin shrinkfilm
- PVC shrink bands
- Skin packaging
- Skin packaging film

COMPETITORS

Georgia-Pacific
Green Bay Packaging
International Paper
Interstate Resources Inc.
Packaging Corp. of America
Southern Container
Weyerhaeuser

HISTORICAL FINANCIALS

Company Type: Private

Income Statement FYE: June 30

	REVENUE ($ mil.)	NET INCOME ($ mil.)	NET PROFIT MARGIN	EMPLOYEES
06/20	2,612	200	7.7%	5,890
06/18	2,498	200	8.0%	—
Annual Growth	2.2%	(0.0%)	—	—

2020 Year-End Financials

Return on assets: 7.8%
Return on equity: 16.7%
Current ratio: 2.60
Cash ($ mil.): 503

PRECISION CASTPARTS CORP.

Precision Castparts Corp. (PCC) is a maker of investment castings and forged and fastener products that have applications in industries from aerospace and energy markets. Products include metal components for aircraft engines and industrial gas turbines (IGT). The company also makes metal forgings including seamless pipe used in power plants downhole casings and tubing pipe for oil and gas production. PCC is also a leading manufacturer of fasteners and fastening systems used in the aerospace construction and machinery industries. It has locations in North America Europe and Asia. The majority of PCC's sales are from purchase orders. The company is a subsidiary of Berkshire Hathaway.

HISTORY

The history of Precision Castparts Corp. (PCC) is not as precise as its castings. The Oregon Saw Company was founded in 1949 and sold in 1953; its buyer wanted neither the future PCC nor a power tools unit so the two became Omark Industries. In 1956 a buyer purchased the power tool business but wasn't interested in castings; that operation was spun off as Precision Castparts Corp.

In the early 1950s a group of Oregon Saw's casting employees developed a process for producing parts as large as 60 inches by use of investment casting making products that rivaled the strength of forged and machined parts at a fraction of the cost. After a two-year search they landed their first aerospace customer — Air Research Corp. — with many to follow. The higher operating temperatures generated by aircraft engines led the company to buy a vacuum furnace in 1959 to fabricate parts that could tolerate greater heat; two more vacuum furnaces were added and sales vaulted toward $10 million by 1967. PCC went public in 1968 and continued to grow. In 1976 the company acquired Centaur Cast Alloys (small investment castings UK) to make parts for the European aerospace industry. By that time General Electric (GE) and Pratt & Whitney accounted for most of PCC's business. Edward Cooley who had masterminded the company's growth since incorporation forged ahead with plans to double production capacity.

In 1980 the airline industry crashed but PCC's sales held at about $90 million. Structural airplane products soon picked up and in 1984 the company bought two titanium foundries in France. To diversify it added TRW's cast airfoils (used in aircraft engines and industrial gas turbines) division in 1986. That acquisition renamed PCC Airfoils increased PCC's annual sales by about 80%; sales reached $443 million by 1989.

The company broadened its offerings again in 1991 when it acquired Advanced Forming Technology which made small complex metal-injection molded parts used in everything from adding machines to military ordnance. The early 1990s recession hit the airline industry and sales dropped. Cooley retired as chairman in 1994 and GE veteran William McCormick replaced him. The next year PCC acquired Quamco Inc. (industrial tools and machines). In 1996 PCC flowed into the fluid management market with the acquisition of NEWFLO for about $300 million.

In 1997 PCC spent $437 million to acquire seven more companies that helped boost sales 75% from 1996 levels. The next year it purchased four metalworking companies that served industries other than aerospace. Having reduced dependence on sales to the aerospace industry to just over 50% PCC began consolidating operations and closing plants to reduce costs.

The company continued to diversify through acquisitions in 1999 but it also expanded its aerospace operations with the purchase of Wyman-Gordon a leading maker of advanced metal forgings for the aerospace market. PCC's 2000 acquisitions included the aerospace division of United Engineering Forgings and Germany-based Convey Engineering (heavy-duty valves). The next year the company bought the assets of Netherlands-based Wouter Witzel and the US's Drop Dies and Forgings Company (renamed Wyman-Gordon Cleveland). In 2002 PCC bought the rest of Western Australian Specialty Alloys (casting and forging alloys) for $27.6 million in cash and PCC shares.

In 2003 Precision Castparts' PCC Structurals unit reached a $400 million agreement with Rolls-Royce to supply large titanium and steel castings. That year the company acquired SPS Technologies a producer of fasteners and other metal components for the aerospace automotive and industrial markets. In 2004 subsidiary SPS Aerospace Fasteners signed a four-year deal with Airbus worth about $72 million to supply collars nuts studs and titanium pins to Airbus plants across Europe.

PCC acquired Air Industries Corporation in early 2005. In 2006 PCC bought Special Metals Corporation (SMC) a maker of nickel alloys and super alloys for $295 million in cash and the assumption of $245 million in SMC debt. PCC intended to use SMC's product as raw materials for its own aircraft engine components. SMC also served the automotive chemical and power generation industries.

Later in 2006 PCC bought Shur-Lok Corporation a manufacturer of aerospace fasteners for about $110 million. The acquisition combined with the 2005 purchase of Air Industries Corporation helped to further PCC's desire to grow its airframe fasteners business.

Early in 2007 PCC completed the purchase of GSC a leading maker of aluminum and steel structural investment casting for the aerospace energy and medical markets. It also acquired Cherry Aerospace which expanded its fastener products portfolio.

In 2009 the company acquired Carlton Forge Works which makes aircraft engines for Boeing and Airbus; California-based Arcturus Manufacturing (hammer forging operations) was included in the transaction. PCC also picked up Airdrome Holdings (fluid fittings) Fatigue Technology (cold expansion technology) and Hackney Ladish (forged pipe fittings) in 2009.

In late summer 2011 PPC purchased Primus International a maker of complex metal industrial parts and assemblies. Its products (machined aluminum and titanium components used in aircraft wings fuselages and engine-related assemblies) cater to Boeing Airbus and other aerospace OEMs. The $900 million deal furthered the company's commitment to the global aerospace industry. In a similar vein the company obtained Unison Engine Components (operating as Tru-Form Rings) from GE Aviation in mid-2011. Tru-Form made flash-welded and cold-rolled rings with jet engine as well as gas turbine applications.

PCC also acquired RathGibson which makes tubing for the oil and gas chemical/petrochemical power-generation and other markets in 2012.

To expand both its Fasteners and Forged Products segments PCC acquired the aerostructures and industrial products businesses of Héroux-Devtek for about CAD$300 million (about $295.5 million) in 2012. Among other benefits the acquisition expanded the company's product line for such OEMs as Lockheed Bombardier and Gulfstream. PCC also inked a deal to purchase the Synchronous Aerospace Group business of private investment firm Littlejohn & Co. in late 2012.

EXECUTIVES

Evp And Cfo, Shawn R. Hagel, $687,500 total compensation

Chairman And Ceo, Mark Donegan, $1,585,000 total compensation

Svp And President Airframe Products, Alan J. (Al) Power

Evp And President Wyman-gordon, Andrew V. Masterman, $592,500 total compensation

Vp And Cio, Byron J. Gaddis

Evp, Steven G. (Steve) Hackett, $708,750 total compensation

Svp And General Counsel, Ruth A. Beyer, $569,000 total compensation

President Aerostructures Products, Joseph I. Snowden, $356,347 total compensation

Svp And President Pcc Airfoils, John P. O'Neill

Svp And President Timet And Special Metals, James R. Pieron

Vice President, Mark Ellis

Vice President, Geoffrey Hawkes

Senior Vice President, Russell Gould

Senior Vice President, Ross Lienhart

Executive Vice President, David Norris

Secretary, Russell Pattee

Auditors: DELOITTE & TOUCHE LLP PORTLAN

LOCATIONS

HQ: PRECISION CASTPARTS CORP.
4650 SW MCDAM AVE STE 300, PORTLAND, OR 97239
Phone: 503 946-4800
Web: WWW.PRECAST.COM

PRODUCTS/OPERATIONS

Selected Products and Services

Fasteners
Advanced forming technology
E/One (for the disposal of residential sanitary waste)
J&L fiber services (for pulp and paper industry)
PCC Precision Tool Group
SPS aerospace fasteners (for commercial/military aircraft)
SPS engineered fasteners (high strength for automotive and construction applications)
Forged products
Special Metals Corporation
Wyman-Gordon Forgings
Investment Cast Products
PCC Airfoils (high-temperature blades and vanes)
PCC Structurals (structural investment castings)
Specialty materials and alloys (alloys waxes and metal processing for investment casting)

COMPETITORS

ATI Ladish
Allegheny Technologies
Arconic
Carpenter Technology
Chicago Rivet
Crane Co.
Curtiss-Wright
ESCO
Farwest Steel Corporation
Federal Screw Works
Georg Fischer
Haynes International
Hitachi Metals
Kennametal
LISI
Mettis Aerospace
SOURIAU PA&E
Swagelok
Teleflex
ThyssenKrupp
United Technologies
Universal Stainless
V & M Tubes (USA)
Volvo Aero

HISTORICAL FINANCIALS

Company Type: Private

Income Statement — FYE: January 3

	REVENUE ($ mil.)	NET INCOME ($ mil.)	NET PROFIT MARGIN	EMPLOYEES
01/16*	7,002	817	11.7%	30,106
03/15	10,005	1,533	15.3%	—
03/14	9,616	1,784	18.6%	—
03/13	8,377	1,429	17.1%	—
Annual Growth	(5.8%)	(17.0%)	—	—

*Fiscal year change

2016 Year-End Financials

Return on assets: 4.0%
Return on equity: 7.0%
Current ratio: 3.90
Cash ($ mil.): 343

PREMIER HEALTHCARE ALLIANCE, L.P.

EXECUTIVES

MBR-Ceo, Susan Devore
MBR-Chb*, Glenn Steel Jr
MBR-V Chb*, Dennis Vonderfecht
Coo*, Michael Alkire
Cfo*, Craig McKasson
Ceo*, Richard A Norling
Sr V Pres*, Ann D Rhoads
Vice-President Information Ser, Larry D Grandia
Lawson Edi Administrat, Rory Flood
Business Continuity and Disast, David A Shimberg
Data Specialist/Membership Gro, Joseph Lawrence

LOCATIONS

HQ: PREMIER HEALTHCARE ALLIANCE, L.P.
13034 BALNTYN CORP PL, CHARLOTTE, NC 282771498
Phone: 704 357-0022
Web: WWW.PREMIERINC.COM

HISTORICAL FINANCIALS

Company Type: Private

Income Statement — FYE: June 30

	REVENUE ($ mil.)	NET INCOME ($ mil.)	NET PROFIT MARGIN	EMPLOYEES
06/12	590	326	55.3%	199
06/11	679	311	45.8%	—
06/09	1,830	0	—	—
Annual Growth	—18233.3%		—	—

2012 Year-End Financials

Return on assets: 72.7%
Return on equity: 92.9%
Current ratio: 5.30
Cash ($ mil.): 129

PREMISE HEALTH HOLDING CORP.

EXECUTIVES

Ceo, Edward Stuart Clark
Coo, Trent Riley
Cfo, Shannon Farrington
Pres, Jami Doucette
Chief Information Officer, Haden McWhorter
Chief Human Resources Officer, Elizebeth Reimer
Chief Compliance Officer, Dana Fields
Chief Information Security Off, Joey Johnson
Exec V Pres, Peter Vasquez
Exec V Pres, Ed McNamara
Operations, Beth Ratliff
Auditors: RSM US LLP CHICAGO ILLINOIS

LOCATIONS

HQ: PREMISE HEALTH HOLDING CORP.
5500 MARYLAND WAY STE 200, BRENTWOOD, TN 370274973
Phone: 615 468-6562
Web: WWW.PREMISEHEALTH.COM

HISTORICAL FINANCIALS

Company Type: Private

Income Statement — FYE: December 31

	REVENUE ($ mil.)	NET INCOME ($ mil.)	NET PROFIT MARGIN	EMPLOYEES
12/17	685	7	1.0%	4,500
12/16	630	(2)	—	—
12/15	581	0	0.0%	—
12/14	303	(14)	—	—
Annual Growth	31.2%	—	—	—

2017 Year-End Financials

Return on assets: 2.1%
Return on equity: 6.4%
Current ratio: 2.20
Cash ($ mil.): 37

PRESBYTERIAN HOSPITAL

EXECUTIVES

Ceo, Carl Armato
Pres*, Lynn Bodgs
Coordinator, Jacqueline Vaughn
Coordinator, Rachel Karo
Supervisor, Cynthia Jackson

LOCATIONS

HQ: PRESBYTERIAN HOSPITAL
200 HAWTHORNE LN, CHARLOTTE, NC 282042528
Phone: 704 384-4000
Web: WWW.NOVANTHEALTH.ORG

HISTORICAL FINANCIALS

Company Type: Private

Income Statement — FYE: December 31

	REVENUE ($ mil.)	NET INCOME ($ mil.)	NET PROFIT MARGIN	EMPLOYEES
12/09	688	68	10.0%	3,100
12/08	500	18	3.7%	—
Annual Growth	37.6%	270.7%	—	—

2009 Year-End Financials

Return on assets: —
Return on equity: 10.0%
Current ratio: —
Cash ($ mil.): —

PRESBYTERIAN MEDICAL CENTER OF THE UNIVERSITY OF PENNSYLVANIA HEALTH SYSTEM

EXECUTIVES

Exec Dir, Michele Volpe
Program Director, Jeanmarie Perch
Operations Manager, Bob Russell
Executive Director Nurse, Diane Maccarone
Operations Manager, Karen Greenfield
Clinical Assistant Professor O, Michael Colucciello
Staff Nurse, Rasheda Peoples
Internist, Andrew W Maier
PA C, Dawn Carson
Anesthesiologist, Dian Lau
Ophthalmologist, Eydie G Miller

LOCATIONS

HQ: PRESBYTERIAN MEDICAL CENTER OF THE UNIVERSITY OF PENNSYLVANIA HEALTH SYSTEM
51 N 39TH ST, PHILADELPHIA, PA 191042692
Phone: 215 662-8000
Web: WWW.PENNMEDICINE.ORG

HISTORICAL FINANCIALS

Company Type: Private

Income Statement				FYE: June 30
	REVENUE ($ mil.)	NET INCOME ($ mil.)	NET PROFIT MARGIN	EMPLOYEES
06/15	546	(0)	—	1,370
06/14	445	21	4.7%	—
06/13	429	7	1.7%	—
06/05	301	(1)	—	—
Annual Growth	6.2%	—	—	—

PRINCE GEORGE'S COUNTY PUBLIC SCHOOLS

EXECUTIVES

Ceo, Kevin Maxwell
Assoc Supt Budget & Fin, Dr Kenneth Brown
Health Professional, William Kurtz
Security Staff, Clifford Mack
Staff, Georgene Arneson
Coordinator, Anthony Dean
Coordinator, Karuna Skariah
Pe Teacher, John Delaney
Teacher, Bryan Pierre
Assistant Supervisor of Garage, David Burgess
Coordinating Supervisor, Mary Bell
Auditors: CLIFTONLARSONALLEN LLP BALTIM

LOCATIONS

HQ: PRINCE GEORGE'S COUNTY PUBLIC SCHOOLS
14201 SCHOOL LN, UPPER MARLBORO, MD 207722866
Phone: 301 952-6000
Web: WWW.PGCPS.ORG

HISTORICAL FINANCIALS

Company Type: Private

Income Statement				FYE: June 30
	REVENUE ($ mil.)	NET INCOME ($ mil.)	NET PROFIT MARGIN	EMPLOYEES
06/14	1,932	(6)	—	22,000
06/13	1,966	43	2.2%	—
06/11	1,855	3	0.2%	—
06/07	1,627	13	0.8%	—
Annual Growth	2.5%	—	—	—

PRINCE WILLIAM COUNTY PUBLIC SCHOOLS

EXECUTIVES

Supt, Steven Walts
Assistant Superintendent, J Keith Johnson
Safety/Security Director, Ronald Crowe
Tech Prep Coordinator, Douglas Wright
Social Worker, Jason Froehlich
Webmaster, Mary Billingsley
Instructor, Debbie Marchio
Grade Teacher, Jocelyn Mishoe
Special Education Teacher, Kay McFarland
Manager Operations, Susan Dooley
Elementary Science Lab Teacher, Jill Hanlon
Auditors: CHERRY BEKAERT LLP TYSONS COR

LOCATIONS

HQ: PRINCE WILLIAM COUNTY PUBLIC SCHOOLS
14715 BRISTOW RD, MANASSAS, VA 201123945
Phone: 703 791-7200
Web: WWW.PWCS.EDU

HISTORICAL FINANCIALS

Company Type: Private

Income Statement				FYE: June 30
	REVENUE ($ mil.)	NET INCOME ($ mil.)	NET PROFIT MARGIN	EMPLOYEES
06/13	1,048	23	2.3%	8,523
06/12	968	(18)	—	—
06/11	887	(66)	—	—
Annual Growth	8.7%	—	—	—

PRISMA HEALTH-UPSTATE

From education and research to primary care and surgery Upstate Affiliate Organization (dba Prisma Health-Upstate formerly Greenville Hospital System) is out to keep residents of the "Golden Strip" (the corridor connecting Charlotte North Carolina and Atlanta) healthy. Originally founded in 1912 the system encompasses eight inpatient hospitals and more than 100 outpatient facilities. Its flagship facility is Prisma Health Greenville Memorial Hospital a referral and academic medical center with more than 800 beds; other facilities include several smaller community hospitals a nursing home and a long-term acute care hospital. Greenville Hospital System merged with Palmetto Health in 2017; the combined system rebranded as Prisma Health in early 2019.

Operations

Prisma Health-Upstate offers a full range of services including a primary care physician network outpatient services and home health care.

The system has teaching affiliations with Medical University of South Carolina and University of South Carolina Medical School and nursing school affiliations with Clemson University and Bob Jones University. Prisma Health-Upstate offers residency programs in about a dozen specialties including internal medicine OB-GYN and vascular surgery. It also performs extensive medical research in partnership with pharmaceutical companies in areas including oncology pediatric oncology women's health cardiology and vascular disease.

Prisma Cancer Institute (formerly GHS Cancer Institute) a regional leader in cancer care offers cancer treatment and prevention trials through the Community Clinical Oncology Program. It also offers Phase 1 clinical trials genetic counseling a blood and marrow transplant program and a number of patient-specific programs.

Strategy

In an effort to reduce unnecessary trips to the emergency room Prisma Health-Upstate has been opening several MD360 urgent care clinics. By diverting patients away from the ER for after-hours and non-emergency health problems GHS hopes to reduce health care costs and increase access to medical care.

Mergers and Acquisitions

In 2017 Greenville Hospital System joined forces with Palmetto Health to create South Carolina's largest health care system. The combined company rebranded itself as Prisma Health in early 2019. Greenville Hospital System became Prisma Health-Upstate.

EXECUTIVES

Vp Information Services And Cio, Rich Rogers
President And Ceo, Michael C. Riordan
Evp And Coo, Gregory J. Rusnak
Evp Medical And Academic Affairs; Dean University Of South Carolina School Of Medicine Greenville, Jerry R. Youkey
Vp Chief Of Staff; System Chief Learning Officer, Tod N. Tappert
Vp Financial Services And Cfo, Terri T. Newsom
Vp Clinical Integration And Chief Medical Officer, Angelo Sinopoli
Vp Physician Engagement And Chief Academic Officer; President Ghs Clinical University, Spence M. Taylor
Vp Patient Care Services And Chief Nursing Officer, Michelle Taylor Smith
President University Medical Group, William Schmidt
Pharmacy Manager, Richard Capps
Director Of Nursing, Cynthia Trout
Director Of Clinical Services And Operations, Julie Martin
Vpma, John Gilpin
Vice President Information Services And Cio, Richard Rogers
Vice President, Bruce Cantrell
Medical Director, Lynn Teague
Medical Director, Parampal Bhullar
Director Of Nursing, Henry Stubbs
Medical Director, Meenu Jindal
Clinical Director Imaging Services, Lisa Stockton
Pharmd Bcps Title: Clinical Assistant Professor, John Howard
Medical Director, Zachary George
Medical Director Of Business Health, Sandra Hardee
Upper Management Vice President, Kim Anderson
Vice Chairman, Margaret L. Jenkins
Chairman, William M. Webster
Secretary, Nancy Owings
Unit Secretary, Jessica Mcmahan
Secretary, Leah Belle
Unit Secretary, Kinetra Ware
Unit Secretary, Shanna Childs
Treasurer, Ryan Hakimi

LOCATIONS

HQ: PRISMA HEALTH-UPSTATE
300 E MCBEE AVE STE 302, GREENVILLE, SC 296012899
Phone: 864 455-1120
Web: WWW.GHS.ORG

PRODUCTS/OPERATIONS

2015 Sales

	$ mil.	% of total
Net patient services	1,973	96
Other operating revenues	82	4
Total	**2,056**	**100**

Selected Operations

Baptist Easley Hospital (with Palmetto Health Easley)
Greenville Memorial Hospital (tertiary academic and referral medical center)
Greer Memorial Hospital (Greer acute care hospital)
Hillcrest Memorial Hospital (Simpsonville general acute care hospital)
Laurens County Memorial Hospital (Clinton)
North Greenville Hospital (long-term acute care hospital)
Oconee Memorial Hospital (Seneca inpatient and outpatient services)
Patewood Memorial Hospital (Greenville inpatient elective hospital and outpatient center)

Selected Services

Behavioral Health
Cancer Institute
Children's Hospital
Heart & Vascular Institute
Medicine
Orthopaedics & Neurosurgery
Radiology
Rehabilitation
Surgery
Women's Health

COMPETITORS

AnMed Health
Blue Ridge HealthCare
Bon Secours Health
CaroMont
Doctors Hospital of Augusta
Grace Hospital
Gwinnett Health System
Laurens County Hospital
MCG Health
Novant Health
Piedmont Athens Regional
Spartanburg Regional Healthcare System
St. Mary's Health Care
Walton Rehabilitation Hospital

HISTORICAL FINANCIALS

Company Type: Private

Income Statement — FYE: September 30

	REVENUE ($ mil.)	NET INCOME ($ mil.)	NET PROFIT MARGIN	EMPLOYEES
09/13	1,001	80	8.1%	7,200
09/05	789	21	2.7%	—
09/04	789	21	2.7%	—
09/03	754	52	7.0%	—
Annual Growth	2.9%	4.4%	—	—

2013 Year-End Financials

Return on assets: —
Return on equity: 8.1%
Current ratio: —
Cash ($ mil.): —

PRO PETROLEUM LLC

EXECUTIVES

Pres, Marcus Griffin
Treas-Cfo, Don Hayden
Stkhldr, B R Griffin
Controller, Betty Catherman
Operator, Chris Thuran
Operator, Jack Worley
Auditors: GARRETT AND SWANN LLP LUBBOC

LOCATIONS

HQ: PRO PETROLEUM LLC
4710 4TH ST, LUBBOCK, TX 794164900
Phone: 806 795-8785
Web: WWW.PROPETROLEUM.COM

HISTORICAL FINANCIALS

Company Type: Private

Income Statement — FYE: December 31

	REVENUE ($ mil.)	NET INCOME ($ mil.)	NET PROFIT MARGIN	EMPLOYEES
12/17	1,075	17	1.6%	150
12/15	1,063	5	0.5%	—
12/14	1,701	4	0.3%	—
12/13	1,815	12	0.7%	—
Annual Growth	(12.3%)	9.4%	—	—

2017 Year-End Financials

Return on assets: 10.6%
Return on equity: 29.1%
Current ratio: 1.30
Cash ($ mil.): 21

PRODUCE ALLIANCE, L.L.C.

EXECUTIVES

MBR, George Melshenker
MBR, Scott Weber
Exe V Pres, Mike Williams
Partner Executive Vice Preside, Joe Collier
V Pres, Melissa Melshenker Ackerman
Cfo, Rob Feldgreber
Executive Implementation Manag, Cassie Young
Sales Staff, Adam Kramer
Executive Vice-President, Stephanie Blanton
Executive Customer Account Man, Gennifer Thompson
Business, Nate Montgomery
Auditors: MILLER COOPER & CO LTD DEE

LOCATIONS

HQ: PRODUCE ALLIANCE, L.L.C.
100 LEXINGTON DR STE 201, BUFFALO GROVE, IL 600896937
Phone: 847 808-3030
Web: WWW.PRODUCEALLIANCE.COM

HISTORICAL FINANCIALS

Company Type: Private

Income Statement — FYE: December 31

	REVENUE ($ mil.)	NET INCOME ($ mil.)	NET PROFIT MARGIN	EMPLOYEES
12/19	572	0	0.0%	75
12/18	504	0	0.1%	—
12/17	441	1	0.3%	—
12/16	381	2	0.7%	—
Annual Growth	14.5%	(56.8%)	—	—

PRODUCTION TECHNOLOGIES, INC.

EXECUTIVES

Chm, John Maclennon
Ceo, Mark Utley
V Pres, Michael Lundequam
Marketing Agent, Martha Timmers

LOCATIONS

HQ: PRODUCTION TECHNOLOGIES, INC.
7651 WASHINGTON AVE S, EDINA, MN 554392417
Phone: 952 944-1076
Web: WWW.PTIMN.COM

HISTORICAL FINANCIALS

Company Type: Private

Income Statement — FYE: December 31

	REVENUE ($ mil.)	NET INCOME ($ mil.)	NET PROFIT MARGIN	EMPLOYEES
12/16	3,289	580	17.6%	25
12/15	3,488	719	20.6%	—
12/14	3,880	348	9.0%	—
12/11	4	0	9.8%	—
Annual Growth	280.1%	327.2%	—	—

PROHEALTH CARE INC

That cheddar-and-beer diet take a toll on your health? Might be time to turn your health over to the pros. ProHealth Care provides health care services to southeastern Wisconsin through a network of three hospitals (Waukesha Memorial Oconomowoc Memorial and the Rehabilitation Hospital of Wisconsin) about two dozen clinics assisted living facilities (Regency Senior Communities) a rehabilitation partnership home health care services and a hospice facility. The community-based organization's specialized services include advanced cancer care cardiology orthopedic and obstetrical and neonatal intensive care.

Operations

ProHealth Care's total operations include Waukesha Memorial Hospital Oconomowoc Memorial Hospital Rehabilitation Hospital of Wisconsin (RHOW) ProHealth Care Medical Associates ProHealth Home Care and Hospice West Wood Health & Fitness Center and senior living facilities.

The RHOW is a 40-bed hospital that is the result of a partnership between ProHealth Care and Centerre Healthcare to meet the increased rehabilitation needs of the region.

Oconomowoc Memorial Hospital has 58 available beds and provides general acute care and support activities in Oconomowoc Wisconsin and surrounding communities.

Financial Performance

In 2014 ProHealth Care's net sales increased by 3% due to higher sales from net patient service revenues less provision for bad debts. Patient service revenues net of contractual allowances and discounts was comprised of $657.9 million from third party payors and $7.3 from self-pay payors.

Net income decreased by $107.1 million in 2014 due to lower excess of revenues over expenses (due to unrealized investment loss and change in interest rate swap value) and pension-related changes other than net periodic benefit cost partially offset by increased revenues.

Net cash provided by the operating activities increased by 16% due to changes in patient accounts receivable and accounts payable.

Company Background

ProHealth Care in 2012 merged the foundations serving its two hospitals in Waukesha County in an effort to optimize the efficiency of its operations. With the merger the Waukesha Memorial Hospital Foundation and Oconomowoc Memorial Hospital Foundation became the ProHealth Care Foundation. The integration combined the foundation boards donors and volunteers into one organization.

ProHealth Care was established as a not-for-profit corporation in 1998.

EXECUTIVES

President And Ceo, Susan Edwards
Cio, Christine Bessler
Vice President Ambulatory Services, John May
Vice President Planning, Darcy Lorenzon
Medical Director, John Ostergaard
Chairman, Janet Swandby
Auditors: PLANTE & MORAN PLLC GRAND RA

LOCATIONS

HQ: PROHEALTH CARE INC
1111 DELAFIELD ST STE 100, WAUKESHA, WI 531883407
Phone: 262 928-4300
Web: WWW.PROHEALTHCARE.ORG

PRODUCTS/OPERATIONS

2014 Sales

	%
Net patient service revenues	91
Other operating revenues	9
Total	**100**

Selected Medical Services

Allergies
Birthing
Bones Joints and Muscles
Brain and Nerves
Breast Health
Cancer
CyberKnife
Diabetes
Diagnostic Services
Digestive
Ear Nose and Throat
Emergency Services/Urgent Care
Eyes and Vision
Gastrointestinal Services
Hearing
Heart and Vascular
Home Care and Hospice
Integrative Medicine
Kidneys and Urinary System
MAKOplasty
Mammography
Men's Health
Mental Health
Multiple Sclerosis
Occupational Health Services
Orthopedic
Pain
Palliative Medicine
Primary Care
Physical Therapy and Rehabilitation Services
Senior Services
Sleep
Spine Care
Stroke
Travel Medicine
Weight Loss
Women's Health
Women's Sexual Health
Wound Care

COMPETITORS

Beaver Dam Community Hospitals
Children's Hospital and Health System
Columbia St. Mary's
FHN
Froedtert Hospital
Hospital Sisters Health System
KishHealth
Ministry Health Care
Rockford Health System
SwedishAmerican Health System
UW Medical Foundation
University of Wisconsin Hospital and Clinics

HISTORICAL FINANCIALS

Company Type: Private

Income Statement — FYE: September 30

	REVENUE ($ mil.)	NET INCOME ($ mil.)	NET PROFIT MARGIN	EMPLOYEES
09/20	865	21	2.5%	3,000
09/19	852	66	7.8%	—
09/18	820	111	13.6%	—
09/17	765	127	16.6%	—
Annual Growth	4.2%	(44.7%)	—	—

2020 Year-End Financials

Return on assets: 1.2%
Return on equity: 1.8%
Current ratio: 1.40
Cash ($ mil.): 68

PROVIDENCE HEALTH & SERVICES

EXECUTIVES

Ceo, Rod Hochman
Pres- Chief Dev Officer, Laurie Kelley
Exec V Pres-Cfo, Todd Hofheins
Technology, Henry Morgan
Coordinator, Mayra Graves
Security Engineering Consultan, Diana Bullion
Admin Assistant, Alex Figueroa
Pharmacy Director, Helen Noonan-Harnsber
Chief Human Resources Officer, Ron Chavira
Executive Director, Terri Warren
Senior Financial Analyst Real, Tuan Nguyen
Auditors: KPMG LLP SEATTLE WA

LOCATIONS

HQ: PROVIDENCE HEALTH & SERVICES
1801 LIND AVE SW, RENTON, WA 980573368
Phone: 425 525-3355
Web: WWW.PROVIDENCE.ORG

HISTORICAL FINANCIALS

Company Type: Private

Income Statement — FYE: December 31

	REVENUE ($ mil.)	NET INCOME ($ mil.)	NET PROFIT MARGIN	EMPLOYEES
12/15	14,433	49	0.3%	130
12/12	280	14	5.3%	—
12/08	7,026	(156)	—	—
12/07	6,348	434	6.8%	—
Annual Growth	10.8%	(23.8%)	—	—

2015 Year-End Financials

Return on assets: 0.3%
Return on equity: 0.6%
Current ratio: 1.40
Cash ($ mil.): 729

PROVIDENCE HEALTH & SERVICES - OREGON

EXECUTIVES

Pres-Ceo, John Koster
Sr V Pres-Cfo, Mike Butler
Pres, Rodney Hochman
SEC, Cindy Strauss
Treas, Todd Hofheins
Proj Coordinator, Jeanette Staley
Coordinator, Sandy Tingley
Access Supervisor, Schmidt Susan
Manager Reimbursement, Soderman Shirley
Head of School, Joe Sciuto
Director, Beth Hegde
Auditors: CLARK NUBER PS BELLEVUE WA

LOCATIONS

HQ: PROVIDENCE HEALTH & SERVICES - OREGON
1801 LIND AVE SW, RENTON, WA 980573368
Phone: 425 525-3355
Web: WWW.PROVIDENCE.ORG

HISTORICAL FINANCIALS

Company Type: Private

Income Statement — FYE: December 31

	REVENUE ($ mil.)	NET INCOME ($ mil.)	NET PROFIT MARGIN	EMPLOYEES
12/17	3,479	781	22.5%	8,511
12/09	2,057	57	2.8%	—
12/08	73	7	10.5%	—
Annual Growth	53.6%	67.2%	—	—

2017 Year-End Financials

Return on assets: 24.4%
Return on equity: 29.7%
Current ratio: 3.00
Cash ($ mil.): 327

PROVIDENCE HEALTH & SERVICES-WASHINGTON

EXECUTIVES

Pres-Ceo, Michael Butler
Treas*, Jo Ann Escasa-Haigh
Corp SEC*, Cindy Strauss
Asst Corp SEC*, John Whipple
Asst SEC*, Shannon Dwyer
Asst SEC For Enrollment*, Donald Anderson Jr
Asst Corp SEC*, Tammy Teodosio
Sterile Processing Coordinator, Anna Shannon
Chief Marketing Officer (provi, Brad Garrigues
Physician, Peter Benziger
Auditors: CLARK NUBER PS BELLEVUE WA

LOCATIONS

HQ: PROVIDENCE HEALTH & SERVICES-WASHINGTON
1801 LIND AVE SW 9016, RENTON, WA 980573368
Phone: 425 525-3355
Web: WWW.PROVIDENCE.ORG

HISTORICAL FINANCIALS

Company Type: Private

Income Statement — FYE: December 31

	REVENUE ($ mil.)	NET INCOME ($ mil.)	NET PROFIT MARGIN	EMPLOYEES
12/09	3,178	(37)	—	9,700
12/08	26	(0)	—	—
12/07	6,348	434	6.8%	—
12/06	2,055	113	5.5%	—
Annual Growth	15.6%	—	—	—

2009 Year-End Financials

Return on assets: (-0.8%)
Return on equity: (-2.4%)
Current ratio: —
Cash ($ mil.): 314

PUBLIC EMPLOYEE RETIREMENT SYSTEM, IDAHO

EXECUTIVES

Director, Don Drumd
Information Specialist, Branden Kennah
Deputy Director, Don Drum
Auditors: EIDE BAILLY LLP BOISE IDAHO

LOCATIONS

HQ: PUBLIC EMPLOYEE RETIREMENT SYSTEM, IDAHO
607 N 8TH ST, BOISE, ID 837025518
Phone: 208 334-3365
Web: WWW.PERSI.IDAHO.GOV

HISTORICAL FINANCIALS

Company Type: Private

Income Statement — FYE: June 30

	REVENUE ($ mil.)	NET INCOME ($ mil.)	NET PROFIT MARGIN	EMPLOYEES
06/19	2,221	1,145	51.6%	62
06/18	2,160	1,157	53.6%	—
06/17	2,586	1,625	62.9%	—
06/16	878	(40)	—	—
Annual Growth	36.3%	—	—	—

2019 Year-End Financials

Return on assets: 5.8%
Return on equity: 5.9%
Current ratio: 1.40
Cash ($ mil.): 11

PUBLIC HEALTH TRUST OF MIAMI DADE COUNTY

Jackson Memorial Hospital is the flagship facility of the Jackson Health System (JHS). It has roughly 2450 beds and offers a wide variety of services including burn treatment trauma pediatrics rehabilitation obstetrics and transplants. It is also a teaching facility for the University of Miami School of Medicine. JHS also operates Holtz Children's Hospital a rehabilitation hospital a mental health hospital primary and specialty care centers two long-term care nursing facilities six corrections health clinics and two community hospitals. Jackson Memorial Hospital and JHS are overseen by The Public Health Trust of Miami-Dade County.

Operations

Jackson Memorial Hospital's Ryder Trauma Center is Miami-Dade County's only adult and pediatric Level 1 trauma center.

JHS is its region's primary provider of charity care spending some $700 million annually to administer health care to Florida's uninsured and underinsured populations. Along with Jackson Memorial Hospital JHS delivers medical care to Floridians through the Jackson South Community Hospital (226 beds) and the Jackson North Medical Center (382 beds) which also serves as a teaching hospital for the Florida International University College of Medicine. Holtz Children's Hospital is one of the largest children's hospitals in the state and one of three in the US that specializes in pediatric multi-organ transplants.

Strategy

The system has acquired a site to build a new campus (Jackson West) that will include a children's outpatient center and a free-standing emergency department. JHS is also adding a new walk-in facility on South Beach. The company has invested in bringing new lab equipment and software to its facilities.

Other initiatives have included adjusting prices to be more competitive doing business with HMOs and drawing in more affluent patients through first-class offerings.

Company Background

The Public Health Trust was created in 1973 by the Board of County Commissioners as an independent governing body to provide leadership for joint planning between Jackson Health System the University of Miami Miller School of Medicine Miami-Dade County and other private and community organizations. Today the Public Health Trust is considered the hospital system's governing board picking its CEO and overseeing the system's operations.

EXECUTIVES

President And Ceo Jackson Health System, Carlos A. Migoya
Evp And Coo Jackson Health System, David R. Small
Chief Administrative Officer Jackson Memorial Hospital And Jackson Rehabilitation Hospital, Alex Contreras-Soto
Chief Administrative Officer Jackson Behavioral Health Hospital, R. John Repique
Associate Vice President For Communications, Christine Morris
Medical Director, Nicolette Schreiber
Vice President Managed Care, Karen Lang
Executive Vice President Chief, Jeffrey Crudele
Medical Director, Diana Cardenas
Director Of Pharmacy, Paul Eger
Medical Director, Shashi Razdan
Vice President Facilities Design And Construction, Isa Nez
Vice President Marketing And Communications, Lisbet Fernandez-Vina
Medical Records Director, Kim Lucas
Vice President Transplant Institute (miami), Luke Preczewski
Unit Secretary, Cristal Lozada
Treasurer, Ann Fleming

LOCATIONS

HQ: PUBLIC HEALTH TRUST OF MIAMI DADE COUNTY
1611 NW 12TH AVE, MIAMI, FL 331361005
Phone: 305 585-1111
Web: WWW.JACKSONHEALTH.ORG

COMPETITORS

Baptist Health South Florida
Broward Health
Continucare
Encompass Health
HCA
Larkin Community Hospital
MJHHA
Miami Children's Hospital
Mount Sinai Medical Center of Florida
NCH Healthcare
Plantation General
South Broward Hospital District
South Miami Hospital
University of Miami Hospital

HISTORICAL FINANCIALS

Company Type: Private

Income Statement — FYE: September 30

	REVENUE ($ mil.)	NET INCOME ($ mil.)	NET PROFIT MARGIN	EMPLOYEES
09/18	1,166	206	17.7%	11,000
09/17	1,160	184	15.9%	—
09/15*	883	200	22.7%	—
06/05	0	0	—	—
Annual Growth	—	—	—	—

*Fiscal year change

2018 Year-End Financials

Return on assets: 8.8%
Return on equity: 33.2%
Current ratio: 1.30
Cash ($ mil.): 308

PUBLIC HOSPITAL DISTRICT 1 OF KING COUNTY

EXECUTIVES

Admin-Ceo, Richard D Roodman
Cfo*, Michael Bernstein
Comm*, Carole Anderson
Coo*, Paul Hayes
Doctor, Olga V Khait-Palant
Doctor, Shreeketa M Mehta
Anesthesiology, Andrew O Smith
Doctor, Joyce V Gauthier
Anesthesiology, Sidney W Postma
Coordinator, Cheryl Webster
Doctor, Arthur Lew
Auditors: KPMG LLP SEATTLE WASHINGTON

LOCATIONS

HQ: PUBLIC HOSPITAL DISTRICT 1 OF KING COUNTY
400 S 43RD ST, RENTON, WA 980555714
Phone: 425 228-3440
Web: WWW.VALLEYMED.ORG

HISTORICAL FINANCIALS

Company Type: Private

Income Statement				FYE: June 30
	REVENUE ($ mil.)	NET INCOME ($ mil.)	NET PROFIT MARGIN	EMPLOYEES
06/19	694	12	1.7%	2,700
06/18	653	40	6.2%	—
06/16*	519	11	2.2%	—
12/07	327	25	7.8%	—
Annual Growth	7.1%	(6.6%)	—	—

*Fiscal year change

2019 Year-End Financials

Return on assets: 1.6%
Return on equity: 4.4%
Current ratio: 1.60
Cash ($ mil.): 35

PUBLIC UTILITY DISTRICT 1 OF SNOHOMISH COUNTY

Keeping its customers' safety is priority No. 1 at Public Utility District No. 1 of Snohomish County Washington (Snohomish County PUD) which distributes electricity to over 360000 electric customers in Washington State. The utility the second largest PUD in the state with over 2200 sq. ml. service area purchases most of its power supply from third parties (Bonneville Power Administration and other producers). It sells surplus power into the wholesale power transactions to balance its supply load. Snohomish County PUD also serves more than 21000 water utility customers.

Operations

Snohomish County PUD's operations consist of three systems: the Electric System the Generation System and the Water System.

The Electric System (about 95% of sales) is made up of electric transmission and distribution system.

The Generation System (some 5%) is composed of the company's Jackson Hydroelectric Project and four smaller hydroelectric projects.

The Water System (less than 5%) is made up of water distribution system.

Overall around 90% of total sales came from its retail sales while wholesale sales and others account for the rest.

Geographic Reach

The company is headquartered in Everett Washington.

Sales and Marketing

The PUD serves three categories of customers: Residential (around 305915) Commercial (about 30795) Industrial (nearly 75) and other (roughly 230).

The company offers a wide range of energy-efficiency solutions for business customers.

Financial Performance

PUD's revenue decreased from $695.8 million in 2018 to $685.7 million in 2019 which resulted from a decrease in wholesale sales and others.

Net income was $82.2 million a 2% increase compared to the previous year.

Cash and cash equivalents at the end of the year were $45.6 million 51% less compared to $45.6 million in the previous year. Cash provided by operating activities was $87.4 million. Financing activities used $142.3 million primarily from capital construction while investing activities provided $5.6 million primarily from sale of special funds and investment securities.

Strategy

In 2019 the PUD completed its first Community Solar project located at the home of the future Microgrid and Clean Energy Technology Center in Arlington. The 500-kilowatt array is the largest community solar project in the state.

With the launch of Community Solar the PUD also awarded its final Planet Power solar energy grants to five community-focused and nonprofit organizations: Eagle Creek Elementary Snohomish County Fire District No. 22 YMCA-Everett Farmer Frog and Camp Killoqua.

Thanks to customer contributions to the Planet Power program through the years an additional 329 kilowatts of solar energy has been added to the PUD's grid across 39 individual projects - 112 kilowatts in 2019 alone.

In addition to the hydropower resources available through Bonneville Power the PUD continued to invest in its own hydroelectric projects. In 2019 the PUD completed the last of the capital improvements specifically identified in the new license for the Henry M. Jackson Hydroelectric Project near Sultan which is capable of supplying power to over 53000 homes. The PUD also continued to invest in and benefit from its four smaller projects at Woods Creek Youngs Creek Calligan Creek and Hancock Creek.

The PUD's other renewable energy resources include long-term contracts for wind projects in Central Washington and Oregon and contracts with locally owned and operated biomass and biodigester facilities.

Company BackgroundIn 2013 solar energy capacity stood at two MW enough to serve 170 homes. More than 350 PUD customers cover part of their electricity needs through their own solar energy units. The PUD's Solar Express program offers financial incentives and technical assistance for solar photovoltaic and solar hot water systems. In 2012 the company amended a power contract with Hampton Lumber (a fuel supplier since 2007) that will boost the level of biomass energy the utility will receive from the lumber company's Darrington plant. The new agreement will allow Snohomish County PUD to receive up to 2.5 MW of energy from Hampton Lumber enough energy to power about 2000 homes. Supported by $15.8 million in matching federal stimulus dollars in 2011 Snohomish County PUD completed its first major project as part of a long-term upgrade of its electric grid with smart grid technology. The upgrade includes the installation of more than 160 miles of fiber optic cable and connecting them to 62 substations two radio sites and other utility buildings. The company began providing water utility service to parts of Snohomish County in 1946. Public Utility District No. 1 of Snohomish County began operating as power utility in 1949 providing publicly owned electric and water utility service to the residents of Snohomish County and Camano Island.

EXECUTIVES

President Send An, Toni Olson
General Manager, Steve Klein
Assistant General Manager Water Resources Division, Kim Moore
Chief Information Officer, Benjamin Beberness
President Board Of Commissioners, Kathleen (Kathy) Vaughn
Auditors: BAKER TILLY MADISON WI

LOCATIONS

HQ: PUBLIC UTILITY DISTRICT 1 OF SNOHOMISH COUNTY
2320 CALIFORNIA ST, EVERETT, WA 982013750
Phone: 425 257-9288
Web: WWW.SNOPUD.COM

PRODUCTS/OPERATIONS

2014 Sales

	$ mil.	% of total
Retail sales	554	86
Wholesale sales	59	9
Other	30	5
Total	**645**	**100**

COMPETITORS

Avista
Chelan County PUD
Grant County Public Utility District
Public Utility District No. 1 of Clark County
Puget Energy
Tacoma Public Utilities

HISTORICAL FINANCIALS

Company Type: Private

Income Statement				FYE: December 31
	REVENUE ($ mil.)	NET INCOME ($ mil.)	NET PROFIT MARGIN	EMPLOYEES
12/19	685	82	12.0%	879
12/18	695	80	11.5%	—
12/17	686	75	11.1%	—
12/16	657	60	9.2%	—
Annual Growth	1.4%	10.8%	—	—

2019 Year-End Financials

Return on assets: 3.7%
Return on equity: 5.4%
Current ratio: 2.30
Cash ($ mil.): 45

PUBLISHING OFFICE, US GOVERNMENT

The US Government Printing Office (GPO) keeps America informed in print and online. The GPO is the Federal government's primary centralized resource for gathering cataloging producing providing and preserving published information in all its forms. Part of the legislative branch the GPO offers Congress the courts and other government agencies centralized services to enable them to easily produce printed documents according to uniform Federal specifications. The GPO also offers the publications for sale to the public and makes them available at no cost through the Federal Depository Library Program. The GPO is run like a business and requires payment from its government customers for services rendered.

EXECUTIVES

Managing Director, Ricardo Garcia
Auditors: KPMG LLP WASHINGTON DC

LOCATIONS

HQ: PUBLISHING OFFICE, US GOVERNMENT
732 N CAPITOL ST NW, WASHINGTON, DC 204010002
Phone: 202 512-0000
Web: WWW.GPO.GOV

HISTORICAL FINANCIALS

Company Type: Private

Income Statement				FYE: September 30
	REVENUE ($ mil.)	NET INCOME ($ mil.)	NET PROFIT MARGIN	EMPLOYEES
09/19	937	51	5.5%	1,880
09/18	874	52	6.0%	—
09/17	874	58	6.7%	—
09/16	875	71	8.1%	—
Annual Growth	2.3%	(10.1%)	—	—

2019 Year-End Financials

Return on assets: 4.8%
Return on equity: 7.2%
Current ratio: 2.80
Cash ($ mil.): 675

QUALITY OIL COMPANY, LLC

With more services than your average oil company Quality Oil helps its customers get fueled up cooled off and well rested. And they can smoke if they want to. The company distributes fuel oil and propane to customers in the Winston-Salem area of North Carolina. Quality Oil provides air conditioning and heating equipment service operates 47 convenience stores (Quality Marts) and about 20 service stations and owns hotels in five southern states. In addition the company operates 60 Quality Plus locations at which drivers can buy cigarettes at discount prices. The company also provides Right-a-Way oil change services at many of its gas stations.

Operations

In addition the company's real estate unit (Quality Oil Real Estate) operates a diverse portfolio of retail and hotel sites industrial units residential subdivision developments and a shopping center. Quality Marts and Quality Plus also provide heating and cooling and fleet fueling services.

Geographic Reach

Quality Oil owns and operates four Hampton Inns two Hampton Inn & Suites and one Homewood Suites in the Carolinas Florida Georgia and Virginia. Affiliate Reliable Tank Line LLC transports petroleum products and provides fleet fueling services at 10 locations in North Carolina northern South Carolina eastern Virginia and eastern Tennessee. Quality Oil Heating-Cooling has assets throughout North Carolina and parts of South Carolina Virginia Florida and Tennessee and serves Forsyth County Stokes County Davie County Davidson County Yadkin County Rowan County and Iredell County.

Sales and Marketing

The company markets Shell oil products.

Strategy

To sharpen its competitive edge in 2013 Quality Oil created a new department – Retail Technology – to maintain PDI Pricebook and POS Systems and test and implement future technological developments.

To increase operational efficiency in 2012 Quality Oil installed Professional Datasolutions Inc. (PDI) scanning software at all of its retail outlets.

Mergers and Acquisitions

To complement its existing oil and propane business in 2012 Quality Oil acquired regional gas station and convenience store operator Horn Oil Co. in Mocksville North Carolina.

Company Background

Expanding its store network in 2011 the company opened Quality Mart locations #46 and #47 in Kernersville and Morrisville.

Quality Oil was founded in 1929 by Joe Glenn and Bert Bennett as a Shell oil products distributor and is still owned and operated by descendants of the founders.

EXECUTIVES

Vice President Information Technology, Thomas Rieke
Auditors: BUTLER & BURKE LLP WINSTON-S

LOCATIONS

HQ: QUALITY OIL COMPANY, LLC
1540 SILAS CREEK PKWY, WINSTON SALEM, NC 271273705
Phone: 336 722-3441
Web: WWW.QUALITYOILNC.COM

PRODUCTS/OPERATIONS

Selected Brands

Hampton Inn
Quality Heating and Air Conditioning
Quality Mart
Quality Oil Appliance Sales and Service
Quality Oil Commercial Heating and On-Site Fueling
Quality Oil Fuel Oil
Quality Oil Gas Logs and Heaters
Quality Oil Propane
Quality Plus
Reliable Tank Line
Shell Oil products

Selected Mergers and Acquisitions

COMPETITORS

Cumberland Farms
E-Z Mart Stores
Hyatt
Marriott
Racetrac Petroleum
WilcoHess

HISTORICAL FINANCIALS

Company Type: Private

Income Statement				FYE: December 31
	REVENUE ($ mil.)	NET INCOME ($ mil.)	NET PROFIT MARGIN	EMPLOYEES
12/09	634	11	1.9%	1,000
12/08	806	27	3.4%	—
12/07	619	10	1.8%	—
12/06	542	15	2.8%	—
Annual Growth	5.4%	(8.1%)	—	—

2009 Year-End Financials

Return on assets: 9.9%
Return on equity: 13.1%
Current ratio: 0.90
Cash ($ mil.): 11

R. DIRECTIONAL DRILLING & UNDERGROUND TECHNOLOGY, INC.

EXECUTIVES

Pres-Ceo, Jose M Ruiz
V Pres of Oprs*, Aurelio Ruiz
V Pres of Sls*, Derek Reeve
Office Manager, Colleen Hale
Job Coordinator, Denise Lenz
Fleet Manager, Tim Howe
Auditors: KEN DUSSEAU PC

LOCATIONS

HQ: R. DIRECTIONAL DRILLING & UNDERGROUND TECHNOLOGY, INC.
8560 N 77TH DR, PEORIA, AZ 853457969
Phone: 602 374-3173
Web: WWW.DRILLRDD.COM

HISTORICAL FINANCIALS

Company Type: Private

Income Statement				FYE: December 31
	REVENUE ($ mil.)	NET INCOME ($ mil.)	NET PROFIT MARGIN	EMPLOYEES
12/12	7,667	(1,040)	—	61
12/11*	7	2	29.9%	—
09/10	2	0	27.4%	—
Annual Growth	5174.7%	—	—	—

*Fiscal year change

2012 Year-End Financials

Return on assets: (-24.0%)
Return on equity: (-48.7%)
Current ratio: 1.30
Cash ($ mil.): 416

R. E. MICHEL COMPANY, LLC

Blowing hot and cold is good for R.E. Michel. The company is one of the nation's largest wholesale distributors of heating air-conditioning and refrigeration (HVAC-R) equipment parts and supplies. The family-owned and operated firm offers more than 16000 items through about 2 sales offices located across the Southern Mid-Atlantic and Northeastern regions of the country. R.E. Michel ships more than 20000 items each day from its 900000-sq.-ft. distribution center in Maryland. Its Exclusive Supplier Partnership (ESP) program offers customers inventory control advertising and marketing support. R.E. Michel was founded in 1935 as a supplier to the home heating oil burner industry.

Geographic Reach

The HVAC wholesaler maintains a handful of offices to cater to customers located in the Southern US as well as in the Mid-Atlantic and Northeastern regions. Most recently opened offices reside in Ohio California Virginia Florida South Carolina Arizona and Tennessee.

Sales and Marketing

R.E. Michel uses up to 50 trailers to ship its more than 10000 items each day. To this end the company also ships more than 3200 items via the United Parcel Service each week. As part of its business it publishes a 1300 page catalog that includes 20000 catalog line items.

EXECUTIVES

Vice President Of Operations, Gene Winters
Exec Vp, Ronald Miller
Vice President Of Fin Human Resources, Holly Porter
Auditors: CLIFTONLARSONALLEN LLP BALTIM

LOCATIONS

HQ: R. E. MICHEL COMPANY, LLC
1 RE MICHEL DR, GLEN BURNIE, MD 210606408
Phone: 410 760-4000
Web: WWW.REMICHEL.COM

PRODUCTS/OPERATIONS

Selected Products & Services
Air conditioning & heating
Indoor air quality
Boilers
Water heating equipment
Hydronic & steam systems
Valves
Pipe & fittings
Fuel oil systems
Gas systems
Chemicals
Refrigeration equipment & supplies
Controls
Electrical supplies
Motors
Air handling products
Venting products
Duct registers & grilles
Tools & test instruments
O.E.M. Parts

COMPETITORS

Emco Corporation
Ferguson Enterprises
Gensco
HD Supply
Lowe's
MSC Industrial Direct
W.W. Grainger
WinWholesale

HISTORICAL FINANCIALS

Company Type: Private

Income Statement — FYE: December 31

	REVENUE ($ mil.)	NET INCOME ($ mil.)	NET PROFIT MARGIN	EMPLOYEES
12/19	939	48	5.2%	1,960
12/18	898	37	4.1%	—
12/17	804	26	3.2%	—
12/16	763	23	3.1%	—
Annual Growth	7.2%	26.8%	—	—

2019 Year-End Financials

Return on assets: 11.9%
Return on equity: 17.2%
Current ratio: 2.90
Cash ($ mil.): 2

R. M. PARKS OF MEXICO, INC.

EXECUTIVES

Pres, R M Parks
V Pres, Tim Callison
SEC-Treas, Marilyn Callison
Offc Mgr, Jason Patterson
Accounting Manager, Sherrill Morris
Auditors: GUMBINER SAVETT INC SANTA MO

LOCATIONS

HQ: R. M. PARKS OF MEXICO, INC.
1061 N MAIN ST, PORTERVILLE, CA 932571686
Phone: 559 784-2384
Web: WWW.RMPARKSINC.COM

HISTORICAL FINANCIALS

Company Type: Private

Income Statement — FYE: October 31

	REVENUE ($ mil.)	NET INCOME ($ mil.)	NET PROFIT MARGIN	EMPLOYEES
10/18	571	0	0.0%	20
10/17	477	(0)	—	—
10/16	448	0	0.2%	—
10/15	534	0	0.2%	—
Annual Growth	2.3%	(73.9%)	—	—

2018 Year-End Financials

Return on assets: 0.1%
Return on equity: 0.2%
Current ratio: 1.30
Cash ($ mil.): —

R.C. WILLEY HOME FURNISHINGS

R.C. Willey Home Furnishings does its best to be top dog. The company drives traffic by giving away over 350000 hot dogs a year in more than 15 stores in Utah Nevada California and Idaho. Despite Sunday store closures and operations in only four states R.C. Willey is one of the nation's largest furniture retailers. It sells furniture (Skyline Baxton Lumisource) appliances (GE Maytag) electronics (Sony Samsung) and flooring. The company also sells mattresses (Serta Malouf Sleep Inc). R.C. Willey is owned by the investment giant Warren Buffett of Berkshire Hathaway.

Operations

R.C. Willey boasts more than 1.7 million sq. ft. of retail space across its nearly a dozen retail stores a pair of retail clearance facilities and three distribution centers to support its entire operation. The company is known for its large selection and reliable brand names. It carries General Electric Whirlpool LG Maytag KitchenAid Sony Traeger Thermado Samsung Electrolux La-Z-Boy Aireloom Bose and Tempur Pedic among others.

Geographic Reach

Utah-based R.C. Willey operates its furniture business nationwide primarily in a handful of states.

Sales and Marketing

A plus to R.C. Willey Home Furnishings customers the company offers financing through its R.C. Willey Credit Card.

EXECUTIVES

President, Jeffrey S. (Jeff) Child
Cfo, Curtis Child
Chairman, William H. (Bill) Child

LOCATIONS

HQ: R.C. WILLEY HOME FURNISHINGS
2301 S 300 W, SALT LAKE CITY, UT 841152516
Phone: 801 461-3900
Web: WWW.RCWILLEY.COM

PRODUCTS/OPERATIONS

Selected Products
Appliances
Electronics
Fitness
Flooring
Furniture
Mattresses

COMPETITORS

Abbey Carpet
Best Buy
Costco Wholesale
Ethan Allen
Fry's Electronics
Home Depot
J. C. Penney Company
La-Z-Boy
Lowe's
Pier 1 Imports
RadioShack
Williams-Sonoma

HISTORICAL FINANCIALS

Company Type: Private

Income Statement — FYE: December 31

	REVENUE ($ mil.)	NET INCOME ($ mil.)	NET PROFIT MARGIN	EMPLOYEES
12/17	807	19	2.4%	2,700
12/16	800	26	3.3%	—
12/14	712	17	2.4%	—
12/13	664	15	2.3%	—
Annual Growth	5.0%	6.3%	—	—

2017 Year-End Financials

Return on assets: 2.1%
Return on equity: 2.5%
Current ratio: 4.10
Cash ($ mil.): 62

RADY CHILDREN'S HOSPITAL AND HEALTH CENTER

EXECUTIVES

Pres-Ceo, Donald B Kearns
Cmo*, Irvin A Kaufman
Exec V Pres*, Margareta E Norton
Sr V Pres-Cfo*, Roger G Roux
Coo*, Nicholas Holmes
Network Administrator, Jim Ward
Coordinator, Giuseppe Principato
Scientist, Andrea Hazen
Coordinator, Carrie Arii
Coordinator, Deborah Ferreira
Coordinator, Maria Guzman
Auditors: LB KPMG LLP LOS ANGELES CA

LOCATIONS

HQ: RADY CHILDREN'S HOSPITAL AND HEALTH CENTER
3020 CHILDRENS WAY, SAN DIEGO, CA 921234223
Phone: 858 576-1700
Web: WWW.RCHSD.ORG

HISTORICAL FINANCIALS

Company Type: Private

Income Statement — FYE: June 30

	REVENUE ($ mil.)	NET INCOME ($ mil.)	NET PROFIT MARGIN	EMPLOYEES
06/20	1,334	(20)	—	4,033
06/19	1,354	167	12.3%	—
06/18	1,243	205	16.5%	—
06/17	1,092	220	20.2%	—
Annual Growth	6.9%	—	—	—

2020 Year-End Financials

Return on assets: (-0.8%)
Return on equity: (-1.3%)
Current ratio: 5.40
Cash ($ mil.): 213

RADY CHILDREN'S HOSPITAL-SAN DIEGO

Rady Children's Hospital-San Diego handles the big injuries of pint-sized patients. Serving as the region's only pediatric trauma center the nonprofit hospital boasts more than 520 beds. As part of its services Rady Children's Hospital-San Diego offers comprehensive pediatric care including surgical services convalescent care a neonatal intensive care unit and orthopedic services. Across its service area the hospital also operates about 25 satellite centers that provide such primary and specialized care services as physical therapy and hearing diagnostics. Rady Children's Hospital a teaching hospital affiliated with the University of California San Diego Medical School was founded in 1954.

Operations

Rady Children's operates its own 36-bed emergency department – The Sam S. and Rose Stein Emergency Care Center – that each day sees up to 300 patients. It is the only regional emergency center solely dedicated and equipped to care for children. The hospital also operates California's only pediatric skilled nursing facility – The Helen Bernardy Center – to provide 24-hour care to disabled and medically fragile children in a homelike environment.

For treating non-life-or-limb-threatening injuries and illnesses the hospital operates neighborhood urgent care centers in Escondido La Mesa Oceanside and San Diego.

Through its medical school affiliation Rady Children's engages in nearly 500 clinical trials in all pediatric specialties. It collaborates with University of California San Diego the Sanford-Burnham Medical Research Institute The Scripps Research Institute the Salk Institute for Biological Studies and St. Jude Children's Research Hospital. Specialized research facilities on campus include the Autism Discovery Institute the Blair L. Sadler Center for Quality and the Child and Adolescent Services Research Center.

The hospital operates a LEED-certified Acute Care Pavilion which holds a neonatal intensive care unit the Peckham Center for Cancer and Blood Disorders and the Warren Family Surgical Center. It serves those suffering from eating disorders through its inpatient center to allow for intensive psychiatric therapy for patients with anorexia and bulimia and to aid families with home care.

In 2014 the hospital had 18782 inpatient admissions 230383 outpatient visits nearly 85000 emergency department visits and more than 54000 urgent care visits. It performed about 20000 surgeries.

Geographic Reach

Rady Children's Hospital serves as the pediatric medical center that caters to the California region of San Diego Imperial and southern Riverside counties. It has more than 30 offices throughout San Diego and southern Riverside counties with satellite locations in Chula Vista El Centro Encinitas Escondido La Jolla La Mesa Murrieta Oceanside San Diego and Solana Beach.

EXECUTIVES

Chairman Rady Pediatric Genomics And Systems Medicine Institute, David F. Hale, age 71
President And Ceo Rady Pediatric Genomics And Systems Medicine Institute, Stephen Kingsmore
Svp And Coo, Margareta E. (Meg) Norton
President And Ceo, Donald Kearns
Vp And Cio, Albert Oriol
Vp And Chief Nursing Executive, Mary Fagan
Chief Medical Officer, Irvin A. Kaufman
Svp And Coo, Nicholas Holmes
Executive Director Rady Children's Hospital Foundation And Svp Rady Children's Hospital, Stephen Jennings
Physician-in-chief And Chief Scientific Officer And Chairman Of Pediatrics Uc San Diego, Gabriel G. Haddad
Svp Rady Children's Specialists Of San Diego, Herb Kimmons
Respiratory Therapy Director, Toni Popien
Senior Vice President, Steve Jennings
Clinical Director, Carolina Schaber
Vice President And Chief Operating Officer Rcssd, Charles Davis
Vice Chairman, Michael P. (Mike) Peckham
Chairman, Theodore D. (Ted) Roth, age 69

LOCATIONS

HQ: RADY CHILDREN'S HOSPITAL-SAN DIEGO
3020 CHILDRENS WAY, SAN DIEGO, CA 921234223
Phone: 858 576-1700
Web: WWW.RCHSD.ORG

Selected Satellite Locations

Chula Vista
El Centro
Encinitas
Escondido
La Jolla
La Mesa
Murrieta
Oceanside
San Diego
Solana Beach

PRODUCTS/OPERATIONS

Selected Services

Allergy/Immunology
Attention Deficit Hyperactivity Disorder
Audiology/Hearing
Autism Discovery Institute
Behavioral Health
Brachial Plexus Clinic
Cancer & Blood Disorders
Cardiology
Cardiovascular Surgery
Celiac Disease Clinic
Center for Healthier Communities
Cerebral Palsy Center
Chadwick Center For Children & Families
Child & Adolescent Psychiatry Services (CAPS)
Child & Adolescent Services Research Center (CASRC)
Child Life Services
Children's Care Connection (C3)
Children's Hospital Emergency Transport (CHET)
Cleft Palate Clinic
Craniofacial Disorders
Critical Care
Cystic Fibrosis Center
Dental Surgery
Dermatology
Developmental Evaluation Clinic
Developmental-Behavioral Pediatrics
Developmental Screening & Enhancement Program (DSEP)
Developmental Services
Down Syndrome Center
Eating Disorders/
Medical-Behavioral Disorders Unit
Emergency Medicine
Endocrinology/Diabetes
Fatty Liver Clinic
Feeding Team
Gastroenterology Hepatology & Nutrition
Genetics/Dysmorphology
Heart Institute
Helen Bernardy Center for Medically Fragile Children
Hematology/Oncology
HomeCare
Hospice
Infectious Diseases
Kawasaki Disease Clinic
Kidney/Liver Tranplant Program
Kidney Disease
Laboratory Services/Pathology
Liver Disease
Liver Transplant
Muscle Disease Clinic
Metabolic Medicine
Neonatology
Nephrology
Neurology
Neurosurgery
Newborn Screening Program
Nutrition Clinic
Occupational Therapy
Ophthalmology
Orthopedics
Otolaryngology/ENT
Pain Services
Palliative Care
Pediatric Surgery
Pediatrics & Hospital Medicine
Pharmacy Services
Physical Therapy
Prader-Willi Syndrome Clinic
Psychiatry
Pulmonary/Respiratory Medicine
Radiology
Rehabilitation Medicine
Rheumatology
Sleep Center
Speech/Language Pathology
Spiritual Care
Sports Medicine
Surgery
Toddler School (Alexa's PLAYC)
Trauma Center
Urgent Care
Urology
Weight & Wellness Center

COMPETITORS

All Children's Hospital
Children's Health System
Children's Hospital & Research Center at Oakland
Children's Hospital of Orange County
Children's Hospital of Philadelphia
Children's Hospital of Richmond
Children's Specialized Hospital
Childrens Hospital Los Angeles
Cook Children's Health Care System
Dell Children's Medical Center
Nationwide Children's Hospital
Palomar Health
Scripps Health
Seattle Children's Hospital
Sharp HealthCare
Shriners Hospitals For Children
St. Jude Children's Research Hospital
Sutter Health
Tri-City Healthcare District
UCSF Medical

HISTORICAL FINANCIALS

Company Type: Private

Income Statement — FYE: June 30

	REVENUE ($ mil.)	NET INCOME ($ mil.)	NET PROFIT MARGIN	EMPLOYEES
06/20	1,267	73	5.8%	2,313
06/19	1,300	208	16.0%	—
06/15	522	104	20.1%	—
06/14	838	82	9.8%	—
Annual Growth	7.1%	(2.0%)	—	—

2020 Year-End Financials

Return on assets: 3.0%
Return on equity: 5.0%
Current ratio: 5.10
Cash ($ mil.): 212

RALEY'S

Raley's has to stock plenty of fresh fruit and great wines — it sells to the people that produce them. The company operates about 130 supermarkets and superstores in California and Nevada. In addition to about 80 flagship Raley's Superstores the company operates about 20 Bel Air Markets (in the Sacramento area) and Nob Hill Foods (an upscale Bay Area chain with some 20 locations). Raley's stores typically offer groceries natural foods and liquor as well as in-store pharmacies. Founded during the Depression by Thomas Porter Raley the company is still owned and run by the Raley family.

Operations

In addition to Raley's Bel Air and Nob Hill supermarkets Raley's operates nearly 10 discount warehouse stores under the Food Source banner in Northern California and Nevada and one Market 5-ONE-5 neighborhood market in downtown Sacramento. The company offers online shopping and delivery in some markets.

Geographic Reach

Raley's approximately 130 stores are located primarily in Central and Northern California with a cluster around its headquarters city of Sacramento. It has about 20 locations in Nevada.

Strategy

Raley's strategy is centered around providing health fresh food at affordable prices. To that end in late 2018 it divested its Aisle 1 fuel stations which are adjacent to Raley's supermarkets to focus on core operations. It has also launched new products to appeal to changing tastes for healthy natural foods and prepared meals including a line of chef-created fresh meal kits vegetable sides (introduced in late 2018). Earlier in 2018 the company removed soda and candy from its check-out stands reducing its overall sugar offerings by 25%.

Raley's has also invested in technology to better serve customers and in 2018 launched a new website and campaign to promote online shopping and introduced a pharmacy mobile app.

Company Background

Raley's traces its roots to Placerville California and the 1935 opening of a grocery store by Tom Raley. The company has grown organically and through acquisitions; it acquired Bel Air Markets in 1992 and Nob Hill Foods in 1998. It remains family-owned.

EXECUTIVES

Vice President Information Technology, Jeff Szczesny
Ceo, Michael J. (Mike) Teel
Svp Store Operations, Kevin Konkel
Vp Nonperishables Sales And Merchandising, Kevin Curry
Cfo And Controller, Ken Mueller
Svp Marketing, Deirdre A. Zimmermann
President And Coo, Keith Knopf
Svp Sales And Merchandising, Paul Gianetto
Board Of Directors, Dale Henley

LOCATIONS

HQ: RALEY'S
500 W CAPITOL AVE, WEST SACRAMENTO, CA 956052696
Phone: 916 373-3333
Web: WWW.RALEYS.COM

2018 Stores

	No.
California	110
Northern Nevada	18
Total	**128**

PRODUCTS/OPERATIONS

2018 Stores

	No.
Supermarkets	
Raley's	78
Nob Hill	20
Bel Air	20
Food Source	8
Other	2
Total	**128**

COMPETITORS

Andronico's Market
Costco Wholesale
Food 4 Less Holdings
Grocery Outlet
Kroger
Lunardi's Super Market
Ralphs Grocery
Safeway
Save Mart
Trader Joe's
Wal-Mart
Whole Foods
WinCo Foods

HISTORICAL FINANCIALS

Company Type: Private

Income Statement — FYE: June 30

	REVENUE ($ mil.)	NET INCOME ($ mil.)	NET PROFIT MARGIN	EMPLOYEES
06/12	3,162	(1)	—	14,000
06/10	3,064	0	—	—
06/09	0	0	—	—
Annual Growth	—	—	—	—

2012 Year-End Financials

Return on assets: (-0.2%)
Return on equity: (-0.6%)
Current ratio: 0.90
Cash ($ mil.): 26

RAYMOND JAMES & ASSOCIATES INC

Does everybody love Raymond James & Associates (RJA)? Raymond James Financial hopes so. RJA is that company's primary subsidiary and one of the largest retail brokerages in the US. The unit provides brokerage financial planning investments and related services to consumers. It performs equity and fixed income sales trading and research for institutional clients in North America and Europe. Its investment banking group provides corporate and public finance debt underwriting and mergers and acquisitions advice. RJA also makes markets for approximately 1000 stocks including thinly traded issues. Planning Corporation of America a wholly-owned subsidiary of RJA sells insurance and annuities.

Operations

RJA is engaged in most aspects of securities distribution and investment banking.

Geographic Reach

The company has more than 200 branches and satellite offices concentrated in the Mid-Atlantic Midwest Southeast and Southwest portions of the US in addition to ten institutional sales offices in Europe.

Sales and Marketing

RJA has many big name clients across dozens of industries. In 2013 Titan Medical announced that it has retained RJA to provide advisory services and present options which could include a possible sale.

Strategy

In 2012 the company's parent completed its acquisition of Morgan Keegan & Co. and MK Holding Inc. from Regions Financial Corporation. Some of the equity capital markets and fixed income operations of were integrated into RJA.

EXECUTIVES

Senior Vice President, Charles Stubbs
Vice President, William Wallace
Vice President, Scott Cutliff
Vice President Investments Financial Advisor, Aamsa Zuniga
Vice President Investments, Hall Sumner
Senior Vice President Corporate Risk Management New Products, Tarek Helal
Auditors: KPMG LLP TAMPA FL

LOCATIONS

HQ: RAYMOND JAMES & ASSOCIATES INC
880 CARILLON PKWY, SAINT PETERSBURG, FL 337161100
Phone: 727 567-1000
Web: WWW.RAYMONDJAMES.COM

COMPETITORS

Ameriprise
Charles Schwab
E*TRADE Financial
Edward D. Jones
Edward Jones
FMR
Janney Montgomery Scott
Merrill Lynch
Scottrade
TD Ameritrade
Wells Fargo Advisors

HISTORICAL FINANCIALS

Company Type: Private

Income Statement — FYE: September 30

	ASSETS ($ mil.)	NET INCOME ($ mil.)	INCOME AS % OF ASSETS	EMPLOYEES
09/17	9,917	198	2.0%	10,000
09/16	10,689	145	1.4%	—
09/15	7,893	167	2.1%	—
09/14	6,955	182	2.6%	—
Annual Growth	12.6%	2.8%	—	—

2017 Year-End Financials

Return on assets: 2.0%
Return on equity: 7.8%
Sales ($ mil): 3,255

RAYMOURS FURNITURE COMPANY, INC.

Raymours Furniture is heating up the oft-chilly Northeast doing business as Raymour & Flanigan. The company operates in several states through 94 retail stores including nearly a dozen clearance centers. It sells furniture for just about every room in the house (bedroom dining room home office living room) offering such pieces as bookcases entertainment centers headboards mattresses nightstands recliners sofas and tables. Brands such as Broyhill La-Z-Boy Natuzzi and Tempur Sealy are represented. Raymours is run by founding Goldberg family.

Operations

The company boasts 94 full-line showrooms about a dozen clearance centers 15 customer service centers and four distribution centers in New York New Jersey Pennsylvania Connecticut Massachusetts Delaware and Rhode Island. Raymours also operates more than a dozen customer distribution centers. Its one warehouse property is located in Quakertown Pennsylvania.

Geographic Reach

Based in New York Raymours has become the largest furniture retailer in the Northeast. Through a contractor it provides furniture delivery across the continental US.

Sales and Marketing

Raymours sells its furniture and accessories through its retail stores and online.

Strategy

Following significant expansion in 2008 Raymours has focused in recent years on expanding its presence on the Internet to entice more customers to shop. It added rugs and home decor items such as lamps throw pillows wall art and silk florals to its online furniture catalog. It also extended its furniture delivery area to all states within the continental US through a partnership with a contracted delivery service.

Raymours also expanded its existing partnership with Kathy Ireland Worldwide (led by its namesake model-actress) by adding 10 upholstered pieces to its Kathy Ireland Home furniture collection. The Kathy Ireland pieces are sold exclusively through Raymours.

The company has been expanding its New York distribution center in Rockland County spending some $46 million to purchase and renovate the 839000-sq.-ft. facility which will serve as its primary regional warehouse and distribution hub for the New York New Jersey and Connecticut areas.

In 2015 Raymours purchased the North Oaks Shopping Plaza. The majority of the complex located at 1345 Route 1 South in North Brunswick had been vacant for years. Raymours will become the plaza's new anchor.

Since 2013 Raymours has been prudently adding furniture showrooms in New York one in Brooklyn in 2013 on Fulton Street and another in 2014 in Queens which spans 22000 sq. ft. on multiple levels.

Company Background

Founded in 1947 by brothers Arnold and Bernard Goldberg Raymour & Flanigan is run by president and CEO Neil Goldberg and EVPs Michael and Steven.

EXECUTIVES

Chb, Neil Goldberg
Exec V Pres*, Michael Goldberg
Exec V Pres*, Steven Goldberg
Cfo*, James Poole
Coordinator, Marcelino Berrios
Customer Representativ, Phillip Barnett
Inventory Control Manager, Corin McManus
Home Furnishings Consultant, Brian Brown
Showroom Manager, Corey Tatun
Home Furnishings Consultant, Inez Milligan
Home Furnishings Consultant, Linda Salerno
Auditors: GREEN & SEIFTER SYRACUSE NEW

LOCATIONS

HQ: RAYMOURS FURNITURE COMPANY, INC.
7248 MORGAN RD, LIVERPOOL, NY 130904535
Phone: 315 453-2500
Web: WWW.RAYMOURFLANIGAN.COM

PRODUCTS/OPERATIONS

Selected Products

Accents
Area Rugs
Bedrooms
Dining Rooms
Entertainment
Home Decor
Home Office
Living Rooms
Mattresses
Youth Bedrooms

Selected Brands
Berkline
Bernhardt
Broyhill
Cindy Crawford Home
Kathy Ireland Home
La-Z-Boy
Natuzzi
Rowe
Sealy
Stanley Furniture
Stearns & Foster
Tempur-Pedic

COMPETITORS

ABC Home Furnishings
American Signature
Bassett Furniture
Bob's Discount Furniture Bob's Discount Furnitu
Crawford Furniture
Dillard's
Ethan Allen
Euromarket Designs
Jennifer Convertibles
La-Z-Boy
Room & Board
Rooms To Go
Williams-Sonoma

HISTORICAL FINANCIALS

Company Type: Private

Income Statement — FYE: December 29

	REVENUE ($ mil.)	NET INCOME ($ mil.)	NET PROFIT MARGIN	EMPLOYEES
12/07	881	30	3.4%	6,166
12/06	780	23	3.0%	—
12/05	655	21	3.2%	—
Annual Growth	16.0%	20.2%	—	—

2007 Year-End Financials

Return on assets: 13.5%
Return on equity: 38.1%
Current ratio: 1.50
Cash ($ mil.): —

RDO EQUIPMENT CO.

RDO Equipment has built a business herding Deere in a big way. The company sells and rents new and used trucks and heavy equipment to customers in the agriculture and construction industries. As one of the largest independent dealer of John Deere and Vermeer equipment RDO Equipment operates more than 75 locations in nearly 10 states. Its RDO Truck Centers offer heavy-duty Volvo GMC Isuzu and Mack trucks. RDO Integrated Controls is the company's acquisitive positioning division. RDO Equipment also supplies lawn and garden equipment and provides maintenance and repair services and replacement parts. Ronald Offutt founded the family-owned and operated company in 1968.

Geographic Reach

North Dakota-based RDO Equipment has stores in Arizona California Minnesota Montana Oregon South Dakota Texas and Washington. Outside the US the company operates through partnerships in Africa Australia Mexico Russia and Ukraine.

EXECUTIVES

Chair And Ceo, Christi J. Offutt
Vp Organizational Development, Gean Zimmerman
Evp And Cfo, David Frear
President; Chief Content Officer, Scott Greenstein
Evp With Responsibility For The Company&rsquo, Ryan Offutt
Coo, Chris Cooper
Executive Vice President Serves On The Board Of Directors, Keith Kreps
Executive Vice President Steve Connelly, Jean Zimmerman
Vice President, Ronald Offutt
Vice President, Bradford Freeman
Vice President Of Aftermarket, Terry Tolbert
V. President, Lance Zachariason
Vice President Public Relations And Media Communications, Ken Horner
Secretary And Director, Allan Knoll
Auditors: PRICEWATERHOUSECOOPERS LLP MI

LOCATIONS

HQ: RDO EQUIPMENT CO.
700 7TH ST S, FARGO, ND 581032704
Phone: 701 239-8700
Web: WWW.RDOEQUIPMENT.COM

PRODUCTS/OPERATIONS

Selected Brands

Hitachi
John Deete
Sakai
Topcon
Vermeer
Wirtgen

Selected Products
Balers
Chippers
Combines
Dozers
Drills
Excavators
Planters
Scrapers
Tractors
Trenchers
Wheel loaders

COMPETITORS

Briggs Equipment
Herc Holdings
Home Depot
Komatsu America
Mustang CAT
Scott Equipment

HISTORICAL FINANCIALS

Company Type: Private

Income Statement — FYE: April 30

	REVENUE ($ mil.)	NET INCOME ($ mil.)	NET PROFIT MARGIN	EMPLOYEES
04/20	2,242	48	2.1%	1,500
04/19	2,095	52	2.5%	—
/* 0	0	—	—	
Annual Growth	—	—	—	—

*Fiscal year change

2020 Year-End Financials

Return on assets: 3.3%
Return on equity: 10.0%
Current ratio: 1.80
Cash ($ mil.): 28

READING HOSPITAL

No it's not a square on the game of Monopoly but The Reading Hospital and Medical Center does treat patients in Berks County Pennsylvania and the surrounding area. Operating as Reading Health System the not-for-profit 735-bed medical center provides acute care and rehabilitation programs as well as behavioral and occupational health services. Specialty units include cancer cardiovascular weight management diabetes orthopedic trauma (level II) and women's health centers. In addition to the main hospital the Reading Health System includes Reading Health Rehabilitation Hospital and medical centers in nearby communities as well as laboratory imaging and outpatient centers throughout its region.

Operations

The system also delivers academic clinical training through its School of Health Sciences and Residency programs and operates the 113-acre Highlands at Wyomissing retirement community.

Altogether Reading Health System operates more than 45 locations with roughly 800 combined beds including primary and specialty care centers operated by Reading Health Physician Partners Reading Health Medical Services and the Quick Care and Urgent Care organizations. It employs some 1000 physicians and serves a population of more than 750000 residents. The Reading Health System served about 124400 emergency room patients during 2014; it also handled more than 31000 inpatient discharges and 19000 surgeries.

More than 90% of the company's revenues come from patient care services while residential (rehabilitation) and other services account for the rest.

Geographic Reach

Reading Health System's main hospital campus is located on a 22-building campus on 36 acres in West Reading Pennsylvania.

The system serves Berks County and the surrounding area.

Financial Performance

Reading Health System reported revenues of $901.1 million in fiscal 2014 (ended June) with net income of $62.8 million. Cash flow from operations totaled $30.2 million.

Strategy

Like most other hospitals Reading Health System sees its fair share of uninsured or underinsured patients seeking care at the ER for problems that are often not emergencies which can put a strain on hospital finances. Reading works to divert these patients to its Quick Care and Urgent Care Centers to help reduce some of that burden. The organization is also working to increase the size of its primary care network.

Within the main hospital Reading Health System is working to add new specialists such as interventional neuroradiologists and pediatric hospitalists as well as physicians who specialize in cardiac revascularization and robotic surgery procedures. It is also working to modernize technologies build new facilities and expand partnerships with area health care organizations. For example in 2013 it implemented its Reading HealthConnect electronic health record (EHR) system.

In addition the network broke ground on a $354 million expansion at the main West Reading hospital campus. The facility which is expected to open in 2016 will include new surgery and emergency treatment capacity and will add 150 private patient rooms; the project also includes conversion of existing rooms to private status. In 2015 Reading Health System opened a new family health care center; a new medical facility (featuring primary care physicians' offices imaging services and a laboratory) in Douglassville is also in the works.

Company Background

The Reading Hospital and Medical Center was founded in 1868 as The Reading Dispensary.

EXECUTIVES

Medical Director, Elaine Lewis
Vice President Medical Director, Jerry Malick
Medical Director, Gregory Mokrynski
Auditors: PRICEWATERHOUSECOOPERS LLP PH

LOCATIONS

HQ: READING HOSPITAL
420 S 5TH AVE, READING, PA 196112143
Phone: 484 628-8000
Web: WWW.READING.TOWERHEALTH.ORG

Selected Pennsylvania Operations

The Reading Health Dispensary (Reading)
The Reading Hospital (West Reading)
Reading Health Medical Services
Reading Health Medical Services at Muhlenberg (Reading)
Reading Health Medical Services at Northern Berks (Hamburg)
Reading Health Medical Services at Spring Ridge (Wyomissing)
Reading Health Medical Services at Wyomissing (Wyomissing)
Reading Health Medical Services at Wyomissing Plaza (Reading)
Reading Health Physicians
Reading Health Rehabilitation Hospital (Wyomissing)
QuickCare Centers (regional)
Urgent Care Centers (regional)

Selected Services

Audiology
Behavioral Health Services
Behavioral Medicine Pain Management
Center for Public Health
Chaplaincy Services
Chest Pain Center
Cleft Palate Clinic
Cochlear Implant Program
da Vinci Surgical System
Diabetes Center
Emergency Services
Epilepsy Monitoring Unit
Family Risk Assessment Program (FRAP)
HelpLine
Hospitalist Program
Infusion Center
Interventional Radiology
Laboratory Services
Library Services
Mammography Services
Nutrition Services
Occupational Health Services
Occupational Therapy
Pain Management
Palliative Care Program
Pediatrics - St' Chris Care
PET/CT Imaging
Physical Therapy
QuickCare -Reading Health Physician Network
Radiology Services
Rehabilitation Services
Respiratory Care
Senior Assessment Program
Sleep Center
Social Service
Speech and Hearing Center
Stroke Center
The Reading Hospital Home Care
Tobacco-Free Wellness Program
Travel Immunization Service
Women's Health Services
Wound Healing and Hyperbaric Medicine Center

COMPETITORS

Ascension Health
Doylestown Hospital
LVHN
Lancaster General
Main Line Health System
Moses Taylor Hospital
Sacred Heart Hospital of Allentown
St. Luke's University Health Network
Universal Health Services
University of Pennsylvania Health System
Wyoming Valley Health Care System

HISTORICAL FINANCIALS

Company Type: Private

Income Statement — FYE: June 30

	REVENUE ($ mil.)	NET INCOME ($ mil.)	NET PROFIT MARGIN	EMPLOYEES
06/09	675	42	6.2%	5,500
06/08	640	50	7.8%	—
06/06	783	0	—	—
Annual Growth	—	—	—	—

2009 Year-End Financials

Return on assets: 5.4%
Return on equity: 103.7%
Current ratio: 1.80
Cash ($ mil.): 43

RECKSON OPERATING PARTNERSHIP, L.P.

EXECUTIVES

Pres-Ceo, Marc Holliday
Cfo-Cao-Treas, Matthew J Diliberto
Gen Ptnr, Wyoming Acquisition GP LLC

LOCATIONS

HQ: RECKSON OPERATING PARTNERSHIP, L.P.
420 LEXINGTON AVE, NEW YORK, NY 101700002
Phone: 212 594-2700
Web: WWW.SLGREEN.COM

HISTORICAL FINANCIALS

Company Type: Private

Income Statement — FYE: December 31

	ASSETS ($ mil.)	NET INCOME ($ mil.)	INCOME AS % OF ASSETS	EMPLOYEES
12/18	7,009	199	2.8%	279
12/17	8,541	198	2.3%	—
12/16	8,754	313	3.6%	—
12/15	8,858	362	4.1%	—
Annual Growth	(7.5%)	(18.1%)	—	—

2018 Year-End Financials

Return on assets: 2.8%
Return on equity: 3.2%
Sales ($ mil): 816

RECTOR & VISITORS OF THE UNIVERSITY OF VIRGINIA

The nation's third president Thomas Jefferson founded the University of Virginia in 1819. Named Rector and Visitors of the University of Virginia the university is known as UVa today. It is said to be Jefferson's proudest achievement and boasts an enrollment of about 23800 students throughout its 12 graduate and undergraduate schools. One of the most prestigious public universities in the US the school has been noted for its law program English department and its more than 160-year-old student-enforced conduct code (the Honor System). The school also includes the University of Virginia Health System which trains future doctors and other health care workers at its Medical Center hospital.

Operations

UVa is an agency of the Commonwealth of Virginia governed by the university's Board of Visitors. The university comprises three divisions: the Academic Division the University of Virginia's College at Wise and the Medical Center Division. Its College at Wise focuses on the humanities arts science and professional disciplines concentrating on instruction research and public service. The Medical Center Division offers both routine and ancillary patient services via its full-service hospital and clinics.

The university which has a 14:1 student-faculty ratio employs some 3200 full-time faculty and research staff supported by 14200 full-time staff members. It runs the College and Graduate School of Arts & Sciences Darden School of Business Frank Batten School of Leadership and Public Policy McIntire School of Commerce as well as the School of Architecture School of Continuing & Professional Studies and School of Data Science among its schools. The university has about 16000 undergraduates and about 7800 graduate students.

Geographic Reach

The University of Virginia operates its 12 schools and medical center in Charlottesville while its College at Wise is in the Southwest Virginia town of Wise.

EXECUTIVES

Vp And Cio, James L. Hilton
Dean Darden School Of Business, Robert F. Bruner
Dean Mcintire School Of Commerce, Carl P. Zeithaml
Dean School Of Engineering And Applied Science, James H. Aylor
Dean College And Graduate School Of Arts And Sciences, Meredith J. E. Woo
Dean School Of Nursing, Dorrie K. Fontaine
Dean School Of Law, Paul G. Mahoney
Dean Curry School Of Education, Robert C. Pianta
Dean School Of Medicine, Steven T. (Steve) DeKosky
Evp And Provost, Thomas C. Katsouleas
President, Teresa A. Sullivan
Dean Frank Batten School Of Leadership And Public Policy, Harry Harding
Dean School Of Architecture, Kim Tanzer
Dean School Of Continuing And Professional Studies, Billy K. Cannaday
Dean Undergraduate Admission, Gregory W. Roberts
Chancellor College At Wise, Donna Price Henry
Evp And Coo, Patrick D. Hogan
Vice President, Gertrude Fraser
Associate Vice President And Dean Of Students, Allen Groves
Associate Vice President For Student Affairs, Christina Morell
Vice President Professional Responsibilities, Malcolm Bell
Communication Assistant To The Assistant Vice President For Public Affairs, Charles M Mccance
Vice President, Steve Thornton
Vice Presient Information Technology, Ronald Hutchins
Vice President And Chief Human Resource Officer, Kelley Stuck
Assistant Vice President Financial Planning And Analysis, Nicole Ferretti
Assistant Vice President Financial Operations, Gerald Burke
Assistant Vice President Enterprise Infrastructure, Clayton Lockhart
Assistant Vice President Clery Act Compliance, Gabriel Gates
Assistant Vice President Department, Jeffrey Legro
First Vice President Investments, Nena Brackett
Educator Tcvpo Post Surgery, Judy Smith
Vice President Academic Student Affair, Suttonwallace Pamela
Vice President, Lori Aylor
Executive Vice President Health Affairs, Rick Shannon
Vice President Of Programming, Rachel Vadhan
Vice President, Devon Sherrerd
Vice President Of New Member Education, Caroline Fowler
Assistant Vice President Of New Member Education, Colleen Cox
Vice President Of Finance, Elizabeth Trotta
Assistant Vice President Of Finance, Dani Motte
Vice President Of Communication, Kaitlyn Bryan
Assistant Vice President Of Membership, Jessica Grubbs
Assistant Vice President Of Philanthropic Services, Samantha Adams
Rector, Helen E. Dragas
Vice Rector, George K. Martin
Secretary, Karen Bennett
Treasurer, Bob Bremer
Treasurer, Cindy Penzes
Treasurer, Esther Thatcher
Secretary, Jenny Hinebaugh
Auditors: WALTER J KUTCHARSKI RICHMOND

LOCATIONS

HQ: RECTOR & VISITORS OF THE UNIVERSITY OF VIRGINIA
1001 EMMET ST N, CHARLOTTESVILLE, VA 229034833
Phone: 434 924-0311
Web: WWW.VIRGINIA.EDU

PRODUCTS/OPERATIONS

Selected Schools

College and Graduate School of Arts & Sciences
Curry School of Education
Darden Graduate School of Business Administration
McIntire School of Commerce
School of Architecture
School of Continuing & Professional Studies
School of Engineering and Applied Science
School of Law
School of Medicine
School of Nursing

HISTORICAL FINANCIALS

Company Type: Private

Income Statement — FYE: June 30

	REVENUE ($ mil.)	NET INCOME ($ mil.)	NET PROFIT MARGIN	EMPLOYEES
06/11	1,909	909	47.6%	13,300
06/10	524	97	18.6%	—
06/08	2,181	312	14.3%	—
06/07	2,121	1,114	52.5%	—
Annual Growth	(2.6%)	(5.0%)	—	—

2011 Year-End Financials

Return on assets: 11.4%
Return on equity: 14.5%
Current ratio: 1.40
Cash ($ mil.): 324

REDNER'S MARKETS, INC.

Redner's Markets operates about 45 warehouse club-style supermarkets under the Redner's Warehouse Markets banner and more than a dozen Quick Shoppe convenience stores. Most of the company's stores are located in eastern Pennsylvania but the regional grocer also operates several locations in Maryland and Delaware having closed its one New York supermarket. Redner's Warehouse Markets house bakery deli meat produce and seafood departments as well as in-store banks. The employee-owned company was founded by namesake Earl Redner in 1970. It is still operated by the Redner family including chairman and CEO Richard and COO Ryan Redner.

Financial Performance

Redner's Markets rang up an estimated $865 million in sales in fiscal 2012 (ends September) up from about $859 million in sales the previous year.

Strategy

Redner's has been tinkering with its store portfolio shuttering underperforming locations including several in its core Pennsylvania market while building new stores in existing and new markets. The regional chain has grown to four stores each in Delaware and Maryland since entering those markets in 2008 and 2005 respectively. Redner's is also growing its Web presence doubling its online traffic in the first year of a digiral shopper marketing program conducted in partnership with Google Shopping Network.

EXECUTIVES

Vice President Retail And Perishable Operations, Gary O'Brien
Vice President Human Resources, Robert McDonough
Vice President Purchasing, Dan Eberhart
Vice President And General Counsel, Jason Hopp
Auditors: RKL LLP WYOMISSING PENNSYLV

LOCATIONS

HQ: REDNER'S MARKETS, INC.
3 QUARRY RD, READING, PA 196059787
Phone: 610 926-3700
Web: WWW.REDNERSMARKETS.COM

2012 Warehouse Market Stores

	No.
Pennsylvania	36
Delaware	4
Maryland	4
Total	**44**

PRODUCTS/OPERATIONS

2012 Stores

	No.
Redner's Warehouse Market	44
Quick Shoppe	14
Total	**58**

COMPETITORS

7-Eleven
A&P
Cumberland Farms
Giant Food Stores
Sheetz
Wal-Mart
Wawa Inc.
Wegmans
Weis Markets

HISTORICAL FINANCIALS

Company Type: Private

Income Statement FYE: October 1

	REVENUE ($ mil.)	NET INCOME ($ mil.)	NET PROFIT MARGIN	EMPLOYEES
10/16*	864	4	0.6%	4,800
09/15	884	6	0.7%	—
09/14	902	1	0.2%	—
09/13	892	4	0.5%	—
Annual Growth	(1.1%)	1.8%	—	—

*Fiscal year change

2016 Year-End Financials

Return on assets: 3.0%
Return on equity: 4.0%
Current ratio: 3.40
Cash ($ mil.): 56

REGAL ENTERTAINMENT GROUP

Regal a subsidiary of the Cineworld Group operates one of the largest and most geographically diverse theatre circuits in the United States consisting of over 7200 screens in almost 550 theatres in over 40 states along with American Samoa the District of Columbia Guam and Saipan as of 2019.

Operations

Regal Entertainment offers IMAX RealD RPX ScreenX 4DX Auro and Dolby Atmos.

Geographic Reach

Tennessee-based Regal Entertainment operates in over 40 US states the District of Columbia Guam Saipan and American Samoa. The chain targets midsized metropolitan markets and suburban growth areas of larger cities. It has a large number of theaters in California Florida and New York; those three states together account for nearly a third of Regal Entertainment's locations.

Sales and Marketing

Regal Entertainment employs an interactive marketing program for specific films and concession items to increase attendance and consumption. Its Regal Crown Club loyalty program rewards frequent moviegoers with deals of concessions and more.

The company uses the internet mobile and social media print and multimedia advertising to promote its service. Regal Entertainment conducts special interactive marketing programs for specific films and concessions items.

EXECUTIVES

Vice President Human Resources, Jackie McClure
Chairman And Ceo, Amy E. Miles, $1,024,850 total compensation
Evp General Counsel And Secretary, Peter B. Brandow, $504,700 total compensation
President And Coo, Gregory W. (Greg) Dunn, $612,850 total compensation
Evp Cfo And Treasurer, David H. Ownby, $566,500 total compensation
Vice President, Rob Westerling
Vice President Of Technical Services, Matt Basford
Vice President Of Tax, Chris Frye
Vice President, Alan Davy
Vice President Real Estate, Jerry Grewe
Senior Vice President Of Real Estate, John Roper
Vice President, John Curry
Vice President Film Marketing, Ken Foreman
Treasurer, Chris Dzambo
Auditors: KPMG LLP KNOXVILLE TENNESSEE

LOCATIONS

HQ: REGAL ENTERTAINMENT GROUP
101 E BLOUNT AVE STE 100, KNOXVILLE, TN 379201605
Phone: 865 922-1123
Web: WWW.REGMOVIES.COM

PRODUCTS/OPERATIONS

2017 Sales

	$ mil.	% of total
Admissions	2,008	64
Concessions	930	29
Other	224	7
Total	**3,163**	**100**

Selected Operations

Cinemas
Edwards Theatres
Regal Cinemas
United Artists Theatre Company
Theater advertising
National CineMedia (20%)

COMPETITORS

AMC Entertainment
Alamo Drafthouse
Carmike Cinemas
Cinemark
Cineplex
Landmark Theatres
Marcus Corporation
National Amusements
Netflix
Pacific Theatres
Reading International
Redbox

HISTORICAL FINANCIALS

Company Type: Private

Income Statement FYE: December 31

	REVENUE ($ mil.)	NET INCOME ($ mil.)	NET PROFIT MARGIN	EMPLOYEES
12/17	3,163	112	3.6%	25,359
12/16	3,197	170	5.3%	—
12/15*	3,127	153	4.9%	—
01/15	2,990	105	3.5%	—
Annual Growth	1.9%	2.2%	—	—

*Fiscal year change

2017 Year-End Financials

Return on assets: 999.0%
Return on equity: —
Current ratio: 0.80
Cash ($ mil.): —

REGENTS OF THE UNIVERSITY OF MICHIGAN

Ranking among the top US public universities Regents of the University of Michigan (or simply University of Michigan) boasts more than 64580 students in southeast Michigan. Its three campuses in Ann Arbor Dearborn and Flint offer more than 275 undergraduate and graduate degree programs in fields including architecture education law medicine music and social work. The university has a student to faculty ratio of 15:1. The University of Michigan Health System includes three hospitals and more than 125 health clinics/centers. The university is supported by $12.5 billion endowment.

Operations

The university's about 15 undergraduate schools and colleges offer architecture & urban planning; art & design; business; dental hygiene; education; engineering; information; kinesiology; literature science and the arts (LSA); music theatre & dance; nursing; pharmacy; public health; and public policy. Its seven academic units accept first-year applications: LSA; engineering; architecture & urban planning; art & design; kinesiology; music theatre & dance; and nursing. Its graduate programs include certificate doctoral and master's in the areas of anthropology architecture biophysics business chemical biology and criminal study among others.

Geographic Reach

From its primary campuses in southeast Michigan the university attracts students from more than 80 Michigan counties nearly 50 states and about 140 countries.

Financial Performance

University of Michigan's revenue increased 7% to $8 billion in 2019 from $7.5 billion in 2018. Student tuition and fees sponsored programs patient care revenues and others increased that year.

Cash and cash equivalents at the end of the year were $397.3 million $263.9 million higher from the year prior. Operating activities used $317.9 million in 2019 while investing activities provided $411.3 million from sales and maturities of investments.

Strategy

The University of Michigan aims to serve the people of Michigan and the world through preeminence in creating communicating preserving and applying knowledge art and academic values and in developing leaders and citizens who will change the present and enrich the future.

In late 2020 UM launched a record 31 start-ups in the fiscal year 2020 a 40% increase during a period that included a pandemic and temporarily shuttered labs. U-M inventors went to market with a wide range of discoveries including those from a company using machine learning predictive modeling to help cities like Flint replace their lead-tainted water pipes to another that pivoted from prostate cancer screening to rapid COVID-19 testing during a global health crisis.

The University of Michigan School of Music Theatre & Dance and Grammy Award-winning baritone Thomas Hamson's Hampsong Foundation formed a new partnership to strengthen the work of both organizations in song research vocal performance and education at all levels. This new collaboration strengthened previous work allowing both organizations to amplify the preservation study and practice of song more broadly and in new contexts.

EXECUTIVES

Vp Government Relations, Cynthia H. Wilbanks
Vp Development, Jerry A. May
Chancellor University Of Michigan-dearborn, Daniel Little
Evp And Cfo, Kevin P. Hegarty, age 64
Chairman Victors For Michigan, Stephen M. Ross
President, Mark S. Schlissel
Dean School Of Public Health, Martin Philbert
Vp Information Technology And Cio, Kelli Trosvig
Dean Stamps School Of Art And Design, Gunalan Nadarajan
Dean School Of Dentistry, Laurie McCauley
Dean Law School, Mark D. West
Chancellor University Of Michigan-flint, Susan E. Borrego
Interim Provost And Evp Academic Affairs, Paul N. Courant
Evp Medical Affairs; Dean Medical School; Ceo Michigan Medicine, Marschall S. Runge
Vp And General Counsel, Timothy G. Lynch
Vp Research, S. Jack Hu
Interim Dean Taubman College Of Architecture And Urban Planning, Robert Fishman

Edward J. Frey Dean Ross School Of Business, Scott DeRue
Dean School Of Education, Elizabeth Birr Moje
Dean School Of Engineering, Alec D. Gallimore
Dean School Of Information, Thomas A. Finholt
Dean School Of Kinesiology, Lori Ploutz-Snyder
Dean College Of Literature Science And The Arts, Andrew D. Martin
Dean College Of Music Theatre And Dance, Aaron Dworkin
Interim Dean School Of Natural Resources And Environment, Dan Brown
Dean School Of Nursing, Patricia D. Hurn
Dean College Of Pharmacy, James T. Dalton
Dean School Of Social Work, Lynn Videka
Dean Rackham Graduate School; Vice Provost Academic Affairs Graduate Studies, Carol A. Fierke
Vice President Research, Stephen Forrest
Associate Vice President And Executive Director For Research Administration, Marvin Parnes
Associate Vice President Development, Julie Sparkman
Vice President Marketing, Rachelle Caoagas
Assistant Vice President Estate, Diane Tracy
Associate Vice President Facilities And Operations, Henry D Baier
Vice President Marketing, Fred Howard
Vice President Client Team Leader, Andrew Crawford
Associate Vice President For Research Douvan Collegiate Professor Of Psychology Research Professor, Toni Antonucci
Vice President Of Technology, Trung Nguyen
Vice President Technology, Jamila Power
Vice President Technology, Mehra Rohit
Clinical Director, Donn Hilker
First Vice President, Rob Geer
Vice President Of Administration, Andy White
Vice President For Finance, Kelli Pape
Vice President Student Government Budget Allocations Committee, Mackenzie Swart
Director Of Admissions And Orientation, Deb Peffer
Vice President Of Sales, Bill Bobrowsky
Vice President Finance Technology, William Hausman
Vice President For Research University Administration, Linda Wilson
Associate Vice President And Deputy General Counsel, Kara Morgenstern
Int Assistant Vice President Academic Human Resources, Donna Lartigue
Vice President, Erik J Rebbe
Vice President In Operations, William Chan
Vice President Finance, Kevin Kuo
Interim Vp Information Technology And Cio, Andrew Rosenberg
Director Of Clinical Services And Research; Assistant Professor Of Psychiatry, Renee Hoste
Vice President Program Delivery, Dave Schueler
Interim Vice President For Communications, Kate Michael
Vice President Of Finance, Morgan Slaff
Uofm Emba Vice President, Eric James Forster
Vice President, Mohammed Islam
Vice President Finance, Dennis Diebolt
Dsp Xi Vice President Of Alumni Relations, Moynawk Gangopadhyay
Vice President, Amani Echols
Vice President Beta Alpha Psi, Emily Wolney
Vice President Of Projects Net Impact Advanced Fellow, Charlene Franke
Medical Director, Darrell Campbell
Vice President, Olivia Herron
Vice President And Corporate Counsel, Gael Tisack
Vice President, Shiuh Lee
Vice President, Beatrice Thaman
Vp Of Women In Mathematics, Vijita Kamath
Vice President, Margaret Perrett
Vice President, Robert Carter
External Vice President, Erika Chow
Investment Banking Vice President, Vikram Chandrasekaran
Vice President, Seth Kaufman
Vice President, Andrew Odesky
Vice President, Faye Racovitis
Vice President, Yervant Demirjian
Medical Director, William Kennedy
Vice President, Debra Thomas-darke
Vice President: Finance, Caroline Kelly
Vice President, Adam Oakley
Vice President Of Communications, Ally Reis
Vice President Of Social Responsibility, Alexander Krupiak
Vice President For Global Communications And Strategic Initiatives, Debbie Serwach
Vice President Of Finance, Nizamuddin Alavi
Vice President, Martha McKinnon
Vice President, Georga Armstrong
Vice President Sales, Chris Wallbank
Director Of Pharmacy, Mike Dabaja
Vice President, Colleen Crouch
Vice President Finance, Chris Winkelmann
Vice President Internal Operations, Ethan Tubbs
Vice President Public Relations, Ashton Russo
Vice President Of Membership, Stav Nachum
Vice President, Adam Greer
Vice President, Kyra Fleming
Vice President Strategy, Elif Sagsen-ercel
Vice Chairman, Michael J. Behm
Chairman, Mark J. Bernstein
Program Secretary, Frances Liao
Senior Business Analyst Treasurers Office Department, Kristopher Covietz
Secretary, Jeff Evans
Secretary Iv Law School Department, LauraA Shiltz
Secretary Iii Department Of Family Medicine Department, SophiaS Scoma
Board Member, Shary Balius
Board Member, Neil Elkin
Secretary Office Of Early Childhood Education And Family Services, Martin Stroud
Secretary, Mary Burton
Secretary Iii, Qiana London
Treasurer, Eleonore Edgell
Senior Secretary, Andrew Mcintyre
Secretary Iv, Allisssa Ebenhoeh
Secretary B Temp Flint Ecdc, Kristina Russo
Secretary Of The University Office Of, Roberta Ruth Palmer
Secretary Senior, Debra Most
Lead Secretary, Amber French
Board Member, Ellen Toronto
Assistant Secretary Of The University, Erin Katz
Secretary Office Of The Vice President For Government Relations, Jill Crane
Board Member, John White
Secretary, Sara VanLooy
Treasurer, Kathleen Ropella
Theta Delta Chi Treasurer And Executive Board, Brandon Goethals
Treasurer, Theodore Zimbo
Treasurer, Chris Attar
Treasurer, Gabrielle Zimbler
Secretary, Jill Katic
Secretary, Alison Bradley
Board Member, Andrew Noh
Auditors: PRICEWATERHOUSECOOPERS LLP DE

LOCATIONS

HQ: REGENTS OF THE UNIVERSITY OF MICHIGAN
503 THOMPSON ST, ANN ARBOR, MI 481091340
Phone: 734 764-1817
Web: WWW.UMICH.EDU

PRODUCTS/OPERATIONS

Selected Academic Units
Architecture and urban planning
Art and design
Business administration
Dentistry
Education
Engineering
Kinesiology
Law
Literature science and the arts
Medicine
Music
Natural resources and environment
Nursing
Pharmacy
Public health
Public policy
Social work

HISTORICAL FINANCIALS

Company Type: Private

Income Statement — FYE: June 30

	REVENUE ($ mil.)	NET INCOME ($ mil.)	NET PROFIT MARGIN	EMPLOYEES
06/20	7,955	(276)	—	34,624
06/19	7,989	522	6.5%	—
06/18	7,466	920	12.3%	—
06/17	7,079	1,275	18.0%	—
Annual Growth	4.0%	—	—	—

2020 Year-End Financials

Return on assets: (-1.1%)
Return on equity: (-1.9%)
Current ratio: 1.70
Cash ($ mil.): 1,284

REGIONAL TRANSPORTATION AUTHORITY

EXECUTIVES

Exec Dir, Richard J Bacigalupo
Chb, Thomas J McCraken Jr
Dep Exec Dir-Cfo, Joseph G Costello
Treas, Allan Sharkey
Prin, Julie Gomez
Prin, Carole Brown
Manager, Roxann Galvan
Director, Michael Vandekreke
Senior Financial Analyst, Alejandro Montero
Accountant, Anita Anderson
Programmer Analyst, Xiaoni Wu
Auditors: RSM US LLP CHICAGO ILLINOIS

LOCATIONS

HQ: REGIONAL TRANSPORTATION AUTHORITY
175 W JACKSON BLVD # 1650, CHICAGO, IL 606042711
Phone: 312 913-3200
Web: WWW.RTACHICAGO.ORG

HISTORICAL FINANCIALS

Company Type: Private

Income Statement — FYE: December 31

	REVENUE ($ mil.)	NET INCOME ($ mil.)	NET PROFIT MARGIN	EMPLOYEES
12/19	618	(102)	—	80
12/16	637	(99)	—	—
12/15	805	(77)	—	—
12/14	755	(3)	—	—
Annual Growth	(3.9%)	—	—	—

2019 Year-End Financials

Return on assets: (-12.0%)
Return on equity: —
Current ratio: 1.70
Cash ($ mil.): 123

REGIONS HOSPITAL

EXECUTIVES

Pres, Megan Remark
Hematologist Oncologist, Balkrishna N Jahagirdar
Lab Technician, Becky Green
Director PA Residency, Bradley Hernandez
Emergency Medicine Specialist, Casey M Woster
Hematologist Oncologist, Colleen Morton
Trauma Program Manager Coordin, Heidi Altamirano
Director of Risk Management, Jeremy Sundheim
Neurosurgeon, Jon I McIver
Chief Engineer, Josh Knoll
Senior Manager, Michaela Timmers
Auditors: KPMG LLP MINNEAPOLIS MINNESO

LOCATIONS

HQ: REGIONS HOSPITAL
640 JACKSON ST, SAINT PAUL, MN 551012595
Phone: 651 254-3456
Web: WWW.REGIONSHOSPITAL.COM

HISTORICAL FINANCIALS

Company Type: Private

Income Statement — FYE: December 31

	REVENUE ($ mil.)	NET INCOME ($ mil.)	NET PROFIT MARGIN	EMPLOYEES
12/19	847	52	6.2%	21
12/14	636	40	6.4%	—
Annual Growth	5.9%	5.3%	—	—

2019 Year-End Financials

Return on assets: 5.4%
Return on equity: 8.5%
Current ratio: 3.10
Cash ($ mil.): 184

REGIONS HOSPITAL

Auditors: KPMG LLP MINNEAPOLIS MN

LOCATIONS

HQ: REGIONS HOSPITAL
8170 33RD AVE S, MINNEAPOLIS, MN 554254516
Phone: 952 883-6280
Web: WWW.HEALTHPARTNERS.COM

HISTORICAL FINANCIALS

Company Type: Private

Income Statement — FYE: December 31

	REVENUE ($ mil.)	NET INCOME ($ mil.)	NET PROFIT MARGIN	EMPLOYEES
12/19	847	52	6.2%	47
12/17	790	47	6.0%	—
12/14	691	40	5.9%	—
12/09	515	17	3.4%	—
Annual Growth	5.1%	11.5%	—	—

2019 Year-End Financials

Return on assets: 5.4%
Return on equity: 8.5%
Current ratio: 3.10
Cash ($ mil.): 184

REGIONS HOSPITAL FOUNDATION

If you live around the Twin Cities Regions Hospital can help with your medical needs. The not-for-profit hospital has more than 450 beds and provides acute medical and emergency care services as well as specialty programs in areas including behavioral health rehabilitation burn care cancer cardiovascular orthopedic pediatrics and women's care. Regions Hospital is one of a handful of level I trauma centers in Minnesota and is also a teaching and residency center for the University of Minnesota Medical School. Regions Hospital is part of HealthPartners which operates a network of medical centers and a health plan in the Twin Cities area.

Operations

In 2012 Regions Hospital operated at a 78% occupancy rate with some 25000 inpatient visits. It also handled 78000 emergency center visits 13000 surgeries and some 2500 births. It has about 650 physicians on its staff plus another 800 affiliated doctors who are members of the HealthPartners Medical Group physician practice organization.

The hospital provided some $56 million in community benefits during 2012 including charity care and outreach programs.

Geographic Reach

Regions Hospital serves the St. Paul Minnesota metropolitan area as well as patients from other areas across Minnesota and in western Wisconsin. It also sees visitors from other Midwest states.

Strategy

The hospital has expanded its facilities in recent years to meet the demands of a growing Twin Cities population and address certain underserved community health needs. For instance in 2012 Regions Hospital completed construction of a new $36 million eight-story inpatient mental health center with about 100 beds designed to replace its aging mental health facility. In addition in 2009 the hospital wrapped up a $180 million expansion and renovation project that gave it a new 10-story patient tower with 20 new operating rooms more than 35 private patient beds and shell space for further expansion in the future.

In addition the hospital looks to enhance services through new equipment and procedural offerings as well as through partnerships with other area providers.

Company Background

Established in 1872 Regions Hospital became part of the HealthPartners network in 1993.

EXECUTIVES

Pres, Brock Nelson
Cfo*, Greg Klugherz
Internist, Matthew Turner
Admin Secretary Surgical Servi, Monica Knack
Vice President of Human Resour, Alicia Gilbert
Vice President Affa, Bret Haake
Vice President of Patient Care, Chris Boese
Staff, Deb Kelly
Vice President, Heidi Conrad
Vice President of Care Deliver, Kari Toft
Vice President of Regions Hosp, Keevan Kosidowski

LOCATIONS

HQ: REGIONS HOSPITAL FOUNDATION
640 JACKSON ST, SAINT PAUL, MN 551012595
Phone: 651 254-3456
Web: WWW.REGIONSHOSPITAL.COM

PRODUCTS/OPERATIONS

Selected Specialties and Divisions

Behavioral Health
Birth Center
Breast Health Center
Burn Center
Cancer Care Center
Center for Dementia and Alzheimer's Care
Digestive Care Center
Emergency Center
Heart Center
Level I Trauma Center
Level I Pediatric Trauma Center
Neurosciences
Orthopedics
Palliative Care Unit
Rehabilitation Institute
Spine Center
Stroke Center
Surgery Center

COMPETITORS

Allina Hospitals
Amery Regional Medical Center
Catholic Health Initiatives
CentraCare Health
Children's Hospitals and Clinics of Minnesota
Fairview Health
Gillette Children's
HealthEast Care System
Mayo Clinic
North Memorial Health Care
Olmsted Medical
Paynesville Area Healthcare System

HISTORICAL FINANCIALS

Company Type: Private

Income Statement — FYE: December 31

	REVENUE ($ mil.)	NET INCOME ($ mil.)	NET PROFIT MARGIN	EMPLOYEES
12/12	581	36	6.3%	3,000
12/06	413	4	1.0%	—
12/05	430	12	2.8%	—
12/04	7	0	0.0%	—
Annual Growth	71.3%	320.5%	—	—

2012 Year-End Financials

Return on assets: 6.2%
Return on equity: 6.3%
Current ratio: 1.70
Cash ($ mil.): 64

RESEARCH TRIANGLE INSTITUTE INC

The scientists at Research Triangle Institute address the problems of a sphere (the planet). Operating mainly under its trade name RTI International (RTI) the not-for-profit enterprise conducts research in such areas as advanced technologies environmental resources and medicine. It provides such services and materials testing as well as software used in laboratories and research projects. Serving the US federal government other governments nonprofits and for-profit companies RTI offers analytical perspectives on public policy and has researchers working in offices around the world.

Operations

The company offers analytical perspectives on public policy. Its staff members represent more than 90 nationalities and speak approximately 90 languages enabling RTI to communicate and collaborate effectively with peer researchers clients and stakeholders around the world.

The company delivers independent objective and scientifically rigorous research development and technical services to support projects around the world. With renowned experts state-of-the-art facilities and proven approaches the company applies its capabilities across key practice areas (education and workforce development energy research environmental sciences food security and agriculture health innovation ecosystems and international development) that intersect with the needs of its clients including government agencies academia foundations global NGOs and commercial companies.

Geographic Reach

North Carolina-based RTI serves clients in more than 75 countries. It has nearly 15 US offices and offices in Canada China El Salvador India Indonesia Kenya Malaysia Spain Sweden the UAE and the UK.

Sales and Marketing

The organization works with clients in government academia foundations global NGOs and commercial companies. RTI's main clients are the Department of Health and Human Services and the US Agency for International Development. RTI's some private sector clients have included Abbott Chevron Nielsen PTC Therapeutics and The Hershey Company among others.

Strategy

RTI delivers reliable data thorough analysis innovative methods novel technologies and sustainable programs that help clients inform public policy and ground practice in evidence. RTI made several strategic partnerships and acquisitions for growth in recent years. In late 2019 RTI invested in BioIQ a healthcare engagement and gap closure company. The relationship will further BioIQ's health plan member engagement outcomes and both organizations' objectives to improve the human condition. RTI also partnered with USAID to conduct a two-year research project in Somalia; as well as with Shatterproof to launch an online platform to help people find quality addiction treatment called ATLAS with both partnerships made in 2020.

In addition RTI acquired Medical Data Analytics (MDA) in early 2020. The acquisition expands existing services of the RTI Health Solutions business unit in the design and conduct of observational research with MDA's capabilities in data collection and management and physician and site recruitment.

Mergers and Acquisitions

In early 2020 RTI has closed its acquisition of Medical Data Analytics (MDA) a provider of real-world evidence (RWE) generation to the pharmaceutical and biotechnology industry. The acquisition expands existing services of the RTI Health Solutions business unit in design and conduct of observational research with MDA's capabilities in data collection and management and physician and site recruitment. Deal terms were not disclosed.

EXECUTIVES

Evp And Coo, James J. (Jim) Gibson
Evp Rti Health Solutions, Allen W. Mangel
President And Ceo, E. Wayne Holden
Evp International Development Group, Aaron S. Williams
Evp Social Statistical And Environmental Sciences, Timothy J. (Tim) Gabel
Evp And Cfo, Michael H. (Mike) Kaelin
Chair Fellow Program And Distinguished Fellow Early Childhood Development, Don Bailey
Unit Vice President, John Mitchell
Vice President Contracts, Mary Reiss
Vice President, Chris Buchholtz
Vice President Research Services, Howard Speizer
Executive Vice President International Development, Paul Weisenfeld
Vice President And Head Of Corporate Development, Matt Jenkins
Vice President Division For Research On Healthcare Value Equity And The Lifespan, Robin Weinick
Vice President, Justin Eiler
Vice President, Sam Field
Vice Chairman, Peter M. Scott
Chairman, William M. Moore
Auditors: DELOITTE & TOUCHE LLP RALEIGH

LOCATIONS

HQ: RESEARCH TRIANGLE INSTITUTE INC
3040 CORNWALLIS RD, DURHAM, NC 277090155
Phone: 919 541-6000
Web: WWW.RTI.ORG

PRODUCTS/OPERATIONS

Selected Research Areas

Advanced technology research and development
Drug discovery and development
Economic and social
Education and training
Energy
Environmental
Health
International development
Laboratory and chemistry
Statistics
Survey

COMPETITORS

Battelle Memorial
QSS Group
Sandford Burnham Institute
Urban Institute

HISTORICAL FINANCIALS

Company Type: Private

Income Statement — FYE: September 30

	REVENUE ($ mil.)	NET INCOME ($ mil.)	NET PROFIT MARGIN	EMPLOYEES
09/17	972	22	2.4%	3,117
09/16	884	15	1.8%	—
09/15	831	40	4.9%	—
09/14	788	31	4.0%	—
Annual Growth	7.2%	(10.4%)	—	—

2017 Year-End Financials

Return on assets: 3.3%
Return on equity: 5.5%
Current ratio: 2.10
Cash ($ mil.): 29

REX HEALTHCARE, INC.

Part of the UNC HealthCare System UNC REX Healthcare is a not-for-profit health care provider that serves residents of Raleigh and the rest of Wake County North Carolina. Founded in 1894 UNC REX Healthcare includes the more than 430-bed acute-care Rex Hospital and two nursing homes with nearly 230 beds as well as primary and specialty care clinics throughout the area. Specialty centers and clinics provide services such as birthing cancer treatment same-day surgery heart and vascular care pain management and sleep disorder therapy. UNC REX also provides home health and mobile emergency medical services. UNC HealthCare also includes affiliate UNC Hospitals.

Operations

The health care system employs a medical staff of more than 1100 physicians and 1700 nurses. Its operations consist of an acute care hospital five wellness centers a pair of skilled nursing facilities (for rehabilitation and long-term nursing care) six suburban campuses and freestanding outpatient diagnostic urgent care and surgery centers.

Each year Rex has approximately 34000 in-patient visits 6000 births 30000 surgeries and 58000 emergency room visits.

Geographic Reach

UNC REX operates facilities in Wake County North Carolina in the cities of Apex Cary Garner Holly Springs Knightdale Wakefield and Raleigh.

Financial Performance

In 2015 net patient service revenue increased 14% to $814 million largely due to higher amounts of cardiovascular and oncology care provided. Operating income rose to $42 million and net income totaled $4 million.

Strategy

The company's venture capital investment fund REX Health Ventures was established to invest in researchers entrepreneurs and inventors and to support start-up companies.

In late 2014 UNC REX began construction on its new $200 million eight-story cardiac care tower. The following year it opened a new breast surgery clinic; it plans to open a new vascular disease center as well.

EXECUTIVES

Vice President Physician, Bob Ricker
Coo, Susan Sandberg
Svp Cfo And Interim Cio, Bernadette Spong
Vp Rex Healthcare Foundation, Sylvia Hackett
Coo, Steve Burriss
Vp Surgical Services, Jane Byrd
Vp Medical Affairs Chief Medical Officer And Chief Medical Information Officer, Linda Butler
Cfo, Andrew Zukowski
Vp Patient Care Services And Chief Nursing Officer, Joel Ray
Director Of Pharmacy, Jane Green
Medical Director Respiratory Therapy Program, Rohit Ahuja
Medical Director Of Bariatric Surgery, Lindsey Sharp
Vice President, Debbie Marshall
Chairman, A. Dale Jenkins
Unit Secretary, Annette Laster

Unit Secretary, Melody Adams
Secretary, Dorvetta Ford
Auditors: CLIFTON LARSON ALLEN LLP CHAR

LOCATIONS

HQ: REX HEALTHCARE, INC.
4420 LAKE BOONE TRL, RALEIGH, NC 276077505
Phone: 919 784-3100
Web: WWW.REXHEALTH.COM

PRODUCTS/OPERATIONS

Selected Specialty Services

Oncology
Heart and vascular
Surgical Services: Bariatric Heartburn and GI
Orthopedic Neuro and Spine
Rehabilitation
Emergency and Urgent Care
Women's Services
Wound Healing

COMPETITORS

Carolinas HealthCare System
Cone Health
Cumberland County Hospital System
Danville Regional Medical Center
Duke University Health System
FirstHealth of the Carolinas
Morehead Memorial Hospital
Novant Health
Vidant Health
WakeMed

HISTORICAL FINANCIALS

Company Type: Private

Income Statement — FYE: June 30

	REVENUE ($ mil.)	NET INCOME ($ mil.)	NET PROFIT MARGIN	EMPLOYEES
06/20	1,180	(2)	—	5,500
06/13	731	8	1.2%	—
06/12	719	34	4.8%	—
06/11	1,669	0	—	—
Annual Growth	—	—	—	—

2020 Year-End Financials

Return on assets: (-0.2%)
Return on equity: (-0.4%)
Current ratio: 2.30
Cash ($ mil.): 430

REX HOSPITAL, INC.

EXECUTIVES

Pres, Steve Burriss
Vp Legal Affairs, Tate Bombard
Vp Medical Affairs/ Cmo, Linda Butler
Vp/Rex Healthcare Foundation, Sylvia Hackett
Vp Patient Care Services / Cno, Joel Ray
Vp Physician Services, Bob Ricker
Vp Heart & Vascular Services, Kirsten Riggs
Ccmo, Lisa Schiller
Vp, Tammie Stanton
Vp Regional Hospitalist Servic, Sean Tehrani
Vp Ambulatory Services, Tom Williams

LOCATIONS

HQ: REX HOSPITAL, INC.
4420 LAKE BOONE TRL, RALEIGH, NC 276076599
Phone: 919 784-3100
Web: WWW.REXHEALTH.COM

HISTORICAL FINANCIALS

Company Type: Private

Income Statement — FYE: June 30

	REVENUE ($ mil.)	NET INCOME ($ mil.)	NET PROFIT MARGIN	EMPLOYEES
06/16	904	106	11.8%	3,500
06/15	813	4	0.5%	—
06/14	724	25	3.6%	—
06/13	701	7	1.0%	—
Annual Growth	8.9%	145.0%	—	—

2016 Year-End Financials

Return on assets: 10.9%
Return on equity: 25.0%
Current ratio: 1.50
Cash ($ mil.): 91

RHODE ISLAND HOSPITAL

EXECUTIVES

Ceo, Margaret Van Bree
Svp-Cno*, Cynthia Danner
Director of Laboratory, Marilyn McAllister
Associate Director, Nicholas Ward
Doctor, Andrew Maslow
Doctor, Ronald A Delellis
Coordinator, Ann Roberto
Doctor, James M Klinger
Chief of Medicine, John Murphy
Coordinator, Marna Jones
Doctor, Andrew Cohen

LOCATIONS

HQ: RHODE ISLAND HOSPITAL
593 EDDY ST, PROVIDENCE, RI 029034923
Phone: 401 444-4000
Web: WWW.HASBROCHILDRENSHOSPITAL.ORG

HISTORICAL FINANCIALS

Company Type: Private

Income Statement — FYE: September 30

	REVENUE ($ mil.)	NET INCOME ($ mil.)	NET PROFIT MARGIN	EMPLOYEES
09/14	1,016	(5)	—	6,400
09/13	1,048	49	4.7%	—
09/07	918	110	12.0%	—
Annual Growth	1.5%	—	—	—

2014 Year-End Financials

Return on assets: (-0.5%)
Return on equity: (-1.2%)
Current ratio: 1.70
Cash ($ mil.): 32

RICELAND FOODS, INC.

Handling more than 110 million bushels of grain a year Riceland Foods is ingrained in its business. The agricultural cooperative processes and markets the rice soybeans and wheat. Each grains are grown in the US and then shipped to its locations in Missouri and Arkansas to be stored and milled. One of the world's largest rice millers it sells white and brown rice plus flavored rices and meal kits under the Riceland and private-label brands. The co-op sells to food retailers and food service and food manufacturing companies worldwide. Riceland also makes cooking oils and processes soybeans bran and lecithin and offers rice bran and hulls to pet food makers and livestock farmers as feed and bedding.

Operations

Riceland's Research and Technical Center (Stuttgart Arkansas) is staffed by scientists and technicians with experience in rice edible oil and lecithin chemistry applications and process engineering.

The facility houses separate soybean and rice research laboratories to conduct product development product and process improvement and customer support. Riceland's business lines are supported by on-site analytical food applications and regulatory compliance labs consumer and foodservice test kitchens and a well-equipped pilot plant. An ongoing research program reinforces Riceland's position as a premier supplier of rice edible oils and lecithin.

In addition to being a leader in rice milling the cooperative is a major soybean processor. Indeed its soybean processing plant in Stuttgart provides high-protein soybean meal and soybean mill run for almost 60 years to many Mid-South and Southwestern feed mills and livestock producers along with shipping raw soybeans for the export market. From raw unprocessed soybeans to soybean feed ingredients Riceland offers a full range of industrial soy products.

Geographic Reach

Arkansas-based Riceland provides marketing services to farmers in its home state. Each grain is proudly grown in the rich soils of the US. It is then shipped to the heartland to be stored and milled at our locations in Missouri and Arkansas.

Riceland markets rice products under the Riceland label private labels as ingredients and in bulk. Riceland's products are sold across the US and in more than 75 foreign destinations.

Sales and Marketing

A major rice exporter and edible oil producer Riceland markets its rice and oil products under the Riceland and Chefway (vegetable oil and shortening) labels.

Rice and oil products are supplied to many of America's leading restaurants fast-food chains cafeterias and military installations. Packaged and flavored rice products are marketed under the Riceland brand. Vegetable oil and shortening products are sold under Riceland and private label brands. Soybeans are sold to US buyers.

EXECUTIVES

Ceo, Danny Kennedy
Auditors: BKD LLP LITTLE ROCK ARKANSA

LOCATIONS

HQ: RICELAND FOODS, INC.
2120 S PARK AVE, STUTTGART, AR 721606822
Phone: 870 673-5500
Web: WWW.RICELAND.COM

PRODUCTS/OPERATIONS

Selected Products

Consumer
Saffron Yellow Rice Mix
Rice N Easy Mix Wild Rice
Long Grain & Wild Mix Rice N Easy Mix
Broccoli & Cheese Rice N Easy Mix
Spanish Rice Mix Rice N Easy Mix
Chicken Rice Mix Rice N Easy Mix
Long Grain Rice Riceland Extra Long Grain Rice
Riceland GOLD Perfected Rice
Riceland Jasmine Rice

Riceland Natural Brown Rice
Riceland Plump & Tender Medium Grain Rice
Food Service
Oil
Rice
Food Ingredients
Long grain milled rice
Long grain brown rice
Medium grain milled rice
Parboiled rice
Broken grains

COMPETITORS

AarhusKarlshamn
American Rice
CHS
Cereal Byproducts
Connell Company
Ebro Foods
Farmers Rice Milling
Farmers' Rice Cooperative
Goya
JFC International
Lotus Foods
Louis Dreyfus Group
Producers Rice Mill
Riviana Foods
Specialty Rice

HISTORICAL FINANCIALS

Company Type: Private

Income Statement — FYE: July 31

	REVENUE ($ mil.)	NET INCOME ($ mil.)	NET PROFIT MARGIN	EMPLOYEES
07/17	941	0	0.0%	1,646
07/16	1,007	5	0.6%	—
07/15	1,122	9	0.9%	—
07/14	1,148	2	0.2%	—
Annual Growth	(6.4%)	(54.4%)	—	—

2017 Year-End Financials

Return on assets: —
Return on equity: 0.1%
Current ratio: 3.10
Cash ($ mil.): 2

RICH PRODUCTS CORPORATION

Starting in 1945 with "the miracle cream from the soya bean" Rich Products has grown from a niche maker of soy-based whipped toppings and frozen desserts to a leading global US frozen foods maker. The family-owned business has developed other products such as toppings and icings and Coffee Rich (nondairy coffee creamer). It has expanded its product line to include frozen bakery and pizza doughs and ingredients for the food service and in-store bakery markets plus appetizers and snacks (Farm Rich) baked goods frozen ice cream cakes (Carvel) seafood (SeaPak) meatballs and barbecue meat.

Operations

Rich Products offers cakes desserts and bakery products; breads and rolls; pizza and flatbreads; seafood appetizers and snacks; and gluten-free and plant-based items.

Geographic Reach

United States-based Rich Products has operations in North America Asia Latin America Europe Africa Australia and Middle East.

EXECUTIVES

Vice President Finance, Mary Kiener
President And Ceo, William G. (Bill) Gisel
Evp Sales And Marketing, Kevin R. Malchoff
President Rich's Entertainment Group, Melinda R. (Mindy) Rich
Executive Vp Chief Financial Officer, James R. (Jim) Deuschle
Executive Vp Chief Operating Officer, Richard M. Ferranti
Vice President Of National Account Sales, Paul J Rich
Executive Vice President, Dwight Gram
Vice President Engineering, Tim Falken
Senior Vice President Of Operations, Dave Konst
Vice President, Marty Hurley
Executive Vice President, Edward Moore
Vice President Marketing, Deborah Andrews
Senior Vice President, Paul Klein
Senior Vice President Customer Experience, Ted Rich
National Account Manager, Tony Murphy
National Sales Manager, Susan Duran
National Account Manager, Tamara Boyer
Senior Vice President Global Supply Chain, David Cowperthwait
Vice President Of Finance, Eric Eynon
Assistant To Thomas R Greco Executive Vice President And Cco Pepsi, Sharon Delozier
Vice President Of Strategic Technology, Joel Cristall
Vice President, Matthew Wilson
Vice President Of Sales, Margaret Russo
Chairman, Robert E. (Bob) Rich

LOCATIONS

HQ: RICH PRODUCTS CORPORATION
1 ROBERT RICH WAY, BUFFALO, NY 142131701
Phone: 716 878-8000
Web: WWW.RICHS.COM

PRODUCTS/OPERATIONS

Selected Product Categories

Appetizers and snacks
Bakery products
BBQ
Breads and rolls
Cakes & desserts
Cooking creams
Gluten-free and all-natural
Meatballs and pasta
Pizza
Shrimp and seafood
Syrups and soaked cakes
Toppings and icings

Selected Consumer Brands

Byron's
Carvel
Casa
Coffee Rich
Farm Rich
Freal
French Meadow Bakery
Rich's
SeaPak

COMPETITORS

BakeMark
Campbell Soup
Canada Bread Company
ConAgra
Dawn Food Products
Dean Foods
General Mills
Gonnella Baking
Gorton's
Heinz
Hom/Ade Foods
Nestlé
Pinnacle Foods
Schwan's
Windsor Foods

HISTORICAL FINANCIALS

Company Type: Private

Income Statement — FYE: December 31

	REVENUE ($ mil.)	NET INCOME ($ mil.)	NET PROFIT MARGIN	EMPLOYEES
12/12	2,858	0	—	10,536
12/11	2,736	0	—	—
12/10	2,465	0	—	—
Annual Growth	7.7%	—	—	—

RITE-HITE HOLDING CORPORATION

EXECUTIVES

Chb-Ceo, Michael H White
Pres*, Mark Petri
V Pres*, Clem Maslowski
Cfo*, Mark S Kirkish
Engineer, Norbert Hahn
Senior Programmer Analyst, Louis Lieberman
Vice President Manager Directo, Ellen Kosidowski
Valuation Manager, Kevin Krug
Production Control Supervisor, Kelly Palmer
Senior Technical Anal, Jason Carter
Operations Manager, Mike Trump

LOCATIONS

HQ: RITE-HITE HOLDING CORPORATION
8900 N ARBON DR, MILWAUKEE, WI 532232451
Phone: 414 355-2600
Web: WWW.RITEHITE.COM

HISTORICAL FINANCIALS

Company Type: Private

Income Statement — FYE: December 31

	REVENUE ($ mil.)	NET INCOME ($ mil.)	NET PROFIT MARGIN	EMPLOYEES
12/19	767	0	—	1,000
12/18	779	0	—	—
12/05	274	0	—	—
Annual Growth	7.6%	—	—	—

RIVER CITY PETROLEUM, INC.

EXECUTIVES

Ceo, Jeanne Haskell
Cfo*, Kurt Schmidl
Customer Staff, Lydia Castellanos
Coordinator, Jeremy Bautista
Information Technology, Chris Gaither
Assistant, Kreidler John
Assistant Staff Accountant, Macie Wightman
General Manager, Brad Folkins
Assistant Credit Manager, John Kreidler
Government Affairs Manager, Cindy Moua
Auditors: BFBA LLP SACRAMENTO CALIFOR

LOCATIONS

HQ: RIVER CITY PETROLEUM, INC.
3775 N FREEWAY BLVD # 101, SACRAMENTO, CA 958341959
Phone: 916 371-4960
Web: WWW.RCPFUEL.COM

HISTORICAL FINANCIALS

Company Type: Private

Income Statement FYE: December 31

	REVENUE ($ mil.)	NET INCOME ($ mil.)	NET PROFIT MARGIN	EMPLOYEES
12/13	655	1	0.2%	55
12/12	579	1	0.2%	—
12/11	656	2	0.4%	—
Annual Growth	(0.1%)	(34.5%)	—	—

2013 Year-End Financials

Return on assets: 2.1%
Return on equity: 6.0%
Current ratio: 1.30
Cash ($ mil.): 4

RIVERSIDE HEALTHCARE ASSOCIATION, INC.

Extra! Extra! Read all about it! Residents of Newport News (and about a dozen other cities in Eastern Virginia) Turn to Riverside Health for Medical Care. The not-for-profit health care provider administers general emergency and specialty medical services from five hospitals Riverside Regional Medical Center Riverside Walter Reed Hospital Riverside Tappahannock Hospital and Riverside Shore Memorial Hospital and Riverside Doctors Hospital as well as a psychiatric hospital a physical rehabilitation facility and retirement communities. Riverside also operates physician offices and medical training facilities. Specialty centers provide home and hospice care cancer treatment and dialysis.

Operations

Combined Riverside's hospitals (including rehabilitation and psychiatric) are home to nearly 1000 beds. Its major hospitals include Riverside Regional Medical Center (450-bed flagship hospital); Riverside Walter Reed Hospital (67-bed acute care facility); Riverside Tappahannock Hospital (67-bed serving the Northern Neck rural area); Riverside Shore Memorial Hospital (143-bed facility); and Riverside Doctors' Hospital Williamsburg (40 private rooms). It also operates specialty medical facilities including a psychiatric hospital a physical rehabilitation facility and retirement communities.

Geographic Reach

It serves Eastern Virginia including cities of Gloucester Hampton Newport News Poquoson Richmond Tappahannock West Point Williamsburg and Yorktown; Eastern Shore Area of Virginia; Counties of Essex Gloucester Isle of Wight James City King and Queen King William Lancaster Mathews Middlesex New Kent Northumberland Richmond and Surry.

Strategy

To keep up with demand Riverside Health has been upgrading its older facilities and building new ones.

In 2013 the company opened a new hospital the Doctors Hospital in Williamsburg. The 40 room hospital provides acute and emergency care as well as specialty services including cardiology neurology and pulmonary care.

That year Riverside broke ground on the new Riverside Shore Memorial Hospital in Onley which is expected to be completed in late 2015. It will have 57 private inpatient rooms with the ability to add 12 more in the future.

In 2012 Riverside Walter Reed Hospital opened a new intensive care unit.

It is also investing in technology physician expertise and patient services. In 2013 Riverside Shore Medical Center at Metompkin converted to digital mammography equipment offering patients a superior diagnostic tool to film mammograms.

Company Background

The original charter for Riverside dates back to 1915 when the company began as one hospital founded by the community. In 1962 the hospital was relocated to the present site in central Newport News.

EXECUTIVES

Vice President And Chief Pharmacy Officer, Cindy Williams
Director Of Nursing, Gaynor Callis
Director Of Physical Therapy, Chris Mchose
Auditors: ERNST & YOUNG LLP RICHMOND V

LOCATIONS

HQ: RIVERSIDE HEALTHCARE ASSOCIATION, INC.
701 TOWN CENTER DR # 1000, NEWPORT NEWS, VA 236064283
Phone: 757 534-7000
Web: WWW.RIVERSIDEONLINE.COM

Selected Facilities – Virginia

HOSPITALS
Riverside Behavioral Health Center (Hampton)
Riverside Doctors' Hospital (Williamsburg)
Riverside Regional Medical Center (Newport News)
Riverside Rehabilitation Institute (Williamsburg)
Riverside Tappahannock Hospital (Tappahannock)
Riverside Shore Memorial Hospital (Nassawadox)
Riverside Walter Reed Hospital (Gloucester)
RETIREMENT COMMUNITIES
Patriots Colony (Williamsburg)
Sanders (Gloucester)
Warwick Forest (Newport News)
SURGERY CENTERS
Doctors Surgery Center (Williamsburg)
Peninsula Surgery Center (Newport News)
Riverside Hampton Surgery Center (Hampton)

COMPETITORS

Alleghany Regional Hospital
Bon Secours Health
Carilion Clinic
Centra Health Inc.
Children's Hospital of The King's Daughters
Franklin Hospital Corp.
Novant Health
Sentara Healthcare

HISTORICAL FINANCIALS

Company Type: Private

Income Statement FYE: December 31

	REVENUE ($ mil.)	NET INCOME ($ mil.)	NET PROFIT MARGIN	EMPLOYEES
12/15	1,149	21	1.8%	8,000
12/14	1,059	(86)	—	—
12/13	1,017	101	10.0%	—
12/12	948	41	4.4%	—
Annual Growth	6.6%	(20.3%)	—	—

2015 Year-End Financials

Return on assets: 1.5%
Return on equity: 2.9%
Current ratio: 1.50
Cash ($ mil.): 1

RIVERSIDE HOSPITAL, INC.

Riverside Hospital operates as Riverside Regional Medical Center a 450-bed acute-care facility that serves the residents of Newport News Virginia. Founded in 1916 the hospital moved to its current 72-acre campus in 1963 providing more than 30 medical specialties including cancer treatment cardiology birthing and diagnostic imaging. It specializes in cardiovascular and neurological surgeries and provides radiosurgery (radiation surgery) through a partnership with the University of Virginia Health System. Its emergency department is a 42-room Level II Trauma Center that treats more than 57000 patients each year. Riverside Hospital is part of the Riverside Health System.

Operations

As part of its operations Riverside Hospital operates a heart center neonatal center 18-bed neonatal intensive care unit cancer care center and radiosurgery center through a partnership with Chesapeake Regional and the University of Virginia Health System. Riverside Hospital works to prevent diagnose and treat diseases of the stomach intestines esophagus pancreas gall bladder liver and biliary tract through its Peninsula Gastroenterology & Riverside Endoscopy Center.

Geographic Reach

Riverside Hospital serves the health care needs of those who reside in and around Newport News Virginia.

EXECUTIVES

Director Of Pharmacy, Lindsay Enzor
Director Of Pharmacy, Catherine Richwine
Auditors: ERNST YOUNG RICHMOND VA

LOCATIONS

HQ: RIVERSIDE HOSPITAL, INC.
500 J CLYDE MORRIS BLVD, NEWPORT NEWS, VA 236011929
Phone: 757 594-2000
Web: WWW.RIVERSIDEONLINE.COM

PRODUCTS/OPERATIONS

Selected Services

Diagnostic Services
- Cardiac testing
- CT
- Digital mammography
- Electrocardiography
- Magnetic resonance imaging
- Nuclear medicine
- PET
- Ultrasound

Nutrition Services
- Radiosurgery Center
- Leksell Gamma Knife Synergy S Radiosurgery
- Gastroenterology Procedures
- Colonoscopy and polypectomy
- Flexible sigmoidoscopy
- Upper endoscopic exams and therapy
- Endoscopic retrograde cholangiopancreatography (ERCP)
- Percutaneous endoscopic gastrostomy (PEG)
- Capsule/Cam (M2A) study of the small intestine
- Esophageal dilation
- Esophageal and anal manometry
- BRAVO pH study of the esophagus

Pulmonary Rehabilitation
Surgical Services

COMPETITORS

Alleghany Regional Hospital
Bon Secours Health
Carilion Clinic
Centra Health Inc.
Children's Hospital of The King's Daughters
Franklin Hospital Corp.
Novant Health
Sentara Healthcare

HISTORICAL FINANCIALS

Company Type: Private

Income Statement FYE: December 31

	REVENUE ($ mil.)	NET INCOME ($ mil.)	NET PROFIT MARGIN	EMPLOYEES
12/18	618	61	10.0%	8,000
12/17	611	57	9.4%	—
12/16	636	65	10.3%	—
12/11	466	36	7.8%	—
Annual Growth	4.1%	7.9%	—	—

RIVERSIDE MIDDLE PENINSULA HOSPITAL, INC.

EXECUTIVES

Pres, William Downey
Auditors: ERNEST YOUNG RICHMOND VA

LOCATIONS

HQ: RIVERSIDE MIDDLE PENINSULA HOSPITAL, INC.
7519 HOSPITAL DR, GLOUCESTER, VA 230614178
Phone: 757 875-7545
Web: WWW.RIVERSIDEONLINE.COM

HISTORICAL FINANCIALS

Company Type: Private

Income Statement FYE: December 31

	REVENUE ($ mil.)	NET INCOME ($ mil.)	NET PROFIT MARGIN	EMPLOYEES
12/12	948	41	4.4%	50
12/11	59	10	17.3%	—
12/10	53	8	16.1%	—
12/09	53	10	19.8%	—
Annual Growth	160.1%	57.6%	—	—

2012 Year-End Financials

Return on assets: 3.4%
Return on equity: 6.0%
Current ratio: 1.50
Cash ($ mil.): 53

RIVERSIDE REGIONAL MEDIAL CENTER

EXECUTIVES

Principal, Debbie Davis
Vp of Ambulatory Care, Susan Mc Andrews

LOCATIONS

HQ: RIVERSIDE REGIONAL MEDIAL CENTER
500 J CLYDE MORRIS BLVD, NEWPORT NEWS, VA 236011929
Phone: 757 856-7030
Web: WWW.RIVERSIDEONLINE.COM

HISTORICAL FINANCIALS

Company Type: Private

Income Statement FYE: December 31

	REVENUE ($ mil.)	NET INCOME ($ mil.)	NET PROFIT MARGIN	EMPLOYEES
12/14	544	73	13.5%	1
12/08	301	0	0.2%	—
Annual Growth	10.4%	123.6%	—	—

RIVERSIDE UNIFIED SCHOOL DISTRICT

EXECUTIVES

Supt, Dr David Hansen
Supt*, Michael H Fine
Pres*, Lynn Carmen Day
V Pres*, Charles L Beaty PHD
Teacher, Candace Mendoza
Teacher, Jenna King
Administrative Secretary, Leticia Romero
Manager, Marcus A Ridley
Teacher, Matthew Schiller
Teacher, Monica Schalow
Teacher, Neil Schlesener
Auditors: NIGRO & NIGRO PC MURRIETA C

LOCATIONS

HQ: RIVERSIDE UNIFIED SCHOOL DISTRICT
3380 14TH ST, RIVERSIDE, CA 925013810
Phone: 951 788-7135
Web: WWW.RIVERSIDEUNIFIED.ORG

HISTORICAL FINANCIALS

Company Type: Private

Income Statement FYE: June 30

	REVENUE ($ mil.)	NET INCOME ($ mil.)	NET PROFIT MARGIN	EMPLOYEES
06/19	592	(31)	—	3,740
06/18	540	(8)	—	—
06/17	513	75	14.7%	—
06/16	499	18	3.6%	—
Annual Growth	5.8%	—	—	—

2019 Year-End Financials

Return on assets: (-3.0%)
Return on equity: (-27.5%)
Current ratio: —
Cash ($ mil.): 258

RIVERVIEW HOSPITAL

Riverview Hospital (which changed its operating name to Riverside Health in 2014) provides general medical and surgical care to residents in central Indiana. With about 155 beds and 300 physicians representing more than 35 medical specialties the hospital is a full-service facility that offers specialty care in a number of areas including heart disease cancer women's health and orthopedics. Besides its main campus Riverview operates several outpatient facilities including an occupational health center a community health clinic and several rehab and fitness centers.

Operations

The Indiana hospital which admits some 6500 patients each year provides family medicine pediatrics OB/GYN care cardiac care surgery orthopedics and sports medicine cancer care interventional pain management wound care diabetes and endocrinology internal medicine and imaging among other services. Also part of its operations the health care facility runs a community health clinic rehab and fitness centers and an occupational health center.

Its Riverview Medical Group is a network of affiliated primary and specialty care doctors with 20 offices located throughout Hamilton and Tipton counties.

Geographic Reach

Riverview serves patients who reside in Indiana's Hamilton and Tipton Counties particularly the service area north of Indianapolis in central Indiana. It has locations in Carmel Cicero Fishers Noblesville Sheridan Tipton and Westfield.

Strategy

To better reflect the organization's full scope of inpatient and outpatient services in 2014 the hospital changed its name from Riverview Hospital to Riverview Health.

Expanding its services in 2014 the hospital began building the Mugg-Z Café an internet café and gift shop for elders.

EXECUTIVES

Vice President Of Medical Affairs, Dennis Pippenger
Director Of Pharmacy, Brian Peters
Vice President Of Operations, Mary Valdez
Executive Vice President Of Information Technology, Nicole Klein
Executive Vice President Of Fiscal Services, Joyce Woods
Head Nurse, Andria Fitzgerald
Vice President, Nikki Swiney
Board Of Directors, Sarah Cookman
Vice Chair, Andrew Cornell
Secretary Treasurer, Aaron Coers

LOCATIONS

HQ: RIVERVIEW HOSPITAL
395 WESTFIELD RD, NOBLESVILLE, IN 460601434
Phone: 317 773-0760
Web: WWW.RIVERVIEW.ORG

PRODUCTS/OPERATIONS

Selected Services

Cancer Services
Diabetes and Endocrinology
Emergency Services
Heart and Vascular Services
Internal Medicine Services
Laboratory Services
Occupational Health Services
Orthopedic Services
Pediatric Services
Radiology and Imaging Services
Rehabilitation Services
Sleep Disorders Services
Surgery Services
Women's Health Services
Wound Care Services

COMPETITORS

Ascension Health
Community Health Network
Franciscan Alliance
Henry County Memorial Hospital
IU Health
Kosciusko Community Hospital
St. Vincent Health
Wabash County Hospital

HISTORICAL FINANCIALS

Company Type: Private

Income Statement				FYE: December 31
	REVENUE ($ mil.)	NET INCOME ($ mil.)	NET PROFIT MARGIN	EMPLOYEES
12/18	574	2	0.4%	949
12/17	179	8	4.8%	—
12/16	171	1	1.1%	—
12/15	162	1	0.8%	—
Annual Growth	52.5%	16.4%	—	—

2018 Year-End Financials

Return on assets: 0.5%
Return on equity: 0.8%
Current ratio: 1.60
Cash ($ mil.): 87

ROBERT BOSCH LLC

Robert Bosch LLC is your one-stop shop for German-engineered auto parts appliances and power tools. The North American subsidiary of German giant Robert Bosch GmbH Bosch LLC makes and markets automotive original equipment and aftermarket products industrial drive and control technology packaging technology power tools home appliances security and communication systems thermotechnology and software solutions. Robert Bosch LLC's biggest area Mobility Solutions makes products aimed at the next generation of automobiles particularly around connectivity automation and electrification. Active since 1906 Bosch LLC has grown to around 70 primary North American locations.

Operations

Robert Bosch LLC comprises four reporting segments Mobility Solutions Industrial Technology Consumer Goods and Energy and Building Technology.

The Mobility Solutions segment represents two-thirds of sales and is active in injection technology and powertrain peripherals for internal-combustion engines powertrain electrification steering systems safety and driver-assistance systems car multimedia vehicle-to-vehicle and vehicle-to-infrastructure communication repair-shop concepts and technology and services.

The Industrial Control segment produces drive and control products and packaging technology and generates around 10% of sales. The Consumer Goods segment accounts for around a fifth of sales and consists of Robert Bosch's US power tools home appliances business. Energy and Building Technology segment (5% of sales) outfits buildings with heating ventilation and lighting infrastructure.

Geographic Reach

Robert Bosch LLC accounts for 15% of global sales. It has around 70 primary facilities in the US Canada and Mexico

Financial Performance

Robert Bosch LLC's sales grew 6% to $14.5 billion in 2018.

Strategy

One of Robert Bosch's major markets North America continues to receive substantial investment. It has expanded Mobility Solutions plants in Charleston and Anderson South Carolina and a dishwasher factory and central distribution center in New Bern North Carolina. It has also broke earth in the construction of a $120 million plant in Celaya Mexico. The 225000 sq. ft. factory will produce electronic control units which are used in connected mobility for the American market. Most recently Bosch opened a technology and innovation hub in Guadalajara Mexico.

EXECUTIVES

President Bosch Security Systems, Christopher P. Gerace
Cfo; Evp Controlling Finance And Administration, Maximiliane Straub
President And Ceo Bosch Rexroth Corporation, Berend Bracht
Regional President Gasoline Systems North America, Sujit Jain
Regional President Chassis Systems Control, D. Scott Winchip
Regional President Car Multimedia North America, Juergen Peters
Evp Original Equipment Sales Ford, Manfred Mueller
President And Ceo Bsh Home Appliances, Michael Traub
Regional President Automotive Electronics North America, Timothy (Tim) Frasier
Regional President Diesel Systems North America, Bernd Boisten
President, Mike Mansuetti
Regional President Robert Bosch Automotive Aftermarket Division, Odd Joergenrud
Evp Original Equipment Sales General Motors, Clesio Honma
Regional President Electrical Drives, Peter Denk
Regional President Starter Motors And Generators North America, Pres Lawhon
Regional President Bosch Engineering Group North America, Wayne (Keith) Andrews
President Robert Bosch Healthcare Systems Inc., Micha Kirchhoff
Vp Original Equipment Sales Chrysler, Paul Thomas
Vice President Business Development, Michael Barhaug
Vice President Purchasing, Scott Schafer
Vice President, Tim Williams
Vice President, Christine Zimmerman
Executive Vice President Finance And Administ, Cara Reynolds
Vice President Sales, George Kostopoulos
Senior Vice President, Martin Kueper
Vice President, Heiko Weller
Vice President Of Sales, Doug Arnold
Vice President Automotive Aftermarket, Karen Folger
Vice President Of Information Technology, James Puttick
National Sales Manager, Robert Dono
Vice President Of Sales, Rajesh Darji
Vice President Marketing And Business Strategy, Andreas Sambel
Vice President Sales Marketing And Aftermarket, Ross Long
Vice President Mergers And Acquisitions, Marcia Medendorp
Senior Vice President Sales, Stefan Thiel
Vice President And General Manager, Erwin Wieckowski
Chairman, Werner Struth

LOCATIONS

HQ: ROBERT BOSCH LLC
38000 HILLS TECH DR, FARMINGTON HILLS, MI 483313418
Phone: 248 876-1000
Web: WWW.BOSCH.US

PRODUCTS/OPERATIONS

2019 Sales

	% of total
Mobility Solutions	66
Consumer Goods	18
Industrial Technology	10
Energy and Building Technology	6
Other	3
Total	**100**

Selected Products

Automotive Technology
- Aftermarket
- Alternators
- Brake pads
- Car audio products
- Diesel parts
- Filters
- Fuel pumps
- Ignition products
- Oxygen sensors
- Spark plugs
- Spark plug wire sets
- Starters
- Wiper blades
- Original equipment
- Actuators
- Braking and chassis systems
- Car multimedia
- Electrical systems
- Electronic systems
- Powertrain systems - diesel
- Powertrain systems - gasoline

Consumer Goods and Building Technology
- Household appliances
- Cooktops
- Dishwashers
- Ovens
- Washers and dryers
- Power tools
- Angle grinders
- Belt sanders
- Circular saws
- Drill bits
- Drills
- Drywall drivers
- Impact wrenches
- Jigsaws
- Orbit sanders/polishers
- Planers
- Reciprocating saws
- Rotary hammers
- Routers
- Screwdriver bits and accessories
- Wet/dry vacuums
- Security Systems
- Access control
- Communications
- Fire detection
- Security management
- Video surveillance
- Thermotechnology
- Indoor climate control (heating and cooling and hot water production)

Industrial Technology
- Drive and control
- Assembly
- Electric drives and controls
- Gears
- Hydraulics
- Linear motion
- Pneumatics
- Packaging
- Confectionary cosmetics and chemicals
- Packaging machines
- Packaging services
- Pharmaceuticals
- Production tools
- Air assembly tools
- Cordless assembly tools
- DC electric assembly tools

Electric assembly tools
Solar Energy
Crystalline PV modules
Solar cells
Thin-film modules
Wafers

COMPETITORS

AISIN World Corp.
Advanced Security & Controls
DENSO America
Dana
Delphi Automotive Systems
GE
Hitachi Automotive Systems Americas
LG Electronics
Makita
Molins
Motorcar Parts
NGK Spark Plugs
Neaton Auto Products
Stanley Black and Decker
Visteon
Whirlpool

HISTORICAL FINANCIALS

Company Type: Private

Income Statement FYE: December 31

	REVENUE ($ mil.)	NET INCOME ($ mil.)	NET PROFIT MARGIN	EMPLOYEES
12/14	10,474	181	1.7%	12
12/10	6,810	326	4.8%	—
12/09	5,464	59	1.1%	—
Annual Growth	13.9%	25.1%	—	—

2014 Year-End Financials

Return on assets: 2.7%
Return on equity: 13.0%
Current ratio: 0.90
Cash ($ mil.): 832

ROBERT W. BAIRD & CO. INCORPORATED

Employee-owned Robert W. Baird & Co. brings midwestern sensibility to the high-flying world of investment banking. The company offers brokerage asset management and investment banking services to middle-market corporations institutional clients and wealthy individuals and families. Its investment banking activities include underwriting and distributing corporate securities mergers and acquisition advisory and institutional sales and trading. The company also conducts equity research on more than 600 US firms. Baird manages more than $97 billion in client assets.

Operations

The company manages about 10 bond and equity mutual funds: Baird Advisors manages fixed income investments while Baird Investment Management handles the equities side. Baird also invests in private equity and venture capital.

Geographic Reach

The firm has more than 100 offices in North America Asia and Europe where it owns 48% of Baird UK. More than half of Baird's locations are wealth management offices in the US.

Sales and Marketing

Baird is the marketing name for Robert W. Baird & Co. Incorporated and its subsidiaries and affiliates worldwide.

Financial Performance

The company's revenues increased by 9% in 2011 and net income grew by 2%.

Strategy

The driving forces for the company's growth have been its wealth management and investment banking operations. Unlike many financial services firms Baird has been adding staff and opening new offices in the US.

The company has also turned to the East for its fortunes. Its private equity group recently has an office in Shanghai hoping to capitalize on China's increasingly business-friendly environment. The outpost focuses on small high-growth businesses that have been overlooked by other venture capitalists. Baird has also expanded its investment banking operations in the region.

In 2012 Baird formed a strategic alliance with Axis Capital the investment banking subsidiary of Axis Bank with an initial focus on cross-border mergers and acquisitions between India and Europe and India and the US.

Company Background

Founded in 1919 Baird had been majority-owned by Northwestern Mutual since 1982. However employees bought back the company's stock in a series of purchases that culminated in 2004.

EXECUTIVES

Coo, Russell P. (Russ) Schwei
Chief Investment Officer, Mary Ellen Stanek
Cfo, Terrance P. (Terry) Maxwell
President Private Wealth Management, Michael J. (Mike) Schroeder
Director Fixed Income Capital Markets, Patrick S. (Pat) Lawton
Managing Director And Director Institutional Equity Services, William W. (Bill) Mahler
Co-head Global Investment Banking, Brian S. Doyal
President And Coo, Steven G. (Steve) Booth
Co-head Global Investment Banking, Brian McDonagh
Director Risk Management, Mark A. Roble
Managing Partner Baird Capital, Gordon G. Pan
Head Global Equities And Director Equity Research, Jon A. Langenfeld
Cio, Timothy (Tim) Byrne
Senior Vice President, Jay Schwister
Vice President, Mark Zalewski
Vice President, Peter Klode
Vice President Vice President Administration, Thomas Seidcheck
Vice President, Joseph G Verdi
Senior Vice President, Dustin Hutter
Senior Vice President, Karen Heintz
Vice President Technology Product Manager, Lesley Augustine
Vice President, Tom Coburn
Senior Vice President Of Wealth Management Office, Paul McWane
Senior Vice President Supervisory Analyst, Keith Dorris
Vice President Information Technology Architect, Jim Cornelius
Vice President, Charles Galarza
Vice President, Robert Ferriman
Senior Vice President, Peter Hammond
Vice President Financial Analyst, Lori Jackson
Senior Vice President Investments, Cory Davis
Senior Vice President, Jayson C Bales
Senior Vice President And Senior Portfolio Manager, Daniel Tranchita
Senior Vice President, Michael Chorley
First Vice President, Trish M Young
Vice President, Janet Holsclaw
Vice President, Marla Regan
First Vice President Purchase And Sales, Dean Markofski
Vice President, Jonathan Dekker
Vice President, Dalena Welkomer
Vice President, Adrianne Limjoco
Vice President, Ryan Unthank
First Vice President, Eileen Wingenter
Assistant Vice President, Tonia G Morris
Senior Vice President, Richard Palm
Vice President, Dale Rudow
Assistant Vice President Compliance Officer, Heidi Mclemore
Compliance Officer Vice President, Edgar Sturkey
Assistant Vice President Private Asset Management, Robert Filetti
Vice President, Mike Monfeli
Vice President Financial Advisor, Dan Koth
Vice President Private Wealth Management, Rebecca Ross
Senior Vice President Private Wealth Management, Matthew H Schmitt
Senior Vice President, Shawn B Smith
Senior Vice President Public Relations, Angela Pittman Taylor
Assistant Vice President, Dominic Burrescia
Vice President, Abhishek Pulakanti
Senior Vice President, Douglas Stencel
First Vice President Tech And Systems, Dennis Weishan
Vice President Financial Advisor, Jeff Pedersen
Vice President And Art Director, Virginia Sunu
Vice President, Mike Malone
Vice President Wealth Management, Theresa Rynaski
Vice President Information Technology Project Services, Jim Whittet
Senior Vice President, Chuck Cairns
Vice President, Frank Downey
Vice President Financial Advisor, Blaine Gibson
Assistant Vice President And Marketing Specialist, Karen Sweeney
First Vice President, Bryan Fiene
Vice President, Mary E Levar
Vice President, Michael Halloran
Assistant Vice President, Genise Brandt
Senior Vice President, Baron Becker
Senior Vice President, Rob Zwiebel
Assistant Vice President, Heather Melzer
Assistant Vice President, Kathy Cobb
Senior Vice President Private Wealth Management, Bryan Sampson
Senior Vice President Internal Audit Director, David Cook
Vice President Investments, Thomas Olson
Senior Vice President Director Of Application Development, Jason Montague
Vice President Quantitative Analyst, Jordan Masnica
Vice President Investment Banking, Christopher Hildreth
Vice President, Alex Ballantine
Vice President Portfolio Analyst, Aaron Benson
Vice President, Suzanne King
Senior Vice President, Gail Bivens-rose
First Vice President, Terry Lineberger
Vice President And Financial Advisor, Jon Bolton
Vice President, Rich Nigro
Senior Vice President Investments, Ronald Christian
Vice President, Marcy Finley
Senior Vice President, Mike Parrott
Senior Vice President, David Schwarz
Vice President, Greg Pauly
Vice President Senior Research Associate, Luke Junk
Vice President, Chase Hinderstein
Vice President, Joe Vruwink
Vice President, Brian Ellenbecker
Assistant Vice President, Stacey Leigh
Assistant Vice President, Deanne Soetenga
Vice President, Frederick Jetter
Vice President Private Wealth Management, Robert King
Assistant Vice President, Bernadette Ross
Vice President, Ryan Cox
Vice President, Ralph Cefalu
Senior Vice President, Douglas Crandall
Vice President, Randall McLaughlin
Vice President, Richard Roesch
Senior Vice President, Orlando C Montesino

First Vice President Research, Ron Freisleben
Vice President Private Wealth Management, Phyllis Lovrien
Vice President Investment Banking, John Sun
Vice President, Brian Kelso
Vice President Investments, John Barnefield
Vice President, Tyson Eubanks
Vice President, Gavin Amato
Vice President Private Wealth Management, Larry Magid
Vice President Senior Estate Planner, Rick Holman
Vice President, Alex Lawhorn
Vice President, Jay Bitter
Vice President Investments, Frances D Bobbie
Assistant Vice President, Ginny Moye
Vice President, Peter Philpott
Senior Vice President, Mary Howard
Vice President, James Cain
Vice President Private Wealth Management, Wes Oliver
Assistant Vice President, Dale Jacques
Senior Vice President, Gerald Jarzabek
Senior Vice President, Jan Bayle
Assistant Vice President, Mary Zavaglia
Assistant Vice President, Judie Meriweather
Vice President Pwm, Clay Ryan
Assistant Vice President, Mary Walters
Senior Vice President And Associate General Counsel, Andrew Ketter
Vice President Resources Consultant Business Partner Human Capital, Lynn Rudolph
Senior Vice President Investments, Lewis Krinsky
Assistant Vice President, Michelle Hernandez
Vice President, Alice Ambrowiak
First Vice President, Kelly Kontowski
Vice President, Phillip Banta
Vice President And Senior Investment Consultant, Penny Cruse
Assistant Vice President, Robert Schultz
Senior Vice President, Joyce Linker
Vice President Pwm, George Gamez
Assistant Vice President Registered Client Relationship Specialist, Shawn Zoltak
Vice President Public Finance, Andrew Arndt
Senior Vice President, Robert Slater
Senior Vice President And Wealth Managaement, Brian Mcgrath
Financial Adviser Senior Vice President, Cliff Henrickson
Vice President Information Technology, Steve Acton
Senior Vice President Regional Director Private Wealth Management, William T Johnson
Vice President, Matthew Anderson

LOCATIONS

HQ: ROBERT W. BAIRD & CO. INCORPORATED
777 E WISCONSIN AVE FL 29, MILWAUKEE, WI 532025391
Phone: 414 765-3500
Web: WWW.BAIRDFINANCIALADVISOR.COM

PRODUCTS/OPERATIONS

Business Groups
Asset Management
Equity Capital Markets
Fixed Income Capital Markets
Private Equity
Private Wealth Management

COMPETITORS

Citigroup Global Markets
Cowen Group
Goldman Sachs
Greenhill
Jefferies Group
Morgan Stanley
Piper Jaffray
Raymond James Financial
Stephens
Stifel Financial
Thomas Weisel Partners
William Blair

HISTORICAL FINANCIALS

Company Type: Private

Income Statement — FYE: December 31

	ASSETS ($ mil.)	NET INCOME ($ mil.)	INCOME AS % OF ASSETS	EMPLOYEES
12/09	2,063	41	2.0%	2,298
12/08	1,080	36	3.4%	—
12/07	1,712	50	2.9%	—
Annual Growth	9.8%	(8.6%)	—	—

2009 Year-End Financials

Return on assets: 2.0%
Return on equity: 11.2%
Sales ($ mil): 699

ROBERT WOOD JOHNSON UNIVERSITY HOSPITAL, INC.

Robert Wood Johnson University Hospital (RWJUH) is the flagship medical center of the RWJBarnabas health system. The hospital consists of four campuses offering acute and tertiary care services including cardiovascular transplant pediatric trauma cancer neurology and women's health care. Founded in 1884 the facility serves as a teaching center for the Rutgers Robert Wood Johnson Medical School. The hospital is part of the RWJBarnabas Health organization.

Operations

RWJUH has four campuses: RWJUH-New Brunswick RWJUH-Somerset RWJUH-Rahway and RWJUH-Hamilton.

The main RWJUH-New Brunswick campus includes a Level I trauma center a Clinical Neurosciences Center and the Bristol-Myers Squibb Children's Hospital. It also operates the Cancer Hospital of New Jersey which is the main hospital partner of the Rutgers Cancer Institute of New Jersey. The New Brunswick campus also serves as the primary teaching hospital for the Rutgers Robert Wood Johnson Medical School.

RWJUH operates satellite clinics near its hospital campuses including wellness wound healing laboratory and physical therapy facilities.

The broader RWJBarnabas Health network operates about a dozen hospitals. Outside of the RWJUH facilities major facilities include Monmouth Medical Center Newark Beth Israel Medical Center and Saint Barnabas Medical Center. The system also operates outpatient locations providing ambulatory care behavioral health trauma emergency geriatric pharmacy and home health and hospice care.

Geographic Reach

RWJUH's main campus is in New Brunswick New Jersey; it has other campuses in Somerset Hamilton and Rahway New Jersey. Parent RWJBarnabas operates throughout the state.

Strategy

To widen its operations RWJUH has expanded its main campus facilities; it has also acquired or opened new satellite locations. The main New Brunswick hospital campus launched an emergency department expansion project to increase capacity and reduce wait times in 2017 with scheduled completion in 2020. The facility will help meet a growing need for emergency and trauma care services in Central New Jersey.

As part of a partnership formed in 2018 between parent RWJBarnabas and Rutgers University RWJBarnabas is building a new cancer research facility and a new ambulatory care facility in New Brunswick.

Company Background

RWJUH was founded in 1884. In 2014 Somerset Medical Center was merged into RWJUH adding more than 300 beds and providing RWJUH entry into the Somerset community.

RWJUH's parent company Robert Wood Johnson Health System merged with fellow New Jersey hospital system Barnabas Health in 2015 creating the largest hospital system in New Jersey. The combined entity began operating under the name RWJBarnabas Health.

EXECUTIVES

President, John Gantner
President Somerset, Anthony V. Cava
Head Nurse, Jennifer Mackown
Vice President Oncology Services, David Fernandez
Medical Records Director, Giovanni Goodrich
Vice President Critical Care, Julie Arsenault
Nursing Director Pediatric Critical Care Pediatric Transport Program Pediatric Oncology And Pacct, Linda Palkoski
Nursing Director, Nicole Mcelvery
Vice President Is, Robert Irwin
Director Of Radiology, Barbara Richardson
Vice President Leasing, Chris Calello
Head Nurse, Laura Viggiano
Vice President Foundation And Development, Mark Hanichak
Medical Secretary, Tarra Stevenson
Board Member, Carlos Burnett
Auditors: KPMG LLP NEW YORK NY

LOCATIONS

HQ: ROBERT WOOD JOHNSON UNIVERSITY HOSPITAL, INC.
1 ROBERT WOOD JOHNSON PL, NEW BRUNSWICK, NJ 089011928
Phone: 732 828-3000
Web: WWW.RWJBH.ORG

PRODUCTS/OPERATIONS

Selected Services
Bariatric Surgery
Bloodless Surgery
Cardiothoracic Surgery
Colorectal Surgery
Comprehensive Sleep Disorders Center
Diabetes
Digestive Disorders
Emergency Department
Executive Health Program
Heart Transplantation
Injury Prevention
Kidney and Pancreas Transplantation
Lab Services (blood work and blood collection)
Level 1 Trauma Center
Neurosciences
  Clinical Neurosciences Center
  Deep Brain Stimulation for Movement Disorders
  Laser Ablation for Brain Tumor Treatment
  Neurosurgery
  New Jersey Brain Aneurysm & AVM Program
  Parkinson's Disease Information and Referral Center
  Stroke Center
  The Gamma Knife Center: Advanced Treatment for Brain and Spine
New Jersey Pain Institute at RWJUH
Orthopedic Surgery
Outpatient Radiology: University Radiology at Robert Wood Johnson
Palliative Care Program
Pastoral Care
Pelvic Floor and Incontinence Program
Physical and Occupational Therapy
Prostate Cancer Surgery
Radiation Oncology
  Gynecologic Brachytherapy

Prostate Brachytherapy
TomoTherapy
Total Skin Electron Beam Therapy
Radiology (including CT MRI and ultrasound)
Speech and Hearing Program
The Center for Wound Healing
The Limb Preservation Program
Therapeutic Apheresis
Thoracic Surgery
Vascular Surgery

COMPETITORS

Bergen Regional Medical
Capital Health System
Princeton HealthCare
Raritan Bay Medical Center
Saint Peter's University Hospital
St. Joseph's Healthcare System

HISTORICAL FINANCIALS

Company Type: Private

Income Statement FYE: December 31

	REVENUE ($ mil.)	NET INCOME ($ mil.)	NET PROFIT MARGIN	EMPLOYEES
12/19	1,451	(89)	—	4,674
12/18	1,337	(3)	—	—
12/17	1,249	(59)	—	—
Annual Growth	7.8%	—	—	—

2019 Year-End Financials

Return on assets: (-5.0%)
Return on equity: (-10.7%)
Current ratio: 3.90
Cash ($ mil.): —

ROCHESTER CITY SCHOOL DISTRICT

EXECUTIVES

Supt, Jean C Brizard
Supt*, Bolgen Vargas
RES*, Malik Evans
V-Pres*, Jose Cruz
V Pres*, Van Henri White
Central Office Assistant Perso*, Mary Adams
MBR-Board of Edu*, Melisza Campos
MBR-Board of Edu*, Cynthia Elliot
Mgr-Board of Edu*, Willa Powell
Human Resources Secretary II, Annette Ramos
Executive Director of Health, Carlos Cotto
Auditors: FREEDMAXICK CPA PC ROCHEST

LOCATIONS

HQ: ROCHESTER CITY SCHOOL DISTRICT
131 W BROAD ST, ROCHESTER, NY 146141103
Phone: 585 262-8100
Web: WWW.RCSDK12.ORG

HISTORICAL FINANCIALS

Company Type: Private

Income Statement FYE: June 30

	REVENUE ($ mil.)	NET INCOME ($ mil.)	NET PROFIT MARGIN	EMPLOYEES
06/13	708	74	10.6%	5,470
06/11	681	(19)	—	—
Annual Growth	1.9%	—	—	—

2013 Year-End Financials

Return on assets: 8.7%
Return on equity: 123.6%
Current ratio: —
Cash ($ mil.): 315

ROCHESTER GAS AND ELECTRIC CORPORATION

Upstate New York residents count on Rochester Gas and Electric (RG&E) to keep the lights turned on. The regulated utility provides electricity to about 370000 customers and natural gas to 306000 customers. RG&E operates 22500 miles of power transmission and distribution lines and has a generating capacity of approximately 400 MW from interests in fossil-fueled and hydroelectric power plants. RG&E and sister utility company New York State Electric & Gas (NYSEG) are subsidiaries of regional power and gas distribution player Avangrid).

Change in Company Type

In 2012 ultimate parent company IBERDROLA reorganized consolidating Iberdrola Renewables Holdings and IBERDROLA USA under a new Avangrid holding company. Intermediate holding company Iberdrola USA Networks was then created to hold all of IBERDROLA's regulated US electric and gas utilities including RG&E.

Geographic Reach

RG&E's service territory contains a substantial suburban area and a large agricultural area in parts of nine counties including and surrounding the city of Rochester New York with a population of 1 million.

Financial Performance

The company operates under the Network business of IBERDROLA. The Network business accounted for 25% of IBERDROLA's 2013 revenues; some 28% of Network sales came from US operations. IBERDROLA generated 10% of its total revenues from the US in 2013.

Strategy

To reduce its carbon emissions RG&E along with affiliate NYSEG is pushing green energy options including a wind energy power program whereby residents can choose to have their power supply from wind generated sources.

In 2013 the company announced plans to retire its 18-MW Rochester 9 natural gas-fired combustion turbine as it would be too expensive to repair the equipment failures that forced the unit offline that year.

Company Background

Between 2008 and the end of 2010 NYSEG or RG&E interconnected six landfill gas plants with a total of 26MW of generating capacity three wind farms with 209 wind turbines (381 MW of generating capacity) in Wyoming and Steuben counties a new 30 MW combined heat and power facility for Cornell University and a lithium-ion battery energy storage facility for AES Corporation.

EXECUTIVES

Pres, Mark S Lynch
Vp-Contrl-Treas*, Joseph J Syta
Executive Officer, Kathleen Case
Staff, Timothy King
Customer Staff, Kim Lawton
Manager, Stephanie Hughes
Analyst Credit, Jennifer Burgess
Customer Staff, Tina Leiker
Program Inspector, Craig Rauber
Coordinator, Sue Flood
Engineer, Mary Masters
Auditors: KPMG LLP NEW YORK NEW YORK

LOCATIONS

HQ: ROCHESTER GAS AND ELECTRIC CORPORATION
89 EAST AVE, ROCHESTER, NY 146490002
Phone: 800 295-7323
Web: WWW.RGE.COM

COMPETITORS

CH Energy
Con Edison
National Fuel Gas
New York Power Authority
Niagara Mohawk

HISTORICAL FINANCIALS

Company Type: Private

Income Statement FYE: December 31

	REVENUE ($ mil.)	NET INCOME ($ mil.)	NET PROFIT MARGIN	EMPLOYEES
12/17	850	83	9.8%	865
12/16	1,042	80	7.7%	—
12/10	982	54	5.5%	—
Annual Growth	(2.0%)	6.3%	—	—

2017 Year-End Financials

Return on assets: 2.3%
Return on equity: 8.8%
Current ratio: 1.20
Cash ($ mil.): —

ROCHESTER INSTITUTE OF TECHNOLOGY (INC)

The Rochester Institute of Technology (RIT) is a privately endowed university with nine colleges focused on providing career-oriented education to nearly 18670 students. The school which has a student-faculty ratio of about 13:1 offers approximately 85 bachelor's degree programs in art and design business engineering science and hospitality. RIT also confers more than 75 master's and eight doctorate degrees. The university's National Technical Institute for the Deaf is the first and largest technological college for learners who suffer from hearing loss. RIT which traces its roots back to 1829 counts among its alumni the CEOs of Kodak and The Associated Press.

Operations

RIT's campus serves about 15740 undergraduate and around 2930 graduate students with help from its faculty and staff of more than 4040. More than 900 deaf and hard-of-hearing students live study and work alongside hearing students on the RIT campus. Tuition runs more than $33650 for general students and more than $17275 for deaf and hard-of-hearing students.

RIT operates a campus in Dubai's Silicon Oasis a not-for-profit global campus technological-focused. The campus serves the university's goal of growing its reputation worldwide and expanding international opportunities for students. RIT Dubai offers undergraduate and graduate degree programs in engineering business information technology and leadership.

Geographic Reach

Spanning some 1300 acres in Rochester New York it has international campuses in China Croatia Dubai and Kosovo. The university's students come from all 50 states and more than 100 nations around the world.

Strategy

RIT has acquired the former Radisson Hotel Rochester Airport located next to its campus on Jefferson Road in Henrietta. RIT will renovate the entire facility and use it for housing students and university guests.

EXECUTIVES

Svp Finance And Administration, James H. Watters
Dean Kate Gleason College Of Engineering, Harvey Palmer
President, William W. (Bill) Destler
Dean College Of Applied Science And Technology, H. Fred Walker
Svp Academic Affairs And Provost, Jeremy A. Haefner
Vp And Dean Institute Of Health Sciences And Technology, Daniel B. Ornt
Dean College Of Imaging Arts & Sciences, Lorraine Justice
Dean College Of Liberal Arts, James J. Winebrake
Dean College Of Science, Sophia Maggelakis
Dean And President National Technical Institute For The Deaf, Gerard J. Buckley
Svp Enrollment Management And Career Services, James Miller
Dean B. Thomas Golisano College Of Computing And Information Sciences, Anne Haake
Dean Saunders College Of Business, Jacqueline Mozrall
Dean Graduate Studies, Hector Flores
Svp Student Affairs, Sandra Johnson
Secretary Of The Institute And Chief Of Staff, Karen Barrows
President Kosovo Campus, Sharon Y. Hart
Vice President Government And Community Relations, Deborah Stendardi
Student Affiars Vice Presidents Office, Kathy Routly
Department Head, Risa Robinson
Academic Affiars Vice President S Office, Lynne Mazadoorian
Associate Vice President Student Auxlliary Services, Howard Ward
Associate Vice President For Academic Affairs, Stephen Aldersley
Vice President's Office, Sandy Johnson
Assistant Vice President Human Resources, Judy Bender
Senior Vice President's Office, Maureen Glegg
Student Affiars Vice President S Office, Nicole Boulais
Assistant Vice President Registrar, Joseph Loffredo
Assistant Vice President Of Student Wellness Student Affairs, Donna Rubin
Associate Vice President Of Academic Affairs And Registrar, Joe Loffredo
Department Chair Professor, Hiroko Yamashita
Vice President, Dawn Lucas
Vice President Of The Association Of Computing, Vicki Hanson
Associate Vice President And Director Of Financial Aid, Larry Chambers
Associate Vice President For Student Health, Wendy Gelbard
Department Chair, Rebecca Edwards
Department Chair And Associate Professor, Shal Khazanchi
Assistant Vice President For Alumni Relations, Katherine Redder
Vice President For Enrollment Management, Ian Mortimer
Vice President, Bao Ha
Eboard External Vice President, George Matta
Eboard External Vice President, Nathan Nasby
Department Chair, Kenneth Hoffmann
Board Of Directors Secretary, Tori Budgeon Baker
Eboard Secretary, Marcela Lopez
Secretary, Kaltrine Miftari
Auditors: PRICEWATERHOUSECOOPERS LLP RO

LOCATIONS

HQ: ROCHESTER INSTITUTE OF TECHNOLOGY (INC)
1 LOMB MEMORIAL DR, ROCHESTER, NY 146235698
Phone: 585 475-2411
Web: WWW.RIT.EDU

PRODUCTS/OPERATIONS

Selected Colleges

College of Applied Science and Technology
School of Engineering Technology
School of International Hospitality and Service Innovation
E. Philip Saunders College of Business
B. Thomas Golisano College of Computing and Information Sciences
Kate Gleason College of Engineering
College of Health Sciences and Technology
College of Imaging Arts and Sciences
School for American Crafts
School of Art
School of Design
School of Film and Animation
School of Media Sciences
School of Photographic Arts and Sciences
College of Liberal Arts
National Technical Institute for the Deaf
College of Science

Selected Graduate & Undergraduate Programs

Accounting
Applied Networking & Systems Administration
Applied Statistics
Biochemistry
Business
Civil Engineering Technology
Clinical Chemistry
Computer Integrated Machining Technology
Computer Science
Digital Imaging & Publishing Technology
Electrical/Mechanical Engineering Technology
Environmental Science
Finance
Glass & Glass Sculpture
Health Systems Administration
Healthcare Billing & Coding Technology
Imaging Arts: Photography
Industrial & Systems Engineering
Instruction Technology
Management
Medical Illustration
Metals/Jewelry Design
Ophthalmic Optical Finishing Technology
Print Media
Psychology
Service Leadership and Innovation
Voice Communication
Woodworking and Furniture Design

HISTORICAL FINANCIALS

Company Type: Private

Income Statement — FYE: June 30

	REVENUE ($ mil.)	NET INCOME ($ mil.)	NET PROFIT MARGIN	EMPLOYEES
06/18	579	203	35.2%	3,300
06/17	560	74	13.2%	—
06/12	490	16	3.4%	—
06/06	370	45	12.2%	—
Annual Growth	3.8%	13.4%	—	—

2018 Year-End Financials

Return on assets: 10.4%
Return on equity: 14.2%
Current ratio: —
Cash ($ mil.): 62

ROCHESTER REGIONAL HEALTH

EXECUTIVES

Pres, Eric Bieber
Director, Mike Meath
Director, Christopher Jordan
Senior Engineer, Craig Unterborn
Director, Daniel Newcomb
Director, Diane Farnsworth
Supervisor, Laura Caceci
Financial Analyst, Lori Falzone
Vice President, Lorri J McCoy
Vice President, Matt Drake
Network Engineer, Matt Kassel

LOCATIONS

HQ: ROCHESTER REGIONAL HEALTH
100 KINGS HWY S STE 700, ROCHESTER, NY 146175541
Phone: 585 922-4000
Web: WWW.ROCHESTERREGIONAL.ORG

HISTORICAL FINANCIALS

Company Type: Private

Income Statement — FYE: December 31

	REVENUE ($ mil.)	NET INCOME ($ mil.)	NET PROFIT MARGIN	EMPLOYEES
12/18	2,189	38	1.8%	16,000
12/17	2,059	54	2.6%	—
Annual Growth	6.3%	(28.6%)	—	—

2018 Year-End Financials

Return on assets: 1.8%
Return on equity: 7.0%
Current ratio: 1.60
Cash ($ mil.): 170

ROCKIES EXPRESS PIPELINE LLC

EXECUTIVES

Account Director, Deborah Fishel

LOCATIONS

HQ: ROCKIES EXPRESS PIPELINE LLC
370 VAN GORDON ST # 4000, LAKEWOOD, CO 802281519
Phone: 877 546-5877
Web: WWW.TALLGRASSENERGYLP.COM

HISTORICAL FINANCIALS

Company Type: Private

Income Statement — FYE: December 31

	REVENUE ($ mil.)	NET INCOME ($ mil.)	NET PROFIT MARGIN	EMPLOYEES
12/19	927	284	30.7%	30
12/18	967	487	50.4%	—
12/17	893	298	33.4%	—
12/16	730	178	24.5%	—
Annual Growth	8.3%	16.7%	—	—

ROPER ST. FRANCIS HEALTHCARE

CareAlliance Health Services (doing business as Roper St. Francis Healthcare) operates four hospitals – the 370-bed Roper Hospital the 200-bed Bon Secours St. Francis Hospital the 85-bed Mount Pleasant Hospital and the Roper Rehabilitation Hospital. Besides providing home health services it also operates outpatient emergency primary care and diagnostic facilities. Roper St. Francis Healthcare serves Charleston South Carolina and surrounding communities. Its Roper St. Francis Physician Partners is one of the region's largest physician practices.

Operations

The health system comprises Roper Hospital Bon Secours St. Francis Hospital Roper St. Francis Mount Pleasant Hospital Roper St. Francis Foundation and Roper St. Francis Physicians Network. Altogether it boasts three acute care hospitals with 655-plus beds one specialty hospital 15 centers for outpatient services three industrial medicine sites five emergency rooms and two urgent care centers.

Roper St. Francis Healthcare has a medical staff of some 800 physicians. The Roper St. Francis Physician Partners organization has more than 230 physicians who offer primary and specialty care including family practice internal medicine and pediatrics.

Geographic Reach

Altogether Roper St. Francis Healthcare operates about 90 facilities in seven counties in the lowcountry region of South Carolina.

Strategy

The health system in 2014 signed an agreement with Trendlines Lab to collaborate on the development of new medical device inventions as well as low-cost solutions for clinical problems. The partnership will work to create devices that will address unmet needs identified by physicians and other health care providers.

Company Background

Roper St. Francis Healthcare was formed through the merger of Roper Hospital and Bon Secours St. Francis Hospital in 1998.

Roper St. Francis Physician Partners was formed through the 2009 combination of Roper St. Francis Physicians' Network and Lowcountry Medical Associates.

EXECUTIVES

President And Ceo, David L. Dunlap
Vp And Cio, Mike Taylor
Vice President Of Medical Affairs & Chief Medical Officer, Steven Shapiro
Svp And Cfo, Bret Johnson
Ceo Roper Hospital And Svp Operations, Matthew Severance
Ceo Roper St. Francis Mount Pleasant Hospital And Vp Operations, John Sullivan
Ceo Bon Secours St. Francis Hospital And Svp Operations, Allen Carroll
Chairman Roper St. Francis Foundation, John B. Holloway
Vice Chairman Roper St. Francis Foundation, Charles T. Cole
Vice President Nursing & Senior Nurse Executive Bon Secours St. Francis, Pennie Peralta
Ceo Rsf Physician Partners & Rsfh Vice President & Chief Strategy Officer, Douglas Bowling
Pharmacy Manager, Thomas Baxley
Vp Operations, Capers Limehouse
Vice President Quality And Training, Tanya Lott
Medical Director, Katherine Minnick
Vice President Of Nursing, P Floyd
Director Of Pharmacy, Holly Balcer
Vice President Of Finance, Lynn Roberts
Vice President And Chief Diversity And Inclusion Officer, Toni Flowers
Vice President Of Medical Affairs, Stanley Wilson
Physical Therapy Director, Troy Powell
Chairman Of The Board, Pierre Manigault
Auditors: DELOITTE & TOUCHE LLP CHARLO

LOCATIONS

HQ: ROPER ST. FRANCIS HEALTHCARE
125 DOUGHTY ST STE 760, CHARLESTON, SC 294035785
Phone: 843 724-2000
Web: WWW.RSFH.COM

Selected South Carolina Facilities

Hospitals
Mt. Pleasant Hospital Campus - Mount Pleasant
Roper Hosp
Roper Rehabilitation Hospital
St. Franci
Outpatient Centers
After Hours Care - James Island
Kiawah-Seabrook Medical & Urgent Care
Roper Hosp
Roper Hospital Ambulatory Surgery & Pain Management - James Island
Roper Hosp
Roper Hosp
Roper Hosp
Roper Hosptial Diagnostics - Goose Creek
Roper Hosptial Diagnostics - James Island
Roper Hosp
Roper Hosptial Diagnostics - Moncks Corner
Roper Hospital Imaging - Wesley Drive
Roper Hospital Imaging - Wingo Way

COMPETITORS

Beaufort Memorial Hospital
Conway Medical Center
Georgetown Hospital System
Grand Strand Regional Medical Center
HCA
Medical University of South Carolina
Tenet Healthcare

HISTORICAL FINANCIALS

Company Type: Private

Income Statement — FYE: December 31

	REVENUE ($ mil.)	NET INCOME ($ mil.)	NET PROFIT MARGIN	EMPLOYEES
12/14	793	(2)	—	6,000
12/09	682	56	8.3%	—
12/08	618	(51)	—	—
Annual Growth	4.3%	—	—	—

2014 Year-End Financials

Return on assets: (-0.3%)
Return on equity: (-0.7%)
Current ratio: 1.30
Cash ($ mil.): 54

ROUND ROCK INDEPENDENT SCHOOL DISTRICT (INC)

EXECUTIVES

Supt, Dr Jess H Chvez
Prin*, Georgia Mill
Supt*, Dr Steven Flores
Information Specialist, Debby Acevedo
Coordinator, Nicole Shannon
Information Technology/Interne, Brent Engelhardt
Administrative Assistant, Jackie Gordon
Director, Tonya Davis
Administrator, Olivia Carreno
Programmer Analyst, Steve Wager
Assistant Director, Maria Green
Auditors: MAXWELL LOCKE & RITTER LLP AU

LOCATIONS

HQ: ROUND ROCK INDEPENDENT SCHOOL DISTRICT (INC)
1311 ROUND ROCK AVE, ROUND ROCK, TX 786814941
Phone: 512 464-5000
Web: WWW.ROUNDROCKISD.ORG

HISTORICAL FINANCIALS

Company Type: Private

Income Statement — FYE: June 30

	REVENUE ($ mil.)	NET INCOME ($ mil.)	NET PROFIT MARGIN	EMPLOYEES
06/19	600	174	29.0%	4,500
06/18	546	(70)	—	—
06/17	533	(65)	—	—
06/16	523	64	12.3%	—
Annual Growth	4.7%	39.3%	—	—

2019 Year-End Financials

Return on assets: 11.8%
Return on equity: 139.2%
Current ratio: 7.90
Cash ($ mil.): 554

ROUSE'S ENTERPRISES, L.L.C.

EXECUTIVES

MBR, Anthony J Rouse Sr
MBR*, Donald J Rouse
MBR*, Thomas B Rouse
GM, Perry Byrne
Director of Human Resources, Steven Galtier
Auditors: TS KEARNS & CO THIBODAUX

LOCATIONS

HQ: ROUSE'S ENTERPRISES, L.L.C.
1301 SAINT MARY ST, THIBODAUX, LA 703016527
Phone: 985 447-5998
Web: WWW.SHOP.ROUSES.COM

HISTORICAL FINANCIALS

Company Type: Private

Income Statement FYE: December 29

	REVENUE ($ mil.)	NET INCOME ($ mil.)	NET PROFIT MARGIN	EMPLOYEES
12/10	691	24	3.5%	5,200
12/09	689	21	3.1%	—
12/06	247	11	4.8%	—
Annual Growth	29.4%	19.7%	—	—

2010 Year-End Financials

Return on assets: 15.7%
Return on equity: 25.8%
Current ratio: 2.00
Cash ($ mil.): 8

ROYAL TEN CATE (USA), INC.

EXECUTIVES

Ceo, Loek De Vries
Vice Pres-Cfo*, Joseph W Averette
SEC*, Henry Hope
Director, David Clarke
Extrusion Manager, Tony Pilgrim

LOCATIONS

HQ: ROYAL TEN CATE (USA), INC.
365 S HOLLAND DR, PENDERGRASS, GA 305674625
Phone: 706 693-2226
Web: WWW.TENCATEGEO.US

HISTORICAL FINANCIALS

Company Type: Private

Income Statement FYE: December 31

	REVENUE ($ mil.)	NET INCOME ($ mil.)	NET PROFIT MARGIN	EMPLOYEES
12/14	640	0	—	1,500
12/13	613	0	—	—
12/12	626	0	—	—
12/11	178	0	—	—
Annual Growth	53.0%	—	—	—

2014 Year-End Financials

Return on assets: —
Return on equity: —
Current ratio: 3.00
Cash ($ mil.): 18

RUDOLPH AND SLETTEN, INC.

Rudolph and Sletten ... the little-known tenth reindeer? More like the elves who built Santa's workshop. The firm is a mainstay of the California construction scene especially Silicon Valley. It has built corporate campuses for Apple Microsoft and Wells Fargo as well as Lucasfilm's Skywalker Ranch production facility. Rudolph and Sletten is one of the US' largest general building contractors with site selection design/build and construction management capabilities. Key projects also include biotech labs hospitals and schools. Onslow "Rudy" Rudolph founded the company in 1959 and was joined by partner Kenneth Sletten in 1962. Rudolph and Sletten is a subsidiary of Tutor Perini Corporation .

Geographic Reach

Redwood City California-based Rudolph and Sletten has regional offices in San Francisco Sacramento Irvine San Diego and Stockton California. The firm is licensed to build in California Arizona Nevada Washington Colorado Idaho Oregon Oklahoma and Texas.

Sales and Marketing

Big name clients have included a number of prestigious institutions such as Childrens Hospital Los Angeles The University of Southern California Genentech and the Monterey Bay Aquarium. The company reports that more than 95% of its business comes from repeat customers.

Financial Performance

California is Rudolph and Slatten's largest market representing an estimated $666 million in revenue in 2013.

Strategy

To capitalize on San Francisco's building boom the firm hired several San Francisco construction veterans in early 2014 to expand its operations there. Rudolph and Sletten is currently working on projects in Mission Bay and the Financial District.

The firm is renowned for its green building practices with nearly half the staff Leadership in Energy and Environmental Design (LEED)-accredited; it aims for 100% accreditation by 2013. Its own corporate headquarters was Gold LEED-certified based on its use of recycled materials energy and water efficiency and sustainable site. Other sustainable projects undertaken by Rudolph and Sletten include the Lawrence Berkeley National Laboratory and the NOAA Fisheries Services Southwest Science Center.

EXECUTIVES

Senior Vice President Preconstruction Services, Michael Mohrman
Sr. Vice President, Jon Foad
Auditors: DELOITTE & TOUCHE LLP LOS AN

LOCATIONS

HQ: RUDOLPH AND SLETTEN, INC.
2 CIRCLE STAR WAY FL 4, SAN CARLOS, CA 940706200
Phone: 650 216-3600
Web: WWW.RSCONSTRUCTION.COM

PRODUCTS/OPERATIONS

Major Markets

Biotechnology/pharmaceutical
Commercial office and corporate campuses
Education
Gaming and hospitality
Government
Health care
Industrial
Justice
Sports and entertainment
Technology

Selected Services

Estimating
Scheduling
Value engineering
Constructibility review
Building Information Modeling (BIM)
Construction
Construction management
Project management
Quality control
Disruption management
Commissioning
Self performed work
Sustainable cpnstruction
Safety

COMPETITORS

Charles Pankow Builders
Clark Construction Group
DPR Construction
Devcon Construction
Hathaway Dinwiddie Construction
Hensel Phelps Construction
Kitchell
McCarthy Building
PCL Constructors
Summit Builders
Swinerton
Turner Construction
Webcor Builders
Whiting-Turner

HISTORICAL FINANCIALS

Company Type: Private

Income Statement FYE: December 31

	REVENUE ($ mil.)	NET INCOME ($ mil.)	NET PROFIT MARGIN	EMPLOYEES
12/16	1,307	14	1.1%	700
12/15	940	7	0.7%	—
12/14	637	3	0.5%	—
12/13	665	(0)	—	—
Annual Growth	25.2%	—	—	—

RUSH UNIVERSITY MEDICAL CENTER

EXECUTIVES

Pres-Ceo, Omar Lateef
Exec V Pres-Coo, Wayne E Keathley
Chief of Medicine, David Amsell
Accounting Staff, Donna Ameismeier
General, Fred A Cbet
Dental Assistant Supervisor, George Katsoyannis
Coordinator, Janie Voyles
Staff, John S Weitzner
Doctor, Juan-Miguel Mosquera
Accounting Staff, Mable Kyles
Doctor, Robert D Samuel Higgins
Auditors: DELOITTE & TOUCHE LLP CHICAG

LOCATIONS

HQ: RUSH UNIVERSITY MEDICAL CENTER
1620 W HARRISON ST, CHICAGO, IL 606123801
Phone: 312 942-5000
Web: WWW.RUSH.EDU

HISTORICAL FINANCIALS

Company Type: Private

Income Statement FYE: June 30

	REVENUE ($ mil.)	NET INCOME ($ mil.)	NET PROFIT MARGIN	EMPLOYEES
06/17	2,267	302	13.3%	8,000
06/16	1,502	83	5.6%	—
06/15	1,408	(22)	—	—
06/14	1,969	208	10.6%	—
Annual Growth	4.8%	13.2%	—	—

2017 Year-End Financials

Return on assets: 7.9%
Return on equity: 13.7%
Current ratio: 0.90
Cash ($ mil.): 99

RYMAN HOSPITALITY PROPERTIES, INC.

Ryman Hospitality Properties (formerly Gaylord Entertainment) may be hollerin' for attention in the hospitality game but it's no corporate hayseed. Its properties consist of resort hotels tethered closely to attractions that appeal to the meetings and conventions market. They include the Gaylord Opryland Resort & Convention Center in Nashville the Gaylord Palms Resort in Florida (close to Disney World) the Gaylord Texan Resort near Dallas and the Gaylord National Resort and Convention Center in the Washington DC area. Ryman's hotels are managed by hotel giant Marriott.

HISTORY

The origins of Gaylord Entertainment can be traced back to the Oklahoma Publishing Co. a newspaper publishing company founded by Edward K. Gaylord Ray Dickinson and Roy McClintock in 1903. The publisher of The Daily Oklahoman Oklahoma Publishing branched into radio in 1928 with the purchase of Oklahoma City radio station WKY. With its 1949 creation of Oklahoma City television station WKY-TV Oklahoma Publishing made the leap into television.

Edward K. Gaylord died in 1974 at the age of 101 and his son Edward L. Gaylord was appointed CEO. Under his leadership the company purchased Opryland USA in 1983 – an acquisition that netted it the Grand Ole Opry Opryland Themepark and the Opryland Hotel. Opryland USA also launched country music cable network The Nashville Network that year.

In 1991 the increasingly diverse Oklahoma Publishing spun off its entertainment and broadcast holdings in the form of public company Gaylord Entertainment which established its headquarters in Nashville Tennessee. Gaylord Entertainment acquired a majority interest in cable music network Country Music Television (CMT) the same year. It later expanded CMT into Latin America Asia and the Pacific Rim. CMT also made a brief foray into Europe but that initiative was ended in 1998.

Facing a consolidating entertainment and media landscape Gaylord sold The Nashville Network and the US operations of CMT to Westinghouse (now CBS) in 1997. It also sold television station KSTW that year. The company expanded its reach into Christian music with the purchase of Word Entertainment and its 1997 acquisition of Blanton Harrell Entertainment gave Gaylord a presence in artist management. Terry London was appointed CEO in 1997.

The company closed its Opryland theme park in 1998 in the face of declining attendance and broke ground at the same site for the Opry Mills entertainment shopping and restaurant complex (opened 2000). Gaylord also purchased a Nashville Ramada Inn in 1998 (later renaming it Radisson Hotel at Opryland). With its 1998 acquisition of Paris-based Pandora Investment Gaylord branched into film distribution.

In 1999 the company formed Opryland Hospitality Group to oversee expansion of the Opryland hotel concept across the US. It also sold its last television station KTVT in Dallas/Fort Worth to CBS. Edward K. Gaylord II succeeded his father as chairman in 1999. That year the company launched its Internet division GETdigitalmedia (later renamed Gaylord Digital) and moved online with the purchase of Christian Web sites Musicforce.com and Lightsource.com. Later the same year the company expanded its Internet presence with the purchase of Songs.com a music Web site focused on independent artists. But in late 2000 the company announced it would close its Internet unit. Also in 2000 the company bought Corporate Magic a firm focused on producing entertainment events for corporate audiences.

At the end of 2000 Gaylord sold Musicforce.com to Christian Book Distributors. Following that sale it sold Lightsource.com to LifeAudio.com in early 2001. That year the company sold its film and television production units and announced a restructuring in order to cut costs. It also renamed Opryland Hotels to Gaylord Opryland while expanding into Texas and Florida. Colin Reed was appointed CEO in 2001.

Between 2001 and 2003 Gaylord Entertainment sold Word Entertainment to Warner Music Group the Opry Mills shopping and restaurant complex to The Mills Corporation the Acuff-Rose Music Publishing business to Sony/ATV two of its Nashville radio stations to Cumulus Media and its majority interest in the Oklahoma City Redhawks minor league baseball team.

Edward L. Gaylord officially retired from the company in 2003 at age 83. Also that year the company significantly expanded its hospitality business with the purchase of ResortQuest a vacation and condominium property management firm. In 2004 the Gaylord family sold more than half its shares in the company making Gabelli Funds the majority owner.

In 2005 Gaylord acquired 50% of Corporate Magic a Dallas-based provider of production support for corporate meetings and events. It did so to support its meeting and convention facilities.

The company unloaded its minority interest in minor league hockey team the Nashville Predators in 2005. Two years later it sold ResortQuest to a subsidiary of Leucadia National Corp. for $35 million. Also in 2007 it sold its interest in sporting goods store operator Bass Pro Group. In 2008 the company opened the Gaylord National Resort and Convention Center in the Washington DC area. The property has some 2000 rooms and approximately 450000 square feet of meeting space.

Also in 2008 Gaylord terminated plans to acquire the Westin La Cantera Resort in San Antonio for about $253 million citing a tough economic environment. In addition the 2008 sale of its ResortQuest subsidiary an online booking service in vacation rentals property management and resort real estate sales fit the company's strategy of selling off assets that aren't related to its Grand Ole Opry or its operations in the meetings and convention market.

In 2009 the company responded to weak earnings by cutting approximately 500 jobs across all areas of the business. Gaylord reported steep dip in profits in 2010 primarily due to harsh flooding in Nashville when the Cumberland River rose to historic levels flowing over protective levees. The flood resulted in property damage and temporary closures at its properties in Nashville causing lost revenues and an increase in expenses. Also in 2010 Gaylord sold its 50% stake in Corporate Magic back to that company's CEO.

The company changed its name to Ryman Hospitality Properties in 2012. It also converted to an REIT and sold the Gaylord brand to Marriott which now manages Ryman's hotel properties and certain other entertainment holdings.

EXECUTIVES

Evp Ryman Hospitality Properties; President Opry Entertainment Group, Stephen G. (Steve) Buchanan

Chairman And Ceo, Colin V. Reed, age 72, $782,830 total compensation

Svp Investments Design And Construction, Bennett D. Westbrook, age 53, $318,447 total compensation

President And Cfo, Mark Fioravanti, age 58, $469,407 total compensation

Svp Asset Management, Patrick Chaffin, age 46, $274,975 total compensation

Svp General Counsel And Secretary, Scott J. Lynn, age 46, $364,876 total compensation

Senior Vice President And Corporate Controller, Jennifer Hutcheson

Vice President Information Technology, Sharon Asmus

Vice President, James Chamblin

Vice President Human Resources, Shawn Smith

Svp Of Marketing, Laura Hollingsworth

Board Member, Michael J Bender

Board Member, Patrick Moore

Member Board Of Directors, Fazal Merchant

Auditors: ERNST & YOUNG LLP NASHVILLE

LOCATIONS

HQ: RYMAN HOSPITALITY PROPERTIES, INC.
1 GAYLORD DR, NASHVILLE, TN 372141207

Phone: 615 316-6000

Web: WWW.RYMANHP.COM

PRODUCTS/OPERATIONS

2015 Sales

	$ mil.	% of total
Hospitality	994	91
Entertainment (previously Opry and Attractions)	97	9
Total	**1,092**	**100**

2015 Sales

	$ mil.	% of total
Food and beverage	461	42
Rooms	404	37
Other hotel revenue	129	12
Entertainment (previously Opry and Attractions)	97	9
Total	**1,092**	**100**

Select Operations

Hospitality
- Gaylord Opryland Resort & Convention Center (Tennessee)
- Gaylord Palms Resort & Convention Center (Florida)
- Gaylord Texan Resort & Convention Center
- Radisson Hotel at Opryland (Tennessee)

Attractions
- Gaylord Springs Golf Links (golf club Tennessee)
- General Jackson Showboat
- Grand Ole Opry
- Ryman Auditorium
- Wildhorse Saloon
- WSM-AM

COMPETITORS

CKX
Caesars Entertainment
Disney Parks & Resorts
Elvis Presley Enterprises
Herschend Entertainment
Hershey Entertainment
Hilton Worldwide
Kennywood
Las Vegas Sands
Live Nation Entertainment
MGM Resorts
Marriott
New York Convention Center Operating Corporation
SeaWorld
Welk Group

HISTORICAL FINANCIALS

Company Type: Private

Income Statement				FYE: December 31
	ASSETS ($ mil.)	NET INCOME ($ mil.)	INCOME AS % OF ASSETS	EMPLOYEES
12/16	2,405	159	6.6%	177,000
12/15	2,331	111	4.8%	—
12/14	2,413	126	5.2%	—
12/13	2,424	113	4.7%	—
Annual Growth	(0.3%)	12.0%	—	—

2016 Year-End Financials

Return on assets: 6.6%
Return on equity: 43.3%
Sales ($ mil): 1,149

S & B ENGINEERS AND CONSTRUCTORS, LTD.

S & B Engineers and Constructors (S&B) makes it possible for others to burn the midnight oil. The employee-owned company specializes in engineering procurement construction and fabrication services to multiple industries. It primarily focuses on NGL fractionation import / export terminals pipelines petrochemicals & polymers and refining. S&B also flexes its engineering muscle on transportation waste and wastewater and environmental and telecommunications projects for public sector clients. Founded in 1967 by James Slaughter and William Brookshire to serve refineries and other process plants along the Texas and Louisiana gulf coasts the company has expanded services globally with two offices in India.

Operations

The company has divisions that focus on specific geographic areas and services. S&B's Engineers and Constructors division provides engineering procurement and construction services for combustion turbine combined and simple cycle projects as well as environmental AQCS retrofit projects for existing coal plants.

Ford Bacon & Davis does much of its business in the southern US where it takes on engineering and design projects for oil gas and chemical companies. It not only constructs new plants but is often hired to rebuild facilities that have been damaged by fires or explosions.

The firm's Plant Services division provides small capital construction supplemental maintenance turnaround professional services asset management and other plant services including productivity studies and specialty training. S&B Infrastructure caters to private and government clients – ranging from federal to state to local authorities – while its private sector services extend from land development to industrial to pipeline client needs.

S&B India services its parent company's US clients as well as clients in India and other countries.

Geographic Reach

Houston-based S&B boasts more than five offices throughout Texas (including its modular operation) its Northeast office in Canonsburg Pennsylvania a handful of offices in Louisiana and a single office in Greenville South Carolina also in Morrisville North Carolina and Kingsport Tennessee. S&B India has engineering centers in Bangalore and New Delhi.

Sales and Marketing

The company primarily serves midstream industry which is nearly 30% of its project. The petrochemical and polymers industry accounts 25% of its projects. Other industries includes terminals/transportation refining and power.

EXECUTIVES

Senior Vice President Of Sales, Rich Akin
President, James G. Slaughter
Svp Engineering, Charles R. Reid
Svp Construction, Tommy H. Collins
Vice President Construction Home Office Services, Randy Walker
Vice President Business Development, Terry A Doyle
Vice President Procurement, Kent Malone
Vice President, James Harrod
Vice President Process Technology, Guy Suffridge
Legal Secretary, Raymond Harper
Vice President Business Development, Harvey Hensley
Vice President Business Development, Justin Borchardt
Vice President Project Services, Sandy Lee
Vice President Human Resources, Ralph Morales
Vice President Field Operations Manager, David Taylor
Vice President Business Development, Blane Vincent
Co-founder And Chairman, William A. Brookshire
Auditors: ERNST & YOUNG LLP HOUSTON TX

LOCATIONS

HQ: S & B ENGINEERS AND CONSTRUCTORS, LTD.
7825 PARK PLACE BLVD, HOUSTON, TX 770874697
Phone: 713 645-4141
Web: WWW.SBEC.COM

Selected Locations

US

Austin TX
Baton Roug
El Paso TX
Fort Worth TX
Freeport TX
Greenville SC
Houston
Longview TX
McAllen TX
Monroe LA
New Orleans
San Antonio

India

Bangalore
New Delhi

PRODUCTS/OPERATIONS

Selected Projects

Sulfur Tailgas Treating Unit Blaine WA
Crude Upgrade Project El Segundo CA
Pipeline Terminal Project Los Angeles CA
Refinery Revamp Project Bakersfield CA
Fractionation Expansion Project Billings MT
Gas Plant Project Meeker CO
SMR Project Port Arthur TX
ABF Program BP Refinery Texas City
Low Sulfur Gasoline & Diesel Projects Houston TX
Fine Paper Machine Project Kingsport TN

Selected Services

Construction
Engineering
Modules and skids
Plant services
Procurement
Project management

Selected Divisions

Ford Bacon & Davis
S&B India
S&B Infrastructure
S&B Plant Services
S&B Power Division

COMPETITORS

Bechtel
Fluor
Jacobs Engineering
KBR
KBR Building Group
Parsons Corporation
Turner Industries
Zachry Inc.

HISTORICAL FINANCIALS

Company Type: Private

Income Statement				FYE: December 31
	REVENUE ($ mil.)	NET INCOME ($ mil.)	NET PROFIT MARGIN	EMPLOYEES
12/19	2,415	0	—	3,000
12/18	679	0	—	—
12/17	679	0	—	—
12/16	950	0	—	—
Annual Growth	36.5%	—	—	—

2019 Year-End Financials

Return on assets: —
Return on equity: —
Current ratio: 1.30
Cash ($ mil.): 314

SACRAMENTO CITY UNIFIED SCHOOL DISTRICT

EXECUTIVES

Supt, Jose Banda
Cfo*, Tom Barrinson
C-Level Human Resources, Robert Garcia
Teacher, Bre Rizzo
K12 Project Manager, Jay Elmquist
Auditors: CROWE LLP SACRAMENTO CALIFOR

LOCATIONS

HQ: SACRAMENTO CITY UNIFIED SCHOOL DISTRICT
5735 47TH AVE, SACRAMENTO, CA 958244528
Phone: 916 643-7400
Web: WWW.SCUSD.EDU

HISTORICAL FINANCIALS

Company Type: Private

Income Statement				FYE: June 30
	REVENUE ($ mil.)	NET INCOME ($ mil.)	NET PROFIT MARGIN	EMPLOYEES
06/19	690	(57)	—	6,500
06/18	635	(45)	—	—
06/17	625	71	11.5%	—
06/16	656	47	7.2%	—
Annual Growth	1.7%	—	—	—

SACRAMENTO MUNICIPAL UTILITY DISTRICT

The Sacramento Municipal Utility District (SMUD) doesn't want its name to be mud. One of the largest locally owned electric utilities in the US SMUD serves more than 640710 residential and commercial customer meters (a service area population of approximately 1.5 million) in California's Sacramento and Placer counties. SMUD is responsible for the acquisition generation transmission and distribution of electric power to its service area. It began serving Sacramento in 1946.

Operations

The utility operates more than 10910 miles of transmission and distribution lines across its 900-sq.-mi. service area. It gets power from varied sources including hydropower natural-gas-fired generators renewable energy (such as solar and wind power) and purchases power on the wholesale market.

The company has installed some 600000 smart meters at customer locations across its entire service area.

Geographic Reach

SMUD generates transmits and distributes electricity to a territory that includes Sacramento Sacramento County and a small portion of Placer and Yolo Counties.

Sales and Marketing

The company has over 640710 customer contracts in some 1.5 million service area population.

Financial Performance

SMUD's revenue is $1.6 billion similar to the previous year due to fluctuations in the company's segment revenues.Cash and cash equivalents at the end of the year were $308.1 million 21% higher than in the previous year. Cash provided by operating activities was $415.9 million. Financing activities and investing activities used $313.7 million and $4.1 million respectively. Main cash uses were repayments of commercial paper construction expenditures and purchases of securities.

Strategy

In 2019 SMUD continued its partnership with Habitat for Humanity by establishing a 2-year partnership to incentivize electrification and EV-ready homes and install rooftop solar. Building electrification programs resulted in a partnership with D.R. Horton to build more than 100 new all-electric homes. And through SMUD's Smart Homes Program SMUD received commitments from local and national homebuilders to build approximately 1900 new all electric homes by the end of 2022. SMUD has continued to grow its Greenergy program and is now one of the largest of its kind in the nation. Through its economic development program SMUD played a key role in the attraction retention and expansion of several companies in its service territory which led to the creation of over 700 jobs.

As part of the hydro relicensing process SMUD entered into long-term contracts to provide certain services to four different government agencies ? U.S. Department of Interior Bureau of Land Management U.S. Department of Agriculture Forest Service El Dorado County and the California Department of Parks and Recreation. On Dec. 31 2019 and 2018 the liability for these contract payments was $63.4 million and $58.8 million respectively.

SMUD also has a long-term agreement with the Western Area Power Administration (WAPA) to purchase power generated by the Central Valley Project a series of federal hydroelectric facilities operated by the U.S. Bureau of Reclamation.

Company Background

In 2012 SMUD announced that it is the leading utility in the US in terms of new homes which had solar panels installed during construction. The utility commenced the SMUD Solar Smart Homes program in 2006 and had constructed more than 1000 homes with solar panels by 2012.

The company has been delivering power to customers in the region since 1946 but its history goes back to 1923 when citizens voted to create SMUD as a community-owned electric service. However years of engineering studies political battles and legal wrangling delayed SMUD's purchase of PG&E' s local electrical system.

In March 1946 the California Supreme Court denied PG&E's final petition to halt the sale and nine months later SMUD finally began operations.

EXECUTIVES

Director Business Planning And Budget And Chief Risk Officer, James A. (Jim) Tracy
Ceo And General Manager, Arlen Orchard
Chief Grid Strategy And Operations Officer, Paul Lau
Board Vice President, Rob Kerth
Vice President, Brad Gacke
Vp Board Of Directors, Nancy Bui-Thompson
Assistant Treasurer, Tim Ryan
Assistant Treasurer, Larry Stark
Treasurer, Noreen Roche-Carter
Treasurer, Dale Johnson
Auditors: BAKER TILLY VIRCHOW KRAUSE L

LOCATIONS

HQ: SACRAMENTO MUNICIPAL UTILITY DISTRICT
6201 S ST, SACRAMENTO, CA 958171818
Phone: 916 452-3211
Web: WWW.SMUD.ORG

PRODUCTS/OPERATIONS

2015 Sales

	% of total
Commercial & industrial	47
Residential	42
Wholesale power	6
Street lighting & other	5
Total	**100**

Selected Products and Services

Conservation programs
Customer billing programs
Diagnostic services
Electric vehicle charging stations
Energy assistance programs
Energy-efficient appliances and equipment
Energy management
Green energy programs
Power quality and environmental services
Security lighting
Shade trees for customers
Solar water heating
Surge protection
Tree trimming

COMPETITORS

AES
Avista
Duke Energy
Edison International
Los Angeles Water and Power
PG&E Corporation
Sempra Energy

HISTORICAL FINANCIALS

Company Type: Private

Income Statement — FYE: December 31

	REVENUE ($ mil.)	NET INCOME ($ mil.)	NET PROFIT MARGIN	EMPLOYEES
12/19	1,559	78	5.1%	2,213
12/18	1,595	209	13.1%	—
12/17	1,559	181	11.6%	—
12/16	1,494	195	13.1%	—
Annual Growth	1.4%	(26.1%)	—	—

2019 Year-End Financials

Return on assets: 1.2%
Return on equity: 4.4%
Current ratio: 1.90
Cash ($ mil.): 255

SADDLE BUTTE PIPELINE LLC

Auditors: HEIN & ASSOCIATES LLP DENVER

LOCATIONS

HQ: SADDLE BUTTE PIPELINE LLC
858 MAIN AVE UNIT 301, DURANGO, CO 813015496
Phone: 970 375-3150
Web: WWW.SBPIPELINE.COM

HISTORICAL FINANCIALS

Company Type: Private

Income Statement — FYE: December 31

	REVENUE ($ mil.)	NET INCOME ($ mil.)	NET PROFIT MARGIN	EMPLOYEES
12/12	689	656	95.2%	30
12/11	69	(10)	—	—
12/10	68	0	0.0%	—
Annual Growth	218.1%	19913.8%	—	—

2012 Year-End Financials

Return on assets: 425.0%
Return on equity: 433.6%
Current ratio: 50.40
Cash ($ mil.): 144

SAINT ALPHONSUS REGIONAL MEDICAL CENTER INC.

EXECUTIVES

Pres-Ceo, Sally Jeffcoat
Cco*, Steven Nemerson
Director, Sarah Berg
Managing Partner, Elizabeth Criner
Account Manager, Lois Soito

LOCATIONS

HQ: SAINT ALPHONSUS REGIONAL MEDICAL CENTER INC.
1055 N CURTIS RD, BOISE, ID 837061309
Phone: 208 367-6899
Web: WWW.SARMC.ORG

HISTORICAL FINANCIALS

Company Type: Private

Income Statement — FYE: June 30

	REVENUE ($ mil.)	NET INCOME ($ mil.)	NET PROFIT MARGIN	EMPLOYEES
06/18	937	50	5.4%	40
06/15	37	(5)	—	—
06/14	29	(5)	—	—
06/11	0	(0)	—	—
Annual Growth	—	—	—	—

2018 Year-End Financials

Return on assets: 4.5%
Return on equity: 6.8%
Current ratio: 3.40
Cash ($ mil.): 208

SAINT ALPHONSUS REGIONAL MEDICAL CENTER, INC.

Saint Alphonsus Regional Medical Center makes medical care its primary mission. The 384-bed hospital provides Boise Idaho and the surrounding region (including eastern Oregon and northern Nevada) with general acute and specialized health care services. Its facilities and operations include a level II trauma center an orthopedic spinal care unit an air transport service and a home health and hospice division. Saint Alphonsus Regional Medical Center is part of Trinity Health's four-hospital Saint Alphonsus Health System which serves Boise and Nampa in Idaho and Ontario and Baker City in Oregon. The Sisters of the Holy Cross founded the hospital in 1894.

Operations

Saint Alphonsus Regional Medical Center provides outpatient services through the 70 affiliated physician practices that make up the Saint Alphonsus Medical Group. It also operates the Saint Alphonsus Health Plaza which provides urgent care and outpatient surgery laboratory rehabilitation and primary care services.

The hospital also offers rural or homebound patients telemedicine services through which remote physician visits are conducted using audio or video.

Geographic Reach

Saint Alphonsus Regional Medical Center serves a territory that includes portions of southwestern Idaho northern Nevada and eastern Oregon.

Strategy

Saint Alphonsus Regional Medical Center expands its facilities to improve medical care in its service territory. In 2014 it opened its newly expanded and renovated emergency department which included a 30% increase in square footage. Also that year it became the first hospital in the region to utilize the EndoWrist Stapler technology on the da Vinci robotic system for minimally invasive surgeries.

EXECUTIVES

Vice President Quality Services, James Robert Polk
Vice President System Philanthropy Marketing Communications Advocacy Saint Alphonsus Health System, Linda Smith
Medical Director Of Physician Relations, Patrice Burgess
Medical Director, Rick Turner
Vice President Corporate Development Marketing, Jean Basom
Vice President, Pamela Thomas
Vice President Of Operations, David Kirk
Treasurer, Richard Presnell
Board Of Directors, Sabrena James

LOCATIONS

HQ: SAINT ALPHONSUS REGIONAL MEDICAL CENTER, INC.
1055 N CURTIS RD, BOISE, ID 837061309
Phone: 208 367-2121
Web: WWW.SAINTALPHONSUS.ORG

COMPETITORS

Ascension Health
HCA
Intermountain Health Care
St. Luke's Health System

HISTORICAL FINANCIALS

Company Type: Private

Income Statement — FYE: June 30

	REVENUE ($ mil.)	NET INCOME ($ mil.)	NET PROFIT MARGIN	EMPLOYEES
06/14	572	46	8.0%	3,500
06/13	545	43	7.9%	—
06/10	449	13	3.1%	—
Annual Growth	6.2%	35.2%	—	—

2014 Year-End Financials

Return on assets: 6.4%
Return on equity: 10.6%
Current ratio: 1.30
Cash ($ mil.): 3

SAINT ELIZABETH MEDICAL CENTER, INC.

It doesn't have much to do with the Holy Trinity except for the fact that St. Elizabeth Medical Center (operating as St. Elizabeth Healthcare) does business in a trinity of states. The system provides health care services to residents in Kentucky Ohio and West Virginia. St. Elizabeth Healthcare's programs include stroke and cardiac care hospice services and neurosurgery. The system is home to six hospitals with about 1200 beds and dozens of primary care offices. St. Elizabeth Healthcare was formed through a merger between St. Elizabeth Medical and nearby St. Luke Hospitals. The organization has one board of directors and one management structure and is sponsored by the Catholic Diocese of Covington.

EXECUTIVES

President, Garren Colvin
Evp And Coo, Gary Blank
Cfo, Lori Ritchey-Baldwin
Assistant Vice President Of Planning And Marketing, Rosanne Nields
Senior Vice President Chief Medical Office, Laroy Kendall
Vice President Business Development, Julie Siemer
Vice President Of Foundation, Larry Warkoczeski
Assistant Vice President, Vera Hall
Director Of Pharmacy, R Frey
Vice President Of Sales, Cynthia Glass
Vice President Oncologist, Jack Basil
Senior Vice President Facilities, Harry Watson
Vice President Foundation, Carri Chandler
Assistant Vp Clinical Transformation, Karl Schmitt
Co Medical Director, Ryan Moon
Vice President Of Finance, Judy Dunman
Medical Director, Jeremy Solberg
Secretary To Director, Lisa Robinson
Secretary, Starr Baxter
Secretary Perioperative, Lora Saylor

LOCATIONS

HQ: SAINT ELIZABETH MEDICAL CENTER, INC.
1 MEDICAL VILLAGE DR, EDGEWOOD, KY 410173403
Phone: 859 301-2000
Web: WWW.STELIZABETH.COM

Selected locations

St. Elizabeth Covington (Covington Kentucky)
St. Elizabeth Edgewood (Edgewood Kentucky)
St. Elizabeth Grant (Williamstown Kentucky)
St. Elizabeth Ft. Thomas (St. Thomas Kentucky)
St. Elizabeth Florence (Florence Kentucky)
St. Elizabeth Falmouth (Falmouth Kentucky)

COMPETITORS

Adventist Health System Sunbelt Healthcare
Bethesda North
Catholic Health Initiatives
Cincinnati Children's Hospital
Deaconess Associations
HCA
Kettering Health Network
Mount Carmel Health
OhioHealth
Regency Hospital
Tenet Healthcare
The Christ Hospital Corporation
TriHealth
UC Health
Universal Health Services

HISTORICAL FINANCIALS

Company Type: Private

Income Statement — FYE: December 31

	REVENUE ($ mil.)	NET INCOME ($ mil.)	NET PROFIT MARGIN	EMPLOYEES
12/14	633	45	7.1%	6,227
12/13	984	124	12.7%	—
12/08	623	(32)	—	—
12/06	483	49	10.2%	—
Annual Growth	3.4%	(1.0%)	—	—

2014 Year-End Financials

Return on assets: 3.9%
Return on equity: 6.1%
Current ratio: 1.40
Cash ($ mil.): 22

SAINT FRANCIS HOSPITAL AND MEDICAL CENTER FOUNDATION, INC.

Saint Francis takes care of the hearts of Hartford Connecticut. The Saint Francis Hospital and Medical Center is a not-for-profit regional medical center with some 620 beds and 65 bassinets. The hospital specializes in cardiology oncology neurology orthopedics and women's and children's health services. It also offers behavioral health weight management trauma care and injury rehabilitation programs. Saint Francis serves as a teaching hospital affiliated with the University of Connecticut Schools of Medicine and Dentistry. It also operates laboratories a home health and hospice agency and other entities.Saint Francis is part of Catholic health care system Trinity Health.

Operations

Saint Francis' on-campus specialty centers include the Hoffman Heart and Vascular Institute which specializes in open-heart surgeries and catheterization procedures.

Strategy

Saint Francis has initiated a number of internal cost-reduction efforts to keep its operations and finances healthy. It is also improving its internal information management systems to increase efficiencies at its facilities.Trinity Health which acquired Saint Francis in 2015 is investing at least $275 million through 2020 towards capital projects and programmatic investments in the hospital's region. Recently introduced programs include the Center for Diabetes and Metabolic Care's Inpatient Glycemic Initiative.

Company Background

Saint Francis joined the Trinity Health Network in 2015.

EXECUTIVES

President, John Rodis
Vp Finance, Jennifer S. Schneider
Vp Facilities Support Services And Construction, Robert J. (Bob) Falaguerra
Vp And Chief Development Officer Saint Francis Foundation, Lynn Rossini
Vp Operations, Thomas M. Burke
Vp Professional Nursing Practice And Quality; Chief Nursing Officer, Denise M. Peterson
Physical Therapy, Dan Henck
Director Of Admissions, Albert Costa
Vice President Human Resources, Dennis Sparks
Vice President Payor Partnerships And Strategic Initiatives, John Sunde
Vice Chair, Jeri Hepworth

LOCATIONS

HQ: SAINT FRANCIS HOSPITAL AND MEDICAL CENTER FOUNDATION, INC.
114 WOODLAND ST, HARTFORD, CT 061051208
Phone: 860 714-4006
Web: WWW.TRINITYHEALTHOFNE.ORG

COMPETITORS

Backus
Bristol Hospital
Connecticut Children's Medical Center
Griffin Health
Hartford Health Care
Hospital of Central Connecticut
Lawrence & Memorial Hospital
MidState Medical Center
Stamford Health
University of Connecticut Health Center
Yale New Haven Health System

HISTORICAL FINANCIALS

Company Type: Private

Income Statement — FYE: September 30

	REVENUE ($ mil.)	NET INCOME ($ mil.)	NET PROFIT MARGIN	EMPLOYEES
09/18	871	90	10.4%	3,270
09/17	769	52	6.8%	—
09/14	670	17	2.6%	—
09/10	651	(10)	—	—
Annual Growth	3.7%	—	—	—

2018 Year-End Financials

Return on assets: 11.2%
Return on equity: 34.4%
Current ratio: 3.50
Cash ($ mil.): 4

SAINT FRANCIS HOSPITAL, INC.

EXECUTIVES

Ceo, Jake Henry
Human Resources, Brenda Garner
Director, Karen Cochran
Vice-President, Marcus McKinney
Senior Vice-President, Pete Aran
Director, Philip Marcus
Director, Tiffani Fagan
V Chm, Peter C Boylan
Vice-President Engineering, Mike Wilson
Coordinator, April M Borg
Family and General Dentistry, Larry Lander

LOCATIONS

HQ: SAINT FRANCIS HOSPITAL, INC.
6161 S YALE AVE, TULSA, OK 741361992
Phone: 918 502-2050
Web: WWW.SAINTFRANCIS.COM

HISTORICAL FINANCIALS

Company Type: Private

Income Statement — FYE: June 30

	REVENUE ($ mil.)	NET INCOME ($ mil.)	NET PROFIT MARGIN	EMPLOYEES
06/16	913	128	14.0%	4,000
06/15	877	171	19.6%	—
06/13	910	190	21.0%	—
06/12	838	157	18.7%	—
Annual Growth	2.2%	(5.0%)	—	—

2016 Year-End Financials

Return on assets: 5.6%
Return on equity: 6.5%
Current ratio: 8.90
Cash ($ mil.): 312

SAINT LOUIS UNIVERSITY

This university gives students a SLU of opportunities. Saint Louis University (SLU) is a Jesuit Catholic school offering nearly 90 undergraduate more than 100 graduate and a host of professional degree programs through about a dozen schools and colleges including a school of medicine and a campus in Madrid Spain. Most programs require core classes in philosophy and theology. SLU has an enrollment of nearly 12855 students. Its student-teacher ratio is 9:1. Saint Louis University was founded in 1818 by Reverend Louis William Du Bourg Catholic Bishop of Louisiana.

Operations

In addition to its extensive educational programs SLU's students and staff are involved in a number of research projects in areas including cancer infectious disease liver disease aging and brain disorders and heart/lung disease.

SLU also operates primary and specialty medical care clinics (some through its SLU Physicians organization) on its medical school campus. The university's School of Medicine is fully accredited by the Liaison Committee on Medical Education (LCME) the accrediting body for medical education in the US.

Geographic Reach

SLU's students hail from all 50 US states and more than 80 countries. In addition to its main campus in St. Louis Missouri the university operates a campus in Madrid Spain.

Company Background

Saint Louis University was founded in 1818 by Reverend Louis William Du Bourg Catholic Bishop of Louisiana.

EXECUTIVES

Treasurer And Chief Investment Officer, Gary L. Whitworth
President, Fred P. Pestello
Vp Medical Affairs, Philip O. Alderson
Vp And Cfo, David Heimburger
Vp And Cio, David Hakanson
Assistant Vice President, Jill Carnaghi
Vice President Of Human Resources, Michael Luna
Vice President Diversity And Community Engagement, Jonathan Smith
Assistant Vice President Public Safety, James Moran
Academic Department Chair, Sara Den
Director Of Admissions, Heidi Buffington
Associate Vice President For Facilities Services, Michael Lucido
Assistant Vice President University Development, Ted Cox
Vice President Facilities Services, Antoinette Dean
Director Of Government Relations, Marc Scheessele
Associate Vice President, Diana Carlin
Chairman, J. Joe Adorjan
Vice Chairman, Patrick J. Sly
Secretary Medical, Mary Streif
Secretary Medical, Nola Johnsen
Secretary Medical, Jan Heizer
Secretary Medical, Georgene Menshouse
Secretary Administrative, Megan Osborn
Secretary Administrative, Vicki Shipp
Secretary Medical, Loletta Zasaretti
Assistant Treasurer, Jim Fugel
Secretary, Meg Smith
Auditors: KPMG LLP COLUMBUS OH

LOCATIONS

HQ: SAINT LOUIS UNIVERSITY
1 N GRAND, SAINT LOUIS, MO 63103
Phone: 314 977-2500
Web: WWW.SLU.EDU

PRODUCTS/OPERATIONS

Colleges Schools and Degree Granting Centers

Advanced Dental Education Center for (CADE)
Arts and Sciences College of
Business John Cook School of
Education and Public Service College of
Engineering Aviation and Technology Parks College of
Health Care Ethics Albert Gnaegi Center for
Health Sciences Doisy College of
Law School of
Madrid Spain Campus
Medicine School of
Nursing School of
Outcomes Research Center for (SLUCOR)
Philosophy and Letters College of
Professional Studies School for
Public Health School of
Social Work School of

HISTORICAL FINANCIALS

Company Type: Private

Income Statement — FYE: June 30

	REVENUE ($ mil.)	NET INCOME ($ mil.)	NET PROFIT MARGIN	EMPLOYEES
06/10	750	28	3.8%	7,500
06/09	697	0	—	—
06/08	633	(54)	—	—
Annual Growth	8.9%	—	—	—

2010 Year-End Financials

Return on assets: 1.7%
Return on equity: 2.3%
Current ratio: —
Cash ($ mil.): 141

SAINT LUKE'S HEALTH SYSTEM, INC.

Caring for the residents of Missouri's largest city is no mean feat but Saint Luke's Health System manages it through 10 area hospitals and a host of clinics located throughout Kansas City. The not-for-profit system's flagship facility is Saint Luke's Hospital which offers a Level I trauma center and internationally recognized cardiac and stroke care. Its Crittenton Children's Center is a behavioral health center serving children and their families on an inpatient and outpatient basis. Saint Luke's Health System is a network of almost 320 doctors providing primary and specialty care through clinics and other locations. The system is affiliated with the University of Missouri- Kansas City School of Medicine.

Operations

The health system offers a heart transplant program treatment for complex brain and spinal cord diseases advanced surgical care liver and kidney transplantation programs and a Level III neonatal intensive care unit. Other specialized services include women's health cancer treatment rehabilitation and home care.

Saint Luke Health System also engages extensively in medical research; its more than 330 researchers conduct more than 430 studies each year. Its activities have drawn funding and sponsorship from the National Institutes of Health the American Heart Association and the Saint Luke's Hospital Foundation.

Saint Luke's Health System BJC HealthCare of St. Louis CoxHealth of Springfield (Missouri) and Memorial Health System of Springfield Illinois make up The BJC Collaborative. Through economies of scale and the sharing of resources the multi-system Collaborative seeks to achieve higher quality care for the patients served by these independent not-for-profit health care organizations.

While remaining independent Collaborative members have more than 4820 hospital beds in Missouri Illinois and Kansas and combined annual revenues of almost $7 billion allowing the members of the BJC Collaborative to focus on achieving savings; deploying clinical programs and services to improve access to quality of health care for patients; lowering health care costs; and creating additional efficiencies.

Geographic Reach

In addition to the Kansas City metropolitan area (some 2 million people) Saint Luke's Health System's service area spans 67 counties in Missouri and Kansas.

Strategy

To expand its market penetration the system will open two Convenient Care clinics — one in Kansas and another in Missouri — during 2016. Additionally Saint Luke's has broken ground on a specialty clinic in Mission Farms in Kansas. That project is expected to be complete in 2017. Also in 2017 a specialty clinic will be opened in Blue Springs Missouri.

Company Background

The predecessor to Saint Luke's Hospital was founded in 1882 by Episcopal priest Henry David Jardine.

EXECUTIVES

Svp Hospital Operations, Julie L. Quirin
Svp And Chief Nurse Executive, Katherine A. (Kathy) Howell
Ceo Saint Luke's Hospital Of Kansas City, Jani L. Johnson
Svp Finance And Administration And Cfo, Chuck Robb
President And Ceo, Melinda L. Estes
Svp And Chief Physician Executive, Leonardo J. Lozada
Director Of Radiology, Robert Moore
Radiology Director, BOB MOORE
Operating Room Dir, APRIL PENDLETON
Medical Director, Tim Pluard
Vice President, Joann Paul
Vice President Supply Chain, Michael Darling
Director Of Medical Records, Nancy Moran
Director Of Home Healthcare Srv, Jill Guenther
Nursing Director, Bernie Jore
Director Physician Recruitment, Rob Diennen
Radiology Director, Lisa Oakes
Treasurer, John Holland
Board Member, Kory Barrett

LOCATIONS

HQ: SAINT LUKE'S HEALTH SYSTEM, INC.
901 E 104TH ST, KANSAS CITY, MO 641314517
Phone: 816 932-2000
Web: WWW.SAINTLUKESKC.ORG

PRODUCTS/OPERATIONS

2015 Sales

	$ mil.	% of total
Hospital	1,501	61
Other university	962	39
Total	2,463	100

Selected facilities

Anderson County Hospital (Garnett Kansas)
Crittenton Children's Center (Kansas City Missouri)
Hedrick Medical Center (Chillicothe Missouri)
Saint Luke's Cushing Hospital (Leavenworth Kansas)
Saint Luke's East (Lee's Summit Missouri)
Saint Luke's Hospital (Kansas City Missouri)
Saint Luke's Northland Hospital (Kansas City Missouri)
Saint Luke's Northland Hospital (Smithville Missouri)
Saint Luke's South (Overland Park Kansas)
Wright Memorial Hospital (Trenton Missouri)

Selected Services

Cancer services
Heart and vascular
Home care and hospice
Neuroscience
Surgical services
Transplant services
Women's and maternity services

COMPETITORS

Ascension Health
Children's Mercy Hospital
CoxHealth
Heartland Regional Medical
Shawnee Mission Medical Center
Truman Medical Centers
University of Kansas Medical Center
Via Christi Health System

HISTORICAL FINANCIALS

Company Type: Private

Income Statement — FYE: December 31

	REVENUE ($ mil.)	NET INCOME ($ mil.)	NET PROFIT MARGIN	EMPLOYEES
12/19	2,100	131	6.3%	5,111
12/18	1,901	42	2.2%	—
12/17	1,721	88	5.2%	—
12/15	155	(3)	—	—
Annual Growth	91.7%	—	—	—

2019 Year-End Financials

Return on assets: 4.6%
Return on equity: 8.4%
Current ratio: 3.00
Cash ($ mil.): 304

SAINT LUKE'S HOSPITAL OF BETHLEHEM, PENNSYLVANIA

EXECUTIVES

Pres, Richard A Anderson
Sr V-Pres Finance*, Thomas P Lichtenwalner
Human Resources Director, Andrew Seidel
Gynecology/Obstetrics, Christopher B Gilbert
Security Staff, William Paslawsky
Senior Director, Jared King
Coordinator, Lisa Johnson
Orthopedic Surgeon, William Delong Jr
Manager, Scott Siegfried
Accounting Staff, Zoraida Zeno
Administrator, Brian Repetz
Auditors: WITHUMSMITHBROWN PC MORRISTOW

LOCATIONS

HQ: SAINT LUKE'S HOSPITAL OF BETHLEHEM, PENNSYLVANIA
801 OSTRUM ST, BETHLEHEM, PA 180151000
Phone: 484 526-4000
Web: WWW.SLHN.ORG

HISTORICAL FINANCIALS

Company Type: Private

Income Statement FYE: June 30

	REVENUE ($ mil.)	NET INCOME ($ mil.)	NET PROFIT MARGIN	EMPLOYEES
06/19	956	205	21.4%	9,154
06/18	890	126	14.2%	—
06/15	660	31	4.8%	—
06/14	629	36	5.8%	—
Annual Growth	8.7%	41.2%	—	—

2019 Year-End Financials

Return on assets: 10.2%
Return on equity: 25.7%
Current ratio: 1.60
Cash ($ mil.): 90

SAINT LUKE'S HOSPITAL OF KANSAS CITY

EXECUTIVES

Ceo, Jani L Johnson
V Pres-Cno*, Debbie Wilson
Coo*, Jane Peck
Cfo*, Amy Nachtigal
Chief of Medicine, George A Pagels
Optometrists, Terry D Anderson
Executive of Information Techn, Denise Kintigh
Doctor, Richard Hill
Internal Medicine Practitioner, Amit Sharma
Internal Medicine Practitioner, Chernet Teklemichael
Emergency Medicine Specialist, Christopher Bowser

LOCATIONS

HQ: SAINT LUKE'S HOSPITAL OF KANSAS CITY
4401 WORNALL RD, KANSAS CITY, MO 641113241
Phone: 816 932-2000
Web: WWW.SAINTLUKESKC.ORG

HISTORICAL FINANCIALS

Company Type: Private

Income Statement FYE: December 31

	REVENUE ($ mil.)	NET INCOME ($ mil.)	NET PROFIT MARGIN	EMPLOYEES
12/18	803	4	0.5%	5,000
12/17	699	63	9.1%	—
12/16	641	26	4.1%	—
12/15	561	0	0.0%	—
Annual Growth	12.7%	198.0%	—	—

2018 Year-End Financials

Return on assets: 0.3%
Return on equity: 0.5%
Current ratio: 3.10
Cash ($ mil.): 33

SAINT MARYS HOSPITAL

EXECUTIVES

Pres, Robert R Waller
Clinical Director, Joyce Dube
Chief Marketing Officer, Kathy Zarling
Diagnostic Radiologist, Sanjay Misra
Chief of Pediatrics, Ann Reed
Security Director, Byron Callis
Admissions Director, Cydni Smith
Pharmacy Director, Jason Christiansen
Chemical Substance Abuse Dir, Jody Boone
Food Director, Kelly Novicki
Radiology Director, Michelle Northland

LOCATIONS

HQ: SAINT MARYS HOSPITAL
1216 2ND ST SW, ROCHESTER, MN 559021970
Phone: 507 255-5123
Web: WWW.MAYOCLINIC.ORG

HISTORICAL FINANCIALS

Company Type: Private

Income Statement FYE: December 31

	REVENUE ($ mil.)	NET INCOME ($ mil.)	NET PROFIT MARGIN	EMPLOYEES
12/16	2,091	556	26.6%	3,250
12/15	1,963	503	25.6%	—
Annual Growth	6.6%	10.6%	—	—

2016 Year-End Financials

Return on assets: 27.3%
Return on equity: 33.4%
Current ratio: 4.10
Cash ($ mil.): —

SALEM HEALTH

Salem Hospital serves the healthcare needs of residents in and around Oregon's Willamette Valley. The acute care hospital boasts about 455 beds and a medical staff of 440-plus physicians that represents some 45 specialty areas such as oncology joint replacement obstetrics diabetes weight loss and mental health among others. The not-for-profit hospital offers a range of services from emergency and critical care to rehabilitation and community wellness programs. Its Center for Outpatient Medicine provides cancer care outpatient surgery and imaging services and has a sleep disorders center. Salem Hospital is part of Salem Health which also includes West Valley Hospital and Willamette Health Partners.

Operations

The Oregon hospital also has a Family Birth Center that offers family-health education services and neonatal intensive-care services. Additionally it provides space to community support services to benefit families.

Salem Hospital operates under the guidance of a 15-member volunteer Board of Trustees.

Strategy

As with many healthcare institutions in this age of reform Salem Hospital is working hard to improve patient experience and the quality of healthcare it provides while reducing the cost of care and eliminating waste within its systems. It has been improving clinical documentation to ensure payments are received standardizing care processes improving scheduling of surgeries leaving 30 open positions unfilled and cutting another 30 positions.

Inspired by Toyota's lean production processes the hospital entered into a five-year contract with John Black and Associates in 2010 to begin what it projects to be a transformation that will be accomplished incrementally over the next 20 years. Its goal is to improve care using a holistic patient-centered approach and reduce waste in terms of waits inventory and other day-to-day processes.

Salem Hospital set a goal of becoming a Magnet hospital in 2003 and accomplished the feat in 2010. (Only 6% of hospitals in the US have achieved Magnet status.) Magnet certification is awarded to hospitals that meet a set of criteria that measures the quality and strength of their nursing staffs as set by the American Nurses' Credentialing Center an affiliate of the American Nurses Association. Criteria includes patient outcomes job satisfaction and low turnover.

In 2009 the hospital opened a new patient tower. In 2010 it sold its money-losing home care department to LHC Group as a way of cutting operating costs.

EXECUTIVES

Vice President Kaizen Quality Safety And Pt Care Services, Leah Mitchell
Medical Director, Lisa Lewis
Nursing Director Adult Health Services, Dana Hawkes
Vice President Of Community Engagement, Leilani Slama
Vice President, Bahaa Wanly
Vice President, Aaron McClung
Medical Director Of Urgent Care, Diana Villanueva
Secretary Of Medical Staff Svs, Louann Hettwer
Auditors: KPMG LLP PORTLAND OREGON

LOCATIONS

HQ: SALEM HEALTH
890 OAK ST SE, SALEM, OR 973013905
Phone: 503 561-5200
Web: WWW.SALEMHEALTH.ORG

PRODUCTS/OPERATIONS

Selected Services

Bariatrics

Cancer

Diabetes

Gynecology

Heart
Joint replacement
Neurosciences
Obstetrics
Orthopedics
Pain management
Psychiatric medicine
Psychology
Rehabilitation
Spine
Sleep
Stroke
Weight-loss surgery
Wound care

COMPETITORS

Adventist Health System West
Asante Health System
Kadlec Regional Medical Center
Kaiser Foundation Hospitals
Legacy Emanuel Hospital and Health Center
Legacy Health System
Oregon Health & Science University
PeaceHealth Southwest Medical Center
Providence St. Joseph Health

HISTORICAL FINANCIALS

Company Type: Private

Income Statement				FYE: June 30
	REVENUE ($ mil.)	NET INCOME ($ mil.)	NET PROFIT MARGIN	EMPLOYEES
06/19	820	86	10.5%	3,400
06/18	773	99	12.8%	—
Annual Growth	6.1%	(13.1%)	—	—

2019 Year-End Financials

Return on assets: 6.2%
Return on equity: 8.6%
Current ratio: 1.40
Cash ($ mil.): 13

SALT RIVER PROJECT AGRICULTURAL IMPROVEMENT AND POWER DISTRICT

One of the US's largest government-owned utilities Salt River Project (SRP) provides Phoenix with two types of currents: electric and water. Electricity comes from the Salt River Project Agricultural Improvement and Power District a political subdivision of the State of Arizona. It operates the Salt River Project a federal reclamation project under contracts with the Salt River Valley Water Users' Association including its obligations to the United States of America for the care operation and maintenance of the project. The district owns and operates an electric system that generates purchases transmits and distributes electric power and energy and provides electric service to residential commercial industrial and agricultural power users in parts of Maricopa Gila and Pinal counties. The district sells excess power to wholesale customers.

Operations

Staying true to its mission of providing water and electricity to SRP customers the company owns or has stakes in about 15 major power generating plants fueled by diverse sources including nuclear fuel and steam. SPR also operates several dams along the Salt and Verde River and the canal system that produce electricity. SRP's portfolio of renewable energy sources includes solar geothermal wind and biomass.

Some 90% of sales were generated from its retail electric.

Geographic Reach

Headquartered in Arizona the company serves residential commercial industrial and agricultural power customers in a 2900-square-mile service territory spanning parts of Maricopa Gila and Pinal counties in Arizona. In addition the enterprise has mining loads in an adjacent 2400-square-mile area in Gila and Pinal counties.

The SRP electric service area includes major portions of the cities of Phoenix Apache Junction Avondale Glendale Guadalupe Paradise Valley Queen Creek Scottsdale Mesa Tempe Chandler Peoria Scottsdale and Tolleson; the Town of Gilbert; and the Fountain Hills.

Financial Performance

The company's revenue in 2020 decreased by 7% to $3.1 billion. The decrease was primarily due to lower retail electric and wholesales revenue.

Cash held by the company at the end of fiscal 2020 increased to $567.7 million compared to the prior year with $474.7 million in the prior year. Cash provided by operations and financing activities were $654.1 million and $557.5 million respectively. Cash used for investing activities was $1.1 billion mainly for capital expenditure.

Strategy

SRP's supplier diversity mission is to promote a composition of corporate spending reflective of the community it serves by utilizing diverse businesses including: small firms; minority suppliers and contractors; woman business enterprises; and veteran and service disabled veteran enterprises.

Company Background

SRP was founded in 1903 under the Natural Reclamation Act.

EXECUTIVES

Ceo And General Manager, Mark B. Bonsall
Associate General Manager And Ceo Power System, Mike Hummel
Associate General Manager And Chief Financial Executive, Aidan McSheffrey
President, David Rousseau
Vice President, John R. Hoopes
Auditors: PRICEWATERHOUSECOOPERS LLP PH

LOCATIONS

HQ: SALT RIVER PROJECT AGRICULTURAL IMPROVEMENT AND POWER DISTRICT
1500 N MILL AVE, TEMPE, AZ 852811252
Phone: 602 236-5900
Web: WWW.SRPNET.COM

PRODUCTS/OPERATIONS

2016 Sales

	$ mil.	% of total
Retail electric	2,749	90
Water	15	1
Other	282	9
Total	**3,047**	**100**

Selected Subsidiaries

Salt River Project Agricultural Improvement and Power District (electric utility)
New West Energy Corporation (energy support services)
Papago Park Center Inc. (real estate facility management)
SRP Captive Risk Solutions Ltd. (domestic captive property boiler and machinery insurer)
Salt River Valley Water Users' Association

COMPETITORS

American States Water
American Water
Calpine
NV Energy
PG&E Corporation
PNM Resources
PacifiCorp
Pinnacle West
Sempra Energy
Southwest Gas
UNS Energy
Xcel Energy

HISTORICAL FINANCIALS

Company Type: Private

Income Statement				FYE: April 30
	REVENUE ($ mil.)	NET INCOME ($ mil.)	NET PROFIT MARGIN	EMPLOYEES
04/20*	3,121	126	4.1%	4,336
01/10	2,217	517	23.3%	—
04/05	2,251	362	16.1%	—
Annual Growth	2.2%	(6.8%)	—	—

*Fiscal year change

2020 Year-End Financials

Return on assets: 0.9%
Return on equity: 2.3%
Current ratio: 1.40
Cash ($ mil.): 361

SAMARITAN HEALTH SERVICES, INC.

EXECUTIVES

Ceo, Doug Boysen
Gynecology/Obstetrics, Jodell J Boyle
Administrative Assistant, Barbara Croney
Coordinator, Lisa Ely
Executive Officer, Pat Zeller
Chief of Medicine, Paul Daskalos
Director of Pharmacy, Penny Reher
Technical Manager, Dennis Ballard
Health Professional, Barry Smith
Oncologist, Holly Almond
Assistant Professor, Thomas Lissman

LOCATIONS

HQ: SAMARITAN HEALTH SERVICES, INC.
3600 NW SAMARITAN DR, CORVALLIS, OR 973303737
Phone: 541 757-5111
Web: WWW.SAMHEALTH.ORG

HISTORICAL FINANCIALS

Company Type: Private

Income Statement				FYE: December 31
	REVENUE ($ mil.)	NET INCOME ($ mil.)	NET PROFIT MARGIN	EMPLOYEES
12/19	1,233	32	2.6%	4,550
12/18	1,168	9	0.8%	—
12/17	1,101	26	2.4%	—
12/08	1	0	—	—
Annual Growth	87.1%	—	—	—

2019 Year-End Financials

Return on assets: 3.7%
Return on equity: 7.7%
Current ratio: 1.90
Cash ($ mil.): 142

SAMARITAN'S PURSE

EXECUTIVES

Chb-Ceo, Franklin Graham
V Pres, Phyllis Payne
South Sudan Country Direc, Phil Ewert
Administrative Assistant, Amber Light
Computer Operations Manager, Tracy Norris
Assistant Manager, Brad Osborne
Executive Assistant To Vice PR, Anita Donnelly
Web, Chris Hampton
Vice President of North Americ, Luther Harrison
Real Estate Agent, Michael Lagazo
Haiti Projects Logistics Manag, Pierre Julien
Auditors: DIXON HUGHES GOODMAN LLP CHA

LOCATIONS

HQ: SAMARITAN'S PURSE
801 BAMBOO RD, BOONE, NC 286078721
Phone: 828 262-1980
Web: WWW.SAMARITANSPURSE.ORG

HISTORICAL FINANCIALS

Company Type: Private

Income Statement				FYE: December 31
	REVENUE ($ mil.)	NET INCOME ($ mil.)	NET PROFIT MARGIN	EMPLOYEES
12/18	709	22	3.1%	525
12/17	800	189	23.7%	—
12/16	634	51	8.0%	—
12/15	599	82	13.7%	—
Annual Growth	5.7%	(35.3%)	—	—

2018 Year-End Financials

Return on assets: 3.1%
Return on equity: 3.4%
Current ratio: 13.10
Cash ($ mil.): 216

SAN ANTONIO INDEPENDENT SCHOOL DISTRICT FAC

EXECUTIVES

Supt, Dr Sylvester Syl Perez
Pres*, Ed Garza
V Pres*, Olga M Hernandez
SEC*, Arthur V Valdez
Information Specialist, Mark McRae
Law Specialist, Andrea Tena
Child Nutrition Coordinator, Olga Perez
Web Administrator, Brad Wehring
Assistant Athletic Director, Brian Clancy
Technology Business, Ray Tena
Director, Tiffany Grant
Auditors: GARZA/GONZALEZ & ASSOCIATES S

LOCATIONS

HQ: SAN ANTONIO INDEPENDENT SCHOOL DISTRICT FAC
141 LAVACA ST, SAN ANTONIO, TX 782101039
Phone: 210 554-2200
Web: WWW.SAISD.NET

HISTORICAL FINANCIALS

Company Type: Private

Income Statement				FYE: June 30
	REVENUE ($ mil.)	NET INCOME ($ mil.)	NET PROFIT MARGIN	EMPLOYEES
06/19	681	136	20.0%	7,600
06/16	659	43	6.5%	—
06/15	624	(14)	—	—
06/14	600	(110)	—	—
Annual Growth	2.6%	—	—	—

2019 Year-End Financials

Return on assets: 8.0%
Return on equity: 88.9%
Current ratio: —
Cash ($ mil.): 362

SAN ANTONIO WATER SYSTEM

Wasting water is a sore point in drought-prone South Texas and San Antonio Water System (SAWS) seeks to husband this precious resource the best it can. The company serves about 511300 water customers and some 457600 wastewater customers or about 1.9 million people in the San Antonio metropolitan area (including most of the city of San Antonio Medina Anatascosa counties and adjacent parts of Bexar County). In addition to serving its own retail customers SAWS provides wholesale water supplies to several smaller utility systems in its service area. The utility is owned by the City of San Antonio.

Operations

SAWS oversees more than 12880 miles of water and sewer mains.

SAWS is the only sewage treatment agency in this area and it charges a fee to the military bases and suburban cities which maintain their own wastewater collection systems. SAWS also provides collection and treatment services by contract to developments outside its defined service area to avoid unnecessary proliferation of state wastewater discharge permits.

SAWS includes all water resources properties facilities and plants owned operated and maintained by the city relating to supply storage treatment transmission and distribution of treated potable water; collection and treatment of wastewater; and distribution of recycled water. Additionally SAWS owns and operates four thermal energy facilities providing chilled water services to governmental and private entities.

Around 35% of the company's total sales were generated through its wastewater systems while water delivery and supply system both generated about 30% each. The chilled water and steam system and non-operating revenue accounts for the rest.

Geographic Reach

The company serves Texas customers in Bexar County as well as parts of Medina and Atascosa counties. Its main office is located in San Antonio Texas.

Sales and Marketing

The company serves retail customers and also provides wholesale water supplies to several smaller utility systems. The population includes more than 511300 water customers and approximately 457600 wastewater customers (around 1.9 million people). Both water and wastewater connections represent about 95% of the customers in Bexar County.

Financial Performance

In 2019 SAWS' net revenue increased by 7% to $765.8 million as operating revenues increased from $691 million in 2018 to $733.2 million in 2019. An average rate increase of 4.7% took effect in January an increase in billed water usage of 3.1% and customer growth of 1.8% contributed to the increased in operating revenue in 2019.

The company's net position (income) increased by 19% to $147.5 million mainly due to higher net revenue.

Cash and cash equivalents at the end of the year were $292.6 million. Net cash provided by operating activities was $381.9 million and cash added from investing activities was $272.1 million. Financing activities used $475.6 million for acquisitions of plant and equipment and payment of bonds.

Strategy

In mid-November SAWS started the sewer main replacement along U.S. Highway 90 and SW Military Drive near Joint Base San Antonio-Lackland that involves five miles of tunneling more than 100 feet below ground to avoid disrupting traffic and military activity.

The much-needed infrastructure project in the planning stages since 2007 will cost up to $210 million and serve more than 500000 San Antonians. SAWS officials say it's the most costly complex sewer pipeline project in the city's history. Construction is expected to be completed in 2023.

Company Background

SAWS and a neighboring water authority the Lower Colorado River Authority signed an agreement in 2002 to study the feasibility of drawing water from the lower Colorado River basin for use by San Antonio. The LCRA reported in 2009 that it had found that there was not a sufficient amount of extra water available to build a proposed reservoir. SAWS sued LCRA for $1.2 billion over the results of the study but the suit was tossed out by a state district judge.

SAWS was formed in 1992 through a merger of three entities: the City Water Board the City Wastewater Department and the Alamo Water Conservation and Reuse District.

EXECUTIVES

Senior Vice President And Chief Operating Officer, Steve Clouse
Svp And Coo, Steven (Steve) Clouse
Svp And Cfo, Douglas (Doug) Evanson
Vp Distribution And Collection Operations, Mike Brinkmann
President And Ceo, Robert R. Puente
Senior Director Sewer System Improvements, Jeff Haby
Chief Information Systems, Joe Samples
Vp Water Resources And Conservation, Charles E. Ahrens
Auditors: BAKER TILLY VIRCHOW KRAUSE

LOCATIONS

HQ: SAN ANTONIO WATER SYSTEM
2800 US HIGHWAY 281 N, SAN ANTONIO, TX 782123106
Phone: 210 704-7297
Web: WWW.SAWS.ORG

PRODUCTS/OPERATIONS

2014 Sales

	$ mil.	% of total
Operating revenues		
Wastewater system	210	42
Water supply system	150	30
Water delivery system	127	25
Chilled water and steam system	11	2
Non-operating revenues	5	1
Total	**505**	**100**

HISTORICAL FINANCIALS

Company Type: Private

Income Statement				FYE: December 31
	REVENUE ($ mil.)	NET INCOME ($ mil.)	NET PROFIT MARGIN	EMPLOYEES
12/17	666	240	36.1%	1,700
12/16	622	213	34.3%	—
12/12	0	0	—	—
Annual Growth	—	—	—	—

2017 Year-End Financials

Return on assets: 3.9%
Return on equity: 8.4%
Current ratio: 3.00
Cash ($ mil.): 36

SAN BERNARDINO CITY UNIFIED SCHOOL DISTRICT

EXECUTIVES

Spdt, Dale Marsden
Staff, Susie Sellas
Security Specialist, Rita Munoz
Coordinator, Terry Comnick
Director, Adriane Robles
Administrative Assistant Email, Sylvia Ross
Human Resources, Harold Vollkommer
Teacher, Isabel Guerrero
Clerk, Sabrina Ramirez
Speech Therapist, Tina Lozano
Program Facilitator Teacher, Cheryl Togashi

LOCATIONS

HQ: SAN BERNARDINO CITY UNIFIED SCHOOL DISTRICT
777 N F ST, SAN BERNARDINO, CA 924103017
Phone: 909 381-1100
Web: WWW.SBCUSD.COM

HISTORICAL FINANCIALS

Company Type: Private

Income Statement — FYE: June 30

	REVENUE ($ mil.)	NET INCOME ($ mil.)	NET PROFIT MARGIN	EMPLOYEES
06/19	775	46	5.9%	6,000
06/18	712	27	3.8%	—
06/08	759	97	12.8%	—
06/05	0	0	—	—
Annual Growth	92.0%	—	—	—

SAN FRANCISCO BAY AREA RAPID TRANSIT DISTRICT

If you're going to San Francisco – from Oakland Berkeley or another Bay Area community – San Francisco Bay Area Rapid Transit District (BART) can take you there. BART's trains carry about 365000 daily weekday riders from more than 45 stations over more than 100 miles of track including the 3.6 mile Transbay Tube under the San Francisco Bay that links the City by the Bay with Oakland and other East Bay communities. Directors elected from nine districts in Alameda Contra Costa and San Francisco counties oversee BART which operates with an annual budget of about $480 million. Construction on the rail system began in 1964 and BART carried its first passengers in 1972.

Operations

BART which has the oldest fleet in the US has awarded Bombardier about $896 million to design and make more than 400 train cars that may be ready for use by 2017. The contract represents the first phase of a $2.5 billion project to replace BART's fleet of some 670 cars with a larger fleet of more than 770 new cars. Three-fourths of the project's cost is being paid by the federal government with the remainder coming from BART.

Another major project is the $1.3 billion Earthquake Safety Program which is almost finished and scheduled for completion in 2016. The program includes bolting 2.5-inch steel plates on the concrete wall of the Transbay Tube – which carries about half of BART's daily weekday riders – and similar strengthening measures for more than 30 stations more than 20 miles of elevated track and other facilities.

Geographic Reach

BART serves the Bay Area through its 45 stations spanning the four counties of Alameda Contra Costa San Francisco and San Mateo.

Financial Performance

In 2014 the company's revenue increased by 4% to $463 million due to a spike in passenger fares along with higher parking rates implemented in 2014 at several stations. BART was also helped by an increase in advertising revenue and a rise in ground lease revenue resulting from the reassignment of its original ground lease at West Dublin Station to a new lessee. In addition its net income increased by 8% in 2014 due to the increase in revenues along with lower transportation expenses.

EXECUTIVES

Vice President Information Technology, William Longstaff
Auditors: MACIAS GINI & O'CONNELL LLP W

LOCATIONS

HQ: SAN FRANCISCO BAY AREA RAPID TRANSIT DISTRICT
300 LAKESIDE DR FL 22, OAKLAND, CA 946123534
Phone: 510 464-6000
Web: WWW.BART.GOV

HISTORICAL FINANCIALS

Company Type: Private

Income Statement — FYE: June 30

	REVENUE ($ mil.)	NET INCOME ($ mil.)	NET PROFIT MARGIN	EMPLOYEES
06/19	554	218	39.4%	3,347
06/18	605	212	35.2%	—
06/16	545	331	60.8%	—
06/06	275	(2)	—	—
Annual Growth	5.5%	—	—	—

2019 Year-End Financials

Return on assets: 2.2%
Return on equity: 3.2%
Current ratio: 2.50
Cash ($ mil.): 253

SAN JUAN UNIFIED SCHOOL DISTRICT

EXECUTIVES

Supt, Pat Jaurequi
Supt*, Glynn Thompson
Information Technology/Interne, Bart Hubbard
Teacher, Carla Elkins
Teacher, Kristen Allen
Teacher, Mary McClain
Teacher, Mike Shepherd
Teacher, Markam Cruz
Financial Executive, Lynn Brown
Assistant Superintendent, Debra Calvin
Assistant Superintendent, Melissa Bassanell
Auditors: CROWE HORWATH LLP SACRAMENTO

LOCATIONS

HQ: SAN JUAN UNIFIED SCHOOL DISTRICT
3738 WALNUT AVE, CARMICHAEL, CA 956083099
Phone: 916 971-7700
Web: WWW.SANJUAN.EDU

HISTORICAL FINANCIALS

Company Type: Private

Income Statement — FYE: June 30

	REVENUE ($ mil.)	NET INCOME ($ mil.)	NET PROFIT MARGIN	EMPLOYEES
06/19	631	105	16.7%	4,200
06/18	620	(38)	—	—
06/17	577	104	18.2%	—
06/16	576	(6)	—	—
Annual Growth	3.1%	—	—	—

SANFORD

Sanford (operating as Sanford Health) is one of the largest not-for-profit integrated health care systems in the US. It primarily serves rural areas through its network of about 45 regional and community hospitals in nine states including the Dakotas Iowa Minnesota and Nebraska. The organization also operates about 300 local clinics and specialty outpatient practices. Specialist service include cancer cardiology vascular health neurology orthopedics pediatrics virology and women's health. Sanford Health added more than 200 senior care locations in 24 states by acquiring Good Samaritan Society in 2019.

Operations

In addition to its 40-plus hospitals Sanford's network includes about 200 senior living facilities (long-term care assisted-living and independent living centers) and 140 clinics. Altogether the facilities in the Sanford Health network handle some 50000 inpatient admissions and about 1.35 million outpatient visits each year. The network's 1400 physicians provide care in more than 80 specialist fields.

Along with its health care facilities Sanford Health also operates Sanford Laboratories based in Sioux Falls and Rapid City South Dakota. The system maintains Sanford Research a not-for-profit research organization that draws upon the physicians of Sanford Health and researchers at the University of South Dakota. Sanford Research conducts some $100 million in research projects each year. Finally the Sanford Health Plan is a not-for-profit health plan that serves individuals and employers across the system's region.

Geographic Reach

Sanford Health has hospital and clinic locations in communities in nine states including California Iowa Minnesota Nebraska North Dakota Oklahoma Oregon and South Dakota. The company also operates about 200 senior care facilities in 24 states. It also has clinical affiliates in locations including Ghana Africa; Karmiel Israel; and Baja Mexico.

Strategy

Growth plans for Sanford Health include the construction of hospital and clinic facilities in Minnesota and North Dakota and new health care and research facilities in South Dakota. A $700 million gift from local philanthropist T. Denny Sanford is enabling the establishment of several new facilities.

That contribution is also supporting the organization's research programs in children's health and initiatives to find cures for conditions including breast cancer and type 1 diabetes.

In addition Sanford Health expands by acquiring small community medical centers. The system is also growing by striking partnerships with small regional health care providers. In 2018 and 2019 it expanded in research and senior care by acquiring the Neuropsychiatric Research Institute and senior housing operator Good Samaritan Society.

The company agreed to merge with Iowa Health System which operates as UnityPoint Health in 2019 but the deal was terminated later that year. The transaction would have created a system with more than 75 hospitals in 26 states.

Mergers and Acquisitions

In early 2019 Sanford merged with senior health services provider The Evangelical Lutheran Good Samaritan Society. The transaction combined Sanford's hospital system with Good Samaritan's senior living facilities creating an integrated health care research and insurance entity.

In 2018 Sanford Research absorbed Neuropsychiatric Research Institute which focuses on eating disorders and obesity. With that acquisition Sanford intends to establish a major research program in Fargo North Dakota.

A deal to merge with Iowa Health System which operates as UnityPoint Health was canceled in 2019. The merger would have created a health network with about 75 hospitals in 26 states.

Company Background

Sanford was created from the 2009 merger of two Dakota health care legends: South Dakota's Sanford Health and North Dakota's MeritCare Health System. Both date back to the 1890s. Following the merger the two units briefly kept their separate identities but in 2010 organized under the Sanford Health-MeritCare name. The operating name was later shortened to Sanford Health.

EXECUTIVES

Vice President Chief Of Staff, Mike Begeman
Director Of Clinical Services, Ann Mays
Vice President Of Research Sanford Health, David Pearce
Physical Therapy, Kris Naig
Vice President Major Initiatives, Brian Bonde
Director Of Nursing, Kellee Johnk
Vice President Marketing, Karoliina Slack
Vice President Marketing Fargo Region, Jennifer Cresap
Managing Director, Barbara Bentz
Medical Director, William Klava
Nursing Director, Jeri Schons
Occupational Therapy Dir, MELISSA GREWE
Pharmacy Manager, Julie Kauffman
Vice President, Misty Anderson
Senior Vice President, Martha Leclerc
Auditors: DELOITTE & TOUCHE LLP MINNEAP

LOCATIONS

HQ: SANFORD
801 BROADWAY N, FARGO, ND 581023641
Phone: 701 234-6000
Web: WWW.SANFORDHEALTH.ORG

PRODUCTS/OPERATIONS

Selected Major Regional Medical Centers

Sanford Bemidji Medical Center (Bemidji Minnesota)
Sanford Medical Center Bismarck (Bismarck North Dakota)
Sanford Medical Center Fargo (Fargo North Dakota)
Sanford USD Medical Center Sioux Falls (Sioux Falls South Dakota)

COMPETITORS

Altru Health
Avera Health
Catholic Health Initiatives
Mayo Clinic
North Memorial Health Care
Rapid City Regional Hospital
St. Alexius Medical Center
St. Mary's Healthcare
Wellmark

HISTORICAL FINANCIALS

Company Type: Private

Income Statement — FYE: June 30

	REVENUE ($ mil.)	NET INCOME ($ mil.)	NET PROFIT MARGIN	EMPLOYEES
06/18	4,639	117	2.5%	50,000
06/17	4,411	175	4.0%	—
06/16	4,231	108	2.6%	—
06/14	3	(11)	—	—
Annual Growth	486.1%	—	—	—

2018 Year-End Financials

Return on assets: 2.7%
Return on equity: 4.6%
Current ratio: 1.60
Cash ($ mil.): 185

SANFORD HEALTH

EXECUTIVES

Pres, Kelby K Krabbenhoft
Sr V Pres-Coo*, Becky Nelson
Pres-Clinic, Dan Blue
Pres-Regional Health Services*, Ed Weiland
Pres-Foundation*, Brian Mortensen
Pres-Health Plan*, Ruth Krystopolski
Ex V Pres*, Dave Link
Cfo*, Michelle Bruhn
Health Information Management, Melissa Schumacher
Pediatrician, Nancy Free
Health Information Management, Roberta Winge
Auditors: DELOITTE & TOUCHE LLP MINNEAP

LOCATIONS

HQ: SANFORD HEALTH
1305 W 18TH ST, SIOUX FALLS, SD 571050401
Phone: 605 333-1720
Web: WWW.SANFORDHEALTH.ORG

HISTORICAL FINANCIALS

Company Type: Private

Income Statement — FYE: December 31

	REVENUE ($ mil.)	NET INCOME ($ mil.)	NET PROFIT MARGIN	EMPLOYEES
12/18*	4,819	141	2.9%	2,939
06/17	4,411	175	4.0%	—
06/16	4,231	114	2.7%	—
06/12	2,516	72	2.9%	—
Annual Growth	9.7%	10.1%	—	—

*Fiscal year change

2018 Year-End Financials

Return on assets: 3.3%
Return on equity: 5.3%
Current ratio: 1.80
Cash ($ mil.): 109

SANFORD HEALTH

Auditors: DELOITTE TAX LLP MINNEAPOLIS

LOCATIONS

HQ: SANFORD HEALTH
1305 W 18TH ST, SIOUX FALLS, SD 571050401
Phone: 605 333-1000

HISTORICAL FINANCIALS

Company Type: Private

Income Statement — FYE: June 30

	REVENUE ($ mil.)	NET INCOME ($ mil.)	NET PROFIT MARGIN	EMPLOYEES
06/17	3,741	138	3.7%	2
06/10	1,038	35	3.4%	—
Annual Growth	20.1%	21.4%	—	—

2017 Year-End Financials

Return on assets: 5.0%
Return on equity: 11.9%
Current ratio: —
Cash ($ mil.): 78

SANFORD NORTH

EXECUTIVES

Prin, Roger L Gilbertson
Cfo*, Lisa Carlson
Coordinator, Pammie Dohman
Pediatrician, Brenda Thurlow
Blood Bank Supervisor, Delilah Rosecrans

LOCATIONS

HQ: SANFORD NORTH
801 BROADWAY N, FARGO, ND 581023641
Phone: 701 234-2000
Web: WWW.SANFORDHEALTH.ORG

HISTORICAL FINANCIALS

Company Type: Private

Income Statement — FYE: June 30

	REVENUE ($ mil.)	NET INCOME ($ mil.)	NET PROFIT MARGIN	EMPLOYEES
06/10	677	(15)	—	7,200
06/08	112	2	2.0%	—
Annual Growth	145.1%	—	—	—

2010 Year-End Financials

Return on assets: (-10.0%)
Return on equity: (-24.5%)
Current ratio: 1.40
Cash ($ mil.): —

SANTA BARBARA COTTAGE HOSPITAL FOUNDATION

EXECUTIVES

Ceo*, Ronald C Werft
Exec V Pres*, Steven Fellows
Cfo*, Brett Tande
Chief of Medicine, Robert S Wright
Coordinator, Ruben Orozco
Executive Assistant, Teresa Guzman-Petter
Director Neurovascular, Alois Zauner
Vice President Information TEC, Bill Worthington
Registered Nurse, Cat Demourkas
Manager Environmental, Jo Vargas
Clinical Pharmacist, Pam Johnson

LOCATIONS

HQ: SANTA BARBARA COTTAGE HOSPITAL FOUNDATION
400 W PUEBLO ST, SANTA BARBARA, CA 931054353
Phone: 805 682-7111
Web: WWW.COTTAGEHEALTH.ORG

HISTORICAL FINANCIALS

Company Type: Private

Income Statement				FYE: December 31
	REVENUE ($ mil.)	NET INCOME ($ mil.)	NET PROFIT MARGIN	EMPLOYEES
12/17	646	178	27.6%	1,786
12/16	603	42	7.0%	—
12/15	610	(15)	—	—
12/14	38	32	83.3%	—
Annual Growth	156.0%	77.2%	—	—

2017 Year-End Financials

Return on assets: 10.6%
Return on equity: 17.3%
Current ratio: 1.90
Cash ($ mil.): 13

SANTA CLARA VALLEY TRANSPORTATION AUTHORITY

EXECUTIVES

Ceo, Nuria Fernandez
Prin, Carroll W Huff
Assistant Superintendent, Cheryl Gonzales
Procurement Manager, George Eaton
Supervisor, Gurpreet Gill
Marketing Communications Speci, Lupe Solis
Human Resources Analyst, Bethany Cramer
Light Rail Maintenance Instruc, Greg Bushner
Senior Real Estate Agent, Jessie Solis
Environmental Health, Tracy Casimiro
Trasnportation Project Enginee, Arshad Syed
Auditors: VAVRINEK TRINE DAY & CO LL

LOCATIONS

HQ: SANTA CLARA VALLEY TRANSPORTATION AUTHORITY
3331 N 1ST ST, SAN JOSE, CA 951341906
Phone: 408 321-2300
Web: WWW.VTA.ORG

HISTORICAL FINANCIALS

Company Type: Private

Income Statement				FYE: June 30
	REVENUE ($ mil.)	NET INCOME ($ mil.)	NET PROFIT MARGIN	EMPLOYEES
06/19	1,204	830	68.9%	2,053
06/17	16	(2)	—	—
06/16	19	(0)	—	—
06/15	27	(0)	—	—
Annual Growth	156.5%	—	—	—

SAPP BROS., INC.

Need air in those 18 wheels? Sapp Bros Travel Centers (formerly Sapp Bros Truck Stops) has the usual air gas food but also offers human conveniences such such as laundry rooms mailbox rentals private showers and TV lounges. The company operates a chain of some 15 truck stops — readily identifiable by the giant red-and-white coffeepot logo — along interstate highways from Utah to Pennsylvania; with a concentration in Nebraska. Half of the locations also operate service centers offering oil changes new tires and safety checks. Its sister company Sapp Bros Petroleum distributes fuels and lubricants to more than 200 retailers. The firm is run by CEO Bill Sapp one of the four founding Sapp brothers.

Geographic Reach

Omaha-based Sapp Bros. has travel centers in eight states: Nebraska Iowa Utah Colorado Wyoming Kansas Illinois and Pennsylvania.

Strategy

To raise its profile and rev up its business Sapp Bros. in 2013 joined the roster of VP Racing Fuels's retail brand partners. The benefits of the affiliation include association with an attractive retail image competitive credit card rates and the ability to source unbranded fuel for its travel centers.

EXECUTIVES

Board Of Directors, Allen Marsh
Auditors: KPMG LLP OMAHA NEBRASKA

LOCATIONS

HQ: SAPP BROS., INC.
9915 S 148TH ST, OMAHA, NE 681383876
Phone: 402 895-7038
Web: WWW.SAPPBROS.NET

2012 Locations

	No.
Nebraska	8
Iowa	2
Colorado	1
Illinois	1
Kansas	1
Pennsylvania	1
Utah	1
Wyoming	1
Total	16

COMPETITORS

Exxon Mobil
Love's Country Stores
Pilot Flying J
Stuckey's
TravelCenters of America

HISTORICAL FINANCIALS

Company Type: Private

Income Statement				FYE: September 30
	REVENUE ($ mil.)	NET INCOME ($ mil.)	NET PROFIT MARGIN	EMPLOYEES
09/19	1,194	4	0.4%	1,700
09/18	1,259	11	0.9%	—
09/17	990	11	1.2%	—
09/16	802	18	2.3%	—
Annual Growth	14.2%	(37.4%)	—	—

2019 Year-End Financials

Return on assets: 2.9%
Return on equity: 7.6%
Current ratio: 1.40
Cash ($ mil.): 5

SARASOTA COUNTY PUBLIC HOSPITAL DISTRICT

Sarasota County Public Hospital Board which does business as the Sarasota Memorial Health Care System is a publicly owned hospital system serving residents in and around Sarasota on Florida's western coast. It operates Sarasota Memorial Hospital a not-for-profit acute-care facility with more than 800 beds (and more than 900 doctors) that provides general medical and surgical care as well as specialized care in areas such as heart disease cancer and neuroscience. The system also features a skilled nursing facility walk-in medical centers an outpatient surgical center and home health care operations. Additionally the hospital conducts clinical trials and has an educational affiliation with Florida State University.

Operations

Sarasota Memorial has the only obstetrics program and neonatal intensive care unit in the county and its Bayside Center includes one of the county's only inpatient behavioral health facilities. The health care system's Charter Health Plan program offers group health insurance to local business owners.

Sarasota Memorial receives some 32000 inpatient visits and 950000 outpatient and physician visits each year.

Geographic Reach

Sarasota Memorial serves Florida's Sarasota County.

Sales and Marketing

Medicare and Medicaid combined account for some 60% of Sarasota Memorial's net patient service revenue. Self-pay and managed care make up the remainder.

Financial Performance

Sarasota's total revenues increased by 9% in fiscal 2016 (ended September) due to a 9% increase in net patient revenue due to higher volume. The company reported $107 million in excess revenues over expenses that year a 13% decline versus the prior year. Operating expenses including salaries fringe benefits and supplies costs all increased in 2016.

Cash flow from operations increased 38% to $85.8 million thanks to an increase in cash received from patient care services.

Strategy

Sarasota Memorial seeks to improve its financial performance by pursuing profitable inpatient and outpatient growth through an aggressive focus on physician alignment and integration and capturing new patients residing in high growth areas. The system has also been opening new facilities to boost patient service revenues. In 2016 it opened its sixth urgent care center. The following year it opened a 74000-sq.-ft. Rehabilitation Pavilion the only site of its kind in Sarasota County to offer comprehensive inpatient and outpatient rehabilitation services.

The system also introduced its nurse residency program and an internal medicine residency program in 2017.

Company Background

Sarasota Memorial was founded as a community hospital in 1925.

EXECUTIVES

Vp And Cio, Denis Baker
Cfo Sarasota Memorial Health Care System, David Verinder, age 53
Chief Nursing Officer, Jan Mauck
Cfo, William Woeltjen
Chief Of Medical Operations, R. Stephen Taylor
Medical Director Research, Ricardo Yaryura
Medical Records Director, Diane Settle
Director Of Nursing Resources Picc Team, Janet Steves
Medical Director Of All Children, Jennifer Mayer
Radiology Director, Debbie Bohanon
Medical Director Hospitalist Program, John Moritz
Vice President And Chief Legal Officer, Carol Kalish
Board Secretary, Donna Desisto
Chairman, Gregory Carter
Chairman, Marguerite G. Malone
First Vice Chairwoman, Alex Miller

LOCATIONS

HQ: SARASOTA COUNTY PUBLIC HOSPITAL DISTRICT
1700 S TAMIAMI TRL, SARASOTA, FL 342393509
Phone: 941 917-9000
Web: WWW.SMH.COM

PRODUCTS/OPERATIONS

2016 Sales

	% of total
County Public Hospital District	
Sarasota Memorial Hospital	59
Corporate Division	2
Nursing & Rehabilitation Center	1
Charter Plan	-
SMH Health Care Inc.	33
Physician Services Inc.	5
Total	100

COMPETITORS

All Children's Hospital
Bayfront Health
Encompass Health
Florida Hospital Tampa Bay Division
HCA
St. Joseph's-Baptist Health Care
Tampa General Hospital

HISTORICAL FINANCIALS

Company Type: Private

Income Statement — FYE: September 30

	REVENUE ($ mil.)	NET INCOME ($ mil.)	NET PROFIT MARGIN	EMPLOYEES
09/17	793	99	12.6%	4,200
09/16	12	0	4.0%	—
09/15	590	131	22.3%	—
09/14	524	92	17.6%	—
Annual Growth	14.8%	2.6%	—	—

2017 Year-End Financials

Return on assets: 6.0%
Return on equity: 9.7%
Current ratio: 1.00
Cash ($ mil.): 27

SAVANNAH-CHATHAM COUNTY BOARD OF EDUCATION

EXECUTIVES

Pres, Jolene Byrne
Executive of Information Techn, Cathy Mc Culloch
Chief Operating Officer, Mike Young
Auditors: KRT CPAS PC SAVANNAH GEOR

LOCATIONS

HQ: SAVANNAH-CHATHAM COUNTY BOARD OF EDUCATION
208 BULL ST, SAVANNAH, GA 314013843
Phone: 912 395-5534
Web: WWW.MASSIEHERITAGECENTER.WORDPRESS.COM

HISTORICAL FINANCIALS

Company Type: Private

Income Statement — FYE: June 30

	REVENUE ($ mil.)	NET INCOME ($ mil.)	NET PROFIT MARGIN	EMPLOYEES
06/19	569	86	15.2%	4,800
06/18	525	41	7.8%	—
06/17	500	(30)	—	—
06/16	493	21	4.3%	—
Annual Growth	4.9%	59.4%	—	—

SAVE THE CHILDREN FEDERATION, INC.

Save the Children helps poor and malnourished children in some 15 US states and nearly 120 countries focusing on such areas as health and nutrition economic development education child protection and HIV/AIDS. The humanitarian organization also participates in international disaster relief efforts focusing on children and their families. Save the Children spends about 90% of its budget on program services with the rest allocated to administration and fundraising. The group was founded in 1932 inspired by the international children's rights movement begun in the UK in 1919 by Eglantyne Jebb founder of the British Save the Children Fund. It is a member of the International Save the Children Alliance.

Operations

Some 43% of the humanitarian organization's work is centered in Asia with 34% in Africa. Save the Children spends the rest of its time in the US Latin America and the Middle East.

In 2012 alone Save the Children helped 125 million girls and boys worldwide.

Geographic Reach

Save the Children operates programs in some 120 countries including the US. It comprises 29 member organizations worldwide.

Financial Performance

The global aid organization's revenue declined by 3.5% in 2012 versus 2011 due largely to a 12% drop in private gifts grants and contributions which account for nearly half of its total revenue. Save the Children directed 89% of its expenses to programs which benefit children and allow the humanitarian organization to keep private costs (includes fundraising and management and general) at about 10% – one of the best ratios for nonprofit organizations.

Strategy

With about 28% of its program services devoted to emergencies and 20% to education Save the Children in 2014 partnered with The Malala Fund to help vulnerable Syrian and Jordanian children return to school. As part of the partnership Save the Children is launching a pair of education projects. Another large portion of Save the Children's program services are focused on Health and Nutrition (25%) and Hunger & Livelihoods (10%).

EXECUTIVES

Vice President Policy And Humanitarian Response, Michael Klosson
Associate Vice President Helath And Nutrition, David Oot
Vice President, Gary Shaye
Vice President, Robert Clay
Vp Of U.s. Programs, Bill Corwin
Associate Vice President, Anna Schowengerdt
Associate Vice President, John Farden
Associate Vice President G And C And Global Finance, Eid Natour
Auditors: KPMG LLP NEW YORK NY

LOCATIONS

HQ: SAVE THE CHILDREN FEDERATION, INC.
501 KINGS HWY E STE 400, FAIRFIELD, CT 068254861
Phone: 203 221-4000
Web: WWW.SAVETHECHILDREN.ORG

Selected Countries of Operation

Australia

Brazil

Canada

Denmark
Dominican Republic
Fiji
Finland
Germany
Guatemala
Honduras
Hong Kong
Iceland
India
Italy
Japan
Jordan
Korea
Lithuania
Mexico

Netherlands
New Zealand
Norway
Romania
South Africa
Spain
Swaziland
Sweden
Switzerland
United Kingdom
United States

HISTORICAL FINANCIALS

Company Type: Private

Income Statement FYE: December 31

	REVENUE ($ mil.)	NET INCOME ($ mil.)	NET PROFIT MARGIN	EMPLOYEES
12/16	652	(7)	—	3,000
12/15	678	(10)	—	—
Annual Growth	(3.9%)	—	—	—

2016 Year-End Financials

Return on assets: (-2.8%)
Return on equity: (-4.1%)
Current ratio: 1.50
Cash ($ mil.): 46

SCAI HOLDINGS, LLC

SCAI Holdings (dba SCA or Surgical Care Affiliates) can stitch 'em up and move 'em out. The company operates one of the largest networks of outpatient surgery centers in the US. (Also known as ambulatory surgical centers or ASCs these facilities charge less than hospitals to perform routine surgeries.) SCA operates more than 200 surgery centers and surgical hospitals in about 35 states. The centers offer non-emergency day surgeries in orthopedics ophthalmology gastroenterology pain management otolaryngology (ear nose and throat) urology and gynecology. The company went public in 2013 but was acquired by insurance giant UnitedHealth in 2017 for some $2.3 billion.

Change in Company Type

In early 2017 Surgical Care Affiliates agreed to be acquired by UnitedHealth for some $2.3 billion. The renamed SCAI joined UnitedHealth's OptumHealth division which itself operates hundreds of health care facilities.

Operations

SCA's outpatient surgery centers are operated in partnership with more than 40 health care systems such as Indiana University Health Sutter Health Texas Health Resources and MemorialCare. It has approximately 3000 physician partners.

Geographic Reach

SCA's facilities are located in 34 states across the US. Its largest markets are Texas California and North Carolina which respectively accounted for 14% 14% and 13% of net patient revenues in 2014. Other large markets include Alabama Connecticut Florida and Idaho.

Sales and Marketing

SCA's sales and marketing efforts are directed at physicians who are responsible for referring patients to its facilities. It also directly negotiates agreements with insurance companies and Medicare. Outpatient surgery centers which perform procedures that don't require an overnight stay are able to charge less than full service hospitals. This 'day surgery' model can be attractive to both patients and insurance companies looking to keep costs down.

As such SCA sees a lot of opportunity in building up its portfolio of outpatient surgery centers. The company estimates there are approximately 5400 Medicare-certified centers in the US and still plenty of opportunity to invest and partner in new facilities.

Payments from non-governmental third-party payors represented more than 60% of the firm's net patient revenues in 2014; Medicare payments accounted for 20%.

Financial Performance

SCA has seen solid revenue growth for the past four years. In 2014 revenue increased 9% to $897.3 million on higher net patient revenue a result of both higher admission numbers and the addition of more facilities. Management fee revenues also rose that year (again thanks to acquisitions).

After four years of reporting losses the company became profitable in 2014 with net income of $32 million. This was driven by the higher revenue as well as the absence of loss from extinguishment of debt and a decline in interest expenses. At the end of 2014 the company's accumulated deficit totaled $176 million.

Cash flow from operations has been on the rise as of late. In 2014 it increased 27% to $210.6 million.

Strategy

In order to expand its network of facilities SCA strives to buy existing surgical facilities and develop new facilities in partnership with area physicians and health care systems. During 2014 it acquired controlling stakes in 28 consolidated facilities. It also added three affiliated facilities with three new health system partners.

Mergers and Acquisitions

In 2014 Surgical Care Affiliates acquired a controlling interest in 15 ASCs for $138.1 million. Other purchases that year included a 51% stake in an ASC in California and a 59% stake in an ASC in Maryland.

Company Background

SCA is the former outpatient surgery unit of HealthSouth. HealthSouth sold the division to private equity firm TPG in 2007.

EXECUTIVES

Evp And Cfo, Peter Clemens
President And Ceo, Andrew P. Hayek
Evp And Chief Development Officer, Joseph T. (Joe) Clark
Evp And Coo, Michael Rucker
Svp Sales And Market Development, Winborne Macphail
Svp Perioperative Services, Gerry Biala
Svp Clinical Services And Training, Linda Lansing
Evp And General Counsel, Rich Sharff
Vice President Sales And Market Development Surgical Care Affiliates, Matt Stewart
Vice President Tax, Lea Harbor
Executive Vice President, Joe Clark
Vice President, Ali Reza
Group Vice President Operations, Chip Zahn
Regional Vice President Of Operations, Diana Shi
Vice President Finance And Investor Relations, Leslie Wachsman
Group Vice President, Jack Pocorobba
Vp Midwest Region Operations, Cory Kruger
Senior Vice President Of Development, Mark Langston
Senior Vice President Development, Tim Buono
Vice President Of Anesthesia Services Surgical Care Affiliates, James Martin
Vice President Operations, David Cutter
Vice President Operations, Jordan Cox
Vice President Operations, Thomas Lally
Clinical Director, Renee Hunt
Senior Vice President Operations, Paul Davis
Senior Vice President, Marie Edler
Vice President Total Rewards And Hris, Dale Moyer
Rvp, Robert Harmon
Vice President Business Development, Daniel Conroy
Group Vice President, Nicole Semeraro
Vice President Finance And Corporate Controller, Jordan Jones
Group Vice President, Nick Laperriere
Medical Director, Jack Nicholas
Chairman, Todd B. Sisitsky
Board Of Directors, Curtis Lane
Auditors: PRICEWATERHOUSECOOPERS LLP BI

LOCATIONS

HQ: SCAI HOLDINGS, LLC
510 LAKE COOK RD STE 400, DEERFIELD, IL 600155031
Phone: 847 236-0921
Web: WWW.SCASURGERY.COM

PRODUCTS/OPERATIONS

2014 Sales by Payor

	% of total
Managed care & other discount plans	62
Medicare	20
Workers' compensation	10
Patients & other third-party payors	5
Medicaid	3
Total	100

2014 Sales

	$ mil.	% of total
Net patient revenues	788	91
Management fee revenue	58	7
Other revenues	17	2
Total	864	100

COMPETITORS

HCA
Novamed Inc.
Symbion
Tenet Healthcare
United Surgical Partners
Universal Health Services

HISTORICAL FINANCIALS

Company Type: Private

Income Statement FYE: December 31

	REVENUE ($ mil.)	NET INCOME ($ mil.)	NET PROFIT MARGIN	EMPLOYEES
12/16	1,281	226	17.7%	5,248
12/15	1,051	273	26.0%	—
12/14	864	157	18.2%	—
12/13	802	52	6.6%	—
Annual Growth	16.9%	62.5%	—	—

2016 Year-End Financials

Return on assets: 8.5%
Return on equity: 19.6%
Current ratio: 1.30
Cash ($ mil.): 131

SCHAUMBOND GROUP, INC.

EXECUTIVES

Pres-Ceo, Baohua Zheng
CPA, Kevin Hsu

LOCATIONS

HQ: SCHAUMBOND GROUP, INC.
225 S LAKE AVE STE 300, PASADENA, CA 911013009
Phone: 626 215-4998

HISTORICAL FINANCIALS

Company Type: Private

Income Statement — FYE: December 31

	ASSETS ($ mil.)	NET INCOME ($ mil.)	INCOME AS % OF ASSETS	EMPLOYEES
12/07	65	4	7.5%	550
12/06	50	4	9.6%	—
Annual Growth	28.2%	(0.0%)	—	—

2007 Year-End Financials

Return on assets: 7.5%
Return on equity: 8.0%
Sales ($ mil): 2,200

SCHOOL BOARD OF BREVARD COUNTY

EXECUTIVES

Chairperson, Andy Ziegler
Chairperson*, Amy Kneessy
Budget Specialist, Joseph Strohfus
Coordinator, Jason Faulds
Coordinator, Diane McAlister
Senior Analyst, Andrea Young
Assistant, Brittany Postlethweight
Technology Repair Technician V, Bryan Rouse
Food Director, Cynthia Barrett
Technology Support, Gary Beasley
Pdcp, Lynnette Thorstensen
Auditors: MOORE STEPHENS LOVELACE PA

LOCATIONS

HQ: SCHOOL BOARD OF BREVARD COUNTY
2700 JDGE FRAN JMESON WAY, VIERA, FL 329406699
Phone: 321 633-1000
Web: WWW.BREVARDSCHOOLS.ORG

HISTORICAL FINANCIALS

Company Type: Private

Income Statement — FYE: June 30

	REVENUE ($ mil.)	NET INCOME ($ mil.)	NET PROFIT MARGIN	EMPLOYEES
06/14	626	7	1.2%	9,031
06/09	613	(19)	—	—
06/06	628	100	15.9%	—
06/05	564	43	7.8%	—
Annual Growth	1.2%	(18.0%)	—	—

2014 Year-End Financials

Return on assets: 0.7%
Return on equity: 1.9%
Current ratio: 2.40
Cash ($ mil.): 64

SCHOOL BOARD OF BROWARD COUNTY, THE (INC)

EXECUTIVES

Chair, Nora Rupert
V Chair*, Heather Brinkworth
Asst Contrl, Lauris N Hazelwood
Accounting Staff, Darla Timmons
Staff, Carol Burton
Coordinator, Bernadette Lohrer
Accounting Staff, Chanda Peoples
Coordinator, Jennifer Austin
Acting Director, Lori Canning
Coordinator, Rachael Garafola
Purchasing Agent, Debra Swain
Auditors: MOORE STEPHENS LOVELACE PA O

LOCATIONS

HQ: SCHOOL BOARD OF BROWARD COUNTY, THE (INC)
600 SE 3RD AVE, FORT LAUDERDALE, FL 333013125
Phone: 754 321-0000
Web: WWW.BROWARDSCHOOLS.COM

HISTORICAL FINANCIALS

Company Type: Private

Income Statement — FYE: June 30

	REVENUE ($ mil.)	NET INCOME ($ mil.)	NET PROFIT MARGIN	EMPLOYEES
06/19	2,924	167	5.7%	3,839
06/18	2,806	(65)	—	—
06/17	2,738	5	0.2%	—
06/09	2,548	(274)	—	—
Annual Growth	1.4%	—	—	—

SCHOOL BOARD OF ORANGE COUNTY FLORIDA

EXECUTIVES

Chairperson, Bill Sublette
Supt*, Barbara M Jenkins
Cfo*, Toni Greene
Executive of Information Techn, Jim Wolf
Occupational Specia, Yesenia Rivera
Staff, Beth McCaules
Coordinator, Frenchie Porter
Athletic Director, Julie Sanford
Assistant, Mabel Rios
Assistant Director, Peter Berry
Assistant, Robert Ryner
Auditors: CHERRY BEKAERT LLP ORLANDO F

LOCATIONS

HQ: SCHOOL BOARD OF ORANGE COUNTY FLORIDA
445 W AMELIA ST LBBY, ORLANDO, FL 328011153
Phone: 407 317-3200
Web: WWW.ORANGECOUNTYFL.NET

HISTORICAL FINANCIALS

Company Type: Private

Income Statement — FYE: June 30

	REVENUE ($ mil.)	NET INCOME ($ mil.)	NET PROFIT MARGIN	EMPLOYEES
06/12	1,823	30	1.7%	25,000
06/11	1,895	24	1.3%	—
Annual Growth	(3.8%)	26.1%	—	—

2012 Year-End Financials

Return on assets: 0.6%
Return on equity: 1.0%
Current ratio: —
Cash ($ mil.): 194

SCHOOL BOARD OF PALM BEACH COUNTY

EXECUTIVES

Chmn, Chuck Shaw
Choice Program Coordinator, Brooke Brink
Government, Cindi Walker
Executive Secretary, Claudia Robbins
Manager, Donald Scantlan
Administrative Assistant To Ch, Pat Haight
Chief Operating Officer, Donald Fennoy
Fleet Executive, Angela Barbato
It Infrastructure Network, Michael Sims
Information Technology Support, Sean Ache
Management Support Technician, Ann-Marie Haddad

LOCATIONS

HQ: SCHOOL BOARD OF PALM BEACH COUNTY
3300 FOREST HILL BLVD C316, WEST PALM BEACH, FL 334065813
Phone: 561 434-8000
Web: WWW.PALMBEACHSCHOOLS.ORG

HISTORICAL FINANCIALS

Company Type: Private

Income Statement — FYE: June 30

	REVENUE ($ mil.)	NET INCOME ($ mil.)	NET PROFIT MARGIN	EMPLOYEES
06/08	2,093	(68)	—	21,000
06/07	2,010	501	24.9%	—
06/05	1,657	(121)	—	—
06/04	1,290	61	4.8%	—
Annual Growth	12.9%	—	—	—

2008 Year-End Financials

Return on assets: (-1.4%)
Return on equity: (-3.4%)
Current ratio: —
Cash ($ mil.): 1,290

SCHOOL DISTRICT 1 IN THE CITY AND COUNTY OF DENVER AND THE STATE OF COLORADO

EXECUTIVES

Spdt, Tom Boasberg
Pres*, Carrie Olson
Principal, Emillo Esquibel
Teacher Secondary Middle, Leslie Aguilar
Teacher, Carolyn Lohr
Facility Management Crew Membe, Christopher Gettler
Senior Data Analyst, Curt O'Hara
2nd Grade Teacher, Diani Riopelle
Program Leader, Jenia Hooper
Hr School Partner, Kristine Lequerique
Careerspark Coordinator, Laura Eley
Auditors: CLIFTONLARSONALLEN LLP GREENW

LOCATIONS

HQ: SCHOOL DISTRICT 1 IN THE CITY AND COUNTY OF DENVER AND THE STATE OF COLORADO
1860 N LINCOLN ST, DENVER, CO 802037301
Phone: 720 423-3200
Web: WWW.DPSK12.ORG

HISTORICAL FINANCIALS

Company Type: Private

Income Statement — FYE: June 30

	REVENUE ($ mil.)	NET INCOME ($ mil.)	NET PROFIT MARGIN	EMPLOYEES
06/12*	916	(100)	—	14,965
12/08	0	(0)	—	—
06/08	790	(38)	—	—
Annual Growth	3.8%	—	—	—

*Fiscal year change

2012 Year-End Financials

Return on assets: (-7.5%)
Return on equity: —
Current ratio: —
Cash ($ mil.): 348

SCHWAB CHARITABLE FUND

EXECUTIVES

Exec Dir, Susan Heldman
Pres, Kim Laughton
Chb*, Carrie Schwab-Pomerantz
Dir, Brooks Walker
Mgr, Margae Diamond
Offc Mgr, Michael Smithwick
Auditors: DELOITTE & TOUCHE LLP SAN FRA

LOCATIONS

HQ: SCHWAB CHARITABLE FUND
211 MAIN ST, SAN FRANCISCO, CA 941051905
Phone: 415 667-9131
Web: WWW.SCHWABCHARITABLE.ORG

HISTORICAL FINANCIALS

Company Type: Private

Income Statement — FYE: June 30

	REVENUE ($ mil.)	NET INCOME ($ mil.)	NET PROFIT MARGIN	EMPLOYEES
06/18	3,465	1,549	44.7%	26
06/17	3,147	1,551	49.3%	—
06/16	2,018	819	40.6%	—
06/12	722	172	23.9%	—
Annual Growth	29.9%	44.1%	—	—

2018 Year-End Financials

Return on assets: 12.0%
Return on equity: 12.0%
Current ratio: 1.50
Cash ($ mil.): 12

SCL HEALTH - FRONT RANGE, INC.

Exempla aims to provide exemplary health care to residents in the Denver area. The Exempla medical network operating as Exempla Healthcare includes three hospitals: Exempla Saint Joseph Hospital (570 beds) Exempla Lutheran Medical Center (400 beds) and Good Samaritan Medical Center (more than 230 beds). It also operates the Exempla Physician Network a chain of primary care clinics. The company employs more than 2100 physicians. Among its specialties are cardiovascular services and surgeries rehabilitation cancer care orthopedics and women's and children's services. Exempla Healthcare is sponsored by the Catholic faith-based Sisters of Charity of Leavenworth Health System (SCL Health System).

Strategy

Exempla is investing in expansion of the facilities at Lutheran Medical Center. It is also constructing a new building for Saint Joseph Hospital that is set to open in 2015.

Company Background

Exempla Healthcare was formed in 1998 when Saint Joseph Hospital and Lutheran Medical Center combined.

EXECUTIVES

Vice President Finance, Judy Boller
211947989431 Vice President Strategy Business Development Elmc, Jennifer Wrona
Senior Vice President And Chief Communications And Marketing Officer, Christine Woolsey
Senior Vice President And Chro, Tamara Saunaitis
Vice President Ethics And Theology, Ken Homan
Vice President Strategic Financial Plan, Robert Fries
Director Of Pharmacy, Troy Butcher
Director Of Home Healthcare Services, Adrie Taylor
Pharmacy Manager, Lori Gumone
Senior Vice President Clinical Services, Stacey Jensen
Vice President Of Human Resources Interim, Scott Murphy
Auditors: ERNST & YOUNG US LLP PHOENIX

LOCATIONS

HQ: SCL HEALTH - FRONT RANGE, INC.
2420 W 26TH AVE, DENVER, CO 802115301
Phone: 303 813-5000
Web: WWW.SCLHEALTH.ORG

PRODUCTS/OPERATIONS

2009 Revenues

	$ mil.	% of total
Exempla Saint Joseph Hospital	377	40
Exempla Lutheran Medical Center	302	32
Exempla Good Samaritan Medical Center	217	23
Exempla Physician Network	22	2
Colorado Lutheran Home & Exempla West Pines Behavioral Health	22	2
Exempla Lutheran Collier Hospice	6	1
Total	948	100

COMPETITORS

Catholic Health Initiatives
Centura Health
Denver Health and Hospital Authority
HealthONE
Porter Adventist Hospital
Presbyterian/St. Luke's Medical Center
Rose Medical Center
University of Colorado Hospital

HISTORICAL FINANCIALS

Company Type: Private

Income Statement — FYE: December 31

	REVENUE ($ mil.)	NET INCOME ($ mil.)	NET PROFIT MARGIN	EMPLOYEES
12/09	597	7	1.3%	5,300
12/05	472	30	6.5%	—
12/04	335	37	11.2%	—
12/02	267	27	10.1%	—
Annual Growth	12.2%	(16.2%)	—	—

2009 Year-End Financials

Return on assets: 0.9%
Return on equity: 2.2%
Current ratio: 0.40
Cash ($ mil.): 53

SCOTT & WHITE MEMORIAL HOSPITAL

EXECUTIVES

Ceo, Robert Pryor
Pres*, Shahin Motakef
Coo*, Donny Sequin
Cfo*, Ken Johnson
Accounting Staff, Bud Watson
Cardiac Physician, Daniel Larsen
General Surgeon, Richard Symmonds
Anesthesiologist, William Culp
Senior Network Administrator, Ted Gaines
Orthopedician, Hanes Brindley
Anesthesiologist, Jack F Lay Jr

LOCATIONS

HQ: SCOTT & WHITE MEMORIAL HOSPITAL
2401 S 31ST ST, TEMPLE, TX 765080001
Phone: 254 724-2111
Web: WWW.BSWHEALTH.COM

COMPETITORS

Baylor Health
Community Health Systems
Cook Children's Health Care System
Dell Children's Medical Center
HCSC
Hill Country
Seton Healthcare Network
Shriners Hospitals For Children
St. David's Health Care
St. David's Round Rock Medical Center
Texas Children's Hospital

HISTORICAL FINANCIALS

Company Type: Private

Income Statement — FYE: June 30

	REVENUE ($ mil.)	NET INCOME ($ mil.)	NET PROFIT MARGIN	EMPLOYEES
06/14*	832	87	10.5%	8,000
08/13	881	76	8.6%	—
08/10	902	41	4.6%	—
Annual Growth	(2.0%)	20.3%	—	—

*Fiscal year change

2014 Year-End Financials

Return on assets: 7.0%
Return on equity: 8.1%
Current ratio: 1.40
Cash ($ mil.): 47

SCOTT AND WHITE HEALTH PLAN

The Scott & White Health Plan (SWHP) works to keep its members Safe & Well. The not-for-profit company provides health insurance plans and related services to more than 200000 members across some 50 counties in and around Central Texas. Owned by the Scott & White network of hospitals and clinics SWHP has employer-sponsored plans (including HMO PPO and consumer choice options) as well as several choices for individuals and families. It also offers COBRA state-administered continuation plans the Young Texan Health Plan for children Medicare and dental and vision benefits. The company began offering its services in 1982. Owner Scott & White is exploring a merger with Baylor Health Care System.

EXECUTIVES

Vice President Information Systems, Troy Stillwagon
Vice President Facilities And Constructon, Scott Liles
Secretary, Deborah Kennedy
Auditors: ERNST & YOUNG US LLP INDIANAP

LOCATIONS

HQ: SCOTT AND WHITE HEALTH PLAN
1206 WEST CAMPUS DR, TEMPLE, TX 765027124
Phone: 254 298-3000
Web: WWW.SWHP.ORG

PRODUCTS/OPERATIONS

Selected Products

Employer plans
Individual and family plans
Medicare plans
Vital Care programs

COMPETITORS

Aetna
Blue Cross and Blue Shield of Texas
CIGNA
Centene
Humana
Texas Health Resources
USHEALTH Group
UnitedHealth Group

HISTORICAL FINANCIALS

Company Type: Private

Income Statement — FYE: December 31

	REVENUE ($ mil.)	NET INCOME ($ mil.)	NET PROFIT MARGIN	EMPLOYEES
12/09	660	13	2.0%	426
12/08	621	(4)	—	—
12/07	586	8	1.4%	—
12/06	557	3	0.7%	—
Annual Growth	5.8%	54.1%	—	—

2009 Year-End Financials

Return on assets: 8.5%
Return on equity: 18.4%
Current ratio: 1.50
Cash ($ mil.): 8

SCOTTSDALE HEALTHCARE CORP.

Scottsdale Healthcare a not-for-profit organization serves the health care needs of central Arizona residents. Its operations include three acute care hospitals that combined boast some 900 beds. Scottsdale Healthcare also operates other campuses that offer physician offices a cancer center home health and other health care services. It conducts clinical research through the Scottsdale Healthcare Research Institute. The group's Essential Touch Wellness Center and Boutique provides spa-like stress-reduction therapies. With nearly 2000 medical and surgical staff members the company offers some 35 medical specialties. Scottsdale Healthcare is an affiliate of Scottsdale Lincoln Health Network along with John C. Lincoln Health Network.

Operations

The group's hospitals are Scottsdale Healthcare Osborn Medical Center (trauma orthopedics neurosurgery cardiovascular and critical care) Scottsdale Healthcare Shea Medical Center (full-service hospital including emergency medical and surgical critical care cardiovascular and oncology services) and Scottsdale Healthcare Thompson Peak (patient-family centered medical/surgical hospital). Additionally Scottsdale Healthcare operates five Urgent Care Plus clinics the Piper Outpatient Surgery Center at the Shea Medical Center the Greenbaum Surgical Specialty Hospital at Osborn Medical center and the Scottsdale Healthcare Primary Care network of primary care physicians.

Geographic Reach

Scottsdale Healthcare serves central Arizona specifically in an around the entire Northeast Valley as well as the area north of Loop 101.

Strategy

Since 2012 the health care network has been expanding into Northeast Phoenix to deepen its relationships with community physicians and diversify beyond its three-hospital Scottsdale campuses. To this end it opened new Scottsdale Healthcare Primary Care physician offices in 2013 – one each in Phoenix and Tempe – to join existing locations in Arcadia Scottsdale and Grayhawk.

What makes Scottsdale Healthcare stand out is its military training program the only one of its kind in the country. Its Readiness Skill Sustainment Training Program gives National Guard Air Force Reserve and nearby Air Force base personnel 12 days of training in treating trauma burns and other wounds they might encounter when deployed in a war zone. Participants also work in intensive care ride along with EMS personnel and get orthopedics and operating room practice. It has since expanded the program to include a $1.6-million military trauma training center which serves military medical personnel with classroom and simulation training and trains civilian paramedics and firefighters.

The organization performs clinical research through the Scottsdale Healthcare Research Institute. Through the institute the organization conducts clinical trials in a range of disciplines including cancer and other complex diseases.

In 2014 Scottsdale Healthcare formed an affiliation with John C. Lincoln Health Network. The combined networks operating under the moniker Scottsdale Lincoln Health Network include five hospitals with some 3700 affiliated physicians and an extensive outpatient services network.

The group opened a new 28-bed unit at its Scottsdale Healthcare Thompson Peak Hospital in 2013. The unit provides care to orthopedic and spine surgery patients.

Company Background

Scottsdale Healthcare was established in 1962 as City Hospital of Scottsdale.

EXECUTIVES

Vp And Cio, James R. (Jim) Cramer
President And Ceo, Thomas J. (Tom) Sadvary
Svp Medical Affairs, James F. Burke
Svp And Chief Clinical Officer, Peggy J. Reiley
Evp Healthcare Operations, Gary E. Baker
President Scottsdale Healthcare Foundation, John N. Ferree
Svp And Cfo, Todd LaPorte
Vp And Administrator Thompson Peak Hospital, Kim Post
Chief Medical Officer; Vp Physician Alignment, Richard Silver
Evp, Laura R. Grafman
Chief Operating Officer, Bruce Pearson
Assistant Vice President Supply Chain Consolidated Services, Michael Hildebrandt
Clinical Director, Shirley Righi
Vice President Marketing, Gilberto Brito
Vice President Worldwide Operations, Carol Henderson
Vice President Research, Mark Slater
Medical Director, Robert Marlow
Vice President, Kathy Zarubi
Medical Director Critical Care, Jack Applefeld
Vice President Finance, Brian Steines
Medical Director, Robin Blackstone
Assistant Vice President Project Management Office, Amy Clay
Medical Records Director, Apollonia Seianna
Assoc. Vp Workplace And Public Safety, Todd Larson
Associate Vp Enterprise Pmo, Eric Zuhlke
Associate Vice President Care Management, Pamela Foster
Vice President Procurement And Supply Chain, Tim Miller
Associate Vice President Analytics And Quality Operations, Lisa Taylor
Associate Vp Supply Chain Operations, Ryan Kirane
Chairman, Steven M. (Steve) Wheeler, age 72
Vice Chairman, Brad A. Gazaway
Board Of Directors, Mike Welborn
Auditors: ERNST & YOUNG LLP PHOENIX AZ

LOCATIONS

HQ: SCOTTSDALE HEALTHCARE CORP.
8125 N HAYDEN RD, SCOTTSDALE, AZ 852582463
Phone: 480 882-4000
Web: WWW.HONORHEALTH.COM

PRODUCTS/OPERATIONS

Selected Services
Bariatric Weight Loss Surgery
Cancer Care
Community Health
Corporate Health
Diabetes Management
Diagnostic Imaging Services
Digestive Health
Emergency Services
Heart & Vascular
Home Health Services
Infusion & Treatment Services
Minimally Invasive Surgery
Neurosciences
Nutrition Services
Orthopedic Services
Outpatient Therapy Services
Pediatrics
Sleep Disorders Center
Trauma Center
Wound Management
Urgent Care Plus
Urology Services

COMPETITORS

Banner Health
Community Health Systems
Dignity Health
Flagstaff Medical Center
Mayo Clinic
Phoenix Children's Hospital
Sun Health
Universal Health Services
University of Arizona Health Network
Yuma Regional Medical Center

HISTORICAL FINANCIALS

Company Type: Private

Income Statement — FYE: December 31

	REVENUE ($ mil.)	NET INCOME ($ mil.)	NET PROFIT MARGIN	EMPLOYEES
12/18	1,967	77	3.9%	17,000
12/17	1,763	104	6.0%	—
12/16	1,716	92	5.4%	—
12/14	88	9	11.2%	—
Annual Growth	117.3%	67.2%	—	—

2018 Year-End Financials

Return on assets: 3.1%
Return on equity: 5.4%
Current ratio: 5.30
Cash ($ mil.): 217

SCRIPPS HEALTH

Scripps Health houses many a script-writing physician in its hospitals. The not-for-profit health system serves the San Diego area through five acute-care hospitals. Altogether the health system is home to approximately 1700 inpatient beds and a network of outpatient clinics. The system also offers home health care and operates community outreach programs. Its hospitals along with several outpatient Scripps Clinic and Scripps Coastal Medical Center locations employ some 3000 affiliated general practice and specialty physicians.

Operations

Scripps Health's facilities include the 700-bed Scripps Mercy Hospital which has a main campus in San Diego and a satellite campus in Chula Vista as well as Scripps Green Hospital (173 beds in La Jolla) Scripps Memorial Hospital Encinitas (138 beds) and Scripps Memorial Hospital La Jolla (444 beds). The system's network also includes the new Prebys Cardiovascular Institute (168 beds) about a dozen coastal medical centers two wellness centers and about 20 specialty centers.

In 2016 the system had more than 445000 hospital outpatient visits 21500 surgeries and 1.2 million medical office visits.

Scripps Health is the official health care provider for the San Diego Padres baseball team.

Financial Performance

Scripps Health had $2.9 billion in revenues in fiscal 2016 (ended September). Some $2.2 billion of that revenue came from net patient service income while $0.5 billion came from capitation premiums. After operating expenses the system had $292.3 million in excess of revenues over expenses attributable to controlling interests.

Strategy

Scripps Health's overall strategy is to remain on the cutting edge of technology in order to treat patients more effectively therefore reporting better patient outcomes (which in turns makes it eligible for certain government incentives). It also aims to make itself the destination of choice for patients — both locally and globally — for cardiac cancer and other types of specialty care. For example it partners with renowned oncology center MD Anderson to operate the Scripps MD Anderson Cancer Center slated to open in mid-2018.

As a major provider in the larger San Diego area Scripps Health is constantly evaluating its scope of services to meet the ever-increasing demand for health care. The company is building several outpatient clinics including cancer treatment and cardiac care centers. It is also expanding and upgrading its hospitals. In addition Scripps Health has launched an initiative to increase the number of clinical trials conducted at its facilities.

However after missing its budget for the first time in more than a dozen years Scripps Health announced plans to lower operating costs through restructuring efforts. It ultimately aims to rely more heavily on outpatient care and wellness services to reduce hospital visits. Layoffs are part of the restructuring plans: For example the system eliminated the CEO positions at its five hospitals. The hospitals are now led by chief operations executives reporting to regional (North and South) CEOs. Additionally Scripps Health shut down its loss-making hospice operations in 2017.

EXECUTIVES

Svp And Chief Executive Scripps Green Hospital, Robin B. Brown
Svp And Chief Executive Scripps Memorial Hospital La Jolla, Gary G. Fybel
Svp And Chief Executive Scripps Mercy Hospital, Tom Gammiere
Cfo And Treasurer, Richard K. Rothberger
Svp And Chief Executive Scripps Memorial Hospital Encinitas, Carl J. Etter
President And Ceo, Christopher D. Van Gorder
Corporate Svp And Chief Medical Officer, James LaBelle
Svp And Chief Executive Scripps Medical Foundation, Shiraz M. Fagan
Corporate Svp And Cio, Andy Crowder
Assistant Vice President Supply Chain Management, Cecile Hozouri
Assistant Vice President Information Services, Clark Kegley
Vice President Finance, June Komar
Corporate Senior Vice President, Barbara Price
Senior Vice President Human Resources Interim Employee Training Devel, Vic Buzachero
Radiology Medical Director, David Buckley
Medical Director, Martin Charlat
Vice President Managed Care, Karri Rodgers
Corporate Vice President And Chief Audit And Compliance Executive, Gerry Soderstrom
Medical Director, Gabriela Mogrovejo
Medical Director Of Respiratory Care, Bao Q Luu
Medical Director Scripps Md Anderson Cancer Center, Thomas Buchholz
Vice President For Nursing Operations, Mary E Doyle
Assistant Vp Care Line Services, Matthew Cantonis
Health Care Director, Susana Medrano
Vice Chairman, Mark Sherman
Secretary, Nancy Bernardy

LOCATIONS

HQ: SCRIPPS HEALTH
10140 CAMPUS POINT DR # 415, SAN DIEGO, CA 921211520
Phone: 800 727-4777
Web: WWW.SCRIPPS.ORG

Selected Facilities
Scripps Clinic (outpatient centers)
Scripps Coastal Medical Center (outpatient centers)
Scripps Green Hospital (La Jolla)
Scripps Memorial Hospital Encinitas
Scripps Memorial Hospital La Jolla
Scripps Mercy Hospital (San Diego)
Scripps Mercy Hospital Chula Vista

COMPETITORS

Adventist Health System West
Cedars-Sinai Medical Center
Community Health Systems
Dignity Health
Grossmont Hospital
HCA
Palomar Health
Paradise Valley Hospital
Prospect Medical
Rady Children's Hospital
Sharp HealthCare
Tenet Healthcare

HISTORICAL FINANCIALS

Company Type: Private

Income Statement — FYE: September 30

	REVENUE ($ mil.)	NET INCOME ($ mil.)	NET PROFIT MARGIN	EMPLOYEES
09/15	2,943	371	12.6%	5,445
09/08	1,953	18	0.9%	—
09/07	1,781	223	12.6%	—
Annual Growth	6.5%	6.5%	—	—

2015 Year-End Financials

Return on assets: 8.3%
Return on equity: 12.0%
Current ratio: 0.80
Cash ($ mil.): 464

SCRIPPS NETWORKS INTERACTIVE, INC.

Lifestyle TV is a livelihood for this company. Scripps Networks Interactive operates six lifestyle cable networks including Home & Garden Television (home building and decoration) the Food Network (culinary programs) DIY - Do It Yourself Network (home repair and improvement) the Cooking Channel (culinary how-to programming) and the Travel Channel (travel and tourism). The company additionally owns music channel Great American Country and has minority interests in Asian Food Channel and regional sports network FOX Sports Net South. It also owns a 50% stake in UKTV.

Trusts for the Scripps family own majority control of the company.In 2017 Discovery Communications agreed to buy Scripps Networks in a $14.6 billion deal.

Operations

Scripps Networks has two reportable segments: US networks and International Networks. Its US network segment accounts for almost 85% of total revenue.

Geographic Reach

Scripps Networks is based in Knoxville Tennessee. The company has additional offices located in Atlanta Chicago Dallas Detroit Los Angeles New York City San Francisco Miami Chevy Chase Maryland and Washington DC. Scripps Networks maintains international offices in London Milan S o Paulo Sydney the Philippines and Singapore.

The company's Cooking Channel is available in Canada. HGTV is available in the Asia-Pacific region the Middle East North Africa and New Zealand. Scripps Networks has also expanded Food Network across Latin America and Australia.

Sales and Marketing

Cable programmers such as Scripps Networks generate most of their revenue through advertising and carriage fees paid by cable system operators and satellite TV service providers. To help keep viewer loyalty and ratings high the company targets its channels toward specific interests rather than airing programming for a general audience.

The company advertises its products through broadcast television networks online and mobile outlets radio programming and print media. Scripps Networks spent $161.1 million on advertising and promotions in fiscal 2016.

Financial Performance

Scripps Networks reported about $3.4 billion in revenue for fiscal 2016. That was an increase of more than $400 million compared to the $3 billion the company reported for revenue the previous fiscal year. The increase was due to increased advertising sales and affiliate fee revenues.

Scripps Networks' net income was $673 million in fiscal 2016. That was an increase of about $67 million compared to the prior fiscal period when the company claimed a net income of $606 million primarily as a result of an increase in total revenue.

The company ended fiscal 2016 with $948 million in cash from operating activities which was an increase compared to fiscal 2015 when Scripps Networks ended the year with $814 million in cash from operations.

Strategy

Scripps Networks is focused on growing advertising revenues by increasing video plays and attracting more unique visitors to its websites through site enhancements and adding more video. Its strategy also includes trying to attract a broader audience through programming on national video streaming sites developing new sources of revenue that capitalize on traffic growth at the company's own websites and capitalizing on the movement of advertising dollars to mobile platforms.

The growth of the company's international business continues to be a strategic priority. Scripps Networks has expanded in Asia Europe and Latin America in recent years.

EXECUTIVES

Chairman President And Ceo, Kenneth W. (Ken) Lowe, age 70, $1,683,858 total compensation

Coo, Burton F. Jablin, age 61, $1,110,000 total compensation

Evp Operations And Cto, Mark S. Hale, age 61, $600,000 total compensation

Head Of International Lifestyle Channels, Derek Chang, age 52

President International And Interim President Tvn, Jim Samples

Evp Finance, Lori A. Hickok, age 56, $775,000 total compensation

President Ad Sales And Marketing And Branded Entertainment, Steven J. (Steve) Gigliotti

Cio, Bob Baskerville, age 56

President Content Distribution And Marketing, Henry Ahn

Chief Programming Content And Brand Officer, Kathleen Finch

Evp Digital Sales, Beth Lawrence

Evp Digital, Tamara Franklin

Evp Corporate Giving And Community Relations, James B. (Jim) Clayton

Evp Legal, Cynthia L. Gibson, age 56, $680,000 total compensation

President National Ad Sales And Marketing, Jon Steinlauf

Evp And Chief Communications Officer, Dylan P. Jones

Svp Culinary, Katherine Alford

Evp And Chief Human Resources Officer, Nello-John (NJ) Pesci, age 58

Senior Vice President Finance, Mark Livingston

Senior Vice President Engineering And Distribution Technologies, Mike Donovan

Vice President Programming And Production, John Feld

Vice President Content Accounting, Melissa Birkholz

Svp Digital Product And Operations, Jennifer Goforth

Senior Vice President Program Planning And Strategy U.s. Networks, Julie Taylor

Vice President Production Operations, Johanna Hammond Hoover

Vice President Corporate Finance, Peter Feret

Senior Vice President Business And Legal Affairs And Corporate Secretary, Eleni Stratigeas

Senior Vice President Ad Sales Food Network And Cooking Channel, Karen Grinthal

Vice President Legal Affairs, Erik Hestnes

Vice President Project Management, Bud Ketterl

Senior Vice President Ad Sales Hgtv And Diy Network, Donna Stephens

Senior Vice President Programming Food Network Travel Channel And Cooking Channel, Courtney White

Vp Media And Content Delivery, Chuck Hurst

Vice President Marketing And Production, Adriana Alcantara

Senior Vice President Internal Audit, Andy Broyles

Vice President Programming And Development Food Network Cooking Channel And Travel Channel, Lynn Sadofsky

Vice President Engineering And Distribution Technologies, Bart Palmer

Vice President Content Distribution And Marketing, Lauren Baynes

Vice President Legal And Government Affairs, Kimberly Hulsey

Vice President Of Video Product Management, Christopher Mccown

Vice President Human Resources, Laura A Schmidt

Vice President Operations And Data Strategy, Jeff Kissinger

Vice President Programming And Developme, Todd Weiser

Auditors: DELOITTE & TOUCHE LLP CINCIN

LOCATIONS

HQ: SCRIPPS NETWORKS INTERACTIVE, INC.
9721 SHERRILL BLVD, KNOXVILLE, TN 379323330
Phone: 865 694-2700
Web: WWW.CORPORATE.DISCOVERY.COM

2016

	$ mil.	% of total
United States	2,884	85
Poland	443	13
Other International	73	2
Total	**3,401**	**100**

PRODUCTS/OPERATIONS

2016 sales

	$ mil.	% of total
operating revenue		
U.S Networks	2,871	84
International Networks	557	16
Total	**3,428**	**100**

2016 sales

	$ mil.	% of total
Advertising	2,416	71
Distribution	894	26
other	90	3
Total	**3,401**	**100**

Selected Operations

Lifestyle media
- Cooking Channel
- DIY Network
- Food Network (75%)
- Fox Sports Net South (7%)
- Great American Country
- HGTV (Home & Garden Television)
- Travel Channel (65%)
- UKTV (50%)
- Asian Food Channel (100%)

Interactive Services
- CookingChanneltv.com
- DIYNetwork.com
- FoodNetwork.com
- GACTV.com
- HGTV.com
- TravelChannel.com

COMPETITORS

A&E Networks
ABC Cable Networks
AMC Networks
MTV Networks
NBCUniversal
PBS
Turner Broadcasting

HISTORICAL FINANCIALS

Company Type: Private

Income Statement — FYE: December 31

	REVENUE ($ mil.)	NET INCOME ($ mil.)	NET PROFIT MARGIN	EMPLOYEES
12/17	3,561	814	22.9%	3,500
12/16	3,401	847	24.9%	—
12/15	3,018	778	25.8%	—
12/14	2,665	726	27.3%	—
Annual Growth	10.1%	3.9%	—	—

2017 Year-End Financials

Return on assets: 12.5%
Return on equity: 26.2%
Current ratio: 3.10
Cash ($ mil.): 130

SEALASKA CORPORATION

Sealaska Corporation is a native-owned investment firm active in natural resources manufacturing services and gaming. The holding company owns land in southeastern Alaska home to the Tlingit Haida and Tsimshian peoples. Sealaska core holdings include Sealaska Timber Corporation Alaska Coastal Aggregates Sealaska Constructors Sealaska Environmental Services and Colorado-based information technology services provider Managed Business Solutions. Subsidiary End-to-End Enterprises manages the company's gaming business. Sealaska's subsidiaries operate throughout North America and around the world. Its companies often win government contracts for construction environmental and engineering projects.

Operations

More than 60% of Sealaska's revenues came from its services segment during 2015 which includes subsidiary Sealaksa Environmental Services Sealaksa Constructors Sealaska Government Services Sealaska Technical Services Synergy Systems and Managed Business Solutions.

Nearly 30% of Sealaska's revenues are earned by its natural resources business which oversees land management and stewardship functions for all Sealaska lands. Sealaska owns about 290000 acres of timberland as well as the minerals rights to construction-grade aggregates on more than 565000 acres. Sealaska Timber harvest timber and markets logs for the domestic and export markets.

The company's Investment Business Segment (5% of revenues) comprised the Majorie V. Young Shareholder Permanent Fund and the Investment and Growth Fund. Its Gaming segment is managed by its subsidiary End-to-End Enterprises.

Geographic Reach

Juneau-based Sealaska has offices through the US and several other countries including Canada and Mexico as well as Europe.

Financial Performance

Sealaska's annual revenues have fallen 65% since 2012 as its portfolio holdings (such as its civil construction business in Hawaii and its natural resources business) haven't all fared well. The firm has rebounded from losses in 2013 however as it's sold off its less successful businesses and reduced costs.

The firm's revenue fell 10% to $109.4 million during 2015 with volatile markets causing a nearly $7 million decline in investment gains.

Revenue declines in 2015 caused Sealaska's net income to plunge 20% to $12 million though operational improvements helped dampen the blow. The firm's services business in particular managed to grow its profits despite a small sales decline as it focused more on higher value added work. Sealaska's operating cash levels spiked nearly 80% to $18.62 million after adjusting its earnings for non-cash expenses such as investment losses.

Strategy

Sealaska continued in 2016 to target acquisitions in businesses operating in the natural foods and seafood maritime services environmental service niche construction and data analytics sectors.The company adopted a 2012-2017 plan designed to transform Sealaska into a financially sustainable and profitable company driven by its core cultural values. To that end in 2013 the company sold its interest in its Nypro K˜naak joint venture and the Sealaska Global Logistics business and exited the security guard services business (acquired in 2010) to support future acquisitions.

Company Background

Sealaska is the largest of 13 corporations formed under the Alaska Native Claims Settlement Act (ANCSA) of 1971 which promised some 44 million acres of land to Alaska natives. The company is owned by some 21600 tribal member shareholders.

Subsidiary Haa Aan (meaning "our land") was established in 2009 as a way to promote the culture social and economic viability of Southeast Alaska. Haa Aan has assisted tribal members with their efforts to establish businesses such as a new oyster farms in southeastern Alaska. Haa Aan also promotes renewable energy initiatives such as a biomass heating system for commercial buildings. In 2012 Haa Aan launched a non-profit community development financial institution in order to provide financing and promote economic development.

EXECUTIVES

Evp, Richard P. (Rick) Harris, $240,000 total compensation
President And Ceo, Chris E. McNeil, $350,000 total compensation
Manager Information Systems, Robert (Rob) Johnson
Director Accounting And Corporate Controller, Doug Morris
Director Group Operations, Russell A. Dick
President And Ceo, Anthony Mallott
Manager Natural Resources, Ron Wolfe
President And Ceo Sealaska Timber Corporation (stc), Wade Zammit
President And Ceo Sealaska Environmental Services, Derik Frederiksen
President And Ceo Managed Business Solutions (mbs) And Mbs Systems, Jon Duncan
Coo, Terry Downes
Coo Sealaska Environmental Services, Lewis Ivers
Chairman, Albert M. Kookesh, age 71
Vice Chair, Rosita F. Worl, age 82
Auditors: RSM US LLP ANCHORAGE ALASKA

LOCATIONS

HQ: SEALASKA CORPORATION
1 SEALASKA PLZ STE 400, JUNEAU, AK 998011276
Phone: 907 586-1512
Web: WWW.SEALASKA.COM

PRODUCTS/OPERATIONS

2014 Sales

	$ mil.	% of total
Services	81	67
Natural Resources	33	28
Investments	6	5
Gaming	0	-
Corporate & other	0	-
Total	**121**	**100**

Selected Subsidiaries

Alaska Coastal Aggregates
End-to-End Enterprises LLC (gaming)
Haa Aaní; LLC
Managed Business Solutions (majority owned)
Sealaska Constructors LLC
Sealaska Environmental Services
Sealaska Timber Corporation

COMPETITORS

Tembec
West Fraser Timber
chugach alaska

HISTORICAL FINANCIALS

Company Type: Private

Income Statement — FYE: December 31

	REVENUE ($ mil.)	NET INCOME ($ mil.)	NET PROFIT MARGIN	EMPLOYEES
12/19	699	86	12.3%	1,400
12/18	429	69	16.1%	—
12/17	293	45	15.6%	—
12/16	145	15	11.0%	—
Annual Growth	68.8%	75.3%	—	—

2019 Year-End Financials

Return on assets: 12.5%
Return on equity: 20.4%
Current ratio: 3.30
Cash ($ mil.): 31

SEATTLE PUBLIC SCHOOLS

EXECUTIVES

Supt, Raj Manhas
Dir*, Carol Johnson
Dir of Fin*, Sephen Nielson
Customer Staff, Alma Clark
Coordinator, Bernardo Ruiz
Facilities, Silas Potter
Reading Specialist, Anne Presecan
Teacher, Amy Ferguson
Planning Staff, Anita Demahy
Teacher, Hersh Mandelman
Teacher, Tim Snyder

LOCATIONS

HQ: SEATTLE PUBLIC SCHOOLS
2445 3RD AVE S, SEATTLE, WA 981341923
Phone: 206 252-0000

HISTORICAL FINANCIALS

Company Type: Private

Income Statement — FYE: August 31

	REVENUE ($ mil.)	NET INCOME ($ mil.)	NET PROFIT MARGIN	EMPLOYEES
08/18	1,042	39	3.8%	4,650
08/06	553	4	0.8%	—
08/05	429	10	2.4%	—
Annual Growth	7.1%	11.0%	—	—

2018 Year-End Financials

Return on assets: 8.2%
Return on equity: 24.0%
Current ratio: —
Cash ($ mil.): 271

SECURITY FINANCE CORPORATION OF SPARTANBURG

Folks looking for a little financial security just might turn to Security Finance Corporation of Spartanburg. Founded in 1955 the consumer loan company provides personal loans typically ranging from $100 to $600 (some states however allow loan amounts as high as $3000). Customers can also turn to Security Finance for credit reports and tax preparation services. The company operates approximately 900 offices in more than 15 states that are marketed under the Security Finance Sunbelt Credit and PFS banner names. A subsidiary of Security Group the financial institution also has locations operating as Security Financial Services in North Carolina and Longhorn Finance in Texas.

Operations

Security Finance boasts some 900 offices nationwide that operate under the Security Finance Sunbelt Credit and PFS names. The company specializes in offering consumers loans to individuals. It also provides consumer credit reports and assistance as well as tax preparation services.

Geographic Reach

From its headquarters in South Carolina Security Finance boasts offices in more than 15 states nationwide.

Company Background

Security Finance exited Colorado in 2010 after the state's attorney general general office filed a compliant that the company had been refinancing some consumer loans more than three times a year (the limit under Colorado law). The company agreed to repay acquisition fees that it had charged the customers for refinancing the loans.

EXECUTIVES

Pres, Heidi Bolton
Chb*, Susan A Bridges
V Chb*, C H Edwards
Treas-Cfo*, A Greg Williams
SEC*, Marshall T Walsh
Asst Treas*, Beadie H Townsel
Coo*, Judy Perkins
Unix Administrator, Bob Saccamano
Software Manager, Mark Libner
Cash Management, Brenda Seagle
Auditors: ELLIOTT DAVIS DECOSIMO LLC G

LOCATIONS

HQ: SECURITY FINANCE CORPORATION OF SPARTANBURG
181 SECURITY PL, SPARTANBURG, SC 293075450
Phone: 864 582-8193
Web: WWW.SECURITYFINANCE.COM

Selected Locations

Alabama
Florida
Georgia
Idaho
Illinois
Louisiana
Missouri
Nevada
New Mexico
North Carolina
Oklahoma
South Carolina
Tennessee
Texas
Utah
Wisconsin

PRODUCTS/OPERATIONS

Selected Banners

Longhorn Finance (Texas)
PFS
Security Finance
Security Financial Services (North Carolina)
Sunbelt Credit

COMPETITORS

1st Franklin Financial
ACE Cash Express
Advance America
Bank of America
Capital One
Cash Plus
Community Choice Financial
DFC Global
EZCORP
FirstCash
OneMain
OneMain Financial
Value Financial Services
World Acceptance

HISTORICAL FINANCIALS

Company Type: Private

Income Statement — FYE: December 31

	ASSETS ($ mil.)	NET INCOME ($ mil.)	INCOME AS % OF ASSETS	EMPLOYEES
12/16	625	70	11.3%	2,500
12/15	651	78	12.1%	—
12/14	648	83	12.8%	—
12/13	616	62	10.2%	—
Annual Growth	0.5%	4.1%	—	—

2016 Year-End Financials

Return on assets: 11.3%
Return on equity: 20.6%
Sales ($ mil): 558

SECURITY GROUP, INC.

EXECUTIVES

Chb, Susan A Bridges
V Chb*, Clarence Edwards
Pres, Ray Biggs
V Pres-Fin, A Greg Williams
Treas, Beadie H Townsel
Software Analyst, Danh Truong
Senior Vice President, Lisa Burroughs
Payroll Specialist, Marilyn Likes
Auditors: ELLIOTT DAVIS DECOSIMO LLC G

LOCATIONS

HQ: SECURITY GROUP, INC.
181 SECURITY PL, SPARTANBURG, SC 293075450
Phone: 864 582-8193
Web: WWW.SECURITYFINANCE.COM

HISTORICAL FINANCIALS

Company Type: Private

Income Statement — FYE: December 31

	ASSETS ($ mil.)	NET INCOME ($ mil.)	INCOME AS % OF ASSETS	EMPLOYEES
12/16	1,002	87	8.8%	2,500
12/15	1,020	97	9.6%	—
12/14	1,040	135	13.0%	—
12/13	1,263	107	8.5%	—
Annual Growth	(7.4%)	(6.4%)	—	—

2016 Year-End Financials

Return on assets: 8.8%
Return on equity: 12.7%
Sales ($ mil): 635

SECURITY HEALTH PLAN OF WISCONSIN, INC.

Security Health Plan of Wisconsin provides health insurance coverage and related services to some 200000 members in more than 35 Wisconsin counties. Its managed network of providers includes more than 4000 physicians 40 hospitals and health care facilities as well as 55000 pharmacies across the US. Security Health Plan provides policies for groups and individuals. Its products include HMO coverage plans and supplemental Medicare plans as well as prescription drug and equipment coverage disease management programs and administration services for self-funded plans. Established in 1986 the company is the managed healthcare arm of Marshfield Clinic which operates medical practices across the state.

Operations

Since it is affiliated with a medical care provider Security Health Plan's coverage decisions are directly impacted by the practicing physician. The company's provider network consists of independent physician locations and parent Marshfield Clinic's more than 50 locations in Wisconsin.

In addition to HMO plans the firm's comprehensive medical coverage plans include POS (point of service) and high-deductable offerings. Security Health Plan offers health care reimbursement accounts through third-party provider agreements with Employee Benefits Corporation and Diversified Benefits Services. In addition the company provides community education and wellness programs.

Geographic Reach

Headquartered in the town of Marshfield Security Health Plan serves the counties of Adams Ashland Barron Bayfield Burnett Chippewa Clark Columbia Dane Douglas Dunn Eau Claire Forest Iron Jackson Juneau Langlade Lincoln Marathon Marquette Monroe Oneida Pepin Portage Price Rusk Sauk Sawyer Shawano Taylor Trempealeau Vilas Washburn Waupaca Waushara and Wood.

Sales and Marketing

Security Health Plan serves individuals families and small to large employer groups.

Strategy

Originally started in 1986 as an offshoot of the Greater Marshfield Community Health Plan Security Health Plan's service territory has grown over the years. For instance in 2012 the company extended its Advocare Medicare Advantage plan offering into several new counties. Security Health Plan also regularly adds primary care and specialty providers to its network to provide a broader range of accessible care services to its members as well as to strengthen its operations in underserved regions. The company is also looking to enhance its IT systems to allow for greater information access communication methods and collaboration among its providers and members.

EXECUTIVES

Medical Director, Dharmesh Babaria
Auditors: KPMG LLP MINNEAPOLIS MN

LOCATIONS

HQ: SECURITY HEALTH PLAN OF WISCONSIN, INC.
1515 N SAINT JOSEPH AVE, MARSHFIELD, WI 544491343
Phone: 715 221-9555
Web: WWW.SECURITYHEALTH.ORG

COMPETITORS

Aetna
Blue Cross Blue Shield of Wisconsin
CIGNA
Centene
Dean Health Plan
Group Health Cooperative
Gundersen Lutheran
Humana
UnitedHealth Group
Unity Health Plans Insurance
WEA Trust
Wisconsin Physicians Service Insurance Corporation

HISTORICAL FINANCIALS

Company Type: Private

Income Statement — FYE: December 31

	REVENUE ($ mil.)	NET INCOME ($ mil.)	NET PROFIT MARGIN	EMPLOYEES
12/17	1,234	9	0.8%	1,006
12/09	814	27	3.4%	—
12/05	385	0	—	—
12/04	369	17	4.7%	—
Annual Growth	9.7%	(4.4%)	—	—

2017 Year-End Financials

Return on assets: 2.8%
Return on equity: 5.7%
Current ratio: 1.10
Cash ($ mil.): 159

SEMCO ENERGY, INC.

Alaska and Michigan have more in common than a cold climate. SEMCO ENERGY serves approximately 423000 natural gas consumers in both states. The company's main subsidiary is utility SEMCO ENERGY Gas which distributes gas to more than 290000 customers in 24 Michigan counties. SEMCO's ENSTAR Natural Gas unit distributes gas to more than 133000 customers in and around Anchorage Alaska. The company's unregulated operations include propane distribution in Michigan and Wisconsin; pipeline and storage facility operation; and information technology outsourcing. In 2012 SEMCO ENERGY was acquired by AltaGas.

EXECUTIVES

Vice President Manager Director, Tracy Vincent
Auditors: ERNST & YOUNG LLP DETROIT MI

LOCATIONS

HQ: SEMCO ENERGY, INC.
1411 3RD ST STE A, PORT HURON, MI 480605480
Phone: 810 987-2200
Web: WWW.SEMCOENERGYGAS.COM

COMPETITORS

AEP
ARB
Chugach Electric
Consumers Energy
DTE Electric
Halliburton
Southwest Gas
Tengasco
WEC Energy

HISTORICAL FINANCIALS

Company Type: Private

Income Statement — FYE: December 31

	REVENUE ($ mil.)	NET INCOME ($ mil.)	NET PROFIT MARGIN	EMPLOYEES
12/16	575	51	9.0%	500
12/14	674	51	7.6%	—
12/13	608	48	8.0%	—
12/12	582	41	7.2%	—
Annual Growth	(0.3%)	5.5%	—	—

2016 Year-End Financials

Return on assets: 3.2%
Return on equity: 9.0%
Current ratio: 1.20
Cash ($ mil.): 4

SEMINOLE ELECTRIC COOPERATIVE, INC.

This Seminole is not only a native Floridian but it has also provided electricity in the state since 1948. Seminole Electric Cooperative generates and transmits electricity for 10 member distribution cooperatives that serve 1.4 million residential and business customers in 42 Florida counties. Seminole Electric has more than 3350 MW of primarily coal-fired generating capacity. The cooperative also buys electricity from other utilities and independent power producers and it owns 350 miles of transmission lines. Some 90% of its power load uses the transmission systems of other utilities through long-term contracts.

Operations

Seminole Electric's primary resources include the 1300 MW Seminole Generating Station and the 810 MW Richard J. Midulla Generating Station. The coop's renewable energy resources include waste-to-energy facilities landfill gas-to-energy facilities and a biomass facility. It also buys power as needed on the market.

Seminole Electric has more than 350 miles of transmission line.

Geographic Reach

The company serves customers in 45 counties in northeast south central and southeast Florida.

Financial Performance

In 2013 the coop's revenues declined by 1% due to lower rates and as well as a reduction in Member energy requirements and lower volumes sold to Non-Members.

Seminole Electric's net income increased by 48% in 2013 thanks to lower operating costs as a result of the absence of asset impairment costs and a drop in interest expenses.

The company's operating cash inflow increased to $86.05 million in 2013 (from $34.81 million in 2012) primarily due to improved net income and a change in working capital.

Strategy

The coop is seeking to respond to the State of Florida's push to get more power generation from renewable sources. In 2014 the company generating about 58% of its electricity from coal 35% from natural gas and 7% from green energy sources (up from 5.5% in 2011 making Seminole Electric one of the largest green energy providers in Florida).

Company Background

In 2012 it also made major environmental improvements to its main power plant the coal-fired Seminole Generating Station. In 2011 Seminole Electric boosted its portfolio of purchased green energy to more than 140 MW (including 113 MW from waste-to-energy facilities).

Seminole Electric was formed in 1948 to aggregate the power demands of its members and is governed by a board of trustees representing the 10 member utilities. The cooperative built its first power plant in the 1970s.

EXECUTIVES

Vp Administration, Al Garcia
Vice President Of Power Production, Charles W Huguenard
Auditors: PRICEWATERHOUSECOOPERS LLP TA

LOCATIONS

HQ: SEMINOLE ELECTRIC COOPERATIVE, INC.
16313 N DALE MABRY HWY, TAMPA, FL 336181427
Phone: 813 963-0994
Web: WWW.SEMINOLE-ELECTRIC.COM

PRODUCTS/OPERATIONS

Members

Central Florida Electric Cooperative
Clay Electric Cooperative
Glades Electric Cooperative
Lee County Electric Cooperative
Peace River Electric Cooperative
Sumter Electric Cooperative
Suwannee Valley Electric Cooperative
Talquin Electric Cooperative
Tri-County Electric Cooperative
Withlacoochee River Electric Cooperative

COMPETITORS

Duke Energy
Florida Power & Light
Florida Public Utilities
JEA
NextEra Energy
Progress Energy
Southern Company
TECO Energy

HISTORICAL FINANCIALS

Company Type: Private

Income Statement — FYE: December 31

	REVENUE ($ mil.)	NET INCOME ($ mil.)	NET PROFIT MARGIN	EMPLOYEES
12/18	1,083	21	1.9%	528
12/17*	1,067	23	2.2%	—
03/17	1,052	33	3.2%	—
12/16	1,067	20	1.9%	—
Annual Growth	0.7%	2.1%	—	—

*Fiscal year change

2018 Year-End Financials

Return on assets: 1.1%
Return on equity: 5.4%
Current ratio: 1.10
Cash ($ mil.): 35

SENTARA HOSPITALS - NORFOLK

EXECUTIVES

Ceo, David L Bernd
Pres, Howard Kern
SEC, Jeffrey King
Cfo, Robert A Broermann
Pres-Cfo, Kern Howard P
Cardiologist, Gary Zeevi
Nurse, Brenda Smith
Lab Safety Officer, Dan Scungio
Otolaryngologist, Joseph Han
Team Coordinator, Viswanathan Venkataraman
Neurosurgeon, Dana Adkins
Auditors: KPMG LLP NORFOLK VIRGINIA

LOCATIONS

HQ: SENTARA HOSPITALS - NORFOLK
600 GRESHAM DR, NORFOLK, VA 235071904
Phone: 757 388-3000
Web: WWW.SENTARA.COM

HISTORICAL FINANCIALS

Company Type: Private

Income Statement — FYE: December 31

	REVENUE ($ mil.)	NET INCOME ($ mil.)	NET PROFIT MARGIN	EMPLOYEES
12/17	877	63	7.2%	172
12/16	831	100	12.1%	—
12/15	791	92	11.7%	—
12/14	748	76	10.2%	—
Annual Growth	5.5%	(6.2%)	—	—

SERVCO PACIFIC INC.

Servco Pacific's business flows through an ocean's worth of enterprises. The company sells passenger vehicles (including Toyota Subaru Suzuki and Chevrolet models) and commercial trucks through dealerships in Hawaii and Australia. In addition Servco Home & Appliance wholesales kitchen and bath products to building professionals throughout the South Pacific; Servco Raynor Overhead Doors installs residential and commercial garage doors; Servco Insurance Services offers insurance coverage for businesses and individuals; and Servco School & Office Furniture outfits educational institutions and government agencies with desks seating and other furnishings. Servco Pacific was founded by Peter Fukunaga in 1919.

Operations

The diversified firm sells insurance through Servco Insurance Services (SIS) in Washington state. It clients are in the fishing shipping and cargo industries in several states including Alaska. SIS also operates in Hawaii where sister chains Servco Home & Appliance Servco Forklift & Industrial Equipment and Servco Automotive also operate. Sercvo Tire Company sells tires on Maui and in Honolulu.

Geographic Reach

Honolulu-based Servco Pacific has insurance offices in Seattle and Tacoma Washington. Its other businesses operate in Hawaii (Kauai Maui Oahu and the Big Island); and Australia (New South Wales Queensland).

Financial Performance

The private company reports revenue of approximately $800 million annually.

Strategy

Servco Pacific through its Australian subsidiary has been expanding its Toyota dealer operations in recent years. During 2010 the company acquired majority stakes in Sunshine Toyota of Queensland and Dubbo City Toyota of New South Wales. It also purchased Pacific Toyota in Cairns in 2009. The deals have significantly grown Servco Pacific's business in Australia part of a bid to strengthen its international presence; altogether Servco Pacific owns five dealerships in the country. The firm started operating in Australia in late 2007 with the acquisition of a Toyota dealership in Brisbane. Closer to home Servco is acquiring dealerships in Hawaii amid a influx of off-island businesses including Lithia Motors to Hawaii.

Mergers and Acquisitions

In February 2014 Servco acquired the assets of Maui's Island Subaru dealership in Kahului. The newly-acquired dealership will operate as Servco Subaru.

EXECUTIVES

Senior Vice President, Glenn Inouye
Senior Vice President, Brian Horikami
Group Vice President Cio, John Harris
Vice President Finance, Craig Mishina
Senior Vice President Human Resources, Peter Hirano
Vice President And Corporate Tax Director, John Lee
Executive Vice President, Peter Dames
Vice President Director If Parts, Beverly Sato
Senior Vice President, Thor Toma
Senior Vice President, Peter Dooher
Vice Chairman, Eric Fukunaga
Auditors: ACUCITY LLP HONOLULU HAWAII

LOCATIONS

HQ: SERVCO PACIFIC INC.
2850 PUKOLOA ST STE 300, HONOLULU, HI 968194475
Phone: 808 564-1300
Web: WWW.SERVCO.COM

PRODUCTS/OPERATIONS

Selected Operations

Automotive

Rex Tire and Supply
Scion Dealers of Hawaii
Subaru Dealers of Hawaii
Suzuki Dealers of Hawaii
Servco Australia
Servco Chevy
Servco Lexus
Servco Truck & Commercial
Toyota Dealers of Hawaii
Servco Home and Appliance Distribution
Servco Insurance Services
Servco Raynor Overhead Doors
Servco School and Office Furniture

COMPETITORS

AutoNation
Citigroup
Fletcher Jones
HD Supply
Inchcape
Lithia Motors

HISTORICAL FINANCIALS

Company Type: Private

Income Statement — FYE: December 31

	REVENUE ($ mil.)	NET INCOME ($ mil.)	NET PROFIT MARGIN	EMPLOYEES
12/18	1,802	66	3.7%	1,000
12/17	1,629	26	1.6%	—
12/16	1,435	29	2.1%	—
12/12	923	15	1.7%	—
Annual Growth	11.8%	27.1%	—	—

2018 Year-End Financials

Return on assets: 8.1%
Return on equity: 24.9%
Current ratio: 1.20
Cash ($ mil.): 61

SES HOLDINGS, LLC

EXECUTIVES

Pres, Kelly Stanley
V Pres*, Faye McCarrell
Cfo*, Eric Mattson
Principal, John D Schmitz
Auditors: KPMG LLP DALLAS TX

LOCATIONS

HQ: SES HOLDINGS, LLC
1820 N INTERSTATE 35, GAINESVILLE, TX 762402179
Phone: 940 668-1818
Web: WWW.SELECTENERGYSERVICES.COM

HISTORICAL FINANCIALS

Company Type: Private

Income Statement — FYE: December 31

	ASSETS ($ mil.)	NET INCOME ($ mil.)	INCOME AS % OF ASSETS	EMPLOYEES
12/12	941	2	0.3%	1,700
12/11	1,019	131	12.9%	—
12/10	617	57	9.3%	—
Annual Growth	23.5%	(78.7%)	—	—

2012 Year-End Financials

Return on assets: 0.3%
Return on equity: 0.6%
Sales ($ mil): 945

SEVENTY SEVEN ENERGY LLC

Seventy Seven Energy (formerly Chesapeake Oilfield Services) is a company that was spun off from Chesapeake Energy one of the top onshore energy companies in the US. Chesapeake Energy reorganized six of its oilfield services subsidiaries into then Chesapeake Oilfield Services to create a new publicly traded entity that offers drilling hydraulic fracturing and trucking services as well as renting tools and manufacturing natural gas compressor equipment. It operates in onshore plays in the US. The company filed for Chapter 11 bankruptcy protection in 2016. In 2017 the company was bought by Patterson-UTI in a $1.76 billion stock deal including debt.

Operations

The company conducts business through three operating segments: Hydraulic Fracturing Drilling and Oilfield Rentals.

The hydraulic fracturing segment (51% of Seventy Seven Energy's total revenues in 2015) operates through Performance Technologies and provides high-pressure hydraulic fracturing services and other well stimulation services. This unit owns 11 hydraulic fracturing fleets with an aggregate of 440000 horsepower and six of these fleets are contracted in the Anadarko Basin and the Eagle Ford and Utica Shales. The fracturing process consists of pumping a fracturing fluid into a well at sufficient pressure to fracture the formation.

The drilling segment (38%) operates through Nomac Drilling and provides land drilling services for oil and natural gas E&P activities.

The oilfield rentals segment (11%) operates through Great Plains Oilfield Rental and provides premium rental tools and specialized services for land-based oil and natural gas drilling completion and workover activities. It offers an extensive line of rental tools including a full line of tubular products specifically designed for horizontal drilling and completion with high-torque premium-connection drill pipe drill collars and tubing.

Geographic Reach

Seventy Seven Energy operates in the Anadarko and Permian Basins and the Eagle Ford Haynesville Marcellus Niobrara and Utica Shales.

Sales and Marketing

The company got 70% of its revenues from Chesapeake Energy (CHK) and its affiliates in 2015.

Financial Performance

In 2015 Seventy Seven Energy's net revenues decreased by 46%.

Drilling revenues decreased due to lower revenue days driven by a drop in demand by non-CHK customers.

Hydraulic fracturing revenues declined due to a decrease in revenue per stage driven by market pricing pressure.

Oilfield rental revenues decreased due to a decline in utilization and pricing pressure.

In 2015 Seventy Seven Energy's net loss grew by 2675% due to lower revenues loss on sale of a business loss on sales of property and equipment net and impairment of goodwill.

Cash from operating activities increased by 7% due to the changes in the timing of collection of accounts receivable and the decline in overall operational activity.

Strategy

Chesapeake Energy decided to spin off its oilfield services in order to keep that activity separate from exploration and production. With exploration production and oilfield services under one umbrella the company only had one customer - itself. By separating the oilfield services unit Chesapeake Energy reduces its risk should exploration and production slow down much as it did with natural gas drilling and the shift to natural gas liquids.

Nomac Drilling continued to upgrade its rig fleet in 2015 making 80% of its rig fleet capable of drilling on multi well pads. As one of the most active drillers in the United States Nomac also continues to diversify its customer base serving more than 20 different operators.

Seventy Seven Energy expects to spend $100 million in aggregate growth and maintenance capital expenditures in 2016. It also intends to explore opportunistic complementary acquisitions particularly within the hydraulic fracturing segment.

In 2015 the company completed the previously disclosed sale of Hodges Trucking Company L.L.C. to a wholly-owned subsidiary of Aveda Transportation and Energy Services Inc. for $42 million.

Company Background

The company was formed in October 2011 and filed to go public in April 2012 in an initial public offering seeking up to $862.5 million. It completed the spinoff in July 2014 and renamed the company Seventy Seven Energy.

EXECUTIVES

Svp Corporate Development Cfo And Treasurer, John E. Vollmer, age 64
President And Ceo, William A. (Andy) Hendricks, age 55
Auditors: PRICEWATERHOUSECOOPERS LLP OK

LOCATIONS

HQ: SEVENTY SEVEN ENERGY LLC
777 NW 63RD ST, OKLAHOMA CITY, OK 731167601
Phone: 405 608-7777
Web: WWW.77NRG.COM

PRODUCTS/OPERATIONS

SERVICES

Drilling

Pumping

Rentals

Selected Subsidiaries

Compass Manufacturing L.L.C. (maufatures natural gas compression equipment)
Great Plains Oilfield Rental L.L.C. (tool and equipment rental)
Hodges Trucking Company L.L.C. (trucking services)
Nomac Drilling L.L.C. (drilling services)
Oilfield Trucking Solutions L.L.C. (trucking services)
Performance Technologies L.L.C. (hydraulic fracturing)

2015 Sales

$ in mil.	% of total
Drilling 436.4	38
Hydraulic fracturing	575.4 51
Oilfield rentals	76.5 7
Oilfield trucking	42.7 4
other operations	0.2 -
Total 1131.2	100

COMPETITORS

Baker Hughes
Basic Energy
FTS International
Halliburton
Helmerich & Payne
Key Energy
Nabors Industries
Oil States International
Parker Drilling
Patterson-UTI Energy
Precision Drilling
RPC
Schlumberger
Superior Energy
Trinidad Drilling
Weatherford International

HISTORICAL FINANCIALS

Company Type: Private

Income Statement — FYE: December 31

	REVENUE ($ mil.)	NET INCOME ($ mil.)	NET PROFIT MARGIN	EMPLOYEES
12/15	1,131	(221)	—	1,700
12/14	2,080	(7)	—	—
Annual Growth	(45.6%)	—	—	—

2015 Year-End Financials

Return on assets: (-11.0%)
Return on equity: (-186.3%)
Current ratio: 2.10
Cash ($ mil.): 130

SGT, LLC

Like its acronym name suggests SGT (aka Stinger Ghaffarian Technologies) is used to taking military orders; in this case very specific technical ones. An engineering services firm SGT provides aerospace engineering project management IT systems development and related services to NASA the US Navy the US Air Force and other primarily military-related government entities through contracts. The company also offers science-related services such as earth climate and planetary modeling and analysis. SGT's facilities are located near airfields and other military facilities.

Geographic Reach

SGT operates a more than dozen offices including in Houston Cleveland and Los Angeles White Sands (New Mexico) and Wallops Island (Virginia).

Sales and Marketing

The company serves the aerospace and aeronautics sectors in addition to civilian agencies and national security entities.

Strategy

SGT grows by signing contracts and working with other partners. In early 2017 it won a $45 million contract to support the National Oceanic and Atmospheric Administration (NOAA). Under the contract SGT will support the National Mesonet Program which brings non-federal meteorological data sources to NOAA for use in operations at weather forecast offices and numerical modeling information at the National Centers for Environmental Protection. To achieve this SGT is working in partnership with Earth Networks Weather Telematics WeatherFlow Synoptic Data Corp. Sonoma Technology Inc. Panasonic Avionics Corp. and the University of Oklahoma.

Company Background

SGT was founded in 1994 by Harold Stinger and Kam Ghaffarian.

EXECUTIVES

Evp Business Development, Charlie Goorevich
President And Ceo, Kam Ghaffarian
Cfo, Joe Morway
Coo, Dave Wolt
Svp Civil Defense Business, Wayne Friedman
Vice President Sales Marketing, Ron Marinzel
Vice President Finance Chief F, Mike Gigliotti
Vice President Business Development, Mary Armstrong
Vice President Air Force Programs, Walt Faulconer
Sr. Vp Business Development, Charles Goorevich
Chairman, Harold Stinger
Auditors: GRANT THORNTON LLP MCLEAN VI

LOCATIONS

HQ: SGT, LLC
7701 GREENBELT RD STE 400, GREENBELT, MD 207706521
Phone: 301 614-8600
Web: WWW.KBR.COM

COMPETITORS

Ball Aerospace
CACI International
CDI Government Services
Digital Fusion
Lockheed Martin Space Systems
QSS Group
Sierra Nevada Corp
Techshot
United Space Alliance

HISTORICAL FINANCIALS

Company Type: Private

Income Statement — FYE: September 30

	REVENUE ($ mil.)	NET INCOME ($ mil.)	NET PROFIT MARGIN	EMPLOYEES
09/15	570	23	4.2%	2,300
09/13	416	15	3.7%	—
09/12	374	9	2.4%	—
09/08	292	8	2.8%	—
Annual Growth	10.0%	16.3%	—	—

2015 Year-End Financials

Return on assets: 20.1%
Return on equity: 69.0%
Current ratio: 1.40
Cash ($ mil.): —

SHAMROCK FOODS COMPANY

Shamrock Foods Company is one of the nation's leading foodservice distributors with a strong presence in the western US. It primarily serves restaurants healthcare facilities and hospitality customers by providing everyday staples such as meats produce dry goods beverages and supplies as well as ethnic foods and artisanal gourmet and other specialty foods. Proprietary brands include Gold Canyon Markon Jensen Foods and Ridegline. Through Shamrock Farms the company is also one of the largest family-owned and -operated dairies in the country. Founded in 1922 as a mom-and-pop dairy Shamrock Foods Company is still owned and operated by the founding McClelland family.

Operations

Shamrock Foods is now one of the top 10 largest foodservice distributors nationwide. Its products include high-quality meats dairy fruits and vegetables beverages dry goods and groceries and kitchen supplies and equipment among others.

Shamrock Foods exclusive brands include Bountiful Harvest Fair Meadow ProPak ProClean and ProWare. The company also works with national brands such as B&G Foods Ecolab Nestle Kellogg's Kraft Heinz and more.

Geographic Reach

Headquartered in Phoenix Arizona Shamrock Foods has broadline distribution warehouses located in Phoenix Arizona; Boise Idaho; Denver Colorado; Albuquerque New Mexico; and Eastvale California. The company also has systems distribution warehouses in Phoenix Arizona; Denver Colorado; Sacramento California; and Portland Oregon.

Sales and Marketing

Shamrock Foods serves in restaurants healthcare casinos and entertainment lodging schools and other industries.

Mergers and Acquisitions

In late 2019 Shamrock Foods has acquired the Boise Idaho operations of Food Services of America (FSA). The acquisition expands Shamrock Foods' reach in the West and will provide customers expanded offerings and best-in-class technology solutions. "The addition of the FSA Boise operations will complement and strengthen our offerings" said Kent McClelland President and Chief Executive Officer at Shamrock Foods Company.

EXECUTIVES

President Shamrock Farms Company, Norman McClelland
National Sales Manager, Paul Hohmann
Svp Cfo Secretary And Treasurer, F. Phillips (Phil) Giltner
President, Kent McClelland
Vp & Cio, Rob Baxter
Vice President Eastern Operations, Jack West
Vp Human Resources, Vince Daniels
Vice President Marketing, Andy Johnston
National Sales Manager Food Service, Wendy Martin
Vice President, Daniel Malechuk
Vice President Farms Div, Jim Whitehurst

LOCATIONS

HQ: SHAMROCK FOODS COMPANY
3900 E CAMELBACK RD # 300, PHOENIX, AZ 850182615
Phone: 602 477-2500
Web: WWW.SHAMROCKFOODS.COM

PRODUCTS/OPERATIONS

Selected Products

Beverages
Center of the plate (meats)
Dairy
Cleaning supplies
Dry goods and groceries
Ethnic foods
Frozen foods
Paper and disposable products
Produce
Specialty
Supplies and equipment

COMPETITORS

Blue Bell
C&S Wholesale
California Dairies Inc.
Dairy Farmers of America
Dean Foods
Land O'Lakes
McLane
Meadowbrook Meat Company
Performance Food Group
Services Group of America
Stonyfield Farm
Sysco
US Foods
United Dairymen of Arizona
Wells' Dairy

HISTORICAL FINANCIALS

Company Type: Private

Income Statement — FYE: September 30

	REVENUE ($ mil.)	NET INCOME ($ mil.)	NET PROFIT MARGIN	EMPLOYEES
09/19	4,016	0	—	4,600
09/18	3,900	0	—	—
09/17	3,447	0	—	—
Annual Growth	7.9%	—	—	—

2019 Year-End Financials

Return on assets: —
Return on equity: —
Current ratio: 1.50
Cash ($ mil.): 99

SHANDS JACKSONVILLE HEALTHCARE, INC.

EXECUTIVES

Pres, Susan Brownie
Internal Medicine Practitioner, Robert Kim
Cardiac Physician, Theodore Bass
Internal Medicine Practitioner, Hammad Bhatti
Internal Medicine Practitioner, Myint Thway
Internal Medicine Practitioner, Mohammad Shahid
Internal Medicine Practitioner, Tifinni Romero
Director, Jessica Schacht
Research, Joan Sacerio
Accounting Staff, Michael Lawton
Cardiovascular Disease, Ambar M Patel

LOCATIONS

HQ: SHANDS JACKSONVILLE HEALTHCARE, INC.
655 W 8TH ST, JACKSONVILLE, FL 322096511
Phone: 904 244-0411
Web: WWW.UFHEALTHJAX.ORG

HISTORICAL FINANCIALS

Company Type: Private

Income Statement — FYE: June 30

	REVENUE ($ mil.)	NET INCOME ($ mil.)	NET PROFIT MARGIN	EMPLOYEES
06/16	665	22	3.3%	3,000
06/13	522	(5)	—	—
06/12	515	(22)	—	—
Annual Growth	6.6%	—	—	—

2016 Year-End Financials

Return on assets: 3.8%
Return on equity: 11.6%
Current ratio: 2.40
Cash ($ mil.): 73

SHANDS JACKSONVILLE MEDICAL CENTER, INC.

Close to the shifting sands of the northern Florida coast Shands Jacksonville Medical Center (doing business as UF Health Jacksonville) offers a range of services to the 19 counties it serves in Florida and southern Georgia. The 695-bed hospital includes a cardiovascular center Level III neonatal intensive care unit and a Level I trauma center. It also operates primary and specialty clinics in the Jacksonville area. The medical center is affiliated with the University of Florida and is the largest of seven hospitals in the Shands HealthCare family.

Operations

UF Health Jacksonville operates about 40 outpatient care centers. Overall its facilities handle some 34000 inpatient visits and 600000 outpatient visits per year. The hospital's affiliation with the University of Florida (UF) includes collaborative treatment and research programs in areas including cancer cardiovascular neurology orthopedic and pediatric care.

Together with its UF colleagues and affiliates UF Health Jacksonville provides a wide range of health care services across the continuum of care on an inpatient and outpatient basis. Backed by a team of more than 400 faculty physicians it offers nearly 100 specialty services.

Geographic Reach

UF Health Jacksonville's facilities are located in Jacksonville Florida and surrounding areas of northeastern Florida and southeastern Georgia.

Financial Performance

The company's revenues increased by 3% in 2014 due to growth in net patient service revenues as a result of a growth in inpatient and outpatient volumes. Medicare accounted for 25% net patient revenues; Medicaid 31%.

UF Health Jacksonville reported net income of $3 million in 2014 over a net loss in 2013 due to higher interest and a loss on the disposal of capital assets.

Operating cash flow in 2014 decreased by 8% due to higher payments to suppliers and vendors.

Strategy

UF Health Jacksonville has plans to build a second campus on the north side of Jacksonville to meet the needs of a growing community. It's also exploring ways to increase clinical efficiencies such as implementing an electronic health record (EHR) system (with help from federal stimulus funding); it also is looking to maximize funding opportunities for its research programs.

The company is looking to develop a Health Science Center Medical Education on Jacksonville Regional Campus including undergraduate graduate and health-related professions.

It also plans to build a 92-bed hospital wing for the North Campus which will provide greater access to more health care services for the center's residents as well as those living in surrounding communities. Construction is scheduled to begin in 2015 with completion in 2017.

In 2015 UF Health North opened the six-story 210000-square-foot outpatient medical complex in North Jacksonville which includes a 28-bed emergency room advanced imaging a midwife-led birth center rehabilitation services and more than 20 specialty services.

Company Background

Founded in 1870 as the Duval Hospital and Asylum UF Health Jacksonville started the first cancer program in Florida in 1948.

EXECUTIVES

Director Of Nursing, Angel Mills
Medical Director Fl Poison Information Center Jacksonville, Tom Kunisaki
Medical Director, Eric Stewart
Medical Records Director, Amy Connell
Auditors: CROWE LLP FORT LAUDERDALE

LOCATIONS

HQ: SHANDS JACKSONVILLE MEDICAL CENTER, INC.
655 W 8TH ST, JACKSONVILLE, FL 322096511
Phone: 904 244-0411
Web: WWW.UFHEALTHJAX.ORG

PRODUCTS/OPERATIONS

Selected Services
Cancer services
Cardiovascular services
Neuroscience services
Orthopaedic services
Pediatrics
Poison Center
Trauma and critical care services
Women and families

COMPETITORS

Baptist Health System
Bay Medical Center
Brooks Rehabilitation
Florida Hospital Tampa Bay Division
Mayo Clinic Jacksonville
Nemours Foundation
North Florida Regional Medical Center
Ocala Regional Medical Center
Orange Park Medical
Orlando Health
Palms West Hospital
St. Vincent's Health System

HISTORICAL FINANCIALS

Company Type: Private

Income Statement FYE: June 30

	REVENUE ($ mil.)	NET INCOME ($ mil.)	NET PROFIT MARGIN	EMPLOYEES
06/16	663	23	3.6%	3,000
06/15	480	10	2.2%	—
06/10	592	19	3.2%	—
Annual Growth	1.9%	3.5%	—	—

2016 Year-End Financials

Return on assets: 4.0%
Return on equity: 12.3%
Current ratio: 2.50
Cash ($ mil.): 68

SHANDS TEACHING HOSPITAL AND CLINICS, INC.

While its full name is Shands Teaching Hospital and Clinics most people call it UF&Shands. The network affiliated with the University of Florida Health Science Center provides health care services to patients in north-central and northeast Florida. The company is made up of seven not-for-profit acute care community and specialty hospitals as well as more than 80 physician practices and outpatient rehabilitation centers. It also operates a home health care agency. The Shands network has some 1700 licensed beds and about 1000 affiliated University of Florida doctors. Specialty services include oncology pediatrics cardiovascular transplants and neurological care.

Operations

In 2013 the organization along with the University of Florida launched the UF Health brand for their combined operations.

UF&Shands consists of the main teaching hospital at the University of Florida; it includes UF Health Shands Cancer Hospital UF Health Shands Psychiatric Hospital UF Health Shands Rehab Hospital as well as outpatient rehabilitation centers and a home health care agency. UF Health Jacksonville has some 700 beds and 400 full-time faculty members.

The hospital has a 40% stake in Community Health Systems which operates three rural community hospitals in Lake City Starke and Live Oak Florida.

Geographic Reach

UF&Shands operates hospitals in Gainesville and Jacksonville Florida.

Financial Performance

Revenues increased 3% to $1.2 billion in 2014 as net patient revenues and other operating revenues rose. Net income fell by 7% though to $66 million that year as a result of rising non-operating costs such as interest expenses and net losses on disposal of assets.

Cash flow from operations declined 7% to $127 million in 2014 as a result of increased salary and benefit expenses as well as supplier and vendor payments.

Strategy

UF&Shands operates with the goal of improving the diversity of its academic health center and engagement within its communities. It focuses on patient care education and research. Its Gainesville campus is getting an expansion gaining a new building that will include 216 beds and 20 operating rooms. In 2015 it was announced that its neonatal intensive care unit on the same campus will get a $20.7 million renovation and expansion; that project is expected to be completed in 2017.

EXECUTIVES

Svp And Cfo, William J. (Bill) Robinson
Interim Ceo, Ed Jimenez
Vp Nursing And Patient Services, Irene Alexaitis
Svp And Cio, Kari Cassel
Evp Regional And Governmental Affairs, Timothy M. Goldfarb
President And Svp Health Affairs, David S. Guzick
Senior Vice President And Chief Communications Officer Ufandshands, Melanie Fridl Ross
Vice President, Marvin Dewar
Vp And Campaign Events Associate, Kalliope King
Vice President, Gussie Boatwright
Vice President International Sales, Charlie Roberson
Secretary, Suzanne Dekay

LOCATIONS

HQ: SHANDS TEACHING HOSPITAL AND CLINICS, INC.
1600 SW ARCHER RD, GAINESVILLE, FL 326103003
Phone: 352 265-0111
Web: WWW.UFHEALTH.ORG

PRODUCTS/OPERATIONS

Selected Hospitals

UF Health Jacksonville (Jacksonville)
UF Health Physicians (Gainesville and Jacksonville)
UF Health Shands HomeCare and Shands Jacksonville Home Health (Gainesville and Jacksonville)
UF Health Shands Hospital (Gainesville)
UF Health Shands Psychiatric Hospital (Gainesville)
UF Health Shands Rehab Centers (Gainesville)
UF Health Shands Rehab Hospital (Gainesville

COMPETITORS

Baptist Health System
Bay Medical Center
Brooks Rehabilitation
Florida Hospital Tampa Bay Division
Florida Hospital Waterman
Lawnwood Medical Center
Mayo Clinic Jacksonville
North Florida Regional Medical Center
Orlando Health
Palms West Hospital
St. Vincent's Health System

HISTORICAL FINANCIALS

Company Type: Private

Income Statement FYE: June 30

	REVENUE ($ mil.)	NET INCOME ($ mil.)	NET PROFIT MARGIN	EMPLOYEES
06/14	1,243	66	5.3%	3,000
06/10	1,040	(67)	—	—
06/09	1,735	(183)	—	—
Annual Growth	(6.4%)	—	—	—

2014 Year-End Financials

Return on assets: 3.6%
Return on equity: 7.1%
Current ratio: 0.60
Cash ($ mil.): 7

SHARP HEALTHCARE ACO, LLC

Sharp HealthCare stands on the cutting edge of health care delivery in Southern California. The system of not-for-profit hospitals and health care facilities is the largest in the San Diego area. The network includes four acute-care hospitals (Sharp Chula Vista Sharp Coronado Sharp Grossmont and Sharp Memorial) as well as three specialty hospitals for women's care psychiatry and chemical dependence. It also operates two physician medical groups and a number of urgent care and outpatient facilities and clinics. With some 2100 beds and about 2600 physicians Sharp HealthCare offers cancer and cardiac care fertility and maternity services surgical procedures and hospice care.

Operations

Altogether the Sharp HealthCare facilities handle 1600 surgeries each year. In addition to medical services the organization operates its own health plan; the Sharp Health Plan is a not-for-profit HMO serving tens of thousands of members in and around San Diego.

The Sharp Grossmont hospital which serves eastern San Diego County is run by Grossmont Hospital Corporation a subsidiary holding a 30-year lease to manage the facility. One of the system's specialty operations Sharp Mary Birch Hospital for Women & Newborns claims to deliver more babies than any other hospital in California. Sharp's two medical groups are Sharp Community and Sharp Rees-Stealy which between them comprise more than 1100 doctors providing both primary and specialty care.

Geographic Reach

In addition to its operating bases in San Diego Sharp HealthCare has California facilities in Carmel Valley Chula Vista El Cajon La Mesa Mira Mesa Otay Ranch Point Loma Rancho Bernado San Diego Scripps Ranch Serra Mesa and Sorrento Mesa.

Financial Performance

Sharp's net revenues have trended upward in recent years. The company's revenues grew by $100 million in 2014 due to increase in net patient revenue and premiums. Revenues from the Medicare and Medi-Cal programs accounted for 30% and 24% respectively of Sharp's gross patient charges.

The company's net income decreased by 4% due to pension-related changes other than net periodic pension cost and increase in employee benefits and medical fees expenses.

Sharp's operating cash flow decreased by 48% in 2014.

Strategy

Sharp HealthCare improves its services to area residents through facility upgrades.

In 2015 the company launched Sharp Health News an online news site featuring engaging and original stories about medical breakthroughs new technology and health and wellness.

In 2014 Sharp HospiceCare opened its newest hospice residence BonitaView the first facility of its kind in the South Bay area of San Diego County for end-of-life care designed around the needs of patients and their families.

The organization installed new imaging equipment at the Sharp Memorial Outpatient Pavilion in 2013 and a opened the new Sharp Rees-Stealy center in Del Mar in 2014.

Company Background

In 2011 the system doubled the capacity of Sharp Chula Vista Medical Center's emergency department at a cost of $12 million and in 2012 the Chula Vista hospital opened a new cancer center.

The system began as a single hospital in 1955 named for a local pilot who died in WWII.

EXECUTIVES

Senior Vice President Human Resources, Ky Lewis
President And Ceo, Michael W. (Mike) Murphy
Evp Hospital Operations, Daniel L. (Dan) Gross
Svp And Ceo Sharp Healthcare Foundation, Bill Littlejohn
Svp And Cio, Ken Lawonn
President And Ceo Sharp Health Plan, Melissa Hayden-Cook
Svp And Ceo Sharp Memorial Hospital, Tim Smith
Svp And Ceo Sharp Chula Vista Medical Center, Pablo Velez
Svp And Ceo Sharp Coronado Hospital, Susan Stone
Ceo Sharp Rees-stealy Medical Group, Stacey Hrountas
Svp And Ceo Sharp Mary Birch Hospital For Women & Newborns, Trisha Khaleghi
Svp Marketing And Communications, Diane Gage Lofgren
Svp And Ceo Sharp Grossmont Hospital, Scott Evans
Svp And Cfo, Staci Dickerson
Ceo Sharp Community Medical Group, Paul Durr
Legal Secretary, Jenna Haynes
Vice President Business Development, Mary Keithgiordano
Director Of Nursing And Patient Care Services, Maryjo Webb
Vice President Clinical Informatics, Julie Mccoy
Vice President Of Compensation And Benefits, Anne Stephenson
Vice President Corporate Compliance, Paul Belton
Vice President Government Relations, Sara Steinhoffer
Director Of Pharmacy, Kenneth Schell
Vice President And Chief Business Development Officer, Michael Byrd
Vice President Information Services, Kara Marx
Vice President Clinical Operations, Anthony Damico
Vice President Patient Care Information Systems, Sandra Mccullough
Vice President, Jacqueline Schwoerke
Medical Director, Mark Jabro
Senior Vice President Sharp Healthcare, Amy Adome
Vice President Quality, Patricia J Atkins
Vice President Patient Care Gh, Louise White
Medical Director, Lloyd Kuritsky
Pharmd, Shaban Barzanjy
Svp Hr And Talent Management, Lisa Allen
Vice President System Pharmacy And Clinical Nutrition, Suzanne Shea
Medical Director, Jim Lyon
Medical Director, Dale Fox
Medical Director, Vincent Kater
Chair, Richard Freeman
Vice Chair, Lori Moore
Department Secretary, Aileen Carr
Department Secretary, Denise Long
Board Member, Henry Garcia
Department Secretary, Donna Whitehouse
Department Secretary, Irma Samudio
Department Secretary, Lacie Paige
Department Secretary, Gloria Rivera
Department Secretary, Sandra Powers
Department Secretary, Carmen Ramirez
Secretary, Nancy Earl
Department Secretary, Alyssa Heu
Auditors: ERNST & YOUNG LLP SAN DIEGO

LOCATIONS

HQ: SHARP HEALTHCARE ACO, LLC
8695 SPECTRUM CENTER BLVD, SAN DIEGO, CA 921231489
Phone: 858 499-4000
Web: WWW.SHARP.COM

PRODUCTS/OPERATIONS

2014 Sales

	$ mil.	% of total
Net patient revenue	1,806	62
Premium	1,024	35
Other	97	3
Total	**2,928**	**100**

Selected Programs and Services

Alcohol and drug dependency
Bloodless medicine
Cancer treatment
Complimentary and alternative medicine
Diabetes
Ear nose and throat
Eating disorders
Emergency and trauma
Endoscopy
Executive health
Eye care
Flu care
Health and wellness
Heart and vascular care
  Heart valve surgery
Home care
Hospice
Integrative and complementary medicine
International patient services
Laboratory services
Men's health
Mental health
Neurology
Nutrition
Occupational health
Orthopedics
Pediatrics
Pregnancy and childbirth
Primary care and family health
Radiology and diagnostic imaging
Rehabilitation and physical therapy
Robotic surgery
Safety and injury prevention
Senior care and services
Skilled nursing
Sleep disorders
Stroke and neurology
Transplant
Travel medicine
Urgent care
Weight loss
  Weight management support
  Weight-loss surgery (bariatric)
Women's care
Worksite wellness
Wound care and hyperbaric medicine

Selected Facilities

Sharp Chula Vista Medical Center (340 beds)
Sharp Coronado Hospital (180 beds)
Sharp Grossmont Hospital (540 beds La Mesa)
Sharp Mary Birch Hospital for Women & Newborns (170 beds San Diego)
Sharp McDonald Center (20 beds San Diego)
Sharp Memorial Hospital (675 beds San Diego)
Sharp Mesa Vista Hospital (150 beds San Diego)

COMPETITORS

Adventist Health System West
Dignity Health
HCA
Palomar Health
Paradise Valley Hospital
Rady Children's Hospital
Scripps Health
Sutter Health
Tenet Healthcare
Tri-City Healthcare District

HISTORICAL FINANCIALS

Company Type: Private

Income Statement — FYE: September 30

	REVENUE ($ mil.)	NET INCOME ($ mil.)	NET PROFIT MARGIN	EMPLOYEES
09/15	3,396	355	10.5%	14,000
09/14	1,234	(12)	—	—
09/13	1,158	(11)	—	—
09/09	897	(0)	—	—
Annual Growth	24.8%	—	—	—

2015 Year-End Financials

Return on assets: 9.1%
Return on equity: 13.7%
Current ratio: 1.90
Cash ($ mil.): 305

SHARP MEMORIAL HOSPITAL

The docs and the scalpels are sharp at Sharp Memorial Hospital. The flagship facility of Sharp HealthCare the not-for-profit hospital has roughly 675 beds and is a designated trauma center for San Diego County. Specialties include cardiac care women's health multi-organ transplantation and cancer treatment. It also provides skilled nursing home health and hospice services. Sharp Memorial Hospital first opened in 1955. Sharp HealthCare completed reconstruction efforts on the Sharp Memorial facility in 2009; the new hospital has improved inpatient surgery emergency trauma and intensive care facilities.

Operations

Along with a full range of inpatient services Sharp Memorial's Outpatient Pavilion provides patients with cancer care women's imaging and endoscopy services. The center also conducts outpatient surgery procedures ranging from LASIK to orthopedic surgeries. More and more hospitals are adding outpatient services to their roster because they tend to be reimbursed at higher rates. The facility also provides patient education services such as community health classes.

Sharp Memorial which provides some $199 million in community benefits (including charity care and outreach efforts) each year is affiliated with a number of other hospitals clinics and physician groups through its parent organization.

EXECUTIVES

Senior Vice President Of Business Development Sharp Healthcare, Alison J Fleury
Pharmacy Manager, Kim Allen
Senior Vice President And Chief Information Officer, Ken Lawonn
Department Secretary, Lawanda Martin

LOCATIONS

HQ: SHARP MEMORIAL HOSPITAL
7901 FROST ST, SAN DIEGO, CA 921232701
Phone: 858 939-3636
Web: WWW.SHARP.COM

COMPETITORS

Adventist Health System West
Grossmont Hospital
Palomar Health
Rady Children's Hospital
Scripps Health
Tenet Healthcare
Tri-City Healthcare District

HISTORICAL FINANCIALS

Company Type: Private

Income Statement				FYE: September 30
	REVENUE ($ mil.)	NET INCOME ($ mil.)	NET PROFIT MARGIN	EMPLOYEES
09/18	1,306	247	19.0%	3,500
09/17	1,158	237	20.5%	—
09/16	1,200	290	24.2%	—
09/15	1,195	240	20.1%	—
Annual Growth	3.0%	1.0%	—	—

2018 Year-End Financials

Return on assets: 8.6%
Return on equity: 10.2%
Current ratio: 19.90
Cash ($ mil.): 1

SHAWMUT WOODWORKING & SUPPLY, INC.

Shawmut Woodworking & Supply which does business as Shawmut Design and Construction provides beginning-to-end construction services from preconstruction planning to post-construction quality assurance checks. The national construction management firm that generates nearly $225 million annual revenue has experience building retail hotel gaming spa and life science facilities. It also handles corporate interiors and high-end residential construction and boasts expertise in cultural and historical preservation projects. The employee-owned company serves clients nationwide from offices in a handful of US states.

Operations

The company provides a wide range of construction management services including lean construction integrated project delivery design/build sustainable construction virtual construction services and mechanical electrical plumbing services. Other services includes BIM?building information modeling 3D MEP coordination/clash detection building technology/peer review historic preservation consulting/peer review last planner system collaborative web-based documentation management furnishings coordination 24-hour/7-day-a-week emergency services commissioning warranty services and asset management.

Geographic Reach

Shawmut Woodworking & Supply operates from offices in Boston (headquarters); New York; Los Angeles; Las Vegas; Chicago Illinois; Irvine California; Providence Rhode Island; North Haven Connecticut; Miami Florida; and West Springfield Massachusetts.

Sales and Marketing

Shawmut Woodworking & Supply serves a range of markets with varying needs with projects involving corporate interiors cultural and historic structures healthcare restaurants retail and health clubs sports venues and universities.

Its clients have included Lacoste Louis Vuitton Balmain Dyson Walgreens Waldorf Astoria Nobu McKinsey & Company One Beacon Street and Legal Sea Foods.

Strategy

Shawmut Woodworking & Supply built on its world-class safety program and developed a robust plan to minimize coronavirus exposure?rolling out safety protocols new job-site innovations and an exhaustive risk assessment and response strategy for all project sites across the country.

Through its technology partnerships pilot programs and grassroots innovation by project team members in the field Shawmut created effective safety procedures that have been rolled out to all sites throughout the region including underway projects at Pace University Parker New York Hotel The Glasshouse Tiffany & Co. and Cultural Services of the French Embassy to name a few. These sites are equipped with Shawmut technology such as Shawmut Vitals and Smartvid.io.

Shawmut also partnered with Cottonwood Group in mid-2020 to expand both their combined real estate capabilities and portfolio in the education sector in the United States. The new partnership will further strengthen and enhance Cottonwood's development capabilities with academic real estate by allowing the firm to tap into Shawmut's solid and time-proven construction platform deep regional expertise and extensive industry sector experience.

EXECUTIVES

Ceo, Les Hiscoe
Vp And Cfo, Roger C. Tougas
Vp Chief Legal Officer And Cio, Doug Lareau
Vice President, Ron Simoneau
Vice President Field Operations, Paul Doherty
Vice President Retail, William Pisani

LOCATIONS

HQ: SHAWMUT WOODWORKING & SUPPLY, INC.
560 HARRISON AVE STE 200, BOSTON, MA 021182632
Phone: 617 622-7000
Web: WWW.SHAWMUT.COM

PRODUCTS/OPERATIONS

Selected Markets

Academic
Commercial
Corporate interiors
Cultural and historic
Gaming
Healthcare and science
Restaurants
Retail
Spas and healthclubs
Sports venues

Selected Services

Services

Pre-Construction
- Master planning services
- Master project scheduling
- Lease review
- Value engineering
- Feasibility studies
- Green design services
- Drawing reviews
- Facilities audits and campus assessments
- Collaborative approach with architect/design team
- Comprehensive conceptual estimating
- BIM and virtual construction
- In-house M/E/P expertise
- Bid packages
- Constructability reviews
- Due diligence and site surveys
- Pre-qualification of subcontractors
- Management of permitting and approvals
- Development of specific phasing schedules and delivery methods
- Open book subcontractor bidding
- Logistics planning
- National purchasing power

Construction
- Master project scheduling
- Weekly project team meetings
- Sites monitored by a Safety Manager
- Zero-tolerance safety program
- BIM and virtual construction services
- LEED documentation certification and green building techniques
- Permitting services
- Design/build services
- Communication with surrounding community
- Coordination of owner-supplied items and vendors
- Procurement solutions
- Schedule and budget controls
- 24-hour/7 days-a-week emergency services
- Specialized services for program clients
- Indoor air quality management
- Construction and demolition waste recycling
- Customized waterproofing details

Post-Construction
- Commissioning and close-out services
- O&M manuals and training
- Project services division
- 1-year warranty walkthrough

COMPETITORS

Andrew Velez Construction
BBL Construction Services
Barr & Barr
Conti Enterprises
E.W. Howell
Skanska USA Building
Structure Tone
Turner Corporation

HISTORICAL FINANCIALS

Company Type: Private

Income Statement				FYE: November 30
	REVENUE ($ mil.)	NET INCOME ($ mil.)	NET PROFIT MARGIN	EMPLOYEES
11/14	957	7	0.7%	1,476
11/11	662	3	0.6%	—
11/09*	618	(21)	—	—
12/05	440	3	0.7%	—
Annual Growth	9.0%	9.9%	—	—

*Fiscal year change

2014 Year-End Financials

Return on assets: 2.4%
Return on equity: 14.5%
Current ratio: 1.20
Cash ($ mil.): 74

SHEA HOMES LIMITED PARTNERSHIP, A CALIFORNIA LIMITED PARTNERSHIP

EXECUTIVES

Ptnr, Jim Shontere
Ptnr, John F Shea LP
Treasurer, Robert Odell
Chief Information Officer, Bruce Verker
Sales Director, Janet Benavidez
Customer Manager, Chip Pennington
Sales Executive, Adam Heib
Technology/Computer Coordinato, Bert Selva
Sales Executive, Eric Snider
Sales Executive, Heather Stevenson
Sales Executive, Ken Peterson
Auditors: ERNST & YOUNG LLP LOS ANGELES

LOCATIONS

HQ: SHEA HOMES LIMITED PARTNERSHIP, A CALIFORNIA LIMITED PARTNERSHIP
655 BREA CANYON RD, WALNUT, CA 917893078
Phone: 909 594-9500
Web: WWW.SHEAHOMES.COM

HISTORICAL FINANCIALS

Company Type: Private

Income Statement				FYE: December 31
	REVENUE ($ mil.)	NET INCOME ($ mil.)	NET PROFIT MARGIN	EMPLOYEES
12/14	1,140	133	11.7%	1,200
12/13	930	125	13.5%	—
12/12	680	29	4.3%	—
12/99	1,793	184	10.3%	—
Annual Growth	(3.0%)	(2.1%)	—	—

2014 Year-End Financials

Return on assets: 8.0%
Return on equity: 24.0%
Current ratio: 1.40
Cash ($ mil.): 236

SHELL MEDICAL PLAN

Auditors: PNCEWATERHOUSECOOPERS LLP PIT

LOCATIONS

HQ: SHELL MEDICAL PLAN
, PHOENIX, AZ 85072
Phone: 800 352-3705

HISTORICAL FINANCIALS

Company Type: Private

Income Statement				FYE: December 31
	REVENUE ($ mil.)	NET INCOME ($ mil.)	NET PROFIT MARGIN	EMPLOYEES
12/16	617	5	1.0%	2
12/15	571	(40)	—	—
12/13	536	6	1.2%	—
Annual Growth	4.8%	(1.6%)	—	—

2016 Year-End Financials

Return on assets: 10.1%
Return on equity: 10.1%
Current ratio: —
Cash ($ mil.): 58

SHI INTERNATIONAL CORP.

Businesses that need more than boxes of hardware and software can call SHI International. The company distributes scores of computer hardware and software products from suppliers such as Adobe Cisco Microsoft VMware Symantec and Lenovo. It resells PCs networking products data storage systems printers software and keyboards among other items. SHI offers a range of professional services including software licensing asset management managed desktop services systems integration and vocational training. The company serves corporate government and health care customers from approximately 35 offices across the US Canada the UK Germany France and Hong Kong. SHI was founded in 1989 by Chairman Koguan Leo.

Operations

SHI serves several sectors and verticals. The company specializes in software and hardware procurement deployment planning configuration data center optimization IT asset management and cloud computing as well as custom IT solutions.

The company's popular product categories include laptops desktop tablets printers and monitors. Featured brands include Acer Citrix Samsung LG Nvidia and HP among others.

Geographic Reach

Based in Somerset New Jersey SHI has a global reach through approximately 35 offices worldwide including its five international offices in Canada France Hong Kong Ireland Singapore and in the UK.

Sales and Marketing

SHI has some 5000 experts from every area of IT operations from volume licensing to security data center to mobility and collaboration supporting approximately 10 million end-users.

Strategy

SHI International made a strategic investment in mLogica a developer of technologies for migrating on-premises databases and applications to the cloud.

With the agreement SHI will have full access to mLogica's technologies and will be authorized to deliver services based on that technology alone or in partnership with mLogica.

mLogica has three focus areas that are of strategic importance to SHI. The first is an automated migration suite for migrating databases and applications to the cloud in an expedited fashion. The second is mLogica's MCAP big data and analytics platform for real-time ingesting and processing of data. The third is mLogica's managed services that dovetail into SHI's own managed services.

EXECUTIVES

Vice President Finance, Paul Ng
President And Co-ceo, Thai Lee, age 63
Vp And General Manager, Hal Jagger
Vice President Internal Audit And Finance Operations, Kevin Boyles
Vice President, Melissa Graham
Chairman, Koguan Leo
Auditors: COHN REZNICK LLP WHITE PLAINS

LOCATIONS

HQ: SHI INTERNATIONAL CORP.
290 DAVIDSON AVE, SOMERSET, NJ 088734145
Phone: 732 764-8888
Web: WWW.SHI.COM

PRODUCTS/OPERATIONS

Selected Products

Accessories
Peripherals
Hardware
Memory
Software

Selected Services

Cloud services
Computer vocational training services
Data center services
Events
Hardware services
Networking
POLARIS Software asset management
Storage
Strategic consulting
Webinars

COMPETITORS

ASI Computer Technologies
Agilysys
Arrow Electronics
Avnet
CDW
CompuCom
Computacenter
Ingram Micro
Insight Enterprises
PC Mall
Softchoice
Tech Data

HISTORICAL FINANCIALS

Company Type: Private

Income Statement				FYE: December 31
	REVENUE ($ mil.)	NET INCOME ($ mil.)	NET PROFIT MARGIN	EMPLOYEES
12/19	10,372	253	2.4%	5,000
12/18	9,767	245	2.5%	—
12/17	8,243	197	2.4%	—
12/16	7,268	104	1.4%	—
Annual Growth	12.6%	34.3%	—	—

2019 Year-End Financials

Return on assets: 10.4%
Return on equity: 36.9%
Current ratio: 1.30
Cash ($ mil.): 63

SIERRA NEVADA CORPORATION

For Sierra Nevada Corp. (SNC) space is the frontier. The company a leading supplier of space systems to Space Systems Commercial Solutions and National Security and Defense has participated in more than 450 missions to space including Mars. The company's Dream Chaser spacecraft is scheduled for a 2021 launch for a trip to the International Space Station. SNC's space efforts include propulsion systems satellites and space technologies & subsystems. The company also supplies instruments and systems for defense applications and its commercial products include flight vision systems and radio and communications equipment. SNC's subsidiaries are Orbital Technologies and Spacedev. The privately held company was founded in 1963.

Operations

SNC offers technology products in a range of industries including aerospace avionics electronics communications systems micro-satellite propulsion solar energy and space. Its divisions are Electronic & Information Systems ISR (Intelligence Surveillance and Reconnaissance) Aviation & Security Integrated Mission Systems and Space Systems.

Geographic Reach

SNC based in Sparks Nevada operates from more than 35 offices in about 20 states across the US and at customer sites around the world. It has offices in England Germany and Turkey.

Sales and Marketing

SNC counts the US Government including the US Army US Navy and the US Department of Defense among its key clients. The company delivers its solutions through partners/suppliers to customers worldwide. Its existing supplier is Exostar.

EXECUTIVES

Ceo, Fatih Ozmen
Chairman And President, Eren Ozmen
Vice President Special Programs, Jeff Summers
Vp Information Technology, Greg Burgess
Vice President Engineering, Matt Wagner
Vice President, David Klingler
Vice President Technology, Charlie Leber
Vice President, Jennifer Jensen
Vice President, Lev Sadovnik
Vice President Engineering And Technology, Kirk Slenker
Vice President Of Operations, Jason Priebe
Vice President Technology, Michael Bertman

Executive Vice President Operations, Gerald Harvey
Vp Isr Persistent Surveillance, David Bullock
Vice President Business Development, Gregory Cox
Vice President, Derek Hess
Vice President Of International Programs, Ali Dian
Senior Vice President, Fred Rost
Vice President Procurement, Ed Mills
Vp Human Resources, Anne Bruce
Vice President Aviation Systems, Robert Horky
Vice President Engineering, Luke Thompson
Vice President Advanced Program Development, Michael Orr
Vice President Training And Operations Support, Ed Topps
Vice President Integrated Tactical Solutions, Tim Woods
Auditors: DELOITTE & TOUCHE LLP LOS ANG

LOCATIONS

HQ: SIERRA NEVADA CORPORATION
444 SALOMON CIR, SPARKS, NV 894349651
Phone: 775 331-0222
Web: WWW.SNCORP.COM

PRODUCTS/OPERATIONS

Business Units

Dream Chaser
Integrated ISR Solutions
Aircraft Design Modification and Support
Rotary-Wing Integration & Remanufacturing
Space Exploration
Cyber Security
Navigation Guidance & Landing
Spacecraft & Satellite Solutions
Electronic Warfare Systems

COMPETITORS

Argon ST
BAE SYSTEMS
DRS Technologies
Exelis
General Dynamics
Honeywell International
L3 Technologies
Lockheed Martin
Northrop Grumman
Raytheon
United Technologies

HISTORICAL FINANCIALS

Company Type: Private

Income Statement — FYE: December 31

	REVENUE ($ mil.)	NET INCOME ($ mil.)	NET PROFIT MARGIN	EMPLOYEES
12/14	1,481	0	—	3,063
12/13	1,623	0	—	—
12/12	1,400	0	—	—
Annual Growth	2.9%	—	—	—

2014 Year-End Financials

Return on assets: —
Return on equity: —
Current ratio: 1.50
Cash ($ mil.): 22

SIGNATURE FINANCIAL LLC

EXECUTIVES

Ceo-MBR, Joseph J Depaolo
MBR, Eric Howell
Senior Vice President, Ann Buzzo
Senior Vice President, Anne Doligale
Senior Vice President, Lisa Wente
Senior Vice President, Marietta Mullane
Vice President, Brandon Tran
Vice President, Jason Chess
Senior Vice President, John Mangan
Senior Vice President, Tim Moran
Vice President, Brad Kranich

LOCATIONS

HQ: SIGNATURE FINANCIAL LLC
565 5TH AVE AT46TH, NEW YORK, NY 100172413
Phone: 646 865-0767
Web: WWW.SIGNATURENY.COM

HISTORICAL FINANCIALS

Company Type: Private

Income Statement — FYE: December 31

	ASSETS ($ mil.)	NET INCOME ($ mil.)	INCOME AS % OF ASSETS	EMPLOYEES
12/18	47,364	505	1.1%	10
12/17	43,119	387	0.9%	—
12/16	39,047	396	1.0%	—
12/15	33,450	373	1.1%	—
Annual Growth	12.3%	10.6%	—	—

2018 Year-End Financials

Return on assets: 1.1%
Return on equity: 11.5%
Sales ($ mil): 1,733

SINAI HOSPITAL OF BALTIMORE, INC.

Sinai Hospital of Baltimore part of the LifeBridge Health network provides medical care in northwestern Baltimore. The 470-bed hospital is a not-for-profit medical center that includes such facilities as a heart center a children's hospital a cancer institute and a rehab center. Other specialties include orthopedics neurology and women's care. Medical students from Johns Hopkins University and the University of Maryland do some of their training at the hospital. Sinai Hospital of Baltimore was founded in 1866 as the Hebrew Hospital and Asylum and became a subsidiary of LifeBridge when it merged with other area providers in 1998.

Operations

The Sinai Hospital of Baltimore handles about 26000 inpatient admissions and some 75000 emergency room visits per year. It also conducts about 20000 inpatient and outpatient surgeries annually.

The medical center conducts a number of education and training programs including residencies and fellowships for about 400 medical students each year. It is a designated training site for the Johns Hopkins University's ambulatory and internal medicine clerkships.

Strategy

Sinai Hospital of Baltimore has completed several expansion efforts in recent years. In 2012 it opened a new dedicated inpatient hospice unit as well as a new center for geriatric surgery. In addition the 20-bed Friedman Neurological Rehabilitation Center was completed that year.

EXECUTIVES

Ceo, Neil Meltzer
Chief Medical Officer*, Daniel C Silverman
Chm*, Brian L Moffet
Treas*, Barry F Levin
SEC*, Nancy Hackerman
Staff, Roger Sheets
Occupational Specia, Amy Herman
Laboratory Information, John Wall
MD, Bel Air
MD, Glen Burnie
Doctor In Physical Therapy, Maureen Abenoja

LOCATIONS

HQ: SINAI HOSPITAL OF BALTIMORE, INC.
2401 W BELVEDERE AVE, BALTIMORE, MD 212155270
Phone: 410 601-5678
Web: WWW.LIFEBRIDGEHEALTH.ORG

PRODUCTS/OPERATIONS

Selected Centers

Alvin & Lois Lapidus Cancer Institute at LifeBridge Health
Center for Joint Preservation and Replacement
Children's Hospital at Sinai
ER-7 Emergency Center
Heart Center at Sinai
International Center for Limb Lengthening
Krieger Eye Institute
Louis and Phyllis Friedman Neurological Rehabilitation Center
Rubin Institute for Advanced Orthopedics
Sandra and Malcolm Berman Brain & Spine Institute
Sinai Rehabilitation Center
The Spine Center at Sinai

Selected Services

Allergy and Immunology
Anesthesia
Cardiology
Cancer/Medical Oncology
Dermatology
Dialysis
Emergency Medicine
Endocrinology and Metabolism
Family Medicine
Gastroenterology
General Internal Medicine
Geriatric Medicine
Infectious Diseases
Nephrology (kidneys)
Pulmonary and Critical Care Medicine
Rheumatology (joints tendons)
Neurology
Neurosurgery
Obstetrics and Gynecology
Ophthalmology (eye care)
Oral and Maxillofacial Surgery and Dentistry
Orthopedic Surgery
Otolaryngology (ear nose & throat)
Pathology
Pediatrics
Pharmacy
Physical Medicine and Rehabilitation
Psychiatry
Radiation Oncology
Radiology
Surgery
Urology

COMPETITORS

Anne Arundel Medical Center
Ascension Health
Bon Secours Health
Franklin Square Hospital Center
GBMC
Johns Hopkins Health System
MedStar Health
Meritus Health
University of Maryland Medical System

HISTORICAL FINANCIALS

Company Type: Private

Income Statement FYE: June 30

	REVENUE ($ mil.)	NET INCOME ($ mil.)	NET PROFIT MARGIN	EMPLOYEES
06/19	803	41	5.1%	4,497
06/17	769	63	8.2%	—
06/16	690	26	3.9%	—
06/15	677	45	6.7%	—
Annual Growth	4.4%	(2.3%)	—	—

2019 Year-End Financials

Return on assets: 7.5%
Return on equity: 33.3%
Current ratio: 1.90
Cash ($ mil.): 38

SKANSKA USA CIVIL INC.

Skanska USA Civil builds some of the world's largest cable-stayed bridges. Part of the US operations of Swedish engineering and construction giant Skanska Skanska USA Civil focuses on infrastructure projects throughout the country. Along with sister firm Skanska USA Building it is a market leader in the New York area where it has worked on the Brooklyn Bridge the AirTrain light-rail system and the Roosevelt Island Bridge. It builds roads tunnels and rail systems in addition to bridges and industrial and marine facilities such as power and water filtration plants gas-treatment plants and dry docks.

Operations

Parent-company Skanska USA operates Skanska USA Civil and three sister business units with different specialties such as Skanska USA Building Infrastructure Development USA and Commercial Development USA. The parent boasts a staff of nearly 11000 US employees (as of mid-2016).

Among Skanska USA Civil's divisions is Bayshore Concrete which produces precast concrete components for tunnel bridge dock and pier construction. Bayshore Concrete's plant in Virginia focuses on East Coast shipments. Skanska Koch which is based in New Jersey has built or worked on some of the country's most recognizable structures such as Yankee Stadium and the Brooklyn Bridge.

Another division Underpinning & Foundation Skanska is a heavy foundation contractor based in New York. It offers underpinning and pile-driving services for private and public projects that range from single-story buildings to skyscrapers.

Geographic Reach

While the firm's largest market is in its home state of New York it serves the US from offices in California Washington Arizona and Florida. Parent Skanska USA has 31 offices across the US and works on projects in nearly all 50 states the District of Columbia and Puerto Rico (as of mid-2016). The US is Skanska AB's largest market accounting for 37% of its global revenue during 2015.

Sales and Marketing

Skanska USA Civil provides public and private clients with construction services in the civil mechanical industrial marine foundation and environmental sectors.

Financial Performance

Parent-company Skanska USA's revenue has been growing in recent years and reached $7.1 billion in 2015.

Strategy

Parent Skanska USA ranked the third-largest building/manufacturing contractor by revenue and the third-largest heavy contractor by revenue on Engineering News-Record's rankings in 2015. The Skanska USA Civil division in particular has built a dominating presence on the East Coast since completing major projects such as the Meadowlands Football Stadium and Boston's Central Artery.

Skanska USA Civil in 2015 secured a contract with Competitive Power Ventures Holdings (CPV) to build the CPV Valley Energy Center in Wawayanda New York with an order value of SEK 2.1 billion ($250 million); a new contract with MTA New York City Transit to rebuild three rail stations in Brooklyn with an order value of SEK 670 million ($80 million); and a new joint-venture contract in California to improve State Route 58 near Hinkley with Skanska USA's share of the order value worth SEK 640 million ($76 million).

Sister division Skanska USA Building in 2015 secured a SEK 750 million ($89 million) contract from existing customer Tahoma School District to construct a new high school and learning center in Maple Valley Washington. That year the division also won a SEK 730 million ($87 million) contract to build Boeing's Commercial Airplane Decorative Paint Facility in Charleston South Carolina.

Company Background

Civil construction which is often publicly funded was less affected by the economic downturn that hindered other construction segments such as home building. However Skanska is looking to diversify its business and become less dependent on public projects. In 2011 the company acquired US-based Industrial Contractors for $135 million. Industrial Contractors (integrated into Skanska US Civil) works on power and energy commercial and light industrial and heavy industrial projects.

EXECUTIVES

Pres-Ceo, Salvatore Mancini
Project Manager, James Tweedall
Project Manager, Jessica Miller
Purchasing Director, Vinnie Santangelo
Management, Choice Sterling
Project Engineer, Dennis Neblett
Management, Michael Germanetto
Project Engineer, Steve Revitsky
Equipment Superintendent, Chris Brown
Accountant, Lisa Chen
Auditors: KPMG LLP NEW YORK NY

LOCATIONS

HQ: SKANSKA USA CIVIL INC.
7520 ASTORIA BLVD STE 200, EAST ELMHURST, NY 113701135
Phone: 718 340-0777
Web: WWW.SKANSKA.COM

PRODUCTS/OPERATIONS

Selected Services

Commercial development
Construction management
Design-build
Financial services
Pharmaceutical validation
Pre-construction
Public-private validation
Self-performance

Operating Units

Bayshore Concrete Products
Industrial Construction Skanska
PCI Skanska
Skanska Koch
Underpinning & Foundation Skanska

COMPETITORS

A & L
American Civil Constructors Holdings
American Infrastructure
Balfour Beatty Infrastructure
Bechtel
Flatiron Construction
Fluor
Granite Construction
J.L. Patterson & Associates
Jones Bros.
Lane Construction
Parsons Brinckerhoff
Parsons Corporation
Peter Kiewit Sons'
RailWorks
Ruscilli Construction
Tutor Perini
Vecellio Group

HISTORICAL FINANCIALS

Company Type: Private

Income Statement FYE: December 31

	REVENUE ($ mil.)	NET INCOME ($ mil.)	NET PROFIT MARGIN	EMPLOYEES
12/08	1,753	54	3.1%	5,200
12/07	1,611	52	3.2%	—
Annual Growth	8.8%	5.2%	—	—

2008 Year-End Financials

Return on assets: 6.1%
Return on equity: 13.6%
Current ratio: 1.50
Cash ($ mil.): 172

SKANSKA USA CIVIL NORTHEAST INC.

EXECUTIVES

Ceo, Richard Cavallaro
Sr V Pres*, Ralph Russo
Contracts Director, Barry Nosowitz
Chief Engineer, Alfredas Daugiala
Human Resources Executive, Frank Varisco
Project Manager, Alper Ayar
Design Build Manager, David Tullis
Subcontract Manager, Brian Aitchison
Project Manager, James Sartorio
Project Executive, Donald Fusco

LOCATIONS

HQ: SKANSKA USA CIVIL NORTHEAST INC.
7520 ASTORIA BLVD STE 200, EAST ELMHURST, NY 113701135
Phone: 718 340-0777
Web: WWW.SKANSKA.COM

HISTORICAL FINANCIALS

Company Type: Private

Income Statement FYE: December 31

	REVENUE ($ mil.)	NET INCOME ($ mil.)	NET PROFIT MARGIN	EMPLOYEES
12/08	816	51	6.3%	1,500
12/07	622	27	4.5%	—
12/06	467	17	3.7%	—
12/05	487	12	2.6%	—
Annual Growth	18.8%	59.9%	—	—

2008 Year-End Financials

Return on assets: 12.0% Cash ($ mil.): 121
Return on equity: 25.1%
Current ratio: 1.70

SKF USA INC.

SKF USA is a subsidiary of Swedish ball bearing giant AB SKF and a global supplier of bearings seals lubricants linear motion components and condition monitoring systems. It also specializes in related services from repair and rebuilding to consulting logistics and training. Its repair stations also provide bearing inspection repair and overhaul services. With hundreds of manufacturing sales and authorized distribution locations across the US SKF USA's offerings are geared at a wide range of industries including aerospace automotive construction machine tooling and alternative energy. Brand names include Alemite Lincoln Reelcraft and S2M.

Operations

SKF USA groups its technologies across five platforms: bearings and units seals lubrication systems mechatronics (combining mechanics and electronics into intelligent systems) and services.

Although bearings and seals are core product lines the company isn't just focused on traditional hardware. It is increasingly launching performance-based products that help to extend the lifecycle of those bearings and seals. Recent products include a portable user-friendly technology for performing bearing grease condition assessments directly in the field. It offers a hydraulic-driven lubricator that eliminates the need for manual lubrication of construction and off-highway equipment attachments. And the product line perhaps showing the most promising growth is its "smart" condition monitoring systems which consist of hardware and software and in some cases sensors that work together to collect store and analyze data.

Geographic Reach

The company has almost 30 manufacturing sites in the US where it provides customized application engineering services through factories in Houston and Cleveland. The company additionally operates a technical Center in Plymouth Michigan that provides a range of engineering and testing services.

Sales and Marketing

SKF USA sells thousands of products and services through a network of over 4000 US-based authorized distributors. For the auto industry it serves the aftermarket for cars and commercial vehicles.

Strategy

SKF USA markets its condition monitoring systems particularly to alternative energy customers in the US a market that is experiencing good growth as a result of tightening environmental regulations.

However following several fiscal quarters of declining sales amid a slow industrial market the company's Sweden-based parent SKF throughout 2016 began consolidating several North American facilities including closing its sites in San Diego and Baltimore. Outside the US SKF also closed its Y-Bearing and Units production channels in Puebla Mexico which served North American agriculture customers.

EXECUTIVES

Treasurer, Brian J. Duffy
President Skf North America, Poul Jeppesen
National Account Manager, Lakshmi Yalamanchili
National Account Manager, Bob Young
Vice President, Gunilla Nilsson
Vice President Of Sales And Marketing, Greg Markow
Vice President Corporate Accounts, Mark Keaveny
Vice President Of Human Resources, Laszlo Haraszti

LOCATIONS

HQ: SKF USA INC.
890 FORTY FOOT RD, LANSDALE, PA 194464303
Phone: 267 436-6000
Web: WWW.CHICAGO-RAWHIDE.COM

PRODUCTS/OPERATIONS

PRODUCTS
Actuation systems
Bearings units & housings
Condition monitoring
Coupling systems
Linear motion
Lubrication solutions
Magnetic systems
Maintenance products
Power transmission
Seals
Test & measurement equipment
Vehicle aftermarket
SERVICES
Asset management services
Business consulting
Customer training
Engineering consultancy
Logistics
Mechanical maintenance
Remanufacturing & maintenance services
Service contracts

COMPETITORS

A. Stucki Company
Accuride International
EnPro
FAG Kugelfischer
Hoover Precision Products
JTEKT
Kaydon
MinebeaMitsumi
NN Inc.
NSK
NTN Bearing Corp. of America
Nippon Bearing
RBC Bearings
Schaeffler
Timken
Waukesha Bearings

HISTORICAL FINANCIALS

Company Type: Private

Income Statement FYE: December 31

	REVENUE ($ mil.)	NET INCOME ($ mil.)	NET PROFIT MARGIN	EMPLOYEES
12/14	3,138	155	5.0%	4,000
12/13	2,554	95	3.7%	—
12/12	2,397	138	5.8%	—
Annual Growth	14.4%	6.0%	—	—

2014 Year-End Financials

Return on assets: 3.8% Cash ($ mil.): 29
Return on equity: 16.4%
Current ratio: 2.40

SMITHSONIAN INSTITUTION

The Smithsonian Institution has many hats from the one worn by Harrison Ford in the Indiana Jones movies to the one worn by Abraham Lincoln the night he was assassinated. One of the world's leading cultural institutions the Smithsonian houses some 155 million objects in about 20 museums gardens zoo and galleries most of which are on the National Mall in Washington DC. Nearly 3.5 million people visit every year to view the Smithsonian's exhibits on art music TV and film science history and other subjects. Admission to all but one of the Smithsonian's facilities is free; only the Cooper-Hewitt National Design Museum in New York charges admission.

Operations

A board of regents that includes the vice president and the chief justice of the US six members of Congress and nine private citizens leads the institution. The Smithsonian's exhibits display items such as the Declaration of Independence the ruby slippers worn by Judy Garland in The Wizard of Oz and the Wright brothers' first airplane. Along with its museums and galleries the Smithsonian also operates the National Zoo and nine research facilities and publishes magazines and books.

Among its museums are the African American Museum Archives of American Art Natural History Museum and the Smithsonian Castle.

Geographic Reach

The Smithsonian Institution is located in Washington DC.

Sales and Marketing

Smithsonian has a total visits of about 3.5 million in 2020.

Financial Performance

In 2019 the company had an operating revenue of $1.4 billion a minor increase from the previous year.

Strategy

The company has a five-year strategic plan that was launched in 2017. The strategic plan has a number of goals which Includes:

Be One Smithsonian - The company will work together as One Smithsonian to amplify the power of the stories it tells increasing reach and impact. It will also view all of its exhibitions and spaces as an Institution-wide portfolio to be deployed strategically. Additionally the company will be setting standards to create a seamless visitor experience across the Smithsonian by creating a unified customer relationship approach.

Catalyze new conversations and address complex challenges - The company will be magnifying its national and global reach through new collaborative approaches. It will also create new forums across the Smithsonian to proffer solutions to problems of national and global import.

Reach 1 billion people a year with a digital-first strategy - The company will create a digital laboratory to test and develop emerging museum-related digital technologies. The company will also be forging transformative strategic partnerships with major digital leaders and create new digital platforms for scholars and educators to better access Smithsonian collections research and education resources.

Understand and impact 21st-century audiences - The company is working on learning how demographic changes new learning styles and new technologies affect the relevance of cultural institutions. It will also tell the complete American story in person and online in all of its museums exhibits and programs?and across them?with a focus on all Americans nationally and locally.

HISTORY

English chemist James Smithson wrote a proviso to his will in 1826 that would lead to the creation of the Smithsonian Institution. When he died in 1829 he left his estate to his nephew Henry James Hungerford with the stipulation that if Hungerford died without heirs the estate would go to the US to create "an Establishment for the increase and diffusion of knowledge among men."

Hungerford died in 1835 without any heirs and the US government inherited more than $500000 in gold.

Congress squandered the money after it was received in 1838 but perhaps feeling pangs of guilt covered the loss. The Smithsonian was finally created in 1846 and Princeton physicist Joseph Henry was named its first secretary. That year it established the Museum of Natural History the Museum of History and Technology and the National Gallery of Art. The Smithsonian's National Museum was developed around the collection of the US Patent Office in 1858. The Smithsonian continued to expand adding the National Zoological Park in 1889 and the Smithsonian Astrophysical Observatory in 1890.

The Freer Gallery a gift of industrialist Charles Freer opened in 1923. The National Gallery was renamed the National Collection of Fine Arts in 1937 and a new National Gallery created with Andrew Mellon's gift of his art collection and a building opened in 1941. The Air and Space Museum was established in 1946.

More museums were added in the 1960s including the National Portrait Gallery in 1962 and the Anacostia Museum (exhibits and materials on African-American history) in 1967. The Kennedy Center for the Performing Arts was opened in 1971. The Collection of Fine Arts was renamed the National Museum of American Art and the Museum of History and Technology was renamed the National Museum of American History in 1980.

The Smithsonian placed its first-ever contribution boxes in four of its museums in 1993.

A planned exhibit featuring the Enola Gay – the plane that dropped the atomic bomb on Hiroshima – created a firestorm in 1994 with critics charging that the exhibit downplayed Japanese aggression and US casualties in WWII. The original exhibit was canceled in 1995 the director of the Air and Space Museum resigned and a scaled-down version of the exhibit premiered. In 2004 the exhibit attracted more protestors prompting Smithsonian officials to evacuate and temporarily close the museum.

Large contributions from private donors continued in the 1990s; the Mashantucket Pequot tribe gave $10 million from its casino operations in 1994 for the Smithsonian's planned American Indian museum and prolific electronics inventor Jerome Lemelson donated $10.4 million in 1995. The museum celebrated its sesquicentennial in 1996 amid news that $500 million in repairs were needed over the next 10 years.

California real estate developer Kenneth Behring gave the largest cash donation ever to the museum in 1997 – $20 million for the National Museum of Natural History. Short of funds the Smithsonian had to cut back on its 150th-anniversary traveling exhibit that year. The Smithsonian announced a $26 million renovation for the National Museum of Natural History in 1998. Two years later Behring quadrupled his record-breaking 1997 donation of $20 million by giving $80 million to the National Museum of American History. Catherine Reynolds withdrew most of her $38 million gift in 2002 after the Smithsonian Institution refused to implement her ideas for an exhibit at the National Museum of American History.

The National Museum of the American Indian opened on the National Mall in 2004.

Secretary Lawrence Small resigned under pressure in March 2007 amid criticism of his spending practices. Cristi ˜n Samper director of the Smithsonian's National Museum of Natural History was named acting secretary. A report on the matter issued by the Smithsonian in June said its Board of Regents failed to provide the oversight that might have prevented Small's extravagant spending.

In July 2008 Wayne Clough became the 12th secretary of the Smithsonian.

EXECUTIVES

John And Adrienne Mars Director National Air And Space Museum, John R. (Jack) Dailey
Director Government Relations, Penelope (Nell) Payne, age 63
Director External Affairs, Virginia B. (Ginny) Clark
Secretary, David J. Skorton
Director National Postal Museum, Allen R. Kane
Director National Museum Of African American History And Culture, Lonnie G. Bunch, age 65
Director Equal Employment And Minority Affairs, Era L. Marshall
Director Smithsonian Marine Station At Fort Pierce, Valerie J. Paul
Director Smithsonian Affiliations, Harold A. Closter
Director Smithsonian Institution Libraries, Nancy E. Gwinn
Ombudsman, Chandra P. Heilman
Director Smithsonian Center For Education And Museum Studies, Stephanie L. Norby
Chief Of Staff Office Of The Regents, John K. Lapiana
Director Smithsonian Environmental Research Center, Anson (Tuck) Hines
Director Smithsonian Institution Archives, Anne Van Camp
Acting Under Secretary For History Art And Culture, Richard Kurin
Director National Museum Of African Art, Johnnetta B. Cole
Director Smithsonian Tropical Research Center, Matthew Larsen
Deputy Under Secretary For Collections And Interdisciplinary Support, Scott Miller
General Counsel, Judith E. Leonard
Director Harvard-smithsonian Center For Astrophysics, Charles R. Alcock
Director Smithsonian Latino Center, Eduardo D az
Director Smithsonian Museum Conservation Institute, Robert J. Koestler
Director Cooper-hewitt Smithsonian Design Museum, Caroline Baumann
Director National Zoological Park, Dennis Kelly
Director Consortia For The Humanities, Michelle Anne Delaney
Director Office Of Facilities Engineering And Operations, Nancy Bechtol
President Smithsonian Enterprises, Christopher Liedel
Inspector General, Cathy Helm
Director Smithsonian Exhibits, Susan Ades
Cio, Deron Burba
Editor-in-chief Smithsonian Magazine, Michael Caruso
Director Finance And Accounting, Jean Garvin
Director Office Of Planning Management And Budget, David Voyles
Acting Director Office Of Policy And Analysis, Whitney Watriss
Director Office Of Fellowships And Internships, Eric Woodard
Director The Smithsonian Associates, Fredie Adelman
Director Smithsonian American Art Museum And The Renwick Gallery, Elizabeth (Betsy) Broun
Director Hirshhorn Museum And Sculpture Garden, Melissa Chiu
Director National Museum Of American History Behring Center, John Gray
Director Archives Of American Art, Kate Haw
Director National Museum Of Natural History, Kirk Johnson
Director Smithsonian's Center For Folklife And Cultural Heritage, Michael Atwood Mason
Director Freer Gallery Of Art And Arthur M. Sackler Gallery, Julian Raby
Director National Portrait Gallery, Kim Sajet
Interim Director Smithsonian Institution Traveling Exhibition Service, Myriam Springuel
Director Consortia For Science, Pierre Comizzoli
Chancellor Board Of Regents, John G. Roberts, age 66
Auditors: KPMG LLP WASHINGTON DC

LOCATIONS

HQ: SMITHSONIAN INSTITUTION
1000 JEFFERSON DR SW, WASHINGTON, DC 205600009
Phone: 202 633-1000
Web: WWW.SI.EDU

PRODUCTS/OPERATIONS

2016 Operating Revenue

	% of total
Federal appropriations	53
Contributions & private grants	18
Business activities	11
Government grants & contracts	8
Endowment	5
Other	5
Total	**100**

Selected Museums and Research Centers

Anacostia Community Museum
Arthur M. Sackler Gallery
Arts and Industries Building
Center for Folklife and Cultural Heritage
Conservation and Research Center
Cooper-Hewitt National Design Museum (New York)
Freer Gallery of Art
Hirshhorn Museum and Sculpture Garden
National Air and Space Museum
National Museum of African Art
National Museum of American History
National Museum of Natural History
National Museum of the American Indian
National Museum of the American Indian - George Gustav Heye Center (New York)
National Science Research Center
National Portrait Gallery
National Postal Museum
National Zoological Park
Smithsonian American Art Museum
Smithsonian Astrophysical Observatory
Smithsonian Center for Latino Initiatives
Smithsonian Center for Materials Research and Education
Smithsonian Environmental Research Center (SERC)
Smithsonian Institution Building (The Castle)
Smithsonian Museum Conservation Institute
Smithsonian Tropical Research Institute

HISTORICAL FINANCIALS

Company Type: Private

Income Statement — FYE: September 30

	REVENUE ($ mil.)	NET INCOME ($ mil.)	NET PROFIT MARGIN	EMPLOYEES
09/19	1,375	180	13.1%	6,100
09/18	1,563	177	11.3%	—
09/17	1,514	153	10.1%	—
09/16	1,541	192	12.5%	—
Annual Growth	(3.7%)	(2.2%)	—	—

2019 Year-End Financials

Return on assets: 3.3%
Return on equity: 4.2%
Current ratio: 1.00
Cash ($ mil.): 785

SMMH PRACTICE PLAN, INC.

Auditors: KPMG LLP PITTSBURGH PA

LOCATIONS

HQ: SMMH PRACTICE PLAN, INC.
7175 SALTSBURG RD, PITTSBURGH, PA 152352252
Phone: 412 795-6069

HISTORICAL FINANCIALS

Company Type: Private

Income Statement — FYE: June 30

	REVENUE ($ mil.)	NET INCOME ($ mil.)	NET PROFIT MARGIN	EMPLOYEES
06/15	2,060	27	1.3%	26
06/14	2,005	570	28.4%	—
06/13	1,985	402	20.3%	—
06/12	1,976	(90)	—	—
Annual Growth	1.4%	—	—	—

2015 Year-End Financials

Return on assets: 4.8% — Cash ($ mil.): 49
Return on equity: 1.3%
Current ratio: 0.60

SNAKE RIVER SUGAR COMPANY

EXECUTIVES

Prin, Duane Grant
Pres*, Vic Jaro
Exec Dir*, Terry L Ketterling
SEC*, John McCreedy
Cfo*, Wayne Neely
Information Technology Manager, Ano Sundara
Information Technology Directo, Dennis Costesso
Technical, Jerry Wagner
Auditors: EIDEBAILLY LLP BOISE IDAHO

LOCATIONS

HQ: SNAKE RIVER SUGAR COMPANY
1951 S SATURN WAY STE 100, BOISE, ID 837092924
Phone: 208 383-6500
Web: WWW.AMALGAMATEDSUGAR.COM

HISTORICAL FINANCIALS

Company Type: Private

Income Statement — FYE: August 31

	REVENUE ($ mil.)	NET INCOME ($ mil.)	NET PROFIT MARGIN	EMPLOYEES
08/11	876	13	1.5%	2,500
08/10	839	18	2.2%	—
08/09	658	22	3.4%	—
Annual Growth	15.3%	(23.8%)	—	—

2011 Year-End Financials

Return on assets: 1.9% — Cash ($ mil.): 17
Return on equity: 4.8%
Current ratio: 0.80

SNYDER'S-LANCE, INC.

If you're familiar with the munchies named Toastchee Nip Chee and Captain's Wafers Snyder's-Lance (formerly Lance) has undoubtedly helped you satisfy a snack attack. The company produces single-serve multi-pack and family-sized packages of bakery products and sweet and savory snack foods including cookies crackers nuts potato chips and pretzels. Its snacks are sold under the Lance Cape Cod Tom's Archway and Snyder's brands at food retailers mass merchants and convenience and club stores in the US. International brands include Kettle Chips and Metcalfe's popcorn. The company also makes private-label and branded snacks for food makers. Snyder's-Lance agreed to its acquisition by The Campbell Soup company in 2017 in a $4.9 billion deal.

Change in Company Type

In late 2017 Snyder's-Lance agreed to its acquisition by The Campbell Soup Company which is looking to boost its snack foods division. The deal is expected to close for around $4.9 billion.

Operations

Synder's-Lance manufactures pretzels sandwich crackers kettle cooked chips pretzel crackers cookies potato chips tortilla chips restaurant style crackers popcorn nuts and other salty snacks. It generates around 80% of its sales from its owned branded products with the remainder coming from third-party branded products and other branded products.

The company has R&D facilities in Hanover Pennsylvania and Salem Oregon.

Geographic Reach

Based in North Carolina Snyder's-Lance operates manufacturing facilities in the US in California North Carolina Oregon Pennsylvania Iowa Indiana Georgia Arizona Massachusetts Florida Ohio and Wisconsin as well as in the UK.

Sales and Marketing

The snack food giant sells its products to mass merchandisers club stores discount stores convenience stores foodservice operators and other retailers the likes of drug stores the military schools and government facilities. Wal-Mart its largest customer represents nearly 15% of the company's revenues.

The company distributes snack food products nationwide using a large direct-store-delivery (DSD) network consisting of some 3000 distribution routes served mostly by Independent Business Owners (IBOs) and others that are company-owned.

Financial Performance

After a few years of sluggish growth in fiscal 2016 Snyder's-Lance's sales jumped 27% to $2.1 billion thanks to the acquisitions of Diamond Foods in February and Metcalfe in September of that year. The company also grew its core business particularly its Lance sandwich crackers Snack Factory pretzel crisps Cape Cod chips and the Late July brand.

Net income fell $35.2 million to $14.9 million due to acquisition expenses higher advertising spend and impairment charges relating to changes in manufacturing operations.

Cash from operations increased 79% to $261.2 million due to lower income tax as the company used net operating losses acquired in the Diamond Foods transaction to offset taxes payable.

Strategy

Snyder's-Lance seeking revenue growth abroad through acquisitions. In 2016 it acquired Diamond Foods which does a roaring trade for its Kettle Chips brand in the UK as well as the US; and Metcalfe which makes the UK's best-selling upmarket ready-to-eat popcorn. The two acquisitions also play into Snyder's-Lance's strategy of growing its "better-for-you" product segment.

Mergers and Acquisitions

In early 2016 the company acquired Diamond Foods makers of Diamond and Emerald nuts for about $1.3 billion. The move added snack brands as well as UK and US distribution might to Snyder's-Lance. Later in 2016 to maintain focus on its core products the company sold its Diamond of California culinary nut business to private equity firm Blue Road Capital. Diamond of California had been one of four Diamond Foods brands at the time of Snyder's-Lance's acquisition.

Also in 2016 it acquired all of Metcalfe's Skinny Limited (it previously owned a 26% stake) the maker of the UK's leading upmarket popcorn brand as well as a range of corn and rice cake products.

EXECUTIVES

President Ceo And Director, Brian J. Driscoll, age 62
Svp And Chief Supply Chain Officer, Patrick S. Mclnerney, $379,950 total compensation
Svp And Chief Marketing And Innovation Officer, Rodrigo F. Troni Pena, age 53, $338,250 total compensation
Evp And Cfo, Alexander W. Pease, age 48, $90,538 total compensation
President Dsd Division, Francis B. (Frank) Schuster, age 53, $341,813 total compensation
President Direct Division, John T. Maples
President Clearview Division, Peter L. Michaud
Managing Director Kettle Foods Limited (uk), Ashley Hicks
Division Vp And General Manager Growth And Developing Markets, Matthew T. Insolia
Vice President Corporate Human Resources, Vanessa Higgins
Vice President Marketing, Eric Van De Wal
National Account Manager, David Wright
Vice President Food Safety And Quality, David Whitman
Vice President Of Engineering, Rob Miller
Vice President Information Technology Global Thermal Equipment And Services, Robert F Foster
Vice President National Account Strategy, John McGinn
Vice President Of Strategic Innovation, Tim Old
Vice President Marketing, Eric Vandewal
Chairman, James W. Johnston, age 73
Auditors: PRICEWATERHOUSECOOPERS LLP CH

LOCATIONS

HQ: SNYDER'S-LANCE, INC.
13515 BALNTYN CORP PL, CHARLOTTE, NC 282772706
Phone: 704 554-1421
Web: WWW.SNYDERSLANCE.COM

PRODUCTS/OPERATIONS

2015 Revenue

	$ mil.	% of total
Branded products	1,155	70
Private brands	335	20
Other	165	10
Total	**1,656**	**100**

Selected Brands

Archway
Brent
Bugles
Cape Cod Potato Chips
Captain's Wafers
Choc-o-Lunch
Delicious
Diamond of California
Don Pablo's
EatSmart
Emerald
Grande

Jays
Kettle brand
KETTLE
Krunchers!
Lance
Nekot
Nipchee
Pop Secret
Pretzel Crisps
Sam's
Salerno
Snyder's of Hanover
Stella D'oro
Texas Pete
Thunder
Toastchee
Toasty
Tom's
Van-o-Lunch
Vista

COMPETITORS

American Pop Corn
Beer Nuts
Bridgford Foods
Campbell Soup
Chattanooga Bakery
ConAgra
Evans Food Products
Flowers Foods
Frito-Lay
General Mills
Golden Enterprises
Inventure foods
John Sanfilippo & Son
Kellogg U.S. Snacks
Kettle Foods
King Nut Companies
Legacy Bakehouse
McKee Foods
Mondelez International
Old Dutch Foods
Otis Spunkmeyer
Pepperidge Farm
Poindexter Nut
Pretzels Inc.
Procter & Gamble
Snappy Popcorn
Weaver Popcorn Company

HISTORICAL FINANCIALS

Company Type: Private

Income Statement FYE: December 30

	REVENUE ($ mil.)	NET INCOME ($ mil.)	NET PROFIT MARGIN	EMPLOYEES
12/17	2,226	149	6.7%	5,900
12/16*	2,109	14	0.7%	—
01/15	1,620	192	11.9%	—
12/13	1,761	79	4.5%	—
Annual Growth	6.0%	17.2%	—	—

*Fiscal year change

2017 Year-End Financials

Return on assets: 4.1%
Return on equity: 7.4%
Current ratio: 1.60
Cash ($ mil.): 18

SOLSTICE HOLDINGS INC.

EXECUTIVES

Pres, Mr Doug L Devos
Chm, Stephen Van Andel
Exec V Pres-Cfo, Russ Evans
Exec V Pres-Coo, Alvin Koop
V Pres, Mr Michael Mohr
Cntrl, Mr Craig V Witcher
Senior Software Developer, Carolyn Knott

LOCATIONS

HQ: SOLSTICE HOLDINGS INC.
7575 FULTON ST E, ADA, MI 493550001
Phone: 616 787-1000

HISTORICAL FINANCIALS

Company Type: Private

Income Statement FYE: December 31

	REVENUE ($ mil.)	NET INCOME ($ mil.)	NET PROFIT MARGIN	EMPLOYEES
12/08	8,235	0	—	14,000
12/07	7,168	0	—	—
12/06	6,387	0	—	—
Annual Growth	13.5%	—	—	—

2008 Year-End Financials

Return on assets: —
Return on equity: —
Current ratio: 1.10
Cash ($ mil.): 1,072

SOUTH BROWARD HOSPITAL DISTRICT

South Broward Hospital District (dba Memorial Healthcare System) is a community-owned health services network that provides health service to residents of Florida's Broward Dade and Palm Beach counties. The system's major hospitals include Memorial Regional Hospital Memorial Hospital Pembroke Memorial Hospital West and Memorial Hospital Miramar. The hospitals have a combined capacity of roughly 1900 licensed beds and provide services including diagnostic emergency surgical and rehabilitative care. Memorial also operates a pediatric hospital cardiac and vascular medicine institute a cancer treatment center and a center for women's health as well as nursing home facilities (120 beds) and community clinics.

Operations

The system's hospitals include Memorial Regional Memorial Regional South Joe DiMaggio Children's Memorial West Memorial Miramar Memorial Pembroke and the Memorial Manor nursing home.

Memorial Regional offers a cardiac and vascular institute a cancer institute and a neuroscience center.

Geographic Reach

Memorial Healthcare System operates health care facilities in Florida and Washington.

Financial Performance

In 2015 revenue increased 12% to $1.8 billion as net patient service earnings rose primarily due to an increase in surgical procedures given. Net income rose 89% to $191.4 million that year due to the higher revenue and a decrease in depreciation and amortization. Operating cash flow also increased rising 68% to $292.4 million.

Strategy

Memorial Healthcare System provides care in a number of ways including through home health services and health care plans. It is adding two additional health plans in 2016 to reach a goal of managing more than 100000 lives in the network.

During 2016 the company entered into a partnership with Holy Cross Physician Partners creating the Atlantic Coast Health Network. The new network represents some 1400 physicians.

EXECUTIVES

President And Ceo, Frank V. Sacco
Evp And Chief Administrative Officer, Matthew J. Muhart
Svp And Chief Medical Officer, Stanley W. Marks
Evp And Coo, Aurelio M. Fernandez
Pharmacy Manager, Margaretta Kearson
Director Physician Recruitment, Ken Bolis
Vice President Information Technology, Oscar Perez
Vice President Of Property Management, David Schlemmer
Vice President Marketing Communications, S S Khan
Vice President Of Managed Care, Sandra Dilts
Respiratory Therapy Director, Sandy Santoro
Respiratory Therapy Director, Darlene Moretti
Director Of Nursing, Barbara Bertot
Director Of Pharmacy, Dorinda Segovia
Vice President Management, Anita Warrick
Respiratory Therapy Director, Son Nguyen
Associate Vice President Patient Services, Paige Smith
Vice President Strategic Planning, Robert Alonso
Chairman, Jose Basulto
Vice Chairman, Vic Narang
Secretary, Juan Espinosa
Secretary, Debbie Delotta
Secretary, Ruth Marcus
Department Secretary, Tracy Kalinowski
Department Secretary, Lynda Blakney
Unit Secretary, Sandra Baptiste
Medical Transcriptionist Secretary, Cheryl Rainwater
Unit Secretary, Patty Fernandez
Pharmacy Secretary, Patricia Sigler
Auditors: ERNST & YOUNG LLP MIAMI FL

LOCATIONS

HQ: SOUTH BROWARD HOSPITAL DISTRICT
3501 JOHNSON ST, HOLLYWOOD, FL 330215421
Phone: 954 987-2000
Web: WWW.JDCH.COM

PRODUCTS/OPERATIONS

2015 Sales

	$ mil.	% of total
Net patient service	1,630	92
Disproportionate share distribution	83	5
Other operating revenue	49	3
Total	**1,764**	**100**

Selected Facilities

Esther L. Grossman Women's Health & Resource Center
Memorial Cancer Institute
Memorial Hospital Miramar
Memorial Hospital Pembroke
Memorial Hospital West
Memorial Manor
Memorial Outpatient Center
Memorial Primary Care Center - Dania Beach
Memorial Primary Care Center - Hollywood
Memorial Primary Care Center - Miramar
Memorial Primary Care Center - West Hollywood
Memorial Regional Hospital
Joe DiMaggio Children's Hospital
Memorial Regional Hospital South
Memorial Regional Hospital Fitness & Rehabilitation Center
Memorial Same Day Surgery Center
Memorial Urgent Care Center
Same Day Surgery Center at Memorial Hospital West

COMPETITORS

Baptist Health South Florida
Boca Raton Regional Hospital
Broward Health
Continucare
Florida Hospital Heartland
HCA
Jackson Health System
MJHHA
South Miami Hospital

HISTORICAL FINANCIALS

Company Type: Private

Income Statement				FYE: April 30
	REVENUE ($ mil.)	NET INCOME ($ mil.)	NET PROFIT MARGIN	EMPLOYEES
04/20	2,159	156	7.3%	9,200
04/19	2,148	165	7.7%	—
04/18	2,014	64	3.2%	—
04/17	1,937	134	6.9%	—
Annual Growth	3.7%	5.3%	—	—

2020 Year-End Financials

Return on assets: 4.2%
Return on equity: 6.5%
Current ratio: 6.20
Cash ($ mil.): 634

SOUTH CAROLINA PUBLIC SERVICE AUTHORITY (INC)

This company turns the lights on in South Carolina. South Carolina Public Service Authority known as Santee Cooper (after two interconnected river systems) provides wholesale electricity to 20 cooperatives and two municipalities that serve more than 2 million customers in South Carolina. It directly retails electricity to more than 174000 customers. One of the largest US state-owned utilities Santee Cooper operates in all 46 counties in South Carolina and has stakes in power plants (fossil-fueled nuclear hydro and renewable) that give it more than 5180 MW of generating capacity. Its Santee Cooper Regional Water System also distributes water to customers in its service area.

Operations

Santee Cooper operates 5029 miles of transmission lines and more than 2841 miles of distribution lines. It also operates 105 transmission stations and 54 distribution substations. The company is the leading renewable energy producer in South Carolina.

Geographic Reach

In addition to supplying power to 20 cooperatives in all 46 counties in South Carolina Santee Cooper also supplies power directly to 29 large industrial customers in 10 counties Charleston Air Force Base the town of Bamberg and the City of Georgetown.

Sales and Marketing

The company serves more than 2 million customers in South Carolina. It directly retails electricity to more than 174000 customers.

Financial Performance

In 2015 Santee Cooper's net revenues decreased by 6% to $1.9 billion compared due to lower kilowatt-hour sales (down 3%) and demand usage (down 2%).

The company's net income decreased by 73% to $34.4 million as the result of lower net revenues and higher electric maintenance expenses.

In 2015 Santee Cooper's operating cash inflow decreased by 77% to $237.6 million.

Strategy

With a eye toward getting 40% of its power from non-carbon emitting sources and conservation by 2020 the company has begun to invest heavily in nuclear solar wind and other renewable energy sources.

In 2015 the company agreed to changes in its agreement with Westinghouse Electric which acquired assets of a second partner in the V.C. Summer Nuclear Station plant construction consortium giving Westinghouse more control over the project.

In 2014 Santee Cooper in collaboration with Central Electric Power Cooperative and the state's electric cooperatives agreed to buy the total energy output of Colleton Solar Farm a utility-scale solar power farm being built by TIG Sun Energy a subsidiary of the North Charleston-based InterTech Group. The solar array consists of 10010 photovoltaic panels. Some panels are fixed while other panels follow the direction of the sun to maximize the production of solar energy.

South Carolina Resources Santee Cooper Central Electric Power Cooperative and the state's electric cooperatives agreed in 2013 to build Colleton Solar Farm the largest solar farm in the state (3000 kilowatts of electricity).

Mergers and Acquisitions

In 2014 South Carolina Electric & Gas Company (SCE&G) principal subsidiary of SCANA Corporation and Santee Cooper announced an agreement for SCE&G to acquire from Santee Cooper a 5% ownership interest in the two new nuclear units which are under construction at V.C. Summer Nuclear Station in Jenkinsville. Under the ownership agreement SCE&G owns 55%; Santee Cooper 45%. The 5% ownership interest would be acquired in three stages with 1% to be acquired at the commercial operation date of the first new nuclear unit (late 2017 or the first quarter of 2018); an additional 2% to be acquired no later than the first anniversary of such commercial operation date; and the final 2% to be acquired no later than the second anniversary date of such commercial operation date.

Company Background

Santee Cooper is a government-owned entity.

Historically the $48.2 million Santee Cooper project (55% federal loan and 45% federal grant) which connected the Santee and Cooper rivers and established hydroelectric dams and a transmission grid began to generate electricity for the first time in 1942. It was founded in 1934.

EXECUTIVES

Vice President Human Resource Management, W Brown
Svp Corporate Planning And Bulk Power, Lonnie N. Carter
Svp And Cfo, Jeff Armfield
Svp Nuclear Energy, Michael Crosby
Evp Competitive Markets And Generation, Marc R. Tye
Svp And Cio, Dom Maddalone
Svp Power Delivery, Arnold R. Singleton
2nd Vice Chairman, Barry Wynn
Chairman, W. Leighton Lord
1st Vice Chairman, William A. Finn
Auditors: CHERRY BEKAERT LLP RALEIGH N

LOCATIONS

HQ: SOUTH CAROLINA PUBLIC SERVICE AUTHORITY (INC)
1 RIVERWOOD DR, MONCKS CORNER, SC 294612998
Phone: 843 761-4121
Web: WWW.SANTEECOOPER.COM

PRODUCTS/OPERATIONS

2015 Sales

	$ mil.	% of total
Electricity	1,856	99
Water	8	-
Other	15	1
Total	**1,879**	**100**

COMPETITORS

Delmarva Power
Dominion Energy
Duke Energy
Florida Public Utilities
MLGW
North Carolina Electric Membership
PS Energy
Progress Energy
SCANA
TVA
Utilities Inc.

HISTORICAL FINANCIALS

Company Type: Private

Income Statement				FYE: December 31
	REVENUE ($ mil.)	NET INCOME ($ mil.)	NET PROFIT MARGIN	EMPLOYEES
12/19	1,722	(231)	—	1,748
12/17	1,756	90	5.2%	—
12/15	1,879	34	1.8%	—
12/13	1,816	65	3.6%	—
Annual Growth	(0.9%)	—	—	—

2019 Year-End Financials

Return on assets: (-2.0%)
Return on equity: (-11.2%)
Current ratio: 1.70
Cash ($ mil.): 311

SOUTH FLORIDA WATER MANAGEMENT DISTRICT LEASING CORP.

EXECUTIVES

Chb, Daniel O'Keefe
V Cbb*, Kevin Powers
MBR*, Lennart Lindahl
V Pres*, Mitch Hutchcraft
Scientist, Patricia Robertshaw
Coordinator, Guangliang Liu
Compliance Staff, Jay Floyd
Coordinator, Peter Harlem
Senior Electrical Engineer, Jack Barton
Diversity, Robin Clemons
Section Leader, Alberto Naya

LOCATIONS

HQ: SOUTH FLORIDA WATER MANAGEMENT DISTRICT LEASING CORP.
3301 GUN CLUB RD, WEST PALM BEACH, FL 334063007
Phone: 561 686-8800
Web: WWW.SFWMD.GOV

HISTORICAL FINANCIALS

Company Type: Private

Income Statement				FYE: September 30
	REVENUE ($ mil.)	NET INCOME ($ mil.)	NET PROFIT MARGIN	EMPLOYEES
09/10	595	(42)	—	1,200
09/08	910	(64)	—	—
09/06	947	51	5.4%	—
Annual Growth	(11.0%)	—	—	—

SOUTH SHORE HOSPITAL, INC.

EXECUTIVES

Ceo, Gene E Green
Pres*, Pamela Daley Whelton
Cfo-Sr V Pres*, Michael Cullen
Sr V Pres*, Margaret Holda
Sr V Pres*, Christopher J Oconnor
Coo*, Joseph Cahill
V Pres Clinical*, Edward Liao
Pres Acute Care Oprs*, Timothy Quigley
Medical Staff, Joseph Jiang
Medical Staff, A K Elamine
Vice-President Sales and Marke, Margaret M Holda

LOCATIONS

HQ: SOUTH SHORE HOSPITAL, INC.
55 FOGG RD, SOUTH WEYMOUTH, MA 021902455
Phone: 781 624-8000
Web: WWW.SOUTHSHOREHEALTH.ORG

HISTORICAL FINANCIALS

Company Type: Private

Income Statement — FYE: September 30

	REVENUE ($ mil.)	NET INCOME ($ mil.)	NET PROFIT MARGIN	EMPLOYEES
09/18	575	10	1.9%	2,375
09/17	563	9	1.7%	—
09/16	558	17	3.1%	—
09/15	522	50	9.6%	—
Annual Growth	3.3%	(40.2%)	—	—

2018 Year-End Financials

Return on assets: 1.6%
Return on equity: 3.5%
Current ratio: 1.50
Cash ($ mil.): 33

SOUTHCOAST HOSPITALS GROUP, INC.

When you feel more than a little physically washed up get to one of the Southcoast Hospitals Group facilities. The not-for-profit company provides medical services in the southeastern corner of Massachusetts and in Rhode Island. Its primary facilities in Massachusetts are the Charlton Memorial Hospital (with about 330 beds) in Fall River St. Luke's Hospital (420 beds) in New Bedford and Tobey Hospital (65 beds) in Wareham which provide acute medical care and specialty services including cardiology neurology orthopedics and women's care. Southcoast Hospitals Group also operates about 20 ancillary facilities including nursing and assisted-living facilities and home health and hospice agencies.

Auditors: DELOITTE TAX LLP JERICHO NY

LOCATIONS

HQ: SOUTHCOAST HOSPITALS GROUP, INC.
363 HIGHLAND AVE, FALL RIVER, MA 027203703
Phone: 508 679-3131
Web: WWW.SOUTHCOAST.ORG

COMPETITORS

Baystate Health
Boston Medical Center
Care New England
CareGroup
Hallmark Health
Lifespan Corporation
McLean Hospital
Memorial Hospital of Rhode Island
Partners HealthCare
Roger Williams Medical Center
Steward Health Care
Yale New Haven Health System

HISTORICAL FINANCIALS

Company Type: Private

Income Statement — FYE: September 30

	REVENUE ($ mil.)	NET INCOME ($ mil.)	NET PROFIT MARGIN	EMPLOYEES
09/13	687	22	3.3%	3,853
09/12	704	49	7.0%	—
09/06	506	14	2.8%	—
09/04	445	13	3.1%	—
Annual Growth	4.9%	5.4%	—	—

2013 Year-End Financials

Return on assets: 6.9%
Return on equity: 3.3%
Current ratio: 0.60
Cash ($ mil.): 6

SOUTHEAST PETRO DISTRIBUTORS, INC.

EXECUTIVES

Pres, Mahesh Shah
V Pres-SEC, Rashmi Shah
V Pres, Shah Summit
Director of Operations, Lori Lemay
Retail Accountant, Doreen Mezzacappa
Director of Business Developme, Ryan Firth
Hr Manager, Chrissy Council
Accounting Receptionist, Ginger Respass
Operations Manager, Helen Waugh
Prin, Mahesh R Shah
Senior Director, Michael Gazzalla
Auditors: JAMES MOORE & CO PL GAINE

LOCATIONS

HQ: SOUTHEAST PETRO DISTRIBUTORS, INC.
402 HIGH POINT DR STE A, COCOA, FL 329266600
Phone: 321 631-0245
Web: WWW.SOUTHEASTPETRO.COM

HISTORICAL FINANCIALS

Company Type: Private

Income Statement — FYE: December 31

	REVENUE ($ mil.)	NET INCOME ($ mil.)	NET PROFIT MARGIN	EMPLOYEES
12/11	553	5	1.0%	12
12/10	416	5	1.3%	—
12/09	331	4	1.5%	—
12/02	57	0	0.9%	—
Annual Growth	28.6%	29.8%	—	—

2011 Year-End Financials

Return on assets: 13.1%
Return on equity: 35.4%
Current ratio: 1.20
Cash ($ mil.): 8

SOUTHERN BAPTIST HOSPITAL OF FLORIDA INC.

EXECUTIVES

Pres, Hugh Greene
Oo, John Wilbanks
Chmn, M C Harden
V Pres, Harvey Granger
Executive Vice President, John Wilbanks
SEC-Treas, Richard L Sisisky
Health Professional, Christopher Carroll
Coordinator, John Polisknowski
Facilities Manager, Larry Peterson
Director Education, Pamela Turner
Perinatal, Cicely Brooks
Auditors: ERNST & YOUNG LLP JACKSONVIL

LOCATIONS

HQ: SOUTHERN BAPTIST HOSPITAL OF FLORIDA INC.
800 PRUDENTIAL DR, JACKSONVILLE, FL 322078202
Phone: 904 202-2000
Web: WWW.BAPTISTJAX.COM

HISTORICAL FINANCIALS

Company Type: Private

Income Statement — FYE: September 30

	REVENUE ($ mil.)	NET INCOME ($ mil.)	NET PROFIT MARGIN	EMPLOYEES
09/19	1,398	186	13.3%	4,000
09/18	1,234	209	17.0%	—
09/17	1,151	296	25.8%	—
09/16	1,129	205	18.2%	—
Annual Growth	7.4%	(3.2%)	—	—

2019 Year-End Financials

Return on assets: 6.0%
Return on equity: 8.9%
Current ratio: 0.70
Cash ($ mil.): —

SOUTHERN CAL SCHOOLS VOL EMP BENEFITS ASSOC

EXECUTIVES

Prin, George McGregor
Auditors: ROSNER BROWN TOUCHSTONE & KELL

LOCATIONS

HQ: SOUTHERN CAL SCHOOLS VOL EMP BENEFITS ASSOC
8885 RIO SAN DIEGO DR # 327, SAN DIEGO, CA 921081624
Phone: 619 278-0021

HISTORICAL FINANCIALS

Company Type: Private

Income Statement FYE: December 31

	REVENUE ($ mil.)	NET INCOME ($ mil.)	NET PROFIT MARGIN	EMPLOYEES
12/14	598	4	0.7%	8
12/13	551	5	1.0%	—
Annual Growth	8.6%	(29.1%)	—	—

2014 Year-End Financials

Return on assets: 6.6%
Return on equity: 19.6%
Current ratio: 2.30
Cash ($ mil.): 38

SOUTHERN ILLINOIS HEALTHCARE ENTERPRISES, INC.

Southern Illinois Healthcare a nonprofit health care system operates the flagship 145-bed tertiary-care Memorial Hospital of Carbondale as well as Herrin Hospital (with 114 beds) and St. Joseph Memorial Hospital (with 25 beds). The hospitals serve residents of across southern Illinois. The nearly 280-bed system provides services such as birthing cardiac cancer and emergency care as well as surgery and rehabilitation. Its cardiac care is offered through an affiliation with the Prairie Heart Institute at St. John's Hospital in Springfield Illinois. The medical school at Southern Illinois University conducts its Family Practice Residency Program at Memorial Hospital of Carbondale.

Operations

Across its health system Southern Illinois Healthcare employs more than 3000 people. Physicians at its primary hospital Memorial Hospital of Carbondale represent nearly 40 medical specialties. It maintains the only dedicated pediatric unit in the region as well as the largest birthing center with Level II Plus Special Care Nursery.

St. Joseph Memorial Hospital is a full-service critical access hospital.

In addition to the patient hospitals the system includes two clinics two physician professional buildings an urgent care clinic and dedicated neurology cancer heart sleep and rehabilitation centers.

Geographic Reach

Most of Memorial Hospital of Carbondale's inpatient and outpatient visits come from residents of seven Illinois counties (Jackson Franklin Williamson Perry Johnson Union and Saline). St. Joseph Memorial Hospital serves the Murphysboro community.

Strategy

Teaming up to provide better care independent not-for-profit health care organizations BJC HealthCare of St. Louis CoxHealth of Springfield Missouri Memorial Health System of Springfield Illinois. and Saint Luke's Health System of Kansas City Missouri created The BJC Collaborative L.L.C. (in 2012). Blessing Health System of Quincy and Southern Illinois Healthcare joined the Collaborative in 2013.

Company Background

During 2012 Southern Illinois Healthcare collaborated with community partners to conduct a Community Health Needs Assessment to spotlight health and quality of life issues in the communities served by Southern Illinois Healthcare.

Southern Illinois Healthcare was first established by four doctors in 1946 as the Southern Illinois Hospital Corporation.

EXECUTIVES

Vice President Quality And Risk, Shelly Pierce
Vice President And Administrator, Bart Millstead
Medical Director, Naresh Ahuja
Medical Director, Amanda Bleichner
Medical Director, Linda Bobo
Auditors: RSM US LLP SPRINGFIELD ILLIN

LOCATIONS

HQ: SOUTHERN ILLINOIS HEALTHCARE ENTERPRISES, INC.
1239 E MAIN ST STE C, CARBONDALE, IL 629013176
Phone: 618 457-5200
Web: WWW.SIH.NET

PRODUCTS/OPERATIONS

Selected Facilities

Herrin Hospital
Memorial Hospital of Carbondale
St. Joseph Memorial Hospital

Selected Services

Birthing Center
Cancer
Senior Renewal
Heart
Infusion Therapy
Neurosciences
Occupational Health
Pediatrics
Rehabilitation
Robotic-assisted Surgery
Sleep Medicine
Stroke
Surgical Services
Weight Loss Surgery
Wound Healing

COMPETITORS

Community Health Systems
Heartland Health
Memorial Hospital (Illinois)
Saint Francis Medical Center
St. John's Hospital (Illinois)

HISTORICAL FINANCIALS

Company Type: Private

Income Statement FYE: March 31

	REVENUE ($ mil.)	NET INCOME ($ mil.)	NET PROFIT MARGIN	EMPLOYEES
03/20	696	(45)	—	3,493
03/19	685	22	3.2%	—
03/18	624	30	4.9%	—
03/17	1	0	41.4%	—
Annual Growth	649.8%	—	—	—

2020 Year-End Financials

Return on assets: (-4.4%)
Return on equity: (-7.7%)
Current ratio: 1.50
Cash ($ mil.): 25

SOUTHERN ILLINOIS UNIVERSITY INC

Southern Illinois University (SIU) helps to train future doctors dentists and other other professionals. The university enrolls some 32000 students at its two institutions – Southern Illinois University at Carbondale (SIUC which includes medical and law schools) and Southern Illinois University at Edwardsville (SIUE which houses education dental and nursing schools) – as well as smaller satellite centers. SIU offers associate baccalaureate master's doctoral and professional degrees. It also boasts a number of study abroad partnerships with international universities. Tracing its roots back to 1869 SIU is known for its extensive research programs.

Operations

Students across SIU's institutions hail from all 50 states and more than 100 countries. Combined the campuses have some 2600 faculty members and an annual budget of $870 million.

The Carbondale campus was chartered in 1869 as a teachers college while the Edwardsville campus was founded in 1957. Most of the university's doctoral programs are housed at the SIUC campus which conducts residencies through the School of Medicine. A majority of the institutions master's degrees are conferred at the SIUE campus.

Undergraduate and research programs are conducted at both primary SIU campuses. Students and faculty members participate in research programs in a number of fields including biology biodiversity and molecular science. The university receives $78.5 million in research grants annually.

Geographic Reach

From its flagship campus in Carbondale Illinois SIU reaches to Edwardsville and to other parts of Southern Illinois including Springfield through satellite campus locations. Its satellite schools include SIU School of Medicine SIU School of Dental Medicine and SIU School of Nursing.

Financial Performance

SIU logged increases of 2% in fiscal 2012 as compared to 2011 pointing to a rise in student tuition and fees private grants and contracts and sales and services for the gains. Net income for the same reporting period rose 17% due to a boost in non-operating revenues attributable to increases in gifts and contributions investment income and payments on behalf of the university.

Strategy

As part of its focus SIU is working to strengthen its undergraduate graduate and professional education. It's also concentrating on streamlining its administrative process while expanding its inter-campus and intra-campus collaboration through degree programs international education distributed learning fundraising and research opportunities for both students and faculty. SIU is also establishing partnerships with public and private sector groups.

EXECUTIVES

Pres, Randy J Dunn
Sr V Pres*, Duane Stucky
Staff, John Massie
Assistant Professor, William Eichfeld
Automotive Parts Manager Asa, Cynthia Gerlock
Director, Michelle Richerson
Administrative Aide, Jane Meuth
Chief Academic Adviser College, Tamora Workman
Accountant, Judy Wright
Assistant Professor, Reza Habib
Assistant Professor, Robin Warne

LOCATIONS

HQ: SOUTHERN ILLINOIS UNIVERSITY INC
1400 DOUGLAS DR, CARBONDALE, IL 629014332
Phone: 618 536-3475
Web: WWW.SIUE.EDU

HISTORICAL FINANCIALS

Company Type: Private

Income Statement				FYE: June 30
	REVENUE ($ mil.)	NET INCOME ($ mil.)	NET PROFIT MARGIN	EMPLOYEES
06/19	581	28	4.9%	9,576
06/18	584	139	23.9%	—
06/17	601	(59)	—	—
06/16	740	(104)	—	—
Annual Growth	(7.7%)	—	—	—

2019 Year-End Financials

Return on assets: 2.4%
Return on equity: 4.8%
Current ratio: 1.80
Cash ($ mil.): 66

SOUTHERN INDIANA GAS & ELECTRIC COMPANY

EXECUTIVES

Ceo, Carl L Chapman
Ceo*, Niel C Ellerbrook
Exec V Pres-Cfo*, Jerome A Benkert Jr
Sr V Pres*, Ronald E Christian
V Pres-Treas*, Robert Goocher
V Pres-Controller*, M Susan Hardwick
Pres*, William S Doty
V Pres*, Daniel Bugher
V Pres*, Ellis S Redd
V Pres*, Eric J Schach
Vp, Darin Carroll
Auditors: DELOITTE & TOUCHE LLP INDIAN

LOCATIONS

HQ: SOUTHERN INDIANA GAS & ELECTRIC COMPANY
1 VECTREN SQ, EVANSVILLE, IN 477081209
Phone: 812 424-6411
Web: WWW.VECTREN.COM

HISTORICAL FINANCIALS

Company Type: Private

Income Statement				FYE: December 31
	REVENUE ($ mil.)	NET INCOME ($ mil.)	NET PROFIT MARGIN	EMPLOYEES
12/17	661	86	13.1%	779
12/16	692	95	13.9%	—
12/03	438	48	11.1%	—
12/02	693	59	8.6%	—
Annual Growth	(0.3%)	2.6%	—	—

2017 Year-End Financials

Return on assets: 3.8%
Return on equity: 9.7%
Current ratio: 1.80
Cash ($ mil.): 2

SOUTHERN METHODIST UNIVERSITY INC

What do former first lady Laura Bush actress Kathy Bates and NFL Hall-of-Famer Doak Walker have in common? They're all graduates of Southern Methodist University (SMU). Founded in 1911 by what is now The United Methodist Church SMU is a nonsectarian private institution offering undergraduate graduate and professional degrees in arts business engineering humanities law science and theology through eight schools. It's one of a handful of schools nationwide to offer an academic major in human rights. Nearly 12375 students attend the university which has a student-faculty ratio of 11:1. About 85% of full-time faculty hold the doctorate or highest degree in their fields.

Operations

The university offers more than 100 majors and 85 minors to choose from as well as double and triple major opportunities and accelerated degree programs through eight schools. Some areas to study include accounting advertising art business entrepreneurship chemistry data sciences and earth sciences.

Geographic Reach

SMU is housed of some 130 buildings on about 235 acres five miles north of downtown Dallas County. SMU's Taos campus is nearly 425 acres with about 30 buildings located within the Carson National Forest and surrounded by the Sangre de Cristo Mountains. Students came from all 50 states the District of Columbia and approximately 90 foreign countries. Students represent diverse economic ethnic and religious backgrounds.

Financial Performance

The SMU endowment ended the fiscal year in 2019 (ended May) with a market value of $1.6 billion. Substantial endowment gifts of $25.7 million were received during the year while endowment distributions of $81.0 million an all-time high provided support to the University.

EXECUTIVES

Vice President Of Sales, Lori White
President, R. Gerald Turner, age 74
Dean Edwin L. Cox School Of Business, Albert W. Niemi, age 77
Dean Dedman School Of Law, John B. Attanasio
Dean And Director Central University Libraries, Gillian M. McCombs
Provost And Vp Academic Affairs, Paul W. Ludden
Vp Business And Finance, Christine (Chris) Regis
Dean Meadows School Of The Arts, José A. Bowen
Dean Annette Caldwell Simmons School Of Education And Human Development, David Chard
Dean Perkins School Of Theology, William B. Lawrence
Dean Research And Graduate Studies, James E. Quick
Cio, Joe Gargiulo
Chief Investment Officer And Treasurer, Michael A. Condon
Dean Dedman College Of Humanities And Sciences, William M. Tsutsui
Dean Lyle School Of Engineering, Marc P. Christensen
President Smu Student Body, Alexander Mace
President Smu Faculty Senate, Jose L. Lage
Vice President Executive Affairs, Thomas E Barry
Department Chair And O. Paul Corley Distinguished Chair In Organizational Behavior, Miguel Quinones
Vice President, Andrea Smith
Department Chair Fire And Ems Technology, Mattie Eiland
Vice President For Development, Dominique Sims
Department Chair, Robert Gregory
Associate Vice President Information Technology Services, George Chrisman
Professor And Department Chair, Karen Lupo
Vice President, Cchea Nugent
Vice President For Administration, Smu Swvf
Vice President, Kit Swain
Senior Vice President, James Gallegos
Senior Vice President Community Development, Wayne Watts
Provost And Vice President For Academic Affairs, Steven Currall
Assistant Vice President Developer, Robert Bucker
Vice President, Vishal Goel
Vice President Academic Excellence, Olivia Waidmann
Associate Vice President Human Resources And Business Services, William Detwiler
Vice President And Treasurer, Andrew Hornung
Associate Vice President, Barry Ernie
Vice President Of Programming, William Hagens
Provost And Vice President Academic Affairs, Tom Tunks
Vice President For Business And Finance, Chris Regis
Vice President Finances, Lizzie Ranshaw
Avp Of Marketing And Communications At Smu, Regina Moldovan
Vice President Engineering, Stephen Smith
Assistant Vice President, Paula Voyles
Vice President, John Unkcd Phillips
Chair, Caren Prothro
Ward Secretary, Julio Lopez
Treasurer, Liz Williams
Department Secretary, Tiffany Powell
Secretary, Suzanne Nelsen
Vice President Legal Affairs And Government Relations Secretary And General Counsel, Leon S Bennett
Treasurer And Chief Investment Officer, Rakesh Dahiya
Ward Secretary, Dan Howard
Treasurer, Garima Singh
Secretary, Scott Kingsley
Treasurer, Marcia Felts
Treasurer, Cole Bildstein
Treasurer, Wynne Casteel
Board Member, Michael Martin
Auditors: KPMG LLP DALLAS TX

LOCATIONS

HQ: SOUTHERN METHODIST UNIVERSITY INC
6425 BOAZ LN, DALLAS, TX 75205
Phone: 214 768-2000
Web: WWW.SMU.EDU

PRODUCTS/OPERATIONS

Selected Schools and Divisions

Annette Caldwell Simmons School of Education and Human Development
Bobby B. Lyle School of Engineering
Cox School of Business
Dedman College of Humanities and Sciences
Dedman School of Law
Meadows School of the Arts
Perkins School of Theology

HISTORICAL FINANCIALS

Company Type: Private

Income Statement — FYE: May 31

	REVENUE ($ mil.)	NET INCOME ($ mil.)	NET PROFIT MARGIN	EMPLOYEES
05/18	652	96	14.7%	2,200
05/17	580	56	9.8%	—
05/13	563	115	20.5%	—
05/11	602	58	9.6%	—
Annual Growth	1.1%	7.4%	—	—

2018 Year-End Financials

Return on assets: 2.9%
Return on equity: 4.6%
Current ratio: —
Cash ($ mil.): 183

SOUTHERN NATURAL GAS COMPANY, L.L.C.

Now here's a company that pipes in the goods that keep the South fueled naturally. Southern Natural Gas operates an 7600-mile long natural gas pipeline (SNG System) which serves major markets across the southeastern US. This system transports more than 3 billion cu. ft. of natural gas per day. The SNG pipeline system has about 60 billion cu. ft. of underground working natural gas storage capacity. Major customers include Atlanta Gas Light Company Alabama Gas Southern Company and SCANA . Southern Natural Gas is a unit of El Paso Pipeline Partners.

EXECUTIVES

Pres-Ceo, Norman G Holmes
Exec V Pres-Cfo, John R Sult
V Pres-Controller-Cao, Rosa P Jackson
Gas Accountant, Mike Rockett
Senior Vice President, Larry Powell
Project Manager, Barry Smith

LOCATIONS

HQ: SOUTHERN NATURAL GAS COMPANY, L.L.C.
1001 LOUISIANA ST, HOUSTON, TX 770025089
Phone: 713 420-2600
Web: WWW.KINDERMORGAN.COM

COMPETITORS

Alagasco
American Midstream Partners
Bridgeline
Crestwood Midstream Partners LP
Gulf South Pipeline
Panhandle Eastern Pipe Line
Piedmont Natural Gas
U.S. Transmission

HISTORICAL FINANCIALS

Company Type: Private

Income Statement — FYE: December 31

	REVENUE ($ mil.)	NET INCOME ($ mil.)	NET PROFIT MARGIN	EMPLOYEES
12/17	606	143	23.7%	3
12/16	609	169	27.8%	—
Annual Growth	(0.6%)	(15.2%)	—	—

2017 Year-End Financials

Return on assets: 5.2%
Return on equity: 10.8%
Current ratio: 0.90
Cash ($ mil.): 3

SOUTHERN NUCLEAR OPERATING COMPANY, INC.

The night the lights went out in Georgia they should have called Southern Nuclear Operating Company. The company a subsidiary of Southern Company since 1990 operates six nuclear power units at three plant locations which combined provide about 20% of the electricity used in Alabama and Georgia. Southern Nuclear's Joseph M. Farley Nuclear Plant began commercial operation in 1977. The Edwin I. Hatch Nuclear Plant and the Alvin W. Vogtle Electric Generating Plant are jointly owned by Southern Company's Georgia Power (50%) Oglethorpe Power (30%) the Municipal Electrical Authority of Georgia (18%) and the city of Dalton.

EXECUTIVES

Vice President Of Fleet Operations Support, Bradley Adams

LOCATIONS

HQ: SOUTHERN NUCLEAR OPERATING COMPANY, INC.
42 INVERNESS CENTER PKWY, HOOVER, AL 352424809
Phone: 205 992-5000
Web: WWW.SOUTHERNCOMPANY.COM

COMPETITORS

Duke Energy
NextEra Energy
Progress Energy

HISTORICAL FINANCIALS

Company Type: Private

Income Statement — FYE: December 31

	REVENUE ($ mil.)	NET INCOME ($ mil.)	NET PROFIT MARGIN	EMPLOYEES
12/16	922	0	0.0%	2,960
12/04	479	0	—	—
12/03	441	0	—	—
12/02	455	0	—	—
Annual Growth	5.2%	—	—	—

2016 Year-End Financials

Return on assets: —
Return on equity: 0.1%
Current ratio: 1.00
Cash ($ mil.): 14

SOUTHWEST RESEARCH INSTITUTE INC

If you're looking for research at an institute in the Southwest look no further. Founded in 1947 by oilman and rancher Thomas Slick Jr. Southwest Research Institute (SwRI) is an independent not-for-profit research and development institution that contracts to explore subjects in areas including automation and data systems applied physics space science and engineering and chemistry. SwRI has about 2700 scientists engineers and support staff at laboratories and offices in the US China and the UK. Customers include the private sector and government agencies. SwRI's Signature Science subsidiary researches national security environmental management and biotechnology.

Operations

SwRI provides contract research and development services to industrial and government clients. It keeps the scope of its work confidential and assigns patent rights arising from its sponsored research to the client. SwRI generally retains rights to Institute-funded advancements and holds more than 1300 patents awarded to staff members.

The company operates through nearly a dozen technical divisions including Aerospace Electronics; Systems Engineering & Training; Applied Physics Chemistry & Chemical Engineering; Engine Emissions & Vehicl; Research; Geosciences & Engineering; Mechanical Engineering; and Space Science & Engineering.

Geographic Reach

The company is based in San Antonio Texas and the Institute has technical offices and laboratories in Ann Arbor Michigan; Beijing China; Boulder Colorade; Hill Air Force Base (Ogden) Utah; Hanover and Rockville Maryland; Minneapolis Minnesota; Oklahoma City Oklahoma; Warner Robins Georgia; and Durham New Hampshire.

Strategy

SwRI is a research and development problem solver providing independent premier service to government and industry clients. Its multidisciplinary nature allows it to rapidly assemble diverse teams to tackle problems from multiple directions. SwRI has been known to provide solutions that not only benefit the government but also the industry and the public through innovative science and technology.

In addition it has formed a consortium to conduct research and code development and apply advanced ROS (Robot Operating System) software to industrial applications. With ROS SwRI has been able to deliver technologically complex or previously infeasible systems for much lower costs. To date SwRI has leveraged ROS applications in the areas of industrial robotics & automation; robotics research & development; ROS-Industrial; and automated driving systems & UGVs.

SwRI also completed the construction of the building housing the Supercritical Transformational Electric Power (STEP) pilot plant a $112 million 10-megawatt supercritical carbon dioxide facility. The STEP pilot plant is a collaboration between SwRI GTI GE Research and the US Department of Energy/National Energy Technology Laboratory. The facility is designed to demonstrate a new form of power generation that is considerably more efficient and cost-effective.

EXECUTIVES

Executive Manager, Scott Mullin
Associate Vice President, Scott Bolton
Assistant Vice President, Matt Majors
Treasurer, Linda Boehme
Secretary, Loida Vergara
Treasurer, Debra Streeter
Secretary, Melody Cherry
Senior Secretary Cap Om, Sylvia Rodriguez
Secretary, Sheri Baetz
Secretary, Dorothea Martinez
Auditors: RSM US LLP SAN ANTONIO TEXAS

LOCATIONS

HQ: SOUTHWEST RESEARCH INSTITUTE INC
6220 CULEBRA RD, SAN ANTONIO, TX 782385100
Phone: 210 684-5111
Web: WWW.SWRI.ORG

PRODUCTS/OPERATIONS

Selected Technical Divisions
Aerospace Electronics and Information Technology
Applied Physics
Applied Power
Automation and Data Systems
Chemistry and Chemical Engineering
Engine Emissions and Vehicle Research
Fuels and Lubricants Research
Geosciences and Engineering
Mechanical Engineering
Signal Exploitation and Geolocation
Space Science and Engineering
Training Simulation and Performance Improvement

COMPETITORS

Battelle Memorial
Berkeley Lab
Brookhaven Lab
Lawrence Livermore Lab
QinetiQ
Southern Research Institute

HISTORICAL FINANCIALS

Company Type: Private

Income Statement FYE: September 27

	REVENUE ($ mil.)	NET INCOME ($ mil.)	NET PROFIT MARGIN	EMPLOYEES
09/19	673	33	5.0%	2,754
09/18	583	38	6.6%	—
09/17	498	11	2.3%	—
09/16	559	6	1.2%	—
Annual Growth	6.4%	69.6%	—	—

2019 Year-End Financials

Return on assets: 4.4%
Return on equity: 5.7%
Current ratio: 3.80
Cash ($ mil.): 9

SOUTHWEST WASHINGTON HEALTH SYSTEM

EXECUTIVES

Pres-Ceo, Joe Kortum
Emergency Medicine Specialist, Erik Denninghoff
Internist, Joan Hunter

LOCATIONS

HQ: SOUTHWEST WASHINGTON HEALTH SYSTEM
400 NE MOTHER JOSEPH PL, VANCOUVER, WA 986643200
Phone: 360 514-2000
Web: WWW.PEACEHEALTH.ORG

HISTORICAL FINANCIALS

Company Type: Private

Income Statement FYE: December 31

	REVENUE ($ mil.)	NET INCOME ($ mil.)	NET PROFIT MARGIN	EMPLOYEES
12/09	601	9	1.5%	3,500
12/08*	110	(38)	—	—
09/08	10	(0)	—	—
Annual Growth	5757.2%	—	—	—

*Fiscal year change

2009 Year-End Financials

Return on assets: 1.4%
Return on equity: 2.9%
Current ratio: 1.40
Cash ($ mil.): 13

SPARROW HEALTH SYSTEM

Ailing residents of central Michigan fly to Sparrow Health System for care. The not-for-profit network's hospitals include the flagship Sparrow Hospital Sparrow Clinton Memorial Hospital Sparrow Specialty Hospital and Carson City Hospital. The health system also operates dozens of satellite clinics a long-term-care center a hospice care provider medical equipment rental unit and athletic club. Through affiliate Physicians Health Plan Sparrow Health provides health plan coverage to some 70000 Michigan residents. Its Sparrow Physicians Health Network includes some 1000 physicians in the region.The system traces its roots back to 1896.

Operations

The Sparrow Health System is a not-for-profit community-governed organization. Its flagship facility Sparrow Hospital is a 700-bed regional referral hospital providing a range of general and specialty services. Community service is important to Sparrow Health as the organization provides millions of dollars worth of charity care underfunded services and community outreach services each year.

Geographic Reach

Sparrow Health's hospitals are located in Lansing St. John's Ionia and Carson City Michigan. It also has dozens of satellite care sites throughout central Michigan.

Strategy

Over the years Sparrow Health System has expanded its services and geographic reach through a series of affiliations. It is part the Mayo Clinic Care Network which allows it to improve the care it provides its patients. In 2016 Sparrow formalized its long-time affiliation with Hayes Green Beach Memorial Hospital which will become an official affiliate by 2019. That hospital is now undergoing a renovation and expansion.

To provide health care to a more sizable population the system regularly opens new health care facilities and expands its physicians care network; it has also been investing in modernizing itself through technological advances. Its Sparrow Care Network a physician-led clinically integrated organization has grown to include more than 650 physicians. In 2016 the system opened additional retail clinics (dubbed "Fast Care" sites) within area grocery stores. And in 2017 the system opened its Herbert-Herman Cancer Center and Plaza.

Sparrow has also been growing its mobile health clinics in partnership with local agencies and organizations.

One of Sparrow's hospitals Sparrow Carson Hospital has come under fire for infection-control issues. In 2018 it was dropped from its Medicare contract after an audit showed it wasn't in compliance with sterilization procedures. The accusations are serious as hospital-based infections are the third leading cause of deaths in the US.

Sparrow closed its St. Lawrence emergency department in mid-2018. It added about a dozen beds to its primary hospital to make up for the closure. It also opened a new urgent care center giving patients a choice of health care based on the severity of their ailments.

Company Background

Sparrow Health got its start in 1896 when a group of women set out with $400 a house on Ottawa Street (in Lansing Michigan) and a mission to care for the sick.

EXECUTIVES

President Ceo, Dennis Swan
President Php, Scott Wilkerson
Vp And Cio, Thomas A. (Tom) Bres
Cfo, Paula Reichle
Vp Sparrow Medical Group, Peter Graham
President Sparrow Clinton Hospital, Ed Bruun
President And Ceo Sparrow Ionia Hospital, William Roeser
Ceo Sparrow Specialty Hospital, Kira Carter-Robertson
Coo And Chief Nursing Officer, Barbara (Barb) McQuillan
Vp Strategic Planning And Marketing, Melissa Sears
Medical Director, Stephen Guertin
Senior Vice President Chief Administrative Officer And Chief Information Officer, Tom Bres
Medical Director Pediatric Emergency Services, Pamela Coffey
Vice President Marketing Communications, Ilene Cantor
Vice President Sparrow Medical Group, Douglas Edema
Vice President Of Finance, William Howe
Vp Chief Medical Information Officer And Chief Transformation Officer, Mike Zaroukian
Vice President Of Patient Care And Chief Nurse Executive, Beth Daugherty
Medical Director Of Stroke Services, Syed Hussain
Chair, Barbara Given
Secretary, Teressia Green
Auditors: PLANTE & MORAN LLC GRAND RAP

LOCATIONS

HQ: SPARROW HEALTH SYSTEM
1215 E MICHIGAN AVE, LANSING, MI 489121811
Phone: 517 364-5000
Web: WWW.SPARROW.ORG

PRODUCTS/OPERATIONS

Selected Services
Emergency room/Urgent Care
Laboratory
Medical Supply
Outpatient Rehabilitation
Pharmacy
Radiology

COMPETITORS

Bronson Battle Creek
Covenant HealthCare
Crittenton Hospital
Detroit Medical Center
Genesys Health System
Genesys Regional Medical Center
Henry Ford Health System
Hurley Medical Center
McLaren Health Care
Munson Healthcare
Sheridan Community Hospital
St. John Health
Trinity Health (Novi)

HISTORICAL FINANCIALS

Company Type: Private

Income Statement FYE: December 31

	REVENUE ($ mil.)	NET INCOME ($ mil.)	NET PROFIT MARGIN	EMPLOYEES
12/19	1,340	99	7.4%	3,400
12/18	1,281	(57)	—	—
12/17	1,259	49	3.9%	—
12/16	1,286	63	5.0%	—
Annual Growth	1.4%	16.1%	—	—

2019 Year-End Financials

Return on assets: 5.2%
Return on equity: 10.4%
Current ratio: 2.50
Cash ($ mil.): 115

SPARTANBURG REGIONAL HEALTH SERVICES DISTRICT, INC.

Spartanburg Regional Health Services District (dba Spartanburg Regional Healthcare System or SRHS) provides a wide range of care options to northeast South Carolina. It operates four hospitals: Spartanburg Medical Center Pelham Medical Center Spartanburg Hospital for Restorative Care and Union Medical Center. The 540-bed Spartanburg Medical offers services including pediatrics diagnostic imaging and behavioral health. It houses the Gibbs Cancer Center as well as centers specializing in heart vascular women's health and outpatient care. SRHS also operates clinics specialty outpatient centers and long-term care home health and hospice facilities.

Operations

SRHS also operates the Ellen Sagar Nursing Center a 113-bed long-term care skilled nursing facility. Its multidisciplinary Medical Group of the Carolinas has more than 300 physicians across seven counties in North and South Carolina. Other offerings include a level I trauma center (at Spartanburg Medical Center) and Advicare a licensed HMO.

Each year the system sees more than 130000 emergency department visits delivers more than 2700 babies and completes more than 28000 surgical procedures.

Geographic Reach

SRHS provides health care services in South Carolina's Spartanburg Cherokee and Union counties and in North Carolina's Polk and Rutherford counties.

Financial Performance

Revenue increased 23% to $982 million in 2014 as net patient service and premium revenues grew. Net patient service revenues increased as patient volumes rose new services were offered and the system participated in the Medicaid Upper Payment Limit program. Meanwhile premium earnings of $73.4 million were reported as the system's Advicare managed care organization began operations.

Net income nearly doubled that year rising 97% to $36 million as net non-operating revenues (investment earnings and grants and contributions) grew. Cash flow from operations rose 48% to $71 million.

Mergers and Acquisitions

In 2015 SRHS took over the operations of the 50-bed Wallace Thomson Hospital (now Union Medical Center) and Ellen Sagar Nursing Home (now Ellen Sagar Nursing Center) in Union South Carolina. Wallace Thomson had filed for Chapter 9 bankruptcy in 2014 struggling to stay afloat in its rural setting with declining insurance coverage and Medicare and Medicaid reimbursements. SRHS plans to buy land and build a new facility for Union Medical in 2017.

EXECUTIVES

Vp Operational Support Services And Cio, Ray Shingler
President And Ceo, Bruce Holstien
Cfo, Mark Aycock
Chief Of Staff, Christopher Lombardozzi
Medical Director Chief Of Staff Chief Marketing Officer, Frank Singletary
Vice President Human Resources, Jim Walker
Director Of The Vascular Surgery Section And Medical Director Of The Vascular Lab, Cuyler Calton
Senior Vice President Business Relations, Paul Butler
Vice President Of Nursing, Susan Duggar
Director Of Nursing, Regina Edge
Nursing Director, Evelyn Lollis
Medical Director Of Nuclear Medicine, William Joyce
Vice President, Thomas Eison
Vice President Clinical Integration And Medical Director Case Management, Eg Ulmer
Medical Director Of Case Management And Clinical Services, Nick Ulmer
Vice President Finance, Bruce Davis
Medical Director Emergency Medicine, Chris Lombardozzi
Medical Director Of Information Technology, Vincent Slater
Director Of Pharmacy, Vashti Ray
Vice President Human Resources, Raymond Gambardella
Vice President Marketing, Maria Williamson
Secretary, Pamela Wolfe

LOCATIONS

HQ: SPARTANBURG REGIONAL HEALTH SERVICES DISTRICT, INC.
101 E WOOD ST, SPARTANBURG, SC 293033040
Phone: 864 560-6000
Web: WWW.SPARTANBURGREGIONAL.COM

PRODUCTS/OPERATIONS

2014 Sales

	$ mil.	% of total
Net patient service revenue	872	89
Premium revenue	73	7
Other operating revenue	36	4
Total	**982**	**100**

Selected Facilities

AccessHealth
Ellen Sagar Nursing Center in Union
Gibbs Cancer Center & Research Institute
Hospice Home
Medical Group of the Carolinas (MGC)
Pelham Medical Center in Greer
Regional HealthPlus (RHP)
Spartanburg Medical Center (SMC)
The Sports Medicine Institute
Union Medical Center

Selected Services

Bearden-Josey Center for Breast Health
Chest Pain Center
Comprehensive Pain Center
Congregational Nursing
Corporate Health
Emergency Center (Level I Trauma Center)
Emergency Medical Services (EMS)
Gibbs Cancer Center & Research Institute
Heart Center
Heart Wellness Program
Home Health
Hospice (Hospice Home)
Imaging and Laboratory Services
Neonatal Intensive Care Unit (Level III)
Neurology
Orthopaedic Services
Palliative Care Services
Pediatrics and Pediatric Intensive Care Unit
Rehabilitation Services
Robotic Surgery
Sleep Services
Stroke Center
Surgery (including minimally invasive)
Urology
Weight Loss Services
Women's Health
Wound Healing Center

COMPETITORS

AnMed Health
Bon Secours Health
CaroMont
Community Health Systems
Doctors Hospital of Augusta
Laurens County Hospital
Novant Health
Palmetto Health
Upstate Affiliate

HISTORICAL FINANCIALS

Company Type: Private

Income Statement — FYE: September 30

	REVENUE ($ mil.)	NET INCOME ($ mil.)	NET PROFIT MARGIN	EMPLOYEES
09/20	1,468	18	1.3%	5,000
09/19	1,365	42	3.1%	—
09/18	1,147	28	2.5%	—
Annual Growth	13.1%	(19.1%)	—	—

2020 Year-End Financials

Return on assets: 1.2%
Return on equity: 20.3%
Current ratio: 1.80
Cash ($ mil.): 348

SPECTRA ENERGY CORP

Spectra Energy covers the spectrum of natural gas activities – gathering processing transmission storage and distribution. The company now part of Enbridge operates more than 15400 miles of transmission pipeline and has 305 billion cu. ft. of storage capacity in the US and Canada. Units include U.S. Gas Transmission Texas Eastern Transmission Natural Gas Liquids Division and Market Hub Partners. It also has stakes in DCP Midstream Maritimes & Northeast Pipeline Gulfstream Natural Gas System Spectra Energy Income Fund and 75% of Spectra Energy Partners. Its Union Gas unit distributes gas to 1.5 million Ontario customers. In 2017 Spectra merged with Enbridge creating the largest energy infrastructure company in North America.

Change in Company Type

In 2017 Enbridge acquired Spectra Energy for $28 billion. The combination of the two companies created the largest energy infrastructure company in North America with a pro-forma enterprise value of about $127 billion. Enbridge shareholders owned 57% of the combined company (Enbridge) and Spectra Energy shareholders 43%.

Operations

Spectra Energy has managed its businesses in four reportable segments: Spectra Energy Partners Distribution Western Canada Transmission & Processing and Field Services.

Spectra Energy Partners provides transmission storage and gathering of natural gas for customers in various regions of the Midwestern northeastern and southeastern US and operates a crude oil pipeline system that connects Canadian and U.S. producers to refineries in the U.S. Rocky Mountain and Midwest regions. Spectra Energy Partners has accounted for about 50% of the company's revenue.

Distribution about 30% of revenue provides retail natural gas distribution service (its Union Gas unit distributes gas to 1.5 million customers in 400 communities in Ontario). It also provides natural gas transportation and storage services to other utilities and energy market customers.

Western Canada Transmission & Processing about 20% of revenue provides its customers with transportation services to move natural gas natural gas gathering and processing services and NGL extraction fractionation transportation storage and marketing services.

Field Services gathers processes treats compresses transports and stores natural gas; it also fractionates transports gathers processes stores markets and trades NGLs. Its DCP Midstream joint venture is 50% owned by Phillips 66. DCP operates in 17 US states.

Transportation storage and processing of natural gas have accounted for about two-thirds of Spectra Energy's revenue.

Geographic Reach

Spectra Energy's Spectra Energy Partners operates in northeastern and southeastern US and operates a crude oil pipeline system that connects Canadian and US producers to refineries in the Rocky Mountains and the Midwest. The Distribution segment serves natural gas customers in Ontario Canada. Western Canada Transmission & Processing serves customers in western Canada and the northern US. Field Services gathers natural gas from the Mid-Continent Rocky Mountain East Texas-North Louisiana Barnett Shale Gulf Coast South Texas Central Texas Antrim Shale and Permian Basin.

All told Spectra Energy has more than 100 facilities across North America.

Sales and Marketing

Spectra Energy's customers (end-users) purchase gas directly from suppliers or marketers as well as through retail and wholesale outlets.

Financial Performance

Spectra Energy reported a 6% decline in revenue in 2016 to $4.9 billion from 2015. Each segment posted lower revenue for 2016. Lower energy prices were passed on to customers and warmer weather meant they used less energy. Revenue also was hurt by a weaker Canadian dollar. The Distribution segment did see some growth with additional customers and the Dawn Parkway Expansion Project.

The company's net income jump some 250% to $693 million in 2016 from 2015 mostly because of charges and costs the company had in 2015 but not 2016.

Spectra has cash flow from operations of about $2 billion in 2016 down from about $2.2 billion in 2015. The difference was driven by non-cash goodwill impairments in 2015 offset by higher earnings.

Company Background

In 2012 Spectra Energy acquired one-third of DCP Sand Hills Pipeline and DCP Southern Hills Pipeline (NGL pipelines) from DCP Midstream for $459 million.

In 2012 Spectra Energy opened a new natural gas processing plant in Dawson Creek British Columbia part of its $1.5 billion investment strategy in infrastructure. That year it also signed a deal with BG Group to develop a pipeline from northeast British Columbia to serve BG Group's potential LNG export facility in Prince Rupert on the northwest coast of the province.

To raise cash in 2012 it sold a 38.76% interest in Maritimes & Northeast Pipeline to Spectra Energy Partners for $375 million.

In a move to boost its Gulf Coast natural gas storage position in 2010 Spectra Energy acquired the Bobcat Gas Storage asset from Haddington Energy Partners and GE Energy Financial Service for about $540 million.

The company was founded in 2006.

EXECUTIVES

Cfo, J. Patrick (Pat) Reddy, $634,900 total compensation
Vice President Of It, Mark Wyatt
Vice President, John Bremner
Chief Administrative Officer, Dorothy M. Ables, $475,488 total compensation
Chairman President And Ceo, Gregory L. (Greg) Ebel, $1,133,000 total compensation
President Spectra Energy Transmission West And Canadian Lng, R. Mark Fiedorek
President Us Transmission And Storage, William T. (Bill) Yardley, $409,500 total compensation
President Union Gas, Stephen W. (Steve) Baker
General Counsel, Reginald D. (Reggie) Hedgebeth, $568,033 total compensation
Chief Development Officer, Guy G. Buckley, $438,333 total compensation
Vice President, Gregory Rizzo
Senior Vice President, Carlo V Dechiro
Vice President And Chief Compliance Officer, Christopher Agbe-davies
Vice President Information Technology, Steve Craft
Auditors: DELOITTE & TOUCHE LLP HOUSTON

LOCATIONS

HQ: SPECTRA ENERGY CORP
5400 WESTHEIMER CT, HOUSTON, TX 770565353
Phone: 713 627-5400
Web: WWW.SPECTRAENERGY.COM

2016 Sales

	$ mil.	% of total
U.S.	2,461	50
Canada	2,455	50
Total	**4,916**	**100**

PRODUCTS/OPERATIONS

2016 Sales

	$ mil.	% of total
Spectra Energy Partners	2,533	52
Distribution	1,370	28
Western Canada Transmission & Processing	1,005	20
Others	8	-
Total	**4,916**	**100**

2016 Sales

	$ mil.	% of total
Transportation storage and processing of natural gas	3,251	66
Distribution of natural gas	1,144	23
Transportation of crude oil	359	7
Sales of natural gas liquids	68	2
Other	94	2
Total	**4,916**	**100**

Selected Mergers and Acquisitions

COMPETITORS

Entergy
Enterprise Products
Kinder Morgan
Koch Industries Inc.
Piedmont Natural Gas
TransMontaigne
Williams Companies

HISTORICAL FINANCIALS

Company Type: Private

Income Statement FYE: December 31

	REVENUE ($ mil.)	NET INCOME ($ mil.)	NET PROFIT MARGIN	EMPLOYEES
12/16	4,916	1,020	20.7%	8,700
12/15	5,234	460	8.8%	—
Annual Growth	(6.1%)	121.7%	—	—

SPECTRUM HEALTH HOSPITALS

EXECUTIVES

Pres, Kevin R Splaine
V Pres*, Joseph J Fifer
Pres*, David M Krhovsky
V Pres, William L Bush
Physician, Peter Vasiu
Chief of Obstetrics Gynecology, Rodman Taber
Executive Assistant, Rhonda McCarthy
Director of Engineering, Duane Nelson
Telecommunications Manager, Larry Walter
Vice President of Finance, Ron Knaus
Internist, Vetriselvi Moorthy

LOCATIONS

HQ: SPECTRUM HEALTH HOSPITALS
100 MICHIGAN ST NE, GRAND RAPIDS, MI 495032560
Phone: 616 391-1774
Web: WWW.SPECTRUMHEALTH.ORG

HISTORICAL FINANCIALS

Company Type: Private

Income Statement FYE: June 30

	REVENUE ($ mil.)	NET INCOME ($ mil.)	NET PROFIT MARGIN	EMPLOYEES
06/16	1,905	196	10.3%	11,000
06/15	1,764	196	11.1%	—
06/08	2,595	(21)	—	—
06/06	1,013	77	7.6%	—
Annual Growth	6.5%	9.8%	—	—

2016 Year-End Financials

Return on assets: 7.9%
Return on equity: 22.0%
Current ratio: 1.90
Cash ($ mil.): 206

SPECTRUM HEALTH SYSTEM

Offering more health services than colors in the rainbow Spectrum Health is a regional health system serving western Michigan. The not-for-profit network operates 12 hospitals that boast more than 1900 beds. Its health system provides a variety of services from general surgery to specialized cancer care. Besides its Spectrum Health Medical Group and West Michigan Heart Spectrum Health also operates Priority Health a health plan with 648000 members and Helen Devos Children's Hospital. The group runs more than 170 service sites including urgent care centers primary care physician offices community clinics rehabilitation and other outpatient facilities and continuing care residences for the elderly.

Operations

Spectrum Health's other hospitals include Blodgett Hospital Butterworth Hospital Kelsey Hospital Reed City Hospital and United Hospital.

Spectrum Health conducts hundreds of research studies each year through its Institutional Review Board. The organization has more than 300 physicians involved in research as investigators and at least 6000 patients enrolled in heart and cancer clinical studies.

The company is western Michigan's largest provider of post-acute care. It provided some $294.6 million in community benefits during fiscal 2014.

Geographic Reach

Spectrum Health provides patient services at community hospitals in Big Rapids East Grand Rapids Fremont Greenville Lakeview Ludington Reed City and Zeeland.

Sales and Marketing

Managed care and other represented more than half of Spectrum's net patient revenues in 2014; Medicare accounted for 26% and Medicaid represented another 15%.

Financial Performance

Spectrum Health's revenues increased 5% to $4.1 billion in fiscal 2014 (versus $3.9 billion in fiscal 2013) due to increases in net patient revenues and revenues from health plans. Net income rose by less than half of a percent to $377 million; impacting net income growth were factors including a decline in non-operating revenue and an increase in operating expenses.

Cash flow from operations rose a modest 2% to $181 million in 2014 due to changes in accounts payable accrued salaries and wages health care claims payable and other operating liabilities.

Strategy

Spectrum Health regularly expands its footprint. In 2015 it began construction on its newest integrated care campus. The new 10000 square foot facility will be located in front of the Meijer store at 2770 South State Road in Berlin Township near Ionia.

In also recently opened a 14-story building for its Helen DeVos Children's Hospital. The health network is also focused on expanding its health plan operations which account for about half of annual revenues. To this end Priority Health has added about 100000 customers in recent years by offering plans in eight new counties in northern Michigan and by adding the Bronson Healthcare provider network in southwestern Michigan.

In 2015 Spectrum Health and Munson Healthcare agreed to form a joint venture between Aero Med's northern operations and North Flight EMS Air Division. The new organization will enhance critical care air emergency transport services in northern Michigan. Aero Med will continue to serve West Michigan from its operations based at the Gerald R. Ford International Airport in Grand Rapids. North Flight's fleet of ground ambulances in northern Michigan will continue to operate as North Flight EMS.

Spectrum Health also focuses on recruiting new physicians and strengthening its community hospital offerings.

Mergers and Acquisitions

Spectrum Health has expanded its health network in recent years through acquisitions. In 2018 it acquired the three-hospital system Lakeland Health which is now a division of Spectrum.

Company Background

Spectrum Health was formed through the 1997 merger of Blodgett Hospital and Butterworth Hospital. Kent Community Hospital joined the organization in 1999 and the United Memorial Health System (Kelsey Hospital and United Hospital) became a member in 2003.

EXECUTIVES

Medical Director, David Kutsche
President And Ceo, Richard C. (Rick) Breon
Evp And Cfo; President And Ceo Priority Health, Michael P. (Mike) Freed
Svp And Cio, Patrick J. O'Hare
Evp; President Spectrum Health Hospital Group, Matthew G. (Matt) Van Vranken
Evp And Chief Strategy Officer, John B. Mosley
President Blodgett Hospital, James (Jim) Wilson
President Helen Devos Children's Hospital, Robert H. (Bob) Connors
Chief Clinical Systems And Improvement Officer, James M. Tucci
President Spectrum Health Grand Rapids, Kevin Splaine
Svp And Chief Human Resource Officer, Roger E. Jansen
President Spectrum Health Hospital Group, Tina Freese-Decker
Chief Medical Officer; President Spectrum Medical Group, Seth W. Wolk
President Spectrum Health Big Rapids And Reed City Hospitals, Mary Kay VanDriel
Coo Spectrum Health Grand Rapids, Gwen G. Sandefur
Vice President General Counsel And Secretary, Kimberly Thomas
Senior Vice President Communit, Steven Heacock
Vice President Operations, Karen Pakkala
Vice President Human Resources Sh System, Julie Lepzinski
Vice President, John Frein
Vice President Of Finance, Joe Fifer
Vice President, Mona Null Wojtas
Senior Vice President Human Resources, Brian Krupiczewicz
Vice President, John Heiser
Medical Director Heart Failure And Heart Transplant Spectrum Health Grand Rapids, Michael Failure
Vice President, Tom Koprowski
Radiology Director, James Viewig
Secretary, David Leonard
Unit Secretary, Dianna Gable
Unit Secretary, Rachel Martorano
Admisitrative Secretary, Elvia Myers
Treasurer, David Dyke

LOCATIONS

HQ: SPECTRUM HEALTH SYSTEM
100 MICHIGAN ST NE, GRAND RAPIDS, MI 495032560
Phone: 616 391-1774
Web: WWW.SPECTRUMHEALTH.ORG

PRODUCTS/OPERATIONS

2014 Sales

	$ mil.	% of total
Health plan	2,136	52
Net patient service revenue	1,868	45
Other	102	3
Total	**4,107**	**100**

Selected Services

Cancer
Continuing care
Digestive disease
Heart & vascular
Neurosciences
Orthopedics
Outpatient
Pediatric
Rehabilitation
Transplant
Women's health

Selected Operations

Helen DeVos Children's Hospital
Priority Health
Spectrum Health Blodgett Hospital
Spectrum Health Butterworth Hospital
Spectrum Health Continuing Care
Spectrum Health Kent Community Campus
Spectrum Health Gerber Memorial Hospital
Spectrum Health Pennock Hospital
Spectrum Health Reed City Hospital
Spectrum Health Special Care Hospital
Spectrum Health United Memorial
  Kelsey Hospital
  United Hospital

COMPETITORS

Ascension Health
Borgess Health
Bronson Battle Creek
Bronson Health Care
CareSource
Covenant HealthCare
Great Lakes Health Plan
Hayes Green Beach Memorial Hospital
Health Alliance Plan of Michigan
McLaren Bay
McLaren Health Care
Mercy Health Hackley
Munson Healthcare
OmniCare Health Plan
Sheridan Community Hospital
Total Health Care
Zeeland Community Hospital

HISTORICAL FINANCIALS

Company Type: Private

Income Statement — FYE: June 30

	REVENUE ($ mil.)	NET INCOME ($ mil.)	NET PROFIT MARGIN	EMPLOYEES
06/19	6,884	332	4.8%	16,996
06/18	6,004	332	5.5%	—
06/17	5,681	357	6.3%	—
06/10	1,446	142	9.9%	—
Annual Growth	18.9%	9.9%	—	—

SPIRE MISSOURI INC.

EXECUTIVES

Pres-Ceo, Steven L Lindsey
Chb*, Suzanne Sitherwood
Cfo*, Steven P Rasche
Asst V Pres-Reg Admin, R Lawrence Sherwin

LOCATIONS

HQ: SPIRE MISSOURI INC.
700 MARKET ST, SAINT LOUIS, MO 631011829
Phone: 314 342-0500
Web: WWW.SPIREENERGY.COM

HISTORICAL FINANCIALS

Company Type: Private

Income Statement — FYE: September 30

	REVENUE ($ mil.)	NET INCOME ($ mil.)	NET PROFIT MARGIN	EMPLOYEES
09/18	1,285	129	10.1%	2,271
09/17	1,171	113	9.6%	—
09/16	1,087	105	9.7%	—
09/15	1,416	105	7.4%	—
Annual Growth	(3.2%)	7.1%	—	—

2018 Year-End Financials

Return on assets: 3.5%
Return on equity: 6.2%
Current ratio: 0.50
Cash ($ mil.): 2

SPIRIT REALTY CAPITAL, INC.

EXECUTIVES

Pres-Ceo, Jackson Hsieh
Exec V Pres-Cfo, Phillip D Joseph Jr
Exec V Pres-Chief Acquisitions, Boyd Messmann
Exec V Pres Asset Management, Mark L Manheimer
Sr V Pres-Chief Hr Officer, Michelle M Greenstreet
Sr V Pres-Cao, Prakash J Parag
Chb, Richard I Gilchrist
Evp-Cfo, Michael Hughes
Asset Management Analyst, Charlie Bernet
Information Technology Directo, Colin Lane
Commercial Risk Mana, Gayle Hazlett
Auditors: ERNST & YOUNG LLP DALLAS TEX

LOCATIONS

HQ: SPIRIT REALTY CAPITAL, INC.
2727 N HARWOOD ST STE 300, DALLAS, TX 752012407
Phone: 480 606-0820
Web: WWW.SPIRITREALTY.COM

HISTORICAL FINANCIALS

Company Type: Private

Income Statement — FYE: December 31

	ASSETS ($ mil.)	NET INCOME ($ mil.)	INCOME AS % OF ASSETS	EMPLOYEES
12/17	7,263	77	1.1%	85
12/16	7,677	97	1.3%	—
12/14	8,017	(33)	—	—
12/13	7,231	1	0.0%	—
Annual Growth	0.1%	160.4%	—	—

2017 Year-End Financials

Return on assets: 1.1%
Return on equity: 2.3%
Sales ($ mil): 668

SPORTS, INC.

EXECUTIVES

Pres, Tony Cardinal
Pres-Dir*, Barry Cory
V Pres*, Chad Wyffels
V Pres & Asst SEC-Treas*, Nancy Wilson
Dir*, Mark Daniels
Dir*, John Phillips
Executive Officer, Frances Hines
Accounting Staff, Shannon Peterschick
Accounts Payable, Roxanne Gordon
Shipping Supervisor, Craig Kriskovich
Outdoor Program Manager, Kale Schwede
Auditors: JUNKERMIER CLARK CAMPANELLA

LOCATIONS

HQ: SPORTS, INC.
333 2ND AVE N, LEWISTOWN, MT 594572700
Phone: 406 538-3496
Web: WWW.SPORTSINC.US

HISTORICAL FINANCIALS

Company Type: Private

Income Statement — FYE: December 31

	REVENUE ($ mil.)	NET INCOME ($ mil.)	NET PROFIT MARGIN	EMPLOYEES
12/19	983	0	0.0%	38
12/18	960	0	0.0%	—
12/17	913	0	0.0%	—
12/16	963	0	0.0%	—
Annual Growth	0.7%	2.9%	—	—

2019 Year-End Financials

Return on assets: 0.1%
Return on equity: 0.9%
Current ratio: 1.10
Cash ($ mil.): 3

SPRING BRANCH INDEPENDENT SCHOOL DISTRICT (INC)

EXECUTIVES

Supt, Scott R Muri
Transportation Director, Sherri Lawson
Elementary Assistant, Sherrie Folger
Administrative Assistant, Betty Head
Payroll Specialist, Evelyn Medrano
Director, Jessica M Hughes
Field Supervisor, Jessica Jackowski
Production Specialist, Kristen Cain
Purchasing Clerk, Martha Cantu
Program Supervisor, Michelle Dickson
Dance Director, Wendy Reeves
Auditors: WHITLEY PENN HOUSTON TEXAS

LOCATIONS

HQ: SPRING BRANCH INDEPENDENT SCHOOL DISTRICT (INC)
955 CAMPBELL RD, HOUSTON, TX 770242803
Phone: 713 464-1511
Web: WWW.SPRINGBRANCHISD.COM

HISTORICAL FINANCIALS

Company Type: Private

Income Statement — FYE: June 30

	REVENUE ($ mil.)	NET INCOME ($ mil.)	NET PROFIT MARGIN	EMPLOYEES
06/20	540	161	29.9%	4,484
06/19	582	22	3.9%	—
06/18	513	135	26.4%	—
06/17	500	(4)	—	—
Annual Growth	2.6%	—	—	—

2020 Year-End Financials

Return on assets: 10.9%
Return on equity: 99.6%
Current ratio: —
Cash ($ mil.): 14

SRCTEC, LLC

EXECUTIVES

Pres, Drew James
Treas*, Deborah Sabella
SEC*, Mary Pat Hartnett
Scientist, Laura Morlacci
Manufacturing Engineer, Tom Chappini
Director, Stephen Winslow
Senior Financial Analyst, Andrea Emery
Director, Bill Kramer
Senior Quality Engineer, Bill Laveck
Manager of Financial Planning, Deb E Sabella
Chief Financial Officer, Phil Fazio

LOCATIONS

HQ: SRCTEC, LLC
5801 E TAFT RD STE 7, SYRACUSE, NY 132123382
Phone: 315 452-8700
Web: WWW.SRCINC.COM

HISTORICAL FINANCIALS

Company Type: Private

Income Statement — FYE: September 30

	REVENUE ($ mil.)	NET INCOME ($ mil.)	NET PROFIT MARGIN	EMPLOYEES
09/10	583	42	7.3%	150
09/09	365	19	5.4%	—
Annual Growth	59.7%	115.0%	—	—

2010 Year-End Financials

Return on assets: 14.3%
Return on equity: 7.3%
Current ratio: 1.30
Cash ($ mil.): 44

SSM HEALTH CARE CORPORATION

The mission of SSM Health began with five nuns who fled religious persecution in Germany in 1872 only to arrive in St. Louis in the midst of a smallpox epidemic. They formed their first hospital there in 1877. Today the Midwest-based not-for-profit system sponsored by the Franciscan Sisters of Mary owns some 25 acute care hospitals with about 4500 licensed beds; it also has management or affiliation agreements with a number of other area hospitals. Additionally the company offers more than 300 outpatient facilities including physicians' practices home care and hospice services post-acute facilities and an insurance company.

Operations

In southern Wisconsin SSM Health facilities include St. Clare Hospital in Baraboo St. Mary's Janesville Hospital in Janesville and St. Mary's Hospital in Madison. Southern Illinois locations include St. Mary's Good Samaritan Hospital in Mount Vernon and St. Mary's Hospital in Centralia. The company owns and operates about 10 hospitals in Missouri; these include Cardinal Glennon Children's Hospital and DePaul Hospital. Oklahoma hospitals include St. Anthony Hospital in Oklahoma City and St. Anthony Shawnee Hospital in Shawnee.

SSM Health has some 9500 physicians on its staff. The system has some 176000 inpatient admissions and some 1.6 million outpatient visits each year.

The system participates in a Medicare Accountable Care Organization (ACO). It also has a pharmacy benefit arm.

Geographic Reach

SSM Health's facilities are located in Illinois Missouri Oklahoma and Wisconsin.

Sales and Marketing

Managed care payments account for about half of SSM Health's net patient revenue before provision for uncollectible accounts; Medicare accounts for about 30% and Medicaid accounts for about 15%.

The system spent $20666 on advertising on 2016 up from $17956 in 2015.

Financial Performance

SSM Health's operating revenue increased 12% to $6.1 billion due largely to a rise in net patient service revenues and an increase in other revenue. Premiums earned and investment income also rose that year.

However operating expenses increased across most areas and the system reported a decrease in excess of revenues over expenses which fell 52% to $99.4 million. Similarly operating cash flow fell 51% to $220.4 million in 2016. Factors contributing to that drop included an increase in pension-related changes and in provisions for uncollectible accounts and bad debts.

Strategy

SSM Health often partners with other care providers which helps it expand without having to invest in new facilities from the ground up.

Like most health systems SSM has been challenged with lower government reimbursement rates. It is implementing a financial improvement initiative which includes some company layoffs.

Mergers and Acquisitions

SSM Health has been making a number of acquisitions to expand its network. For example in 2016 it doubled its stake in St. Clare Surgical Center to 60% and acquired the rest of Physicians Surgery Center at DePaul it didn't already own. SSM also took over the operations of about 25 health clinics located in Walgreens stores in Greater St. Louis.

In early 2018 the system acquired Agnesian HealthCare and Monroe Clinic (both based in Wisconsin) adding four hospitals eight post-acute facilities and several outpatient facilities.

EXECUTIVES

President And Ceo, William P. Thompson
Svp Finance, Kris A. Zimmer
President Hospital Operations, Chris Howard
Evp; President Health Care Delivery Finance And Integration, Gaurov Dayal
Svp Strategy Communications And Marketing, Paula J. Friedman
President Ssm St. Joseph Health Center, Mike Bowers
Evp; President Physician And Ambulatory Operations, Shane Peng
Chief Nursing Officer, Maggie Fowler
Svp And Cio, Phillip Loftus
President St. Mary's Hospital, Jon Rozenfeld
President Ssm Health At Home, Alison Ruehl
Regional Vp Medical Affairs, Kersey Winfree
Vice President, Stacy Coleman
Auditors: DELOITTE & TOUCHE LLP ST LOU

LOCATIONS

HQ: SSM HEALTH CARE CORPORATION
10101 WOODFIELD LN # 120, SAINT LOUIS, MO 631322937
Phone: 314 994-7800
Web: WWW.SSMHEALTH.COM

PRODUCTS/OPERATIONS

Selected Facilities

Illinois

St. Mary's Good Samaritan (joint sponsorship with Felician Services two hospitals in Mt. Vernon and Centralia)

Missouri

St. Francis Hospital & Health Services (Maryville)
St. Mary's Health Center (Jefferson City)
SSM Cardinal Glennon Children's Medical Center (St. Louis)
SSM DePaul Health Center (Bridgeton)
SSM St. Clare Health Center (St. Louis)
SSM St. Joseph Health Center (St. Charles)
SSM St. Joseph Health Center (Wentzville)
SSM St. Joseph Hospital West (Lake St. Louis)
SSM St. Mary's Health Center (Richmond Heights)

Oklahoma

Bone & Joint Hospital (Oklahoma City)
Shawnee Medical Center Clinic (Shawnee)
St. Anthony Hospital (Oklahoma City)
Unity Health Center (Shawnee)

Wisconsin

Boscobel Area Health Care (managed hospital and clinics Boscobel)
Columbus Community Hospital (affiliate Columbus)
Edgerton Hospital and Health Services (Edgerton)
St. Clare Hospital (Baraboo)
St. Clare Meadows Care Center (nursing home Madison)
St. Mary's Care Center (nursing home Madison)
St. Mary's Hospital (Madison)
St. Mary's Janesville Hospital (Janesville)
Stoughton Hospital (affiliate Stoughton)
Uplands Hill Health (affiliate hospital and nursing care Dodgeville)

COMPETITORS

Adventist Health System Sunbelt Healthcare
Advocate Health Care
Allina Hospitals
Ascension Health
BJC HealthCare
Carle Physician Group
Community Health Systems
HCA
Hospital Sisters Health System
Mayo Clinic
Mercy Health
Meriter Health Services
MetroSouth Medical
Rush System for Health
Tenet Healthcare
University of Wisconsin Hospital and Clinics
VITAS Healthcare

HISTORICAL FINANCIALS

Company Type: Private

Income Statement — FYE: December 31

	REVENUE ($ mil.)	NET INCOME ($ mil.)	NET PROFIT MARGIN	EMPLOYEES
12/17	6,497	245	3.8%	24,230
12/16	6,109	(30)	—	—
12/13	1,177	32	2.8%	—
Annual Growth	53.3%	65.9%	—	—

2017 Year-End Financials

Return on assets: 3.3%
Return on equity: 10.5%
Current ratio: 0.80
Cash ($ mil.): 126

ST BARNABAS MEDICAL CENTER (INC)

Part of the RWJBarnabas Health system Saint Barnabas Medical Center is a 600-bed acute-care hospital that provides a full range of health services to residents of Livingston New Jersey and surrounding areas. The not-for-profit medical center provides general inpatient and outpatient care programs as well as burn and perinatal care. It also houses units specializing in organ transplant stroke care cardiac surgery and comprehensive cancer treatment. Its Institute for Reproductive Medicine and Science provides assisted reproductive technology services.

Company Background

New Jersey's first hospital Saint Barnabas Medical Center was founded in 1865 in a private home.

EXECUTIVES

Senior Vice President, Robert Iannaccone
Vice President Human Resources, Arnie Manzo
Medical Director, Adrian L Connolly
Assistant Vice President, Kevin Lawless
Vice President, Thomas Heleotis
Assistant Vice President Legal Affairs, Margaret H Campbell
Auditors: KPMG LLP NEW YORK NY

LOCATIONS

HQ: ST BARNABAS MEDICAL CENTER (INC)
94 OLD SHORT HILLS RD # 1, LIVINGSTON, NJ 070395668
Phone: 973 322-5000
Web: WWW.RWJBH.ORG

COMPETITORS

Atlantic Health
Children's Specialized Hospital
Chilton Medical Center
East Orange General Hospital
Hackensack Meridian Health
Hackensack University Medical Center
JFK Medical Center
Newark Beth Israel Medical Center
Raritan Bay Medical Center
Robert Wood Johnson University Hospital
Robert Wood Johnson University Hospital at Rahway
Saint Peter's University Hospital
St. Joseph's Healthcare System
Trinitas Regional Medical Center
Virtua Health

HISTORICAL FINANCIALS

Company Type: Private

Income Statement — FYE: December 31

	REVENUE ($ mil.)	NET INCOME ($ mil.)	NET PROFIT MARGIN	EMPLOYEES
12/18	818	113	13.9%	4,000
12/17	818	113	13.9%	—
12/16	760	84	11.1%	—
12/15	728	87	12.0%	—
Annual Growth	4.0%	9.0%	—	—

2018 Year-End Financials

Return on assets: 7.5%
Return on equity: 11.3%
Current ratio: 9.20
Cash ($ mil.): —

ST LOUIS CHILDREN'S HOSPITAL

EXECUTIVES

Act Pres, Peggy Gordin
Sr V Pres*, Michael Dehaven
V Pres*, David Aplington
Pres*, Joan Magruder
Distribution/Shipping/Transpor, Lynne Andreski
General Manager, Ellie Glenn
Manager of Child Life, Jill Malan
Bereavement Coordinator, Mary Lucido
Pediatric Nurse Practitioner, Michelle Nadler
Clinical Nurse Manager GI, Tammy Keeling
Lab Supervisor, David Baker

LOCATIONS

HQ: ST LOUIS CHILDREN'S HOSPITAL
1 CHILDRENS PL FL 2, SAINT LOUIS, MO 631101081
Phone: 314 454-6000
Web: WWW.STLOUISCHILDRENS.ORG

HISTORICAL FINANCIALS

Company Type: Private

Income Statement — FYE: December 31

	REVENUE ($ mil.)	NET INCOME ($ mil.)	NET PROFIT MARGIN	EMPLOYEES
12/18	668	65	9.8%	2,959
12/17	609	62	10.2%	—
12/16	563	58	10.3%	—
12/15	527	50	9.5%	—
Annual Growth	8.2%	9.1%	—	—

2018 Year-End Financials

Return on assets: 11.1%
Return on equity: 13.1%
Current ratio: 2.20
Cash ($ mil.): —

ST LUKE'S HOSPITAL & HEALTH NETWORK INC

EXECUTIVES

Pres, Richard A Anderson
Sr V Pres, Rthomas P Lichtenwalner
Coordinator, Kathleen Hedges
Administrative Assistant, Emilia Dossantos
Network Director Real Estate, James Reyes
Senior Director, Jeff Stone
Patient Experience Manager, Lisa Litak
Information Technology Directo, Mike Owsinsky
Front Office Coordinator, Nicole Ihle
Purchasing Agent, Barbara Lorenzo
Director, Cheryl Davidson

LOCATIONS

HQ: ST LUKE'S HOSPITAL & HEALTH NETWORK INC
801 OSTRUM ST, BETHLEHEM, PA 180151000
Phone: 484 526-4000
Web: WWW.SLHN.ORG

HISTORICAL FINANCIALS

Company Type: Private

Income Statement — FYE: June 30

	REVENUE ($ mil.)	NET INCOME ($ mil.)	NET PROFIT MARGIN	EMPLOYEES
06/16	648	47	7.4%	75
06/15	602	38	6.4%	—
Annual Growth	7.6%	24.9%	—	—

2016 Year-End Financials

Return on assets: 5.1%
Return on equity: 130.2%
Current ratio: 1.30
Cash ($ mil.): 43

ST LUKE'S HOSPITAL OF KANSAS CITY

LOCATIONS

HQ: ST LUKE'S HOSPITAL OF KANSAS CITY
4401 WORNALL RD, KANSAS CITY, MO 641113220
Phone: 816 932-2000
Web: WWW.SAINTLUKESHEALTHSYSTEM.ORG

HISTORICAL FINANCIALS

Company Type: Private

Income Statement — FYE: December 31

	REVENUE ($ mil.)	NET INCOME ($ mil.)	NET PROFIT MARGIN	EMPLOYEES
12/13	647	11	1.8%	4
12/09	479	13	2.7%	—
Annual Growth	7.8%	(2.8%)	—	—

2013 Year-End Financials

Return on assets: 1.0%
Return on equity: 1.4%
Current ratio: 0.40
Cash ($ mil.): 34

ST. CHARLES HEALTH SYSTEM, INC.

EXECUTIVES

Pres-Ceo, Joe Sluka
Coordinator, Sue Takemoto
Operating Room Dir, Carla Stevens
Chief Operations Officer, Iman Simmons
Manager, Alan Burke
Clinical Oncology Pharmacist, Alexis Barr
Licensed Clinical Social Worke, John Walkenhorst
Human Resources Specialist, Kristi Durr
Point of Care Coordinator, Lura Wilhelm
Director Community Hea, Robert Ross
Survivorship, Wendy Rudy

LOCATIONS

HQ: ST. CHARLES HEALTH SYSTEM, INC.
2500 NE NEFF RD, BEND, OR 977016015
Phone: 541 382-4321
Web: WWW.STCHARLESHEALTHCARE.ORG

HISTORICAL FINANCIALS

Company Type: Private

Income Statement — FYE: December 31

	REVENUE ($ mil.)	NET INCOME ($ mil.)	NET PROFIT MARGIN	EMPLOYEES
12/17	809	41	5.1%	3,200
12/13	631	40	6.4%	—
12/07	367	8	2.4%	—
12/06	173	0	—	—
Annual Growth	15.0%	—	—	—

2017 Year-End Financials

Return on assets: 3.9%
Return on equity: 6.4%
Current ratio: 0.50
Cash ($ mil.): 57

ST. DOMINIC HEALTH SERVICES, INC.

EXECUTIVES

Chb, Mary Dorothea
Manager, Janet McAdory
Chief of Medicine, Dan Woodliff
Coordinator, Stacey Ferguson
Scientist, Keshia Mallett
Executive, Patrick Bufkin
Plastic Surgeon, Adrian R Smith
Doctor, Preston Foster
Senior Accountant, Sam Yeager
Executive Assistant Informatio, Shana Watkins
Family Medicine, Arturo Blanco
Auditors: HORNE LLP RIDGELAND MS

LOCATIONS

HQ: ST. DOMINIC HEALTH SERVICES, INC.
969 LAKELAND DR, JACKSON, MS 392164606
Phone: 601 200-2000
Web: WWW.STDOM.COM

HISTORICAL FINANCIALS

Company Type: Private

Income Statement — FYE: June 30

	REVENUE ($ mil.)	NET INCOME ($ mil.)	NET PROFIT MARGIN	EMPLOYEES
06/20*	560	397	71.0%	2,500
12/17	2	2	87.6%	—
12/13	0	0	—	—
12/12	2	(0)	—	—
Annual Growth	118.4%	—	—	—

*Fiscal year change

2020 Year-End Financials

Return on assets: 56.3%
Return on equity: 100.0%
Current ratio: 1.60
Cash ($ mil.): 138

ST. FRANCIS HOSPITAL, ROSLYN, NEW YORK

Sure St. Francis Hospital can handle your gall bladder and sinus difficulties but it's really on top of your heart problems. The hospital's Heart Center – New York State's only specially designated cardiac center – provides surgical diagnostic and treatment services. The 365-bed St. Francis Hospital also has centers for ENT (ear nose and throat) orthopedic vascular prostate cancer gastrointestinal and general surgery services. As part of Catholic Health Services of Long Island St. Francis opened its doors in 1954 to children and adults. It was originally established as St. Francis Hospital and Sanatorium for Cardiac Children in 1936.

Operations

St. Francis Hospital's Heart Center performs about 8000 cardiac catheterizations 3000 coronary angioplasties and about 1500 open-heart operations every year. The center's DeMatteis Center for Cardiac Research and Education works to develop improved techniques for heart disease diagnosis including conducting clinical trials through partnerships with device and equipment makers and provides patient education and fitness programs.

Geographic Reach

St. Francis Hospital is located in Roslyn New York. In addition it has satellite New York locations in Greenvale (DeMatteis Center for Cardiac Research and Education) West Islip (South Bay Cardiovascular Center) and Hicksville (Bishop McHugh Health Center) as well as administrative offices in Port Washington.

Strategy

St. Francis Hospital has expanded in recent years to keep up with growing patient demand. It opened the Bishop McHugh Health Center to provide outpatient primary care services for uninsured and underinsured patients in 2012.

The hospital completed its largest expansion project to date in 2009 with the construction of the $190 million Nancy and Frederick DeMatteis Pavilion; the project increased the hospital's clinical space by about 40% and added 85 beds.

EXECUTIVES

Pres-Ceo, Alan Guerci
Sr V Pres-Cfo*, William C Arms
Sr Vp-Coo*, Martin A Bieber
Vp-Development & Public Relati*, Linda Cavallo-Miller
R.N., Sr V Pres*, Ann Cella Rn
Vp-Human Resources*, Betty Anson
Exec V Pres*, Ruth Hennessey
Sr V Pres*, Jack Soterakis
PH 516 705-1925, Jenny Mitchell
Chief Anesthesiology, H Sinan Berkay
Director of Discharge Planning, Mary Anne Highland
Auditors: PRICEWATERHOUSECOOPERS LLP NE

LOCATIONS

HQ: ST. FRANCIS HOSPITAL, ROSLYN, NEW YORK
100 PORT WASHINGTON BLVD, ROSLYN, NY 115761347
Phone: 516 562-2000
Web: WWW.CHSLI.ORG

PRODUCTS/OPERATIONS

Selected Services

Anesthesiology
Breast Surgery
Cardiology
Cardiothoracic Surgery
Diabetes Care Center
Emergency Medicine
Gastroenterology
General Surgery
Hematology/Oncology
Nephrology
Neurology
Orthopedic Surgery
Otolaryngology
Podiatry
Psychiatry
Pulmonary Medicine
Radiology
Rehabilitation
Urology
Vascular Services
Women's Center

COMPETITORS

Bronx-Lebanon Hospital
Brookhaven Memorial Hospital Medical Center
Calvary Hospital
Continuum Health Partners
Franklin Hospital
Huntington Hospital
Mather Memorial Hospital
MediSys Health Network
Memorial Sloan-Kettering
New York City Health and Hospitals
NewYork-Presbyterian Healthcare
Northwell Health
NuHealth

HISTORICAL FINANCIALS

Company Type: Private

Income Statement — FYE: December 31

	REVENUE ($ mil.)	NET INCOME ($ mil.)	NET PROFIT MARGIN	EMPLOYEES
12/15	614	37	6.2%	2,184
12/08	385	28	7.4%	—
12/04	366	47	12.9%	—
12/02	828	0	—	—
Annual Growth	—	152.0%	—	—

2015 Year-End Financials

Return on assets: 3.9%
Return on equity: 5.5%
Current ratio: —
Cash ($ mil.): 34

ST. JOHN HEALTH SYSTEM, INC.

St. John Health System aims to bring health into the lives of the ill. The not-for-profit system provides health care services to residents of Tulsa and surrounding areas in northeastern Oklahoma and southern Kansas. In addition to flagship facility St. John Medical Center it owns or manages eight other community hospitals as well as urgent care and long-term care facilities. St. John Health System provides primary and specialty medical care through OMNI Medical Group and offers health insurance through CommunityCare health plan. Established in 1926 by the Sisters of the Sorrowful Mother the health system is part of Marian Health.

Operations

Facilities owned managed or sponsored by St. John Health System include hospitals Oklahoma State University Medical Center St. John Sapulpa St. John Owasso St. John Broken Arrow Pawhuska City Hospital Sedan City Hospital Nowata Hospital and Jane Phillips Medical Center. The company's senior living facilities include Franciscan Villa Frances Streitel Villa Heartsworth House and Rosewood Terrace.

Strategy

St. John Health System will periodically add services to its offerings to meet community demand. In early 2011 St. John Health opened the St. John Weight Management Institute to offer its patients weight loss options including bariatric surgery. The health system's newest hospital St. John Broken Arrow near Tulsa was constructed in 2009.

In 2012 Marian Health entered talks with another Catholic health system operator Ascension Health over the possibility of merging St. John Health System and other Marian organizations into the Ascension organization.

EXECUTIVES

Vice President, Ann Paul
Pharmacy Manager, Cornell Nathan
Secretary Iv, Julie Anderson

LOCATIONS

HQ: ST. JOHN HEALTH SYSTEM, INC.
1923 S UTICA AVE, TULSA, OK 741046520
Phone: 918 744-2180
Web: WWW.HEALTHCARE.ASCENSION.ORG

PRODUCTS/OPERATIONS

Selected Facilities and Operations – Oklahoma

CommunityCare (health plan)
Nowata Hospital
Oklahoma State University Medical Center (managed facility in Tulsa)
OMNI Medical Group (physicians group)
Pawhuska City Hospital
Regional Medical Laboratory (clinical lab testing)
Sedan City Hospital
St. John Broken Arrow Hospital
St. John Medical Center (Tulsa)
St. John Owasso Hospital
St. John Physicians
St. John Sapulpa Hospital

COMPETITORS

Anthem
Ardent Health Services
CIGNA
Catholic Health Initiatives
Community Health Systems
Deaconess Health Care
HCA
Hillcrest Medical Center
INTEGRIS Health
Kindred Healthcare
Marian Health System
Norman Regional Health
Presbyterian Healthcare Services
SSM Health Care
Saint Francis Health System
UnitedHealth Group

HISTORICAL FINANCIALS

Company Type: Private

Income Statement — FYE: June 30

	REVENUE ($ mil.)	NET INCOME ($ mil.)	NET PROFIT MARGIN	EMPLOYEES
06/14*	1,056	79	7.5%	4,011
09/12	977	74	7.7%	—
09/11	895	17	2.0%	—
Annual Growth	5.7%	64.9%	—	—

*Fiscal year change

2014 Year-End Financials

Return on assets: 5.2%
Return on equity: 9.9%
Current ratio: 1.70
Cash ($ mil.): 44

ST. JOHN HOSPITAL AND MEDICAL CENTER

St. John Hospital & Medical Center is part of the larger Detroit area-based St. John Health regional health care system. Besides providing acute and trauma care the 770-bed teaching hospital operates specialized cancer and pediatric centers a hip and knee center an inpatient mental health unit and a Parkinson's Disease clinic. It also operates the only emergency trauma center on Detroit's East Side. The hospital was established in 1952 and has grown to include a 200-physician medical team that specializes in more than 50 medical and surgical fields. It boasts 34000 admissions; 14500 surgical visits; and more than 126500 emergency center visits each year.

Operations

Its emergency center is a Level II Trauma Center that boasts Chest Pain Center and Heart Failure Center accreditations. St. John Hospital also operates a large inpatient pediatric unit PICU and Level III NICU or Level II Special Care Nursery. The hospital runs the Van Elslander Cancer Center.

Strategy

St. John Hospital expanded its operations by opening the Elaine E. Blatt Endoscopy Department and a new pediatric burn treatment room both in 2012. It also expanded its mammography service capabilities with the purchase of Lakeshore Mammograph giving it more than a dozen new mammography sites across southeastern Michigan. In addition St. John Hospital opened a new cardiac catheterization lab that brought new diagnostic options to patients in the Michigan Blue Water Area.

EXECUTIVES

Physical Therapy Director, Roger Anderson

LOCATIONS

HQ: ST. JOHN HOSPITAL AND MEDICAL CENTER
28000 DEQUINDRE RD, WARREN, MI 480922468
Phone: 313 343-4000
Web: WWW.HEALTHCARE.ASCENSION.ORG

PRODUCTS/OPERATIONS

Selected Services and Operations

Alternative Health
Breast Care
Breast Feeding (Lactation) Consultation
Cracchiolo Inpatient Rehabilitation Center
Diabetes Education and Care
Diagnostic and Imaging Services
Echocardiogram
Emergency
Heart and Vascular Care
Hip and Knee Center
Minimally Invasive Surgery
Minor Emergency
Neonatal Intensive Care Unit (NICU)
Obstetrics
Oncology (cancer)
Parkinson's Movement Disorder Clinic
Pediatrics
Physical Therapy
Spine Center
TravelCare
Urgent Care
Wound Care

COMPETITORS

Beaumont Health System
Crittenton Hospital
Detroit Medical Center
Henry Ford Health System
Mount Clemens Regional Medical Center
Trinity Health (Novi)

HISTORICAL FINANCIALS

Company Type: Private

Income Statement — FYE: June 30

	REVENUE ($ mil.)	NET INCOME ($ mil.)	NET PROFIT MARGIN	EMPLOYEES
06/15	753	36	4.8%	5,000
06/09	638	1	0.3%	—
06/05	0	0	—	—
06/03	1,642	9	0.6%	—
Annual Growth	(6.3%)	12.0%	—	—

2015 Year-End Financials

Return on assets: 3.0%
Return on equity: 6.1%
Current ratio: 2.20
Cash ($ mil.): 1

ST. JOSEPH HEALTH SYSTEM

EXECUTIVES

Ceo-Pres, Richard Afable
Pres-Strat, Annette M Walker
Exec V Pres-Gen Counsel, Shannon Dwyer
Exec V Pres-Cfo, Jo Ann Escasa-Halgh
Reg-Exec V Pres, Kevin Klockenga
Event Coordinator and Developm, Katie Gozzarino
Manager, Vanessa De Gier
Chief Information Officer, Benjamin R Williams
Coordinator, Hala Abduljalil
Coordinator, Kimberly Reynolds
Project Manager, Albert Nguyen
Auditors: ERNST & YOUNG LLP IRVINE CA

LOCATIONS

HQ: ST. JOSEPH HEALTH SYSTEM
3345 MICHELSON DR STE 100, IRVINE, CA 926120693
Phone: 949 381-4000
Web: WWW.STJHS.ORG

COMPETITORS

Adventist Health
Arrowhead Medical Center
Banner Health
Catholic Health Initiatives
Cedars-Sinai Medical Center
Citrus Valley Health Partners
City of Hope
Dignity Health
HCA
Kaiser Permanente
Loma Linda University Medical Center
Los Angeles County Health Department
Memorial Health Services
Pasadena Hospital Association
Prospect Medical
Scripps health
Sutter Health
Tenet Healthcare
Western Medical Center - Santa Ana

HISTORICAL FINANCIALS

Company Type: Private

Income Statement — FYE: June 30

	REVENUE ($ mil.)	NET INCOME ($ mil.)	NET PROFIT MARGIN	EMPLOYEES
06/13	4,955	2,082	42.0%	129
06/10	4,268	268	6.3%	—
Annual Growth	5.1%	98.1%	—	—

2013 Year-End Financials

Return on assets: 3.6%
Return on equity: 42.0%
Current ratio: 0.80
Cash ($ mil.): 329

ST. JOSEPH HOSPITAL OF ORANGE

If you're feeling green or blue in Orange County St. Joseph Hospital of Orange is there to help get back to feeling pink and rosy. The California hospital provides general medical and surgical services as well as specialty care such as women's health mental health services oncology cardiology and physical rehabilitation. Part of the St. Joseph Health System the hospital provides primary care and specialty outpatient services through a network of affiliated physician practices. It also operates low-income and mobile clinics. The hospital has about 468 beds and a medical staff of some 1000.

Operations

In addition to physician group affiliates St. Joseph Hospital Affiliated Physicians and St. Joseph Heritage Medical Group the hospital also partners with the Childrens Hospital of Orange County to help expand pediatric care throughout the region. The hospital has more than 20100 inpatient discharges and about 290400 outpatient visits a year.

Geographic Reach

St. Joseph Hospital serves Orange County California and the greater Los Angeles metropolitan area.

Strategy

St. Joseph Hospital has been working to expand its community outreach programs related to cancer through a number of projects including offering improved access to clinical trials; providing better overall access to cancer care; and implementing measures to garner support for the implementation of cancer electronic health records. St. Joseph Hospital is using stimulus money and about a $3 million award from the National Cancer Institute Community Cancer Centers Program to help fund its various projects.

Company Background

The company was founded in 1929 by the Sisters of St. Joseph of Orange.

EXECUTIVES

Vice President Management, Terry Alvarez
Executive Medical Director, Lawrence D Wagman
Vice President Performance Improvement, Mary Ann Vincent
Vice President Foundation And Chief Development Officer, Richard Green
Director Of Nursing, Carole Adam
Vice President Site Administrator Sj Wayne Hospital, Daniel Kline
Medical Director For Quality Improvement, Donald Krause
Vice President And Administrator, Charles Foster
Medical Director, Anita Lawrence
Medical Director, Elena Furrow
Director Of Home Healthcare Services, Heidi Ketch
Vice President Global Information Technology, Gary King
Vice President Chief Medical Officer, Amy Herold
Director Of Nursing, Marie Schickler

Vice President Information Technology Infrastructure And Operations St Joseph Health System, Rob Rice
Board Member, Aa Jewel Box

LOCATIONS

HQ: ST. JOSEPH HOSPITAL OF ORANGE
1100 W STEWART DR, ORANGE, CA 928683891
Phone: 714 633-9111
Web: WWW.SJO.ORG

PRODUCTS/OPERATIONS

Selected Services

Bariatric Surgery
Behavioral Health
Cancer
Nasal & Sinus Center
Heart & Vascular Center
Kidney Dialysis Center
Maternity
Orthopedic Services
Sleep Disorders Center

COMPETITORS

Anaheim Regional Medical Center
Children's Hospital of Orange County
Citrus Valley Health Partners
Hoag Memorial Hospital
Memorial Health Services
Pasadena Hospital Association
Providence St. Joseph Health
Southwest Healthcare
Sutter Health
Tenet Healthcare
Torrance Memorial Medical Center
Trinity Health (Novi)
Western Medical Center - Santa Ana

HISTORICAL FINANCIALS

Company Type: Private

Income Statement — FYE: June 30

	REVENUE ($ mil.)	NET INCOME ($ mil.)	NET PROFIT MARGIN	EMPLOYEES
06/18	627	40	6.5%	3,300
06/17	655	29	4.5%	—
06/16	599	11	2.0%	—
06/15	567	2	0.5%	—
Annual Growth	3.4%	144.6%	—	—

2018 Year-End Financials

Return on assets: 5.2%
Return on equity: 14.4%
Current ratio: 1.20
Cash ($ mil.): 17

ST. JOSEPH'S HEALTH, INC.

St. Joseph's Healthcare System takes care of northern New Jersey. The system includes St. Joseph's Regional Medical Center a tertiary teaching hospital with about 650 beds that includes the 120-bed St. Joseph's Children's Hospital. The regional hospital boasts a state-designated trauma center and provides such specialty services as cardiology oncology obstetrics behavioral health and neurology. The system also operates St. Joseph's Wayne Hospital a community medical center with about 230 beds. Other operations include St. Vincent's Nursing Home a home health agency and a community clinic network. St. Joseph's Healthcare System is sponsored by the Sisters of Charity of Saint Elizabeth.

Operations

With a total of some 1400 physicians and more than 1000 beds the St. Joseph's Healthcare facilities serve more than 1.6 million patients each year. The St. Joseph Regional facility handled some 1.3 million inpatient and outpatient visits as well as 123000 emergency room visits while the St. Joseph's Wayne center saw 680000 patients including 27000 ER visitors.

Geographic Reach

St. Joseph's facilities are located in Cedar Grove Paterson Totowa and Wayne in northern New Jersey.

Financial Performance

Revenue rose by 2% in fiscal 2013 to $714 million from $700 million in 2012. Income grew $110 million to $89 million from a net loss in 2012.

Medicare accounts for about 34% of net patient revenues while Medicaid accounts for 8%.

Strategy

The St. Joseph's Wayne and St. Joseph's Regional centers are undergoing a multi-year facility improvement project that boasts a total cost of some $250 million. The first phase was completed in 2009 and expanded St. Joseph's Regional outpatient services in areas including neurology orthopedics ophthalmology and pediatrics. And the facility completed a new lobby and conference center in 2010. In 2012 its St. Joseph's Children's Hospital completed expansion efforts on its emergency and MRI facilities; it also opened a new birth defects center and launched a telemedicine suite through a partnership with St. Jude Children's Research Hospital. At the St. Joseph's Wayne facility a new cardiac catheterization lab was added in 2012.

In addition in 2012 the St. Joseph's Children's Hospital added a new specialist facility to serve residents of Paramus and nearby communities. In 2012 St. Joseph's Children's Hospital in Tampa opened its new Steinbrenner Children's Emergency/Trauma Center.

Company Background

St. Joseph's Healthcare traces its roots to the 1867 opening of the St. Joseph's Hospital by the Sisters of Charity of Saint Elizabeth.

EXECUTIVES

Medical Director, Amer Akmal
Senior Vice President Operations, Christine Maher
Vice President Finance, Joanne Dunay
Vice President Of Operations, Jim Haynes
Senior Vice President Population Health And Physician Integration, Robert Hood
Vice President Sales, Liz Gallegos-toledo
Vp Wayne Site Administrator, Jennifer Mendrzycki
Vice President Facilities Operations, James Haynes
Vice President Of Business Development, Jeffrey OMalley
Vice President Of Operations, Jane Reed
Secretary, Michael Larson
Secretary, Linda Cimmino
Secretary, Vena Ramoutar
Secretary, Theresa Podrugiel
Treasurer, Michael Steinberg
Secretary And Treasurer, Elizabeth Barnet
Auditors: DELOITTE TAX LLP JERICHO NY

LOCATIONS

HQ: ST. JOSEPH'S HEALTH, INC.
703 MAIN ST, PATERSON, NJ 075032621
Phone: 973 754-4500
Web: WWW.STJOSEPHSHEALTH.ORG

PRODUCTS/OPERATIONS

Selected Facilities

St. Joseph's Regional Medical Center (Paterson)
St. Joseph's Children's Hospital (Paterson)
St. Joseph's Wayne Hospital (Wayne)
St. Vincent's Nursing Home (Cedar Grove)
Visiting Health Services of New Jersey Inc. (Totowa)

Selected Services

Blood Bank/Donation
Care Management/Social Work
Clinical and Educational Services
Driver Rehabilitation Program
Food and Nutrition Services
Identifying Obstacles
Information Technology
Laboratory Services
Mission Services
Pain Management Services
Pain Medicine Center
Palliative Care
Pathology/Laboratory
Pharmacy Services
Radiology
Rehabilitation
Swallowing Center
Telemedicine
Telemedicine Programs at St. Joseph's
Transfer Center

COMPETITORS

Atlantic Health
CentraState Healthcare System
Children's Specialized Hospital
Chilton Medical Center
East Orange General Hospital
Hackensack University Medical Center
Newton Medical Center
Princeton HealthCare
Raritan Bay Medical Center
Robert Wood Johnson University Hospital
Robert Wood Johnson University Hospital at Rahway
Trinitas Regional Medical Center
Virtua Health

HISTORICAL FINANCIALS

Company Type: Private

Income Statement — FYE: December 31

	REVENUE ($ mil.)	NET INCOME ($ mil.)	NET PROFIT MARGIN	EMPLOYEES
12/19	827	(4)	—	16,132
12/18	808	(22)	—	—
12/17	0	0	—	—
12/16	796	(13)	—	—
Annual Growth	1.3%	—	—	—

2019 Year-End Financials

Return on assets: (-0.5%)
Return on equity: (-2.3%)
Current ratio: 2.60
Cash ($ mil.): 60

ST. JOSEPH'S HOSPITAL HEALTH CENTER

With about 450 inpatient beds St. Joseph's Hospital Health Center serves the residents of 16 central New York counties. The not-for-profit hospital system provides general emergency and surgical care as well as specialty services in areas such as obstetrics cardiology dialysis and wound care. In addition to its inpatient facilities the organization operates a home health agency a nursing school medical and dental residency programs and several outpatient care centers. Its Franciscan Companies affiliate offers some ancillary services including the provision of medical supplies home health equipment and senior services. St. Joseph's Hospital Health Center was founded in 1869 and became part of Trinity Health in 2015.

Geographic Reach

St. Joseph's Hospital Health Center's service territory includes the New York counties of Broome Cayuga Chenango Cortland Delaware Herkimer Jefferson Lewis Madison Oneida Onondaga Oswego Otsego St. Lawrence Tioga and Tompkins.

EXECUTIVES

Vice President Chief Integrity, Jennifer Reschke Bolster
Secretary, Mary Narvaez

LOCATIONS

HQ: ST. JOSEPH'S HOSPITAL HEALTH CENTER
301 PROSPECT AVE, SYRACUSE, NY 132031899
Phone: 315 448-5882
Web: WWW.SJHSYR.ORG

PRODUCTS/OPERATIONS

Selected Services

Centers of Excellence
- Cardiac Services
- The Center for Orthopedic and Spine Care
- Vascular Services
- Women and Children's Services
- Wound Care
- Home Care
- Dialysis
- Bariatric (Weight Loss) Services

Other Services and Centers
- Aesthetic Services
- Behavioral Health
- da Vinci Robotic Surgery
- Emergency Services
- Imaging
- Infusion (CPEPCNY)
- Interventional Radiology
- Medical Equipment
- Obstetric Services
- Palliative Care
- Pharmacy
- Physical Medicine & Rehabilitation
- Pulmonary Services
- Sleep Laboratory
- Social Adult Day Care
- Surgical Services
- Urology Services

Outpatient Services
- Dental Services
- Family Medicine Center
- Obstetrics and Gynecology
- Pediatric Office
- Physician Health
- Primary Care
- Westside Family Health Center

COMPETITORS

Catholic Health System
Ellis Hospital
Kaleida Health
Lifetime Health
Oneida Healthcare Center
SUNY Upstate Medical University
United Health Services Hospitals
Upstate University Hospital at Community General

HISTORICAL FINANCIALS

Company Type: Private

Income Statement — FYE: December 31

	REVENUE ($ mil.)	NET INCOME ($ mil.)	NET PROFIT MARGIN	EMPLOYEES
12/15	542	(2)	—	3,300
12/14	523	0	0.1%	—
12/09	436	5	1.2%	—
12/08	399	6	1.6%	—
Annual Growth	4.5%	—	—	—

2015 Year-End Financials

Return on assets: (-0.6%)
Return on equity: (-3.9%)
Current ratio: 1.80
Cash ($ mil.): 36

ST. JOSEPH'S HOSPITAL, INC.

EXECUTIVES

Pres, Lorraine Lutton
Pres*, Isaac Mallah
Cfo*, Cathy Yoder
V Pres-Fin*, Tommy Inzina
Pres*, Kimberly Guy
Pres*, Paula McGuiness
Cmo*, Peter Charvat
C-Level Human Resources, Craig Brethauer
Executive of Information Techn, Brenda Pingle
Manager Food 6075bc, Erica Salgado
Cardiac Cath Lab Director, Michelle Hare

LOCATIONS

HQ: ST. JOSEPH'S HOSPITAL, INC.
3001 W DR MRTN LTHER KING, TAMPA, FL 336076307
Phone: 813 554-8500
Web: WWW.BAYCARE.ORG

HISTORICAL FINANCIALS

Company Type: Private

Income Statement — FYE: December 31

	REVENUE ($ mil.)	NET INCOME ($ mil.)	NET PROFIT MARGIN	EMPLOYEES
12/14	872	141	16.2%	300
12/09	719	75	10.4%	—
12/08	663	29	4.5%	—
12/06	565	63	11.2%	—
Annual Growth	5.6%	10.6%	—	—

2014 Year-End Financials

Return on assets: 11.0%
Return on equity: 12.5%
Current ratio: 5.40
Cash ($ mil.): —

ST. JOSEPH'S UNIVERSITY MEDICAL CENTER INC

EXECUTIVES

Pres-Ceo, Kevin Slavin
Cfo*, Dennis Roemer
Chm*, Patricia Thiele
Coo*, Lisa Brady
Chief of Neonatology, Adel M Zauk
Administrative Assistant To Vp, Christine Strangeway
Director of Environmental Svs, John Di' Giovani
Chief of Pulmonary Medicine, M Aness Khan
Doctor, Aldo Khoury
Vice President Human Resources, John P Bruno
Chief of Medicine, Robert C Amoruso

LOCATIONS

HQ: ST. JOSEPH'S UNIVERSITY MEDICAL CENTER INC
703 MAIN ST, PATERSON, NJ 075032621
Phone: 973 754-2000
Web: WWW.STJOSEPHSHEALTH.ORG

HISTORICAL FINANCIALS

Company Type: Private

Income Statement — FYE: December 31

	REVENUE ($ mil.)	NET INCOME ($ mil.)	NET PROFIT MARGIN	EMPLOYEES
12/19	821	(8)	—	6,000
12/18	798	(12)	—	—
12/16	763	(12)	—	—
12/15	752	60	8.0%	—
Annual Growth	2.2%	—	—	—

2019 Year-End Financials

Return on assets: (-1.0%)
Return on equity: (-4.5%)
Current ratio: 2.70
Cash ($ mil.): 59

ST. JUDE HOSPITAL

EXECUTIVES

Ceo-Pres, Robert Fraschetti
Ceo*, Lee Penrose
Coo-Ceo*, Doreen Dann
Staff Pharmacist, Sue J Kim
Chief of Medicine, Lytton Smith
Administrative Assistant, Leslee Mc Gregor
Staff Pharmacist, Norman Q Jung
Chief Staff, James L Benoit
Chief of Pathology, Patrick L Fitzgibbons
Staff Pharmacist, Huong V Le
Radiologist, Hao Q Ngo

LOCATIONS

HQ: ST. JUDE HOSPITAL
101 E VALENCIA MESA DR, FULLERTON, CA 928353875
Phone: 714 871-3280
Web: WWW.STJUDEMEDICALCENTER.ORG

COMPETITORS

Anaheim Regional Medical Center
Children's Hospital of Orange County
Hoag Memorial Hospital
Memorial Health Services
Western Medical Center - Santa Ana

HISTORICAL FINANCIALS

Company Type: Private

Income Statement — FYE: June 30

	REVENUE ($ mil.)	NET INCOME ($ mil.)	NET PROFIT MARGIN	EMPLOYEES
06/18	557	50	9.1%	2,600
06/17	544	45	8.3%	—
06/16	490	4	0.9%	—
06/15	458	8	2.0%	—
Annual Growth	6.8%	77.9%	—	—

ST. LUKE'S HEALTH NETWORK, INC.

St. Luke's University Hospital (formerly St. Luke's Hospital - Bethlehem Campus) serves residents of Pennsylvania's Lehigh Valley with primary specialty and emergency care services. The not-for-profit teaching hospital has about 480 acute-care beds. Its medical specialties include trauma oncology cardiology orthopedics neurology open-heart surgery radiology and robotic surgery. The medical center also operates outpatient surgery centers and general physician care clinics and it operates home health and community wellness programs. St. Luke's University Hospital was founded in 1872 and is part of the St. Luke's University Health Network.

EXECUTIVES

Medical Director Emergency Medicine, Christopher Stromski
Vp Finance, Carl Alberto
Secretary, Linda Keefe
Auditors: WITHUMSMITHBROWN PC MORRISTOW

LOCATIONS

HQ: ST. LUKE'S HEALTH NETWORK, INC.
801 OSTRUM ST, BETHLEHEM, PA 180151000
Phone: 610 954-4000
Web: WWW.STLUKESPAWILDMED.COM

PRODUCTS/OPERATIONS

Selected Services
Cancer Center
Children's health
Diagnostic and Treatment Centers
Emergency
Heart Center
Neuroscience
Orthopaedics
Radiology/Imaging
Regional Breast Center (Center Valley)
Urgent Care Centers
Women's Imaging & Health Centers

COMPETITORS

Ascension Health
Evangelical Community Hospital
LVHN
Moses Taylor Hospital
Reading Hospital and Medical Center
Sacred Heart Hospital of Allentown
Wyoming Valley Health Care System

HISTORICAL FINANCIALS

Company Type: Private

Income Statement — FYE: June 30

	REVENUE ($ mil.)	NET INCOME ($ mil.)	NET PROFIT MARGIN	EMPLOYEES
06/19	2,116	59	2.8%	2,958
06/18	1,844	159	8.6%	—
06/17	1,521	121	8.0%	—
06/15	0	0	—	—
Annual Growth	—	—	—	—

2019 Year-End Financials

Return on assets: 2.5%
Return on equity: 6.7%
Current ratio: 1.50
Cash ($ mil.): 100

ST. LUKE'S HEALTH SYSTEM, LTD.

To Catholics St. Luke is also known as the "beloved physician" and St. Luke's Health System strives to live up to its namesake. The regional not-for-profit health system provides a range of health services to residents of Idaho eastern Oregon and northern Nevada. St. Luke's is home to six general acute care hospitals with a total of about 860 beds. Its flagship facility is the 400-bed St. Luke's Boise Medical Center which also includes a full-service children's hospital. St. Luke's also runs a network of cancer care sites under the name Mountain States Tumor Institute as well as a number of urgent care family practice and specialty health centers.

Operations

St. Luke's hospitals handle about 50000 inpatient visits 35000 surgeries and 8000 births each year. The network also sees about 700000 outpatients annually through its urgent care family health and specialty care centers. The company's diagnostic care operations include about five imaging centers and eight breast cancer detection clinics. Overall St. Luke's employs about 1000 physicians.

The Boise campus is home to its tertiary care services - cancer heart and the Children's Hospital - meaning the most acute cases from the region are brought there for the most specialized care. St. Luke's Children's Hospital sees 85000 patient visits a year has Idaho's first and only Pediatric Intensive Care Unit and has the state's largest and most experienced Level III Newborn Intensive Care Unit. Its Boise campus is also the base of St. Luke's Mountain States Tumor Institute (MSTI which cares for about 820 cancer patients a day) and St. Luke's Heart services one of the top 50 cardiovascular programs in the US.

Geographic Reach

St. Luke's has Idaho operations in Boise Caldwell Eagle Fruitland Jerome Ketchum McCall Meridian Mountain Home Nampa and Twin Falls.

Strategy

The growing need for care from each of these leading service lines is a significant part of the Integrated Care Model that has guided the company's Master Plan. St. Luke's has been investing a significant amount of money to upgrade and expand its facilities in recent years.

In 2014 the federal courts ordered St. Luke's to divest Saltzer Medical Group (Idaho's state's largest independent multi-specialty physician practice) after concluding that St. Luke's 2012 acquisition of Saltzer violated Section 7 of the Clayton Act and the Idaho Competition Act.

Company Background

In 2011 St. Luke's completed a $130 million project to rebuild the St. Luke's Magic Valley Medical Center. The new hospital building had about 190 beds and expanded emergency cancer and cardiac centers. The health system was also working to expand its Boise Medical Center's heart and vascular and pediatric departments as well as its system-wide MSTI facilities.

The health system has also expanded its outpatient network to include new family practice emergency care and urgent care clinics in recent years. The network opened a St. Luke's Nampa emergency care clinic and medical complex in 2012. In addition to updating its facilities the St. Luke's Health System was working to upgrade its information technology assets.

St. Luke's added its fifth and sixth acute care hospitals in 2010 and 2011 when the 15-bed St. Luke's McCall (formerly McCall Memorial Hospital) and 25-bed St. Luke's Jerome (formerly St. Benedicts Medical Center) hospitals joined the health network through affiliation and merger agreements.

The health system was formed in 2006 when the three hospitals of the old St. Luke's Regional Medical Center network (Boise Meridian and Wood River) merged with Magic Valley Regional Medical Center a former county facility in Twin Falls Idaho.

EXECUTIVES

President Ceo And Director, David C. Pate
Nursing Director, Katie Schimmelpfennig
Vice President And Chief Legal Officer, Christine Neuhoff
Vice President And Chief Nursing Officer, Deborah White
Medical Director Mountain States Tumor Institute, Thomas Beck
Chairman, Jon Miller
Treasurer, Lisa Barker
Auditors: DELOITTE & TOUCHE LLP BOISE

LOCATIONS

HQ: ST. LUKE'S HEALTH SYSTEM, LTD.
190 E BANNOCK ST, BOISE, ID 837126241
Phone: 208 381-2222
Web: WWW.STLUKESONLINE.ORG

PRODUCTS/OPERATIONS

Selected Idaho Facilities
St. Luke's Boise Medical Center (Boise)
St. Luke's Children's Hospital
St. Luke's Clinics (multiple locations)
St. Luke's Eagle Urgent Care (Eagle)
St. Luke's Jerome Medical Center (Jerome)
St. Luke's Magic Valley Medical Center (Twin Falls)
St. Luke's McCall Memorial Hospital (McCall)
St. Luke's Meridian Medical Center (Meridian)
St. Luke's Mountain States Tumor Institute (multiple locations)
St. Luke's Wood River Medical Center (Hailey/Ketchum)

COMPETITORS

Ascension Health
Benedictine Health System
HCA
Intermountain Health Care
Saint Alphonsus Regional Medical Center
Trinity Health (Novi)

HISTORICAL FINANCIALS

Company Type: Private

Income Statement — FYE: September 30

	REVENUE ($ mil.)	NET INCOME ($ mil.)	NET PROFIT MARGIN	EMPLOYEES
09/19	2,894	91	3.2%	7,891
09/18	2,602	34	1.3%	—
09/17	2,327	10	0.4%	—
09/16	1,937	48	2.5%	—
Annual Growth	14.3%	24.1%	—	—

2019 Year-End Financials

Return on assets: 3.5%
Return on equity: 8.0%
Current ratio: 1.10
Cash ($ mil.): 118

ST. LUKE'S REGIONAL MEDICAL CENTER, LTD.

EXECUTIVES

Pres, Edwin Dahlberg
V Pres*, Gary Fletcher
V Pres-Fin*, Clarence Pumeroy
Health Professional, Colleen Walker-Vamos
Emergency Medicine Specialist, Bradley Chatlin
Emergency Medicine Specialist, Marlene Olson
Oncologist, Silvana Bucur
Internist, Carissa Pereda

Pediatrics, Katherine Stevens
Diagnostic Radiologist, Michael Fisher
Diagnostic Radiologist, Michael Fuchs

LOCATIONS

HQ: ST. LUKE'S REGIONAL MEDICAL CENTER, LTD.
190 E BANNOCK ST, BOISE, ID 837126241
Phone: 208 381-5500
Web: WWW.STLUKESONLINE.ORG

HISTORICAL FINANCIALS

Company Type: Private

Income Statement FYE: September 30

	REVENUE ($ mil.)	NET INCOME ($ mil.)	NET PROFIT MARGIN	EMPLOYEES
09/14	1,255	31	2.5%	4,500
09/13	1,121	(19)	—	—
09/08	898	44	4.9%	—
Annual Growth	5.7%	(5.5%)	—	—

2014 Year-End Financials

Return on assets: 1.7%
Return on equity: 4.6%
Current ratio: 5.60
Cash ($ mil.): 258

ST. MARY'S HEALTH, INC.

St. Mary's Medical Center of Evansville is a 433-bed hospital serving Indiana's River City. It is the primary facility in regional St. Mary's Health System which is in turn part of Ascension Health. The Evansville hospital provides emergency trauma diagnostic surgical and rehabilitative services as well as specialized cancer cardiac orthopedic and neurological services. With a total of some 750 physicians St. Mary's Health System also includes St. Mary's Hospital for Women & Children (100 beds adjacent to the main hospital) and St. Mary's Warrick (a 25-bed hospital in Boonville Indiana) as well as specialty outpatient surgical cancer and home health units in surrounding areas of southern Indiana.

Operations

St. Mary's Medical Center of Evansville admits some 17000 inpatients annually. It also handles around 64000 emergency room visits and performs approximately 4700 inpatient and 18000 outpatient surgeries each year.

Company Background

St. Mary's Medical Center of Evansville was originally a Marine Hospital built by the US government. When the government shuttered its doors city business leaders bought the building in 1872 and partnered with the Daughters of Charity to operate a community hospital.

EXECUTIVES

Medical Director, Donald Brake
Board Member, Anthony Stephens
Auditors: DELOITTE TAX LLP INDIANAPOLIS

LOCATIONS

HQ: ST. MARY'S HEALTH, INC.
3700 WASHINGTON AVE, EVANSVILLE, IN 477140541
Phone: 812 485-4000

PRODUCTS/OPERATIONS

Selected Services

Breast Center
Cancer Care Services
Children's Health Care Services and Programs
Community Outreach Services
Convenient Care Centers
Diabetic Foot Clinic
Diabetes Services
Emergency Services Department
Endoscopy Suite
Foundation
Heart Services
Home Health Services
Hospitalists
Imaging/Radiology
Infusion Center
Laboratory Services
LifeFlight
Medical Equipment
Mental Health Services
Neurosciences & Stroke Care
Occupational Medicine Services
Orthopedic Healthcare
Palliative Care
Pastoral Care
Quality and Patient Safety
Rehabilitation Services
Respiratory Care
Senior Services
Sleep Disorders Center
Surgical Services
Trauma Services
Volunteers & Auxiliary
Weight Management Center
Women's Services and Programs
Women's Wellness Center

COMPETITORS

Ball Memorial Hospital
Community Health Network
Daviess Community Hospital
Deaconess Health System
Good Samaritan Hospital (IN)
Henry County Memorial Hospital
Kosciusko Community Hospital
Memorial Hospital (Logansport)

HISTORICAL FINANCIALS

Company Type: Private

Income Statement FYE: June 30

	REVENUE ($ mil.)	NET INCOME ($ mil.)	NET PROFIT MARGIN	EMPLOYEES
06/15	574	52	9.2%	3,500
06/13	468	48	10.4%	—
06/11	0	0	—	—
Annual Growth	—	—	—	—

2015 Year-End Financials

Return on assets: 6.4%
Return on equity: 9.1%
Current ratio: 2.80
Cash ($ mil.): 12

ST. PETER'S HEALTH CARE SERVICES

EXECUTIVES

Ceo, Ann Errichettii
Vice President For Facilities, Charles Gianfagna
Network Manager, Kyle Stark
Director, Linda Berner
Manager, Anne Martin
Scientist, Alfonzo Diblasio
Director of Surgery, Kathleen Marsch
Chief of Pathology, Russell Newkirk
Pharmacist, Carmen Mojica
Telecommunications Executive, George Seabury
Chief of Cardiology, Steve Cameron
Auditors: DELOITTE & TOUCHE LLP ROCHEST

LOCATIONS

HQ: ST. PETER'S HEALTH CARE SERVICES
315 S MANNING BLVD, ALBANY, NY 122081707
Phone: 518 525-1550
Web: WWW.SPHP.COM

HISTORICAL FINANCIALS

Company Type: Private

Income Statement FYE: June 30

	REVENUE ($ mil.)	NET INCOME ($ mil.)	NET PROFIT MARGIN	EMPLOYEES
06/17	1,327	37	2.9%	6,000
06/16	552	39	7.1%	—
06/15	527	44	8.5%	—
06/14	509	21	4.1%	—
Annual Growth	37.6%	21.7%	—	—

2017 Year-End Financials

Return on assets: 2.7%
Return on equity: 4.4%
Current ratio: 2.60
Cash ($ mil.): 124

STAN BOYETT & SON, INC.

EXECUTIVES

Pres, Dale Boyett
V Pres*, Scott Castle
Accounting Staff, Laverne Couch
District Manager, James Martin
Coordinator, Martha Garcia
Sales, Samantha Falk
Account Executive, Kristine Freitag
Marketing, Michelle Gill
Account Executive, Cesar Betancourt
Account Executive, Chris Kwietkauski
Account Executive, Carl Haney

LOCATIONS

HQ: STAN BOYETT & SON, INC.
601 MCHENRY AVE, MODESTO, CA 953505411
Phone: 209 577-6000
Web: WWW.BOYETT.NET

HISTORICAL FINANCIALS

Company Type: Private

Income Statement FYE: December 31

	REVENUE ($ mil.)	NET INCOME ($ mil.)	NET PROFIT MARGIN	EMPLOYEES
12/08	656	0	0.1%	170
12/07	559	0	0.0%	—
12/06	475	0	0.1%	—
12/05	416	0	0.1%	—
Annual Growth	16.4%	28.4%	—	—

2008 Year-End Financials

Return on assets: 3.3%
Return on equity: 17.6%
Current ratio: 1.00
Cash ($ mil.): 2

STANFORD HEALTH CARE

Doctors patients medical students and researchers gather at Stanford Health Care (formerly Stanford Hospital and Clinics). As Stanford University's primary medical teaching facility the more than 600-bed Stanford Hospital specializes in such areas as cardiac care cancer treatment neurology surgery and organ transplant. The affiliated Stanford Clinics is a physician group practice organization that represents more than 100 specialized fields of medicine. Stanford Health Care is part of the Stanford Medicine organization which also includes the nearby Stanford University School of Medicine and the 310-bed Lucile Packard Children's Hospital (named for the wife of Hewlett-Packard co-founder David Packard).

Operations

Stanford Health Care handles some 25000 inpatient admissions each year more than 50000 emergency room visits and about 425000 outpatient encounters. The organization boasts such specialized clinics as the Byers Eye Institute the Stanford Comprehensive Cancer Center the Stanford Center for Marfan Syndrome and Aortic Disorders and the California VitreoRetinal Center. It also operates centers for orthopedic brain blood and marrow transplant and other specialist procedures.

Educational programs include medical and graduate student training as well as residency and fellowship programs. The organization also conducts research in medical and biological fields.

Additionally the system owns stakes in physician network University HealthCare Alliance radiation therapy facility Stanford Emanuel Radiation Oncology Center health care advocacy firm CareCounsel and HMO plan University HealthCare Advantage.

Geographic Reach

Stanford Health Care operates in more than 15 locations in the San Francisco Bay Area.

Sales and Marketing

Stanford Health Care receives 70% of its revenues from managed care (commercial insurance) providers. Another 20% of patient service income is sourced to Medicare and Medicaid programs.

Financial Performance

Revenue increased 10% to $3 billion in fiscal 2014 (ended August) due to higher net patient service revenues primarily from managed care and Medicare fee increases. However net income dropped 22% to $432.2 million that year as operating costs rose and the system reported losses on investments.

Cash flow from operations grew 8% to $366.5 million in fiscal 2014 largely due to a change in working capital items.

Strategy

To remain at the forefront of medicine and technology the hospital is constructing a new $2 billion 600-bed facility next to its existing building. Local high-tech firms including Apple Hewlett-Packard and Intel are kicking in $15 million and technology partnerships to support the project. As corporate partners the firms will help to develop and integrate state-of-the-art information technology for the new facility.

Other growth projects include the construction of a new outpatient cancer clinic in San Jose. The center opened in 2014.

Also in 2014 the system changed its name from Stanford Hospitals and Clinics to Stanford Health Care. That change signified the broader scope of its operations which go beyond inpatient and outpatient facilities to include affiliated physician practices and health plans.

In fiscal 2015 Stanford Health Care engineers developed and launched a new MyHealth mobile application for the iPhone. The app connects with Epic electronic health records and Apple's HealthKit enabling patients to monitor their health data. MyHealth provides consumers with such capabilities as telehealth (video) physician visits appointment scheduling online payments and the ability to manage prescriptions and access test results.

EXECUTIVES

President And Ceo, David Entwistle
Vp And Chief Marketing Officer, Deborah Italiano
Chief Risk Officer, Jeff Driver
Vp Clinical Cancer Center And Cardiovascular Health, Sridhar Seshadri
Senior Associate Dean For Adult Clinical Affairs Stanford University School Of Medicine, Norman W. Rizk
Coo, Quinn L. McKenna
Cio, Pravene Nath
Coo, James Hereford
Interim Cfo, David Connor
Chief Quality Officer, Raj Behal
Chief Medical Information Officer, Christopher (Topher) Sharp
Vice President, Doug Olson
Director Of Respiratory Therap, Robert Shields
Western Region Vice President, Todd Walter
Ambulatory Services Dir, Catherine Krna
Vice President Operations, Gaguik Khachatourian
Department Head, Craig Burkhart
Vice President, Jaclyn Tandler
Ambulatory Services Dir, Sue Hoopes
Assistant Secretary, Susan King
Secretary, Anne Chen
Auditors: PRICEWATERHOUSECOOPERS LLP SA

LOCATIONS

HQ: STANFORD HEALTH CARE
300 PASTEUR DR, STANFORD, CA 943052200
Phone: 650 723-4000
Web: WWW.STANFORDHEALTHCARE.ORG

PRODUCTS/OPERATIONS

2014 Sales

	$ mil.	% of total
Net patient service revenue	2,839	95
Premium revenue	60	2
Other revenue	98	3
Total	**2,998**	**100**

Selected Services

Heart Center
Neurosciences
Orthopaedics
Sports Medicine
Stanford Cancer Center
Surgical Services
Transplant

COMPETITORS

Dignity Health
Sequoia Capital
Sutter Health
UCSF Medical

HISTORICAL FINANCIALS

Company Type: Private

Income Statement — FYE: August 31

	REVENUE ($ mil.)	NET INCOME ($ mil.)	NET PROFIT MARGIN	EMPLOYEES
08/20	5,567	104	1.9%	14,100
08/18	4,910	456	9.3%	—
08/17	4,454	450	10.1%	—
08/15	3,570	372	10.4%	—
Annual Growth	9.3%	(22.4%)	—	—

2020 Year-End Financials

Return on assets: 1.1%
Return on equity: 2.4%
Current ratio: 1.60
Cash ($ mil.): 1,642

STANFORD HEALTH SERVICES

Auditors: PRICEWATERHOUSECOOPERS LLP BO

LOCATIONS

HQ: STANFORD HEALTH SERVICES
300 PASTEUR DR, STANFORD, CA 943052200
Phone: 650 723-4000
Web: WWW.STANFORDCHILDRENS.ORG

HISTORICAL FINANCIALS

Company Type: Private

Income Statement — FYE: August 31

	REVENUE ($ mil.)	NET INCOME ($ mil.)	NET PROFIT MARGIN	EMPLOYEES
08/11	2,510	415	16.6%	4
08/10	2,141	186	8.7%	—
Annual Growth	17.2%	123.2%	—	—

2011 Year-End Financials

Return on assets: —
Return on equity: 16.6%
Current ratio: 0.50
Cash ($ mil.): 395

STAPLE COTTON COOPERATIVE ASSOCIATION

Referred to as Staplcotn the Staple Cotton Cooperative has been a staple of its member-producers' business lives since 1921. One of the oldest and largest cotton marketing co-ops in the US it provides domestic and export marketing cotton warehousing and agricultural financing to some 9730 members in 47 states. As of 2011 the co-op handles nearly 14000 farm accounts in 10 states. Staplcotn's inventory is consigned by member-producers and averages from 2.5 million to 3 million bales of cotton a year. The co-op operates though 15 warehouses serving the mid-south and southeastern US to supply more than 25% of the cotton consumed by the US textile industry as well as the needs of textile mills overseas.

EXECUTIVES

Vp Sales Operations, David Camp
Vp Human Resources, Russell Robertson
Vice President Customer Service And Support, Sterling Jones

LOCATIONS

HQ: STAPLE COTTON COOPERATIVE ASSOCIATION
214 W MARKET ST, GREENWOOD, MS 389304329
Phone: 662 453-6231
Web: WWW.STAPLCOTN.COM

PRODUCTS/OPERATIONS

Selected Services
Cotton services
Loans
Mill Sales Program
Marketing
Stapldiscount
Warehouse

COMPETITORS

Alabama Farmers Cooperative
Calcot
Cargill
Dunavant Enterprises
International Cotton Marketing
J.G. Boswell Co.
JB Cotton
King Ranch
Louis Dreyfus Group
Noble Group
Olam
Plains Cotton
Southern States
Tennessee Farmers Co-op
Weil Brothers Cotton

HISTORICAL FINANCIALS

Company Type: Private

Income Statement — FYE: August 31

	REVENUE ($ mil.)	NET INCOME ($ mil.)	NET PROFIT MARGIN	EMPLOYEES
08/13	1,138	5	0.5%	312
08/12	1,236	8	0.7%	—
08/11	963	875	90.8%	—
Annual Growth	8.7%	(91.7%)	—	—

2013 Year-End Financials

Return on assets: 2.5%
Return on equity: 5.3%
Current ratio: 1.80
Cash ($ mil.): 33

STATE OF ALABAMA

EXECUTIVES

Governor, Kay Ivey
Comptroller*, Kathleen D Baxter
Atty Gen, Troy King
Cmptlr, Robert Childree
Director and State Law Librari, Timothy Lewis
Associate Justice, Tom Parker
Chief of Staff, Jo Bonner
Program Manager, Donna Jordan
Donor Relations Coordinator, Cherie H Smith
Information Technology Operati, Janice Majors
Web Resources Librarian, Myra Sabel
Auditors: RONALD L JONES MONTGOMERY A

LOCATIONS

HQ: STATE OF ALABAMA
300 DEXTER AVE, MONTGOMERY, AL 361043741
Phone: 334 242-7100
Web: WWW.ALABAMA.GOV

HISTORICAL FINANCIALS

Company Type: Private

Income Statement — FYE: September 30

	REVENUE ($ mil.)	NET INCOME ($ mil.)	NET PROFIT MARGIN	EMPLOYEES
09/19	23,698	677	2.9%	37,659
09/18	22,258	(34)	—	—
09/17	21,740	1,393	6.4%	—
09/16	21,126	349	1.7%	—
Annual Growth	3.9%	24.6%	—	—

2019 Year-End Financials

Return on assets: 1.1%
Return on equity: 2.2%
Current ratio: —
Cash ($ mil.): 6,719

STATE OF ALASKA

EXECUTIVES

Governor, Michael Dunleavy
Lt. Governor, Kevin Meyer
Accounting Staff, Nove Barril
Coordinator, Sara Chambers
Accounting Staff, Christine Spence
Accounting Staff, Amy Johnson
Accounting Staff, Caroline Byford
Coordinator, Heidi Hedberg
Coordinator, Katie Reilly
Employee, Dinah Aquino
Senior Adviser On Fish and Gam, Ephraim Froehlich
Auditors: KRIS CURTIS CPA CISA JUNEAU

LOCATIONS

HQ: STATE OF ALASKA
120 4TH ST, JUNEAU, AK 998011162
Phone: 907 465-3500
Web: WWW.ALASKA.GOV

HISTORICAL FINANCIALS

Company Type: Private

Income Statement — FYE: June 30

	REVENUE ($ mil.)	NET INCOME ($ mil.)	NET PROFIT MARGIN	EMPLOYEES
06/19	12,421	2,275	18.3%	4,300
06/18	12,318	2,779	22.6%	—
06/17	12,693	3,224	25.4%	—
Annual Growth	(1.1%)	(16.0%)	—	—

STATE OF ARIZONA

EXECUTIVES

Governor, Doug Ducey
Attor Gen*, Terry Goddard
Treas*, David Petersen
Acctng Mgr, Jean Bell
Sergeant, Joe Kubacki
Chief Information Security Off, Mike Lettman
U.S. District Court Judge, Susan Brnovich
Member, Nancy Barto
Member, Frank Pratt
Manager, Ted Hale
Information Technology Infrast, Allan Gazza
Auditors: LINDSEY PERRY CPA CFE PHOENI

LOCATIONS

HQ: STATE OF ARIZONA
1700 W WASHINGTON ST FL 7, PHOENIX, AZ 850072808
Phone: 602 542-4331
Web: WWW.AZ.GOV

HISTORICAL FINANCIALS

Company Type: Private

Income Statement — FYE: June 30

	REVENUE ($ mil.)	NET INCOME ($ mil.)	NET PROFIT MARGIN	EMPLOYEES
06/19	34,554	1,496	4.3%	34,161
06/18	32,354	539	1.7%	—
06/17	31,295	385	1.2%	—
06/16	871	4	0.6%	—
Annual Growth	241.0%	570.6%	—	—

2019 Year-End Financials

Return on assets: 2.7%
Return on equity: 4.8%
Current ratio: 1.70
Cash ($ mil.): 6,980

STATE OF ARKANSAS

EXECUTIVES

Governor, Asa Hutchinson
Lt Gov*, Tim Griffin
Chief of Staff*, Morril Harriman
Acting Manager, Tom Smith
State Chief Security Officer, Franklin Andrews
Coordinator, Carla Jordan
Information Specialist, Justin Villines
Information Specialist, Ken Giesbrecht
Coordinator, Randall Anderson
Coordinator, Randie Jones
Dhhs Division of Administrativ, Gail Boykins
Auditors: ROGER A NORMAN JD CPA CFE

LOCATIONS

HQ: STATE OF ARKANSAS
4 CAPITOL MALL RM 403A, LITTLE ROCK, AR 722011013
Phone: 501 682-2345
Web: WWW.ARKANSAS.GOV

HISTORICAL FINANCIALS

Company Type: Private

Income Statement — FYE: June 30

	REVENUE ($ mil.)	NET INCOME ($ mil.)	NET PROFIT MARGIN	EMPLOYEES
06/19	13,821	997	7.2%	28,272
06/18	17,966	40	0.2%	—
06/17	17,915	(91)	—	—
06/16	17,333	161	0.9%	—
Annual Growth	(7.3%)	83.5%	—	—

2019 Year-End Financials

Return on assets: 3.3%
Return on equity: 5.8%
Current ratio: 4.20
Cash ($ mil.): 5,050

STATE OF CALIFORNIA

EXECUTIVES

Governor, Gavin Newsom
Lt. Governor*, Eleni Kounalakis
Consultant, A Kirk McKenzie
Chief Licensing/Information Te, Brian Desmarais
Chief Information Security Off, Carol Kelly
Budgets and Fiscal STA, Caroline McNeil
Computer Support Staff Represe, Cheryl Drefs
Budgets and Fiscal STA, Diane Herteg
Chief Technology Support Servi, Jim Rengstorff
AG Technician II, Jose Antonio Diaz
Analyst, Karen Bianchi Walsh
Auditors: MICHAEL S TILDEN CPA SACRAM

LOCATIONS

HQ: STATE OF CALIFORNIA
STATE CAPITAL, SACRAMENTO, CA 95814
Phone: 916 445-2864
Web: WWW.CA.GOV

HISTORICAL FINANCIALS

Company Type: Private

Income Statement — FYE: June 30

	REVENUE ($ mil.)	NET INCOME ($ mil.)	NET PROFIT MARGIN	EMPLOYEES
06/16	255,725	4,798	1.9%	208,580
06/15	249,923	6,252	2.5%	—
06/14	219,871	8,082	3.7%	—
06/13	204	8	3.9%	—
Annual Growth	976.7%	742.3%	—	—

STATE OF COLORADO

EXECUTIVES

Governor, Jared Polis
Lt Gov*, Dianne Primavera
Treasurer*, Dave Young
Sergeant, Ron Watkins
Information Technology Special, Martin Pullam
Acting Communications Director, Holly Shrewsbury
Staff, Jessika Shipley
Director, John Penn
Press Secretary, Jacque Montgomery
Vice-President Research and Te, Gert Thygesen
Staff, Ron Kirk
Auditors: DIANNE E RAY CPA DENVER CO

LOCATIONS

HQ: STATE OF COLORADO
200 E COLFAX AVE STE 91, DENVER, CO 802031716
Phone: 303 866-5000
Web: WWW.COLORADO.GOV

HISTORICAL FINANCIALS

Company Type: Private

Income Statement — FYE: June 30

	REVENUE ($ mil.)	NET INCOME ($ mil.)	NET PROFIT MARGIN	EMPLOYEES
06/17	22,949	(240)	—	81,349
06/16	23,139	(295)	—	—
06/13	18,658	788	4.2%	—
06/12	17,586	472	2.7%	—
Annual Growth	5.5%	—	—	—

2017 Year-End Financials

Return on assets: (-0.5%)
Return on equity: (-1.4%)
Current ratio: 2.20
Cash ($ mil.): 5,708

STATE OF DELAWARE

EXECUTIVES

Governor, John Carney
Lt Gov, Bethany Hall-Long
Prin, Beau Biden
Treas, Chip Flowers
Prin, Thomas Wagner Jr
Comm, Karen Weldin Stewart
Information Specialist, Tim LI
Information Technology Custome, John Trabaudo
Information Technology Custome, Dorothy Kope
Adjutant General, Michael Berry
Team Leader, Colleen Gause
Auditors: KPMG LLP PHILADELPHIA PENNSY

LOCATIONS

HQ: STATE OF DELAWARE
860 SILVER LAKE BLVD # 1, DOVER, DE 199042402
Phone: 302 744-4101
Web: WWW.DELAWARE.GOV

HISTORICAL FINANCIALS

Company Type: Private

Income Statement — FYE: June 30

	REVENUE ($ mil.)	NET INCOME ($ mil.)	NET PROFIT MARGIN	EMPLOYEES
06/19	8,124	371	4.6%	25
06/17	7,368	(351)	—	—
06/16	7,106	(347)	—	—
06/15	6,955	62	0.9%	—
Annual Growth	4.0%	55.9%	—	—

2019 Year-End Financials

Return on assets: 2.3%
Return on equity: —
Current ratio: —
Cash ($ mil.): 333

STATE OF GEORGIA

EXECUTIVES

Governor, Brian Kemp
Lt Governor*, Geoff Duncan
Treas*, Lynnette Riley
Microbiologist, Amanda Balish
Director, Andrew Dent
Microbiologist, Anne Whitney
Officer, Catherine McLean
Supreme Court Judge, Charlie Bethel
Information Technology Special, Cheri Gatland-Lightne
Court of Appeals Judge, Christian A Coomer
Public Affairs Specialist, Courtney Lenard
Auditors: GREG S GRIFFIN STATE AUDITOR

LOCATIONS

HQ: STATE OF GEORGIA
206 WSHNGTON ST 111 STATE, ATLANTA, GA 30334
Phone: 404 656-1776
Web: WWW.GEORGIA.GOV

HISTORICAL FINANCIALS

Company Type: Private

Income Statement — FYE: June 30

	REVENUE ($ mil.)	NET INCOME ($ mil.)	NET PROFIT MARGIN	EMPLOYEES
06/19	45,109	1,235	2.7%	67,139
06/17	42,410	1,167	2.8%	—
06/16	40,422	1,513	3.7%	—
06/15	38,901	512	1.3%	—
Annual Growth	3.8%	24.6%	—	—

2019 Year-End Financials

Return on assets: 1.5%
Return on equity: 3.4%
Current ratio: —
Cash ($ mil.): 6,236

STATE OF HAWAII

EXECUTIVES

Gov, David Ige
Lt. Gov*, Josh Green
Chief Information Security Off*, Vincent Hoang
Director of Operations, Jing Xu
Supervisor, Kristine Shimogawa
Director, Hawaii Officer of Pl, Mary Alice Evans
Hawaii Attorney General, Russell Suzuki
Deputy Admin Director, Walter Ozawa
Director, Zheng Fang
Information Specialist, Andrew Jackson
Executive Officer, Charlene Tamanaha
Auditors: ACCUITY LLP HONOLULU HAWAII

LOCATIONS

HQ: STATE OF HAWAII
201 MERCHANT ST STE 1805, HONOLULU, HI 968132963
Phone: 808 695-4620
Web: WWW.PORTAL.EHAWAII.GOV

HISTORICAL FINANCIALS

Company Type: Private

Income Statement — FYE: June 30

	REVENUE ($ mil.)	NET INCOME ($ mil.)	NET PROFIT MARGIN	EMPLOYEES
06/19	11,744	57	0.5%	44,201
06/18	11,316	(39)	—	—
06/17	10,516	435	4.1%	—
06/16	10,309	574	5.6%	—
Annual Growth	4.4%	(53.5%)	—	—

2019 Year-End Financials

Return on assets: 0.2%
Return on equity: —
Current ratio: —
Cash ($ mil.): 3,062

STATE OF IDAHO

EXECUTIVES

Governor, Brad Little
Lt Governor*, Janice McGeachin
Cmsnr*, Tom Katsilometes
Cmsnr*, Rich Jackson
Cmsnr*, Elliot Werk

Information Specialist, Cory Woodbury
Admin Idaho Div Veterans Serv, Marv Hagedorn
Project Coordinator, Elizabeth Ultis
Executive Director, Laura Wilder
Supervisor, Lisa Tordjman
Senior Project Manager, Margie Kennedy
Auditors: APRIL RENFRO CPA MANAGER BO

LOCATIONS

HQ: STATE OF IDAHO
700 W JEFFERSON ST, BOISE, ID 837200001
Phone: 208 334-2100
Web: WWW.IDAHO.GOV

HISTORICAL FINANCIALS

Company Type: Private

Income Statement — FYE: June 30

	REVENUE ($ mil.)	NET INCOME ($ mil.)	NET PROFIT MARGIN	EMPLOYEES
06/19	8,615	157	1.8%	429
06/18	8,403	542	6.5%	—
06/17	7,788	473	6.1%	—
06/15	7,219	426	5.9%	—
Annual Growth	4.5%	(22.0%)	—	—

2019 Year-End Financials

Return on assets: 0.8%
Return on equity: 1.0%
Current ratio: —
Cash ($ mil.): 826

STATE OF ILLINOIS

EXECUTIVES

Governor, J B Pritzker
Lt Gov, Julianna Stratton
SEC of State, Jesse White
Treasurer, Michael Frerichs
Deputy Governor, Sol Flores
General Counsel, Roma Larson
Director, Pamela Simon
Deputy Director, Ryan Prehn
Quality Assurance Director, Scott Hughes
Executive Director, Scott McFarland
Accounting Manager, Tracy McGee
Auditors: WILLIAM G HOLLAND

LOCATIONS

HQ: STATE OF ILLINOIS
207 STATE HOUSE, SPRINGFIELD, IL 627060001
Phone: 217 782-6830

HISTORICAL FINANCIALS

Company Type: Private

Income Statement — FYE: June 30

	REVENUE ($ mil.)	NET INCOME ($ mil.)	NET PROFIT MARGIN	EMPLOYEES
06/13	62,451	1,596	2.6%	59,659
06/12	58,747	(522)	—	—
06/11	55,157	869	1.6%	—
Annual Growth	6.4%	35.5%	—	—

2013 Year-End Financials

Return on assets: 2.1%
Return on equity: —
Current ratio: —
Cash ($ mil.): 11,764

STATE OF INDIANA

EXECUTIVES

Lt Gov*, Suzanne Crouch
Director of Finance, Carl Zapfe
Public Relations Executive, Carlos Pettiford
Commissioner, Christine Klika
Manager-Geo-Spatial Is, Chuck Carufel
Mis, Ron Bolander
Marketing Director, Stephanie Genrich
SEC, Stephene Reeve
Superintendent, Suellen Reed
Data, Anthony Barker
Auditors: PAUL D JOYCE CPA INDIANAPOL

LOCATIONS

HQ: STATE OF INDIANA
200 W WA ST STE 201, INDIANAPOLIS, IN 462042731
Phone: 317 232-4567
Web: WWW.STATE.IN.US

HISTORICAL FINANCIALS

Company Type: Private

Income Statement — FYE: June 30

	REVENUE ($ mil.)	NET INCOME ($ mil.)	NET PROFIT MARGIN	EMPLOYEES
06/19	36,469	986	2.7%	33,000
06/18	33,877	408	1.2%	—
06/17	32,576	(78)	—	—
Annual Growth	5.8%	—	—	—

STATE OF IOWA

EXECUTIVES

Governor, Kim Reynolds
Lt Governor, Adam Gregg
Consultants, Jillian Dotson
Indexing Supervisor, Kristin Wentz
Performance Investigation Divi, Annette Campbell
Deputy Medicaid Director, Julie Lovelady
Assistant Aud 6, Michelle Meyer
Teacher Visually Impair, Michelle Tauke
Phys Supervisor Human, Mohammad Rehman
Ddm Contractor, Balaji Punukula
Administrative Law Judge, Jeanene Elder
Auditors: MARY MOSIMAN CPA DES MOINES

LOCATIONS

HQ: STATE OF IOWA
1007 E GRAND AVE RM 105, DES MOINES, IA 503199003
Phone: 515 281-5211
Web: WWW.IOWA.GOV

HISTORICAL FINANCIALS

Company Type: Private

Income Statement — FYE: June 30

	REVENUE ($ mil.)	NET INCOME ($ mil.)	NET PROFIT MARGIN	EMPLOYEES
06/19	18,006	471	2.6%	24,304
06/18	17,093	(79)	—	—
06/17	16,806	(130)	—	—
06/16	16,563	(297)	—	—
Annual Growth	2.8%	—	—	—

STATE OF KANSAS

EXECUTIVES

Governor, Laura Kelly
Treasurer*, Jake Laturner
Chief Information Technology O*, Lee Allen
City Clark, Adam Moore
Staff, Marc Galbraith
Staff, Stan Frownfelter
Communications Director, Kara Zeyer
Member, Elaine Bowers
Director of Program Finance, Adam Proffitt
Accountant, Becky Bahr
Program Director, Bryna Stacey
Auditors: CLIFFTONLARSONALLEN LLP BROOM

LOCATIONS

HQ: STATE OF KANSAS
534 S KANSAS AVE STE 1210, TOPEKA, KS 666033434
Phone: 785 354-1388
Web: WWW.KANSAS.GOV

HISTORICAL FINANCIALS

Company Type: Private

Income Statement — FYE: June 30

	REVENUE ($ mil.)	NET INCOME ($ mil.)	NET PROFIT MARGIN	EMPLOYEES
06/19	14,988	794	5.3%	22,375
06/18	14,322	895	6.3%	—
06/17	12,935	(187)	—	—
06/16	12,563	(240)	—	—
Annual Growth	6.1%	—	—	—

2019 Year-End Financials

Return on assets: 2.6%
Return on equity: 4.3%
Current ratio: —
Cash ($ mil.): 3,200

STATE OF LOUISIANA

EXECUTIVES

Governor, Bobby Jindal
Lt Gov, Jay Dardenne
Director, Margaret Gehdauer
Treasurer, John Schroder
Compensation Division Administ, Brandy Malatesta
Finance, Marella Houghton
Sphr Human Resources Director, Sophia Pipsair
Vice President Management, Joseph Livingston
Information Technology Technic, Mike Cavell
Senior, Alden Clement
Specialist, Brooke Guidry
Auditors: DARYL G PURPERA CPA CFE BA

LOCATIONS

HQ: STATE OF LOUISIANA
900 N 3RD ST FL 4, BATON ROUGE, LA 708025236
Phone: 225 342-0991
Web: WWW.LOUISIANA.GOV

HISTORICAL FINANCIALS
Company Type: Private

Income Statement — FYE: June 30

	REVENUE ($ mil.)	NET INCOME ($ mil.)	NET PROFIT MARGIN	EMPLOYEES
06/19	30,034	1,386	4.6%	47,937
06/18	28,849	829	2.9%	—
Annual Growth	4.1%	67.2%	—	—

2019 Year-End Financials

Return on assets: 2.5%
Return on equity: 10.8%
Current ratio: —
Cash ($ mil.): 7,170

STATE OF MAINE

EXECUTIVES

Governor, Janet Mills
Senior Health Policy Adviser, Nick Adolphsen
Senior Policy Adviser, Sean Ingram
Legislative Policy Coordinator, Andrew Bracy
Information Specialist, Dale Irish
Sergeant, Jonathan Shapiro
Accounting Staff, Laura Larrabee
Procurement Staff, Marie Malloy
Sergeant, Mark Tibbetts
Coordinator, Michael Laberge
Coordinator, Michael Mayo
Auditors: POLA A BUCKLEY CPA CISA/MAR

LOCATIONS

HQ: STATE OF MAINE
1 STATE HOUSE STA, AUGUSTA, ME 043330001
Phone: 207 287-3531
Web: WWW.MAINE.GOV

HISTORICAL FINANCIALS
Company Type: Private

Income Statement — FYE: June 30

	REVENUE ($ mil.)	NET INCOME ($ mil.)	NET PROFIT MARGIN	EMPLOYEES
06/19	8,155	357	4.4%	12,000
06/18	7,798	110	1.4%	—
06/17	7,623	146	1.9%	—
06/16	7,389	179	2.4%	—
Annual Growth	3.3%	25.9%	—	—

2019 Year-End Financials

Return on assets: 2.1%
Return on equity: 8.4%
Current ratio: 2.60
Cash ($ mil.): 1,407

STATE OF MICHIGAN

EXECUTIVES

Governor, Gretchen Whitmer
Lt Governor*, Garlin Gilchrist
SEC*, Joseph Gordon
Chief Deputy Treasurer*, Jeff Guilfoyle
Member Advisor, Alyssa Vanhyfte
Accounting Staff, Anita Westry
Senior Management Analyst, Bill Bartels
Trade Developmen, Chris Bosio
Business Capital Relationship, Chris Cook
Scientist, Clarence Jones
Director, Eric Dean
Auditors: DOUG A RINGLER CPA CIA LAN

LOCATIONS

HQ: STATE OF MICHIGAN
111 S CAPITOL AVE, LANSING, MI 489331555
Phone: 517 373-7910
Web: WWW.MICHIGAN.GOV

HISTORICAL FINANCIALS
Company Type: Private

Income Statement — FYE: September 30

	REVENUE ($ mil.)	NET INCOME ($ mil.)	NET PROFIT MARGIN	EMPLOYEES
09/18	54,684	832	1.5%	55,416
09/17	52,459	702	1.3%	—
09/16	52,181	168	0.3%	—
Annual Growth	2.4%	122.5%	—	—

2018 Year-End Financials

Return on assets: 1.1%
Return on equity: 3.5%
Current ratio: 2.70
Cash ($ mil.): 11,188

STATE OF MINNESOTA

EXECUTIVES

Governor, Tim Walz
Lt Governor, Peggy Flanagan
ATT Gen, Mike Hatch
St Treas, Carol C Johnson
SEC of State, Mary Kiffmeyer
Security Staff, William Fowler
Coordinator, Evie Wold
Minnesota Adjutant General, Jon A Jensen
Supreme Court Judge, Paul Thissen
Court of Appeals Judge, Randall J Slieter
Court of Appeals Judge For Six, Jeanne M Cochran
Auditors: JAMES R NOBLES/CECILE M FERK

LOCATIONS

HQ: STATE OF MINNESOTA
116 VETERAN SERVICE BLD, SAINT PAUL, MN 551550001
Phone: 218 828-2400
Web: WWW.STATE.MN.US

HISTORICAL FINANCIALS
Company Type: Private

Income Statement — FYE: June 30

	REVENUE ($ mil.)	NET INCOME ($ mil.)	NET PROFIT MARGIN	EMPLOYEES
06/19	41,741	1,040	2.5%	35,217
06/17	37,751	793	2.1%	—
06/16	36,717	479	1.3%	—
06/15	35,721	812	2.3%	—
Annual Growth	4.0%	6.4%	—	—

2019 Year-End Financials

Return on assets: 1.4%
Return on equity: 3.0%
Current ratio: 2.90
Cash ($ mil.): 16,977

STATE OF MISSISSIPPI

EXECUTIVES

Governor, Phil Bryant
Lieutenant Governor*, Tate Reeves
Executive Director*, Kevin J Upchurch
Executive Assistant, Dorthy Kuykendall
Administrator, Dana Kidd
Scientist, Kerwin Cuevas
Procurement Staff, Vicki Brown
Special Projects Officer IV, Kenneth Judie
Staff, Susanne Merchant
U.S. Marshal, Southern Distric, Mark B Shepherd
Communications Director, Kathy Waterbury
Auditors: STEPHANIE C PALMERTREE CPA

LOCATIONS

HQ: STATE OF MISSISSIPPI
501 NW ST STE 1301 WLFOL, JACKSON, MS 39201
Phone: 601 359-3100
Web: WWW.MISSISSIPPI.GOV

HISTORICAL FINANCIALS
Company Type: Private

Income Statement — FYE: June 30

	REVENUE ($ mil.)	NET INCOME ($ mil.)	NET PROFIT MARGIN	EMPLOYEES
06/19	16,887	773	4.6%	27,775
06/18	16,518	(9)	—	—
06/17	16,436	156	0.9%	—
06/16	16,438	158	1.0%	—
Annual Growth	0.9%	69.8%	—	—

2019 Year-End Financials

Return on assets: 2.2%
Return on equity: 4.2%
Current ratio: 3.00
Cash ($ mil.): 1,725

STATE OF MISSOURI

EXECUTIVES

Governor, Mike Parson
Lt Gov, Mike Kehoe
Comm, Doug Nelson
Security Staff, Scotty Allen
Scientist, Alica Alexander
Coordinator, Karen Cassmeyer
Scientist, Tracey Mason
Server Administrator, Billy Sarver
Actuary, David Cox
Director, Dean Linneman
Alcohol and Tobacco Enforcemen, Keith Hendrickson
Auditors: THOMAS A SCHWEICH JEFFERSON

LOCATIONS

HQ: STATE OF MISSOURI
301 W HIGH ST RM 570, JEFFERSON CITY, MO 651011517
Phone: 573 751-4013
Web: WWW.MO.GOV

HISTORICAL FINANCIALS

Company Type: Private

Income Statement FYE: June 30

	REVENUE ($ mil.)	NET INCOME ($ mil.)	NET PROFIT MARGIN	EMPLOYEES
06/19	25,748	309	1.2%	51,488
06/18	25,326	110	0.4%	—
06/17	24,769	(153)	—	—
06/16	24,115	267	1.1%	—
Annual Growth	2.2%	5.0%	—	—

2019 Year-End Financials

Return on assets: 0.5%
Return on equity: 0.9%
Current ratio: —
Cash ($ mil.): 3,174

STATE OF MONTANA

EXECUTIVES

Prin, Steve Bullock
Information Specialist, Amy Moore
Coordinator, Donna Coffman
Staff, Matt Chambers
Compliance Staff, Mitch Leslie
Coordinator, Steve Becker
Coordinator, Sullivan Dan
Analyst, Bob Decker
Manager, Angela Smith
Petroleum Brownfields Coordina, Betsy Hovda
Claims Manager, Brad Cozzie
Auditors: CINDY JORGENSON CPA HELENA

LOCATIONS

HQ: STATE OF MONTANA
1301 E 6TH AVE FL 2, HELENA, MT 596013875
Phone: 406 444-3111
Web: WWW.MT.GOV

HISTORICAL FINANCIALS

Company Type: Private

Income Statement FYE: June 30

	REVENUE ($ mil.)	NET INCOME ($ mil.)	NET PROFIT MARGIN	EMPLOYEES
06/19	6,740	509	7.6%	418
06/18	6,228	95	1.5%	—
06/17	5,921	(195)	—	—
06/16	5,558	(89)	—	—
Annual Growth	6.6%	—	—	—

2019 Year-End Financials

Return on assets: 2.8%
Return on equity: 4.3%
Current ratio: —
Cash ($ mil.): 2,578

STATE OF NEBRASKA

EXECUTIVES

Governor, Pete Ricketts
Lt. Gov*, Mike Foley
Staff, Traci Cooney
Acting Superintendent, Russ Stanczyk
Coordinator, John Rockenbach
Fire Marshal, Christopher Cantrell
Information Technology Infrast, Garry Kapperman
Operations Consultant, Jesse Cushman
Legal Counsel, Ron Theis
Law Enforcement Officer, Scott Eveland
Government Official, Steve Burns
Auditors: PHILIP J OLSEN CPA CISA LI

LOCATIONS

HQ: STATE OF NEBRASKA
521 S 14TH ST STE 400, LINCOLN, NE 685082707
Phone: 402 471-2311
Web: WWW.NEBRASKA.GOV

HISTORICAL FINANCIALS

Company Type: Private

Income Statement FYE: June 30

	REVENUE ($ mil.)	NET INCOME ($ mil.)	NET PROFIT MARGIN	EMPLOYEES
06/19	9,322	401	4.3%	18,653
06/18	8,643	(108)	—	—
06/17	8,449	(266)	—	—
Annual Growth	5.0%	—	—	—

2019 Year-End Financials

Return on assets: 1.6%
Return on equity: 1.9%
Current ratio: —
Cash ($ mil.): 1,657

STATE OF NEVADA

EXECUTIVES

Governor, Steve Sisolak
Lt. Governor, Kate Marshall
Attorney General, Catherine Cortez Masto
Chief of Staff, Gerald Gardner
State Contrl, Kim Wallin
SEC of State, Ross Miller
Dir, Jim Groth
General Counsel, Kathryn Reynolds
Chief Information Security Off, Brian Wilcox
Communications Director, Mari St Martin
Chief Manager, Robert Dehnhardt
Auditors: EIDE BAILLY LLP RENO NEVADA

LOCATIONS

HQ: STATE OF NEVADA
101 N CARSON ST STE 1, CARSON CITY, NV 897017011
Phone: 775 684-5670
Web: WWW.NV.GOV

HISTORICAL FINANCIALS

Company Type: Private

Income Statement FYE: June 30

	REVENUE ($ mil.)	NET INCOME ($ mil.)	NET PROFIT MARGIN	EMPLOYEES
06/16	10,436	301	2.9%	14,790
06/15	9,446	(144)	—	—
06/14	8,131	161	2.0%	—
06/13	7,965	171	2.2%	—
Annual Growth	9.4%	20.6%	—	—

STATE OF NEW HAMPSHIRE

EXECUTIVES

Governor, Chris Sununu
Commissioner, Beth Edes
Park Manager IV, Andrew Zboray
Payroll Officer I, Angela Theberge
Secretary II, Anita Terrio
Facility Supervisor, Anne Bailey
Secretary II, Annie M Laurendeau
Payroll Officer I, Bonita M Huckins
Registered Nurse I, Brian Mortimer
Sergeant, Casey Shingleton
Senior Audit Manager, Christine L Young
Auditors: KPMG LLP BOSTON MA

LOCATIONS

HQ: STATE OF NEW HAMPSHIRE
107 N MAIN ST, CONCORD, NH 033014951
Phone: 603 271-1110
Web: WWW.STATE.NH.US

HISTORICAL FINANCIALS

Company Type: Private

Income Statement FYE: June 30

	REVENUE ($ mil.)	NET INCOME ($ mil.)	NET PROFIT MARGIN	EMPLOYEES
06/19	5,955	110	1.9%	12,280
06/18	5,874	145	2.5%	—
06/17	5,585	8	0.1%	—
06/16	5,562	322	5.8%	—
Annual Growth	2.3%	(30.0%)	—	—

2019 Year-End Financials

Return on assets: 1.0%
Return on equity: 3.2%
Current ratio: 2.50
Cash ($ mil.): 867

STATE OF NEW MEXICO

EXECUTIVES

Governor, Michelle Lujan Grisham
Lt. Governor*, Howie Morales
Dep Chief of Staff*, Scott Darnell
Auditor*, Wayne Johnson
Coordinator, Laura Dalemarre
Court of Appeals Judge, Zachary A Ives
Chief of Police, Tim Johnson
Deputy Chief, Robert O Thornton III
Deputy Chief, Nick Aragon
Deputy Chief, Carolyn N Huynh
Member, Deborah A Armstrong
Auditors: CLIFTONLARSONALLEN LLP ALBUQU

LOCATIONS

HQ: STATE OF NEW MEXICO
237 DON GASPAR AVE, SANTA FE, NM 875012178
Phone: 505 827-3000
Web: WWW.NEWMEXICO.GOV

HISTORICAL FINANCIALS

Company Type: Private

Income Statement				FYE: June 30
	REVENUE ($ mil.)	NET INCOME ($ mil.)	NET PROFIT MARGIN	EMPLOYEES
06/19	18,370	3,033	16.5%	22,217
06/18	17,364	2,968	17.1%	—
06/17	32	1	3.6%	—
06/16	14,929	(828)	—	—
Annual Growth	7.2%	—	—	—

2019 Year-End Financials

Return on assets: 5.8%
Return on equity: 9.3%
Current ratio: 3.10
Cash ($ mil.): 2,670

STATE OF NEW YORK MORTGAGE AGENCY

The State of New York Mortgage Agency (SONYMA pronounced "Sony Mae") is a public benefit corporation of the State of New York that makes homebuying more affordable for low- and moderate-income residents of the state. SONYMA has two program divisions: Its single-family programs and financing division provides low-interest rate mortgages to first-time homebuyers with low and moderate incomes through the issuance of mortgage revenue bonds while its mortgage insurance fund provides mortgage insurance and credit support for multi-family affordable residential projects and special care facilities throughout the state.

EXECUTIVES

Vice President, Daniel Murphy
Assistant Vice President, Robert Rosado
Vice President Special Projects, Mark Flescher
Assistant Vice President Senior Underwriter, Maria Lasorsa
Vice President Internal Audit, Stephen Chopey
Senior Vice President, Michael Friedman
Assistant Vice President, Olivia Jervis
Auditors: ERNST & YOUNG LLP NEW YORK N

LOCATIONS

HQ: STATE OF NEW YORK MORTGAGE AGENCY
641 LEXINGTON AVE FL 4, NEW YORK, NY 100224503
Phone: 212 688-4000
Web: WWW.HCR.NY.GOV

HISTORICAL FINANCIALS

Company Type: Private

Income Statement				FYE: October 31
	ASSETS ($ mil.)	NET INCOME ($ mil.)	INCOME AS % OF ASSETS	EMPLOYEES
10/19	5,936	392	6.6%	221
10/18	5,324	147	2.8%	—
10/17	5,228	34	0.7%	—
10/16	5,187	63	1.2%	—
Annual Growth	4.6%	83.2%	—	—

2019 Year-End Financials

Return on assets: 6.6%
Return on equity: 13.2%
Sales ($ mil): 221

STATE OF NORTH CAROLINA

EXECUTIVES

Governor, Roy Cooper
Lt Gov*, Dan Forest
Chief of Staff*, Thomas Stith
Controller*, Linda M Combs
District Court Judge, Judicial, Annette Turik
Staff, Barry Anderson
Staff, Beth P Mills
Staff, Betty M Jones
Coordinator, Bill Davis
Dep Adv-Jobs & Economy, Blannie Cheng
Cdsa Manager, Brian Deese
Auditors: BETH A WOOD CPA RALEIGH NO

LOCATIONS

HQ: STATE OF NORTH CAROLINA
20301 MAIL SERVICE CTR, RALEIGH, NC 276990300
Phone: 919 715-1411
Web: WWW.NC.GOV

HISTORICAL FINANCIALS

Company Type: Private

Income Statement				FYE: June 30
	REVENUE ($ mil.)	NET INCOME ($ mil.)	NET PROFIT MARGIN	EMPLOYEES
06/19	48,977	836	1.7%	69,869
06/18	46,551	208	0.4%	—
06/17	45,371	1,172	2.6%	—
06/16	44,395	1,501	3.4%	—
Annual Growth	3.3%	(17.7%)	—	—

2019 Year-End Financials

Return on assets: 0.7%
Return on equity: 1.2%
Current ratio: —
Cash ($ mil.): 16,804

STATE OF NORTH DAKOTA

EXECUTIVES

Governor, Doug Burgum
Lt Gov*, Brent Sanford
Auditor*, Bob Peterson
Coo*, Jodi Uecker
Cao*, Jodee Hanson
Chief People Officer*, Kelsey Roth
Information Technology/Interne, Jason Bryhn
Dept of Agriculture Livestoc, Becky Gietzen
Dept of Agriculture Exec Srv, Bonnie Sunby
Instructional Special, Cheryl Thompson
Dept of Agriculture Plant In, Elaine Sayley
Auditors: JOSHUA C GALLION BISMARCK N

LOCATIONS

HQ: STATE OF NORTH DAKOTA
600 E BOULEVARD AVE # 101, BISMARCK, ND 585050601
Phone: 701 328-4905
Web: WWW.ND.GOV

HISTORICAL FINANCIALS

Company Type: Private

Income Statement				FYE: June 30
	REVENUE ($ mil.)	NET INCOME ($ mil.)	NET PROFIT MARGIN	EMPLOYEES
06/19	7,860	1,955	24.9%	8,800
06/17	6,408	172	2.7%	—
06/16	5,667	(1,080)	—	—
06/15	7,902	1,203	15.2%	—
Annual Growth	(0.1%)	12.9%	—	—

2019 Year-End Financials

Return on assets: 5.8%
Return on equity: 7.7%
Current ratio: —
Cash ($ mil.): 1,010

STATE OF OHIO

EXECUTIVES

Governor, Mike Dewine
Lt Govnr*, Jon Husted
Chief of Staff, AVI Zaffini
Communications Director, Joshua Eck
Dpty Communications Director, Eve Mueller
Press Secretary, Dan Tierney
Minority Affairs Liaison, Ronald C Todd
Chief of Staff, Laurel Dawson
Director, Washington DC Office, Nikki Guilford
Vice Chair, Chris Widener
Manager, Angela Albrecht
Auditors: KEITH FABER COLUMBUS OHIO

LOCATIONS

HQ: STATE OF OHIO
30 E BROAD ST FL 40, COLUMBUS, OH 432153414
Phone: 614 466-3455
Web: WWW.OHIO.GOV

HISTORICAL FINANCIALS

Company Type: Private

Income Statement				FYE: June 30
	REVENUE ($ mil.)	NET INCOME ($ mil.)	NET PROFIT MARGIN	EMPLOYEES
06/19	60,384	1,717	2.8%	57,631
06/17	56,959	(267)	—	—
Annual Growth	3.0%	—	—	—

2019 Year-End Financials

Return on assets: 1.3%
Return on equity: 4.2%
Current ratio: —
Cash ($ mil.): 14,916

STATE OF OKLAHOMA

EXECUTIVES

Governor, Kevin Stitt
Lt Gov*, Matt Pinnell
General Counsel-Sec*, James Williamson
Sec, Science and Innovation, Kayse Shrum
Sec, Health and Mental Health, Jerome Loughridge
Contracting Andamp, Kathy Hallum
Coordinator Mark, Barbara Charlet
Senior Screening Consultant, Dane Libart

Editor, Donna Bruce
DOT Public Works Director, Ernestine Mbroh
Board of Trustees Member, James Hixon
Auditors: GARY A JONES CPA CFE OKLAH

LOCATIONS

HQ: STATE OF OKLAHOMA
421 NW 13TH ST STE 220, OKLAHOMA CITY, OK 731033784
Phone: 405 521-2342
Web: WWW.OK.GOV

HISTORICAL FINANCIALS

Company Type: Private

Income Statement — FYE: June 30

	REVENUE ($ mil.)	NET INCOME ($ mil.)	NET PROFIT MARGIN	EMPLOYEES
06/19	19,784	1,636	8.3%	37,613
06/18	17,805	602	3.4%	—
06/17	17,175	48	0.3%	—
06/16	16,789	(1,025)	—	—
Annual Growth	5.6%	—	—	—

2019 Year-End Financials

Return on assets: 3.4%
Return on equity: 5.3%
Current ratio: 3.10
Cash ($ mil.): 8,766

STATE OF OREGON

EXECUTIVES

Governor, Kate Brown
State SEC, Bev Clarno
Staff, Caroline Zavitkovski
Public Safety Policy Adviser, Constantin Severe
Human Resources Administration, Donna Minor
Deputy Health Care Policy Advi, Jackie Yerby
North Coast Regional, Jennifer Purcell
Coordinator, Jessica Guerrero
Communications Specialist, Jessica Sall
Dhs Human, Larry Nicholson
Security Staff, Mike Meza
Auditors: OFFICE OF THE ACCOUNTANCY OF S

LOCATIONS

HQ: STATE OF OREGON
900 COURT ST NE STE 160, SALEM, OR 973014046
Phone: 503 378-3111
Web: WWW.STATE.OR.US

HISTORICAL FINANCIALS

Company Type: Private

Income Statement — FYE: June 30

	REVENUE ($ mil.)	NET INCOME ($ mil.)	NET PROFIT MARGIN	EMPLOYEES
06/19	28,230	2,142	7.6%	36,176
06/18	26,037	874	3.4%	—
06/17	24,296	1,536	6.3%	—
06/16	23,578	1,568	6.7%	—
Annual Growth	6.2%	10.9%	—	—

2019 Year-End Financials

Return on assets: 3.5%
Return on equity: 6.7%
Current ratio: 4.50
Cash ($ mil.): 13,410

STATE OF RHODE ISLAND AND PROVIDENCE PLANTATIONS

EXECUTIVES

Gov, Gina M Raimondo
Lt Gov, Daniel J McKee
State Controller, Lawrence C Franklin Jr
Research Scientist, Adam Miller
Grant Manager, Andrea Creach
Research Technician, Caitlin Oconnor
Human Resources Manager, Cecille Antonelli
Associate Director, Cheryl Burrell
Human Resources Rep, Crystine Marandola
Labor, Diane Buerger
Communications Director, Evan England
Auditors: DENNIS E HOYLE CPA PROVIDEN

LOCATIONS

HQ: STATE OF RHODE ISLAND AND PROVIDENCE PLANTATIONS
82 SMITH ST STE 102, PROVIDENCE, RI 029031121
Phone: 401 222-2080
Web: WWW.RI.GOV

HISTORICAL FINANCIALS

Company Type: Private

Income Statement — FYE: June 30

	REVENUE ($ mil.)	NET INCOME ($ mil.)	NET PROFIT MARGIN	EMPLOYEES
06/19	7,547	(49)	—	13,535
06/17	7,012	215	3.1%	—
06/16	6,860	(10)	—	—
06/15	6,787	160	2.4%	—
Annual Growth	2.7%	—	—	—

2019 Year-End Financials

Return on assets: (-0.3%)
Return on equity: (-1.9%)
Current ratio: 2.10
Cash ($ mil.): 1,905

STATE OF SOUTH CAROLINA

EXECUTIVES

Gov, Henry Dargan McMaster
Lt Gov*, Pamela S Evette
Exec Asst*, Kara Smoak
Atty Gen, Henry McMaster
Governors Aid, Susane Cooper
Director of Information Techno, Andrew Blais
Branch Manager, Robert Liming
Adjutant General, R Van McCarty
Professional Responsibility, Kenneth Phelps
Administrative Coordinator, Bonnie Brooks
Assistant District Maintenance, Dusty S Turner
Auditors: GEORGE L KENNEDY III COLUMB

LOCATIONS

HQ: STATE OF SOUTH CAROLINA
1205 PENDLETON ST, COLUMBIA, SC 292013756
Phone: 803 734-2100
Web: WWW.SC.GOV

HISTORICAL FINANCIALS

Company Type: Private

Income Statement — FYE: June 30

	REVENUE ($ mil.)	NET INCOME ($ mil.)	NET PROFIT MARGIN	EMPLOYEES
06/19	24,767	1,774	7.2%	67,816
06/15	21,191	224	1.1%	—
06/14	20,459	613	3.0%	—
06/13	19,706	944	4.8%	—
Annual Growth	3.9%	11.1%	—	—

2019 Year-End Financials

Return on assets: 2.6%
Return on equity: 6.6%
Current ratio: —
Cash ($ mil.): 8,923

STATE OF SOUTH DAKOTA

EXECUTIVES

Governor, Kristi L Noem
Lt. Governor*, Larry Rhoden
SEC of State*, Chris Nelson
State Auditor*, Rich Sattgast
Attorney General*, Larry Long
Director of Finance Compliance, Ron Wire
Attorney, Michael F Shaw
Administrative Assistant, Quynn Verhelst
Staff, Dj Hausmann
Compliance Staff, Paige Olson
Supervisor, Stacy Ellwanger
Auditors: MARTIN L GUINDON CPA PIERRE

LOCATIONS

HQ: STATE OF SOUTH DAKOTA
500 E CAPITOL AVE, PIERRE, SD 575015007
Phone: 605 773-3378
Web: WWW.SD.GOV

HISTORICAL FINANCIALS

Company Type: Private

Income Statement — FYE: June 30

	REVENUE ($ mil.)	NET INCOME ($ mil.)	NET PROFIT MARGIN	EMPLOYEES
06/19	3,945	71	1.8%	8,256
06/18	3,828	87	2.3%	—
06/17	3,820	153	4.0%	—
06/16	3,539	(62)	—	—
Annual Growth	3.7%	—	—	—

2019 Year-End Financials

Return on assets: 0.6%
Return on equity: 0.8%
Current ratio: —
Cash ($ mil.): 1,736

STATE OF TENNESSEE

EXECUTIVES

Governor-Prin, Bill Haslam
Lt Gov*, Ron Ramsey
Speaker - House, James O Naifeh
Speaker - Senate, John S Wilder
East TN Field Dr, Harlow Sumerford
Staff, Amanda Carter
Assistant Chief, Glenn Moates
Coordinator, Steve Cross
Director - Communications, Jennifer Donnals
Staff Assistant To Treasur, Ashley Humphrey
Specialist, Barry Bryant
Auditors: DEBORAH V LOVELESS CPA DIRE

LOCATIONS

HQ: STATE OF TENNESSEE
312 ROSA L PARKS AVE, NASHVILLE, TN 372431102
Phone: 615 741-2001
Web: WWW.TN.GOV

HISTORICAL FINANCIALS

Company Type: Private

Income Statement — FYE: June 30

	REVENUE ($ mil.)	NET INCOME ($ mil.)	NET PROFIT MARGIN	EMPLOYEES
06/19	32,779	754	2.3%	37,737
06/18	32,194	902	2.8%	—
06/17	31,145	981	3.2%	—
06/16	30,452	1,162	3.8%	—
Annual Growth	2.5%	(13.4%)	—	—

2019 Year-End Financials

Return on assets: 1.2%
Return on equity: 1.6%
Current ratio: —
Cash ($ mil.): 12,711

STATE OF TEXAS

EXECUTIVES

Governor, Greg Abbott
Chief of Staff*, Luis Saenz
Deputy Chief of Staff*, David Whitley
Chief Operating Officer*, Reed Clay
Deputy Chief of Staff*, Jordan Hale
Senior Adviser For State Opera, Steven Albright
Texas District Attorney, Andria Bender
Senior Adviser, Sarah Hicks
Chief of Staff, Amy Bruno
Shift Coordinator, Darrell Taylor
Administrator, David Carter
Auditors: LISA R COLLIER CPA CFE CID

LOCATIONS

HQ: STATE OF TEXAS
1100 SAN JACINTO BLVD, AUSTIN, TX 787011935
Phone: 512 463-2000
Web: WWW.TEXAS.GOV

HISTORICAL FINANCIALS

Company Type: Private

Income Statement — FYE: August 31

	REVENUE ($ mil.)	NET INCOME ($ mil.)	NET PROFIT MARGIN	EMPLOYEES
08/17	115,336	1,882	1.6%	144,175
08/15	107,350	1,993	1.9%	—
08/14	109,860	8,184	7.4%	—
08/13	0	0	—	—
Annual Growth	—	—	—	—

2017 Year-End Financials

Return on assets: 0.6%
Return on equity: 1.1%
Current ratio: 1.90
Cash ($ mil.): 29,217

STATE OF UTAH

EXECUTIVES

Governor, Gary Herbert
Gov, Gary R Herbert
Lt Gov, Spencer J Cox
Exec-Dir, Q Val Hale
General Counsel, Ron Gordon
Accounting Staff, Susan Lundquist
Local Area Network Administrat, Cindy Talboe
Senior Information Tea, Dan Cox
Department of Workforce Servic, Elizabeth Thorpe
Specialist, Jill Grimm
Department of Workforce Servic, Julie Thurston
Auditors: OFFICE OF THE STATE AUDITOR

LOCATIONS

HQ: STATE OF UTAH
350 N STATE ST STE 200, SALT LAKE CITY, UT 841140002
Phone: 801 538-1000
Web: WWW.UTAH.GOV

HISTORICAL FINANCIALS

Company Type: Private

Income Statement — FYE: June 30

	REVENUE ($ mil.)	NET INCOME ($ mil.)	NET PROFIT MARGIN	EMPLOYEES
06/19	14,316	696	4.9%	29,821
06/18	13,582	986	7.3%	—
06/17	12,668	199	1.6%	—
06/16	11,723	55	0.5%	—
Annual Growth	6.9%	132.2%	—	—

2019 Year-End Financials

Return on assets: 1.3%
Return on equity: 1.8%
Current ratio: —
Cash ($ mil.): 5,160

STATE OF VERMONT

EXECUTIVES

Governor, Phil Scott
Lt Governor*, David Zuckerman
Chief of Staff*, Liz Miller
Coordinator, Amy Tucker
Staff, Diane Hahn
Staff, Judith Barbera
Supervisor, Sgt Prevost
Law Specialist, Nancy Williams
Acting Washington County Atty, Rory Thibault
Policy, Austin Davis
Public Safety Barracks Clerk, Hannah Neilson

LOCATIONS

HQ: STATE OF VERMONT
109 STATE ST STE 4, MONTPELIER, VT 056090003
Phone: 802 828-1452
Web: WWW.VERMONT.GOV

HISTORICAL FINANCIALS

Company Type: Private

Income Statement — FYE: June 30

	REVENUE ($ mil.)	NET INCOME ($ mil.)	NET PROFIT MARGIN	EMPLOYEES
06/19	5,868	(13)	—	8,795
06/18	5,790	144	2.5%	—
Annual Growth	1.3%	—	—	—

2019 Year-End Financials

Return on assets: (-0.1%)
Return on equity: (-1.2%)
Current ratio: 2.30
Cash ($ mil.): 1,483

STATE OF WASHINGTON

EXECUTIVES

Governor, Jay Inslee
Lt Govnr*, Brad Owen
SEC State*, Sam Reed
Treas*, Michael Murphy
Pub Inst*, Terry Bergeson
Exec SEC*, Sue Martin
Chief of Staff*, Mary Alice Heuschel
Senior Adviser, Joby Shimomura
Manager, Linda Garland
Deputy Chief Information Offic, Debbie Hoxit
Manager, Ginny Schenck
Auditors: PAT MCCARTHY OLYMPIA WA

LOCATIONS

HQ: STATE OF WASHINGTON
106 LEGISLATIVE BUILDING, OLYMPIA, WA 985040001
Phone: 360 902-4111
Web: WWW.ACCESS.WA.GOV

HISTORICAL FINANCIALS

Company Type: Private

Income Statement — FYE: June 30

	REVENUE ($ mil.)	NET INCOME ($ mil.)	NET PROFIT MARGIN	EMPLOYEES
06/19	50,993	264	0.5%	57,659
06/18	49,114	2,692	5.5%	—
06/17	46,269	1,100	2.4%	—
06/16	43,294	1,096	2.5%	—
Annual Growth	5.6%	(37.8%)	—	—

2019 Year-End Financials

Return on assets: 0.2%
Return on equity: 1.0%
Current ratio: —
Cash ($ mil.): 17,528

STATE OF WEST VIRGINIA

EXECUTIVES

Governor, Jim Justice
State Auditor*, Glen Gainer III
Chief of Staff*, Chris Stadelman
Chief of Staff*, Nick Casey
Member, L W Linger
Assistant Treasurer, Josh Stowers
Director Participant Accountin, Diane Holcomb
Supreme Court of Judge, John Hutchison
Debt Manager, Bryan Archer
Web Designer, Jeff Takarsh
Local Government Dire, Ora Ash
Auditors: ERNST & YOUNG LLP CHARLESTON

LOCATIONS

HQ: STATE OF WEST VIRGINIA
1900 KANAWHA BLVD E, CHARLESTON, WV 253050009
Phone: 304 558-2000
Web: WWW.WV.GOV

HISTORICAL FINANCIALS

Company Type: Private

Income Statement FYE: June 30

	REVENUE ($ mil.)	NET INCOME ($ mil.)	NET PROFIT MARGIN	EMPLOYEES
06/19	12,469	649	5.2%	19,357
06/17	11,650	(2)	—	—
06/16	11,147	(231)	—	—
06/15	11,175	(159)	—	—
Annual Growth	2.8%	—	—	—

2019 Year-End Financials

Return on assets: 2.2%
Return on equity: 5.0%
Current ratio: 3.20
Cash ($ mil.): 6,813

STATE OF WISCONSIN

EXECUTIVES

Governor, Tony Evers
Lt. Governor*, Mandela Barnes
Coordinator, Lisa Jorgensen
Project Coordinator, Cynthia Moore
Office Press Secretary, Amy Hasenberg
Deputy Chief of Staff, Jack Jablonski
Chief of Staff, Eric Schutt
Specialist, Erika Ryerson
Civil Engineering Supervisor, David Castleberg
Revenue Section Chief, Dawn Wenzel
Accountant, Doug Meek
Auditors: JOE CHRISMAN MADISON WI

LOCATIONS

HQ: STATE OF WISCONSIN
115 E CAPITOL, MADISON, WI 537020015
Phone: 608 266-1212
Web: WWW.WISCONSIN.GOV

HISTORICAL FINANCIALS

Company Type: Private

Income Statement FYE: June 30

	REVENUE ($ mil.)	NET INCOME ($ mil.)	NET PROFIT MARGIN	EMPLOYEES
06/19	31,683	693	2.2%	35,522
06/17	28,874	474	1.6%	—
06/16	28,533	357	1.3%	—
06/15	28,158	(537)	—	—
Annual Growth	3.0%	—	—	—

2019 Year-End Financials

Return on assets: 1.1%
Return on equity: 2.0%
Current ratio: —
Cash ($ mil.): 9,163

STATE UNIVERSITY OF NEW YORK

SUNY days are ahead for many New Yorkers seeking higher education. With an enrollment of more than 460000 students The State University of New York (SUNY) is vying with California State University System for the title of largest university system in the US. Most students are residents of New York State. Students come from all 50 states as well as 160 countries. SUNY maintains 64 campuses around the state including four university centers about two dozen university colleges 30 community colleges and a handful of technical colleges as well as medical centers. The system has a student-teacher ratio of about 16:1.

Operations

The school offers more than 7500 undergraduate programs of study – including engineering business literature medicine agriculture performing arts and human services. SUNY also offers about 400 study abroad programs.

EXECUTIVES

Vice President For Business And Finance, Wendy Gilman
Secretary, Beth Osborne
Secretary, Heather Soroka
Secretary Treasurer Levin Foundation; Founding Chief Operating And Financial Officer The Levin Ins, Michael DiGiacomo
Auditors: KPMG LLP ALBANY NY

LOCATIONS

HQ: STATE UNIVERSITY OF NEW YORK
353 BROADWAY, ALBANY, NY 122462915
Phone: 518 320-1100
Web: WWW.SUNY.EDU

HISTORICAL FINANCIALS

Company Type: Private

Income Statement FYE: June 30

	REVENUE ($ mil.)	NET INCOME ($ mil.)	NET PROFIT MARGIN	EMPLOYEES
06/12	5,961	(374)	—	88,024
06/06*	4	(2)	—	—
10/05	0	0	—	—
Annual Growth	—	—	—	—

*Fiscal year change

2012 Year-End Financials

Return on assets: (-2.5%)
Return on equity: —
Current ratio: 1.50
Cash ($ mil.): 1,642

STATEN ISLAND UNIVERSITY HOSPITAL

Staten Island University Hospital (SIUH) ferries health care services to residents of New York City's fastest growing borough and surrounding areas at its two medical campuses. Established in 1861 SIUH maintains about 715 beds and is a teaching affiliate of the State University of New York's Brooklyn Health Science Center. Its larger north campus includes units specializing in cardiology pathology cancer blood-related diseases burn treatment trauma and women's health. The south campus site offers specialty programs such as sleep medicine geriatric psychiatry and substance abuse services. A member of Northwell Health SIUH employs approximately 1200 physicians.

Operations

SIUH's Heart Institute of Staten Island located on the north campus is a joint venture between the hospital and Richmond University Medical Center. The Heart Institute specializes in cardiac diagnostics and "beating heart" surgeries.

The hospital operates several general physician practice and specialty health clinics on Staten Island. It also provides a home visit program and hospital-based hospice services.

SIUH is an affiliate of the SUNY Health Science Center at Brooklyn; its campuses serve as clinics for the Hofstra North Shore-LIJ School of Medicine which SIUH owns in partnership with Hofstra University.

In 2013 SIUH had nearly 3000 births nearly 45000 hospital discharges about 126000 emergency department visits and more than 16000 ambulatory surgeries.

EXECUTIVES

Pres, Anthony C Ferreri
Exec V Pres*, Robin Wittenstein
V Pres-Fin-Controller*, John Steiger
Cfo*, Thomas Reca
Exec V Pres*, Nicholas Caruselle
Sr V Pres*, Margaret Dialto
V Pres*, John P Demoleas
SEC*, Arthur Fried
Exec Dir*, Donna Proske
Staff, Vincent Logatto
Sr Hr Rep, Jenie Grodowski

LOCATIONS

HQ: STATEN ISLAND UNIVERSITY HOSPITAL
475 SEAVIEW AVE, STATEN ISLAND, NY 103053436
Phone: 718 226-9000
Web: WWW.SIUH.NORTHWELL.EDU

PRODUCTS/OPERATIONS

Selected Services

Behavioral Health
Cancer Services
Cardiac Services
Cardiovascular and Thoracic Surgery
Medical Services including Endocrinology Gastroenterology Nephrology and Pulmonary
Neuroscience and Spine Services
Orthopedic Services
Pediatrics
Rehabilitation Medicine

Surgical Services including General Surgery Colorectal Head & Neck and Urology
Trauma and Burn Services
Women's Health

Selected Centers of Care

Center for Bariatric Surgery
Comprehensive Breast Center
Heart Institute
Institute of Sleep Medicine
Level III Perinatal Center
New York Head & Neck Institute at Staten Island University Hospital
Regional Burn Center
Stroke Center
The Elizabeth A. Connelly Emergency and Trauma Center
The Sanford R. Nalitt Institute for Cancer and Blood Related Diseases; Children's Cancer Center

COMPETITORS

Bronx-Lebanon Hospital
Catholic Healthcare System
CenterLight Health System Inc.
Continuum Health Partners
Eger Health Care
Kingsbrook Jewish Medical Center
Maimonides Medical Center
MediSys Health Network
New York City Health and Hospitals
NewYork-Presbyterian Healthcare

HISTORICAL FINANCIALS

Company Type: Private

Income Statement — FYE: December 31

	REVENUE ($ mil.)	NET INCOME ($ mil.)	NET PROFIT MARGIN	EMPLOYEES
12/18	934	(33)	—	5,700
12/17	891	69	7.8%	—
12/16	871	57	6.6%	—
12/15	850	41	4.9%	—
Annual Growth	3.2%	—	—	—

2018 Year-End Financials

Return on assets: (-3.1%)
Return on equity: (-6.7%)
Current ratio: 3.50
Cash ($ mil.): 34

STEPHEN GOULD CORPORATION

Others can worry about what's inside – Stephen Gould Corporation concentrates on the package. The company provides a full range of packaging-related design and printing services for customers worldwide. Its products include gift packaging point-of-purchase displays product merchandising and retail and industrial packaging. Stephen Gould Corporation also provides graphic design and package-engineering services as well as assembly and fulfillment. The company was originally founded in 1939 by Stephen Gould David Golden and Leonard Beckerman.

Geographic Reach

Stephen Gould Corporation operates from about 40 facilities; branches are located primarily in the US (more than 20 states) but also in China Ireland Malaysia and Mexico.

EXECUTIVES

Executive Vice President Operations, John Golden

LOCATIONS

HQ: STEPHEN GOULD CORPORATION
35 S JEFFERSON RD, WHIPPANY, NJ 079811043
Phone: 973 428-1500
Web: WWW.GOULDNY.COM

PRODUCTS/OPERATIONS

Selected Products and Services

Products
Aerospace reusable cases
Corrugated containers
Gift packaging
Industrial packaging
Point of sale packaging
Protective packaging
Services
Creative services
Logistics & facilities
Package design & engineering

COMPETITORS

Consolidated Carqueville
Focus Packaging & Display group
Fort Dearborn
Metro Packaging and Imaging
R.R. Donnelley
WS Packaging Group

HISTORICAL FINANCIALS

Company Type: Private

Income Statement — FYE: December 31

	REVENUE ($ mil.)	NET INCOME ($ mil.)	NET PROFIT MARGIN	EMPLOYEES
12/19	757	5	0.8%	525
12/16	665	11	1.8%	—
12/13	526	3	0.7%	—
12/12	442	0	—	—
Annual Growth	—	310.7%	—	—

2019 Year-End Financials

Return on assets: 2.0%
Return on equity: 7.0%
Current ratio: 2.20
Cash ($ mil.): 7

STEVENS TRANSPORT, INC.

Staying cool is a must for Stevens Transport. An irregular-route refrigerated truckload carrier (or reefer) Stevens hauls temperature-controlled cargo throughout the US covering the 48 contiguous states. Through alliances Stevens also covers every province in Canada and every state in Mexico. The company operates a fleet of about 2000 Kenworth and Peterbuilt tractors and 3500 Thermo King refrigerated trailers from a network of more than a dozen service centers. Partnerships with railroads allow Stevens to arrange intermodal transport of temperature-controlled cargo. The company also provides third-party logistics services. Stevens Transport was founded in 1980.

Operations

The company owns 49% of B2B Transport which provides an array of transportation related services to large mid-sized and small companies throughout North America.

Geographic Reach

Stevens Transport maintains its operations across Canada Mexico and the US through its partnerships with BNSF Norfolk Southern CSX and Union Pacific. It has 13 logistics offices located in Canada and throughout the US.

Sales and Marketing

Stevens has provided refrigerated shipping services for such big names as General Mills Kraft Foods M&M Mars Procter & Gamble and Wal-Mart.

Strategy

Even in a US economy ripe with unpredictable fuel costs and a decline in consumer confidence one thing has always worked in Stevens' favor: people will always need their food. The company has managed to maintain a steady growth rate by keeping costs down updating the technology of its trucking equipment and maintaining an efficient operating structure. Along these lines in 2012 it implemented new mobile computing platforms across its fleet of tractors to enhance its customer services and optimize productivity.

EXECUTIVES

Vice President Risk Management, William Tallent
Executive Vice President, Mike Richey
Vice Chairman, Todd Aaron
Auditors: SADDOCK & CO PLLC DALLAS T

LOCATIONS

HQ: STEVENS TRANSPORT, INC.
9757 MILITARY PKWY, DALLAS, TX 752274805
Phone: 972 216-9000
Web: WWW.STEVENSTRANSPORT.COM

PRODUCTS/OPERATIONS

Selected Services

Intermodal

International

Logistics

Truckload

COMPETITORS

C.R. England
Central Refrigerated Service
Comcar
Covenant Transportation
Frozen Food Express
Henderson Trucking
Jim Palmer Trucking
KLLM Transport Services
Marten Transport
Navajo Shippers
Prime Inc.
Southern Refrigerated Transport
TransAm Trucking
Watkins Associated Industries
Willis Shaw Express

HISTORICAL FINANCIALS

Company Type: Private

Income Statement — FYE: December 31

	REVENUE ($ mil.)	NET INCOME ($ mil.)	NET PROFIT MARGIN	EMPLOYEES
12/15	668	87	13.0%	2,100
12/12	607	85	14.0%	—
12/11	566	76	13.5%	—
12/08	550	0	0.0%	—
Annual Growth	2.8%	505.7%	—	—

2015 Year-End Financials

Return on assets: 13.0%
Return on equity: 16.3%
Current ratio: 4.60
Cash ($ mil.): 152

STEWARD HEALTH CARE SYSTEM LLC

Steward Health Care System is a steward of its patients' good health. With a total of some 7300 beds Steward Health operates 36 hospitals in 10 states including Holy Family Hospital Norwood Hospital St. Elizabeth's Medical Center The Medical Center of Southeast Texas and Pikes Peak Regional Hospital. Several of the hospitals are affiliated with Boston-area medical schools. The company also has managed operations in Arizona Utah and Massachusetts. Steward Health also includes a physician practice organization an outpatient clinic network and a home care and hospice agency. Steward which is owned by Cerberus Capital Management merged with IASIS Healthcare in 2017 to become the US' largest private for-profit hospital operator.

Operations

Steward Health is a community-based care organization that offers a full range of health care services. Its operations include integrated network physicians 36 hospital campuses more than 25 affiliated urgent care providers more than 40 preferred skilled nursing facilities and other services.

The three main components of the system are: Steward Medical Group (which has more than 1400 providers and has more than 1 million patient encounters per year in 10 states); Steward Health Care Network (a fully integrated care management company with some 4800 providers and 2 million patient encounters per year); and Steward Hospitals.

Other operations include Steward Home Care and Hospice Steward Urgent Care and Steward Insurance Plans

Strategy

Steward Health provides care for patients across the care spectrum. By providing health care services in a coordinated and more efficient manner the system is able to control costs and improve quality eliminate care fragmentation and reduce duplication of services in the delivery of health care.In 2016 sold its hospitals to Medical Properties Trust in a sale-leaseback transaction that provided capital to pay down debt make improvements at its facilities and pursue geographic expansion.

Among the company's initiatives has been to expand beyond its base in Massachusetts as evidenced by its 2017 acquisition of IASIS Healthcare (which added 18 hospitals to its network). It made a sale-leaseback arrangement with Medical Properties Trust for 10 hospitals gained in the IASIS transaction.

The largest private hospital operator in the US Steward Health is very secretive with its financial statements.

Mergers and Acquisitions

In 2017 Steward Health completed a major acquisition when it bought eight hospitals from Community Health Systems for $304 million. The hospitals located in Ohio Pennsylvania and Florida were the company's first outside of New England. The deal added some 1800 beds to its operations.

Later that year the company made an even bigger smash when it merged with IASIS Healthcare to create a system with 36 hospitals (with some 7500 beds) in 10 states as well as managed care operations in three states.

Company Background

The company changed its name from Caritas Christi to Steward Health after being acquired by Cerberus Capital Management in 2010; it had previously been operated by the Catholic Archdiocese of Boston. The acquisition by Cerberus was worth some $895 million and provided operational funding and capital for hospital improvement projects; it also helped pay down debt obligations. As a result of the transaction Steward Health became a for-profit corporation; however a stipulation of the deal mandated that the health system's hospitals retain their pastoral and charitable care policies. The sale to Cerberus was not the first attempt by the Archdiocese of Boston to sell the ailing Caritas Christi system which had been suffering from financial troubles for several years prior to the deal.

EXECUTIVES

Senior Vice President Chief Marketing Officer, Brian Carty
Coo, Joshua S. Putter
President Steward Medical Network, Mark Girard
Chairman And Ceo, Ralph de la Torre
Evp And General Counsel, Joseph Maher
Cfo, Mark Rich
Evp, Robert E. (Bob) Guyon
President - Steward Medical Group, Michael G. Callum
Chief Information Officer, Drexel DeFord
President, Craig A. Jesiolowski
Executive Vice President Network Insurance And Physician Operations, John Polanowicz
Vice President Of Operations, Marisela Marrero
Vp Hr, Patrick Lombardo

LOCATIONS

HQ: STEWARD HEALTH CARE SYSTEM LLC
1900 N PEARL ST STE 2400, DALLAS, TX 752012470
Phone: 469 341-8800
Web: WWW.STEWARD.ORG

Services

Behavioral Health Services
Centers for Cancer Care
Center for Advanced Cardiac Surgery
Centers for Cardiac and Vascular Care
Centers for Weight Control
Home Care and Hospice
MAKOplasty®; Services
Maternity Services

Selected Hospitals

Arizona
Mountain Vista Medical Center (Mesa)
St. Luke's Medical Center (Phoenix)
Tempe St. Luke's Hospital
Arkansas
Wadley Regional Medical Center at Hope
Colorado
Pikes Peak Regional Hospital & Surgery Center (Woodland Park)
Florida
Rockledge Regional Medical Center
Sebastian River Medical Center
Louisiana
Glenwood Regional Medical Center (West Monroe)
Massachusetts
Carney Hospital (Dorchester)
Good Samaritan Medical Center (Brockton)
Holy Family Hospital (Methuen)
Morton Hospital (Taunton)
Nashoba Valley Medical Center (Ayer)
New England Sinai Hospital (Stoughton)
Norwood Hospital
Quincy Community Care Network
Saint Anne's Hospital (Fall River)
St. Elizabeth's Medical Center (Brighton)
Ohio
Northside Regional Medical Center (Youngstown)
Trumbull Regional Medical Center (Warren)
Pennsylvania
Easton Hospital
Sharon Regional Medical Center
Texas
Southwest General Hospital (San Antonio)
The Medical Center of Southeast Texas (Port Arthur)
The Medical Center of Southeast Texas — Victory Campus (Beaumont)
Utah
Davis Hospital and Medical Center (Layton)
Jordan Valley Medical Center (West Jordan)
Mountain Point Medical Center (Lehi)

COMPETITORS

Adventist Health System Sunbelt Healthcare
Berkshire Health Systems
Boston Medical Center
Cambridge Health Alliance
Cape Cod Healthcare
Care New England
CareGroup
Children's Hospital Boston
Emerson Hospital
Hallmark Health
John C. Lincoln Health Network
New England Alliance for Health
Northeast Health System
Partners HealthCare
Southcoast Hospitals Group
University of Utah Hospitals & Clinics
Winchester Healthcare

HISTORICAL FINANCIALS

Company Type: Private

Income Statement — FYE: September 30

	REVENUE ($ mil.)	NET INCOME ($ mil.)	NET PROFIT MARGIN	EMPLOYEES
09/07	1,240	30	2.5%	37,000
09/06	1,220	47	3.9%	—
09/05	27	2	8.0%	—
Annual Growth	572.6%	272.9%	—	—

2007 Year-End Financials

Return on assets: 3.6%
Return on equity: 10.8%
Current ratio: 1.10
Cash ($ mil.): 73

STEWART'S SHOPS CORP.

I scream you scream we all scream for Stewart's ice cream — especially if we live in upstate New York or Vermont home to some 330 Stewart's Shops. The chain of convenience stores sells more than 3000 products across 30-plus counties. They include dairy items groceries food to go (soup sandwiches hot entrees) beer coffee gasoline and of course ice cream. In addition to its retail business the company owns about 100 rental properties including banks hair salons and apartments near its stores. Stewart's Shops formerly known as Stewart's Ice Cream Company was established in 1945. The founding Dake family owns about two-thirds of the company; employee compensation plans own the rest.

Operations

The convenience store chain which spans New York and Vermont offers consumers milk ice creams coffee to-go foods beer gasoline and groceries. As part of its business Stewart's Shops also acquires and develops (preferably adjacent) properties the likes of shops banks hair salons and apartments that it then leases or sells.

Stewart's Shops makes its own dairy products including its own ice cream in more than 50 flavors that are hand-dipped and packaged. Recognized for its quality products the company relies on a group of about 45 farmers in New York to supply its milk.

The vertically-integrated company which makes about 75% of the items it sells also offers private-label goods and national brands in its stores. Its private-label brands extend far beyond dairy products to include soda chips bread and juices.

Geographic Reach

Based in New York Stewart's Shops operates a chain of convenience stores across upstate New York and in Vermont.

Sales and Marketing

Stewart's Shops serves consumers through its New York and Vermont shops; two-thirds of its stores sell gas.

Strategy

The convenience store operator regularly extends its reach. In 2014 it's focused on Syracuse New York following several store openings in 2013 in Keeseville Herkimer Rotterdam and Heuvelton New York. The latter shops boast an expanded cooler walk-in beer cave and seating.

The company is also investing in environmentally friendly facilities. In 2013 for instance it had 2400 solar panels installed at its manufacturing and distribution center. Stewart's Shops anticipates that the effort will save nearly $40000 a year in energy costs at the plant after about a 5-year period.

It enlisted the help of Paragon Software in 2014 to automate the planning of daily and seasonal deliveries. In turn Stewart's Shops aims to lower mileage reduce fuel usage and improve truckload efficiencies.

EXECUTIVES

Pres, Gary C Dake
Chm*, William P Dake
V Pres*, Nancy Trimbur
Asst Treas*, David Farr
Treas*, Michael Cocca
SEC*, Matthew Gutch
Distribution/Shipping/Transpor, Chris Burby
Merchandizer, Carrie Niciu
Real Estate Conultant, Chuck Marshall
Project Coordinator, Mike Cannizzo
Human Resources Compliance and, Shannon Potter
Auditors: BST & CO CPAS LLP ALBANY

LOCATIONS

HQ: STEWART'S SHOPS CORP.
2907 STATE ROUTE 9, BALLSTON SPA, NY 120204201
Phone: 518 581-1201
Web: WWW.STEWARTSSHOPS.COM

PRODUCTS/OPERATIONS

Selected Products

Beverages

Coffee
Ice Cream
Food to go
Gasoline
Groceries
Milk

COMPETITORS

7-Eleven
Ben & Jerry's
Carvel
Cumberland Farms
Exxon Mobil
Friendly's Ice Cream
Golub
Hannaford Bros.
Kroger
McDonald's
Sunoco
TravelCenters of America

HISTORICAL FINANCIALS

Company Type: Private

Income Statement — FYE: December 29

	REVENUE ($ mil.)	NET INCOME ($ mil.)	NET PROFIT MARGIN	EMPLOYEES
12/19	1,699	124	7.3%	3,800
12/17	1,542	92	6.0%	—
12/16	1,405	80	5.7%	—
12/14	1,610	59	3.7%	—
Annual Growth	1.1%	15.7%	—	—

2019 Year-End Financials

Return on assets: 14.9%
Return on equity: 18.5%
Current ratio: 4.30
Cash ($ mil.): 137

STILLWATER MINING COMPANY

EXECUTIVES

Pres-Ceo, Michael J McMullen
Cfo*, Christopher M Bateman
V Pres Safety Health & Hr*, Kristen K Koss
V Pres Mine Oprs*, Dee L Bray
Accounting Team Member, Luttschwager Yvonne
Senior Site Accountant, Joyce Weber
Financial Planning, Ashlee Mendive
Executive Vpres, Richard Stewart
Information Technology Manager, Cheryl Kennedy
Parks Director, Christy Waters
Processing Coordinator, Mike Gaustad
Auditors: KPMG LLP BILLINGS MONTANA

LOCATIONS

HQ: STILLWATER MINING COMPANY
536 E PIKE AVE, COLUMBUS, MT 590197616
Phone: 406 373-8700
Web: WWW.STILLWATERCOUNTYNEWS.COM

COMPETITORS

Anglo American Platinum
Aquarius Platinum
Diadem Resources
Franco-Nevada
Impala Platinum
Lonmin
North American Palladium
Vale Limited

HISTORICAL FINANCIALS

Company Type: Private

Income Statement — FYE: December 31

	REVENUE ($ mil.)	NET INCOME ($ mil.)	NET PROFIT MARGIN	EMPLOYEES
12/16	711	9	1.3%	1,432
12/15	726	(23)	—	—
12/14	943	68	7.3%	—
12/13	1,039	(302)	—	—
Annual Growth	(11.9%)	—	—	—

2016 Year-End Financials

Return on assets: 0.7%
Return on equity: 1.0%
Current ratio: 7.00
Cash ($ mil.): 123

STOCKTON UNIFIED SCHOOL DISTRICT

EXECUTIVES

Supt, Dr Steve Lowder
Pres*, Sara L Cazares
Vice Pres*, Gloria Allen
Research/Development Director, Mong Thi Nguyen
Mechanical Division Manager, Tabatha Hoak
Kindergarten Teacher, Tracey Gray
Executive Assistant II, Carmen Jimenez
Program Technician, Cathy Holman
Superintendent, Denise Birdwell
Coo, Louis Hartwell
Sr Administrative Assistant, Mee Yang
Auditors: CROWE LLP SACRAMENTO CALIFOR

LOCATIONS

HQ: STOCKTON UNIFIED SCHOOL DISTRICT
701 N MADISON ST, STOCKTON, CA 952021634
Phone: 209 933-7000
Web: WWW.STOCKTONUSD.NET

HISTORICAL FINANCIALS

Company Type: Private

Income Statement — FYE: June 30

	REVENUE ($ mil.)	NET INCOME ($ mil.)	NET PROFIT MARGIN	EMPLOYEES
06/19	602	8	1.3%	3,000
06/18	536	(24)	—	—
06/17	557	36	6.6%	—
06/16	527	98	18.6%	—
Annual Growth	4.5%	(56.5%)	—	—

STORMONT-VAIL HEALTHCARE, INC.

EXECUTIVES

Ceo, Randall Peterson
Ceo*, Randy Peterson
Vice Pres*, Tracy O'Rourke
Sr V Pres-Medi Dir, Kent Palmberg
V Pres-Medi Svc Div*, Deb Yocum
V Pres-Chf Info Offc*, Janet Stanek
V Pres-Patient Care Svcs*, Carol Perry
V Pres-Fclty Mgmt*, David Cuningham
V Pres-Hr*, Bernard Becker
Cfo*, Kevin Han
Svp-Gen Counsel-Chief Complian*, Kevin Steck
Auditors: RSM US LLP DAVENPORT IOWA

LOCATIONS

HQ: STORMONT-VAIL HEALTHCARE, INC.
1500 SW 10TH AVE, TOPEKA, KS 666041301
Phone: 785 354-6000
Web: WWW.STORMONTVAIL.ORG

HISTORICAL FINANCIALS

Company Type: Private

Income Statement				FYE: September 30
	REVENUE ($ mil.)	NET INCOME ($ mil.)	NET PROFIT MARGIN	EMPLOYEES
09/18	719	88	12.4%	4,500
09/17	654	70	10.8%	—
09/16	634	30	4.8%	—
09/15	582	(9)	—	—
Annual Growth	7.3%	—	—	—

2018 Year-End Financials

Return on assets: 11.0%
Return on equity: 18.3%
Current ratio: 2.50
Cash ($ mil.): 101

STRACK AND VAN TIL SUPER MARKET INC.

One of Chicagoland's leading grocery chains Strack & Van Til operates more than 35 supermarkets in and around Chicago and northern Indiana. Stores operate under the banners of Strack & Van Til Town & Country Food Market and Ultra Foods. The regional grocery chain offers fresh and packaged foods and has delicatessen and bakery divisions in each of its stores. Its websites offer weekly circulars and coupons as well as feature recipes cooking videos meal planners and food-related articles. The company is owned by Chicago-based grocery distributor Central Grocers which also operates supermarkets under the Berkot's and Key Market banners.In 2017 Central Grocers filed for Chapter 11 bankruptcy protection and put Strack & Van Til up for sale as part of the filing.

Strategy

Strack & Van Til and its regional rivals are facing increased competition from national chains including Wal-Mart and Trader Joe's moving into the market while taking advantage of the woes of smaller ones. Rather than retreat the grocery chain is pursuing a growth strategy acquiring seven stores in its market area in late 2012. (With Safeway-owned Dominick's Supermarkets on the block its stores are in play.) It is also investing in its existing stores and stocking more organic foods to compete with the likes of Whole Foods. The company is revamping supermarkets in Valpariso Hobart and Chesterton was well as an Ultra Foods store in Highland Strack's supermarkets in Munster and Schereville and an Ultra in Lansing are slated for upgrades as well.

Wal-Mart which had been expanding aggressively in the Chicago suburbs has begun opening supercenters and smaller Walmart Express stores within the city limits. Its arrival has sparked fierce price competition among area grocers. Other relative newcomers to the Illinois grocery market include Roundy's and non-traditional grocery chains such as SuperTarget stores and limited-assortment ALDI. To take on nationwide retailers Strack & Van Til bands together with other independent stores as members of the Central Grocers cooperative. The combined buying power helps the stores to offer competitive pricing and product selection.

In late 2013 the grocery chain launched a new marketing campaign I'm a Strack & Van Til Shopper to appeal to a wide audience while maintaining the company's value proposition.

Mergers and Acquisitions

In December 2012 Strack & Van Til acquired seven grocery stores from Indiana-based WiseWay Supermarkets. Four of the stores were converted to the Strack & Van Til banner while three became Ultra Foods stores. Like Strack & Van Til WiseWay was also supplied by Central Grocers.

EXECUTIVES

Pres, David Wilkinson
V Pres*, Andrew Raab
V Pres*, Jeff Strack
Cfo*, Keith Bruxvoort
V Pres*, Robert Wasiuta
V Pres*, Rex Mudge
V Pres*, Joe Kolavo
SEC*, Jim Denges
Director, Mike Mulle
Field Supervisor, Gale Mote
Grocery Manager, George Frencl
Auditors: MCGLADREY & PULLEN LLP CHICAG

LOCATIONS

HQ: STRACK AND VAN TIL SUPER MARKET INC.
2244 45TH ST, HIGHLAND, IN 463222629
Phone: 219 924-7588
Web: WWW.STRACKANDVANTIL.COM

COMPETITORS

ALDI
Jewel Osco
Kmart
Meijer
Roundy's
Target Corporation
Trader Joe's
Wal-Mart
Whole Foods

HISTORICAL FINANCIALS

Company Type: Private

Income Statement				FYE: August 1
	REVENUE ($ mil.)	NET INCOME ($ mil.)	NET PROFIT MARGIN	EMPLOYEES
08/10	961	15	1.7%	2,000
08/09	995	13	1.4%	—
Annual Growth	(3.4%)	16.1%	—	—

2010 Year-End Financials

Return on assets: 7.7%
Return on equity: 12.9%
Current ratio: 1.40
Cash ($ mil.): 10

SUASIN CANCER CARE INC.

Auditors: ERNST & YOUNG US LLP SAN DIEG

LOCATIONS

HQ: SUASIN CANCER CARE INC.
1301 PUNCHBOWL ST, HONOLULU, HI 968132402
Phone: 512 583-0205

HISTORICAL FINANCIALS

Company Type: Private

Income Statement				FYE: June 30
	REVENUE ($ mil.)	NET INCOME ($ mil.)	NET PROFIT MARGIN	EMPLOYEES
06/15	1,003	50	5.0%	4
06/14	851	31	3.7%	—
06/13	856	109	12.8%	—
Annual Growth	8.2%	(32.4%)	—	—

2015 Year-End Financials

Return on assets: 3.4%
Return on equity: 7.9%
Current ratio: 0.30
Cash ($ mil.): 29

SUFFOLK CONSTRUCTION COMPANY, INC.

Suffolk Construction Company provides construction services from top to bottom. The company kicks off the building process with pre-construction services and follows through with design/build and construction management. Suffolk Construction builds for both the public and private organizations in the science and technology health care education government and commercial sectors operating in the Northeast South and West Coast regions of the US. Founded in 1982 the privately-held firm is owned by president and CEO John Fish whose family has been in construction for four generations.

Operations

Suffolk Construction provides value throughout the entire project lifecycle by leveraging its core construction management services with vertical service lines that include real estate capital investment design self-perform construction services technology start-up investment and innovation research/development. Some projects have included 78 Haight housing development in San Francisco a ground-up construction of Agua Caliente Casino Resort & Spa luxury boutique hotel Alila Marea Beach Resort and the construction of construction of two modern hotel Aloft and Element Hotels on D Street.

Geographic Reach

The Boston-based construction firm operates nationwide across the Northeast South and West Coast regions. Its offices are located Oakland and San Jose California; Texas; Boston; Miami; Los Angeles; San Diego; San Francisco; New York; West Palm Beach and Estero Florida.

Sales and Marketing

Suffolk Construction offers its services for projects in the assisted living aviation and transportation commercial education entertainment government healthcare hospitality non-profit residential retail and science and technology sectors.

The company has also worked on projects for federal and local governments. In the past Suffolk has built for the Army Corps of Engineers the US Marine Corps and US Navy.

Strategy

Suffolk made a diversification and rebranding effort to expand services beyond construction into startup funding and academic research and development.

The diversification strategy focused on leveraging its core competency of construction and expanding into additional service lines to create a fully integrated platform.

As part of its new strategy Suffolk plans to build "The Garage" an incubator with up to 30000 sq. ft. for academic partnerships startups co-working spaces and industry-related research and experimentation adjacent to the firm's Boston headquarters. The firm says this will allow for in-house product development and industry problem solving.

Company Background

Already a successful builder in the New England area Suffolk Construction has expanded nationally in the past through acquisitions. In 2009 it bought Massachusetts-based William A. Berry & Son creating Suffolk's Berry Division which specializes in health care and biomedical projects.

Suffolk Construction also acquired The Dietze Construction Group based in Ashburn Virginia in 2010. The deal strengthened Suffolk's position in the Mid-Atlantic region and expanded its ability to serve the government health care education science/technology and commercial sectors. Giving the company a boost in the West Suffolk Construction acquired Southern California-based ROEL Construction in 2011.

EXECUTIVES

Chairman And Ceo, John F. Fish
President West Region, Andrew J. (Andy) Ball
Evp And Cfo, Michael (Mike) Azarela
Director Operations Special Projects Division, Mark L. DiNapoli
President & General Manager Southeast Region, Rex B. Kirby
General Manager San Diego, Wayne Hickey
Chief Operating Officer San Francisco Office, Michael (Mike) DiNapoli
Executive Vice President Work Acquisition Northeast Region, Peter Welsh
President Healthcare/science And Technology & Chief Innovation Officer, Peter Campot
Vice President And Chief Information Officer, Corren Collura
Evp And General Manager Mid-atlantic Region, Stephen Skinner
Vice President & Chief Operating Officer Commercial Education And Government Northeast Region, Angus Leary
Executive Vice President Of National Business Development, Christopher Woods
Senior Vice President Chief Information Officer, Kevin McDonough
Executive Vice President And General Manager, Jeffrey Gouveia
Vice President Retail, Mike DiNapoli
Executive Vice President And Chief Innovation Officer, Chris Mayer
Vice President Customer Soluti, Chris Gedrich
Vice President Preconstruction, David Slomsky
Vice President, Christopher Debruin
Treas, Mike Lindblom

LOCATIONS

HQ: SUFFOLK CONSTRUCTION COMPANY, INC.
65 ALLERTON ST, BOSTON, MA 021192923
Phone: 617 445-3500
Web: WWW.SUFFOLK.COM

PRODUCTS/OPERATIONS

Selected Services

Building information modeling
Construction management
Design/build
General contracting
Preconstruction
Sustainable building

COMPETITORS

Balfour Beatty Construction
Clark Enterprises
DooleyMack
Kraus-Anderson
McCarthy Building
Pepper Construction
Swinerton
Turner Corporation
Tutor Perini
Walsh Group
Whiting-Turner

HISTORICAL FINANCIALS

Company Type: Private

Income Statement — FYE: August 31

	REVENUE ($ mil.)	NET INCOME ($ mil.)	NET PROFIT MARGIN	EMPLOYEES
08/15	2,500	0	—	1,150
08/14	1,761	0	—	—
08/13	1,825	0	—	—
Annual Growth	17.0%	—	—	—

2015 Year-End Financials

Return on assets: —
Return on equity: —
Current ratio: 1.10
Cash ($ mil.): 126

SUMMIT COUNTY

EXECUTIVES

Prin, Russell M Pry
Exec Director*, Jim McCarthy
Deputy Dir*, Patrick Bravo
Training, Dave Rankin
Human Resources, Donna Testa
Social Worker, Jillian Palowski
Licensed Social Worker, Judie Sturgill
Information Technology Manager, Todd Schauffler
Highway Technician, Lisa King
Auditors: DAVE YOST COLUMBUS OHIO

LOCATIONS

HQ: SUMMIT COUNTY
650 DAN ST, AKRON, OH 443103909
Phone: 330 643-2500
Web: WWW.CO.SUMMITOH.NET

HISTORICAL FINANCIALS

Company Type: Private

Income Statement — FYE: December 31

	REVENUE ($ mil.)	NET INCOME ($ mil.)	NET PROFIT MARGIN	EMPLOYEES
12/19	544	126	23.2%	3,354
12/18	421	(4)	—	—
12/17	412	(7)	—	—
12/16	401	0	0.1%	—
Annual Growth	10.7%	589.9%	—	—

2019 Year-End Financials

Return on assets: 10.7%
Return on equity: 32.9%
Current ratio: —
Cash ($ mil.): 5

SUN COAST RESOURCES, INC.

Breaking the glass ceiling with large containers of Texas tea woman-owned Sun Coast Resources buys refined oil and sells it to more than 10000 third-party customers such airlines and construction educational energy industrial and retail companies in about 40 states. The company has an extensive truck fleet (more than 1000 vehicles) and delivers gasoline and diesel fuels marine and aviation fuels and lubricants. It also provides oilfield transportation and services onsite and fleet fueling petroleum tanks and generator fueling services. Sun Coast was founded in 1985 by president and CEO Kathy Lehne.

Operations

Sun Coast carries a full line of Chevron oils and lubricants and is one of Chevron's largest lubricant distributors in the US. Other Sun Coast services include additive packages bulk storage and warehousing a computerized fleet tracking system and customized schedule and deliveries. The company has approximately 1 billion gallons of bulk fuel storage more than 10000 fuel and lubricant tanks including skid tanks aviation certified tanks emergency ISO tanks and others. Its truck fleet includes bobtails lowboys lube trucks pick-ups roll-backs and vacuum trucks.

Its transport trucks are capable of hauling approximately 6000 gallons of diesel fuel and approximately 8600 gallons of gasoline. Sun Coast's lubricant trucks are capable of hauling 2000 gallons of bulk lubricants as well as drums totes and other packaged products.

The company's products include aviation gasoline (avgas) gasoline jet fuel kerosene marine diesel ultra-low sulfur diesel fuel and Chevron Conoco Mystik Phillips 66 and TOTAL lubrication products. It also offers services card lock service filtration and fluid purification fleet fueling and mobile on-site fueling spill response and other services.

Geographic Reach

Sun Coast owns and operates more than 15 offices in Arkansas New Mexico Mississippi Oklahoma Texas and Louisiana. It also has of office and warehouse space in nine facilities in Texas. It markets its products in about 40 US states. Sun Coast also provides equipment and services in fast-growing shale plays including the Eagle Ford Eagle Ford Bryan Permian Haynesville Cline Woodford and Marcellus.

Sales and Marketing

Sun Coast provides fuel supply services and related equipment to communication companies delivery services firms government entities utilities and other fleet operators.

Company Background

It expanded into Louisiana in 2012 with the purchase of St. Martin Oil and Gas which operated a small fleet of fuel transportation trucks from two bulk storage facilities in St. Martinville and Denham Springs.

Further expanding its portfolio in 2012 the company acquired assets from bankrupt SMF Energy including its wholly owned affiliate H&W Petroleum Co. Properties included more than 100 fuel trucks and support vehicles previously used by SMF's mobile refueling operations outside of Texas and about 100 fuel and chemical transportation and support vehicles from H&W its Lufkin blending facility and fuel storage tanks across Texas.

That year Sun Coast further expanded its branded and unbranded fuel and lubricant distribution business by buying Houston-based ADA Resources.

In 2011 the company bought the commercial fuel and disaster response businesses of Cypress Texas-based Roy Moffitt Customized Fueling.

EXECUTIVES

President And Ceo, Kathy Lehne
Vp Sales And Marketing, Kyle Lehne
Director Information Technology, Bryan Frazier
President And Cfo, Sheila Kahanek
Operations Manager, Larry Bothmann

LOCATIONS

HQ: SUN COAST RESOURCES, INC.
6405 CAVALCADE ST BLDG 1, HOUSTON, TX 770264315
Phone: 713 844-9600
Web: WWW.SUNCOASTRESOURCES.COM

PRODUCTS/OPERATIONS

Selected Products

Petroleum Products
- Aviation gasoline
- High sulfur diesel fuel
- Jet fuel
- Kerosene
- Lubricants
- Marine fuels
- Mid-grade fuel
- Low sulfur diesel fuel
- Premium low sulfur diesel fuel
- Premium unleaded gasoline
- Unleaded gasoline

Oils and Lubricants
- Automatic transmission fluid
- Chain oils
- Food-grade oils
- Fuel Additives
- Gear oils
- Greases
- Heat transfer oils
- Hydraulic oils
- Metal-working oils
- Motor oils
- Refrigeration oils
- Solvents and chemicals

Selected Mergers and Acquisitions

COMPETITORS

George Warren
Global Partners
Gulf Oil
J.A.M. Distributing
Martin Resource Management
Mercury Air Group

HISTORICAL FINANCIALS

Company Type: Private

Income Statement — FYE: December 31

	REVENUE ($ mil.)	NET INCOME ($ mil.)	NET PROFIT MARGIN	EMPLOYEES
12/07	1,064	2	0.3%	1,649
12/06	864	7	0.8%	—
12/05	867	13	1.6%	—
12/04	697	3	0.4%	—
Annual Growth	15.1%	(2.7%)	—	—

2007 Year-End Financials

Return on assets: 2.3%
Return on equity: 13.4%
Current ratio: 3.30
Cash ($ mil.): —

SUN MAR MANAGEMENT SERVICES

EXECUTIVES

Ceo, Frank Johnson
Cfo, Bill Presnell
Director of Quality Assurance, Susanne Dean

LOCATIONS

HQ: SUN MAR MANAGEMENT SERVICES
3050 SATURN ST STE 201, BREA, CA 928216278
Phone: 714 577-3880

HISTORICAL FINANCIALS

Company Type: Private

Income Statement — FYE: March 31

	REVENUE ($ mil.)	NET INCOME ($ mil.)	NET PROFIT MARGIN	EMPLOYEES
03/09*	742	0	0.1%	500
12/08	6	(0)	—	—
Annual Growth	***********%	—	—	—

*Fiscal year change

SUNBELT SUPPLY L.P.

EXECUTIVES

Ceo-Pres, Scott Jackson
S Vp of Fin, Joao Vaz
Sr V Pres-Gen Counsel, Suzanne Mailes-Dineff
Senior Vice President of Busin, Dan Sisney
Purchasing Assistant, Brooke Kinsey
Sales, Jessica Tena
Branch Manager, Chuck Brock
Senior Account Manager, Don Lamb
Area Sales Manager, Gus Vasquez
Outside Sales, Jamie Jamieadams
Pff Purchasing, Jorie Landry

LOCATIONS

HQ: SUNBELT SUPPLY L.P.
3750 HWY 225, PASADENA, TX 77503
Phone: 713 672-2222
Web: WWW.SUNBELTSUPPLY.COM

HISTORICAL FINANCIALS

Company Type: Private

Income Statement — FYE: January 31

	REVENUE ($ mil.)	NET INCOME ($ mil.)	NET PROFIT MARGIN	EMPLOYEES
01/14	657	24	3.8%	573
01/13	668	28	4.3%	—
Annual Growth	(1.6%)	(14.5%)	—	—

SUNDT CONSTRUCTION, INC.

EXECUTIVES

Ceo-Pres, G Michael Hoover
Svp-Gen Counsel*, Ronald Stuff
Svp/Cfo/Treas*, Kevin M Burnett
Payroll Staff, Karolyn Comstock
Vice-President Business Develo, Cade Rowly
Coordinator, Kimberly Evans
Pres-Industrial Group, Richard Keil
Contractor, Dave Fleming
Project Director, Hal Hardister
Operations Manager, Jim Pullen
Talent Acquisition Specialist, Sarah Clapper
Auditors: MAYER HOFFMAN & MCCANN

LOCATIONS

HQ: SUNDT CONSTRUCTION, INC.
2620 S 55TH ST, TEMPE, AZ 852821903
Phone: 480 293-3000
Web: WWW.SUNDT.COM

HISTORICAL FINANCIALS

Company Type: Private

Income Statement — FYE: September 30

	REVENUE ($ mil.)	NET INCOME ($ mil.)	NET PROFIT MARGIN	EMPLOYEES
09/18	1,432	0	—	1,000
09/17	1,134	0	—	—
09/16	813	0	—	—
09/13	895	0	—	—
Annual Growth	9.8%	—	—	—

2018 Year-End Financials

Return on assets: —
Return on equity: —
Current ratio: 1.70
Cash ($ mil.): 140

SUNKIST GROWERS, INC.

Sunkist Growers is one business that is least susceptible to an outbreak of scurvy among its employees. America's oldest continually operating citrus cooperative the company is owned by California and Arizona citrus growers who farm some 300000 acres of citrus trees. Sunkist offers traditional and organic fresh oranges lemons limes grapefruit and tangerines worldwide. The co-op which operates some 20 packing facilities also makes juice and cut fruit packaged in jars. Fruit that doesn't meet fresh market standards is turned into oils and peels for use in food products made by other manufacturers. Sunkist's customers include food retailers and manufacturers and foodservice providers worldwide.

Operations

The cooperative's seasonal citrus includes Meyer lemons mandarin oranges Clementine oranges blood oranges and tangelos. Sunkist is one of the most recognized brand names in the world.

Through some 40 licensing agreements the Sunkist name appears on more than 600 beverages and other products – from vitamins to candy to soda to pistachios. It offers Sunkist Fruit Gems (gummie candies) made for the company by the Jelly Belly Candy Company.

Some 45% of Sunkist's fresh fruit sales revenues come from markets outside the US as well as more than 20% of its processed products revenues. To maintain its reach abroad Sunkist works with the US government and the governments of foreign countries to open new markets that are off limits to Western citrus growers.

Geographic Reach

California-based Sunkist operates in the Americas Europe the Middle East and Asia Pacific.

Sales and Marketing

Sunkist regularly advertises worldwide to encourage use of its citrus products and build its brand. Additionally the company leverages television to get its name out such as its alliance with the NBC motivational weight loss competition The Biggest Loser .

Sunkist which has operated a centralized sales organization since 2009 sells its products primarily to food retailers and manufacturers as well as to foodservice providers worldwide. The company is the largest marketing cooperative in the global fruit and vegetable industry.

Financial Performance

Gross annual sales of Sunkist-brand products exceed $1.2 billion worldwide.

Strategy

The company has been focused on market and portfolio expansion and getting the most from its citrus juice and oils and for-profit businesses. It is working to extend its reach to new markets such as India the Middle East and Eastern Europe where its core product has not historically been traded. To reach beyond citrus and expand its products portfolio Sunkist is concentrating on table grapes. Through a pilot program with its existing citrus growers the company markets Sunkist-branded California table grapes grown by them.

It also worked in recent years to improve the productivity of its Tipton juice processing plant. To this end Sunkist in 2012 entered a 50:50 joint venture agreement with fellow juice processor Ventura Coastal. Under the name Ventura Coastal LLC the entity operates the Ventura Coastal plant in Visalia and the Sunkist plant in Tipton. Beginning in 2013 Sunkist also partnered with Greene River Marketing to sell its Florida citrus in promising domestic and export markets.

The 2011-2012 growing season got off to a late start thanks to slow maturing fruit. Its navel orange crop grew to a manageable 88 million cartons as compared to a challenging 93-million-carton crop the previous year. Lemons started slowly as well but both demand and price picked up. Protected groves fared well during the year while unprotected ones – those outside the traditional growing areas – did not. More susceptible to the cold mandarins crops have suffered.

EXECUTIVES

Managing Director Sunkist Global, Michael Nomoto
Coo And Vp, Christian Harris
Auditors: MOSS ADAM LLP STOCKTON CALIF

LOCATIONS

HQ: SUNKIST GROWERS, INC.
27770 ENTERTAINMENT DR, VALENCIA, CA 913551092
Phone: 661 290-8900
Web: WWW.SUNKIST.COM

PRODUCTS/OPERATIONS

Selected Products

Fresh fruit
- Grapefruit
- Melo Golds
- Oro Blancos
- Pummelos
- Sweeties
- Texas Rio Star
- Western

Lemons
- Eurkea/Lisbon
- Meyer

Limes
- Key
- Persian

Mandarins
- Clementine
- Honey
- Royal
- Satsuma
- Shasta Gold
- W. Murcott

Oranges
- Cara Cara
- Moro
- Navel
- Valencia

Tangelos
- Minneola
- Orlando

Tangerines
- Dancy
- Fairchild
- Pixie

Packaged fruit
- Beverage concentrates
- Carbonated beverages (under license)
- Chilled fruit jellies (under license)
- Fruit juice
- Fruit juice drinks
- Fruit snacks (under license)
- Powdered fruit drinks
- Vitamins (under license)

COMPETITORS

Alico Inc.
Big Heart Pet Brands
Chiquita Brands
Citrus World
Coca-Cola
Dole Food
Dundee Citrus Growers
Edinburg Citrus
Fresh Del Monte Produce
Freshco
Great Western Juice
King Ranch
Lake Placid Groves
Lionel Hitchen
Louis Dreyfus Group
M&B Products
Old Orchard
Orchard House Foods
R & Z Ventures
Silver Springs
Southern Gardens Citrus
Sunny Delight
Tropicana
U.S. Sugar
Wonderful Company

HISTORICAL FINANCIALS

Company Type: Private

Income Statement FYE: October 31

	REVENUE ($ mil.)	NET INCOME ($ mil.)	NET PROFIT MARGIN	EMPLOYEES
10/19	1,147	6	0.5%	500
10/18	1,359	2	0.2%	—
10/17	1,299	9	0.7%	—
10/16	1,207	7	0.6%	—
Annual Growth	(1.7%)	(3.8%)	—	—

2019 Year-End Financials

Return on assets: 2.7%
Return on equity: 4.8%
Current ratio: 1.30
Cash ($ mil.): 23

SUNOCO PIPELINE L.P.

LOCATIONS

HQ: SUNOCO PIPELINE L.P.
4041 MARKET ST, UPPER CHICHESTER, PA 190143121
Phone: 610 859-5700

HISTORICAL FINANCIALS

Company Type: Private

Income Statement FYE: December 31

	REVENUE ($ mil.)	NET INCOME ($ mil.)	NET PROFIT MARGIN	EMPLOYEES
12/17	804	1,419	176.6%	3
12/16	1,070	796	74.4%	—
Annual Growth	(24.9%)	78.2%	—	—

SUNTORY INTERNATIONAL CORP.

Suntory USA established in the 1960s on the other side of the globe from its parent Japanese trading giant Suntory Holdings Limited imports Suntory products to the US market from its New York headquarters. Well-known offerings include wine beer and distilled spirits such as Yamazaki Single Malt Whisky and Zen Green Tea and Midori Melon liqueurs. Other operations handled by Suntory USA include a soft drink bottling business (Pepsi Bottling Ventures) a winery various restaurants and its parent's bottled water division Suntory Water Group once the second-largest bottled water producer in the US. Altogether Suntory USA comprises 17 companies contributing 4% of its parent's 2013 revenue.

EXECUTIVES

Pres, Tsuyoshi Nishizaki
Exec V Pres, Yoshihiko Kunimoto
Cfo, Tsutomu Santoki
Treas, Yoshito Shihara
SEC, Masaru Ijima
Agent, David L Hayutin
Sales Manager, Mauro Vidale
Auditors: PRICEWATERHOUSECOOPERS LLP NE

LOCATIONS

HQ: SUNTORY INTERNATIONAL CORP.
4141 PARKLAKE AVE STE 600, RALEIGH, NC 276122380
Phone: 917 756-2747

PRODUCTS/OPERATIONS

Selected Products & Brands

Beer & Happoshu
- Diet Draft Happoshu
- Hop's Draft Happoshu
- Jokki Beer
- Kinmugi Beer
- Magnum Dry Happoshu
- Malt's Beer
- The Premium Malt's Beer

Cocktails
- Calori
- Cocktail Bar
- Cocktail Calori
- Ginza Cocktail
- Super Chu-hi

Distilled Spirits
- Barley Shochu Wanko
- Daijuhyo Ko-rui Shochu
- HAKUSHU Blended Whiskey
- Hanauta Shochu Nanco
- HIBIKI Blended Whiskey
- KAKUGBIN Whiskey
- Ko-otsu Blended Shochu
- Kyogetsu GREEN
- Midori Melon liqueur
- Otsu-rui Sochu
- Suntory Shirofuda Whiskey

Sweet Potato Shochu Wanco
YAMAZAKI Single Malt Whiskey
Zen Green Tea liqueur
Wine
Akadama Sweet Wine
Delica Maison Delicious Wine
Sankaboshizai Mutenka Wine
Tomi no oka Wine
Tomi Wine
Yukisaibai Budo no Oishii Wine

COMPETITORS

Anheuser-Busch
Aquaterra Corporation
Asahi Breweries
Coca-Cola
Coca-Cola Bottling Consolidated
Coca-Cola Refreshments
Coke United
Danone Water
Diageo
Dr Pepper Snapple Group
Heineken
Kirin Holdings Company
Kokubu
Kyowa Hakko Kirin
Naked Juice
Nestlé Waters
Odwalla
PepsiCo
SABMiller
Sapporo
Takara

HISTORICAL FINANCIALS

Company Type: Private

Income Statement — FYE: December 31

	REVENUE ($ mil.)	NET INCOME ($ mil.)	NET PROFIT MARGIN	EMPLOYEES
12/10	790	60	7.7%	2,199
12/09	13	5	42.0%	—
Annual Growth	5928.4%	1002.2%	—	—

2010 Year-End Financials

Return on assets: 8.1%
Return on equity: 13.8%
Current ratio: 1.50
Cash ($ mil.): 60

SUPERIOR COMMUNICATIONS, INC.

EXECUTIVES

Chb, Solomon Chen
Pres*, Jeffrey Banks
Sr V Pres*, Robert Chen
Cfo*, Keith Kam
Legal Counsel*, Jennifer Ju
Stckhldr*, Michael Cavanah
Coo*, Mike Cost
Dir of Credit & Payables Recei*, Ava Cheung
Cmo*, Scott Shanks
Purchasing Director, Armando Jara
Procurement Coordinator, Caroline Chin
Auditors: PRICEWATERHOUSECOOPERS LLP IR

LOCATIONS

HQ: SUPERIOR COMMUNICATIONS, INC.
5027 IRWINDALE AVE # 900, IRWINDALE, CA 917062187
Phone: 877 522-4727
Web: WWW.SUPERIORCOMMUNICATIONS.COM

HISTORICAL FINANCIALS

Company Type: Private

Income Statement — FYE: December 31

	REVENUE ($ mil.)	NET INCOME ($ mil.)	NET PROFIT MARGIN	EMPLOYEES
12/14*	734	6	0.9%	273
06/13	296	2	0.7%	—
12/12	1,365	0	—	—
Annual Growth	(26.7%)	177565.4%	—	—

*Fiscal year change

2014 Year-End Financials

Return on assets: 2.2%
Return on equity: 73.8%
Current ratio: 1.10
Cash ($ mil.): 25

SUTTER BAY HOSPITALS

Sutter West Bay Hospitals (doing business as California Pacific Medical Center or CPMC) is a health care complex located in the heart of hospital-heavy San Francisco. The private not-for-profit center's four area campuses (California Davies Pacific and St. Luke's) offer acute and specialty care including obstetrics and gynecology cardiovascular services pediatrics neurosciences orthopedics and organ transplantation. With more than 1300 beds between its campuses the center also conducts professional education and biomedical clinical and behavioral research. CPMC is part of the West Bay Region division of the Sutter Health hospital system.

Operations

CPMC's Sutter Health West Bay Region also includes Novato Community Hospital Sutter Lakeside Hospital and Sutter Medical Center of Santa Rosa. In addition to acute medical services CPMC also provides outpatient services at clinics in the San Francisco area operates home health and hospice organizations and conducts health education and charity care programs.

In 2011 CPMC's Research Institute conducted more than 200 clinical trials including studies on aging cancers epilepsy diabetes cardiovascular disease osteoporosis organ transplantation and more. That year CPMC's Kidney and Pancreas Transplant Program performed the first ever single-hospital five-way kidney swap transplant in California. CPMC's Joint Replacement Center is one of the leading joint replacement centers in the Bay Area performing roughly 1200 hip knee shoulder and elbow procedures per year. It has 1859 CPMC Medical Staff (including St. Luke's) and 109 medical residents and fellows.

That year the healthcare system reported about 619400 outpatient visits and 30300 inpatient cases.

Geographic Reach

CPMC serves patients from San Francisco Marin San Mateo Oakland Berkeley Palo Alto Santa Rosa San Jose. and the Bay Area.

Strategy

In order to meet California's seismic construction standards CPMC plans to renovate or rebuild most of its hospital campuses which are among the oldest medical centers in the San Francisco area. Its $2.5 billion reorganization plan includes the construction of a new 550-bed Cathedral Hill Campus that will include a full acute care hospital plus specialized women's and children's departments. CPMC also plans to rebuild and downsize the St. Luke's campus and convert the Pacific and California campuses into ambulatory care clinics. Reconstruction efforts at the Davies campus will include a new patient pavilion and a new Davies Neurosciences Institute for expanded neurological care. Major construction projects began in 2011 and will extend through 2015.

In 2010 the company sold its outpatient kidney dialysis operations to DaVita to focus on core operations.

Company Background

In 2007 parent Sutter Health merged St. Luke's Hospital into California Pacific to help keep the ailing St. Luke's afloat; St. Luke's provides care to many of San Francisco's low-income patients. CPMC had announced plans to turn St. Luke's into an outpatient facility in 2007; however the company rescinded those plans after San Franciscans objected to the proposal.

EXECUTIVES

Board Member, Steven Cummings
Auditors: ERNST & YOUNG US LLP SAN DIEG

LOCATIONS

HQ: SUTTER BAY HOSPITALS
633 FOLSOM ST FL 5, SAN FRANCISCO, CA 941073623
Phone: 415 600-6000
Web: WWW.CPMC.ORG

PRODUCTS/OPERATIONS

Selected Hospitals

California Campus (aka Children's Hospital of San Francisco)
Davies Campus (aka Davies Medical Center or Franklin Hospital)
Pacific Campus (aka Presbyterian Medical Center)
St. Luke's Campus (aka St. Luke's Hospital)

COMPETITORS

Children's Hospital & Research Center at Oakland
Dignity Health
HCA
John Muir Health
Stanford Health Care
Tenet Healthcare
UCSF Medical
ValleyCare Health System

HISTORICAL FINANCIALS

Company Type: Private

Income Statement — FYE: December 31

	REVENUE ($ mil.)	NET INCOME ($ mil.)	NET PROFIT MARGIN	EMPLOYEES
12/11	1,616	67	4.1%	3,597
12/09	1,245	159	12.8%	—
12/08	830	168	20.3%	—
Annual Growth	24.9%	(26.5%)	—	—

2011 Year-End Financials

Return on assets: 4.3%
Return on equity: 6.6%
Current ratio: 1.20
Cash ($ mil.): 76

SUTTER HEALTH SACRAMENTO SIERRA REGION

EXECUTIVES

Ceo, Patrick E Fry
Sr Staff Pres, Darling Lones
Coordinator, Sue Hawley
Orthopedic Surgeon, Philip Orisek
Interventional Radiology, Christine Chao
Nephrology, Don Chang
Nephrology, Jackson Wang
Emergency Medicine, John Bauer
Urology, Matthew Janiga
Hospitalist, Murray Batt
Radiology, Scott Foster
Auditors: ERNST & YOUNG US LLP SAN DIEG

LOCATIONS

HQ: SUTTER HEALTH SACRAMENTO SIERRA REGION
2200 RIVER PLAZA DR, SACRAMENTO, CA 958334134
Phone: 916 733-8800
Web: WWW.SUTTERHEALTH.ORG

HISTORICAL FINANCIALS

Company Type: Private

Income Statement — FYE: December 31

	REVENUE ($ mil.)	NET INCOME ($ mil.)	NET PROFIT MARGIN	EMPLOYEES
12/13	1,884	148	7.9%	4,000
12/11	1,752	(16)	—	—
12/09	1,453	154	10.6%	—
12/02	4,634	322	6.9%	—
Annual Growth	(7.9%)	(6.8%)	—	—

2013 Year-End Financials

Return on assets: 8.6%
Return on equity: 30.8%
Current ratio: 0.30
Cash ($ mil.): 69

SUTTER ROSEVILLE MEDICAL CENTER

EXECUTIVES

Ceo, Patrick Brady
Pharmacist, Charles Elliot
Human Resources Manager, Julie Fralick
Case Manager, Mary Nourot
Senior Officer, Rebecca Thompson
Hospitalist, Prasad Jogu
Associate Planner, Lance Lowe
Senior Financial Analyst, Marthea Johnson

LOCATIONS

HQ: SUTTER ROSEVILLE MEDICAL CENTER
1 MEDICAL PLAZA DR, ROSEVILLE, CA 956613037
Phone: 916 781-1000
Web: WWW.SUTTERROSEVILLE.ORG

HISTORICAL FINANCIALS

Company Type: Private

Income Statement — FYE: December 31

	REVENUE ($ mil.)	NET INCOME ($ mil.)	NET PROFIT MARGIN	EMPLOYEES
12/17	669	126	18.9%	1,700
12/16	628	121	19.3%	—
12/15	558	74	13.3%	—
12/12	484	95	19.6%	—
Annual Growth	6.7%	5.9%	—	—

2017 Year-End Financials

Return on assets: 35.4%
Return on equity: 129.3%
Current ratio: 3.70
Cash ($ mil.): —

SUTTER VALLEY HOSPITALS

EXECUTIVES

Ceo, Anne Platt
Chief of Emergency Room, Paul R Beatty
Internal Medicine Practitioner, Prabjit Singh
Director of Business Office, Melanie Stroberg
Patient Education Director, Joanne Hasson
Director of Nursing, Nicki Allen
Human Resources Manager, Beverly Revels
Human Resources Manager, Kathy Collins
Pediatrics, Kathy Lewis
Mobile Solution, Kranthi Vallamreddy
Technical Analyst II, Raychiel Craven

LOCATIONS

HQ: SUTTER VALLEY HOSPITALS
2200 RIVER PLAZA DR, SACRAMENTO, CA 958334134
Phone: 916 733-8800
Web: WWW.SUTTERAMADOR.ORG

HISTORICAL FINANCIALS

Company Type: Private

Income Statement — FYE: December 31

	REVENUE ($ mil.)	NET INCOME ($ mil.)	NET PROFIT MARGIN	EMPLOYEES
12/19	3,614	12	0.3%	405
12/17	80	1	2.4%	—
12/16	83	8	10.3%	—
12/15	80	8	10.1%	—
Annual Growth	159.0%	10.3%	—	—

2019 Year-End Financials

Return on assets: 0.5%
Return on equity: 1.2%
Current ratio: 1.60
Cash ($ mil.): 22

SUTTER VALLEY MEDICAL FOUNDATION

EXECUTIVES

Ceo, Tom Blinn
Project Coordinator, Dalena Spahr
Coordinator, Rebeca Colom
Regional Director Nutrition, Jack Breezee
Project Manager III, Mark Hajny
Radiology, Hani Greiss
Network Engineering Manager, Robert Haubeck
Surgeon, Eric London
Director of Education, Ali Myers
Clinical Laboratory Technical, Christine Manley
External Affairs Associate, Thomas Trejo
Auditors: ERNST & YOUNG LLP ROSEVILLE

LOCATIONS

HQ: SUTTER VALLEY MEDICAL FOUNDATION
2700 GATEWAY OAKS DR, SACRAMENTO, CA 958334337
Phone: 916 887-7122
Web: WWW.SUTTERHEALTH.ORG

HISTORICAL FINANCIALS

Company Type: Private

Income Statement — FYE: December 31

	REVENUE ($ mil.)	NET INCOME ($ mil.)	NET PROFIT MARGIN	EMPLOYEES
12/19	1,651	23	1.4%	700
12/18	1,556	(2)	—	—
12/09	505	(21)	—	—
12/02	111	(7)	—	—
Annual Growth	17.2%	—	—	—

2019 Year-End Financials

Return on assets: 3.5%
Return on equity: 11.6%
Current ratio: 1.10
Cash ($ mil.): 132

SWEDISH HEALTH SERVICES

Swedish Health Services doing business as Swedish Medical Center is the largest not-for-profit health provider in the greater Seattle area. Swedish Medical operates five acute care hospitals; it also runs two ambulatory care centers and the Swedish Medical Group physician practice organization which has more than 100 primary and specialty care offices in the greater Puget Sound region. Swedish Medical is affiliated with Providence St. Joseph Health a Catholic not-for-profit organization with 50 hospitals in seven states.

Operations

Swedish Medical has more than 2800 physicians and its hospitals are home to more than 1500 beds. The network's facilities see over 57000 inpatients per year as well as 175000 emergency room visits more than 9000 births and about 39000 surgeries. Swedish Medical operates numerous institutes across its campuses including its Cancer Institute Heart and Vascular Institute Neuroscience Institute and Orthopedic Institute. Other medical specialties include transplants pediatrics and women's health.

Swedish Medical also conducts clinical research programs with as many as 700 trials being conducted at one time making it one of the largest clinical trial sites in the US. The network's research programs are supported by government and commercial partners.

Geographic Reach

Swedish Medical has three hospital locations in Seattle as well as hospitals in Edmonds and Issaquah Washington. Its ambulatory centers (with emergency and specialty facilities) are located in Redmond and Everett Washington.

Financial Performance

In 2013 the system reported $2 billion in revenue (96% of which came from patient care services) and $59 million in net operating income.

Strategy

The company grows both organically and through partnerships. Through its affiliation with Providence St. Joseph Health Swedish Medical combined with Providence's Washington facilities under a new not-for-profit holding company. The two health systems retain their independent identities but share clinical and IT resources to work towards reducing medical costs and increasing the quality of care in the region.

The company announced a $63.5 million expansion to its Swedish Edmonds hospital campus in 2014. The two-story expansion will include a new emergency department and an outpatient diagnostic imaging center.

Also in 2014 Swedish Medical launched a hematologic malignancies program to research and treat blood-based cancers such as leukemia multiple myeloma and lymphoma.

To balance the costs of growth Swedish Medical occasionally exits underperforming businesses. In 2012 for instance the company ceased operations of its Swedish Visiting Nurse Services program which provide home health care hospice and therapy services. The unit had incurred continuous losses since 2009.

Company Background

Not-for-profit Swedish Medical began in 1910 as a single hospital with 24 beds.

EXECUTIVES

Vice President Human Resources, Joanne Suffis
Interim Chief Executive Swedish Medical Group, Jon Younger, age 66
Chief Operating And Administrative Officer, June Altaras
Ceo, R. Guy Hudson
Interim Chief Medical Officer, Charles Watts
President And Chief Development Officer Swedish Medical Center Foundation, Harold A. (Jay) Vogelsang
Vice President Medical Affairs, Sandeep Sachdeva
Vice President Of Patient Care Services Chief Nursing Officer, Nancy Wood
Respiratory Therapy Director, Jim Kumpula
Senior Vice President Corporate Strategy And Marketing, Shelley Britton
Director Of Nursing, Emmett Londo
Chairman, Teresa Bigelow

LOCATIONS

HQ: SWEDISH HEALTH SERVICES
747 BROADWAY, SEATTLE, WA 981224379
Phone: 206 386-6000
Web: WWW.SWEDISH.ORG

PRODUCTS/OPERATIONS

Selected Washington Facilities

Ballard Campus (Seattle)
Cherry Hill Campus (Seattle)
Edmonds Campus (Edmonds)
First Hill Campus (Seattle)
Issaquah Campus (Issaquah)
Mill Creek Campus (ambulatory center in Everett)
Redmond Campus (ambulatory center in Redmond)

Selected Institutes and Services

Cancer Institute
Emergency Services
Heart and Vascular Institute
Neuroscience Institute
Orthopedic Institute
Pediatric Specialty Care
Primary Care
Pregnancy and Childbirth
Surgical Services
Transplant Program
Women's Health

COMPETITORS

Franciscan Health System
Harrison Medical Center
MultiCare Health System
Overlake Hospital
PeaceHealth
Seattle Children's Hospital
University of Washington
Wenatchee Valley Medical Center
Yakima Valley Memorial

HISTORICAL FINANCIALS

Company Type: Private

Income Statement — FYE: December 31

	REVENUE ($ mil.)	NET INCOME ($ mil.)	NET PROFIT MARGIN	EMPLOYEES
12/17	2,438	(9)	—	9,699
12/16	1,278	(2)	—	—
12/15	1,240	56	4.6%	—
12/14	1,127	79	7.1%	—
Annual Growth	29.3%	—	—	—

2017 Year-End Financials

Return on assets: (-0.3%)
Return on equity: (-1.2%)
Current ratio: —
Cash ($ mil.): 51

SWEDISHAMERICAN HOSPITAL

EXECUTIVES

Ceo, Bill Gorski
V Pres-Oprs*, Michael F Richter
Cfo*, Don Haring
Exec V Pres*, John R Mecklenburg
SEC*, David R Rydell
Information Specialist, Amira Christiansen
Coordinator, Dick Robinson
Information Specialist, Nathan Sweeney
Coordinator, Patricia R Yocum
Security Staff, Matthew Bartsch
Coordinator, Julie Gadow

LOCATIONS

HQ: SWEDISHAMERICAN HOSPITAL
1401 E STATE ST, ROCKFORD, IL 611042315
Phone: 815 968-4400
Web: WWW.SWEDISHAMERICAN.ORG

HISTORICAL FINANCIALS

Company Type: Private

Income Statement — FYE: June 30

	REVENUE ($ mil.)	NET INCOME ($ mil.)	NET PROFIT MARGIN	EMPLOYEES
06/20	553	4	0.7%	1,599
06/19	555	33	6.1%	—
06/18	527	31	6.0%	—
06/17	495	16	3.4%	—
Annual Growth	3.8%	(38.0%)	—	—

2020 Year-End Financials

Return on assets: 0.4%
Return on equity: 0.8%
Current ratio: 1.20
Cash ($ mil.): 97

SWEETWATER UNION HIGH SCHOOL DISTRICT

EXECUTIVES

Supt, Karen Janney
Senior Buyer, Don Prince
School Psychologist, Rosa Ruiz
Planning Project Manager, Frank Mendoza
Senior Administrative Assistan, Erika Gonzales
Buildings, Douglas Knapp
Buildings, Isaias Arroyo
Chief Financial Officer, Javier Islas
Bus Finance Purchasing Dir, Nancy Picone
School Psychologist, Nitza Romero
Substitute Teacher, Aaron Ferguson
Auditors: CHRISTYWHITE ACCOUNTANCY CORPO

LOCATIONS

HQ: SWEETWATER UNION HIGH SCHOOL DISTRICT
1130 FIFTH AVE, CHULA VISTA, CA 919112812
Phone: 619 691-5500
Web: WWW.SWEETWATERSCHOOLS.ORG

HISTORICAL FINANCIALS

Company Type: Private

Income Statement — FYE: June 30

	REVENUE ($ mil.)	NET INCOME ($ mil.)	NET PROFIT MARGIN	EMPLOYEES
06/19	601	22	3.8%	3,521
06/18	553	(17)	—	—
06/17	546	(48)	—	—
06/16	525	77	14.8%	—
Annual Growth	4.6%	(33.7%)	—	—

SWINERTON BUILDERS, INC.

Swinerton Builders a subsidiary of Swinerton focuses on commercial and sustainable construction and renovation projects. Operating primarily in the western US its interiors group offers interior tenant finishes and remodeling working on such projects as high-tech and lab renovations hospitals retail facilities and seismic upgrades. The employee-owned company's building group focuses on new construction and retrofitting for such projects as the San Francisco Museum of Modern Art a Lockheed Martin launch vehicle assembly plant in Colorado and the Bay Bridge toll operations building in San Francisco. Swinerton Builders operates from offices in California Colorado Hawaii Texas New Mexico and Washington.

Operations

As part of its business Swinerton Builders is involved in high-tech and lab renovations hospitals retail facilities and seismic upgrades as well as new construction and retrofitting projects.

Swinerton Builders also constructs many buildings to meet environmental standards. Green projects have ranged from fire stations and retail outlets to college facilities and hotels. Swinertons' own corporate offices in California are solar powered.

Geographic Reach

The building arm of Swinerton serves the western US through offices in California Colorado Hawaii Texas Oregon and Washington. Its offices are located across California as well as in Austin Texas; Denver Colorado; Portland Oregon; Seattle Washington; and Honolulu Hawaii.

Sales and Marketing

Swinerton Builders serves a variety of sectors involving: critical facilities education government healthcare hospitality interiors multi-family residential native American and renewable energy projects. Its clients have included NASA the Federal Aviation Administration Bureau of Indian Affairs and several military and governmental entities including the US Air Force US Army US Department of Agriculture US Department of Homeland Security and the US National Park Service.

Strategy

Swinerton Builders continues to work on high-value projects around the country. In 2015 after being selected from a two-phase best value selection process the company secured a contract to lead the design-build construction project of a $46 million parking building (with some 1795 parking spaces) at the Denver International Airport (DIA) in Colorado.

The company's Swinerton Renewable Energy unit which builds and offers services to the solar utility industry expanded its capabilities in 2013 by adding comprehensive operations and maintenance (O&M) services for any solar facility across North America. The unit also launched a monitoring platform named SOLV to manage all the operational needs of customers with solar utility plants.

EXECUTIVES

Vice President, John Capener
Auditors: CLIFTONLARSONALLEN LLP WALNU

LOCATIONS

HQ: SWINERTON BUILDERS, INC.
2001 CLAYTON RD STE 700, CONCORD, CA 945202792
Phone: 415 421-2980
Web: WWW.SWINERTON.COM

PRODUCTS/OPERATIONS

Selected Services

BIM/VD&C
Corporate Services
Critical Facilities
General Contracting
Government Construction
Management & Consulting
Preconstruction
Renewable Energy
Sustainable Construction/LEED

COMPETITORS

Andersen Construction
Charles Pankow Builders
Clark Builders Group
Cordoba
DPR Construction
Devcon Construction
Gilbane Building Company
Hathaway Dinwiddie Construction
Hensel Phelps Construction
J.F. Shea
Jaynes Companies
Kitchell
Torix General Contractors
Turner Corporation
W. L. Butler
Webcor Builders
Whiting-Turner

HISTORICAL FINANCIALS

Company Type: Private

Income Statement — FYE: December 31

	REVENUE ($ mil.)	NET INCOME ($ mil.)	NET PROFIT MARGIN	EMPLOYEES
12/19	4,272	46	1.1%	900
12/18	3,541	38	1.1%	—
12/17	3,306	39	1.2%	—
12/16	3,664	53	1.5%	—
Annual Growth	5.2%	(4.8%)	—	—

2019 Year-End Financials

Return on assets: 3.3%
Return on equity: 14.6%
Current ratio: 1.30
Cash ($ mil.): 243

SWINERTON INCORPORATED

Swinerton is building up the West just as it helped rebuild San Francisco after the 1906 earthquake. One of the largest contractors in California the construction group builds commercial industrial and government facilities including resorts subsidized housing public schools soundstages hospitals and airport terminals. Through its subsidiaries (including Swinerton Builders) Swinerton offers general contracting and design/build services as well as construction and program management. The firm also provides property management for conventional subsidized and assisted living residences and is active in the renewable energy sector. The 100% employee-owned company traces its roots to 1888.

Operations

Swinerton has a special renewable energy division (Swinerton Renewable Energy) focused on solar and wind projects.

For North American solar power facilities the company also offers comprehensive operations and maintenance (O&M) services which include performance monitoring and alerting parts management service ticketing reporting preventive and corrective maintenance warranty administration and site maintenance (including vegetation mitigation and module washing).

Swinerton also has a special division to handle government construction projects delivering large-scale complex design and construction services for government agencies. Through the division Swinerton has worked on federal courthouses and administrative buildings training centers VA hospitals and military housing projects.

Geographic Reach

San Francisco-based Swinerton has more than a dozen offices throughout California Colorado Hawaii Texas Oregon and Washington.

Financial Performance

With the California construction market experiencing some of the strongest growth the industry has seen since 2008 Swinerton posted nearly $1.8 billion in revenue in 2013 about $1.4 billion of which was rung up in California.

Strategy

Swinerton's renewable energy division has been busy with a series of projects and new services coming to the fold in recent years. In 2014 Duke Energy awarded Swinerton a contract to develop a pair of 20-megawatt solar farms called the Pumpjack and Wildwood solar power projects which will power some 10000 households in central California once they're completed. In 2013 the company began offering comprehensive operations and maintenance (O&M) services for any North American solar facility.

The company also continues to work on other projects in recent years. In 2014 it started building the five-story 117000-square-foot building on behalf of the developer Breevast which secured a 12-year lease agreement on the building with file-sharing service provider Dropbox. In 2013 it started work on Telecom Real Estate Services' Block Data Center in Las Vegas with the goal of turning an existing warehouse facility into a Tier III modular data center. That year it also began construction on Chevron's 340000 square-foot office complex and campus in Midland Texas.

As one of the top waste-reducing companies in California Swinerton employs green building construction and design practices to conserve resources reduce waste and create healthier environments. The company's own headquarters building in San Francisco received Gold LEED-EB (Leadership in Energy & Environmental Design for Existing Buildings) – a top certification from the U.S. Green Building Council. Swinerton also built the LEED platinum rated NASA Ames Research Center Sustainability Base the greenest government building in history.

EXECUTIVES

Vice President Operations Manager, Gerald Mejia
Auditors: CLIFTONLARSONALLEN LLP WALNUT

LOCATIONS

HQ: SWINERTON INCORPORATED
2001 CLAYTON RD FL 7 FLR 7, SAN FRANCISCO, CA 94107
Phone: 415 421-2980
Web: WWW.SWINERTON.COM

PRODUCTS/OPERATIONS

Selected Companies and Divisions

Cameron Swinerton
Harbison-Mahony-Higgins Builders Inc. (HMH general contracting)
Swinerton Builders (general contracting)
Swinerton Government Services
Swinerton Management & Consulting (property assessment)
Swinerton Property Services (property management)
William P. Young Construction (engineering and civil construction)

Selected Projects

100 Montgomery
AECOM
Agilent Technologies
Andaz Wailea Resort & Villas
Avaya Research & Development
Bank of New York Mellon Newport Beach
Bank of New York Mellon San Francisco
Bright Horizons Colorado
Bright Horizons South Lake Union
Bruceville | 19.15 MWdc
Cache Creek Casino Resort
CalSTRS Office Headquarters
Caltech Solar Project | 1.10 MWdc
Cathedral of the Blessed Sacrament

Christopher High School
Ciné;polis Del Mar
City Center Plaza and Entry Upgrades
City Target at the Metreon
CNET Headquarters
Columbia 3 | 11.06 MWdc Columbia Sportswear
de Young Museum
Delta Airlines Sky Club
Dillard | 12.03 MWdc

COMPETITORS

A.G. Spanos
Bechtel
Beck Group
Charles Pankow Builders
Clark Construction Group
Cordoba
DPR Construction
Devcon Construction
Gilbane
Hathaway Dinwiddie Construction
Hensel Phelps Construction
J.F. Shea
JCM Partners
Kitchell
McCarthy Building
Menas Realty
PCL Construction Enterprises
Rudolph & Sletten
Skanska USA Building
Sundt
Turner Corporation
Tutor-Saliba
Webcor Builders
Western National Group
Whiting-Turner

HISTORICAL FINANCIALS

Company Type: Private

Income Statement FYE: December 31

	REVENUE ($ mil.)	NET INCOME ($ mil.)	NET PROFIT MARGIN	EMPLOYEES
12/19	4,304	42	1.0%	900
12/18	3,631	36	1.0%	—
12/17	3,365	31	0.9%	—
12/16	0	0	—	—
Annual Growth	—	—	—	—

2019 Year-End Financials

Return on assets: 2.6%
Return on equity: 14.0%
Current ratio: 1.30
Cash ($ mil.): 285

TA CHEN INTERNATIONAL, INC.

EXECUTIVES

Ceo, Johnny Hsieh
V Pres*, James Chang
V Pres*, John Hellighausen
Cfo*, Andrew Chang
Software Engineer, Chin Wang
Account Manager, Billy Reeder
Director, Bruce Ferguson
Vice President, Danny Tu
Operation Warehouse Manager, Lee Groover
Analyst Information TEC, Lexie Chan
Specialist, Phina Castillo
Auditors: CHEN & FAN ACCOUNTANCY COPR

LOCATIONS

HQ: TA CHEN INTERNATIONAL, INC.
5855 OBISPO AVE, LONG BEACH, CA 908053715
Phone: 562 808-8000
Web: WWW.TACHEN.COM

HISTORICAL FINANCIALS

Company Type: Private

Income Statement FYE: December 31

	REVENUE ($ mil.)	NET INCOME ($ mil.)	NET PROFIT MARGIN	EMPLOYEES
12/17	1,257	32	2.6%	557
12/14	1,178	27	2.3%	—
12/13	904	8	1.0%	—
Annual Growth	8.6%	38.0%	—	—

2017 Year-End Financials

Return on assets: 3.2%
Return on equity: 7.8%
Current ratio: 6.10
Cash ($ mil.): 3

TACOMA PUBLIC SCHOOLS

EXECUTIVES

Supt, Carla Fantorno
Pres*, Debbie Winskill
V Pres*, Kurt Miller
Coo*, Christopher Williams
Coordinator, Deana Siegel
Payroll Staff, Maggie Thomas
Technology/Computer Coord, Shaun Taylor
Director of Budget, Kristin Bell
Psychologist, Tracy Pennington
Officer, John Hines
Director of Internal Audit, Paul Walker

LOCATIONS

HQ: TACOMA PUBLIC SCHOOLS
601 S 8TH ST, TACOMA, WA 984054614
Phone: 253 571-1000
Web: WWW.TACOMASCHOOLS.ORG

HISTORICAL FINANCIALS

Company Type: Private

Income Statement FYE: August 31

	REVENUE ($ mil.)	NET INCOME ($ mil.)	NET PROFIT MARGIN	EMPLOYEES
08/19	544	(57)	—	3,700
08/18	495	(50)	—	—
08/17	469	3	0.8%	—
08/06	41	(2)	—	—
Annual Growth	21.9%	—	—	—

2019 Year-End Financials

Return on assets: (-4.3%)
Return on equity: (-16.6%)
Current ratio: —
Cash ($ mil.): 8

TALEN ENERGY SUPPLY, LLC

EXECUTIVES

Svp And Chief Administrative Officer, James E. (Jim) Schinski
Svp And Chief Commercial Officer, Clarence J. (Joe) Hopf
President And Ceo, Paul A Farr
Svp Cfo And Chief Accounting Officer, Jeremy R. McGuire
Svp And Chief Nuclear Officer, Timothy S. Rausch
Auditors: ERNST & YOUNG LLP PHILADELPHI

LOCATIONS

HQ: TALEN ENERGY SUPPLY, LLC
600 HAMILTON ST STE 600 # 600, ALLENTOWN, PA 181012130
Phone: 888 211-6011
Web: WWW.PPLWEB.COM

HISTORICAL FINANCIALS

Company Type: Private

Income Statement FYE: December 31

	REVENUE ($ mil.)	NET INCOME ($ mil.)	NET PROFIT MARGIN	EMPLOYEES
12/19	2,597	(8)	—	4,981
12/18	2,714	(37)	—	—
12/16	3,913	(352)	—	—
12/15	4,481	(341)	—	—
Annual Growth	(12.7%)	—	—	—

2019 Year-End Financials

Return on assets: (-0.1%)
Return on equity: (-0.4%)
Current ratio: 1.10
Cash ($ mil.): 72

TALLAHASSEE MEMORIAL HEALTHCARE, INC.

Tallahassee Memorial HealthCare (TMH) aims to take the hassle out of health care. The community health system serves residents of Florida's state capital and its surrounding communities. The system is anchored by Tallahassee Memorial Hospital a not-for-profit facility with more than 770 beds and about 560 physicians on staff who represent some 50 different specialties. TMH provides general medical and surgical care as well as specialty care in areas such as oncology rehabilitation women's and children's health obesity and diabetes. TMH also has a trauma center offers a family practice residency program and provides primary medical care through a handful of regional clinics.

Operations

TMH is Florida's eighth-largest hospital boasting more than 24000 inpatient admissions per year. As part of its operations TMH has a 60-bed psychiatric hospital and offers adult day care and home health care services. It operates the only Level II trauma center in the region which benefits from newly added telemedicine equipment that includes videoconferencing. Trauma centers are specially trained and equipped to handle severe injuries and all such patients in the area are routed to trauma certified facilities.

The system partners with the H. Lee Moffitt Cancer Center & Research Institute in Tampa to allow cancer patients to participate in clinical trials and other experimental and research opportunities.

The system offers a range of cardiovascular services from diagnostic procedures to open-heart surgery a designated acute brain and spinal cord injury center and a 110000-sq.-ft. childbirth facility – the region's only Level Three Neonatal Intensive Care Unit.

In 2014 the hospital had 122100 emergency and urgent care visits and 29586 general admissions.

Geographic Reach

TMH serves 17 counties across North Florida and South Georgia.

Financial Performance

In 2014 TMH's net revenues increased by 7% due to higher net patient service revenues (net of contractual allowances and discounts).

The company's net income rose by 15% due to higher net revenues and a decrease in interest.

TMH's operating cash inflow in 2014 increased by 16%.

Strategy

The medical facility operates the Tallahassee Memorial Transition Center created in partnership with Capital Health Plan and Florida State University College of Medicine. The center was designed to improve wellness through new approaches and collaborative research. Looking to position itself as a regional center for healthcare Tallahassee Memorial has plans to roll out more new services and add physicians.

In 2015 the hospital and Apalachee Center expanded their agreement to include administrative management of Tallahassee Memorial behavioral health services by Apalachee Center to improve behavioral health services in the community. As part of an earlier agreement the company will continue to provide some psychiatric medical coverage for Apalachee Center's inpatient services as well as providing all psychiatric medical services at the Tallahassee Memorial Behavioral Health Center.

In 2014 TMH and Doctors' Memorial Hospital signed an agreement to create an equal governance partnership between the two institutions that will ultimately enhance services to Doctors' Memorial Hospital and expand its role in Taylor County's health care system.

To expand its capabilities TMH opened the Tallahassee Memorial Emergency Center - Northeast in mid-2013 and broke ground in 2013 on a new surgery and adult intensive care facility that's anticipated to cost as much as $175 million.

Company Background

TMH was founded in 1948.

EXECUTIVES

Vp And Cfo, William (Bill) Giudice
Vp And Coo, Jason Moore
Vp And Cio, Don Lindsey
President And Ceo Tmh Foundation, Paula Fortunas
Chief Medical Officer, Dean Watson
Administrator Behavioral Health Center, Carl Mahler
Director Premier Health And Fitness Center, Len Harvey
Administrator Orthopedic And Neurological Services, Judy Greenwald
Administrator Surgery Services, David Thompson
President And Ceo, G. Mark O'Bryant
Vp And Chief Nursing Officer, Barbara Alford
Administrator Cancer Center, Matt Sherer
Interim Administrator Emergency Medicine Services, Eric Hartigan
Administrator Heart And Vascular Center, Terri McDonald
Administrator Regional Development Population Health And Telemedicine, Lauren Faison
Administrator Women's Pavilion And Children's Center, Connie Styons
Director Of Nursing, Bradley Stewart
Vice President, Stephanie Derzypolski
Medical Records Director, Gail Robinson
Chairman, Glenda Thornton
Medical Secretary, Jan Raymond
Unit Secretary, Tracy Blue
Unit Secretary, Jureen Lamb
Department Secretary, Shirley Heuring
Unit Secretary In Surgery, Doris Chester
Md Secretary, Carlos Campo

LOCATIONS

HQ: TALLAHASSEE MEMORIAL HEALTHCARE, INC.
1300 MICCOSUKEE RD, TALLAHASSEE, FL 323085054
Phone: 850 431-1155
Web: WWW.TMH.ORG

PRODUCTS/OPERATIONS

2014 sales

	% of total
Hospitals	97
TMHV	1
Medicus	2
Total	**100**

Selected Services

Behavioral Health Center
Rehabilitation Center
Cancer Center
Bixler Emergency Center
Heart & Vascular Center
Diabetes Center
Orthopedic Center
NeuroScience Center
Surgical Services
Women's Pavilion
Home Health Care
Clinical Genetics Center
Bariatric Center
Chronic Pain Management
Lipid Center

COMPETITORS

Adventist Health System Sunbelt Healthcare
Baptist Health System
Bay Medical Center
H. Lee Moffitt Cancer Center & Research Institute
HCA
Jackson County Hospital of Florida
Munroe Regional Health System
Sacred Heart Health System
UF&Shands

HISTORICAL FINANCIALS

Company Type: Private

Income Statement — FYE: September 30

	REVENUE ($ mil.)	NET INCOME ($ mil.)	NET PROFIT MARGIN	EMPLOYEES
09/15	589	38	6.5%	6,430
09/14	532	33	6.2%	—
09/13	566	31	5.6%	—
09/12	479	40	8.4%	—
Annual Growth	7.1%	(1.4%)	—	—

2015 Year-End Financials

Return on assets: 6.3%
Return on equity: 14.0%
Current ratio: 3.60
Cash ($ mil.): 227

TALLGRASS ENERGY, LP

Tallgrass Energy holds 22.5% of (and manages) Tallgrass Equity which itself owns (through Tallgrass MLP GP LLC) all of Tallgrass Energy Partners' (TEP) incentive distribution rights and a 1.4% general partner interest in TEP. Tallgrass Equity owns a 32.75% limited partner interest in TEP. TEP's business consists of the Tallgrass Interstate Gas Transmission (TIGT) system (in Colorado Kansas Missouri Nebraska and Wyoming); the Trailblazer Pipeline (Colorado Wyoming and Nebraska); a 66.7% membership interest in Tallgrass Pony Express Pipeline; the Casper and Douglas natural gas processing plants; and the West Frenchie Draw natural gas treating facility. It went public in 2015.

IPO

Tallgrass Energy raised $1.2 billion in its May 2015 IPO. It used the proceeds buy a 22.5% stake in Tallgrass Equity. As a result of the offering Kelso & Co. the Energy & Minerals Group and Tallgrass Energy company executives and directors reduced their collective holdings in the company from 99% to 77%.

Strategy

The company looks to TEP's stable fee-based cash flow and strong potential for future distribution growth to directly benefit the company as a result of Tallgrass Energy's interest in Tallgrass Equity.

EXECUTIVES

Ceo, William R Moler
Pres, Matthew Sheehy
Coo, Crystal Heter
Technology Associate, Carl West
Operations Manager, Charles McCoy
Supervisor Measurement, Charles Sprackling
Chief Commercial Officer, Damon Daniels
Measurement Technician, Daniel Brennan
Director, David Dehaemers
Director, Doug Griffin
General Manager, Doug Johnson
Auditors: PRICEWATERHOUSECOOPERS LLP DE

LOCATIONS

HQ: TALLGRASS ENERGY, LP
4200 W 115TH ST STE 350, LEAWOOD, KS 662112733
Phone: 913 928-6060
Web: WWW.TALLGRASSENERGYLP.COM

COMPETITORS

Colorado Interstate Gas
Kinder Morgan
Merit Energy
Newfield Exploration
Stone Energy
Western Gas Partners

HISTORICAL FINANCIALS

Company Type: Private

Income Statement — FYE: December 31

	REVENUE ($ mil.)	NET INCOME ($ mil.)	NET PROFIT MARGIN	EMPLOYEES
12/19	868	448	51.6%	800
12/18	793	467	59.0%	—
12/17	655	223	34.1%	—
12/16	605	243	40.2%	—
Annual Growth	12.8%	22.7%	—	—

2019 Year-End Financials

Return on assets: 7.2%
Return on equity: 20.5%
Current ratio: 0.70
Cash ($ mil.): 9

TARRANT COUNTY HOSPITAL DISTRICT

If Fort Worth residents are searching for health care they need look no further than Tarrant County Hospital District (dba JPS Health Network). Founded in 1906 in Fort Worth Texas the network's flagship facility John Peter Smith Hospital has approximately 540 beds and provides specialty services including orthopedics cardiology and women's health. JPS Health Network also includes behavioral health treatment center Trinity Springs Pavilion and the JPS Diagnostic & Surgery Hospital of Arlington. The company provides family medical dental and specialty care through dozens of health care centers in northern Texas.

Operations

JPS Hospital is a member of the Council of Teaching Hospitals and Health Systems (COTH).

Sales and Marketing

The health system carries a Level 1 Trauma designation across the spectrum of health care specialties meaning it is the referral hospital of choice for patients who are terribly injured.

Strategy

The health system works to improve the health of Tarrant County as a whole by training health care workers and physicians about working outside the hospital walls and within the community. The institution sponsors programs that are accredited through the Accreditation Council for Graduate Medical Education (ACGME) American Osteopathic Association (AOA) and the Council on Podiatric Medical Education (CPME).

JPS Health Network opened JPS Medical Home Southeast Tarrant a primary and specialty care facility in 2014. The following year the system relocated its Pain Management Clinic to a renovated site in Fort Worth.

EXECUTIVES

Cfo, David Salsberry
Executive Vice President Chief Medical Officer, Gary Floyd
Coo, Bill Whitman
Vice President, Scott Rule
Senior Vice President Of Human Resources And Learning, Nikki Sumpter
Vice President Of Support Services, Charles Williams
Vice President Communications And Community Affairs, Taffee Becker
Vice President Finance, Jeanna Adler
Department Chairman, Kellie Flood-Shaffer
Senior Vice President Erm, Ronald Skillens
Manager, Scott W. Fisher
Vice-chair, Trent Petty

LOCATIONS

HQ: TARRANT COUNTY HOSPITAL DISTRICT
1500 S MAIN ST, FORT WORTH, TX 761044917
Phone: 817 921-3431
Web: WWW.JPSHEALTHNET.ORG

Primary Locations – Texas

Ambulatory Surgery Center (Fort Worth)
Cardiology Center (Fort Worth)
Enrollment & Eligibility Center (Fort Worth)
Family Medicine & Surgical Specialty Center (Fort Worth)
Healing Wings AIDS Center (Fort Worth)
John Peter for Cancer Care (Fort Worth)
JPS Urgent Care Center (Fort Worth)
Lifespan Family Medicine & Pediatrics (Fort Worth)
Patient Care Pavilion (Fort Worth)
Professional Building-Medicine Clinic (Fort Worth)
Trinity Springs Pavilion for Psychiatric Services (Fort Worth)

PRODUCTS/OPERATIONS

Selected Services

Behavioral Services
Cancer
Cardiology
Dental
Geriatrics
Healing Wings HIV/AIDS Center
Orthopedics and Sports Medicine
Robotic Surgery
School-Based Health Centers
Sexual Assault Nurse Examiner Program
Stroke / N
Surgical Services
Trauma Services
Women's Services

COMPETITORS

Baylor University Medical Center
CHRISTUS Health
Community Health Systems
Cook Children's Health Care System
HCA
Harris Methodist Fort Worth Hospital
Parkland Health & Hospital System
Presbyterian Hospital of Dallas
Southwestern Medical Center
Tenet Healthcare
Texas Health Resources
The Methodist Health System
Universal Health Services

HISTORICAL FINANCIALS

Company Type: Private

Income Statement — FYE: September 30

	REVENUE ($ mil.)	NET INCOME ($ mil.)	NET PROFIT MARGIN	EMPLOYEES
09/18	632	(3)	—	3,000
09/16	576	18	3.2%	—
09/15	557	48	8.7%	—
09/14	285	48	16.9%	—
Annual Growth	22.0%	—	—	—

2018 Year-End Financials

Return on assets: (-0.3%)
Return on equity: (-0.4%)
Current ratio: 4.30
Cash ($ mil.): 161

TARRANT COUNTY TEXAS (INC)

EXECUTIVES

Administrator, G K Manieus
Cfo*, B Glen Whitley
County Exe.sec, Judy Scott
Coordinator, Lori McEndree
Finance Manager, Charles Jackson
Commissioner, Andy Nguyen
Treasurer, Charlotte Hogan-Price
Supervisor of Mental Health SE, Cobi Tittle
Deputy Assistant Director, Deborah Butler
Elections Coordinator, Germaine Woolridge
Commissioner, Roy Brooks
Auditors: KPMG LLP DALLAS TX

LOCATIONS

HQ: TARRANT COUNTY TEXAS (INC)
100 E WEATHERFORD ST, FORT WORTH, TX 761960206
Phone: 817 884-1111
Web: WWW.ACCESS.TARRANTCOUNTY.COM

HISTORICAL FINANCIALS

Company Type: Private

Income Statement — FYE: September 30

	REVENUE ($ mil.)	NET INCOME ($ mil.)	NET PROFIT MARGIN	EMPLOYEES
09/19	687	19	2.9%	3,945
09/18	650	(10)	—	—
09/17	625	(20)	—	—
09/16	597	5	1.0%	—
Annual Growth	4.8%	49.2%	—	—

TAUBER OIL COMPANY

No liquid petrochemical product is taboo for oil refiner and marketer Tauber Oil. The family-owned company markets refined petroleum products carbon black feedstocks liquefied petroleum gases chemicals and petrochemicals (including benzene styrene monomer and methanol). Tauber Oil is one of the US's leading suppliers of feedstocks for reforming and olefin cracking. It also has oil and gas exploration and production operations. Subsidiary Tauber Petrochemical was created to beef up the company's international petrochemical business. Tauber Oil which is owned by David and Richard Tauber maintains a fleet of more than 500 rail cars to supply its customers.

Operations

Tauber Oil's blending group works with refineries and producers to create a market for by-product/co-product streams. It also supplies liquid petroleum products to marine diesel customers fuel to power generators cutters for bunker blending clients and a number of other fuel applications.

The company's natural gas liquids department works with producers and consumers to create a market; the refined products department trades refined products with refiners traders distributors and other customers.

Tauber Petrochemical markets a range of products including alkylate benzene C9 aromatics ethyl benzene pyrolysis gasoline styrene monomer toluene and xylene.

Geographic Reach

The company's rail and barge fleet moves products from inland to Gulf Coast markets. It gathers blends and distributes out of tankage in Houston Texas City and on the Mississippi River. Tauber Oil's has oil and gas exploration and production operations in the East Texas South Texas the Gulf Coast of Texas Southern Louisiana and Oklahoma. (Additionally Tauber participates in 3-D seismic projects lease acquisitions and funding for geological and geophysical projects). Its Canadian Crude group works with heavy crude oil producers.

Sales and Marketing

The company transports its products via ship barge tank truck and rail car. It maintains a fleet of more than 500 rail cars to supply on-time delivery requirements to customers.

Company Background

To strengthen its finances and to focus on its core oil chemical and petrochemical businesses in 2012 the company merged its natural gas division with Interconn Resources Inc. to form Interconn Resources LLC. Interconn Resources specializes in delivering competitively priced natural gas to municipal industrial retail and governmental customers across the southeastern US.

Tauber Oil was founded in 1953 by O. J. Tauber Sr. He gained his oil and petroleum products trading experience working for a small Houston refinery called Eastern States Refining.

His son (and company executive) Richard Tauber is also the president of a small affiliated oil company Tauber Exploration and Production.

EXECUTIVES

Vice President, Steven Elliott
Vp Credit Finance, Stephen E. Hamlin
Owner And Principal, David W. Tauber
Owner And Principal, Richard E. Tauber
Vice President Residual Fuels, Ed Naspinski
Vice President Refined Products, Blake Hale
Vice President, Bob Mackenzie
Vice President Finance And Corporate Development, Matthew Crotts
Auditors: MOHLE ADAMS HOUSTON TEXAS

LOCATIONS

HQ: TAUBER OIL COMPANY
55 WAUGH DR STE 700, HOUSTON, TX 770075837
Phone: 713 869-8700
Web: WWW.TAUBEROIL.COM

PRODUCTS/OPERATIONS

Selected Products:

Natural Gas Liquids
- Butane
- Ethane
- Isobutane
- Propane

Petrochemicals
- Benzene
- Methanol
- MTBE
- Styrene monomer
- Toluene
- Xylene

Refined
- Aviation jet fuel
- Kerosene
- Low sulfur diesel
- No. 2 fuel oil

COMPETITORS

Cabot Oil & Gas
Devon Energy
Exxon Mobil
George Warren
Global Partners
Marathon Oil
Occidental Petroleum
Tesoro
Valero Energy

HISTORICAL FINANCIALS

Company Type: Private

Income Statement — FYE: December 31

	REVENUE ($ mil.)	NET INCOME ($ mil.)	NET PROFIT MARGIN	EMPLOYEES
12/14	4,831	10	0.2%	135
12/13	4,769	16	0.3%	—
12/12	5,088	21	0.4%	—
Annual Growth	(2.6%)	(29.0%)	—	—

2014 Year-End Financials

Return on assets: 2.7%
Return on equity: 6.9%
Current ratio: 1.50
Cash ($ mil.): 15

TECHNIP USA, INC.

EXECUTIVES

V Pres, Matthew Seinsheimer
Pres, Deanna Goodwin
Designer, Allan Salvador
Coordinator, Christopher Bennett
Procurement Staff, Sam Daik
Manager, Natalie Michulka
Senior Project Manager, James Lee
Refurbishment, Brett Folmar
Applications Engineer Ucos, Carlos Alvarez
Senior Buyer, Charlie Reynoso
Buyer, Constance Rice

LOCATIONS

HQ: TECHNIP USA, INC.
11740 KATY FWY STE 100, HOUSTON, TX 770791254
Phone: 281 870-1111
Web: WWW.TECHNIP.COM

HISTORICAL FINANCIALS

Company Type: Private

Income Statement — FYE: December 31

	REVENUE ($ mil.)	NET INCOME ($ mil.)	NET PROFIT MARGIN	EMPLOYEES
12/08	1,377	111	8.1%	4,346
12/04	609	(1)	—	—
12/97	225,116	0	0.0%	—
Annual Growth	(37.1%)	79.2%	—	—

2008 Year-End Financials

Return on assets: 10.7%
Return on equity: 26.5%
Current ratio: 1.20
Cash ($ mil.): 205

TECUMSEH PRODUCTS COMPANY LLC

Named for the legendary Shawnee chief Tecumseh Products makes a line of hermetically sealed compressors and heat pumps for residential and commercial refrigerators and freezers water coolers air conditioners dehumidifiers and vending machines. The company's line of scroll compressor models are suited for demanding commercial refrigeration applications and consist primarily of reciprocating and rotary designs. Tecumseh sells its products to OEMs and aftermarket distributors in more than 100 countries worldwide with more than 80% of its sales generated outside of the US. In mid-2015 Tecumseh agreed to be acquired by affiliates of Mueller Industries and Atlas Holdings for $123 million.

Geographic Reach

Tecumseh's products are manufactured in about a dozen plants in the US Brazil France (five facilities) and India (two facilities); assembly plants are located in Canada Malaysia and Mexico. Some of the company's facilities are made possible through joint ventures; one such venture is Song Jiang in China.

Sales and Marketing

The company serves 1600 customers including Whirlpool and Electrolux which together generate about 12% of the company's business. In 2014 almost 45% of the sales from its Brazilian location were made to its three largest customers. The company sells its products in 97 countries primarily through its own sales staff as well as independent sales representatives and authorized wholesale distributors. It markets its products under brand names that include Celseon Tecumseh Wintsys Masterflux Silensys and Vector.

Financial Performance

Tecumseh has suffered four straight years of declining revenues and two straight years of net losses. Revenues fell 12% from $824 million in 2013 to $724 million in 2014 as the company posted a net loss of $33 million in 2014.

The decrease in revenue for 2014 was primarily due to a 8% drop in sales of compressors used in commercial refrigeration and aftermarket applications a 23% decrease in sales of compressors for air conditioning applications and a 13% drop in sales for compressors used in household refrigeration and freezer applications. Tecumseh was also negatively affected by a competitive pricing environment in Brazil and soft market conditions in North America throughout 2014.

Strategy

Focused on growing internationally Tecumseh has invested in research and development engineering laboratories in North America Europe South America and India. It also partners with R&D facilities at universities throughout the globe to provide life science research on how its products interface with the environment.

HISTORY

Master toolmakers Ray Herrick (friend and advisor to Henry Ford and Thomas Edison) and Bill Sage founded the Michigan-based company in 1930 as Hillsdale Machine & Tool. Its first products included small tools toys and car and refrigerator parts. By 1933 Herrick controlled the company. The next year the company bought a facility in Tecumseh Michigan where it began mass-producing car and refrigerator parts. The company changed its name to Tecumseh Products in 1934 and went public in 1937.

By the end of the 1930s Tecumseh was a major producer of hermetic compressors. In 1941 its focus shifted to WWII efforts and it began making anti-aircraft projectile casings and aircraft engine parts. Herrick's son Kenneth began working for Tecumseh in 1945. Two years later a company-made compressor was used in the first home window air-conditioning unit.

Tecumseh bought two Ohio companies in 1950 and 1952 and introduced an AC compressor for cars in 1953. Two years later the company bought compressor designer Tresco and hired Joseph Layton as Tecumseh's president and CEO. Tecumseh gained entry into the gasoline engine market with the purchase of Wisconsin's Lauson Engine (1956) and Power Products (1957). Acquisitions in the 1960s allowed Tecumseh to tap into the power-train market.

EXECUTIVES

Vp Of It, Mario Gauna
Vice President Of Sales North America, Ben Long

LOCATIONS

HQ: TECUMSEH PRODUCTS COMPANY LLC
5683 HINES DR, ANN ARBOR, MI 481087901
Phone: 734 585-9500
Web: WWW.TECUMSEH.COM

2014 Sales

	$ mil.	% of total
Europe	191	26
South America		
Brazil	182	25
Other countries	45	6
North America		
US	125	18
Other countries	15	2
Asia		
India	105	14
China	13	2
Other countries	5	1
Middle East & Africa	39	6
Total	**724**	**100**

PRODUCTS/OPERATIONS

2014 Sales

	% of total
Commercial refrigeration	62
Household refrigerator & freezer	19
Residential & specialty air conditioning	19
Total	100

Selected Products

Compressors (all hermetically sealed)
- Reciprocating (for air conditioning and commercial refrigeration)
- Rotary (for room and mobile air conditioning)
- Scroll (especially designed for demanding commercial refrigeration applications)
- Highlighted Products
- A Legend Reborn
- Tecumseh "K” Kits

COMPETITORS

Brasmotor
Bristol Compressors
Daikin
Danfoss Turbocor
Emerson Electric
LG Electronics
Lennox
Mitsubishi Electric
Panasonic Corp
SANYO
Sullair
Trane Inc.
WEG Electric

HISTORICAL FINANCIALS

Company Type: Private

Income Statement FYE: December 31

	REVENUE ($ mil.)	NET INCOME ($ mil.)	NET PROFIT MARGIN	EMPLOYEES
12/14	724	(32)	—	5,800
12/13	823	(37)	—	—
12/12	854	22	2.6%	—
Annual Growth	(7.9%)	—	—	—

2014 Year-End Financials

Return on assets: (-8.3%)
Return on equity: (-21.8%)
Current ratio: 1.40
Cash ($ mil.): 42

TEKNOR APEX COMPANY

Teknor Apex offers a wide-ranging portfolio of chemicals and synthetic polymers. The company's six business divisions provide colorants (through its Teknor Color unit) vinyl compounds thermoplastic elastomers engineering thermoplastics chemicals for the polyvinyl chloride (PVC) plasticizer market and garden hoses. The company's compounds are used for building and construction consumer products industrial manufacturing electrical and electronic devices medical tools packaging and vehicular components. Founded in 1924 by Alfred A. Fain and his son-in-law Albert Pilavin Teknor invented the first plasticized (flexible) PVC.

Operations

Teknor Apex operates via six business segments.

The company's Teknor Color unit offers standard and custom colorants for polymers including olefins styrenics polyethylene terephthalate (PET) engineering thermoplastics and thermoplastic elastomers.

Teknor's vinyl products include flexible and rigid polyvinyl chloride (PVC) fire-resistant plenum PVC PVC elastomers PVC blends (including rigid blends) chlorinated PVC PVC film and halogen-free flame retardant.

The company's thermoplastic elastomers lineup comprises styrenic block copolymer (SBC) compounds polyolefin blends thermoplastic vulcanizates polyurethane compounds and other specialty blends.

Through its Engineering Thermoplastics business Teknor markets three nylon-based compounds that are used in outdoor power equipment hinges furniture and cars ? including chassis exterior and interior parts and engine components.

The company's Chemicals segment produces esters for the PVC plasticizer market under its TruVis brand. Its offerings include adipate low-viscosity trimellitate high-viscosity trimellitate and polyol esters. The chemicals are used as base stocks and additives for automotive and industrial applications metalworking fluid and grease.

Teknor also sells hoses under brands like ZeroG Neverkink Flexalloy and Apex for gardens professional landscaping farms and ranches RVs and marine vehicles industrial and construction applications and food and services.

Geographic Reach

Pawtucket Rhode Island-based Teknor Apex has about 10 US manufacturing plants (including one manufacturing plant and sales office) in California Kentucky Massachusetts the Carolinas Rhode Island Tennessee Texas and Vermont; one plant in each of Belgium Germany and China; one sales office in each of Germany the Netherlands and China; and a plant and sales office in Singapore.

Sales and Marketing

Teknor Apex serves a diverse client base including building and construction firms consumer goods producers electrical and electronics companies industrial manufacturers healthcare providers packaging companies and vehicle fabricators.

Strategy

Teknor Apex released a series of acrylic-based compounds for highly weatherable dark-color outer or "cap" layers in PVC exterior products. The company has given the entire range of these capstocks the new brand name Weatherguard.

The company and Covestro cooperated closely on compounding thermoplastic polyurethane (TPU) and signed a cooperation agreement to this effect. The products made from the agreement will be marketed under the name Desmoflex.

Company Background

The company was founded in 1924 as a tire distributor and retreader by Alfred Fain in 1924. Fain's grandson now leads the privately held company.

EXECUTIVES

Vice President Human Resources, Laurie Meisner
President, Jonathan D. Fain
Evp, Bertram M. Lederer
President, William J. (Bill) Murray
Cio, Peter Matteo
Vice President Of Information Technology, Craig White
Vice President Business Development, Robert Brookman
Senior Vice President Of Manufacturing, Bill Murray
National Accounts Manager, John Mcdermott
National Account Manager, Chris Bates
Vice President Of Human Resources, Lori Meisner
Vice President Technology, Ryszard Brzoskowski
Vice President Of The Consumer Products Division, Gil Blanchette
National Accounts Manager, Mary Newell
Treasurer, Shauneen Bourgeois
Auditors: PICCERELLI GOLSTEIN & COMPANY

LOCATIONS

HQ: TEKNOR APEX COMPANY
505 CENTRAL AVE, PAWTUCKET, RI 028611900
Phone: 401 725-8000
Web: WWW.TEKNORAPEX.COM

PRODUCTS/OPERATIONS

Selected Products and Services

Vinyl
FLEXIBLE PVC COMPOUNDS
Apex Flexible PVC
FireGuard LS FR PVC
Flexalloy PVC Elastomers
Apex PVC Blends
RIGID PVC COMPOUNDS
Apex Rigid PVC
AquaGuard CPVC
Apex Rigid PVC Blends
CALENDERED PVC FILM
Apex Calendered PVC Film
Thermoplastic Elastomers (TPE)
TPS TPV TPO AND TPU COMPOUNDS
Medalist Medical TPEs
Monprene
Sarlink
Elexar
Engineering Thermoplastics
POLYAMIDES
Chemlon
Creamid
Polyolefins
HalGuard LS HFFR Compounds
Colorants
Teknor Color
Color Store
Esters
TruVis Esters
Garden Hose

COMPETITORS

GLS
NatureWorks
PMC Global
PolyOne
RB Rubber
Synthomer
Tekni-Plex
Vulcan International

HISTORICAL FINANCIALS

Company Type: Private

Income Statement FYE: July 31

	REVENUE ($ mil.)	NET INCOME ($ mil.)	NET PROFIT MARGIN	EMPLOYEES
07/14	996	50	5.0%	2,808
07/05	574	0	—	—
Annual Growth	6.3%	—	—	—

2014 Year-End Financials

Return on assets: 6.8%
Return on equity: 5.0%
Current ratio: 2.40
Cash ($ mil.): 74

TEKSYSTEMS, INC.

TEKsystems a subsidiary of staffing giant Allegis provides IT consulting and staffing services from locations in North America Europe and Asia. Considered one of the nation's largest IT staffing firms the company places more than 80000 technical professionals each year who work in a variety of fields including telecommunications construction and engineering. TEKsystems has more than 100 locations serving about 6000 clients. Spinning off of fellow Allegis unit Aerotek TEKsystems was formed in 1994 to focus on the IT needs of clients.

Operations

TEKsystems is an industry in full-stack technology services talent services and real-world application. It offers services such as cloud enablement data analytics and insights DevOps and automation digital experience enterprise applications modern enterprise management risk and security telecom design implementation and operations.

Geographic Reach

Headquartered in Hanover Maryland the company has more than 100 locations throughout North America Europe and Asia.

Sales and Marketing

TEKsystems works to help its clients control cost mitigate risk and deliver quality product outcomes.

The company is working with over 6000 customers including 80% of the Fortune 500. It serve various industries primarily communications financial services healthcare services and government. Additional industries the company serves are aerospace and defense food and beverage agriculture automotive among others.

Strategy

TEKsystems acquired 1Strategy to leverage a mutual familiarity with the expanding portfolio of AWS cloud solutions.

Mergers and Acquisitions

In 2019 TEKsystems acquired 1Strategy a Premier Consulting partner in the AWS Partner Network. The acquisition is to leverage a mutual familiarity with the expanding portfolio of AWS cloud solutions.

EXECUTIVES

President, Keith Bozeman
Vp Of Communications, Kevin Bird
Vice President, Matthew Hannigan
Vice President Finance, Paul Oldham
Regional Vice President, Dustin Hunt
Executive Vice President Human Resources, Janet Agnello
Vice President, Jessica Schamburg
Vice President Human Resources, Jessica Duff
Auditors: PRICEWATERHOUSECOOPERS LLP BA

LOCATIONS

HQ: TEKSYSTEMS, INC.
7437 RACE RD, HANOVER, MD 210761112
Phone: 410 540-7700
Web: WWW.TEKSYSTEMS.COM

PRODUCTS/OPERATIONS

SELECTED SERVICES

IT STAFFING SOLUTIONS
Communications Staffing Services
Digital Services
End User Services
IT Applications Staffing Services
IT Direct Placement Services
Network Infrastructure Staffing Services
TEKsystems Staffing Quality Process
Time and Expense
IT SERVICES
Applications Services
Education Services
Global Delivery Network
Infrastructure Services
Project Governance
IT TALENT MANAGEMENT EXPERTISE
Local Market

Selected Markets Served

Communications
Financial services
Government
Information technology
Expertise

COMPETITORS

Acro Service
Adecco
CDI
CorSource Technology Group
Info Technologies
Kelly Services
ManpowerGroup
Prosum
Robert Half

HISTORICAL FINANCIALS

Company Type: Private

Income Statement FYE: December 31

	REVENUE ($ mil.)	NET INCOME ($ mil.)	NET PROFIT MARGIN	EMPLOYEES
12/19	4,927	0	—	2,900
12/18	4,677	0	—	—
12/17	4,350	0	—	—
12/16	4,132	0	—	—
Annual Growth	6.0%	—	—	—

2019 Year-End Financials

Return on assets: —
Return on equity: —
Current ratio: 3.50
Cash ($ mil.): 12

TEMPLE UNIVERSITY HEALTH SYSTEM, INC.

Temple University Health System (TUHS) is a network of academic and community hospitals associated with the Temple University School of Medicine. It provides primary secondary and tertiary care to residents in the Philadelphia County (Pennsylvania) area. The system includes 722-bed Temple University Hospital (a Level 1 trauma center) and a pair of community-based hospitals that provide acute and emergency care as well as the Jeanes Hospital and TUH-Episcopal Campus (home to a 120-bed behavioral health unit). TUHS supports programs in cardiology organ transplantation and oncology. In late 2019 the health system agreed to sell the Fox Chase Cancer Center to Philadelphia-based Thomas Jefferson University.

Operations

The $1.4-billion academic health system comprises Temple University Hospital TUH-Episcopal Campus TUH-Northern Campus Fox Chase Cancer Center Jeanes Hospital Temple Transport Team and Temple Physicians. It's affiliated with Temple University School of Medicine. Bermuda-based TUHS Insurance Company Ltd. is a captive insurance company established to reinsure the professional liability claims of TUHS subsidiaries.

It offers everything from specialized cardiac care and spinal rehabilitation to a lung care center a burn center and stroke treatments.

Medicare and Medicaid account for 65% of net patient revenues.

Geographic Reach

Temple University Health System serves the residents of Philadelphia.

Sales and Marketing

TUHS markets itself through TV commercials and print and billboard advertising.

Financial Performance

In fiscal 2012 revenue rose by 37% to $1.35 billion vs. 2011. It attributes the double-digit gains to increases in net patient service revenue research revenue and other revenue. The system logged $107 million in net income during the reporting period as compared to a net loss in 2011.

Strategy

TUHS concentrates on adding services and expanding its geographic reach. It added Fox Chase Cancer Center in 2012; opened the women's care center in Elkins Park Pennsylvania in 2012; opened a third urgent care facility in Jenkintown Pennsylvania in 2013; and expanded into new markets by opening the Temple Health Center City facility.

EXECUTIVES

Ceo, Michael Young
Pres*, Richard M Englert
Vp For Public Affairs*, William T Bergman
Administrative Coordinator, Diana Douglas
Manager, Kanchana Perera
Auditors: DELOITTE & TOUCHE LLP PHILADE

LOCATIONS

HQ: TEMPLE UNIVERSITY HEALTH SYSTEM, INC.
2450 W HUNTING PARK AVE, PHILADELPHIA, PA 191291302
Phone: 215 707-2000
Web: WWW.TEMPLEHEALTH.ORG

COMPETITORS

Albert Einstein Healthcare Network
Aria Health
Children's Hospital of Philadelphia
Community Health Systems
Crozer-Keystone Health System
Doylestown Hospital
Jefferson Health
Main Line Health System
Mercy Health System
North Philadelphia Health System
Northwestern Human Services
Our Lady of Lourdes Medical Center
Pennsylvania Hospital
The Magee Memorial Hospital for Convalescents
University of Pennsylvania Health System

HISTORICAL FINANCIALS

Company Type: Private

Income Statement FYE: June 30

	REVENUE ($ mil.)	NET INCOME ($ mil.)	NET PROFIT MARGIN	EMPLOYEES
06/12	1,004	(48)	—	7,573
06/11	994	45	4.6%	—
06/09	0	(0)	—	—
Annual Growth	1819.9%	—	—	—

2012 Year-End Financials

Return on assets: (-5.1%)
Return on equity: (-22.0%)
Current ratio: 2.30
Cash ($ mil.): 103

TEMPLE UNIVERSITY-OF THE COMMONWEALTH SYSTEM OF HIGHER EDUCATION

Temple University's owl mascot reflects its start as a night school but the owl's sagacity also points to the school's educational credentials. Roughly 40000 undergraduate graduate and professional students are enrolled in its more than 500 academic programs across the Philadelphia university's 17 schools. Its Health Sciences Center includes Temple University Hospital and schools that teach medicine and dentistry. Part of Pennsylvania's Commonwealth System of Higher Education Temple has eight different campuses in the Philadelphia area as well campuses in Tokyo and Rome and educational programs in China Greece France Israel Spain and the UK. The system has a student-teacher ratio of about 13:1. Dr. Russell

Conwell founded the university in 1884; it was incorporated as Temple University in 1907.

Operations

Temple's campus in suburban Ambler Pennsylvania offers programs in community and regional planning horticulture and landscape architecture. Together all of its campuses offer a combined total of about 170 bachelor's 180 master's nearly 55 doctoral and 15 doctoral professional degrees. Students can obtain professional degrees in dentistry law medicine pharmacy and podiatric medicine among others.

EXECUTIVES

Dean Fox School Of Business And Management, M. Moshe Porat
Vp Computer Services And Cio, Timothy C. O'Rourke
Dean Katz School Of Medicine, Larry R. Kaiser
Provost And Svp Academic Affairs, Hai-Lung Dai
Dean Boyer College Of Music And Dance, Robert T. Stroker
Vp Cfo And Treasurer, Ken Kaiser
President, Neil D. Theobald
Dean Of Students, Stephanie Ives
Interim Dean Tyler School Of Art, Hester Stinnett
Dean Kornberg School Of Dentistry, Amid I. Ismail
Dean College Of Education, Gregory Anderson
Dean Beasley School Of Law, JoAnne A. Epps
Dean School Of Media And Communication, David Boardman
Dean School Of Pharmacy, Peter Doukas
Dean School Of Podiatric Medicine, John A. Mattiacci
Dean College Of Public Health, Laura A. Siminoff
Dean College Of Science And Technology, Michael L. Klein
Assistant Vice President Human Resources Operations, Karen Ward
Assistant Vice President Benefits, Jennifer Silvestri
Associate Vice President And Controller, Frank Annunziato
Department Chair, Alice Hausman
Vice President, Michael Guglielmo
Associate Vice President Care Management, Steven Carson
Vice President Of Information Services, Raymond Johnson
Assistant Vice President, Anne Nadol
Associate Vice President, Larry Brandolph
Associate Vice President, Dozie Ibeh
Assistant Vice President, Shawn Kleitz
Asst. Vp Hr, Sharon Boyle
Vice President, Ryan Olson
Associate Vice President, Timm Rinehart
Senior Vice President For Government C, Karin Mormando
Associate Vice President Budget And Planning, Rick Chant
Vice President, Deanna Geddes
Assoicate Vice President Human Resources, Kim Sakil
Vice President Finance, Lee Shirley
First Vice President, Kelsey Boyd
Assoc Vice President Acad Computing Service, Sheri Stahler
Vice President, Jack Zhang
Assistant Vice President, Adam Ferrero
Associate Vice President For Finance And Administration, Joe De Jesus
Assistant Vice President For Community Relations And Economic Development, Beverly Coleman
Assistant Vice President Government Rltns, Dennis Lynch
Assistant Vice President, Nancy L Hinchcliff
Director Of Admissions, Brian F Hahn
Assistant Vice President Comp Service, Michael Taylor
Associate Vice President Bus Services, Rich Rumer
Director Of Admissions, Karin West
Vice President Student, Ariel Pierre
Vice President, Jim Cawley
Vice President Finance(treasurer), Ramesh Narasimhan
Chairman, Patrick J. (Pat) O'Connor
Vice Chairman, Anthony J. Scirica
Secretary, Mary Vesey
Secretary, Rosa Grier
Secretary, Ruby Hammond
Secretary, Valentina Cleary
Secretary, Myrla Barksdale
Secretary, Cynthia Grabusic
Secretary, Monica Dukes
Surgery Secretary, Devonna Smith
Treasurer Mens Club Soccer, Alec Jule
Secretary, Natissa L King
Graduate Secretary, Patricia Mcfadden
Secretary, Patrick Aragon
Board Member, Melissa Watts
Auditors: DELOITTE & TOUCHE LLP PHILADE

LOCATIONS

HQ: TEMPLE UNIVERSITY-OF THE COMMONWEALTH SYSTEM OF HIGHER EDUCATION
1801 N BROAD ST, PHILADELPHIA, PA 191226003
Phone: 215 204-1380
Web: WWW.TEMPLE.EDU

Selected Campuses

Philadelphia
Ambler
Center City
Fort Washington
Harrisburg
Main
Podiatric Medicine
Health Sciences Center
International
Japan
Rome Italy

HISTORICAL FINANCIALS

Company Type: Private

Income Statement — FYE: June 30

	REVENUE ($ mil.)	NET INCOME ($ mil.)	NET PROFIT MARGIN	EMPLOYEES
06/20	3,628	154	4.3%	9,061
06/13	2,635	192	7.3%	—
06/12	2,254	(37)	—	—
06/08	2,034	228	11.2%	—
Annual Growth	4.9%	(3.2%)	—	—

2020 Year-End Financials

Return on assets: 2.8%
Return on equity: 4.9%
Current ratio: 3.00
Cash ($ mil.): 930

TENASKA ENERGY, INC.

EXECUTIVES

Chb-Ceo, Howard L Hawks
Pres-Dir*, Jerry K Crouse
Dir*, Thomas E Hendricks
Exec V Pres*, Michael C Lebens
SEC*, Ronald N Quinn
Assistant Controller, Lisa Jones
Executive Vice President, David Schettler
Maintenance Manager, David Wilroy
Marketing, Heather Delmas
Executive Administrator, INA Schumacher
Marketing, Jeff Rohrig

LOCATIONS

HQ: TENASKA ENERGY, INC.
14302 FNB PKWY, OMAHA, NE 681544446
Phone: 402 691-9500
Web: WWW.TENASKA.COM

HISTORICAL FINANCIALS

Company Type: Private

Income Statement — FYE: December 31

	REVENUE ($ mil.)	NET INCOME ($ mil.)	NET PROFIT MARGIN	EMPLOYEES
12/07	654	0	—	300
12/05	10,020	0	—	—
Annual Growth	(74.4%)	—	—	—

2007 Year-End Financials

Return on assets: —
Return on equity: —
Current ratio: 1.70
Cash ($ mil.): 142

TERRACON CONSULTANTS, INC.

Employee-owned Terracon Consultants (Terracon) provides geotechnical environmental construction material evaluation pavement engineering and construction management and facilities engineering services. One of the nation's top design firms the company serves the agriculture oil & gas telecommunications commercial development and transportation sectors as well as government clients. The company has more than 150 offices in all 50 US states. It helps its customers comply with new building codes and environmental regulations assess environmental hazards and tackle the problem of aging structures.

Operations

Terracon provides practical solutions to environmental facilities geotechnical and materials engineering challenges. Environmental services includes asbestos and lead services brownfields and site redevelopment environmental management systems regulatory compliance and solid waste planning and design among others. It also provides facility engineering including building enclosure condition assessments MEP consulting engineering diagnostics structural analysis and design geotechnical consulting construction monitoring & support and construction material evaluation.

Geographic Reach

Kansas-based Terracon has operations throughout the US.

Sales and Marketing

Terracon serves variety of industries such as agriculture aquatics commercial/retail disaster response federal financial healthcare industrial oil & gas power generation/transmission telecommunications and transportation/infrastructure.

Some of its agricultural partners includes Agriliance LLC Cenex/Harvest States Helena Chemical Company Murphy Family Farms Seaboard Farms United Agri Products Terra Industries as well as its government clients such as US Air Force US Department of Agriculture NASA Department of Commerce and Federal Highway Administration.

Strategy

Terracon continues to expand its business and geographic reach through strategic acquisitions. Among its recent acquisitions are Environmental

Services Inc. and Geotechnical & Environmental Consultants Inc. Skelly and Loy and Environmental Planning Group. These acquisitions expand Terracon's business operations geographically across Georgia the Mid-Atlantic and the Southwest.

Terracon's acquisition of Environmental Services Inc. and Geotechnical & Environmental Consultants Inc. enhances the company's geographic presence and depth of services in Georgia and the Southeast. ESI and GEC's expertise and services complement its existing environmental geotechnical and materials capabilities and will allow Terracon to support its clients throughout the Southeast even more nimbly.

While Terracon's acquisition of Skelly and Loy allows it to further strengthen its service offerings and geographic resources in Pennsylvania and the Mid-Atlantic. In joining forces the companies' shared capabilities and focus on outstanding client experience allows it to bring even greater resources to clients regionally and nationally. In addition the acquisition of the Environmental Planning Group brings a tremendous wealth of experience and strong professional presence in the region further enhancing its environmental engineering and consulting services in the Southwest and Western US.

Aside from acquisitions Terracon also implemented key organizational changes in late 2019 designed to guide the company as it continues its pattern of growth.

Mergers and Acquisitions

Terracon has expanded its geotechnical environmental engineering and testing capabilities with a string of recent purchases.

In 2013 it expanded its presence in the Northeast with the acquisition of New Hampshire-based environmental consulting firm New England EnviroStrategies Inc.

In 2012 Terracon acquired California-based Earthtec Inc. a provider of geotechnical environmental special inspection and other services to clients in Northern California. Also in 2012 it purchased Utah-based IHI Environmental a provider of industrial hygiene occupational safety and environmental consulting services to public and private sector clients across the western US. Previously Terracon bought Colorado firm Geotechnical Engineering Group boosting its presence in the West; and Stafford Consulting Engineers a building envelope system specialist with a presence in the Southeast. Also that year Terracon acquired Dressler Consulting Engineers a building forensics engineering firm based in Kansas and Nodarse & Associates a Florida-based environmental geotechnical and construction materials engineering firm.

Company Background

The company was founded in Iowa in 1965 as a joint venture between Shive Hall and Hattery (civil consulting) Soil Testing Services (geotechnical testing) and Gerald Olson P.E. (the company's founder and a project engineer).

Terracon is owned by its employees. The firm was ranked 51st on the Employee Ownership 100 the list of the top 100 largest majority employee-owned companies in the US in 2012.

EXECUTIVES

Chairman President And Ceo, David Gaboury
Cfo, Roger R. Herting
Evp And Director, Dan Israel
President And Director, Swaminathan (Vasan) Srinivasan
Senior Vice President, David Harwood
Vice President Of Human Resources, Jarrett Boesche
Vice President And Regional Manager, James Bierschwale
Senior Vice President And Senior Principal And Division Manager, Alex Goharioon
Vice President National Director Power Generation And Transmission, Blair Loftis
National Account Manager, Greg Malmgren
General. Senior Vice President Division Manager, Joseph Aldern
National Account Manager, Catherine Rocky
Secretary, Blanca Jacquez
Auditors: BKD LLP KANSAS CITY MISSOUR

LOCATIONS

HQ: TERRACON CONSULTANTS, INC.
10841 S RIDGEVIEW RD, OLATHE, KS 660616456
Phone: 913 599-6886
Web: WWW.TERRACON.COM

PRODUCTS/OPERATIONS

Selected Services

Materials

Special InspectionsOn-site Observation and MonitoringConstruction Quality Control and Quality Assurance ProgramsField and Laboratory Testing and AnalysisDesign and Review of Concrete Grout and Asphaltic Concrete MixesStructural Steel Nondestructive Testi

Geotechnical
- Subsurface exploration and testing
- Foundation analysis and design
- Soil stabilization
- Groundwater control
- Pavement design

Environmental
- Site assessment
- Industrial hygiene and occupational safety
- Regulatory compliance
- Solid waste planning and design

Facilities
- Roof/waterproofing consulting
- Foundation/structural consulting
- Life cycle cost analysis
- Peer reviews
- Seismic risk assessments
- Construction administration

Selected Markets

Agriculture
Commercial/Retail
Energy
Federal
Financial
Industrial
Telecommunications
Transportation/Infrastructure

COMPETITORS

AECOM
Fluor
HNTB Companies
Jacobs Engineering
KBR

HISTORICAL FINANCIALS

Company Type: Private

Income Statement — FYE: December 31

	REVENUE ($ mil.)	NET INCOME ($ mil.)	NET PROFIT MARGIN	EMPLOYEES
12/19	804	21	2.7%	4,000
12/18	751	22	2.9%	—
Annual Growth	7.0%	(2.8%)	—	—

2019 Year-End Financials

Return on assets: 7.2%
Return on equity: 12.9%
Current ratio: 3.00
Cash ($ mil.): 6

TESLA ENERGY OPERATIONS, INC.

Ready to get off the grid? SolarCity can help. The company sells installs finances and monitors turnkey solar energy systems that convert sunlight into electricity. Its systems either mounted on a building's roof or the ground are used by residential commercial and government customers such as eBay Intel Wal-Mart and Homeland Security. SolarCity doesn't manufacture its systems but uses solar panels from Trina Solar Yingli Green Energy and Kyocera Solar and inverters from Power-One SMA Solar Technology and Schneider Electric. In late 2016 SolarCity was acquired by Tesla Motors in a deal worth $2.6 billion.

Change in Company Type

SolarCity was acquired by Tesla Motors for $2.6 billion in late 2016. Both companies will be led by Elon Musk and expect to achieve cost synergies of $150 million in the first full year after closing. By combining Tesla's new electric vehicles with SolarCity's newest solar products the companies expect to lower hardware costs reduce installation costs and improve their manufacturing efficiency.

Operations

SolarCity's main selling point is that it offers renewable energy for less than traditional utility companies. While customers feel good about choosing an alternative energy source they're also usually saving money. Much of the costs associated with new installation and monthly fees are offset by SolarCity's investment funds. To date the company has formed more than 20 investment funds and raised more than $1.5 billion from banks and other companies such as Credit Suisse Google PG&E Corporation and U.S. Bancorp. (Two funds however are being audited by the IRS.) SolarCity also depends on federal and state tax rebates and credits to lower costs and create incentives for fund investors. For example the federal government offers a tax credit of 30% to install solar power through 2016. (After 2016 the tax credit will fall to 10%.)

Electricity is sold under long-term contracts; generally customers agree to a 20-year term. Customers are either signed up as leases or power purchase agreements. Lease customers pay a fixed monthly rate while the rate for power purchase agreement customers depends on the amount of electricity the solar energy system produces. The vast majority of its customers (some 90%) "rent" the solar installations instead of buying them outright in order to keep SolarCity in charge of the product warranty.

Geographic Reach

California-based SolarCity serves customers in 16 states and the District of Columbia. Its offices and warehouses reside in Arizona California Colorado Connecticut Hawaii Maryland Massachusetts Nevada New Jersey New York Oregon Texas Canada and China. The company earned over 75% of its revenue collectively from California Arizona Colorado Hawaii and New York.

Sales and Marketing

The company's client list includes residential customers commercial entities such as Wal-Mart eBay Intel and Safeway and government entities such as the U.S. Military. SolarCity sells its products and services through a direct outside sales force from 64 sales offices in 16 states and Washington DC. (Most states have one sales office but its home state of California has 12.) It also has a call center.

Financial Performance

Fast-growing SolarCity is posting impressive revenue gains but no profits yet. Indeed the solar services company reported $255 million in sales in 2014 an increase of 56% versus 2013. The company credited the double-digit gain for 2014 to a major increase in the installation and operation of solar energy systems under lease and power purchase agreements in new and existing markets along with an increase in sales of solar energy systems and components. SolarCity's net loss for 2014 was fueled by an increase in sales and marketing costs and interest expenses.

Strategy

SolarCity installs about one of every four solar energy systems in the US but is still hungry for more. The company's products and services are available through home-improvement-retail-giant The Home Depot. Also in 2014 the company partnered with electronics retailer Best Buy to offer its products and services through some 60 Best Buy stores in California Arizona Hawaii New York and Oregon. SolarCity also partners with more than 100 homebuilders including Pulte and Del Webb. Other channel partners include Tesla Motors Viridian Energy Honda Acura and BMW.

While residential customers are important to the company going forward SolarCity is seeking to install larger solar energy systems for businesses and government customers. The company is also growing its business through acquisitions.

Mergers and Acquisitions

In mid-2014 SolarCity acquired Silevo a solar panel technology and manufacturing company. The acquisition helped to manage the company's supply chain and control the design and manufacturing of solar cells and photovoltaic panels that are a key component of its solar energy systems. The deal also enabled SolarCity to utilize and combine Silevo's technology with economies of scale to achieve significant cost reductions.

Company Background

SolarCity was founded in 2006 by CEO Lyndon Rive and his brother COO and CTO Peter Rive. The Rives are cousins of non-executive chairman Elon Musk a notable entrepreneur who co-founded PayPal and also heads Tesla Motors and SpaceX.

EXECUTIVES

Ceo, Lyndon R. Rive, $275,000 total compensation
Cto, Peter J. Rive, $275,000 total compensation
Evp General Counsel And Secretary, Seth R. Weissman, $270,000 total compensation
Evp Strategy And Global Markets, Marco Krapels
Evp Customer Operations, Brendon Merkley
Cfo, J. Radford Small
President Global Sales And Customer Experience, Toby Corey
Vice President Customer Account Management Group, Paul Brandt
Vice President Regional Sales, Courtney Reynolds
Senior Vice President Of Product Engineering, Jiunn Heng
Vice President Of Information Technology, John Germain
Vice President Inside Sales, Paul Bajus
Chairman, Elon Musk
Board Member, Antonio Gracias
Auditors: ERNST & YOUNG LLP LOS ANGELES

LOCATIONS

HQ: TESLA ENERGY OPERATIONS, INC.
3055 CLEARVIEW WAY, SAN MATEO, CA 944023709
Phone: 888 765-2489

PRODUCTS/OPERATIONS

2013 Sales

	$ mil.	% of total
Operating leases	82	51
Solar energy system	81	49
Total	**163**	**100**

Selected Products and Services

Products
Solar energy systems (panels inverters and mounting racks)

Services

Energy efficiency upgrades
Home energy evaluations

COMPETITORS

AEE Solar
Ameresco
Chevron
Conergy Inc.
First Solar
REC Solar
Real Goods Solar
SolarCraft Services
SunEdison
SunPower
Sunvalley Solar

HISTORICAL FINANCIALS

Company Type: Private

Income Statement — FYE: December 31

	REVENUE ($ mil.)	NET INCOME ($ mil.)	NET PROFIT MARGIN	EMPLOYEES
12/16	730	(820)	—	12,000
12/15	399	(768)	—	—
12/14	255	(375)	—	—
12/13	163	(151)	—	—
Annual Growth	64.6%	—	—	—

2016 Year-End Financials

Return on assets: (-9.0%)
Return on equity: (-42.5%)
Current ratio: 0.50
Cash ($ mil.): 290

TEXAS AROMATICS, LP

EXECUTIVES

Pres, Melbern G Glasscock
V Pres, Trenton L Kelley
Treasurer, Staci Voll
Accounting Team Member, Vivian Mursuli
Vice President, Edwin Echols
Scheduler, Natalie Pappas
Distribution Coordinator, Tiffany Buck
Scheduler, Anastasia Swanson
Administrative Assistant, Ann Loyo
Scheduler, Jeanette Lusk
Distribution Coordinator, Lauren Hall
Auditors: WEAVER AND TIDWELL LLP HOUST

LOCATIONS

HQ: TEXAS AROMATICS, LP
3555 TIMMONS LN STE 700, HOUSTON, TX 770276450
Phone: 713 520-2900
Web: WWW.TEXASAROMATICS.COM

HISTORICAL FINANCIALS

Company Type: Private

Income Statement — FYE: December 31

	REVENUE ($ mil.)	NET INCOME ($ mil.)	NET PROFIT MARGIN	EMPLOYEES
12/18	567	5	0.9%	20
12/17	470	9	2.0%	—
12/16	449	11	2.6%	—
12/15	531	10	2.0%	—
Annual Growth	2.2%	(20.4%)	—	—

2018 Year-End Financials

Return on assets: 7.4%
Return on equity: 13.6%
Current ratio: 2.20
Cash ($ mil.): 27

TEXAS CHILDREN'S HOSPITAL

Texas Children's Hospital (TCH) is the flagship facility of Texas Children's Hospital Integrated Delivery System. Founded in 1954 the not-for-profit hospital provides full-service medical care for children conducts extensive research and trains pediatric medical professionals. Part of the Texas Medical Center complex it has clinical facilities for every ailment ranging from psychological troubles to surgery and physical rehabilitation as well as specialized heart cancer and neurological care. TCH is the primary pediatric training facility for Baylor College of Medicine.

Operations

TCH comprises a 491-bed tertiary care pediatric facility a 115-bed obstetrics and gynecological care facility focusing on high-risk births (both located on the Texas Medical Center campus) and a 44-bed full-service pediatric facility in west Houston. The hospital includes the Jan and Dan Duncan Neurological Research Institute and the Feigin Center for pediatric research.

The hospital's staff includes more than 1500 primary physicians and other medical specialists as well as some 6000 nurses. The hospital has satellite facilities in and around Houston and it operates the Texas Children's Pediatric Associates primary care network of more than 170 physicians. The company also runs the Texas Children's Health Plan which offers Medicaid and Texas CHIP (Children's Health Insurance Plan) programs.

TCH's International coordinates care for sick children who come to Texas Children's Hospital from abroad. The international segment also sends out medical teams to care for critically ill children throughout Latin America the Middle East Europe Africa and Asia. For instance it has established a number of AIDS clinics in African countries.

The hospital performs more than 25000 surgeries annually. It has some 1.9 million patient encounters some 31000 admissions and about 117000 emergency department visits each year.

Geographic Reach

TCH includes four main facilities – its main hospital and Texas Children's Pavilion for Women at the Medical Center Texas Children's West Campus in the Houston suburb of Katy and Texas Children's The Woodlands in that suburb (opening in 2017).

Financial Performance

Though most of its revenue comes from patient care fees TCH relies heavily on donations and federal funding to supplement its operations. For instance the hospital and Baylor College of Medicine represent one of the most active and well-funded pediatric research programs in the US with more than 800 basic research and clinical studies backed by more than $100 million in annual grants.

Increased patient revenue and premiums led to a 9% rise in revenue for 2014 from $2.3 billion to $2.5 billion. Net income fell 29% to $257 million due to a decline in investment returns and increased operating expenses including salaries and benefits supplies and pharmaceuticals. Cash flow from operations rose 63% to $257 million as a result of higher accounts payable.

Strategy

TCH has been opening new facilities some in suburban locations and expanding others to reach additional patients. In 2013 it introduced the da Vinci robotic system and expanded its children's hematology center to include a dozen exam rooms and four acute care rooms. It also opened its oculoplastic clinic for pediatric patients.

In 2014 the hospital opened its in vitro fertilization lab the first in Houston to utilize the EmbryoScope embryo monitoring system. It is also building an eight-bed isolation unit at its west campus.

EXECUTIVES

Senior Vice President Human Resources And Organizational Development, Linda Aldred
Vice President Strategic Capital Projects, Robert McCleskey
President And Ceo, Mark A. Wallace, age 68
Physician-in-chief, Mark W. Kline
Evp And Cfo, Benjamin (Ben) Melson
Obstetrician/gynecologist-in-chief, Michael A. Belfort
President Texas Children's Hospital The Woodlands, Michelle Riley-Brown
President Texas Children's Hospital West Campus, Chanda Cashen Chac n
Cio, Myra Davis
Vice President Business Operations, Carlos Rodriguez
Senior Vice President For Development, John Scales
Vice President, Tabitha Rice
Assistant Vice President Facilities Operations, Bert Gumeringer
Senior Executive Assistant To H. Mallory Caldwell Senior Vice President, Leticia Ybarra
Nursing Director, Tangula Taylor
Vice President Of Public Affairs, Claire M Bassett
Vice President And General Counsel, Lance Lightfoot
Medical Director, Silvana Lawrence
Medical Director, Edward Mason
Vice President, Douglas Spade
Medical Director, Jed Nuchtern
Vice President, Maria Javallana
Vice President For Public Affairs, Shawn Davis
Assistant Vice President For Finance, Kimberly Cotner
Senior Vice President, David Holcomb
Senior Vice President, Linda Waldred
Vice President, Debra Kahanek
Medical Director Blue Bird Circle Multiple Sclerosis Clinic, Timothy Lotze
Vice President, Debra Ward
Senior Vice President Chief Information Officer, Myrar Davis
Medical Director, Brandie Nichols
Medical Director, Angie Medellin
Vice President Marketing, Jenny Dudley
Vice President Of Purchasing, Sabrina Cowans
Vice President, Dan DiPrisco
Assistant Vice President, Sara Montenegro
Medical Director, Catherine Healy
Vice President Marketing, Bobby Alford
Senior Vice President Technology, Samuel Wu
Vice President Audit Services, Randy Langenderfer
Treasurer Hospital, Doreen Mascari
Treasurer, Dorine Mascari
Unit Secretary, Maya Cross
Board Member, George Bisset
Department Secretary, Philip Abin
Department Secretary, Mayra Williams
Secretary, Susan Boykin

LOCATIONS

HQ: TEXAS CHILDREN'S HOSPITAL
6621 FANNIN ST, HOUSTON, TX 770302399
Phone: 832 824-1000
Web: WWW.TEXASCHILDRENS.ORG

PRODUCTS/OPERATIONS

2014 Sales

	$ mil.	% of total
Net patient revenue	1,530	60
Premium revenue	876	34
Medicaid & other supplemental reimbursement	59	2
Net assets released from restrictions for operations	28	1
Grants	21	1
Other income	41	2
Total	**2,558**	**100**

2014 Net Patient Revenue

	% of total
Managed care	61
Medicaid managed care	15
Medicaid	13
Self-pay	6
Commercial	5
Total	**100**

Selected Serives

Bariatric/weight control services
Certified trauma center
Chemotherapy
Dental services
Heart catheterization;diagnostic (child)
Genetic testing/counseling
HIV-AIDS services
Heart catheterization;treatment (child)
Kidney dialysis
Chemotherapy
Physical rehabilitation
Psychiatric services (Child/adolescent services Consultation and Outpatient care)
Sleep center
Sports medicine
Urgent-care center
Women's health center
Wound management services

COMPETITORS

CHRISTUS Health
Children's Hospital of Philadelphia
Children's Medical Center of Dallas
Cook Children's Health Care System
Dell Children's Medical Center
Mayo Clinic
Memorial Hermann Healthcare
Methodist Hospital System
Shriners Hospitals For Children
St. Jude Children's Research Hospital
St. Luke's Episcopal Hospital
Tenet Healthcare

HISTORICAL FINANCIALS

Company Type: Private

Income Statement — FYE: September 30

	REVENUE ($ mil.)	NET INCOME ($ mil.)	NET PROFIT MARGIN	EMPLOYEES
09/15	1,546	96	6.3%	6,000
09/14	1,383	70	5.1%	—
09/13	1,229	78	6.4%	—
09/12	2,043	289	14.2%	—
Annual Growth	(8.9%)	(30.6%)	—	—

2015 Year-End Financials

Return on assets: 2.1%
Return on equity: 3.0%
Current ratio: 1.10
Cash ($ mil.): 93

TEXAS CHRISTIAN UNIVERSITY INC

Home of the Horned Frogs (the school mascot) Texas Christian University (TCU) offers bachelor's master's and doctorate degrees in approximately 220 fields of study. More than 11000 undergraduate and graduate students attend the university's ten colleges and schools the cover fields of study ranging from liberal arts to engineering to business. TCU has nearly 700 full-time faculty members and a student-to-faculty ratio of 13:1. It also has one of the NCAA's top football programs. TCU is affiliated with the Disciples of Christ a Protestant denomination.

Operations

The TCU academic programs are organized under ten schools in fields including liberal arts communication education fine arts science and engineering nursing and health and business. It offers more than 115 bachelors approximately 65 masters and nearly 40 doctoral degrees.

Tuition fees room and board and books cost about $66600 per year for undergraduate and nearly $50540 for graduate/professional.

Geographic Reach

TCU's campus takes up about 295 acres about five miles from downtown Fort Worth.

Strategy

TCU's strategy includes fostering a diverse and inclusive university for all; promoting academic excellence and elevating its academic profile and reputation through focused and dynamic academic planning; providing a highly engaging and inclusive its student experience and recruiting and retaining a diverse world-class workforce; and telling compelling stories of TCU and its students faculty and staff.

Company Background

Brothers Addison and Randolph Clark established the school in 1873 as Addran Male and Female College (the school changed its name to Texas Christian University in 1902).

EXECUTIVES

Chancellor, Victor J. Boschini
Vice Chancellor Academic Affairs And Provost, R. Nowell Donovan
Vice Chancellor Finance And Administration, Brian G. Gutierrez
Chief Investment Officer, James R. Hille
Cto, Bryan Lucas
Dean Addran College Of Liberal Arts, F. Andrew Schoolmaster
Dean Neeley School Of Business, O. Homer Erekson
Vice Chancellor Marketing And Communication, Tracy Syler-Jones
Dean College Of Science And Engineering, Philip S. (Phil) Hartman
Vice Chancellor For Human Resources, Yohna Chambers
Dean Harris College Of Nursing & Health Sciences Professor And Executive Director Of The Health Innovation Institute, Susan Weeks
Dean Of The Bob Schieffer College Of Communication, Kris Bunton

Dean College Of Fine Arts, Anne Helmreich
Director Of Admissions, Sandra Mackey
Vice President Of Membership Development, Gillian Hogan
Panhellenic Vice President Of Community Involvement, Katie Hamilton
Vice President Of External Affairs, Jake Neal
Panhellenic Vice President Of Finance An, Nicole Dinatale
Financial Vice President Of Delta Sigma Pi, Julie Brandenburg
Panhellenic Vice President Recruitment, Simone Elices
Sigma Kappa Vice President Of Communicat, Alexandra Kester
Sigma Phi Epsilon Vice President Of Communications, Dillon Smith
Vice President Finance, Carol Campbell
Student Body Vice President For External Affairs, Hillary Shepheard
Executive Vice President, Nancy Ramsay
Senior Vice President, Emmet Smith
Vice President Of New Member Education, Mackenzie Hagge
Student Body Vice President, Ryker Thompson
Vice President Public Relations, Morgan Relyea
Ama Vice President Of Licensing, Jacky Meacham
Collegiate Scholars Vice President, Natalie Shelton
Vice President Of Communication, Alexandra Peters
Vice President Of Membership, Blake Brumley
Vice President, John Hillman
Nfso Vice President Of External Outreach, Lynsey Malin
Vice President, Alex Noetzel
Vp Of Operations, Kat Nestor
Vice President Public Relations, Madison Benveniste
Vice President Of Membership, Amanda Jackson
Autism Vice President, Carlota Silva
Vice President, Carl Stephens
Executive Vice President, Madison White
Vice President, Rich Robinson
Vice President, Rob Decamp
Vice President Of Philanthropic Service, Sam Silva
Vice President Of Communication, Jaena Delahunt
Vice President, Nick Dimento
Vice President Of Finance, Hannah Davidian
Vice President, Michael Dial
Vice President, Peyton Hance
Chairman, Clarence Scharbauer
Vice Chairman, Mark L. Johnson
Vice Chair, Kit Tennison Moncrief
Treasurer, Jack Anspach
Treasurer, James Moon
Auditors: GRANT THORNTON LLP DALLAS TE

LOCATIONS

HQ: TEXAS CHRISTIAN UNIVERSITY INC
2800 S UNIVERSITY DR, FORT WORTH, TX 761290001
Phone: 817 257-7000
Web: WWW.TCU.EDU

PRODUCTS/OPERATIONS

Selected Colleges and Schools
AddRan College of Liberal Arts
College of Communication
College of Education
College of Fine Arts
College of Science and Engineering
Harris College of Nursing and Health Sciences
John V. Roach Honors College
Neeley School of Business
Relationship with Brite Divinity School

HISTORICAL FINANCIALS

Company Type: Private

Income Statement — FYE: May 31

	REVENUE ($ mil.)	NET INCOME ($ mil.)	NET PROFIT MARGIN	EMPLOYEES
05/20	562	(47)	—	3,400
05/19	558	26	4.8%	—
05/18	521	185	35.6%	—
05/17	499	123	24.7%	—
Annual Growth	4.1%	—	—	—

2020 Year-End Financials

Return on assets: (-1.4%)
Return on equity: (-2.0%)
Current ratio: —
Cash ($ mil.): 16

TEXAS COUNTY AND DISTRICT RETIREMENT SYSTEM

EXECUTIVES

Exec Dir, Gene Glass
Cao*, Ray Smith
Deputy Dir*, Amy Bishop
Staff, Brad Eddins
Network Analyst, Brad Watkins
Contrl, Vincent Prendergast
Hedge Associate, Derek Bergquist
Investment Executive Assistant, Rachel Epstein
Accounting Manager, Tom Shephard
Investment Administrator, Vickie Dodson
Employer Plan Management Analy, Allison Coffey
Auditors: KPMG LLP AUSTIN TX

LOCATIONS

HQ: TEXAS COUNTY AND DISTRICT RETIREMENT SYSTEM
901 S MO PAC EXPY STE V50, AUSTIN, TX 787465776
Phone: 512 328-8889
Web: WWW.TCDRS.ORG

HISTORICAL FINANCIALS

Company Type: Private

Income Statement — FYE: December 31

	ASSETS ($ mil.)	NET INCOME ($ mil.)	INCOME AS % OF ASSETS	EMPLOYEES
12/16	26,387	1,761	6.7%	108
12/15	24,654	(182)	—	—
12/14	24,832	0	—	—
12/10	18,116	2,178	12.0%	—
Annual Growth	6.5%	(3.5%)	—	—

2016 Year-End Financials

Return on assets: 6.7%
Return on equity: 6.7%
Sales ($ mil): 3,030

TEXAS DEPARTMENT OF TRANSPORTATION

Bob Wills saw Miles and Miles of Texas and the Texas Department of Transportation (TxDOT) makes sure that we do too. TxDOT builds and maintains interstate US and state highways as well as farm-to-market roads throughout the state. It also oversees public transportation systems in the state. The aviation division helps local governments manage funds for airport development. In 2009 the agency transferred some its responsibilities including issuing license plates and vehicle titles to the newly created Texas Department of Motor Vehicles. The governor-appointed five-member Texas Transportation Commission oversees TxDOT's work. The agency dates back to the Texas Highway Department created in 1917.

Operations

The Texas Department of Transportation is divided into 25 districts that each supervise the construction and maintenance of state highways in their jurisdictions. These districts are further divided into four administrative regions that provide such services as information technology purchasing accounting and project management support for the districts. A major Texas city is included in each of the four regions.

Current TxDOT projects include widening Interstate 35 to six lanes throughout Central Texas and reconstructing the State Loop 12/State Highway 114 interchange to improve traffic conditions in the Dallas/Fort Worth area.

EXECUTIVES

Exec Dir, James M Bass
P.e, Deputy Exec Dir*, Marc D Williams
Chief of Staff*, Richard McMonagle
Chief Planning and Project Off, Russell Zapalac
Chief Strategy and Innovation, Darran Anderson
Revenue Accounting, Nigel Lewis
Chief Audit & Compliance Ofcr, Benito Ybarra
Chief Procurement Off, Lauren Garduno Pe
Chief Engineer, Bill Hale
Supervisor Judge Roy Bean Tic, Miguel Zuniga
Purchaser, Keith Reiss

LOCATIONS

HQ: TEXAS DEPARTMENT OF TRANSPORTATION
150 E RIVERSIDE DR, AUSTIN, TX 787041202
Phone: 512 463-8588
Web: WWW.TXDOT.GOV

HISTORICAL FINANCIALS

Company Type: Private

Income Statement — FYE: August 31

	REVENUE ($ mil.)	NET INCOME ($ mil.)	NET PROFIT MARGIN	EMPLOYEES
08/19	12,069	1,107	9.2%	14,720
08/18	10,993	1,123	10.2%	—
08/17	8,143	1,526	18.8%	—
08/16	8,699	332	3.8%	—
Annual Growth	11.5%	49.3%	—	—

2019 Year-End Financials

Return on assets: 0.8%
Return on equity: 1.2%
Current ratio: 4.00
Cash ($ mil.): 8,683

TEXAS EASTERN TRANSMISSION, LP

EXECUTIVES

Pres-Ceo-Ptnr, Martha B Wyrsch
Supervisor, Jon Huckels
Vice President of Business Dev, David Shammo
Administrative Asst III, Deanna Cordova
Sr Analyst, Eric Munsayac
Legal Secretary, Felecia Lee
Chief Communications Officer, Julie Dill
Tax Research and Planning, Lawonda Love
GM, Leah Moss
Administrative Assistant, Nancy Price
Vp Regulatory, Richard Kruse
Auditors: DELOITTE & TOUCHE LLP HOUSTO

LOCATIONS

HQ: TEXAS EASTERN TRANSMISSION, LP
5400 WESTHEIMER CT, HOUSTON, TX 770565353
Phone: 713 627-5400
Web: WWW.SPECTRAENERGY.COM

HISTORICAL FINANCIALS

Company Type: Private

Income Statement — FYE: December 31

	REVENUE ($ mil.)	NET INCOME ($ mil.)	NET PROFIT MARGIN	EMPLOYEES
12/17	1,389	347	25.0%	700
12/16	1,350	329	24.4%	—
12/12	956	406	42.5%	—
Annual Growth	7.8%	(3.1%)	—	—

TEXAS HEALTH HARRIS METHODIST HOSPITAL FORT WORTH

Harris Methodist Fort Worth Hospital is the largest and busiest hospital in Fort Worth. It is a private not-for-profit almost 730-bed tertiary care hospital serving the residents of Tarrant County and nearby communities in Texas. Harris Methodist provides both inpatient and outpatient care through its main medical center and on-site health clinics. Specialized services include emergency medicine trauma care orthopedics occupational health women's health oncology and rehabilitation. Its Harris Methodist Heart Center has about 100 beds. The hospital is the flagship facility of the Texas Health Resources hospitals system.

Operations

Harris Methodist also known as Texas Health Harris Methodist Hospital Fort Worth serves as a regional referral center. The hospital employs a medical staff of about 1000 physicians.

Sales and Marketing

To promote its services to area residents Harris Methodist uses a range of marketing avenues including print television online radio and outdoor advertising.

Strategy

To meet the growing needs of Fort Worth area residents in 2012 Harris Methodist launched a $58 million construction project to add a new emergency care center adjacent to the medical center campus. The 75000-sq. ft. center scheduled for completion in 2014 will increase the hospital's emergency room capacity from about 60 beds to 90 beds. A sky bridge will connect the new emergency care center to the main hospital.

Mergers and Acquisitions

To further expand outpatient services in 2012 Harris Methodist acquired the Clear Fork Surgery Center (now named Texas Health Outpatient Surgery Center Fort Worth). The ambulatory surgery center is located on the Harris Methodist hospital campus and was previously operated through a venture with Symbion and a group of physicians. The center performs about 10000 procedures per year.

Company Background

The organization opened its doors in 1930 the leadership of Dr. Charles Harris and the Methodist Church.

EXECUTIVES

President, Lillie Biggins
Chief Medical Officer*, Joseph Prosser
Chief Nursing Officer*, Elaine Nelson
Sr Asst, Elizabeth Goenn
Staff, Carla A Castaneda
Purchasing Coordinator, Chris Benson
Assistant Vice President Marke, Pam Marecki
Supervisor, Tommy Jackson
Evs Manager, Angela Jackson
Hospitalist, Cynthia Dockins
Senior Administrative Assistan, Roshonda Helm

LOCATIONS

HQ: TEXAS HEALTH HARRIS METHODIST HOSPITAL FORT WORTH
1301 PENNSYLVANIA AVE, FORT WORTH, TX 761042122
Phone: 817 250-2000
Web: WWW.TEXASHEALTH.ORG

PRODUCTS/OPERATIONS

Selected Centers and Services

Breast Center
Breastfeeding Resource Center
Business Health Services
Cancer
Complementary or Alternative Medicine
Diabetes
Emergency Trauma Services
Executive Health Program
Fitness Center
Heart and Vascular
Gastroenterology
Home Health
Hospitalist Program
Imaging
Infertility
Mobile Health Unit
Neurosciences
Occupational Health
Orthopedics
Outpatient Physical Therapy
Respiratory
Weight Loss
Texas Health Physician Offices Saginaw
Palliative Care
Rehabilitation
Sports Medicine
Primary Stroke Center
Surgery
Texas Health Physician Offices Keller
Vascular and Interventional Radiology
Women and Infants
Wound Care

COMPETITORS

Baylor University Medical Center
Cook Children's Health Care System
Encompass Health
HCA
JPS Health Network
Parkland Health & Hospital System
Tenet Healthcare
The Methodist Health System

HISTORICAL FINANCIALS

Company Type: Private

Income Statement — FYE: December 31

	REVENUE ($ mil.)	NET INCOME ($ mil.)	NET PROFIT MARGIN	EMPLOYEES
12/17	843	55	6.5%	3,500
12/15	770	55	7.1%	—
Annual Growth	4.6%	0.1%	—	—

TEXAS HEALTH RESOURCES

Texas Health Resources (THR) provides care of the Dallas/Fort Worth and North Texas region. The not-for-profit system includes about 30 acute care and short-stay hospitals including owned managed and joint venture facilities. THR also operates outpatient and surgical centers and physicians' offices and it maintains affiliations with imaging diagnostic rehabilitation facilities and home health agencies. THR's network includes more than 5500 doctors and more than 3800 licensed beds. Its Research and Education Institute for Texas Health Resources provides clinical studies management medical device testing and medical training services.

Operations

THR's hospitals operate under names including Texas Health Presbyterian Texas Health Arlington Memorial Texas Health Harris Methodist and Texas Health Huguley. The company operates 20 outpatient facilities and it coordinates general practice care through its physician practice groups. Its Texas Health MedSynergies unit provides office management services for doctors' offices.

Geographic Reach

THR's primary service territory includes about 25 counties in north-central Texas. It has locations in towns including Allen Alliance Arlington Azle Burleson Cleburne Craig Ranch Dallas Denton Flower Mound Fort Worth Huguley Kaufman Plano Richardson Rockwall Southlake Stephenville and Sherman.

Sales and Marketing

The organization promotes its medical services through print television outdoor online and radio advertising.

Strategy

In order to keep up with the growing population of North Texas in 2007 THR launched a $1.5 billion initiative to expand its facilities over a 10-year period. Project efforts thus far have included establishing a joint venture hospital in Flower Mound and the expansion of existing facilities. For instance in 2015 it opened a 70000 sq. ft. cancer center at Presbyterian Hospital Dallas. In 2017 it completed an expansion at its Texas Health Alliance facility which included adding 24 private beds; the same facility will also expand its emergency department. THR has also opened a number of outpatient surgery imaging wellness and specialist centers and it is now building a new 74-bed hospital campus in Frisco Texas.

In 2016 the system established a joint venture with emergency room operator Adeptus Health through which Adeptus' 27 North Texas First Choice Emergency Rooms as well as its First Texas Hospital in Carrollton became part of THR. The move helped THR as it works to expand its access points to emergency health care (an area it has struggled with).

Other expansion moves include the 2016 purchase of Forest Park Medical Center Fort Worth for $141 million and the creation of a jointly owned health plan with health insurer Aetna.

THR has also built up its information technology networks including the implementation of electronic health record (EHR) systems. In addition the organization is adding new medical professional training programs.

Company Background

THR was formed in 1997 by the merger of Harris Methodist Health System Presbyterian Healthcare System and Arlington Memorial Hospital Foundation. In 2008 the organization rebranded its hospitals unifying them all under the Texas Health Resources name.

THR had originally been the minority shareholder in a venture with Triad Hospitals to own Presbyterian Hospital of Denton. However THR grew dissatisfied when Triad was acquired by Community Health Systems in 2007. After a long legal tussle THR paid $100 million to acquire the hospital outright in 2009 and changed its name to Texas Health Presbyterian Hospital Denton. Texas Health Presbyterian found itself the focus of international media attention in 2014 when it treated the first case of Ebola on US soil.

EXECUTIVES

Evp People And Culture, Bonnie Bell
Evp Southeast Zone Operations Leader, Oscar L. Amparan
Sevp And Chief Clinical Officer, Daniel W. Varga
Evp And Cfo, Ronald R. (Ron) Long
Evp North Zone Operations Leader, Brett S. McClung
Sevp And Coo, Barclay E. Berdan
Svp And Chief Nurse Executive, Joan S. Clark
Executive Vice President And Southwest Zone Operations Leader, Kirk King
Sevp And Coo, Jeffrey L. Canose
Evp Southwest Zone Clinical Leader, Harold Berenzweig
Evp Southeast Zone Clinical Leader, Mark C. Lester
Evp North Zone Clinical Leader, Elizabeth Ransom
Evp Population Health; President Texas Health Population Health Education And Innovation Center, Tricia Nguyen
President Texas Health Physicians Group, Shawn D. Parsley
Vice President Of Information Systems, Joe Hodge
Senior Vice President Of Brand Experience, Paul Szablowski
Vice President Chief Nursing Officer, Rosemarie Aznavorian
Senior Vice President Of Care Continuum And Collaborations, Krystal Mims
Services Cmrp Senior Vice President Supply Chain Management, Shaun Clinton
Vice President Chief Learning Officer, Daniel Gandarilla
Vice President, John Wilson
Director Of Radiology Services, Tammy Ormuz
Director Of Pharmacy, Randy Martin
Vice President Treasury Services, Sandy Reeves
Radiology Medical Director, David Robinson
Director Of Health Information, Bonnie Blevins
Vice President And Chief Nursing Officer, Deborah Bostic
Vice President Human Resources, Molly Thompson
Vice President Corporate Controller, David Jackson
Vice President Applications And Ehr, Cynda Grimes
Senior Vice President Legal Counsel, Ken Kramer
Vice President Supply Chain Management, Becky Daniel
Director Of Nursing, Michelle Pecenka
Director Of Nursing, Vickie Turner
Physical Therapy Tech, Lanandra Hamilton
Senior Vice President, Robert Jones
Vice President Financial Planning, Luke Gorman
Director Of Radiology, Kevin Stone
Director Of Pharmacy, Rebecca Wilson Turner
Vice President Stakeholder Engagement, Mark Riordan
Director Of Radiology And Women's Imaging Services, Darlene Rodriguez
Ache Member Vice President Strategy And Business, Virginia Rose
Medical Director, Steven Stanley
Vice President, Teresa Martin
Medical Director, Sheila Poston
Medical Director, William Posten
Vice President Of Finance, Kay Mason
Operating Room Dir, Cheryl Moore
Director Of Pharmacy, Kimberly Machala
Medical Director, Timothy Everett Williams
Chairman, John R. Ferguson
Vice Chairman, Wesley R. Turner
Board Of Director, Mitchel Kruger
Secretary, Stacey Mcjunkin
Unit Secretary, Tina Sosebee
Secretary, Bernadina Richey
Unit Secretary, Claudia Love
Unit Secretary, Mary Kinman
Unit Secretary, Monica Dillard
Secretary, Shandlyn Hearn
Unit Secretary, Maureen Yamada
Unit Secretary, Karessa Griggs
Auditors: KMPG LLP DALLAS TEXAS

LOCATIONS

HQ: TEXAS HEALTH RESOURCES
612 E LAMAR BLVD STE 400, ARLINGTON, TX 760114125
Phone: 682 236-7900
Web: WWW.TEXASHEALTH.ORG

PRODUCTS/OPERATIONS

Selected Facilities and Affiliates

Acute Care and Specialty Hospitals
- Texas Health Arlington Memorial
- Texas Health Harris Methodist Hospital Fort Worth
- Texas Health Huguley Hospital Fort Worth South
- Texas Health Presbyterian Hospital Dallas
- Texas Health Presbyterian Hospital Flower Mound
- Texas Health Presbyterian Hospital Rockwall
- Texas Health Center for Diagnostics & Surgery Plano
- Texas Heath Heart & Vascular Hospital Arlington
- USMD Hospital at Arlington
- USMD Hospital at Fort Worth

Affiliates
- Envision Imaging of North Fort Worth
- Texas Rehabilitation Partners
- Two Forest Imaging Dallas
- Southwest Diagnostic Imaging Center

COMPETITORS

Community Health Systems
Cook Children's Health Care System
HCA
JPS Health Network
Parkland Health & Hospital System
Southwestern Medical Center
Tenet Healthcare
The Methodist Health System

HISTORICAL FINANCIALS

Company Type: Private

Income Statement — FYE: December 31

	REVENUE ($ mil.)	NET INCOME ($ mil.)	NET PROFIT MARGIN	EMPLOYEES
12/17	4,688	869	18.6%	21,277
12/13	718	285	39.8%	—
12/09	334	2	0.9%	—
12/06	2,287	2,299	100.5%	—
Annual Growth	6.7%	(8.5%)	—	—

2017 Year-End Financials

Return on assets: 9.8%
Return on equity: 14.2%
Current ratio: 1.60
Cash ($ mil.): 435

TEXAS PERMANENT SCHOOL FUND MANAGEMENT COMPANY, INC.

EXECUTIVES

Prin, Elizabeth Jones
Auditors: LISA R COLLIER CPA CFE CID

LOCATIONS

HQ: TEXAS PERMANENT SCHOOL FUND MANAGEMENT COMPANY, INC.
1701 CONGRESS AVE STE 5, AUSTIN, TX 787011402
Phone: 512 463-1814
Web: WWW.TEXAS.GOV

HISTORICAL FINANCIALS

Company Type: Private

Income Statement — FYE: August 31

	REVENUE ($ mil.)	NET INCOME ($ mil.)	NET PROFIT MARGIN	EMPLOYEES
08/17	5,375	4,154	77.3%	4
08/16	2,691	1,519	56.5%	—
Annual Growth	99.7%	173.4%	—	—

2017 Year-End Financials

Return on assets: 9.3%
Return on equity: 10.0%
Current ratio: —
Cash ($ mil.): 3,584

TEXAS STATE UNIVERSITY SYSTEM

EXECUTIVES

Chancellor, Brian McCall
Vice Chancellor For Finance, Claire Jackson
Director, Scott Cupp
Abroad Coordinator Follow, Josh Andrews

Assistant Director of Admissio, Joshua Hector
Assistant Professor of Dance, Joshua Manculich
General Counsel, Randall Sarosdy
Director Email, Rusti Wade
Graduate Teaching Assistant, Daniel Barton
Accounting Clerk, Heather Adams
Associate Professor of Art, Martin Amorous

LOCATIONS

HQ: TEXAS STATE UNIVERSITY SYSTEM
601 COLORADO ST, AUSTIN, TX 787012904
Phone: 512 463-1808
Web: WWW.TSUS.EDU

HISTORICAL FINANCIALS

Company Type: Private

Income Statement — FYE: August 31

	REVENUE ($ mil.)	NET INCOME ($ mil.)	NET PROFIT MARGIN	EMPLOYEES
08/19	878	(61)	—	3,196
08/18	862	190	22.0%	—
08/17	854	145	17.1%	—
08/16	846	126	14.9%	—
Annual Growth	1.3%	—	—	—

2019 Year-End Financials

Return on assets: (-1.4%)
Return on equity: (-4.6%)
Current ratio: 1.10
Cash ($ mil.): 410

TEXLA ENERGY MANAGEMENT, INC.

EXECUTIVES

Pres, Lacy H Williams II
Cfo-V Pres, Randy Miller
Administrator, George Fritz
Trade Analyst, Nathan Offers
Auditors: MOHLE ADAMS LLP HOUSTON TEXA

LOCATIONS

HQ: TEXLA ENERGY MANAGEMENT, INC.
1100 LA ST STE 4700, HOUSTON, TX 77002
Phone: 713 655-9900
Web: WWW.TEXLAENERGY.COM

HISTORICAL FINANCIALS

Company Type: Private

Income Statement — FYE: December 31

	REVENUE ($ mil.)	NET INCOME ($ mil.)	NET PROFIT MARGIN	EMPLOYEES
12/18	1,462	2	0.2%	19
12/17	1,291	3	0.3%	—
12/04	949	2	0.3%	—
12/03	596	1	0.2%	—
Annual Growth	6.2%	4.0%	—	—

2018 Year-End Financials

Return on assets: 1.7%
Return on equity: 11.1%
Current ratio: 1.20
Cash ($ mil.): 26

THE ADMINISTRATORS OF THE TULANE EDUCATIONAL FUND

EXECUTIVES

Vice President For Development, Luann Dozier
Assistant Vice President Of University Financial Aid, Georgia Whiddon
Vice President For Finance, JP Gooderham
Associate Vice President For Student Affairs, John Nonnamaker
Assistant Vice President For Student Affairs, Brian Johnson
Vice President Of Enrollment Management, Satyajit Dattagupta
Tsba Vice President, Lynne Firmin
Avp Information Security And Ciso, Robert Fink
Senior Executive Assistant To The Senior Vice President, Diane Gromelski
Vice President, Kristi Miller
Secretary To The Associate Dean, Linda Civello
Secretary, Mildred Freemon
Auditors: DELOITTE & TOUCHE LLP NEW ORL

LOCATIONS

HQ: THE ADMINISTRATORS OF THE TULANE EDUCATIONAL FUND
6823 SAINT CHARLES AVE, NEW ORLEANS, LA 701185665
Phone: 504 865-5000
Web: WWW.TULANE.EDU

Selected Campuses

Tulane University main uptown campus
The F. Edward Hebert Research Center (Louisiana)
The School of Continuing Studies (Louisiana and Mississippi)
The Health Sciences downtown campus
School of Medicine
School of Public Health and Tropical Medicine
Tulane Medical Center and Technology Services
The North Shore campus
Tulane National Primate Research Center (Louisiana)
The A.B. Freeman School of Business (Texas)

PRODUCTS/OPERATIONS

Selected Schools and Colleges

A.B. Freeman School of Business
Faculty of Liberal Arts and Sciences
Graduate School
Law School
Newcomb College
School of Architecture
School of Engineering
School of Medicine
School of Public Health and Tropical Medicine
School of Social Work
Tulane College
University College

HISTORICAL FINANCIALS

Company Type: Private

Income Statement — FYE: June 30

	REVENUE ($ mil.)	NET INCOME ($ mil.)	NET PROFIT MARGIN	EMPLOYEES
06/16	924	(63)	—	5,500
06/15	1,054	40	3.9%	—
06/10	738	48	6.5%	—
06/09	737	0	—	—
Annual Growth	3.3%	—	—	—

2016 Year-End Financials

Return on assets: (-2.7%)
Return on equity: (-4.5%)
Current ratio: —
Cash ($ mil.): 22

THE AEROSPACE CORPORATION

A not-for-profit company the Aerospace Corporation provides space-related research development and advisory services primarily for US government programs. Its chief sponsor is the US Air Force and its main customer have included the Space and Missile Systems Center of Air Force Space Command. Other clients have included NASA and the National Oceanic and Atmospheric Administration as well as commercial enterprises universities and international organizations. Areas of expertise include launch certification process implementation systems engineering and technology application. The Aerospace Corporation was established in 1960 and operates in around two dozen locations across about 10 states.

Operations

Officially The Aerospace Corporation operates a federally funded research and development center or FFRDC for the Air Force. FFRDCs fill a unique role in service to the government and the nation. Along with commercial industry and academia FFRDCs support government science engineering and technology development. The company also focuses in the areas of launch assurance spanning all stages of the space lifecycle from concept to operations mission success. Satellite technology includes space debris and space traffic management and satellite docking tool. Space exploration such as laser for studying the solar system testing Orion's impenetrable heat shield as well as creating astronauts' space suit.

Geographic Reach

The Aerospace Corporation's headquarters with engineering and laboratory facilities is located in El Segundo California. Major regional offices are located in Chantilly Virginia and Colorado Springs Colorado. The company has testing and research center for space systems with more than 80 specialized laboratories test analyze and troubleshoot virtually every aspect of rocket and satellite systems.

Strategy

In mid-2020 Aerospace started building a second facility in Colorado Springs. This facility recently approved by the Aerospace Board of Trustees is planned to be 70 percent classified space and includes a multi-purpose high-technology center to meet the growing requirements of the US Space Command the US Space Force and a variety of other customers.

Construction started in July with ground-breaking activities planned for this fall. Completion and occupancy are scheduled for spring 2022.

Company Background

Founding of The Aerospace Corporation in 1960 the progress of the corporation's work in support of the U.S. Air Force paralleled the advances that the country witnessed in the fields of science and technology.

EXECUTIVES

Senior Vice President General Counsel Secretary, Gordon Louttit
Evp, David J. Gorney
General Manager Computers And Software, William C. (Willie) Krenz
Vp Vaeros, Edward M. (Ed) Swallow
Svp National Systems Group, Catherine J. Steele
Acting Principal Director Finance Directorate Assistant Cfo And Assistant Treasurer, Ellen M. Beatty

Svp Operations And Support Group, Wayne H. Goodman
President And Ceo, Steven J. (Steve) Isakowitz
Vp Space Launch Operations, Randolph L. (Randy) Kendall
Vp Space Program Operations, Malina M Hills
Vice President Space Launch Operations, Ray F Johnson
Executive Vice President, Glenn E Peterson
Vice President Director Manager, Mindy Dayton
Vice President Space Program Operations, Stephen E Burrin
Vice President Director Manager, Jeanne Campanella
Vice President, George Paulikas
Vice President Director Manager, James Jusko
Vice President, Shirley Dohzen
Vice President Technology, Lawrence Greenberg
Vice President, Ed Swallow
Vice President Chief Human Resources Officer, Heather Laychak
Vice President, Jamie Morin
Senior Vice President Systems Planning, Rand Fisher
Vice President, Helen Wong
Vice President Space Program Operations, Wayne Bauman
Chairman, Barbara M. Barrett, age 68
Vice Chairman, Michael B. Donley
Board Member, Kathryn Brenan
Secretary, Yvonne Peltz
Treasurer, Jerome Morin
Auditors: DELOITTE & TOUCHE LLP LOS ANG

LOCATIONS

HQ: THE AEROSPACE CORPORATION
2310 E EL SEGUNDO BLVD, EL SEGUNDO, CA 902454609
Phone: 310 336-5000
Web: WWW.AEROSPACE.ORG

PRODUCTS/OPERATIONS

Selected Services
Civil and Commercial
CORDS
Cyber Security
Labs
Launch Support
Mission Assurance
Systems Engineering
Technical Resources

COMPETITORS

AKKA Technologies
Orbital Research
QinetiQ

HISTORICAL FINANCIALS

Company Type: Private

Income Statement — FYE: September 30

	REVENUE ($ mil.)	NET INCOME ($ mil.)	NET PROFIT MARGIN	EMPLOYEES
09/15	916	(15)	—	3,920
09/14	881	5	0.6%	—
09/13	868	0	0.0%	—
09/12	903	4	0.5%	—
Annual Growth	0.5%	—	—	—

2015 Year-End Financials

Return on assets: (-2.3%)
Return on equity: —
Current ratio: 1.10
Cash ($ mil.): 23

THE AMALGAMATED SUGAR COMPANY LLC

The Amalgamated Sugar Company with roots reaching back to 1915 turns beets into sweets. It's the second-largest US sugar producer processing sugar beets grown on about 180000 acres in Idaho Oregon and Washington. The company manufactures granulated coarse powdered and brown consumer sugar products marketed under the brand White Satin. It also makes products for retail grocery chains under private labels. The sugar company produces beet pulp molasses and other beet by-products for use by food and animal-feed manufacturers. Since 1997 Amalgamated Sugar has been owned by the Snake River Sugar Company a cooperative that comprises sugar beet growers in Idaho Oregon and Washington.

Operations

The Amalgamated Sugar Company processes up to 1.6 billion pounds of sugar each year. Along with processing the cooperative's crops the company provides its owner-farmers with agronomy advice and services runs workshops and seminars operates a co-op store and sells used equipment.

The company's key management team is employed on a contract basis. A seven-member Management Committee oversees the management team. The committee comprises members of the cooperative's board of directors.

Geographic Reach

The Idaho-based company's sugar beets which are grown in Idaho Oregon and Washington are processed through the three sugar processing facilities it operates in Idaho. The Amalgamated Sugar Company's warehouses and bulk transfer stations are strategically located from the Midwest to the West Coast.

Sales and Marketing

The Amalgamated Sugar Company markets its sugar primarily in the nation's North Central Intermountain and Northwest regions. The company competes with not only cane sugar refiners but also manufacturers of other forms of sweeteners such as regular and high fructose corn syrup (HFCS) and non-nutritive high intensity sweeteners the likes of aspartame.

Financial Performance

The Amalgamated Sugar Company generates some 90% of its annual sales through the sale of refined sugar. The balance of its revenue comes from animal feed derived from beet pulp and molasses and other by-products as a result of sugar beet processing.

Strategy

The industry's return to the use of real sugar in soft drinks and other beverages has become a boon for The Amalgamated Sugar Company. To this end Pepsi Bottling Ventures has tapped the sugar beet processor to supply the bottler with granulated sugar. During the past few decades more beverage makers have moved to using lesser-expensive high fructose corn syrup (HFCS) to sweeten their beverages as a way to cut costs and boost profits but the shift spurred by consumers to return to sugar-sweetened drinks has become profitable for sugar processors the likes of The Amalgamated Sugar Company.

EXECUTIVES

Pres-Ceo, John McCreedy
V Pres-Coo, Joe Huff
V Pres, Pat Laubacher
V Pres-Fins, Craig Hanks
V Pres-SEC, Scott Blickenstaff
Purchasing Clerk, Christa Anderson
Purchasing Clerk, Faith Larios
Safety, Michael Shuey
Area Governor Maintenance Repa, Shane Rucker
Member, Jeff Henry
Manager, Troy Lentell
Auditors: EIDE BAILLY LLP BOISE IDAHO

LOCATIONS

HQ: THE AMALGAMATED SUGAR COMPANY LLC
1951 S SATURN WAY STE 100, BOISE, ID 837092924
Phone: 208 383-6500
Web: WWW.AMALGAMATEDSUGAR.COM

PRODUCTS/OPERATIONS

Selected Products
Bakers' special sugar
Brown sugar
Dark brown sugar
Extra-fine granulated sugar
Fine granulated sugar
Gel gran granulated sugar
Industrial coarse sugar
Powdered sugar 10x and 12x
Sugar packets
Sugar standards
Type 50 medium invert sugar
Type O liquid sucrose (66.5 brix)
Type O liquid sucrose (67.5 brix)

COMPETITORS

Alico Inc.
American Crystal Sugar
Associated British Foods
C&H Sugar
Cosun
Cumberland Packing
Eurosugar
Florida Crystals
Imperial Sugar
Ingredion
M. A. Patout
Merisant
Michigan Sugar Company
Minn-Dak Co-op
Nippon Beet Sugar
Nordzucker
NutraSweet
SMBSC
Sterling Sugars
Sugar Cane Growers Cooperative of Florida
S dzucker
U.S. Sugar
Western Sugar Cooperative

HISTORICAL FINANCIALS

Company Type: Private

Income Statement — FYE: December 31

	REVENUE ($ mil.)	NET INCOME ($ mil.)	NET PROFIT MARGIN	EMPLOYEES
12/13	953	62	6.6%	1,500
12/12	907	14	1.6%	—
12/11	886	46	5.3%	—
Annual Growth	3.7%	16.0%	—	—

2013 Year-End Financials

Return on assets: 8.0%
Return on equity: 54.7%
Current ratio: 0.90
Cash ($ mil.): 1

THE AMERICAN ENDOWMENT FOUNDATION

EXECUTIVES

Administrator, Dawn Davis
Executive Vice President, John Farren
Administrator, Kristin Wilcoxson
Grants Administrator, Anne Wise
Treasurer, Gail Tobin
Grant Administrator, Elyse Smith
Vp Marketing, Eric Kinaitis
Senior Grants Administrator, Michelle Cozens
Account Administrator, Sue Presper
Vp, William Hewitt
Vice President Investments, Jeff Scherer
Auditors: MALONEY NOVOTNY LLC CANTON O

LOCATIONS

HQ: THE AMERICAN ENDOWMENT FOUNDATION
5700 DARROW RD STE 118, HUDSON, OH 442365026
Phone: 330 655-7552
Web: WWW.AEFONLINE.ORG

HISTORICAL FINANCIALS

Company Type: Private

Income Statement — FYE: December 31

	REVENUE ($ mil.)	NET INCOME ($ mil.)	NET PROFIT MARGIN	EMPLOYEES
12/16	848	349	41.2%	5
12/15	640	335	52.3%	—
12/12	133	86	64.7%	—
12/11	68	42	61.6%	—
Annual Growth	65.4%	52.6%	—	—

2016 Year-End Financials

Return on assets: 23.9%
Return on equity: 24.3%
Current ratio: 21.30
Cash ($ mil.): 70

THE ANDREW W MELLON FOUNDATION

Recipients of funds from The Andrew W. Mellon Foundation don't take the organization for granted. One of the leading charitable foundations in the US the organization provides about $280 million annually in grants including awards in five core areas: including higher education and scholarship performing arts and museums and art conservation. Recent grant recipients include the Detroit Symphony Orchestra Oberlin College and the Metropolitan Museum of Art. The foundation was created in 1969 when Paul Mellon and Ailsa Mellon Bruce the son and daughter of banking titan Andrew W. Mellon merged their charitable foundations (Old Dominion Foundation and Avalon Foundation).

EXECUTIVES

Pres, William G Bowen
V Pres*, Harriet Zuckerman
V Pres-Fin*, John Hull
Executive Vice President*, Michele Warman
Chief Financial Officer*, Thomas Sanders
Accounting Manager, Christy Cicatello
Manager, Oscar Cruz
Facilities Manager, Ronnie Shepard
Portfolio Manager, Karen Inal
Senior Portfolio Manager, Monica Spencer
Director Facilities, Ronald Sheppard
Auditors: PRICEWATERHOUSECOOPERS LLP NE

LOCATIONS

HQ: THE ANDREW W MELLON FOUNDATION
140 E 62ND ST, NEW YORK, NY 100658124
Phone: 212 838-8400
Web: WWW.MELLON.ORG

HISTORICAL FINANCIALS

Company Type: Private

Income Statement — FYE: December 31

	REVENUE ($ mil.)	NET INCOME ($ mil.)	NET PROFIT MARGIN	EMPLOYEES
12/19	782	435	55.6%	70
12/18	54	(285)	—	—
12/17	980	655	66.9%	—
12/16	487	151	31.1%	—
Annual Growth	17.1%	42.2%	—	—

2019 Year-End Financials

Return on assets: 6.2%
Return on equity: 6.4%
Current ratio: —
Cash ($ mil.): 9

THE ASSOCIATED PRESS

This just in: The Associated Press (AP) is reporting tonight and every night wherever news is breaking. AP is one of the world's largest news gathering organizations with news bureaus in about 100 countries. It provides news photos graphics and audiovisual services that reach people daily through print radio TV and the Web. It also offers advertising management and distribution services. The not-for-profit cooperative is owned by 1500 US daily newspaper members. A group of New York newspapers founded the AP in 1846 in order to chronicle the US-Mexican War more efficiently. Founding papers include The New York Sun The Journal of Commerce The Courier and Enquirer The New York Herald and The Express .

Operations

The AP has about 3200 employees globally working around 280 locations worldwide.

Geographic Reach

The Associated Press is headquartered in New York City. The AP serves 1700 newspapers and 5000 radio and television outlets in the US many of which are members.

Financial Performance

In fiscal 2014 the AP's total annual revenue increased by 1% to $604 million compared to $595 million in fiscal 2013. The company's net income increased dramatically to $140 million in fiscal 2014 compared to $3.26 million in fiscal 2013 mainly due to increased gross revenue and interest income.

Strategy

In recent years the AP has shifted its focus away from providing content to newspapers and towards serving online media sources; some of the company's biggest customers now include media outlets such as Google MSN and Yahoo!. It has also focused on developing AP Direct its live video news agency service. It sells its back catalog of video through AP Video Archives.

To cope with the decline in print readership the news co-op is continuing to invest in digital initiatives. It is currently undergoing a multimillion-dollar upgrade of its newsgathering infrastructure to increase its video coverage of global events. It is also pushing to increase its high definition footage to broadcast and digital markets and ensure that its video and images integrate seamlessly with new digital workflows to drive value for customers.

HISTORY

The Associated Press traces its roots to 1846 when New York Sun publisher Moses Yale Beach agreed to share news arriving by telegraph about the Mexican-American War with four other New York newspapers. The cooperative news gathering effort was later established as the AP which began selling wire reports to other papers and started creating regional associations. Adapting to changing technologies and public interests AP began covering sports financial and public interest stories in the 1920s and was selling news reports to radio stations in the 1940s. Advancements during WWII included using transatlantic cable and radio-teletype circuits to deliver news and photos.

In the late 1960s AP and Dow Jones introduced services to improve business and financial reporting. AP improved photo delivery reception and storage in the 1970s with the advent of Laserphoto and the Electronic Darkroom. It began transmitting news by satellite and offering color photographs to newspapers in the 1980s. In 1985 Louis Boccardi took over the job as president and CEO of AP.

AP adjusted to the media-heavy culture of the 1990s by launching the APTV international news video service and the All News Radio network in 1994. It then moved onto the Internet with The WIRE in 1996 and began offering online access to its Photo Archive in 1997. It bought Worldwide Television News in 1998 combining it with APTV to form AP Television News Limited (APTN). The following year it purchased the radio news contracts of UPI after the rival organization announced it was getting out of broadcast news.

In 2000 AP created an Internet division AP Digital to focus on marketing news to online providers. The cooperative continued its Internet focus the following year launching AP Online en Español (news for Spanish-language websites) and AP Entertainment Online (multimedia entertainment news for websites). Also that year AP bought the Newspaper Industry Communication Center from the Newspaper Association of America.

In 2002 the company launched an expanded editorial partnership with Dow Jones Newswires increasing the amount of financial news distributed on AP wires. Later that year it acquired Capitolwire a provider of state government news. Boccardi stepped down as CEO in 2003 handing the reins to former USA TODAY publisher Tom Curley.

AP relocated in 2004 from Rockefeller Plaza (its home for 65 years) to a new headquarters on the west side of Manhattan that features a 105000-sq.-ft. newsroom and serves as a central hub of digital news streams.

The organization moved to strengthen its sports information coverage in 2005 merging its AP MegaSports operation with News Corporation's STATS Inc. to form STATS LLC a 50-50 joint venture that provides sports-related information content and statistical analysis.

The following year AP launched The Online Video Network (OVN) service to provide news video to AP member and customer websites. The co-op responded to the harsh economy by cutting costs in 2008 with consolidation of its print broadcast and digital sales and marketing units. It continued its cost-cutting efforts in 2009 when it cut some 90 jobs instituted a hiring freeze and bought out about 100 employees.

EXECUTIVES

Director, Gary B. Pruitt, age 62
Svp And Executive Editor, Kathleen Carroll
Svp And Cio, Lorraine Cichowski
Svp And Cfo, Ken Dale
Svp And Cto, Gianluca D'Aniello
First Vice President, Justin Casson
Senior Vice President, Timothy Sheehan
Senior Vice President And Deputy General Counsel, Chuck Gerber
Director, Mary E. Junck, age 73
Auditors: ERNST & YOUNG LLP NEW YORK N

LOCATIONS

HQ: THE ASSOCIATED PRESS
200 LIBERTY ST FL 19, NEW YORK, NY 102812102
Phone: 212 621-1500
Web: WWW.AP.ORG

PRODUCTS/OPERATIONS

Selected Products and Services

AP Digital News (Internet and wireless news delivery)
AP Images (photo services)
AP Mobile (mobile applications)
APTN (AP Television News international television news service)
ENPS (electronic news production system)
Online Video Network (video content distribution)

COMPETITORS

Agence France-Presse	GlobeNewswire
Bloomberg L.P.	Marketwire
Business Wire	New York Times
Comtex News	PR Newswire
Corbis	Reuters
Dow Jones	TEGNA
E. W. Scripps	Tribune Media
Getty Images	UPI

HISTORICAL FINANCIALS

Company Type: Private

Income Statement — FYE: December 31

	REVENUE ($ mil.)	NET INCOME ($ mil.)	NET PROFIT MARGIN	EMPLOYEES
12/16	556	1	0.3%	3,533
12/15	568	183	32.3%	—
12/14	604	140	23.3%	—
Annual Growth	(4.0%)	(89.4%)	—	—

2016 Year-End Financials

Return on assets: 0.4% Cash ($ mil.): 24
Return on equity: —
Current ratio: 0.60

THE BLOOMBERG FAMILY FOUNDATION INC

EXECUTIVES

Prin, Steve Fadem
Associate, Matt Lipsky
Auditors: GELLER & COMPANY LLC NEW YORK

LOCATIONS

HQ: THE BLOOMBERG FAMILY FOUNDATION INC
909 3RD AVE, NEW YORK, NY 100224731
Phone: 212 205-0100
Web: WWW.BLOOMBERG.ORG

HISTORICAL FINANCIALS

Company Type: Private

Income Statement — FYE: December 31

	REVENUE ($ mil.)	NET INCOME ($ mil.)	NET PROFIT MARGIN	EMPLOYEES
12/15	1,194	736	61.7%	2
12/14	1,328	1,048	79.0%	—
12/13	809	538	66.5%	—
12/09	452	279	61.8%	—
Annual Growth	17.6%	17.5%	—	—

2015 Year-End Financials

Return on assets: 10.3% Cash ($ mil.): 73
Return on equity: 10.3%
Current ratio: —

THE BOLDT GROUP INC

EXECUTIVES

Pres, Oscar C Boldt
V Pres*, Thomas J Boldt
SEC*, Michelle M Gawinski
Project Financial Coordinator, Maria Drezek
Project Engineer, Brian Cutler
Senior Designer, Eric Siebers
Project Coordinator III, Tammie Beitz
Superintendent Childrens Hospi, Brian Caminiti
Project Executive, Dan Schmidt
Director, Daren Maas
Planning and Scheduling, Ginelle Hussin
Auditors: SCHENCK SC APPLETON WISCONSI

LOCATIONS

HQ: THE BOLDT GROUP INC
2525 N ROEMER RD, APPLETON, WI 549118623
Phone: 920 739-7800
Web: WWW.THEBOLDTCOMPANY.COM

HISTORICAL FINANCIALS

Company Type: Private

Income Statement — FYE: December 31

	REVENUE ($ mil.)	NET INCOME ($ mil.)	NET PROFIT MARGIN	EMPLOYEES
12/18	1,046	(11)	—	1,500
12/17	989	0	—	—
12/16	1,022	17	1.7%	—
12/15	978	0	—	—
Annual Growth	2.2%	—	—	—

2018 Year-End Financials

Return on assets: (3.8%) Cash ($ mil.): 39
Return on equity: (30.9%)
Current ratio: 1.10

THE BOND FUND OF AMERICA INC

EXECUTIVES

President, Abner D Goldstine

LOCATIONS

HQ: THE BOND FUND OF AMERICA INC
333 S HOPE ST FL 55, LOS ANGELES, CA 900713061
Phone: 213 486-9200
Web: WWW.CAPITALGROUP.COM

HISTORICAL FINANCIALS

Company Type: Private

Income Statement — FYE: December 31

	REVENUE ($ mil.)	NET INCOME ($ mil.)	NET PROFIT MARGIN	EMPLOYEES
12/18	1,140	1,775	155.6%	2
12/17	866	1,056	122.0%	—
Annual Growth	31.7%	68.0%	—	—

2018 Year-End Financials

Return on assets: 4.0% Cash ($ mil.): 26
Return on equity: 4.5%
Current ratio: —

THE BRIGHAM AND WOMEN'S HOSPITAL INC

EXECUTIVES

Pres, Elizabeth G Nabel
Immunologist, Annemieke De Jong
Chief Officer, Stanley W Ashley
Chief Officer, Susan Rapple
Coordinator, Amanda Harless
Director Cardiovascular Divisi, Raymond Kwong
Physician, Benjamin D Sommers
Scientist, Beverly Hope
Inventory Manager Angio, Frantz Pierre
Pathologist, Jane E Brock
Executive Director, Kathy McManus

LOCATIONS

HQ: THE BRIGHAM AND WOMEN'S HOSPITAL INC
75 FRANCIS ST, BOSTON, MA 021156106
Phone: 617 732-5500
Web: WWW.BRIGHAMANDWOMENS.ORG

HISTORICAL FINANCIALS

Company Type: Private

Income Statement — FYE: September 30

	REVENUE ($ mil.)	NET INCOME ($ mil.)	NET PROFIT MARGIN	EMPLOYEES
09/18	2,257	171	7.6%	8,376
09/17	2,128	55	2.6%	—
09/16	1,938	94	4.9%	—
09/15	1,811	60	3.4%	—
Annual Growth	7.6%	41.4%	—	—

2018 Year-End Financials

Return on assets: 5.6% Cash ($ mil.): 39
Return on equity: 20.6%
Current ratio: 1.30

THE BROAD INSTITUTE INC

EXECUTIVES

Pres-Ceo-Dir, Eric Lander
Principal*, Derek Martyn
Exec V Pres-V Pres*, Alan Fein
Dir*, David Baltimore
Coo*, Samantha Singer
Chief Scientific Officer*, Todd Golub
Cdo*, Justine Levin
Cco*, Clare Midgley
Cpo*, Andy Porter
Scientist, Ashlee M Earl
Scientist, Heng LI
Auditors: PRICEWATERHOUSECOOPERS LLP BO

LOCATIONS

HQ: THE BROAD INSTITUTE INC
415 MAIN ST, CAMBRIDGE, MA 021421027
Phone: 617 714-7000
Web: WWW.BROADINSTITUTE.ORG

HISTORICAL FINANCIALS

Company Type: Private

Income Statement — FYE: June 30

	REVENUE ($ mil.)	NET INCOME ($ mil.)	NET PROFIT MARGIN	EMPLOYEES
06/20	551	53	9.6%	800
06/19	551	53	9.6%	—
06/18	466	(18)	—	—
06/17	451	23	5.2%	—
Annual Growth	6.9%	31.4%	—	—

2020 Year-End Financials

Return on assets: 3.2%
Return on equity: 5.0%
Current ratio: 1.70
Cash ($ mil.): 248

THE CHARLES STARK DRAPER LABORATORY INC

The Charles Stark Draper Laboratory (also known as Draper Lab) guides research into space under water and across continents. The not-for-profit corporation develops guidance navigation and control technologies for aircraft missiles and spacecraft. It works with NASA to develop technologies and fabricate prototypes. The organization also solves healthcare problems with its work in biomedical engineering.

Operations

Draper Lab's innovations include a personal navigation system that allows soldiers to find their way in GPS-denied areas. The corporation boasts expertise in guidance navigation and control sytems; advanced algorithms and software; fault-tolerant computing; modeling and simulation; and microelectromechanical system (MEMS) and multichip module technology.

Geographic Reach

Headquartered in Cambridge Massachusetts Draper Lab maintains operations in Huntsville Alabama; Annapolis Junction Maryland; Cambridge and Road Pittsfield Massachusetts; Houston; Huntsville Alabama; Cape Canaveral Tampa and St. Petersburg Florida; Houston Texas; Reston Virginia; and Washington D.C.

Sales and Marketing

The company provide engineering services directly to government commercial companies and academia.

Strategy

Fueled by the brain power and expertise of its hundreds of engineers Draper Lab aims to solve problems by designing developing and deploying solutions built using advanced technologies. Its primary areas of focus include space exploration security healthcare and energy.

In late 2019 Draper Lab unveiled its LiDAR-on-a-Chip that uses patented all digital MEMS optical switches for beamsteering. Draper has successfully built a high-resolution solid-state LiDAR that images objects at 50 meters. This new offering adds to Drapers' growing portfolio of autonomous system and self-driving car capabilities. Draper's latest addition to this portfolio was in 2020 with its new PathScout system which equips drivers with a system that alerts them to nearby pedestrians when it detects GPS signals emitted by their mobile phones.

Draper also continues its collaborations with other organizations. In early 2019 Draper Lab and 3Derm collaborated to create new automated capabilities for 3Derm's high0quality skin imaging systems with the aim of improving the management of chronic inflammatory skin disease such as psoriasis and eczema. Draper also collaborated with Bristol-Myers Squibb in developing a unique liver tissue model for screening the toxicity of drugs in which Draper used its Human Organ Systems (HOS) platform.

Draper has also been selected by government institutions for various projects. NASA has selected Dynetics and Draper to develop and demonstrate a Human Landing System (HLS) to return humans to the lunar surface by 2024. The Department of Defense is also working with Draper to address challenges and improve upon UAV software to give it an autonomy architecture and software package that can enable UAVs to do more than ever before.

Company Background

The organization was founded in 1932 by MIT professor Charles Stark Draper as a teaching lab.

EXECUTIVES

Vice President For Programs, Darryl Sargent
Cfo, Elizabeth Mora
President And Ceo, Kaigham (Ken) Gabriel
Vice President, Len Polizzotto
Vice President, Ted Rye
Vice President Of Information Technology, Diane Chilante
Vice President For Strategic Systems, Steve DiTullio
Vice President Engineering, John Lupien
Vice President Government And Public, Jennifer Gibson
Director, Franklin C. (Frank) Miller
Auditors: GRANT THORNTON LLP BOSTON MA

LOCATIONS

HQ: THE CHARLES STARK DRAPER LABORATORY INC
555 TECHNOLOGY SQ, CAMBRIDGE, MA 021393539
Phone: 617 258-1000
Web: WWW.DRAPER.COM

PRODUCTS/OPERATIONS

Selected Research Areas

Biomedical engineering
- Tissue engineering
- Sensor development

Space systems
- Military space systems
- Planetary exploration
- Scientific spacecraft
- Space transportation

Special operations
- Robotics
- Small low-power electronics
- Surveillance systems

Strategic systems
- Inertial guidance systems

Tactical systems
- Precision engagement systems
- Manned/unmanned systems
- Missile defense

COMPETITORS

Applied Research Associates
Institute for Defense Analyses
QinetiQ
Quantum Research

HISTORICAL FINANCIALS

Company Type: Private

Income Statement — FYE: July 31

	REVENUE ($ mil.)	NET INCOME ($ mil.)	NET PROFIT MARGIN	EMPLOYEES
07/16*	676	36	5.5%	1,800
06/14	522	28	5.4%	—
06/13	542	17	3.2%	—
06/12	514	(20)	—	—
Annual Growth	7.1%	—	—	—

*Fiscal year change

2016 Year-End Financials

Return on assets: 6.0%
Return on equity: 9.7%
Current ratio: 1.50
Cash ($ mil.): 51

THE CHEROKEE NATION

EXECUTIVES

Chief, Chad Smith
Accounting Manager, Larry T Smith
Reporter, Jami Custer
Information Specialist, Melissa Bostwick
Education, Wade Blevins
Contracts Manager, Mike Robinson
Family Practitioner, Clinton Childs
Finance, David James
Gis Specialist, Eric Dean
Occupational Therapist, Felipe Zamarron
Chief of Parties, Guy Caughron

LOCATIONS

HQ: THE CHEROKEE NATION
17675 S MUSKOGEE AVE, TAHLEQUAH, OK 744645492
Phone: 918 453-5000

HISTORICAL FINANCIALS

Company Type: Private

Income Statement — FYE: September 30

	REVENUE ($ mil.)	NET INCOME ($ mil.)	NET PROFIT MARGIN	EMPLOYEES
09/16	541	1	0.4%	5,500
09/15	511	(15)	—	—
09/05	226	15	6.7%	—
09/04	203	14	6.9%	—
Annual Growth	8.5%	(15.3%)	—	—

2016 Year-End Financials

Return on assets: 0.1%
Return on equity: 0.1%
Current ratio: —
Cash ($ mil.): 313

THE CHILDREN'S HOSPITAL CORPORATION

The Children's Hospital Corporation dba Boston Children's Hospital is a 400-bed hospital that offers acute health care and specialty services for children from birth through age 21. The medical center is Harvard Medical School's main teaching hospital for children's health care and it is the world's largest pediatric research center. Its John F. Enders Pediatric Research facility provides research for the treatment of childhood diseases. Specialty services are offered in the fields of cardiovascular surgery digestive care neurology oncology ophthalmology orthopedics autism spectrum disorder blood diseases and fetal care. The not-for-profit hospital was founded in 1869.

Operations

Boston Children's Hospital handles about 25000 inpatient visits per year as well as 27000 surgeries and more than 200000 radiological exams. Its 200+ specialized clinical programs handle about 560000 appointments annually. The hospital is considered a safety-net hospital and as such is one of the largest providers of medical care to low-income children in the state. About 30% of the hospital's patients are either uninsured or have health care coverage through public assistance.

In addition to its educational and research partnerships with Harvard the medical center collaborates with other universities as well as drug makers medical equipment firms and research institutes. Altogether it has some 1100 scientists at its research centers including the Enders Pediatric Research Laboratories and the Karp Family Research Laboratories. Children's Hospital Boston receives up to some $225 million in research funding per year.

Along with the main hospital the system operates a handful of primary and specialty care centers throughout the Boston area. It also operates a cancer clinic within the main campus through a partnership with the Dana Farber Cancer Institute.

In 2017 Boston Children's Hospital was named the country's best pediatric hospital by U.S. News & World Report for the fifth year in a row.

Geographic Reach

Boston Children's Hospital has satellite locations and affiliates throughout Massachusetts. In addition to its main campus in Boston it has satellites in Lexington North Dartmouth Peabody and Waltham; doctors' offices in Brockton Milford Norwood and Weymouth; and affiliates in Beverly Fall River Milford New Bedford South Weymouth Wareham and Winchester.

Strategy

Due to increasing economic troubles and health reform measures in the US Boston Children's Hospital has been working to cut costs. Despite the cost-control efforts the main campus is undergoing expansion renovation and modernization efforts as part of a 10-year expansion plan.

EXECUTIVES

Svp Network Development, Wendy Warring
Ceo And Trustee, James Mandell
President Coo And Trustee, Sandra L. Fenwick, age 69
Cfo, Doug Vanderslice
Cio, Daniel Nigrin
Svp Patient Care Operations, Eileen Sporing
Surgeon-in-chief And Trustee, James Kasser
Anesthesiologist-in-chief, Paul R. Hickey
Executive Director Satellite Clinical Operations, Julee Bolg
President Children's Hospital Trust, Lynn Susman
Svp And Chief Marketing And Communications Officer, Margaret Coughlin
Chief Investment Officer, Phil Rotner
Executive Director Satellite Administrative Operations, Jane Venti
Executive Vice President Of, Kevin Churchwell
Medical Director, Michael Rivkin
Vice President For Research Chief Scientific Off, Bruce Zetter
Director Of Pharmacy, Crystal Tom
Medical Director, Terra Lafranchi
Medical Director, Xianhua Piao
Medical Director Child Protection Program, Celeste Wilson
Executive Vice President, Andrea Pettinato
Operating Room Dir, Yolanda Milliman-richard
Executive Vice President, George Phillips
Medical Director, James Wall
Director Of Medical Records, Mary Radley
Vp Human Resources, Inez Stewart
Vice President Research Administration, August Cervini
Vice President, Henry Tomasuolo
Icu Intensitvist Vice President Of Cardiology, Patricia Hickey
Senior Vice President Network Development And Strategic Partnerships, Warring Wendy
Vice President Corporate, Carola Cadley
Vice President, Brian Landry
Clinical Director, Leslie Lehmann
Vice President Finance, Sophia G Holder
Vice President, Michael Gillespie
Senior Vice President And General Counsel, Michele Garvin
Vice President Research, Gus Cervini
Senior Vice President International Services, Cynthia Haines
Senior Vice President, Lisa Hogarty
Vice President Major Partnerships And Mergers, Susan Alesina
Medical Director, Seeta Badrinath
Vice President Development, Sophia Monaghan
Vice President Business Operations, Courtney Cannon
Vice President Corporate Development And Special Events, Michael Bornhost
Vice President, Mary Poyner Reed
Vice President Marketing And Communications, David Perry
Senior Vice President Foundation And Chief Development Officer, Brad Barber
Vice President, Danny Stancill
Vice President Of Sales, Jessie Garcia
Vice President, Eric Trentman
Vice President, Christopher T Holbrook
Vice President Of Information Technology, Tony Johnston
Executive Vice President, Katherine Lapp
Medical Director, Ann Nicoloff Becker
Chair, Stephen R. Karp
Director Finance Corporate Service And Assistant Treasurer, Bruce Balter
Medical Secretary, Stephanie Ferrer
Secretary, Kay Barr
Sec Treas, William Towler
Secretary Treasurer, Geraldine Grombir
Treasurer Secretary, Mary Cloutier
Treasurer, Craig Nesta
Database Vice Chair, David Wypij

LOCATIONS

HQ: THE CHILDREN'S HOSPITAL CORPORATION
300 LONGWOOD AVE, BOSTON, MA 021155737
Phone: 617 355-6000
Web: WWW.CHILDRENSHOSPITAL.ORG

PRODUCTS/OPERATIONS

Selected Services

Major centers
- Brain Center
- Cancer and Blood Diseases Center
- Heart Center
- Orthopedic Center
- Transplant Center

Other Services
- Airway breathing and lungs
- Allergies and asthma
- Anatomy and function
- Bone joint and muscle
- Brain and nervous system
- Cancer and blood disorders
- Common childhood health topics and conditions
- Craniofacial anomalies
- Diet and nutrition
- Digestive metabolic and renal disorders
- Ears nose and throat
- Emergency medicine and trauma
- Eyes and vision
- Genetic disorders and birth defects
- Heart blood and circulation
- International patient care
- Medical tests
- Newborns
- Psychiatric (mental) conditions
- Reproductive and urinary conditions
- Skin and vascular
- Viruses and infections

COMPETITORS

Baystate Medical Center
Beth Israel Deaconess Medical Center
Boston Medical Center
Cambridge Health Alliance
Cape Cod Hospital
Children's Hospital of Philadelphia
Nemours Foundation
Newton-Wellesley Hospital
Northeast Health System
Partners HealthCare
Shriners Hospitals For Children
Steward Health Care
Sturdy Memorial

HISTORICAL FINANCIALS

Company Type: Private

Income Statement — FYE: September 30

	REVENUE ($ mil.)	NET INCOME ($ mil.)	NET PROFIT MARGIN	EMPLOYEES
09/14	1,514	111	7.3%	8,000
09/09*	1,348	94	7.0%	—
06/05	4	0	13.0%	—
Annual Growth	89.2%	77.5%	—	—

*Fiscal year change

2014 Year-End Financials

Return on assets: 2.5%
Return on equity: 3.6%
Current ratio: 0.30
Cash ($ mil.): —

THE CHILDREN'S HOSPITAL OF ALABAMA

EXECUTIVES

Ceo, William Michael Warren Jr
Exec V Pres-Coo*, Thomas G Shufflebarger
Exec V Pres*, Mike McDevitt
Facilities Manager, David Cantrell
Department Director, Greg Lockridge
Sleep Disorders Center Manager, Aneshia Williams
Director, Kelvin Knight
Facilities Supervisor, Corey Cunningham
Chief Engineer, Dale Williams
Msn, Ehrica Speigner
Director, Emily Hornak
Auditors: WARREN AVERETT LLC BIRMINGHA

LOCATIONS

HQ: THE CHILDREN'S HOSPITAL OF ALABAMA
1600 7TH AVE S, BIRMINGHAM, AL 352331711
Phone: 205 939-9100
Web: WWW.CHILDRENSAL.ORG

HISTORICAL FINANCIALS

Company Type: Private

Income Statement FYE: December 31

	REVENUE ($ mil.)	NET INCOME ($ mil.)	NET PROFIT MARGIN	EMPLOYEES
12/19	751	165	22.0%	3,329
12/18	733	17	2.4%	—
12/17	736	113	15.4%	—
12/16	713	86	12.1%	—
Annual Growth	1.8%	24.3%	—	—

2019 Year-End Financials

Return on assets: 9.9%
Return on equity: 12.8%
Current ratio: 7.40
Cash ($ mil.): 190

THE CHILDREN'S HOSPITAL OF PHILADELPHIA

In the City of Brotherly Love sick little boys and girls have a place to get better at the The Children's Hospital of Philadelphia (CHOP). As a leading pediatric hospital CHOP also has one of the largest pediatric research programs in the world. The nation's first hospital devoted exclusively to the care of children it has about 530 beds at its primary facility and is a leader in formal pediatric medical training pediatric emergency medicine and adolescent medicine. In addition to its main hospital facilities CHOP operates a pediatric health care network with owned or affiliated offices clinics and research facilities in Delaware New Jersey and Pennsylvania. The hospital was founded in 1855.

Operations

CHOP is consistently ranked among the best pediatric health facilities in the nation. Its primary specialties are diabetes care neonatology cardiology pulmonary care endocrinology gastroenterology urology orthopedics and oncology. The hospital's extended regional network includes the CHOP Care Network a group of more than 50 pediatric practices and specialty care centers in Pennsylvania and New Jersey.

CHOP's doctors also provide pediatric care at half a dozen affiliated hospitals in Pennsylvania and New Jersey as well as neonatal care at about 10 regional hospitals including Pennsylvania Hospital Holy Redeemer Hospital and Medical Center and Shore Memorial Hospital.

The hospital conducts hundreds of research programs under the auspices of its Children's Hospital of Philadelphia Research Institute and many programs are conducted in partnership with the University of Pennsylvania. Its research programs include investigations into pediatric AIDS fetal surgery sickle cell disease and child safety. CHOP also conducts medical training and residency programs in partnership with University of Pennsylvania.

CHOP's Colket Translational Research Building holds four laboratory floors (two of which are focused on cancer research) a two-story ground floor lobby and four administrative office floors three of which are convertible to future laboratory use.

Each year the hospital has more than 1 million outpatient visits and inpatient admissions; it also receives more than 86000 emergency department visits.

Financial Performance

In 2014 the hospital's revenue increased 7% to $2.4 billion driven by 9% growth in net patient service revenues.

Like many other health care providers CHOP faces some challenges related to health reform measures and reimbursement changes in the US. The hospital is especially reliant on reimbursement from Medicaid which is the largest national payer of pediatric services. However its strong industry ranking research program funding and private insurance reimbursement rates balance the reliance on federal and state health programs.

Strategy

In mid-2015 CHOP opened the new Buerger Center for Advanced Pediatric Care a 12-story facility with the capacity to accommodate more than 200000 outpatient appointments annually. The center offers specialties including orthopedics oncology radiology and otolaryngology.

Future growth plans include CHOP's ambitious South Campus program. The hospital is building new outpatient buildings imaging centers and day medicine centers on its South Campus at a cost of about $1 billion. The South Campus will also include new research facilities.

EXECUTIVES

Vice President;chief Scientific Officer;executive Vice President And Chief Scientific Officer, Philip R Johnson
Evp And Coo, Douglas G. (Doug) Hock
Evp And Cfo, Thomas J. Todorow
Evp And Chief Scientific Officer, Bryan A. Wolf
Evp And Chief Administrative Officer, Margaret M. Jones
President And Ceo, Madeline Bell
Evp And General Counsel, Jeffrey D. Kahn
Evp And Chief Development Officer, Stuart P. Sullivan
Medical Director Lung Transplantation, Samuel Goldfarb
Medical Director, Michael Levine
Clinical Director, David Langdon
Assistant Vice President Operations, Deborah Smith
Vice President, Judith Kraft
Medical Director Of Clinical Operations, Evan Fieldston
Director Of Nursing, Paula Agosto
Chief Investment Officer And Senior Vice President, Nicholas Procyk
Vice President Gov Affairs Comm Relations, Peter M Grollman
Director Of Radiology Informatics, Devida Rembert
Medical Staff Vice President, Robyn Lorfink
Medical Staff Vice President, Monica Lotty
Vice President Financial Strategy, Spencer Kowal
Director Media Relations, Betsy Duffy
Medical Director, Susan N Ortolao
Secretary To Chief, Jane E Koller
Board Member, Stephen Paridon
Treasurer, John Milligan
Medical Secretary I, Joanne Hofmann
Medical Secretary I, Joan J Leahy
Treasurer, Kenisha Campbell
Medical Secretary I, Kathleen Haugland
Board Member, Nicholas Lunig

LOCATIONS

HQ: THE CHILDREN'S HOSPITAL OF PHILADELPHIA
3401 CIVIC CENTER BLVD, PHILADELPHIA, PA 191044319
Phone: 215 590-1000
Web: WWW.CHOP.EDU

PRODUCTS/OPERATIONS

2014 Sales

	$ mil.	% of total
Net patient revenue	2,021	84
Research	211	9
Contributions	64	4
Other operating revenue	104	3
Total	**2,401**	**100**

Selected Specialties

Behavioral health
Blood and marrow transplantation program
Cardiac center
Center for fetal diagnosis and treatment
Center for airway disorders
Center for inflammatory bowel disease
Craniofacial reconstruction center
Diagnostic imaging center
Endocrinology
Gastroenterology
Hematology
Intensive care
Liver disease center
Neurosurgery
Orthopedic surgery
Pathology
Pediatric oncology
Pain management
Reconstructive surgery
Sickle cell center
Sports medicine and performance center
Stroke center
Surgery (general thoracic and fetal)
Transplant center
Urology

COMPETITORS

Aria Health
Children's Hospital Boston
Children's Hospital of Pittsburgh
Fox Chase Cancer Center
Main Line Health System
Nemours Foundation
North Philadelphia Health System
Shriners Hospitals For Children
St. Jude Children's Research Hospital
St. Luke's University Health Network
TUHS
Tenet Healthcare
Universal Health Services
University of Pennsylvania Health System

HISTORICAL FINANCIALS

Company Type: Private

Income Statement FYE: June 30

	REVENUE ($ mil.)	NET INCOME ($ mil.)	NET PROFIT MARGIN	EMPLOYEES
06/19	3,057	469	15.4%	13,519
06/10	1,425	135	9.5%	—
06/09	1,439	197	13.7%	—
Annual Growth	7.8%	9.1%	—	—

2019 Year-End Financials

Return on assets: 6.5%
Return on equity: 8.5%
Current ratio: 3.00
Cash ($ mil.): 731

THE CHILDRENS HOSPITAL LOS ANGELES

Childrens Hospital Los Angeles (CHLA) is dedicated to treating the youngest critical care patients in the region. The about 570-bed hospital specializes in treating seriously ill and injured children from its neonatal intensive care unit to its pediatric organ transplant center. CHLA's pediatric specialists also provide care at its ambulatory care center in Arcadia and through about 40 off-site practice sites. The hospital's pediatric specialties include cancer kidney failure and cystic fibrosis care. CHLA serves more than 107000 children every year. It is one of only 12 children's hospitals in the nation (and the only one in California) ranked in all 10 pediatric specialties by U.S. News & World Report .

Operations

The CHLA medical staff includes about 600 physicians most of which are members of the CHLA Medical Group. Its emergency department treats some 71000 patients and the hospital sees more than 343000 outpatients annually. Nearly 50% of its patients are under the age of four. CHLA is also the only freestanding level I Pediatric Trauma Center in LA County approved by the Committee on Trauma of the American College of Surgeons and among only 5% of US hospitals to be designated as a Magnet Hospital by the American Nurses Credentialing Center.

It is also a teaching hospital through its affiliation with the Keck School of Medicine of the University of Southern California and is home to the Saban Research Institute which conducts biomedical research into pediatric diseases. CHLA's training programs include 575 medical students 85 full-time residents three chief residents and 98 fellows.

Financial Performance

Revenue decreased 7% to $803 million in 2014 due to a decline in net patient service revenue. Also that year the company reported a net loss of $30 million due to the decline in revenue and higher operating expenses.

Strategy

CHLA is expanding its facilities to keep up with demand. In 2015 it opened the doors of a new outpatient center in Encino.

Company Background

Although it sometimes operates as Children's Hospital Los Angeles the absent apostrophe in the legal Childrens Hospital of Los Angeles name is no accident. The intentional spelling honors the original incorporation documents filed in 1901 when the institution was founded as Childrens Hospital Society of Los Angeles.

EXECUTIVES

Vice President, Terence Sanger
Assistant Vice President, Christian Nelson
Vice President Marketing, Joanne Reyes
Vice President Information Technology Operations, Dave Abbott
Vice President. Foundation, Anna Weiser
Vice President Of Research Operations, Jodi Ogden
Senior Vice President, Lara M Khouri
Senior Vice President Technology, Paul Viviano
Senior Vice President, Mamoon Syed
Auditors: DELOITTE & TOUCHE LLP LOS ANG

LOCATIONS

HQ: THE CHILDRENS HOSPITAL LOS ANGELES
4650 W SUNSET BLVD, LOS ANGELES, CA 900276062
Phone: 323 660-2450
Web: WWW.CHLA.ORG

COMPETITORS

Cedars-Sinai Medical Center
Children's Hopsital of Chicago
Children's Hospital & Research Center at Oakland
Children's Hospital Boston
Children's Hospital of Orange County
Children's Hospital of Philadelphia
Children's National Medical Center
Cincinnati Children's Hospital
Cook Children's Health Care System
Dignity Health
Good Samaritan Hospital (Los Angeles)
Hollywood Presbyterian Medical Center
Nationwide Children's Hospital
Shriners Hospitals For Children

HISTORICAL FINANCIALS

Company Type: Private

Income Statement FYE: June 30

	REVENUE ($ mil.)	NET INCOME ($ mil.)	NET PROFIT MARGIN	EMPLOYEES
06/20	1,325	47	3.6%	3,000
06/19	1,485	216	14.6%	—
06/18	1,393	247	17.8%	—
06/17	1,035	(14)	—	—
Annual Growth	8.6%	—	—	—

2020 Year-End Financials

Return on assets: 2.0%
Return on equity: 2.8%
Current ratio: 2.70
Cash ($ mil.): 122

THE CHRIST HOSPITAL

Perched on the hilltop of Mt. Auburn The Christ Hospital oversees the health of ailing residents throughout Greater Cincinnati. Along with the flagship 528-bed hospital the organization operates about 100 outpatient and physician practice locations throughout the area. The Christ Hospital offers specialized care in a variety of fields including cardiac care cancer treatment kidney transplantation spine treatment and orthopedics. The not-for-profit hospital also provides an internal medicine residency program a family medicine residency program and a school of nursing. The Christ Hospital conducts research through its Lindner Clinical Trial Center.

Operations

The Christ Hospital is a general medical and surgical facility with 24977 admissions a year. It performed 7320 annual inpatient and 17373 outpatient surgeries and its emergency room had 52066 visits.

Physicians at the center have participated in more than 1000 clinical research trials in obesity diabetes adult stem cell protocols and congestive heart failure among a range of other therapeutic specialties.

The hospital works with the Ohio Heart & Vascular Center to provide comprehensive heart care to Cincinnati and the surrounding region. As part of the affiliation The Christ Hospital owns some assets related to the Ohio Heart & Vascular Center and employs its physicians and other staff. The agreement allows the two to make use of each others resources and to better serve heart patients in rural areas.

Strategy

In 2015 The Christ Hospital completed the expansion of its main campus at Mt. Auburn in a major $265 million initiative that included a new orthopedic and spine center with connectors to its existing buildings a parking garage and a materials management building.

That year the hospital opened its Montgomery Outpatient Center in Ohio and a new primary care office in Kenwood. It also announced plans to build a comprehensive medical center in the fast growing Butler County community of Liberty Township.

Company Background

The hospital expanded its outpatient capabilities in 2012 by opening its newly constructed The Christ Hospital Outpatient Center in Green Township and by adding a new center in Fort Wright Kentucky. The Green Township center is home to physician practices in cardiology OB-GYN internal and family medicine. It also offers physical and occupational therapy laboratory services and diagnostic testing services including digital X-ray ultrasound echocardiogram and vascular screening. The Fort Wright center offers cardiovascular care and screening services family medicine diagnostic imaging (X-ray screening mammography and general ultrasound) and wound healing obstetrics and gynecology and lab services.

Along with expanding via new construction The Christ Hospital grows its outpatient locations by acquiring local physician practices in a range of specialties. The system was particularly focused on increasing its orthopedic and urogynecological holdings during 2010 while acquisitions in 2011 and 2012 include a breast surgery practice a family medicine center a hematology-oncology group and an internal medicine practice.

The Christ Hospital was founded in 1889. At one time it was a part of UC Health a health care organization based in Ohio until the two ended their affiliation following a years-long court battle. It began operating independently again in 2008.

EXECUTIVES

President Ceo, Susan Croushore
Vp And Chief Nursing Officer, Deborah (Debbie) Hayes
Vp And Chief Medical Officer, Berc Gawne
Vp And Cfo, Chris Bergman
Cio, Alex Vaillancourt
President Of The Christ College Of Nursing, Nathan Long
President Of The Christ Hospital Foundation, Richard F. Kammerer
Vice President Patient Services, Susan Wietholter

LOCATIONS

HQ: THE CHRIST HOSPITAL
2139 AUBURN AVE, CINCINNATI, OH 452192989
Phone: 513 585-2000
Web: WWW.THECHRISTHOSPITAL.COM

PRODUCTS/OPERATIONS

Selected Services
Cancer Services
Comprehensive Medicine
Heart & Vascular
Orthopaedics & Sports Medicine
Primary Care
Spine
Women's Health

COMPETITORS

Bethesda North
Cincinnati Children's Hospital
Deaconess Associations
Kettering Health Network
Premier Health Partners
St. Elizabeth Healthcare
TriHealth
UC Health

HISTORICAL FINANCIALS

Company Type: Private

Income Statement FYE: June 30

	REVENUE ($ mil.)	NET INCOME ($ mil.)	NET PROFIT MARGIN	EMPLOYEES
06/18	742	95	12.9%	4,000
06/17	929	14	1.5%	—
06/16	681	90	13.2%	—
06/15	647	89	13.9%	—
Annual Growth	4.7%	2.1%	—	—

2018 Year-End Financials

Return on assets: 5.8%
Return on equity: 8.9%
Current ratio: 8.10
Cash ($ mil.): 28

THE CITY OF SEATTLE-CITY LIGHT DEPARTMENT

City of Seattle - City Light Department (Seattle City Light) keeps guitars humming and coffee grinders running in the Seattle metropolitan area. The US's 10th largest municipally owned power company Seattle City Light transmits and distributes electricity to almost 1 million residential commercial industrial and government customers and owns hydroelectric power plants with more than 1800 MW of generation capacity. The utility also purchases power from the Bonneville Power Administration and other generators and it sells power to wholesale customers.

Operations

The company owns and operates generating transmission and distribution facilities and supplies electricity to 408000 customer meters in Seattle and certain surrounding communities. It also supplies electrical energy to other City agencies at rates prescribed by City ordinances.

Geographic Reach

The Seattle City Light service area includes all of the City of Seattle portions of the cities of Burien Tukwila SeaTac Shoreline Lake Forest Park and Renton as well as parts of unincorporated King County.

Financial Performance

Seattle City Light reported a revenue increase of 5% (to $842.2) in 2013 primarily due to increased retail power revenues stemming from a 4% rate increase and a 1.2% Bonneville Power Administration pass-through rate adjustment.

It net income increased that year due to higher retail power sales rate stabilization account unearned revenue transferred-in power related revenues and capital contributions. These were partially offset by higher expenses for generation customer service administrative and general taxes depreciation interest and lower investment earnings.

In 2013 Seattle City Light's operating cash inflow decreased to $229.7 (from $243.5 million in 2012) was due to higher tax paid and increased cash paid to a supplier.

Strategy

The company's long term objective is to continue to secure reliable low-cost and environmentally-sensitive power for its customers. To lower costs the utility is pushing its customers to conserve by taking green energy options such as installing more energy-efficient appliances and by buying renewable energy credits (allowing customers to pay for slightly higher costs of integrating renewable energy into the region's power grid).

Seattle City Light's six-year strategic plan adopted in 2012 calls for an annual rate increase of 4.7% to pay for expanding Seattle City Light's infrastructure and services including building its first electric substation for 30 years.

In 2013 the company added two new service request types to the 'Find It Fix It' smartphone app enabling Smartphone to report illegal dumping and streetlight outages in addition to its existing features for reporting abandoned vehicles graffiti potholes and parking enforcement issues.

That year Seattle City Light and the Seattle Aquarium announced the start of construction for the largest solar array at any aquarium on the West Coast as part of the utility's Community Solar and Green Up programs. The $330000 system will cover a large portion of the south side of the Seattle Aquarium's roof. Most of its 247 solar panels will produce electricity on behalf of City Light customers who want to buy solar power through the utility's Community Solar program. The rest of the panels are being installed as a demonstration project through the utility's voluntary Green Up renewable energy program with the electricity produced helping to power the Aquarium's operations.

Company Background

Evolving from several neighborhood electric companies that began serving Seattle in 1886 Seattle City Light was created in 1910 to power the city's streetlights. In 2005 the electric utility became the first in the US to become greenhouse gas neutral in its power generation.

EXECUTIVES

Superintendent, Jorge Carrasco
President City University Of Seattle, Richard Carter
Chief Technical Officer, Michael Mattmiller
Auditors: BAKER TILLY VIRCHOW KRAUZE LLP

LOCATIONS

HQ: THE CITY OF SEATTLE-CITY LIGHT DEPARTMENT
700 5TH AVE STE 3200, SEATTLE, WA 981045065
Phone: 206 684-3200
Web: WWW.SEATTLE.GOV

PRODUCTS/OPERATIONS

2013 Sales

	% of total
Non-residential	63
Residential	37
Total	**100**

COMPETITORS

Avista
Cascade Natural Gas
IDACORP
NV Energy
NW Natural
PacifiCorp
Portland General Electric
Puget Energy
Xcel Energy

HISTORICAL FINANCIALS

Company Type: Private

Income Statement FYE: December 31

	REVENUE ($ mil.)	NET INCOME ($ mil.)	NET PROFIT MARGIN	EMPLOYEES
12/18	991	162	16.4%	1,600
12/17	989	120	12.2%	—
12/16	903	85	9.4%	—
12/09	723	34	4.7%	—
Annual Growth	3.6%	18.9%	—	—

2018 Year-End Financials

Return on assets: 3.3%
Return on equity: 10.8%
Current ratio: 1.20
Cash ($ mil.): 135

THE CLEVELAND CLINIC FOUNDATION

The not-for-profit Cleveland Clinic Foundation operates about 20 hospitals in Ohio Florida Abu Dhabi Toronto and soon in London. Combined the foundation's hospitals have more than 6000 beds. Its flagship location is its namesake Cleveland Clinic an academic medical center in Cleveland Ohio. The campus specializes in cardiac care digestive disease treatment and urological and kidney care along with education and research opportunities. It has an international care center children's hospital and an outpatient center; it also contains research and educational institutes covering clinical drug research ophthalmic studies and cancer research as well as physician and scientist training programs.

Operations

The Cleveland Clinic operates approximately 220 outpatient facilities in northern Ohio. These include outpatient family health centers ambulatory surgery centers physician offices specialized cancer centers and wellness centers.

The foundation operates the Lerner College of Medicine and the Lerner Research Institute through a partnership with Case Western Reserve University and it has continuing education nursing and residency programs. It also operates Cleveland Clinic Innovations a unit that oversees collaborative research and technology commercialization programs with partners including MedStar Health and the University of Notre Dame. Cleveland Clinic educates about 1975 residents and fellows and receives more than $305 million in research funding (from grants contracts and federal support) each year.

Altogether the medical centers known as the Cleveland Clinic Health System include more than

6000 beds and employ more than 4500 full-time physicians. The group handles almost 308770 hospital admissions and more than 9.5 million outpatient visits each year. In 2019 it had more than 255000 surgical cases.

Geographic Reach

In addition to its primary campus Cleveland Clinic operates regional hospitals and numerous family and specialty health centers in northeastern Ohio. It operates a handful of facilities in Florida and several brain clinics in Nevada.

Internationally it operates a health and wellness center in Canada and manages health centers in the United Arab Emirates.

Its corporate headquarters is located in Cleveland Ohio.

Strategy

In late 2019 Cleveland Clinic and American Well are partnering on a first-of-its-kind initiative to provide broad access to comprehensive and high-acuity care services via telehealth. Together the organizations will form a Cleveland-based joint venture company named The Clinic which will offer virtual care from Cleveland Clinic's highly specialized experts through American Well's well-established digital health technology platform.

Mergers and Acquisitions

In early 2019 Cleveland Clinic expanded its operations in the Sunshine State when it acquired Martin Health System and its three hospitals (with more than 520 beds) in Southeast Florida. It also acquired Indian River Medical Center which has more than 330 beds and is located on Florida's Treasure Coast. The system plans to invest millions in the newly added operations over the next few years.

Company Background

Cleveland Clinic Foundation traces its roots to 1921 when a group of Cleveland doctors teamed up to improve medical care and education. Its main campus has conducted breakthrough medical innovations through its history such as the first face transplant in 2008 and it is regularly named to the US News & World Report's list of America's Best Hospitals.

EXECUTIVES

Cio, C. Martin Harris
Chairman And Ceo, Delos M. (Toby) Cosgrove
Ceo Cleveland Clinic Regional Hospitals, David L. Bronson
Controller And Chief Accounting Officer, Steven C. Glass
Ceo Cleveland Clinic Abu Dhabi, A. Marc Harrison
Chief Medical Operations Officer, Robert Wyllie
Chief Of Operations, William (Bill) Peacock
Interim Ceo Sheikh Khalifa Medical City, Ben Frank
Interim Executive Chief Nursing Officer, K. Kelly Hancock
Chair Department Of Palm Ccm, Herbert Wiedemann
Vice President, Sanford Timen
Medical Director, Kevin Hopkins
Director Of Health Information, Bryan Holtz
Vice President Of Medical Operations, William Riebel
Medical Director, Cheryl Hubbard
Vice President Of Operations, Kris Bennett
Vice President, Toribio Flores
Medical Director, Damon Kralovic
Medical Director, Michael Machuzak
Assistant Vice President Operations, Janet Gulley
Medical Director, John Donohue
Medical Director, Hany Aziz
Associate Medical Director, Faith Factora
Medical Director, Purva Grover
Vice President Oncology Services West, Susan Dunson
Pharmacy Manager Transitions Of Care, Erick Sokn
Regional Vice President Cv Services East, Dan Sutton
Vice President Market Leader, Grace Jen
Senior Vice President System Operations, Steve Abdenour
Chairman, Robert E. (Bob) Rich
Vice Chairman, Joseph M. (Joe) Scaminace
Medical Secretary, Brenda Hammond
Surgical Operations Secretary, Denise Slovan
Secretary, Lynn Meyers
Medical Secretary, Lisa Yospur
Medical Secretary, Mattie Dalton
Medical Secretary, Judith Burdett
Medical Secretary, Sally Cooper
Secretary, Pam Staub
Medical Secretary, Joyce Velazquez
Board Member, Donna Munic-Miller
Unit Secretary, Karen Ginley
Medical Secretary, Heather Karn
Appt Secretary, Robin Allen
Secretary, Joye Grebb
Department Secretary, Chris Morchak
Secretary, Marianne Simon
Medical Secretary, Charylie Rivers
Medical Secretary, Lucy Bufkin
Medical Secretary, Linda Rosa
Ap Secretary, Patricia Lichtenfeld
Secretary Medical Education, Barb Salak
Auditors: ERNST & YOUNG LLP CLEVELAND

LOCATIONS

HQ: THE CLEVELAND CLINIC FOUNDATION
9500 EUCLID AVE, CLEVELAND, OH 441950002
Phone: 216 636-8335
Web: WWW.CLEVELANDCLINIC.ORG

Selected Facilities

Ashtabula County Medical Center (Ashtabula Ohio; management contract)
The Cleveland Clinic (Cleveland Ohio)
- Cleveland Clinic Children's Hospital
- Cleveland Clinic International Center

Cleveland Clinic Canada (Toronto)
Cleveland Clinic Children's Hospital for Rehabilitation (Shaker Campus in Cleveland Ohio)
Cleveland Clinic Family Health Centers (multiple locations in northeast Ohio)
Cleveland Clinic Florida (Weston Florida)
Cleveland Clinic Florida (West Palm Beach Florida)
Cleveland Clinic Lou Ruvo Center for Brain Health (Elko Nevada)
Cleveland Clinic Lou Ruvo Center for Brain Health (Las Vegas Nevada)
Cleveland Clinic Lou Ruvo Center for Brain Health (Reno Nevada)
Euclid Hospital (Euclid Ohio)
Fairview Hospital (Cleveland Ohio)
Hillcrest Hospital (Mayfield Heights Ohio)
Lakewood Hospital (Lakewood Ohio)
Lutheran Hospital (Cleveland Ohio)
Marymount Hospital (Garfield Heights Ohio)
Medina Hospital (Medina Ohio)
Richard E. Jacobs Health Center (Avon Ohio)
South Pointe Hospital (Warrensville Heights Ohio)

Selected Institutes

Cleveland Clinic Institutes
- Anesthesiology and Pain Management
- Bariatric and Metabolic
- Cancer Center/Taussig Cancer Institute
- Cleveland Clinic Children's and Pediatric
- Dermatology and Plastic Surgery
- Digestive Disease and Surgery
- Emergency Services
- Endocrinology and Metabolism
- Genomics
- Head and Neck
- Heart and Vascular
- Imaging
- Medicine
- Neurological
- Nursing
- Orthopaedic and Rheumatologic
- Pathology and Laboratory Medicine
- Respiratory
- Urology and Kidney
- Wellness

Special Expertise Institutes
- Arts and Medicine
- Body Donation
- Patient Experience
- Philanthropy
- Professional Staff Affairs
- Quality and Patient Safety
- Research

PRODUCTS/OPERATIONS

2018 Sales

	$ mil.	% of total
Net patient service revenue		
Self-pay	4,465	50
Managed care & commercial	2,871	32
Medicare	649	7
Medicaid	45	1
Other	895	10
Total	**8,927**	**100**

COMPETITORS

Akron Children's Hospital
Catholic Health Initiatives
Deaconess Associations
Kettering Health Network
Lake Health
Mayo Clinic
Memorial Sloan-Kettering
MetroHealth System
OhioHealth
Parma Community General Hospital
Premier Health Partners
Robinson Memorial Hospital
Shriners Hospitals For Children
Summa Health System
University Hospitals Health System

HISTORICAL FINANCIALS

Company Type: Private

Income Statement — FYE: December 31

	REVENUE ($ mil.)	NET INCOME ($ mil.)	NET PROFIT MARGIN	EMPLOYEES
12/19	10,559	2,239	21.2%	44,000
12/18	8,927	176	2.0%	—
12/17	8,407	1,150	13.7%	—
12/16	8,037	513	6.4%	—
Annual Growth	9.5%	63.4%	—	—

2019 Year-End Financials

Return on assets: 11.2%
Return on equity: 19.0%
Current ratio: 1.10
Cash ($ mil.): 505

THE CLEVELAND ELECTRIC ILLUMINATING COMPANY

The Cleveland Electric Illuminating Company (CEI) has a glowing reputation. The utility commonly referred to as The Illuminating Company distributes electricity to a base population of about 1.8 million inhabitants in a 1600 sq. ml. area of northeastern Ohio. CEI has 33210 miles of distribution lines. In 2010 the utility met 4420 MW of hourly maximum generating demand from interests in fossil-fueled and nuclear power plants (which are operated by fellow FirstEnergy subsidiaries). It also engages in wholesale energy transactions with other power companies. CEI is also a competitive retail electric service provider in Ohio alongside sister companies Ohio Edison and Toledo Edison.

EXECUTIVES

Pres, John E Skory
Exec V Pres-Cfo, Mark T Clark
V Pres-Contrl, Harvey L Wagner
Exec V Pres-Gen Cnsl, L L Vespoli
V Pres-Treas, J F Pearson
Auditors: PRICEWATERHOUSECOOPERS LLP CL

LOCATIONS

HQ: THE CLEVELAND ELECTRIC ILLUMINATING COMPANY
76 S MAIN ST, AKRON, OH 443081812
Phone: 800 589-3101
Web: WWW.FIRSTENERGYCORP.COM

COMPETITORS

Columbia Gas of Ohio
DPL
Dominion East Ohio
Duke Energy Ohio
Ohio Power
Vectren Energy Delivery of Ohio

HISTORICAL FINANCIALS

Company Type: Private

Income Statement — FYE: December 31

	REVENUE ($ mil.)	NET INCOME ($ mil.)	NET PROFIT MARGIN	EMPLOYEES
12/16	928	37	4.0%	897
12/10	1,221	73	6.0%	—
12/09	1,676	(10)	—	—
12/08	1,815	284	15.7%	—
Annual Growth	(8.0%)	(22.4%)	—	—

THE COMMUNITY HOSPITAL GROUP INC

JFK Medical Center plays a central role in health care in central New Jersey. The medical center is an acute care facility with some 500 beds and 950 physicians providing emergency surgical trauma and other inpatient services. The hospital includes the JFK New Jersey Neuroscience Institute which treats stroke and other neurological conditions and the JFK Johnson Rehabilitation Institute which treats traumatic injuries. JFK Medical Center also offers diagnostic imaging cancer care senior and hospice care and family practice services. It is also a teaching hospital affiliated with several area universities. The hospital is part of the JFK Health System.

Strategy

To expand its capacity for emergency services JFK Medical Center launched construction of a new ER pavilion in 2013. The project includes the addition of a three-story structure above the existing ER facilities. To keep pace with cutting-edge medical technologies the hospital has also made recent investments in upgrades to its diagnostic imaging cardiac catheterization and wound healing equipment.

EXECUTIVES

Director Of Radiology, Srikanth Jaikumar
Medical Director Vice President, Sara Cuccurullo
Auditors: BAKER TILLY

LOCATIONS

HQ: THE COMMUNITY HOSPITAL GROUP INC
98 JAMES ST STE 400, EDISON, NJ 088203902
Phone: 732 321-7000
Web: WWW.JFKMC.ORG

PRODUCTS/OPERATIONS

Selected Centers and Affiliates

Adult Medical Day Program
Haven Hospice
JFK at Home
JFK Dental Clinic
JFK Family Medicine Center
JFK Hartwyck Nursing Convalescent and Rehabilitation Centers
JFK Johnson Rehabilitation Institute (JRI)
JFK Mediplex Surgery Center
JFK New Jersey Neuroscience Institute
JFK Medical Center Muhlenberg Campus/JFK-Muhlenberg Snyder Schools
Whispering Knoll Assisted Living

COMPETITORS

Ball Memorial Hospital
Bergen Regional Medical
Capital Health System
CentraState Healthcare System
Henry County Memorial Hospital
Monmouth Medical Center
Newton Medical Center
Princeton HealthCare
Robert Wood Johnson University Hospital
Saint Peter's University Hospital
St. Joseph's Healthcare System

HISTORICAL FINANCIALS

Company Type: Private

Income Statement — FYE: December 31

	REVENUE ($ mil.)	NET INCOME ($ mil.)	NET PROFIT MARGIN	EMPLOYEES
12/17	551	(13)	—	3,000
12/16	532	28	5.3%	—
12/14	467	(3)	—	—
12/10	427	(17)	—	—
Annual Growth	3.7%	—	—	—

2017 Year-End Financials

Return on assets: (-4.9%)
Return on equity: (-46.5%)
Current ratio: 1.40
Cash ($ mil.): 39

THE CONLAN COMPANY

EXECUTIVES

Ceo, Gary D Condron
Pres*, Kevin Turpin
V Pres*, Tom Lutz
V Pres*, Ryan Triesenberg
Cfo*, Bill Hayne
Exec V Pres*, David Staley
Exec V Pres*, Stuart Price
Sr V Pres*, Scott Austin
V Pres*, Charles King
V Pres*, Ronnie Cupp
Human Resources Compliance, Larry Robbins
Auditors: SMITH ADCOCK & COMPANY LLP A

LOCATIONS

HQ: THE CONLAN COMPANY
1800 PARKWAY PL SE # 1010, MARIETTA, GA 300678293
Phone: 770 423-8000
Web: WWW.CONLANCOMPANY.COM

HISTORICAL FINANCIALS

Company Type: Private

Income Statement — FYE: December 31

	REVENUE ($ mil.)	NET INCOME ($ mil.)	NET PROFIT MARGIN	EMPLOYEES
12/18	953	40	4.2%	391
12/17	930	40	4.3%	—
12/16	772	41	5.3%	—
12/15	589	13	2.3%	—
Annual Growth	17.3%	42.9%	—	—

2018 Year-End Financials

Return on assets: 16.3%
Return on equity: 90.9%
Current ratio: 1.20
Cash ($ mil.): 93

THE CORE GROUP LTD

EXECUTIVES

Pres, James K Jacobs
SEC, Dennis Barber
Dir of Fin, John Verhoff
Auditors: MAYER HOFFMAN MCCANN PC PHO

LOCATIONS

HQ: THE CORE GROUP LTD
3036 E GREENWAY RD, PHOENIX, AZ 850324414
Phone: 602 494-0800
Web: WWW.COREGROUPSALES.COM

HISTORICAL FINANCIALS

Company Type: Private

Income Statement — FYE: December 31

	REVENUE ($ mil.)	NET INCOME ($ mil.)	NET PROFIT MARGIN	EMPLOYEES
12/19	1,004	14	1.4%	150
12/18	1,000	17	1.7%	—
Annual Growth	0.5%	(18.7%)	—	—

2019 Year-End Financials

Return on assets: 4.9%
Return on equity: 37.1%
Current ratio: 1.10
Cash ($ mil.): 55

THE COUNTY OF BUCKS

EXECUTIVES

Chief, David Steinbach
Chb*, Michael G Fitzpatrick
Treas*, William R Snyder
Interim Coo*, Leader Brian Hessenthaler
Coronor, Thomas J Rosko
Register of Wills, Barbara G Reilly
Human Resources, Suzanne Colonna
Instructor, June Lane
Coordinator, Karen Platts
Auditors: ZELENKOFSKE AXELROD LLC JAMIS

LOCATIONS

HQ: THE COUNTY OF BUCKS
55 E COURT ST FL 5, DOYLESTOWN, PA 189014318
Phone: 215 348-6424
Web: WWW.BUCKSCOUNTY.ORG

HISTORICAL FINANCIALS

Company Type: Private

Income Statement — FYE: December 31

	REVENUE ($ mil.)	NET INCOME ($ mil.)	NET PROFIT MARGIN	EMPLOYEES
12/19	549	(42)	—	2,500
12/18	549	16	3.0%	—
12/17	514	(28)	—	—
12/16	508	8	1.6%	—
Annual Growth	2.6%	—	—	—

2019 Year-End Financials

Return on assets: (-4.0%)
Return on equity: (-12.1%)
Current ratio: —
Cash ($ mil.): 172

THE DAVID AND LUCILE PACKARD FOUNDATION

One of the wealthiest philanthropic organizations in the US The David and Lucile Packard Foundation primarily provides grants to not-for-profit entities. The foundation focuses on operating in three areas: conservation and science; children families and communities; and population. The David and Lucile Packard Foundation boasts approximately $4.6 billion in assets. In 2009 the organization committed $100 million for the expansion of the Lucile Packard Children's Hospital at Stanford. The late David Packard (co-founder of Hewlett-Packard) and his wife the late Lucile Salter Packard created the foundation in 1964. Their children run the organization.

EXECUTIVES

Managing Director Of Marketable Securities, Kimberly Sargent
Auditors: PRICEWATERHOUSECOOPERS LLP

LOCATIONS

HQ: THE DAVID AND LUCILE PACKARD FOUNDATION
300 2ND ST, LOS ALTOS, CA 940223694
Phone: 650 917-7167
Web: WWW.PACKARD.ORG

HISTORICAL FINANCIALS

Company Type: Private

Income Statement — FYE: December 31

	REVENUE ($ mil.)	NET INCOME ($ mil.)	NET PROFIT MARGIN	EMPLOYEES
12/10	701	412	58.8%	85
12/09	398	74	18.8%	—
12/06	809	587	72.6%	—
12/05	0	0	69.6%	—
Annual Growth	302.5%	289.2%	—	—

2010 Year-End Financials

Return on assets: 6.7%
Return on equity: 6.8%
Current ratio: 2.00
Cash ($ mil.): 213

THE DCH HEALTH CARE AUTHORITY

The DCH Healthcare Authority is concerned with the Druid City's health. The company which does business as DCH Health System provides health services to residents of Tuscaloosa and several other communities in Western Alabama. Its flagship facility is the 580-bed DCH Regional Medical Center a full-service teaching hospital located near the University of Alabama campus. DCH Health System also includes the Northport and Fayette medical centers which together houses more than 385 acute-care beds. The hospitals offer a full range of inpatient and outpatient services including primary diagnostic emergency surgical rehabilitative and home health care.

Operations

Several of the system's hospitals operate specialty centers. For instance DCH Regional has cancer and cardiology clinics while the Northport Medical Center has specialty rehabilitation and mental health departments. In addition Fayette Medical Center houses a 120-bed nursing home.

Geographic Reach

The company's headquarters is located at Tuscaloosa Alabama along with DCH Regional Medical Center.

Strategy

Employees of the DCH Health System give their time and talents in service to others in West Alabama at work and in their community. Throughout the year customers will see DCH employees volunteering their time to support community events that benefit organizations such as the March of Dimes the American Heart Association and the American Cancer Society.

DCH Health System employees and physicians are out in their schools churches malls and at civic organizations sharing practical information on how to stay healthy. DCH sponsors health fairs and free screenings including an annual prostate screening and a breast screening and education program.

Many support groups that help people in the community with special needs are supported by DCH and DCH supports education by participating in the Adopt-A-School program. DCH Health System Hospitals shows their support for the community by providing health care to individuals who cannot afford it. The citizens of Tuscaloosa County have helped DCH meet its mission of service. Of the county's 3-cent sales tax 7% is set aside for DCH Regional Medical Center to help pay for health care for indigent patients from Tuscaloosa County. DCH provides 17 dollars in care to the indigent for every dollar it receives.

Company Background

The "DCH" in the organization's name stands for Druid City Hospital the name of the system's first hospital which opened in 1923. Druid City is a nickname for Tuscaloosa.

EXECUTIVES

President And Ceo, Bryan N. Kindred
Cfo, John Winfrey
Administrator Dch Regional Medical Center, Bill Cassels
Administrator Pickens County Medical Center, Wayne McElroy
Administrator Northport Medical Center, Luke Standeffer
Administrator Fayette Medical Center, Barry S. Cochran
Director Of Nursing, Jutta Beams
Pharmacy Manager And Hematology Oncology Specialist, Hind Hamid
Medical Director, Peter G Casten
Physical Therapy Assistants, Dana Taylor
Medical Director, Dick Owens
Chairman, Samuel F. Clabaugh
Auditors: MORRISON & SMITH LLP TUSCALO

LOCATIONS

HQ: THE DCH HEALTH CARE AUTHORITY
809 UNIVERSITY BLVD E, TUSCALOOSA, AL 354012029
Phone: 205 759-7111
Web: WWW.DCHSYSTEM.COM

PRODUCTS/OPERATIONS

Selected Alabama Facilities

DCH Regional Medical Center (Tuscaloosa)
Fayette Medical Center (Fayette)
Northport Medical Center (Northport)
Pickens County Medical Center (Carrollton)

COMPETITORS

Baptist Health (AL)
Children's Health System
East Alabama Medical Center
Gadsden Regional Medical Center
Health Care Authority of the City of Huntsville
Jackson Hospital & Clinic of Alabama
University of South Alabama Health System

HISTORICAL FINANCIALS

Company Type: Private

Income Statement — FYE: September 30

	REVENUE ($ mil.)	NET INCOME ($ mil.)	NET PROFIT MARGIN	EMPLOYEES
09/19	547	26	4.8%	4,683
09/18	520	6	1.3%	—
09/17	516	8	1.7%	—
09/16	531	23	4.5%	—
Annual Growth	1.0%	3.4%	—	—

2019 Year-End Financials

Return on assets: 3.7%
Return on equity: 5.9%
Current ratio: 2.10
Cash ($ mil.): 71

THE DETROIT INSTITUTE OF ARTS

EXECUTIVES

Dir-Pres-Ceo, Graham W J Beal
Chm*, Eugene A Gargaro Jr
Coo*, Nettie Seabrooks
Internal Medicine Practitioner, Lisa Lorenzo
Vice-President, H W Burdett
Bishop, Johnf White

LOCATIONS

HQ: THE DETROIT INSTITUTE OF ARTS
5200 WOODWARD AVE, DETROIT, MI 482024094
Phone: 313 833-7900
Web: WWW.DIA.ORG

HISTORICAL FINANCIALS

Company Type: Private

Income Statement FYE: June 30

	REVENUE ($ mil.)	NET INCOME ($ mil.)	NET PROFIT MARGIN	EMPLOYEES
06/15	606	28	4.7%	350
06/14	52	13	26.0%	—
06/09	47	0	—	—
06/08	58	(8)	—	—
Annual Growth	39.7%	—	—	—

2015 Year-End Financials

Return on assets: 8.4%
Return on equity: 11.8%
Current ratio: —
Cash ($ mil.): 49

THE DREES COMPANY

The Drees Company is a big homebuilder in Cincinnati and one of the nation's top private builders. Drees targets first-time and move-up buyers with homes that are priced from about $100000 to more than $1 million. Drees also builds condominiums townhomes and patio homes. Its homes portfolio ranges from its former Zaring Premier Homes luxury division to the company's more financially accessible and modest Marquis Homes division. Drees is active in Florida Indiana Kentucky Maryland North Carolina Ohio Tennessee Texas Virginia and Washington DC. The family-owned firm was founded in 1928.

Operations

In addition to home building architecture energy efficiency upgrades and design services Drees also provides new construction financing solutions through its subsidiary and mortgage lending business First Equity Mortgage which has closed more than $1 billion in loans.

Geographic Reach

Headquartered in Fort Mitchell Kentucky Drees operates across nearly 10 states in cities including Cincinnati and Cleveland Ohio; Indianapolis; Nashville; Raleigh North Carolina; Jacksonville Florida; Austin Houston and Dallas Texas; and the Greater Washington DC area.

Sales and Marketing

In recent years Drees has concentrated on the fast-growing "move up" segment market targeting home buyers looking to upgrade into larger houses.

In 2012 Drees converted its longtime Zaring Premier Homes luxury brand name to its flagship Drees Homes brand. While the move required rebranding in the greater Cincinnati area Drees is banking on its brand reputation and recognition. It also allowed the residential homebuilder to consolidate its advertising sales and marketing efforts.

Financial Performance

While full details of the private company could not be found Drees' CEO David Drees announced in July 2013 that he expected the company to reach $629 million in revenue by April 1 2014.

Looking further back Drees had revenues as high as $1.2 billion in 2006 which slid dramatically following the financial crisis to $490 million in revenue in 2010. To its benefit Texas markets – specifically Austin and Dallas – remained active throughout the recession. Drees was also helped by entering the recession with a relatively low debt load of $364 million. By March 2013 Drees had sold land to generate cash flow and reduced its debt to $125 million.

Strategy

Ranked among the top 25 largest national homebuilders by BUILDER Magazine Drees has been steadily expanding over the past few years to capitalize on an improving housing market.

In recent years Drees has concentrated on the fast-growing and lucrative "move up" segment of the homebuyer's market targeting home owners that are looking to upgrade to larger houses with higher-end amenities. In late 2014 the company landed a $100 million contract to build 237 homes in three Cincinnati-based residential communities with the average house priced between $307000 and $360000. In September 2014 the company entered its first ever foray into the Houston Texas market with plans to price its houses there for more than $300000 – prime pricing to lure these "move up" buyers.

Company Background

A family-operated enterprise since its founding by immigrant Theodore Drees in 1928 the company is run by the third generation of the Drees family.

EXECUTIVES

Chb-Ceo, Ralph Drees
Pres-Coo, David Drees
V Pres-Sec-Treas, Lawrence Herbst
Market Manager, Heather Williams
Director of Communications, Jocelyn Cates
Sales Manager, Adam Dirkhising
Market Manager, Carla Houdek
Architecture Specialist, Saavan Patel
Auditors: DELOITTE & TOUCHE LLP CINCINN

LOCATIONS

HQ: THE DREES COMPANY
515 S CAPTAL OF TEXAS HWY, WEST LAKE HILLS, TX 787464314
Phone: 859 578-4200
Web: WWW.DREESHOMES.COM

Selected Locations

Florida
Jacksonville
Indiana
Indianapolis
Kentucky
Fort Mitchell
Maryland
Frederick
North Carolina
Raleigh
Ohio
Cincinnati
Cleveland
Dayton
Tennessee
Nashville
Texas
Austin
Dallas
Washington DC

COMPETITORS

D.R. Horton
Fischer Homes
KB Home
Lennar
M/I Homes
PulteGroup

HISTORICAL FINANCIALS

Company Type: Private

Income Statement FYE: March 31

	REVENUE ($ mil.)	NET INCOME ($ mil.)	NET PROFIT MARGIN	EMPLOYEES
03/16	722	31	4.3%	549
03/15	669	36	5.4%	—
03/14	683	35	5.3%	—
03/13	584	19	3.3%	—
Annual Growth	7.3%	17.6%	—	—

2016 Year-End Financials

Return on assets: 6.5%
Return on equity: 14.1%
Current ratio: 1.90
Cash ($ mil.): 10

THE EMPIRE DISTRICT ELECTRIC COMPANY

Empire District Electric (EDE) light ups the middle of the US. The utility transmits and distributes electricity to a population base of more than 450000 (about 217000 customers in southwestern Missouri and adjacent areas of Arkansas Kansas and Oklahoma. It also supplies water to three Missouri towns and natural gas throughout most of the state. EDE's interests in fossil-fueled and hydroelectric power plants give it a generating capacity of 1377 MW; it also wholesales power. The company also provides fiber-optic services. In early 2017 the company was bought by an Algonquin Power & Utilities unit in a C$3.2 billion (US$2.3 billion) deal.

Operations

EDE operates its businesses in three segments: electric gas and other. The electric segment serves an area of 10000 sq. ml. located principally in southwestern Missouri and also includes smaller areas in southeastern Kansas northeastern Oklahoma and northwestern Arkansas. It also provides water service to three towns in Missouri.

Coal-fired generating units 1 and 2 at the Iatan Plant are jointly-owned by KCP&L (a subsidiary of Great Plains Energy) Missouri Joint Municipal Electric Utility Commission Kansas Electric Power Cooperative and EDE with EDE's share of ownership being 12% in each plant. The Plum Point Energy Station is a 670-MW coal-fired generating facility near Osceola Arkansas of which EDE owns 50 MW of capacity.

EDE's natural gas operations distribute natural gas through The Empire District Gas Company. Its principal gas utility properties consist of about 87 miles of transmission mains and approximately 1160 miles of distribution mains.

EDE's other segment consists of its fiber optics business (which it also uses in its own utility operations).

In 2013 the company generated about 90% of its revenue from its electric segment.

Geographic Reach

The company serves customers in Arkansas Kansas Missouri and Oklahoma.

Sales and Marketing

EDE supplies retail electric service to 119 incorporated communities (and to various unincorporated areas) and wholesale service to four municipally owned distribution systems. The largest urban area it serves is the city of Joplin Missouri and its immediate vicinity with a population of 160000. Its three largest classes of customers are residential commercial and industrial which provided 43% 30% and 15% respectively of its electric operating revenues in 2013. The company derived about 90% of its retail electric revenues from Missouri.

Its gas operations serve 44000 customers in northwest north central and west central Missouri. It provides natural gas distribution to 48 communities and 377 transportation customers. The largest urban area it serves is the city of Sedalia with a population of more than 20000. Residential and commercial provided 63% and 27% respectively of its gas operating revenues in 2013.

EDE also has 118 fiber customers.

Financial Performance

The company's revenues increased by 7% in 2013 due to improved revenues across all of its segments. Electric sales increased due to higher electric rates a growth in customers and colder weather (which increased demand). However commercial sales decreased due to a net unbilled sales adjustment recorded in 2012; Industrial sales decreased due to operating reductions by several large industrial customers; and it wholesale sales decreased due to the closure of a large dairy facility in Monett Missouri.

EDE's gas retail sales and revenues increased due to the colder weather; and other revenues also increased due to a growth in Southwest Power Pool transmission revenues in 2013.

The company's net income increased by 14% in 2013 primarily due to higher revenues and as well as an increased allowance for equity funds used during construction.

EDE has seen growth in revenues since 2009 however it decreased in 2012 due to lower demand as a result of milder winter temperatures that year. The company has seen a healthy growth in cash flow from operations since 2009.

Strategy

The company has been boosting its generating capacity including through its partial ownership in the Plum Point Energy Station in Arkansas and through several wind farm contracts. Total property additions for the three years ending in 2013 totaled $398 million and retirements during the same period totaled $39 million.

Seeking to boost its revenues to cover maintenance and expansion costs in 2013 EDE filed for rate increases for its Arkansas and Missouri electric customers.

In 2013 the company filed an Integrated Resource Plan with the Missouri Public Service Commission to introduce additional demand-side management programs to help its customers use energy more efficiently.

Company Background

In May 2011 EDE's power system suffered extensive damage as as a result of the major tornado that tore through Joplin Missouri. Initial damage reports from the Joplin tornado included the loss of 130 transmission poles.

Mild weather and the global recession suppressed demand and revenues in 2009 but lower gas and power costs helped EDE post an increase in operating income for that year. Cooler-than-normal winter weather and warmer-than-usual summer weather and a rate increase helped to boost power usage and lifted the company's revenues in 2010. A shrinking gas customer base due to depressed economic conditions led to lower gas revenues that year. Lower expenses allowed EDE to report an overall improved net income position in 2010.

EXECUTIVES

President Ceo And Director, Bradley P. Beecher, $532,500 total compensation
Vp And Coo Gas, Ronald F. Gatz, $262,500 total compensation
Vp And Coo Electric, Kelly S. Walters, $312,500 total compensation
Vp Finance And Cfo, Laurie A. Delano, $295,000 total compensation
Vp Energy Supply And Delivery Operations, Blake A. Mertens, $240,000 total compensation
Chairman, D. Randy Laney
Treasurer, Mark Timpe

LOCATIONS

HQ: THE EMPIRE DISTRICT ELECTRIC COMPANY
602 S JOPLIN AVE, JOPLIN, MO 648012337
Phone: 417 625-5100
Web: WWW.LIBERTYUTILITIES.COM

PRODUCTS/OPERATIONS

Selected Subsidiaries
EDE Holdings Inc. (nonregulated operations)
Empire District Industries Inc. (fiber-optic services)
The Empire District Gas Company

COMPETITORS

AEP
Ameren
Associated Electric
Berkshire Hathaway Energy
Charter Communications
Entergy
Grand River Dam Authority
Great Plains Energy
OGE Energy
Southern Union
Spire
Westar Energy
Western Farmers Electric
Xcel Energy

HISTORICAL FINANCIALS

Company Type: Private

Income Statement — FYE: December 31

	REVENUE ($ mil.)	NET INCOME ($ mil.)	NET PROFIT MARGIN	EMPLOYEES
12/17	584	36	6.3%	749
12/16	568	64	11.3%	—
12/15	605	56	9.3%	—
12/14	652	67	10.3%	—
Annual Growth	(3.6%)	(18.2%)	—	—

2017 Year-End Financials

Return on assets: 1.5%
Return on equity: 4.4%
Current ratio: 1.20
Cash ($ mil.): 5

THE EVANGELICAL LUTHERAN GOOD SAMARITAN SOCIETY

The Evangelical Lutheran Good Samaritan Society strives to be a good neighbor to all particularly to the elderly people in need of housing and health care. The not-for-profit organization owns or leases some 200 senior living facilities including nursing homes assisted living facilities and affordable housing projects for seniors. Through its facilities it also provides home health care services outpatient rehabilitation adult day care and a variety of other services such as specialized units for people with Alzheimer's disease and related dementias. Good Samaritan Society merged with hospital system Sanford Health in early 2019.

EXECUTIVES

Vice President Workforce Systems, Dean Mertz
Medical Records Director, Melissa Rapoza
Director Of Nursing Services, Mari Stelter
Director Of Nursing Services, Amy Larsen
Director Of Medical Records, Laura Fresk
Medical Records Director, KERRI MOULTON
Medical Records Director, Kelly Fletcher
Medical Records Director, Kimberly Geldhardt
Medical Records Director, Dawn Gisch
Medical Director, Sherry Billups
Medical Director, Michael Goodhope
Medical Director, Rodney Dill
Medical Director, David Jameson
Medical Director, David Little
Medical Director, Steven Senseney
Medical Records Director, Rita Dotson
Medical Director, Lyle Wadsworth
Medical Director, Elizabeth Petty
Medical Director, Marc Campbell
Medical Director, Zoltan Pek
Medical Director, Eric Slane
Medical Records Director, VICKI PRUST
Medical Director, Lindy Eatwell
Medical Director, ED STEIN
Medical Director, Jerzy Slomka
Medical Director, KEITH COWARD
Medical Records Director, Magda Estrada
Medical Director, MARK SILVER
Medical Director, DAVID REESE
Vice President, Glomer Lute
Medical Records Director, Lisa Berry
Medical Records Director, Deanna Jensen
Medical Director, Mark Boyce
Medical Director, Bruce Kocourek
Medical Records Director, Betty Maggert
Medical Records Director, Sherry Finnesand
Medical Director, Wayne Wetzbarger
Medical Records Director, Jenni Dvorak
Medical Records Director, Barb Robinson
Medical Records Director, Vicki Curtis
Medical Records Director, Stacy Logue
Medical Records Director, Tami Tompkins
Medical Records Director, Liz Mitchell
Medical Records Director, Kahki Barnett
Medical Records Director, Joyce Hussey
Medical Records Director, Alex Greer
Medical Director, Henry Middleton
Medical Director, Christa Danielson
Vice President, Alena Goergen
Auditors: CLIFTON LARSON ALLEN LLP MINN

LOCATIONS

HQ: THE EVANGELICAL LUTHERAN GOOD SAMARITAN SOCIETY
4800 W 57TH ST, SIOUX FALLS, SD 571082239
Phone: 866 928-1635
Web: WWW.GOOD-SAM.COM

COMPETITORS

BPM Senior Living
Brookdale Senior Living
Enlivant
Extendicare
Five Star Senior Living
Genesis Healthcare
Golden Horizons
Kindred Healthcare
RehabCare
Select Medical
Sunrise Senior Living

HISTORICAL FINANCIALS

Company Type: Private

Income Statement — FYE: December 31

	REVENUE ($ mil.)	NET INCOME ($ mil.)	NET PROFIT MARGIN	EMPLOYEES
12/15	1,011	(33)	—	24,000
12/13	979	0	0.0%	—
12/07	841	17	2.1%	—
12/06	836	44	5.3%	—
Annual Growth	2.1%	—	—	—

2015 Year-End Financials

Return on assets: (-1.9%)
Return on equity: (-4.5%)
Current ratio: 2.30
Cash ($ mil.): 17

THE FINISH LINE INC

The Finish Line sells performance and casual footwear and apparel through more than 900 Finish Line stores and branded shops inside Macy's department stores across the US. Its core Finish Line stores are bigger than those of competitors and offer a wider array of clothing accessories and other merchandise including jackets backpacks sunglasses and watches. Finish Line offers big brand names (such as adidas NIKE and Timberland) and also markets its own private-label line of T-shirts socks and other basics. The company also sells athletic shoes and apparel online. It is a subsidiary of European sports retailer JD Sports.

Operations

Finish Line delivers the EPIC FINISH by providing the most desirable sneakers latest trends and exclusives from the best brands.

Geographic Reach

Indianapolis-based Finish Line has stores across the US. Its largest markets are Texas Florida California Illinois New York and Ohio.

Sales and Marketing

Nearly all of Finish Line's merchandise is shipped directly from suppliers to its different retail stores where the company processes and ships the merchandise by contract and common carriers to its stores/shops or directly to customers. The company also sell products online through its official website.

Company Background

In 1976 boyhood friends Alan Cohen (a lawyer) and David Klapper (a retailer) founded Athletic Enterprises the Indiana franchisee for The Athlete's Foot. By 1981 they had all The Athlete's Foot stores that the state's big malls could hold – about a dozen. To expand beyond those confines the pair teamed up with Dave Fagin and Larry Sablosky and formed The Finish Line.

EXECUTIVES

Vice President And Corporate Controller, Beau J Swenson
Evp And Cfo, Edward W. (Ed) Wilhelm, age 62, $530,000 total compensation
Evp And President Running Specialty Group, Bill Kirkendall, age 66, $355,385 total compensation
Evp And Coo, Melissa Greenwell, age 53
Ceo, Samuel M. (Sam) Sato, age 56, $635,000 total compensation
Evp And Chief Omnichannel Officer, Imran Jooma, age 48, $31,673 total compensation
Vp Supply Chain, Dan Marous
Vice President Information Technology, Awilda Hernandez
Vice President Of Customer Experience, Mark Roper
Vice President Of Human Resources And Payroll, Cindy Cook
Vice President Store Operations And Trai, Greg Davis
Evp Of Chief Information And Technology Officer, Albert Sutera
Senior Vice President Legal And Human Resources And General Counsel And Corporate Secretary, Chris Eck
Executive Vice President Chief Information And Technology Officer, AJ Sutera
Vice President, Pam Zaremba
Vice President, Joyce Ribet
Vice President, Satish Khatana
Vp Dmm Apparel And Accessories, Celeste Richardson
Evp Chief Merchandise Officer And Vp Apparel, Glenn S. Lyon, age 70
Board Member, Richard Crystal
Board Member, Torrence Boone
Board Member, Catherine Langham
Member Board Of Directors, Dolores Kunda
Board Member, Stephen Goldsmith
Board Member, Alyssa Jackson
Auditors: ERNST & YOUNG LLP INDIANAPOLI

LOCATIONS

HQ: THE FINISH LINE INC
3308 N MITTHOEFER RD, INDIANAPOLIS, IN 462352332
Phone: 317 899-1022
Web: WWW.FINISHLINE.COM

PRODUCTS/OPERATIONS

Selected Brands

adidas
Asics
Brooks
Lacoste
Mizuno
New Balance
NIKE
Pastry
Puma
Reebok
Saucony
The North Face
Timberland
Under Armour

Selected Products

Accessories
- Athletic equipment
- Athletic socks
- Backpacks
- Gym bags
- Headbands and sweatbands
- Shoe care
- Shoe insoles and liners
- Shoe laces
- Sunglasses
- Watches

Fan
- High school
- MLB
- NBA
- NCAA
- NFL
- Kids
- Shoes
- Clothing

Men's
- Caps
- Hats
- Jackets
- Jerseys
- Pants
- Shoes
- Shorts
- Socks
- Sweatshirts/fleece
- Tanks
- T-shirts
- Workout clothing

Women's
- Caps
- Hats
- Jackets
- Jerseys
- Pants
- Shoes
- Shorts
- Socks
- Sweatshirts/fleece
- Tanks
- T-shirts
- Team clothing
- Workout clothing

COMPETITORS

Academy Sports
DSW
Dick's Sporting Goods
Foot Locker
Genesco
Hat World
Hibbett Sports
Kmart
Modell's
Patagonia Inc.
REI
Rack Room Shoes
Sports Authority
Target Corporation
Wal-Mart
Zappos.com
shoebuy.com

HISTORICAL FINANCIALS

Company Type: Private

Income Statement — FYE: March 3

	REVENUE ($ mil.)	NET INCOME ($ mil.)	NET PROFIT MARGIN	EMPLOYEES
03/18*	1,838	14	0.8%	13,500
02/17	1,844	(18)	—	—
02/16	1,888	21	1.2%	—
02/15	1,820	79	4.4%	—
Annual Growth	0.3%	(43.5%)	—	—

*Fiscal year change

2018 Year-End Financials

Return on assets: 2.1%
Return on equity: 3.2%
Current ratio: 2.70
Cash ($ mil.): 93

THE FIRST DISTRICT ASSOCIATION

EXECUTIVES

Ceo, Clinton Fall
SEC*, Kevin Schueler
Controller, Tom Middendorf

LOCATIONS

HQ: THE FIRST DISTRICT ASSOCIATION
101 S SWIFT AVE, LITCHFIELD, MN 553552800
Phone: 320 693-3236
Web: WWW.FIRSTDISTRICT.COM

HISTORICAL FINANCIALS

Company Type: Private

Income Statement — FYE: September 30

	REVENUE ($ mil.)	NET INCOME ($ mil.)	NET PROFIT MARGIN	EMPLOYEES
09/18	556	14	2.6%	150
09/17	609	19	3.2%	—
09/16	553	19	3.5%	—
09/15	615	13	2.2%	—
Annual Growth	(3.3%)	2.2%	—	—

THE FORD FOUNDATION

As one of the nation's largest philanthropic organizations the Ford Foundation can afford to be generous. The foundation offers grants to individuals and institutions worldwide that work to meet its goals of strengthening democratic values reducing poverty and injustice promoting international cooperation and advancing human achievement. The Ford Foundation's charitable giving has run the gamut from A (Association for Asian Studies) to Z (Zanzibar International Film Festival). The foundation has an endowment of about $10 billion. Established in 1936 by Edsel Ford whose father founded the Ford Motor Company the foundation no longer owns stock in the automaker or has ties to the founding family.

Operations

The foundation which is governed by an international board of trustees makes grants in all 50 US states and supports programs in more than 50 countries.

It boasts about 10 regional offices in Latin America Africa the Middle East and Asia.

Geographic Reach

Based in New York the Ford Foundation is a grantmaking foundation that primarily serves the US but also global programs.

Strategy

The Ford Foundation's programs address several social justice issues including democratic and accountable government freedom of expression access to education economic fairness and opportunity sexuality and reproductive rights sustainable development social justice metropolitan opportunity and human rights.

A small portion of its endowment is set aside for social investing. The foundation's funds typically finance critical projects set new business models and develop sustainable organizations. By investing $1 million or more in initiatives the Ford Foundation's investment strategy aims to make a noteworthy impact and encourage other investors to also fund projects.

EXECUTIVES

Secretary, Karen Mcburnie

LOCATIONS

HQ: THE FORD FOUNDATION
320 E 43RD ST FL 4, NEW YORK, NY 100174890
Phone: 212 573-5370
Web: WWW.FORDFOUNDATION.ORG

PRODUCTS/OPERATIONS

Selected Core Issues

Democratic and accountable government
Economic fairness
Education opportunity and scholarship
Freedom of expression
Human rights
Metropolitan opportunity
Sexuality and reproductive health rights
Social justice philanthropy
Sustainable development

HISTORICAL FINANCIALS

Company Type: Private

Income Statement — FYE: December 31

	ASSETS ($ mil.)	NET INCOME ($ mil.)	INCOME AS % OF ASSETS	EMPLOYEES
12/15	12,114	(270)	—	556
12/14*	12,400	(7)	—	—
09/11	10,344	(5)	—	—
09/09	10,234	0	—	—
Annual Growth	2.8%	—	—	—

*Fiscal year change

2015 Year-End Financials

Return on assets: (-2.2%)
Return on equity: (-2.3%)
Sales ($ mil): 486

THE FRESH MARKET INC

When it comes to food fresh is best. The Fresh Market operates about 160 full-service upscale specialty grocery stores in over 20 US states from Florida to New York. As the name suggests the chain specializes in perishable goods including fruits and vegetables meat and seafood. The initial 14000-square-foot store differentiated itself from conventional supermarkets with a farmer's market atmosphere. Founded by husband-and-wife team Ray and Beverly Berry who opened their first store in 1982 The Fresh Market was acquired by Apollo Global Management in 2016.

Operations

The Fresh Market Inc. delivers fresh produce and exceptional meat and seafood signature baked goods and thousands of organic options. Other products include deli and prepared foods bread floral Asian foods nuts frozen food and body care among others.

Geographic Reach

Headquartered in Greensboro North Carolina it currently operates nearly 160 stores in over 20 states across the U.S.

Sales and Marketing

The company serves more than 25000 U.S. customers. Aside from its retail stores it also gets sales from its e-commerce website.

Strategy

Over the past six months the specialty grocer has elevated its restaurant-quality meals and has expanded its meal and party platter offerings. For the main event The Fresh Market offers five different options of complete ready-to-heat holiday meals that range in size to accommodate gatherings of all sizes. In addition to the ready-to-heat holiday meals The Fresh Market also has more than 50 different made-in-store party platters to help simplify small gatherings.

In early 2020 the grocer launched a new online store: https://shop.thefreshmarket.com/ along with a corresponding mobile app expanding on the successful partnership with Instacart rolled out last year. The new site makes it even easier to shop either by department or by collections such as new items easy meals and seasonal offerings. Customers can also plan and build a menu for special meals or save their favorite items to a regular shopping list. The list can be used for shopping in the store or can be moved into a virtual shopping basket and placed for a delivery order. Another feature is the ability to filter products by special dietary need such as gluten free vegan or organic or can filter by items on sale The Fresh Market private label items or new items.

EXECUTIVES

President And Ceo, Richard A. (Rick) Anicetti, age 63
Svp Merchandising And Marketing, Marc Jones, age 48, $285,697 total compensation
Svp And General Counsel, Scott Duggan, age 54, $254,510 total compensation
Evp And Cfo, Jeffrey (Jeff) Ackerman, age 56, $407,231 total compensation
Svp Real Estate And Development, Randy Young, age 62, $279,971 total compensation
Vice President Finance, Jeffrey B Short
Vice President Store Development Construction And Facilities, David Sibert
President, Ray Berry, age 79
Auditors: ERNST & YOUNG LLP CHARLOTTE

LOCATIONS

HQ: THE FRESH MARKET INC
628 GREEN VALLEY RD # 500, GREENSBORO, NC 274087791
Phone: 336 272-1338
Web: WWW.THEFRESHMARKET.COM

2016 Stores

	No.
Florida	45
North Carolina	22
Virginia	16
Georgia	15
Illinois	9
Tennessee	9
South Carolina	9
Alabama	6
Indiana	5
Louisiana	5
New York	5
Ohio	5
Pennsylvania	5
Maryland	4
Connecticut	3
Kentucky	3
New Jersey	3
Arkansas	2
Wisconsin	2
Delaware	1
Massachusetts	1
Mississippi	1
New Hampshire	1
Oklahoma	1
Total	**178**

COMPETITORS

Earth Fare
Food Lion
Kroger
Publix
Safeway
Sprouts
Target Corporation
Trader Joe's
Wal-Mart
Wegmans
Weis Markets
Whole Foods
Winn-Dixie

HISTORICAL FINANCIALS

Company Type: Private

Income Statement — FYE: January 31

	REVENUE ($ mil.)	NET INCOME ($ mil.)	NET PROFIT MARGIN	EMPLOYEES
01/16	1,857	65	3.5%	12,600
01/15	1,753	63	3.6%	—
01/14	1,511	50	3.4%	—
01/13	1,329	64	4.8%	—
Annual Growth	11.8%	0.7%	—	—

2016 Year-End Financials

Return on assets: 11.3%
Return on equity: 18.0%
Current ratio: 1.10
Cash ($ mil.): 60

THE GEISINGER CLINIC

EXECUTIVES

Ceo, Glenn D Steele Jr
Sr V Pres-Treas, Frank J Trembulak
Vice-President Information Ser, David Macko
Emergency Room Directo, John Skiendzielewski
Technical Analyst, Sean Spangler

LOCATIONS

HQ: THE GEISINGER CLINIC
100 N ACADEMY AVE, DANVILLE, PA 178229800
Phone: 570 271-6211
Web: WWW.GEISINGER.ORG

HISTORICAL FINANCIALS

Company Type: Private

Income Statement — FYE: June 30

	REVENUE ($ mil.)	NET INCOME ($ mil.)	NET PROFIT MARGIN	EMPLOYEES
06/18	1,290	(163)	—	12,000
06/15	991	(12)	—	—
06/14	849	(3)	—	—
06/10	572	(3)	—	—
Annual Growth	10.7%	—	—	—

2018 Year-End Financials

Return on assets: (-42.0%)
Return on equity: (-102.7%)
Current ratio: —
Cash ($ mil.): 14

THE GEORGE WASHINGTON UNIVERSITY

The George Washington University's name is just one more reminder of the regard the nation holds for its first president. The private coeducational university's more than 26000 students are scattered across its primary campus at Foggy Bottom as well as its campuses in Mount Vernon and Ashburn Virginia. With nearly 1225 non-medical and nearly 1270 medical faculty staff the school's student-teacher ratio is about 13:1. Its academic programs spread across some 10 schools run the gamut from business to law to medicine. Notable alumni include former First Lady Jacqueline Kennedy Onassis actor Alec Baldwin and former US Secretary of State Colin Powell.

Operations

George Washington University the largest institution of higher education in the District of Columbia has students enrolled in a range of disciplines from forensic science and creative writing to international affairs and computer engineering as well as medicine public health the law and public policy.

It runs the Columbian College of Arts & Sciences Corcoran School of the Arts & Design School of Business Graduate School of Education & Human Development School of Engineering & Applied Science as well as the Elliott School of International Affairs GW Law School of Media & Public Affairs School of Medicine & Health Sciences School of Nursing Graduate School of Political Management College of Professional Studies Milken Institute School of Public Health Trachtenberg School of Public Policy & Public Administration.

More than 45% of its total sales generates from student tuition fees about 15% from patient care and more than 10% from grants and contracts including indirect cost recoveries. It also generates small amount from auxiliary enterprises endowments medical education agreements contributions and investments.

Geographic Reach

The George Washington University's more than 26000 students comes from all 50 US states the District of Columbia and more than 130 other countries.

Financial Performance

For the year ended June 2020 the company had $1.7 billion in revenue a 9% increase from the previous year.

The company had a net gain of $45.7 million for the year ended June 2020.

The company's cash for the year ended June 2020 was $696.4 million. Operating activities generated $39.1 million and investing activities generated $201.8 million. Financing activities generated another $293 million.

Strategy

The George Washington University's strategic initiatives are five important areas of focus:

Student Experience - GW students experience the university in many ways?in classrooms residence halls and student space through interactions with faculty and staff. Each experience should be positive and students' GW careers from enrollment to graduation should be supported by a service-oriented community that cares about their success;

Research - The university will build on the research progress it has made exploring ways to support research that continues to generate groundbreaking discoveries and innovative ideas;

Philanthropy & Constituent Engagement - GW relies on the support of its alumni parent and friend communities to advance priorities and sustain the university mission. It is committed to strengthening these GW communities as partners in the success and growth of the university;

Medical Enterprise- With its clinical and academic partners GW is committed to a strategic planning process and enhanced alignment in its joint pursuit of preeminence as an academic medical enterprise.; and

Institutional Culture - The university's institutional culture affects the experience of each member of its community. GW's culture should foster and maintain a commitment to service engagement belonging and respect creating a positive warm and welcoming environment for all.

Company Background

Chartered by the US Congress in 1821 as The Columbian College in the District of Columbia the university adopted its present name in 1904.

EXECUTIVES

President, Steven Knapp
Evp And Treasurer, Louis H. Katz
Deputy Evp And Treasurer, Ann McCorvey
Dean Law School, Blake D. Morant
Dean Columbian College Of Arts And Sciences, Ben Vinson
Dean School Of Engineering And Applied Science, David S. Dolling
Dean College Of Professional Studies, Ali Eskandarian
Dean Graduate School Of Education And Human Development, Michael J. Feuer
Dean School Of Nursing, Pamela R. Jeffries
Dean Milken Institute School Of Public Health, Lynn R. Goldman
Vp Health Affairs And Dean School Of Medicine And Health Sciences, Jeffrey S. Akman
President, Thomas J. LeBlanc
Evp Academic Affairs And Provost, Forrest Maltzman
Dean Elliott School Of International Affairs, Reuben E. Brigety
Dean Of Libraries And Academic Innovation, Geneva Henry
Senior Vice President, John Och
Director Of Admissions, Joke Ogundiran
Executive Vice President Academic Affairs, Donald Lehman
Assistant Vice President Information Security And Compliance Services, Dennis Devlin
Vice President, Leo Chalupa
Vice President, Emily Reisch
Associate Vice President For Communications, Sarah Baldassaro
Associate Vice President For Financial Management Schools, Debra Dickenson
Assistant Vice President Academic Life, Natalie Fleischman
Assistant Vice President, Sharon Sullivan
Evp And Cfo, Mark Diaz
Vice President For Development And Alumni Relations, Donna Arbide
Avp University Programs, Katie Turcotte
Vice President, Jamie Meltzer
Assistant Vice President For Corporate And Industry Research, Thomas Russo
Vice President, Penelope Lantz
Senior Vice President, Joseph Duffey
Second Vice President Personal Trust Assistant Relationship Manager, Colleen Reed
Vice President, Seokyong Choi
Chairman, Nelson A. Carbonell
Secretary, Emily Brown
Secretary Faculty Support, Green Jacob L
Treasurer, Adam Ricker
Board Member, Kenechi Ejebe
Board Member, Steven Kelly
Auditors: PRICEWATERHOUSECOOPERS LLP MC

LOCATIONS

HQ: THE GEORGE WASHINGTON UNIVERSITY
1918 F ST NW, WASHINGTON, DC 200520042
Phone: 202 994-6600
Web: WWW.GWU.EDU

PRODUCTS/OPERATIONS

Selected Schools

College of Professional Studies
Columbian College of Arts and Sciences
Elliott School of International Affairs
George Washington School of Business
George Washington University Law School
Graduate School of Education and Human Development
Graduate School of Political Management
School of Engineering and Applied Science
School of Media and Public Affairs
School of Medicine and Health Sciences
School of Public Health and Health Services

HISTORICAL FINANCIALS

Company Type: Private

Income Statement — FYE: June 30

	REVENUE ($ mil.)	NET INCOME ($ mil.)	NET PROFIT MARGIN	EMPLOYEES
06/13	1,177	59	5.0%	5,000
06/06	921	146	15.9%	—
06/05	832	115	13.8%	—
Annual Growth	4.4%	(7.9%)	—	—

2013 Year-End Financials

Return on assets: 1.7%
Return on equity: 3.1%
Current ratio: —
Cash ($ mil.): 224

THE GEORGETOWN UNIVERSITY

Georgetown University is the oldest Catholic university in the US. The institution's 17400 undergraduate and graduate students are instructed by more than 2340 faculty members (representing both full- and part-time) in nine schools ranging from the university's renowned Law Center to the Edmund A. Walsh School of Foreign Service and the Georgetown School of Medicine. The system has a student-teacher ratio of about 10:1. The university is also home to the Georgetown University Medical Center and has forged numerous ties with its neighboring institutions in the Washington DC community.

Operations

The Georgetown University Medical Center provides a variety of medical services to area residents in addition to serving as a teaching and research facility for the university. The medical center has several specialty medicine and research programs through a partnership with MedStar's Georgetown University Hospital including Huntington disease care and brain development studies. Georgetown's research institutes are working to discover new medical treatments including potential breast cancer therapies. The university receives some $179 million in research funding each year.

Geographic Reach

Georgetown University's main campus (54 buildings including the medical center) is located on about 100 acres on the banks of the Potomac in Washington DC. It also has locations in downtown Washington DC and in Arlington Virginia.

Internationally Georgetown University operates a School of Foreign Service campus in Qatar. The university also has study abroad programs in Argentina Turkey China Chile Italy and England and a nursing study program with the Australian Catholic University.

Financial Performance

Georgetown University reported about $1.12 billion in revenues in fiscal 2014 virtually flat with the previous year. Its earnings come from student tuition and fees grants and contracts auxiliary activities and other sources. In fiscal 2015 undergraduate tuition was $46200 per student (up from $44280 in fiscal 2014 and $42360 in fiscal 2013).

Strategy

Georgetown University expands and upgrades its facilities periodically to keep pace with modern technologies and appeal to a variety of students.

To expand its outreach programs Georgetown University built a new location for its School of Continuing Studies in downtown Washington DC. The new campus located near the Law Center opened in late 2013 and extends the reach of the university's presence downtown as it works to expand beyond its historical campus. It also officially launched its McCourt School of Public Policy in 2013.

It also launches new degree programs such as the MIDP (master's of international development policy) and the Master of Science in Global Health.

Company Background

In 2010 Georgetown University received its largest philanthropic gift ever when it was granted a nearly $90 million endowment to support medical research at the university's medical center from a charitable trust established by the will of the late Harry Toulmin in 1965.

Georgetown University was founded in 1789 by John Carroll the nation's first Catholic bishop. At the time of its founding Georgetown University's historic campus was located in Georgetown Maryland; the location is now part of the Washington DC metropolitan area. Among Georgetown University's alumni are President Bill Clinton basketball great Patrick Ewing and former US Surgeon General Antonia Novello.

EXECUTIVES

Associate Vice President Administrative Services, Lennie Carter
Senior Vice President And Treasurer, Christopher Augostini
Associate Vice President Risk Management, Joseph A Yohe
Assistant Vice President For Student Health, James Welsh
Associate Vice President Alumni Relations, William Reynolds
Vice President For Strategic Development And External Affairs, Kevin Conry
Associate Vice President And Dean Of Students, Mitchell Bailin
Assistant Vice President, Regina Bleck
Associate Vice President Campaign Operations, Stephanie Jacobson-Landon
Vice President Corporate Engagement, Ellen Carberry
Associate Vice President Advancement Services, Jo Grainger
Assistant Vice President For Student Health, Vince WinklerPrins
Assistant Vice President For Emergency Management, Tonya Coultas
Vice President Of Marketing And Communications Student Government Association Mba Class Of 2018, Mercedes Castro
Associate Vice President For Strategic Communications, Meghan Dubyak
Associate Vice President Communications Office Of Advancement, Amy Levin
Associate Vice President, Margie Bryant
Vice President, Sandra Horvathpeterson
Associate Vice President Auxiliary Services, Joelle Wiese
Medical Director, Michelle Roett
Director Of Admissions Center For Security Studies, Jessica Gershuny
Associate Vice President For Community Engagement And Strategic Initiatives, Lauralyn Lee
Vice President Diversity Equity And Inclusion Evening Student Government Association Manager Business Analysis Candidate 2018, Zoya Awan
Vice President, Jason Martin
Assistant Vice President, Darlene Steil
Medical Director, Deborah Wilson
Vice President, Sharon Roeder
Svp Business Development And Publisher Partnerships, Aimee Irwin
Vice President Mba Technology Club Mba Candidate Class Of 2019, Anuj Mahajan
Vice President Manager Analysis Candidate 2019 Mcdonough School Of Business Washington, Robert Weitzel
Vice President Alumni Relations Startup Hoyas Vice President Community Building, Ankita Kochhar
Vice President, Richard Kennedy
Secretary, Jacqueline Summers
Secretary Of The University, Edward Quinn
Board Member, Charlene Simmons
Board Member, Aaron Eastman
Board Of Advisors, Richard Kerschner
Auditors: PRICEWATERHOUSECOOPERS LLP MC

LOCATIONS

HQ: THE GEORGETOWN UNIVERSITY
37TH AND O ST NW, WASHINGTON, DC 200570001
Phone: 202 687-0100
Web: WWW.GEORGETOWN.EDU

PRODUCTS/OPERATIONS

Selected Schools

Edmund A. Walsh School of Foreign Service
Georgetown College
Graduate School of Arts and Sciences
Law Center
McCourt School of Public Policy
Robert E. McDonough School of Business
School of Medicine
School of Nursing and Health Studies
School for Summer and Continuing Education

HISTORICAL FINANCIALS

Company Type: Private

Income Statement — FYE: June 30

	REVENUE ($ mil.)	NET INCOME ($ mil.)	NET PROFIT MARGIN	EMPLOYEES
06/19	1,330	(77)	—	9,700
06/18	1,249	130	10.4%	—
06/17	1,203	185	15.4%	—
Annual Growth	5.1%	—	—	—

2019 Year-End Financials

Return on assets: (-2.2%)
Return on equity: (-4.5%)
Current ratio: —
Cash ($ mil.): 295

THE GOLUB CORPORATION

Supermarket operator The Golub Corporation offers tasty come-ons such as table-ready meals gift certificates automatic discount cards and a hotline where cooks answer food-related queries. Golub operates supermarkets under the Price Chopper Market 32 and Market Bistro banners in six states in the northeastern US (New York is its largest market). Some New York stores provide shopping and delivery service through the Instacart program. The company also provides catering foodfare pharmacy cooking school and Kosher services.

Geographic Reach

Golub's Price Chopper chain is active in six US states such as New York Connecticut Massachusetts Vermont Pennsylvania and New Hampshire.

Sales and Marketing

The company sells its products in its stores and online. It serves customers in pharmaceutical school and food service industries.

Strategy

The company partners with Instacart to offer the customer the convenience of grocery delivery and pickup service. Instacart's network of personal shoppers will grocery shop for the customers and either deliver their order directly at their doorstep or have it ready for pickup.

Company Background

Like many other retailers the company is experimenting with new formats. In May 2012 it opened its first small-format store known as Price Chopper Limited. The 19000-square-foot store (about a third of the size of a typical Price Chopper supermarket) is located in a residential neighborhood in downtown Saratoga Springs New York. The "Limited" store offers an edited selection of Price Chopper's most popular products a bakery full-service meat deli and seafood departments and a cafe with eat-in or take-out meals.

In fall 2011 Price Chopper launched a new online ordering and home delivery program called Price Chopper Shops4U . The service charges a service fee of $10 with an additional $6 fee for delivery. Customers can either pick up their orders at the store or have them delivered.

Brothers Bill and Ben Golub founded the company in 1932.

EXECUTIVES

President And Ceo, Jerel T. (Jerry) Golub
Vp Public Relations And Consumer Services, Mona J. Golub
Svp Administration, David Golub
Vp Produce & Floral Merchandising, Rick Reed
Vice President Advertising, Shawn Gonzalez
Vice President Marketing Analytics, Glen Bradley
Vice President Talent Management, Paul Rollins
Vice President Merchandising Group, Scott Evans
Senior Vice President Sales And Merchandising, Jerry Golub
Pharmd, Alisha Roberts
Vice President Risk Management, Anne Davis
Vice President Engineering And Construction, Ryan Hill
Vice President Supply Chain, Bernie Socha
Chairman And Ceo, Neil M. Golub

LOCATIONS

HQ: THE GOLUB CORPORATION
461 NOTT ST, SCHENECTADY, NY 123081812
Phone: 518 355-5000
Web: WWW.PRICECHOPPER.COM

2013 Stores

	No.
New York	81
Massachusetts	16
Vermont	15
Connecticut	8
Pennsylvania	8
New Hampshire	4
Total	**132**

COMPETITORS

7-Eleven
A&P
ALDI
BJ's Wholesale Club
Big Y Foods
CVS
Costco Wholesale
Cumberland Farms
DeMoulas Super Markets
Gerrity's
Hannaford Bros.
Shaw's
Stewart's Shops
Stop & Shop
TOPS Markets
Target Corporation
Wal-Mart
Wegmans

HISTORICAL FINANCIALS

Company Type: Private

Income Statement — FYE: April 24

	REVENUE ($ mil.)	NET INCOME ($ mil.)	NET PROFIT MARGIN	EMPLOYEES
04/16	3,427	8	0.2%	19,500
04/15	3,476	21	0.6%	—
04/14	3,472	18	0.5%	—
Annual Growth	(0.7%)	(32.3%)	—	—

2016 Year-End Financials

Return on assets: 1.2%
Return on equity: 13.3%
Current ratio: 0.70
Cash ($ mil.): 22

THE HEALTH CARE AUTHORITY OF THE CITY OF HUNTSVILLE

Health Care Authority of the City of Huntsville ensures that residents get the medical attention they need. The volunteer board consists of nine members that governs the more than 880-bed Huntsville Hospital one of the largest medical centers in Alabama with a staff of more than 650 physicians as well as other medical facilities. Huntsville Hospital is also a teaching facility for the University of Alabama-Birmingham. The Health Care Authority of the City of Huntsville provides a list of nominees for board members to the City Council which decides who is appointed to the board.

EXECUTIVES

Eo, David Spillers
Cfo*, Kelly Towers
V Pres, Michael W Brown
Chief of Medicine, Richard Spera
Chief of Psychology/Psychiatry, Anupama Yedla
MD, Kevin S Ellis
Auditors: WARREN AVERETT LLC HUNTSVILL

LOCATIONS

HQ: THE HEALTH CARE AUTHORITY OF THE CITY OF HUNTSVILLE
101 SIVLEY RD SW, HUNTSVILLE, AL 358014421
Phone: 256 265-1000
Web: WWW.HUNTSVILLEHOSPITAL.ORG

HISTORICAL FINANCIALS

Company Type: Private

Income Statement — FYE: June 30

	REVENUE ($ mil.)	NET INCOME ($ mil.)	NET PROFIT MARGIN	EMPLOYEES
06/19	1,700	218	12.9%	14,000
06/18	1,524	53	3.5%	—
06/17	1,407	46	3.3%	—
06/07	591	49	8.3%	—
Annual Growth	9.2%	13.3%	—	—

2019 Year-End Financials

Return on assets: 11.7%
Return on equity: 16.4%
Current ratio: 1.40
Cash ($ mil.): 88

THE HERTZ CORPORATION

EXECUTIVES

Ceo-Pres, Paul E Stone
Non Exec Chb*, Henry R Keizer
Exec V Pres-Cfo, Jamere Jackson
Exec V Pres-Cmo, Jodi J Allen
Exec V Pres-General Counsel-SE, M David Galainena
Sr V Pres-Cao, Richard E Esper
Manager, Al Greene
Associate, Alexander Mejia
Project Manager, Andrew Roberson
Human Resources Programs Speci, Annasuela Fritz
Business Transformation Manage, Ben Wylie
Auditors: PRICEWATERHOUSECOOPERS LLP FO

LOCATIONS

HQ: THE HERTZ CORPORATION
8501 WILLIAMS RD, ESTERO, FL 339283325
Phone: 239 301-7000
Web: WWW.HERTZ.COM

HISTORICAL FINANCIALS

Company Type: Private

Income Statement — FYE: December 31

	REVENUE ($ mil.)	NET INCOME ($ mil.)	NET PROFIT MARGIN	EMPLOYEES
12/17	8,803	332	3.8%	38,000
12/16	8,803	(488)	—	—
12/15	10,535	276	2.6%	—
Annual Growth	(8.6%)	9.7%	—	—

2017 Year-End Financials

Return on assets: 1.7%
Return on equity: 21.8%
Current ratio: —
Cash ($ mil.): 1,072

THE INCOME FUND OF AMERICA INC

EXECUTIVES

Chb, Janet McKinley
Pres, Darcy Kopcho
Treas, Dayna Yamabe
Sr V Pres, Stephen E Bepler
Sr V Pres, Abner K Goldstein
V Pres, John Smet
SEC, Patrick F Quan
Auditors: DELOITTE & TOUCHE LLP COSTA

LOCATIONS

HQ: THE INCOME FUND OF AMERICA INC
1 MARKET PLZ, SAN FRANCISCO, CA 941051101
Phone: 415 421-9360

HISTORICAL FINANCIALS

Company Type: Private

Income Statement — FYE: July 31

	REVENUE ($ mil.)	NET INCOME ($ mil.)	NET PROFIT MARGIN	EMPLOYEES
07/19	4,050	160	4.0%	7
07/18	4,051	2,343	57.9%	—
07/16	3,577	6,660	186.2%	—
Annual Growth	4.2%	(71.1%)	—	—

2019 Year-End Financials

Return on assets: 0.1%
Return on equity: 0.1%
Current ratio: —
Cash ($ mil.): 29

THE JAMAICA HOSPITAL

Jamaica Hospital Medical Center has been operating in the Queens Borough of New York since before the nation of Jamaica even was born. The hospital serves Queens and eastern Brooklyn with general medical pediatric psychiatric and ambulatory care services. The facility has about 430 beds. Its specialty services include a coma recovery unit a dialysis center a psychiatric emergency department a rehabilitation center as well as a traumatic brain injury recovery unit. The hospital also operates a nursing home with more than 220 beds as well as family practice ambulance and home health services. Jamaica Hospital Medical Center is a subsidiary of MediSys Health Network.

Operations

Jamaica Hospital Medical Center treats some 130000 patients annually through its emergency department which contains a level I regional trauma center. The hospital also handles about 2000 births each year in its labor and delivery wing.

In addition to acute care services the hospital is a teaching facility associated with several educational organizations including Cornell University's Weill Medical College the Mount Sinai School of Medicine and St. George's University School of Medicine. It provides residency and training programs in areas including dentistry podiatry physician assistant and osteopathic medicine. Some of its residency programs are conducted in partnership with other regional health centers including the New York Hospital and the Montefiore Medical Center.

The Ambulatory Care Centers include a Sleep Clinic where sleep disorders in adults and children are evaluated and treated.

In 2014 the hospital had nearly 120000 patients were treated in the Emergency Department; 300000 patients were seen in the Ambulatory Care Centers (with locations at the main campus and also at the offsite centers in the community); and some 2904 deliveries were performed.

Geographic Reach

Jamaica Hospital Medical Center serves a population greater than 1.2 million in Queens and eastern Brooklyn.

Strategy

To improve care for area residents Jamaica Hospital Medical Center has expanded its sleep medicine division to include a new sleep disorder diagnosis center for adults and children. The hospital has also expanded its community care provisions through partnerships with area businesses and organizations.

Upgrading its technology in 2015 the company introduced da Vinci Robot Now at its Flushing location.

Company Background

Jamaica Hospital Medical Center was founded in 1892.

EXECUTIVES

Vice President Finance, Manzar Sassani
Pharmacy Manager, William Tomasulo
Executive Vice President And Chief Operating Officer, Bill Lynch
Vp Of Finance, Arleen Hurtarte

LOCATIONS

HQ: THE JAMAICA HOSPITAL
8900 VAN WYCK EXPY FL 4N, RICHMOND HILL, NY 114182897
Phone: 718 206-6290
Web: WWW.JAMAICAHOSPITAL.ORG

PRODUCTS/OPERATIONS

Selected Centers and Services

Advanced Center for Psychotherapy
Allergy and Immunology
Ambulatory Care
Anesthesia
Cardiology
Clinical Services
Corporate Health
Critical Care Medicine
Dental
Dermatology
Dialysis-Island Rehabilitation
Emergency Medicine
Family Medicine
Gastroenterology
Home Health
Infectious Disease
Lupus Center
MediSys Family Care Centers
Nephrology
Neurology
Nursing
OB-GYN
Oncology
Orthopedic Surgery
Palliative Care
Pathology
Pediatrics
Podiatry
Prehospital Care
Psychiatry
Pulmonary Medicine
Radiology
Rehabilitation
Rheumatology
Surgery
TCU
The Brady Institute
Trump Pavilion~Jamaica Hospital Nursing Home
Women's Health
Women's Health Center

COMPETITORS

Catholic Healthcare System
Continuum Health Partners
Maimonides Medical Center
Montefiore Medical
New York City Health and Hospitals
NewYork-Presbyterian Healthcare
Northwell Health

HISTORICAL FINANCIALS

Company Type: Private

Income Statement — FYE: December 31

	REVENUE ($ mil.)	NET INCOME ($ mil.)	NET PROFIT MARGIN	EMPLOYEES
12/19	789	27	3.5%	3,251
12/18	739	15	2.1%	—
12/17	436	(45)	—	—
12/16	439	(7)	—	—
Annual Growth	21.5%	—	—	—

2019 Year-End Financials

Return on assets: 11.9%
Return on equity: —
Current ratio: 1.10
Cash ($ mil.): 16

THE JOHNS HOPKINS HEALTH SYSTEM CORPORATION

Named after philanthropist Johns Hopkins the Johns Hopkins Health System (JHHS) gifts Baltimore residents with an array of health care services. The health system is an affiliate of world-renowned Johns Hopkins Medicine and oversees six hospitals: All Children's Hospital Johns Hopkins Hospital Bayview Medical Center Howard County General Hospital Sibley Memorial Hospital and Suburban Hospital. The not-for-profit teaching hospitals offer inpatient and outpatient health services that include general medicine emergency/trauma care pediatrics maternity care senior care and numerous specialized areas of medicine. JHHS also operates community health and satellite care facilities.

Operations

JHHS facilities handle 2.8 million patient encounters each year including 115000 inpatient admissions and 350000 emergency room visits. In addition to the six Johns Hopkins Medicine hospitals (which combined house more than 2600 beds) the JHHS organization includes four surgery centers two dozen primary care clinics associated with the Johns Hopkins Community Physicians practice organization and a home health care services agency. JHHS offers unified shared services to its members including advertising purchasing finance legal and other administrative functions.

The Johns Hopkins name is well-known for health care but is probably equally as well-known for its medical education and research initiatives. The health system's hospitals are affiliated with Johns Hopkins University offering physicians-in-training a whole host of residency options.

Geographic Reach

The JHHS inpatient and outpatient facilities are located throughout Maryland and the Washington DC-area as well as in Florida. The system operates a handful of outpatient surgery and imaging centers as well. The group's hospitals serve visitors from all over the world.

Strategy

The organization regularly expands through small to large construction efforts as well as through acquisitions. For example it has acquired two hospitals (All Children's Hospital in Florida and Sibley Memorial Hospital in Washington DC) since 2010.

EXECUTIVES

Pres, Ronald R Peterson
Chb*, C Micheal Amstrong
V Pres Fin-Cfo*, Ronald J Werthman
V Pres-Medical Affairs*, Beryl Rosenstein
Corp SEC*, Hannah Jones
Manager, Bridget Carver
Coordinator, Matthew Trojanowski
Senior Vice-President, Bertrand M Emerson
Scientist, Edina Avdic
Assistant Professor, Ming-Hsien Wang
Coordinator, Tiesha Mobley
Auditors: PRICEWATERHOUSECOOPERS LLP BA

LOCATIONS

HQ: THE JOHNS HOPKINS HEALTH SYSTEM CORPORATION
600 N WOLFE ST, BALTIMORE, MD 212870005
Phone: 410 955-5000
Web: WWW.HOPKINSMEDICINE.ORG

PRODUCTS/OPERATIONS

Selected Facilities

All Children's Hospital (St. Petersburg FL)
Bayview Medical Center (Baltimore MD)
Howard County General Hospital (Columbia MD)
Johns Hopkins at Cedar Lane (Columbia MD)
Johns Hopkins at Greenspring Station (Lutherville MD)
Johns Hopkins at Odenton (Odenton MD)
Johns Hopkins at White Marsh (White Marsh MD)
Johns Hopkins Hospital (Baltimore MD)
Johns Hopkins Outpatient Center (Baltimore MD)
Sibley Memorial Hospital (Washington DC)
Suburban Hospital (Bethesda MD)

COMPETITORS

Anne Arundel Medical Center
Ascension Health
Bon Secours Health
Carilion Clinic
Christiana Care
Dimensions Healthcare
Franklin Square Hospital Center
GBMC
Good Samaritan Hospital of Maryland
Harbor Hospital
Levindale Hospital
LifeBridge Health
MedStar Health
MedStar Union Memorial Hospital
Sinai Hospital of Baltimore
St. Agnes HealthCare
St. Joseph Medical Center
University of Maryland Medical System
Upper Chesapeake Health

HISTORICAL FINANCIALS

Company Type: Private

Income Statement — FYE: June 30

	REVENUE ($ mil.)	NET INCOME ($ mil.)	NET PROFIT MARGIN	EMPLOYEES
06/20	7,110	(306)	—	13,000
06/19	6,826	(59)	—	—
06/18	6,558	308	4.7%	—
Annual Growth	4.1%	—	—	—

2020 Year-End Financials

Return on assets: (-3.3%)
Return on equity: (-8.1%)
Current ratio: 1.20
Cash ($ mil.): 892

THE LANCASTER GENERAL HOSPITAL

Lancaster General Health (LG Health) is a 690-bed integrated health care delivery system serving residents of Lancaster County Pennsylvania and surrounding areas. Its flagship Lancaster General Hospital (LGH) - opened in 1893 - is known for its cardiology orthopedic and intensive care specialties. A separate Women & Babies hospital cares for those just making it into the world. The not-for-profit system also includes multiple outpatient clinics a rehab hospital home care services and a nursing center and health care college as well as a medical group of more than 300 physicians operating at more than 40 practices throughout the region.

Operations

Facilities in the LG Health system include the 533-bed flagship LGH the 98-bed Women & Babies Hospital the 59-bed Lancaster Rehabilitation Hospital and 14 outpatient centers. Specialty services include open-heart surgery obstetrics neurosurgery trauma care and behavioral health. The system also operates a number of outpatient programs such as a diabetes and nutritional Center and a sleep medicine center.

Every year LG Health sees some 972000 outpatients delivers some 4000 babies and performs around 38000 surgeries.

Geographic Reach

The system serves Pennsylvania's Lebanon Berks Dauphin York Chester and Lancaster counties.

Sales and Marketing

Commercial and HMO payments together account for about 40% of net patient revenues; Medicare accounts for another 35% while Medicaid accounts for some 10%.

Financial Performance

LG Health's revenue rose 5% to $969 million in fiscal 2014 (ended June) on higher net patient revenue and medical services revenue. However net income fell 51% to $117 million as income from contributions and gifts declined; a change in pension liability also hurt the system's bottom line.

Cash flow from operations declined 43% to $43 million in fiscal 2014 as more cash was used in patient accounts receivable and changes were made in prepaid expenses assets and benefits.

Strategy

LG Health continues to make strategic investments to better serve its patients and the community. In 2013 the health system completed construction on the Ann B. Barshinger Cancer Center which opened its doors that year. Two years later it announced plans to expand LGH in a $60 million project that will add a new eight-story patient tower. With the addition of 60 new private rooms and the space for 80 more rooms as demand requires the hospital will have the room to convert its existing semi-private rooms to private rooms.

The system also partners with others in the community to improve patient care. In 2014 it formed an alliance with the University of Pennsylvania Health System to develop innovative care research and education programs.

EXECUTIVES

Senior Vice President Business Development, Susan Wynne
Medical Director Of The Blood Bank, Susan Bator
Medical Director, Frederick Rogers
Svp And Cio, Gary Davidson
Evp Chief Population Health Officer; President Lg Health Innovation Solutions Inc., Marion A. McGowan
President And Ceo, Thomas E. (Tom) Beeman
Evp Chief Administrative And Legal Officer And Corporate Secretary, Robert P. Macina
Svp Post-acute Care, Geoffrey W. Eddowes
Evp And Cfo, Dennis R. Roemer
Svp Chief Physician Executive And Chief Medical Officer, Lee M. Duke
Svp Hospital Operations And Nurse Executive; President Lancaster General Hospital, Karen Flaherty-Oxler
Medical Director, Jeffrey Kirchner
Senior Vice President, Joseph Puskar
Vp Operations, Christopher Maley
Vice President Legal Services, Margaret F Costella
Vice President Of Operations, Rich Paoletti
Vice President Of Customer Service, Carolyn Carlson
Medical Director, Lora Regan
Medical Director, John Eichenlaub
Vice President And Controller, Doug Rinehart
Medical Director Oncology Program, Randall Oyer
Director Of Nursing, Valerie Adams
Senior Vice President Hospital Operations, William Mccune
Director Of Nursing, Shirley Heisey
Medical Director Healthy Weight Management And Bariatric Surgery, Joseph R Mcphee
Medical Director Team Physician, Amy Myers
Chairman, C. Clair McCormick
Vice Chairman, Philip R. Wenger
Secretary, Susan Dickel
Board Member, Christine Vlassis
Secretary, Jennifer Edmonds
Electrophysiology Secretary, Beth A Bumgardner
Secretary, Pamela Miller
Pharmacy Secretary, Cindy Jenner
Secretary, Sheila Loreto

LOCATIONS

HQ: THE LANCASTER GENERAL HOSPITAL
555 N DUKE ST, LANCASTER, PA 176022207
Phone: 717 544-5511
Web: WWW.LANCASTERGENERALHEALTH.ORG

PRODUCTS/OPERATIONS

2014 Sales

	$ mil.	% of total
Net patient services revenue less provision for bad debts	920	95
Medical services	10	4
Other revenue	35	1
Other	2	-
Total	**969**	**100**

Selected Specialties

Cardiology
Emergency medical
Intensive care
Neurology
Oncology
Radiology
Rehabilitation
Urology

COMPETITORS

Altoona Regional
Ascension Health
Catholic Health Initiatives
Evangelical Community Hospital
Hanover Healthcare
Holy Spirit
Lewistown Hospital
Main Line Health System
Memorial Hospital (PA)
PinnacleHealth System
Saint Vincent Health System
St. Luke's University Health Network
University of Pennsylvania Health System
WellSpan Health

HISTORICAL FINANCIALS

Company Type: Private

Income Statement — FYE: June 30

	REVENUE ($ mil.)	NET INCOME ($ mil.)	NET PROFIT MARGIN	EMPLOYEES
06/16	958	122	12.8%	7,000
06/15	920	110	12.1%	—
06/14	867	(13)	—	—
06/13	823	(15)	—	—
Annual Growth	5.2%	—	—	—

2016 Year-End Financials

Return on assets: 14.5%
Return on equity: 28.6%
Current ratio: 2.50
Cash ($ mil.): 23

THE LANE CONSTRUCTION CORPORATION

Lane likes people to be in the fast lane. For more than a century the heavy civil contractor and its affiliates have been widening paving and constructing lanes for highways bridges runways railroads dams and mass transit systems in the eastern and southern US. The group also produces bituminous and precast concrete and mines aggregates at plants and quarries in the northeastern mid-Atlantic and southern US. Additionally it sells and leases construction equipment. Founded in 1902 Lane Construction has offices in more than 20 states and is owned by descendants of Lane and employees.

Operations

Lane Construction specializes in heavy civil construction services and products in the transportation infrastructure and energy industries. During the past decade Lane Construction has participated in more than 70 design-building projects with a combined value of more than $4 billion.

Beyond its construction projects Lane operates divisions that manufacture bituminous and precast concrete with mine aggregates at 70 plants and 12 quarries throughout the U.S.

Lane's business divisions are spread across the US and include: Civil Wall Solutions Cold River Materials Prestress of the Carolinas Senate Asphalt Virginia Paving Company and Virginia Sign & Lighting Company.

Lane affiliates include New Hampshire-based Cold River Materials Senate Asphalt of Washington D.C. and Virginia Paving and Virginia Sign & Lighting Co. among about a half a dozen others. In 2013 its Rea Contracting division in the Carolinas changed its name to Lane Construction Corp.

Geographic Reach

Lane Construction has offices in more than 20 US states including Florida Illinois Maine North Carolina Pennsylvania Texas and Virginia. While most of Lane's projects take place along the East Coast it also operates in the South/Southwest and has international operations – under the Lane Worldwide Infrastructure Inc. name – in the Middle East.

Financial Performance

While full financials of the privately-held company were not available Lane Construction has posted annual revenues of more than $1 billion since 2010.

Strategy

The company continues to work for both public and private entities on a variety of high-value projects. In early 2015 the contractor was working on a joint-venture project with Skanska and Granite Construction Company on the $2.3 billion "I-4 Ultimate project" which involves design build finance operating and maintenance work on 21 miles of Interstate 4 from Orange County to Seminole County in Florida.

Also as of early 2015 Lane reported that it recently completed its $1.5-billion construction project on the I-495 Express Lanes in Virginia in one of the largest public-private joint ventures in the US. The same team also completed a $722 million expansion and improvement project on 29 miles of the I-95 Express (high occupancy toll road) lanes in Virginia. Both of these Virgina-based projects were completed ahead of schedule.

EXECUTIVES

Assistant Vice President Engineering, Tom Larson
Senior Vice President, Tim Reichwein
Vice President General Counsel, Seth T Firmender
Executive Vice President Human Resources And Organization, Adolfo Criscuolo
Auditors: KPMG LLP HARTFORD CT

LOCATIONS

HQ: THE LANE CONSTRUCTION CORPORATION
90 FIELDSTONE CT, CHESHIRE, CT 064101212
Phone: 203 235-3351
Web: WWW.LANECONSTRUCT.COM

PRODUCTS/OPERATIONS

Selected Projects

Airports
Bridges
Design-Build
Federal
Heavy Civil
Highways
Public Private Partnerships
Plants & Paving
Rail
Specialty Paving

Selected Divisions

Civil Wall Solutions
Cold River Materials Prestress of the Carolinas
Senate Asphalt
Sunquip
Sunrise Materials
Virginia Paving Company
Virginia Sun & Lighting Company
Wardwell
White Bros.

COMPETITORS

Angelo Iafrate
Austin Industries
Balfour Beatty Inc
Bechtel
Clark Enterprises
Granite Construction
J.F. White Contracting
MBC Holding
Peter Kiewit Sons'
Sargent Corp
Skanska USA Civil
The Middlesex Corporation
Turner Corporation
Tutor-Saliba
Vecellio & Grogan
Walsh Group

HISTORICAL FINANCIALS

Company Type: Private

Income Statement — FYE: December 31

	REVENUE ($ mil.)	NET INCOME ($ mil.)	NET PROFIT MARGIN	EMPLOYEES
12/18	847	76	9.0%	3,500
12/17	1,476	18	1.3%	—
12/16	1,196	39	3.3%	—
12/15	1,115	(16)	—	—
Annual Growth	(8.7%)	—	—	—

2018 Year-End Financials

Return on assets: 7.6%
Return on equity: 15.2%
Current ratio: 1.80
Cash ($ mil.): 136

THE MARY IMOGENE BASSETT HOSPITAL

EXECUTIVES

Pres-Ceo, Tommy Ibrahim
Chm, Douglas Hastings
Exec V Pres-Coo, Bertine McKenna
V Pres-Cfo, Sue Andrews
Cco, Steven Heneghan
Evp-Chief Operating Officer, Ronette Wiley
Svp-Coo, Jeff Joyner
Svp-Chief Stategy&transformati, Lisa Betrus
Vp-Chief of Staff, Cailin Purcell
Svp-Cpe, Reginald Knight
Svp-CNE, Denise Robinson

LOCATIONS

HQ: THE MARY IMOGENE BASSETT HOSPITAL
1 ATWELL RD, COOPERSTOWN, NY 133261394
Phone: 607 547-3456
Web: WWW.BASSETT.ORG

HISTORICAL FINANCIALS

Company Type: Private

Income Statement — FYE: December 31

	REVENUE ($ mil.)	NET INCOME ($ mil.)	NET PROFIT MARGIN	EMPLOYEES
12/17	547	4	0.8%	3,200
12/16	443	5	1.3%	—
12/15	412	(2)	—	—
12/14	486	18	3.7%	—
Annual Growth	4.0%	(39.0%)	—	—

2017 Year-End Financials

Return on assets: 1.0%
Return on equity: 1.5%
Current ratio: 0.70
Cash ($ mil.): 2

THE MASSACHUSETTS GENERAL HOSPITAL

The General Hospital Corporation is no soapy daytime drama. Doing business as Massachusetts General Hospital (or Mass General) the 200-year-old acute care facility is Harvard Medical School's original and largest teaching hospital. With some 1000 beds Mass General has its main campus in Boston and operates several health centers in surrounding communities. Its specialized medical departments include cancer cardiology and heart surgery; neurology and neurosurgery; and diabetes and endocrinology. As a leading research facility Mass General hosts a number of clinical drug and device trials and has an annual research budget of more than $850 million. The hospital is a founding member of the Partners HealthCare System (along with Brigham and Women's).

Operations

Founded in 1811 Mass General is the oldest and largest general hospital in New England as well as one of the oldest hospitals in the nation. It holds Level I certifications for adult and pediatric trauma and burn care making it a regional referral center for other area hospitals. The hospital also provides outpatient care through doctors' offices of the Mass General Physicians Organization.

Mass General Hospital for Children administers pediatric care services including primary care and rare disease treatment.

Additionally Mass General operates one of the largest hospital-based research networks in the nation consisting of more than 30 clinical departments and centers and conducting some 1200 clinical trials at any given time. With Harvard Mass General offers about 30 residency programs 145 fellowships and continuing medical education programs.

Each year the hospital has some 48000 inpatients more than 100000 emergency department visits and performs more than 42000 operations.

Geographic Reach Mass General's main hospital is located in downtown Boston. The medical center also operates clinics and community locations in Boston Charleston Chelsea Danvers Everett Foxborough Revere and Waltham.

EXECUTIVES

President And Trustee, Peter L. Slavin
Chief Radiation Oncology, Jay S. Loeffler
Chief Neurosurgery, Robert L. Martuza
Chief Orthopaedic Surgery, Harry E. Rubash
Director Cancer Center, Daniel A. Haber
Chief Of Pathology, David N. Louis
Chief Dermatology, David E. Fisher
Chief Molecular Biology, Robert E. Kingston
Chief Of Radiology, James Brink
Surgeon-in-chief And Chair Department Of Surgery, Keith D. Lillemoe
Chief Urology Service, Michael L. Blute
Physician-in-chief Department Of Medicine, Katrina A. Armstrong
Chief Department Of Emergency Medicine, David FM Brown
Chief Neurology Service, Merit Ester Cudkowicz
Chief Department Of Obstetrics And Gynecology, Jeffrey Lawrence (Jeff) Ecker
Chief Pediatric Surgery And Surgeon-in-chief Massgeneral Hospital For Children, Allan Moises Goldstein
Physician-in-chief Of Massgeneral Hospital For Children And Chief Of Partners Pediatrics, Ronald Ellis Kleinman
Chief Of Psychiatry, Jerrold Frank Rosenbaum

Chief Oral And Maxillofacial Surgery, Maria J. Troulis
Chief Of Anesthesia Critical Care And Pain Medicine, Jeanine P. Wiener-Kronish
Chief Physical Medicine And Rehabilitation, Ross D. Zafonte
Medical Director, Leonard Kaban
Director Of Him, Jackie Raymond
Medical Director, Mary Sabatini
Clinical Director, David Ebb
Nursing Director, Hiyam Nadel
Medical Director, David Berger
Pharmacist Manager, Jen Noce
Nursing Director, Christina Stone
Nursing Director, Lee Tata
Vice President National Sales, Mccauley Denise
Medical Director, Depathy Mark
Medical Director, Thomas Horn
Vice President Regulatory Compliance, Dalma Winkler
Trustee, Cathy E. Minehan, age 72
Assoc Vice Chair Psychiatry, Deborah Blacker
Board Member, Cathleen Poliquin
Board Member, Robert Neer

LOCATIONS

HQ: THE MASSACHUSETTS GENERAL HOSPITAL
55 FRUIT ST, BOSTON, MA 021142696
Phone: 617 726-2000
Web: WWW.MASSGENERAL.ORG

Selected Research Centers

AIDS

Cancer
Cardiovascular research
Computational and integrative biology
Cutaneous biology
Human genetics
Medical imaging
Neurodegenerative disorders
Photomedicine
Regenerative medicine
Reproductive biology
Systems biology
Transplantation biology

COMPETITORS

Beth Israel Deaconess Medical Center
Boston Medical Center
Cambridge Health Alliance
Cape Cod Hospital
Care New England
CareGroup
Catholic Medical Center
Children's Hospital Boston
Dana-Farber
Elliot Health System
Emerson Hospital
Milford Regional Medical Center
New England Alliance for Health
Northeast Health System
Southcoast Hospitals Group
Steward Health Care
Sturdy Memorial
Winchester Healthcare

HISTORICAL FINANCIALS

Company Type: Private

Income Statement — FYE: September 30

	REVENUE ($ mil.)	NET INCOME ($ mil.)	NET PROFIT MARGIN	EMPLOYEES
09/14	2,201	186	8.5%	10,156
09/13	2,274	148	6.5%	—
09/12	2,281	267	11.7%	—
Annual Growth	(1.8%)	(16.5%)	—	—

2014 Year-End Financials

Return on assets: 7.7%
Return on equity: 17.7%
Current ratio: 1.40
Cash ($ mil.): 38

THE MEDICAL CENTER OF CENTRAL GEORGIA INC

EXECUTIVES

Ceo, Ninfa M Saunders
Coo*, Mike Gilstrap
Sr V Pres-Cfo*, Virgil E Cooper Jr
Cfo*, Rhonda S Perry
SEC*, Kenneth B Banks
Chief of Medicine, Charles Buafo
Prin, David King

LOCATIONS

HQ: THE MEDICAL CENTER OF CENTRAL GEORGIA INC
777 HEMLOCK ST, MACON, GA 312012155
Phone: 478 633-1000
Web: WWW.NAVICENTHEALTH.ORG

HISTORICAL FINANCIALS

Company Type: Private

Income Statement — FYE: September 30

	REVENUE ($ mil.)	NET INCOME ($ mil.)	NET PROFIT MARGIN	EMPLOYEES
09/16	660	2	0.4%	3,750
09/15	717	93	13.0%	—
09/14	683	80	11.8%	—
09/09	656	10	1.7%	—
Annual Growth	0.1%	(18.3%)	—	—

2016 Year-End Financials

Return on assets: 0.2%
Return on equity: 0.3%
Current ratio: 14.00
Cash ($ mil.): 29

THE MEDICAL UNIVERSITY OF SOUTH CAROLINA

Established in 1824 the Medical University of South Carolina (MUSC) provides Charleston with a wide range of health-related services including medical care training and research. The 50-acre medical school has 1300 faculty members and trains about 2750 full- and part-time students and residents each year through its six schools which cover medical pharmacy nursing dental health professional and graduate training. The MUSC Health organization includes the MUSC Medical Center in Charleston which has some 700 beds and includes a children's hospital and a psychiatric institute as well as the University Medical Associates physician practice organization.

Operations

MUSC has extensive research facilities and programs in areas including bioengineering and translational sciences. The university also participates in drug discovery clinical trial research programs. Its technology transfer program allows small start-up companies to license or purchase research programs that are nearing commercial development stages.

Financial Performance

MUSC is primarily funded by grants and contracts (27% of revenue) and sales and services (also 27% in revenue). State and capital appropriations account for 15% of revenue while student tuition and fees account for 13%. In fiscal 2014 (ended June) the university reported a less-than 1% rise in total revenue to $642.4 million versus $640.7 million in 2013. The modest rise was attributed to an increase in tuition earnings but slightly offset by reductions in both grants/contracts and sales/services revenues.

Strategy

The MUSC strategic plan is focused around four major expansion initiatives: innovation and technology entrepreneurial activity cross-departmental collaboration and globalization. The innovation technology and entrepreneurial goals are centered around the MUSC medical and clinical research organizations which aim to increase external funding resources through grants collaborations and technology transfer agreements. Its collaboration initiative aims to increase inter-professional relationships across its patient care education and research divisions. The university has also been expanding its educational and research facilities.

The university has a total operating budget of some $1.1 billion.

Mergers and Acquisitions

In 2018 MUSC agreed to buy four hospitals in South Carolina from Community Health Systems for an undisclosed price. The purchase will more than double the beds in the university's portfolio. The hospitals including Springs Memorial in Lancaster will be the first ever acquired by MUSC.

Company Background

MUSC was created by an act of South Carolina's General Assembly in 1824. It is historically recognized as the first medical school in the South.

EXECUTIVES

Evp Finance And Operations, Lisa P. Montgomery
Dean College Of Medicine, Raymond N. DuBois
President, David Cole
Interim Vp Medical Affairs, Bruce Elliott
Vp Clinical Operations; Ceo And Executive Director Medical Center, Patrick J. Cawley
Cio, Michael J. Caputo
Director Of Respiratory Therapy, Seo Na Ji
Vice President, Yue Cao
Assistant Vice President And Director Of Student Servic, Matthew Burns
Medical Director Meducare Ground, Dustin Leblanc
Auditors: KPMG LLP GREENSBORO NC

LOCATIONS

HQ: THE MEDICAL UNIVERSITY OF SOUTH CAROLINA
171 ASHLEY AVE, CHARLESTON, SC 294258908
Phone: 843 792-2123
Web: WWW.MUSC.EDU

COMPETITORS

Beaufort Memorial Hospital
Carolinas Hospital System
Conway Medical Center
Duke University
Grand Strand Regional Medical Center
North Carolina State University
Roper St. Francis Healthcare

HISTORICAL FINANCIALS

Company Type: Private

Income Statement FYE: June 30

	REVENUE ($ mil.)	NET INCOME ($ mil.)	NET PROFIT MARGIN	EMPLOYEES
06/18	992	4	0.4%	5,500
06/17	914	9	1.0%	—
06/13	780	26	3.3%	—
06/09	836	3	0.4%	—
Annual Growth	1.9%	1.8%	—	—

2018 Year-End Financials

Return on assets: 0.3%
Return on equity: 3.8%
Current ratio: 3.70
Cash ($ mil.): 322

THE METHODIST HOSPITAL

Houston Methodist (formerly The Methodist Hospital) owns and operates seven Houston-area medical centers including the flagship location which has more than 800 beds and is known for innovations in urology and neurosurgery among other specialties. Other hospitals include Houston Methodist West Houston Methodist Sugar Land Houston Methodist San Jacinto Houston Methodist Willowbrook Houston Methodist St. John and Houston Methodist St. Catherine. Together the hospitals have nearly 2000 beds and employ more than 4500 physicians. In addition to hospitals the organization operates emergency care imaging outpatient and rehab centers and manages a physician organization of nearly 400.

Operations

The health system has been recognized for high performance in several specialty areas including cancer diabetes nephrology pulmonology and geriatrics. It's also been lauded for its specialties in cardiology and heart surgery endocrinology gastroenterology and GI surgery gynecology neurology and neurosurgery orthopedics and urology.

Houston Methodists family of hospitals include the main Houston Methodist Hospital Sugar Land Hospital West Hospital San Jacinto Hospital Willowbrook Hospital St. John Hospital St. Catherine Hospital. It also has long-term acute care facilities emergency care centers imaging centers and a research institute.

The hospital has educational and research affiliations with Cornell University's Weil Cornell Medical College the New York-Presbyterian Hospital University of Houston Baylor College of Medicine Texas A&M and other organizations.

Geographic Reach

Operating mostly in and around Houston Texas Houston Methodist has hospitals and medical facilities in Sugar Land Missouri City the Woodlands Baytown Nassau Bay Pearland Clear Lake and Katy.

Strategy

To widen its capacity for medical care Houston Methodist has been expanding its service network around the Houston area in recent years. In early 2015 it opened a new 36-bed patient care unit in the Houston Methodist Willbrook Hospital's North Pavilion. Houston Methodist's primary care group also broke ground on a new 7200-square-foot primary care practice which will be staffed with six board-certified primary care physicians who will serve adults and children in the Northwest Houston area starting in May 2015.

In 2014 Houston Methodist began work on a new patient tower at its Sugar Land Hospital which will add 104 beds (mostly for intensive care and medical/surgical patients)as part of its $131 million expansion effort at that location. The group also started working on a 390-bed hospital in The Woodlands Texas with completion expected in 2017. Also scheduled for completion in 2017 is a new patient tower with advanced heart and neurosurgery operating rooms at the main Houston Methodist Hospital location.

EXECUTIVES

Senior Vice President Of Corporate Finance, Edward Tyrrell
President And Ceo, Marc L. Boom
Ceo Houston Methodist Sugar Land Hospital, Chris Siebenaler
Interim Ceo San Jacinto Methodist Hospital, Donna Gares
Ceo Houston Methodist Willowbrook Hospital; Svp Houston Methodist, Beryl Ramsey
President And Ceo Houston Methodist Research Institute, Mauro Ferrari
Svp Houston Methodist; Ceo Houston Methodist West Hospital, Wayne Voss
Vice President Support Services, Sharon Johnson
Nursing Director, Maggie Duplantis
Executive Vice President Project Manager, Sara Loewy
Medical Director, Jeanette Ferrer
Director Of Nursing, Elaine Creekmore
Medical Director, Jett Brady
Vp And Chief Nursing Officer, Jim Renneker
Chairman, Ewing Werlein
Vice Chairman, David M. Underwood
Secretary Iii, Rhonda Robinett
Secretary Ii, Sharda Kelly
Secretary, Phelps Mildred
Auditors: DELOITTE & TOUCH LLP HOUSTON

LOCATIONS

HQ: THE METHODIST HOSPITAL
6560 FANNIN ST STE B2-32, HOUSTON, TX 770302711
Phone: 713 441-2340
Web: WWW.HOUSTONMETHODIST.ORG

PRODUCTS/OPERATIONS

Selected Houston-Area Hospitals

Houston Methodist Hospital - Texas Medical Center (Houston)
Houston Methodist Sugar Land Hospital
Houston Methodist Willowbrook Hospital (Houston)
Houston Methodist West Hospital (Houston)
Houston San Jacinto Methodist Hospital (Baytown)
Houston Methodist St. John Hospital (Texas)
Houston Methodist St. Catherine Hospital (Texas)

Selected Services

Cancer / Oncology
Diabetes / Endocrinology
Digestive Diseases
Ear Nose & Throat
Emergency Care
Heart & Vascular
Imaging / Radiology
Internal Medicine
Neurology
Neurosurgery
Obstetrics & Gynecology
Ophthalmology
Oral and Maxillofacial Surgery & Dentistry
Orthopedics & Sports Medicine
Otolaryngology Head & Neck Surgery
Pathology & Genomic Medicine
Plastic & Reconstructive Surgery
Psychiatry
Rehabilitation
Robotic Surgery
Transplant
Urology
Weight Management
Wellness

COMPETITORS

CHRISTUS Health
Dynacq Healthcare
HCA
Johns Hopkins Medicine
MD Anderson Cancer Center
Mayo Clinic
Memorial Hermann Healthcare
St. Luke's Episcopal Health System
Tenet Healthcare
Texas Children's Hospital
Texas Health Resources
Tomball Regional
Universal Health Services

HISTORICAL FINANCIALS

Company Type: Private

Income Statement FYE: December 31

	REVENUE ($ mil.)	NET INCOME ($ mil.)	NET PROFIT MARGIN	EMPLOYEES
12/19	5,225	1,275	24.4%	15,000
12/18	4,496	291	6.5%	—
12/17	3,887	531	13.7%	—
Annual Growth	15.9%	54.9%	—	—

2019 Year-End Financials

Return on assets: 12.2%
Return on equity: 16.1%
Current ratio: 1.10
Cash ($ mil.): 198

THE METROHEALTH SYSTEM

Helping Cleveland's metropolitan citizens stay healthy (and healing them when they aren't) is what MetroHealth System is all about. At the center of the system is MetroHealth Medical Center a level I trauma center and acute care hospital that serves as a teaching affiliate for Case Western Reserve University. Services include oncology behavioral health vascular care orthopedics burn care and pediatrics. The system also operates outpatient clinics long-term care facilities a regional rehabilitation clinic a heart and vascular center two skilled nursing centers an outpatient center and a medical helicopter program. MetroHealth is owned by Ohio's Cuyahoga County.

Operations

More than 550 primary care and specialty care physicians and more than 1700 registered nurses practice within MetroHealth. On an annual basis MetroHealth Medical Center provides care to more than 28000 inpatients and delivers 2900 newborns. More than 950000 visits are recorded in the medical center's outpatient centers along with 17500 surgical cases and 100000 emergency room visits.

The system affiliates with Akron Children's Hospital to expand access to pediatric care throughout the region. Through the partnership Akron Children's provides specialty care at MetroHealth's main campus in the areas of pediatric cardiology gastroenterology cancer and blood disorders and critical care. The MetroHealth affiliation is Akron Children's fourth location in Cuyahoga County.

Geographic Reach

MetroHealth is one of the largest most comprehensive health care providers in Northeast Ohio serving the medical needs of the Greater Cleveland area through more than 15 locations.

Strategy

As emergency rooms continue to burst at the seams more hospitals are finding ways to divert non-emergency patients to more appropriate care settings. MetroHealth has done that with its MetroExpressCare unit for residents who need to see a doctor and would probably otherwise end up at the emergency room. The family medicine physicians who see patients at MetroExpressCare are also available to establish longer-term relationships with patients coming to MetroHealth for the first time. If the physician determines that it's a more serious problem the patient can be referred to MetroHealth's emergency department.

Having options such as MetroExpressCare available is especially important to MetroHealth because it is its region's safety net hospital. As such it receives the lion's share of uninsured patients many of whom end up in the ER because ERs are required to see all patients regardless of their ability to pay under the Emergency Medical Treatment and Active Labor Act. Being able to provide a less expensive option to those patients decreases MetroHealth's bad debt (or unpaid patient bills) and helps reduce crowding at its ER.

To serve non-ER patients Metrohealth opens a new clinic each year on average.

Mergers and Acquisitions

In 2018 MetroHealth agreed to buy Recovery Resources a not-for-profit organization that provides behavioral health and addiction services. MetroHealth will work with Recovery Resources to offer mental illness and addiction care the latter of which is very much in the nation's consciousness. In fact opioid addiction is one of MetroHealth's key areas of focus for the future. The deal will also expand MetroHealth's operations into Cuyahoga County. The purchase price was not disclosed.

Company Background

MetroHealth has been serving the medical needs of the Greater Cleveland community since 1837. It has been a major affiliate of Case Western Reserve University since 1914.

EXECUTIVES

Coo, Daniel K. Lewis
President And Ceo, Akram Boutros
Vp Marketing And Communications, Elizabeth Heller Allen, age 66
Chief Patient Experience Officer, Sara Laskey
Chief Nursing Officer, Mavis Bechtle
Chief Medical Officer And Chief Quality Officer, Alfred F. Connors
Cfo, Craig Richmond
Vp And Associate Cio, Donald Reichert
President Medical Staff, Sherrie Dixon-Williams
Medical Director, Annette Kyprianou
Medical Director, Carolyn Dziwis
Medical Director, Michael Infeld
Vice President, Geoff Himes
Executive Vice President Chief Clinical Officer, Bernard Boulanger
Pharmacy Manager, Barb Isabella
Vp Cio, Dave Fiser
Vice Chairman, J. B. Silvers
Chairman, Thomas M. McDonald
Secretary, Emigda Gabriel
Secretary Organizational Development, Tina Erickson
Auditors: RSM US LLP CLEVELAND OHIO

LOCATIONS

HQ: THE METROHEALTH SYSTEM
2500 METROHEALTH DR, CLEVELAND, OH 441091900
Phone: 216 398-6000
Web: WWW.METROHEALTH.ORG

Selected Locations

J. Glen Smith Health Center (In partnership with the City of Cleveland Cleveland)
MetroHealth Asia Town Health Center (Cleveland)
MetroHealth Beachwood Health Center (Beachwood Ohio)
MetroHealth Broadway Health Center (Cleveland)
MetroHealth Brooklyn Health Center (Cleveland)
MetroHealth Buckeye Health Center (Cleveland)
MetroHealth Center for Sleep Medicine South Campus (Independence Ohio)
MetroHealth Center for Sleep Medicine West Campus (Westlake Ohio)
MetroHealth Lakewood Health Center (Lakewood)
MetroHealth Lee-Harvard Health Center (Cleveland)
MetroHealth Medical Center Main Campus (Cleveland)
MetroHealth Old Brooklyn Campus (Cleveland)
MetroHealth Pepper Pike Health Center (Pepper Pike Ohio)
MetroHealth Premier Health Center (Westlake Ohio)
MetroHealth Rehabilitation Institute of Ohio (Cleveland)
MetroHealth Strongsville Health Center (Strongsville Ohio)
MetroHealth West 150th Health and Surgery Center (Cleveland)
MetroHealth Westlake Health Center (Westlake)
MetroHealth West Park Health Center (Cleveland)
The Elisabeth Severance Prentiss Center for Skilled Nursing Care at MetroHealth (Cleveland)
Thomas F. McCafferty Health Center (In partnership with the City of Cleveland Cleveland)

PRODUCTS/OPERATIONS

MetroHealth System Departments and Services

Aamoth Family Pediatric Wellness Center
Adolescent Clinic (Teen Health)
Advanced Gynecology (Center for Advanced Gynecology)
Advantage (MetroHealth Advantage)
Allergy & Immunology Clinic
Allergy Services (Department of Ear Nose & Throat)
Amigas Unidas Program
Anesthesiology
Art Therapy
Arthritis Center (Rheumatology)
Audiology
Bariatric Surgery (Weight Loss Surgery Program)
Behavioral Health (Child and Teen Mental Health Services)
Birth Control Procedures
Birthing Services
Bone Health and Surgery (Orthopaedics
BREAST Program (Community Breast Cancer Outreach)
Burn Care Center
Cancer Care Center
Cardiology Cardiovascular (Heart & Vascular Center)
Center for Advanced Gynecology
Center for Behavioral Health (Child and Teen Mental Health Services)
Centers for Community Health
Center for Sleep Medicine
Cerebrovascular
Childbirth Education
Child Life and Education
Children's Health (Pediatrics)
Children's Health Specialties
Closing the Gap (MetroHealth Buckeye Health Center)
Comprehensive Care Program (Services for Children with Special Needs)
Concussion Clinic
Cosmetic Dermatology
Dentistry and Oral Health
Dermatology
Diabetes Self-Management Program
Digital Mammogram
Ear Nose and Throat (ENT/Otolaryngology)
Emergency Medicine/Emergency Department
Endocrinology
Endoscopy Suite (Gastroenterology)
ExpressCare (MetroExpressCare)
Family Medicine Clinic at MetroHealth Medical Center
Fertility Services
Freedom From Smoking
Gastroenterology and Endoscopy Suite
Genetics Clinic
Geriatrics (Senior Health & Wellness Center)
Gynecology
Gynecology Advanced (Center for Advanced Gynecology
Gynecologic Oncology
Hand Center
Heart & Vascular Center
Hematology and Oncology (Cancer Care Center)
High-Risk Pregnancy Services
Hospital Medicine
Immunology (Allergy & Immunology Clinic)
Infectious Disease
Infertility Clinic
Infusion Therapy (Allergy & Immunology Clinic)
Internal Medicine Clinic at MetroHealth Medical Center
Internal Medicine and Pediatrics (Med-PEDS)
Kids' Health (Pediatrics
Kids' Korner Free Daycare Service at MetroHealth Medical Center
Latina Clinic: English | En espa ol
LGBT Pride Clinic (At Thomas F. McCafferty Health Center Health Center)
Life Flight (Metro Life Flight)
Long-Term/Skilled Nursing Care
Maternal-Fetal Medicine (High-Risk Pregnancy Services)
Medicine (Department of Medicine)
Mental Health (Psychiatry)
Metro Life Flight
MetroHealth Advantage
MetroExpressCare
MetroHealth Rehabilitation Institute of Ohio
MetroHealth Select Health Plan
MetroHealth Simulation Center
Mi MetroHealth Mi Comunidad
MyChart
Neonatology Neonatal Intensive Care Unit (NICU)
Nephrology
Neurology
Neurosciences
Northeast Ohio Chapter of the National Spinal Cord Injury Association (NSCIA)
Northeast Ohio Regional Spinal Cord Injury System (NORSCIS)
Nose Ear and Throat (ENT Otolaryngology)
Nursing
Nutrition
Obstetrics
Obstetrics and Gynecology
Occupational Medicine
Oncology (Cancer Care Center)
Opthalmologic (Eye) Surgery
Oral Health (Dentistry)
Oral and Maxillofacial Surgery
Orthopaedics
Osteopathic Medicine
Otolaryngology (Ear Nose and Throat)
Pain Management
Palliative Care
Pastoral Care
Pathology
Pediatrics
Permanent Birth Control Procedures
Pharmacy
Pregnancy Resources
Pride Clinic (At Thomas F. McCafferty Health Center Health Center)
Psychiatry (Behavioral/Mental Health)
Pulmonary and Critical Care
Quality Indicators
Radiology
Rehab Rehabilitation Services (MetroHealth Rehabilitation Institute of Ohio)
Reiki
Reproductive Endocrinology and Infertility Clinic
Rheumatology (Arthritis Center)

Select Health Plan

Senior Health and Wellness Center
Simulation Center
Skeletal (Orthopaedics)
Skilled Nursing/Long-Term Care
Sleep Medicine Sleep Studies
Spanish-language Information
Special Needs Services for Children (Comprehensive Care)
Spine Center
Stroke Stroke & Cerebrovascular Center
Surgery
Throat (Otolaryngology ENT)
Teen Health
Trauma Burns and Critical Care
Travel Clinic
Urgent Care (MetroExpressCare
Urology
Vascular Health and Surgery (Heart & Vascular Center
Weight Loss Surgery Program (Bariatric Surgery)
X-ray (Radiology)

COMPETITORS

AdCare
Catholic Health Initiatives
Cincinnati Children's Hospital
Community Health Systems
Kettering Health Network
Lake Health
OhioHealth
Premier Health Partners
Robinson Memorial Hospital
The Cleveland Clinic
University Hospitals Health System

HISTORICAL FINANCIALS

Company Type: Private

Income Statement FYE: December 31

	REVENUE ($ mil.)	NET INCOME ($ mil.)	NET PROFIT MARGIN	EMPLOYEES
12/15	888	37	4.2%	7,700
12/13	813	41	5.1%	—
12/09	673	58	8.7%	—
Annual Growth	4.7%	(7.1%)	—	—

2015 Year-End Financials

Return on assets: 3.6%
Return on equity: 20.0%
Current ratio: 1.10
Cash ($ mil.): 4

THE MIDDLE TENNESSEE ELECTRIC MEMBERSHIP CORPORATION

Middle Tennessee Electric Membership Corporation's service territory is smack dab in the middle of Tennessee. The utility cooperative distributes electricity to 190750 residential and business customers (member/owners) in four counties (Cannon Rutherford Williamson and Wilson) via more than 10470 miles of power lines connected to 34 electric distribution substations. Middle Tennessee Electric purchases its power supply from the Tennessee Valley Authority. The corporation is Tennessee's largest electric cooperative and the sixth largest in the US.

Geographic Reach

The cooperative serves customers in Cannon Rutherford Williamson and Wilson counties. According to a US Census report three of Tennessee's five fastest growing counties (Rutherford Williamson and Wilson) are in Middle Tennessee Electric's service area which also includes three of Tennessee's top five fastest-growing cities — LaVergne Smyrna and Franklin.

Strategy

To harness green energy as a way to limit fossil fuel power sources and reduce carbon emissions the utility cooperative is installing solar panels for customers. In 2012 the company completed a 850-panel solar field next to the City of Franklin's water plant. That year Middle Tennessee Electric had 70 solar projects operating across its service area and 30 more in the planning stages.

Company Background

Middle Tennessee Electric was formed in 1936 as part of a national rural electrification push.

EXECUTIVES

Vice President Of Operations, Jeff Gill
Vice President Of Information Systems, John Florida
Vice President Of Operations, Dan Dement
Vice President Communications And Member Services, Robert White
Board Of Directors, Jim Mills
Vice Chairman, William Jordan
Secretary Treasurer And Director, Will Jordan
Secretary Treasurer And Director, Mike Woods
Secretary, Jon Hood
Auditors: WINNETT ASSOCIATES PLLC SHELB

LOCATIONS

HQ: THE MIDDLE TENNESSEE ELECTRIC MEMBERSHIP CORPORATION
555 NEW SALEM HWY, MURFREESBORO, TN 371293390
Phone: 615 890-9762
Web: WWW.MTEMC.COM

HISTORICAL FINANCIALS

Company Type: Private

Income Statement FYE: June 30

	REVENUE ($ mil.)	NET INCOME ($ mil.)	NET PROFIT MARGIN	EMPLOYEES
06/16	542	10	1.9%	410
06/13	524	27	5.3%	—
06/12	510	19	3.8%	—
06/11	1,841	0	—	—
Annual Growth	—	781.4%	—	—

2016 Year-End Financials

Return on assets: 1.7%
Return on equity: 2.5%
Current ratio: 2.20
Cash ($ mil.): 74

THE MITRE CORPORATION

Politicians try to engineer a better government but MITRE governs the country's best engineering. A private not-for-profit organization MITRE Corporation provides consulting engineering and technical research services primarily for agencies of the federal government. It has primary research facilities in Massachusetts and Virginia. It also manages serveral federally funded research and development centers serving organizations such as the Department of Defense the Federal Aviation Administration the Internal Revenue Service and the Department of Veterans Affairs. MITRE was founded in 1958 by former MIT researchers.

Operations

MITRE also supports the Department of Homeland Security (DHS). For the DHS MITRE provides systems engineering practices and acquisition expertise.

MITRE brings innovative ideas into existence in areas as varied as artificial intelligence intuitive data science quantum information science health informatics space security policy and economic expertise trustworthy autonomy cyber threat sharing and cyber resilience.

The company operates federally funded research and development centers (FFRDCs) a unique organizations that assist the United States government with scientific research and analysis; development and acquisition; and systems engineering and integration. It also have an independent research program that explores new and expanded uses of technologies to solve our sponsors' problems.

Geographic Reach

In addition to primary research facilities in Bedford Massachusetts and McLean Virginia MITRE has international operations in Germany Italy Japan the Netherlands Singapore and the UK.

Sales and Marketing

MITRE works in the public interest across federal state and local governments as well as industry and academia.

Strategy

In 2020 MITRE established MITRE Labs restructuring research and development (R&D) capabilities and talent to further extend its impact across federally funded R&D centers and in collaboration with academia and industry.

In 2020 MITRE and Mayo Clinic announced a strategic relationship to improve public health outcomes. The organizations will work together to conduct research and development on common data elements for oncology cardiology and COVID-19. The collaborative research will further the development of platforms for intelligent automation including mCODE and mCARD common data standards for oncology and cardiology to the improve quality and coordination of patient care. MITRE and Mayo will also work together to create a platform known as mCOVID to support planning containment and mitigation of COVID-19 which will be adaptable for potential future pandemics.

Company Background

The MITRE Corporation was chartered in 1958 as a private not-for-profit company to provide engineering and technical guidance for the federal government. Since then MITRE has operated at the intersection of advanced technology and vital national concerns. The company grown to serve a variety of government agencies at the highest levels through the operation of federally funded research and development centers (FFRDCs).

EXECUTIVES

Svp Programs And Technology Center For Connected Government, Richard J. Byrne
President And Ceo, Jason F. Providakes
Vp And Director Center For Enterprise Modernization, James E. (Jim) Cook
Vp And Cio, Joel Jacobs
Svp And Coo, Peter Sherlock
Vp And Cto, Jay Schnitzer
Vp And Director Centers For Medicare & Medicaid Services (cms) Alliance To Modernize Healthcare, Patricia C. Steinbrech
Vp Joint And Services Portfolio National Security Engineering Center, Gregory K (Greg) Crawford
Vp Public Sector Programs Center For Programs And Technology, John M. Kreger
Vp Joint And Services Programs Center For Programs And Technology, Eileen M. Boettcher
Vp Intelligence Programs Center Programs And Technology, Kerry Buckley
Svp And General Manager Mitre National Security Sector, William LaPlante
Vp Air Force Portfolio National Security Engineering Center, Sarah MacConduibh
Vp And Cfo, Jean C. Milbrandt
Vp Air Force Programs Center For Programs And Technology, Douglas Robbins
Vp Intelligence Portfolios Mitre National Security Sector, Lori M. Scherer
Vp Programs And Technology, John A. Wilson
Vp And Director Center For Enterprise Modernization Veterans Affairs Portfolio, Jacklyn Mitchell Wynn
Vice President Information Technology, Dwayne Allain
Vice President, Kathy Saunders
Vice President And Director Center For Cem Fet Ffrdc, Beth Meinert

Department Head Agile And Adaptive Software Engineering, Carole Mahoney
Department Head, David Hodulich
Department Head, George Wilson
Department Head, Thomas Wilk
Manager Government Relations, William Klein
Vice Chairman, Donald M. Kerr
Chairman, John J. Hamre
Assistant Treasurer, Julie Trudeau

LOCATIONS

HQ: THE MITRE CORPORATION
202 BURLINGTON RD, BEDFORD, MA 017301420
Phone: 781 271-2000
Web: WWW.MITRE.ORG

COMPETITORS

Altarum
Battelle Memorial
Berkeley Lab
ComGlobal Systems
EDSI
General Atomics
Institute for Defense Analyses
Leidos
QinetiQ
SITA
SRI International
Sandia National Laboratories
SwRI
The Scripps Research Institute
Wyle Information Systems

HISTORICAL FINANCIALS

Company Type: Private

Income Statement — FYE: October 5

	REVENUE ($ mil.)	NET INCOME ($ mil.)	NET PROFIT MARGIN	EMPLOYEES
10/08	1,234	22	1.8%	7,000
10/07	1,113	23	2.1%	—
Annual Growth	10.9%	(4.6%)	—	—

2008 Year-End Financials

Return on assets: —
Return on equity: 1.8%
Current ratio: 0.80
Cash ($ mil.): 36

THE MOSES H CONE MEMORIAL HOSPITAL

EXECUTIVES

Ceo, Terry Akin
Exec V Pres-Cfo*, Jeff Jones
Coo*, Judy Schanel
Trustee, William V Nutt
Vice President of Information, Frank V Aluisio
Accountant Wide, Frank Kauder
Registered Nurse BSN, Heather Carter
Pharm D, Jenny Clapp
Senior Executive Assistant, Marsha Honeycutt
Director, Michelle Rothrock
Administrative Clinical Assist, Tina Brown
Auditors: DELOITTE & TOUCHE LLP RALEIG

LOCATIONS

HQ: THE MOSES H CONE MEMORIAL HOSPITAL
1200 N ELM ST, GREENSBORO, NC 274011020
Phone: 336 832-7000
Web: WWW.CONEHEALTH.COM

HISTORICAL FINANCIALS

Company Type: Private

Income Statement — FYE: September 30

	REVENUE ($ mil.)	NET INCOME ($ mil.)	NET PROFIT MARGIN	EMPLOYEES
09/20	2,293	172	7.5%	12,000
09/19	2,194	23	1.1%	—
09/18	2,001	88	4.4%	—
09/17	1,836	142	7.7%	—
Annual Growth	7.7%	6.6%	—	—

2020 Year-End Financials

Return on assets: 5.2%
Return on equity: 8.9%
Current ratio: 0.90
Cash ($ mil.): 328

THE NATURE CONSERVANCY

The Nature Conservancy is a nonprofit dedicated to preserving the diversity of Earth's wildlife by saving more than 125 million acres of land and 100 marine areas in every US state and about 80 countries worldwide. The Nature Conservancy originally carried out missions which tackles climate change protection of land and water and building healthy cities. The organization partners with government corporate and private entities to reduce harmful use of natural areas to create conservation-friendly public policy and to increase conservation funding. The Nature Conservancy was founded in 1951.

Operations

The Nature and Conservancy gets more than 55% of its support and revenues from private contributions followed by the Government contributions which gives about 15% land sales and gifts more than 10% and the rest comes from investments and other income.

Geographic Reach

Based in Arlington Virginia The Nature Conservancy operates in about 80 countries worldwide and in all 50 US states. The organization works in Africa the Asia-Pacific region the Caribbean Europe Canada India and the Americas.

Financial Performance

The Nature Conservancy raised more than $1.1 billion in total revenue and support in 2019. This includes nearly $600 million in private support similar to the three prior record-setting years for the organization excluding an extraordinary gift of $165 million in 2018.

Strategy

In July 2019 The Nature Conservancy announced a massive new land deal that helps conserve a broad swath of forest in the central Appalachian Mountains?a haven for biodiversity that scientists predict will become even more valuable as climate change moves the habitable zones of many plants and animals.

The Conservancy's impact investment arm NatureVest created a $130 million fund to pursue the purchases. The Conservancy drafted plans to manage the lands for improved biodiversity and to bring in revenues from sustainable timber harvesting carbon capture and recreational leases. The projects can support local jobs in conservation forestry and the region's burgeoning outdoor industry.

EXECUTIVES

Coo, Lois E. Quam, age 59
President And Ceo, Mark R. Tercek
Evp, Peter Wheeler
Cfo And Chief Administrative Officer, Stephen (Steve) Howell
Chief External Affairs Officer, Glenn T. Prickett
Evp Latin America, Joseph (Joe) Keenan
Regional Managing Director Africa, David Banks
Regional Managing Director Asia Pacific, Charles E. Bedford
Evp And Managing Director North America Region, Mark Burget
Evp Global Conservation Initiatives, William (Bill) Ginn
Senior Science Advisor, Peter Kareiva
Chief Conservation Officer, Brian McPeek
Chief External Affairs Officer, Glenn Pricket
Global Managing Director Lands, Justin Adams
Chief Development Officer, Jim Asp
Global Managing Director Water, Giulio Boccaletti
Global Managing Director Oceans, Maria Damanaki
Global Managing Director Cities, Pascal Mittermaier
Regional Managing Director Latin American Region, Aurelio Ramos
Managing Director Public Policy, Lynn Scarlett
Acting Chief Scientist, Heather Tallis
Chief Of Staff And Acting Chief Marketing Officer, Janine M. Wilkin
Vice President, Laurel Mayer
Director Of Government Relations, April Donnelly
Vice President, Joe Keenan
Director Of Government Relations, Susan Donovan
Government Relations Director, Mark Aagenes
Vice Chairman, James E. (Jim) Rogers
Chairman, Thomas J. Tierney
Board Director, Teresa Beck
Board Member, John Randall
Auditors: PRICEWATERHOUSECOOPERS LLP MC

LOCATIONS

HQ: THE NATURE CONSERVANCY
4245 FAIRFAX DR STE 100, ARLINGTON, VA 222031650
Phone: 703 841-5300
Web: WWW.NATURE.ORG

Selected Areas of Operation

Africa

Australia
Asia & the Pacific Islands
Caribbean
Central America
Europe
North America
South America

PRODUCTS/OPERATIONS

2014 Support & Revenue

		% of total
Dues & contributions		50
Investment income		22
Land sales & gifts		**138.5**
12		
Government grants	120	11
10ther income	59	5
Total	**1,114**	**100**

2014 Dues & Contributions

	%
Individuals	37
Foundations	28
Bequests	23
Other organizations	6
Corporations	6
Total	**100**

HISTORICAL FINANCIALS

Company Type: Private

Income Statement — FYE: June 30

	REVENUE ($ mil.)	NET INCOME ($ mil.)	NET PROFIT MARGIN	EMPLOYEES
06/19	992	118	11.9%	3,400
06/16	803	(8)	—	—
06/14	949	201	21.2%	—
06/13	859	106	12.4%	—
Annual Growth	2.4%	1.7%	—	—

2019 Year-End Financials

Return on assets: 1.5%
Return on equity: 1.8%
Current ratio: —
Cash ($ mil.): 193

THE NEBRASKA MEDICAL CENTER

Cornhuskers take note: If health care is what you seek The Nebraska Medical Center aims to please. The not-for-profit health system provides tertiary care at two campuses in Omaha University Hospital and Clarkson Hospital that collectively house about 680 licensed beds. The medical center the largest health care facility in Nebraska is the primary teaching facility of the University of Nebraska Medical Center (UNMC). It also serves as a designated trauma facility for eastern Nebraska and western Iowa and provides highly specialized care including organ transplantation. Its Clarkson West Medical Center campus houses outpatient surgery facilities an emergency room and doctors' offices.

Operations

The system has more than 1000 physicians. In 2013 it had some 51000 emergency department visits more than 24500 inpatient admissions and about 428000 outpatient visits.

In addition to University Hospital and Clarkson Hospital Nebraska Medical Center operates a network of 40 specialty and primary care clinics in and around Omaha. The health system's Centers of Excellence include its Cancer Center Heart Center Neurological Sciences Transplant Center and Women's Health.

Geographic Reach

In addition to serving the residents of Omaha the Nebraska Medical Center serves as a designated trauma facility for patients in eastern Nebraska and western Iowa.

Strategy

Like most other health care providers the Nebraska Medical Center is looking for ways to cut costs in the face of decreasing reimbursements from federal payers (such as Medicare and Medicaid) and as pressure from health care reform mounts and hospitals are required to implement expensive digital record-keeping and physician order entry systems. One way that Nebraska Medical Center has sought to reduce its expenses it by signing up with companies such as Medassets to receive sourcing and group purchasing (GPO) medical device and clinical consulting services for items used most by its physicians and for its pharmacy services.

The medical center and its sponsoring university are looking to expand its medical facilities to keep pace with a growing and aging population. UNMC is developing a new cancer center at the medical center's Omaha campus. Plans include three facilities - a multidisciplinary outpatient clinic a 98-lab research tower and a hospital tower with 108 beds dedicated to oncology patients. The project (estimated to cost $370 million) is expected to create 1200 new jobs by 2020 and pump $100 million annually into Nebraska's economy.

The system is also working with UNMC to add a new outpatient center to the university's midtown campus. The Lauritzen Outpatient Center will feature 10 operating rooms including four dedicated to opthalmic surgical procedures.

EXECUTIVES

Respiratory Therapy Director, Marlon Mcgough
Medical Director, Ron Kirschner
Auditors: KPMG LLP OMAHA NE

LOCATIONS

HQ: THE NEBRASKA MEDICAL CENTER
987400 NEBRASKA MED CTR, OMAHA, NE 681980001
Phone: 402 552-2000
Web: WWW.NEBRASKAMED.COM

PRODUCTS/OPERATIONS

Selected Services

Cancer Center
General Health Services
Heart and Vascular Services
Neurological Sciences
Transplantation

COMPETITORS

BryanLGH Medical Center
CHI Health
Children's Hospital & Medical Center
Fremont Area Medical Center
Madonna Rehabilitation Hospital
Methodist Health System
Saint Elizabeth Regional Medical Center

HISTORICAL FINANCIALS

Company Type: Private

Income Statement — FYE: June 30

	REVENUE ($ mil.)	NET INCOME ($ mil.)	NET PROFIT MARGIN	EMPLOYEES
06/17	1,389	74	5.4%	4,100
06/16	1,119	60	5.4%	—
Annual Growth	24.1%	22.1%	—	—

2017 Year-End Financials

Return on assets: 5.2%
Return on equity: 9.0%
Current ratio: 2.40
Cash ($ mil.): 67

THE NEW JERSEY TRANSIT CORPORATION

Government-owned New Jersey Transit (NJ TRANSIT) provides bus rail and light rail passenger transportation services. Its systems connect major points in New Jersey and provide links to the neighboring New York City and Philadelphia metropolitan areas. Overall the NJ TRANSIT service area spans about 5325 sq. miles. One of the largest transportation companies of its kind in the US NJ TRANSIT operates a fleet of more than 2200 buses approximately 1230 trains and about 95 light rail vehicles. Collectively the agency's passengers make nearly 270 million trips a year. NJ TRANSIT oversees public transportation programs for the elderly people with disabilities and people in rural areas.

Operations

Aside from bus rail and light rail passenger transportation services NJ TRANSIT also offers bike abroad program where customers are permitted to carry bicycles on all NJ Transit's trains buses and light rails with some restrictions and schedules.

Geographic Reach

NJ TRANSIT is headquartered in New Jersey.

Sales and Marketing

NJ TRANSIT has an application where customers can plan and buy tickets for the company's services. The company also offers deals and discounts to its customers including students with its promotional partners.

Financial Performance

Total operating revenues for NJ TRANSIT were $1059.5 million in the fiscal year 2019 an increase of $3.2 million or less than 1% compared to the prior fiscal year. Passenger revenue increased by $5.6 million or 1%. Other operating revenues net decreased by $2.4 million or 3%.

Cash held by the company at the end of 2019 decreased by $7.6 million to $178.4 million compared to $186.0 million in the prior year. Cash used for operations was $1.4 billion while cash provided by investing and financing were $2.6 million and $182.4 million respectively.

Strategy

In 2020 NJ TRANSIT is launching new features on its mobile app in a pilot program that allows rail and bus customers to see how full their ride is before they step on board making a better-informed personal decision that optimizes their comfort level as they return to the system.

In June 2020 NJ Transit launches strategic and capital plans that will guide the agency though 2030 called NJT2030: A 10-Year Strategic Plan" and a complementary 5-Year Capital Plan. Together these plans provide the vision for the agency to build the future of transportation in New Jersey and with it drive a 21st century economy in an accountable transparent and environmentally-sustainable way.

As the first strategic plan of its kind for NJ TRANSIT NJT2030 begins with a vision to transform the agency into an innovative world-class public transportation provider that meets the travel needs of every customer. To achieve that vision NJT2030 establishes five over-arching goals: ensure the reliability and continued safety of its transit system; deliver a high-quality experience for all its customers with the customer's entire journey in mind; power a stronger and fairer economy for all communities in the region; promote a more sustainable future for its planet; build an accountable innovative and inclusive organization that delivers for New Jersey.

Company Background

NJ TRANSIT was founded in 1979 by the New Jersey legislature.

EXECUTIVES

Executive Director, Veronique (Ronnie) Hakim
Vice President Of Diversity, Leo Sanders
Vice President, Leotis Sanders
Vice Chairman, Bruce Meisel
Chairman, Jamie Fox
Auditors: DELOITTE & TOUCHE LLP PARSIPP

LOCATIONS

HQ: THE NEW JERSEY TRANSIT CORPORATION
1 PENN PLZ E, NEWARK, NJ 071052245
Phone: 973 491-7000
Web: WWW.NJTRANSIT.COM

COMPETITORS

Port Imperial Ferry Corp.

HISTORICAL FINANCIALS

Company Type: Private

Income Statement				FYE: June 30
	REVENUE ($ mil.)	NET INCOME ($ mil.)	NET PROFIT MARGIN	EMPLOYEES
06/19	1,059	22	2.1%	1,000
06/18	1,056	(67)	—	—
06/04	583	256	44.0%	—
06/03	569	482	84.7%	—
Annual Growth	4.0%	(17.5%)	—	—

2019 Year-End Financials

Return on assets: 0.3%
Return on equity: 0.6%
Current ratio: 0.90
Cash ($ mil.): 75

THE NEW YORK AND PRESBYTERIAN HOSPITAL

The New York and Presbyterian Hospital is a learned institution: The not-for-profit hospital is affiliated with both the Columbia University College of Physicians & Surgeons and the Weill Cornell Medical College of Cornell University. Known as NewYork-Presbyterian Hospital the organization includes two major medical centers Columbia University Medical Center and Weill Cornell Medical Center which conduct educational and research programs in partnership with the universities. The two facilities combined have about 2600 beds and offer specialized programs for burns digestive diseases pediatrics women's health and other conditions. NewYork-Presbyterian Hospital is part of the NewYork-Presbyterian Healthcare System.

Operations

Altogether the NewYork-Presbyterian Hospital campuses handle some 2 million patient visits each year (both on an inpatient and outpatient basis) including inpatient admissions and more than 310000 emergency room visits and about 15000 births. The facilities employ a total of more than 6500 physicians including residents and fellows. NewYork-Presbyterian Hospital provides more than $108 million in charity and community care services each year.

Geographic Reach

In addition to its flagship campuses NewYork-Presbyterian/Columbia and NewYork-Presbyterian/Weill Cornell NewYork-Presbyterian Hospital operates two small community hospitals in Manhattan – the Allen Hospital and the Lower Manhattan Hospital – and an inpatient mental health facility (the Westchester Division). The broader NewYork-Presbyterian Healthcare System operates facilities in other areas of New York as well as in New Jersey and Connecticut. The NewYork-Presbyterian Hospital/Columbia campus houses the Morgan Stanley Children's Hospital as well as other specialist units.

Sales and Marketing

Medicare and Medicaid recipients account for more than 60% of NewYork-Presbyterian Hospital's patients. Commercial managed care organizations and insurance firms as well as self-pay customers account for the rest.

Financial Performance

NewYork-Presbyterian Hospital's revenue in fiscal 2015 totaled $4.8 billion.

Strategy

As the health care landscape has become increasingly complex and competitive especially with changing regulations and the push to provide more integrated patient care NewYork-Presbyterian Hospital has made some major organizational changes. Chief among its goals is to provide a patient-centered model of care creating a system that can easily be accessed by its patient consumers. It recently established its Community and Population Health division which includes community programs and initiatives ambulatory care network sites and the management of its new Accountable Care Organization.

It has also expanded beyond its former base of Manhattan in order to provide a regional system of care. For example the system took ownership of former affiliate Brooklyn Methodist in early 2017 with the intention of investing in the hospital's development; the move falls in line with its strategy of providing integrated care for communities particularly in light of a number of recent hospital failures in the borough.

Mergers and Acquisitions

New York Methodist Hospital (now NewYork-Presbyterian Brooklyn Methodist Hospital) was added to the organization in early 2017. Brooklyn Methodist will gain funds for a new $400 million ambulatory care building as part of the new relationship.

Company Background

NewYork-Presbyterian Hospital was formed through the 1998 merger of the New York Hospital (founded in 1771) and the Presbyterian Hospital (founded in 1868). New York Hospital was known for advancing care in areas including women's health and surgery while the Presbyterian Hospital was known for its pediatric division and its cancer center.

EXECUTIVES

Vice President Risk Management And Associate General Counsel, John Campano
Vice President, Valerie Punnett
Vice President Medical Director, Philip Wilner
Svp Cfo And Treasurer, Phyllis R. Lantos
President And Ceo, Steven J. (Steve) Corwin
Chief Nursing Officer; Vp Patient Services Newyork-presbyterian/columbia, Wilhelmina Manzano
Evp And Coo, Laura L. Forese
Vp Medical Affairs And Associate Chief Medical Officer, Richard S. Liebowitz
Cio, William Lee
Evp Chief Legal Officer And General Counsel, Maxine Frank
Finance Vice President, Ana Arroyo
Director Of Health Information, Deborah Forde
Vice President Compensation Benefits And Hris, Mary Falkowitz
Vice President Nursing, Michaelle Williams
Vice President Human Resources, Lorraine Orlando
Vice President Finance, William Farrell
Finance Vice President, Salvatore Logiudice
Senior Vice President And Chief Quality, Henry Ting
Vice President Of Human Resources, April Rodgers
Vice President Public Affairs, Karen Sodomick
Clinical Director, Gina A Rivera
Vice President Finance, Lugeion Y Carter
Vice President, Tanya Clark
Senior Vice President Chief Information Officer, Daniel Barchi
Vice President And Chief Administrative Officer, Kim Roldan-sanchez
Vice President Support Services East Campus, Mila Henn
Vice President Legal Affairs, Fred Title
Assistant Vice President Patient Financial Services, Elizabeth Carnevale
Vp Operations And Engagement, Keren Rozenfeld
Asst Vp, Jennifer Donovan
Vice President, Diego Rodriguez
Medical Director, Robert H Birkhahn
Director Of Medical Records, Alexandra Velnik
Director Of Pharmacy, Alexander Melchert
Director Of Radiology, Joseph Cianci
Group Senior Vice President Facilities And Real Estate, Joe Ienuso
Vice President Patient Flow And Capacity Management, Mary Godfrey
Vice President Quality And Patient Safety, Mary Kincart
Vice Chairman, Frank A. Bennack, age 87
Executive Vice Chair, Herbert Pardes, age 86
Treasurer, Karen Turi
Assistant Treasurer, Sedare Coradine
Surgical Secretary, Eileen Chavez
Assistant Secretary, Mary Braunsdorf

LOCATIONS

HQ: THE NEW YORK AND PRESBYTERIAN HOSPITAL
525 E 68TH ST, NEW YORK, NY 100654870
Phone: 212 746-5454
Web: WWW.NYP.ORG

PRODUCTS/OPERATIONS

2016 Patient Mix

	% of total
Medicare Managed	9
Medicare FFS	22
Medicaid Managed	23
Medicaid FFS	7
Managed Care and Other	37
Self-Pay	1
Workers Comp	1
Total	**100**

Selected Services

Cancer
Children's Health
Digestive
Geriatrics
Heart
Mens Health
Neuroscience
Orthopedic
Psychiatry
Rehabilitation Medicine
Transplant
Vascular
Womens Health

COMPETITORS

Ascension Health
Beth Israel Medical Center
Bronx-Lebanon Hospital
Catholic Healthcare System
Continuum Health Partners
Lenox Hill Hospital
Lutheran HealthCare
Maimonides Medical Center
MediSys Health Network
Memorial Sloan-Kettering
Montefiore Medical
New York City Health and Hospitals
Northwell Health
Winthrop-University Hospital
Yale New Haven Health System

HISTORICAL FINANCIALS

Company Type: Private

Income Statement				FYE: December 31
	REVENUE ($ mil.)	NET INCOME ($ mil.)	NET PROFIT MARGIN	EMPLOYEES
12/18	8,483	526	6.2%	23,709
12/17	5,616	762	13.6%	—
12/16	4,935	496	10.1%	—
12/14	4,206	197	4.7%	—
Annual Growth	19.2%	27.8%	—	—

2018 Year-End Financials

Return on assets: 3.7%
Return on equity: 6.3%
Current ratio: 2.50
Cash ($ mil.): 590

THE NEWTRON GROUP L L C

Some contractors bomb but The Newtron Group keeps on ticking. Through subsidiaries The Newtron Group offers a variety of industrial electrical and other specialty construction and contracting services nationwide. Services include instrumentation and control systems installation and maintenance; fiber optic installation and testing; industrial pipe and panel fabrication; and electrical heat tracing. The Newtron Group serves clients in such industries as refining power generation mining petrochemical and gas transmission. Subsidiaries include electrical contractor Triad Electric & Controls and control panel fabrication Triad Control Systems. Founded in 1973 The Newtron Group serves the US from offices in California Louisiana Nevada and Texas.

Operations

The Newtron Group's projects range in size from small-capital projects and maintenance contracts to multi-million dollar grassroots projects with services including industrial electrical & instrumentation commercial and residential electrical industrial mechanical process automation advanced analytical electric heat trace fabrication & integration and communications networking and security.

It held half a dozen subsidiary companies with four under the Newtron brand including Newtron which constructs and maintains electrical and instrumentation systems; Newtron Mechanical which deals with mechanical systems; Newtron Electrical Services which works with electrical meters breaker box replacement parking lot light and other electrical systems and Newtron Heat Trace.

Other subsidiaries include: Triad Electric & Controls an open-shop contractor for electrical and instrumentation projects and Triad Control Systems.

Geographic Reach

Baton Rouge-based The Newtron Group works on projects across the contiguous US from offices in California and on the coasts of Louisiana Nevada and Texas.

Sales and Marketing

The Group serves primarily the refining data centers petrochemical power generation pulp and paper mining and materials pharmaceutical healthcare government banking single/multi-family residential and gas & water transmission industries among others.

Strategy

The Newtron Group can save its clients time and money providing its services turn-key. The group is one of the few providers who can offer clients a comprehensive solution. With its offices across the southeast and west coast it has performed work across the United States and has established strong partnerships with manufacturers suppliers and vendors. This enables Newtron to secure the best prices possible and pass those savings on to its customers.

Newtron is also looking to expand geographically to further its reach and better serve its customers. In 2019 Newtron opened an office in Sparks Nevada to perform work in and around the Reno-Tahoe area.

Company Background

The Newtron Group founded in 1973 is one of the largest privately-owned Specialty Construction companies in the US and among the nation's leading Electrical and Instrumentation providers.

EXECUTIVES

Vp Marketing, Duff Schempf
President, Glen Redd
Auditors: HANNIS T BOURGEOIS LLP BATON

LOCATIONS

HQ: THE NEWTRON GROUP L L C
8183 W EL CAJON DR, BATON ROUGE, LA 708158093
Phone: 225 927-8921
Web: WWW.THENEWTRONGROUP.COM

PRODUCTS/OPERATIONS

Selected Subsidiaries

Com-Net Services Inc. (fiber optics)
Executive Aviation Inc. (hangar space fuel supplies)
Newtron Inc. (electrical and instrumentation)
Newtron Heat Trace (industrial heat tracing)
Newtron Mechanical (industrial mechanics)
Triad Electric and Controls Inc. (electrical and instrumentation)
Triad Control Systems Inc. (control panel fabrication)

Selected Industries

Cement
Electronics
Food processing
Gas transmission
Metals and mining
Petrochemical
Pharmaceuticals
Power generation
Pulp and paper
Refining
Semiconductors
Waste treatment

COMPETITORS

EMCOR
Fisk Electric
Industrial Specialty Contractors
Jelec
MMR Group
Motor City Electric
Pike Corporation

HISTORICAL FINANCIALS

Company Type: Private

Income Statement				FYE: June 30
	REVENUE ($ mil.)	NET INCOME ($ mil.)	NET PROFIT MARGIN	EMPLOYEES
06/19	622	0	—	3,500
06/18	489	0	—	—
06/17	450	0	—	—
06/16	436	0	—	—
Annual Growth	12.6%	—	—	—

2019 Year-End Financials

Return on assets: —
Return on equity: —
Current ratio: 1.70
Cash ($ mil.): 60

THE NORTH CAROLINA MUTUAL WHOLESALE DRUG COMPANY

EXECUTIVES

Ceo, David S Moody
Pres*, Thomas P Davis
SEC*, Michael C Broome
V Pres*, Hal Harrison
Accounts Payable, Tammy Roycroft
Programmer, Brad Bigger
Rx Buyer, John Hall
Administration, Jessica Watson
Auditors: THOMAS KNIGHT TRENT KING AN

LOCATIONS

HQ: THE NORTH CAROLINA MUTUAL WHOLESALE DRUG COMPANY
816 ELLIS RD, DURHAM, NC 277036019
Phone: 919 596-2151
Web: WWW.MUTUALDRUG.COM

HISTORICAL FINANCIALS

Company Type: Private

Income Statement				FYE: March 31
	REVENUE ($ mil.)	NET INCOME ($ mil.)	NET PROFIT MARGIN	EMPLOYEES
03/10	1,035	0	0.0%	160
03/09	1,024	0	0.1%	—
03/08	1,007	1	0.2%	—
Annual Growth	1.4%	(64.1%)	—	—

2010 Year-End Financials

Return on assets: 0.2%
Return on equity: 0.8%
Current ratio: 1.20
Cash ($ mil.): 53

THE OHIO STATE UNIVERSITY WEXNER MEDICAL CENTER

EXECUTIVES

Pres, Michael V Drake
Director, Jennifer Lanter
Division Administrator, Missy Kaufman
Research Dietitian, Elizabeth Grainger
Assistant Director of Competit, Charles Anderson
Radiation Oncologist, Karl Haglund
Prin, Robert N Pompa
Radiology, Adele Lipari
Deputy Director, Bence Boelcskevy
Professor, Brandon Biesiadecki
Professor, Christina Arnold

LOCATIONS

HQ: THE OHIO STATE UNIVERSITY WEXNER MEDICAL CENTER
410 W 10TH AVE, COLUMBUS, OH 432101240
Phone: 614 293-8000
Web: WWW.WEXNERMEDICAL.OSU.EDU

HISTORICAL FINANCIALS

Company Type: Private

Income Statement	REVENUE ($ mil.)	NET INCOME ($ mil.)	NET PROFIT MARGIN	EMPLOYEES
				FYE: June 30
06/19	3,433	39	1.2%	35,000
06/18	3,106	137	4.4%	—
06/16	2,628	126	4.8%	—
Annual Growth	9.3%	(31.9%)	—	—

2019 Year-End Financials

Return on assets: 1.0%
Return on equity: 6.2%
Current ratio: 4.40
Cash ($ mil.): 987

THE ORANGE COUNTY PUBLIC SCHOOL DISTRICT

EXECUTIVES

Supt, Barbara Jenkins
Executive of Information Techn, Giovanna Bravo
Coordinator, Jody Bernier
Administrator, Steve McHale
Senior Buyer, Belinda Biddle
Information Technology Sap, Charlie Boston
Teacher 6th Grade, Malcolm Rawlings
Teacher, Christy Malandra
Teacher Science, James Lis
Information Technology Project, Nancy Cox
Mentoring Director, Rebecca Watson
Auditors: CHERRY BEKAERT LLP ORLANDO

LOCATIONS

HQ: THE ORANGE COUNTY PUBLIC SCHOOL DISTRICT
445 W AMELIA ST, ORLANDO, FL 328011128
Phone: 407 317-3200
Web: WWW.OCPS.NET

HISTORICAL FINANCIALS

Company Type: Private

Income Statement	REVENUE ($ mil.)	NET INCOME ($ mil.)	NET PROFIT MARGIN	EMPLOYEES
				FYE: June 30
06/20	2,661	(26)	—	24,000
06/19	2,646	95	3.6%	—
06/18	2,506	107	4.3%	—
06/17	2,341	(25)	—	—
Annual Growth	4.4%	—	—	—

2020 Year-End Financials

Return on assets: (-0.4%)
Return on equity: (-0.6%)
Current ratio: —
Cash ($ mil.): 377

THE PARSONS CORPORATION

Industrial construction giant Parsons provides engineering construction and other services for corporate institutional and government projects worldwide. The company designs and builds structures; provides environmental remediation services including hazardous materials cleanup; and adds improvements to airports rail systems bridges and highways. Parsons developed significant expertise and differentiated capabilities in key areas of cybersecurity missile intelligence defense C5ISR space geospatial and connected communities. The company was founded in 1944. North America accounts for more than 80% of revenues.

Operations

The company operates in two reporting segments: Federal Solutions and Critical Infrastructure.

Its Critical Infrastructure business provides integrated design and engineering services for complex physical and digital infrastructure around the globe. The segment accounts more than half of the company revenues.

The Federal Solutions segment serves the defense environmental intelligence and security markets. It offers systems engineering intelligence services IT facility management and environmental/energy solutions to US government agencies worldwide. The segment has provided staff for space exploration US homeland security cybersecurity and ordinance cleanup. This segment accounts for about 50% of revenues.

Geographic Reach

Centreville Virginia-based Parsons has operations in more than 35 states and about 15 countries. North America accounts for more than 80% of revenues Middle East accounts for more than 15% of revenues and the rest of the world generates the remaining.

Sales and Marketing

The company serves a diverse global customer base including federal state municipal and industry customers such as Los Angeles World Airports Canada's Metrolinx Dubai's Roads and Transport Authority and the Port Authority of New York and New Jersey.

Financial Performance

Total revenue for 2019 was $4 billion an 11% increase from the previous year. The increase was due to higher sales in all of the company's segments.

The company's net income dropped 46% from $222.3 million in 2018 to $120.5 million in 2019.

Parsons' cash at the end of 2019 $195.4 million. Operating activities provided $220.2 while investing activities used $570.8 million mainly for payments for acquisitions. Financing activities provided another $266 million mainly from proceeds from borrowings.

Strategy

Parsons' growth strategy is focused on three pillars: Enhance Extend and Transform. These include continually enhancing and optimizing its core business processes extending its core business into high-growth and opportunity-rich adjacent markets and acquiring and integrating companies that possess transformative and disruptive technologies.

Mergers and Acquisitions

In 2019 Parsons Corporation completed its acquisition of QRC from private equity firm DC Capital Partners for $215 million to expand its offerings in the radio frequency environment and signals intelligence market. The transaction is consistent with the company's transformation strategy of acquiring high-growth defense and intelligence technology companies with hardware and intellectual property that enhance its technology and transactional revenue growth and margin profile.

Also in 2019 Parsons announced its acquisition of Virginia-based OGSystems an innovative solutions provider with advanced technologies in geospatial intelligence big data analytics and threat mitigation. OGSystems' core defense and intelligence customers include the National Geospatial-Intelligence Agency (NGA) the National Reconnaissance Office (NRO) and Special Operations Command (SOCOM). Terms were not disclosed.

EXECUTIVES

President Transportation, James R. (Jim) Shappell
Chairman And Ceo, Charles L. (Chuck) Harrington
President Parsons Infrastructure And Technology, Thomas L. (Tom) Roell
President Transportation Group, Todd K. Wager
President Emea, Garold B. (Gary) Adams
President Water And Infrastructure, Anthony F. (Tony) Leketa
Evp Cfo And Treasurer, George L. Ball
President Middle East And North Africa, Jeffrey F. Squires
Evp And Global Business Development Manager Commercial Technology, Brent F. Harvey
Vp And Defense & Security Sector Manager, Kurt H Tripp
Svp And National Security & Defense Division Manager, Biff Lyons
President Government Services Group, Mary Ann Hopkins
Vice President And Regional Manager, David A Brown
Vice President, Robert Mannebach
Senior Vice President, Dean Radeloff
Senior Vice President And General Counsel, Clyde Ellis
Vice President Investor Relations, Spille Joins
Board Member, Curtis Bower
Auditors: PRICEWATERHOUSECOOPERS LLP LO

LOCATIONS

HQ: THE PARSONS CORPORATION
5875 TRINITY PKWY STE 300, CENTREVILLE, VA 201201971
Phone: 703 988-8500
Web: WWW.PARSONS.COM

PRODUCTS/OPERATIONS

Selected Markets and Services

Parsons Commercial Technology
- Advanced manufacturing
- Commercial facilities
- Data management services
- Educational facilities
- Entertainment
- Health care
- Industrial environmental remediation
- Life sciences
- Mission critical facilities
- Telecommunications
- Vehicle inspection and compliance
- Wireless telecommunications systems

Parsons Infrastructure and Technology
- Community relations
- Construction
- Construction management
- Design
- Engineering
- Estimating
- Operations
- Operator training
- Procurement
- Program management
- Start-up and operations

Parsons Transportation
- Aviation

Bridges
Highways
Railroads
Revenue collection and management systems
Systems engineering
Transportation consumer services
Transportation planning
Tunneling
Urban Transit
Parsons Water and Infrastructure
Biosolids management
Combined sewer overflows
Construction/Construction management
Desalination and membrane technology
Design-build
Emergency response support
Environmental planning and restoration
Master planning
Ocean outfalls
Operations and maintenance
Storm water management
Utility tunneling
Wastewater collection systems
Wastewater treatment
Water resources
Water supply and pipelines

COMPETITORS

ABB
AECOM
ARCADIS
Bechtel
Black & Veatch
Bouygues
Day & Zimmermann
Fluor
Gilbane
Granite Construction
HOCHTIEF
Halliburton
Hill International
Hyundai Engineering and Construction
Jacobs Engineering
KBR
KBR Building Group
Kaiser Group
Layne Christensen
Lend Lease
Louis Berger
M. A. Mortenson
Michael Baker
Mott MacDonald
Paragon Project Resources
Pernix Group
Peter Kiewit Sons'
RBF Consulting
RailWorks
TIC Holdings
Turner Corporation
Tutor-Saliba
Vecellio & Grogan

HISTORICAL FINANCIALS

Company Type: Private

Income Statement FYE: December 31

	REVENUE ($ mil.)	NET INCOME ($ mil.)	NET PROFIT MARGIN	EMPLOYEES
12/18	3,560	239	6.7%	15,633
12/15	846	28	3.4%	—
Annual Growth	61.4%	102.7%	—	—

2018 Year-End Financials

Return on assets: 9.2%
Return on equity: —
Current ratio: 1.50
Cash ($ mil.): 280

THE PENNSYLVANIA HOSPITAL OF THE UNIVERSITY OF PENNSYLVANIA HEALTH SYSTEM

Early to bed early to rise may have made Ben Franklin healthy wealthy and wise. But for those not so healthy he (along with Dr. Thomas Bond) found it wise to establish Pennsylvania Hospital the nation's first such medical institution. The hospital is now a part of the University of Pennsylvania Health System (UPHS) and offers a comprehensive range of medical surgical and diagnostic services to the Philadelphia County area. Housing some 520 beds Pennsylvania Hospital offers specialized care in areas such as orthopedics vascular surgery neurosurgery and obstetrics; it is also a leading teaching hospital and a center for clinical research.

Operations

Pennsylvania Hospital has an average of about 29000 inpatient admissions per year including 5200 births as well as 115000 outpatient and emergency care visits. The medical center has more than 800 physicians on its medical staff. In addition to its extensive medical care services the company conducts medical training programs through its relationship with the University of Pennsylvania School of Medicine. Medical and clinical research programs are conducted with the school and with other research entities including government agencies. The hospital also collaborates with other UPHS entities including the Penn Presbyterian Medical Center and the Hospital of the University of Pennsylvania. The medical center also provides educational services across academic programs inlcuding Clinical Psychology Internship Program Medicine OB/GYN Pathology Radiology Sports Medicine Fellowship Surgery and Vascular Surgery Fellowship.

Financial Performance

For the fiscal year 2014 (ended June 30) Pennsylvania Hospital's revenues increased by 8.4% with a 9% increase in net patient service revenues 94% of total revenues); offset by a 1% decline in other revenues.

The company's net loss for the year decreased by 38% due to higher revenues and a decline in employee benefits paid.

Strategy

To improve the quality of care in the region UPHS is expanding specialist programs at its facilities.

In 2014 Pennsylvania Hospital opened its new Well Mother & Baby Unit which will represent Philadelphia's first all-private maternity suite unit. The new unit is part of Pennsylvania Hospital's $61 million long-range facility master plan and expands the company's offerings by providing private rooms to all of their maternity patients along with an array of obstetrical services from conception to discharge from the hospital following childbirth.

In 2013 UPHS expanded the orthopedic surgery program at Pennsylvania Hospital. The medical center is also enhancing services in fields including stroke care and women's health.

Company Background

The hospital was founded in 1751 by Benjamin Franklin and Dr. Thomas Bond to care for the sick-poor and insane of Philadelphia.

EXECUTIVES

Vice President, Kevin Guynn
Clinical Director, Dan Wilson
Medical Director, Charles Orellana
Medical Records Director, Scott Gilyard
Chair Department Of Neurology, Francisco Gonzalez-scarano
Medical Director Department Of Emergency Medicine, Kathleen Nasci
Vice President, Arthur Bartolozzi
Clinical Performance Vice President, John M Bruza
Vice President For Government Relations, Mary R Young
Auditors: LB PRICEWATERHOUSECOOPERS LLP

LOCATIONS

HQ: THE PENNSYLVANIA HOSPITAL OF THE UNIVERSITY OF PENNSYLVANIA HEALTH SYSTEM
800 SPRUCE ST, PHILADELPHIA, PA 191076130
Phone: 215 829-3000
Web: WWW.AAHAMPHILA.ORG

PRODUCTS/OPERATIONS

Selected Centers

ALS Center
Birthing Suite
Center for Bloodless Medicine and Surgery
Crisis Response Center
CyberKnife
Diabetes Education Center
Joan Karnell Cancer Center
Pain Management Center
Parkinson's Disease and Movement Disorders Center
Penn Comprehensive Neurosciences Center
Penn Orthopaedic Institute
Penn Center for Voice
Sports Medicine and Rehabilitation Center
Sleep Disorders Center
Vascular Center
Women's Imaging Center

Selected Services

Behavioral health
Heart and vascular
Neonatology
Neurosurgery
Obstetrics (including high-risk maternal and fetal services)
Orthopedics
Otorhinolaryngology (ENT)
Urology
Vascular medicine/surgery

COMPETITORS

Abington Memorial Hospital
Albert Einstein Healthcare Network
Aria Health
Bryn Mawr Hospital
Children's Hospital of Philadelphia
Crozer-Keystone Health System
Fox Chase Cancer Center
Jefferson Health
North Philadelphia Health System
TUHS
The Magee Memorial Hospital for Convalescents

HISTORICAL FINANCIALS

Company Type: Private

Income Statement FYE: June 30

	REVENUE ($ mil.)	NET INCOME ($ mil.)	NET PROFIT MARGIN	EMPLOYEES
06/15	579	21	3.7%	2,200
06/14	534	(2)	—	—
06/10	485	27	5.7%	—
06/09	453	0	—	—
Annual Growth	4.2%	—	—	—

2015 Year-End Financials

Return on assets: 3.2%
Return on equity: 4.8%
Current ratio: 0.40
Cash ($ mil.): —

THE PENNSYLVANIA STATE UNIVERSITY

The Pennsylvania State University system is one of the top of the world universities. Penn State has an enrollment of 96400 students; 15300 of them are graduate students. It offers more than 190 graduate programs and more than 275 undergraduate programs at 20 campuses. The school's oldest and largest campus with about half of the system's undergraduate students is at University Park in central Pennsylvania. Other sites include the Penn State College of Medicine in Hershey Pennsylvania and the Dickinson School of Law in Carlisle Pennsylvania.

Operations

It's more than 275 undergraduate programs include majors such as agriculture and natural resources biological science business engineer humanities and language and social science. Penn State offers more than 190 graduate major programs several stand-alone graduate minor programs and approximately 100 graduate and post-baccalaureate certificate programs. Some majors include accounting aerospace engineering anatomy architectural engineering art and astrobiology.

Geographic Reach

Its two dozen campuses are located throughout Pennsylvania including in Abington Altoona Behrend Berks Carlisle Great Valley (School of Graduate Professionals) Wilkes-Barre University Park (largest Penn State campus) and York.

Strategy

Through its Invent Penn State program the university has opened 21 innovation hubs across Pennsylvania that are designed to foster entrepreneurial and small business development.

Company Background

Chartered in 1855 to apply scientific principles to farming Penn State has conferred almost 800000 degrees since its founding.

The university's storied football program was hit in 2012 with a four year postseason ban the significant reduction of scholarships the vacating of 112 wins and a $60 million fine all stemming from the school's handling of the child molestation scandal involving former coach Jerry Sandusky. However in 2015 the NCAA reversed its decision on the vacating of wins restoring the late head coach Joe Paterno as the winningest coach in major college football history.

EXECUTIVES

Vice President For Student Affairs, Damon Sims
Svp Finance And Business And Treasurer, David J. Gray
Dean University Libraries And Scholarly Communications, Barbara I. Dewey
Dean Undergraduate Education, Robert N. Pangborn
Dean College Of Medicine, A. Craig Hillemeier
Dean College Of Arts And Architecture, Barbara O. Korner
Dean College Of Earth And Mineral Sciences, William E. Easterling
Dean College Of Education, David H. Monk
Dean College Of Health And Human Development, Ann C. (Nan) Crouter
Dean College Of The Liberal Arts, Susan Welch
Dean College Of Nursing, Paula Milone-Nuzzo
Dean Schreyer Honors College, Christian M. M. Brady
President, Eric J. Barron, age 69
Dean Smeal College Of Business, Charles H. Whiteman
Evp And Provost, Nicholas P. Jones
Chief Investment Officer, John Pomeroy
Dean Graduate School, Regina Vasilatos-Younken
Dean College Of Agricultural Sciences, Richard Roush
Dean College Of Communications, Marie Hardin
Dean College Of Engineering, Amr S. Elnashai
Vice President For Commonwealth Campuses, Madlyn Hanes
Department Head Learning And Performance Systems, Roy Clariana
Student Affairs Vice President Financial Officer, Rachael Diamond
Department Head, Mark Morrisson
Senior Vice President For Development And Alumni Relations, Tresa Ciprich
Vice President, Victor Sparrow
Vice President, Sandy Rothrock
Vice President For Governmental Affairs, Mike Diraimo
Department Head Geospatial And Decision Support, Shawn Hough
Department Head Recreation Park And Tourism Management, Peter Newman
Vice President For Administration, Frank Guadagnino
Vice President, Emily Sandall
Vice Provost For Affirmative Action, Ken Lehrman
Assistant Vice President For Research And Industrial Partnerships, James Delattre
Vice President Development And Alumni Relations, Orrin Bundy
Associate Vice President And Chief Executive Officer Of The Penn State Alumni Association, Paul Clifford
Chair Department Of Ophthlmlgy, David Quillen
Vice President Tajai Carrington, Ann Rogers
Department Head, David Stensrud
Associate Vice President, Rachel Pell
Vice President, Katie Bridgens
Vice President, Christina Platt
Vice Chairman, Ira M. Lubert, age 70
Chairman, Keith E. Masser
Board Member, Jim Kustenbauter
Club Secretary, Jessica Baker
Board Member, Christine Igoe
Secretary, Bob Corman
Secretary Bookkeeper, Missie Estep
Board Member, Robert Martin
Board Member, Vickie Cunningham
Board Member, Ken Fohringer
Secretary [pulmonary Medicine, Joann Tucker
Treasurer, Bobbie Johannes
Secretary, Erin Mcginley
Auditors: DELOITTE & TOUCHE LLP PHILADE

LOCATIONS

HQ: THE PENNSYLVANIA STATE UNIVERSITY
201 OLD MAIN, UNIVERSITY PARK, PA 168021503
Phone: 814 865-4700
Web: WWW.PSU.EDU

PRODUCTS/OPERATIONS

Selected Colleges

College of Agricultural Sciences
College of Arts and Architecture
Smeal College of Business
College of Communications
College of Earth and Mineral Sciences
College of Education
College of Engineering
College of Health and Human Development
College of Information Sciences and Technology
School of International Affairs
School of Law
College of the Liberal Arts
College of Medicine
School of Nursing
Eberly College of Science
Graduate School
Schreyer Honors College

Selected Campuses

Penn State Abington Penn State Altoona
Penn State Beaver
Penn State Berks
Penn State Brandywine
Penn State DuBois
Penn State Erie The Behrend College
Penn State Fayette The Eberly Campus
Penn State Greater Allegheny
Penn State Harrisburg
Penn State Hazleton
Penn State Lehigh Valley
Penn State Mont Alto
Penn State New Kensington
Penn State Schuylkill
Penn State Shenango
Penn State Wilkes-Barre
Penn State Worthington Scranton
Penn State York

HISTORICAL FINANCIALS

Company Type: Private

Income Statement FYE: June 30

	REVENUE ($ mil.)	NET INCOME ($ mil.)	NET PROFIT MARGIN	EMPLOYEES
06/20	6,795	(712)	—	44,000
06/19	6,576	583	8.9%	—
06/18	6,363	1,081	17.0%	—
06/17	6,059	635	10.5%	—
Annual Growth	3.9%	—	—	—

2020 Year-End Financials

Return on assets: (-4.1%)
Return on equity: (-7.3%)
Current ratio: 2.80
Cash ($ mil.): 2,359

THE PEPPER COMPANIES INC

EXECUTIVES

Pres-Ceo, J Stanley Pepper
SEC, Richard S Pepper
Exec V Pres-Gen Counsel, Thomas M O'Leary
Exec V Pres, Christopher R Averill
Superintendent, Dave Lewis
Project Engineer I, John Mueting
Project Manager II, Tiffany Lomax
Auditors: DELOITTE & TOUCHE LLP CHICAGO

LOCATIONS

HQ: THE PEPPER COMPANIES INC
643 N ORLEANS ST, CHICAGO, IL 606543608
Phone: 312 266-4703
Web: WWW.PEPPERCONSTRUCTION.COM

HISTORICAL FINANCIALS

Company Type: Private

Income Statement — FYE: September 30

	REVENUE ($ mil.)	NET INCOME ($ mil.)	NET PROFIT MARGIN	EMPLOYEES
09/17	1,119	22	2.0%	1,100
09/16	1,179	21	1.8%	—
09/11	1,177	10	0.9%	—
09/10	911	7	0.9%	—
Annual Growth	3.0%	15.8%	—	—

2017 Year-End Financials

Return on assets: 5.9%
Return on equity: 20.9%
Current ratio: 1.20
Cash ($ mil.): 41

THE PRESIDENT AND FELLOWS OF HARVARD COLLEGE

Auditors: PRICEWATERHOUSECOOPERS LLP B

LOCATIONS

HQ: THE PRESIDENT AND FELLOWS OF HARVARD COLLEGE
600 ATLANTIC AVE, BOSTON, MA 022102211
Phone: 617 495-1502
Web: WWW.WEBMEDIAUNIVERSITY.COM

HISTORICAL FINANCIALS

Company Type: Private

Income Statement — FYE: June 30

	REVENUE ($ mil.)	NET INCOME ($ mil.)	NET PROFIT MARGIN	EMPLOYEES
06/14	4,408	4,607	104.5%	11,500
06/13	4,214	1,056	25.1%	—
06/12	4,037	(1,446)	—	—
06/09	0	0	—	—
Annual Growth	—	—	—	—

2014 Year-End Financials

Return on assets: 7.2%
Return on equity: 104.5%
Current ratio: —
Cash ($ mil.): 87

THE PRIDDY FOUNDATION

EXECUTIVES

President, David Wolverton
Director, Debbie White

LOCATIONS

HQ: THE PRIDDY FOUNDATION
807 8TH ST STE 1010, WICHITA FALLS, TX 763013310
Phone: 940 723-8720
Web: WWW.PRIDDYFDN.ORG

HISTORICAL FINANCIALS

Company Type: Private

Income Statement — FYE: December 31

	REVENUE ($ mil.)	NET INCOME ($ mil.)	NET PROFIT MARGIN	EMPLOYEES
12/13	8,791	3	0.0%	4
12/12	3	(4)	—	—
12/10	32	27	86.7%	—
12/09	0	0	—	—
Annual Growth	—	—	—	—

2013 Year-End Financials

Return on assets: 2.5%
Return on equity: 2.5%
Current ratio: —
Cash ($ mil.): 14

THE QUEEN'S HEALTH SYSTEMS

EXECUTIVES

Pres-Ceo, Gary A Okamoto
Ceo, Arthur A Ushijima
Exec V Pres, Tracy Woo
Asst Treas, Kanoe Margol
Pres, William G Obana
V Pres, Mark Yamakawa
V Pres, Eric K Martinson
V Pres, Janice Kalanihuia
CIO, Harold Moscho
Coo, Jason C Chang
Vice President Human Resources, Nona Tamanaha
Auditors: KPMG LLP HONOLULU HI

LOCATIONS

HQ: THE QUEEN'S HEALTH SYSTEMS
1301 PUNCHBOWL ST, HONOLULU, HI 968132402
Phone: 808 691-5900
Web: WWW.QUEENS.ORG

HISTORICAL FINANCIALS

Company Type: Private

Income Statement — FYE: June 30

	REVENUE ($ mil.)	NET INCOME ($ mil.)	NET PROFIT MARGIN	EMPLOYEES
06/17	1,279	173	13.6%	4,500
06/15	118	7	6.0%	—
06/11	24	3	14.2%	—
06/10	25	5	22.4%	—
Annual Growth	75.2%	63.1%	—	—

2017 Year-End Financials

Return on assets: 6.9%
Return on equity: 11.3%
Current ratio: 4.90
Cash ($ mil.): 80

THE REGENTS OF THE UNIVERSITY OF COLORADO

The University of Colorado System spans four campuses and some 60000 students. The Boulder campus home to about 30000 students provides more than 2500 courses in 150-plus fields through nine colleges and schools. The University of Colorado at Denver has an enrollment of more than 14000 and has 120 study programs at a dozen schools and its nearby Anschutz Medical Campus serves more than 500000 patients annually. The smallest campus University of Colorado at Colorado Springs has six colleges with about 10000 students and offers nearly 60 undergraduate graduate and doctoral degree programs. The system which began in Boulder as the University of Colorado in 1876 boasts more than 4000 faculty members.

EXECUTIVES

Vice President Of Communications, Shawn M Goehl
Assistant Vice President Risk Management, Terry Lee
Vice President Of Programming, Crystal Watson
Board Of Regents Member, Peter Steinhauer
Treasurer, David Lee
Auditors: CLIFTONLARSONALLEN LLP GREENW

LOCATIONS

HQ: THE REGENTS OF THE UNIVERSITY OF COLORADO
3100 MAR ST STE 481 572 U, BOULDER, CO 803090001
Phone: 303 735-6624
Web: WWW.COLORADO.EDU

PRODUCTS/OPERATIONS

Selected Campuses

University
University of Colorado - Colorado Springs
University
University of Colorado Anschutz Medical Campus

HISTORICAL FINANCIALS

Company Type: Private

Income Statement — FYE: June 30

	REVENUE ($ mil.)	NET INCOME ($ mil.)	NET PROFIT MARGIN	EMPLOYEES
06/20	4,239	584	13.8%	12,980
06/18	3,833	(197)	—	—
06/17	3,728	77	2.1%	—
06/16	3,451	72	2.1%	—
Annual Growth	5.3%	68.2%	—	—

2020 Year-End Financials

Return on assets: 7.4%
Return on equity: 22.0%
Current ratio: 3.90
Cash ($ mil.): 221

THE RESEARCH FOUNDATION FOR THE STATE UNIVERSITY OF NEW YORK

The Research Foundation of State University of New York (The Research Foundation) collects and administers research and education grants from state and federal governments corporations and foundations on behalf of the 24-campus State University of New York known as SUNY. The foundation has formed several affiliated divisions – including Long Island High Technology Incubator and NanoTech Resources – to operate research facilities encourage scientific collaboration and otherwise facilitate research for the university. It facilitates research for studies such as engineering and nanotechnology; physical sciences and medicine; life sciences and medicine; social sciences; and computer and information sciences.

Operations

The foundation manages SUNY's research portfolio. Research Foundation administrators help SUNY faculty students and staff through every step of the research grant process allowing them to focus on their work and ensuring compliance with university grant sponsor and government requirements.

The Research Foundation protects SUNY's intellectual property (SUNY ranks among the nation's top faculty to commercialize their inventions for the public good).

The organization makes strategic investments to maximize the collective impact of SUNY research to drive investment and job growth. SUNY's Networks of Excellence assemble scientists and scholars from all campuses to collaborate on research projects in areas ranging from advanced manufacturing and energy to health and the humanities.

The Research Foundation is an integral partner in the execution and administration of the START-UP NY initiative to transform SUNY campuses and university communities across the state into tax-free communities for new and expanding businesses.

The organization funds its operations primarily from recoveries of indirect costs provided from grants and contracts.

Geographic Reach

The Research Foundation comprises a central office and operating units at 31 campus locations across New York State.

Financial Performance

The Research Foundation reported $1 billion in revenues in 2014 compared to $1.07 billion in 2013. The primary reason for the decline was due to decreased sales from federal grants and contracts private grants and contracts and investment income.

Investment income/loss included dividends and interest realized and unrealized gains and losses and equity adjustments from the foundation's investment in the Brookhaven Science Associates partnership.

The organization's net income decreased by $30 million in 2014 due to lower revenues and increased other program expenses.

Net cash provided by the operating activities increased by $127.7 million due to changes in interest payments on capital debts and other payments.

Strategy

In 2014 Iliad Neurosciences a company focused on the development of innovative approaches to diagnosing and treating Autism Spectrum Disorders entered into an Exclusive License Agreement with The Research Foundation for The State University of New York. Under this deal Iliad will provide a new biomarker to identify an abnormality in folate transport to the brain associated with susceptibility to Autism Spectrum Disorders. . The identification of this defect could lead to a targeted therapy that may improve the transport of folate to the brain in children and to the fetus in pregnant women who test positive for the folate receptor autoantibody.

Company Background

The Research Foundation was established in 1951 just three years after SUNY itself.

EXECUTIVES

Office Of The Vice President For Research, Edward Zablocki
Associate Vice President For Marketing And Media Outreach, Kristin Haacker
Assistant Vice President Metrology, Steve Novak
Assistant Vice President Special Events And Programs, Laura Wheeler
Vice President, Patricia Bucklin
Auditors: KPMG LLP BOSTON MA

LOCATIONS

HQ: THE RESEARCH FOUNDATION FOR THE STATE UNIVERSITY OF NEW YORK
35 STATE ST, ALBANY, NY 122072826
Phone: 518 434-7000
Web: WWW.RFSUNY.ORG

PRODUCTS/OPERATIONS

2014 Revenues

	% of total
Federal grants & contracts	50
Private grants & contracts	23
State grants & contracts	17
Investments	2
Inventions & licenses	2
Local grants & contracts	2
Investment income	0
Gifts capital gifts & grants	0
Other	4
Total	**100**

HISTORICAL FINANCIALS

Company Type: Private

Income Statement — FYE: June 30

	REVENUE ($ mil.)	NET INCOME ($ mil.)	NET PROFIT MARGIN	EMPLOYEES
06/13	1,079	42	3.9%	16,330
06/12	1,114	12	1.2%	—
06/09	985	(71)	—	—
Annual Growth	2.3%	—	—	—

2013 Year-End Financials

Return on assets: 7.2%
Return on equity: —
Current ratio: 1.30
Cash ($ mil.): —

THE RUDOLPH/LIBBE COMPANIES INC

The corporate model of a conglomerate composed of independent unrelated businesses is not for The Rudolph/Libbe Companies. The group of companies can build or oversee real estate projects (general contractor Rudolph/Libbe Inc.); perform mechanical electrical and structural work (GEM Industrial); and then represent those properties in the market (RLWest Properties). Operating in the Ohio/Michigan corridor the group provides site selection design/build and construction management. Its portfolio includes industrial retail municipal residential educational health care and mixed-use projects. Fritz and Phil Rudolph and their cousin Allan Libbe founded flagship subsidiary Rudolph/Libbe Inc. in 1955.

EXECUTIVES

Chm, Bill Rudolph
Pres*, Allan J Libbe
SEC*, John A Libbe
Treas-Cfo*, Robert Pruger
Pres*, Frederick W Rudolph
Pres*, Philip J Rudolph
Project Engineer, Joel Curcio
Business Manager, Brandon Gartee
Project Manager Estimator, Jay Gillette
Business Manager, Michelle Dean
Safety Manager, Neil Smith
Auditors: REHMANN ROBSON TOLEDO OH

LOCATIONS

HQ: THE RUDOLPH/LIBBE COMPANIES INC
6494 LATCHA RD, WALBRIDGE, OH 434659788
Phone: 419 241-5000
Web: WWW.RLGBUILDS.COM

COMPETITORS

Albert M. Higley
Atlas Industrial Holdings
Danis
Messer Construction
Ruhlin
Skanska USA Building

HISTORICAL FINANCIALS

Company Type: Private

Income Statement — FYE: December 31

	REVENUE ($ mil.)	NET INCOME ($ mil.)	NET PROFIT MARGIN	EMPLOYEES
12/18	573	16	2.8%	600
12/17	567	20	3.5%	—
12/16	502	23	4.8%	—
12/15	425	16	3.8%	—
Annual Growth	10.5%	(0.2%)	—	—

2018 Year-End Financials

Return on assets: 7.4%
Return on equity: 25.9%
Current ratio: 1.30
Cash ($ mil.): 16

THE SAINT CLOUD HOSPITAL

EXECUTIVES

Pres, Craig Broman
Cfo*, Greg Klugherz
Coordinator, Kevin Mentzer
Chief of Medicine, Richard Jolkovsky
Chief of Medicine, Peter Charvat
Board Member, Betsy Horsch
Analyst, Chris Stavros
Chief of Internal Medicine, Joe Mercuri
Cardiologist, Richard Aplin
Infectious Disease, Richard Backes
Psychologist, Stephanie Baas
Auditors: MCGLADREY LLP MINNEAPOLIS MN

LOCATIONS

HQ: THE SAINT CLOUD HOSPITAL
1406 6TH AVE N, SAINT CLOUD, MN 563031901
Phone: 320 251-2700
Web: WWW.CENTRACARE.COM

HISTORICAL FINANCIALS

Company Type: Private

Income Statement — FYE: June 30

	REVENUE ($ mil.)	NET INCOME ($ mil.)	NET PROFIT MARGIN	EMPLOYEES
06/18	864	39	4.5%	4,957
06/16	756	3	0.5%	—
06/15	767	170	22.2%	—
06/14	754	72	9.6%	—
Annual Growth	3.5%	(14.3%)	—	—

2018 Year-End Financials

Return on assets: 3.2%
Return on equity: 5.3%
Current ratio: 1.90
Cash ($ mil.): 33

THE SALVATION ARMY

EXECUTIVES

Pres-Trus, William A Bamford III
President-Trustee*, William A Bamfordiii
V Pre-Trustee*, Kenneth O Johnson Jr
Chb-Trustee*, David E Jeffrey
Treasurer-Trustee*, Donald W Lance
Secretary*, Michael J Southwick
Fist Asst Treas-Trustee*, D Sue Foley
Second Asst Treas*, Thomas O Henson
Asst SEC-Legal*, Richard D Allen
Asst Sec-Property*, Jorge E Diaz
Second Asst Sec-Property*, Adolph M Orlando
Auditors: GRANT THORNTON LLP NEW YORK

LOCATIONS

HQ: THE SALVATION ARMY
440 W NYACK RD OFC, WEST NYACK, NY 109941739
Phone: 845 620-7200
Web: WWW.SACONNECTS.ORG

HISTORICAL FINANCIALS

Company Type: Private

Income Statement — FYE: September 30

	REVENUE ($ mil.)	NET INCOME ($ mil.)	NET PROFIT MARGIN	EMPLOYEES
09/16	859	(224)	—	10,447
09/12	1,034	207	20.0%	—
09/09	782	(96)	—	—
09/08	288	(463)	—	—
Annual Growth	14.6%	—	—	—

2016 Year-End Financials

Return on assets: (-5.4%)
Return on equity: (-9.7%)
Current ratio: 0.30
Cash ($ mil.): 122

THE SALVATION ARMY

EXECUTIVES

Chb, David Jeffrey
Pres*, Donald Bell
Treas*, James Seiler
Assis Treas*, Stephen Ellis
SEC*, Ward Matthews
V Pres*, Ralph Bukiewicz
MBR*, Susan Bukiewicz
MBR*, William Mockabee
Cfo*, Alberto Flores
Senior Manager, Colonel B Bailey
Director, Joann Avery

LOCATIONS

HQ: THE SALVATION ARMY
1424 NORTHEAST EXPY NE, BROOKHAVEN, GA 303292088
Phone: 404 728-1300
Web: WWW.SALVATIONARMYSOUTH.ORG

HISTORICAL FINANCIALS

Company Type: Private

Income Statement — FYE: September 30

	REVENUE ($ mil.)	NET INCOME ($ mil.)	NET PROFIT MARGIN	EMPLOYEES
09/09	830	(220)	—	16,168
09/08	533	(336)	—	—
09/07	1,185	318	26.9%	—
Annual Growth	(16.3%)	—	—	—

2009 Year-End Financials

Return on assets: (-6.7%)
Return on equity: (-8.6%)
Current ratio: 1.30
Cash ($ mil.): 89

THE SCHOOL BOARD OF MIAMI-DADE COUNTY

EXECUTIVES

Chb, Perla Tabares Hantman
Staff, Martin A Berkowitz
Auditors: MCGLADREY LLP MIAMI FLORIDA

LOCATIONS

HQ: THE SCHOOL BOARD OF MIAMI-DADE COUNTY
1450 NE 2ND AVE, MIAMI, FL 331321308
Phone: 305 995-1000
Web: WWW.DADESCHOOLS.NET

HISTORICAL FINANCIALS

Company Type: Private

Income Statement — FYE: June 30

	REVENUE ($ mil.)	NET INCOME ($ mil.)	NET PROFIT MARGIN	EMPLOYEES
06/19	3,948	(14)	—	9
06/18	3,868	(46)	—	—
06/17	3,728	448	12.0%	—
06/16	3,631	136	3.8%	—
Annual Growth	2.8%	—	—	—

2019 Year-End Financials

Return on assets: (-0.2%)
Return on equity: (-5.2%)
Current ratio: 4.60
Cash ($ mil.): 427

THE SCHOOL DISTRICT OF OSCEOLA COUNTY FL

EXECUTIVES

Supt, Melba Luciano
Cbfo*, Bill Collins
Principal, George Sullivan
Coordinator, Jean Riggs
Public Information Director, Dana Lee Schafer
Management Info Dir, Robert Curran Sr
Senior Buyer, Megan Pearison
Executive Director, Janice Franceschi
Editor, Laura Elam
Tech Prep Coordinator, Melanie Stefanowicz
School Board Member, Kelvin Soto
Auditors: MOORE STEPHENS LOVELACE PA

LOCATIONS

HQ: THE SCHOOL DISTRICT OF OSCEOLA COUNTY FL
817 BILL BECK BLVD, KISSIMMEE, FL 347444492
Phone: 407 870-4600
Web: WWW.OSCEOLASCHOOLS.NET

HISTORICAL FINANCIALS

Company Type: Private

Income Statement — FYE: June 30

	REVENUE ($ mil.)	NET INCOME ($ mil.)	NET PROFIT MARGIN	EMPLOYEES
06/19	787	25	3.2%	6,250
06/18	695	13	2.0%	—
06/17	638	117	18.4%	—
06/16	601	37	6.2%	—
Annual Growth	9.4%	(12.2%)	—	—

2019 Year-End Financials

Return on assets: 1.7%
Return on equity: 3.7%
Current ratio: —
Cash ($ mil.): 225

THE SCHOOL DISTRICT OF PHILADELPHIA

EXECUTIVES

Spdt, William Hite Jr
Cfo*, Matthew E Stanski
Food Director, Wayne T Grasela
Teacher, Abram Taber
Specialist, Danielle Schultz
Webmaster, Ezra Miller
Health, Julia Smith
Director, Majeedah Scott
Personnel Assistant, Michelle Stokes
Health, Brandon Coleman
Health Coordinator, Paula Miller
Auditors: CHRISTY BRADY CPA PHILADELPH

LOCATIONS

HQ: THE SCHOOL DISTRICT OF PHILADELPHIA
440 N BROAD ST, PHILADELPHIA, PA 191304090
Phone: 215 400-4000
Web: WWW.PHILASD.ORG

HISTORICAL FINANCIALS

Company Type: Private

Income Statement — FYE: June 30

	REVENUE ($ mil.)	NET INCOME ($ mil.)	NET PROFIT MARGIN	EMPLOYEES
06/18	3,473	210	6.1%	21,065
06/17	3,250	220	6.8%	—
06/16	3,064	23	0.8%	—
06/11	2,930	(259)	—	—
Annual Growth	2.5%	—	—	—

2018 Year-End Financials

Return on assets: 5.7%
Return on equity: —
Current ratio: —
Cash ($ mil.): 190

THE SCHOOL DISTRICT OF WEST PALM BEACH COUNTY

EXECUTIVES

Coordinator, Elizabeth Parsley
Staff, Linda Esta
Coordinator, Noemi Moreno
Technician, Edith Brown
Reading Teacher, Amy McGregor
Financial Applications Manager, Angela Saccareccia
School Counselor, Anne Kim
Teacher, Annie Yarensky
Executive Secretary, Barbara Fraga
Networking Administrat, Bryan Borck
Director of Employee Benefits, Dianne Howard
Auditors: RSM US LLP WEST PALM BEACH

LOCATIONS

HQ: THE SCHOOL DISTRICT OF WEST PALM BEACH COUNTY
3300 FOREST HILL BLVD, WEST PALM BEACH, FL 334065813
Phone: 561 434-8747
Web: WWW.BELIEVERSACADEMYINC.ORG

HISTORICAL FINANCIALS

Company Type: Private

Income Statement — FYE: June 30

	REVENUE ($ mil.)	NET INCOME ($ mil.)	NET PROFIT MARGIN	EMPLOYEES
06/18	2,307	136	5.9%	28,910
06/17	2,146	78	3.7%	—
06/16	1,986	64	3.2%	—
06/15	1,903	(61)	—	—
Annual Growth	6.6%	—	—	—

2018 Year-End Financials

Return on assets: 2.8%
Return on equity: 9.2%
Current ratio: —
Cash ($ mil.): 959

THE SCOULAR COMPANY

The Scoular Company doesn't move food from farm to table but it does handle a good portion of the trip. The company buys sells stores handles processes and transports agricultural products (mainly grains) worldwide. It gets the mainstays of farming ? corn millet rye peas and lentils soybeans and wheat ? where they need to go. The company transports these products via rail truck barge shipping partners. Scoular's other divisions offer fishmeal products for farm-animal pet and aquaculture feeds; ingredients for food manufacturers; and renewable fuels as well as a host of risk management logistics and product-related services. It has customers worldwide.

Operations

Scoular facilitates solutions for its customers at every step in the agricultural supply chain. It provides solutions for grains food ingredients animal feed ingredients pet food ingredients international trades and transportation.

The company has the network confidence and creativity to make connections between farmers processors manufacturers facilities shippers and carriers worldwide. When it comes to animal feed the company delivers flexible and valuable nutrition solutions whether it's for a dairy feedmill or another animal feed manufacturer. Its indirect wholly owned and independently operated subsidiary Petsource provides comprehensive freeze-dried pet food manufacturing capabilities for ultimate quality control.

Scoular's grain products include barley flaxseed soybean and sunflower seeds among others. Other products include fats and oils fibers flours sweeteners and more.

Geographic Reach

In addition to the company's headquarters in Omaha Nebraska and corporate offices in Overland Park Kansas and Minneapolis Minnesota Scoular has more than 90 locations around the world.

Sales and Marketing

Scoular serves local regional national and international customers in the food feed and renewable fuel markets.

Financial Performance

As a non-public company Scoular doesn't publicly release full financials. It reported 2020 revenue however of $4.6 billion.

Strategy

The Scoular Company announced in August 2020 that it has selected Jerome Idaho as the location to manufacture a new sustainable plant-based alternative protein made from barley. Scoular will build a 15000-square-foot facility to manufacture the product called barley protein concentrate for use in aquaculture feed and pet food. The building will be constructed on 4 acres south of Scoular's existing livestock feed ingredients facility in Jerome. The operation is expected to create 13 jobs and begins manufacturing in May 2021.

The new manufacturing plant is projected to process 1.9 million bushels of barley annually with capacity projected to expand over the next several years. A high-energy liquid feed supplement for cattle feeders will be co-produced. This facility and innovative barley product will create a new market and greater stability for farmers in the Magic Valley region and throughout Idaho.

Company Background

George Scoular founded the George Scoular Grain & Lumber Company in Nebraska in 1892. It was family-owned until 1967 when it was sold to a group of grain industry executives. It grew through acquisitions and partnerships over the following decades.

EXECUTIVES

Vice President, Randall Foster
Senior Vice President, Joan Maclin
Chairman And President, David M. Faith
Svp And Division General Manager, Todd McQueen
Svp And Division General Manager, John Messerich
Cfo, Richard A. (Rick) Cogdill
Ceo, Paul T. Maass
Cio, Jeff Schreiner
Svp And Division General Manager, Bob Ludington
Vice President Finance And Tre, Roger Barber
Vice President Finance, Omer Sagheer
Vice President Talent Management And Human Resources, Theresa Ruby
Senior Vice President And General Counsel, Megan Belcher
Auditors: KPMG LLP OMAHA NEBRASKA

LOCATIONS

HQ: THE SCOULAR COMPANY
2027 DODGE ST, OMAHA, NE 681021240
Phone: 402 342-3500
Web: WWW.SCOULAR.COM

COMPETITORS

ADM
Andersons
Bartlett and Company
Bunge Limited
CHS
Cargill
DeBruce Grain
Excel Maritime Carriers
Louis Dreyfus Group
Syntroleum
TBS International
TORM

HISTORICAL FINANCIALS

Company Type: Private

Income Statement — FYE: May 31

	REVENUE ($ mil.)	NET INCOME ($ mil.)	NET PROFIT MARGIN	EMPLOYEES
05/19	4,226	23	0.6%	801
05/18	4,486	22	0.5%	—
05/17	4,366	25	0.6%	—
05/16	4,667	(10)	—	—
Annual Growth	(3.3%)	—	—	—

2019 Year-End Financials

Return on assets: 2.5%
Return on equity: 7.3%
Current ratio: 1.40
Cash ($ mil.): 14

THE SIMONS FOUNDATION INC

EXECUTIVES

Pres, Marilyn Simons
V Pres*, Mark Silver
Chb*, James H Simons
Cfo*, Marlow Kee
Coo*, Euan Robertson
Information Technology Manager, Chris Fleisch
Vice President, Marion Greenup
Director, Apoorva Mandavilli
Accounting Manager, Lawrence Bianco
Human Resources Director, Kathleen Savarese
Operations Manager, Monika Lenard

LOCATIONS

HQ: THE SIMONS FOUNDATION INC
160 5TH AVE FL 7, NEW YORK, NY 100107037
Phone: 646 654-0066
Web: WWW.SIMONSFOUNDATION.ORG

HISTORICAL FINANCIALS

Company Type: Private

Income Statement FYE: December 31

	REVENUE ($ mil.)	NET INCOME ($ mil.)	NET PROFIT MARGIN	EMPLOYEES
12/19	786	302	38.5%	350
12/18	619	283	45.8%	—
12/17	645	236	36.7%	—
12/16	267	(39)	—	—
Annual Growth	43.2%	—	—	—

2019 Year-End Financials

Return on assets: 7.6%
Return on equity: 9.6%
Current ratio: 0.20
Cash ($ mil.): 151

THE SOUTHEASTERN CONFERENCE

EXECUTIVES

Commissioner, Greg Sankey
Commissioner*, Michael Flive
Commissioner*, Mark Womack
Associate Media Relations Dire, Tammy Wilson
Associate Director, Sylvia Hagan
Director, Torie Johnson
Director Ticket Operations, John Gibson
Auditors: BARFIELD MURPHY SHANK & SMITH

LOCATIONS

HQ: THE SOUTHEASTERN CONFERENCE
2201 RICHARD ARRINGTN JR, BIRMINGHAM, AL 352031103
Phone: 205 949-8960
Web: WWW.SECSPORTS.COM

HISTORICAL FINANCIALS

Company Type: Private

Income Statement FYE: August 31

	REVENUE ($ mil.)	NET INCOME ($ mil.)	NET PROFIT MARGIN	EMPLOYEES
08/19	720	23	3.3%	30
08/16	639	17	2.7%	—
08/15	527	17	3.3%	—
08/14	325	2	0.7%	—
Annual Growth	17.2%	58.9%	—	—

2019 Year-End Financials

Return on assets: 22.1%
Return on equity: 22.1%
Current ratio: —
Cash ($ mil.): 28

THE ST FRANCIS HOSPITAL FOUNDATION INC

EXECUTIVES

Pres- Ceo, Alan Guerci
Doctor, Antonio Madrid
Nurse Case Manager, Patricia Witchey
Manager Information, Charles Faverio
Human Resources Business Partn, Eric Curtin
Internist, Maria Fedoseeva
Anesthesiologist, Michael Dutt
Emergency Medicine Specialist, Patricia Phan
Rn, Sandra Sofka
Diagnostic Radiologist, Scott Springer
Senior Vice President, Martin Bieber

LOCATIONS

HQ: THE ST FRANCIS HOSPITAL FOUNDATION INC
100 PORT WASHINGTON BLVD, ROSLYN, NY 115761347
Phone: 516 563-7964
Web: WWW.STFRANCISHEARTCENTER.CHSLI.ORG

HISTORICAL FINANCIALS

Company Type: Private

Income Statement FYE: December 31

	REVENUE ($ mil.)	NET INCOME ($ mil.)	NET PROFIT MARGIN	EMPLOYEES
12/18	803	75	9.3%	4
12/17	755	76	10.1%	—
Annual Growth	6.4%	(1.2%)	—	—

2018 Year-End Financials

Return on assets: 6.3%
Return on equity: 8.6%
Current ratio: 0.80
Cash ($ mil.): 32

THE STAMFORD HOSPITAL

EXECUTIVES

Ceo-Pres, Brian Grissler
Exec V Pres*, Kathleen Silard
Cfo*, Kevin Gage
Cmo*, Sharon Kiely
Sr V Pres*, Darryl McCormick
Dentist, David B Weinstein DDS
Vp- Ambulatory Network Dev't, Andrew Snyder
Librarian, Guillaume V Moorsel
Coordinator, Joyce Potter
Coordinator, Marcel Souza
Procurement Staff, Gloria Vallo
Auditors: ERNST & YOUNG LLP NEW YORK

LOCATIONS

HQ: THE STAMFORD HOSPITAL
1 HOSPITAL PLZ, STAMFORD, CT 069023602
Phone: 203 325-7000
Web: WWW.STAMFORDHEALTH.ORG

HISTORICAL FINANCIALS

Company Type: Private

Income Statement FYE: September 30

	REVENUE ($ mil.)	NET INCOME ($ mil.)	NET PROFIT MARGIN	EMPLOYEES
09/19	608	(44)	—	2,000
09/18	574	3	0.7%	—
Annual Growth	6.0%	—	—	—

2019 Year-End Financials

Return on assets: (-4.5%)
Return on equity: (-12.3%)
Current ratio: 1.60
Cash ($ mil.): 79

THE SUNDERLAND FOUNDATION

EXECUTIVES

Prin, Lester T Sunderland

LOCATIONS

HQ: THE SUNDERLAND FOUNDATION
5700 W 112TH ST STE 320, LEAWOOD, KS 662111759
Phone: 913 319-6194
Web: WWW.SUNDERLANDFOUNDATION.ORG

HISTORICAL FINANCIALS

Company Type: Private

Income Statement FYE: December 31

	REVENUE ($ mil.)	NET INCOME ($ mil.)	NET PROFIT MARGIN	EMPLOYEES
12/18	1,552	1,429	92.1%	3
12/10	6	2	35.2%	—
12/09	2	(2)	—	—
Annual Growth	105.9%	—	—	—

2018 Year-End Financials

Return on assets: 95.8%
Return on equity: 95.8%
Current ratio: —
Cash ($ mil.): 542

THE SUNDT COMPANIES INC

Sundt has put its stamp on the Southwest. Through Sundt Construction and other subsidiaries The Sundt Companies offers preconstruction construction management general contracting and design/build services for commercial government and industrial clients. Projects include commercial buildings military bases light rails airports and schools. It builds mostly in Arizona Nevada California New Mexico and Texas. Sundt has overseen some notable projects including the development of the top-secret town of Los Alamos New Mexico (where the first atomic bomb was built) and the relocation of the London Bridge to Arizona. Sundt Companies was formed in 1998 as a holding company for various company interests.

Operations

The Sundt Companies performs its work through various divisions: Industrial; concrete; building; heavy civil; and federal. The building division is divided into geographic regions: California; Southwest; and Texas; as well as a Federal Division.

Strategy

Like its peers Sundt is dealing with the lingering effects of the construction downturn that greatly impacted the Southwest. (The company lost more than $750 million in government projects due to state budget constraints.) Indeed Sundt anticipates that it may be 2015 before it sees a strong economy for construction. In the meantime the firm has relied on a healthy backlog of projects and diversification efforts to sustain its business. To that end it entered new geographic markets in 2012 including New Mexico where it is building new dorms at New Mexico State University. It also recently began construction of new schools in El Paso Texas its first in the city. The firm formed a new Criminal Justice Specialization group in 2012 to win courthouse and detention facility work.

Sundt also has focused on making investments in improving technology used in the preconstruction and construction process. It also grew its self-perform work capabilities when it acquired Foley Masonry and Tile Inc. in 2010. Also that year Sundt opened a new office in San Antonio as part of the company's growth plan. The company expanded once again in 2011. It opened new offices to support projects in New Mexico North Carolina and Texas.

EXECUTIVES

Pres-Ceo, Mike Hoover
Svp/Cfo*, Kevin M Burnett
Sr V Pres-Gen Counsel*, Ronald Stuff
Vice President Engineering, Nobuyuki Kuroki
Auditors: MAYER HOFFMAN & MCCANN

LOCATIONS

HQ: THE SUNDT COMPANIES INC
2015 W RIVER RD STE 101, TUCSON, AZ 857041676
Phone: 520 750-4600
Web: WWW.SUNDT.COM

PRODUCTS/OPERATIONS

Selected Projects

Aviation
Commercial buildings
Concrete construction
Courthouses
Federal government
Hospitality
Hospitals & health care
Infrastructure & site development
Juvenile detention facilities
K-12 schools
Mining
Mission critical/Data center
Municipal buildings
Parking structures
Power plants & alternative energy
Prisons
Research & development facilities
Residential
Retail
Roads & bridges
Student housing & dormitories
Universities & community colleges
Water & wastewater treatment

Selected Services
Build-to-suit
Construction manager at risk (CMAR)
Construction/program manager
Design-bid-build/general contractor (DBB)
Preconstruction
Self-perform contracting

COMPETITORS

Austin Industries
CORE Construction
Charles Pankow Builders
DPR Construction
Granite Construction
Hunt Construction
Kitchell
McCarthy Building
Meadow Valley
O'Neil Industries
Peter Kiewit Sons'
Swinerton
Tutor Perini
Weitz

HISTORICAL FINANCIALS

Company Type: Private

Income Statement — FYE: September 30

	REVENUE ($ mil.)	NET INCOME ($ mil.)	NET PROFIT MARGIN	EMPLOYEES
09/18	1,432	0	—	1,800
09/17	1,134	0	—	—
09/16*	813	0	—	—
06/16	0	0	—	—
Annual Growth	—	—	—	—

*Fiscal year change

2018 Year-End Financials

Return on assets: —
Return on equity: —
Current ratio: 1.30
Cash ($ mil.): 82

THE TRUSTEES OF PRINCETON UNIVERSITY

This prince's kingdom is covered with ivy. As one of the eight elite Ivy League schools in the Northeastern US Princeton is a research university that offers students degrees across 35 departments and 55 interdisciplinary undergraduate certificate programs. It boasts more than 8855 students (more than 5265 undergraduate around 2945 graduate and nearly 645 international students). The highly selective school which enjoys an undergraduate student-faculty ratio of 5:1 admits nearly 5% of its total applicants. Nobel Prize winners associated with Princeton include professor of physics emeritus James Peebles Woodrow Wilson writer Toni Morrison. One of the nation's wealthiest universities Princeton has an endowment of approximately 26.6 billion.

Operations

The Princeton campus comprises six residential colleges that are organized by grade level (freshmen sophomores juniors and seniors).

The university which is supported by nearly 1290 faculty members that include visitors and part-time appointments operates three schools: the School of Architecture School of Engineering and Applied Science and the Woodrow Wilson School of Public and International Affairs. Its research areas focus on engineering and applied science humanities natural sciences and social sciences. Some 60% of the university's undergraduate students receive financial aid.

It generates most of its revenue from investment earnings for about 65% of total sales 15% from government grants and contracts and the remainder from tuition fees auxiliary sales and services and others.

Geographic Reach

Located in Princeton New Jersey Princeton's campus includes more than 200 buildings that cover about 600 acres.

Financial Performance

The University's revenue totaled $2.2 billion a 1% increase compared to the previous year. The increase is primarily due to a higher sales volume in the company's Government Grants and Contracts segment.

The University's cash for the year ended 2020 was $945 million. Operating activities used $777.2 million primarily for net realized and unrealized gains on investments. Investing activities and financing activities provided $912.6 million and $495.5 million respectively.

Strategy

As part of its investment strategy the University enters into transactions utilizing a variety of financial instruments and strategies including futures swaps options short sales and forward foreign currency contracts. These financial instruments and strategies allow the University to fine-tune the asset allocation of the investment portfolio.

Company Background

Founded in 1746 as the College of New Jersey Princeton is the fourth-oldest college in the nation. In 1756 the college was moved to Nassau Hall which served as the temporary capitol of the US in 1783 and is still part of the Princeton campus.

EXECUTIVES

Vp Finance And Treasurer, Carolyn N. Ainslie
President, Christopher L. Eisgruber
Dean Admission, Janet L. Rapelye
Dean Undergraduate Students, Kathleen Deignan
President Princeton University Investment Co., Andrew K. Golden
Dean Religious Life And The Chapel, Alison L. Boden
Dean Wilson School Of Public And International Affairs, Cecilia E. Rouse
Vp Information Technology And Cio, Jay Dominick
Dean School Of Engineering And Applied Science, H. Vincent Poor
Provost, David S. Lee
Dean Of The Faculty, Deborah A. Prentice
Dean Graduate School, Sanjeev R. Kulkarni
Dean Of The College, Jill S. Dolan
Dean Research, Pablo G. Debenedetti
Dean School Of Architecture, Monica Ponce de Leon
Evp, Treby Williams
Program Assistant Vice President For Pppl, Janice Huang
Communications Specialist Office Of The Vice President For Facilities, Cynthia L Suter
Executive Assistant Office Of The Vice President For Development, Deborah A Small
Vice President, David McComas
Avp Human Capital Management Systems, Elaine Cha
Vice President For Development And Alumni Affairs, Kristin I Brathole
Assistant Vice President For Academic Development, Charlotte E Collins
Special Assistant To The Assistant Vice President, Liz Patten
Vice President, Jacqueline J Knowlton
Vp For Facilities, Kyujung Whang
Trustee, Kathryn A. Hall
Vice Chairman, Brent L. Henry
Secretary, Crystal Sada
Secretary, Elizabeth Haile
Secretary Mechanical Engineer Engineering And Technical Infrastructure Princeton Plasma Physics Lab, Tyrrell Marianne
Auditors: PRICEWATERCOOPERS LLP NEW YOR

LOCATIONS

HQ: THE TRUSTEES OF PRINCETON UNIVERSITY
1 NASSAU HALL, PRINCETON, NJ 085442001
Phone: 609 258-3000
Web: WWW.PRINCETON.EDU

PRODUCTS/OPERATIONS

Select Councils Institutes and Centers

Bendheim Center for Finance
Center for Migration and Development
Center for the Study of Religion
Council of the Humanities
Council on Science and Technology
Davis Center for Historical Studies
James Madison Program in American Ideals and Institutions
Lewis-Sigler Institute for Integrative Genomics
Liechtenstein Institute on Self-Determination
Princeton Environmental Institute (PEI)
Princeton Institute for International and Regional Studies (PIIRS)
Princeton Institute for the Science and Technology of Materials (PRISM)
Princeton Writing Program
Program of Freshman Seminars in the Residential Colleges
Program in Law and Public Affairs
Program in Neuroscience
University Center for Human Values

COMPETITORS

Brown University
Columbia University
Cornell University
Dartmouth
Harvard University
Penn
Rutgers University
Yale University

HISTORICAL FINANCIALS

Company Type: Private

Income Statement — FYE: June 30

	REVENUE ($ mil.)	NET INCOME ($ mil.)	NET PROFIT MARGIN	EMPLOYEES
06/20	2,173	383	17.7%	6,000
06/19	2,146	677	31.6%	—
06/18	2,012	2,582	128.3%	—
06/17	1,813	2,096	115.6%	—
Annual Growth	6.2%	(43.2%)	—	—

2020 Year-End Financials

Return on assets: 1.2%
Return on equity: 1.3%
Current ratio: —
Cash ($ mil.): 105

THE TURNER CORPORATION

The Turner Corporation a subsidiary of German construction giant HOCHTIEF is the leading general building and construction management firm in the US (as ranked by Engineering News-Record) ahead of rivals Bechtel and Fluor. The firm operates primarily through subsidiary Turner Construction and has worked on notable projects such as Madison Square Garden the UN headquarters Yankee Stadium the Taipei 101 Tower and the 68000-seat open-air stadium for the San Francisco 49ers. Known for its large projects also offers services for midsized and smaller projects and provides interior construction and renovation services.

Operations

Turner works on more than 1500 projects in a year totaling $8 billion in volume. The group has divisions dedicated to serving the aviation health care biotechnology public assembly sports education justice and industrial sectors. Its homeland security group was established in order handle a growing demand for security systems and protection. The unit installed detection equipment in some 450 airports throughout the US. Turner Corporation also has an arm specializing in green building with a focus on Leadership in Energy and Environmental Design (LEED) -certified projects. Turner Green Building has more than 400 LEED projects and green projects either completed or in progress.

Turner Corporation has subsidiaries providing auxiliary operations. Turner's risk management department offers contract review project safety and claims handling. Turner Logistics handles procurement and supply chain management for projects and Turner Facilities Management Solutions offers ongoing operations services. Also the Turner School of Construction Management provides training for local subcontractors.

Geographic Reach

Dallas-based Turner Corporation boasts a network of offices across the US (with most in California and Ohio) and Canada (Vancouver and Toronto) with an global presence in 20 countries in Europe Africa East Asia India Latin America and the Caribbean.

Sales and Marketing

Turner works on variety of projects from several sectors. It's known for its work in the categories of healthcare education offices commercial properties cultural facilities sports facilities and hotels. The company is also a leader in the green building category.

Strategy

With the construction market rebounding from the economic downturn Turner is looking to high-growth markets in the US and overseas. As of early 2015 it was working on more than 1900 projects 80% of which were Education Commercial or Interior project-related. Some of these projects included the 17000 sq. ft- interior remodel for Salesforce's Vancouver office; the 325000 sq. ft- construction of the LEED-Certified RAND Corporation Headquarters in Santa Monica California; and the 25000-seat Charlotte Coliseum event arena for the City of Charlotte North Carolina.

The company has also been making moves to expand its business abroad in recent years. In 2012 for example Turner partnered with one of India's largest real estate developers Sahara Prime City Ltd. to form Sahara Turner which would lead the development and construction of multiple townships across the country with an approximate value of $2.5 billion by 2017. It also purchased a majority stake in Clark Builders Canada to capitalize on the country's growing construction market.

Turner often partners with fellow US-based HOCHTIEF subsidiary Flatiron which specializes in civil engineering. Examples of the teamwork are the expansions of airports in San Diego and Sacramento.

HISTORY

At the turn of the century an engineer and devout Quaker named Henry Chandlee Turner was convinced that a new type of steel-reinforced concrete (called the Ransome system) would change the construction industry. With this conviction and with the help of his partner D. H. Dixon Turner bought the rights to the technology for $25000 and in 1902 founded Turner Construction Company.

One of the company's early projects was building the stairways for New York's first subway stations. As the Ransome method proved to be successful Turner's reputation grew. Defense contracts during WWI raised Turner's take to $35 million in 1918.

Before the Depression Turner was building high-rises hotels and stadiums. During the economic crash that started in 1929 the company survived by building retail stores churches and public buildings a strategy it would employ successfully in later recessions.

Henry Turner retired in 1941. His brother Archer Turner managed the company during most of the war effort. As WWII raged more than 80% of the company's work was defense-related. Projects included building and managing a submarine base in Oak Ridge Tennessee during the development of the atomic bomb.

In 1947 Henry C. Turner Jr. the founder's son became president and within four years he had led the company to more than $100 million in sales. By the time he stepped down as chairman in 1970 the firm had built skyscrapers futuristic airports and such landmarks as Madison Square Garden and the United Nations Secretariat and Plaza in New York City. Turner went public in 1969.

Howard S. Turner (the final family member to head the business) led the company during the 1970s. The company extended its global presence opening offices in more countries including Iran Pakistan and the United Arab Emirates. Turner also developed construction management services.

In 1984 The Turner Corporation was formed as a holding company for the construction company and the subsidiaries created or acquired as a result of diversification. Property development was one of these activities but by 1987 Turner had begun to dispose of its real estate holdings. It did not move quickly enough however and when the real estate market crashed Turner was caught with a large portfolio.

As commercial projects slowed Turner sought work in more sectors including public works and amusement projects (aquariums arenas hospitals and universities). By 1994 these areas accounted for 70% of business. In 1993 as the building slump continued Turner began a cost-cutting plan which included laying off workers and closing offices. That year the company set up an $8.5 million restructuring reserve and as the real estate market eased into recovery Turner sold more of its real estate holdings.

In 1996 Turner won a contract to build a 10000-seat arena in Salt Lake City to be used for the 2002 Winter Olympics. In 1997 Turner contracted to renovate 811 schools and build two campuses in California's San Fernando Valley and in 1998 it was chosen to manage the construction of the Kansas City Motor Speedway.

Profits were recovering quickly. Nonetheless in 1999 the company agreed to be acquired by German construction giant HOCHTIEF in a $370 million deal that ended Turner's joint venture with Switzerland's Karl Steiner. The company also relocated its corporate headquarters to Dallas that year to take advantage of the construction boom in the US Southwest.

In 2000 Turner created three new business groups to serve the aviation pharmaceutical and sports sectors. By the next year Turner's sports group was working on 17 projects. In 2001 the company was a member of the construction team that responded to the September 11 devastation at Ground Zero in New York City.

The next year the company celebrated its 100th anniversary with an exhibit at the National Building Museum in Washington DC; the exhibit featured drawings and photos of some of Turner's notable projects during the past century. In 2003 Turner Construction acquired the assets of Tompkins Builders the third-largest construction company in the Washington DC area from former rival J.A. Jones Construction Co.

Turner Construction which celebrated its 100th anniversary in 2002 has ranked among the leading general builders in the US since WWI. For 80 of the 100 years the group had a Turner among its senior executives. Howard S. Turner was the last member of the family to serve in the company's senior ranks. The company's appointment of Peter Davoren in 2003 as president of Turner Construction reflected the rise of a new generation of leaders for the unit. Davoren was additionally appointed chairman and CEO in 2007.

Turner Construction announced in 2008 that it had signed the contract on its 15000th major project.

EXECUTIVES

Pres-Chb-Ceo, Peter J Davoren
Sr V Pres-Cfo & Treas, Karen Gould
V Pres-Finance & Asst Treas, Don Oshiro
Attrny, Richard L Smith Jr
Svp, Turner, Thomas B Gerlach Jr
Project Engineer, Bernardo Lomeli
Procurement Agent, Paul Dempsey
Superintendent, Austin Armstrong
Purchasing Agent, Jared Posvistak
Superintendent, Michael Depoortere
Project Engineer, Sam Padovano
Auditors: DELOITTE & TOUCHE LLP PRINCET

LOCATIONS

HQ: THE TURNER CORPORATION
375 HUDSON ST RM 700, NEW YORK, NY 100143667
Phone: 212 229-6000
Web: WWW.TURNERCONSTRUCTION.COM

PRODUCTS/OPERATIONS

Selected Related Companies

E. E. Cruz (infrastructure)
Flatiron Construction Corp. (transportation construction civil engineering)
Clark Builders (51% Canada)

Selected Markets Served

Aviation
Commercial
Cultural and entertainment
Data center
Education
Government
Green building
Health care
Infrastructure
Industrial
Interiors
Pharmaceutical
Public Assembly
Religious
Research and development
Residential/hotel
Sports

Selected Services

Building information modeling
Building maintenance
Construction management
Design-build
Design-build/finance
Facilities management
General construction
Lean construction
Logistics
Medical planning and procurement
Preconstruction consulting
Program management
Project management

COMPETITORS

Balfour Beatty Construction
Bechtel
Clark Construction Group
Fluor
Gilbane Building Company
Hunt Construction
Imperial Construction Group
Jacobs Engineering
Parsons Corporation
Peter Kiewit Sons'
Skanska
Structure Tone

HISTORICAL FINANCIALS

Company Type: Private

Income Statement FYE: December 31

	REVENUE ($ mil.)	NET INCOME ($ mil.)	NET PROFIT MARGIN	EMPLOYEES
12/15	10,523	107	1.0%	5,000
12/14	10,560	95	0.9%	—
12/13	9,522	80	0.8%	—
12/12	8,575	74	0.9%	—
Annual Growth	7.1%	12.9%	—	—

2015 Year-End Financials

Return on assets: 2.9%
Return on equity: 16.5%
Current ratio: 1.00
Cash ($ mil.): 880

THE UCLA FOUNDATION

Helping to make La-La Land a little more erudite The UCLA Foundation raises manages and disperses funds to help support the tripartite education research and service mission of UCLA. With more than $1 billion in assets the organization funds the aforementioned purposes as well as campus improvements and special programs. About half of the foundation's gifts received are provided by foundations; corporations and alumni each account for some 15% of gifts. The UCLA Progress Fund predecessor of the foundation was established in 1945 by the school's alumni association.

EXECUTIVES

Secretary To Ucla Fund, Wendy Lohman
Auditors: PRICEWATERHOUSECOOPERS LLP LO

LOCATIONS

HQ: THE UCLA FOUNDATION
10920 WILSHIRE BLVD # 200, LOS ANGELES, CA 900246502
Phone: 310 794-3193
Web: WWW.UCLAFOUNDATION.ORG

HISTORICAL FINANCIALS

Company Type: Private

Income Statement FYE: June 30

	ASSETS ($ mil.)	NET INCOME ($ mil.)	INCOME AS % OF ASSETS	EMPLOYEES
06/18	3,539	336	9.5%	317
06/17	3,050	346	11.4%	—
Annual Growth	16.0%	(3.1%)	—	—

2018 Year-End Financials

Return on assets: 9.5%
Return on equity: 10.7%
Sales ($ mil): 691

THE UNITED ILLUMINATING COMPANY

EXECUTIVES

Pres-Ceo, James P Torgerson
Chb*, Nathaniel D Woodson
Pres-Coo*, Anthony J Vallillo
V Pres-Finance-Cfo*, Richard Nicholas
Vp-Info Tech/CIO*, W Marie Zanavich
Vp-Controller*, Steven P Favuzza
Business Analyst, James Pellegrino
Commercial Collection Represen, Javier Velez
Recruiter, Katherine Autuori
Technical Manager, Kevin McCormick
Senior Administrative Clerk, Kimberly Sampiere

LOCATIONS

HQ: THE UNITED ILLUMINATING COMPANY
180 MARSH HILL RD, ORANGE, CT 064773629
Phone: 203 499-2000
Web: WWW.UINET.COM

HISTORICAL FINANCIALS

Company Type: Private

Income Statement FYE: December 31

	REVENUE ($ mil.)	NET INCOME ($ mil.)	NET PROFIT MARGIN	EMPLOYEES
12/17	921	105	11.4%	920
12/16*	866	84	9.7%	—
06/00	344	34	10.0%	—
Annual Growth	5.6%	6.4%	—	—

*Fiscal year change

THE UNIVERSITY OF CENTRAL FLORIDA BOARD OF TRUSTEES

The University of Central Florida (UCF whose mascot is a stylized knight) is part of the State University System of Florida. Boasting an enrollment of more than 69000 students UCF offers more than 220 degree programs through a dozen colleges. Areas of study include psychology health sciences biomedical sciences nursing computer science mechanical engineering biology integrated business finance and hospitality management. In addition to its main campus UCF operates more than a dozen locations throughout Central Florida.

Operations

The University offers about a hundred bachelor's 90 master's around 30 research doctorates three professional doctorates and three specialist degree programs. The university's research programs annually attract more than $192 million in funding.

In addition to more traditional areas of study the university also boasts the Florida Interactive Entertainment Academy where graduate students learn video-game development including art programming and production. The academy is funded jointly by the State of Florida and UCF.

Geographic Reach

UCF is located on a 1400-acre campus in Orlando. Through its main campus and its satellite locations UCF serves around a dozen of county service areas including Brevard Citrus Flagler Indian River Lake Levy Marion Orange Osceola Polk Seminole Sumter and Volusia. Its students hail from all 50 US states and nearly 150 international countries. The university also conducts study abroad programs in about 35 countries.

Strategy

UCF leverages innovative learning discovery and partnerships fostering social mobility while developing the skilled talent needed to advance industry for its region state and beyond.

The university partnered with Adobe in late 2020. UCF specifically is working with Adobe on a digital reading project that aims to reduce information overload. The project is part of Adobe's continuing efforts toward creating products that empower people to change the world such as its recent collaboration with a UCF-spin-off the non-profit Limbitless Solutions Inc.

UCF has also added a new physical therapy program solely focused on pain. The 12-week summer course debuted in 2019 and teaches students about the physical psychological and social aspects of pain management. The course helps students apply and understand the new overall wellness model of patient care. UCF also added a new hybrid-class format called BlendFlex. The new class strategy includes some face-to-face and online components and has been added to the lineup of fully online and face-to-face classes.

Company Background

The school was founded in 1963 as Florida Technological University and held its first classes five years later. UCF changed its name to the current moniker in 1978.

EXECUTIVES

President, John C. Hitt
Vp And Cfo, William F. Merck
Dean College Of Health And Public Affairs, Michael Frumkin
Dean Burnett Honors College, Alvin Wang
Dean Rosen School Of Hospitality Management, Abraham Pizam
Provost And Evp, A. Dale Whittaker
Dean College Of Undergraduate Studies, Elizabeth Dooley
Vp Information Technologies And Resources, Joel Hartman
Assistant Vp Strategic Communications And Marketing, Christine Dellert
Dean College Of Arts And Humanities, José Fern ˇndez
Dean College Of Medicine, Deborah German
Dean College Of Engineering And Computer Science, Michael Georgiopoulos
Dean College Of Education And Human Performance, Pameela (Sissi) Carroll
Dean College Of Graduate Studies, Mubarak Shah
Dean College Of Business Administration, Paul Jarley
Dean College Of Sciences, Michael Johnson
Dean College Of Optics And Photonics, Bahaa Saleh
Dean College Of Nursing, Mary Lou Sole
Assistant Vice President News And Information, Chad Binette
Vice Chairman, Robert A. (Bob) Garvy
Chairman, Marcos R. Marchena
Auditors: SHERRILL F NORMAN CPA TALLA

LOCATIONS

HQ: THE UNIVERSITY OF CENTRAL FLORIDA BOARD OF TRUSTEES
4000 CENTRAL FLORIDA BLVD, ORLANDO, FL 328168005
Phone: 407 823-2000
Web: WWW.UCF.EDU

PRODUCTS/OPERATIONS

Selected Colleges and Schools

Burnett Honors College
College of Arts and Humanities
College of Business Administration
College of Education
College of Engineering and Computer Science
College of Graduate Studies
College of Health and Public Affairs
College of Medicine
College of Nursing
College of Optics and Photonics
College of Sciences
Interdisciplinary Studies
Rosen College of Hospitality Management

HISTORICAL FINANCIALS

Company Type: Private

Income Statement — FYE: June 30

	REVENUE ($ mil.)	NET INCOME ($ mil.)	NET PROFIT MARGIN	EMPLOYEES
06/19	558	89	16.0%	6,500
06/08	374	108	28.9%	—
06/07	382	152	40.0%	—
06/06	311	61	19.6%	—
Annual Growth	4.6%	3.0%	—	—

2019 Year-End Financials

Return on assets: 4.1%
Return on equity: 7.5%
Current ratio: 4.20
Cash ($ mil.): 6

THE UNIVERSITY OF CHICAGO MEDICAL CENTER

It may have received its official dedication on Halloween but The University of Chicago Medical Center (UCMC) works hard to make visiting the hospital a little less spooky. UCMC is a complex of facilities located on The University of Chicago campus that include the acute care Mitchell Hospital-hyde park campus the Comer Children's Hospital a women's health and maternity facility and an outpatient care center. Established in 1927 (and dedicated on Halloween of that year) the complex includes the affiliated University of Chicago Pritzker School of Medicine and forms the clinical arm of The University of Chicago Division of Biological Sciences. UCMC houses about 810 beds.

Operations

Its Bernard A. Mitchell Hospital includes emergency level-one pediatric trauma services and regional burn and peri-natal units. The more than 170-bed Comer Children's Hospital offers disease care education and research as well as expanded newborn intensive care services.

UCMC sees some 33700 inpatients and more than 108000 emergency room visits per year. The hospital is one of the largest providers of uncompensated care in Illinois providing millions of dollars in charity care every year.

As part of the university's Biological Sciences division UCMC operates medical research centers focused on cancer immunology diabetes cardiology and neurology. The cancer center is especially intent on discovering improved treatment and prevention measures using gene and protein-based treatments. The Gwen and Jules Knapp Center for Biomedical Discovery works on discovery programs for a variety of medical conditions including diabetes cancer and pediatrics.

Geographic Reach

UCMC is located in Hyde Park on the south side of Chicago. Its main medical campus includes the Center for Care and Discovery Comer Children's Hospital Bernard A. Mitchell Hospital Chicago Lying-in Hospital and Duchossois Center for Advanced Medicine. UCMC also manages a network of area physicians and specialty clinics located in Chicago and its suburbs.

Its corporate headquarters is located in Chicago Illinois.

Company Background

The University of Chicago was founded in 1890 and expanded into medicine in 1898. Under then-University President William Rainey Harper the University of Chicago temporarily became affiliated with the Rush Medical College with "the distinct purpose" of establishing a medical school when funds became available according to Harper's Decennial address in 1902.

In 1916 the University of Chicago Board of Trustees set aside $5.3 million for construction equipment and an endowment for an expansion into health care. However World War I put a halt to the development. The project resumed in 1921 eventually reaching completion in 1927. By that time costs had skyrocketed to nearly five times the original estimate.

EXECUTIVES

President, Sharon O'Keefe
Evp Medical Affairs; Dean Division Of The Biological Sciences And Pritzker School Of Medicine, Kenneth S. Polonsky
Evp Corporate Strategy And Public Affairs, Susan S. Sher
Coo And Associate Dean, Carolyn S. Wilson
Cfo, James M. Watson
Vice President Managed Care And Program Development, Mayumi Fukui
Medical Director, Sanghyun Paik
Vice President Revenue Cycle, Charlie Brown
Vp And Cio, Heather Nelson
Vice President Operational Excellence, Greg Horner
Executive Vice President Business Development And Chief Strategy Officer, Audre Bagnall
Vice President, Stanley Gonner
Respiratory Therapy Director, Russel Hall
Vice Chairman, Craig J. Duchossois
Vice Chairman, James S. (Jim) Frank
Chairman, Emily Nicklin
Auditors: PRICEWATERHOUSECOOPERS LLP WA

LOCATIONS

HQ: THE UNIVERSITY OF CHICAGO MEDICAL CENTER
5841 S MARYLAND AVE, CHICAGO, IL 606371443
Phone: 773 702-1000
Web: WWW.UCHICAGOMEDICINE.ORG

PRODUCTS/OPERATIONS

Selected Services

Cancer
Endocrinology
Gastroenterology
Geriatrics
Heart

Kidney disease
Neurosciences
Orthopaedics
Respiratory disease
Surgery
Transplantation
Women's services

Selected Facilities

Bernard A. Mitchell Hospital
Center for Care and Discovery
Chicago Lying-in Hospital (Maternity and Women's Hospital)
Comer Children's Hospital
Duchossois Center for Advanced Medicine (outpatient care and diagnostics)
Gwen and Jules Knapp Center for Biomedical Discovery
LaRabida Children's Hospital (affiliated facility)
Mercy Hospital (affiliated facility)
University of Chicago Pritzker School of Medicine
Weiss Memorial Hospital (affiliated facility)

COMPETITORS

Advocate Health Care
Alexian Brothers Health System
Covenant Ministries
Elmhurst Memorial Healthcare
Loyola University Health System
Mercy Hospital and Medical Center
NorthShore University HealthSystem
Northwest Community Healthcare
Northwestern Memorial HealthCare
Rush System for Health
Silver Cross Hospital
Sinai Health System
St. Bernard Hospital and Health Care Center

HISTORICAL FINANCIALS

Company Type: Private

Income Statement — FYE: June 30

	REVENUE ($ mil.)	NET INCOME ($ mil.)	NET PROFIT MARGIN	EMPLOYEES
06/20	2,547	(53)	—	5,000
06/19	2,387	27	1.2%	—
06/18	2,212	49	2.2%	—
06/15	1,610	148	9.2%	—
Annual Growth	9.6%	—	—	—

2020 Year-End Financials

Return on assets: (-1.3%)
Return on equity: (-3.0%)
Current ratio: 1.30
Cash ($ mil.): 538

THE UNIVERSITY OF DAYTON

More than 11600 students make the University of Dayton one of the nation's largest Catholic universities and the largest private university in Ohio. The institution offers more than 80 undergraduate and 50 graduate and doctoral programs. Students are recruited on a national basis and from foreign countries. The student population more than 8300 undergraduate and more than 3000 graduate students. It has a student-to-faculty ratio of 14:1. Well-known alumni include the late author and columnist Erma Bombeck and Super Bowl-winning NFL coaches Jon Gruden and Chuck Noll.

Operations

The university academic units include College of Arts and Sciences School of Business Administration School of Education and Health Sciences School of Engineering and School of Law. Its program has included accounting aerospace engineering art history biochemistry biology chemistry communication economics finance and music.

Geographic Reach

The university is located in Dayton Ohio.

Strategy

Partnerships and Exchanges seeks builds and maintains relationships with institutions and organizations all over the world for the purpose of increasing direct global opportunities for UD faculty staff students and partners abroad. Partnerships and Exchanges support activities that include education abroad programs joint international research dual degree agreements faculty mobility to teach and achieve professional development and other special enrollment programs.

Company Background

The University of Dayton was founded in 1850 by the Society of Mary (the Marianists).

EXECUTIVES

Vice President, Thomas Burkhardt
Associate Provost And Cio, Thomas D. (Tom) Skill
Dean University Libraries, Kathleen M. Webb
President, Eric F. Spina
Dean College Of Arts And Science, Paul H. Benson
Dean School Of Business Administration, Paul M. Bobrowski
Dean School Of Education And Health Sciences, Kevin R. Kelly
Dean College Of Arts And Sciences, Jason Pierce
Dean School Of Law, Andrew L. Strauss
Dean School Of Engineering, Eddy Rojas
Vp Finance And Administrative Services, Andy Horner
Assistant Vice President Of Enrollment Management, Rob Durkle
Associate Vice President For Student Development And Dean Of Students, Christine Schramm
Vice President Enrollment Management Marketing, Jason Reinoehl
Chair Department Of Philosophy, John Inglis
Assistant Vice President And Treasurer, Phillip Chick
Assistant Vice President Of Athletics, Mike Kelly
Assistant Vice President, Robert Durkle
Vice President For Student Development, Bill Fischer
Vice President Finanace And Administration, Tom Burkhardt
Vice President For Diversity And Inclusion University Of Dayton, Lawrence Burnley
Vice President University Advancement, Jennifer Howe
Vice President For Finance And Administrative Services, Andrew Horner
Vice President Of Communication: Vice President Of Finance, Erin Clark
Associate Vice President For Financial Support Services, Thomas Madden
Vice President For Facilities Management And Planning, Rick Assoc
Vice President, Colin Wuebker
Vice President, Kayleigh Morris
Vice President, Andrea Knuth
Vice President, Wilbur Sharpe
Vice President, Brian Cabell
Vice President, Matthew Cambizaca
Vice President, Sarah Bonn
Vice President, Camron Greer
Vp Of Communications, Ryan Doyle
Vice President, Corey Reichel
Vice President, Kelly Stewart
Vice President, Sebastian Duban
Vice President, Hunter Hemminger
Vice President, Leanna Henry
Vice President, Parker Getz
Vice President, Jayson Breier
Vice President, Alec Trautman
Vice President, Meagan Lovin
Vice President, David Puzder
Vice President, Scott Elter
Vice President, Carly Evatz
Vice President, Sarah Olszewski
Vice President, Erik Chidester
Vice President, Robert Orourke
Chairman, Steven D. Cobb
Vice Chairman, Martin A. Solma
Director Board Of Directors, Robert Rosenfelder
Registration Secretary, Denise Quillen
Academic Secretary, Michael Duricy
Board Member, Sean Falkowski
Secretary, Bruce Craver
Academic Secretary, Kathy Winters
Secretary, Elizabeth Lopresti
Treasurer, Colleen Jutte
Secretary, Maya Smith-custer
Treasurer, Brendan Roberts
Treasurer, Joseph Gaccione
Secretary, Stephen Pressley
Treasurer, Megan Barga
Treasurer, Antonia Schafer
Secretary, Caitlin Fitzgerald
Secretary, Adriana Paonessa
Treasurer, Caroline Krumme
Treasurer, Megan Taschner
Secretary, Christopher Baldasare
Treasurer, Mark Lauterbach
Auditors: RSM US LLP DAYTON OHIO

LOCATIONS

HQ: THE UNIVERSITY OF DAYTON
300 COLLEGE PARK AVE, DAYTON, OH 454690002
Phone: 937 229-2919
Web: WWW.UDAYTON.EDU

HISTORICAL FINANCIALS

Company Type: Private

Income Statement — FYE: June 30

	REVENUE ($ mil.)	NET INCOME ($ mil.)	NET PROFIT MARGIN	EMPLOYEES
06/19	774	30	4.0%	4,500
06/16	521	(11)	—	—
Annual Growth	14.1%	—	—	—

2019 Year-End Financials

Return on assets: 1.8%
Return on equity: 2.5%
Current ratio: 0.40
Cash ($ mil.): 41

THE UNIVERSITY OF IOWA

The University of Iowa Hawkeyes see clearly from their perch as one of the state's largest university. Founded in 1847 the University of Iowa has some 31730 students (and a student-faculty ratio of about 16:1) at its Iowa City campus. It is home to a dozen colleges spanning more than 200 areas of study including distinguished programs in audiology physics and astronomy speech pathology nursing service administration and creative writing. Its Writers' Workshop was the nation's first creative writing advanced degree program. It also includes programs in law engineering teaching and medicine as well as the affiliated University of Iowa Hospitals and Clinics health care organization.

EXECUTIVES

President, J. Bruce Harreld, age 70

Svp And University Treasurer, Douglas K. True
Dean College Of Law, Gail B. Agrawal
Cio, Steve R. Fleagle
Dean Graduate College, John C. Keller
Dean College Of Dentistry, David C. Johnsen
Evp And Provost, P. Barry Butler
Dean College Of Public Health, Susan J. Curry
Dean College Of Liberal Arts And Sciences, Chaden Djalali
Dean Tippie College Of Business, Sarah Fisher Gardial
Dean College Of Engineering, Alec B. Scranton
Dean Carver College Of Medicine, Debra Schwinn
Dean College Of Nursing, Rita A. Frantz
Dean College Of Pharmacy, Donald E. Letendre
Dean University College, Beth F. Ingram
Vice President Of Community Service, Tony Maiers
Vice President Of Marketing And Public Relations, James Oconnor
Vice President For Student Life, Melissa Shivers
Associate Vice President Donor Relations, Erin Lewis
Assistant Vice President For Economic Development, David Conrad
Associate Vice President For Legal Affairs, Joseph Clamon
Vice President, Gina Guerrieri
Executive Vice President Gamma Iota Sigma, Patrick Ergastolo
Senior Business Intelligence Developer, Siva Krishna
Vice President, Conrad Hoover
Assistant Vice President, Diane Brownlee
President Board Of Regents, Bruce L. Rastetter, age 63
President Pro Tem Board Of Regents, Katie S. Mulholland
Secretary, Kathy Bell
Secretary Transplant, Catherine A Chapman
Secretary Ii, Laura Gusomano
Secretary Ii, Kimberly Broszeit
Secretary Iii To The Dental Registrar, Shannon Knipfer
Treasurer, Katherine Lu
Treasurer, Alton Croker
Auditors: MARLYS K GASTON CPA DES MOI

LOCATIONS

HQ: THE UNIVERSITY OF IOWA
5W JEFFRSON ST 101 JSSUP, IOWA CITY, IA 52242
Phone: 319 335-3500
Web: WWW.UIOWA.EDU

PRODUCTS/OPERATIONS

Selected Colleges
College of Dentistry
College of Education
College of Engineering
College of Law
College of Liberal Arts and Sciences
College of Nursing
College of Pharmacy
College of Public Health
Graduate College
Henry B. Tippie College of Business
Roy J. and Lucille A. Carver College of Medicine

HISTORICAL FINANCIALS

Company Type: Private

Income Statement — FYE: June 30

	REVENUE ($ mil.)	NET INCOME ($ mil.)	NET PROFIT MARGIN	EMPLOYEES
06/19	3,404	254	7.5%	17,000
06/16	2,859	253	8.9%	—
06/11	2,067	253	12.3%	—
06/08	1,684	150	8.9%	—
Annual Growth	6.6%	4.9%	—	—

2019 Year-End Financials

Return on assets: 3.5%
Return on equity: 5.5%
Current ratio: 1.00
Cash ($ mil.): 132

THE UNIVERSITY OF IOWA

EXECUTIVES

V Pres, Marty Scholtz
Assistant Professor, Adam Ward
Oral and Maxillofacial Surgeon, Emma Cole
Oral and Maxillofacial Surgeon, Grace Chabal
Scientist, Youhua Tang
Assistant Professor, Megan Gilster
Project Coordinator, Nick Benson
Executive Officer, Nitin Karandikar
Assistant Professor, Phuong Nguyen
Assistant Professor, Shea Brown
Assistant Professor, Hai Fu

LOCATIONS

HQ: THE UNIVERSITY OF IOWA
2660 UCC, IOWA CITY, IA 52242
Phone: 319 335-2119
Web: WWW.UIOWA.EDU

HISTORICAL FINANCIALS

Company Type: Private

Income Statement — FYE: June 30

	REVENUE ($ mil.)	NET INCOME ($ mil.)	NET PROFIT MARGIN	EMPLOYEES
06/18	3,176	588	18.5%	13
06/17	2,950	144	4.9%	—
Annual Growth	7.7%	308.5%	—	—

2018 Year-End Financials

Return on assets: 8.6%
Return on equity: 13.6%
Current ratio: 1.10
Cash ($ mil.): 145

THE UNIVERSITY OF KANSAS HOSPITAL AUTHORITY

EXECUTIVES

Ceo, Bob Page
Prin, Angela Cook
Pediatric Urologist, J Pat Murphy
Chief of Medicine, Bart McCann
Principal, Linsey Gregory
Internal Medicine Practitioner, Ahmad Tarakji
Neurology Specialist, Bhavana Patel
Internal Medicine Practitioner, Calvin Madrigal
Internal Medicine Practitioner, Donald Campbell Jr
Anesthesiologist, Nicholas Kaup
Anesthesiologist, Nicolas Patonai

LOCATIONS

HQ: THE UNIVERSITY OF KANSAS HOSPITAL AUTHORITY
4000 CAMBRIDGE ST, KANSAS CITY, KS 661608501
Phone: 913 588-5000
Web: WWW.KUMC.EDU

HISTORICAL FINANCIALS

Company Type: Private

Income Statement — FYE: June 30

	REVENUE ($ mil.)	NET INCOME ($ mil.)	NET PROFIT MARGIN	EMPLOYEES
06/15	1,362	156	11.5%	40
06/02	321	6	2.0%	—
Annual Growth	11.8%	28.1%	—	—

2015 Year-End Financials

Return on assets: 9.4%
Return on equity: 17.3%
Current ratio: 2.00
Cash ($ mil.): 140

THE UNIVERSITY OF NORTH CAROLINA

Tar heels can sink their feet into academia and athletics at The University of North Carolina. The system of 17 universities including the flagship University of North Carolina at Chapel Hill campus counts more than 220000 undergraduate and graduate students across its campuses. It offers degrees in more than 200 disciplines. The university system chartered in 1789 is home to medical schools a teaching hospital law schools a veterinary school at NC State a school of pharmacy nursing programs schools of education schools of engineering and a school for the arts. In addition the system also operates the NC School of Science and Mathematics a public residential high school for gifted students.

Operations

The university system comprises 17 public institutions that grant baccalaureate degrees. It also operates a public residential high school for gifted students under the name NC School of Science and Mathematics.

Each year the university graduates more than 30000 students.

Geographic Reach

The University of North Carolina system serves students worldwide. Of its enrollment the system attracts far more in-state students than out-of-state students.

Financial Performance

Revenue for fiscal 2014 was $1.9 billion.

Strategy

To extend its reach The University of North Carolina partners with half a dozen affiliates. They include UNC Center for Public Television The North Carolina Arboretum The North Carolina State Approving Agency The North Carolina Center for International Understanding The North Carolina State Education Assistance Authority and The University of North Carolina Press.

In 2013 the system adopted a five-year strategic plan entitled "Our Time Our Future." The plan's goals were designed to set priorities allocate resources plan programs and refine academic missions.

EXECUTIVES

Assistant Vice President Campus Safety And Emergency Operations, Brent Herron
Assistant Vice President, Tracey Ford
Vice President Of State Government Relations, Drew Moretz
Medical Director, Melissa Miller
Vice President, Bobbi Owen
Associate Vice President For Legal Affairs, Thomas Shanahan
Senior Vice President External Affairs, Kevin Howell
Vice President, Timothy A Minor
Senior Associate Vice President For Leadership And Talent Development, Lynn Duffy
Associate Vice President For Legal Affairs, Brooks Skinner
Vice President Government Relations, Elizabeth Morra
Assistant Vice President Of Development And Gift Planning, Stephen Watt
Senior Vice President Finance, Mark Miller
Senior Vice President Of Operations, Janet Hadar
Medical Director, Thomas Shea
Vice President, Sarah Morrison
Treasurer, Gail Mazzocco
Board Member, Channing Der
Vice Chair, Tim Ives

LOCATIONS

HQ: THE UNIVERSITY OF NORTH CAROLINA
910 RALEIGH RD, CHAPEL HILL, NC 275143916
Phone: 919 962-2211
Web: WWW.NORTHCAROLINA.EDU

PRODUCTS/OPERATIONS

Selected Institutions

Appalachian State University
East Carolina University
Elizabeth City State University
Fayetteville State University
NC A&T State University
North Carolina Central University
NC State University
UNC Asheville
UNC Chapel Hill
UNC Charlotte
UNC Greensboro
UNC Pembroke
UNC Wilmington
UNC School of the Arts
Western Carolina University
Winston-Salem State University
NC School of Science and Mathematics

HISTORICAL FINANCIALS

Company Type: Private

Income Statement — FYE: June 30

	REVENUE ($ mil.)	NET INCOME ($ mil.)	NET PROFIT MARGIN	EMPLOYEES
06/13	1,838	267	14.6%	55,000
06/12	0	(0)	—	—
06/06	30	(9)	—	—
Annual Growth	79.3%	—	—	—

2013 Year-End Financials

Return on assets: 3.3%
Return on equity: 5.9%
Current ratio: 5.00
Cash ($ mil.): 520

THE UNIVERSITY OF TEXAS HEALTH SCIENCE CENTER AT SAN ANTONIO

EXECUTIVES

Pres*, William L Henrich
Exec V Pres*, Steven A Wartman
Sr V Pres*, Michael E Black
Prin*, Mary G Delay
Endocrinology, Chris Mc Daniel
Thoracic Surgeon, Sreenath V Reddy
Assistant Professor, Jason Morrow
Project Coordinator, Sharon Bressette
Assistant Professor, Beth Thai
Assistant Professor, Sandeep Patel
Assistant Professor, Cristina Boccalandro

LOCATIONS

HQ: THE UNIVERSITY OF TEXAS HEALTH SCIENCE CENTER AT SAN ANTONIO
7703 FLOYD CURL DR, SAN ANTONIO, TX 782293901
Phone: 210 567-7000
Web: WWW.UTHSCSA.EDU

HISTORICAL FINANCIALS

Company Type: Private

Income Statement — FYE: August 31

	REVENUE ($ mil.)	NET INCOME ($ mil.)	NET PROFIT MARGIN	EMPLOYEES
08/11	767	62	8.2%	6,000
08/05	289	56	19.6%	—
08/04	289	56	19.6%	—
Annual Growth	15.0%	1.5%	—	—

2011 Year-End Financials

Return on assets: 4.3%
Return on equity: 4.9%
Current ratio: 1.60
Cash ($ mil.): 99

THE UNIVERSITY OF TOLEDO

One of Ohio's 14 state universities The University of Toledo (UT) is the third-largest by operating budget. It enrolls more than 20200 students and offers more than 270 programs of study including master's degree and doctoral programs. The university has a student-to-faculty ratio of 19:1. Its about 15 colleges focus on subjects ranging from visual and performing arts to business and innovation as well as education engineering law medicine nursing pharmacy languages and chemistry. The school also operates the University of Toledo Medical Center.

Operations

The University of Toledo Medical Center affiliated with UT provides advanced care and healing in a patient-centered environment. It has access to the latest clinical trials and medical research and committed to teaching the next generation of health-care professionals.

The UT Medical Center features a Level I trauma center and extensive medical training programs on UT's Health Science Campus. It provides treatments for strokes and cancer that are unique within the state. Other specialties include kidney transplants and cardiology.

Geographic Reach

UT students come from more than 40 US states and about 85 international countries. The school has an extensive distance learning program. In addition to the main campus in Toledo UT operates several satellite centers in Toledo (including the Health Science Campus the Scott Park Campus and the Center for the Visual Arts facility) and the Lake Erie Research and Education Center in Oregon Ohio.

Strategy

UT continues to work on its five-year strategic plan that ends in 2022 which includes promoting student success and academic excellence; improving research scholarship and creative activities; taking care of faculty staff and alumni; and improving the university's fiscal positioning and infrastructure among others.

Company Background

UT and the Medical University of Ohio merged in 2006. UT is accredited by the Higher Learning Commission of the North Central Association of Colleges and Schools.

UT was established in 1872 and became a member of the state university system in 1967.

EXECUTIVES

Interim Svp Finance And Administration, Lawrence (Larry) Kelley
Interim Dean Scott Honors College, Kelly Moore
Dean College Of Pharmacy And Pharmaceutical Sciences, Johnnie L. Early
President, Sharon L. Gaber
Dean College Of Engineering, Nagi Naganathan
Evp; Ceo Ut Medical Center, David R. Morlock
Interim Provost And Evp Academic Affairs, John A. Barrett
Evp; Dean College Of Medicine And Life Sciences, Christopher J. Cooper
Vice Provost; Executive Dean College Of Applied Science And Technology, Todd A. Rickel
Dean College Of Health Sciences, Christopher D. Ingersoll
Dean College Of Languages Literature And Social Sciences, Jamie Barlowe
Dean College Of Natural Sciences And Mathematics, Karen S. Bjorkman
Dean College Of Communication And The Arts, Debra A. Davis
Interim Dean College Of Social Justice And Human Service, Thomas G. (Tom) Gutteridge
Dean College Of Business And Innovation, Gary S. Insch
Dean College Of Graduate Studies, Patricia R. Komuniecki
Dean College Of Adult And Lifelong Learning, Dennis S. Lettman
Vp Cio And Cto, William McCreary
Interim Dean Herb College Of Education, Virginia Keil
Dean College Of Law, D. Benjamin Barros
Interim Dean College Of Nursing, Kelly Phillips
Interim Dean Youcollege, Julie Fischer-Kinney
Associate Vice President For Finance, Bryan Dadey
Executive Vice President, David Morlock
Nursing Director, Andrew Fox
Administrative Support Analyst To The Vice President And Chief Information Officer Of Information Technology, Lisa Gaynor
Vice President, Brenda Grant
Associate Vice President, Jovita Williams
Vice President, Sakui Malakpa
Vice President Student Affairs, David Meabon

Interim Vice President For Student Affairs, Phillip Cockrell
Interim Vice President For Enrollment Management, Stephanie Sanders
Associate Vice President For Development, Barbara Tartaglia Poure
Assistant Vice President, Shanda Gore
Vice President Student Body, Cameron Forsythe
Associate Vice President, Stephen Schissler
Student Vice President, Edvin Rosic
Chairman, Sharon S. Speyer
Vice Chairman, Steven M. Cavanaugh
Secretary, Susan Rouppas
Secretary Ii, Patricia Baldwin
Secretary, Elaine Coopshaw
Ward Secretary, Pamela Thayer
Ward Secretary, Wendy Frick
Secretary 2 Radiation Safety, Deborah Frye
Secretary 1 Neurology, Mildred Wegener
Secretary 2 Medicine, Michelle McKenzie
Secretary 2 Medicine, Lisa Johnston
Secretary 1 College Of Nursing, Roni Hoskins
Board Member, Matthew Miller
Secretary Communication, Patricia Damschroder
Secretary, Nora Longsworth
Secretary 2 5ab Medical Surgery, Maura Luettke
Secretary, Gregory Gilchrist
Secretary 1 Pediatrics, Michele Agocs
Secretary, Traci Mcdaniel
Secretary, Amada Esquivel
Secretary 2 Psychiatry, Jacquelyn Mcbee
Secretary I, Tamara Golkiewicz
Secretary 1 College Of Nursing, Margaret Desmond
Department Secretary, Bonnie Edmonds
Secretary, Kayla Wiemers
Secretary Ii, Laurie Flowers
Secretary, Tana Felkey
Ward Secretary, James Zeller
Secretary 2, Connie Butler
Secretary 1, Lilla Horton
Secretary, Laura Leady
Secretary, Lauri Vanwormer
Department Secretary, Lisa Edwards
Auditors: CLIFTONLARSONALLEN LLP TOLEDO

LOCATIONS

HQ: THE UNIVERSITY OF TOLEDO
2801 W BANCROFT ST, TOLEDO, OH 436063390
Phone: 419 530-4636
Web: WWW.UTOLEDO.EDU

HISTORICAL FINANCIALS

Company Type: Private

Income Statement — FYE: June 30

	REVENUE ($ mil.)	NET INCOME ($ mil.)	NET PROFIT MARGIN	EMPLOYEES
06/18	716	55	7.8%	7,000
06/17	728	(62)	—	—
Annual Growth	(1.6%)	—	—	—

2018 Year-End Financials

Return on assets: 4.7%
Return on equity: 176.9%
Current ratio: 1.20
Cash ($ mil.): 40

THE UNIVERSITY OF UTAH

The University of Utah (U of U) has offered instruction since long before the Beehive State was a state. Founded in 1850 as the University of Deseret the "U of U" has a total enrollment of more than 33000 undergraduate and graduate students with a student-to-faculty ratio of some 17:1. It offers over 100 major subjects at the undergraduate and graduate level at more than 15 colleges and schools; its business science humanities and engineering departments are the university's largest. It also offers medical nursing and pharmacy programs as well as health and social science research programs. U of U confers nearly 8950 baccalaureate masters and doctoral degrees annually.

Operations

The university includes an academic health system University Health Care (UHC) which includes the U of U School of Medicine and the University of Utah Hospitals & Clinics. The University of Utah School of Medicine combines teaching research and clinical expertise to train future physicians for the rapidly changing world of medicine. With a faculty of more than 1000 physicians and researchers and more than 20 clinical and basic science departments the School of Medicine trains the majority of Utah physicians trough MD degrees physician assistant training residencies fellowship specialty training degrees in public health degrees in medical laboratory science and science and research. U of U also includes institutes that conduct research programs in a variety of fields — including health math fine arts and engineering — as well as technology commercialization projects.

Approximately half of total sales generated from patient services about a quarter for sales and services and the remainder sales came from grants contracts and auxiliary and tuition and fees.

Geographic Reach

The 1500 acre campus is located along the foothills of the Wasatch Mountains the westernmost branch of the Rockies overlooking Salt Lake City. U of U's international students hail from more than 130 countries which some are from Latin American Bosnian Pacific Islander and Sri Lankan communities.

Financial Performance

The company's revenue has been rising in the last five years with an overall growth of 35% between 2016 and 2020.

Revenue increased 5% from $4.8 billion in 2019 to $5.1 billion in 2019. All of the company's segments had a hand in this increase.

Cash for the year ended 2020 was $1.7 billion. Operating activities generated $29.3 million. Investing and financing activities generated $570.5 million and $758.2 million respectively.

EXECUTIVES

Associate Vice President, Joan Gines
President, David W. Pershing
Svp Health Sciences And Dean School Of Medicine And Ceo University Health Care, Vivian S. Lee
Svp Academic Affairs, Ruth V. Watkins
Cio, Steve Hess
Senior Chief Administrative Officer And Cfo, John E. Nixon
Vice President Government And Regulatory Affairs, Laura Nelson
Vice President Student Affairs, Barbara Snyder
Vice President Human Resources, Wayne Imbrescia
Assistant Vice President, Jennifer W Molock
Vice President Of Information Security, David Glod
Bs Pharmd, David Stenehjem
Vice President, David Warren
Assistant Vice President Student Development, Kari Ellingson
Technology Corporate Ambassador Office Of Vp For Resear, Andrew Buffmire
Ustar Professor And Department Chair, Gianluca Lazzi
Vice President, Kay Harward
Interim Associate Vice President For Equity And Diversity, Kathryn Stockton
Assistant Vice President, Gordon Wilson
Department Chair Humanities College Of Dean, Fernando Rubio
Department Chair Humanities College Of Dean, Ed Rubin
Panhellenic Vice President Of Judicial And Risk Reduction, Ginny Mitchell
Membership Vice President, Wendy Warner
Associate Vice President Of Academic Affairs, Martha Bradley
Pharmacy Manager, Jay Lewandowski
Medical Director, Feras Bader
Vice President, Scammon Debra
Chief Sales Officer, Matt Gregory
Pharmd, Patricia Jeppson
Medical Director Molecular Oncology, Larissa Furtado
Office Assistant For Vp Of Institutional Advancement, James Gessel
Svp Of Academic Affairs, Dan Reed
Associate Vice President Academic Administration, Cypers Breanna
Pharmacy Manager Inpatient Operations, Russell Findlay
Vice President, William Couldwell
Medical Director, Kirsten Lee Stoesser
Pharmacy Manager, Jerel Bullock
Vice President Uhsc Services, Kathleen Carlson
Vice President Emerging Channels, Thomas Mitchell
Chair, Michele Mattsson
Vice Chair, Phillip W. Clinger
Treasurer, Johanna Watzinter
Secretary, Jeremy Freed
Board Member, James Rogers
Medical Secretary, Tracey Mcgee
Clinical Secretary, Mary Looser
Medical Secretary, Ashley Adams
Secretary, Ivie Blussette Sofia
Medical Secretary, Christian Seiter
Medical Secretary, Chani Brown
Medical Secretary, Jonci Robey
Secretary, Roche Mike
Advisory Board Member, Jessica Anderson
Secretary, Janet Cummings
Medical Secretary, Felicia Barney
Medical Secretary, Amy Short
Medical Secretary, Rinda Hardy
Auditors: OFFICE OF THE UTAH STATE AUDIT

LOCATIONS

HQ: THE UNIVERSITY OF UTAH
201 PRESIDENTS CIR, SALT LAKE CITY, UT 841129049
Phone: 801 581-7200
Web: WWW.UTAH.EDU

PRODUCTS/OPERATIONS

2015 Sales

	$ mil.	% of total
Patient services net	1,816	53
Sales and services	740	21
Grants and contracts	362	10
Tuition and fees net	304	9
Auxiliary and other	237	7
Total	**3,460**	**100**

Selected Colleges

College of Architecture and Planning
College of Education
College of Engineering
College of Fine Arts
College of Health
College of Humanities
College of Law
College of Mines and Earth Sciences
College of Nursing
College of Pharmacy
College of Science

College of Social and Behavioral Sciences
College of Social Work
David Eccles School of Business
Graduate School
Honors College
School of Medicine

HISTORICAL FINANCIALS

Company Type: Private

Income Statement				FYE: June 30
	REVENUE ($ mil.)	NET INCOME ($ mil.)	NET PROFIT MARGIN	EMPLOYEES
06/13*	2,907	186	6.4%	18,000
12/08	0	0	—	—
06/08	22	(10)	—	—
Annual Growth	164.4%	—	—	—

*Fiscal year change

2013 Year-End Financials

Return on assets: 3.7%
Return on equity: 4.8%
Current ratio: 3.60
Cash ($ mil.): 486

THE UNIVERSITY OF VERMONT HEALTH NETWORK INC

EXECUTIVES

Ceo, John Brumsted
Coordinator, Linnea Oosterman
Staff, Lynz Parker
Coordinator, Mercy Gingras
Director Human Resources Total, Thomas Kess
Director of Accreditation, Carol Muzzy
Supervisor, Brian Douglas
Information Analyst, Katelyn Muir
Director of Supply Chain Servi, Ken Jensen
Local Network Administrator, Dale Devino
or Staff Rn Cnor, Eamon Mahoney
Auditors: PRICEWATERHOUSECOOPERS LLP BO

LOCATIONS

HQ: THE UNIVERSITY OF VERMONT HEALTH NETWORK INC
462 SHELBURNE RD, BURLINGTON, VT 054016947
Phone: 844 886-4325
Web: WWW.UVMHEALTH.ORG

HISTORICAL FINANCIALS

Company Type: Private

Income Statement				FYE: September 30
	REVENUE ($ mil.)	NET INCOME ($ mil.)	NET PROFIT MARGIN	EMPLOYEES
09/18	2,169	129	6.0%	1,300
09/17	1,933	161	8.4%	—
09/16	1,748	92	5.3%	—
Annual Growth	11.4%	18.3%	—	—

2018 Year-End Financials

Return on assets: 5.5%
Return on equity: 10.0%
Current ratio: 2.20
Cash ($ mil.): 246

THE UNIVERSITY OF VERMONT MEDICAL CENTER INC

The University Of Vermont Medical Center (formerly Fletcher Allen Health Care) provides medical care in the Green Mountain State. The company operates an academic medical center in alliance with the University of Vermont. The not-for-profit health system serves residents of Vermont and northern New York through three primary hospital campuses and more than 130 outpatient clinics patient care sites and outreach programs. Its acute care medical centers have a combined 560-bed capacity and a medical staff of some 800 health care providers representing medical specializations including emergency/trauma care pediatrics and women's health. The health care system is a subsidiary of Fletcher Allen Partners.

Operations

The health system receives some 60000 emergency visits each year and its hospitals handle more than 50000 inpatient and outpatient visits per year as well as 2000 births.

Working with the University of Vermont's College of Medicine and College of Nursing and Health Sciences The University Of Vermont Medical Center helps connect bedside experience with medical research to improve overall quality of care. It also provides hands-on educational services for medical and nursing students as well as professionals undergoing specialty training.

Geographic Reach

The University Of Vermont Medical Center serves 160000 people who live in Vermont's Chittenden and Grand Isle counties.

Financial Performance

The company's revenues accounted for 68% of Fletcher Allen Partners' total revenues in 2014.

Strategy

In order to provide a cohesive health network in the region the health system is working to create an integrated care network in its service territory. It is also working to build out its IT and data management capabilities

The University of Vermont Medical Center also has affiliations with other area providers to increase referrals and cooperative care including Alice Hyde Medical Center Canton-Potsdam Hospital Moses Ludington Hospital Central Vermont Medical Center Champlain Valley Physicians Hospital and the Elizabethtown Community Hospital. It seeks to form new partnerships with additional facilities.

In 2015 the company changed its name from Fletcher Allen Health Care to The University of Vermont Medical Center as part of a branding strategy approved by the Fletcher Allen Partners and University of Vermont boards.

Company Background

The hospital system was created through the 1995 merger of the Fanny Allen Hospital (which opened in 1894) the Medical Center Hospital of Vermont (or Mary Fletcher Hospital founded in 1876) and the University Health Center (formed in 1971). The hospitals are now known as Fanny Allen Campus Medical Center Campus and UHC Campus.

Fletcher Allen Health Care completed the implementation of an electronic health records (EHR) system that connects patient records at all of its facilities in 2010.

EXECUTIVES

Medical Director, Terry Rabinowitz
Svp And Cio, Charles (Chuck) Podesta
President And Ceo, John R. Brumsted
Svp And Cfo, Roger Deshaies
President And Ceo University Of Vermont Medical Group, Paul Taheri
Vp Marketing And Communications, Teresa Murphy
Svp Coo And Chief Nursing Officer, Sandra L. Felis
Chief Medical Officer, Stephen Leffler
Interim President Uvm Medical Group Fletcher Allen, Howard Schapiro
Chief Medical Information Officer, Adam P. Buckley
Ceo Inter-lakes Health, Chip Holmes
Assistant Vice President Support Services And Radiation Oncology, Brian Irwin
Medical Director, Kennith Sartorelli
Director Of Pharmacy, William Rogers
Medical Director, Janusz Kikut
Medical Director, Karen Leonard
Vice President Hospital Services, Dawn Lebaron
Director Of Radiology, Paula Gonyea
Pharmacy Manager, Lisa Jackman
Network Senior Vice President External Relations, Theresa Alberghini Dipalma
Radiology Director, Jennifer Gagnon
Chairman, John Powell
Vice Chair, Mark Fung
Unit Secretary, Shirley Beecher
Unit Secretary, Carla Levesque
Secretary, Micheline Lafontaine
Unit Secretary, Melissa Brooks
Auditors: PRICEWATERHOUSECOOPERS LLP BO

LOCATIONS

HQ: THE UNIVERSITY OF VERMONT MEDICAL CENTER INC
111 COLCHESTER AVE, BURLINGTON, VT 054011473
Phone: 802 847-0000
Web: WWW.UVMHEALTH.ORG

PRODUCTS/OPERATIONS

Selected Services

Cancer Care
Heart & Vascular
Orthopedics
Primary Care
Urgent Care
Women's Health

COMPETITORS

Albany Medical Center
Ellis Hospital
New England Alliance for Health
NewYork-Presbyterian Healthcare
Northwell Health
Rutland Regional Medical Center
Southwestern Vermont Health Care
Springfield Hospital
St. Peter's Health Partners

HISTORICAL FINANCIALS

Company Type: Private

Income Statement				FYE: September 30
	REVENUE ($ mil.)	NET INCOME ($ mil.)	NET PROFIT MARGIN	EMPLOYEES
09/18	1,363	68	5.1%	7,000
09/17	1,246	129	10.4%	—
09/16	1,181	85	7.2%	—
Annual Growth	7.4%	(10.0%)	—	—

2018 Year-End Financials

Return on assets: 4.1%
Return on equity: 7.1%
Current ratio: 2.00
Cash ($ mil.): 144

THE UNIVERSITY OF VIRGINIA

EXECUTIVES

Pres, Lindsay H Kidd
Cardiologist, Michael Ragosta
Associate Professor, Ulrike Lorenz
Assistant Professor, Brian Pusser
Director, David Bearinger
Senior Human Resources, Donna Kauffman
Doctor, Robert A Sinkin
Associate Professor, Emad Abdelrahman
Assistant Professor, Sara Dexter
Professor, Zhenqi Liu
Doctor, Brian W Behm

LOCATIONS

HQ: THE UNIVERSITY OF VIRGINIA
1215 LEE ST, CHARLOTTESVILLE, VA 229080816
Phone: 434 924-0000
Web: WWW.VIRGINIA.EDU

HISTORICAL FINANCIALS

Company Type: Private

Income Statement — FYE: June 30

	REVENUE ($ mil.)	NET INCOME ($ mil.)	NET PROFIT MARGIN	EMPLOYEES
06/19	2,915	350	12.0%	1
06/18	2,788	544	19.5%	—
Annual Growth	4.5%	(35.6%)	—	—

2019 Year-End Financials

Return on assets: 2.7%
Return on equity: 3.9%
Current ratio: 1.00
Cash ($ mil.): 149

THE VALLEY HOSPITAL INC

The Valley Hospital is second to none when it comes to its Same-Day Service program. More than one-third of the company's annual patients experience its longstanding continuum of one-day service; fully half the surgeries performed are same-day. The not-for-profit hospital is a 450-bed facility providing general and emergency services to residents of New Jersey's Bergen County. The hospital belongs to the Valley Health System which also includes subsidiaries Valley Home Care and Valley Health Medical Group and is an affiliate member of NewYork-Presbyterian Healthcare. The Valley Hospital New Jersey's second busiest has more than 800 physicians on its medical staff.

Operations

The Valley Hospital is well known for its cardiology cancer maternity and neonatal care programs (including its neonatal ICU). Its key services also include emergency care orthopedics and neurosciences. The hospital's emergency department treated more than 75000 patients in 2013. That year the hospital also admitted more than 49240 patients and the delivered almost 3200 babies.

The Valley Hospital's cardiac service includes a full range of diagnostic and interventional cardiac treatment services including cardiac surgery coronary angioplasty and electrophysiology studies. The hospital is also known for its work in lung cancer diagnosis and treatment radiation oncology (including tomotherapy) chemotherapy and infusion GYN oncology prostate cancer care and other clinical and support services.

Geographic Reach

The hospital serves more than 440000 people in 32 towns in Bergen County and surrounding communities.

Strategy

The medical system is looking to improve its facilities and technology in order to keep up with demand. The Valley Hospital is the first and only hospital in northern New Jersey to offer brain and spinal surgery with a state-of-the-art O-arm® surgical imaging system purchased through a $1 million grant from The Bolger Foundation.

In 2012 The Valley Hospital Valley became the first hospital in northern New Jersey to offer the latest breast imaging technology – 3D breast tomosynthesis.

That year it also enhanced its capacity to perform minimally invasive surgery with the acquisition of the robotic da Vinci® Surgical System funded by a $1.6 million donation from The Bolger Foundation.

In 2012 the hospital opened a new Women's and Children's Resource Center to coordinate wide range of services for women and their families.

EXECUTIVES

Director Of Pharmacy, Ron Krych

LOCATIONS

HQ: THE VALLEY HOSPITAL INC
223 N VAN DIEN AVE, RIDGEWOOD, NJ 074502736
Phone: 201 447-8000
Web: WWW.VALLEYHEALTH.COM

PRODUCTS/OPERATIONS

Selected Services

Adoption Screening and Evaluation Program
Ambulatory Infusion Center
Anticoagulation Management Service
Autism Services
Auxiliary
Barrett's Esophagus Center
Bariatric Surgery
Bereavement Services
Biplane
Bladder Cancer Care
Breast Center
Cancer Care
Capsule Endoscopy
Cardiac MRI
Cardiac Rehabilitation
Cardiac Surgery
Cardiology
Center for Childbirth
Kireker Center for Child Development
Center for Metabolic and Weight Loss Surgery
Center for Family Education
Center for Women's Heart Health
Center for Youth Fitness
Clinical Trials Oncology
Clinical Trials Cardiology
Colonoscopy
Community Resources
Complementary Medicine
Concussion Management Program
Continence Services
Cosmetic Laser Treatment
Critical Care
Diabetes Support Services
Diagnostic Imaging
Doula Program
Emergency Services
Emergency Services Pediatric
Employee Recognition
Endoscopic Ultrasound
Epilepsy Monitoring Program Adult
Epilepsy Center Pediatric
ERCP
Esophagogastroduodenoscopy (EGD)
Extended Care

COMPETITORS

Bergen Regional Medical
Englewood Hospital and Medical Center
Hackensack Meridian Health
Hackensack University Medical Center
Jersey City Medical Center
Newton Medical Center
Raritan Bay Medical Center
Robert Wood Johnson University Hospital at Rahway

HISTORICAL FINANCIALS

Company Type: Private

Income Statement — FYE: December 31

	REVENUE ($ mil.)	NET INCOME ($ mil.)	NET PROFIT MARGIN	EMPLOYEES
12/18	695	128	18.4%	2,900
12/17	657	80	12.2%	—
12/16	638	73	11.6%	—
12/15	621	83	13.4%	—
Annual Growth	3.8%	15.4%	—	—

2018 Year-End Financials

Return on assets: 10.5%
Return on equity: 12.9%
Current ratio: 1.00
Cash ($ mil.): 2

THE VANDERBILT UNIVERSITY

The house that Cornelius built Vanderbilt University was founded in 1873 with a $1 million grant from industrialist Cornelius Vanderbilt. Since then the university's endowment has grown to $6.3 billion making the Nashville school a haven for its more than 12300 students and nearly 4360full-time faculty members. Boasting a 7:1 student-faculty ratio Vanderbilt offers undergraduate and graduate programs in areas such as education and human development divinity engineering and the arts and sciences. The university operates some 10 schools and colleges. Vanderbilt's Owen Graduate School of Management and its medical school regularly rank near the top in national surveys.

Operations

Top-ranked in both academics and financial aid Vanderbilt offers residential undergraduate experience with programs in the liberal arts and sciences engineering music education and human development. The university also is home to nationally and internationally recognize graduate schools of law education business medicine nursing and divinity and offers robust graduate-degree programs across a range of disciplines.

Vanderbilt is closely affiliated with the comprehensive Vanderbilt University Medical Center (VUMC) which manages more than 2 million patient visits yearly and collaborates closely with the university through education and research. Its home to an acute care hospital a children's hospital and several clinics as well as the university's medical school research facilities and nursing programs.

Geographic Reach

Its 340.7 acres campus is located a mile and a half southwest of downtown Nashville Tennessee and it has around 180 buildings. Vanderbilt Dyer Observatory located about nine miles from campus also is listed on the National Register of Historic Places.

Company Background

During its first 40 years of existence Vanderbilt was under the auspices of the Methodist Episcopal Church South. The Vanderbilt Board of Trust severed its ties with the church in 1914 after a dispute with the bishops over who would appoint university trustees.

EXECUTIVES

Chancellor, Nicholas S. Zeppos
Vice Chancellor Health Affairs And Dean School Of Medicine, Jeffrey R. Balser
Dean Of The Blair School Of Music, Mark Wait
Dean Peabody College, Camilla Benbow
Associate Provost And Dean Of Students, Mark Bandas
Dean Of The School Of Divinity, Emilie M. Townes
Vice Chancellor Finance And Cfo, Brett Sweet
Dean Of The Law School, Chris Guthrie
Vice Chancellor For Information Technology, John M. Lutz
Dean Of The School Of Engineering, Philippe Fauchet
Vice Chancellor General Counsel And Secretary, Audrey J. Anderson
Provost And Vice Chancellor For Academic Affairs, Susan Wente
Vice Chancellor For Administration, Eric Kopstain
Vice Provost For Enrollment And Dean Of Admissions, Douglas L. Christiansen
Interim Dean Of Libraries, Joseph D. Combs
Dean Of The Owen Graduate School Of Management, M. Eric Johnson
Dean Of The School Of Nursing, Linda Norman
Pediatric Medical Director Center Of Ems Excellence, Michele Walsh
Evp And Chief Development Officer, Zeena M Abdulahad
Department Chairperson Professor, John York
Vice President For Diversity And Inclusion Atandt, Belinda Grant-anderson
Senior Vice President Human Resources Global Operations Hewlett Packard Company, Mike Dallas
Department Chairperson Professor, Lisa Kachnic
Vice Chairman, Jackson W. Moore, age 71
Chairman, Mark F. Dalton, age 69
Vice Chairman, John Winkelried
Board Member, Gail Yount
Auditors: PRICEWATERHOUSECOOPERS LLP N

LOCATIONS

HQ: THE VANDERBILT UNIVERSITY
2301 VANDERBILT PL, NASHVILLE, TN 372350002
Phone: 615 322-7311
Web: WWW.VANDERBILT.EDU

PRODUCTS/OPERATIONS

Selected Schools and Colleges

Blair School of Music
College of Arts and Science
Divinity School
Graduate School
Law School
Owen Graduate School of Management
Peabody College of Education and Human Development
School of Engineering
School of Medicine
School of Nursing

HISTORICAL FINANCIALS

Company Type: Private

Income Statement — FYE: June 30

	REVENUE ($ mil.)	NET INCOME ($ mil.)	NET PROFIT MARGIN	EMPLOYEES
06/18	1,366	511	37.4%	21,000
06/17	1,311	374	28.6%	—
06/16	1,270	(569)	—	—
06/15	4,121	131	3.2%	—
Annual Growth	(30.8%)	57.3%	—	—

2018 Year-End Financials

Return on assets: 7.1%
Return on equity: 8.1%
Current ratio: —
Cash ($ mil.): 602

THE WALSH GROUP LTD

Operating through subsidiaries Walsh Construction Walsh Canada and Archer Western Contractors The Walsh Group provides design/build general contracting and construction services for industrial public and commercial projects. The family-owned company offers complete project management services from demolition and planning to general contracting and finance. The company is involved in the construction of highways water treatment facilities airports hotels convention centers correctional facilities and commercial industrial and residential buildings. Walsh operates out of roughly 20 offices in North America. The company was founded in 1898 by Matthew Myles Walsh.

Operations

Walsh Group offers seamlessly integrated services to plan finance build operate and maintain the full life-cycle of a project including preconstruction design-build public-private partnerships operations & maintenance logistics lean construction sustainability self-performance and building information modelling (BIM).

Geographic Reach

Walsh Group operates in about 20 regional offices across the United States and Canada each strategically located to support maximum quality and responsiveness to a growing customer base. Walsh Construction Archer Western and Walsh Canada headquarters are located in Chicago Illinois; Atlanta Georgia; and in Toronto Ontario respectively.

Strategy

Walsh Group opened new offices to support maximum responsiveness to the company's growing customer base. The new location reflects the company's commitment to the region's construction market and its talented workforce.

Company Background

The company was founded in the year 1898 by Matthew Myles Walsh. In 2012 Walsh Group acquired California-based R&L Brosamer which specializes in heavy highway and other transportation projects. R&L Brosamer often works on projects for Bay Area Rapid Transit California Department of Transportation and Los Angeles World Airports. The deal helped Walsh strengthen its presence in California and bordering states including Nevada and Arizona.

In 2011 Walsh was awarded its first overseas embassy project a $200 million contract to build the New American Embassy at Oslo Norway.

EXECUTIVES

Co-chairman And Ceo, Matthew M. (Matt) Walsh
President Building Division, Michael Whelan
President Heavy Civil Division, Don Gillis
Cfo, Tim Gerken
Vp Heavy/civil Division, Daniel Walsh
Vp Corporate Equipment, Michael Gibbons
Vp Building Division, Matthew Walsh
President Walsh Construction, Sean Walsh
Co-chairman, Daniel J. Walsh
Auditors: WOLF & COMPANY LLP OAKBROOK T

LOCATIONS

HQ: THE WALSH GROUP LTD
929 W ADAMS ST, CHICAGO, IL 606073021
Phone: 312 563-5400
Web: WWW.WALSHGROUP.COM

PRODUCTS/OPERATIONS

Projects

Airports
Athletic facilities
Bridges
Conference centers
Correctional facilities
Data centers
Educational facilities
Entertainment
Government
Health care
High rise residential
Highways and bridges
Hotels
Interiors
Laboratories
Parking garages
Renovations
Retail centers
Senior housing
Treatment plants
Warehouse and distribution

COMPETITORS

Bechtel
Black & Veatch
Brasfield & Gorrie
C. G. Schmidt
Flatiron Construction
Fluor
Granite Construction
Hunt Companies
Hunt Construction
Jacobs Engineering
James McHugh
Lane Construction
MWH Global
McCarthy Building
Peter Kiewit Sons'
Skanska
TIC Holdings
Turner Corporation
Vecellio & Grogan

HISTORICAL FINANCIALS

Company Type: Private

Income Statement — FYE: December 31

	REVENUE ($ mil.)	NET INCOME ($ mil.)	NET PROFIT MARGIN	EMPLOYEES
12/10	3,462	186	5.4%	5,000
12/09	3,316	191	5.8%	—
12/08	3,534	203	5.8%	—
Annual Growth	(1.0%)	(4.4%)	—	—

2010 Year-End Financials

Return on assets: 11.9%
Return on equity: 27.9%
Current ratio: 1.80
Cash ($ mil.): 656

THE WASHINGTON UNIVERSITY

Washington University also known as Washington University in St. Louis (WUSTL) is the gateway to higher education for more than 13000 students. Founded in 1853 the independent university offers 90 bachelor's master's and doctoral degrees and has about 3400 faculty members. It offers approximately 1500 courses in fields such as arts and sciences business design and visual arts engineering law medicine and social work. WUSTL which has multiple campuses in and near the city of St. Louis also offers associate degree and continuing education programs. The affiliated Washington University Medical Center is an acute-care hospital that also provides educational training and research services.

Operations

The Medical Campus conducts extensive collaborative studies between students faculty and hospital staff as well as external institutions. Areas of research include genome sequencing of cancer patients and children's developmental studies. The 2000-acre Tyson Research Center outside the city is a biological field station that conducts environmental studies and research activities including renewable energy and sustainability programs some of which is coordinated with outside groups.

The university has an 8:1 student-to-faculty ratio. Its libraries contain more than 3.6 million books journals and other print materials and have access to more than 65000 electronic journals and a half million e-books.

In the academic year ending spring 2015 annual undergraduate educational costs totaled $45700.

Geographic Reach

In addition to the main 170-acre Danforth Campus in St. Louis WUSTL's facilities include the nearby 165-acre Medical Campus (housing the School of Medicine and the hospital facilities). Other operations include three smaller satellite academic campuses and music research and art centers in the greater St. Louis area.

Financial Performance

In fiscal 2015 revenue increased 9% to $2.7 billion on higher tuition and fees endowment spending distribution gifts and patient services. However a decline in non-operating revenue such as investment returns led to a 71% drop in net income which fell to $270 million.

Cash flow from operations spiked 522% to $104 million as less cash was used in net gains on investments.

Strategy

WUSTL has made efforts to extend its collaborations with third parties which can help bring in academic and research funds. In addition the university has worked to attract more government research grants in recent years. It is also upgrading some classroom and student facilities as well as hiring more experienced teachers and medical staff members to maintain its tuition auxiliary enterprise (lodging and vending) health services and research income expectations.

EXECUTIVES

Executive Vice Chancellor Administration, Henry S. Webber
Executive Vice Chancellor Alumni And Development Programs, David T. Blasingame
Executive Vice Chancellor And General Counsel, Michael R. Cannon
Chancellor, Mark S. Wrighton, age 71
Vice Chancellor Finance And Cfo, Barbara A. Feiner
Executive Vice Chancellor Medical Affairs And Dean School Of Medicine, Larry J. Shapiro
Dean Olin Business School, Mahendra R. Gupta
Dean Sam Fox School Of Design And Visual Arts, Carmon Colangelo
Dean George Warren Brown School Of Social Work, Edward F. Lawlor
Dean School Of Law, Kent D. Syverud
Provost And Executive Vice Chancellor Academic Affairs, H. Holden Thorp, age 56
Dean School Of Engineering And Applied Science, Ralph S. Quatrano
Dean Faculty Of Arts And Sciences, Barbara A. Schaal
Dean College Of Arts And Sciences, Jennifer R. Smith
Dean Graduate School Of Arts And Sciences, Richard J. Smith
Cio, Michael P. (Mike) Caputo
Head Nurse, Stacy Pokorny
Vice Chairman, John F. McDonnell, age 81
Vice Chairman, David W. Kemper, age 69
Vice Chairman, Craig D. Schnuck, age 71
Chairman, Stephen F. Brauer, age 75
Secretary, Judith Stockstad
Secretary Receptionist, Carol Kimball
Treasurer, Elizabeth Bohn
Secretary, Melissia Varner
Treasurer, Leanna Jackson
Auditors: PRICEWATERHOUSECOOPERS LLP L

LOCATIONS

HQ: THE WASHINGTON UNIVERSITY
1 BROOKINGS DR, SAINT LOUIS, MO 631304899
Phone: 314 935-8566
Web: WWW.WUSTL.EDU

PRODUCTS/OPERATIONS

2015 Sales

	$ mil.	% of total
Patient service	985	36
Grants	368	14
Tuition & fees	356	13
Endowment spending distribution	266	10
Gifts	186	7
Educational	162	6
Others	382	14
Total	**2,707**	**100**

Selected Schools and Colleges

College of Arts & Sciences
  Graduate School of Arts & Sciences
  University College and Summer School (Arts & Sciences)
George Warren Brown School of Social Work
Sam Fox School of Design & Visual Arts
School of Engineering & Applied Science
School of Law
School of Medicine
Olin Business School

COMPETITORS

Bucknell University
Missouri State University
Saint Louis University
Southeast Missouri State University
University of Missouri

HISTORICAL FINANCIALS

Company Type: Private

Income Statement — FYE: June 30

	REVENUE ($ mil.)	NET INCOME ($ mil.)	NET PROFIT MARGIN	EMPLOYEES
06/20	3,749	719	19.2%	9,600
06/19	3,544	554	15.7%	—
06/18	3,543	1,011	28.6%	—
06/17	3,068	737	24.0%	—
Annual Growth	6.9%	(0.8%)	—	—

2020 Year-End Financials

Return on assets: 4.8%
Return on equity: 6.1%
Current ratio: —
Cash ($ mil.): 316

THE WHITING-TURNER CONTRACTING COMPANY

Whiting-Turner Contracting provides construction management general contracting and design/build services primarily for large commercial institutional and infrastructure projects conducted across the US. A key player in retail construction the employee-owned company also undertakes such projects as biotech cleanrooms theme parks historical restorations senior living residences educational facilities stadiums and corporate headquarters. Clients past and present include the US military AT&T General Motors and Texas A&M University. Whiting-Turner Contracting operates from more than 30 offices across the US.

Geographic Reach

The Baltimore-based company has offices in Arizona California Colorado Connecticut Delaware Florida Georgia Maryland Massachusetts Missouri Nevada New Jersey New York North Carolina Ohio Pennsylvania Texas Virginia and Washington DC.

Sales and Marketing

The contractor works on projects across a wide range of industries related to arts and entertainment education federal and military healthcare industrial office retail multi-family residential sports and fitness transportation and utilities among other fields.

Strategy

Whiting-Turner prefers to grow organically instead of making acquisitions. It has been steadily expanding by opening new offices in places such as California Texas and Virginia. The company in 2016 continued to rank among the Engineering News Record (ENR) top domestic general building contractors in the nation.

Some of the firm's recently awarded projects (as of mid-2016) include the Tropicana Pedestrian Bridge the Jacksonville Lung Bio Facility the Westowne Elementary School the Lexington Market the Costco Meat Production Plant the Sentara Norfolk General Hospital and the CoolSprings Galleria among others.

Whiting-Turner Contracting's past projects include the Joseph B. Whitehead Building at Emory University Vanderbilt Hall at Yale University projects at Universal Studios theme park and a vaccine facility at Chesapeake Biological Laboratories. Projects in the firm's hometown of Baltimore have included the city's convention center and the football stadium for the Baltimore Ravens. More recent projects include the Horseshoe Casino Cleveland University of Maryland Baltimore County (UMBC) Performing Arts & Humanities Naval Facilities Engineering Command (NAVFAC) Jacksonville Sentara Princess Anne Hospital Norwalk Community College Texas A&M University at Galveston Mary Moody Northen Student Center renovation Opry Mills the College of Business & Economics Vinson Hall Parking Garage a Coastal Studies Institute facility a Blue Diamond Growers building and a USPS Call Center.

Company Background

G.W.C. Whiting and LeBaron Turner classmates at MIT founded the company in 1909 to build sewer lines.

EXECUTIVES

Vp Richmond, Dani Niccolucci
Svp Allentown, Jack DaSilva
Division Vp Fort Lauderdale, Robert (Rob) Mitchell
Division Vp Delaware And Maryland, James (Jim) Martini
Svp District Of Columbia, Richard L. Vogel
Division Vp Pleasanton, Troy Caldwell
Svp Irvine, Len Cannatelli
Svp Baltimore, Gino J. Gemignani
Division Vp Dallas, Espen S. Brooks
Vp Bridgewater, Chris Martinson
Svp Atlanta, Keith Douglas
Svp Connecticut, Daniel (Dan) Bauer
Vp Boston, Kevin Shields
Division Vp Las Vegas, Paul Schmitt
Division Vp Chantilly, Kempton C. Haile
Regional Manager (tampa), Brent A. Voyles
Vp Denver, Mark Faul
Vp San Diego, Steven Likins
Vp Orlando, Robert Minutoli
Division Vp Raleigh, Chris Carlson
Vp White Plains, David Brickley
Vp San Antonio, Daryl Steinbeck
Vp Norfolk, John Berotti
Senior Project Manager Sacramento, Jack Stackalis
Vp Cleveland, Jeff Maeder
Regional Manager Kansas City, Adam Eshelbrenner
Regional Manager Charlotte, Chris Woods
Regional Manager Houston, Michael Browning
President And Ceo, Timothy J. Regan, age 64
Vice President Worldwide Operations, Robert Ryan
Vice President, John Giovannone
Vice President Mechanical Electrical Services, David Reitmeyer
Vice President Mission Critical Mechanical Electrical Services, Greg Botteon
Division Vice President, Samuel Wells
Vice President Ashe Chc, Bob Moore
Vice President Finance And Operations, Nick Weiss
Leed Ap Banking Division C Vice President, Patricia Carper
Vice President, Dennis Hunter
Vice President, Karen Evans
Vice President, Jim Groff
Vice President, Irene Knott
Vice President, David McGinnis
Vice President, Damon Ellis
Vice President, Sam Abutaleb
Vice President, Edward Mackowiak
Vice President Information Technology, Joseph Dittmer
Division Vice President, Brian Ott
Vice President, Bill Wahl
Vice President, Jeffrey Baxter
Vice President, Craig Rayner
Division Vice President, Jeff Cochran
Vp Tax And Internal Audit, Bryant Cargile
Vice President, Charles Konkolics
Vice President, Andrew Linden
Vice President, Terry Powell
Senior Vice President, Stephen Lambertson
Vice President, Ray MacKeen
Division Vice President National Healthcare Coodinator, Richard Warhall
Senior Vice President, Kc Haile
Senior Vice President, Ron Eisenberg
Vice President, Thomas Wooden
Vice President, Bill Whiting
Vice President, Ruben Espinoza
Vice President, Christopher Moore
Vice President, Thomas Monticup
Vice President, Pete Valianatos
Vice Chairman, Nick Bloch

LOCATIONS

HQ: THE WHITING-TURNER CONTRACTING COMPANY
300 E JOPPA RD STE 800, BALTIMORE, MD 212863047
Phone: 410 821-1100
Web: WWW.WHITING-TURNER.COM

Selected Locations

Maryland - Baltimore (Headquarters)
California
California - Los Angeles
California
California
California - San Diego
Colorado -
Connecticut - New Haven
Delaware -
District of Columbia
Florida - Ft. Lauderdale
Florida -
Florida -
Georgia -
Maryland -
Massachuse
Missouri - Kansas City
Nevada - Las Vegas
New Jersey
New York - White Plains
North Caro
North Caro
Ohio - Cle
Pennsylvan
Texas - Da
Texas - Ho
Texas - San Antonio
Virginia -
Virginia -
Virginia -

PRODUCTS/OPERATIONS

Selected Services

Construction management
Agency
At-risk
Design/build
General contracting
Preconstruction

Selected Markets

Biotechnology and pharmaceutical
Cleanroom and high-technology
Education
Entertainment
Federal/military
Food/beverage distribution
Health care
Historical restoration
Industrial and manufacturing
Interiors
Life sciences
Lodging and hospitality
Mission critical facilities
Mixed use
Offices and headquarters
Parking garages
Restaurants
Retail
Senior living
Sports
Sustainable
Technology
Microelectronics
Nano
Theme parks
Utilities
Warehouse and distribution

COMPETITORS

Barton Malow
Bechtel
Choate Construction
Clark Construction Group
DPR Construction
Fisher Development
Fluor
Gilbane
Hensel Phelps Construction
Hoffman Corporation
J.E. Dunn Construction Group
Jacobs Engineering
Kitchell
McCarthy Building
Peter Kiewit Sons'
Skanska
Suffolk Construction
Swinerton
Turner Corporation
Tutor Perini
Weitz

HISTORICAL FINANCIALS

Company Type: Private

Income Statement — FYE: December 31

	REVENUE ($ mil.)	NET INCOME ($ mil.)	NET PROFIT MARGIN	EMPLOYEES
12/16	5,522	90	1.6%	4,043
12/15	5,729	80	1.4%	—
12/14	6,347	75	1.2%	—
Annual Growth	(6.7%)	9.8%	—	—

2016 Year-End Financials

Return on assets: 3.6%
Return on equity: 11.4%
Current ratio: 1.40
Cash ($ mil.): 26

THE WILLS GROUP INC

The Wills Group willingly delivers petroleum products and related products and services to its customer base in southern Maryland and adjacent areas. The family-owned company operates four business subsidiaries: Dash-In Convenience Stores (with 35 locations including 18 franchises); DMO (provider of propane heating oil and HVAC equipment); and Southern Maryland Oil (SMO) and SMO Motor Fuels (distribution of diesel gasoline and kerosene products). More than 90% of SMO's gasoline products are Shell-branded fuels. The Wills Group supplies more than 300 dealer-operated gas stations in Delaware southern Maryland and Washington DC.

Operations

The Wills Group divides its business into four operations: Dash-In Convenience Stores (serving the Maryland; Delaware; and Tidewater Virgina regions); DMO (propane heating oil and HVAC equipment maker); and Southern Maryland Oil (SMO) and SMO Motor Fuels (distribution of diesel gasoline and kerosene products).

Company Background

The company was founded in 1926 by Jim Wills and Harold Swann. In 1942 The Wills Group was the first principal fuel supplier to the newly built Patuxent Naval Air Station. In 1972 the company developed the first branded self-service station in Maryland. In 2012 Lock Wills was serving as the president of The Wills Group.

EXECUTIVES

Vice President Of Retail Operations, Mark Samuels
Auditors: RSM US LLP

LOCATIONS

HQ: THE WILLS GROUP INC
6355 CRAIN HWY, LA PLATA, MD 206464267
Phone: 301 932-3600
Web: WWW.WILLSGROUP.COM

COMPETITORS

Dixie Gas & Oil
Petroleum Marketers
Quarles Petroleum
Weis Markets
Woodfin Oil

HISTORICAL FINANCIALS

Company Type: Private

Income Statement FYE: September 30

	REVENUE ($ mil.)	NET INCOME ($ mil.)	NET PROFIT MARGIN	EMPLOYEES
09/18	1,035	66	6.4%	450
09/17	654	27	4.3%	—
Annual Growth	58.1%	137.1%	—	—

2018 Year-End Financials

Return on assets: 14.2%
Return on equity: 29.4%
Current ratio: 0.80
Cash ($ mil.): 27

THEDACARE, INC.

ThedaCare is a community health system that provides a wide range of health services to residents of fourteen northeast Wisconsin counties. It consists of seven hospitals including Appleton Medical Center Theda Clark Medical Center New London Family Medical Center Shawano Medical Center and ThedaCare Medical Center in Waupaca; 35 physician clinics; and community health and wellness programs. The hospitals provide back and pain care neuroscience behavioral health bone muscle & joint pain and heart and vascular services. ThedaCare also operates long-term care and assisted living facilities and provides occupational health and emergency transport services.

Operations

The health system operates seven hospitals and some 35 physician locations and manages approximately 235000 patients per year.

Its offers ThedaCare's Heritage Peabody Manor and Juliette Manor Communities ? choose from independent living assisted living or skilled care units all on the same campus. It manages 24-hour emergency response system and on-site nursing staff.

Geographic Reach

ThedaCare serves patients in about 15 counties in Northeastern Wisconsin.

Strategy

ThedaCare Neuroscience Group and Hand To Shoulder Center of Wisconsin celebrated the groundbreaking of the new Orthopedic Spine and Pain Center. This milestone marks the official start in creating the region's only comprehensive health center specializing in orthopedic spine and pain care. These groups form a team of experts at one location allowing patients to access outstanding individualized care. By enhancing that coordinated care it can live its mission of improving the health of the communities creating peace of mind for all they serve.

Together the partners will focus on creating excellence in key areas including neuro and spine upper extremity total joint foot and ankle sports medicine physical therapy and pain. Patients can be confident knowing they have access to the highest levels of fully integrated care physician talent and training. The local economy was considered as partners determined the importance of moving forward with this project. Approximately 75 healthcare jobs are expected to be created with the opening of the new Center plus the equivalent of an additional 200 construction jobs.

EXECUTIVES

Cio, Keith Livingston
President And Trustee, Dean Gruner, age 65
Chief Medical Officer, Greg Long
Vp Spine And Orthopedic Business, Mary Downs
Cfo, Tim Olson
Coo, Maryjeanne Schaffmeyer
Chief Nursing Executive, Laura Reed
Operating Room Dir, Heather Habeck
Chair, John Davis
Secretary, Lynn Gosse
Auditors: WIPFLI LLP MILWAUKEE WISCONS

LOCATIONS

HQ: THEDACARE, INC.
122 E COLLEGE AVE STE 2A, APPLETON, WI 549115741
Phone: 920 735-5560
Web: WWW.THEDACARE.ORG

PRODUCTS/OPERATIONS

Selected Facilities and Programs

Appleton Medical Center
The Heritage Community (senior living)
ThedaCare Medical Center-New London
Peabody Manor (senior living)
Riverside Medical Center
Shawano Medical Center
Theda Clark Medical Center
ThedaCare at Home
ThedaCare at Work (occupational health services)
ThedaCare Behavioral Health
ThedaCare Physicians

COMPETITORS

Aspirus
Beaver Dam Community Hospitals
Beloit Health System
Benedictine Health System
Children's Hospital and Health System
Columbia St. Mary's
Dean Health Systems Inc.
Howard Young Health Care
Luther Midelfort
Marian Health System
Marshfield Clinic Health System
Sacred Heart Hospital
Tomah Memorial Hospital
UW Medical Foundation
University of Wisconsin Hospital and Clinics

HISTORICAL FINANCIALS

Company Type: Private

Income Statement FYE: December 31

	REVENUE ($ mil.)	NET INCOME ($ mil.)	NET PROFIT MARGIN	EMPLOYEES
12/19	1,057	126	12.0%	7,000
12/18	995	(1)	—	—
12/17	909	88	9.7%	—
12/14	809	76	9.4%	—
Annual Growth	5.5%	10.7%	—	—

2019 Year-End Financials

Return on assets: 8.1%
Return on equity: 13.1%
Current ratio: 5.80
Cash ($ mil.): 78

THOMAS JEFFERSON UNIVERSITY

Thomas Jefferson University named after a founding father of diverse interests is itself diversifying the world of medical training. Its Sidney Kimmel Medical College (formerly Jefferson Medical College) boasts departments in surgery and specialized areas including obstetrics neurology and psychiatry. The Graduate Studies department offers programs in occupational therapy and engineering. The College of Health Professions has programs in nursing pharmacy biotechnology and counseling. Founded as Jefferson Medical College in 1824 it has granted more than 30000 medical degrees. The school merged with Philadelphia University a design-focused liberal arts school.

Operations

Thomas Jefferson University's schools include College of Architecture & The Built Environment College of Health Professions College of Humanities & Sciences College of Life Sciences College of Nursing College of Pharmacy College of Population Health College of Rehabilitation Sciences and Sidney Kimmel Medical College.

It also operates the Institute of Emerging Health Professions Kanbar College of Design Engineering & Commerce School of Business School of Design & Engineering and School of Continuing & Professional Studies. In addition it offers the Philadelphia University Honors Institute.

The university enrolls more than 3700 future healthcare professionals.

The university's medical school tests or treats nearly 43000 inpatients and about 1.5 million outpatients each year.

Geographic Reach

Thomas Jefferson University has campuses in the Center City and East Falls areas of Philadelphia.

Company Background

Thomas Jefferson University was founded in 1824 as Jefferson Medical College. In 1877 Thomas Jefferson University Hospital was established and Jefferson Medical College became the second medical school in the country with a separate teaching hospital. In 1891 the school established the Jefferson Hospital Training College for Nurses and in 1967 the College of Allied Health Sciences.

Thomas Jefferson University was officially established in 1969. In 1991 the NCI-designated Sidney Kimmel Cancer Center was established and in 2006 the university had renamed and added the Schools of Nursing and Health Professions. Two years later the Schools of Pharmacy and Population Health were formed. In 2014 the Sidney Kimmel Foundation bestowed a $110 million gift to Jefferson ? the largest gift in its history ? and Jefferson Medical College became Sidney Kimmel Medical College at Thomas Jefferson University.

In 2015 Thomas Jefferson University merged with Abington Health a Philadelphia health care organization with two hospitals and several clinics. The merger gave Abington access to the university's educational and training facilities and expands the university's reach to the Philadelphia suburbs. In 2016 the organization's medical operations combined forces with Aria Health which now operates as Aria – Jefferson Health.

Jefferson and Philadelphia University merged in 2017 and kept the Thomas Jefferson name. (Philadelphia University was founded in 1884 as the Philadelphia Textile School.)

EXECUTIVES

Medical Director Jefferson Sleep Disorders Center, Karl Doghramji
Vp Finance And Cfo, Richard J. Schmid
President, Stephen K. Klasko
Cio, Doug Herrick
Dean Jefferson Medical College, Richard J. Tykocinski

Dean Graduate School Of Biomedical Sciences, Gerald B. Grunwald
Dean School Of Health Professions, Janice Burke
Dean School Of Nursing, Beth A. Swan
Dean School Of Pharmacy, Rebecca S. Finley
Dean School Of Population Health, David Nash
Dean Students And Admissions, Clara A. Callahan
Evp Chief Operating Officer, Larry Merlis
Vp Research, Steven Mckenzie
Senior Vice President, Mark Tykocinski
Vice President Supply Chain, Robert Burkholder
Pharmacy Manager, Michael Roshko
Vice President For University Affairs, Janice C Marini
Vice President For Musculoskeletal Services, Rick Webster
Vice President, Chris Smith
Vice President Accountable Care, Carol Haines
Vice President Informaticsand Clinical Integration, Charleeda Redman
Associate Vice President, Mark Anderson
Vice President, Daisy Zhang
Vice President, Rebecca McIntosh
Clinical Director, Catherine Piersol
Executive Vp And Chief Growth And Marketing, Charles Lewis
Executive Vice President Chief Growth And Marketing Officer, Chuck Lewis
Assistant Vice President Jefferson Fund, Melissa Salazar
Vice President Oncology, Angel Medina
Vice President, David Klodowski
Medical Director Surgical Intensive Care Unit Se, Rob Hargraves
Medical Director, Voichita Ad
Chairman, Richard C. Gozon, age 82
Treasurer, Maria Gubbiotti
Treasurer, Philip Nimoityn
Secretary, Kathleen Kieser
Vice Chair For Clinical Practice And Quality, Lawrence Ward
Auditors: PRICEWATERHOUSECOOPERS LLP PH

LOCATIONS

HQ: THOMAS JEFFERSON UNIVERSITY
1020 WALNUT ST STE 1, PHILADELPHIA, PA 191075567
Phone: 215 955-6000
Web: WWW.JEFFERSON.EDU

PRODUCTS/OPERATIONS

Selected Research Centers and Institutes

Center for Translational Medicine
Daniel Baugh Institute
Delaware Health Science Alliance
Farber Institute for Neuroscience
Jefferson Coordinating Center for Clinical Research
Jefferson Vaccine Center
Kimmel Cancer Center

Selected Colleges and Schools

Sidney Kimmel Medical College
Jefferson Graduate School of Biomedical Sciences
Jefferson School of Health Professions
Jefferson School of Nursing
Jefferson School of Pharmacy
Jefferson School of Population Health

HISTORICAL FINANCIALS

Company Type: Private

Income Statement — FYE: June 30

	REVENUE ($ mil.)	NET INCOME ($ mil.)	NET PROFIT MARGIN	EMPLOYEES
06/17	3,951	700	17.7%	10,625
06/16	136	8	6.5%	—
Annual Growth	2788.6%	7723.4%	—	—

2017 Year-End Financials

Return on assets: 12.0%
Return on equity: 23.1%
Current ratio: 3.20
Cash ($ mil.): 259

THOMAS JEFFERSON UNIVERSITY HOSPITALS, INC.

Named after the "Man of the People" Thomas Jefferson University Hospitals (dba Jefferson Health) serves the people of the Keystone State with a medical staff of more than 1200 and some 1550 beds. The system provides acute tertiary and specialty medical care from a dozen hospitals nearly 20 outpatient centers and about 10 urgent care centers. The hospital also administers cardiac care at the Jefferson Heart Institute which provides everything from minimally invasive surgical procedures to heart transplants. Additionally Jefferson Health operates as the teaching hospital for Thomas Jefferson University.

Operations

As part of its operations Jefferson Health offers several premier programs to its patients as well as 35 different specialties. The system performed Delaware Valley's first liver transplant and designated a kidney transplant center for live and deceased donor transplants. In addition to transplantation it provides surgical services heart and vascular digestive diseases and bones and joints in addition to its Kimmel Cancer Canter and Jefferson Hospital for Neuroscience. In 2014 the health system logged more than 470000 outpatient visits 45000 admissions and about 115000 emergency room visits.

Geographic Reach

Through a handful of locations Jefferson Health provides health care services to the residents of Philadelphia and the Delaware Valley. It shares a 13-acre campus with Thomas Jefferson University.

Strategy

In October 2017 Jefferson Health merged with New Jersey-based Kennedy Health which operated three hospitals. The transaction followed closely on the heels of Jefferson's mergers with Aria Health and Abington Health.

In 2015 Jefferson Health added a new feature to its telemedicine program JeffConnect called On-Demand Virtual Care which allows patients to connect with an emergency medicine physician via computers and mobile devices.

That year the Philadelphia 76ers partnered with the Rothman Institute and Jefferson Health. The Rothman Institute will provide the Official Orthopedics & Urgent Care of the Philadelphia 76ers as well as the Official Team Physicians; Jefferson Health became an official hospital of the Philadelphia 76ers.

In 2014 the system opened the Jefferson Angioplasty Center the outpatient practice for Jefferson's interventional cardiologists. It is co-located with the Vascular Center allowing for streamlined consultations and convenience as the two specialties often see the same patients.

That year it also introduced genomic analyses of breast cancer in-house using the Prosigna Breast Cancer Prognostic Gene Signature Assay significantly reducing turn-around time for test results and allowing patients to begin effective treatment sooner.

Company Background

Thomas Jefferson University Hospital was founded in 1825.

EXECUTIVES

Blood Bank Director, Jay Herman
Vice President Clinical Resource Management, Patrice Miller
Vice President Hospital Administration, Richard Webster
Vice President Finance, Elizabeth Smith
Vp Human Resources, Kimberly Evans
Director Of Clinical Services Administrator Musculoskeletal Service Line, Kristen Vogl
Senior Vice President Clinical Service, Rebecca Oshea
Vice President Of Information Technology, Kevin Morgan
Secretary, Gerri Anderson

LOCATIONS

HQ: THOMAS JEFFERSON UNIVERSITY HOSPITALS, INC.
111 S 11TH ST, PHILADELPHIA, PA 191074824
Phone: 215 955-6000
Web: WWW.HOSPITALS.JEFFERSON.EDU

PRODUCTS/OPERATIONS

Selected Services

Cancer

Diabetes & Endocrinology
Ear Nose & Throat
Gastroenterology
Geriatrics
Gynecology
Nephrology
Orthopedics
Pulmonology
Rehabilitation
Urology

Selected University Locations

Jefferson at the Navy Yard
Jefferson Medical College
Jefferson College of Graduate Studies
Jefferson Radiology
Jefferson School of Health Professions
Jefferson School of Nursing
Jefferson School of Pharmacy
Jefferson School of Population Health
Jefferson Voorhees

COMPETITORS

Albert Einstein Healthcare Network
Bryn Mawr Hospital
Community Health Systems
Doylestown Hospital
Mercy Health System
North Philadelphia Health System
Our Lady of Lourdes Medical Center
Pennsylvania Hospital
TUHS
Universal Health Services
University of Pennsylvania Health System

HISTORICAL FINANCIALS

Company Type: Private

Income Statement — FYE: June 30

	REVENUE ($ mil.)	NET INCOME ($ mil.)	NET PROFIT MARGIN	EMPLOYEES
06/16	1,495	76	5.1%	4,701
06/15	1,456	42	2.9%	—
06/14	1,510	51	3.4%	—
06/10	1,250	49	4.0%	—
Annual Growth	3.0%	7.7%	—	—

2016 Year-End Financials

Return on assets: 4.4% Cash ($ mil.): 57
Return on equity: 8.7%
Current ratio: 3.20

THOMPSON CREEK METALS COMPANY USA

EXECUTIVES

Pres-Ceo, Jacques Perron
Chb*, Kevin Loughrey
V Pres*, Robert Dorfler
Cfo*, Pamela L Saxton
Accounting Staff, Jamie Patterson
Coordinator, Raymond Gelinas
Manager, Mark Piper
Director, Robert Clifford
Auditors: KPMG LLP DENVER COLORADO

LOCATIONS

HQ: THOMPSON CREEK METALS COMPANY USA
26 W DRY CREEK CIR # 225, LITTLETON, CO 801208064
Phone: 303 761-8801
Web: WWW.RENMARKFINANCIAL.COM

HISTORICAL FINANCIALS

Company Type: Private

Income Statement — FYE: December 31

	REVENUE ($ mil.)	NET INCOME ($ mil.)	NET PROFIT MARGIN	EMPLOYEES
12/14	806	(124)	—	1,700
12/13	434	(215)	—	—
12/12	401	(546)	—	—
Annual Growth	41.8%	—	—	—

2014 Year-End Financials

Return on assets: (-4.4%) Cash ($ mil.): 265
Return on equity: (-14.0%)
Current ratio: 2.50

THRUWAY AUTHORITY OF NEW YORK STATE

Leaving Manhattan or Brooklyn to shuffle off to Buffalo? The New York State Thruway Authority oversees a 641-mile toll road system and a 524-mile canal system. The authority's toll road system known as the Governor Thomas E. Dewey Thruway is the largest in the US. It crosses the state from New York City to Buffalo and more than 80% of the population of New York State lives along the corridor formed by the Thruway's 426-mile main line. Other arms of the Thruway connect with toll roads and other highways in neighboring states. The New York State Canal Corporation oversees the state's canal system of five lakes and four canals which connect bodies of water such as the Hudson River with Lake Champlain.

EXECUTIVES

Xec Dir, Thomas Madison
Exec Dir*, Michael R Fleischer
Chief Operating Officer*, John Bryan
Executive Director*, Bill Finch
Manager, James Benoit
Information Specialist, Shawn Mancini
Assistant To Director, James Chicoine
Legal Staff, Marcy Dikeman
Software Engineer, Gene Greger
Web Developer, Greg Neugebauer
Administrative Aide, Kim Blinstrub
Auditors: TOSKI & CO CPAS PC WILLI

LOCATIONS

HQ: THRUWAY AUTHORITY OF NEW YORK STATE
200 SOUTHERN BLVD, ALBANY, NY 122092018
Phone: 518 436-2700
Web: WWW.THRUWAY.NY.GOV

HISTORICAL FINANCIALS

Company Type: Private

Income Statement — FYE: December 31

	REVENUE ($ mil.)	NET INCOME ($ mil.)	NET PROFIT MARGIN	EMPLOYEES
12/10	674	(127)	—	2,840
12/09	640	(129)	—	—
12/08	598	(129)	—	—
Annual Growth	6.1%	—	—	—

2010 Year-End Financials

Return on assets: (-2.3%) Cash ($ mil.): 203
Return on equity: (-6.1%)
Current ratio: 0.80

TMH PHYSICIAN ORGANIZATION

EXECUTIVES

V Pres-Ceo, John Lyle
Dir-Treas, Mike Giblin
Treas, Edward L Tyrrell
SEC, Marc L Boom
Manager, Ganesh Kalambur
Coordinator, Jennifer Hamilton
Information Specialist, Thomas Daubner
Vice-President, Liisa Ortegon
Vice-President, Hackett Carole
Manager, Jill Roach
Consultant, Jose Solis

LOCATIONS

HQ: TMH PHYSICIAN ORGANIZATION
6565 FANNIN ST STE D200, HOUSTON, TX 770302703
Phone: 713 441-4182
Web: WWW.HOUSTONMETHODIST.ORG

HISTORICAL FINANCIALS

Company Type: Private

Income Statement — FYE: December 31

	REVENUE ($ mil.)	NET INCOME ($ mil.)	NET PROFIT MARGIN	EMPLOYEES
12/18	600	0	0.1%	9
12/17	532	(0)	—	—
12/15	413	0	0.2%	—
12/14	360	1	0.5%	—
Annual Growth	13.6%	(20.1%)	—	—

2018 Year-End Financials

Return on assets: 0.9% Cash ($ mil.): —
Return on equity: —
Current ratio: 0.40

TMV CORP.

EXECUTIVES

Ceo, Mark J Whitt
Chm, Howard L Hawks
Ceo, Fred R Hunzeker
Chief Marketing Officer, Lori A Bruck
Evp-Cfo, John Obermiller
Svp-Bus Devt, Martin E Titus
Svp-Gen Counsel, Mark A McQuade
Vice President, Corey S Kopiasz
Vice President, Gaye L Schaffart
Vice President, Michael H Crabb
Vice President, Todd M Litjen

LOCATIONS

HQ: TMV CORP.
14302 FNB PKWY, OMAHA, NE 681545212
Phone: 402 691-9500
Web: WWW.TENASKA.COM

HISTORICAL FINANCIALS

Company Type: Private

Income Statement — FYE: December 31

	REVENUE ($ mil.)	NET INCOME ($ mil.)	NET PROFIT MARGIN	EMPLOYEES
12/07	10,309	0	—	91
12/05	9,470	0	—	—
12/04	0	0	—	—
12/03	4,940	0	—	—
Annual Growth	20.2%	—	—	—

TOLEDO PROMEDICA HOSPITAL

One of the region's largest acute-care facilities The Toledo Hospital provides medical care to the residents of northwestern Ohio and southeastern Michigan. Boasting nearly 800 beds the facility offers several specialties and services including the Jobst Vascular Center which provides cardiac and vascular services in conjunction with The University of Michigan. The Toledo Hospital which shares a medical complex with the Toledo Children's Hospital also operates trauma emergency outpatient arthritis sleep disorder and women's health centers. The Toledo Hospital is a member of Toledo-based ProMedica Health System a mission-based not-for-profit healthcare organization formed in 1986.

EXECUTIVES

Nursing Director, Deana Sievert

LOCATIONS

HQ: TOLEDO PROMEDICA HOSPITAL
2142 N COVE BLVD, TOLEDO, OH 436063895
Phone: 419 291-4000
Web: WWW.PROMEDICA.ORG

PRODUCTS/OPERATIONS

Selected Services

Arthritis and Osteoporosis Center
Bariatric Surgery
Behavioral Health and Psychiatric Services
Breast Care Center
Cancer Care
Critical Care
Diabetes
Dialysis
Emergency Services
Endoscopy Services
Fertility Services
Heart Care
Hemophilia Outpatient Clinic
Hyperbaric Medicine
Laboratory Services
Lactation Services
Maternal - Fetal Medicine
Mom & Me Boutique
Neurology
Neurophysiology
OccuHealth
Orthopaedics
Outpatient Surgery
Palliative Care
Radiology / Imaging Services
Rehabilitation Services
Respiratory Care
Sleep Medicine
Surgical Services
Trauma Services
Urology /
Vascular Services
Women's Services

COMPETITORS

Firelands Regional Health System
Mercy Health Partners Toledo
Sylvania Franciscan Health
Tenet Healthcare
Trinity Health (Novi)
University of Michigan Health System

HISTORICAL FINANCIALS

Company Type: Private

Income Statement — FYE: December 31

	REVENUE ($ mil.)	NET INCOME ($ mil.)	NET PROFIT MARGIN	EMPLOYEES
12/17	854	(115)	—	5,586
12/14	745	20	2.8%	—
12/09	635	19	3.0%	—
12/08	548	33	6.1%	—
Annual Growth	5.0%	—	—	—

2017 Year-End Financials

Return on assets: (-8.1%)
Return on equity: (-35.3%)
Current ratio: 0.30
Cash ($ mil.): 83

TOWN OF HEMPSTEAD

EXECUTIVES

Sup, Anthony Santino
Clerk*, Nasrin Ahmad
Secretary, Richard Regina
Information Specialist, Arthur Primm
Directo, Fred Parola
Council Member, Dorothy Goosby
Commissioner, Gerald Marino
Water Plant Supervisor II, John Markwalter
Executive, Beverly Hester
Supervisor, Laura Gillen
Analyst, Mike Defilippis
Auditors: ALBRECHT VIGGIANO ZURECK & C

LOCATIONS

HQ: TOWN OF HEMPSTEAD
1 WASHINGTON ST, HEMPSTEAD, NY 115504921
Phone: 516 489-5000
Web: WWW.TOWNOFHEMPSTEAD.ORG

HISTORICAL FINANCIALS

Company Type: Private

Income Statement — FYE: December 31

	REVENUE ($ mil.)	NET INCOME ($ mil.)	NET PROFIT MARGIN	EMPLOYEES
12/19	588	5	0.9%	2,052
12/18	549	48	8.8%	—
12/17	677	71	10.5%	—
12/16	580	(51)	—	—
Annual Growth	0.4%	—	—	—

2019 Year-End Financials

Return on assets: 0.2%
Return on equity: 0.5%
Current ratio: —
Cash ($ mil.): 161

TRAMMO, INC.

Stockpiles of fertilizers liquefied petroleum gas (LPG) and petrochemicals are the "ammo" which international trader Trammo (formerly Transammonia) uses in its battle with competitors. The company trades distributes markets and transports these commodities around the world. Trammo was founded by Ronald P. Stanton in 1965 with the intention of specializing in the international trade of ammonia. Today it remains privately held and manages its operations through its headquarters in New York City and offices worldwide.

Operations

The company is engaged in marketing trading and distribution of a number of commodities with a focus on certain primary businesses in which it is a leading market participant including anhydrous ammonia sulfur sulfuric acid nitric acid and petroleum coke.

Anhydrous ammonia is an alkaline compound consisting of Nitrogen and Hydrogen which is transported worldwide in gaseous or liquid form on board pressurized or refrigerated vessels. These vessels (gas carriers) are also used in transporting liquefied petroleum gas (LPG). Only around 20 million metric tons are available for international marketing and seaborne trade out of more than 200 million metric tons of ammonia produced annually worldwide.

Sulfur is a by-product of oil and gas production and refining with this involuntary production accounting for up to 95% of traded volume. Annual production is about 70 million metric tons of sulfur of which about 40%-45% is available for seaborne trade.

Sulfuric acid is a key element in the production of fertilizer (phosphates and ammonium sulfate) which is its primary use (approximately 65% of total consumption). Sulfuric acid is also used in the mining industry for leaching of copper nickel uranium and other elements from ores (approximately 15% of total consumption). It is also is used in various industrial processes (approximately 20% of total consumption) including the production of titanium dioxide for dyes and pigments the production of other industrial chemicals water treatment the production of cellulose paper and rubber and in the food and glass industries. Sulfuric acid is one of the most widely used chemical commodities its total worldwide annual production is approximately 265 million metric tons.

Nitric acid used predominantly as an intermediate for fertilizer production (mainly ammonium and calcium ammonium nitrate) and for the production of nitro-containing organic intermediates.

Petroleum coke ("petcoke") is a by-product of crude oil refining. The coking processes produce "green coke" which is then further processed into two main products calcined petcoke and fuel grade petcoke. Annual production is around 140 million metric tons (MT). Calcined petcoke (approximately 25% of production) is used for making anodes for aluminum smelting the dioxide industry and production of steel and titanium whiles Fuel grade petcoke (approximately 75% of production) makes up most of the petcoke traded internationally.

Low Density Ammonium Nitrate is one of the main raw materials to manufacture civil explosives such as ANFO (Ammonium Nitrate Fuel Oil) used in the mining industry. It is engineered to have the ideal density and optimal porosity which will obtain a good absorption rate it enhance the performance of the explosive in mining operations.

Geographic Reach

Headquartered in New York NY Trammo has expanded its reach into the global market establishing merchandising and trading offices in Singapore China and the United Arab Emirates. The offices complement its other global operations in Africa Asia Europe the Middle East and North and South America (Brazil and Chile). It also has major representative offices in Dubai and Shanghai.

The company also owns and operates ammonia terminals in Meredosia and Niota Illinois and a nitric acid production facility in North Bend Ohio. Trammo has about 20 offices worldwide.

Sales and Marketing

Sulfur is typically marketed in solid form and transported in bulk around the world on board ocean going vessels globally. It is used in a wide variety of industries most of it after conversion into sulfuric acid as an input for fertilizer production (about 70%) in metal leaching (around 20%) and in various chemical industries (approximately 10%). Approximately 20 million metric tons per year of sulfuric acid are traded in all forms and the seaborne trade comprises only about 11 million metric tons internationally. The vast majority of the 35 million metric tons of calcined petcoke produced is traded directly by producers to end users.

Strategy

In mid-2020 Trammo successfully extended its committed secured revolving credit facility through June 2021 with a syndicate of eight international banks. Co ¶perative Rabobank UA New York Branch will serve as Administrative and Collateral Agent and along with BNP Paribas will serve as joint lead arranger and joint book runner. Other participating banks include ABN AMRO ING Belgium JPMorgan Chase Zurcher Kantonalbank HSBC Trinkaus & Burkhardt and Brown Brothers Harriman.

The $200 million secured facility with an accordion feature that can permit an increase in total commitments up to $275 million is available for working capital and general corporate purposes in support of Trammo's commodities trading and distribution businesses around the world. The over-subscribed syndication was a strong indication of the ongoing commitment and support of Trammo's bank group.

Company Background

In 2013 Transammonia changed its name to Trammo to more accurately represent the broad spectrum of products and services it provides.

In 2010 the company's bulk carriers division entered the commodity shipping business. TA Bulk Carriers operates a fleet of 15 to 20 vessels which trade worldwide but focus on the handysize market (25000-35000 metric tons deadweight) in the Atlantic basin. In 2010 it transported about 2.9 million metric tons of cargo primarily fertilizers and grains.

Ronald Stanton founded the company in 1965 as an international ammonia trader. It branched into fertilizer merchandising and trading in 1967 LPG trading in 1978 and petrochemicals trading in 1987.

EXECUTIVES

Evp Coo And Cfo, Edward G. Weiner
Ceo Chemicals Division, Ashok Kishore
President Ceo Director And Ceo Commodities Division, Brent Hart
Svp Global Risk Management, Oliver K. Stanton
Senior Vice President, Dudley Cox
Vice President, Fred Lowenfels
Senior Vice President Chief Accounting Officer, Robert Lovett
Vice President Of Human Resour, Pat Berry
Assistant Vice President, Donald Madden
Assistant Vice President, Jorge Melazzini
Vice President Finance And Treasury, John Sheehan
Senior Vice President Finance And Treasury, Jim Benfield
Chairman Emeritus, Ronald P Stanton
Auditors: RSM US LLP NEW YORK NEW YORK

LOCATIONS

HQ: TRAMMO, INC.
667 MADISON AVE FL 4, NEW YORK, NY 100658029
Phone: 212 223-3200
Web: WWW.TRAMMO.COM

PRODUCTS/OPERATIONS

Major Subsidiaries
Sea-3 (liquefied propane)Trammo Gas (LPG)
Trammo Gas International Inc. (LPG transportation for third parties.Trammo Petroleum (crude oil and oil products)Trammochem (petrochemicals)Fertilizers and CommoditiesNitrogen BasedAnhydrous Ammo

COMPETITORS

BASF SE	HELM
CF Industries	Koch Industries Inc.
Cargill	Magellan Midstream
ConAgra	Yara

HISTORICAL FINANCIALS

Company Type: Private

Income Statement — FYE: December 31

	REVENUE ($ mil.)	NET INCOME ($ mil.)	NET PROFIT MARGIN	EMPLOYEES
12/19	2,267	22	1.0%	139
12/18	3,212	(12)	—	—
12/16	6,453	(229)	—	—
12/14	11,266	31	0.3%	—
Annual Growth	(27.4%)	(6.1%)	—	—

2019 Year-End Financials

Return on assets: 5.2%
Return on equity: 14.7%
Current ratio: 1.50
Cash ($ mil.): 74

TRC COMPANIES, INC.

RC companies has Environmental Energy Pipeline Services and Planning and Construction. The firm provides engineering construction and remediation services for Power and Utilities Oil Gas and Industrial Transportation Real Estate Water and Government.. Services include energy efficiency and solid- and hazardous-waste management consulting infrastructure improvements and landfill cleanup. TRC's services also include remediation for brownfield sites discontinued industrial operations operating assets and Superfund sites. It offers an Exit Strategy Program in which it assumes complete responsibility for a contaminated site's closure and cleanup. In 2019 TRC acquired Distributed Energy Solutions group of Lockheed Martin. The company was incorporated in Connecticut in 1969.

HISTORY

TRC was born as Travelers Research Center a unit set up in 1953 by Travelers Insurance to do meteorological and industrial hygiene research. In 1969 Travelers (now part of Citigroup) spun off TRC Companies which prospered as government spending on the environment and pollution control increased. It became a free-standing public entity in 1976. When the government began cutting back during the 1980s TRC started courting the commercial market.

In 1994 TRC expanded acquiring Environmental Solutions and Mariah Associates. It increased its international interests forming joint ventures in 1995 and 1996 to help with the remediation of Poland's horrendous pollution.

Sales fell in 1996 and 1997 the result of a weak market and stiff competition in the environmental services industry. TRC responded with a major cost-cutting effort. In 1997 chairman and CEO Vincent Rocco and president Bruce Cowen resigned amid an investigation into options exercised by the two executives that the company's board had not authorized. Richard Ellison head of the TRC Environmental Solutions subsidiary was named chairman president and CEO.

Also in 1997 TRC teamed up with insurer American International Group to introduce a service called the Exit Strategy Program in which TRC is paid to take full responsibility — including liability risks — for a contaminated site's closure and remediation.

In 1998 the company sold its Monitoring Instruments for the Environment subsidiary for about $2.7 million. The next year TRC embarked on a major buying spree: It purchased Alton Geoscience which specialized in installation removal and replacement of fuel tanks; A&H Engineers a transportation consulting and engineering firm in New York City; and Vectre which provided brownfield remediation services in New Jersey. The company also landed an Exit Strategy contract to clean up a Superfund site in Maine.

Continuing to grow through acquisitions in 2000 TRC acquired Texas-based Hunter Associates North Carolina-based Triange Environmental and California-based Lowney Associates. Also that year the TRC twice scored big with its Exit Strategy product: a $103 million contract with Consolidated Edison to clean up a site in New York City and a $21 million contract with Lockheed Martin to clean up sites in California Massachusetts and New Jersey.

TRC kept on snapping up companies in 2001. The company bought Engineered Automation Systems which provided electrical mechanical and environmental controls and ECON a provider of environmental services to the oil and gas companies that was to take on Exit Strategy business in the Gulf Coast region. The company also bought two infrastructure engineering companies LandCon and CSM that were to be combined with Hunter Associates.

The next year eager to expand its outsourcing operations for the power industry TRC acquired engineering firm E/PRO which had experience in the US Northeast in the licensing of hydroelectric plants as well as in designing constructing and managing other power utilities. TRC also completed its acquisition of transportation infrastructure firm SITE-Blauvelt Engineers which targeted mid-Atlantic states.

In 2002 the group expanded westward by acquiring California-based environmental planning training and compliance management firm Essex Environmental. It also enhanced its Midwestern operations by buying Novak Engineering a power transmission and distribution planning and design firm. In 2004 the group won a contract from the Department of Defense to design an "intelligent building" system to optimize energy use and detect threats within the Pentagon.

Ellison retired as president and CEO effective January 1 2006 but remained chairman. Christopher Vincze who had been COO took over as president and CEO.

But TRC began to broaden its reach nationally in all segments of its business in 2010. Since 2010 the company has been marketing its energy and infrastructure services on a national basis and its environmental services are being integrated into its national platform. Its national platform is linked to TRC's corporate sales and marketing organization.

Pursuing strategic acquisitions in 2011 TRC continued acquired Alexander Utility Engineering a San Antonio-based engineering and design firm that specializes in services to the electric utility and communications utility markets. The deal for Alexander which posted earnings of about $3 million in 2010 expands TRC's engineering presence in the Texas market and advances its growth strategy. That same year TRC acquired the environmental business of RMT Inc. a subsidiary of Alliant Energy Corp. The deal expands TRC's growth in the solar wind and geothermal energy markets. The company also picked up environmental consulting company The Payne Firm.

On the heels of acquiring RMT and Payne the company formed a strategic partnership with California-based environmental consulting group EORM to acquire its eastern region operations based in Danvers Massachusetts. The deal enhances TRC's environmental management sustainability and safety operations as well as broadens its geographic reach.

Broadening its geographic coverage in 2012 the company opened an office in London.

In 2013 TRC acquired GE Air Emissions Testing for $3.2 million.

EXECUTIVES

Svp General Counsel And Secretary, Martin H. Dodd, $287,928 total compensation
Chairman And Ceo, Christopher P. (Chris) Vincze, $550,000 total compensation
Cfo, Thomas W. (Tom) Bennet, $323,979 total compensation

Svp And Lead Energy Sector, James Mayer, $352,228 total compensation
Svp And National Environmental Sector Leader, John W. Cowdery, $357,002 total compensation
Senior Vice President, Cynthia Retallick
Vice President, Gary Hunt
Vice President Power Services, Tedd Southern
Senior Vice President, Jim Mayer
Vice President Testing And Commissioning, Jason Hostetter
Vice President Trc Environmental Corp., Carl Stopper
Vice President Oil And Gas, Lauren O'donnell
Vice President, Tom Rooney
Vp Chief Engineer Pipelines, Kevin Bodenhamer
Senior Vice President National Practice, David Tiernan
Svp Procurement And Real Estate, Brad Pittman
Auditors: DELOITTE & TOUCHE LLP

LOCATIONS

HQ: TRC COMPANIES, INC.
21 GRIFFIN RD N, WINDSOR, CT 060951590
Phone: 860 298-9692
Web: WWW.TRCSOLUTIONS.COM

PRODUCTS/OPERATIONS

2016 Sales

	% of total
Environmental	45
Energy	33
Infrastructure	12
Pipeline	10
Total	**100**

2016 Sales

	$ mil.	% of total
Net services	465	97
Insurance recoverable and others	16	3
Total	**481**	**100**

Selected Customers

AES Enterprises
ASARCO
Burlington Northern Santa Fe (BNSF)
Connecticut Resources Recovery Authority
Consolidated Edison
Duke Energy
El Paso Energy
Environmental Protection Agency
Exxon Mobil
Goodyear Tire & Rubber
Kinder Morgan
PG&E Corporation
Sempra Energy
State Departments of Transportation/Power Authorities
- California
- Louisiana
- Massachusetts
- New Hampshire
- New Jersey
- New York
- Pennsylvania
- Texas
- West Virginia

Selected Subsidiaries

Alexander Utility Engineering
Center Avenue Holdings
Cubix Corporation
Environomics Southwest
Hunter Associates
Site-Blauvelt Engineers Inc.
Site Construction Services
TRC Engineers Inc.
TRC Environmental Corporation
TRC Solutions Inc.
Vectre Corporation

COMPETITORS

3E Company
ARCADIS
ATC Associates
Bechtel
Black & Veatch
Clyde Bergemann EEC
Fluor
Weston Solutions

HISTORICAL FINANCIALS

Company Type: Private

Income Statement — FYE: June 30

	REVENUE ($ mil.)	NET INCOME ($ mil.)	NET PROFIT MARGIN	EMPLOYEES
06/19	693	(30)	—	3,700
06/18	590	(48)	—	—
Annual Growth	17.5%	—	—	—

2019 Year-End Financials

Return on assets: (-3.2%)
Return on equity: (-10.9%)
Current ratio: 1.50
Cash ($ mil.): 43

TRI STAR ENERGY, LLC

EXECUTIVES

Mng MBR, John B Jewell III
MBR, Steve Hostetter
Vice President of Retail Opera, Rick Hamilton
MBR, Jeff Williams
Human Resources, Liane Taylor
Senior Vice President of Facil, Charlton Bell
Manager, Randy Alexander
R Credit Manager, Belinda Hilliard
Manager, Jack Cooper
District Manager, Keith Middleton
Database Analyst, Mark Roark
Auditors: LATTIMORE BLACK MORGAAN & CA

LOCATIONS

HQ: TRI STAR ENERGY, LLC
1740 ED TEMPLE BLVD, NASHVILLE, TN 372081850
Phone: 615 313-3600
Web: WWW.TRISTARTN.COM

HISTORICAL FINANCIALS

Company Type: Private

Income Statement — FYE: December 31

	REVENUE ($ mil.)	NET INCOME ($ mil.)	NET PROFIT MARGIN	EMPLOYEES
12/11	730	3	0.5%	500
12/10	635	4	0.7%	—
12/09	547	0	0.0%	—
Annual Growth	15.5%	399.7%	—	—

2011 Year-End Financials

Return on assets: 3.1%
Return on equity: 7.4%
Current ratio: 0.70
Cash ($ mil.): —

TRIBOROUGH BRIDGE & TUNNEL AUTHORITY

EXECUTIVES

V Pres-Pres, Michael C Ascher
Computer Specialist, Paul Kolodizner

LOCATIONS

HQ: TRIBOROUGH BRIDGE & TUNNEL AUTHORITY
ROBERT MOSES BLDG RANDAL, NEW YORK, NY 10035
Phone: 212 360-3000

HISTORICAL FINANCIALS

Company Type: Private

Income Statement — FYE: December 31

	REVENUE ($ mil.)	NET INCOME ($ mil.)	NET PROFIT MARGIN	EMPLOYEES
12/19	2,094	485	23.2%	1,500
12/18	1,999	453	22.7%	—
12/17	1,931	282	14.6%	—
12/16	1,895	202	10.7%	—
Annual Growth	3.4%	33.9%	—	—

2019 Year-End Financials

Return on assets: 5.6%
Return on equity: —
Current ratio: 1.10
Cash ($ mil.): 149

TRINITY HEALTH CORPORATION

Hospitals health centers and nursing homes make up Trinity Health. One of the largest Catholic health care systems in the US Trinity Health runs about 90 hospitals and more than 100 continuing care facilities more than 20 states across the country. In addition to acute care services include behavioral health pediatrics oncology neurology senior housing and home health and hospice care. It also provides senior service management supply chain management research and international consulting services. The company employs more than 7800 physicians and clinicians.

Operations

Trinity Health gets its revenue from acute care inpatient services (about 40% of revenue) outpatient acute care (more than 30%) physician services (10%) long-term and home health (5%) health insurance (5%) and other sources.

Geographic Reach

Based in Livonia Michigan Trinity Health has locations in Alabama California Connecticut Delaware Florida Georgia Idaho Illinois Indiana Iowa Maryland Massachusetts Michigan Nebraska New Jersey New York North Carolina Ohio Oregon Pennsylvania and South Dakota.

Sales and Marketing

Medicare accounts for about 40% of net patient service revenues; Blue Cross accounts for 20% Medicaid for 15% while commercial and other represents about 25%.

Financial Performance

Trinity Health reported some $19.3 billion in revenue in fiscal 2019 (ending June 30) a 5% increase over 2018 results. The growth was attributed to hospital acquisitions volume growth rate increases case mix improvements higher retail pharmacy revenue and other gains. Growth was offset by increased payment denials unfavorable patient mix shifts and reduced health plan earnings.

Excess of revenue over expenses attributable to Trinity Health declined 13% to $786 million in 2019 due to lower investment earnings and affiliate earnings and a change in interest rate swap values.

The company ended 2018 with $474.3 million in cash down $497.4 million from 2017. Operating activities contributed $919.6 million while investing activities used $1.5 billion (mostly property equipment and investment purchases) and financing activities contributed $102.4 million via an expanded credit line.

Trinity Health has net assets of $13.8 billion and a community benefit ministry of $1.2 billion.

Strategy

To meet federal health reform guidelines improve quality of care and lower medical costs Trinity Health is working to coordinate patient care across all regional facilities and upgrade its infrastructure with new information technology systems. The company is shifting its facilities to a common electronic health record (EHR) and revenue cycle platform and it announced plans to create three centralized patient billing service centers in 2019.

Trinity Health expands its network through construction efforts and by acquiring facilities such as the purchase of MacNeal Hospital in Illinois in 2018. The company also grows by forming collaborations with other area providers. In 2018 the company sold a 49% stake in St. Joseph Mercy Chelsea Hospital to the Regents of the University of Michigan to establish a partnership with the university and improve delivery of care in the area.

The company also occasionally divests underperforming or noncore assets. In 2019 it sold its Lourdes Health System unit (Camden New Jersey) to Virtua Health.

In 2018 Trinity Health joined a consortium of health care providers to form a not-for-profit generic drug company Civica Rx which aims to address the excessive costs and shortages of essential medicines that often plague hospitals in the US.

As a not-for-profit health system and a sponsored organization of the Catholic Health Ministries Trinity Health carries out a number of ministry programs including investing in community housing and child care resources and providing health outreach services.

Mergers and Acquisitions

Trinity Health acquired the 370-bed MacNeal Hospital in Berwyn Illinois along with related health entities from Tenet Healthcare in 2018. The hospital was added to the Loyola University Health System subsidiary.

Company Background

Trinity Health was established in 2013 from the merger of Catholic Health East and the former Trinity Health organization.

The predecessor Trinity Health organization was formed through the 2000 merger of Mercy Health Services and Holy Cross Health System. Holy Cross was founded in 1979 but traces its roots to the founding of the Congregation of the Sisters of the Holy Cross in 1841; Mercy Health was founded in 1976 but originates with the Sisters of Mercy establishing operations in Iowa and Michigan in the 1860s and 1870s.

Catholic Health East was formed through the 1998 merger of three health ministries: Franciscan Sisters of Allegany Health System (tracing its roots to 1883 in Boston) Eastern Mercy Health System (1847 Pittsburgh) and Sisters of Providence Health System (1892; Holyoke Massachusetts).

In 2015 New York-based St. Joseph's Hospital Health Center joined the Trinity hospital system.

EXECUTIVES

Executive Vice President Eastern Division, Michael A Slubowski
Evp Governance And Sponsorship, Catherine DeClercq
Svp Treasurer And Chief Investment Officer, James W. Bosscher
Svp And General Counsel, Daniel G. (Dan) Hale
Evp And Cfo, Benjamin R. (Ben) Carter
President And Ceo, Richard J. (Rick) Gilfillan
Evp And Chief Clinical Officer, P. Terrence (Terry) O'Rourke
Evp And Chief Culture And Talent Effectiveness Officer, Debra A. (Deb) Canales
Evp And President East Group, Richard (Rick) O'Connell
Evp And General Counsel, Paul G. Neumann
Evp West/midwest Group, Sally E. Jeffcoat
Evp Continuing Care Group, John Capasso
Evp System Services And Chief Human Resources Officer, Clayton Fitzhugh
Svp And Chief Medical Officer, Donald Bignotti
Svp And Cio, Marcus B. Shipley
Evp Growth Strategy And Innovation, Scott Nordlund
President Saint Francis Hospital And Medical Center, John F. Rodis
Evp And Chief Clinical Officer, Mark I. Froimson
Evp Mission Integration, Mary Persico
Evp And Chief Population Health Officer, Barbara A. Walters
Vice President Labor Relations And Human Resources Operations, Martha Murphy
Vice President Supply Chain Operations, Clay Johnson
Vice President Reimbursement And Revenue Integrity, Lisa Wille
Vice President Clinical Integration, Thomas Anderson
Vice President Patient Financial Services, Linda Schaeffer
Vice President Client Services And Transformation, Chuck Lund
Vice President Clinical Quality Analytics And Improvement, Shanna Johnson
Vice President Asset Management, Beverly Erickson
Medical Records Director, Janice Walsh
Senior Vice President, Dina Richard
Senior Vice President, Paul Marceau
Vice President, Kathy Connor
Vice President Audit Services, Heidi Crosby
Vice President Of Ancillary, Rebekah Smith
Vice President Finance, Lori Shively
Vice President Service Management, Julie Moran
Vice President Technology Services, Frank Abate
Vice President Of Operational Excellence, Jonathan Maner
Vice President, Anna Butrie
Evp Chief Clinical Officer, Dan Roth
Vice President Operations, Anne Lewis
Evp Chief Medical Officer, Jeff Komins
Senior Vice President And Chief Nursing Officer, Nora Triola
Senior Vice President Ma And Partnership Development, Sheri Shapiro
Executive Vice President And Chief Human Resources Officer, Edmund Hodge
Executive Vice President And Chief Clinical Officer, Daniel Roth
Senior Vice President Insurance And Risk Management Services, Ruth Goodell
Vice President, Darren Vianueva
Vice President Advocacy And Government Relations, Daniel Keenan
Vice President Financial Operations And Budget, Kathy Ralston
Vice President, Katherine Zbanek
Vice President Executive Development, Anita Jensen
Vice President Mission Formation, Stephen Surprenant
Vice President Human Resources Strategy And Services, Mark Story
Vice President Provider Contracting And Reimbursement, Rick O'donnell
Vice President Sales And Marketing, Christopher Caserta
Senior Vice President Chief Medical Officer, Tammy Lundstrom
Vice President Finance, Lannie Checketts
Vice President, Brendan Dunnigan
Vice President, Maria Martinico
Vice President Human Resources, Karyn Doran
Operating Room Dir, DAWN PETERS
Director Of Medical Records, Kim Dudich
Senior Vice President Mission Integration Ethics, Philip Boyle
Vice President Performance Leadership, Sara Schmanske
Senior Vice President Chief Mission Officer, Bartholomew Rodrigues
Medical Records Director, Katie Wilson
Chair, Melanie C. Dreher
Assistant Treasurer Th Director Debt, Marianne Cunningham
Auditors: DELOITTE & TOUCHE LLP DETROIT

LOCATIONS

HQ: TRINITY HEALTH CORPORATION
20555 VICTOR PKWY, LIVONIA, MI 481527031
Phone: 734 343-1000
Web: WWW.TRINITY-HEALTH.ORG

Selected Facilities

California
Saint Agnes Medical Center (Fresno)
Idaho and Oregon
Saint Alphonsus Medical Center - Baker City
Saint Alph
Saint Alph
Saint Alphonsus Regional Medical Center (Boise)
Indiana
Saint Joseph Regional Medical Center (South Bend)
Saint Joseph Regional Medical Center (Plymouth)
Illinois
Loyola University Health System (Chicago)
Loyola University Medical Center
Loyola Gottlieb Memorial Hospital
Mercy Hospital & Medical Center (Chicago)
Iowa and Nebraska
Mercy Health Network (Clinton Des Moines Dubuque Dyersville Mason City New Hampton and Sioux City Iowa; Oakland Nebraska)
Maryland
Holy Cross Hospital (Silver Spring)
Michigan
Mercy Health Partners (Muskegon)
Mercy Hospital (Cadillac)
Mercy Hospital (Grayling)
Saint Joseph Mercy Health System (Ann Arbor)
Saint Mary's Health Care (Grand Rapids)
Ohio
Mount Carmel Health System (Columbus)

PRODUCTS/OPERATIONS

2014 Net Patient Revnue

	% of total
Medicare	38
Blue Cross	20
Medicaid	13
Uninsured	4
Commercial and other	25
Total	**100**

2014 Sales

	% of total
Net patient service revenuel less provision for bad debts	87
Capitation and premium revenue	5
Other revenue	8
Total	**100**

COMPETITORS

Advocate Health Care
Amedisys
Ascension Health
Beaumont Health System
Community Health Systems
Encompass Health
HCA
Henry Ford Health System
Hospice of Michigan
Johns Hopkins Medicine
Kindred Healthcare
Mayo Clinic
MedStar Health
Memorial Hospital & Health System
OhioHealth
St. Luke's Health System
Tenet Healthcare
Universal Health Services
University of Chicago Medical Center
VITAS Healthcare
Wheaton Franciscan Services

HISTORICAL FINANCIALS

Company Type: Private

Income Statement FYE: June 30

	REVENUE ($ mil.)	NET INCOME ($ mil.)	NET PROFIT MARGIN	EMPLOYEES
06/18	18,345	1,358	7.4%	51,100
06/15	1,375	19	1.4%	—
Annual Growth	137.1%	314.2%	—	—

2018 Year-End Financials

Return on assets: 5.2%
Return on equity: 10.2%
Current ratio: 1.90
Cash ($ mil.): 971

TRINITY HEALTH-MICHIGAN

EXECUTIVES

Ceo, Rebekah Smith
Cfo*, Mike Gusho
Director of Geriatric Programs, Mary Jo West
Coordinator, Catherine Popour
Coordinator, Jan Hansen
Coordinator, Karen Dalton
Coordinator, Kim Graham
Sleep Lab Manager, Rosemary Bruno
Director of Cyber Security, Shaun Swenson
Chief Pharmacy Informatics Off, Chris Manthey
Senior Vice President, Cynthia Fry

LOCATIONS

HQ: TRINITY HEALTH-MICHIGAN
20555 VICTOR PKWY, LIVONIA, MI 481527031
Phone: 810 985-1500
Web: WWW.STJOESHEALTH.ORG

HISTORICAL FINANCIALS

Company Type: Private

Income Statement FYE: June 30

	REVENUE ($ mil.)	NET INCOME ($ mil.)	NET PROFIT MARGIN	EMPLOYEES
06/18	3,595	303	8.4%	1,500
06/14	2,474	102	4.2%	—
06/13	2,475	138	5.6%	—
06/09	2,096	60	2.9%	—
Annual Growth	6.2%	19.6%	—	—

TRINITY MOTHER FRANCES HEALTH SYSTEM FOUNDATION

Trinity Mother Frances Health System Foundation (dba Trinity Mother Frances Hospitals and Clinics) has a complicated name but a simple mission: to improve patient health. Consisting of three general hospitals several specialist facilities and a large physicians' group Trinity Mother Frances serves northeastern Texas. Its largest acute-care facility is Mother Frances Hospital-Tyler with more than 400 beds offering comprehensive medical surgical trauma and cardiovascular care. Two smaller hospitals in Jacksonville and Winnsboro provide emergency diagnostic surgery and select specialty services. The Trinity Clinic is a multi-specialty physician group that includes 300 doctors in 36 community clinics.

Operations

Trinity Mother Frances Hospitals and Clinics' specialty facilities include the freestanding Trinity Mother Frances Rehabilitation Hospital in Tyler which has 75 beds and is operated through a joint venture with HealthSouth. It also operates the Tyler ContinueCARE Hospital a long-term acute care hospital located within the Mother Frances Hospital-Tyler as well as several urgent care centers.

Strategy

In 2010 the network added the 35-bed Mother Frances Hospital-Winnsboro facility when it took over control of the Texas Health Presbyterian Hospital Winnsboro from Texas Health Resources. The transfer was made to align the Winnsboro hospital with the main Tyler facility where the majority of specialized cases from Winnsboro were already being transferred.

The network also added a freestanding 72-bed cardiac facility the Louis and Peaches Owen Heart Hospital in Tyler. The first phase of the center was added to the existing Mother Frances Hospital-Tyler facilities in 2010; the second stage is a six-story freestanding tower adjacent to the Tyler hospital. Construction on the tower started in early 2011 and was completed by the end of 2012.

Additionally Trinity Mother Frances Hospitals and Clinics is investing in information technology initiatives. It began installing electronic health record (EHR) systems at its facilities during 2012 as part of the US government's health care improvement initiatives.

Company Background

Trinity Mother Frances Hospitals and Clinics was established by the 1995 merger of Mother Frances Hospital and the Trinity Clinic both founded in the 1930s.

EXECUTIVES

President, J. Lindsey Bradley
Evp And Coo, Ray Thompson
Ceo Mother Franes Hospital - Tyler, Laura Owen
President And Chief Medical Officer Tmf; President Trinity Clinic, Steven P. Keuer
Evp; Chief Of Anesthesia Trinity Clinic, Gifford Eckhout
Ceo Mother Frances Hospital - Jacksonville, Tom Cammack
Ceo Mother Frances Hospital - Winnsboro, Janet Coates
Ceo Louis And Peaches Owen Heart Hospital, John McGreevy
Ceo Continuecare Hospital, Stephanie Hyde
Ceo Trinity Mother Frances Rehabilitation Hospital, Sharla Anderson
Vp And Cio, Jeff Pearson
Vice President Of Construction, Kyle Rutherford
Vice President Operations, Chris Glenney
Vice President Finance, Joyce Hester
Senior Vice President Christus Trinity Clinic, Scott Smith
Director Physician Recruitment, Tonya Hamlin
Vice President Tmf Foundation, Mary Jackson
Vice President Revenue Cycle, Andrew Voneschenbach
Vp Of Hospital Based Providers, Christy Bush
Senior Vice President And Chief Human Resources Of, Thomas Wilken
Medical Director, John Larrinaga
Secretary, Regina Hollie
Secretary, Jennifer Copeland
Auditors: ERNST & YOUNG LLP DALLAS TX

LOCATIONS

HQ: TRINITY MOTHER FRANCES HEALTH SYSTEM FOUNDATION
800 E DAWSON ST, TYLER, TX 757012036
Phone: 903 531-5057
Web: WWW.CHRISTUSHEALTH.ORG

PRODUCTS/OPERATIONS

Selected Locations

DirectCARE (urgent care multiple sites)
Louis and Peaches Owen Heart Hospital Tyler
Mother Frances Hospital-Jacksonville
Mother Frances Hospital-Tyler
Mother Frances Hospital-Winnsboro
Trinity Clinics (physician practices multiple sites)
Trinity Mother Frances Rehabilitation Hospital-Tyler
Tyler ContinueCARE Hospital

Selected Services

Anesthesiology
Audiology
Bariatric Surgery Center
Cancer
Cardiac Services
Cardiothoracic Surgery
Critical Care Intensivists
Ear Nose & Throat
Emergency Medicine
Endocrinology
Gastroenterology Hepatology and Endoscopy
Family Medicine
General Surgeons
Genetics
Hospitalists
Imaging Radiology Mammography
Internal Medicine
Neonatology
Neuroscience Institute
Obstetrics & Gynecology
Occupational Medicine - Health At Work
Ophthalmology Optometry & Optical Services
Orthopedics
Pain Medicine
Pediatrics
Physical Medicine and Rehabilitation
Plastic Surgery
Podiatry
Psychiatry
Rehabilitation Hospital
Rheumatology
Sleep Medicine
Sports Medicine
Surgery Services
Trauma Services
Urgent Care
Urology Institute & Continence Center
Vascular Institute
Women & Children
WoundCARE

COMPETITORS

Community Health Systems
East Texas Medical Center Regional Healthcare
Good Shepherd Health System
HCA
Hunt Memorial
Memorial Health System of East Texas
Parkland Health & Hospital System
Southwestern Medical Center
Tenet Healthcare
The Methodist Health System
United Surgical Partners
Wadley Regional Medical Center
Woodland Heights Medical Center

HISTORICAL FINANCIALS

Company Type: Private

Income Statement FYE: June 30

	REVENUE ($ mil.)	NET INCOME ($ mil.)	NET PROFIT MARGIN	EMPLOYEES
06/13	653	21	3.3%	3,551
06/10	603	19	3.3%	—
06/09	901	0	—	—
Annual Growth	—	1364.1%	—	—

2013 Year-End Financials

Return on assets: 3.1%
Return on equity: 7.2%
Current ratio: 1.50
Cash ($ mil.): 47

TRUMAN ARNOLD COMPANIES

TAC (previously Truman Arnold Companies) is one of the largest independent fuel wholesalers and aviation service providers in the US. Its energy business markets and sells more than 2 billion gallons of fuel to customers in industries like energy retail trucking utilities mining and construction. The company supplies refined products like gasoline diesel biodiesel ethanol renewable fuels and Diesel Exhaust Fluid (a non-hazardous product). TAC also serves the aviation industry by selling aviation fuel and providing Fixed Base Operations (aircraft fueling hangar space and transport) through over 15 locations in the US. Providing private charter flights and aircraft maintenance services is a small part of the company's business. TAC was founded in 1964 as Truman Arnold Companies.

Operations

TAC operates through four major businesses: TACenergy; TAC Air; Keystone Aviation; and TAC Investments.

Based in Dallas Texas TACenergy sells an annual fuel volume of more than 2 billion gallons through a vast terminal supply network. This segment also provides a 24/7 logistics call center a bulk trading desk and a real-time inventory intelligence service (matching inventory supply with trading prices) that helps minimize fuel costs for customers.

TAC Air is the company's aviation division which sells competitively priced aviation fuel and provides Fixed Base Operation services including ground handling aircraft fueling hangar space aircraft maintenance cargo handling and de-icing. Through Keystone Aviation the company also provides private charter flights aircraft management and aircraft maintenance.

TAC Investments segment manages the company's capital by investing in a wide pool of assets.

Geographic Reach

TAC is headquartered in Dallas Texas. TAC Air FBO has over 15 locations including Arkansas Colorado Connecticut Kentucky and Louisiana among others.

Sales and Marketing

TACenergy sells branded retail fuel to a range of customers including gasoline and diesel retailers industrial users transportation oil & gas waste disposal & recycling trucking government agencies utilities mining and construction as well as other commercial user or reseller of fuel. The company has a vast terminal supply network with outlets across the continent plus a 24/7 logistical call center.

Strategy

The Arnold Companies is expanding its presence into New York with the addition of its 16th FBO location TAC Air - BUF at Buffalo Niagara International Airport. Acquiring Prior Aviation assets associated with its fixed base operations TAC Air also plans to maintain the 120 associates supporting these operations. The full range of FBO services including fuel hangar and aircraft handling as well as supporting the market's commercial airlines with into-plane fuel charter handling cargo services de-icing and airline maintenance will be offered by TAC Air.

Mergers and Acquisitions

In late 2020 TAC Air a division of TAC is expanding its presence into New York with the addition of its 16th FBO location TAC Air - BUF at Buffalo Niagara International Airport. Acquiring Prior Aviation assets associated with its fixed base operations TAC Air also plans to maintain the 120 associates supporting these operations. The full range of FBO services including fuel hangar and aircraft handling as well as supporting the market's commercial airlines with into-plane fuel charter handling cargo services de-icing and airline maintenance will be offered by TAC Air.

In late 2019 TACenergy a division of TAC acquired the US wholesale petroleum distribution business of IPC (USA) Inc (IPC). Terms of the sale between the companies were not disclosed. Increasing its west coast presence with a majority of the IPC sales team TACenergy will maintain offices in Santa Ana CA Sacramento CA and Seattle WA. The shared expertise and TACenergy resources will allow local sales to continue providing the service expected by existing IPC customers. Along with the competitive fuel prices and reliable supply the TACenergy network offers expanded opportunities to all customers.

Company Background

Truman Arnold Companies was founded in 1964 as a Texas-based Conoco Distributor. It once operated a chain of 125 Road Runner convenience stores in eight states before selling this network to Total Petroleum in 1989. It revived the brand in 2003. The company presently focuses on fuel marketing and providing aviation services doing business under the TAC business name.

EXECUTIVES

General Counsel And Senior Vice President, James H Day
President And Coo, Gregory A. (Greg) Arnold
Svp And Cfo, Steve McMillen
Vp And Cio, Michael Davis
Vice President Marketing, Tad Perryman
Chairman, Truman Arnold
Auditors: THOMAS & THOMAS PLLC TEXARKAN

LOCATIONS

HQ: TRUMAN ARNOLD COMPANIES
701 S ROBISON RD, TEXARKANA, TX 755016747
Phone: 903 794-3835
Web: WWW.THEARNOLDCOS.COM

COMPETITORS

Atlantic Aviation
Million Air
Petroleum Traders Corporation
Sun Coast Resources

HISTORICAL FINANCIALS

Company Type: Private

Income Statement FYE: September 30

	REVENUE ($ mil.)	NET INCOME ($ mil.)	NET PROFIT MARGIN	EMPLOYEES
09/18	3,174	18	0.6%	550
09/17	2,119	18	0.9%	—
09/16	1,525	18	1.2%	—
09/15	1,595	17	1.1%	—
Annual Growth	25.8%	1.2%	—	—

2018 Year-End Financials

Return on assets: 5.2%
Return on equity: 14.2%
Current ratio: 1.30
Cash ($ mil.): 2

TRUMAN MEDICAL CENTER, INCORPORATED

Truman Medical Center (TMC) provides primary and mental health care at two not-for-profit hospitals in the Kansas City (Missouri) area with a combined total of about 540 beds. Its Hospital Hill runs one of the busiest emergency rooms in Kansas City and is known for treatments related to asthma diabetes obstetrics ophthalmology weight management and women's health. TMC Lakewood is a leading academic medical center providing a range of health care services to the greater Kansas City metropolitan area including uninsured patients.

Operations

The hospital system has a combined capacity of more than 540 beds including 353 acute-care beds and 188 long-term-care beds. With a medical staff of more than 500 TMC admits more than 22000 patients and handles more than 322000 medical outpatient visits and more than 226000 mental health visits annually. It also treats more than 101000 emergency room patients every year.

Truman Medical Center Hospital Hill provides an array of acute care and outpatient services. In addition to Emergency Medicine and Trauma TMC Hospital Hill is also noted for treatments of asthma and diabetes and for providing obstetrics ophthalmology weight management and women's health programs.

TMC Lakewood is home to the University of Missouri Kansas City School of Medicine Community and Family Medicine Residency program.

Truman Medical Centers Behavioral Health is a leader in the treatment of mental health and substance abuse treatment. It serves more than 17000 patients a year and provides a comprehensive array of mental health and substance abuse treatment to persons living in the Kansas City Missouri metropolitan area.

Sales and Marketing

Medicare and Medicaid combined account for around half of TMC's net patient revenues; self-pay accounts represent about 35%.

Financial Performance

In fiscal 2014 (ended June) net revenues totaled $422 million.

Strategy

The system expands health care offerings by opening new care centers or by adding on to its existing ones. For example during 2014 it opened The Richard and Annette Bloch Cancer Center. It also opened Fairmount Family Medical Care in Western Independence Missouri a community that hadn't had a comprehensive health care facility since 2007.

It has also recently added a wound care center to its Hospital Hill campus.

Due to state and federal regulations TMC shut down the behavioral health emergency department at Hospital Hill in 2015. Going forward it will either treat incoming patients with acute mental health crises at its 47-bed standard emergency department or send them to another psychiatric facility.

EXECUTIVES

Cfo, Allen (Al) Johnson
Evp Clinical Coordination, Mark S. McPhee
Chief Medical Officer, Mark T. Steele
Coo Behavioral Health, Marsha L. Morgan
Svp Strategy Business Development And Performance Integration; Cio, Mitzi Cardenas
Corporate Quality Medical Director, Shauna R. Roberts
Chief Nursing Officer, Lynette Wheeler
President And Ceo, Charles W. (Charlie) Shields
Vp Professional Health Services, Lynda Donegan
Executive Director Tmc Charitable Foundation, Karlyn Wilkins
Chief Nursing Officer, Amy Peters
Director Of Physical Therapy, Joel Hennenfent
Director Of Pharmacy, Erin Pender
First Vice President, Jerre Wiggans
Vice President Audit And Compliance, Barbara Zubeck
Auditors: BKD LLP KANSAS CITY MO

LOCATIONS

HQ: TRUMAN MEDICAL CENTER, INCORPORATED
2301 HOLMES ST, KANSAS CITY, MO 641082677
Phone: 816 404-1000
Web: WWW.TRUMED.ORG

PRODUCTS/OPERATIONS

Truman Medical Center Hospital Hill
Asthma Center
The Birthplace
Cardiovascular Center
Chiropractic Services KC CORE
Dental Maxillofacial Surgery
Diabetes Center
Emergency Care
Eye Clinic
Eye Foundation
GI Gastrointestinal
Hospital Hill Medical Pavilion
Infectious Disease Clinic
Oncology
Orthopaedics
Pulmonary Fibrosis
Radiology Services
Rehabilitation Services
Sickle Cell Disease Center
Sleep Center
Trauma Services
TruMed Clinic
Weight Management
Women's Care Breast Center
Women's Health Services
TMC Lakewood
Family Medicine Center
Lakewood Family Birthplace
Chiropractic Services
Counseling Services Lakewood
Dental Services
Dental Services Elks Mobile
GI Gastrointestinal
Emergency Medicine
Eye Care Center
Lakewood Medical Pavilion
Longterm Care Center
Medical Detox
Orthopaedic Services
Outpatient Surgery Center
Podiatry
Rehabilitation Services
Sports Medicine
Women's Health Services

COMPETITORS

Ascension Health
Children's Mercy Hospital
CoxHealth
Saint Luke's Health System
Shawnee Mission Medical Center
University of Kansas Medical Center
Via Christi Health System

HISTORICAL FINANCIALS

Company Type: Private

Income Statement FYE: June 30

	REVENUE ($ mil.)	NET INCOME ($ mil.)	NET PROFIT MARGIN	EMPLOYEES
06/19	666	13	2.0%	3,000
06/18	562	22	4.0%	—
06/14	418	(78)	—	—
06/13	493	(4)	—	—
Annual Growth	5.1%	—	—	—

2019 Year-End Financials

Return on assets: 3.0%
Return on equity: 11.9%
Current ratio: 1.10
Cash ($ mil.): 14

TRUSTEES OF BOSTON COLLEGE

Students at Boston College (BC) get both academic excellence and the Red Sox. Operate in the city of Boston the university enrolls some 14600 students. It has a student-teacher ratio of 11:1. BC offers degrees in more than 50 fields of study through its eights schools and colleges on four campuses. Some programs include biology chemistry economics geology philosophy and theology. The university also has more than 35 research centers including the Institute for Scientific Research and the Center for International Higher Education. BC is one of the oldest Jesuit Catholic universities in the nation and has the largest Jesuit community in the world.

Operations

BC offers a variety of graduate degree programs in the humanities social sciences and natural sciences lead to Ph.D. M.A. and M.S. degrees. It include Classical Studies Earth and Environmental Sciences Geophysics History Philosophy and Theology Physics Political Science Psychology and Sociology.

The university is home to more than 35 centers and institutes designated for research and teaching. Research opportunities including participation in faculty research projects exist for both undergraduate and graduate students. It also houses 8 libraries with nearly 3 million volumes.

The cost of tuition stood at $70143.

Geographic Reach

The university has campuses in Brighton Chestnut Hill Dover and Newton Massachusetts. It also operates a campus in Dublin Ireland.

Company Background

The university was founded by Jesuits in 1863. During its first seven decades BC was an exclusively undergraduate institution that served sons of the Irish working class. Its liberal arts emphasis was on the Greek and Latin classics English and modern languages and philosophy and religion. Development into the college it is today did not begin until the 1920s when the Graduate School of Arts and Sciences the Law School and the Evening College (known today as the James A. Woods S.J. College of Advancing Studies) were inaugurated. All classes became co-educational in the 1970s and today BC has a fairly equal split among male and female students.

EXECUTIVES

Financial Vice President And Treasurer, Peter Mckenzie
Vice President Human Resources, Leo Sullivan
President, William P. Leahy
Chancellor, J. Donald Monan
Dean Carroll School Of Management, Andrew C. Boynton
Dean School Of Social Work, Alberto Godenzi
Evp, Patrick J. Keating
Vp Information Technology Services, Michael Bourque
Financial Vp And Treasurer, John D. Burke
Provost And Dean Of Faculties, David Quigley
Dean Of Students, Tom Mogan
Dean School Of Theology And Ministry, Mark Massa
Dean Connell School Of Nursing, Susan Gennaro
Dean Lynch School Of Education, Maureen E. Kenny
Dean Law School, Vincent Rougeau
Interim Dean Morrissey College Of Arts And Sciences, Gregory Kalscheur
Dean Woods College Of Advancing Studies, James Burns
Director Special Projects University Advancement Vice Presidents Office, Elizabeth McLain
Administrative Assistant University Advancement Vice Presidents Office, Judith Speed
Vice President, John Westman
Associate Vice President Human Resources, Robert Lewis
Associate Vice President For Student Affairs, George Arey
Vice President University Mission And, Joseph Appleyard
Assistant Vice President, Steven Sass
Associate Vice President Alumni Relations, Joy Moore
Department Chair Of English, Mary Crane
Vice President, Madeleine G Moore
Office Of The Executive Vice President, Jeanne Marquardt
Vice President For Research, Thomas Chiles
Vice President, Pat Ryan
Associate Vice President For Operations And Planning, Brenda Ricard
Administrative Asst. To Vp Student Affairs, Karen Fiorentino
Media Chair And Vice President, Luiza Justus
Vice President, Dan Bourque
Macro Social Work Intern Government Relations, Julia Macmahon
Associate Vice President Capital Giving, Christine Rinaldi
Associate Vice President, Thomas Mogan
Executive Vice President, Michael Lochhead
Vice President Operations, Kristen Moran
Vice President, Emily Manns

Senior Vice President, John Gallant
Vice President, Jack Burke
Vice President For Enterprise Services Division, Chris Meyer
Vice President, John Foole
Senior Vice President, Joseph Duggan
Vice President, Eleni Papadopoulas
Vice President, Mary Kessler
Vice President, Ryan Valle
Chairman, John F. Fish
Vice Chairman, Peter K. Markell, age 64
Secretary, Gloria Rufo
Investment Officer Office Of The Associate Treasurer, Travis Looker
Assistant Treasurer, Mark Conner
Board Member, Barbara Hebard
Executive Board Member, Emily Leogrande
Secretary Campus School, Susan O'donnell
Treasurer, Michael Mckie
Board Member, Rohan Dixit
Auditors: PRICEWATERHOUSECOOPERS LLP BO

LOCATIONS

HQ: TRUSTEES OF BOSTON COLLEGE
140 COMMONWEALTH AVE, CHESTNUT HILL, MA 024673800
Phone: 617 552-8000
Web: WWW.BC.EDU

PRODUCTS/OPERATIONS

Selected Colleges and Schools
Carolyn A. and Peter S. Lynch School of Education
College of Arts and Sciences
Graduate School of Arts and Sciences
Graduate School of Social Work
James A. Woods S.J. College of Advancing Studies
School of Law
School of Theology and Ministry
Wallace E. Carroll School of Management
William F. Connell School of Nursing

HISTORICAL FINANCIALS

Company Type: Private

Income Statement FYE: May 31

	REVENUE ($ mil.)	NET INCOME ($ mil.)	NET PROFIT MARGIN	EMPLOYEES
05/20	865	(41)	—	2,493
05/18	835	169	20.2%	—
05/17	798	279	34.9%	—
05/14	702	221	31.5%	—
Annual Growth	3.5%	—	—	—

2020 Year-End Financials

Return on assets: (-0.8%)
Return on equity: (-1.2%)
Current ratio: —
Cash ($ mil.): 21

TRUSTEES OF DARTMOUTH COLLEGE

Part of the esteemed Ivy League Dartmouth College is a private four-year liberal arts college with an enrollment of more than 6000 students. The university has an undergraduate college (offering about 40 programs) and graduate schools of business engineering and medicine plus graduate programs in the arts and sciences. Its student-teacher ratio is about 6:1. It is also home to a number of centers and institutes including Children's Hospital at Dartmouth; Dartmouth Center on Addiction Recovery and Education; and Center for Digital Strategies. Notable alumni include Daniel Webster Robert Frost Theodore "Dr. Seuss" Geisel and Nelson Rockefeller.

Operations

Dartmouth is located on a 270-acre campus located in Hanover New Hampshire. It also conducts study-abroad programs in about 20 countries. Through its collective institutes and graduate schools the college conducts a number of research programs in areas including security capitalism energy and infectious disease. Altogether it has about 50 research-focused groups centers and institutes and attracts more than $200 million in sponsored research funding per year.

Financial Performance

For fiscal year 2011 Dartmouth reported revenues of some $763 million. Operating expenses for fiscal 2011 were some $738 million. Dartmouth has an endowment of some $3.5 billion.

Company Background

Dartmouth is the nation's ninth oldest college founded in 1769 by Reverend Eleazar Wheelock a Congregational minister from Connecticut. Land for its campus in Hanover New Hampshire was conveyed by a charter from King George III; it was the last institution of higher education established in the US under colonial rule.

EXECUTIVES

Pres, Philip J Hanlon
Assistant Professor, John D Trout
Assistant Director, Karl Von Dubuche
Assistant Professor, Kelsey Wheeler
Assistant Professor, Linda M Hoover
Assistant Professor, Michael E Cox
Assistant Professor, Beverly J Entwisle
Assistant Professor, Marc L Bertrand
Assistant Professor, Richard F Hobbs
Assistant Professor, William B Gunn
Assistant Professor, Ralph D Beasley
Auditors: PRICEWATERHOUSECOOPERS LLP B

LOCATIONS

HQ: TRUSTEES OF DARTMOUTH COLLEGE
20 LEBANON ST, HANOVER, NH 037553564
Phone: 603 646-1110
Web: WWW.HOME.DARTMOUTH.EDU

PRODUCTS/OPERATIONS

Selected Divisions
Admissions and Financial Aid
Advancement Office
Campus Planning and Facilities
Dean of the College
Faculty of the Arts & Sciences
Finance and Administration
Geisel School of Medicine
President's Office
Provost's Office
Thayer School of Engineering
The Trustees of Dartmouth College
Tuck School of Business

HISTORICAL FINANCIALS

Company Type: Private

Income Statement FYE: June 30

	REVENUE ($ mil.)	NET INCOME ($ mil.)	NET PROFIT MARGIN	EMPLOYEES
06/17	1,369	691	50.5%	5,000
06/16	859	(301)	—	—
06/15	876	236	27.0%	—
Annual Growth	25.0%	71.0%	—	—

2017 Year-End Financials

Return on assets: 8.8%
Return on equity: 12.1%
Current ratio: —
Cash ($ mil.): 176

TRUSTEES OF INDIANA UNIVERSITY

Indiana University has been schooling Hoosiers (and others) since 1820. With a population of some 115000 students from all 50 states and more than 130 countries the university offers more than 1000 associate baccalaureate master's professional and doctoral degree programs at eight campuses: flagship institution IU-Bloomington; regional campuses in Fort Wayne Gary Kokomo New Albany Richmond and South Bend; and an urban campus in Indianapolis that is operated with Purdue University. The university has about 20000 faculty and professional and support staff. It has 200 research centers and institutes and offers courses in more than 70 languages.

Operations

The university offers more than 200 undergraduate majors and more than 300 graduate programs; it also boasts more than 300 study-abroad programs. It has a student-teacher ratio of about 17:1.

Indiana University has more than 306000 total living alumni including nearly 248000 Indiana residents. For the academic year 2014-15 the university charged undergraduate tuition and fees of $10388 for residents and $33240 for non-residents. It awarded $1.1 billion in financial aid that year.

Indiana University-Purdue University Indianapolis (IUPUI) is considered an "up and coming" university by U.S. News and World Report . With nearly 20 schools and degrees granted in more than 200 programs IUPUI enrolls more than 30000 students from both the Indiana University and Purdue University systems.

The IPFW Office of Research Engagement and Sponsored Programs supports research business efforts and establishes partnerships with area public and private organizations.

Geographic Reach

The university has major campuses in Bloomington and Indianapolis and regional campuses in Gary Kokomo New Albany Richmond and South Bend. It enrolls more than 50% of the students from the St. Joseph County area.

Financial Performance

Indiana University's revenues grew 1% in fiscal year 2015 to $2.2 billion. The largest single source of operating revenues for the university is student tuition and fees (accounting for 55% of total revenues). That year a 4% increase in student fees helped to offset a 40% decline in sales and services of educational units.

Net income fell 31% to $138 million in 2015 as interest earnings declined. Operating cash outflow remained flat at $534 million largely due to higher payments to employees.

Strategy

Indiana University is dedicated to keeping tuition increases as low as possible and providing extensive financial aid for qualified students. It also aims to educate its students on managing and reducing their student loan debt.

The university plans to expand and renovate its School of Public and Environmental Affairs building; the project will cost some $12 million and is expected to be complete in early 2017. In mid-2015 a new hall housing the Lilly Family School of Philanthropy was opened on the IUPUI campus. Also that year Indiana University completed the construction of a $53 million building for the new School of Global and International Studies.

The university will also continue to expand its Global Gateway Network. It officially opened offices in China and India in 2014; other target markets include the Middle East Europe Latin America and Africa.

Company Background

An 1820 statute created the Indiana Seminary the predecessor to Indiana University. In 1828 the legislature changed the name of the institution to Indiana College and in 1838 it established Indiana University.

EXECUTIVES

President, Michael A. McRobbie
Chancellor Iu Southeast, Sandra R. Patterson-Randles
Chancellor Iu South Bend, Una Mae Reck
Evp And Chancellor Iu-purdue University Indianapolis, Charles R. Bantz
Provost And Evp, Lauren Robel
Interim Vp Cfo And Treasurer, MaryFrances McCourt
Evp University Regional Affairs Planning And Policy, John S. Applegate
Vp Information Technology And Cio, Bradley C. (Brad) Wheeler
Chancellor Iu Northwest, William J. Lowe
Interim Chancellor Iu East, Larry Richards
Interim Chancellor Iu Kokomo, Susan Sciame-Giesecke
Chancellor Iu-purdue University Fort Wayne, Vicky L. Carwein
President Of Indiana University On, Alfred Ryors
President To Assume Office, David Jordan
President And Professor Of Botany At Indiana University, John Coulter
President On, John Ryan
Vice President For Engagement, William Stephan
Director Of Admissions And Financial Aid, Espen Jensen
Vice President, William Heller
Vice President Events, Bryan Povlinski
Vice President Information Systems, Beverly Church
Assoc. Vice President For International Affairs, Charles Reafsnyder
Vice President Of External, Kerwin Leonard
Vice President, Brad Reis
Vice President International Affairs, Patrick O'Meara
Associate Vice President, Dennis Cromwell
Assistant Vice President Finance, Linda Hunt
Associate Vice President Of Finance, Stew Cobine
Executive Vice President, Peter Bogdanovich
Associate Vice President And Chief Human Resources Officer, John Whelan
Vice President, Julie Head
Vice President Of Engagement, Garrett Lance
Assoc Vice President Information Technology, Brad Wheeler
Director Of Admissions And Financial Aid, James Holmen
Vice President Information Technology Advancement Web Communications, Duane Schau
Vice President, Mike Sample
Vice President Of Information Technology, John Pillans
Assistant Vice President Networks, Dave Jent
Associate Vice President Marketing, Rob Zinkan
Senior Vice President Marketing, Mike Fowler
Mathematics Department Chair, Elizabeth Housworth
Assistant Vice President, Philip Seabrook
Office Of The Vice President For Public Affairs And Government Relations (pagr), Martin McCrory
Vice President Marketing, John Andrews
Vice President Sales, Ivan Strand
Director Of Admissions, Dee Rillo
Vice President Of Finance, Eric Anderson
Vice President Finance, Gina Reel
Vice President And President Elect, Ballard C Campbell
Chief Of Staff Office Of The Vice President For Information Technology, Daniel Calarco
Director Of Admissions, Janet Hein
Senior Vice President Finance, John Buuck
Associate Vice President, James Kennedy
Senior Vice President, Tyna Hunnicutt
Department Head, Vaughn Nuest
Vice President, Jalen Walker
Vice President Of Communications, Andrew Harder
Vice President Of Lending And Hoosier Social Impact Fund, Molly Hallahan
Vice President, Bob Mooney
Vice President, Charlie Nelms
Assoc Vice President Univ Planning Inst Rsrch, Vic Borden
Executive Vice President Of Wright Quad, John Arcaro
Assistant Vice President Of Marketing, Heeter Aimee
Panhellenic Association Vice President Of Recruitment, Monica Dirk
Vice President Of Finance Spruce Hall Student Government, Brianna Wold
Associate Vice President University Academic Affairs, Steve Keucher
Associate Vice President For International Development And Research, Teshome Alemneh
Vice President Of Restructuring Team, Luxi Zhang
Vice President Of Finance Women, Megan Christopher
Vice President, Abhishek Bansal
Vice President, Jimmy Rosen
Vice President Of Membership, Allison Newman
Vice President, Kathryn Lin
Senior Vice President, John Hobson
Vp Of Internal Controls, Josh Hafkin
Vice President Technology, Mitchell Mayer
Vice Provost, Kelly D Rollins
Vp Of Social Events, Baylee Whitehead
Vice Chair, Patrick A. Shoulders
Chair, William R. Cast
Secretary, Sara Sturgeon
Treasurer, Penny Hsu
Treasurer, Teresa Andrews
Secretary, Kim Denny
Department Secretary, Robert Rowe
Accounting Representative And Graduate Secretary, Melissa Hunt
Intramural Secretary, LaMinda Walls
Secretary, Joyce Regester
Treasurer, Donald Lukes
Treasurer Kelley Student Government, Luke Hochgesang
Deputy Treasurer, Gentry Patrick Lee
Athletic Secretary, Sha Sarraf Ravit
Secretary, Wright Nathan A
Senior Secretary, Marilyn Horne
Secretary Treasurer, Ho-fung Hung
(treasurer), Steve Kaplin
Secretary, Donna Levi
Board Member, Hannah Martin
Treasurer, Jim Buher
Secretary Football, Montgomery Lyman
Treasurer, Rachel Sendrow
Auditors: PAUL D JOYCE CPA STATE EXAM

LOCATIONS

HQ: TRUSTEES OF INDIANA UNIVERSITY
107 S INDIANA AVE, BLOOMINGTON, IN 474057000
Phone: 812 855-4848
Web: WWW.TRUSTEES.IU.EDU

PRODUCTS/OPERATIONS

2015 Sales

	$ mil.	% of total
Student fees	1,118	51
Auxiliary enterprises	318	14
Federal grants & contracts	293	13
Non-governement grants & contracts	136	6
Sales and services of educational units	39	2
State & local grants & contracts	21	1
Other revenue	279	13
Total	**2,207**	**100**

HISTORICAL FINANCIALS

Company Type: Private

Income Statement FYE: June 30

	REVENUE ($ mil.)	NET INCOME ($ mil.)	NET PROFIT MARGIN	EMPLOYEES
06/16	2,256	105	4.7%	16,000
06/15	2,207	138	6.3%	—
06/14	2,195	201	9.2%	—
06/13	2,146	189	8.8%	—
Annual Growth	1.7%	(17.7%)	—	—

2016 Year-End Financials

Return on assets: 2.0%
Return on equity: 2.8%
Current ratio: 1.60
Cash ($ mil.): 345

TRUSTEES OF THE ESTATE OF BERNICE PAUAHI BISHOP

Kamehameha Schools provides an education fit for a king ... or queen. The private charitable trust was founded and endowed by Princess Bernice Pauahi Bishop great granddaughter and last royal descendant of Kamehameha the Great. One of the largest independent schools in the US Kamehameha educates more than 5000 elementary middle school and high school students many of whom board at one of its three Hawaii campuses. In addition it operates some 30 preschools with a total enrollment of about 1500. Kamehameha Schools is also the largest private property owner in the state of Hawaii and uses the proceeds from its real estate operations to support its schools.

EXECUTIVES

Vice President Strategic Planning And Implementation, Christopher Pating
Vice President Human Resources, Winona White
Legal Secretary, Diane Lee
Auditors: PRICEWATERHOUSECOOPERS LLP WA

LOCATIONS

HQ: TRUSTEES OF THE ESTATE OF BERNICE PAUAHI BISHOP
567 S KING ST STE 200, HONOLULU, HI 968133079
Phone: 808 523-6200
Web: WWW.KSBE.EDU

COMPETITORS

Edison Learning
Learning Care Group

HISTORICAL FINANCIALS

Company Type: Private

Income Statement FYE: June 30

	REVENUE ($ mil.)	NET INCOME ($ mil.)	NET PROFIT MARGIN	EMPLOYEES
06/15	767	333	43.5%	1,500
06/14	915	482	52.7%	—
06/13	519	109	21.1%	—
06/10	333	(21)	—	—
Annual Growth	18.1%	—	—	—

2015 Year-End Financials

Return on assets: 3.7%
Return on equity: 4.0%
Current ratio: 0.60
Cash ($ mil.): 18

TRUSTEES OF TUFTS COLLEGE

Tufts University wants to light up the minds of New England scholars. The school offers undergraduate and graduate degrees in areas such as education engineering psychology art English music and medicine. The university enrolls some 11000 students and has 1300 faculty members and it offers classes in 70 fields at three campuses in Massachusetts (Boston Medford/Somerville and Grafton). It also has an international campus in Talloires France. Tufts University's Fletcher School of Law and Diplomacy is the oldest continuous international relations graduate program in the country. The school is also home to New England's only Veterinary School.

Operations

Tufts University has a number of research programs at all three campuses including clinical studies in medical dental veterinary and nutritional fields. It also has research programs in areas such as biology engineering and technology many of which are funded through grants and fellowship funds.

Financial Performance

Tufts University has an endowment of about $1.1 billion.

Strategy

Tufts University is working to expand the resources its School of Medicine. In 2012 it moved to add a new medical research lab to study serious infectious diseases (such as tuberculosis) within the Biomedical Research and Public Health Building. It also expanded the Cummings School of Veterinary Medicine by adding a new clinic for the care and study of pets with obesity problems. The university also expands by adding new degree programs such as a doctorate in mamalian genetics in 2011.

Company Background

Tufts was founded in 1852 through a land donation by Boston-area businessman Charles Tufts to the Universalist Church. The school adopted its motto Pax et Lux (Peace and Light) in 1857.

EXECUTIVES

Vice President For Operations, Linda Snyder
Vice President For Human Resources, Julien Carter
Vice President Campus Relations, Talia Inbar
Vice President, Suvi Rajadurai
National Service Product Manager Corporate Vice President Xr, Casey Tray
Co Vice President, Jennifer Kim
Vice President, Kimberly Rzepecki
Secretary, Hannah Gould
Auditors: PRICEWATERHOUSECOOPERS LLP BO

LOCATIONS

HQ: TRUSTEES OF TUFTS COLLEGE
169 HOLLAND ST STE 318, SOMERVILLE, MA 021442401
Phone: 617 628-5000
Web: WWW.TUFTS.EDU

PRODUCTS/OPERATIONS

Schools & Colleges

Cummings School of Veterinary Science
Graduate School of Arts & Sciences
The Fletcher School
Friedman School of Nutrition Science and Policy
Sackler School of Graduate Biomedical Sciences
School of Arts & Sciences
School of Dental Medicine
School of Engineering
School of Medicine
Tisch College of Citizenship and Public Service

HISTORICAL FINANCIALS

Company Type: Private

Income Statement FYE: June 30

	REVENUE ($ mil.)	NET INCOME ($ mil.)	NET PROFIT MARGIN	EMPLOYEES
06/15	914	(25)	—	4,100
06/14	965	68	7.1%	—
06/13	768	127	16.6%	—
06/12	769	(100)	—	—
Annual Growth	5.9%	—	—	—

2015 Year-End Financials

Return on assets: (-0.8%)
Return on equity: (-1.1%)
Current ratio: 0.20
Cash ($ mil.): 37

TRUVEN HOLDING CORP.

EXECUTIVES

Pres- Ceo, Mike Boswood
Exec V Pres, Phil Buckingham
Exec V Pres, Jon Newpol
Coo, Roy Martin
Gen Counsel, Andra Heller
Senior Director Information Te, Bryan Smith
Director Account Management, Roy Crowdis
Auditors: PRICEWATERHOUSECOOPERS LLP NE

LOCATIONS

HQ: TRUVEN HOLDING CORP.
100 PHOENIX DR STE 100 # 100, ANN ARBOR, MI 481082600
Phone: 734 913-3000
Web: WWW.IBM.COM

HISTORICAL FINANCIALS

Company Type: Private

Income Statement FYE: December 31

	REVENUE ($ mil.)	NET INCOME ($ mil.)	NET PROFIT MARGIN	EMPLOYEES
12/15	610	(75)	—	2,110
12/14	544	(37)	—	—
12/13	492	(344)	—	—
12/12	241	(54)	—	—
Annual Growth	36.2%	—	—	—

2015 Year-End Financials

Return on assets: (-6.4%)
Return on equity: —
Current ratio: 0.80
Cash ($ mil.): 14

TUCSON MEDICAL CENTER

EXECUTIVES

Pres-Ceo, Judith F Rich
V Pres*, Linda Wojtowicz
Chief Medical Offc, Palmer Evans
Internist, Jeffrey Robertson
Adminstrative Associate, Leanna Dominguez
Senior Network Engineer, Marcus Medina
Executive Assistant, Becky Hiser
Manager Labor, Debra Derck
Registered Nurse, Erica Kaercher
Vice President, Julia Strange
Chief Human Resources Officer, Alex Horvath

LOCATIONS

HQ: TUCSON MEDICAL CENTER
5301 E GRANT RD, TUCSON, AZ 857122874
Phone: 520 327-5461
Web: WWW.TMCAZ.COM

HISTORICAL FINANCIALS

Company Type: Private

Income Statement FYE: December 31

	REVENUE ($ mil.)	NET INCOME ($ mil.)	NET PROFIT MARGIN	EMPLOYEES
12/17	559	19	3.4%	4,455
12/14	449	12	2.8%	—
12/13	462	16	3.5%	—
Annual Growth	4.9%	4.5%	—	—

2017 Year-End Financials

Return on assets: 4.1%
Return on equity: 7.8%
Current ratio: 0.70
Cash ($ mil.): 29

TUDOR INVESTMENT CORPORATION

EXECUTIVES

Managing Director And Deputy General Counsel, Steve Waldman
Vice President Investor Relations, Susan Briggs
Vice President, Miriam Roiter
Vice President, Alberto Antonini
Vice President Loan Operations, Daniel Silva
Secretary, Stephen Waldman
Auditors: ERNST & YOUNG LLP NEW YORK N

LOCATIONS

HQ: TUDOR INVESTMENT CORPORATION
200 ELM ST STE 200 # 200, STAMFORD, CT 069023826
Phone: 203 863-6700
Web: WWW.TUDOR.COM

COMPETITORS

Actua
Draper Fisher Jurvetson
EnTrust Capital
Hummer Winblad
Kleiner Perkins
Menlo Ventures
NEA
US Venture Partners
Wexford Capital
vCap Investments

HISTORICAL FINANCIALS

Company Type: Private

Income Statement — FYE: December 31

	ASSETS ($ mil.)	NET INCOME ($ mil.)	INCOME AS % OF ASSETS	EMPLOYEES
12/15	831	222	26.7%	291
12/14	819	(80)	—	—
12/13	905	486	53.7%	—
12/11	624	187	30.0%	—
Annual Growth	7.4%	4.4%	—	—

2015 Year-End Financials

Return on assets: 26.7%
Return on equity: 47.5%
Sales ($ mil): 784

TUFTS MEDICAL CENTER, INC.

EXECUTIVES

Int Pres-Ceo, Michael Wagner
Chb*, Malcolm L Sherman
Pres*, Deeb Salem
Cmo*, Saul N Weingart
Professor of Medicine, John Wong
Senior Vice President CIO, Bill Shickolovich
Director, Brian Cohen
Director, Chenchen Wang
Trauma Program Manager, Cheryl Webber
Director of Research, Ed Saltzman
Supervisor Ambulatory Clinics, Geraldine Flaherty
Auditors: DELOITTE & TOUCHE LLP BOSTON

LOCATIONS

HQ: TUFTS MEDICAL CENTER, INC.
800 WASHINGTON ST, BOSTON, MA 021111552
Phone: 617 636-2254
Web: WWW.TUFTSMEDICALCENTER.ORG

HISTORICAL FINANCIALS

Company Type: Private

Income Statement — FYE: September 30

	REVENUE ($ mil.)	NET INCOME ($ mil.)	NET PROFIT MARGIN	EMPLOYEES
09/18	1,121	44	4.0%	3,800
09/17	681	12	1.8%	—
09/16	646	14	2.3%	—
09/15	595	(18)	—	—
Annual Growth	23.5%	—	—	—

2018 Year-End Financials

Return on assets: 4.8%
Return on equity: 18.0%
Current ratio: 1.30
Cash ($ mil.): 72

TURNER CONSTRUCTION COMPANY INC

Turner Construction has been the mastermind for scores of head-turning projects for more than a century. The company that built Madison Square Garden has ranked among the leading general builders in the US since the early 1900s. Turner provides construction and project management services for commercial and multifamily buildings airports and stadiums as well as correctional educational entertainment and manufacturing facilities. The company is also a leader in sustainable or green building practices. Founded in 1902 by Henry Turner the company is the main operating unit of The Turner Corporation which is a subsidiary of German construction group HOCHTIEF.

Operations

Turner Construction works on some 1500 projects each year. For decades Turner has kept tabs on construction prices with its quarterly Building Cost Index which forecasts construction costs by considering labor rates productivity and material prices.

The index is used by federal and state governments to track building costs and pricing trends.

As part of HOCHTIEF's Americas division Turner works alongside other contractors in the US and Canada such as Flatiron its subsidiary E.E. Cruz and Clark Builders.

Geographic Reach

Headquartered in New York Turner Construction has offices across North America and with a presence in about 20 countries. It has operations in Latin America and the Caribbean India Europe Southeast Asia and the Middle East.

Sales and Marketing

Turner Construction works on projects in industries including aviation transportation commercial entertainment government green building manufacturing pharmaceutical research & development retail and sports.

Company Background

Notable projects in Turner Construction's history include the World War II Memorial in Washington DC the John F. Kennedy Memorial Library in Boston and the Rock and Roll Hall of Fame. Turner also built the new Yankee Stadium in New York. The company reached a milestone in 2008 by inking its 15000th major contract.

EXECUTIVES

President, Peter J. Davoren
Vp, Stephen W. Fort
Evp (new York New Jersey Maryland Pennsylvania Connecticut And New England), Pasquale A. (Pat) Di Filippo
Svp, Michael J. (Mike) Kuntz
Svp, Mark A. Boyle
Evp (ohio Nashville Huntsville Atlanta Florida And The Carolinas), Richard P. Homan
Vp, Thomas J. (Tom) Manahan
Svp; President And Ceo Turner International, Abrar Sheriff
Svp And Cfo, Karen O. Gould
Svp (mid-atlantic And Southeast), Tom Reilly
President The Lathrop Company, Steve Johnson
Vp And Construction Executive, Robert Hubner
Vice President, Neil D Jensen
Vice President, Phillip Parker
Senior Vice President, Christa Andresky
Vice President, Christoph Verbeek
Vice President Business Integration, Travis Cole
Vp And Operations Manager Of Central Texas, Jeremiah Hudson
Vice President Operations Manager, Dan VonKossovsky
Vice President And General Manager, Tom Stachowiak
Vice President And Financial Manager, Sarah Garner
Vice President And Construction Executive, Bob Grace
Vp And Operations Manager Of Connecticut, Tom Dutchyshyn
Vice President, Dave Welber
Executive Vice President Operational Services, David Benton
Vice President, Stephen J Spaulding
Vice President, Carlo A Disilvestro
Vice President And Construction Executive Middle Atlantic, Derek Brown
Vice President, Peter S Ramstedt
Vice President, Davey Mass
Vp Of Special Projects Division Of Dallas, Nick Barker
Vice President, Douglas W Cooper
Vice President, Charles Egbert
Vice President, Maureen Kirkpatrick
Vice President, Filippo Restivo
Auditors: DELOITTE & TOUCHE LLP PRINCET

LOCATIONS

HQ: TURNER CONSTRUCTION COMPANY INC
375 HUDSON ST FL 6, NEW YORK, NY 100143667
Phone: 212 229-6000
Web: WWW.TURNERCONSTRUCTION.COM

PRODUCTS/OPERATIONS

Selected Services

Turner Engineering Group
Design+Build
Turner Logistics: Procurement Services
Medical Planning and Procurement
Building Information Modeling (BIM)
Lean Construction

COMPETITORS

Bechtel
C. G. Schmidt
Catamount Constructors
Dimeo Construction
DooleyMack
English Construction Company
F.A. Wilhelm
Fluor
Gilbane Building Company
Hensel Phelps Construction
Hunt Construction
Jacobs Engineering
PCL Employees Holdings
Parsons Corporation
Peter Kiewit Sons'
Shook National
Skanska USA Building
Structure Tone
Tully Construction
Tutor Perini
Winter Construction

HISTORICAL FINANCIALS

Company Type: Private

Income Statement — FYE: December 31

	REVENUE ($ mil.)	NET INCOME ($ mil.)	NET PROFIT MARGIN	EMPLOYEES
12/14	10,516	96	0.9%	5,000
12/13	9,488	76	0.8%	—
12/12	8,552	70	0.8%	—
Annual Growth	10.9%	17.2%	—	—

2014 Year-End Financials

Return on assets: 2.8%
Return on equity: 14.1%
Current ratio: 1.10
Cash ($ mil.): 188

TURTLE & HUGHES, INC

Turtle & Hughes' longevity has demonstrated that slow and steady really does win the race when it comes to distributing electrical and industrial equipment. The company's exhaustive lineup is sold through two divisions: Electrical/Industrial Distribution which operates in more than 15 branches and a pair of distribution centers providing one of the industry's most comprehensive ranges of services and solutions and Turtle & Hughes Integrated Supply (THIS) which provides comprehensive outsource procurement for MRO and storeroom management solutions. Its customers include industrial and construction companies electrical contractors export and utilities and some Fortune 100 companies. Family-owned the company is led by its first non-family CEO Kathleen Shanahan.

Operations

Turtle & Hughes provides electrical products such as alarms signals and annunciators; anchors and plugs; automation products; ballasts; batteries and flashlights; boxes and covers; bus ducts and switchgears; transformers; wires cables and cords; wiring accessories and devices; and others.

The company also offers industrial products such as adhesives/tapes and compounds carbide tools cutting tools fasteners lubricating devices material handling products power transmissions precision tools soldering equipment valves struts/channels tooling accessories and other products.

Geographic Reach

Turtle & Hughes headquartered in Linden New Jersey operates through about 20 branches across the US.

Company Background

Turtle & Hughes was founded in 1923 as an electrical supply house.

EXECUTIVES

Svp, Jack Sinagra
Manager Marketing, Jayne Millard
Manager Corporate Operations, Chuck Noll
Evp; Branch Manager Bridgewater Distribution Center And Plainfield Branch, Rick Reffler
Executive Vice President Build A Brain Trust, Randy Roessle
President, Michael DeVoney
Chief Financial Officer, Chris Rausch
Vice President, Peter Landers
Vp Export Sales, Abdul Hooda
National Accounts Manager, Blake Varbero
National Sales Manager, Melissa Hartpence
Executive Vice President, Randall Roessle
Vice President Sales, Anthony Ventola
Senior Vice President, Al Fernandes
Vice President, William Wresch
Vice President Sales, Ken Pileggi
Vice President And General Manager, Jeff Stroin
Executive Vice President, Ken Mccauley
Executive Vice President, Mark Crowdis
Vice President, Dennis Albert
Chairman President And Ceo, Suzanne Turtle Millard
Auditors: EISNERAMPER LLP ISELIN NEW J

LOCATIONS

HQ: TURTLE & HUGHES, INC
1900 LOWER RD, LINDEN, NJ 070366586
Phone: 732 574-3600
Web: WWW.TURTLE.COM

PRODUCTS/OPERATIONS

Selected Products

Datacom categories
- Anchors and fasteners
- Burial products/innerduct
- Cabinets and enclosures
- Cable management
- Cable tray/ladder rack
- Category rated and coax cable
- Connectivity
- Fiber-optic cable
- Hand tools
- Outside plant
- Power protection
- Raceway and duct systems
- Safety
- Security fencing
- Splices connectors and lugs
- Tools testers and safety

Electrical categories
- Alarms annunciators and signals
- Anchors and plugs
- Automation products
- Ballasts and transformers
- Batteries and flashlights
- Box enclosures
- Breakers panels and switchgears
- Cable trays and struts
- Conduit fittings
- Cord connectors
- Dimming controls
- Electrical tools
- Emergency lighting
- Enclosures
- Fans
- Fluorescent lighting
- Fuse holders and terminal blocks
- Generators
- Groundings
- Heat shrink
- Heating
- High-bay lighting
- Incandescent lighting
- Lamps
- Limit temp. and proximity switch
- Lugs and terminals
- Metering equipment
- Motor control
- Motors AC and DC drivers
- Outdoor lighting
- Pole line products
- Programmable controls
- Relays
- Strut/channel
- Test equipment
- Time clocks
- Transformers
- Wire cable and cord
- Wiring accessories
- Wiring devices

Industrial categories
- Adhesives and tapes
- Brushes and brooms
- Carbide tools
- Cutting fluid/lubricant
- Cutting tools
- Fasteners
- Hand tools
- Hoist chain and accessories
- Industrial abrasives
- Janitorial paper supplies
- Ladders
- Locks
- Lubricating devices
- Material handling
- MRO supplies
- Paint/markets
- Pipe hangers
- Pipe valves and fittings
- Pneumatics
- Pneumatic tools
- Power tools
- Safety equipment
- Saw blades
- Shim/shim stock
- Solenoid valves
- Strut/channel
- Tooling accessories

COMPETITORS

C. R. Laurence
Consolidated Electrical
Dillon Supply
Graybar Electric
Indoff
Interline Brands
Kennametal
MSC Industrial Direct
Prime Advantage
Rexel Inc.
Sonepar USA
Steiner Electric
W.W. Grainger
WESCO International

HISTORICAL FINANCIALS

Company Type: Private

Income Statement — FYE: September 30

	REVENUE ($ mil.)	NET INCOME ($ mil.)	NET PROFIT MARGIN	EMPLOYEES
09/19	758	21	2.8%	900
09/18	754	20	2.7%	—
09/17	671	18	2.7%	—
09/16	628	16	2.6%	—
Annual Growth	6.4%	8.9%	—	—

2019 Year-End Financials

Return on assets: 8.1%
Return on equity: 15.8%
Current ratio: 2.00
Cash ($ mil.): 11

U.S. GENERAL SERVICES ADMINISTRATION

The U.S. General Services Administration (GSA) manages the rental of more than 370 million square feet of real estate in US government-owned properties. In addition to acting as the government's landlord in obtaining office space for over a million federal workers the GSA also manages properties and supplies equipment telecommunications and information technology products to its customer agencies. It spends some $55 billion annually for goods and services supporting about 8700 buildings and more than 250000 vehicles. The agency operates through divisions including the Federal Acquisition Service and Public Buildings Service. The GSA was established in 1949 to streamline the administrative work of the federal government.

Operations

GSA comprises the Federal Acquisition Service (FAS) the Public Buildings Service (PBS) and the Office of Government-wide Policy (OGP). In addition it operates about 10 staff offices and a handful of independent offices. FAS and PBS each generate about half of the agency's revenue; the OGP does not contribute to overall revenue.

Through a network of service providers FAS delivers information technology products and services telecommunications services travel and transportation management motor vehicles and fleet services and issues more than 35 million charge cards.

PBS operates within two divisions?workspace acquisition and property management. It acquires space for the federal government through new construction and leasing and leases almost 370 million square feet of workspace in more than 8700 buildings about 500 of which are on the National Register of Historic Places. PBS also manages the disposal of unused properties. In 2018 it disposed of 140 assets generating more than $123 million in proceeds.

The OGP develops government policy and performance standards and provides data analysis and transparent reporting to drive efficiency across key administrative areas including travel and transportation acquisition fleet management information technology modernization and real estate management.

Geographic Reach

Headquartered in Washington DC the U.S. General Services Administration provides services and support to more than 60 Federal departments and agencies. It delivers goods and services across the country and overseas through more than 10 regional offices located in major US cities.

Strategy

The GSA has been working to streamline access to its Federal marketplace by implementing more efficient systems and processes with a focus on IT modernization data analytics and change management. In 2018 it made data from the government's real property inventory available to the public for the first time making it easier to identify and dispose of underused property. Also in 2018 it introduced its IT Modernization Centers of Excellence (CoE) where the agency is assessing IT resources and technology needs at the US Department of Agriculture and US Department of Housing and Urban Development in hopes of reducing redundancies. GSA also administers the Technology Modernization Fund (TMF) a lending vehicle through which Federal agencies can borrow money to invest in modernizing aging technologies.

In 2019 the agency is working on a shared services initiative to create the infrastructure necessary to centralize administrative functions and systems such as hiring payroll finance and contract processing. There are currently more than 100 systems that track time and attendance for government employees.

Company Background

The U.S. General Services Administration was established by President Harry Truman in 1949 to streamline the administrative work of the federal government. It consolidated the National Archives Establishment the Federal Works Agency the Public Buildings Administration the Bureau of Federal Supply the Office of Contract Settlement and the War Assets Administration into one federal agency delivering and managing supplies and providing workplaces for federal employees.

GSA's original mission was to dispose of war surplus goods manage and store government records handle emergency preparedness and stockpile strategic supplies for wartime.

EXECUTIVES

Commissioner Federal Acquisition Service, James A. Williams
Cfo, Kathleen M. Turco
Acting Associate Administrator Office Of Citizen Services And Communications, Martha Dorris
Acting Administrator, Paul F. Prouty
Acting Commissioner Public Buildings Service, Anthony E. Costa
Acting Associate Administrator Office Of Governmentwide Policy, Stanley F. Kaczmarczyk
Acting Associate Administrator Office Of Small Business Utilization, Mary Parks
Acting Associate Administrator Office Of Performance Improvement, Steven D. McPeek
Acting Chief Office Of Emergency Response And Recovery, Joshua B. (Josh) Sawislak
Director Office Of Management Services, Elizabeth I. Kelley
Chairman Civilian Board Of Contract Appeals, Stephen M. Daniels
Chief Information Officer, Diane Merriett

LOCATIONS

HQ: U.S. GENERAL SERVICES ADMINISTRATION
1800 F ST NW RM 6100, WASHINGTON, DC 204050001
Phone: 202 501-0450
Web: WWW.GSA.GOV

PRODUCTS/OPERATIONS

2018 Sales

	$ mil.	% of total
Federal Buildings Fund		
Building Operations-Leased	6,420	26
Building Operations-Government Owned	5,261	21
Acquisition Services Fund		
Assisted Acquisition Services	7,043	29
Travel Transportation and Logistics	2,060	8
Information Technology	1,786	7
General Supplies and Services	1,300	5
Professional Services and Human Capital	87	-
Other Programs	113	1
Other Funds		
Working Capital Fund	657	3
Other General	37	-
Eliminations	(921)	-
Total	**23,843**	**100**

Selected Products and Services

Facilities & Construction
Construction Related Materials
Facility Related Materials
Facility Related ServicesHuman Capital
Administrative Services
Human Capital and Training Solutions
Human Resources System
General Support Services

HISTORICAL FINANCIALS

Company Type: Private

Income Statement — FYE: September 30

	REVENUE ($ mil.)	NET INCOME ($ mil.)	NET PROFIT MARGIN	EMPLOYEES
09/19	11,785	536	4.5%	13,000
09/16	20,457	290	1.4%	—
09/15*	38,976	486	1.2%	—
12/05	0	0	—	—
Annual Growth	—	—	—	—

*Fiscal year change

U.S. VENTURE, INC.

Privately held US Venture Inc is a North American leader in the distribution of fuel and transportation products. US Oil its division transports more than 2 billion gallons of fuel annually via pipelines rail light oil-barges and trucks. The division maintains over 7.5 million BOE in storage capacity and has access to nearly 200 terminals. Through US AutoForce the company is also a top distributor of tires and car parts to independent tire retailers auto repair shops and dealerships. The company's Lubricants division maintains a competitive business as well set up to blend and market chemical products to automotive industrial and metalworking industries. Through the GAIN Clean Fuel brand US Venture also sells clean biofuels.

Operations

US Venture has six business divisions.

US Oil is a leading distributor of branded and unbranded refined products in the US and Canada. It transports more than 2 billion gallons of energy products annually. US Oil also engages in energy trading.

Tires car parts and lubricants are distributed through the US AutoForce division another industry leader. Its portfolio includes more than 35 tire brands beyond 15 lubricant brands and many branded car parts (mostly brakes chassis repair equipment and exhausts).

US Lubricants blends and distributes lubricants under its THRIVE brand for automotive industrial and metalworking needs. It also provides support services like mobile filtration systems oil analysis lab services and fluids storage and handling systems.

US Venture is also developing and building alternative fuel transportation networks and filling stations in the US. Headed by the US GAIN division the company supplies compressed natural gas (CNG) and renewable natural gas (RNG) to more than 50 fueling stations.

Breakthrough provides innovative transportation and supply chain strategies for the world's leading shippers. IGEN build excise tax software that meets the needs of the motor fuel industry.

Geographic Reach

Headquartered in Appleton Wisconsin US Venture operates throughout North America. US Oil handles fuel supply in the Midwest with 25 terminals and nearly 200 third-party terminal partners. The company has a concentration of fuel tires car parts and convenience store services in the Midwest. It distributes fuels car parts and lubricants in North America.

Sales and Marketing

The US Oil division distributes products from a-dozen major oil brands including BP Shell Exxon Mobil Marathon Citgo Sunoco Clark and Phillips 66. It offers flexible pricing and fixed-fuel contracts and commodity trading. Traded products include gasoline ethanol biodiesel jet fuels propane and butane. In the Midwest the company also owns the Express chain of convenience stores.

US AutoForce offers more than 35 tire brands including Michelin Bridgestone Dunlop Firestone and Goodyear. Together with US Lubricants it serve the agricultural construction forestry marine and mining industries. US Lubricants also supplies its products to automotive dealerships repair shops lube shops and tire centers and customers in commercial transportation as well as industrial and metalworking lubricants.

US Venture is a major sponsor of the USA Luge team.

Company Background

U.S. Oil was established in 1951 as Schmidt Oil by the sons of local fuel distributor Albert Schmidt. The company changed its name to U.S. Venture in 2010 to reflect the company's increasingly diverse portfolio of entrepreneurial businesses. It has remained family-owned since its inception and today it is one of the largest privately held companies in Wisconsin.

EXECUTIVES

President And Ceo, John Schmidt
Vp Marketing And Strategy, Jeff Van Brunt
President U.s. Gain, Mike Koel
Vice President Treasurer Assistant Secretary, Lori Karls
Vp Of Sales And Operations, Kevin Olson
Senior Vice President Merchandise Planning And Allocation, Mark Duenig
Vp Insight And Analytics, Gary Cao
Secretary, Raymond Schmidt
Treasurer, Martin Tomczyk
Secretary And Treasurer, Ray Schmidt
Treasurer, Judy Engen-pazdera
Auditors: DELOITTE & TOUCHE LLP MILWAU

LOCATIONS

HQ: U.S. VENTURE, INC.
425 BETTER WAY, APPLETON, WI 549156192
Phone: 920 739-6101
Web: WWW.USVENTURE.COM

PRODUCTS/OPERATIONS

Selected Operations

U.S. AutoForce (exhaust pipe manufacturing and autoparts distribution)
U.S. Lubricants (motor oil and related products)
U.S. Oil (gasoline fuel oil and natural gas)
U.S Gain (compressed natural gas)

COMPETITORS

American Tire Distributors
Guttman Oil
Petroleum Traders Corporation

HISTORICAL FINANCIALS

Company Type: Private

Income Statement — FYE: July 31

	REVENUE ($ mil.)	NET INCOME ($ mil.)	NET PROFIT MARGIN	EMPLOYEES
07/15	8,076	173	2.1%	1,673
07/14	9,088	49	0.5%	—
07/13	7,346	47	0.6%	—
Annual Growth	4.9%	91.7%	—	—

2015 Year-End Financials

Return on assets: 16.9%
Return on equity: 53.2%
Current ratio: 1.70
Cash ($ mil.): 13

UAW RETIREE MEDICAL BENEFITS TRUST

EXECUTIVES

Head of Trustees, Robert Naftaly
Prin, Rober Naftaly
Senior Manager Human Resources, Karen Blair
Director Communications, Matthew Wood
Strategy Consultant, Vince Ferri
Senior Managing Director, Benjamin Cotton
Corporate Governance Analyst, Ryan Droze
Manager Strategic Opportunitie, Adrian Ohmer
Senior Accountant, Amy Hawkins
Director, Brian Gimotty
Vice President, Cindy Estrada
Auditors: DELOITTE TAX LLP DETROIT MI

LOCATIONS

HQ: UAW RETIREE MEDICAL BENEFITS TRUST
200 WALKER ST STE 400, DETROIT, MI 482074229
Phone: 313 324-5900
Web: WWW.RHAC.COM

HISTORICAL FINANCIALS

Company Type: Private

Income Statement — FYE: December 31

	ASSETS ($ mil.)	NET INCOME ($ mil.)	INCOME AS % OF ASSETS	EMPLOYEES
12/18	60,352	1,176	1.9%	94
12/17	63,225	88	0.1%	—
12/16	58,966	(1,839)	—	—
Annual Growth	1.2%	—	—	—

2018 Year-End Financials

Return on assets: 1.9%
Return on equity: 2.1%
Sales ($ mil): 5,050

UC HEALTH, LLC.

UC Health is Cincinnati's scholarly health care provider. The medical provider is a partnership between the University of Cincinnati the 480-bed University of Cincinnati Medical Center and the University of Cincinnati Physicians organization. Additionally UC Health is home to the 160-bed West Chester Hospital (a full-service community hospital) the Drake Center long-term acute care (rehabilitation) hospital the UC Health Surgical Hospital and the Lindner Center of HOPE (mental health services). Specialized services include cancer cardiovascular neuroscience and metabolic disease treatment. The not-for-profit UC Health was formed in 1994.

Operations

After a major reorganization in 2010 the surviving UC Health organization core operations are comprised of University Medical Center West Chester Medical Center and its primary and specialty care centers. Through its affiliation with the University of Cincinnati the medical organization conducts educational and research programs.

Strategy

UC Health is working to expand its network through acquisitions. For instance it added a new women's health practice to its provider network in 2012 to widen its specialty service offerings.

UC Health acquired full control of the Drake Center from former partner (and former network member) Jewish Hospital in 2011. It also added the Lindner Center of HOPE to its network that year.

Company Background

Formerly known as The Health Alliance of Greater Cincinnati the company changed its name to UC Health in 2010 after a number of its hospital members left the system and the University of Cincinnati took control of the remaining operations. Rumors of dissolution had swirled around the organization since its members began jumping ship starting in 2007.

Four of the organization's founding hospitals ultimately left the system: The 175-bed Fort Hamilton Hospital (now part of Kettering Health Network) and the 210-bed Jewish Hospital (now part of Catholic Healthcare Partners) departed in 2010. Two other hospitals (St. Luke's and Christ Hospital) broke off from the alliance after a long legal struggle in 2007.

EXECUTIVES

Senior Vice President And Chief Human Resources Officer, Bob Griffith
Evp And Cfo, Rick Hinds
President And Ceo, Richard P. Lofgren
Chief Physicians Services, Myles Pensak
Coo, Peter N. Gilbert
President Uc Health Foundation, Chris Smith
Vice President Government Relations Vice President Government Rela Vice President Of Marketing Vice President Chief Marketing Officer, Anthony Condia
Senior Vice President And Cio, Jay Brown
Director Of Nursing, Salyer Heidi
Vice President External Affairs, Tony Condia
Senior Vice President And Chief Human Resources Officer, Clarence Pauley
Senior Vice President Strategic Planning And Business Development, Gayla Harvey
Vice President Information Systems And Technology, Mark Carey
Senior Vice President And General Counsel, Charles Pangburn
Vice President Care Coordination, Andrew Cusher
Senior Vice President, Kyle Taylor
Chair Department Of Radiation Oncology, William Barrett
Medical Records Director, Frances Matre
Vice President Finance, Doug Jarrold
Vp Human Resources, Robert Nelson
Vice President;md, Daniel Niehaus
Senior Vp Inpatient Services, Nancy Smith
Vice President Chief Administrative Officer, Lafe Bauer
Secretary Administrative, Pamela Becker
Medical Secretary, Amanda Morgan
Medical Secretary, Billie Sword
Auditors: DELOITTE TAX LLP CINCINNATI

LOCATIONS

HQ: UC HEALTH, LLC.
3200 BURNET AVE, CINCINNATI, OH 452293019
Phone: 513 585-6000
Web: WWW.UCHEALTH.COM

PRODUCTS/OPERATIONS

Selected Ohio Facilities

Drake Center (Cincinnati)
Linder Center of HOPE (Mason)
UC Health Surgical Hospital (West Chester)
University of Cincinnati Physicians (Cincinnati)
University of Cincinnati Medical Center (Cincinnati)
West Chester Hospital (West Chester)

COMPETITORS

Catholic Health Initiatives
Cincinnati Children's Hospital
Kettering Health Network
Mercy Hospital Springfield
Premier Health Partners
St. Elizabeth Healthcare
The Christ Hospital Corporation
TriHealth

HISTORICAL FINANCIALS

Company Type: Private

Income Statement — FYE: June 30

	REVENUE ($ mil.)	NET INCOME ($ mil.)	NET PROFIT MARGIN	EMPLOYEES
06/18	1,661	40	2.5%	10,000
06/17	1,586	73	4.7%	—
06/10	138	(81)	—	—
06/09	102	0	—	—
Annual Growth	36.3%	—	—	—

2018 Year-End Financials

Return on assets: 2.5%
Return on equity: 4.9%
Current ratio: 4.70
Cash ($ mil.): 76

UFCW & EMPLOYERS TRUST LLC

EXECUTIVES

Administrator, Jody Osterweil
Information Technology, Ken Foulke
Payroll Manager, Norma Villa

Risk Management Consultant, Darren McClain
Auditors: VAVRINEK TRINE DAY & CO LLP S

LOCATIONS

HQ: UFCW & EMPLOYERS TRUST LLC
1000 BURNETT AVE STE 110, CONCORD, CA 945202000
Phone: 800 552-2400
Web: WWW.UFCWTRUST.COM

HISTORICAL FINANCIALS

Company Type: Private

Income Statement — FYE: December 31

	ASSETS ($ mil.)	NET INCOME ($ mil.)	INCOME AS % OF ASSETS	EMPLOYEES
12/18	460	10	2.3%	200
12/17	455	18	4.1%	—
Annual Growth	1.0%	(44.2%)	—	—

2018 Year-End Financials

Return on assets: 2.3%
Return on equity: 3.0%
Sales ($ mil): 555

UFCW & EMPLOYERS TRUST LLC

Auditors: HEMMING MORSE CPA'S AND CONSUL

LOCATIONS

HQ: UFCW & EMPLOYERS TRUST LLC
1000 BURNETT AVE STE 200, CONCORD, CA 945202058
Phone: 925 609-9068
Web: WWW.UFCWTRUST.COM

HISTORICAL FINANCIALS

Company Type: Private

Income Statement — FYE: December 31

	REVENUE ($ mil.)	NET INCOME ($ mil.)	NET PROFIT MARGIN	EMPLOYEES
12/14	553	33	6.0%	4
12/13	544	16	3.0%	—
Annual Growth	1.7%	107.2%	—	—

2014 Year-End Financials

Return on assets: 14.2%
Return on equity: 26.2%
Current ratio: 40.60
Cash ($ mil.): 81

UGI UTILITIES, INC.

EXECUTIVES

Chairman And Ceo, Lon R Greenberg

LOCATIONS

HQ: UGI UTILITIES, INC.
1 UGI DR, DENVER, PA 175179039
Phone: 800 276-2722
Web: WWW.UGI.COM

HISTORICAL FINANCIALS

Company Type: Private

Income Statement — FYE: September 30

	REVENUE ($ mil.)	NET INCOME ($ mil.)	NET PROFIT MARGIN	EMPLOYEES
09/18	1,092	148	13.6%	1,520
09/17	887	116	13.1%	—
Annual Growth	23.1%	28.3%	—	—

2018 Year-End Financials

Return on assets: 4.6%
Return on equity: 13.6%
Current ratio: 0.50
Cash ($ mil.): 10

UMASS MEMORIAL HEALTH CARE INC AND AFFILIATES GROUP RETURN

Auditors: FEELEY & DRISCOLL PC BOSTON

LOCATIONS

HQ: UMASS MEMORIAL HEALTH CARE INC AND AFFILIATES GROUP RETURN
306 BELMONT ST 120, WORCESTER, MA 016041004
Phone: 508 334-5106
Web: WWW.UMMHC.ORG

HISTORICAL FINANCIALS

Company Type: Private

Income Statement — FYE: September 30

	REVENUE ($ mil.)	NET INCOME ($ mil.)	NET PROFIT MARGIN	EMPLOYEES
09/13	2,613	51	2.0%	500
09/10	2,594	65	2.5%	—
Annual Growth	0.2%	(7.7%)	—	—

2013 Year-End Financials

Return on assets: 2.4%
Return on equity: 5.8%
Current ratio: 0.80
Cash ($ mil.): 156

UMASS MEMORIAL MEDICAL CENTER, INC.

EXECUTIVES

Ceo, John Obrien
Exec V Pres, Wendy Waring
Sr V Pres, Gary Lapidas
Treas, Todd Keating
Pres, Eric Dickson M D
Chief of Medicine, Robert Finberg
Vice-President Business Develo, Willis Chandler
Executive of Information Techn, Denise Skrocki
Doctor, William Corbett
Employee, Judith Siegel
Doctor of Medicine, Manisha Desai
Auditors: PRICEWATERHOUSECOOPERS LLP B

LOCATIONS

HQ: UMASS MEMORIAL MEDICAL CENTER, INC.
365 PLANTATION ST STE 185, WORCESTER, MA 016052379
Phone: 508 334-1000
Web: WWW.UMASSMEMORIALHEALTHCARE.ORG

HISTORICAL FINANCIALS

Company Type: Private

Income Statement — FYE: September 30

	REVENUE ($ mil.)	NET INCOME ($ mil.)	NET PROFIT MARGIN	EMPLOYEES
09/19	1,856	16	0.9%	50
09/18	1,712	87	5.1%	—
09/17	1,668	(62)	—	—
09/16	1,621	(130)	—	—
Annual Growth	4.6%	—	—	—

2019 Year-End Financials

Return on assets: 1.2%
Return on equity: 8.3%
Current ratio: 1.80
Cash ($ mil.): 133

UMASS MEMORIAL MEDICAL CENTER, INC.

EXECUTIVES

Internal Medicine Practitioner, Timothy P Fitzgibbons
Manager of Payment, Barry McGrath
Doctor, Jane Sargent
Coordinator, Lorie Gull
Business Operations Manager, Kevin Moran
Cardiac Cath Lab Director, Jay Cyr
Senior Applications An, Adam Cohen
Director Ambulatory Applicatio, Dana Locke
Program Administrator, Tamara Cullen
Pediatrician, Alexander Procaskey
Rn, Amanda Berg
Auditors: PRICEWATERHOUSECOOPERS LLP BO

LOCATIONS

HQ: UMASS MEMORIAL MEDICAL CENTER, INC.
55 LAKE AVE N, WORCESTER, MA 016550002
Phone: 508 334-1000

HISTORICAL FINANCIALS

Company Type: Private

Income Statement — FYE: September 30

	REVENUE ($ mil.)	NET INCOME ($ mil.)	NET PROFIT MARGIN	EMPLOYEES
09/16	1,621	(130)	—	29
09/15	1,332	60	4.5%	—
09/14	1,258	19	1.6%	—
09/13	1,183	68	5.8%	—
Annual Growth	11.1%	—	—	—

2016 Year-End Financials

Return on assets: (-10.0%)
Return on equity: (-83.3%)
Current ratio: 1.20
Cash ($ mil.): 124

UNIFIED SCHOOL DISTRICT 259

EXECUTIVES

Supt, John Allison
Treas-Dir*, Linda Jones
Cfo*, Jim Freeman
Facilities, Debbie Kandt
Office Technician, Mary Halley
Educator, Michele Steinbacher
Risk Coordinator, Weston Schartz
Secretary, Jeanette Parker
Classroom Teacher, Annetta Albright
Teacher, Arvilla Bennett
Communications Specialist, Gretchen Cox
Auditors: ALLEN GIBBS & HOULIK LC W

LOCATIONS

HQ: UNIFIED SCHOOL DISTRICT 259
903 S EDGEMOOR ST, WICHITA, KS 672183337
Phone: 316 973-4000
Web: WWW.USD259.ORG

HISTORICAL FINANCIALS

Company Type: Private

Income Statement — FYE: June 30

	REVENUE ($ mil.)	NET INCOME ($ mil.)	NET PROFIT MARGIN	EMPLOYEES
06/19	688	13	1.9%	5,406
06/18	668	119	17.8%	—
06/17	632	15	2.4%	—
06/16	622	(31)	—	—
Annual Growth	3.4%	—	—	—

2019 Year-End Financials

Return on assets: 1.0%
Return on equity: 12.6%
Current ratio: —
Cash ($ mil.): 219

UNIPRO FOODSERVICE, INC

UniPro Foodservice knows there's strength in numbers. As the largest US food service cooperative its members include more than 650 independent member companies that provide food and food-related products to more than 800000 food service customers including health care and educational institutions military installations and restaurants. UniPro provides training collective purchasing and marketing materials to all distributors. Its products – which include dry groceries and frozen and refrigerated foods – are sold under the brand names CODE ComSource Nifda and Nugget. Suppliers include Kraft Foods Reynolds Food Packaging Solo Cup Tyson Foods and Unilever Foodsolutions.

Operations

The cooperative's Multi-Unit Group (MUG) formed in 1985 to service multi-unit food service operators include some of the largest member distributors in the UniPro network. MUG members are like a one-stop shop for multi-unit operators offering fresh produce paper products and small wares from a single source in an effort to improve efficiency.

Geographic Reach

The Atlanta-based cooperative operates through more than 900 distribution centers across the US. Beyond the US it has distribution operations in Canada Mexico the Bahamas Australia Costa Rica Guam and Japan.

Sales and Marketing

Progressive Group Alliance a business unit distributes and supplies partners with sales marketing and advice to customers. Brands include Alliance Pro (non-food) Coral Princess (seafood) GourMates (condiments) Harvest Gold (cheese butter and dairy-related products) and Premium Recipe (prepared entrees salsas and sauces).

Financial Performance

While privately-owned Unipro Foodservice doesn't report its financial results collectively the cooperatives ring up an estimated $64 billion in sales annually.

Strategy

To enhance its members' competitiveness at home and abroad in 2013 UniPro formed a strategic alliance with Technomic a leading research and consulting firm to the food service industry. As part of the partnership UnPro joined the steering committee of Technomic's Foodservice Category Management Institute.

EXECUTIVES

Vice President Of Finance, Dan Wolfram
Department Vice President Of Accounting Services, Martin Miller
Departmental Vice President Financial Services, Sharon Nesset
Regional Vice President, Gary Butler
Department Vice President Beef And Pork, Phillip Wilson
Executive Vice President Of Procurement, David Huch
Vice President Saels West, Scott Strull
Regional Vice President Of Sales, Bob Bossong
Senior Vice President Sales East, Keith Durnell
Departmental Vice President Vendor Engagement, Dave Devlin
Regional Vice President Mid Central, Bob Fannin
Regional Vice President, Ed Delaney
Department Vice President Of National Brands, Diane Grimsley
Vice President Business Analysis, Van Perry
Regional Vice President Sales, Wayne Harrison
Regional Vice President, Matthew Milcoff
Departmental Vice President, Bob Salo
Departmental Vice President Frozen Fruits And Vegetables Imports, Beverly Deschon
Department Vice President Nesa Buying Group, Mike Beaverson
Auditors: HA&W LLP ATLANTA GEORGIA

LOCATIONS

HQ: UNIPRO FOODSERVICE, INC
2500 CUMBERLAND PKWY SE, ATLANTA, GA 303393942
Phone: 770 952-0871
Web: WWW.UNIPROFOODSERVICE.COM

PRODUCTS/OPERATIONS

Selected Suppliers

Cargill Foodservice
Durable Packaging International
Handgards Inc.
Kraft Foods
Reynolds Foodservice Packaging
Solo Cup Company
Unilever Foodsolutions

COMPETITORS

Ben E. Keith
Foodbuy
Golden State Foods
Keystone Foods
MAINES
Martin-Brower
McLane Foodservice
Meadowbrook Meat Company
Services Group of America
Sysco
US Foods

HISTORICAL FINANCIALS

Company Type: Private

Income Statement — FYE: December 31

	REVENUE ($ mil.)	NET INCOME ($ mil.)	NET PROFIT MARGIN	EMPLOYEES
12/12	987	(0)	—	140
12/11	881	0	—	—
12/10	657	0	—	—
Annual Growth	22.5%	—	—	—

2012 Year-End Financials

Return on assets: (-0.2%)
Return on equity: (-3.5%)
Current ratio: 1.00
Cash ($ mil.): 6

UNITED CONCORDIA LIFE AND HEALTH INSURANCE COMPANY

EXECUTIVES

Ceo, Frederick Merkel
Fo, Daniel Wright
EC, Edward Bittner
Supervisor, Brenda Godusky

LOCATIONS

HQ: UNITED CONCORDIA LIFE AND HEALTH INSURANCE COMPANY
4401 DEER PATH RD, HARRISBURG, PA 171103983
Phone: 717 260-7081
Web: WWW.UNITEDCONCORDIA.COM

HISTORICAL FINANCIALS

Company Type: Private

Income Statement — FYE: December 31

	REVENUE ($ mil.)	NET INCOME ($ mil.)	NET PROFIT MARGIN	EMPLOYEES
12/15	680	34	5.1%	1
12/14	731	57	7.9%	—
Annual Growth	(6.9%)	(39.8%)	—	—

2015 Year-End Financials

Return on assets: 10.3%
Return on equity: 14.3%
Current ratio: 1.10
Cash ($ mil.): 54

UNITED COOPERATIVE

EXECUTIVES

Ceo, David Cramer
Cfo*, Damian Girten
Chm*, Howard Bohl
SEC*, Robin Craker
Vice President Grain Operation, Alan Jentz
Human Resource Recruiter, Jamie Haas

LOCATIONS

HQ: UNITED COOPERATIVE
N7160 RACEWAY RD, BEAVER DAM, WI 539169315
Phone: 920 887-1756
Web: WWW.UNITEDCOOPERATIVE.COM

HISTORICAL FINANCIALS

Company Type: Private

Income Statement FYE: December 31

	REVENUE ($ mil.)	NET INCOME ($ mil.)	NET PROFIT MARGIN	EMPLOYEES
12/17	644	49	7.7%	358
12/16	630	41	6.6%	—
12/15	579	41	7.1%	—
12/14	577	57	10.0%	—
Annual Growth	3.7%	(4.7%)	—	—

2017 Year-End Financials

Return on assets: 8.0%
Return on equity: 12.1%
Current ratio: 2.20
Cash ($ mil.): 22

UNITED DAIRYMEN OF ARIZONA

Its name says it all: United Dairymen of Arizona (UDA) is a group of Arizona-based dairy farmers united together to stabilize and strengthen the market for milk products. Supplied by some 90-member producers the cooperative's plant has the capacity to process 10 million pounds of milk per day about 90% of the milk in the state. Products include sweet cream and butter fluid and condensed skim milk and non-fat dry milk among others. Customers include onsite cheese maker Schreiber Foods fluid milk processors and supermarket chains throughout The Grand Canyon State. UDA also makes dried lactose powder for food manufacturers. Started in 1960 the co-op was formed through a merger of two dairy associations.

EXECUTIVES

Vice President Of Engineering Projects, James Hrusovszky
Vice President Of Business Relations And Development Special Projects, Jimco Hrusovszky
Vice President Of Government Relations, Mike Billotte
Auditors: HERBEIN & COMPANY INC READI

LOCATIONS

HQ: UNITED DAIRYMEN OF ARIZONA
2008 S HARDY DR, TEMPE, AZ 852821211
Phone: 480 966-7211
Web: WWW.UDA.COOP

PRODUCTS/OPERATIONS

Selected Products and Services

Products
- Dried
  - Dry milk blends
  - Kosher powder
  - Lactose powder
  - Milk protein concentrate
  - Nonfat dry milk
- Fluid
  - Butter
  - Cream
  - Condensed skim milk
  - Skim milk

Services
- Emergency repair
- Installation
- Preventative maintenance
- Transportation

Supplies
- Chemical
- Equipment
- Pharmaceutical

COMPETITORS

Associated Milk Producers
Dairy Farmers of America
Dairy Manufacturers
Dean Foods
Goya
Land O'Lakes
Main Street Ingredients
Nestlé
Shamrock Foods
Smucker
Tate & Lyle Ingredients

HISTORICAL FINANCIALS

Company Type: Private

Income Statement FYE: September 30

	REVENUE ($ mil.)	NET INCOME ($ mil.)	NET PROFIT MARGIN	EMPLOYEES
09/11	825	21	2.6%	190
09/10	612	12	2.0%	—
09/09	812	2	0.3%	—
Annual Growth	0.8%	203.7%	—	—

2011 Year-End Financials

Return on assets: 16.2%
Return on equity: 32.4%
Current ratio: 1.40
Cash ($ mil.): 30

UNITED FOOD AND COMMERCIAL WORKERS UNIONS AND FOOD EMPLOYERS BEN FUND

EXECUTIVES

Prin, Richard Klontz
Auditors: HEMMING MORSE CPA'S AND CONSUL

LOCATIONS

HQ: UNITED FOOD AND COMMERCIAL WORKERS UNIONS AND FOOD EMPLOYERS BEN FUND
6425 KATELLA AVE, CYPRESS, CA 906305246
Phone: 714 220-2297
Web: WWW.SCUFCWFUNDS.COM

HISTORICAL FINANCIALS

Company Type: Private

Income Statement FYE: March 31

	REVENUE ($ mil.)	NET INCOME ($ mil.)	NET PROFIT MARGIN	EMPLOYEES
03/18	581	(13)	—	25
03/17	593	3	0.5%	—
03/12	512	(34)	—	—
03/11	460	(74)	—	—
Annual Growth	3.4%	—	—	—

2018 Year-End Financials

Return on assets: (-4.2%)
Return on equity: (-7.0%)
Current ratio: 161.40
Cash ($ mil.): 45

UNITED HEALTH SERVICES HOSPITALS, INC.

United Health Services Hospitals (UHS Hospitals) can service injuries from a slip in the snow or a slipped disc to health that's just plain slipping. The organization operates Binghamton General Hospital (about 200 beds) Wilson Medical Center (some 280 beds) and a group of primary and specialty care clinics in upstate New York. Specialty services include cardiology dialysis neurology rehabilitation pediatrics and psychiatry. The Wilson Medical Center serves as a teaching hospital offering residency and fellowship programs. UHS Hospitals is a subsidiary of United Health Services which operates a network of affiliated hospitals clinics long-term care centers and home health agencies in the region.

Geographic Reach

Binghamton General is located in Binghamton New York while Wilson Medical Center is located in Johnson City New York both within the boundaries of Broome County. UHS Hospitals also operates primary and specialty care clinics in Broome Chenango Delaware and Tioga counties in upstate New York.

Strategy

United Health Services Hospitals is investing in equipment upgrades and facility improvements at Binghamton General to help the facility remain at the forefront of medical technology and services. Wilson Medical Center which acts as a regional referral center in areas including emergency medicine newborn care neurology and heart surgery has also been the subject of enhancement measures. The hospital recently completed construction of the new Decker Center for Advanced Medical Treatment which offers high-tech diagnostic and acute care services.

EXECUTIVES

Vice President Of Quality, Amy Miller
Director Of Home Healthcare Services, Karla Dotts
Auditors: FUST CHARLES CHAMBERS LLP SYR

LOCATIONS

HQ: UNITED HEALTH SERVICES HOSPITALS, INC.
10-42 MITCHELL AVE, BINGHAMTON, NY 139031617
Phone: 607 762-2200
Web: WWW.STMRI.COM

COMPETITORS

Albany Medical Center
Guthrie Healthcare
Kaleida Health
Lifetime Health
Oneida Healthcare Center
SUNY Upstate Medical University
St. Joseph's Hospital Health Center
Upstate University Hospital at Community General

HISTORICAL FINANCIALS

Company Type: Private

Income Statement FYE: December 31

	REVENUE ($ mil.)	NET INCOME ($ mil.)	NET PROFIT MARGIN	EMPLOYEES
12/19	732	32	4.5%	5,000
12/18	685	(0)	—	—
12/16	611	21	3.4%	—
12/15	575	13	2.3%	—
Annual Growth	6.2%	26.0%	—	—

2019 Year-End Financials

Return on assets: 6.2%
Return on equity: 13.9%
Current ratio: 1.60
Cash ($ mil.): 25

UNITED SPACE ALLIANCE, LLC

United Space Alliance (USA) is a space-race heavyweight; the Houston-based prime contractor has run NASA's 173000 pound Shuttles — Discovery Atlantis and Endeavour. USA a joint venture between Lockheed Martin and Boeing was formed in response to NASA's move to consolidate multiple Space Shuttle contracts under a single entity. It is now wrapping up those contracts. USA has supported mission operations astronaut and flight controller training flight software development Shuttle payload integration and vehicle processing launch and recovery. It also has led training and planning for the International Space Station. USA served the Johnson and Kennedy Space Centers and Marshall Space Flight Center.

Operations

The company has consolidated more than 30 heritage contracts which supported the Space Shuttle Program (including the Space Flight Operations contract the Space Program Operations Contract and the Integrated Mission Operations Contract).

Geographic Reach

Based in Houston the company has another location in Titusville Florida.

Strategy

The company served as NASA's primary partner in human space operations for the management of the Space Shuttle fleet and worked together for 55 Space Shuttle missions and more than 35 International Space Station increments.

In 2014 the company had no active contracts and will not pursue future contracts. The company is currently operating in an administrative capacity to close-out its managed government contracts (a process that will take a further about 5-7 years).

Company Background

In 2012 NASA awarded a one-year extension of the Integrated Mission Operations Contract to USA to continue providing mission and flight crew operations support for the International Space Station and Exploration Programs. The deal includes a further option for 2014. Throughout 2012 and 2013 however USA laid off waves of workers that resided in its former Space Shuttle program.

The launch of space shuttle Atlantis in July 2011 marked the end of NASA's 30-year Space Shuttle program. The shuttles have transported astronauts launched recovered and repaired satellites as well as driven new research and built and stocked the International Space Station with parts and provisions.

The joint venture was formed in 1996.

EXECUTIVES

Evp And Coo, Daniel C. (Dan) Brandenstein
President Chief Executive Officer, Virginia A. (Ginger) Barnes
Vp Huntsville Operations, Kimberly B. (Kim) Doering
Vp Launch And Recovery; Site Executive Florida, Mark Nappi
Cio, Toni Russell
Auditors: PRICEWATERHOUSECOOPERS LLP HO

LOCATIONS

HQ: UNITED SPACE ALLIANCE, LLC
3700 BAY AREA BLVD # 100, HOUSTON, TX 770582783
Phone: 281 282-2592
Web: WWW.UNITEDSPACEALLIANCE.COM

PRODUCTS/OPERATIONS

Selected Capabilities

Flight software
Ground operations and processing
GSA (General Services Administration) services
Integrated logistics
Integration and program management
Mission operations
Safety

COMPETITORS

Airbus Group
Arianespace
Astrotech
BAE SYSTEMS
Honeywell Aerospace
Meggitt-USA
Northrop Grumman
Raytheon
SGT
Thales Aerospace

HISTORICAL FINANCIALS

Company Type: Private

Income Statement FYE: December 31

	REVENUE ($ mil.)	NET INCOME ($ mil.)	NET PROFIT MARGIN	EMPLOYEES
12/07	1,859	168	9.0%	8,000
12/06	1,920	146	7.6%	—
Annual Growth	(3.2%)	14.8%	—	—

2007 Year-End Financials

Return on assets: 60.5%
Return on equity: —
Current ratio: 1.00
Cash ($ mil.): 57

UNIVERSITIES OF LOUISIANA SYSTEM

EXECUTIVES

President, Randy Moffett
Exec Dir, Caprice Leyoub
Pres, John Crain

LOCATIONS

HQ: UNIVERSITIES OF LOUISIANA SYSTEM
1201 N 3RD ST STE 7300, BATON ROUGE, LA 708025243
Phone: 225 342-6950
Web: WWW.ULSYSTEM.EDU

HISTORICAL FINANCIALS

Company Type: Private

Income Statement FYE: June 30

	REVENUE ($ mil.)	NET INCOME ($ mil.)	NET PROFIT MARGIN	EMPLOYEES
06/19	942	28	3.0%	4,500
06/18	930	101	10.9%	—
06/17	906	23	2.6%	—
06/16	845	25	3.0%	—
Annual Growth	3.7%	4.4%	—	—

2019 Year-End Financials

Return on assets: 1.0%
Return on equity: —
Current ratio: 1.90
Cash ($ mil.): 247

UNIVERSITY COMMUNITY HOSPITAL, INC.

University Community Health (doing business as Florida Hospital Tampa Bay Division) is a 1000-bed regional health care system with four locations spanning the Hillsborough Pinellas and Pasco counties of Florida. It oversees a network of eight hospitals in Florida's Tampa Bay area. Its four general hospitals — three located in Tampa and one in nearby Tarpon Springs — collectively house some 860 beds and provide emergency surgical and acute medical care as well as provide outpatient services. The system also includes a specialty heart hospital a women's hospital and a long-term acute care hospital. Florida Hospital Tampa Bay Division is part of the Adventist Health System.

Strategy

As part of the Adventist Health System's network the system has access to a broader statewide network of physicians and specialists as well as enhanced administrative and technological services organization.

In 2012 Florida Hospital Tampa Bay Division opened Florida Hospital Wesley Chapel and began work on three major construction projects including a new full-service Emergency Department (ED) expanding The Women's Center and exterior and interior upgrades to the main hospital which should add a total of 54000 sq. ft. to the scope of Florida Hospital Tampa.

Company Background

Its original name of University Community Health (UCH) reflected its proximity to the University of South Florida. UCH teamed up with Adventist Health in 2007 to build Wesley Chapel Medical Center. Buoyed by the success of the venture in 2010 UCH and Adventist Health reached an accord and UCH became a member of Adventist Health.

EXECUTIVES

V Pres, Michael Schultz
Acct*, Lynn Addiscott
Acct*, Ariel De Prada

Coo*, Jack Chubb
Cno*, Theresa Trivette
Chief of Medicine, Mitchell Ohara
Internal Medicine Practitioner, Ashley Robaina
Nurse, Amy Thatavakorn
Supervisor Cardiac Cath Lab, Frank Vansickle
Pediatrician, Alison Simpson
Emergency Medicine Specialist, Andrew Spencer

LOCATIONS

HQ: UNIVERSITY COMMUNITY HOSPITAL, INC.
3100 E FLETCHER AVE, TAMPA, FL 336134613
Phone: 813 971-6000
Web: WWW.ADVENTHEALTH.COM

PRODUCTS/OPERATIONS

Selected Centers
Diabetes and Endocrinology Institute
Don Lau Family Center for Cancer Care
Florida Hospital Pepin Heart Institute
Occupational Health Service
Orthopedic Care Center
Pediatric Care Center
Sleep Center
The Women's Center
Wound Healing Institute

Selected Hospitals
Florida Hospital at Connerton
Florida Hospital Carrollwood
Florida Hospital North Pinellas
Florida Hospital Pepin Heart Institute
Florida Hospital Tampa
Florida Hospital Wesley Chapel
Florida Hospital Zephyrhills
Long Term Acute Care

COMPETITORS

All Children's Hospital
BayCare Health System
Bayfront Health
HCA
Lakeland Regional Medical Center
Northside Hospital and Heart Institute
Tampa General Hospital

HISTORICAL FINANCIALS

Company Type: Private

Income Statement — FYE: December 31

	REVENUE ($ mil.)	NET INCOME ($ mil.)	NET PROFIT MARGIN	EMPLOYEES
12/17	688	66	9.6%	8,000
12/16	483	39	8.2%	—
12/15	460	38	8.4%	—
12/14	381	24	6.5%	—
Annual Growth	21.7%	38.9%	—	—

2017 Year-End Financials

Return on assets: 6.4%
Return on equity: 9.2%
Current ratio: 9.50
Cash ($ mil.): 258

UNIVERSITY HEALTH CARE INC

University Health Care wants to give patients a passport to good health. The company which does business as Passport Health Plan provides managed Medicaid insurance services to about 150000 members throughout 16 counties in Kentucky. Offerings include HMO Medicare Advantage and children's health plans. University Health Care was founded in 1997 by a group of affiliated providers including the University of Louisville Medical Center Jewish Hospital and St. Mary's HealthCare and the Louisville/Jefferson County Primary Care Association. The health plan has an administration partnership with the AmeriHealth Mercy organization a Medicaid managed care joint venture between AmeriHealth and Mercy Health System.

EXECUTIVES

Vice President Of Public Affairs, Jill Bell
Vice President And Chief Medical Officer, Stephen Houghland
Vice President And Chief Compliance Officer, David Henley
Vice President And Chief Of Staff, Joanne McFall
Auditors: MOUNTJOY CHILTON MEDLEY LLP L

LOCATIONS

HQ: UNIVERSITY HEALTH CARE INC
5100 CMMERCE CROSSINGS DR, LOUISVILLE, KY 402292128
Phone: 502 585-7900
Web: WWW.PASSPORTHEALTHPLAN.COM

COMPETITORS

AMERIGROUP
Aetna
Anthem Health Plans of Kentucky
Bluegrass Family Health
CIGNA
Health Net
HealthSpring
Humana
Kaiser Foundation Health Plan
UnitedHealth Group

HISTORICAL FINANCIALS

Company Type: Private

Income Statement — FYE: December 31

	REVENUE ($ mil.)	NET INCOME ($ mil.)	NET PROFIT MARGIN	EMPLOYEES
12/14	1,299	114	8.8%	165
12/00	330	3	1.2%	—
12/99	284	5	2.0%	—
12/98	809	0	—	—
Annual Growth	3.0%	—	—	—

2014 Year-End Financials

Return on assets: 31.8%
Return on equity: 52.2%
Current ratio: —
Cash ($ mil.): 140

UNIVERSITY HEALTH SYSTEM SERVICES OF TEXAS, INC.

As the hospital system of the Bexar County Hospital District University Health System serves residents of San Antonio and the surrounding region. Its flagship facility University Hospital boasts about 720 beds and is the primary teaching facility for The University of Texas Health Science Center at San Antonio. In addition to general medical and surgical care the hospital is a designated Level I trauma center and a Level II pediatric trauma and burn center. The system provides health care for families near its clinic locations including the Robert B. Green Campus Texas Diabetes Institute more than a dozen neighborhood clinics five ExpressMed urgent-care clinics and four outpatient renal dialysis centers.

Operations

The system which has about 800 physicians also operates preventive care centers including the Texas Diabetes Institute which provides treatment research and education for diabetes patients and health care professionals. The University Transplant Center performs a range of procedures such as kidney liver and lung transplants. The Harlandale Independent School District school-based Health Center is a collaboration with Harlandale ISD that helps keep students healthy and learning.

University Health System's emergency department is the busiest in the area taking in nearly 70000 visits annually. In 2013 it had about 22000 inpatient discharges 3000 births and 139000 outpatient visits.

As part of its operations University Health System is joint owner of San Antonio AirLIFE which provides emergency air medical transport services aboard its fleet of Bell 430 helicopters.

University Health System provides health insurance through its Community First Health Plans a not-for-profit HMO with thousands of members in Bexar and surrounding counties.

Geographic Reach

The system's University Hospital is the lead trauma hospital for a 22-county area of Texas serving patients from Bexar County to South Texas and beyond.

Financial Performance

University Health System's revenue rose 11% to $564 million in 2013 thanks to net patient revenue growth. Net income decreased 24% to $75 million that year as operating expenses including salaries and benefits purchased services and supplies rose.

Strategy

To its benefit University Hospital is the only pediatric trauma center that serves San Antonio and the greater South Texas area. Its emergency center remains the busiest in the region averaging nearly 70000 visits annually.

The organization is in the midst of a systemwide capital improvement program aimed at "right-sizing" its facilities to meet growing demand. To this end the system in 2014 completed construction on a $778 million 10-story Sky Tower at University Hospital that features an expanded emergency department 35 new surgical suites and 420 new private patient rooms. It also opened a six-story Clinical Pavilion at its Robert B. Green Campus in 2013. In 2015 the system was granted approval to renovate and expand its emergency department which will convert most semi-private rooms to fully private rooms and provide additional observance and recovery space. The new facilities are part of University Health System's $900 million Capital Improvement Program to expand and renovate facilities at University Hospital and its downtown Robert B. Green Campus.

Additionally University Health System's downtown health center has added services that include acute and crisis care diagnostic imaging and pharmacy.

In 2014 the system launched its healthyUexpress2 mobile health vehicle which extends its new school-based health care initiative throughout Bexar County.

Company Background

University Health System was founded in 1968.

EXECUTIVES

Evp And Cfo, Peggy Deming
Vice President Chief Information Officer, Bill Phillips
Executive Vice President Chief Operating Officer, Christann Vasquez
Vp Managed Care; President Community First Health Plans, Greg Gieseman

Senior Vice President Chief Nursing Officer, Nancy Ray
Evp Chief Medical Officer, Bryan Alsip
President And Ceo Community Medicine Associates, Priti Mody-Baily
President And Ceo, George B. Hernandez
Vice President Of Marketing Sv, Rebecca Thompson
Chairman, James R. Adams
Auditors: BKD LLP DALLAS TEXAS

LOCATIONS

HQ: UNIVERSITY HEALTH SYSTEM SERVICES OF TEXAS, INC.
4502 MEDICAL DR STOP 65-1, SAN ANTONIO, TX 782294402
Phone: 210 358-4000
Web: WWW.UNIVERSITYHEALTHSYSTEM.COM

PRODUCTS/OPERATIONS

2013 Sales

	$ mil.	% of total
Net patient services revenue	462	60
Premium revenue	261	34
Other revenue	49	6
Total	**773**	**100**

2013 Net Patient Revenue

	% of total
Medicare	22
Medicaid	21
Self-Pay including CareLink	37
Commercial insurance	19
Other	1
Total	**100**

Selected Locations

University Hospital
University Health Care
Texas Diabetes Institute
University Family Health Centers

Selected Medical Services

Audiology
Blood Bank
Breast Health
Cancer
Cardiology
Craniosynostosis
Diabetes
ExpressMed
Emergency Center
Endoscopy
Epilepsy
Gynecology
Health Education
Hepatology
HIV/AIDS
Mammography
Maternal-fetal Medicine
Men's Health
Neurosciences
Newborn Services
NICU
Obstetrics
Outpatient Surgery
Pharmacy Services
Pediatrics
Primary Care
Rehabilitation
Respiratory Care
Robot Assisted Surgery
Stroke
Texas Diabetes Institute
Transcatheter Aortic Valve Replacement
Transplant Center
Trauma Center
Vascular
Women's Health

COMPETITORS

CHRISTUS Health
Methodist Healthcare System
Tenet Healthcare
Valley Baptist Health System (Texas)

HISTORICAL FINANCIALS

Company Type: Private

Income Statement — FYE: December 31

	REVENUE ($ mil.)	NET INCOME ($ mil.)	NET PROFIT MARGIN	EMPLOYEES
12/19	1,610	150	9.3%	3,998
12/18	1,488	95	6.4%	—
12/17	1,349	54	4.1%	—
12/16	1,253	82	6.6%	—
Annual Growth	8.7%	22.3%	—	—

2019 Year-End Financials

Return on assets: 4.6%
Return on equity: 11.1%
Current ratio: 3.10
Cash ($ mil.): 308

UNIVERSITY HOSPITALS HEALTH SYSTEM, INC.

University Hospitals Health System (UHHS) is on a mission to teach research and administer good health throughout northeastern Ohio. Its flagship facility University Hospitals of Cleveland (UHC) which operates as University Hospitals Case Medical Center (UHCMC) is a more than 1000-bed tertiary care center serving Cleveland and other parts of northeastern Ohio. The teaching hospital which is affiliated with Case Western Reserve University is also home to Rainbow Babies & Children's Hospital Seidman Cancer Center and MacDonald Women's Hospital. the not-for-profit UHHS is also home to community hospitals outpatient health and surgery centers mental health facilities and senior care centers.

Operations

UHHS' eight community hospitals some of which are operated through affiliation agreements provide a full range of specialty and general acute care from anesthesia to vascular surgery. Along with those the system operates urgent care and neighborhood medical centers throughout the region. The UH Extended Care Campus includes a specialty hospital outpatient rehabilitation and extended care facility. UHHS also operates home health occupational health wellness and managed care (health plan) divisions. The UHHS facilities have a total of some 1800 beds.

Altogether the network's facilities handle some 65000 inpatient visits per year as well as 5.8 million outpatient procedures and 206000 emergency room visits. It delivered more than 5200 babies and conducted more than 60000 surgeries in 2013.

In addition to conducting education and training programs for Case Western Reserve University School of Medicine students UHHS partners with the university to operate the Center for Clinical Research and Technology. The center is the largest biomedical research facility in Ohio and focuses on translational research which connects laboratory research to clinical bedside care.

UHHS' physician network consists of 1700 physicians and 3000 affiliated members. The system provided $270 million for community benefit and provided $253 million for research in 2013.

The hospital system is affiliated with three Cleveland-area health care providers: St. John Medical Center UH Rehabilitation Hospital (a joint venture with Center Healthcare) and Southwest General.

Geographic Reach

UHHS operates about 30 health centers and outpatient office buildings as well as more than 100 physician practice locations across the northeastern Ohio region. It serves 16 counties.

Financial Performance

UHHS' revenues increased by 4% to $2.3 billion in 2013 due to higher patient service revenues.

Operating income increased by 21% $78.6 million that year due to a change in fair value of derivative instruments and a growth in investment income partially offset by higher operating expenses.

UHHS' operating cash flow decreased by $143 million in 2013 due a change in beneficial interest in foundation and perpetual trusts pension liability adjustments and a change in operating assets and liabilities.

Strategy

The medical system is expanding by installing smaller regional and community hospitals and additional specialty care units within its larger facilities including a neonatal intensive care unit emergency care center and a cancer care center within UH Case Medical.

To strengthen its clinical capabilities it also expanded its established areas of excellence and developed new areas to improve access it has forged new hospital partnerships. To enhance care in the communities served by its new partners UHHS has opened satellites of some of its centers of excellence initially for cancer care cardiac care pediatrics and women's health. Pursuant to the growth strategy it has added two community hospitals that are now UHHS' largest: 387-bed UH Elyria Medical Center (formerly EMH Healthcare) and 332-bed UH Parma Medical Center (formerly The Parma Community General Hospital).

The company also plans to break ground on a $28 million state-of-the-art outpatient health center and freestanding emergency department in Broadview Heights with a projected completion date in late 2016. In 2013 University Hospitals Seidman Cancer Center expanded to Parma Community General Hospital providing integrated cancer care to residents in Parma and surrounding communities.

To expand in another neighboring community the system launched renovation of an office building that became the UH Solon Health Center in 2013. It also opened a new outpatient center the UH Aurora Health Center in 2012.

UHHS is also in the process of implementing an electronic health records (EHR) system across its facilities. The EHR system could make the network eligible for certain government incentives if they meet government guidelines for "meaningful use."

On the research front in 2014 UHHS Case Medical Center conducted a Phase 3 clinical trial to evaluate the safety and effectiveness of an investigational medicine called LMTX in people with a type of dementia known as behavioral-variant Frontotemporal Dementia (previously known as Pick's Disease).

Company Background

UHHS completed construction of the UH Ahuja Medical Center a new community hospital in 2011.

The company was founded in 1866.

EXECUTIVES

Vice President, Elizabeth Novak
Auditors: DELOITTE TAX LLP CINCINNATI

LOCATIONS

HQ: UNIVERSITY HOSPITALS HEALTH SYSTEM, INC.
3605 WARRENSVILLE CTR RD, SHAKER HEIGHTS, OH 441229100
Phone: 216 767-8900
Web: WWW.UHHOSPITALS.ORG

PRODUCTS/OPERATIONS

Selected Facilities
Main Campuses
Case Medical Center
MacDonald Women's Hospital
Rainbow Babies & Children's Hospital
Seidman Cancer Center
Community Hospitals
Ahuja Medical Center
Bedford Medical Center (UH Regional Hospitals)
Conneaut Medical Center
Elyria Medical Center
Geauga Medical Center
Geneva Medical Center
Parma Medical Center
Richmond Medical Center (UH Regional Hospitals)

COMPETITORS

Akron Children's Hospital
Akron General Health System
Lake Health
Mercy Medical Center (OH)
MetroHealth System
Parma Community General Hospital
Robinson Memorial Hospital
Summa Health System
The Cleveland Clinic
Trinity Health System

HISTORICAL FINANCIALS

Company Type: Private

Income Statement				FYE: December 31
	REVENUE ($ mil.)	NET INCOME ($ mil.)	NET PROFIT MARGIN	EMPLOYEES
12/17	580	33	5.7%	30,099
12/12	2,266	54	2.4%	—
12/09	1,938	110	5.7%	—
12/08	1,800	(153)	—	—
Annual Growth	(11.8%)	—	—	—

2017 Year-End Financials

Return on assets: 0.8%
Return on equity: 1.6%
Current ratio: 0.20
Cash ($ mil.): 184

UNIVERSITY MEDICAL CENTER INC

EXECUTIVES

Ceo, James Taylor
Pres*, Ken Marshall
Sr V Pres*, Mark Pfeifer
Cfo-Sr V Pres*, Robert P Barbier
SEC*, Amber Denham
Prin*, Mary Jane Adams
Assistant Professor of Radiolo, Peter Hentzen
Assistant Professor of Radiolo, Richard Goldwin
Assistant Professor of Radiolo, Barbara Pawley
Director of Oncology, Den Ellen Coldiron
Director, Hiram C Polk

LOCATIONS

HQ: UNIVERSITY MEDICAL CENTER INC
530 S JACKSON ST, LOUISVILLE, KY 402021675
Phone: 502 562-3000
Web: WWW.UOFLHOSPITAL.ORG

HISTORICAL FINANCIALS

Company Type: Private

Income Statement				FYE: June 30
	REVENUE ($ mil.)	NET INCOME ($ mil.)	NET PROFIT MARGIN	EMPLOYEES
06/19	607	23	3.8%	2,000
06/18	487	(72)	—	—
06/16	501	35	7.1%	—
06/15	484	53	11.1%	—
Annual Growth	5.8%	(18.9%)	—	—

2019 Year-End Financials

Return on assets: 4.5%
Return on equity: 10.2%
Current ratio: 0.70
Cash ($ mil.): 67

UNIVERSITY MEDICAL CENTER MANAGEMENT CORPORATION

EXECUTIVES

Ceo, Danny Hardman
Buyer*, Todd Scurto
General Practitioner, Joseph Kanter
Assistant Professor, Yingnan Zhao
Assistant Professor, Zhe Wang
Admissions Director, Allenda Hendry
Operating Room Dir, Anne Ertel
Pharmacy Director, Anthony Laurent
Radiology Director, Anthony Mosley
Food Director, Candice Gallagher
Utilization Review Director, Connie Brider
Auditors: LAPORTE APAC METAIRIE LA

LOCATIONS

HQ: UNIVERSITY MEDICAL CENTER MANAGEMENT CORPORATION
2000 CANAL ST, NEW ORLEANS, LA 701123018
Phone: 504 903-3000
Web: WWW.UMCNO.ORG

HISTORICAL FINANCIALS

Company Type: Private

Income Statement				FYE: December 31
	REVENUE ($ mil.)	NET INCOME ($ mil.)	NET PROFIT MARGIN	EMPLOYEES
12/18	675	1	0.2%	2,000
12/16	448	(65)	—	—
Annual Growth	22.7%	—	—	—

2018 Year-End Financials

Return on assets: 0.3%
Return on equity: —
Current ratio: 0.70
Cash ($ mil.): 46

UNIVERSITY OF ALABAMA

EXECUTIVES

Exec Dir, Kevin Stevens
Accounting Staff, Lisa H McKinney
Accounting Staff, Tina Dorroh
Assistant Professor, Jane Rasco
Assistant To President, Charles Hilburn
Staff, June Vance
Staff, Paul A Leblanc
Staff, Sunee Lavender
Staff, Michael Steinberg
Staff, Paula House
Staff, Natalie Champion
Auditors: PRICEWATERHOUSECOOPERS LLP BI

LOCATIONS

HQ: UNIVERSITY OF ALABAMA
301 ROSE ADMIN BLDG, TUSCALOOSA, AL 354870001
Phone: 205 348-7840
Web: WWW.OVPRED.UA.EDU

HISTORICAL FINANCIALS

Company Type: Private

Income Statement				FYE: September 30
	REVENUE ($ mil.)	NET INCOME ($ mil.)	NET PROFIT MARGIN	EMPLOYEES
09/19	906	55	6.1%	3,950
09/18	875	188	21.6%	—
09/17	833	224	26.9%	—
Annual Growth	4.3%	(50.2%)	—	—

2019 Year-End Financials

Return on assets: 1.1%
Return on equity: 2.6%
Current ratio: 1.10
Cash ($ mil.): 108

UNIVERSITY OF ALABAMA HEALTH SERVICES FOUNDATION, P.C.

EXECUTIVES

Ceo, Will Ferniany
Pres*, Anton Bueschen
V Pres*, Reed F Jones
Cfo*, Michael Heckman
Pres*, Dr Jim Bonner
Exec V Pres*, Patricia Pritchett
Exec Admin, Melanie Brewer
Project Coordinator, Niki Woodall
Director, Chuck Patrick
Quality Assurance Coordinator, Emily Jones
Executive Administrator, Mark Schmidt
Auditors: PRICEWATERHOUSECOOPERS LLP BI

LOCATIONS

HQ: UNIVERSITY OF ALABAMA HEALTH SERVICES FOUNDATION, P.C.
500 22ND ST S STE 100, BIRMINGHAM, AL 352333110
Phone: 205 731-9600

HISTORICAL FINANCIALS

Company Type: Private

Income Statement — FYE: September 30

	REVENUE ($ mil.)	NET INCOME ($ mil.)	NET PROFIT MARGIN	EMPLOYEES
09/19	705	(19)	—	3,205
09/18	668	12	1.9%	—
09/15	561	1	0.2%	—
09/14	26	0	1.6%	—
Annual Growth	93.1%	—	—	—

2019 Year-End Financials

Return on assets: (-2.2%)
Return on equity: (-5.1%)
Current ratio: 1.00
Cash ($ mil.): 8

UNIVERSITY OF ARKANSAS SYSTEM

Calling "Wooo Pig Sooie" at anyone in The University of Arkansas System (UA) is not an insult. The system encompasses more than a dozen schools institutes and campuses throughout the state including five universities a college of medicine a math and science high school and the Clinton School of Public Service started in 2004 by former president Bill Clinton and offering the only Master of Public Service degree in the country. UA which has an enrollment of more than 60000 hails the razorback or hog as its mascot. "Wooo Pig Sooie" or "hog calling" is the school's cheer at sporting events. Its student-teacher ratio is 19:1; it has about 17000 employees.

EXECUTIVES

Vice President For University Relations, Melissa Rust
Associate Vice President For Finance, Rita Fleming
Vice President Community Service, Robyn Jilg
Executive Vice President Student Alumni Board, Emma Buckner
Vice Chairman, Mark Waldrip
Assistant Secretary, Kelly Eichler
Auditors: ROGER A NORMAN JD CPA CFE

LOCATIONS

HQ: UNIVERSITY OF ARKANSAS SYSTEM
2404 N UNIVERSITY AVE, LITTLE ROCK, AR 722073608
Phone: 501 686-2500
Web: WWW.UASYS.EDU

PRODUCTS/OPERATIONS

Selected Campuses

Arkansas Archeological Survey
Arkansas School for Mathematics Sciences and the Arts (high school)
Clinton School of Public Service
Cossatot Community College of the University of Arkansas
Criminal Justice Institute
Division of Agriculture
Phillips Community College of the University of Arkansas
University of Arkansas Community College at Morrilton
University of Arkansas Fayetteville
University of Arkansas at Fort Smith
University of Arkansas at Little Rock
University of Arkansas for Medical Sciences
University of Arkansas at Monticello
University of Arkansas at Pine Bluff
Winthrop Rockefeller Institute

HISTORICAL FINANCIALS

Company Type: Private

Income Statement — FYE: June 30

	REVENUE ($ mil.)	NET INCOME ($ mil.)	NET PROFIT MARGIN	EMPLOYEES
06/20	2,449	85	3.5%	14,025
06/19	2,515	153	6.1%	—
06/18	2,402	139	5.8%	—
06/17	2,297	88	3.9%	—
Annual Growth	2.1%	(1.3%)	—	—

2020 Year-End Financials

Return on assets: 1.7%
Return on equity: 3.1%
Current ratio: 3.40
Cash ($ mil.): 596

UNIVERSITY OF CALIFORNIA, DAVIS

If you want to grow grapes and make wine in Napa Valley or Sonoma County you might want to swing by the University of California Davis (UC Davis) first. The school one of 10 University of California campuses offers a wide variety of agricultural programs; its Viticulture and Enology department provides professional education for aspiring winemakers. Located between Sacramento and San Francisco UC Davis also has colleges and professional schools in biology engineering education law business medicine and veterinary medicine and it is recognized for its research programs. UC Davis enrolls about 39630 including more than 8645 graduate students and it has a student-faculty ratio of 20:1.

Operations

UC Davis comprises four colleges: Agricultural and Environmental Sciences; Biological Sciences; Engineering; and Letters and Science. The university also operates six professional schools: Education; Law; Management; Medicine; Veterinary Medicine; and the Betty Irene Moore School of Nursing. It also includes a 620-bed acute care teaching hospital in Sacramento (UC Davis Health) and the UC Davis Veterinary Medicine Teaching Research Center in Tulare.

It also has access to approximately 10 million items in the university's library including books journals music and maps in print and digital formats.

Geographic Reach

Spanning approximately 5300 acres campus borders the city of Davis the state capital is 20 minutes away and destinations such as the San Francisco Bay Area Lake Tahoe and the Napa Valley are within a two-hour drive. UC Davis has satellite campuses in San Ramon and Sacramento as well as related educational facilities elsewhere in California and in Nevada. UC Davis also has international students which represents more than 140 countries across six continents.

Company Background

The school was originally known as the University Farm School and accepted its first students at its new campus in the town of Davisville (later changed to Davis) in 1909. The California Legislature in 1905 authorized the establishment of a state agricultural college; the school that became UC Davis was administratively tied to UC Berkeley for decades before gaining its status as an independent university in 1959.

EXECUTIVES

Vice Provost Of Information And Educational Technology And Cio, Viji Murali
Ceo Uc Davis Medical Center, Ann Madden Rice
Chancellor, Linda P.B. Katehi
Executive Vice Chancellor And Provost, Ralph J. Hexter
Vice Chancellor For Finance Operations And Administration And Cfo, Dave Lawlor
Medical Director, Becky Mackey

LOCATIONS

HQ: UNIVERSITY OF CALIFORNIA, DAVIS
1 SHIELDS AVE, DAVIS, CA 956168500
Phone: 530 752-1011
Web: WWW.UCDAVIS.EDU

HISTORICAL FINANCIALS

Company Type: Private

Income Statement — FYE: June 30

	REVENUE ($ mil.)	NET INCOME ($ mil.)	NET PROFIT MARGIN	EMPLOYEES
06/11*	2,697	360	13.4%	17,741
12/08	0	0	9.6%	—
06/08	14	0	6.1%	—
Annual Growth	474.6%	644.1%	—	—

*Fiscal year change

2011 Year-End Financials

Return on assets: 6.5%
Return on equity: 10.4%
Current ratio: 2.50
Cash ($ mil.): 1,114

UNIVERSITY OF CALIFORNIA, SAN FRANCISCO FOUNDATION

EXECUTIVES

Pres, Michael Bishop
Dir, Jim Asp
Rn Is Director, Barbara Koenig

LOCATIONS

HQ: UNIVERSITY OF CALIFORNIA, SAN FRANCISCO FOUNDATION
220 MONTGOMERY ST STE 500, SAN FRANCISCO, CA 941043412
Phone: 415 476-6922
Web: WWW.UCSF.EDU

HISTORICAL FINANCIALS

Company Type: Private

Income Statement				FYE: June 30
	REVENUE ($ mil.)	NET INCOME ($ mil.)	NET PROFIT MARGIN	EMPLOYEES
06/18	628	332	53.0%	73
06/99	33	39	117.7%	—
Annual Growth	16.6%	11.8%	—	—

2018 Year-End Financials

Return on assets: 15.2%
Return on equity: 18.0%
Current ratio: —
Cash ($ mil.): 395

UNIVERSITY OF CHICAGO

LOCATIONS

HQ: UNIVERSITY OF CHICAGO
1414 E 59TH ST, CHICAGO, IL 606372916
Phone: 773 753-2270
Web: WWW.UCHICAGO.EDU

HISTORICAL FINANCIALS

Company Type: Private

Income Statement				FYE: June 30
	REVENUE ($ mil.)	NET INCOME ($ mil.)	NET PROFIT MARGIN	EMPLOYEES
06/13	3,091	182	5.9%	2
06/11	3,056	1,052	34.4%	—
Annual Growth	0.6%	(58.4%)	—	—

2013 Year-End Financials

Return on assets: 1.9%
Return on equity: 2.9%
Current ratio: 0.20
Cash ($ mil.): 45

UNIVERSITY OF CINCINNATI

The University of Cincinnati (UC) is a research institution offering undergraduate graduate and professional education from its three campuses in Ohio. The university enrolls nearly 46800 students and has about 15 colleges. Academic offerings include business law medicine applied science pharmacy and music. The institution offers approximately 85 doctoral programs and about 415 other degree programs. UC was founded in 1819 and became a state university in 1977; the school has an endowment of about $1.5 billion. Notable alumni include former US president William Howard Taft and architect Michael Graves.

Operations

The university has a combined faculty and staff of more than 10375 and a student teacher ratio of 16.1. The school's staff and students engage in experimentation that spans the gamut from basic clinical and translational research to creative works and performance. The largest employer in the region UC has an annual economic impact of more than $4 billion.

Geographic Reach

The university has nearly 120 facilities on about 475 acres land located in Cincinnati Ohio. It attracts students from all 50 states and to nearly 115 countries.

Company Background

UC traces its history all the way back to 1819 when Cincinnati College and the Medical College of Ohio were chartered. In 1870 the city established the University of Cincinnati which later absorbed Cincinnati College and the Medical College of Ohio. In 1906 UC created the first cooperative education program in the world. In 1977 UC joined the University System of Ohio. Today UC is classified as a research university (meaning it has "Very High Research Activity") by the Carnegie Commission and is ranked as one of America's top 25 public research universities by the National Science Foundation.

EXECUTIVES

President, Santa J. Ono
Svp Academic Affairs And Provost, Beverly Davenport
Svp Administration And Finance And Cfo, Robert F. (Bob) Ambach
Vp Information Technology And Cio, Nelson C. Vincent
Assistant Vice President And University Registrar, Douglas Burgess
Vpres Community Affairs Uc Hea, John Tew
Executive Vice President, Ryan M Hays
Vice President Fin Services Controller, Carol Metzger
Department Head, Amy Lind
Associate Vice President For Research And Advanced Studies, Judith Trent
Associate Vice President For Research Research Integrity Officer, Jane Strasser
Senior Vice President Finance, Kathleen Qualls
Clinical Director, Maria Piombo
Vice President For Student Affairs, Debra Merchant
Edd Assistant Vice President Division Of Student Affairs, Nicole Mayo
Provost And Executive Vice President Academic Affairs, Kristi A Nelson
Assistant Vice President, Richard Puff
Associate Vice President, Mary McGrew
Professor And Department Head, Michael Fry
Assistant Vice President, Karen Losekamp
Vice President Of Finance, Patrick Kowalski
Assistant Vice President, Margie Rolf
Senior Vice President And Provost Medical Center, Don Harrison
Medical Director, Floyd Sallee
Assistant Vice President Housing Food And Retail Services, Todd Duncan
Medical Director, Tiffany Diers
Vice President For Governmenta, Greg Vehr
Assistant Vice President Business Core Systems, Robin Pittman
Associate Vice President And Chief Human Resource Officer, Tamie Grunow
Associate Vice President Dorot, Dorothy Air
Assistant Vice President And Chief Risk Officer, Anita Ingram
Internal Vice President, Adam Kluesener
Assistant Vice President For Research Strategic Initiatives, Phil Taylor
Senior Vice President Of Advancement And Campaign Director, Donna Gastevich
Associate Vice President Innovation And Partnerships, Annette Ready
University Of Cincinnati 18 Vice President, Lonna Sedam
Associate Vice President For Human Resources, Linda Bledsoe
Medical Director, Jon Divine
Vice President Of Professional Activities, Devin Lally
Assistant Vice President, Karen Goodwin
Vice President Of Education, Andrew Filak
Vice President, Carrie White
Assistant Vice President For Student Affairs And Dean Of Students, Juan Guardia
Vice President For Safety And Reform, Robin Engel
Vice President Marketing And Communications, Chris Ralston
Department Head, Steve Carlton
Vice President Of Ambulatory Service, Rosemary Keiser
Assistant Vice President Of Development, Kim Francis
Nursing Director, Beverly Bokovitz
Medical Director Emergency Medicine, Andrew Yick
Vp Of Committees, Kacie Lucas
Chairperson Board Of Trustees, Thomas H. (Tom) Humes
Vice Chair Board Of Trustees, Robert E. Richardson
Treasurer, Gary Hunt
Excecutive Secretary, Pat Graman
Secretary, Jamie Adkins
Treasurer, Audra Morrison
Treasurer Office Accounts Payable, Amber Simkins
Ward Secretary, Elizabeth Davis
Medical Secretary, Darlene Pabst
Assistant Treasurer, Susan Albonetti
Assistant Treasurer, Sheri Williams
Treasurer, Benita Webster
Board Member, Jennifer Heisey
Secretary, Robin Lee
Board Member, Debbie Zorn
Treasurer, Amanda Mare
Auditors: BKD LLP CINCINNATI OHIO

LOCATIONS

HQ: UNIVERSITY OF CINCINNATI
2600 CLIFTON AVE, CINCINNATI, OH 452202872
Phone: 513 556-6000
Web: WWW.UC.EDU

PRODUCTS/OPERATIONS

Selected Colleges & Schools

Clermont College (regional campus)
College-Conservatory of Music
College of Allied Health Sciences
College of Applied Science
College of Business
College of Design Architecture Art & Planning
College of Education Criminal Justice and Human Services
College of Engineering
College of Law
College of Medicine
College of Nursing
James L. Winkle College of Pharmacy
McMicken College of Arts & Sciences
Raymond Walters College (regional campus)
School of Social Work

HISTORICAL FINANCIALS

Company Type: Private

Income Statement				FYE: June 30
	REVENUE ($ mil.)	NET INCOME ($ mil.)	NET PROFIT MARGIN	EMPLOYEES
06/11	1,198	48	4.1%	14,600
06/07	594	112	18.9%	—
06/06	557	20	3.6%	—
Annual Growth	16.6%	19.2%	—	—

2011 Year-End Financials

Return on assets: 1.1%
Return on equity: 1.5%
Current ratio: —
Cash ($ mil.): 83

UNIVERSITY OF CINCINNATI MEDICAL CENTER, LLC

EXECUTIVES

Ceo, Bryan Gibler
Chief of Ob/Gyn, Arthur T Evans II
Director Records, Charlesetta Mc Cray
Assistant Professor, Sangita Kapur
Professor, Edward Silberstein
Internal Medicine Practitioner, Mark Andolina
Emergency Medicine Specialist, Matthew K Riddle
Diagnostic Radiologist, Raj Patel
Hematologist, Zartash Gul
Emergency Medicine Specialist, Aaron Murphy-Crews
Internist, Elliott Welford

LOCATIONS

HQ: UNIVERSITY OF CINCINNATI MEDICAL CENTER, LLC
234 GOODMAN ST, CINCINNATI, OH 452192364
Phone: 513 584-1000
Web: WWW.UCHEALTH.COM

HISTORICAL FINANCIALS

Company Type: Private

Income Statement — FYE: June 30

	REVENUE ($ mil.)	NET INCOME ($ mil.)	NET PROFIT MARGIN	EMPLOYEES
06/16	913	57	6.3%	5,000
06/15	873	64	7.4%	—
06/10	633	28	4.6%	—
06/09	562	20	3.6%	—
Annual Growth	7.2%	16.0%	—	—

2016 Year-End Financials

Return on assets: 9.2% — Cash ($ mil.): 2
Return on equity: 9.8%
Current ratio: 18.50

UNIVERSITY OF COLORADO

EXECUTIVES

Exec Dir, Hollie Stevenson
Senior Research Associate, Robin Corley
Director of Special Events, Suzanne Balog
Teaching Assistant History, Elizabeth Ernst
Senior Director of Gift Planni, Lori Goldstein
Physical Therapy, Thomas Colver
Senior Messaging, Tim Crean
Education, Daniela Vergara
Language Technology Specialist, Edwige Simon
Associate Professor, Elizabeth Dunn
Director of Real Estate, Jeff Lipton
Auditors: CLIFTON LARSON ALLEN LLP GRE

LOCATIONS

HQ: UNIVERSITY OF COLORADO
1800 N GRANT ST STE 800, DENVER, CO 802031187
Phone: 303 831-6192
Web: WWW.COLORADO.EDU

HISTORICAL FINANCIALS

Company Type: Private

Income Statement — FYE: June 30

	REVENUE ($ mil.)	NET INCOME ($ mil.)	NET PROFIT MARGIN	EMPLOYEES
06/19	4,097	427	10.4%	1
06/13	2,774	308	11.1%	—
06/12	2,641	141	5.4%	—
Annual Growth	6.5%	17.1%	—	—

2019 Year-End Financials

Return on assets: 5.6% — Cash ($ mil.): 179
Return on equity: 20.6%
Current ratio: 1.20

UNIVERSITY OF COLORADO HEALTH

EXECUTIVES

General Counsel, Emily Weber
Internal Medicine Practitioner, Darlene B Tad-Y
Coordinator, Carrie Macdonald
Coordinator, Jessica Berry
Coordinator, Meredith Snyder
Social Worker Clinical Lcsw CM, Allyson Drago
Nurse Navigator, Christine Frodella
Ems, Joy Schmitter
Case Manager Rn CM, Nicole Allsman
Vp Patient Line, Gary Henry
Clinical Documentation Special, Susan Krage

LOCATIONS

HQ: UNIVERSITY OF COLORADO HEALTH
12401 E 17TH AVE, AURORA, CO 800452548
Phone: 720 848-1031
Web: WWW.UCHEALTH.ORG

HISTORICAL FINANCIALS

Company Type: Private

Income Statement — FYE: June 30

	REVENUE ($ mil.)	NET INCOME ($ mil.)	NET PROFIT MARGIN	EMPLOYEES
06/20	5,055	485	9.6%	7,593
06/19	4,952	773	15.6%	—
06/18	4,341	747	17.2%	—
06/17	3,668	750	20.5%	—
Annual Growth	11.3%	(13.6%)	—	—

2020 Year-End Financials

Return on assets: 5.2% — Cash ($ mil.): 990
Return on equity: 8.5%
Current ratio: 1.20

UNIVERSITY OF COLORADO HOSPITAL AUTHORITY

University of Colorado Hospital Authority doing business as UCHealth operates the University of Colorado Hospital (UCH) in Aurora Colorado. The facility is a teaching institution for – you guessed it – the University of Colorado. UCH is a 400-bed community hospital that includes a number of specialty care facilities including centers specializing in oncology respiratory care and endocrinology. The facility also conducts medical training and research programs in partnership with the University of Colorado's Denver School of Medicine. In addition UCHealth operates 10 primary care clinics in the Denver metropolitan area.

Operations

UCH is located on the University of Colorado's Anschutz Medical Campus along with other health care providers and the University of Colorado's primary medical school campus in Aurora Colorado. Its Anschutz Inpatient Pavilion includes ICU operating imaging pharmacy and other care facilities. It also includes the Anschutz Cancer Pavilion which not only offers cancer treatment but also conducts research; Rocky Mountain Lions Eye Institute for ophthalmic care; and a rehabilitation department offering addiction treatment services.

While UCH's operations are closely tied to the University of Colorado UCH is governed by the UCH Authority a separate legal entity.

Strategy

UCHealth has upgraded its facilities in recent years to provide state-of-the art medical care and educational and research resources. Among its recent projects has been a $20 million renovation and expansion of the Anschutz Cancer Pavilion the addition of a brain tumor treatment lab to the Anschutz Outpatient Pavilion and the construction of a new 12-story emergency department tower.

In 2015 the authority broke ground on another project – the construction of a new $12.3 million emergency center at its Harmony Campus in Fort Collins Colorado. It also acquired a majority stake in a dozen freestanding emergency rooms in Colorado that are operated by Adeptus Health. The facilities (plus two more under construction) operated under the First Choice banner but were rebranded as UCHealth ER.

EXECUTIVES

Vp Clinical Affairs, Gregory V. (Greg) Stiegmann
Vp Ambulatory Services, Suzanne Sullivan
President And Ceo, John P. Harney
President Medical Staff, Robert McIntyre
Vp Patient Services And Chief Nursing Officer, Carolyn Sanders
Vp Finance And Cfo, Barbara Carveth
Coo, Tom Gronow
Executive Director Center For Dependency Addiction And Rehabilitation, Steven Millette
Executive Director Cardiac And Vascular Center, Lorna Prutzman
Executive Director Neurosciences/spine And Rehabilitation Medicine, Kimberly Meyers
President And Ceo University Of Colorado Hospital, Will Cook
Chief Information Officer, Steve Hess
Vice President Of Education, Lauren Carter

LOCATIONS

HQ: UNIVERSITY OF COLORADO HOSPITAL AUTHORITY
4200 E 9TH AVE, DENVER, CO 802203706
Phone: 720 848-0000
Web: WWW.UCHEALTH.ORG

COMPETITORS

Banner Health
Catholic Health Initiatives
Centura Health
Denver Health and Hospital Authority
Exempla Healthcare
HealthONE
Memorial Health System (Colorado)
Poudre Valley Health System
Sisters of Charity of Leavenworth
Valley View Hospital

HISTORICAL FINANCIALS

Company Type: Private

Income Statement — FYE: June 30

	REVENUE ($ mil.)	NET INCOME ($ mil.)	NET PROFIT MARGIN	EMPLOYEES
06/10	795	151	19.1%	4,200
06/09	1	0	—	—
06/05	464	1	0.2%	—
Annual Growth	11.4%	169.7%	—	—

2010 Year-End Financials

Return on assets: 12.0%
Return on equity: 24.3%
Current ratio: 1.30
Cash ($ mil.): 22

UNIVERSITY OF DELAWARE

Delaware brings up images of many things our first president that famous river and now the private University of Delaware (UD). The school's flagship campus in Newark has an enrollment of roughly 17000 undergraduate and close to 4000 graduate students. The school also has four auxiliary campuses around the state. UD offers almost 150 undergraduate degrees about 120 master's programs and more than 50 doctoral programs as well as associate's and dual graduate programs through seven academic schools. Among its instructors are well-known authors scientists artists and Nobel Laureates.

Operations

UD is a Land Grant Sea Grant and Space Grant institution meaning the school is eligible for government grants in each of these areas. The Carnegie Foundation for the Advancement of Teaching also classifies UD as a research university with very high research activity – a designation given to less than 3% of US colleges and universities. UD ranks among the nation's top 100 universities in federal research and development support for science and engineering. The university even has its own 146-foot research vessel (named the Hugh R. Sharp) for undersea exploration.

The school has a student-teacher ratio of about 15:1. It has roughly 1130 faculty members nearly 80% of which are tenured. Almost 90% have doctorate or terminal professional degrees in their field. (A terminal degree is also referred to as a Ph.D and refers to the fact that no higher degree can be obtained on that track.)

UD's 2012-13 tuition and fees were $11682 (in-state) and $28772 (out-of-state).

Geographic Reach

The university has campuses in Dover Georgetown Lewes Newark and Wilmington.

Financial Performance

The school reported a 5% increase in revenues in 2012 as the result of an increase in tuition and fees contributions and sales and services of auxiliary enterprises.

However UD's net income dropped by 118% in 2012 over 2011 due to higher expenses and a larger net realized and unrealized loss and an increase in a post-retirement benefit obligation.

In 2012 the university was supported by $1.21 billion endowment.

Company Background

UD got its start in 1743 as a private academy and was chartered by the state of Delaware in 1833. In athletics the school began NCAA Division I competition for men in 1973 and for women in 1982. US Vice President Joe Biden and his wife Jill are both UD graduates.

EXECUTIVES

Vice President For Human Resources, Wayne Guthrie
Vice President, Branndon Chen
Vice President, Lily Guastella
Vice President Communications And Marketing, Glenn Carter
Vice President And University Secretary, Jeffrey Garland
Vice Presidentres Operations, Gerald Laetsch
Vice President Of Financial, Julia Kane
Vice President, Hannah Watts
Vice President For Research, Mark Barteau
Secretary, Maria Van Venrooy
Secretary, Erin Hogan
Treasurer, Sydney Anunda
Secretary, Chase Thompson
Secretary, Anna Mcgough
Secretary, Eric Nahe
Treasurer, Linda Stacy
Secretary, Julia Amoriello
Treasurer, Susan Zaccaria
Auditors: KPMG LLP PHILADELPHIA PA

LOCATIONS

HQ: UNIVERSITY OF DELAWARE
220 HULLIHEN HALL, NEWARK, DE 197160099
Phone: 302 831-2107
Web: WWW.UDEL.EDU

PRODUCTS/OPERATIONS

Selected Schools and Colleges

Agriculture and Natural Resources
Arts and Sciences
Business and Economics
Earth Ocean and Environment
Education and Human Development
Engineering
Health Sciences

25 Most Popular Majors (2011)

Biological Sciences
Nursing
Finance
Psychology
Elementary Teacher Education
Exercise Science
Mechanical Engineering
Accounting
English
Chemical Engineering
Criminal Justice
Political Science
Civil Engineering
Marketing
Hotel Restaurant & Institutional Management
History
Human Services
Communication Interest
International Relations
Fashion Merchandising
Business Administration
Dietetics
Communication
Management
Pre-Veterinary Medicine & Animal Biosciences

HISTORICAL FINANCIALS

Company Type: Private

Income Statement — FYE: June 30

	REVENUE ($ mil.)	NET INCOME ($ mil.)	NET PROFIT MARGIN	EMPLOYEES
06/19	1,069	60	5.7%	3,600
06/18	1,023	139	13.7%	—
06/17	992	159	16.1%	—
Annual Growth	3.8%	(38.5%)	—	—

2019 Year-End Financials

Return on assets: 1.5%
Return on equity: 2.4%
Current ratio: —
Cash ($ mil.): 111

UNIVERSITY OF FLORIDA

Founded in 1853 the University of Florida (UF) is the state's oldest university and one of the largest in the country with more than 56000 students and nearly 5000 faculty and library staff members. UF is a major land-grant research university encompassing 2000 acres in Gainesville Florida. The university's about 15 colleges offer almost 100 undergraduate majors and over 200 graduate programs including education law medicine psychology and philosophy. It is also a member of the Association of American Universities a confederation of the top research universities in North America. A founding member of the Southeastern Conference UF's athletic teams (the Florida Gators) are typically ranked nationally.

Operations

UF is active in research and operates more than 200 research institutes and centers including the Nanoscale Research Facility the Pathogens Research Facility and the Biomedical Sciences Building. It has helped launch more than 190 startups based on researchers' technologies. The university received a record $838 million in research awards.

UF also has extensive health education programs including nursing and pharmacy colleges. Its medical school conducts teaching and residency programs at several Shands hospitals.

Geographic Reach

The campus consists of approximately 2000 acres and more than 1000 buildings including the first Leadership in Energy and Environmental Design (LEED) Platinum-certified building in the state of Florida. In addition more than 27000 rural acres near Yeehaw Junction in Florida's southern Osceola County has been gifted to the UF for conservation outdoor classroom and laboratory.

Financial Performance

UF's revenue increased from $1.9 billion in 2018 to $2 billion in 2019. This was brought about primarily by an increase in nongovernmental grants and contracts as well as federal grants and contracts.

Net income was $59 million 109% higher compared to $28.2 million in the previous year.

Cash and cash equivalents at the end of the year increased from $6.3 million in 2018 to $13 million in 2019. Cash used by operations was $1.1 billion. Investing activities used $86.4 million for purchase of investments while noncapital financing activities provided $1.3 billion primarily from state noncapital appropriations.

Strategy

UF has adopted a strategic development plan which seeks to shape the University and the surrounding community's future over the next 40 to 50 years. Included in UF's strategic plan is continuing to invest in updated facilities including modern research laboratories and classrooms and attracting and retaining talented faculty and staff with a competitive compensation package.

Company Background

UF's alumni include Robert Cade the inventor of Gatorade; best-selling mystery novelist Michael Connelly; actress Faye Dunaway; and former US Senator and Florida Governor Bob Graham. Other UF alumni include two Nobel Prize winners and three NASA astronauts.

EXECUTIVES

Vp And Cfo, Michael V. (Mike) McKee
Associate Provost Academic Affairs, Joseph (Joe) Glover
Dean Of Students, Jen Day Shaw
Dean Warrington College Of Business Administration, John Kraft
Vp And Cio, Elias G. Eldayrie
Svp Health Affairs; President Uf Health, David S. Guzick
Dean College Of Journalism And Communications, Diane H. McFarlin
Dean College Of Public Health And Health Professions, Michael G. Perri
Dean College Of Medicine, Michael Good
Dean College Of Education, Glenn E. Good
Dean College Of Arts, Lucinda Lavelli
Dean University Libraries, Judith C. Russell
Dean College Of Design Construction And Planning, Christopher Silver
Svp And Coo, Charles E. Lane
President, W. Kent Fuchs
Dean College Of Engineering, Cammy Abernathy
Dean College Of Health And Human Performance, Michael Reid
Interim Dean College Of Liberal Arts And Sciences, David E. Richardson
Interim Dean College Of Dentistry, Boyd Robinson
Dean College Of Nursing, Anna McDaniel
Dean College Of Pharmacy, Julie A. Johnson
Dean College Of Veterinary Medicine, James Lloyd
Dean College Of Agricultural And Life Sciences, Elaine Turner
Dean Ifas Extension, Nick Place
Dean Ifas Research, Jacqueline Burns
Dean Graduate School, Henry T. Frierson
Assistant Vice President, Mary Kay
Vice President, Greg Allen
Vice President Information Technology, Marjorie Chow
Medical Director, Sherri Flax
Assistant Vice President, Lisette Pellot
Senior Advisor To The Vp For Student Affairs, Jaquie Resnick
Chairman, Steven M. Scott
Board Member, Kristi Cheyney
Auditors: SHERRILL F NORMAN CPA TALLA

LOCATIONS

HQ: UNIVERSITY OF FLORIDA
300 SW 13TH ST, GAINESVILLE, FL 326110001
Phone: 352 392-3261
Web: WWW.UFL.EDU

PRODUCTS/OPERATIONS

Selected Colleges

College of Agricultural and Life Sciences
College of Dentistry
College of Design Construction and Planning
College of Education
College of Engineering
College of Health and Human Performance
College of Journalism and Communications
College of Liberal Arts and Sciences
College of Medicine
College of Nursing
College of Pharmacy
College of Public Health and Health Professions
College of the Arts
College of Veterinary Medicine
Levin College of Law
Warrington College of Business Administration

HISTORICAL FINANCIALS

Company Type: Private

Income Statement FYE: June 30

	REVENUE ($ mil.)	NET INCOME ($ mil.)	NET PROFIT MARGIN	EMPLOYEES
06/15	1,735	261	15.1%	5,106
06/12	3,939	64	1.6%	—
06/09	3,846	(343)	—	—
Annual Growth	(12.4%)	—	—	—

2015 Year-End Financials

Return on assets: 7.3%
Return on equity: 11.3%
Current ratio: 3.80
Cash ($ mil.): 2

UNIVERSITY OF GEORGIA

Located in the quintessential college town of Athens The University of Georgia (UGA) offers a wide range of degree programs to nearly 35000 students. Forest resources veterinary medicine and law are a few of the school's academic programs. UGA which also runs 170-plus study-abroad and exchange programs administers the prestigious Peabody Awards which honors media achievements and boasts one of the nation's largest map collections. Famous alumni include former US Senator Phil Gramm TV journalist Deborah Norville and former PBS president Pat Mitchell. The University of Georgia was chartered by the State of Georgia in 1785 and graduated its first class in 1804.

Operations

As part of its business UGA offers nearly two dozen bachelor's degrees in about 140 fields and roughly 35 master's degrees in nearly 140 fields. Its doctorate or professional degrees cover a broad spectrum of disciplines such as law pharmacy veterinary medicine and 90 other areas. The university has a student-teacher ratio of about 12:1.

Sales and Marketing

The university sources 80% of its students from the Peach State. Since 1851 25 Georgia governors have graduated from UGA. The institution also boasts nine Pulitzer Prize recipients 17 presidents or provosts of US colleges and universities and four members of the National Academy of Sciences.

Strategy

Despite its annual endowment of more than $50 million UGA has logged decreases in state appropriations in recent years due to overall declines in Georgia's budget. The result spurred UGA to cut its budget increase undergraduate tuition fees institute a "Special Institutional" mandatory fee of $200 per semester reduce employer health insurance contributions and increase energy conservation measures. Going forward UGA has also not ruled out the possibility of hiking tuition further citing that an increase of up to 30% would help to replace all of the state funding the university has lost due to the recession.

EXECUTIVES

Vice President Information Technology, Timothy M Chester
Franklin Professor Of History And History Department Chair, John Morrow
Auditors: GREG S GRIFFIN ATLANTA GEOR

LOCATIONS

HQ: UNIVERSITY OF GEORGIA
424 E BROAD ST, ATHENS, GA 306021535
Phone: 706 542-2786
Web: WWW.UGA.EDU

PRODUCTS/OPERATIONS

Selected Schools and Colleges

Agricultural and Environmental Sciences
Arts and Sciences Business
Ecology
Education
Environment and Design
Family and Consumer Sciences
Forest Resources
Graduate School
Journalism and Mass Communication
Law
Pharmacy
Public Health
Public and International Affairs
Social Work
Veterinary Medicine
The GHSU/UGA Medical Partnership
Engineering

HISTORICAL FINANCIALS

Company Type: Private

Income Statement FYE: June 30

	REVENUE ($ mil.)	NET INCOME ($ mil.)	NET PROFIT MARGIN	EMPLOYEES
06/19	1,094	72	6.7%	17,800
06/18	997	111	11.2%	—
06/17	975	142	14.6%	—
06/12	776	72	9.3%	—
Annual Growth	5.0%	0.2%	—	—

2019 Year-End Financials

Return on assets: 2.5%
Return on equity: 12.7%
Current ratio: 2.90
Cash ($ mil.): 194

UNIVERSITY OF HAWAI'I OF MANOA

EXECUTIVES

Dir, Terence Wesley-Smith
Chm, David Hanlon
Assistant Professor, Matthew Cain
Graduate Assistant, Daniel Dores
Research Assistant, Julio Rivera
Physician, Jason Kaneshige
Assistant Researcher, Andre Seale
Auxiliary, Beth Lehman
Maui County Administrator, Cynthia Reeves
Assistant Specialist, Robyn Chun
Emer Astronomer, Ann M Boesgaard

LOCATIONS

HQ: UNIVERSITY OF HAWAI'I OF MANOA
2500 CAMPUS RD, HONOLULU, HI 968222217
Phone: 808 956-7700
Web: WWW.HAWAII.EDU

HISTORICAL FINANCIALS

Company Type: Private

Income Statement FYE: June 30

	REVENUE ($ mil.)	NET INCOME ($ mil.)	NET PROFIT MARGIN	EMPLOYEES
06/18	772	51	6.7%	8
06/11	871	139	16.0%	—
Annual Growth	(1.7%)	(13.2%)	—	—

2018 Year-End Financials

Return on assets: 1.2%
Return on equity: —
Current ratio: 2.10
Cash ($ mil.): 122

UNIVERSITY OF HAWAII SYSTEMS

With a reach that extends across half a dozen islands the University of Hawai'i System consists of three university campuses seven community college campuses and several job training and research centers. The public higher education system has an enrollment of more than 60000 students about 85% of which are Hawaii residents. It offers more than 600 different doctorate graduate undergraduate and associate degrees as well as professional certificates in more than 200 fields of study. The University of Hawai'i was founded in 1907 as the College of Agriculture and Mechanic Arts in Honolulu incidentally while Hawaii was still a US territory.

EXECUTIVES

Vice President, Bryan Tanaka
Vice President Korean Student Association Uhm Active Member Accounting Club Shidler College Of Business, Timothy Ahn
It Specialist Office Of The Vice President For Community Colleges, Gordon Furuto
Department Chair, Fletcher Marty
Secretary, Kris Rodrigues
Secretary To The Chancellor, Cynthia Vinluan
Auditors: ACCUITY LLP HONOLULU HAWII

LOCATIONS

HQ: UNIVERSITY OF HAWAII SYSTEMS
2444 DOLE ST, HONOLULU, HI 968222399
Phone: 808 956-8111
Web: WWW.HAWAII.EDU

Selected Campuses

Manoa

Hilo
West O'ahu
Hawai'i
Honolulu
Kapi'olani
Kaua'i
Leeward
Maui
Windward

HISTORICAL FINANCIALS

Company Type: Private

Income Statement FYE: June 30

	REVENUE ($ mil.)	NET INCOME ($ mil.)	NET PROFIT MARGIN	EMPLOYEES
06/19	785	(67)	—	12,000
06/18	772	51	6.7%	—
06/17	771	33	4.3%	—
06/16	799	(116)	—	—
Annual Growth	(0.6%)	—	—	—

2019 Year-End Financials

Return on assets: (-1.6%)
Return on equity: —
Current ratio: 2.30
Cash ($ mil.): 131

UNIVERSITY OF HOUSTON SYSTEM

The University of Houston System can't do much about the heat or humidity but it can provide higher education in Houston. The university system serves more than 72000 students at four Houston-area universities. Flagship institution the University of Houston was founded in 1927 and offers more than 390 bachelor's master's and doctoral degree programs; it also conducts a number of research programs. Also under the system's umbrella are the University of Houston-Clear Lake the University of Houston-Downtown the University of Houston-Victoria as well as a handful of learning centers in the area. The system was established in 1977.

EXECUTIVES

President University Houston - Clear Lake, William A. Staples
Associate Vice Chancellor For Central Computing And Telecommunication Services, Dennis Fouty
President University Houston - Downtown, William V. (Bill) Flores
Executive Vice Chancellor For Administration And Finance, Carl P. Carlucci, age 71
Chancellor; President University Of Houston, Renu Khator
President University Houston - Victoria, Philip Castille
Chairman, Jarvis V. Hollingsworth

LOCATIONS

HQ: UNIVERSITY OF HOUSTON SYSTEM
4302 UNIVERSITY DR, HOUSTON, TX 772042011
Phone: 713 743-0945
Web: WWW.UHSYSTEM.EDU

PRODUCTS/OPERATIONS

Selected Colleges and Schools
University of Houston
C.T. Bauer College of Business
College of Education
College of Liberal Arts and Social Sciences
College of Natural Sciences and Mathematics
College of Optometry
College of Pharmacy
College of Technology
Conrad N. Hilton College of Hotel and Restaurant Management
Cullen College of Engineering
Gerald D. Hines College of Architecture
Graduate College of Social Work
Honors College
Law Center
University of Houston-Clear Lake
School of Business
School of Education
School of Human Sciences and Humanities
School of Science and Computer Engineering
University of Houston-Downtown
College of Business
College of Humanities and Social Sciences
College of Public Service
College of Sciences and Technology
University of Houston-Victoria
School of Arts and Sciences
School of Business Administration
School of Education and Human Development
School of Nursing

HISTORICAL FINANCIALS

Company Type: Private

Income Statement FYE: August 31

	REVENUE ($ mil.)	NET INCOME ($ mil.)	NET PROFIT MARGIN	EMPLOYEES
08/15	605	41	6.9%	12,608
08/14	742	46	6.2%	—
08/13	1	81	6095.0%	—
08/12	688	132	19.3%	—
Annual Growth	(4.2%)	(31.9%)	—	—

UNIVERSITY OF IOWA HOSPITALS AND CLINICS

EXECUTIVES

Ceo, Kenneth P Kates
Ceo, Gordon Williams
Pres, Sally Mason
V Pres, Jean Robillard
Prin, Ann Williamson
Coo, Sabi Singh
Coordinator, Kathy Moser
Pediatrician, Catherina Pinnaro
Diagnostic Radiologist, John D Newell
Internal Medicine Practitioner, Aubrey C Chan
Internal Medicine Practitioner, Andrew Johannes
Auditors: KPMG LLP DES MOINES IOWA

LOCATIONS

HQ: UNIVERSITY OF IOWA HOSPITALS AND CLINICS
200 HAWKINS DR, IOWA CITY, IA 522421009
Phone: 319 356-1616
Web: WWW.UICHILDRENS.ORG

HISTORICAL FINANCIALS

Company Type: Private

Income Statement FYE: June 30

	REVENUE ($ mil.)	NET INCOME ($ mil.)	NET PROFIT MARGIN	EMPLOYEES
06/19	1,834	111	6.1%	7,638
06/18	1,666	296	17.8%	—
06/17	1,502	47	3.2%	—
06/16	1,395	117	8.4%	—
Annual Growth	9.6%	(1.7%)	—	—

2019 Year-End Financials

Return on assets: 4.5%
Return on equity: 6.7%
Current ratio: 1.40
Cash ($ mil.): 16

UNIVERSITY OF LOUISVILLE

Living up to its mandate to be a leading metropolitan research university the University of Louisville (U of L) has hit a few out of the park. The U of L completed the first self-contained artificial heart implant and the first successful hand transplant at its University of Louisville Hospital. The health care focused university offers associate baccalaureate master's professional and doctorate degrees in some 170 fields of study including medicine dentistry nursing and public health as well as arts and sciences education business law music social work and engineering. It has more than 22000 students enrolled in about a dozen colleges and schools on three campuses.

Geographic Reach

U of L's main campus the 290-acre Belknap Campus houses seven of the university's 12 colleges and schools and is located three miles from downtown Louisville. The U of L Health Sciences Center (housing the health-related schools) is located in downtown Louisville while the Shelby Campus is in eastern Jefferson County.

Strategy

Despite its focus on health care pressures on the health care industry (including the high cost of running a full-service hospital) prompted the school to explore a possible merger of the U of L Hospital with two other state health care providers Saint Joseph Health Care and Jewish Hospital & St. Mary's HealthCare (JHSMH) in 2010. However U of L was ultimately left out of the deal (completed in 2012) after Kentucky's governor voiced concerns over the potential loss of control over the U of L Hospital which operates as a regional safety net medical care provider.

Company Background

The origins of the University of Louisville date back to 1798 with a meeting to establish Jefferson Seminary which didn't open its doors until 1813 and closed 16 years later. Subsequent incarnations eventually led to the creation of the University of Louisville in 1846.

Notable alumni include author Sue Grafton US Senator Christopher Dodd and William Akers inventor of the SPF sun protection rating system.

EXECUTIVES

Vice President Business Affairs, Larry Owsley
Executive Vice President And Provost, Shirley Willihnganz
Executive Vice President Health Affairs, Larry Cook
Medical Director, Christine Cook
Second Vice President, Joy Hart
Assistant Vice President For Business Affairs, Terri Rutledge
Vice President For Community E, Daniel Hall
Clinic Director General Pediatrics, Michael Howard
Associate Vice President For Research Services, William King
Senior Vice President For Administration, Jennifer Bobo
Assistant Vice President, Sandra Johnson-Byers
Senior Vice President For Administration, Anita Block
Prof. Of Political Science And Department Chair, Rodger Payne
Vice President Of Recruitment, Angelo Ciliberti
Assistant Vice President For Health Affairs, Peter Diakov
Associate Vice President Business Services, Mark Watkins
Assistant Vice President For Development, Karen Kayser
Vice President Finance, Lisa Ward
Associate Vice President For Facilities Planning And Management, Nancy Tierney
Vice President Of Career Services, Holly Symonds Clark
Assistant Vice President For Government Relations, Shannon Rickett
Second Vice President, Steven Kniffley
Medical Director, Rosemary Ouseph
Department Chair, Prof Poc
Housing Vice President, Jordan Knapp
Secretary Treasurer, William Armstrong
Professor And Senior Vice Chairman, Roland Valdes
Auditors: BKD LLP LOUISVILLE KENTUCKY

LOCATIONS

HQ: UNIVERSITY OF LOUISVILLE
2301 S 3RD ST, LOUISVILLE, KY 402922001
Phone: 502 852-5555
Web: WWW.ULGC.NET

PRODUCTS/OPERATIONS

Selected Colleges and Schools

Arts & Sciences
Brandeis School of Law
Business
Dentistry
Education & Human Development
Kent School of Social Work
Medicine
Music
Nursing
Public Health & Information Sciences
School of Interdisciplinary and Graduate Studies
Speed School of Engineering

HISTORICAL FINANCIALS

Company Type: Private

Income Statement — FYE: June 30

	REVENUE ($ mil.)	NET INCOME ($ mil.)	NET PROFIT MARGIN	EMPLOYEES
06/19	769	23	3.0%	6,275
06/18	717	3	0.4%	—
06/12	559	(36)	—	—
06/11	591	32	5.4%	—
Annual Growth	3.3%	(3.9%)	—	—

2019 Year-End Financials

Return on assets: 1.8%
Return on equity: 3.2%
Current ratio: 1.30
Cash ($ mil.): 110

UNIVERSITY OF MARYLAND MEDICAL SYSTEM CORPORATION

The thirteen academic specialty and community hospitals of the University of Maryland Medical System (UMMS) dot the map of the state's eastern half on both sides of Chesapeake Bay. UMMS one of the largest employers in the Baltimore area has more than 2485 acute care beds and attends to such specialties as trauma care cancer cardiac women's vascular and neuroscience services orthopedic rehabilitation and pediatric care. University of Maryland Medical Center the system's teaching hub is one of the oldest academic hospitals in the US. In addition to its hospitals UMMS also includes community clinics to address mental health rehabilitation and primary care. The system was established in 1984.

Operations

UMMC's members hospitals include the University of Maryland Medical Center Baltimore Washington Medical Center Chester River Home Care ChoiceOne Urgent Care UM Rehabilitation & Orthopedic Institute UM Capital Region Health Mt. Washington Pediatric Hospital UM Shore Health System University of Maryland St. Joseph Medical Center and Upper Chesapeake Health.

University of Maryland Medical Center which houses about 805 beds is staffed entirely by physicians who double as faculty members at the University of Maryland School of Medicine (SOM) the system's longtime partner. The hospital contains additional specialty facilities dedicated to such areas as pediatrics cancer treatment cardiac disease diabetes organ transplants Parkinson's disease and shock trauma.

Aside from its integral partnership with SOM UMMS has in recent years been bolstering its network of member hospitals to reach new markets in Maryland. Its affiliate University of Maryland Upper Chesapeake Health owns a pair of hospitals in northeastern Maryland (UM Upper Chesapeake Medical Center and UM Harford Memorial Hospital).

Geographic Reach

Based in Maryland UMMS provides primary and specialty care at more than 150 locations across the state.

Strategy

The University of Maryland Medical System and CareFirst BlueCross BlueShield (CareFirst) the region's largest not-for-profit healthcare company announced a new five-year partnership to address access and quality of care for the state's most vulnerable populations. The transformative work from this initiative will focus on population health which is an approach to care aiming to improve the health outcomes for entire patient populations while also improving the healthcare experience and effectively managing costs. This includes enhanced support and focused care for the highest-risk patients to help them maintain a high quality of life through more efficient and effective management of their health. As part of this effort CareFirst BlueChoice Inc. will acquire University of Maryland Health Advantage Inc. (UM Health Advantage) a Medicare Dual Eligible Special Needs health plan and University of Maryland Health Partners Inc. a Medicaid Managed Care Organization. Combined UMMS' Health Plans serve 55000 Maryland residents each year.

At the core of this partnership is the development of a jointly operated population health management team which will allow UMMS and CareFirst to collaborate on innovative care models and related resources better enabling both organizations to focus on what they do best. Specifically the work will bring new approaches to using shared data that drive improved population health outcomes by supporting the identification and delivery of the most effective care and support for vulnerable populations. This joint effort allows CareFirst and UMMS to take coordinated action focused on investing in healthier communities and improving health equity in Maryland. This collaboration also marks a shared commitment to expanding partnerships designed to transform care delivery and improve health outcomes.

Company Background

The system's flagship hospital began on its present site in 1823 as Baltimore Infirmary. It later was known for many years as University Hospital until Maryland's legislature changed it from a state-run single-building facility to a private not-for-profit medical system in 1984. In short order UMMS began expanding mainly by adding existing hospitals.

EXECUTIVES

President And Ceo University Of Maryland Medical Center, Jeffrey A. Rivest
Ceo Chester River Health System, James E. Ross
Senior Vice President Chief Information Officer, Jon P. Burns
President And Ceo Maryland General Health Systems And Hospita, Sylvia Smith Johnson
President And Ceo, Karen E. Olscamp, age 60
Evp And Cfo, Henry J. Franey
Medical Director, Melissa Frisch
Vice President Information Technology Services, Brian Cassel
Senior Vice President, Jerry Wollman
Senior Vice President Finance, Hank Franey
Vice President, Mia Zorzi
Director Of Nursing, Margaret Burns
Senior Vice President, Alicia Cunningham
Vice President, Kristin Jones Bryce
Vice President Information Technology, Lisa Vuolo
Vice President It Upper Chesapeake Health, Rick Casteel
Director, Stephen A. Burch, age 70
Medical Secretary I, Shakeya Scott
Vice Chair, Steven Bernstein

LOCATIONS

HQ: UNIVERSITY OF MARYLAND MEDICAL SYSTEM CORPORATION
250 W PRATT ST, BALTIMORE, MD 212012423
Phone: 410 328-8667
Web: WWW.UMM.EDU

PRODUCTS/OPERATIONS

Selected Facilities and Affiliates
Baltimore Washington Medical Center
Chester River Health System
Civista Medical Center
Kernan Orthopaedics and Rehabilitation
Maryland General Hospital
Mt. Washington Pediatric Hospital
Shore Health System
  Dorchester General Hospital
  The Memorial Hospital at Easton
University of Maryland Medical Center
  Marlene and Stewart Greenebaum Cancer Center
  R Adams Cowley Shock Trauma Center
  University of Maryland Hospital for Children
University of Maryland St. Joseph Medical Center
University Specialty Hospital
Upper Chesapeake Health
  Harford Memorial Hospital
  Upper Chesapeake Medical Center

COMPETITORS

Adventist HealthCare
Anne Arundel Medical Center
Ascension Health
Bon Secours Health
Catholic Health Initiatives
Dimensions Healthcare
Franklin Square Hospital Center
GBMC
Johns Hopkins Health System
LifeBridge Health
MedStar Health

HISTORICAL FINANCIALS

Company Type: Private

Income Statement — FYE: June 30

	REVENUE ($ mil.)	NET INCOME ($ mil.)	NET PROFIT MARGIN	EMPLOYEES
06/20	4,364	70	1.6%	12,000
06/19	4,235	36	0.9%	—
06/16	1,358	(29)	—	—
06/15	1,413	13	0.9%	—
Annual Growth	25.3%	39.9%	—	—

2020 Year-End Financials

Return on assets: 1.0%
Return on equity: 2.5%
Current ratio: 1.00
Cash ($ mil.): 961

UNIVERSITY OF MARYLAND, COLLEGE PARK

EXECUTIVES

Pres, Darryll Pines
Acting Chief Diversity Officer, Cynthia Edmunds
Administrative Assistant, Dee Allen
Accounting Staff, Showerman Stacey
Dean, Gregory Bullock
Accounting Staff, Janet Dudley-Eshbach
Manager, Jennifer Shannon
Coordinator, Sheila Goebel
Coordinator, Omar Siddique
Law Specialist, Rebecca Hunsaker
Director Administrative Servic, Bill Katsereles

LOCATIONS

HQ: UNIVERSITY OF MARYLAND, COLLEGE PARK
PATUXENT BLDG 010, COLLEGE PARK, MD 207420001
Phone: 301 405-1000
Web: WWW.ESSIC.UMD.EDU

HISTORICAL FINANCIALS

Company Type: Private

Income Statement — FYE: June 30

	REVENUE ($ mil.)	NET INCOME ($ mil.)	NET PROFIT MARGIN	EMPLOYEES
06/18	1,369	100	7.3%	8,871
06/17	15	1	12.6%	—
Annual Growth	8577.7%	4931.4%	—	—

2018 Year-End Financials

Return on assets: 3.2%
Return on equity: 5.0%
Current ratio: 2.90
Cash ($ mil.): 663

UNIVERSITY OF MASSACHUSETTS

The University of Massachusetts (UMass) has been expanding across the commonwealth since its founding in 1863. About 72000 students are enrolled in UMass programs that range from art to journalism to engineering. The university's flagship campus in Amherst (with a student-teacher ratio of 18:1) offers its 22000 undergrad students degrees in more than 90 areas and its 6400 graduate students master's degrees in nearly 70 areas and doctorates in 50 areas. Its University of Massachusetts Medical School in Worcester has an affiliated teaching hospital and students studying medicine nursing and biomedical sciences. Other UMass campuses can be found in Boston Dartmouth and Lowell.

Operations

UMass Amherst is part of the Five Colleges consortium a partnership with other area universities including Amherst Hampshire Mount Holyoke and Smith colleges through which students at member institutions attend classes and benefit from being able to share resources at all of the schools.

The system's Boston and Dartmouth campuses are renowned for their academic programs. Boston is known as a research university with more than 90% of its faculty holding the highest degree available in their field. Dartmouth is credited with giving its students a "personalized' education that includes internships undergraduate research opportunities and service learning experiences.

Geographic Reach

While UMass serves students from all 50 US states and 100 other countries 80% of incoming freshmen are from the Commonwealth.

Financial Performance

Operating revenue increased at UMass 3% to $2.2 billion in fiscal 2014 due to increases in tuition and fees. Along with grants and contracts auxiliary services and services provided at the Worcester Medical School tuition and fees are the most significant sources of operating revenues.

UMass' endowment reached $758 million in 2014 when the fund grew by 14%. The endowment is being used for projects such as the Charles J. Hoff Scholarship. Created by former UMass trustee and alumnus Charles J. Hoff and his wife Josephine Hoff the scholarship is expected to provide financial support to more than 2500 students by 2017.

Strategy

UMass uses its funds to upgrade and expand it facilities. In 2014 it announced plans to build an academic center and home for administrative offices in downtown Boston. It also opened its first satellite center in Springfield which offers 40 courses in manufacturing cybersecurity IT and casino management based on area business needs. The center works with local community colleges to develop programs that allow students to transition from associate to bachelor degrees.

The university's Boston campus also received a new Integrated Sciences Complex completed in late 2014 and the General Academic Building slated for 2015.

Company Background

Notable UMass alumni include entertainer Bill Cosby singer Natalie Cole and former General Electric CEO Jack Welch.

EXECUTIVES

President, Robert L. Caret, age 72
Evp And Coo, James R. Julian
Svp Administration And Finance, Christine Wilda
Interim Chancellor Umass Boston, J. Keith Motley
Chancellor University Of Massachusetts Amherst, Kumble R. (Swamy) Subbaswamy
Chancellor University Of Massachusetts Worcester, Michael F. Collins
Chancellor University Of Massachusetts Dartmouth, Divina Grossman
Vp And Cio, Robert Solis
Ceo Umass Online, John Cunningham
Chancellor Umass Lowell, Jacquie Moloney
Vice Chairman, Ruben J. King-Shaw, age 59
Vice Chairman, Maria D. Furman
Chairman, Victor Woolridge
Auditors: GRANT THORNTON LLP BOSTON M

LOCATIONS

HQ: UNIVERSITY OF MASSACHUSETTS
1 BEACON ST, BOSTON, MA 021083107
Phone: 617 287-7000
Web: WWW.MASSACHUSETTS.EDU

PRODUCTS/OPERATIONS

Selected Colleges and Schools

College of Engineering
College of Humanities and Fine Arts
College of Natural Sciences and Mathematics
College of Social and Behavioral Sciences
Commonwealth College
Graduate School
School of Education
School of Management
School of Nursing
School of Public Health and Health Sciences

HISTORICAL FINANCIALS

Company Type: Private

Income Statement FYE: June 30

	REVENUE ($ mil.)	NET INCOME ($ mil.)	NET PROFIT MARGIN	EMPLOYEES
06/18	2,468	77	3.1%	13,196
06/17	2,442	325	13.3%	—
06/16	2,403	129	5.4%	—
06/12	2,055	255	12.4%	—
Annual Growth	3.1%	(18.0%)	—	—

2018 Year-End Financials

Return on assets: 1.0%
Return on equity: 3.2%
Current ratio: 1.00
Cash ($ mil.): 103

UNIVERSITY OF MISSISSIPPI MEDICAL CENTER

EXECUTIVES

Interim Chancellor, Larry Sparks
Assistant Professor, Benjamin Stronach
Assistant Professor, Rebecca Sugg
Human Resources Business Partn, Constance Suber
Assistant Professor U M C, Gongchao Yang
Staff Assistant, Peggy Duke
Senior Human Resources, Cecelia Bass
Irb Specialist, Debrah Rogers
Professor Clinical, James Jordan
Lab Reg Med Tech, Robin Galey
Registered Nurse I Inpatient, Amanda Coleman

LOCATIONS

HQ: UNIVERSITY OF MISSISSIPPI MEDICAL CENTER
2500 N STATE ST, JACKSON, MS 392164500
Phone: 601 984-2150
Web: WWW.UMC.EDU

HISTORICAL FINANCIALS

Company Type: Private

Income Statement FYE: June 30

	REVENUE ($ mil.)	NET INCOME ($ mil.)	NET PROFIT MARGIN	EMPLOYEES
06/18	1,252	(87)	—	9,000
06/17	1,204	(78)	—	—
Annual Growth	4.0%	—	—	—

2018 Year-End Financials

Return on assets: (-5.0%)
Return on equity: —
Current ratio: 2.80
Cash ($ mil.): 294

UNIVERSITY OF MISSISSIPPI MEDICAL CENTER

EXECUTIVES

Dir, Daniel W Jones
Administrative Assistant III, Linda Buckley

LOCATIONS

HQ: UNIVERSITY OF MISSISSIPPI MEDICAL CENTER
2500 N STATE ST, JACKSON, MS 392164500
Phone: 601 984-5670
Web: WWW.UMC.EDU

HISTORICAL FINANCIALS

Company Type: Private

Income Statement FYE: June 30

	REVENUE ($ mil.)	NET INCOME ($ mil.)	NET PROFIT MARGIN	EMPLOYEES
06/14	1,042	30	2.9%	20
06/13	940	23	2.5%	—
Annual Growth	10.9%	29.9%	—	—

2014 Year-End Financials

Return on assets: 8.9%
Return on equity: 2.9%
Current ratio: 2.20
Cash ($ mil.): 176

UNIVERSITY OF MISSOURI HEALTH CARE

EXECUTIVES

Ceo-Pres, Mitch Wasden
Dir of Treas*, Ann Toellner
Cfo*, Kevin Necas
Clinic Coordinator, Andrea Beneke
Purchasing Director, Carol Clark
Rheumatologist, Chokkalingam Siva
Doctor, Debra Howenstine
Staff, Rhonda Cuddy
Project Manager, Cecilia Molina-Clark
Internal Medicine Practitioner, Harihoran Regunath
Internal Medicine Practitioner, Hraleen Chela
Auditors: KPMG LLP

LOCATIONS

HQ: UNIVERSITY OF MISSOURI HEALTH CARE
1 HOSPITAL DR, COLUMBIA, MO 652015276
Phone: 573 882-4141
Web: WWW.MUHEALTH.ORG

HISTORICAL FINANCIALS

Company Type: Private

Income Statement FYE: June 30

	REVENUE ($ mil.)	NET INCOME ($ mil.)	NET PROFIT MARGIN	EMPLOYEES
06/16	749	62	8.4%	5,000
06/15	696	64	9.3%	—
06/08	0	0	1.0%	—
Annual Growth	140.0%	212.1%	—	—

2016 Year-End Financials

Return on assets: 5.9%
Return on equity: 10.0%
Current ratio: 1.40
Cash ($ mil.): 27

UNIVERSITY OF MISSOURI SYSTEM

Education isn't just for show in the Show Me State. The University of Missouri (UM) founded in 1839 educates more than 75000 students at four campuses and through a statewide extension program; approximately 60% of students are in graduate or professional programs. The university's campuses include flagship UM-Columbia UM-Kansas City UM-St. Louis and the Missouri University of Science and Technology. Nicknamed "Mizzou" the University of Missouri System has close to 6000 faculty members and a student-teacher enrollment of about 17:1.

Operations

In addition to its university campuses the University of Missouri System operates the University of Missouri Health System which encompasses University Hospital and Clinics Women's and Children's Hospital Ellis Fischel Cancer Center Rusk Rehabilitation Center Missouri Psychiatric Institute Missouri Orthopaedic Institute and University Physicians. Its hospitals and clinics provide high-risk obstetrics orthopedic surgery neurosciences and cardiovascular care among other services. It also has the region's only Level I Trauma Center.

Geographic Reach

The University of Missouri's four campuses are located in Columbia Kansas City Rolla and St. Louis. The system has an exchange program with South Africa through which UM students study at the University of the Western Cape in Bellville (Cape Town) South Africa and vice versa.

EXECUTIVES

Chancellor University Of Missouri-kansas City, Leo E. Morton, age 75
Chancellor University Of Missouri-st. Louis, Thomas F. (Tom) George
Chancellor Missouri University Of Science And Technology, Cheryl B. Schrader
Vp Information Technology, Gary K. Allen
Evp Academic Affairs And Interim Chancellor University Of Missouri-columbia, Henry C. (Hank) Foley
Vp Finance And Cfo, Brian D. Burnett
Chief Investment Officer, Thomas Richards
Interim President, Mike Middleton
Medical Director, Johnathan Lauriello
Pharmacy Manager, Patrick Ege
Vice President Managed Care, Mike Larson
Education Technologist Vice President Undergraduate Studies, Faydre Paulus
Vice President Marketing, Brett Hayes
Events Assistant Vice President Enrollment Management, Cherelle S Washington
Vice President Of Human Resources, Scott Shoener
Chairman, Donald L. Cupps
Vice Chairman, Pamela Q. Henrickson
Secretary To The Board, Cindy Harmon
Secretary To The Board, Kathleen Miller
Secretary, Lynda Larocque
Secretary Senior Mechanical And Aerosp, Cynthia Irsik
Secretary, Lila O'riley

Secretary, Annette Valentine
Secretary, Diane Temmen
Secretary, Jody Meyers
Secretary, Presha Earney
Secretary, Kimberle Holsten
Secretary Henry County, Verlinda Talley
Secretary, Val Germann
Treasurer, Benson Verel
Auditors: BKD LLP KANSAS CITY MISSOUR

LOCATIONS

HQ: UNIVERSITY OF MISSOURI SYSTEM
321 UNIVERSITY HALL, COLUMBIA, MO 652113020
Phone: 573 882-2712
Web: WWW.UMSYSTEM.EDU

PRODUCTS/OPERATIONS

Selected Campuses

University of Missouri-Columbia
University of Missouri Health System (Columbia)
UM-Kansas City
UM-St. Louis
Missouri University of Science and Technology (Rolla)

Selected Colleges and Schools

College of Agriculture Food and Natural Resources
School of Natural Resources
College of Arts and Sciences
School of Music
College of Education
School of Information Science and Learning Technologies
College of Engineering
College of Human Environmental Sciences
School of Social Work
College of Veterinary Medicine
Graduate School
Harry S Truman School of Public Affairs
School of Health Professions
School of Journalism
School of Law
School of Medicine
Sinclair College of Nursing
Trulaske College of Business
School of Accountancy

HISTORICAL FINANCIALS

Company Type: Private

Income Statement — FYE: June 30

	REVENUE ($ mil.)	NET INCOME ($ mil.)	NET PROFIT MARGIN	EMPLOYEES
06/18	2,851	267	9.4%	30,282
06/16	2,702	108	4.0%	—
06/13	2,404	221	9.2%	—
Annual Growth	3.5%	3.8%	—	—

2018 Year-End Financials

Return on assets: 3.1%
Return on equity: 5.5%
Current ratio: 1.30
Cash ($ mil.): 360

UNIVERSITY OF NEW MEXICO

With more than 36630 students The University of New Mexico (UNM) based in Albuquerque is most renowned for its schools of medicine law and education. Students also attend one of the school's four branches located around the northern part of the state at Gallup Los Alamos Rio Rancho Taos and Valencia. Through its schools and colleges the university offers 96 bachelor's degrees 71 master's degrees 37 doctorate degrees as well as professional practice programs in law medicine and pharmacy. Its annual budget tops $2 billion. UNM employs more than 22000 people across the state.

Operations

The university also serves non-traditional students through its Evening and Weekend Degree Program which offers some 1000 classes each semester that contribute to about 40 different degree programs. About 12000 working students attend UNM at night each semester.

Most of its students come from in-state and continue to live in New Mexico after graduation.

In conjunction with the university's health sciences medical nursing and pharmacy school programs the university operates the UNM Health Sciences Center. It's the state's largest integrated health care treatment research and education facility. The teaching hospital operates a trauma center and specialized care units for oncology and pediatrics.

Geographic Reach

UNM's main campus is located in Albuquerque. Satellite campuses are in Gallup Los Alamos Rio Rancho Taos and Valencia. Only Los Alamos and Santa Fe offer graduate and upper division programs.The university hosts some 1500 international students and scholars.

Financial Performance

The majority of UNM's revenues (more than 60%) come from clinical operations and patient services from the UNM hospitals. Grants and contracts make up 18% while tuition and fees only account for 9% of the university's revenues.

In 2016 the university's revenues declined by $30 million to $1.56 billion due to lower other patient-related serivces and lower sales and serivces.

Operating expenses grew by about $112 million to $2.2 billion due to higher instruction research and public service costs and a rise in clinical operation expenses.

Company Background

UNM was founded in 1889.

EXECUTIVES

Dean School Of Engineering, Joseph L. Cecchi
Dean School Of Medicine, Paul B. Roth
Dean College Of University Libraries And Learning Sciences, Richard W. Clement
President, Robert G. Frank
Provost And Evp Academic Affairs, Chaouki T. Abdallah
Interim Dean Anderson School Of Management, Craig G. White
Dean College Of Arts And Sciences, Mark Peceny
Dean College Of Fine Arts, Kymberly Pinder
Dean Graduate Studies, Julie Coonrod
Dean Honors College, Catherine Krause
Dean College Of Nursing, Nancy Ridenour
Dean College Of Pharmacy, Lynda S. Welage
Dean School Of Architecture And Planning, Geraldine Forbes Isais
Dean School Of Law, David J. Herring
Dean School Of Public Administration, Mario Rivera
Dean College Of Education, S. Hector Ochoa
Financial Officer, Nicole Dopson
Cio, Gil Gonzales
President Board Of Regents, Jack L. Fortner
Auditors: MOSS ADAMS LLP ALBUQUERQUE N

LOCATIONS

HQ: UNIVERSITY OF NEW MEXICO
1800 ROMA BLVD NE, ALBUQUERQUE, NM 871310001
Phone: 505 277-0732
Web: WWW.GALLUP.UNM.EDU

PRODUCTS/OPERATIONS

2013 Sales

	% of sales
Clinical operations	42
Grants & contracts	21
Sales & services	16
Tuition & fees	10
Patients services	8
Other	3
Total 0	100

Schools and Colleges

Schools and Colleges
Anderson School of Management
College of Arts & Sciences
College of Education
College of Fine Arts
College of University Libraries & Learning Sciences
Honors College
School of Architecture & Planning
School of Engineering
School of Law
School of Public Administration
University College

HISTORICAL FINANCIALS

Company Type: Private

Income Statement — FYE: June 30

	REVENUE ($ mil.)	NET INCOME ($ mil.)	NET PROFIT MARGIN	EMPLOYEES
06/19	1,913	(137)	—	18,362
06/18	1,826	(181)	—	—
06/17	1,807	11	0.6%	—
06/16	1,893	6	0.3%	—
Annual Growth	0.4%	—	—	—

2019 Year-End Financials

Return on assets: (-4.0%)
Return on equity: (-48.5%)
Current ratio: 3.20
Cash ($ mil.): 397

UNIVERSITY OF NORTH CAROLINA AT CHAPEL HILL

The University of North Carolina at Chapel Hill (UNC-Chapel Hill) has the education market cornered. One of the three original points making up North Carolina's Research Triangle (along with Duke University and North Carolina State University) Carolina is the flagship campus of the University of North Carolina (UNC) system. The institution is consistently among the top-ranked research schools in the US. It enrolls some 29000 students and offers more than 250 undergraduate graduate and professional programs including law and medicine. It has 3200 full-time faculty members.

Operations

The university includes 15 schools and colleges as well as an adult learning center for continuing education programs. Its degree offerings include more than 100 master's degrees and about 70 doctorate programs.

UNC-Chapel Hill conducts extensive research programs in a variety of fields at its five health science schools (medicine dentistry pharmacy nursing and public health) its patient care facilities (operated through the University of North Carolina Hospitals affiliate) and its scientific teaching divisions (at the College of Arts and Sciences). The university attracted some $770 million in research grants and contracts during 2012. Funding sources include the National Institutes of Health. Research funding at UNC-Chapel Hill makes up more than half of awards for the entire UNC system.

Geographic Reach

UNC-Chapel Hill is located on a 730-acre campus that holds about 300 buildings. The university attracts students from all 50 US states and more than 145 international countries. It also has study abroad opportunities.

Financial Performance

UNC-Chapel Hill reported $2.5 billion in total revenues in 2012. Operating revenues make up the majority of earnings ($1.7 billion) from activities including student tuition fees federal grants and contracts and patient services. Non-operating revenues include state appropriations non-capital grants and gifts and investment income. Operating expenses ran at about $2.4 billion for 2012 and the university had a budget for fiscal 2013 of some $2.5 billion.

Strategy

To expand its international education opportunities in 2013 UNC-Chapel Hill formed a dual-degree partnership with Tsinghua University in China. The partnership offers business administration executive master's degrees.

Company Background

Chartered in 1789 Carolina is the oldest public university in the US. Notable alumni include author Thomas Wolfe and President James K. Polk as well as athlete Michael Jordan and journalist Charles Kuralt.

EXECUTIVES

Vice Department Chair Pharmacology, Robert Nicholas
Vice President Of Finance And Administration, Betty M Whichard
Medical Director, James Hill
Senior Vice President Professional And Support Services, Mel Hurston
Auditors: BETH A WOOD CPA RALEIGH NC

LOCATIONS

HQ: UNIVERSITY OF NORTH CAROLINA AT CHAPEL HILL
104 AIRPORT DR, CHAPEL HILL, NC 275995023
Phone: 919 962-1370
Web: WWW.UNC.EDU

PRODUCTS/OPERATIONS

Selected Schools Colleges and Centers

College of Arts and Sciences
Eshelman School of Pharmacy
Friday Center for Continuing Education
General College
Gillings School of Global Public Health
Graduate School
Kenan-Flagler Business School
School of Dentistry
School of Education
School of Government
School of Information and Library Science
School of Journalism and Mass Communication
School of Law
School of Medicine
School of Nursing
School of Social Work

Selected Academic Departments

African and AfroAmerican Studies
Air Force ROTC
Anthropology
Army ROTC
Art
Biology
Chemistry
Classics
Communication Studies
Dramatic Art
Economics
English and Comparative Literature
Exercise and Sport Science
Geography
History
Marine Sciences
Music
Nutrition
Pharmacology
Philosophy
Political Science
Psychology
Religious Studies
Sociology
Surgery

HISTORICAL FINANCIALS

Company Type: Private

Income Statement — FYE: June 30

	REVENUE ($ mil.)	NET INCOME ($ mil.)	NET PROFIT MARGIN	EMPLOYEES
06/19	2,073	229	11.0%	12,204
06/17	1,773	95	5.4%	—
06/11	1,704	391	23.0%	—
06/08	281	149	53.1%	—
Annual Growth	19.9%	3.9%	—	—

2019 Year-End Financials

Return on assets: 8.0%
Return on equity: 378.1%
Current ratio: 2.10
Cash ($ mil.): 240

UNIVERSITY OF NORTH CAROLINA HOSPITALS

University of North Carolina Hospitals (UNCH) is at the heart of the UNC Health Care System (UNC HCS). The medical center provides acute care to the Tar Heel State through North Carolina Memorial Hospital North Carolina Children's Hospital North Carolina Neurosciences Hospital and North Carolina Women's Hospital. Combined the facilities have more than 800 beds. Specialties include cancer treatment at the North Carolina Cancer Hospital organ transplantation cardiac care orthopedics wound management and rehabilitation. Not-for-profit UNC HCS is owned by the state of North Carolina and is affiliated with the UNC-Chapel Hill School of Medicine.

Operations

UNCH operates under the umbrella of UNC HCS.

UNC HCS already extends beyond Chapel Hill and into the greater Triangle area through its network of primary care and specialty physician practices located in Orange Wake Durham Chatham and Lee counties. The system treats some 800000 people at UNC HCS practices and clinics annually.

UNCH handles more than 37000 patients each year and delivers 3500 babies annually.

North Carolina Children's offers 150 inpatient beds and a comprehensive children's outpatient center. Every year provides specialty care to more than 70000 children from all 100 North Carolina counties. The North Carolina Cancer Hospital is the clinical home of the UNC Lineberger Comprehensive Cancer Center. The state's only public cancer hospital the North Carolina Cancer Hospital treats patients from every county in North Carolina with more than 135000 patient visits a year.

Geographic Reach

UNCH not only serves patients from all North Carolina counties with about a third coming from the Research Triangle area it also serves patients from neighboring states.

Strategy

Being one of the primary health care providers in the area UNC HCS is nearly always expanding its services and service areas either through acquisitions or new construction.

In 2015 UNCH filed a petition with state regulators seeking the ability to add 42 acute-care beds at its Chapel Hill campus. If approved UNC estimates it will cost the hospital $17 million and would be completed by mid-2018.

UNC HCS planned to open a new 86-bed acute-care hospital in Hillsborough in 2015 as part of an effort to reduce pressure on its Chapel Hill campus. The construction of the hospital will cost about $200 million. The new facility will offer an emergency department outpatient surgery and a range of inpatient services to our patients in Alamance and Western Orange counties.

Dedicated cancer care and cancer research is another area in which UNC HCS is expanding. It opened a North Carolina Cancer Hospital at Rex Hospital in 2014.

The system is also building an Imaging Research Building expected to open in 2013 to house the Biomedical Research Imaging Center and serve as a state resource for handling the acquisition processing analysis storage and retrieval of scientific images.

In 2013 UNC HCS established the first stage of its Hillsborough campus with the opening of a 60000-square-foot medical office building. The building includes hospital services such as imaging laboratory pharmacy and medical and surgical oncology.

Company Background

In 2011 the hospital opened a new wing of the Newborn Critical Care Unit in the North Carolina Children's Hospital that houses 10 new patient beds bringing the number of beds in the unit to 58.

UNCH was founded in 1952 under the name North Carolina Memorial Hospital. In 1989 the North Carolina General Assembly created UNCH.

EXECUTIVES

Pres, Gary Park
Exec V Pres, Brian P Goldstein
Svp and Cfo, Chris Ellington
Sr V Pres, Mary Beck
V Pres, Amy Bragg
Otolaryngology, Jill A Alexander Ritch
Accounting Staff, Mike Sumner
Coordinator, Samara Robinson
Staff, David Reed
Staff, Douglas Robinson
Coordinator, Margaret Brooks
Auditors: BETH A WOOD CPA RALEIGH NC

LOCATIONS

HQ: UNIVERSITY OF NORTH CAROLINA HOSPITALS
101 MANNING DR BLDG 2, CHAPEL HILL, NC 275144423
Phone: 919 966-5111
Web: WWW.UNCHEALTHCARE.ORG

PRODUCTS/OPERATIONS

Selected Facilities

North Carolina Cancer Hospital (Chapel Hill)
UNC Lineberger Comprehensive Cancer Center
North Carolina Children's Hospital (Chapel Hill)
North Carolina Memorial Hospital (Chapel Hill)
North Carolina Neurosciences Hospital (Chapel Hill)
North Carolina Women's Hospital (Chapel Hill)

COMPETITORS

Alamance Regional Medical Center
Carolinas HealthCare System
Cone Health
Cumberland County Hospital System
Danville Regional Medical Center
Duke University Health System
Emory Healthcare
Grady Health System
High Point Regional Health System
Morehead Memorial Hospital
New Hanover Regional Medical Center
Rowan Regional Medical Center
Vidant Health
WakeMed

HISTORICAL FINANCIALS

Company Type: Private

Income Statement FYE: June 30

	REVENUE ($ mil.)	NET INCOME ($ mil.)	NET PROFIT MARGIN	EMPLOYEES
06/18	1,892	88	4.7%	6,000
06/16	1,551	87	5.6%	—
06/15	1,385	110	8.0%	—
06/07	787	182	23.2%	—
Annual Growth	8.3%	(6.4%)	—	—

2018 Year-End Financials

Return on assets: 3.4%
Return on equity: —
Current ratio: 1.70
Cash ($ mil.): 49

UNIVERSITY OF NORTH TEXAS SYSTEM

EXECUTIVES

Mgr, Cynthia Doll
Chief Human Capital Officer, Barbara Abercrombie
Chancellor, Lesa Roe
Interim Assistant Director, Renee McBride
Vice Chancellor, Gary Rahlfs
Vice Chancellor, Nancy S Footer
Auditors: GRANT THORNTON LLP DALLAS TE

LOCATIONS

HQ: UNIVERSITY OF NORTH TEXAS SYSTEM
1302 TEASLEY LN, DENTON, TX 762057946
Phone: 940 565-2281
Web: WWW.UNTHSC.EDU

HISTORICAL FINANCIALS

Company Type: Private

Income Statement FYE: August 31

	REVENUE ($ mil.)	NET INCOME ($ mil.)	NET PROFIT MARGIN	EMPLOYEES
08/19	657	(83)	—	525
08/18	654	79	12.2%	—
08/17	619	82	13.4%	—
08/16	631	47	7.5%	—
Annual Growth	1.3%	—	—	—

2019 Year-End Financials

Return on assets: (-2.9%)
Return on equity: (-11.5%)
Current ratio: 1.20
Cash ($ mil.): 219

UNIVERSITY OF OREGON

This school's got all its ducks in a row. As one of the largest schools in the state the University of Oregon (UO) has an enrollment of about 22760 students and some 2095 faculty members. It offers its students eight different schools and colleges plus a graduate college with fields of study range from the arts and journalism to business and law. Part of the Oregon University System UO also offers development services an honors program research institutes and continuing education courses. The school's athletic department organizes around 15 sports activities including lacrosse and football; the teams are called The Ducks.

Operations

UO has a student-to-teacher ratio of 16:1 and an average class size of 20. Course offerings range across lecture discussion seminar activity laboratory independent study and independent research formats and UO has a total of more than 300 undergraduate programs more than 80 graduate subject areas and more than 30 research centers and institutes. The university's most popular majors for undergraduates include accounting architecture art biology business administration chemistry education economics english environmental science human physiology journalism political science public relations and sociology. Its freshman retention success rate is nearly 90%.

Geographic Reach

UO is located at some 295-acre campus in Eugene Oregon that includes about 80 buildings. It also has a satellite campus in Portland. Students come to UO from all 50 US states (plus Washington DC and two US territories) as well as about 100 foreign countries. More than half of students are Oregon residents. A number of students also participate in more than 300 study abroad and internship programs in approximately 90 international locations.

Company Background

The Oregon State Legislature created the university in 1872 and students first enrolled in 1876.

EXECUTIVES

Dean School Of Music And Dance, Brad Foley
Interim President, Scott Coltrane
Svp And Provost, Frances Bronet
Vp Finance And Administration, Jamie Moffitt
Vice Provost Information Services And Cio, Melissa Woo
Dean College Of Arts And Sciences, W. Andrew Marcus
Dean Lundquist College Of Business, Cornelis A. (Kees) de Kluyver
Dean College Of Education, Randy Kamphaus
Dean School Of Law, Michael Moffitt
Dean Clark Honors College, Terry Hunt
Interim Dean School Of Journalism And Communication, Julianne Newton
Acting Dean School Of Architecture And Allied Arts, Brook Muller
Dean Graduate School, Scott Pratt
Vice President Academic Affairs, Lorraine Davis
Vice President University Communications, Kyle Henley
Associate Vice President For State And Community Affairs, Hans Bernard
Assistant Vice President For University Initiatives And Collaborations, Charles Triplett
Assistant Vice President, Kelly Pembleton
Vice President, Mike Urbancic
Associate Vice President, Kris Winter
Assensoh Vice President, Yvette Alex
Chairman, Charles M. (Chuck) Lillis
Vice Chairman, Ginevra Ralph
Board Member, Carl Hosticka
Receptionist And Secretary, Risa Saavedra
Academic Secretary, Emily Cornell
Auditors: MOSS ADAMS LLP PORTLAND OR

LOCATIONS

HQ: UNIVERSITY OF OREGON
1585 E 13TH AVE, EUGENE, OR 974031657
Phone: 541 346-1000
Web: WWW.COMMUNICATIONS.UOREGON.EDU

PRODUCTS/OPERATIONS

Colleges and Schools

Charles H. Lundquist College of Business
College of Arts and Sciences
College of Education
Graduate School
Robert D. Clark Honors College
School of Architecture and Allied Arts
School of Journalism and Communication
School of Law
School of Music and Dance

HISTORICAL FINANCIALS

Company Type: Private

Income Statement FYE: June 30

	REVENUE ($ mil.)	NET INCOME ($ mil.)	NET PROFIT MARGIN	EMPLOYEES
06/20	741	329	44.4%	7,971
06/18	740	(8)	—	—
06/17	713	31	4.5%	—
06/16	692	(48)	—	—
Annual Growth	1.7%	—	—	—

2020 Year-End Financials

Return on assets: 11.9%
Return on equity: 25.9%
Current ratio: 1.10
Cash ($ mil.): 137

UNIVERSITY OF PENNSYLVANIA

EXECUTIVES

Pres, Amy Gutmann
Market Researcher, Market Rese, Jane Anderson
Coordinator, Karen Stevenson
College and Career Programs Co, Laurie Engleman
Lsoca Coordinator, Mark Bardsley
University Recruiting Coordina, Marlene Williams
Administrative Coordinator, Patricia Kozak
Computer Analyst, Dan Bachovin Sr
Information Specialist, Caroline Elizabeth
Financial Support Spec, Janice Brown
Assistant Professor, Benjamin Backus
Auditors: PRICEWATERHOUSECOOPERS LLP PH

LOCATIONS

HQ: UNIVERSITY OF PENNSYLVANIA
3451 WALNUT ST RM 100, PHILADELPHIA, PA 191046243
Phone: 215 898-5000
Web: WWW.UPENN.EDU

HISTORICAL FINANCIALS

Company Type: Private

Income Statement				FYE: June 30
	REVENUE ($ mil.)	NET INCOME ($ mil.)	NET PROFIT MARGIN	EMPLOYEES
06/18	10,093	2,326	23.0%	70
06/16	8,576	1,021	11.9%	—
06/15	0	0	—	—
Annual Growth	—	—	—	—

2018 Year-End Financials

Return on assets: 8.8%
Return on equity: 12.5%
Current ratio: —
Cash ($ mil.): 1,431

UNIVERSITY OF PITTSBURGH

The University of Pittsburgh (Pitt for short) operates its flagship campus in the Oakland neighborhood of Pittsburgh. More than 35000 graduate and undergraduate students attend the main campus as well as four regional campuses. Pitt Panthers pursue degrees in about 400 disciplines including arts and sciences business law medicine and engineering. The school has a student-teacher ratio of 14:1. Pitt is also affiliated with the UPMC health system which operates about 20 hospitals numerous clinics and an insurance company. Pitt was founded in 1787 making it one of the oldest universities in the US.

Operations

Pitt is considered a leading US public research university and as such spends more than $700 million annually on research projects. Pitt is recognized for its work in about a dozen disciplines including computer modeling philosophy the humanities international studies aging neuroscience bioengineering commercial innovation education national preparedness drug discovery translational medicine and nanoscience. It was at Pitt that Jonas Salk developed the polio vaccine at what is now known as Salk Hall.

Notable Pitt alumni include Academy Award winner Gene Kelly Nobel Peace Prize winner Wangari Maathai Pulitzer Prize winner Michael Chabon and US Senator Orrin Hatch.

Geographic Reach

In addition to the main campus in Pittsburgh which houses 17 schools colleges and a center for social and urban research Pitt has regional campus locations in Bradford Greensburg Johnstown and Titusville.

Financial Performance

Pitt reported revenues of some $2 billion in 2014. Most of the university's revenues come from grants and contracts followed by student tuition and feescommonwealth appropriation endowment distributions and other sources of income.

Strategy

In addition to providing high quality education programs for its students Pitt works to engage in research scholarly and artistic projects that advance global learning. It also works to collaborate with government agencies and businesses to advance science medicine and technology seeking active partners as well as funding provider to further its programs.

EXECUTIVES

Legal Secretary, Mary Kaye Bucher
Director Of Admissions, Alexandra Linsenmeyer
Managing Director Vice Dean, Ann Thompson
Division Secretary, Dawn Beam
Id Secretary, Susan Sawyers
Resident Assistant Brackenridge Hall Service Chair Epsilon Sigma Alpha, Maria Dechant
Treasurer, Ning Gao
Auditors: KPMG LLP PITTSBURGH PENNSYLV

LOCATIONS

HQ: UNIVERSITY OF PITTSBURGH
4200 5TH AVE, PITTSBURGH, PA 152600001
Phone: 412 624-4141
Web: WWW.PITT.EDU

PRODUCTS/OPERATIONS

Selected Schools and Colleges

The John A. Swanson School of Engineering
The Joseph M. Katz Graduate School of Business
College of Business Administration
Kenneth P. Dietrich School of Arts and Sciences
College of General Studies
School of Dental Medicine
School of Education
School of Health and Rehabilitation Sciences
School of Information Sciences
School of Law
School of Medicine
School of Nursing
School of Pharmacy
School of Public and International Affairs
School of Public Health
School of Social Work
University Center for International Studies
University Honors College

HISTORICAL FINANCIALS

Company Type: Private

Income Statement				FYE: June 30
	REVENUE ($ mil.)	NET INCOME ($ mil.)	NET PROFIT MARGIN	EMPLOYEES
06/20	2,501	(168)	—	9,607
06/19	2,352	111	4.8%	—
06/18	2,276	381	16.8%	—
06/17	2,169	487	22.5%	—
Annual Growth	4.9%	—	—	—

2020 Year-End Financials

Return on assets: (-2.1%)
Return on equity: (-3.4%)
Current ratio: —
Cash ($ mil.): 117

UNIVERSITY OF SOUTH ALABAMA

When you go by the moniker USA and the campus beauty queen wins the Miss USA title year after year (the Pi Kappa Phi Miss USA pageant that is) you're standing on hallowed ground. In this case it's the ground of the University of South Alabama situated on the upper Gulf Coast. The school's crown jewel is its College of Medicine and other facilities including USA Medical Center USA Knollwood Hospital and USA Children's and Women's Hospital. USA also offers degrees in Health Arts and Sciences Business Education Engineering Nursing Computer and Information Sciences Continuing Education and Special Programs and the Graduate School. More than 14880 students call the USA home.

Operations

USA offers 41 different bachelor programs 31 masters programs and 10 doctoral programs.

Financial Performance

The school reported an 8% increase in revenues in 2012 thanks to higher tuition and fee rates and an increase in student enrollment and credit hours taken and a rise in net patient service revenues (29% of total 2012 revenues). Other operating revenues also increased in 2012 thanks to higher revenues from the Electronic Health Records Incentive Program.

USA reported net income in 2012 of $38 million (versus a net loss in 2011) due to decline in operating loss and an increase in non-operating revenues (primarily from higher investment returns and state appropriations).

The university saw an increase in revenues between 2010 and 2012 largely due to organic growth.

Strategy

USA is pushing to expand and strengthen its development program and increase student enrollment. In 2013 the school received a gift of $250000 from alumni Dr. and Mrs. Steven H. Stokes to start a new Center for Environmental Resiliency.

Company Background

Founded in 1963 USA has graduated more than 75000 students including 18200 teachers and school administrators (including 85% of Mobile's public school teachers).

EXECUTIVES

Associate Vice President Academic Affair, Keith Harrison
Interim Associate Vice President For Academic Affairs, Julio Turrens
Department Head, Bob Shipp
Vice President Student Affairs, John Smith
Associate Vice President For Global Engagement, Richard Carter
Vice President, Sandra Corry
Senior Vice President Academic Affairs, Chris Cowley
Swe Vice President, Samantha Hamilton
Alapsa Program Chair Department Of Political Science And Criminal Justice University Of South, Jaclyn Bunch
Assistant Vice President Facilities Management, Moon Randy
Secretary, Marcina Lang
Secretary, Karen Barrick
Secretary V, Deborah Tittle
Secretary, Lisa Callaghan
Laboratory Secretary, Kathy Vrachalus
Secretary, Greta Washington
Secretary, Lord Shari
Secretary V, Lanier Sharon
Secretary Iv, Robin Hamilton
Auditors: KPMG LLP JACKSON MS

LOCATIONS

HQ: UNIVERSITY OF SOUTH ALABAMA
307 N UNIVERSITY BLVD, MOBILE, AL 366883053
Phone: 251 460-6101
Web: WWW.SOUTHALABAMA.EDU

PRODUCTS/OPERATIONS

USA Colleges and Schools

Arts and Sciences
Auburn University School of Pharmacy at USA
Computing
Continuing Education and Special Programs
Education
Engineering
Mitchell College of Business
Medicine

Nursing
Pat Capps Covey College of Allied Health Professions

HISTORICAL FINANCIALS

Company Type: Private

Income Statement FYE: September 30

	REVENUE ($ mil.)	NET INCOME ($ mil.)	NET PROFIT MARGIN	EMPLOYEES
09/20	782	124	15.9%	5,403
09/18	653	(0)	—	—
09/17	662	47	7.2%	—
09/16	624	25	4.1%	—
Annual Growth	5.8%	48.0%	—	—

2020 Year-End Financials

Return on assets: 7.7%
Return on equity: 57.4%
Current ratio: 1.40
Cash ($ mil.): 237

UNIVERSITY OF SOUTH FLORIDA

The University of South Florida (USF) is bullishly educational. The school has about 50830 students at three campuses in Tampa St. Petersburg and Sarasota/Manatee. It offers some 180 undergraduate graduate specialty and doctoral degree programs through some 15 colleges including Arts and Sciences Business Education Engineering Marine Biology Pharmacy and Public Health. USF also offers graduate certificates continuing education courses and teacher certifications and it is a major research institution among US universities. USF was founded in 1956; its mascot is the bull.

Operations

The university has more than 2185 teaching faculty members and maintains a 21:1 student-to-faculty ratio. USF's core offerings include an extensive health sciences program including medical nursing pharmacy and public health colleges grouped under the USF Health banner. The health organization also includes patient care facilities such as family care practices emergency clinics and Alzheimer's centers.

USF Health also hosts medical research programs in areas such as neurological conditions cardiovascular care pediatrics infectious disease and biotechnology. The university also has research programs in a range of science engineering and arts fields such as veteran reintegration. Altogether USF's research programs were granted $405 million in awards and contracts.

Geographic Reach

USF's international students (nearly 10% of the total student population) come from more than 40 US states and more than 145 countries. USF also supports study abroad programs. The university's campuses in Florida encompass some 1645 acres. The main Tampa campus includes the USF Health facilities and health-related schools.

Financial Performance

USF has a budget of $1.9 billion in 2020 and an endowment of $532.2 million.

EXECUTIVES

President And Corporate Secretary, Judy L. Genshaft
Evp And Provost, Ralph Wilcox
Coo, John W. Long
Svp Research Innovation And Economic Development And President Usf Research Foundation, Paul R. Sanberg
Vp Information Technology And Cio, Sidney Fernandes
Vp Business And Finance And Cfo, Nick Trivunovich
Interim Vice President Student Affairs, Kofi Glover
Vice Provost Student Success, Paul J Dosal
Assistant Vice President For Research, Valerie McDevitt
Usf System Vice President, Roger Brindley
Vice President Research, Scott Mann
Vice President Research And Development, Don Clark
Vice President, Ricci Allen
Medical Director Clinic Service, Arthur Andrews
Chair Department Of Mathematics And Statistics, Leslaw Skrzypek
Vice President Acad Affairs Stpetersburg, Melanie Marquez
Assistant Vice President For Donor Services, Tracy Muir
Associate Vp Information Technology, George Ellis
Associate Vice President Academic And Faculty Affairs And Senior Associate Dean, John Curran
Vice President Research, Concetta M Carr
Vice President Acad Affairs St.petersburg, Helen D Levine
Sa Assistant Vice President Dean Of Students, Judy L Polk
Chair Department Of Surgery, Andrew M Smith
Pharmacy Manager, Xilma Lemois
Professor Of German And Chair Department Of World Languages, Stephan Schindler
Senior Vice President For Strategic Development, Edmund Funai
Vice President, Joseph Michalsky
Vice President, Andrew Miles
Vice President, Oscar Ayala-Gonzalez
Vice President Of The New Music Consortium, Lindsey Jones
Assistant Vice President Human Resources And Risk Management, Martinez-kidde Edith
Interfraternity Council Vice President Of Administration, Mathew Bernstein
Vice President, Enzo Ferrara
Associate Vice President, Julie Gillespie
Svp Business And Financial Strategy, David Lechner
Vice President For Service Programming, Manal Ammagui
Medical Director And Professor, James Brownlee
Assistant Vice President, Terrie Daniel
Vice President, Nils Corrales
Vice President Of Administrative Services, Calvin Williams
Vice President Harborside Activities Board Co President Vice President, Kelli Carmack
Vice President Administration, Erica Sells
Executive Vice President American Academy Of Allergy Asthma And Immunology, Thomas Casale
Assistant Vice President For Economic Development And Government Affairs, Casey Welch
Vice President, Priti Shukla
Chair, Harold W. Mullis
Vice Chair, Brian D. Lamb
Senior Secretary, Fran Schoel
Senior Secretary, Kasch Laura
Match Secretary, Tamesha Coney
Treasurer, Richard Cunningham
Treasurer, Dario Milano
Match Secretary, Trelawney Baidsen
Secretary Clinical Services, Aleida Galvez
Auditors: SHERRILL F NORMAN CPA TALLA

LOCATIONS

HQ: UNIVERSITY OF SOUTH FLORIDA
4202 E FOWLER AVE, TAMPA, FL 336208000
Phone: 813 974-2011
Web: WWW.USF.EDU

PRODUCTS/OPERATIONS

2013 Revenue

	% of total
Contracts & grants	26
Student financial aid	26
Tuition	16
General revenue	14
Auxiliary enterprises	11
Intercollegiate athletics	3
Lottery	2
Concessions & fees	2
Total	**100**

Selected Colleges

The Arts
Arts & Sciences
Behavioral & Community Sciences
Business
Education
Engineering
Global Sustainability
Honors College
Marine Science
Medicine
Nursing
Pharmacy
Public Health
University College (graduate school)

COMPETITORS

Florida Atlantic University
Florida International University
Florida State University
University of Central Florida
University of Florida
University of Miami
University of North Florida

HISTORICAL FINANCIALS

Company Type: Private

Income Statement FYE: June 30

	REVENUE ($ mil.)	NET INCOME ($ mil.)	NET PROFIT MARGIN	EMPLOYEES
06/19	849	4	0.5%	16,165
06/18	871	36	4.1%	—
06/09	892	42	4.7%	—
06/07	533	148	27.8%	—
Annual Growth	3.9%	(25.4%)	—	—

2019 Year-End Financials

Return on assets: 0.2%
Return on equity: 0.5%
Current ratio: 6.00
Cash ($ mil.): 50

UNIVERSITY OF TENNESSEE

Whether you want to learn the art of aviation or get ready for a career in public service the University of Tennessee System (UT) is here to help. The 200-year-old school provides undergraduate graduate and professional academic programs to about 50000 students; programs include business engineering law pharmacy medicine and veterinary medicine. It has a student-teacher ratio of about 16:1. Campuses include the flagship Knoxville location as well as the Health Science Center at Memphis the Space Institute at Tullahoma the statewide Institute for Public Service and the Institute of Agriculture. Other UT System campuses are located in Chattanooga and Martin. UT was founded in 1794 as Blount College.

Financial Performance

UT's funding comes from gifts grants and contracts (about 30%) state appropriations (roughly 28%) tuition and fees (20%) and a handful of auxiliary enterprises and independent operations (the remainder).

Company Background

Notable alumni include former Senate Majority Leader Howard Baker Nobel Prize-winning economist James Buchanan and author Cormac McCarthy.

EXECUTIVES

Assistant Vice President, Chuck Shoopman

LOCATIONS

HQ: UNIVERSITY OF TENNESSEE
1331 CIRCLE PARK DR, KNOXVILLE, TN 379163801
Phone: 865 974-2303
Web: WWW.UTK.EDU

PRODUCTS/OPERATIONS

Selected Colleges Schools and Institutes

College of Agricultural Sciences and Natural Resources
College of Allied Health Sciences
College of Architecture and Design
College of Arts and Sciences
College of Business Administration
College of Communication and Information
College of Dentistry
College of Education Health and Human Sciences
College of Engineering
College of Graduate Health Sciences
College of Health Science Engineering
College of Law
College of Medicine
College of Nursing
College of Pharmacy
College of Social Work
College of Veterinary Medicine
Graduate School of Medicine
School of Art
School of Music
Space Institute

HISTORICAL FINANCIALS

Company Type: Private

Income Statement FYE: June 30

	REVENUE ($ mil.)	NET INCOME ($ mil.)	NET PROFIT MARGIN	EMPLOYEES
06/12	1,092	60	5.5%	12,000
06/11*	1,034	296	28.7%	—
12/08	1	0	—	—
Annual Growth	847.7%	—	—	—

*Fiscal year change

2012 Year-End Financials

Return on assets: 1.6%
Return on equity: 2.3%
Current ratio: 1.50
Cash ($ mil.): 357

UNIVERSITY OF UTAH HEALTH HOSPITALS AND CLINICS

Whether you've broken your leg on the ski slopes or need the latest treatment for a neurological condition the University of Utah Hospitals & Clinics is here for you. Part of the University of Utah Health Care system the medical services provider operates an acute and critical care hospital that has some 550 beds as well as a network of community clinics that provide primary health care pharmacy and eye care among other services. The University Hospital provides care in areas including surgery emergency care cardiology radiology and organ transplant services; it also houses centers for medical education training and research.

Operations

Also part of the Hospitals & Clinics system the Huntsman Cancer Institute home to the system's cancer inpatient and outpatient services and the University Orthopaedic Center which offers physical therapy and orthopedic surgery. The University Neuropsychiatric Institute provides inpatient and outpatient behavioral health care.

Strategy

As part of its plan to expand and prepare for the future University of Utah Hospitals & Clinics completed a new $24 million building at the school's College of Nursing in 2012.

EXECUTIVES

Ceo, David Entwistle
Cfo, Gordon Crabtree
Executive Director Service Line Administration Facilities And Support Services, Dan K. Lundergan
Executive Director Huntsman Cancer Hospital, Ray Lynch
Executive Director University Neuropsychiatric Institute, Ross Van Vranken
Executive Director Ambulatory Services Community Clinics And The John A. Moran Eye Center, Wayne Imbrescia
Executive Director University Of Utah Orthopaedic Center, Bart Adams
Cio, Jim Turnbull
Director Of Health Information, Connie Tohara
Technology Corporate Ambassador Office Of Vice President For Research, Andrew Buffmire
Medical Director, Martin Caravati
Associate Vice President Financial And Accounting Services, Jeffrey West
Pharmacy Manager, Jamie Doi
Medical Secretary, Chelsey Olsen
President Board Of Directors, Mac Newbold

LOCATIONS

HQ: UNIVERSITY OF UTAH HEALTH HOSPITALS AND CLINICS
50 N MEDICAL DR, SALT LAKE CITY, UT 841320001
Phone: 801 581-2121
Web: WWW.EMPLOYMENT.UTAH.EDU

COMPETITORS

CHRISTUS Health
Intermountain Health Care
LifePoint Health
Ogden Regional Medical Center
St. Mark's

HISTORICAL FINANCIALS

Company Type: Private

Income Statement FYE: June 30

	REVENUE ($ mil.)	NET INCOME ($ mil.)	NET PROFIT MARGIN	EMPLOYEES
06/14	1,282	20	1.6%	4,200
06/06	0	(0)	—	—
06/05	0	(0)	—	—
Annual Growth	126.0%	—	—	—

2014 Year-End Financials

Return on assets: 2.0%
Return on equity: 4.5%
Current ratio: 2.30
Cash ($ mil.): 179

UNIVERSITY OF VERMONT & STATE AGRICULTURAL COLLEGE

The University of Vermont (UVM) boasts scenic views and comprehensive secondary education. the university offers more than 100 majors through its seven undergraduate colleges as well 46 master's programs and 21 doctoral programs at its Graduate College and College of Medicine. UVM has an enrollment of more than 12820 students including undergraduate graduate medical and continuing education program participants. The university also conducts research programs in areas including translational science cancer care and transportation. UVM a public land grant university has more than 1360 faculty members.

Operations

UVM comes from Universitas Veridis Montis which is Latin for "University of the Green Mountains." Its campus consists of more than a dozen dining facilities – including a pair of convenience stores and Cyber Cafe – and nearly 40 residence halls for on-campus students. Off-campus UVM offers a research park four research farms nine natural areas (including the summit of Mount Mansfield) and the Rubenstein Ecosystem Science Laboratory in the Leahy ECHO Center for Lake Champlain.

Geographic Reach

The UVM campus which spans 460 acres in Burlington Vermont enrolls students from nearly all US states. The university also provides education to some 350 international students from more than 50 countries.

Financial Performance

As a public land grant university UVM draws a portion of its budget from the state of Vermont. Other sources of income include student tuition and fees charitable gifts and returns on investment funds. The university's office of technology commercialization brings in some income by licensing out research discoveries to spinoff entities.

Strategy

To attract and retain a quality student population UVM regularly conducts construction and renovation efforts on its campus facilities in areas ranging from academics and recreation to research and athletics.

Furthermore UVM seeks to provide more flexible education options for students including expanding its onlinep rograms.

Company Background

UVM is the fifth oldest university in the New England area after Harvard Yale Dartmouth and Brown. It's the first institution of higher education to declare public support for the freedom of religion and the first university to admit women and African-Americans into Phi Beta Kappa honor society.

Notable alumni include education philosopher John Dewey and film producer Jon Kilik.

Ira Allen founded the university in 1791 the same year that Vermont became the 14th state. Located in between the Adirondack and Green mountain ranges UVM's motto is the Latin phrase Universitas Viridis Montis or University of the Green Mountains.

EXECUTIVES

Vice President, Lee Stewart
Interim Vice President Of Development And Director Of Principal Gifts, Kathleen Kelleher
Vice President, Margaret Battey
Vice President, Francine Bazluke
Vice President Information Technology, Eric Melton
Vice President Research Admin Office, Eric Clark
Vice President, Ted Winfield
Department Chair, Dale Goldhaber
Vice President, Carol Phillips
Vice President For Executive Operations, Bethany Wolfe
Associate Vice President, Robert Corran
Provost And Senior Vice President, John Hughes
Vice President, Willi Coleman
Vice President Enrollment Management, Christopher Lucier
Director Of Admissions, Sarah Smith
Assistant Vice President For University Operations, Jon Crystal
Vice President, Elizabeth Nuckols
Senior Vice President, Catherine Symans
Vice President Alumni Relations, Alan Ryea
Sga Vice President, Tyler Davis
Vice President Preconstruction Services, John Stetson
Vice President For Development And Campaign Director, Mark Dorgan
Vice President Of Communications, Timothy Cece
Vice President, Frances Carr
Assistant Vice President For Development And Gift Planning, Amy Palmer-ellis
Senior Vice President And Provost, Rebecca L Delaricheliere
Medical Director, Tom Simpatico
Vice President Of Finance, Lincoln Pierce
Professor And Vice Chair, John King
Secretary, Chris Walker
Board Member, Joshua Farley
Board Member, Andrew Rubenstein
Secretary, Virginie Diambou
Technical Secretary, Rachel Berube
Secretary Cardiovascular Group, Pam Burton
Sga Treasurer, Jamie Lapierre
Treasurer, Jesse Cases-villablanca
Auditors: KPMG LLP COLCHESTER VERMONT

LOCATIONS

HQ: UNIVERSITY OF VERMONT & STATE AGRICULTURAL COLLEGE
85 S PROSPECT ST WTRMN, BURLINGTON, VT 054050001
Phone: 802 656-3131
Web: WWW.UVM.EDU

PRODUCTS/OPERATIONS

Selected Colleges and Schools

College of Agriculture and Life Sciences
College of Arts and Sciences
College of Education and Social Services
College of Engineering and Mathematical Sciences
College of Medicine
College of Nursing and Health Sciences
Continuing Education
Graduate College
Honors College
Rubenstein School of Environment and Natural Resources
School of Business Administration

HISTORICAL FINANCIALS

Company Type: Private

Income Statement — FYE: June 30

	REVENUE ($ mil.)	NET INCOME ($ mil.)	NET PROFIT MARGIN	EMPLOYEES
06/20	661	23	3.6%	3,710
06/19	650	39	6.1%	—
06/17	613	34	5.6%	—
06/14	545	27	5.1%	—
Annual Growth	3.3%	(2.3%)	—	—

2020 Year-End Financials

Return on assets: 1.4%
Return on equity: 5.8%
Current ratio: 1.90
Cash ($ mil.): 187

UNIVERSITY OF WASHINGTON INC

The University of Washington (UW) is Husky indeed with an annual enrollment of more than 59380 students. Founded in 1861 as the Territorial University of Washington UW (pronounced "U-dub" by those on campus) has smaller branches in Tacoma and Bothell in addition to its main campus in downtown Seattle. The university whose mascot is a Husky offers undergraduate and more than 370 graduate and professional degree programs through nearly 20 colleges and schools. It also operates four hospitals: University of Washington Medical Center Harborview Medical Center Northwest Hospital and Valley Medical Center.

Operations

University of Washington confers some 12000 bachelor's master's doctoral and professional degrees each year. Around 30 of its undergraduate and 10 of its graduate students be selected as semi-finalists for the Fulbright Student Program. The school's some bachelor degree fields include biology psychology political science economics and communications.

Research is a cornerstone of the university which has about 285 specialized research centers. The school's annual sponsored grant and contract research funding exceeds $1.58billion.

Geographic Reach

The UW is a multi-campus university in Seattle Tacoma and Bothell Washington.

Financial Performance

The University's revenue at the end of 2020 increased by 1% to $5.51 billion compared from the prior year with $5.48 billion. Revenue from student tuition and fees increased a modest $6 million whereas grant and contract revenue recorded another strong year increasing $66 million or 5% over 2019.

Cash held by the University at the end of fiscal 2020 increased to $0.1 million. Cash provided by financing activities was $0.6 million while cash used for operations and investing activities were $0.3 million and $0.2 million.

Strategy

The University continues to expand its campuses invest in information technology and renovate existing facilities to meet the needs of its students patients faculty and staff. Significant capital asset expenditures (greater than $20 million) during the fiscal year 2020 included $115 million for the Population Health Facility $43 million for North Campus Student Housing (Oak Hall) $34 million for the UW Medicine clinical transformation program ("Destination: One") and $23 million for the renovation of Kincaid Hall.

EXECUTIVES

Dean School Of Medicine, Paul G. Ramsey
Svp Finance And Facilities, V'Ella Warren
Chancellor Bothell Campus, Bjong Wolf Yeigh
Dean School Of Law, Kellye Testy
Dean Libraries, Lizabeth A. (Betsy) Wilson
Interim Chancellor Tacoma Campus, Kenyon S. Chan
Dean School Of Public Health, Howard Frumkin
President, Ana Mari Cauce
Dean Undergraduate Academic Affairs, Ed Taylor
Vp Information Technology And Cio, Kelli Trosvig
Dean College Of Arts And Sciences, Robert Stacey
Interim Dean College Of Built Environments, John Schaufelberger
Dean School Of Dentistry, Joel H. Berg
Dean College Of Education, Tom Stritikus
Dean College Of Engineering, Michael B. Bragg
Dean College Of The Environment, Lisa Graumlich
Dean Evans School Of Public Affairs, Sandra Archibald
Dean Foster School Of Business, James Jiambalvo
Dean Graduate School, Dave Eaton
Dean Information School, Harry Bruce
Dean School Of Nursing, Azita Emami
Dean School Of Pharmacy, Thomas Baillie
Dean School Of Social Work, Edwina (Eddie) Uehara
Associate Vice President And Chief Advan, Lynn Hogan
Associate Vice President, Lee Heck
Assistant Vice President For Labor Relations, Peter Denis
Assistant Vice President Campus Human Resources Operations, Jessie Garcia
Medical Director, Jean Haulman
Senior Vice President Ecommerce Mobile D, Brian Jones
Vp Of Marketing, Jennifer Wong
Extension Lecturer Vice President For Continuing Ed, Barbara Bell
Vice President For Student Life, Denzil Suite
Assistant Vice President For Student Life And, Pam Schreiber
Director Of Government Relations, Ian Goodhew
Medical Director, Rob Sweet
Associate Vice President For Information Management, Aaron Powell
Associate Vice President College Access, Patricia Loera
Executive Vice President, Jeffrey Scott
Director Of Admissions, Erin Town
Vice President, Lou Cariello
Medical Director, Matthew Grierson
Associate Vice President, Barbara Wingerson
Research And Graduate Studies Vice President, Kimberly Johns
Medical Director Uw Center For Pain Relief, Brett Stacey
Executive Vice President Provost, Gerald Balsasty
Medical Director, Joe C Huang
Vice President, Sean Campbell
Associate Vice President, Theresa Fujiwara
Vice President Membership, Lisa Dion
Vice President, Caitlin Snaring
Assistant Vice President Campaign, Lisa A Thomas
Legal Secretary, Sandra Webb

Medical Director, David Kauff
Vice President Of Scholarship, Ali Haugh
Vice President, Brian Silva
Vice President, K Edstam
Vice President Of Purchasing, Mark W Majesky
Vice President, David Pitkethly
Director Of Government Relations, Melissa Bailey
Medical Director, Lucy Wang
Vice Chairman, William S. (Bill) Ayer
Chairman, Orin C. Smith
Board Member, Lance Bennett
Secretary Senior Capital Projects Office, Chris Niblack
Secretary Senior, Gregory Daigle
Board Member, Melissa Cunningham
Msim Advisory Board Member, Cheryl Scott
Treasurer, Lizbeth Seebacher
Secretary Senior, Victoria Parker
Board Of Directors, Craig Mauer
Board Member, Dan Brettler
Assistant Secretary, Louise Hine
Treasurer, Thomas Frey
Board Of Directors, Jason Cahill
Auditors: KPMG LLP SEATTLE WASHINGTON

LOCATIONS

HQ: UNIVERSITY OF WASHINGTON INC
4300 ROOSEVELT WAY NE, SEATTLE, WA 981054718
Phone: 206 543-4444
Web: WWW.UW.EDU

PRODUCTS/OPERATIONS

Selected Colleges and Schools
College of Arts and Sciences
College of Built Environments
College of Education
College of Engineering
College of the Environment
Evans School of Public Affairs
The Graduate School
Information School
Michael G. Foster School of Business
School of Dentistry
School of Law
School of Medicine
School of Nursing
School of Pharmacy
School of Public Health
School of Social Work

HISTORICAL FINANCIALS

Company Type: Private

Income Statement — FYE: June 30

	REVENUE ($ mil.)	NET INCOME ($ mil.)	NET PROFIT MARGIN	EMPLOYEES
06/20	5,511	343	6.2%	27,228
06/19	5,485	481	8.8%	—
06/18	5,171	490	9.5%	—
06/17	4,893	363	7.4%	—
Annual Growth	4.0%	(1.9%)	—	—

2020 Year-End Financials

Return on assets: 2.5%
Return on equity: 5.8%
Current ratio: 1.30
Cash ($ mil.): 143

UNIVERSITY OF WISCONSIN HOSPITALS AND CLINICS AUTHORITY

The University of Wisconsin Hospitals and Clinics Authority (UW Hospitals and Clinics) has the last word when it comes to the health of Badger Staters. The centerpiece of the authority is the UW Hospitals and Clinics medical campus which is home to a 650-bed hospital the American Family Children's Hospital a cancer clinic and a small inpatient psychiatric ward as well as Level I adult and pediatric trauma centers. The hospital administers cancer treatment heart and stroke care organ transplantation and a host of other medical services. The UW Hospitals and Clinics organization also operates area health clinics that provide general and specialty outpatient care and emergency room services.

Operations

UW Hospitals and Clinics is a public authority formed to manage the health care facilities all of which are part of the broader University of Wisconsin (UW) Health organization. The teaching hospital and clinics are located adjacent to the university's medical and nursing schools. The system's satellite health centers provide medical care throughout the community. Altogether the UW Hospitals and Clinics provides care to about 27000 inpatients and 580000 outpatient visits per year. UW Hospitals and Clinics also provides outpatient care through affiliated practices that are part of the UW Medical Foundation physician practice organization.

The authority has more than 1200 physicians and 85 outpatient clinics. It also offers six intensive care units (dedicated to trauma and life support pediatrics cardiac care cardiothoracic care burns and neurosurgery) with a total of 83 beds. UW Hospitals and Clinics is one of two organizations in Wisconsin with level I adult and pediatric trauma centers.

UW Hospitals and Clinics works with UW Medical School to perform medical research in an array of disciplines including asthma cancer infectious disease and transplant medicine. About 1000 faculty members work in more than two dozen departments and 18 centers and institutes performing research in most aspects of basic clinical and public health care. The Carbone Cancer Center for instance includes 280 physicians and scientists who work to improve cancer treatment technologies.

Its Home Care Services segment provides patients with visits from licensed nurses and therapists as well as dietitians respiratory therapists and other medical specialists. The organization also supplies home health equipment.

Geographic Reach

UW Hospitals and Clinics' main campus facilities are located in Madison Wisconsin. It also has clinics in about 50 surrounding communities.

Sales and Marketing

Medicare and Medicaid combined accounted for more than 30% of the net patient revenues in fiscal 2014; managed care accounted for more than 50%.

Strategy

The UW Health organization is working to improve the quality of care for patients through a number of initiatives including infrastructure improvements data management upgrades and safety programs. It is upgrading network systems standardizing processes and implementing best practices across its facilities. UW Health is also looking to add new affiliations and academic relationships with other organizations. These goals help serve UW Health's participation in the Medicare Accountable Care Organization (ACO) program as well.

EXECUTIVES

Vp Marketing, Elizabeth Zaher
Svp And Cfo, Michael D. (Mike) Buhl
Vp American Family Children's Hospital, Jeff Poltawsky
President And Ceo, Jeffrey Grossman
President Uw, John Sheehan
Membership Vice President, Elise Rose
Chairman, David Walsh
Vice Chair, Michael (Mike) Weiden
Auditors: RSM US LLP MINNEAPOLIS MINNE

LOCATIONS

HQ: UNIVERSITY OF WISCONSIN HOSPITALS AND CLINICS AUTHORITY
600 HIGHLAND AVE, MADISON, WI 537920001
Phone: 608 263-6400
Web: WWW.UWHEALTH.ORG

PRODUCTS/OPERATIONS

Selected Services
Adult Primary CareFamily MedicineGeriatricsInternal MedicinePrimary CareWomen's Health and WellnessAdult Specialty CareAllergy Asthma and ImmunologyAudiologyBehavioral Health Services (Addiction)Blood and Bone Marrow TransplantBreast Care ServicesBurn Ce

COMPETITORS

Beaver Dam Community Hospitals
Beloit Health System
Dean Health Systems Inc.
Hospital Sisters Health System
Marian Health System
Meriter Health Services
ProHealth Care
SSM Health Care
Stoughton Hospital
ThedaCare Inc.
Tomah Memorial Hospital

HISTORICAL FINANCIALS

Company Type: Private

Income Statement — FYE: June 30

	REVENUE ($ mil.)	NET INCOME ($ mil.)	NET PROFIT MARGIN	EMPLOYEES
06/20	2,075	202	9.8%	1,350
06/19	3,396	231	6.8%	—
06/18	3,213	170	5.3%	—
Annual Growth	(19.6%)	8.8%	—	—

2020 Year-End Financials

Return on assets: 5.3%
Return on equity: 11.3%
Current ratio: 2.00
Cash ($ mil.): 366

UNIVERSITY OF WISCONSIN MEDICAL FOUNDATION, INC.

UW Medical Foundation provides administrative services to faculty physicians at the University of Wisconsin School of Medicine and Public Health. The foundation a not-for-profit entity is a physician practice organization that works in cooperation with the UW Hospital and Clinics and other medical offices and clinics throughout the Badger State. The foundation coordinates clinical sites and provides technical and professional staffing services as well as administrative support for legal marketing information technology and logistics functions.

Operations

UW Medical Foundation provides support services for more than 1200 member doctors located at about 45 physician practices and 60 clinical outreach locations. It also helps clinical practices with quality initiatives. The foundation provides some $200 million in charity care each year. Its community activities include sponsoring health outreach events and donating safety products to low-income families.

Physicians in the organization provide services across a number of medical specialties including oncology gastroenterology women's health kidney care orthopedics respiratory therapy and urology.

Company Background

The organization has expanded over time: UW Medical Foundation merged with Physicians Plus Medical Group in 1998 and with the University Community Clinics in 2003.

EXECUTIVES

Ceo, Alan Kaplan
Chb, Robert Golden
Coo*, Robert Flannery
Sam Poc, Sarah Meyer
Information Specialist, Debra Hopke
Information Specialist, Jamie Buchanan
Hipaa Privacy Officer, Amanda Reese
Clinical Assistant Professiona, Deborah Raehl
Cardiologist, Anwer Dhala
Is Customer Director, Elaine Gerke
Physician, Caroline Paul
Auditors: MCGLADREY LLP PALOS HILLS IL

LOCATIONS

HQ: UNIVERSITY OF WISCONSIN MEDICAL FOUNDATION, INC.
7974 UW HEALTH CT, MIDDLETON, WI 535625531
Phone: 608 821-4223
Web: WWW.UWHEALTH.ORG

COMPETITORS

Ascension Health
Beaver Dam Community Hospitals
Beloit Health System
Catholic Health Initiatives
Dean Health Systems Inc.
Hospital Sisters Health System
Marian Health System
Meriter Health Services
ProHealth Care
SSM Health Care
Stoughton Hospital
ThedaCare Inc.
Tomah Memorial Hospital

HISTORICAL FINANCIALS

Company Type: Private

Income Statement — FYE: June 30

	REVENUE ($ mil.)	NET INCOME ($ mil.)	NET PROFIT MARGIN	EMPLOYEES
06/20	785	7	1.0%	3,200
06/19	796	2	0.3%	—
06/18	784	40	5.2%	—
06/15	766	26	3.4%	—
Annual Growth	0.5%	(22.1%)	—	—

2020 Year-End Financials

Return on assets: 0.7%
Return on equity: 2.1%
Current ratio: 1.20
Cash ($ mil.): 301

UNIVERSITY OF WISCONSIN SYSTEM (INC)

The University of Wisconsin System (UW System) is one of the largest public university systems in the US. Across its vast operations there are almost 15 four-year universities about 25 branch campuses and a statewide extension program that reaches every Wisconsin county. The UW System has more than 170000 students and approximately 39000 faculty and staff members. Its two main campuses are UW at Madison and UW at Milwaukee which offer hundreds of undergraduate and graduate programs including doctoral and professional degrees. The system's more than 350 majors include studies in the arts physical and social sciences business communications engineering education information and public affairs.

Operations

The UW System's largest campus is UW at Madison which offers more than 200 undergraduate majors 250-plus master's doctoral and professional programs to more than 45300 students. The system's other major campus is UW at Milwaukee with more than 26100 students more than 90 undergraduate majors and numerous master's and doctoral degrees. The remaining four-year campuses are smaller while about 15 branch campuses primarily provide two-year degrees.

Geographic Reach

One of the nation's largest public universities the UW System boasts offices or campuses in every county in Wisconsin.

Financial Performance

UW System reported a 2% revenue increase to $5.3 billion in fiscal 2019 (ended June 30 2019). Operating revenues increased $85.6 million since fiscal 2017 with the primary increase in non-resident tuition and all other operating revenues. Non-operating revenues increased $156.1 million between fiscal 2017 and 2019 primarily due to changes in state appropriations gifts investment income and other non-operating revenues.

Operating expenses increased by about 6% to $5.5 billion due to higher instruction student service research public service and other costs.

Cash and equivalents at the end of fiscal 2019 were $1.9 billion a $4.7 million decrease from the year prior. Operating activities used $1.1 billion largely for salaries and fringe benefits and payments to vendors and suppliers. Investing activities provided $29.3 million from interest and dividends on investments and proceeds from sales and maturities of investments. Cash used in capital and related financing activities were $597.3 million mostly for the purchase of capital assets principal payments on capital debt and leases and interest payments on capital debt and leases. Noncapital financing activities provided $1.6 billion mainly from state appropriations gifts and other receipts and additions to permanent endowments.

Strategy

Through the 2020FWD framework the UW System will inspire connect and convene with the people businesses and communities of the State of Wisconsin.

The 2020FWD framework looks to increase the enrollment and success of individuals in all educational experiences throughout their lifetimes. It has the capacity and responsibility to help students at all points in the educational pipeline ? from early childhood through secondary school college and lifelong learning.

It also aims to grow a more creative and engaging educational experience so all learners can compete and succeed in a global environment. The UW System needs to ensure that every student has access to exceptional faculty and staff who in turn have the resources and support enabling them to provide high-impact practices including undergraduate research service learning and study abroad.

Another aspect of the 2020FWD framework is to further expand the Wisconsin Idea to address the state's greatest needs and help Wisconsin businesses and communities become more successful. A central role of the UW System is to identify and articulate the issues affecting people and organizations.

UW System also vigorously pursues transparent efficient and effective operational practices. It will focus on ways to harness the collective power of the UW System to drive down costs while still providing excellent services such as in information technology human resources financial services and procurement.

Company Background

The University of Wisconsin System was created in 1971 through the merger of the University of Wisconsin (established 1848) and Wisconsin State Universities (originating in 1857 as the Normal Schools).

EXECUTIVES

Vp Finance, Deborah A. (Debbie) Durcan
Chancellor Madison Campus, Rebecca M. Blank
President, Kevin P. Reilly
Interim Director Information Services, Lori Docken
Chancellor Eau Claire Campus, Gilles Bousquet
Chancellor Green Bay Campus, Thomas Harden
Chancellor La Crosse Campus, Joe Gow
Chancellor Milwaukee Campus, Michael Lovell
Chancellor Oshkosh Campus, Richard Wells
Chancellor Parkside Campus, Deborah (Debbie) Ford
Chancellor Platteville Campus, Dennis Shields
Chancellor River Falls Campus, Dean Van Galen
Chancellor Stevens Point Campus, Bernie Patterson
Chancellor Stout Campus, Charles W. Sorensen
Chancellor Superior Campus, Renée Wachter
Chancellor Whitewater Campus, Richard J. Telfer
Vice President, Larry Rubin
Vice President Academic Student Affairs, James Henderson
Associate Vice President For Learning And Information Technology Services, Steven Hopper
Vice Provost For Libraries, Lisa Carter
Regent President, Brent Smith
Regent Vp, Michael Falbo
Treasurer, Kelly Wilfert

LOCATIONS

HQ: UNIVERSITY OF WISCONSIN SYSTEM (INC)
1220 LINDEN DR, MADISON, WI 537061525
Phone: 608 262-2321
Web: WWW.WISCONSIN.EDU

PRODUCTS/OPERATIONS

Selected Four-Year Campuses
UW-Eau Claire
UW-Green Bay
UW-La Crosse
UW-Madison
UW-Milwaukee
UW-Oshkosh
UW-Parkside
UW-Platteville
UW-River Falls
UW-Stevens Point
UW-Stout
UW-Superior
UW-Whitewater

Selected Two-Year Colleges
UW-Baraboo/Sauk County
UW-Barron County
UW-Fond du Lac
UW-Fox Valley
UW-Manitowoc
UW-Marathon County
UW-Marinette
UW-Marshfield/Wood County
UW-Richland
UW-Rock County
UW-Sheboygan
UW-Washington County
UW-Waukesha

HISTORICAL FINANCIALS

Company Type: Private

Income Statement FYE: June 30

	REVENUE ($ mil.)	NET INCOME ($ mil.)	NET PROFIT MARGIN	EMPLOYEES
06/18	3,613	203	5.6%	3,190
06/17	3,702	(20)	—	—
Annual Growth	(2.4%)	—	—	—

2018 Year-End Financials

Return on assets: 2.2%
Return on equity: 3.7%
Current ratio: 4.00
Cash ($ mil.): 1,868

UNIVERSITY SYSTEM OF MARYLAND

The University System of Maryland (USM) operates one of the largest public university systems in the country serving more than 135125 students through a dozen institutions including Towson University University of Maryland Global Campus and Bowie State University. Its flagship university in College Park boasts about 41200 students and some of the country's top-ranked education programs. The University of Maryland is also known for its successful athletic teams (named the Terrapins) which compete in the Big Ten Conference. The system also operates the University of Maryland Center for Environmental Science. Maryland established its university system in 1988.

Operations

USM has nearly 1100 buildings including two dozen libraries. The University of Maryland College Park (UMCP) USM's flagship institution and preeminent public research university fueled by $545 million in external research funding. Its colleges and schools include the A. James Clark School of Engineering College of Agriculture and Natural Resources School of Music and School of Public Policy among others.

Geographic Reach

USM's headquarters is located in Baltimore Maryland. It also has an office in Adelphi.

Strategy

US Maryland Momentum Fund has invested $300 thousand in Rockville-based N5 Sensors Inc. a company developing smart microscale wearable sensors to detect gas chemicals and additional environmental conditions for a variety of applications. It plans to leverage this funding to accelerate the commercial release of its products scale up manufacturing and expand its business team.

It has also invested $500 thousand in College Park-based VisiSonics Corporation an early-stage company that develops spatial audio technology and personalization software for audio playback as well as hardware and software for audio capture and analytics fund officials announce today. The company supports VisiSonics as the company positions itself to play a greater role in the audio marketplace.

Company Background

Notable University of Maryland alumni include Muppet creator Jim Henson news anchor Connie Chung Seinfeld creator Larry David and football legend Norman "Boomer" Esiason.

EXECUTIVES

Coo And Vice Chancellor Administration And Finance, Joseph F. Vivona
President University Of Maryland Baltimore County, Freeman A. Hrabowski
Associate Vice Chancellor And Cio, Donald Z. Spicer
Vice Chancellor Communications, Anne Moultrie
President Salisbury University, Janet Dudley-Eshbach
President University Of Maryland Center For Environmental Science, Donald F. (Don) Boesch
Vice Chancellor For Advancement, Leonard R. Raley
President University Of Maryland College Park, Wallace D. Loh
President University Of Maryland Baltimore, Jay A. Perman
President University Of Baltimore, Kurt L. Schmoke
President Bowie State University, Mickey L. Burnim
President Frostburg State University, Jonathan C. Gibralter
Chancellor, William E. Kirwan
Senior Vice Chancellor For Academic Affairs, Joann Boughman
President University Of Maryland Eastern Shore, Juliette B. Bell
President Coppin State University, Mortimer H. Neufville
Interim President Towson University, Timothy J.L. Chandler
President University Of Maryland University College, Javier Miyares
Executive Director Universities At Shady Grove, Stewart Edelstein
Executive Director University System Of Maryland At Hagerstown, Mark Halsey
Clinical Social Worker Vpsa Uhc Mental Health Sum, Jennifer Sherman
Information Technology Support Assistant Svpaap Nyumburu, Aaron Mcgrew
Vice President Of Finance And Chief Officer, Pamela Purcell
Collections Sprv Vpsa Dining Services, Karen Kimmel
Collections Specialist Vpaa Compt Bursars Office, William Damiano
Chaplain Vpsa Chapel, Eli Backman
Information Technology Program Analyst Vpsa Dining Services, Luisa Egan
Grounds Supervisor Vpsa Ds Maintenance, Jason Millar
Interior Designer Vpaa Fm Facilities Planning, Zoe Kyriacos
Postal Service Proc Vpaa Business Service Mail Services, Erik Krug
Mt Mlt Trd Chief Ii Vpsa Res Facilities Comm Maintenance, Joseph Sherman
Food Service Manager Vpsa Ds Bakery, Jeffrey Russo
Housekeeper Lead Vpsa Res Facilities North Campus, Maria Villegas
Motor Equipment Operations Ii Vpsa Transportation Services, Ian Bholai
Assistant Vice President Administration Program Manag, Katrina December
Medical Director Of The Blood Bank, Magali Fontaine
Vice President Chief Nurse Executive, Colleen Roach
Assistant Vice President Advancement Services, Rebecca Boughamer
Chairman Board Of Regents, James L. Shea
Vice Chair Board Of Regents, Barry P. Gossett
Auditors: SB & COMPANY LLC OWINGS MILL

LOCATIONS

HQ: UNIVERSITY SYSTEM OF MARYLAND
3300 METZEROTT RD, ADELPHI, MD 207831651
Phone: 301 445-2740
Web: WWW.USMD.EDU

Selected Institutions
Bowie State University
Coppin State University
Frostburg State University
Salisbury University
Towson University
University of Baltimore
University of Maryland Baltimore
University of Maryland Baltimore County
University of Maryland College Park
University of Maryland Eastern Shore
University of Maryland University College
University of Maryland Center for Environmental Science

Selected Schools and Colleges
College of Agriculture and Natural Resources
School of Architecture Planning and Preservation
College of Arts and Humanities
College of Behavioral and Social Sciences
Robert H. Smith School of Business
College of Chemical and Life Sciences
College of Computer Mathematical and Physical Sciences
College of Education
A. James Clark School of Engineering
The Graduate School
Philip Merrill College of Journalism
College of Information Studies
School of Public Health
School of Public Policy
Office of Undergraduate Studies

HISTORICAL FINANCIALS

Company Type: Private

Income Statement FYE: June 30

	REVENUE ($ mil.)	NET INCOME ($ mil.)	NET PROFIT MARGIN	EMPLOYEES
06/19	3,748	283	7.6%	28,000
06/18	3,601	338	9.4%	—
06/17	3,515	355	10.1%	—
06/16	3,386	516	15.3%	—
Annual Growth	3.4%	(18.1%)	—	—

2019 Year-End Financials

Return on assets: 2.7%
Return on equity: 4.2%
Current ratio: 3.40
Cash ($ mil.): 2,552

UNIVERSITY SYSTEM OF NEW HAMPSHIRE

The University of New Hampshire (UNH) is a liberal arts college that serves about 12600 undergraduate and more than 2200 graduate students. The institution offers more than 100 majors and academic programs of study at nine colleges and schools. The student-faculty ratio is 20:1. UNH is the flagship institution of the University System of New Hampshire. In 2007 the university graduated its first international class in Seoul under a program run by its Whittemore School of Business and Economics. Founded in 1866 as the New Hampshire College of Agriculture and the Mechanic Arts UNH is a designated land-grant sea-grant and space-grant chartered school.

Operations

UNH's most popular bachelor's programs include business administration undeclared liberal arts psychology English and communication followed by mechanical engineering biology biomedical science civil engineering and political science.

The University System of New Hampshire includes Keene State College Plymouth State University and Granite State College in addition to UNH.

Geographic Reach

In addition to its main campus in Durham UNH has a campus in Manchester and its School of Law is in Concord. Almost 60% of the school's student body comes from within state with a concentration of others coming from the northeastern region of the US. UNH is developing new academic programs expanding its online courses and opportunities and creating new international initiatives for faculty and students in Costa Rica Chile Ghana India South Korea and China.

Strategy

UNH is engaged in a strategic plan to support its growth through 2020. Its plan for creating a learning-centered environment includes such initiatives as establishing a New Venture Fund to promote collaborative research and teaching opportunities; developing new programs to support independent research and scholarship; commercializing UNH's intellectual capital; and promoting diversity and inclusiveness as well as international opportunities. It also includes making major capital investments in technology to build a high-capacity cyber-infrastructure and a learning portal to promote interdisciplinary collaboration; renovating restoring and adding on to facilities; and constructing a new center for the arts.

EXECUTIVES

Chancellor, Todd Leach
Pres*, Melinda Treadwell
Vice Chancellor*, Catherine Provelcher
General Counsel*, Ron Rodgers
Pres*, James W Dean Jr
Assistant Professor, Lin Guo
Coordinator, Steve Wright
Assistant Professor, Weiwei MO
Assistant To President, Cheri O'Neil
Coordinator, Cynthia Nizzari-Mcclain
Assistant Professor, Shawna Hollen
Auditors: KPMG LLP BOSTON MA

LOCATIONS

HQ: UNIVERSITY SYSTEM OF NEW HAMPSHIRE
5 CHENELL DR STE 301, CONCORD, NH 033018522
Phone: 603 862-1800
Web: WWW.USNH.EDU

PRODUCTS/OPERATIONS

Selected Colleges and Schools

College of Engineering and Physical Sciences
College of Health and Human Services
College of Liberal Arts
College of Life Sciences and Agriculture
The Graduate School
Thompson School of Applied Science
University of New Hampshire at Manchester
University of New Hampshire School of Law
Whittemore School of Business and Economics
Special Academic Opportunities
Graduate Research Conference
Hamel Center for Undergraduate Reasearch
Honors program
International research opportunities program
Student internships
Study abroad
Undergraduate research opportunities program

HISTORICAL FINANCIALS

Company Type: Private

Income Statement — FYE: June 30

	REVENUE ($ mil.)	NET INCOME ($ mil.)	NET PROFIT MARGIN	EMPLOYEES
06/20	642	(1)	—	16,000
06/19	700	52	7.5%	—
06/16	692	(9)	—	—
06/15	680	32	4.7%	—
Annual Growth	(1.1%)	—	—	—

2020 Year-End Financials

Return on assets: (-0.1%)
Return on equity: (-0.1%)
Current ratio: 1.60
Cash ($ mil.): 65

UPMC

For University of Pittsburgh students and area residents medical care is spelled UPMC. University of Pittsburgh Medical Center (UPMC) is a leading not-for-profit health care delivery system in western Pennsylvania. The organization operates more than 40 hospitals including campuses in the Pittsburgh area regional and community hospitals and specialty facilities such as Children's Hospital of Pittsburgh. Altogether UPMC has about 8400 inpatient beds. In addition the system provides care through hundreds of physician practices outpatient clinics cancer treatment facilities and rehab centers; it also offers health insurance home health care and long-term care through about 25 senior living facilities.

Operations

UPMC is organized into four primary operating divisions: Provider Services Insurance Services UPMC International and UPMC Enterprises.

Provider Service which includes a comprehensive array of tertiary community and regional hospitals; specialty service lines such as transplantation women's health behavioral health pediatrics UPMC Hillman Cancer Center and rehabilitation; in-home care and retirement living options; contract services including pharmacy and clinical laboratories; and nearly 3400 employed physicians and associated practices.

Insurance Services offers health insurance to employers and employees workers' compensation and disability services and behavioral health coverage to Medical Assistance beneficiaries. The division's health plans include UPMC for You UPMC Health Plan UPMC for Kids and UPMC for Life; altogether it serves some 3.8 million members.

UPMC Enterprises functions as the innovation and commercialization arm of UPMC.

UPMC International provides hands on health care and management services with partners around the world.

As an academic medical center affiliated with the University of Pittsburgh's Schools of Health Sciences UPMC also focuses on medical research in a wide range of areas including the fields of regenerative medicine and biosecurity some of which is funded by the National Institutes of Health. The system is also renowned for its organ transplantation programs as well as for its cancer care psychiatric pediatric and neurosurgery.

Geographic Reach

UPMC's primary operating territory is the Pittsburgh area and western and central Pennsylvania. Outside the US UPMC operates health care facilities in Ireland Italy Kazakhstan and China.

Its headquarters is located in Pittsburgh Pennsylvania.

Sales and Marketing

The majority of UPMC's hospital services are rendered to patients under Medicare Highmark Blue Cross Blue Shield (a major area insurer) and medical assistance programs. It also provides management and consulting services partly through partnerships with health equipment and technology firms.

Strategy

The UPMC network of facilities has grown over the years through acquisitions partnerships and the construction of new facilities. For example to address the increasing number of patients seeking high-quality emergency care at UPMC East the hospital has expanded its emergency department more than doubling its capacity in mid-2020.

Also in March 2019 the system broke ground on a new vision and rehabilitation tower at UPMC Mercy as part of its $2 billion investment in specialty care.

Mergers and Acquisitions

In early 2019 Somerset Hospital in Somerset Pennsylvania became an affiliate of UPMC. The hospital is now operating as UPMC Somerset. UPMC plans to invest at least $45 million in the facility over a 10-year period.

Also in 2019 UPMC acquired Clane General Hospital in County Kildare in partnership with the Institute of Eye Surgery (IOES) and is renaming the facility UPMC Kildare Hospital. UPMC will also work with IOES to create a national Ophthalmology Network of Excellence while adding or expanding other needed medical specialties for patients in the region. Terms were not disclosed.

Company Background

UPMC traces its roots to 1893 when Louise Lyle the wife of a Presbyterian minister founded its predecessor. The hospital was incorporated as Presbyterian Hospital of Pittsburgh two years later. In 1930 the hospital joined forces with the University of Pittsburgh and broke ground on a new location which opened its doors in 1938.

EXECUTIVES

President And Ceo, Jeffrey A. Romoff
Evp And Chief Administrative Officer, Gregory Peaslee
Evp And Cfo, Robert A. DeMichiei
Evp President Insurance Services Division And President And Ceo Upmc Health Plan, Diane P. Holder
Evp; President Hospital And Community Services Division, Elizabeth B. Concordia
President Magee Women's Hospital, Leslie C. Davis
Evp And Chief Legal Officer, W. Thomas (Tom) McGough

Evp And President International Commercial Services Division And President Upmc Cancercenter, Charles E. (Chuck) Bogosta
Svp And Chief Of Staff Office Of The President, David M. Farner
Evp Treasurer And President Upmc Enterprises, C. Talbot Heppenstall
Evp And Chief Medical Officer; President Physician Services Division, Marshall W. Webster
Evp Chief Medical And Scientific Officer And President Health Services Division, Steven D. Shapiro
Vice President Information Security And Privacy; Associate General Counsel, John Houston
Vice President Talent Acquisition Human Resources Innovation, Matt Rimer
Svp And Cio, Edward Mccallister
Senior Vice President And Chro, John Galley
Vice President International Technology, Deb Salava
Clinical Director, Debra Frank
Executive Vice President Treasurer And President Upmc Enterprises, C Talbot Heppenstall
Executive Vice President Upmc Enterprises Technology Development, Mark Stabingas
Vice President International Clinical Operations And Quality, Cheryl Brill
Clinical Director, Angela Scolieri
Vice President Of Medical Affairs, Gregory Beard
Cno Vice President Patient Care Services, Sandy Rader
Vice President Strategic Planning, David Russell
Director Of Pharmacy, Jennifer Belavic
Medical Director, Syed Hyder
Clinical Director, Susan Killmeyer
Medical Director Corporate Care Management, Roy Jacobson
Vice President For Medicaid Services For The Insurance Services Division, John Lovelace
Clinical Director, Sharon Hanchett
Director Of Nursing, Donna D Cochran
Senior Vice President Chief Risk Compliance And Ethics Officer, Kc Turan
Associate Medical Director, Richard Ambrosino
Vice President Upmc Imaging Services, Laura Moul
Vice President Government Programs Chief Engineer Ne Pa, Brendan Harris
Medical Secretary, Fay Reed
Secretary, Aleesa Foltz
Vice Chair Clinical Services, Dwight Heron
Auditors: ERNST & YOUNG LLP

LOCATIONS

HQ: UPMC
200 LOTHROP ST, PITTSBURGH, PA 152132536
Phone: 412 647-8762
Web: WWW.UPMC.COM

Selected Pennsylvania Facilities

Children's Hospital of Pittsburgh of UPMC
Magee-Womens Hospital of UPMC (Pittsburgh)
UPMC Bedford Memorial (Everett)
UPMC East (Pittsburgh)
UPMC Hamlot (Erie)
UPMC Horizon (Greenville and Shenango Valley)
UPMC McKeesport (McKeesport)
UPMC Mercy (Pittsburgh)
UPMC Montefiore (Pittsburgh)
UPMC Northwest (Seneca and Oil City)
UPMC Passavant (McCandless and Cranberry)
UPMC Presbyterian (Pittsburgh)
UPMC Shadyside (Pittsburgh)
UPMC St. Margaret (Pittsburgh)
UPMC Western Psychiatric Institute and Clinic (Pittsburgh)

PRODUCTS/OPERATIONS

2018 Sales

	$ mil.	% of total
Net patient services	8,823	47
Insurance enrollment	8,492	45
Other	1,462	8
Total	18,777	100

2018 Sales by Segment

	$ mil.	% of total
Health Services	11,881	57
Insurance Services	9,005	43
Adjustments	(2109)	-
Total	18,777	100

Selected Services

Behavioral and Mental Health Services
Cancer
COPD and Emphysema Center
Dermatology
Diabetes and Endocrinology
Ear Nose and Throat
Emergency Medicine
Family/Primary Care Medicine
Gastroenterology
Geriatrics
Heart and Vascular
Imaging Services
Kidney Disease
Liver
Neurology
Ophthalmology
Pain Medicine
Pathology
Pediatrics
Pulmonology and Respiratory
Rehabilitation
Rheumatology
Sports Medicine
Stroke Care
Thyroid
Urology
Women's Health
Wound Healing Services

COMPETITORS

AmeriHealth Mercy Health Plan
Butler Health System
Capital BlueCross
Conemaugh Health System
Excela Health
Geisinger Health System
HealthAmerica
Heritage Valley Health
Highmark
Independence Blue Cross
Jefferson Regional Medical Center of Pennsylvania
Ohio Valley General
St. Clair Health
Universal Health Services
West Penn Allegheny Health System

HISTORICAL FINANCIALS

Company Type: Private

Income Statement — FYE: December 31

	REVENUE ($ mil.)	NET INCOME ($ mil.)	NET PROFIT MARGIN	EMPLOYEES
12/19*	20,609	462	2.2%	80,000
06/15	614	326	53.1%	—
06/13	10,188	441	4.3%	—
12/11	4,758	(2)	—	—
Annual Growth	20.1%	—	—	—

*Fiscal year change

2019 Year-End Financials

Return on assets: 2.6%
Return on equity: 5.6%
Current ratio: 1.10
Cash ($ mil.): 351

UPMC PINNACLE HOSPITALS

EXECUTIVES

Pres, Michael Young
Analyst, Sherry Stoner
Pres Cumberland Region, Louis Baverso
Auditors: PARENTEBEARD LLC YORK PA

LOCATIONS

HQ: UPMC PINNACLE HOSPITALS
409 S 2ND ST STE 1C, HARRISBURG, PA 171041612
Phone: 717 782-5678
Web: WWW.PINNACLEHEALTH.ORG

HISTORICAL FINANCIALS

Company Type: Private

Income Statement — FYE: June 30

	REVENUE ($ mil.)	NET INCOME ($ mil.)	NET PROFIT MARGIN	EMPLOYEES
06/10	559	14	2.5%	4,500
06/09	538	0	—	—
06/08	513	(14)	—	—
06/06	482	26	5.6%	—
Annual Growth	3.8%	(15.1%)	—	—

2010 Year-End Financials

Return on assets: 2.2%
Return on equity: 7.3%
Current ratio: 0.20
Cash ($ mil.): —

UPMC PRESBYTERIAN SHADYSIDE

EXECUTIVES

Pres, John Innocenti
Cfo, Eileen Simmons
Nurse Practitioner, Kristen Baileys
Nurse Practitioner, Kristin Ermine-Baer
Director of Operations, Melanie Houston
Nurse Practitioner, Patti Gigliotti
Nurse Practitioner, Timothy Coleman
Manager, Vicki Bedel
Member, William S Dietrich II
Managing Partner, William Pietragallo II
Member, John Pelusi Jr
Auditors: ERNST & YOUNG LLP PITTSBURGH

LOCATIONS

HQ: UPMC PRESBYTERIAN SHADYSIDE
200 LOTHROP ST MH-N739, PITTSBURGH, PA 152132536
Phone: 412 647-2345
Web: WWW.UPMC.COM

HISTORICAL FINANCIALS

Company Type: Private

Income Statement				FYE: June 30
	REVENUE ($ mil.)	NET INCOME ($ mil.)	NET PROFIT MARGIN	EMPLOYEES
06/10	8,046	276	3.4%	8,200
06/09	1,723	83	4.8%	—
06/06	1,627	0	—	—
Annual Growth	49.1%	—	—	—

2010 Year-End Financials

Return on assets: 3.5%
Return on equity: 9.1%
Current ratio: 0.80
Cash ($ mil.): 158

UPPER MISSOURI G & T ELECTRIC CO-OPERATIVE INC

EXECUTIVES

President, Roger Sorenson
Ice Pres, Allen Thiessen
Controller, Della Pewonka
Compliance Manager, Rick Engstrom
General Manager, Claire Vigesaa
Auditors: BRENNER AVERETT & CO PC SIDNE

LOCATIONS

HQ: UPPER MISSOURI G & T ELECTRIC CO-OPERATIVE INC
111 2ND AVE SW, SIDNEY, MT 592704017
Phone: 406 433-4100
Web: WWW.UPPERMO.COM

HISTORICAL FINANCIALS

Company Type: Private

Income Statement				FYE: December 31
	REVENUE ($ mil.)	NET INCOME ($ mil.)	NET PROFIT MARGIN	EMPLOYEES
12/18	548	78	14.2%	2
12/17	531	0	—	—
12/16	486	0	—	—
12/14	319	0	—	—
Annual Growth	14.5%	—	—	—

2018 Year-End Financials

Return on assets: 27.5%
Return on equity: 34.7%
Current ratio: 1.00
Cash ($ mil.): 1

URM STORES, INC.

URM Stores is a leading wholesale food distribution cooperative serving more than 160 grocery stores in the Northwest. Its member-owner stores operate under a variety of banners including Family Foods Harvest Foods Super 1 Foods Trading Co. Stores and Yoke's Fresh Market. It also owns the Rosauers Supermarkets chain. In addition to grocery stores URM supplies 1500-plus restaurants hotels and convenience stores; it also offers such services as merchandising store development consulting and technology purchasing. The cooperative was founded in 1921 as United Retail Merchants. The business is privately owned by its members.

Operations

The company's Spokane Washington-based Peirone Produce distribution subsidiary supplies fresh produce including organic produce as well as specialty items source from Arizona California Florida Mexico and Texas. In addition to groceries and produce URM Stores sells insurance to its members and food service customers through URM Insurance Agency. Insurance products include business insurance for stores and personal lines of coverage for owns and their employees.

Geographic Reach

Regional wholesaler URM Stores supplies stores and other customers in much of eastern Washington northern Idaho Oregon and Montana.

Financial Performance

URM Stores rings up sales of about $775 million employs more than 2700 people and has assets exceeding $100 million.

Strategy

In 2010 the company moved its Spokane Washington-based Peirone Produce distribution subsidiary into a larger facility boasting 70000 sq. ft. of warehouse space and 7000 sq. ft. of office space. It is equipped with about 15 docks for loading outgoing trucks and another dozen docks for unloading incoming trucks. The facility is more than twice the size of Peirone's previous building which had nearly 10 docks total. Because of the larger space and greater number of docks Peirone Produce said it has been able to improve its productivity.

EXECUTIVES

Vice President Of Information Technology, Rich Stuber
Vice President Of Human Resources, Linda Wilson
Vice President Software Sales, Carla Thompson
Vice President Procurement, Mike Mcshane
Auditors: BDO USA LLP SPOKANE WA

LOCATIONS

HQ: URM STORES, INC.
7511 N FREYA ST, SPOKANE, WA 992178043
Phone: 509 467-2620
Web: WWW.URMSTORES.COM

PRODUCTS/OPERATIONS

Selected Banners

CenterPlace Market
Family Foods
Harvest Foods
Trading Co. Stores
Rosauers Supermarkets
Super 1 Foods
Yoke's Fresh Market

COMPETITORS

AMCON Distributing
Albertsons
Associated Food
C&S Wholesale
Core-Mark
Farner-Bocken
Fred Meyer Stores
McLane
SUPERVALU
Safeway
Sysco
US Foods
Wal-Mart

HISTORICAL FINANCIALS

Company Type: Private

Income Statement				FYE: August 2
	REVENUE ($ mil.)	NET INCOME ($ mil.)	NET PROFIT MARGIN	EMPLOYEES
08/08*	932	8	0.9%	2,100
07/07	859	7	0.8%	—
07/06	799	4	0.6%	—
Annual Growth	8.0%	41.0%	—	—

*Fiscal year change

2008 Year-End Financials

Return on assets: 3.8%
Return on equity: 11.0%
Current ratio: 1.20
Cash ($ mil.): 2

USG CORPORATION

USG Corporation is a leading manufacturer of building products in the US serving the residential nonresidential and repair & remodel end markets. It is a top seller of wallboard gypsum fiberboard and construction plaster products that are used for finishing interior walls ceilings and floors. The company is also a major North American supplier of building-related performance materials (water fire and mold retardants) ceiling grid and acoustic tiles. Recognized brands include Sheetrock Durock Fiberock and Securock. Thanks to a tie-up with Boral Limited USG also distribute products across Asia and Australia. A merger deal with the Knauf Group (with USG becoming a wholly owned subsidiary) is currently pending (expected 2019).

Change in Company Type

In June 2018 USG Corporation agreed to be acquired by Gebr. Knauf KG the ultimate parent company of the German-based Knauf Group for $7 billion. USG will survive the merger as an indirect wholly owned subsidiary. The merger will make the Knauf Group a global leader in building materials. The deal is expected to close in Q1 2019 but remains on hold as Australian and Mexican governments are yet to approve the merger.

Operations

USG Corporation reports five segments: US Wallboard and Surfaces US Performance Materials US Ceilings Canada and the USG Boral Building Products joint-venture (UBBP).

More than half of its revenue comes from gypsum products that help put the finishing touches on the walls of residential and commercial buildings. This whole business is managed under the US Wallboard and Surfaces segment. Some 15% more sales comes from tiles and grids meant to complete the ceilings of nonresidential buildings reported under US Ceilings. The third big product line of USG beyond wall and ceiling products is its roof-related products like reinforced concrete planes and mold-resistant boards. Housed under Performance Materials these products bring in some 10% of total sales mostly from commercial projects. The rest of its revenue some 15% comes from the company's Canadian segment that sells products from its three other producing segments.

The joint-venture UBBP manufactures and sells plasterboard and non-board lines for metal products in Asia Australia and the Middle East. Its revenue is reported separately.

Geographic Reach

Headquartered in Chicago Illinois USG Corporation operates plants mines and quarries in the US and some parts of Canada (Alberta British Columbia Ontario and Quebec). USG also owns three gypsum mines outside of North America through its UBBP joint venture.

The US accounts for more than 80% of its sales followed by Canada (nearly 15%).

Sales and Marketing

USG Corporation's products are sold through a network of distributors installation contractors and home improvement centers. The company makes most of its revenue through residential and non-residential repair and remodel activity. A quarter of its sales come from The Home Depot with another 15% coming from L&W Supply Corp.

USG's well-known brands include Sheetrock Securock Red Top Imperial Diamond and Supremo (gypsum business line); Durock Fiberock and Levelrock (performance materials); and Radar Eclipse Donn Curvatura and Ensemble (ceiling systems).

USG's advertising expenses was $15 million in 2018.

Financial Performance

USG Corporation has enjoyed a modestly upward trajectory in annual sales for the last five years. Revenue grew from $2.9 billion in 2014 to $3.3 billion by the end of 2018. In 2018 the company grew 3% coming mostly from higher selling prices in Sheetrock branded gypsum products Durock branded cement products and Securock branded roof boards and ceiling tiles.

Net income rose to $196 million in 2018 from $88 million the year before. A year-over-year $204 million reduction in income tax expenses improved company profits. Gross profit declined by $50 million as unit cost of producing its products climbed along with a hike in transportation costs.

The company's cash and cash equivalents fell by $61 million ending 2018 with $328 million on hand. Cash from operations generated $284 million while cash from investing used $195 million ($219 million on CAPEX). Financing activities further used $150 million.

Strategy

USG Corporation is facing two major challenges: anemic growth in the gypsum segment as well as a steep competition from substitute products in its ceiling materials business.

Gypsum market outlook is bleak for 2019 as residential and non-residential activity in the US is expected to remain well below historical averages. Demand in the Australian and South Korean markets are also expected to slow due to a slowing housing market. USG's volume growth of its gypsum board market share in the US shrank by 5%.

Furthermore there is excess wallboard production capacity in the US market and unless housing starts and repair activity pick up in 2019 the conditions won't improve for USG. This means that the company will not be able to charge higher prices for its materials (unlike 2018) going forward.

The Ceilings segment is experiencing an even bigger crisis: the market preference for the construction material of choice has rapidly shifted to open plenum and specialty ceilings products that directly compete with the company's own materials. USG has tried to catch up with this trend by acquiring Ceilings Plus in 2017 but its command over the market has taken a hit in recent years.

Mergers and Acquisitions

In late 2017 the company acquired US-based Ceilings Plus a leading manufacturer of specialty ceiling products for $52 million. The addition of Ceilings Plus made USG a leader in the specialty ceiling market especially in ceiling grid and acoustic ceiling tile products.

Company Background

In 1901 a group of 35 companies joined to form U.S.G. the largest gypsum producing and processing business in the industry. In 1915 the company began producing lime followed by paint manufacturing in 1924.

By 1931 it was producing insulating board and metal lath fields. When the company bought Masonite in 1984 its changed its name to USG the next year.

In 2019 the company is expected to bt acquired by Germany-based company Knauf.

HISTORY

In 1901 a group of 35 companies joined to form U.S.G. the largest gypsum producing and processing business in the industry. Sewell Avery became CEO in 1905 (he led U.S.G. until 1951). U.S.G. began producing lime in 1915. It became United States Gypsum (U.S. Gypsum) in 1920 and began making paint in 1924. By 1931 it was producing insulating board and metal lath fields. It also added two lime businesses and two gypsum concerns.

The company bought Masonite in 1984 and changed its name to USG the next year. It acquired Donn (remodeling materials) in 1986 and DAP (caulk and sealants) in 1987.

EXECUTIVES

Evp And Chief Administrative Officer, Brian J. Cook, $421,167 total compensation

Evp And Cfo, Matthew F. Hilzinger, $600,833 total compensation

Evp And Chief Operations And Innovation Officer, Dominic A. Dannessa, $442,500 total compensation

President And Ceo, Jennifer F. Scanlon, $509,500 total compensation

Svp; President North America, Gregory D. Salah

Vice President Advanced Manufacturing And Corporate Excellence, Ken Banas

Vice President Engineering, Curt Malone

Vice President Sales Operations And Customer Experience, Elaine Chapa

Senior Vice President General Counsel And Corporate Secretary, Michelle Warner

Vice President Sales, Duane Knight

Svp And President Ceilings, Christopher Macey

Vp And Treasurer, Dean Gillen

Vice President Strategy And Transition, Alexander Dadakis

Chairman, Steven F. Leer

Auditors: DELOITTED & TOUCHE LLP CHICAG

LOCATIONS

HQ: USG CORPORATION
550 W ADAMS ST, CHICAGO, IL 606613665
Phone: 312 436-4000
Web: WWW.USG.COM

2018 Sales

	$ mil.	% of total
US	2,871	81
Canada	448	13
Other Foreign	211	6
Geographic transfers	(194)	-
Total	**3,336**	**100**

Subsidiaries

Subsidiaries
United States Gypsum Company
USG Interiors LLC
USG Foreign Investments Ltd.
USG Netherlands Global Holdings B.V.
CGC Inc.
USG Latin America LLC.
USG Holding de Mexico S.A. de C.V.
USG Mexico S.A. de C.V.

Selected schools

School of Dentistry
School of Medicine
School of Nursing
School of Pharmacy (with Oregon State University)
School of Science & Engineering

PRODUCTS/OPERATIONS

2018 Sales (by Segment)

	$ mil.	% of total
US Wallboard and Surfaces	1,927	54
US Performance Materials	392	11
US Ceilings	541	15
Canada	448	13
Other	252	7
Eliminations	(224)	-
Total	**3,336**	**100**

COMPETITORS

Allied Building Products
American Gypsum
Armstrong World Industries
CertainTeed
Continental BP
Georgia-Pacific
James Hardie Industries
LATICRETE
New NGC
Pacific Coast Building Products
Worthington Industries

HISTORICAL FINANCIALS

Company Type: Private

Income Statement — FYE: December 31

	REVENUE ($ mil.)	NET INCOME ($ mil.)	NET PROFIT MARGIN	EMPLOYEES
12/18	3,336	196	5.9%	7,300
12/17	3,204	88	2.7%	—
12/16	3,017	510	16.9%	—
Annual Growth	5.2%	(38.0%)	—	—

2018 Year-End Financials

Return on assets: 5.1%
Return on equity: 10.2%
Current ratio: 2.30
Cash ($ mil.): 328

USS-POSCO INDUSTRIES, A CALIFORNIA JOINT VENTURE

US and Korean steel manufacturing interests come together in the form of USS-POSCO Industries (UPI) a 50/50 joint venture between United States Steel (US Steel) and POSCO. The company operates a steel plant (formerly owned by US Steel) in Pittsburg Northern California. It manufactures flat-rolled steel sheets in various forms: cold-rolled steel galvanized steel and tinplate. In addition USS-POSCO churns out iron oxide which is used to make hard and soft ferrites. UPI sells its products to more than 150 customers in more than dozen states throughout the western US. End products include office furniture computer cabinets metal studs cans culverts and metal building materials.

Operations

UPI's main product lines include cold rolled sheet galvanized sheet hot rolled pickled and oiled sheet and tin plate. It has the capacity to produce about 1.5 million tons of product per year.

Geographic Reach

The company markets its products primarily in the western US.

Sales and Marketing

UPI ships steel products to more than 150 customers across North America. The company sells its products to a wide range of manufacturers whose end products include automotive parts computer cabinets culverts food packaging metal buildings metal studs and office furniture. About 1/3 of UPI's product line is tinplate for the canning industry.

Strategy

Its Korean co-owner supplied high quality raw materials for use at the plant. In order to stay competitive in the face of cheaper steel imports UPI jettisoned non-core product lines to focus on steel sheet and tin. However strong competition and poor market prices forced the company in 2011 to introduce furloughs at the plant and enforce temporary shutdowns of the facility.

Company Background

The company rebounded from a major fire in 2001. In 2010 UPI invested heavily in remediation measures to clean up soil and groundwater impacted by its plant activities.

US Steel teamed up with POSCO (then Pohang Iron & Steel Company) in 1986 as part of a major reorganization of the aging Pittsburg plant which first opened in 1910.

EXECUTIVES

Vice President Supply Chain, Lynnette Giacobazzi
Auditors: KPMG LLP SACRAMENTO CALIFOR

LOCATIONS

HQ: USS-POSCO INDUSTRIES, A CALIFORNIA JOINT VENTURE
900 LOVERIDGE RD, PITTSBURG, CA 945652808
Phone: 800 877-7672
Web: WWW.USSPOSCO.COM

PRODUCTS/OPERATIONS

Selected Steel Products
Cold Rolled Annealed
Hot Dipped Galvanized
Hot Rolled Pickled and Oiled
Tinplate

COMPETITORS

AK Steel Holding Corporation
ArcelorMittal USA
BlueScope Steel
Gerdau Ameristeel
Nucor
Steel Dynamics

HISTORICAL FINANCIALS

Company Type: Private

Income Statement — FYE: December 31

	REVENUE ($ mil.)	NET INCOME ($ mil.)	NET PROFIT MARGIN	EMPLOYEES
12/15	648	(4)	—	759
12/08	1,198	11	1.0%	—
12/07	998	(40)	—	—
12/06	1,034	14	1.4%	—
Annual Growth	(5.1%)	—	—	—

2015 Year-End Financials

Return on assets: (-1.5%)
Return on equity: —
Current ratio: 0.90
Cash ($ mil.): —

UTAH STATE UNIVERSITY

Utah State University (USU) has more than 40 academic departments at colleges of agriculture arts business education and human services engineering science natural resources and humanities and social sciences. It offers about 170 bachelor's degree programs and more than 140 graduate degree programs. Biology elementary education mechanical and aerospace engineering and business administration are among the university's most popular majors. About 29000 students attend its main campus in northern Utah its three branch campuses or extension facilities located across the state. USU was established in 1888 as an agricultural college.

Operations

USU has a student-to-faculty ratio of 18:1. Alumni of the university include Greg Carr founder of the Greg C. Carr Foundation and Charlie Denson former president of NIKE.

Geographic Reach

USU students hail from all 50 US states and some 80 international countries. The university's students have the opportunity to study abroad through partnerships with 140 other institutions located around the world. USU's main campuses or branch offices in Utah are located in Brigham City Logan San Juan Tooele and Uintah Basin.

Financial Performance

Revenues increased at USU by 4% to some $340 million due to increased income from tuition and fees higher enrollment and increased state appropriations. The gain was offset by decreases in gifts grants and contracts. Net income fell 41% to $68 million due to higher operating expenses from salary benefit and other costs.

Strategy

To expand its facilities and meet growing student needs USU is adding a new school of business building and a new athletics center to its main campus. The university recently completed construction of a new $47 million agricultural building on the main campus as well as a new administration building on the USU Eastern campus. In addition USU is building a new distance education building on its Logan campus.

To further expand resources for students USU began offering a Master of Business Administration (MBA) program at the Brigham Young University's Idaho campus in 2013.

EXECUTIVES

Vice President, Tim Vitale
Vice President University Advancement, Fross Peterson
Department Head, Kim Lewis
Vice President For Business And Finance, David Cowley
Associate Vice President, Dwight Davis
Vice President University Advancement, Ross Peterson
Regional Vice President, Melanie Rodraguez
Associate Vice President, Kim Kimberly
Secretary, Vanessa Chambers
Treasurer, Rae Ann
Secretary, Mica McKinney
Auditors: OFFICE OF THE STATE AUDITOR S

LOCATIONS

HQ: UTAH STATE UNIVERSITY
1000 OLD MAIN HL, LOGAN, UT 843221000
Phone: 435 797-1000
Web: WWW.ENGINEERING.USU.EDU

HISTORICAL FINANCIALS

Company Type: Private

Income Statement — FYE: June 30

	REVENUE ($ mil.)	NET INCOME ($ mil.)	NET PROFIT MARGIN	EMPLOYEES
06/20	559	77	13.9%	6,000
06/19	537	94	17.5%	—
06/18	461	39	8.7%	—
Annual Growth	10.1%	39.3%	—	—

2020 Year-End Financials

Return on assets: 3.9%
Return on equity: 5.4%
Current ratio: 1.90
Cash ($ mil.): 110

UTI, (U.S.) HOLDINGS, INC.

EXECUTIVES

Pres-Ceo, Christopher Dale
Treas*, Clinton Smith
Vice Pres*, Mary Anne Henry
Asst Treas*, Matthew Tachouet
Asst SEC*, Kristen Galbreath
Acct, Lorraine Disarlo
Acct Mgr, Patrick Billera
Cash Mgr, Mark Burrow
Director of Information Techno, Craig Jarrett
Vice-President, Tom Riester
Manager, Jay Newey
Auditors: DELOITTE & TOUCHE LLP LOS AN

LOCATIONS

HQ: UTI, (U.S.) HOLDINGS, INC.
400 SW 6TH AVE STE 906, PORTLAND, OR 972041634
Phone: 503 953-1300

HISTORICAL FINANCIALS

Company Type: Private

Income Statement — FYE: January 31

	REVENUE ($ mil.)	NET INCOME ($ mil.)	NET PROFIT MARGIN	EMPLOYEES
01/10	3,567	45	1.3%	5,981
01/08	534	12	2.3%	—
Annual Growth	158.3%	91.3%	—	—

2010 Year-End Financials

Return on assets: 20.5%
Return on equity: 1.3%
Current ratio: 1.20
Cash ($ mil.): 350

VALLEY CHILDREN'S HEALTHCARE FOUNDATION

EXECUTIVES

Ceo, Todd Suntrapak
V Pres*, William Chaltraw
Director of Strategic Planning, Brian Sabbatini
Director of Information Securi, Joe Egan
Director, Rod Benedict
Director, Tim Curley
Director, Michelle Brunetti
Director Recruitment, Suzan Parsons
Director of Patient SA, Samuel Lehman
Clinical Laboratory Scientist, Ashley Owens
Payroll Analyst, Tami Evers

LOCATIONS

HQ: VALLEY CHILDREN'S HEALTHCARE FOUNDATION
9300 VALLEY CHILDRENS PL, MADERA, CA 936368761
Phone: 559 353-3000
Web: WWW.VALLEYCHILDRENS.ORG

HISTORICAL FINANCIALS

Company Type: Private

Income Statement — FYE: September 30

	REVENUE ($ mil.)	NET INCOME ($ mil.)	NET PROFIT MARGIN	EMPLOYEES
09/19	793	159	20.0%	2,800
09/18	698	122	17.6%	—
09/17	604	121	20.1%	—
09/16	601	83	13.9%	—
Annual Growth	9.7%	23.9%	—	—

2019 Year-End Financials

Return on assets: 9.0%
Return on equity: 12.1%
Current ratio: 1.30
Cash ($ mil.): 31

VALLEY CHILDREN'S HOSPITAL

EXECUTIVES

Pres- Ceo, Todd Sunterapak
Cfo*, Michele Waldrin
Coo*, Jessie Hudgins
Executive*, Stephanie Scott
Prin*, Gordon Alexander
Human Resources, Heather San Julian
Director Information Technolog, Denise Zeitler
Manager of Gift Shop, Peggy Ellithorpe
Pediatric Cardiology, Kenneth P Rouillard
MD, Peter Nakaguchi
Doctor, Randall D Morton

LOCATIONS

HQ: VALLEY CHILDREN'S HOSPITAL
9300 VALLEY CHILDRENS PL, MADERA, CA 936368762
Phone: 559 353-3000
Web: WWW.VALLEYCHILDRENS.ORG

HISTORICAL FINANCIALS

Company Type: Private

Income Statement — FYE: September 30

	REVENUE ($ mil.)	NET INCOME ($ mil.)	NET PROFIT MARGIN	EMPLOYEES
09/15	575	24	4.3%	1,800
09/13*	542	103	19.0%	—
06/05	457	(24)	—	—
09/02	219	0	0.3%	—
Annual Growth	7.7%	33.9%	—	—

*Fiscal year change

2015 Year-End Financials

Return on assets: 2.3%
Return on equity: 3.0%
Current ratio: 2.30
Cash ($ mil.): 8

VALLEY HEALTH SYSTEM GROUP RETURN

EXECUTIVES

Ex Dir, Kevin Callanan
Urology Specialist, John Warner
Auditors: VALLEY HEALTH SYSTEM WINCHEST

LOCATIONS

HQ: VALLEY HEALTH SYSTEM GROUP RETURN
220 CAMPUS BLVD STE 310, WINCHESTER, VA 226012889
Phone: 540 536-4302

HISTORICAL FINANCIALS

Company Type: Private

Income Statement — FYE: December 31

	REVENUE ($ mil.)	NET INCOME ($ mil.)	NET PROFIT MARGIN	EMPLOYEES
12/17	904	32	3.6%	7
12/13	625	22	3.7%	—
12/12	628	46	7.4%	—
12/09	538	45	8.5%	—
Annual Growth	6.7%	(4.2%)	—	—

2017 Year-End Financials

Return on assets: 2.3%
Return on equity: 3.9%
Current ratio: 0.40
Cash ($ mil.): 65

VALUE DRUG COMPANY

Value Drug Company (Value Drug) sees a great deal of value in keeping independent pharmacies competitive. The company is a purchasing cooperative of hundreds of independent drugstores that provides wholesale pharmaceutical distribution services to its members primarily in the central Pennsylvania area. Its products include pharmaceuticals and non-prescription medications medical equipment health and beauty aids nutritional supplies and other health care-related products. The company works with some of the world's largest pharmaceutical makers. Value Drug was founded in 1934 and incorporated in 1936. The company is led by president Greg Drew a former Rite-Aid executive.

Operations

The company is not just a pharmaceutical wholesaler but it also provides retail and specialty pharmacy services long-term care pharmacy support and immunization service offerings. Value Drug offers more than 25000 products including brand generic injectable and specialty pharmaceuticals over-the-counter products home health care long-term care supplies health beauty and wellness as well as seasonal and everyday gifts. Value Drug also participates in such retail initiatives as the federal 340B Drug Discount Program an adult immunization tracking program and competitive generic sourcing program OptiSource.

Geographic Reach

Value Drug is located in Duncansville Pennsylvania.

Sales and Marketing

Value Drug customers include pharmacists and business owners. It offers a variety of marketing tools for its customers such as store signage and consumer email communications to physician marketing support for CP specialty pharmacy services. Value Drug provides valuable resources that help generate traffic and its customer's increase sales.

Strategy

Value Drug is committed to providing transparency in its pricing and optimizing manufacturer relationships and purchasing power to improve buying conditions for its members. Value Drug also takes note of the changing consumer and independent pharmacy owners' needs. The company has assembled a diverse portfolio of programs and services that satisfy both the customer's need for convenience and low-cost healthcare and the pharmacist's need to increase growth efficiency and profitability.

Value Drug strives to keep independent pharmacies independent. Its Value Buy/Sell Program was established to assist those seeking to sell their business as well as those looking for new ownership or expansion opportunities. Through its partnership with PRS members have access to industry-leading buying selling and transferring services while its partnership with Sykes & Co. provides members with access to accounting tax and advisory services.

Value Drug also provides resources that help generate traffic and increase sales in pharmacies. It offers a variety of marketing tools to help its members stay top-of-mind with patients and customers in their communities. Through Value Drug's partnerships with leading suppliers clients can purchase high-quality apparel and promotional products featuring the clients' pharmacy's logo and brand designs.

Company Background

Value Drug Company was founded in 1934. Value Drug Company was then incorporated in 1936. The first warehouse occupied was located at 5th Avenue and 24th Street. In 1970 Drenning Trucking Co. was the first delivery service. In 2015 Value Drug introduces the ValueDrugHub mobile app the first pharmaceutical wholesaler to provide a mobile app for order receiving and discrepancies.

EXECUTIVES

National Account Manager, Ellen Breitenbach
Vice President Of Operations, J Bover
Auditors: HILL BARTH & KING LLC WEXFOR

LOCATIONS

HQ: VALUE DRUG COMPANY
195 THEATER DR, DUNCANSVILLE, PA 166357144
Phone: 814 944-9316
Web: WWW.VALUEDRUGCO.COM

COMPETITORS

AmerisourceBergen
Cardinal Health
H. D. Smith Wholesale Drug
Kinray
McKesson
Quality King

HISTORICAL FINANCIALS

Company Type: Private

Income Statement — FYE: March 31

	REVENUE ($ mil.)	NET INCOME ($ mil.)	NET PROFIT MARGIN	EMPLOYEES
03/20*	1,156	0	0.1%	200
12/18	1,034	(0)	—	—
12/17	842	0	0.1%	—
12/16	816	0	0.0%	—
Annual Growth	12.3%	74.6%	—	—

*Fiscal year change

2020 Year-End Financials

Return on assets: 0.4%
Return on equity: 2.8%
Current ratio: 1.50
Cash ($ mil.): 12

VAN ATLAS LINES INC

The main subsidiary of Atlas World Group moving company Atlas Van Lines provides transportation of household goods throughout the US and between the US and Canada. The company is one of the largest movers in the US. Atlas Van Lines also offers specialized transportation services for such cargo as trade show materials fine art electronics pianos store fixtures and even individual cars and motorcycles. It operates through a network of some 500 agents in the US and about 150 in Canada – independent companies that use the Atlas brand in assigned geographic territories and cooperate on interstate moves. Atlas Van Lines was formed in 1948 by a group of 33 small moving companies.

EXECUTIVES

Vice President Customer Services, Mark Spiehler

LOCATIONS

HQ: VAN ATLAS LINES INC
1212 SAINT GEORGE RD, EVANSVILLE, IN 477112364
Phone: 812 424-4326
Web: WWW.ATLASVANLINES.COM

COMPETITORS

AMERCO
Bekins
Graebel
Penske Truck Leasing
SIRVA
United Van Lines

HISTORICAL FINANCIALS

Company Type: Private

Income Statement — FYE: December 31

	REVENUE ($ mil.)	NET INCOME ($ mil.)	NET PROFIT MARGIN	EMPLOYEES
12/08	696	19	2.8%	606
12/06	58	2	4.3%	—
12/05	59	3	6.5%	—
Annual Growth	127.4%	71.0%	—	—

VANDERBILT UNIVERSITY MEDICAL CENTER

The Vanderbilt University Medical Center (VUMC) is one of the top health care organizations in the US with its network of hospitals outpatient centers clinics and specialty institutes. Its medical education programs train hundreds of doctors and nurses each year and the center's Vanderbilt Clinics receive more than 1.5 million annual patient visits. Its Vanderbilt University Hospitals together with the clinics and specialty facilities have more than 1000 beds. VUMC boasts a children's hospital a psychiatric hospital a transplant center and a rehabilitation hospital as well as a biomedical research center and the Vanderbilt-Ingram Cancer Center a National Cancer Institute-designated facility.

Change in Company Type

In mid 2016 Vanderbilt University and VUMC officially split severing their financial and legal ties. The change allows VUMC more financial independence but the two institutions will still partner to provide research and education. VUMC will be reconfigured as a not-for-profit academic medical center; it will retain its current name.

Operations

VUMC includes a level I trauma center and a level IV neonatal intensive care unit (NICU). It also operates a regional burn center and comprehensive regional transplant program. Its nationally designated cancer center has multiple locations. In addition to some 630 beds at the main Vanderbilt University Hospital the medical center campus includes the 270-bed Children's Hospital at Vanderbilt the 90-bed Vanderbilt Psychiatric Hospital and the 90-bed Vanderbilt Stallworth Rehabilitation Hospital. Altogether VUMC's facilities handle some 50000 patient discharges 60000 emergency room visits and 35000 surgeries each year.

Since its establishment in 1875 the Vanderbilt University Medical Center has earned a reputation as a leader in patient care medical education and biomedical research. Its medical and nursing schools train more than 1800 students and its residencies and fellowships groom some 1400 students. Support for VUMC research funding has grown over the last decade with grants from all sources exceeding $570 million in fiscal 2012.

Geographic Reach

VUMC's hospitals affiliates physician practices and clinics cover more than 70 counties in Tennessee and Kentucky.

Strategy

VUMC launched its Vanderbilt Health Affiliated Network (VHAN) in 2013. The network aims to create one of the largest clinically integrated health care networks in the region. VHAN is used as an alternative health plan by Vanderbilt employees; the unit has also received a grant to study chronic disease management practices. Other patient and student service efforts in 2012 and 2013 included enhancing mobile and online applications and learning portals.

EXECUTIVES

President And Ceo, Jeffrey R. Balser
Deputy Ceo And Chief Health System Officer, C. Wright Pinson
Medical Director Acute Operations And Transplant Perioperative Services, Sunil Geevarghese
Vice Chair, Victoria Burrus
Auditors: ERNST & YOUNG LLP NASHVILLE

LOCATIONS

HQ: VANDERBILT UNIVERSITY MEDICAL CENTER
1211 MEDICAL CENTER DR, NASHVILLE, TN 372320004
Phone: 615 322-5000
Web: WWW.VANDERBILTHEALTH.COM

PRODUCTS/OPERATIONS

Selected Facilities

Annette and Irwin Eskind Biomedical Library
Bill Wilkerson Center for Otolaryngology and Communication Sciences
Comprehensive Spine Center
Dayani Center for Health and Wellness
Monroe Carell Jr. Children's Hospital at Vanderbilt
Orthopaedic Institute
School of Medicine
School of Nursing
Sports Medicine Center
Stallworth Rehabilitation Hospital
Transplant Center
Vanderbilt Center for Better Health
The Vanderbilt Clinic
Vanderbilt Heart and Vascular Institute
Vanderbilt Psychiatric Hospital
Vanderbilt University Hospital
Vanderbilt-Ingram Cancer Center

COMPETITORS

American HealthChoice
Ascension Health
Blount Memorial Hospital
Catholic Health Initiatives
Community Health Systems
Covenant Health
Duke University Health System
Emory Healthcare
Erlanger Health System
HCA
LifePoint Health
Mountain States Health
Tennova Healthcare

HISTORICAL FINANCIALS

Company Type: Private

Income Statement — FYE: June 30

	REVENUE ($ mil.)	NET INCOME ($ mil.)	NET PROFIT MARGIN	EMPLOYEES
06/18	4,086	98	2.4%	19,000
06/17	3,894	264	6.8%	—
Annual Growth	4.9%	(62.8%)	—	—

2018 Year-End Financials

Return on assets: 3.1%
Return on equity: 10.6%
Current ratio: 2.20
Cash ($ mil.): 500

VANGUARD CHARITABLE ENDOWMENT PROGRAM

EXECUTIVES

Pres, Benjamin R Pierce
Chief Dev't Officer, David S Ryder
Cfo, Kevin Cavanaugh
Cfo, Mark Froehlich
Marketing Manager, James R Barnes
Senior Philanthropic, Jodi Rosen
Marketing Operations Team Lead, Nicole Acker
Project Manager, Amanda Welsh
Sr Business Execut, Cindy Vanamburgh
Manager, Karen Levandoski
Marketing Coordinator, Kevin Cella
Auditors: PRICEWATERHOUSECOOPERS LLP PH

LOCATIONS

HQ: VANGUARD CHARITABLE ENDOWMENT PROGRAM
100 VANGUARD BLVD G19, MALVERN, PA 193552331
Phone: 888 383-4483
Web: WWW.VANGUARDCHARITABLE.ORG

HISTORICAL FINANCIALS

Company Type: Private

Income Statement FYE: June 30

	REVENUE ($ mil.)	NET INCOME ($ mil.)	NET PROFIT MARGIN	EMPLOYEES
06/13	1,117	608	54.4%	22
06/12	908	424	46.7%	—
06/11	890	402	45.2%	—
06/10	490	15	3.2%	—
Annual Growth	31.6%	239.7%	—	—

2013 Year-End Financials

Return on assets: 16.8%
Return on equity: 16.9%
Current ratio: —
Cash ($ mil.): 14

VARIETY CHILDREN'S HOSPITAL

Miami Children's Hospital (MCH) a not-for-profit medical center boasts some 290 beds and offers more than 40 different health care specialties and sub-specialties represented by more than 650 physicians and more than 130 pediatric sub-specialists. Some specialties include pediatric emergency care cancer treatment orthopedics and rehabilitation services. The hospital's neonatal unit treats newborns referred from other hospitals. Miami Children's Hospital operates the region's only free-standing pediatric trauma center. The MCH Research Institute conducts more than 210 clinical research studies in 26 sub-specialties.

Operations

The health system also operates mobile health units that provide preventive care to uninsured children throughout its service area. The units provide immunizations tuberculosis tests and hearing and vision screenings among other services.

In 2012 the hospital had 11550 inpatient admissions 91901 emergency room visits and 14360 surgical cases. Its neonatology division admits more than 600 newborns each year virtually all of them referred from general acute-care hospitals because they are in need of an advanced level of tertiary care.

In 2012 Radiology performed a total of 129794 Diagnostic x-rays MRI's CT Scans and ultrasounds at the main campus. The LifeFlight Critical Care Transport Team transported 2480 patients by air and ground to Miami Children's Hospital in 2012.

Geographic Reach

MCH caters to young Florida residents and their families as well as those in South America and Europe through its Dan Marino Outpatient Center which assists children with special needs and provides neurological and development services for special needs children. Its six outpatient centers are based in Doral Miami Lakes Palmetto Bay Weston West Kendall and West Palm Beach.

Sales and Marketing

MCH markets its products and services through radio and television advertising

Financial Performance

Net patient revenues accounted for about 90% MCH's revenues in 2012.

Strategy

The hospital is at the tail end of a multiyear nearly $70 million project to install an electronic medical record system at the medical center. The first phase of the project which wrapped up in 2012 included new prescribing methods and lab test protocols. It will also engender better communication between hospital staff. The entire system should be installed by 2015.

In 2013 it also launched a smartphone app for Apple iOS devices that uses Wi-Fi triangulation technology to offer patients the convenience of an on-campus indoor GPS-like way-finding system along with other service enhancements.

Expanding its physical infrastructure in 2014 FIU Health broke ground on a 36000-sq.-ft. ambulatory care center on FIU's Modesto A. Maidique Campus in west Miami-Dade County. In partnership with MCH the campus will house the first dedicated pediatric ambulatory surgical center in South Florida.

As part of an expansion project aimed at meeting the growing needs of the community that year MCH also opened 20 new exam rooms in the Emergency Department.

In 2013 the Florida legislature approved HB 1159 a bill that amends a law to make it possible for MCH to build a 10-bed unit to provide obstetrical services for healthy mothers expecting babies pre-diagnosed with congenital conditions requiring clinical intervention immediately after birth.

In 2012 MCH completed a six-story Advanced Pediatric Care Pavilion and the 21000-sq.-ft. Miami Children's Hospital Midtown Outpatient Center. It also opened Miami Children's Hospital Nicklaus Outpatient Center.

On the media front in 2014 MCH launched the MCH Television Network an in-house television network providing patients and families a customized resource for news research and entertainment that specifically caters to MCH patients and their families. It also revamped its in-house radio station that year.

Company Background

Variety Children's Hospital opened in 1950 and became Miami Children's Hospital in 1986.

The hospital first opened its doors in the 1940s as Miami Tent #33 of Variety Clubs International.

EXECUTIVES

Ceo, Narendra M Kini
V Pres, Mario Murgado
SEC, Keith Ward
Treas, Tim M Birkenstock
Sr V Pres, Timothy Birkenstock
Sr V Pres, Jacqueline L Gonzalez
Sr V Pres, Edward Martinez
SEC, Jefry M Biehler
Vp-Cmo, Marcos Mestre
Mgr, Alfredo Guevara
Immunologist, Susan V Benenati

LOCATIONS

HQ: VARIETY CHILDREN'S HOSPITAL
3100 SW 62ND AVE, MIAMI, FL 331553009
Phone: 305 666-6511
Web: WWW.NICKLAUSCHILDRENS.ORG

PRODUCTS/OPERATIONS

Selected Services

Cardiology and Cardiovascular Surgery
Children's Medical Services Primary Care Program
Clinical Research
Dermatology Early Steps Southernmost Coast
Endocrinology & Diabetes
Gastroenterology
Hematology & Oncology
MCH Pediatric Care Center
Neuroscience Center
Neurosurgery
Ophthalmology
Orthopaedics
Otolaryngology Outpatient Centers
Pediatric Advanced Comprehensive Care Team
Pediatric Critical Care Medicine
Pediatric Hospital Medicine Team Pediatric Medicine
Pediatric Surgery & Anesthesiology
Psychiatry & Psychology
Pulmonology
Radiology
Rehabilitation Services
Rheumatology
Urology

Selected Locations

Miami Children's Hospital Dan Marino Center
Miami Children's Hospital Doral Center
Miami Children's Hospital Miami Lakes Rehabilitation Center
Miami Children's Hospital Nicklaus Care Center
Miami Children's Hospital Palmetto Bay Center
Miami Children's Hospital West Kendall Center

COMPETITORS

Adventist Health System Sunbelt Healthcare
All Children's Hospital
Baptist Health South Florida
Children's Hospital of Philadelphia
HCA
Jackson Health System
Mount Sinai Medical Center of Florida
NCH Healthcare
Shriners Hospitals For Children
South Broward Hospital District
South Miami Hospital
UF&Shands
University of Miami
University of Miami Hospital

HISTORICAL FINANCIALS

Company Type: Private

Income Statement FYE: December 31

	REVENUE ($ mil.)	NET INCOME ($ mil.)	NET PROFIT MARGIN	EMPLOYEES
12/19	680	(44)	—	3,700
12/18	655	(23)	—	—
12/17	674	60	9.0%	—
12/16	625	71	11.5%	—
Annual Growth	2.9%	—	—	—

2019 Year-End Financials

Return on assets: (-3.5%)
Return on equity: (-6.5%)
Current ratio: 3.10
Cash ($ mil.): 150

VCC, LLC

EXECUTIVES

Member, Derek Alley
Superintendent, Iulian Trofin
Superintendent, Dennis Haynes
Superintendent, James McClain
Senior Project Manager, Hayden Herring
Graphic Designer, Brent Murray
Staff, Devon Kalkbrenner
Accountant, Jordys Barr
Preconstruction Manager, Andrew Hubbell
Project Superintendent, Joe Leroux
General Superintendent, John Edminson
Auditors: HOGAN TAYLOR LLP LITTLE ROCK

LOCATIONS

HQ: VCC, LLC
1 INFORMATION WAY STE 300, LITTLE ROCK, AR 722022197
Phone: 214 574-4500
Web: WWW.VCCUSA.COM

HISTORICAL FINANCIALS

Company Type: Private

Income Statement FYE: December 31

	REVENUE ($ mil.)	NET INCOME ($ mil.)	NET PROFIT MARGIN	EMPLOYEES
12/19	746	0	—	350
12/18	779	0	—	—
12/17	682	0	—	—
Annual Growth	4.6%	—	—	—

2019 Year-End Financials

Return on assets: —
Return on equity: —
Current ratio: 1.10
Cash ($ mil.): 51

VCU HEALTH SYSTEM AUTHORITY

EXECUTIVES

Ceo, John Duval
Pres, Michael RAO
Cfo-Evp, Dominic J Puleo
Coo, Deborah Davis
Rn, Carol Clark
Physician Assistant, Katherine Vita
Accountant, Lavonne Teagarden
Residency Program Director, Michael Chang
Instructor Radiation Oncology, William C Sleeman
Assistant Professor of Urology, Aaron Krill
Registered Nurse, Adrienne Harris
Auditors: ERNST & YOUNG LLP RICHMOND

LOCATIONS

HQ: VCU HEALTH SYSTEM AUTHORITY
1250 E MARSHALL ST, RICHMOND, VA 232985023
Phone: 804 828-9000
Web: WWW.VCUHEALTH.ORG

HISTORICAL FINANCIALS

Company Type: Private

Income Statement FYE: June 30

	REVENUE ($ mil.)	NET INCOME ($ mil.)	NET PROFIT MARGIN	EMPLOYEES
06/19	3,895	140	3.6%	7,399
06/18	3,399	162	4.8%	—
06/17	3,014	309	10.3%	—
06/05	899	47	5.3%	—
Annual Growth	11.0%	8.0%	—	—

2019 Year-End Financials

Return on assets: 3.6%
Return on equity: 5.5%
Current ratio: 2.20
Cash ($ mil.): 408

VICTORY INTERNATIONAL GROUP, LLC

EXECUTIVES

Pres, Jiansheng Fan
Vice President, Amanda Meng

LOCATIONS

HQ: VICTORY INTERNATIONAL GROUP, LLC
14748 PIPELINE AVE STE B, CHINO HILLS, CA 917096024
Phone: 949 407-5888
Web: WWW.VICTORYINTLGROUP.COM

HISTORICAL FINANCIALS

Company Type: Private

Income Statement FYE: December 31

	REVENUE ($ mil.)	NET INCOME ($ mil.)	NET PROFIT MARGIN	EMPLOYEES
12/15	873	42	4.8%	25
12/07	87	1	1.4%	—
Annual Growth	33.2%	55.5%	—	—

2015 Year-End Financials

Return on assets: 7.3%
Return on equity: 13.2%
Current ratio: 1.80
Cash ($ mil.): 40

VIRGINIA COMMONWEALTH UNIVERSITY

Virginia Commonwealth University (VCU) serves the common interests of its more than 30000 enrolled students. The university offers more than 200 certificate undergraduate graduate and doctoral programs through its 15 schools. Spread across two campuses in Richmond: Monroe Park and Medical College of Virginia (MCV) which includes the Schools of Allied Health Dentistry Medicine Nursing Pharmacy and Public Health. Specialty facilities include the VCU Medical Center and a branch campus of the School of the Arts in Qatar. Founded in 1917 as the Richmond School of Social Work and Public Health in 1968 the school merged with the Medical College of Virginia to form VCU.

EXECUTIVES

Assistant Vice President For Human Resources, Cindy Andrews
Associate Vice President Facilities Management, Brian Ohlinger
Director Provost And Vice President Academic Affairs, Jamie Stillman
Associate Vice President, David Sarrett
Vice President Research And Development Bioinformatics, David Fenstermacher
Provost And Senior Vice President Academic Affairs, Gail Hackett
Associate Vice President Of Patient Care Services, Shirley Gibson
Vice President, James Wasilewski
Assistant Vice President Academic Affairs, Alison Jones
First National Vice President The U. S. Complete, Art Mourino
Vice President Third, Matthew Balazik
Exec. Secretory Meeting Planners, Cathy Howard
Vice President, Bobby Krzyzanowski
Vice President, Joey Bungard
Vice President, Wiley Lori
Vice President Of Engineering, Matthew Schell
Vice Chair, Van Tassell

LOCATIONS

HQ: VIRGINIA COMMONWEALTH UNIVERSITY
912 W FRANKLIN ST, RICHMOND, VA 232849040
Phone: 804 828-0100
Web: WWW.VCU.EDU

HISTORICAL FINANCIALS

Company Type: Private

Income Statement FYE: June 30

	REVENUE ($ mil.)	NET INCOME ($ mil.)	NET PROFIT MARGIN	EMPLOYEES
06/18	763	12	1.7%	11,000
06/17	760	84	11.1%	—
06/16	737	37	5.1%	—
06/11	2,319	328	14.2%	—
Annual Growth	(14.7%)	(37.1%)	—	—

2018 Year-End Financials

Return on assets: 0.7%
Return on equity: 1.8%
Current ratio: 1.80
Cash ($ mil.): 65

VIRGINIA DEPARTMENT OF TRANSPORTATION

EXECUTIVES

Commissioner, C Kilpatrick
Commissioner*, Charles A Kilpatrick
Assistant Secretary*, Amy Wight
Acting Deputy SEC*, John W Lawson
Payroll Staff, Carol Clatterbaugh
Accounting Staff, Lu Lutero
Business Analyst, Liliya Fedzhora
Safety Manager, Billie Miller
Engineering Manager, Jeff Wyatt
Quality Assurance Manager, Robert Liberatore
Environmental Policy Analyst, Angel Aymond

LOCATIONS

HQ: VIRGINIA DEPARTMENT OF TRANSPORTATION
1401 E BROAD ST, RICHMOND, VA 232192052
Phone: 804 786-2701
Web: WWW.VIRGINIADOT.ORG

HISTORICAL FINANCIALS

Company Type: Private

Income Statement — FYE: June 30

	REVENUE ($ mil.)	NET INCOME ($ mil.)	NET PROFIT MARGIN	EMPLOYEES
06/10	3,240	473	14.6%	10,737
06/06	3,047	410	13.5%	—
06/05	0	0	—	—
06/04	2,857	56	2.0%	—
Annual Growth	2.1%	42.7%	—	—

2010 Year-End Financials

Return on assets: 2.3%
Return on equity: 2.7%
Current ratio: —
Cash ($ mil.): 2,013

VIRGINIA HOUSING DEVELOPMENT AUTHORITY

Though Virginia is famous for its Civil War-era plantations these historic estates represent a lifestyle out of reach for most. For Virginians seeking a more modest homestead there's the Virginia Housing Development Authority (VHDA). The not-for-profit quasi-government agency founded by the Virginia General Assembly in 1972 provides developers of rental properties and low- to moderate-income borrowers with low interest rate loans to renovate or purchase houses and apartments across the state. Its loan products are offered by more than 140 authorized lenders throughout Virginia. The VHDA is self-supporting issuing bonds to raise capital.

EXECUTIVES

Executive Director, Susan F. Dewey
Managing Director Rental Housing, Arthur N. (Art) Bowen
Managing Director Community Outreach, J. Michael Hawkins
Managing Director Executive Services, Llewellyn C. Anderson
Managing Director Homeownership, Janet Wiglesworth
Managing Director Internal Audit And Risk Management, Julie Camus
Managing Director Finance, Pat Carey
Acting Managing Director Information Technology Services, J. Kyle Howard
Vice President Of Operation, Jackie Gibbs
Vice President Of Operation, Sherry Estridge
Executive Vice President Claims And Customer Service Operations, Dyson Darrell
Chairman, Timothy M. Chapman
Vice Chairman, Sarah B. Stedfast
Treasurer, Gary Murray
Auditors: KPMG LLP RICHMOND VIRGINIA

LOCATIONS

HQ: VIRGINIA HOUSING DEVELOPMENT AUTHORITY
601 S BELVIDERE ST, RICHMOND, VA 232206504
Phone: 804 780-0789
Web: WWW.VHDA.COM

HISTORICAL FINANCIALS

Company Type: Private

Income Statement — FYE: June 30

	ASSETS ($ mil.)	NET INCOME ($ mil.)	INCOME AS % OF ASSETS	EMPLOYEES
06/18	7,292	132	1.8%	300
06/16	8,024	171	2.1%	—
06/15	8,070	176	2.2%	—
06/14	8,014	132	1.7%	—
Annual Growth	(2.3%)	(0.1%)	—	—

2018 Year-End Financials

Return on assets: 1.8%
Return on equity: 4.0%
Sales ($ mil): 505

VIRGINIA MASON MEDICAL CENTER

EXECUTIVES

Pres, James Young
V Pres*, James Orlikoff
Treas*, Robert Lemon
SEC*, Dorothy Mann
Chb-Ceo*, Gary S Kaplan
Sr V Pres-Cio-Cfo*, Suzanne Anderson
Pres*, Carolyn Corvi
Physician, Anthony Gerbino
Hospitalist Internal Medicine, Barry Aaronson
Managing Director, Bruce Nitsche
Supervisor, Carolyn Smalley
Auditors: KPMG LLP SEATTLE WA

LOCATIONS

HQ: VIRGINIA MASON MEDICAL CENTER
1100 9TH AVE, SEATTLE, WA 981012756
Phone: 206 223-6600
Web: WWW.VIRGINIAMASON.ORG

HISTORICAL FINANCIALS

Company Type: Private

Income Statement — FYE: December 31

	REVENUE ($ mil.)	NET INCOME ($ mil.)	NET PROFIT MARGIN	EMPLOYEES
12/19*	1,156	29	2.5%	5,000
03/19	274	10	4.0%	—
12/18	1,101	(16)	—	—
12/17	1,025	33	3.2%	—
Annual Growth	6.2%	(6.2%)	—	—

*Fiscal year change

2019 Year-End Financials

Return on assets: 2.3%
Return on equity: 5.6%
Current ratio: 1.50
Cash ($ mil.): 73

VIRGINIA POLYTECHNIC INSTITUTE & STATE UNIVERSITY

Virginia Polytechnic Institute and State University more commonly known as Virginia Tech is the state's largest university enrolling 34440 students. The university offers 280 undergraduate graduate and professional degree programs through nine academic colleges. It has a student-teacher ratio of 14 to 1. The school's most popular majors include agriculture architecture business journalism and computer and information sciences. Virginia Tech which was formed in 1872 serves the surrounding community through outreach and education programs.

Operations

Virginia charges more than $23000 tuition and fees for in-state undergraduates and more than $42175 tuition and fees for out-of-state undergraduates.

Virginia Tech manages a research portfolio of more than $530 million. It has Graduate School Virginia-Maryland College of Veterinary Medicine Virginia Tech Carilion School of Medicine Honors College

Geographic Reach

Virginia Tech has nearly 215 campus buildings a 2600-acre main campus in Blacksburg off-campus educational facilities in Alexandria Arlington Falls Church Leesburg Manassas and Middleburg and a study-abroad site in Switzerland.

Company Background

Virginia Tech was founded as a land-grant college in 1872.

EXECUTIVES

Svp And Provost, Mark G. McNamee
Vp Finance And Cfo, M. Dwight Shelton
Vp And Dean Graduate Education, Karen P. DePauw
Ceo Virginia Tech Foundation, John E. Dooley
Dean Pamplin College Of Business, Robert T. Sumichrast
Dean Virginia-maryland College Of Veterinary Medicine, Cyril Clarke
President, Timothy D. (Tim) Sands
Vp Information Technology And Cio, Scott F. Midkiff
Dean College Of Agriculture And Life Sciences, Alan Grant
Dean College Of Architecture And Urban Studies, A. Jack Davis
Dean College Of Engineering, Richard Benson
Dean College Of Liberal Arts And Human Sciences, Elizabeth Spiller
Dean College Of Natural Resources And Environment, Paul M. Winistorfer
Dean College Of Science, Lay Nam Chang
Dean University Libraries, Tyler O. Walters
Associate Vice President For Research Computing Director Interdisciplinary Center For Applied Mathematics Professor Mathematics, Terry Herdman
Associate Vice President For Engagement, Susan Short
Associate Vice President Human Resources, Hal Irvin
Department Head, Mark Pitt
Vice President, Adrienne Weber
Associate Vice President For Advancement Services, Rhonda Arsenault
Associate Vice President, Richard Beatty

County Vice President, Megan Seibel
Associate Chair Department Of English Associate Professor Of English, Kelly Pender
Vice President For Advancement, Charles Phlegar
Vice President Practice Administration, Christopher Null Reilly
Department Chair, Dave Gerrard
Vice President, Virginia Tech
Undergraduate Student Virginia Tech Triathlon Team Vice President Phi Sigma International Treasurer And Icr, Greg Pfister
Deputy To Interim Vice President For Human Resources Email, Kim Akers
Virginia Tech Senior Associate Vice President, Tracy Vosburgh
English Department Chair, Johan Norstedt
Vice President Corporate Relations I Pamplin Leadership Development Team Treasurer I Block And Bridle Club, Emma Saunders
Department Head, Eric Smith
Associate Vice President For Research Partnerships, Gary Sherman
Associate Vice President For Information Systems And Computing, Patricia Jackson
Executive Vice President And Provost, Shannon Harvey
Associate Vice President For Principal Gifts, Monecia Taylor
Assistant Vice President For Leadership Gifts And Annual Giving, John Torget
Vice Presidenti, Virgil Cook
Senior Vice President And General Manager, Marion Devoe
Professor And Vice President For Research And Innovation, Theresa Mayer
Vice President, Michael Cirbee
Vice President Class, Luvie Abell
Vice President, Gavin Kline
Vice President Financial Planning And Analysis, Paul Atwood
Department Head, W Holbrook
Vice President, Anjali Shingala
Senior Vp, Dave Guido
Vice Chair For Education, John Ferrara
Board Member, Patrick Lowther
Treasurer, Phil Meeks
Secretary External Affairs Athletics, Jean Ann Bailey
Treasurer, Steven Brodnik
Secretary, Arielle Katherine McNally
Executive Board Member, Hannah Stratton
Secretary, Jessica Lyons
Alumni Secretary, Elijah Rinaldi
Treasurer Human Powered Submarine Team, Christine Bodenheimer
Recording Secretary, Carolyn Mottley
Treasurer, Evan Miller
Treasurer, Kaitlyn Revercomb
Treasurer, Michael Brennan
Recording Secretary, Juliana Kreuscher
Treasurer, Matthew Anama
Secretary, Andy Taminger
Auditors: COMMONWEALTH OF VIRGINIA AUDIT

LOCATIONS

HQ: VIRGINIA POLYTECHNIC INSTITUTE & STATE UNIVERSITY
300 TURNER ST NW STE 4200, BLACKSBURG, VA 240616100
Phone: 540 323-1528
Web: WWW.VT.EDU

PRODUCTS/OPERATIONS

Selected Colleges
College of Agriculture and Life Sciences
College Architecture and Urban Studies
College of Engineering
College of Liberal Arts and Human Sciences
College of Natural Resources and Environment
College of Science
Pamplin College of Business
Virginia-Maryland Regional College of Veterinary Medicine

HISTORICAL FINANCIALS

Company Type: Private

Income Statement — FYE: June 30

	REVENUE ($ mil.)	NET INCOME ($ mil.)	NET PROFIT MARGIN	EMPLOYEES
06/19	1,160	130	11.2%	6,866
06/18	1,279	181	14.2%	—
06/17	1,031	64	6.2%	—
06/16	1,020	121	11.9%	—
Annual Growth	4.4%	2.4%	—	—

2019 Year-End Financials

Return on assets: 4.6%
Return on equity: 9.4%
Current ratio: 0.90
Cash ($ mil.): 177

VIRGINIA PREMIER HEALTH PLAN, INC.

EXECUTIVES

Ceo, Linda Hines
Transportation Manager, Randy Ledien
Director of Government Relatio, Blair Hedgepeth
Talent Acquisition Specialist, Jasmine Lewis
Director, Kenneth Hepler
Supervisor, Amy Feathers
Project Management, Ana Dunn
Talent Acquisition Supervisor, Brittany Woolfolk
Business Analyst II, Courtney Eliot
Compliance Analyst I, Dustin Harrel
Vice President, Elizabeth Veliz
Auditors: KPMG LLP MC LEAN VA

LOCATIONS

HQ: VIRGINIA PREMIER HEALTH PLAN, INC.
600 E BROAD ST STE 400, RICHMOND, VA 232191800
Phone: 804 819-5164
Web: WWW.VIRGINIAPREMIER.COM

HISTORICAL FINANCIALS

Company Type: Private

Income Statement — FYE: June 30

	REVENUE ($ mil.)	NET INCOME ($ mil.)	NET PROFIT MARGIN	EMPLOYEES
06/19	1,730	(51)	—	165
06/18	1,372	(14)	—	—
06/15	969	(0)	—	—
06/14	749	14	1.9%	—
Annual Growth	18.2%	—	—	—

2019 Year-End Financials

Return on assets: (-11.0%)
Return on equity: (-55.7%)
Current ratio: 1.20
Cash ($ mil.): 36

VIRGINIA WEST UNIVERSITY HOSPITALS INC

West Virginia University Hospitals (WVUH) has West Virginians covered. The health care system's 530-bed main campus includes the Ruby Memorial Hospital the WVU Children's Hospital and the behavioral health Chestnut Ridge Center as well as outpatient care centers. Other services include centers for eye and dental care cancer treatment and family medicine. WVUH's facilities serve as the primary teaching locations for the West Virginia University's health professions schools. Cheat Lake Physicians is the physicians group associated with the health system. WVUH is a member of the West Virginia United Health System.

Strategy

To increase its capacity for patient services WVUH launched a $230 million project to build a new tower addition at its main Ruby Memorial Hospital facility in 2012. The project will add about 115 general inpatient beds.

WVUH is also working to expand its community outreach capabilities and lower the cost of inpatient care through technology initiatives. The health system is adding a number of tele-health services including psychiatry and stroke programs that allow patients to communicate with doctors via video conferencing systems. These services especially help residents living in rural settings.

EXECUTIVES

Department Chair School Of Public Health, Snehalata Huzurbazar
Secretary, Star Hammond

LOCATIONS

HQ: VIRGINIA WEST UNIVERSITY HOSPITALS INC
1 MEDICAL CENTER DR, MORGANTOWN, WV 265061200
Phone: 304 598-4000
Web: WWW.WVUH.TESTCATALOG.ORG

COMPETITORS

CAMC Health
HCA
West Penn Allegheny Health System

HISTORICAL FINANCIALS

Company Type: Private

Income Statement — FYE: December 31

	REVENUE ($ mil.)	NET INCOME ($ mil.)	NET PROFIT MARGIN	EMPLOYEES
12/18	1,193	(39)	—	6,267
12/12	1,386	96	6.9%	—
12/06	0	0	—	—
Annual Growth	—	—	—	—

2018 Year-End Financials

Return on assets: (-2.3%)
Return on equity: (-5.4%)
Current ratio: 2.50
Cash ($ mil.): 21

VIRTU FINANCIAL LLC

Auditors: DELOITTE & TOUCHE LLP NEW YOR

LOCATIONS

HQ: VIRTU FINANCIAL LLC
1 LIBERTY PLZ, NEW YORK, NY 100061404
Phone: 212 418-0100
Web: WWW.VIRTU.COM

HISTORICAL FINANCIALS

Company Type: Private

Income Statement — FYE: December 31

	ASSETS ($ mil.)	NET INCOME ($ mil.)	INCOME AS % OF ASSETS	EMPLOYEES
12/14	3,324	190	5.7%	18
12/13	3,963	182	4.6%	—
Annual Growth	(16.1%)	4.3%	—	—

2014 Year-End Financials

Return on assets: 5.7%
Return on equity: 89.5%
Sales ($ mil): 723

VIRTUA-WEST JERSEY HEALTH SYSTEM, INC.

EXECUTIVES

Pres-Ceo, Richard Miller
Chm*, Dennis Flanagan
Cfo*, Robert Segin
Treas*, David Kindlick
SEC*, Edward Cloues
Coordinator, Monica Fiorini
Staff, Beverly Crawford
Coordinator, Leha Anderson
Coordinator, Joanne Sebastiano
Scheduler, Sue Obrien
Nurse, Tanya Jones

LOCATIONS

HQ: VIRTUA-WEST JERSEY HEALTH SYSTEM, INC.
1000 ATLANTIC AVE, CAMDEN, NJ 081041132
Phone: 856 246-3000
Web: WWW.VIRTUA.ORG

HISTORICAL FINANCIALS

Company Type: Private

Income Statement — FYE: December 31

	REVENUE ($ mil.)	NET INCOME ($ mil.)	NET PROFIT MARGIN	EMPLOYEES
12/17	919	207	22.6%	4,100
12/04	399	29	7.4%	—
12/03	354	6	1.8%	—
12/02	346	7	2.2%	—
Annual Growth	6.7%	24.6%	—	—

2017 Year-End Financials

Return on assets: 9.7%
Return on equity: 16.1%
Current ratio: 0.20
Cash ($ mil.): 68

VITALANT

Vitalant (formerly Blood Systems) collects blood and provides blood products and services to nearly 1000 hospitals in about 40 states. One of the largest US not-for-profit blood service companies Vitalant operates more than 125 donation centers and conducts more than 30000 mobile blood drives each year. The company's BioCare division distributes plasma derivative products used in medical procedures while Vitalant Research Institute conducts blood-related research studies. Vitalant also provides blood donor testing services through its Creative Testing Solutions (CTS) venture (owned with American Red Cross and OneBlood).

Operations

Its Vitalant Research Institute is engaged in scientific studies ranging from blood donor epidemiology to cellular therapy to virus discovery. Vitalant is a partner in the operation of Creative Testing Solutions a blood donor testing organization. Its BioCare solutions has wide-reaching distribution capabilities to deliver therapeutic biologicals such as albumin coagulation factors and Rh immune globulin. CanyonCARE Rx part of BioCare is a full service pharmacy specializing in medications for hemophilia von Willebrand disease and other bleeding disorders. The organization is self-insured with its wholly-owned subsidiary Canyon State Insurance.

Geographic Reach

Vitalant has locations in Arizona California Colorado Illinois Montana New Jersey Nevada Ohio Pennsylvania South Dakota Tennessee and in Washington among others.

Sales and Marketing

Vitalant provides services to facilities ranging from major medical centers in the largest urban areas to community hospitals in remote rural areas also to clinics and physician offices.

Strategy

Vitalant widens its geographic reach by acquiring smaller donation center networks and by entering new hospital and group purchasing organization (GPO) service contracts in strategic markets. It has doubled the size of its network and extended its operations across the US over the past decade.

The company is expanding in transfusion medicine by researching cellular therapy molecular biology immunology virus discovery and donor epidemiology through its Vitalant Research Institute. One division of the institute is working to develop novel transfusion methodologies and therapeutics; another unit works to reduce transfusion-transmitted diseases. Vitalant is also growing the range of biological products and specialty medications (for bleeding disorders) offered through its BioCare division.

The company changed its name from Blood Systems to Vitalant in 2018 to unify its operating divisions (10 blood-center brands research institute and specialty laboratory) under one brand. Former blood-center brands now operating as Vitalant include BloodSource LifeShare LifeSource United Blood Services and Blood Centers of the Pacific.

Company Background

The company which was founded in 1943 as the Salt River Valley Blood Bank is governed by a voluntary board of directors consisting of community and medical industry leaders.

Acquisitions of blood bank chains have included BloodSource and Lifeblood (both completed in 2015).

In 2018 Blood Systems changed its name to Vitalant and rebranded all of its blood center brands under the Vitalant name.

EXECUTIVES

Evp And General Counsel, Scott M. Nelson
Executive Vice President Chief Financial Officer, Susan L. Barnes
Evp And Chief Quality Officer, Mary Beth Bassett
Evp Business Services, Patrick Holt
President Chief Executive Officer, Daniel Connor
Executive Vice President Chief Medical & Scientific Officer, Ralph R. Vassallo
Medical Director, Hany Kamel
Auditors: GRANT THORNTON LLP PHOENIX A

LOCATIONS

HQ: VITALANT
6210 E OAK ST, SCOTTSDALE, AZ 852571101
Phone: 602 414-3819
Web: WWW.BLOODSYSTEMS.ORG

PRODUCTS/OPERATIONS

2013 Sales

	$ mil.	% of total
Blood component service fees	323	44
Laboratory testing services	208	28
Sales of pharmaceutical products	174	23
Other services & income	37	5
Total	**743**	**100**

Selected Services

Blood Centers
- Blood Components
- Component Therapy
- Commonly Ordered Derivatives
- Modified Blood Components

Laboratory Services
- Donor Counseling
- Histocompatibility Laboratory (HLA)
- Immunohematology Reference Laboratory (IRL)

Special Collections
- Directed Donation
- Perioperative Blood Salvage
- Pre-operative Autologous Donation (PAD)
- Stem Cell Processing
- Therapeutic (Clinical) Apheresis

Transfusion Medicine
- Blood Management Services
- Compatibility Services

COMPETITORS

CSL
Daxor
FFF Enterprises
Grifols Inc.
HemaCare
New York Blood Center
Puget Sound Blood Center
Red Cross
SeraCare Life Sciences

HISTORICAL FINANCIALS

Company Type: Private

Income Statement — FYE: December 31

	REVENUE ($ mil.)	NET INCOME ($ mil.)	NET PROFIT MARGIN	EMPLOYEES
12/16	1,129	1	0.1%	500
12/15	966	2	0.3%	—
12/14	0	(62)	—	—
12/13	743	65	8.8%	—
Annual Growth	15.0%	(71.6%)	—	—

2016 Year-End Financials

Return on assets: 0.2%
Return on equity: 0.4%
Current ratio: 2.60
Cash ($ mil.): 49

VIZIO, INC.

VIZIO is known for its sticker-friendly flat panel plasma LCD HDTVs and TV Brand with Quantum

Dot5. The company also makes and sells Blue-Ray players sound bars and speakers headphones Internet routers PCs and other consumer electronics through retailers and resellers across America. Sourcing its products from China and Taiwan VIZIO sells many of its low-priced electronics through top discount chains including Amazon Best Buy Costco Wholesale Sam's Club Target and Walmart. Thanks to its low prices VIZIO ranked as the #1 American-based TV brand3 and #1 Sound Bar Brand4 in America. In 2019 the company announced the launch of 10 Spanish-speaking channels for its millions of SmartCast viewers across America.

Operations

The company designs a collection of televisions sound bars and the SmartCast smart TV platform with the consumer's desires in mind and has been rated America's Fastest Growing TV Brand with Quantum Dot5 and America's Fastest Growing Sound Bar Brand with Dolby Atmos6. In addition it offers remote controls and built-in bluetooth for streaming music wirelessly.

The company is partnered with Inscape and generates more comprehensive TV viewing data and helps companies gain a deeper and more accurate understanding of their audience.

Geographic Reach

Irvine California-based VIZIO sells its products across North America.

It has office locations across the United States in Dakota Dunes Dallas Denver Seattle San Francisco and other states.

Sales and Marketing

VIZIO offers other businesses to showcase contents or applications in Vizio platform.

Strategy

The company continuously participates in partnerships to expand its offerings.

In late 2020 VIZIO Inc. announced that customers in the US and Canada can now access the Apple TV app on SmartCast TVs to enjoy Apple TV+ Apple TV channels new and popular movies and personalized and curated recommendations. Earlier that year the company announced that Disney+ has been made available directly on SmartCast expanding entertainment options accessible through the platform.

In January the company teamed up with FOX Deportes as an official sponsor of NFLeros as the network makes the most-watched game in football available to Spanish-speaking audiences.

Company Background

The company was founded by William Wang in 2002 and initially sold its TVs at membership retailers such as Costco Wholesale BJ's Wholesale Club and Sam's Club. It then extended its reach to discount retailers Wal-Mart and Sears.

The TV maker entered the market for smart TVs which are integrated with i nternet functionality when it shipped its first model during the second half of 2011.

VIZIO entered the PC market in mid-2012 with a new line of laptops and desktops starting at about $890. By combining its entertainment know-how with the power of the latest Intel Core processors VIZIO hopes to set a new standard for the Windows experience. The line consists of the VIZIO Thin + Light Notebook and All-in-One PC.

EXECUTIVES

Ceo, William Wang
Cfo, Kurt Binder
Vice President Sales And Marketing, Laynie Newsome
Vice President Engineering, Marcus Apitz
Vice President Of Support, Scott Patten
Vice President Direct Sales, Michelle Nguyen
Vice President Of Information, Derrick Beard
Vice President Sales, Hernandez Paul
Chief Sales Officer, Randy Waynick
Senior Vice President, Francis Ahn
National Account Manager, Erin Thompson
National Account Manager, Mark Sevier
Svp Finance And Accounting, Evan Kloch

LOCATIONS

HQ: VIZIO, INC.
39 TESLA, IRVINE, CA 926184603
Phone: 855 833-3221
Web: WWW.VIZIO.COM

PRODUCTS/OPERATIONS

Selected Products

Cables and other accessories
Blue-ray disc players
HDTVs
HD home theater systems
Headphones
Internet routers
Personal computers
Tablet computers
Smartphones
Speakers

COMPETITORS

Acer
Bose
Dell
Funai Electric
Harman International
Hewlett-Packard Limited
Koss
LG Electronics
Lenovo
Panasonic Corp
Philips Electronics
Pioneer Corporation
Samsung Electronics
Sony
Westinghouse

HISTORICAL FINANCIALS

Company Type: Private

Income Statement — FYE: December 31

	REVENUE ($ mil.)	NET INCOME ($ mil.)	NET PROFIT MARGIN	EMPLOYEES
12/08	2,006	10	0.5%	225
12/07	1,929	7	0.4%	—
12/06	671	1	0.2%	—
12/04	46	0	1.0%	—
Annual Growth	155.8%	115.7%	—	—

2008 Year-End Financials

Return on assets: 3.2%
Return on equity: 0.5%
Current ratio: 0.90
Cash ($ mil.): 42

VNS CHOICE

EXECUTIVES

Prin, Mark Flannery
Clinical Field Manager, Alicia Gagne-Giuffo
Geriatric Nurse Practitioner, Barbara Atkins
Manager, Chantal Louisma
Manager, Christine Wynter
Manager, James Balchunas
Clinical Care Manager, Kathleen Petrullo
Adminsitrative Assistant, Laron Foster
Director Compensation, Leslie Dorman
Clinical Director Queens, Maryam Gaibi
Supervisor, Michelle Sosa-Richards
Auditors: KPMG LLP HARTFORD CT

LOCATIONS

HQ: VNS CHOICE
220 E 42ND ST FL 3, NEW YORK, NY 100175806
Phone: 212 609-7235
Web: WWW.VNSNYCHOICE.ORG

HISTORICAL FINANCIALS

Company Type: Private

Income Statement — FYE: December 31

	REVENUE ($ mil.)	NET INCOME ($ mil.)	NET PROFIT MARGIN	EMPLOYEES
12/14	1,388	(72)	—	651
12/13	1,299	(90)	—	—
12/09	419	4	1.0%	—
Annual Growth	27.0%	—	—	—

2014 Year-End Financials

Return on assets: (-18.0%)
Return on equity: —
Current ratio: —
Cash ($ mil.): 1

WABASH VALLEY POWER ASSOCIATION INC

EXECUTIVES

Exec Dir-Ceo, Rick Coons
Cfo*, Jeffrey A Conrad
V Pres*, Katherine A Joyce
V Pres*, Curtis E Taylor
V Pres*, M Keith Thompson
Administrative Assistant, Stephanie Sohn
Controller, Theresay Young
Accounting, Denise Sewell
Manager, Drew Dalton
Vice President Member, Kathy Joyce
Human Resources Specialist, Kim Coons
Auditors: DELOITTE & TOUCHE LLP INDIANA

LOCATIONS

HQ: WABASH VALLEY POWER ASSOCIATION INC
6702 INTECH BLVD, INDIANAPOLIS, IN 462782008
Phone: 317 481-2800
Web: WWW.WVPA.COM

HISTORICAL FINANCIALS

Company Type: Private

Income Statement — FYE: December 31

	REVENUE ($ mil.)	NET INCOME ($ mil.)	NET PROFIT MARGIN	EMPLOYEES
12/19	645	25	3.9%	65
12/18	654	24	3.7%	—
12/17	702	19	2.7%	—
12/16	707	21	3.0%	—
Annual Growth	(3.0%)	6.0%	—	—

2019 Year-End Financials

Return on assets: 2.1%
Return on equity: 10.4%
Current ratio: 2.70
Cash ($ mil.): 80

WAKE COUNTY PUBLIC SCHOOL SYSTEM

LOCATIONS

HQ: WAKE COUNTY PUBLIC SCHOOL SYSTEM
5625 DILLARD DR, CARY, NC 275189226
Phone: 919 431-7343
Web: WWW.WCPSS.NET

HISTORICAL FINANCIALS

Company Type: Private

Income Statement FYE: June 30

	REVENUE ($ mil.)	NET INCOME ($ mil.)	NET PROFIT MARGIN	EMPLOYEES
06/10	1,224	13	1.1%	17,000
06/09	1,425	(7)	—	—
06/08	1,374	(1)	—	—
Annual Growth	(5.6%)	—	—	—

2010 Year-End Financials

Return on assets: 0.5%
Return on equity: 0.5%
Current ratio: 1.40
Cash ($ mil.): 91

WAKEFERN FOOD CORP.

Wakefern Food Corp. is the largest retailer-owned cooperative in the nation with its nearly 50 members owning some 355 supermarkets across the northeastern US. The cooperative offers some $10 billion in purchasing power and provides a host of support services including private label brand development development store layout and design and advertising and marketing as well as technology finance and human resources services. The members' stores operate under the ShopRite The Fresh Grocer Price Rite Marketplace Gourmet Garage and Dearborn Market banners. Wakefern also provides merchandise and services to non-member customers through its wholesale division. It was founded by eight grocers in 1946.

Operations

Wakefern operates its wholesale business with integrity focusing on and consistently meeting the unique needs of its retail customers. From supplying produce and frozen foods to meats and dairy Wakefern is continuously scaling its business and emphasizing teamwork to provide outstanding services. In addition to a milk processing and distribution facility and a seafood processing plant wholesale customers can benefit from a wide range of capabilities offered through Wakefern including transportation quality assurance category management technical support financial support development and store development.

The cooperative's unique brand offerings include Wholesome Pantry Bowl & Basket and Paperbird.

Geographic Reach

Based in Keasbey New Jersey Wakefern's member retailers own and operate about 355 grocery stores across the northeastern US. Markets include Connecticut Delaware Maryland Massachusetts New Jersey New York Pennsylvania Rhode Island and Virginia.

Sales and Marketing

With more than 70000 associates Wakefern's ShopRite serves approximately 7 million customers each week with unprecedented variety and customer service.

Strategy

Wakefern Food Corp. in November announced that Madison Foods a third-generation family grocery business has joined the Wakefern cooperative with plans to convert three Save A Lot stores to Price Rite Marketplace stores in Massachusetts.

Owned and operated by the Slawsby family Madison Foods is a successful local business in the Boston area. The family company will begin converting their Save A Lot stores to Price Rite Marketplace ? a registered trademark and banner of Wakefern Food Corp.

The new Price Rite Marketplace locations will also offer several Wakefern Own Brand products including the new popular Bowl & Basket and Paperbird lines. Shoppers will also be able to purchase Wakefern's award-winning Wholesome Pantry brands which include the Wholesome Pantry Organic line as well as a range of products free from artificial additives and preservatives.

Technology to improve internal efficiency as well as customer experience is also a key element of Wakefern's strategy. In mid-2020 the cooperative partnered with Solutions for Retail Brands (S4RB) a global consulting-led software business to provide new information sharing software for Wakefern and its Own Brand vendors.

S4RB's Affinity platform for Wakefern will allow the retailer to use a proprietary online portal and database to provide real-time data and analytics enabling Wakefern to collaborate with new and existing vendor partners and continue to grow its Own Brand portfolio. The platform will integrate with existing Wakefern systems through all stages of its private brand process from development and launch of new products to product sales and post-purchase review.

Company Background

In 1946 in an effort to assist struggling independent grocers a sales representative from Del Monte Foods introduced cooperative buying to eight independent grocers from Newark New Jersey. By the end of that year each grocer having invested $1000 Wakefern Food Corp. was officially founded.

HISTORY

Wakefern Food was founded in 1946 by seven New York- and New Jersey-based grocers: Louis Weiss Sam and Al Aidekman Abe Kesselman Dave Fern Sam Garb and Albert Goldberg. The company got its name by taking the first letters of the last names of five of the original founders (Weiss Sam and Al Aidekman Kesselman and Fern). Like many cooperatives the association sought to lower costs by increasing its buying power as a group.

They each put in $1000 and began operating a 5000-sq.-ft. warehouse often putting in double time to keep both their stores and the warehouse running. The shopkeepers' collective buying power proved valuable enabling the grocers to stock many items at the same prices as their larger competitors.

In 1951 Wakefern members began pooling their resources to buy advertising space. A common store name — ShopRite — was chosen and each week co-op members met to decide which items would be sale priced. Within a year membership had grown to over 50. Expansion became a priority and in the mid-1950s co-op members united in small groups to take over failed supermarkets. One such group called the Supermarkets Operating Co. (SOC) was formed in 1956. Within 10 years it had acquired a number of failed stores remodeled them and given them the ShopRite name.

During the late 1950s sales at ShopRite stores slumped after Wakefern decided to buck the supermarket trend of offering trading stamps (which could then be exchanged for gifts) figuring that offering the stamps would ultimately lead to higher food prices. The move initially drove away customers but Wakefern cut grocery prices across the board and sales returned. The company did embrace another supermarket trend: stocking stores with nonfood items.

The co-op was severely shaken in 1966 when SOC merged with General Supermarkets a similar small group within Wakefern becoming Supermarkets General Corp. (SGC). SGC was a powerful entity with 71 supermarkets 10 drugstores six gas stations a wholesale bakery and a discount department store. Many Wakefern members opposed the merger and attempted to block the action with a court order. By 1968 SGC had beefed up its operations to include department store chains as well as its grocery stores. In a move that threatened to break Wakefern SGC broke away from the co-op and its stores were renamed Pathmark.

Wakefern not only weathered the storm it grew under the direction of chairman and CEO Thomas Infusino elected shortly after the split. The co-op focused on asserting its position as a seller of low-priced products. Wakefern developed private-label brands including the ShopRite brand. In the 1980s members began operating larger stores and adding more nonfood items to the ShopRite product mix. With its number of superstores on the rise and facing increased competition from club stores in 1992 Wakefern opened a centralized nonfood distribution center in New Jersey.

In 1995 30-year Wakefern veteran Dean Janeway was elected president of the co-op. The company debuted its ShopRite MasterCard co-branded with New Jersey's Valley National Bank in 1996. The following year the co-op purchased two of its customers' stores in Pennsylvania then threatened to close them when contract talks with the local union deteriorated. In 1998 Wakefern settled the dispute then sold the stores.

The company partnered with Internet bidding site Priceline in 1999 offering customers an opportunity to bid on groceries and then pick them up at ShopRite stores. Big V Wakefern's biggest customer filed for Chapter 11 bankruptcy protection in 2000 and said it was ending its distribution agreement with the co-op. In July 2002 however Wakefern's ShopRite Supermarkets subsidiary acquired all of Big V's assets for approximately $185 million in cash and assumed liabilities.

Infusino retired in May 2005 after 35 years with Wakefern Food. He was succeeded by former vice chairman Joseph Colalillo. The cooperative added to its footprint in 2007 when it acquired about 10 underperforming retail locations from Stop & Shop. The stores located mostly in South Jersey were rebranded under the ShopRite banner.

EXECUTIVES

Vice President Pharmacy, Jeffrey Mondelli
Vice President Quality Assurance Food Safety, Michael Ambrosio
Auditors: KPMG LLP SHORT HILLS NJ

LOCATIONS

HQ: WAKEFERN FOOD CORP.
5000 RIVERSIDE DR, KEASBEY, NJ 088321209
Phone: 908 527-3300
Web: WWW.WAKEFERN.COM

COMPETITORS

A&P
Acme Markets
Bozzuto's
C&S Wholesale
CVS
Hannaford Bros.
IGA
Krasdale Foods
SUPERVALU
Stop & Shop
Wal-Mart
Wawa Inc.

HISTORICAL FINANCIALS

Company Type: Private

Income Statement — FYE: September 27

	REVENUE ($ mil.)	NET INCOME ($ mil.)	NET PROFIT MARGIN	EMPLOYEES
09/14	11,871	5	0.0%	3,500
09/13	11,455	0	0.0%	—
09/12	11,010	5	0.0%	—
Annual Growth	3.8%	(0.0%)	—	—

2014 Year-End Financials

Return on assets: 0.3%
Return on equity: 2.7%
Current ratio: 0.80
Cash ($ mil.): 128

WALSH CONSTRUCTION COMPANY

EXECUTIVES

Chb-Ceo, Matthew M Walsh
Pres*, Daniel J Walsh
Project Administrator, Diane Mitchell
Quality Director, Martin Houston
Assistant Project Manager, Grife Mariah
Auditors: WOLF & COMPANY LLP OAKBROOK

LOCATIONS

HQ: WALSH CONSTRUCTION COMPANY
929 W ADAMS ST, CHICAGO, IL 606073021
Phone: 312 563-5400
Web: WWW.WALSHCONSTRUCTION.COM

HISTORICAL FINANCIALS

Company Type: Private

Income Statement — FYE: December 31

	REVENUE ($ mil.)	NET INCOME ($ mil.)	NET PROFIT MARGIN	EMPLOYEES
12/10	1,627	35	2.2%	3,000
12/09	1,711	56	3.3%	—
12/08	1,847	68	3.7%	—
Annual Growth	(6.2%)	(27.7%)	—	—

2010 Year-End Financials

Return on assets: 4.7%
Return on equity: 14.1%
Current ratio: 1.50
Cash ($ mil.): 281

WALTON CONSTRUCTION - A CORE COMPANY, LLC

EXECUTIVES

Mng MBR, James K Jacobs
Director, Joshua Bentley
Executive Vice President, Brad Roberts
Chief Administrative Officer, Tom Budde

LOCATIONS

HQ: WALTON CONSTRUCTION - A CORE COMPANY, LLC
2 COMMERCE CT, NEW ORLEANS, LA 701233225
Phone: 504 733-2212
Web: WWW.CORECONSTRUCTION.COM

HISTORICAL FINANCIALS

Company Type: Private

Income Statement — FYE: December 31

	REVENUE ($ mil.)	NET INCOME ($ mil.)	NET PROFIT MARGIN	EMPLOYEES
12/08	695	0	—	700
12/07	626	0	—	—
12/06	0	0	—	—
12/05	0	0	—	—
Annual Growth	—	—	—	—

2008 Year-End Financials

Return on assets: 15.8%
Return on equity: —
Current ratio: 1.20
Cash ($ mil.): 4

WALTON FAMILY FOUNDATION INC

EXECUTIVES

Exec Dir, Buddy Philpot
Coordinator, Karis Butler
Computer Support Technician, Josh Senty
Senior Program Officer, Cathy N Lund
Training Manager, Janet Post
Focus Area Coordinator, Sarah Burns
Human Resources Coordinator, Leigh Oliver
Program Officer, Yoo Cheong
Program Officer, Morgan Snyder
Senior Program Officer, Sandy Nickerson
Senior Program Officer, Damon Gardenhire

LOCATIONS

HQ: WALTON FAMILY FOUNDATION INC
125 W CENTRAL AVE RM 218, BENTONVILLE, AR 727125248
Phone: 479 273-5605
Web: WWW.WALTONFAMILYFOUNDATION.ORG

HISTORICAL FINANCIALS

Company Type: Private

Income Statement — FYE: December 31

	REVENUE ($ mil.)	NET INCOME ($ mil.)	NET PROFIT MARGIN	EMPLOYEES
12/09	740	368	49.8%	7
12/08	421	244	58.0%	—
12/00	244	190	78.0%	—
Annual Growth	13.1%	7.6%	—	—

2009 Year-End Financials

Return on assets: 20.2%
Return on equity: 20.2%
Current ratio: —
Cash ($ mil.): 24

WASHINGTON HOSPITAL CENTER CORPORATION

Washington Hospital Center (doing business as MedStar Washington Hospital Center) may be the official hospital of the Washington Redskins but you don't have to be a professional football player to make use of the facility's services. The hospital at the heart of the MedStar Health system serves some 500000 patients living in and around the nation's capital each year. Washington Hospital Center has 912 beds and includes specialized care centers for cancer cardiovascular conditions and stroke. Other offerings include organ transplantation a regional burn treatment center and emergency air transportation. MedStar Washington also conducts clinical research and offers educational residency and fellowship programs.

Operations

MedStar Washington has about 1350 doctors and dentists on staff; many of whom are involved in Washington Hospital Center's 520 clinical research studies. The hospital is affiliated with the medical schools of The George Washington University Georgetown University Johns Hopkins and several other regional educational institutions. Its Cardiac Ventricular Assist Device program is accredited by The Joint Commission.

The hospital is also home to MedSTAR one of the country's top shock-trauma and medevac programs and also operates the region's only adult burn center.

MedStar Washington has some 390000 outpatient and 37000 inpatient visits each year. It also provides care for some 3500 births and some 87000 emergency department visits.

Company Background

Washington Hospital Center was created through the merger of three regional hospitals: Emergency Garfield and Episcopal Eye Ear and Throat. The actual idea of the Hospital Center was conceived in 1943 but it took nearly 15 years for funding planning and construction to be completed.

EXECUTIVES

Vp Professional Services, Cathie Monge
President, John Sullivan
Coo, Robert S. Ross
Cfo, William Gayne
Senior Vice President Administrative Services, James Hiltzer
Assistant Secretary And Assistant Treasu, Rafael Convit

LOCATIONS

HQ: WASHINGTON HOSPITAL CENTER CORPORATION
110 IRVING ST NW, WASHINGTON, DC 200103017
Phone: 855 546-1686
Web: WWW.MEDSTARWASHINGTON.ORG

COMPETITORS

Adventist HealthCare
Bon Secours Health
Children's National Medical Center
Dimensions Healthcare
Doctors Community Hospital
HSC Pediatric Center
Inova
Mary Washington Healthcare
Sibley Memorial Hospital
Suburban Hospital

HISTORICAL FINANCIALS

Company Type: Private

Income Statement FYE: June 30

	REVENUE ($ mil.)	NET INCOME ($ mil.)	NET PROFIT MARGIN	EMPLOYEES
06/16	1,166	36	3.1%	5,637
06/15	1,121	23	2.1%	—
06/14	1,107	22	2.1%	—
06/08	1,028	14	1.4%	—
Annual Growth	1.6%	12.3%	—	—

2016 Year-End Financials

Return on assets: 6.6%
Return on equity: 10.6%
Current ratio: 1.20
Cash ($ mil.): —

WASHINGTON SUBURBAN SANITARY COMMISSION (INC)

Used water in clean water out is the job description of the Washington Suburban Sanitary Commission (WSSC). The utility provides water and wastewater services in Maryland's Montgomery and Prince George's counties just outside the nation's capital. WSSC serves 460000 customers representing 1.8 million residents in an area of about 1000 square miles. The agency draws water from the Potomac and Patuxent rivers and maintains three reservoirs. The commission also operates two water filtration plants six wastewater treatment plants and some 11000 miles of sewer and water main lines including a network of nearly 5600 miles of fresh water pipeline and over 5400 miles of sewer pipeline.

Operations

WSSC's three reservoirs (Triadelphia Rocky Gorge and Little Seneca) along with Jennings Randolph Reservoir which it shares with Fairfax Water and the Washington Aqueduct have a total holding capacity of 27 billion gallons. Its two water filtration plants (Patuxent and Potomac) produce nearly 170 million gallons of drinking water daily. The commission handles some 72 million gallons of wastewater daily through its six treatment plants (Damascus Hyattstown Parkway Piscataway Seneca and Western Branch).

Financial Performance

The company reported operating revenue of about $698 million in fiscal 2014 (ended June) up about 2% from the prior year. The growth was powered by an increase in water and sewer billing rates.

WSSC's proposed budgets for 2014 and 2015 were $1.5 billion and $1.3 billion respectively.

Company Background

WSSC was established in 1918.

EXECUTIVES

Chief Engineer, Gary Gumm
General Manager, Jerry N. Johnson
Cfo, Yvette Downs
Cio, Mujib Lodhi
Vpn Technician, Chandra Vavilala
Chairman, Omar M. Boulware
Vice Chairman, Adrienne A. Mandel
Auditors: BCA WATSON RICE LLP WASHINGTO

LOCATIONS

HQ: WASHINGTON SUBURBAN SANITARY COMMISSION (INC)
14501 SWEITZER LN, LAUREL, MD 207075901
Phone: 301 206-8000
Web: WWW.WSSCWATER.COM

HISTORICAL FINANCIALS

Company Type: Private

Income Statement FYE: June 30

	REVENUE ($ mil.)	NET INCOME ($ mil.)	NET PROFIT MARGIN	EMPLOYEES
06/20	749	23	3.2%	2,000
06/19	742	139	18.8%	—
06/18	725	119	16.5%	—
06/17	725	179	24.7%	—
Annual Growth	1.1%	(49.1%)	—	—

2020 Year-End Financials

Return on assets: 0.3%
Return on equity: 0.5%
Current ratio: 0.60
Cash ($ mil.): 37

WASHOE COUNTY SCHOOL DISTRICT

EXECUTIVES

Spdt, Traci Davis
Payroll Staff, Barbara Hawkins
Coordinator, Diana Cox
Coordinator, Josephine J Johnson
Coordinator, Lynette Larson
Coordinator, Marianne Campbell
Coordinator, Mary Green
Information Specialist, Kelli Pennington
Staff, Mariah Evans
Coordinator, Trudy Nunn
School Nurse, Erin Dehahn

LOCATIONS

HQ: WASHOE COUNTY SCHOOL DISTRICT
425 E 9TH ST, RENO, NV 895122800
Phone: 775 348-0200
Web: WWW.WASHOESCHOOLS.NET

HISTORICAL FINANCIALS

Company Type: Private

Income Statement FYE: June 30

	REVENUE ($ mil.)	NET INCOME ($ mil.)	NET PROFIT MARGIN	EMPLOYEES
06/19	713	(95)	—	7,000
06/18	683	190	27.8%	—
06/17	640	57	8.9%	—
06/08	578	38	6.7%	—
Annual Growth	1.9%	—	—	—

WAUKESHA MEMORIAL HOSPITAL, INC.

Waukesha Memorial Hospital is a 300-bed teaching hospital that provides health care services for Wisconsin's Milwaukee Waukesha and Dane counties. With about 670 physicians representing several specialties and 2700 employees the hospital operates centers for excellence focused on cardiology oncology neurology women's health and orthopedics as well as emergency neonatal and family practice services. Additionally Waukesha Memorial Hospital conducts a physician residency program. Established in 1914 the medical facility is a subsidiary of not-for-profit ProHealth Care a medical network that serves southeastern Wisconsin with acute care and specialty health services.

Operations

ProHealth Care runs Waukesha Memorial Hospital alongside its other critical-care hospital Oconomowoc Memorial Hospital. As part of its operations the hospital boasts a neuroscience center orthopedic center regional cancer center regional heart and vascular center and a women's center. Its newborn intensive care unit and its emergency department which averages more than 39000 visits are both Level III.

Geographic Reach

Despite its name Waukesha Memorial Hospital serves the residents of Milwaukee and Dane counties along with Waukesha County.

EXECUTIVES

Vpma, James Gardner
Vice President Of Revenue Cycle, Curtis Glaunert
Rph, Christine Koehler
Auditors: PLANTE & MORAN PLLC GRAND RA

LOCATIONS

HQ: WAUKESHA MEMORIAL HOSPITAL, INC.
725 AMERICAN AVE, WAUKESHA, WI 531885099
Phone: 262 928-1000
Web: WWW.PROHEALTHCARE.ORG

PRODUCTS/OPERATIONS

Selected Services

Birthing
Blood / Ly
Bones Joints & Muscles
Brain & Nerves
Cancer
Cancer Second Opinion
Children's Health
CyberKnife
Diabetes
Diagnostic Services
Digestive
Ear Nose & Throat
Emergency Services/Urgent Care
Eyes & Vision
General Surgery
Genetics
Heart & Vascular
Infections
Integrative Medicine
Kidneys & Urinary System
Lungs / Br
Men's Health
Mental Health
Nutrition
Orthopedic
Pain
Rehabilitation Services
Senior's Health
Sleep
Stroke

Wellness & Lifestyle
Women's Health

COMPETITORS

Children's Hospital and Health System
Columbia St. Mary's
Froedtert Hospital
Hospital Sisters Health System
Ministry Health Care
SwedishAmerican Health System
University of Wisconsin Hospital and Clinics

HISTORICAL FINANCIALS

Company Type: Private

Income Statement — FYE: September 30

	REVENUE ($ mil.)	NET INCOME ($ mil.)	NET PROFIT MARGIN	EMPLOYEES
09/19	543	13	2.5%	2,071
09/18	520	27	5.3%	—
09/17	470	59	12.6%	—
09/16	457	37	8.3%	—
Annual Growth	5.9%	(29.2%)	—	—

2019 Year-End Financials

Return on assets: 2.5%
Return on equity: 8.2%
Current ratio: 1.50
Cash ($ mil.): 6

WAYNE STATE UNIVERSITY

Wayne State University is a public university with an annual enrollment of nearly 27000 students and a student-to-teacher ratio of 16:1. It offers more than 350 bachelor's master's and doctoral degree programs as well as certificate specialist and professional programs through about a dozen colleges and schools. Located in midtown Detroit WSU traces its heritage back to 1868 with the founding of the Detroit Medical College now part of its School of Medicine. Prominent alumni include US Congressman John Conyers radio DJ Casey Kasem and actor Tom Sizemore.

Operations

WSU's areas of study include accountancy finance management education engineering arts as well as nursing pharmacy and social work. It also offers online studies for theatre and dance and information management.

A notable indicator of the research program's success is its classification as a doctoral university highest research activity by the Carnegie Classification of Higher Education. WSU also ranks among the top public institutions for annual research expenditures by the National Science Foundation.

Geographic Reach

WSU's 200-acre campus includes more than 95 academic research and residential buildings. The university also has five satellite campuses around Detroit (and one in Jackson) and six extension centers offering educational programs across southeastern Michigan.

It has affiliations with more than 100 institutions globally and offers study abroad programs in about 15 countries on five continents.

The school hosts students from every US state and 75 countries.

EXECUTIVES

Cio And Associate Vp Computing And Information Technology, Joseph F. Sawasky
President, M. Roy Wilson
Svp Academic Affairs And Provost, Margaret E. Winters
Cfo, Rick Nork
Vice President Research, Hilary Ratner
Associate Department Chair, Kendra L Schwartz
Assistant Vice President For Research Compliance, Phil Cunningham
Department Chair, Eva Powers
Associate Vice President Enrollment Management, Dawn Medley
Assistant Vice President, Mark Byrd
Pharm.d, Victoria Lehr
Vice President Human Resources And Information Technology, Adrienne Mitchell
Vice President For Economic Development, Ned Staebler
External Vice President Class, Sandra Mikhail
Chair, Gary S. Pollard
Vice Chair, Paul E. Massaron
Secretary, Saundra Sumner
Secretary Iii, Lenora Paul
Board Of Governors Member, Lois Avery
Graduate Secretary, Rose Priest
Secretary, Gwendolyn Cotton
Secretary, Kara Cox
Auditors: PLANTE & MORAN PLLC CLINTON

LOCATIONS

HQ: WAYNE STATE UNIVERSITY
5057 WOODWARD AVE # 13001, DETROIT, MI 482024050
Phone: 313 577-2230
Web: WWW.WAYNE.EDU

PRODUCTS/OPERATIONS

Selected Colleges and Schools

College of Education
College of Engineering
College of Fine Performing and Communication Arts
College of Liberal Arts and Sciences
College of Nursing
Eugene Applebaum College of Pharmacy and Health Sciences
Irvin D. Reid Honors College
Law School
School of Business Administration
School of Library and Information Science
School of Medicine
School of Social Work
The Graduate School

HISTORICAL FINANCIALS

Company Type: Private

Income Statement — FYE: September 30

	REVENUE ($ mil.)	NET INCOME ($ mil.)	NET PROFIT MARGIN	EMPLOYEES
09/17	640	46	7.2%	8,500
09/11	520	(15)	—	—
09/05	445	37	8.4%	—
09/04	418	(3)	—	—
Annual Growth	3.3%	—	—	—

2017 Year-End Financials

Return on assets: 3.2%
Return on equity: 7.0%
Current ratio: 1.90
Cash ($ mil.): 355

WELCH FOODS INC., A COOPERATIVE

Welch Foods has a taste for the grape. A company owned by more than 900 farmer families Welch produces the Welch's brand grape and white grape juices and jellies. Its beverage line includes sparkling juices and cocktails. Welch supplies fresh grapes and snacks as well as preserved offerings (jellies jams and spreads). Its products are purchased by grocery retailers and food service operators in the US.

Operations

Welch Foods offers juices jams jellies spreads and cocktails primarily made from grapes which the company harvest in its vineyards located in Northern part of the US.

Geographic Reach

Massachusetts-based Welch Foods has vineyards in four regions across the US where the climate is optimal: the Finger Lakes Region of New York; the shore of Lake Erie in New York Pennsylvania and Ohio; the shore of Lake Michigan in southwestern Michigan; and the Yakima Valley in Washington State. It also operate a vineyard in Ontario Canada.

Sales and Marketing

Welch's products sells across online and retail stores which includes Walmart Target Shoprite Meijer and Kroger among others.

Strategy

As grape juice consumption in the US falls Welch Foods is focused on expanding its product line. In 2019 it partnered with Cornell University and the New York Wine & Grape Foundation to develop technology to neutralize the smell and taste of Concord grape juice; the neutralized juice could then be used as a base wine or blender.

In addition as Welch's is committed to finding ways to help the environment it has replaced its current 10oz juice bottle in early 2020 with a new lighter-weight bottle which uses 15% less plastic.

Company Background

In 1869 Dr. Thomas Bramwell Welch pasteurized Concord grape juice to create a non-alcoholic alternative to wine for his church. The beverage was a hit at the World's Fair in Chicago in 1893 and by 1923 Concord grape jelly was introduced.

The farmers who grew grapes for Welch's took ownership of the company and began operating it as a co-op in 1952.

EXECUTIVES

President And Ceo, Bradley C. Irwin, age 61
Vice President Information Technology, Phyllis Gutz
Chairman Of The Board, Joseph C. Falcone

LOCATIONS

HQ: WELCH FOODS INC., A COOPERATIVE
575 VIRGINIA RD, CONCORD, MA 017422761
Phone: 978 371-1000
Web: WWW.WELCHS.COM

PRODUCTS/OPERATIONS

Selected Brands and Products

BAMA
Jams jellies and preserves
Peanut butter
Welch
Bottled and canned juices
Dried fruit
Fresh table grapes
Frozen juices
Fruit juice bars

Jams jellies and preserves
Pourable concentrated juices
Refrigerated juices
Single-serve juices

COMPETITORS

Chiquita Brands
Citrus World
Coca-Cola
Coloma Frozen Foods
Dole Food
Fresh Del Monte Produce
Great Western Juice
Lion Raisins
Monster Beverage
Mott's
Naked Juice
National Raisin
Ocean Spray
Odwalla
Old Orchard
Silver Springs
Smucker
Snapple
South Beach Beverage
Stapleton-Spence Packing
Sun-Maid
Sunny Delight
Sunview Vineyards
Tree Top
Tropicana
Unilever NV
Wet Planet Beverages

HISTORICAL FINANCIALS

Company Type: Private

Income Statement FYE: August 31

	REVENUE ($ mil.)	NET INCOME ($ mil.)	NET PROFIT MARGIN	EMPLOYEES
08/16	600	83	14.0%	1,000
08/15	609	81	13.3%	—
08/14	609	76	12.6%	—
08/13	608	65	10.7%	—
Annual Growth	(0.5%)	8.8%	—	—

2016 Year-End Financials

Return on assets: 20.6%
Return on equity: 233.2%
Current ratio: 1.40
Cash ($ mil.): 7

WELLMONT HEALTH SYSTEM

At Wellmont Health System wellness is paramount. Wellmont Health System provides general and advanced medical-surgical care to residents of northeastern Tennessee and southwestern Virginia. The health system consists of about a dozen owned and affiliated hospitals that collectively have more than 1000 licensed beds. One of its facilities is a rehabilitation hospital operated in partnership with HealthSouth. The system's Holston Valley Medical Center features a level I trauma center and a level III neonatal intensive care unit (NICU). Wellmont also operates numerous ancillary facilities including an assisted living center a mental health clinic home health care and hospice agencies and outpatient centers.

Operations

Today Wellmont is one of the region's largest employers with a staff of more than 6500 medical professionals. Nearly 600 physicians deliver care at Wellmont's facilities that include eight hospitals in Tennessee and Virginia. Other facilities include an outpatient surgery center a child development center a cancer center urgent care centers and a health network of physicians that include occupational health providers. The hospital also offers urgent care transportation with its Wellmont One Air Transport.

Wellmont is the only health system in Tennessee to offer two major trauma centers (at Holston Valley Medical Center in Kingsport and Bristol Regional Medical Center in Bristol).

Sales and Marketing

Medicare payments accounted for nearly 85% of Wellmont's net patient revenue in fiscal 2013 (ended June); Medicaid and TennCare (Tennessee's state Medicaid program) each accounted for nearly 10%.

Financial Performance

Revenue increased 1% to $798 million in fiscal 2013 (ended June) on higher net patient revenue. However patient volumes were mixed: Some categories declined while others increased. For example emergency department visits dropped 7% as more patients chose to visit the system's more affordable urgent care centers.

Net income rose significantly that year increasing 79% to $47 million. This was due to a change in net unrealized gains on investments and a change in the funded status of benefit plans. Cash flow from operations fell 5% to $74 million.

Strategy

Wellmont has expanded by opening new outpatient facilities including a new physical therapy clinic in 2013 and by acquiring existing medical facilities. For example in 2015 it agreed to buy out Adventist Health in their partnership owning Takoma Regional Hospital in Tennessee. The system also expands its service territory by partnering with other area care providers.

In 2014 the company migrated to a new electronic medical records (EMR) system replacing its four existing EHR platforms.

Mergers and Acquisitions

In 2015 Wellmont announced plans to merge with a neighboring health system Mountain States Health Alliance. By combining operations the two systems hope to better provide care for communities in northeast Tennessee as well as Virginia Kentucky and North Carolina. The states of Tennessee and Virginia have to approve the transaction.

Company Background

Founded in 1996 Wellmont has grown over the years primarily through acquisitions including Lee Regional Medical Center Mountain View Regional Medical Center and Takoma Regional Hospital (through a partnership with Adventist Health).

EXECUTIVES

Svp Business Development And Rural Strategy, David L. Brash
President And Ceo, Bart Hove
President Bristol Regional Medical Center, Greg Neal
Evp And General Counsel, Gary Miller
Svp System Advancement And President Wellmont Foundation, Todd Norris
Chief Executive Medical Officer Wellmont Medical Associates, Stephen Combs
President Holston Valley Medical Center, Tim Attebery
Evp And Coo, Eric Deaton
President Of Hawkins County Memorial Hospital And Hancock County Hospital, Rebecca Beck
President Mountain View Regional Medical Center And Lonesome Pine Hospital, Dale Clark
Interim Cio, Martha O. Chill
Medical Director, Marta Wayt
Vice President Director Of Project Management Office, Kim Whiteaker
Chairman, Roger Leonard
Vice Chairman, Julie Bennett

LOCATIONS

HQ: WELLMONT HEALTH SYSTEM
1905 AMERICAN WAY, KINGSPORT, TN 376605882
Phone: 423 230-8200
Web: WWW.WELLMONT.ORG

PRODUCTS/OPERATIONS

Selected Facilities

Bristol Regional Medical Center (Bristol Tennessee)
Hancock County Hospital (Sneedville Tennessee)
Hawkins County Memorial Hospital (Rogersville Tennessee)
HealthSouth Rehabilitation Hospital of Kingsport (HealthSouth partnership; Kingsport Tennessee)
Holston Valley Medical Center (Kingsport Tennessee)
Lee Regional Medical Center (Pennington Gap Virginia)
Lonesome Pine Hospital (Big Stone Gap Virginia)
Mountain View Regional Medical Center (Norton Virginia)
Takoma Regional Hospital (Greeneville Tennessee)

Selected Services

Cancer Care
Children
Diabetes
Emergency and Trauma
Family Medicine
Hearing Services
Heart Care
Home Care
Hospice
Hospitalists
Marsh Regional Blood Center
Neurology
Occupational Medicine
Orthopedics
Palliative Care
Psychiatry
Radiology
Rehabilitation and Therapy
Sleep Medicine
Stroke Care
Surgical Services
Weight Loss
Women's Health

COMPETITORS

Ascension Health
Baptist Memorial Health Care
Community Health Systems
Cookeville Regional Medical Center
Kindred Healthcare
LifePoint Health
Mountain States Health
Tenet Healthcare

HISTORICAL FINANCIALS

Company Type: Private

Income Statement FYE: June 30

	REVENUE ($ mil.)	NET INCOME ($ mil.)	NET PROFIT MARGIN	EMPLOYEES
06/17	908	53	5.9%	6,114
06/10	622	33	5.5%	—
06/09	2	0	—	—
Annual Growth	104.4%	—	—	—

2017 Year-End Financials

Return on assets: 4.5%
Return on equity: 8.8%
Current ratio: 1.60
Cash ($ mil.): 60

WELLS REAL ESTATE INVESTMENT TRUST II

Auditors: DELOITTE & TOUCHE LLP ATLANT

LOCATIONS

HQ: WELLS REAL ESTATE INVESTMENT TRUST II
1 GLENLAKE PKWY STE 1200, ATLANTA, GA
303287267
Phone: 404 465-2200
Web: WWW.WELLSREITII.COM

HISTORICAL FINANCIALS

Company Type: Private

Income Statement FYE: December 31

	REVENUE ($ mil.)	NET INCOME ($ mil.)	NET PROFIT MARGIN	EMPLOYEES
12/12	576	48	8.3%	9
12/11	613	56	9.2%	—
Annual Growth	(5.9%)	(15.2%)	—	—

2012 Year-End Financials

Return on assets: —
Return on equity: 8.3%
Current ratio: 0.10
Cash ($ mil.): —

WELLSPAN MEDICAL GROUP (INC)

EXECUTIVES

Ceo, Tom McGann
Controller, Steffney Calp
Administrator, Laurie Brown

LOCATIONS

HQ: WELLSPAN MEDICAL GROUP (INC)
140 N DUKE ST, YORK, PA 174011170
Phone: 717 851-6515
Web: WWW.WELLSPAN.ORG

HISTORICAL FINANCIALS

Company Type: Private

Income Statement FYE: June 30

	REVENUE ($ mil.)	NET INCOME ($ mil.)	NET PROFIT MARGIN	EMPLOYEES
06/20	567	(13)	—	709
06/16	375	(43)	—	—
06/15	336	(36)	—	—
06/14	251	(25)	—	—
Annual Growth	14.5%	—	—	—

2020 Year-End Financials

Return on assets: (-10.0%)
Return on equity: (-53.3%)
Current ratio: 0.70
Cash ($ mil.): —

WESCO AIRCRAFT HOLDINGS, INC.

Planes may fly around the world but they can't leave the ground without Wesco Aircraft Holdings. One of the largest logistics and supply chain companies serving the aerospace industry it provides distribution vendor relationship management just-in-time (JIT) delivery quality assurance and kitting. Operating through Wesco Aircraft Hardware and other subsidiaries the company stocks about 565000 different pieces of hardware bearings tools electronic components and machined parts from more than 5000 suppliers. Boeing Airbus and Bombardier are among its largest customers.

Operations

Wesco divides its operations across five main product lines: hardware (48% of total sales) chemicals (41%) electronic components (7%) bearings (2%) and other machined parts (2%).

The company sources its inventory from over 5000 suppliers including Precision Castparts Alcoa Fastening Systems Amphenol Corporation PPG Industries Lisi Aerospace and RBC Bearings.

Geographic Reach

Headquartered at Valencia California the company operates its facilities and offices across nearly 60 locations in 17 countries including Canada Mexico the UK the US and in other European and Asian countries. The US accounts for almost 75% of sales and the UK generates roughly 20%.

Sales and Marketing

Operations and maintenance subcontractors such as Boeing Airbus Bombardier Cessna Gulfstream Embraer and BAE Systems account for 75% of the company's sales. Other customers include distributors airlines and the US government. Its 8000 customers can choose from just-in-time or long-term contracts or ad hoc sales.

Financial Performance

After posting record-setting revenues of $1.5 billion in 2015 Wesco saw its revenues dip marginally by 1% to $1.5 billion in 2016. The revenue dip was attributed to foreign currency impacts which the company estimates reduced sales by $30 million. In addition Westco experienced a $26 million decline in sales due to the end of a large commercial contract and a $10 million decrease of ad hoc sales during 2016.

After posting a net loss of $155 million in 2015 Wesco posted positive net income of $91 million in 2016. The positive net income for 2016 was mostly the result of the absence of about $206 million in losses from discontinued operation it had posted the previous year. The company's operating cash flow has fluctuated over the years; after rising in 2015 cash flow fell from $141 million to $117 million in 2016.

Strategy

In late 2015 the company's management team launched a new strategy of providing integrated supply chain services more tailored to customer demand through long-term contracts and focused forecasted consumption. This involves changes to its inventory purchasing strategy holding inventory for shorter periods and scrapping older more-dated inventory. The company believes the move will allow it to serve customers better and strengthen its balance sheet.

EXECUTIVES

Evp And Cfo, Richard J. (Rick) Weller, $450,000 total compensation
Evp And Cio, Dave Currence
Evp And Chief Legal Officer, John Holland
President And Coo, Alex Murray, $356,395 total compensation
Ceo And Director, Todd Renehan, $357,774 total compensation
Evp And Chief Supply Chain Officer, Dan Snow, $330,490 total compensation
Vice President Tax And Global Cash Management, Michael Apelt
Executive Vice President And Chief Supply Chain Officer, Daniel Snow
Vp Supply Chain And Strategic Initiatives, Jo Sayers
Executive Vice President And Cio, Ryan Worobel
Vice President Manufacturing Operations, Ken Brech
Chairman, Randy J. Snyder
Board Of Directors, Paul Fulchino
Board Of Directors, Jay Haberland
Auditors: PRICEWATERHOUSECOOPERS LLP LO

LOCATIONS

HQ: WESCO AIRCRAFT HOLDINGS, INC.
24911 AVENUE STANFORD, VALENCIA, CA
913551281
Phone: 661 775-7200
Web: WWW.WESCOAIR.COM

2016 Sales

	$ mil.	% of total
North America	1,185	80
Rest of World	292	20
Total	**1,477**	**100**

2016 Sales

	$ mil.	% of total
United States of America	1,087	74
United Kingdom	195	13
Other foreign counties	194	13
Total	**1,477**	**100**

PRODUCTS/OPERATIONS

2016 Sales

	$ mil.	% of total
Hardware	711	48
Chemicals	600	41
Electronic components	105	7
Bearings	34	2
Machined parts and other	26	2
Total	**1,477**	**100**

PRODUCTS

HARDWARE
Blind fasteners
Bolts and screws
Clamps
Hi lok pins and collars
Hydraulic fittings
Inserts
Lockbolts and collars
Nuts
Panel fasteners
Rivets
Springs
Valves
Washers
CHEMICALS
Adhesives
Cleaners and cleaning solvents
Coolants and metalworking fluids
Industrial gases
Lubricants
Oil and grease
Paints and coatings
Sealants and tapes
ELECTRONIC COMPONENTS
Circuit breakers
Connectors
Interconnect accessories
Lighted products
Relays
Switches
Wire and cable
BEARINGS
Airframe control bearings
Ball bearing
Bushings
Needle roller bearings
Precision bearings
Rod ends
Spherical bearings
OTHER PRODUCTS
Brackets
Installation tooling
Milled parts
Shims
Stampings
Turned parts
Welded assemblies

COMPETITORS

AAR Corp.
Align Aerospace
Aviall Services
First Aviation
GECAS Asset Management Services
Kellstrom Industries

HISTORICAL FINANCIALS

Company Type: Private

Income Statement FYE: September 30

	REVENUE ($ mil.)	NET INCOME ($ mil.)	NET PROFIT MARGIN	EMPLOYEES
09/19	1,696	21	1.3%	3,302
09/18	1,570	32	2.1%	—
09/17	1,429	(237)	—	—
09/16	1,477	91	6.2%	—
Annual Growth	4.7%	(38.4%)	—	—

2019 Year-End Financials

Return on assets: 1.2%
Return on equity: 3.0%
Current ratio: 3.60
Cash ($ mil.): 38

WEST PENN POWER COMPANY

EXECUTIVES

Manager, Joe Musco

LOCATIONS

HQ: WEST PENN POWER COMPANY
76 S MAIN ST BSMT, AKRON, OH 443081817
Phone: 800 686-0021
Web: WWW.FIRSTENERGYCORP.COM

HISTORICAL FINANCIALS

Company Type: Private

Income Statement FYE: December 31

	REVENUE ($ mil.)	NET INCOME ($ mil.)	NET PROFIT MARGIN	EMPLOYEES
12/17	1,009	110	11.0%	11
12/16	1,020	116	11.4%	—
Annual Growth	(1.1%)	(5.0%)	—	—

WESLEY MEDICAL CENTER, LLC

EXECUTIVES

Ceo, Bill Voloch
Prin*, Carl Fitch
Cfo*, Matt Leary
Coordinator, Diana Lippoldt
Training and Direc, Sharon Bowles
Director, David Miller
Coordinator, Stacey Wright
Internal Medicine Practitioner, Bob Ragan
Director of Risk Management, Joey Dean
Consultant, Kent Potter
Coordinator, Teena Johnston

LOCATIONS

HQ: WESLEY MEDICAL CENTER, LLC
550 N HILLSIDE ST, WICHITA, KS 672144976
Phone: 316 962-2000
Web: WWW.WESLEYMC.COM

HISTORICAL FINANCIALS

Company Type: Private

Income Statement FYE: December 31

	REVENUE ($ mil.)	NET INCOME ($ mil.)	NET PROFIT MARGIN	EMPLOYEES
12/17	608	80	13.3%	40
12/16	555	56	10.3%	—
12/15	545	60	11.1%	—
12/14	520	88	17.0%	—
Annual Growth	5.3%	(3.0%)	—	—

WEST VIRGINIA UNITED HEALTH SYSTEM, INC.

West Virginia United Health System (WVUHS) helps residents in the Mountain State stay on top of their health. The system operates United Hospital Center (in Clarksburg) as well as hospitals in the West Virginia University Hospitals (WVUH) system including City Hospital (Martinsburg) Jefferson Memorial Hospital (Ranson) and WVUH's home hospital in Morgantown. In addition WVUHS operates WVUH's Cheat Lake physicians ambulatory center as well as a network of about a dozen primary care clinics located throughout central and northern West Virginia. Combined the system's hospitals and clinics have more than 1000 beds and treat approximately 1.4 million patients annually.

EXECUTIVES

Associate Vice President Investments, Jennifer Cunanan
Auditors: DIXON HUGHES GOODMAN LLP CHA

LOCATIONS

HQ: WEST VIRGINIA UNITED HEALTH SYSTEM, INC.
1 MEDICAL CENTER DR, MORGANTOWN, WV 265061200
Phone: 304 598-4000
Web: WWW.WVUMEDICINE.ORG

PRODUCTS/OPERATIONS

Selected facilities

Barbour Country Family Medicine
Bridgeport Physicians Care
Chestnut Ridge Center
City Hospital
Doddridge Family Medicine
Elk Memorial Clinic
Harrisville Medical Center
Jefferson Memorial Hospital
Lumberport Family Medicine
Oakland Family Medicine Center
Pennsboro Medical Center
Pinewood Medical Center
Shinnston Healthcare Clinic
United Hospital Center
United Summit Center
WVU Hospitals

COMPETITORS

CAMC Health
HCA
West Penn Allegheny Health System

HISTORICAL FINANCIALS

Company Type: Private

Income Statement FYE: December 31

	REVENUE ($ mil.)	NET INCOME ($ mil.)	NET PROFIT MARGIN	EMPLOYEES
12/19	2,770	238	8.6%	7,000
12/17	2,172	132	6.1%	—
12/16	1,877	103	5.5%	—
12/15	1,651	23	1.5%	—
Annual Growth	13.8%	77.6%	—	—

2019 Year-End Financials

Return on assets: 6.9%
Return on equity: 14.9%
Current ratio: 2.10
Cash ($ mil.): 199

WEST VIRGINIA UNIVERSITY

West Virginia University (WVU) is the intellectual home of more than 29000 Mountaineers (the school's mascot) and the state's preeminent institution of higher learning. WVU offers more than 180 bachelor's master's doctoral and professional degree programs through some 15 colleges and schools. The university's clinical psychology and forestry programs have been recognized nationally and it boasts 100% post-graduate job placement for its nursing pharmacy and mining engineering majors. WVU also runs a two-year residential school Potomac State College in Keyser West Virginia.

Operations

Its 1099 acres campus university offers a joint petroleum and natural gas engineering major. It also operates eight experimental farms and four forests throughout the state in addition to WVU Jackson's Mill State 4-H Camp and Lifelong Learning Center near Weston. Some 93% of its full-time faculty have earned doctorates or first-professional degrees in their disciplines. More than 800 students traveled to another country for study abroad courses in the 2011-12 academic year. Undergraduate tuition and fees for the 2012-13 year was reported as $9808.

WVU is an independent operating unit of the West Virginia Higher Education Fund.

Geographic Reach

The university's main campus is in Morgantown. It also has divisional campuses in Charleston Keyser Martinsburg and Montgomery.

Financial Performance

The university reported a 4% increase in revenues in 2012 due to a growth in capital grants and gifts revenue tuition and fees as well as revenues from auxiliary enterprise gifts and other sources. Capital grants and gifts increased by $55.9 million thanks to a donation of a master license agreement from Siemens PLM for educational software. Tuition and fees increased by $19.9 million in 2012 thanks to a fee rate hike and an increase in non-resident student enrollment. Auxiliary revenues grew by $12.2 million due to an increase in revenues from room and dining services auxiliary fees and athletics revenues. Organic growth has lifted the company's revenues since 2009.

Net income increased by 51% in 2012 due to a growth in other net non-operating revenues of $3.2 million as a result of a settlement agreement in the amount of $7.2 million partially offset by operating revenues.

Strategy

In addition to WVU's campus-based activities the university is focusing on expanding its online and distance learning options to increase educational access and research activities.

Company Background

WVU was founded in 1867 as a public land-grant institution. It one of only 11 schools in the US that are land-grant doctoral research universities with a comprehensive medical school.

EXECUTIVES

Vice President For Strategic Initiatives, Rob Alsop
Interim Vice President Of Legal Affairs And Interim General Counsel, Mary Brandt
Assistant Vice President Retention Program, Candace Tackett
Vice President, Ghazala Khokar
Secretary, Lisa Berry
Secretary, Megan Blackburn
Auditors: CLIFTONLARSONALLEN LLP PLYMOU

LOCATIONS

HQ: WEST VIRGINIA UNIVERSITY
103 STEWART HL, MORGANTOWN, WV 26506
Phone: 304 293-2545
Web: WWW.THEDAONLINE.COM

PRODUCTS/OPERATIONS

Selected Colleges and Schools

Benjamin M. Statler College of Engineering and Mineral Resources
College of Business and Economics
College of Creative Arts
College of Education and Human Services
College of Law
College of Physical Activity and Sport Sciences
Davis College of Agriculture Natural Resources and Design
Eberly College of Arts and Sciences
Perley Isaac Reed School of Journalism
Potomac State College of WVU
School of Dentistry
School of Medicine
School of Nursing
School of Pharmacy
School of Public Health
WVU Institute of Technology

HISTORICAL FINANCIALS

Company Type: Private

Income Statement — FYE: June 30

	REVENUE ($ mil.)	NET INCOME ($ mil.)	NET PROFIT MARGIN	EMPLOYEES
06/18	808	41	5.1%	6,245
06/17	783	8	1.1%	—
Annual Growth	3.2%	390.3%	—	—

2018 Year-End Financials

Return on assets: 1.8%
Return on equity: 3.9%
Current ratio: 1.40
Cash ($ mil.): 85

WESTCHESTER COUNTY HEALTH CARE CORPORATION

EXECUTIVES

Ceo-Pres, Michael D Israel
Sr V Pres, Anthony Mahler
Cfo, Gary Brudnicki
Gen Counsel, Julie Switzer
Sr V Pres, John Morgan
Public Relations Director, David Billig
Director, Mary Delaney
Information Specialist, Michelle Weinraub
Information Specialist, Omar Ziyadeh
Information Specialist, Ann Addison
Information Specialist, Donna Dozor
Auditors: GRANT THORNTON LLP NEW YORK

LOCATIONS

HQ: WESTCHESTER COUNTY HEALTH CARE CORPORATION
100 WOODS RD, VALHALLA, NY 105951530
Phone: 914 493-7000
Web: WWW.WESTCHESTERMEDICALCENTER.COM

HISTORICAL FINANCIALS

Company Type: Private

Income Statement — FYE: December 31

	REVENUE ($ mil.)	NET INCOME ($ mil.)	NET PROFIT MARGIN	EMPLOYEES
12/19	1,718	12	0.7%	12,000
12/18	1,641	(10)	—	—
12/16	2,008	45	2.3%	—
12/15	1,069	33	3.1%	—
Annual Growth	12.6%	(21.5%)	—	—

2019 Year-End Financials

Return on assets: 0.8%
Return on equity: —
Current ratio: 1.30
Cash ($ mil.): 96

WESTERN FARMERS ELECTRIC COOPERATIVE

Power also comes sweeping down the plain in Oklahoma thanks to the Western Farmers Electric Cooperative. Led by its coal- and natural gas-fueled generating plants — three in Anadarko one in Mooreland and one in Hugo (all in Oklahoma) — the generation and transmission co-op produces more than 1845 MW of capacity. It pipes power over 3700 miles of transmission lines to two-thirds of rural Oklahoma and parts of New Mexico. It also operates 264 substations and 59 switch stations. Western Farmers Electric Cooperative which is owned by its member distribution cooperatives supplies 22 distribution co-ops and Altus Air Force base which serve a total of a half million members.

Operations

The company maintains a well-balanced and diversified portfolio of generation resources reflecting a mix of technologies and fuel types. In 2013 coal represented 33% of Western Farmers Electric Cooperative's energy production with natural gas at 12 percent. Power generated from wind resources represents about 14% of the coop's energy mix hydro 7%. Economy purchases energy imbalance purchases and contract power (primarily natural gas) made up the balance.

Geographic Reach

Western Farmers Electric Cooperative's members consist of 22 distribution cooperatives (serving customers in Kansas Oklahoma New Mexico and Texas) and the Altus Air Force Base in Oklahoma.

Financial Performance

In 2013 the company's revenues increased by 15% to $525.3 million due to a 7.7% energy sales increase. (Its average MWh sales growth rate of 5.5% over the past three year is above the national average). Western Farmers Electric Cooperative also gets a small amount of off-system sales from three of its four New Mexico members. Power sales increased $64 million in 2013 due to higher MWh sales a slight increase in wholesale power rates and a 40% rise in natural gas prices.

Western Farmers Electric Cooperative's net income increased by 61% in 2013 due to higher sales and an increase in noninterest income.

That year the company's operating cash inflow increased to $53.3 million (compared to $21.2 million in 2012) primarily due to higher net income and increased coal and oil inventory.

Strategy

Western Farmers Electric Cooperative has diversified its fuel mix to meet green energy regulations and boasts one of the state's largest renewable energy portfolios. The diversity in generation mix helps reduce exposure to changing market conditions helping to keep rates competitive.

In 2013 the company signed a purchase with Apex Clean Energy through its subsidiary Balko Wind LLC for 100 MW of wind energy from the Balko Wind Project. With this agreement Apex has sold all the capacity of 300 MW project which will produce enough electricity to power over 110000 U.S. homes. This new site represents the fifth Oklahoma wind farm development that is a part of an ongoing commitment to diversify Western Farmers Electric Cooperative's portfolio of generation sources.

That year it also entered into a purchase and sale agreement with community-wind developer National Renewable Solutions to acquire the development assets for the Broadview Wind Projects in New Mexico. The two projects with a combined 19.8 MW capacity will each sell power over the next 20 years to Western Farmers Electric Cooperative. This wind farm site is in the service territory of Western Farmers Electric Cooperative member Farmers' Electric Cooperative.

In 2012 the company teamed up with Enel Green Power which that year began operating the 150-MW Rocky Ridge Wind Project in Kiowa and Washita counties Oklahoma. The energy generated by the wind farm will be bought by Western Farmers Electric Cooperative.

In 2012 Calpine Corporation agreed to supply Western Farmers Electric Cooperative with electric generation capacity and power (up to 280 MW) from Calpine's gas-fired Oneta Energy Center from June 2014 through 2035.

Company Background

Growing its geographic coverage in late 2010 Western Farmers Electric Cooperative added four New Mexico-based cooperatives (Farmers' Central Valley Lea County and Roosevelt County with a total of 400 MW of load) to its membership.

Responding to a growing demand for power in 2009 the power co-op completed an expansion project at its gas-fueled Anadarko plant adding some 145 MW of power generating capacity.

Western Farmers Electric Cooperative was organized in 1941 by western Oklahoma rural electric distribution cooperatives in order to secure power generation and distribution at an affordable rate. The co-op began generating power in 1950.

EXECUTIVES

Secretary Transmission Services, Kelli Keeling
Secretary, Shelly Trammell
Secretary T And D Engineering, Shelli Pearson
Secretary, White Susie
Auditors: KPMG LLP OKLAHOMA CITY OK

LOCATIONS

HQ: WESTERN FARMERS ELECTRIC COOPERATIVE
701 NE 7TH ST, ANADARKO, OK 730052297
Phone: 405 247-3351
Web: WWW.WFEC.COM

COMPETITORS

Empire District Electric
Entergy
Grand River Dam Authority
OGE Energy
ONEOK
PG&E Corporation

HISTORICAL FINANCIALS

Company Type: Private

Income Statement — FYE: December 31

	REVENUE ($ mil.)	NET INCOME ($ mil.)	NET PROFIT MARGIN	EMPLOYEES
12/18	715	14	2.0%	378
12/17	686	13	2.0%	—
12/16	655	24	3.7%	—
12/15	671	31	4.6%	—
Annual Growth	2.2%	(22.8%)	—	—

2018 Year-End Financials

Return on assets: 1.0%
Return on equity: 3.9%
Current ratio: 1.10
Cash ($ mil.): 14

WESTERN GOVERNORS UNIVERSITY

EXECUTIVES

Pres, Scott Pulsipher
Chief Information Officer-Svp*, David Morales
Coo*, David Grow
Mgr, David R Grow
Pres-Academic Advancement, Sally Johnstone
Coordinator, Juan Maestas
Information Technology/Interne, Travis Hitz
Information Specialist, Erik Jorgensen
Coordinator, Kami Hobson
Academic Vp-College of It, Elke Leeds
Webmaster, David Galvan
Auditors: TANNER LLC SALT LAKE CITY UT

LOCATIONS

HQ: WESTERN GOVERNORS UNIVERSITY
4001 S 700 E STE 700, SALT LAKE CITY, UT 841072533
Phone: 801 274-3280
Web: WWW.WGU.EDU

HISTORICAL FINANCIALS

Company Type: Private

Income Statement — FYE: June 30

	REVENUE ($ mil.)	NET INCOME ($ mil.)	NET PROFIT MARGIN	EMPLOYEES
06/19	855	62	7.3%	208
06/15	381	25	6.8%	—
06/14	297	24	8.3%	—
Annual Growth	23.5%	20.4%	—	—

2019 Year-End Financials

Return on assets: 13.4%
Return on equity: 28.8%
Current ratio: 0.30
Cash ($ mil.): 39

WESTERN OREGON UNIVERSITY

EXECUTIVES

Pres, Mark D Weiss
Project Coordinator, Angela Christensen
Staff, Heitho Reuter
Assistant Professor, Lauren Roscoe
Natural Science, Michael Baltzley
Coordinator, Emily Lafon
Associate Professor of Compute, Becka Morgan
Assistant Professor, Erin Barnes
Project Coordinator, Gina Herrera
Project Coordinator, Ruth McDonald
Assistant, Elizabeth Balding

LOCATIONS

HQ: WESTERN OREGON UNIVERSITY
345 MONMOUTH AVE N, MONMOUTH, OR 973611329
Phone: 503 838-8000
Web: WWW.WOU.EDU

HISTORICAL FINANCIALS

Company Type: Private

Income Statement — FYE: June 30

	REVENUE ($ mil.)	NET INCOME ($ mil.)	NET PROFIT MARGIN	EMPLOYEES
06/08	1,251	80	6.4%	706
06/06*	0	(0)	—	—
12/05	1	0	30.1%	—
06/04	1	0	22.9%	—
Annual Growth	483.6%	324.8%	—	—

*Fiscal year change

2008 Year-End Financials

Return on assets: —
Return on equity: 6.4%
Current ratio: 0.70
Cash ($ mil.): 355

WGL HOLDINGS, INC.

WGL Holdings owners of the regulated Washington Gas Light Company sells natural gas to more than 1 million customers in the District of Columbia Maryland and Virginia. It has about 600 miles of transmission mains more than 13000 miles of distribution mains and some 12500 miles of distribution lines. The company's unregulated segment also provides energy marketing clean-energy products and services and midstream asset management. In July 2018 WGL Holdings was bought by Canada-based AltaGas for $6.4 billion deal.

Operations

WGL Holdings has four segments: Regulated Utility Retail Energy-Marketing Commercial Energy Systems and Midstream Energy Services.

Regulated Utility (more than 50% of revenue) consists of Washington Gas (regulated gas distribution/transportation services) and Hampshire Gas (regulated interstate natural gas storage services).

The Retail Energy-Marketing (some 40%) competes with regulated utilities and unregulated third-party marketers to sell natural gas and electricity to some 210000 customers in Maryland Virginia Delaware Pennsylvania and DC.

Commercial Energy Systems sells products like solar PV systems combined heat and power plants and natural gas fuel cells; it also provides installation services for technological upgrades. It generates 340000 megawatt hours of clean energy a year.

Midstream Energy Services manages natural gas storage and transportation assets.

Geographic Reach

WGL Holdings primarily operates in Washington DC Maryland and Virginia. It also serves customers across the US through its non-utility segments. Washington Gas has peak shaving facilities in Springfield Virginia (Ravensworth Plant) and Rockville Maryland (Rockville Plant).

Sales and Marketing

WGL sells and delivers natural gas and/or electricity directly to residential commercial and industrial customers. Washington Gas has some 1.2 million customers in the District of Columbia Maryland and Virginia while its Energy Services business count some 210000 retail customers in the same area.

Financial Performance

WGL has not been a growing company lately. In the last five years company revenue fell from $2.7 billion in 2014 to $2.3 billion in 2018. In 2018 (ended September 30) revenue fell less than a percentage point to $2.34 billion (compared to $2.35 billion in 2017). The fall came due to lower sales volumes in the retail energy (non-utility) business.

Net income slashed from $192 million in 2017 to $49 million in 2018 mostly due to a YOY $364 million increase in operation and maintenance costs related to the merger with AltaGas as well as a YOY $114 million increase in the utility cost of gas. Lower realized margins in the regulated utility segment further reduced its coffers.

Cash holdings at the company shot up from only $8 billion at the end of 2017 to $122 million at 2018 end. Operations provided $322 million and a further $715 million came in from financial activities which was offset by $923 million going into investments.

Company Background

WGL was established in the year 2000 as a Virginia corporation. On January 25 2017 WGL entered into an Agreement and Plan of Merger (Merger Agreement) to combine with AltaGas Ltd. a Canadian Corporation (AltaGas). On July 6 2018 the merger was consummated between AltaGas WGL and Wrangler Inc. (Merger Sub) a newly formed indirect wholly owned subsidiary of AltaGas.

EXECUTIVES

President And Coo Wgl Holdings Inc. And Washington Gas Light Company, Adrian P. Chapman, $551,000 total compensation
Svp And Cfo Wgl Holdings And Washington Gas Light Company, Vincent L. Ammann, $460,000 total compensation
Chairman And Ceo Wgl Holdings And Washington Gas Light Company, Terry D. McCallister, $824,000 total compensation
Vp Strategy Business Development And Non-utility Operations, Gautam Chandra, $420,000 total compensation
Svp General Counsel And Corporate Secretary, Leslie Thornton, $380,000 total compensation
Executive Vice President Business Development Of The Bank, Nigeria Poole

LOCATIONS

HQ: WGL HOLDINGS, INC.
1000 MAINE AVE SW, WASHINGTON, DC 200243494
Phone: 202 624-6011
Web: WWW.WGLHOLDINGS.COM

PRODUCTS/OPERATIONS

2018 Sales

	$ mil.	% of total
Retail energy marketing	1,009	42
Utility	1,248	53
Commercial energy services	79	3
Midstream energy services	40	2
Eliminations	(36.4)	-
Total	**2,341**	**100**

2018 Sales

	$ mil.	% of total
Non-utility	1,112	47
Utility	1,229	53
Total	**2,341**	**100**

Selected Subsidiaries

Hampshire Gas Company (underground natural gas storage)
Wrangler SPE LLC
Washington Gas Light Company (natural gas utility)
Washington Gas Resources Corp. (nonregulated business holding company)
  Washington Gas Energy Services Inc. (retail energy services)
  Washington Gas Energy Systems Inc. (commercial energy systems and HVAC services)

COMPETITORS

Appalachian Power
Comfort Systems USA
Commerce Energy Group
Constellation Energy Group
Dominion Energy
FirstEnergy
Northern Virginia Electric Cooperative
Pepco Holdings
RGC Resources
Rappahannock Electric Cooperative

HISTORICAL FINANCIALS

Company Type: Private

Income Statement — FYE: September 30

	REVENUE ($ mil.)	NET INCOME ($ mil.)	NET PROFIT MARGIN	EMPLOYEES
09/18	2,341	21	0.9%	1,586
09/17	2,354	177	7.6%	—
09/16	2,349	168	7.2%	—
09/15	2,659	132	5.0%	—
Annual Growth	(4.2%)	(45.8%)	—	—

2018 Year-End Financials

Return on assets: 0.3%
Return on equity: 1.2%
Current ratio: 0.60
Cash ($ mil.): 57

WHEATLAND UNION HIGH SCHOOL DISTRICT

EXECUTIVES

Supt, Glenn Sewll
Manager, Johnny Anderson
Auditors: DENNIS COOPER & ASSOCIATES CPA

LOCATIONS

HQ: WHEATLAND UNION HIGH SCHOOL DISTRICT
1010 WHEATLAND RD, WHEATLAND, CA 956929798
Phone: 530 633-3100
Web: WWW.WHEATLANDHIGH.ORG

HISTORICAL FINANCIALS

Company Type: Private

Income Statement — FYE: June 30

	REVENUE ($ mil.)	NET INCOME ($ mil.)	NET PROFIT MARGIN	EMPLOYEES
06/19	11,464	788	6.9%	76
06/18	9	0	7.3%	—
06/17	9,186	(1,399)	—	—
06/16	8,941	94	1.1%	—
Annual Growth	8.6%	103.0%	—	—

WHEATON FRANCISCAN SERVICES, INC.

Wheaton Franciscan Services Inc. (WFSI) is the not-for-profit parent company for more than 100 health care housing and social service organizations in Colorado Illinois Iowa and Wisconsin. Also known as Wheaton Franciscan Healthcare WFSI operates about 15 hospitals including Affinity Health System Rush Oak Park Hospital and United Hospital System with more than 1600 beds total. WFSI also includes long-term care centers home health agencies and physician offices. Its Franciscan Ministries division provides affordable housing units including assisted-living facilities and low-income dwellings. The health system is sponsored by The Franciscan Sisters Daughters of the Sacred Hearts of Jesus and Mary.

Operations

Many of WFSI's hospitals are operated in partnership with other area providers. For instance the Affinity Health System in Wisconsin is jointly sponsored by Wheaton Franciscan Sisters and Ministry Health Care while the Rush Oak Park Hospital in Illinois is operated through a partnership between WFSI and the Rush System for Health.

The health system partners with the YMCA of Milwaukee to try to address chronic health concerns of area residents. The two organizations converted a local YMCA campus into the YMCA Healthy Lifestyle Village. The center offers health screenings health education outpatient therapy and fitness services. WFSI and the YMCA have more Healthy Lifestyle Village campuses planned for other locations within their service areas.

The organization had a total of 1656 beds and 2620 housing units at the end of 2014.

In fiscal 2013 WSFI delivered more than 8000 babies and had more than 330000 emergency department visits. It reported more than 1580000 outpatient visits and some 64000 hospital admissions. It employs more than 500 physicians and has some 2000 affiliated physicians.

Geographic Reach

WFSI operates in Wisconsin Iowa Colorado and Illinois.

Financial Performance

The not-for-profit system's revenues were flat in fiscal 2014 at $1.8 billion. Net income totaled $184 million.

Strategy

To increase the scope of specialty health care services it can provide to the community WFSI recruits new physicians and specialists to the Wheaton Franciscan Medical Group. The system also works to improve communication among its physicians and facilities by adding electronic health record (EHR) systems.

In 2013 the system opened a new 80000-sq.-ft. outpatient center specializing in neurology services.

Company Background

The Franciscan Sisters Daughters of the Sacred Hearts of Jesus and Mary (also known as the Wheaton Franciscan Sisters) founded WSFI in 1983 as a holding company for their ministry operations. The health system traces its roots back to the founding of the St. Mary's Hospital in Racine Wisconsin in 1882.

EXECUTIVES

Vice President Construction And Facilities Services, Ron Boecker
Board Of Director, Michael Murry
Auditors: KPMG LLP CHICAGO IL

LOCATIONS

HQ: WHEATON FRANCISCAN SERVICES, INC.
400 W RIVER WOODS PKWY, GLENDALE, WI 532121060
Phone: 414 465-3000
Web: WWW.MYWHEATON.ORG

PRODUCTS/OPERATIONS

Selected Operations

Franciscan Ministries Inc. (housing in Colorado Illinois Iowa and Wisconsin)
Illinois
  Marianjoy Rehabilitation Hospital (Wheaton)
  Rush Oak Park Hospital (affiliate Oak Park)
Iowa (Wheaton Franciscan Healthcare of Iowa)
  Covenant Medical Center (Waterloo)
  Mercy Hospital (Oelwein)
  Sartori Memorial Hospital (Cedar Falls)
Wisconsin
  Affinity Health System (partnership with Minstry Health Care)
  Calumet Medical Center (Chilton)
  Mercy Medical Center (Oshkosh)
  St. Elizabeth Hospital (Appleton)
  Wheaton Franciscan Healthcare of Southeast Wisconsin
  All Saints Hospital (two campuses in Racine)
  Elmbrook Memorial Hospital (Brookfield)
  Franklin Hospital (Franklin)
  St. Francis Hospital (Milwaukee)
  St. Joseph Hospital (Milwaukee)
  Wisconsin Heart Hospital (Wauwatosa)
  United Hospital System Inc. (affiliated system)
  Kenosha Medical Center (Kenosha)
  St. Catherine's Medical Center (Pleasant Prairie)

COMPETITORS

Advocate Health Care
Alden Management Services
Children's Hospital and Health System
Columbia St. Mary's
Elmhurst Memorial Healthcare
FHN
Froedtert Hospital
Hospital Sisters Health System
KishHealth
Loyola University Health System
Ministry Health Care
Morris Hospital
NorthShore University HealthSystem
OSF Healthcare System
ProHealth Care
Rockford Health System
SwedishAmerican Health System

HISTORICAL FINANCIALS

Company Type: Private

Income Statement FYE: June 30

	REVENUE ($ mil.)	NET INCOME ($ mil.)	NET PROFIT MARGIN	EMPLOYEES
06/15	1,809	18	1.0%	18,000
06/14	1,754	128	7.3%	—
06/13	1,763	177	10.1%	—
06/12	1,723	(112)	—	—
Annual Growth	1.6%	—	—	—

2015 Year-End Financials

Return on assets: 0.8%
Return on equity: 1.6%
Current ratio: 1.30
Cash ($ mil.): 81

WHITE PLAINS HOSPITAL MEDICAL CENTER

EXECUTIVES

Pres-Ceo, Jon B Schandler
Chb, Paul Weissman
Pres, Susan Fox
Exec V Pres-Coo, Edward F Leonard
V Pres-Fin-Cfo, John Schiurba
Chief Operating Officer, Jeffrey Tiesi
Information Specialist, Allison Schurko
Information Specialist, Anna Perselis
Information Specialist, Carmita Pacheco
Information Specialist, Celia Caceres
Information Specialist, Christin Barnett

LOCATIONS

HQ: WHITE PLAINS HOSPITAL MEDICAL CENTER
41 E POST RD, WHITE PLAINS, NY 106014607
Phone: 914 681-0600
Web: WWW.WPHOSPITAL.ORG

HISTORICAL FINANCIALS

Company Type: Private

Income Statement FYE: December 31

	REVENUE ($ mil.)	NET INCOME ($ mil.)	NET PROFIT MARGIN	EMPLOYEES
12/17	620	40	6.5%	2,000
12/16	460	23	5.1%	—
12/15	389	23	6.1%	—
12/14	353	8	2.3%	—
Annual Growth	20.7%	70.9%	—	—

2017 Year-End Financials

Return on assets: 5.9%
Return on equity: 10.1%
Current ratio: 1.00
Cash ($ mil.): 45

WHOLE FOODS MARKET, INC.

Whole Foods Market is the world's largest natural foods grocery chain. Founded in 1980 it pioneered the supermarket concept in natural and organic foods retailing. The company operates more than 500 stores throughout the US Canada and the UK. It sells private-label items through its 365 Organic Everyday Value and Allegro Coffee lines among others and offers a variety of non-GMO vegan and gluten-free foods.

HISTORY

With a $10000 loan from his father John Mackey started SaferWay Natural Foods in Austin Texas in 1978. Despite struggling Mackey dreamed of opening a larger supermarket-sized natural foods store. Two years later SaferWay merged with Clarksville Natural Grocery and Whole Foods Market was born. Led by Mackey that year it opened an 11000-sq.-ft. supermarket in the counterculture hotbed of Austin. The store was an instant success and a second store was added 18 months later in suburban Austin.

The company slowly expanded in Texas opening or buying stores in Houston in 1984 and Dallas in 1986. Whole Foods expanded into Louisiana in 1988 with the purchase of like-named Whole Food Co. a single New Orleans store owned by Peter Roy (who served as the company's president from 1993 to 1998). Sticking to university towns Whole Foods added another store in California the next year and acquired Wellspring Grocery (two stores North Carolina) in 1991. In 1992 it debuted its first private-label products under the Whole Foods name. Seeking capital to expand even more the company raised $23 million by going public in early 1992 with 12 stores.

Every competitor in the fragmented health foods industry became a potential acquisition and the chain began growing rapidly. In 1992 Whole Foods bought the six-store Bread & Circus chain in New England. The next year it added Mrs. Gooch's Natural Foods Markets (seven stores in the Los Angeles area). Its biggest acquisition came in 1996 when it bought Fresh Fields the second-largest US natural foods chain (22 stores on the East Coast and in Chicago). Although the purchase hurt profits in 1996 sales surpassed $1 billion for the first time in fiscal 1997 as Whole Foods neared 70 stores. In 1997 it introduced the less-expensive 365 private label and acquired the Granary Market (Monterey California) and Bread of Life (two stores South Florida) natural foods supermarkets.

Capitalizing on the growing popularity of nutraceuticals (natural supplements with benefits similar to pharmaceuticals) the company paid $146 million in 1997 for Amrion a maker of nutraceuticals and other nutritional supplements (merged with subsidiary WholePeople.com in 2000). It capped the year by buying coffee roaster Allegro Coffee. (Both companies are based in Boulder Colorado home of its former main rival the smaller Wild Oats.) Also in 1997 Whole Foods acquired the six-store Merchant of Vino natural foods and wine shop chain to foster the development of its wine departments.

In 1998 Whole Foods opened its first store in Boulder – a 39000-sq.-ft. superstore with amenities such as a juice bar and a prepared foods section. At year's end Roy resigned as president and was replaced by Chris Hitt. In 1999 Whole Foods bought four-store Boston-area chain Nature's Heartland.

In 2000 Whole Foods merged its online operations (wholefoods.com) with its direct marketing and nutritional supplement unit (Amrion) to form Wholepeople.com. Later that year the company merged Wholepeople.com with lifestyle marketing firm Gaiam; Whole Foods received a minority stake in Gaiam and started selling food online through Gaiam.com.

Hitt resigned in mid-2001 and Mackey took over his duties. Later that year Whole Foods acquired the three upscale Harry's Farmers Market stores in Atlanta; the sale did not include the Harry's In A Hurry stores which later shut down.

In 2002 Whole Foods crossed the border into Canada. Its first foreign store opened in downtown Toronto that May.

Mackey was named Entrepreneur of the Year in 2003 by consulting firm Ernst & Young. That year Whole Foods acquired Select Fish a Seattle-based seafood processor and distributor and opened a seafood distribution facility in Atlanta.

In 2004 Whole Foods opened a 59000-sq.-ft. store in the new Time Warner Center in Manhattan. The new store which includes a 248-seat cafe sushi bar wine shop and gourmet bakery is the largest supermarket in New York City. That year the company acquired the UK organic-food retailer Fresh & Wild for $38 million.

To support its rapid growth in 2004 Whole Foods Market expanded its number of operating regions from eight to 10 by separating the Southwest region into the Southwest and Rocky Mountain regions and the Northern Pacific region into the Northern California and Pacific Northwest region. The company announced the opening of its first Gluten-Free Bakehouse a dedicated gluten-free baking facility located outside Raleigh North Carolina. Overall the company opened 12 new stores in 2004.

In January 2005 Whole Foods launched the Animal Compassion Foundation an independent nonprofit organization dedicated to the compassionate treatment of livestock. The company moved that month to its new corporate headquarters across the street from its old location in downtown Austin. Its new flagship store opened its doors in March at the same location. In October Whole Foods increased its number of operating regions from 10 to 11 by separating the North Atlantic region into the North Atlantic and Tri-State regions. Overall in fiscal 2005 the company opened a dozen new stores including its first in Nebraska and Ohio. In 2006 the company acquired a store in Portland Maine and converted it to the Whole Foods Market banner.

In August 2007 Whole Foods acquired its main competitor – Boulder Colorado-based Wild Oats Markets – in a deal valued at about $565 million (plus $106 million in debt). In early October the company sold 35 Henry's Farmers Market and Sun Harvest stores to a subsidiary of Los Angeles-based Smart & Final for about $166 million. The stores in California and Texas were acquired with Wild Oats.

The company launched a bi-monthly magazine called Whole Foods Market Magazine at its midwestern stores in 2008. On the heels of its disappointing third-quarter results in August 2008 shares of the company's stock fell to a six-year low and Whole Foods suspended its dividend. Blaming the poor economy the company announced the layoffs of some 50 employees at its Austin headquarters in August 2008. Overall in fiscal 2008 the company introduced about 300 new private-label items.

For the first time in its 29-year history Whole Foods reported negative same-store sales in the quarter ended December 2008 as traffic in its stores fell.

In March 2009 the company reached a settlement in its long-running dispute with the FTC over its acquisition of Wild Oats in 2007. Whole Foods agreed to sell 32 stores including 19 Wild Oats locations that had already been closed. In exchange the FTC dropped its crusade to undo the merger. In December 2009 John Elstrott was named chairman of Whole Foods Market after Mackey voluntarily relinquished the chairmanship which he had held since 1980. In May 2010 Walter Robb formerly co-president of the company was promoted to co-CEO of Whole Foods a title he now shares with Mackey.

EXECUTIVES

Ceo, John P. Mackey, $1 total compensation
President And Coo, A. C. Gallo, $501,110 total compensation
President Florida Region, Juan Nuñez
Chairman Whole Kids Foundation And Whole Cities Foundation, Walter E. Robb, $501,110 total compensation
Evp Operations U.s. And Whole Foods 365, David Lannon, $501,110 total compensation
Vp Purchasing Midwest Division, Jeff Turnas
Evp Operations, Christina Minardi
President Southern Pacific Region, Patrick Bradley
President Mid-atlantic Region, Scott Allshouse
President Rocky Mountain Region, Bill Jordan
President Midwest Region, Michael Bashaw
President North Atlantic Region, Laura Derba
Evp And Cio, Jason Buechel, $501,110 total compensation
President South Region, Omar Gaye
President Northern California Region, Rob Twyman
Evp Operations U.s. And The U.k., Kenneth (Ken) Meyer, $486,510 total compensation
Evp Growth And Business Development, James (Jim) Sud, $486,510 total compensation
Evp And Cfo, Keith Manbeck
President Pacific Northwest Region, Angela Lorenzen
Global Vp Marketing, Sonya Gafsi Oblisk
President Northeast Region, Nicole Wescoe
Global Vice President, Bart Beilman
Global Vice President, Lee Matecko
Executive Vice President Operations, Kenny Meyer
Vice President And Marketing Manager, Desa Abbamondi
Vice President Vendor Manager, Ray Hudson
Global Vice President Commmunications, Brooke Buchanan
Vice President And Loan Officer And Branch Manager, Francisco Ibarra
Assistant Vice President Product Manager Marketing, Merijoy Rucker
Regional Vice President, Scott Saulsberry
Regional Vice President, Tim Gates
Vice President Of Information Technology, Shawn Williams
Vice President Digital Marketing Crm Loyalty And Ecommerce, Ryan Linders
Vice President Brand, Madhavi Reese
Chairman, John B. Elstrott
Auditors: ERNST & YOUNG LLP AUSTIN TEX

LOCATIONS

HQ: WHOLE FOODS MARKET, INC.
550 BOWIE ST, AUSTIN, TX 787034644
Phone: 512 477-4455
Web: WWW.WHOLEFOODSMARKET.COM

PRODUCTS/OPERATIONS

Selected Product Categories

Bakery
Body care
Educational products
Floral
Grocery
Household products
Meat and poultry
Nutritional supplements
Pet products
Prepared foods
Produce
Seafood
Specialty (beer wine cheese)
Textiles

COMPETITORS

ALDI
Albertsons
Costco Wholesale
Fiesta Mart
GNC
H-E-B
Kroger
Loblaw
Natural Grocers by Vitamin Cottage
Publix
Safeway
Sprouts
Tesco
Trader Joe's
Wal-Mart

HISTORICAL FINANCIALS

Company Type: Private

Income Statement — FYE: September 24

	REVENUE ($ mil.)	NET INCOME ($ mil.)	NET PROFIT MARGIN	EMPLOYEES
09/17	16,030	245	1.5%	95,000
09/16	15,724	507	3.2%	—
09/15	15,389	536	3.5%	—
09/14	14,194	579	4.1%	—
Annual Growth	4.1%	(24.9%)	—	—

2017 Year-End Financials

Return on assets: 3.7%
Return on equity: 7.1%
Current ratio: 1.60
Cash ($ mil.): 322

WILBUR-ELLIS HOLDINGS II, INC.

"Seed 'em weed 'em and feed 'em" could be the motto of San Francisco's Wilbur-Ellis Co. (aka WECO). Through its agribusiness division WECO sells fertilizer herbicides insecticides seed and farm machinery in North America. The Connell Bros. unit exports and distributes food ingredients and specialty chemicals throughout the Pacific Rim. Its feed division serves international customers in the livestock pet food and aquaculture industries. Additionally WECO provides consulting pesticide application and other agriculture-related services. Beyond North America WECO has operations in about 15 countries in the Asia/Pacific Region. WECO was founded in 1921 by Brayton Wilbur Sr. and Floyd Ellis.

Operations

WECO's Agribusiness division is one of the top marketers and distributors of agricultural products in the US with sales of $2 billion. Connell Bros. is the largest marketer and distributor of specialty chemicals and ingredients with about three dozen offices across the Asia/Pacific region and annual sales of about $815 million. The $500-million-in-sales Feed division supplies value-added feed ingredients and markets for customers' by-products.

Geographic Reach

The San Francisco-based company has agribusiness operations in the West Southwest and Midwest regions on the US. Connell Bros. has offices in 17 countries across the Asia/Pacific Region including Australia China and Vietnam. The Feed unit has operations in North America and in Australia and New Zealand.

Sales and Marketing

WECO's ProMarket business serves such markets as nurseries greenhouses forests and golf courses and sporting facilities. The Connel Bros. division sells ingredients and specialty chemicals to the coatings food personal care plastics paper construction and other industries.

Financial Performance

WECO's annual sales continue to exceed $3 billion.

Strategy

WECO employs a strategy of acquiring successful businesses and integrating them into its existing operations. Geography is no barrier when it comes to buying companies: The group has acquired operations in such faraway places as Malaysia Taiwan the Philippines China Australia and New Zealand. WECO continues to expand both through acquisitions and organically across its three divisions.

Mergers and Acquisitions

The company continued its acquisitive streak in 2014 and 2015. In early 2014 it acquired one of its alliance partners New Horizons Ag Service an agricultural retail business in Elgin North Dakota. New Horizons became part of Wilbur-Ellis Midwest. The company also acquired Accu-Rate Services a full-service agricultural retailer in Sedgwick Kansas and Advanced Ag located in Creston Iowa. Other agribusinesses added in 2014 included retail facility Poynter's Ag Supply (North Dakota) and feed provider Allied Premium Protein.

Also that year WECO's Connell Brothers unit purchased Enzyme Solutions of Melbourne Australia extending its capabilities in enzymes. Furthering its Asia/Pacific business it acquired Bioworld Fine Chemical (Shanghai) which distributes upscale botanical oils and plant extracts.

Agribusiness purchases in 2015 include The Seed House a Nebraska-based professional seed company; Lacey's Farmacy a South Dakota-based agriculture retail outfit and Aero Spray Services an aerial spraying and fire-fighting firm also based in South Dakota.

EXECUTIVES

Vp Treasurer And Cfo, James D. Crawford
President Agribusiness Division, Daniel R. (Dan) Vradenburg
Vp Strategic Planning And Business Development, John P. Thacher
Vp South Central Operations, Steven J. Dietze
Vp Western Operations, Scott Hushbeck
General Manager Canadian Feed Division North Vancouver And Saskatoon, Rob Fullerton
President Wilbur-ellis Japan, Iguchi Shinichi
President Connell Brothers, Azita Owlia
Vice President Finance, Steve Flowers
Chairman, Herbert B. Tully
Auditors: PRICEWATERHOUSECOOPERS

LOCATIONS

HQ: WILBUR-ELLIS HOLDINGS II, INC.
345 CALIFORNIA ST FL 27, SAN FRANCISCO, CA 941042644
Phone: 415 772-4000
Web: WWW.WILBURELLIS.COM

PRODUCTS/OPERATIONS

Selected Products and Services

Agribusiness Division
- Agricultural chemicals
- Fertilizers
- Fungicides
- Herbicides
- Insecticides
- Machinery
- Pesticides
- Seed protectants
- Seed treatments
- Sprayers
- Supply-chain management

Connell Bros. Division
- Industrial chemicals

Feed Division
- Aquaculture products
- Feed ingredients
- Food oils
- Forage products
- Pet food

Professional Products
- Forestry
- Fungicides
- Herbicides
- Golf
- Fungicides
- Landscape
- Fungicides
- Nursery/Greenhouse
- Fungicides
- Vegetation Management
- Selective and nonselective growth regulators

COMPETITORS

ADM
AGRI Industries
Ag Processing Inc.
Andersons
BASF SE
Bayer CropScience
CF Industries
CHS
Cargill
Dow AgroSciences
DuPont Agriculture
Frontier Agriculture
GROWMARK
Goulding Chemicals
Ingredion
JR Simplot
Land O'Lakes Purina Feed
Southern States

HISTORICAL FINANCIALS

Company Type: Private

Income Statement — FYE: December 31

	REVENUE ($ mil.)	NET INCOME ($ mil.)	NET PROFIT MARGIN	EMPLOYEES
12/11	2,812	0	—	4,600
12/10	2,342	0	—	—
12/09	0	0	—	—
12/00	1,100	0	—	—
Annual Growth	8.9%	—	—	—

WILLIAM BEAUMONT HOSPITAL

EXECUTIVES

Ceo-Pres, Gene Michalski
Pres, Brian Connolly
SEC, Gale R Colwell
Treas, Barbara Mahone
Chief Med, Ananias Diokno
Chm, Stephen R Howard
V Chm, Mark Shaevsky
Sr V Pres, Margaret Casey
Fo/Exe V Pres, John Keuten
Director, Hadley Mack French
Director, Martha James Quay

LOCATIONS

HQ: WILLIAM BEAUMONT HOSPITAL
3601 W 13 MILE RD, ROYAL OAK, MI 480736712
Phone: 248 898-5000
Web: WWW.BEAUMONTHOSPITALS.COM

HISTORICAL FINANCIALS

Company Type: Private

Income Statement — FYE: December 31

	REVENUE ($ mil.)	NET INCOME ($ mil.)	NET PROFIT MARGIN	EMPLOYEES
12/18	1,556	91	5.9%	18,050
12/17	1,473	71	4.9%	—
12/16	1,396	118	8.5%	—
12/15	1,300	142	10.9%	—
Annual Growth	6.2%	(13.7%)	—	—

2018 Year-End Financials

Return on assets: 6.3%
Return on equity: 6.5%
Current ratio: 3.00
Cash ($ mil.): 129

WILMINGTON TRUST COMPANY

EXECUTIVES

Chief Executive Officer, Robert Harra
Vice President, Eric Cheung
Assistant Vice President, David Cuocolo
Group Vice President, Richard Marsh
Vice President, Joseph Brooks
Vice President, Mary Pupillo
Vice President, Peter Finkel
Assistant Vice President, Donald Haverstick
Vice President, Steven Cimalore
Vice President Global Capital Markets, Vito Iacovazzi
Vice President Private Banking, Heather Ford
Vp And Manager Business Application Support, Gary Powers
Assistant Vice President, Yvette Howell
Vice President Inv. Management Support Services, Edward Moon
Vice President, Michael Orendorf
Vice President Global Capital Markets, Nicholas Adams
Vice President, Mary Avery
Vice President, Jeanne Oller
Vice President, Margaret Pulgini
Vice President, Sergio Godinho
Assistant Vice President Corporate Trust Custody, Erik Saville
Vice President, Jennifer Matz
Training Manager Vice President, Lynn Dibonaventura
Vice President, Charles Hicks
Assistant Vice President, Steve Barone
Vice President, Lisa Fricke
Vice President Wilmington Trust Fsb, Josh Stump
Vice President, Wendy White
Vice President, Sandra Plowinske
Vice President, Janice Cirillo
Vice President, George Chen
Assistant Vice President Talen, Kathryn Spencer
Assistant Vice President, Adam Vogelsong
Vice President Of Data Center, Ed Olkowski
Vice President, Thomas Raymond
Vice President Corporate Client Services, Christie Longo
Vice President Client Development, Rob Barnett
Vice President, Jeanette Madaya
Vice President, Kevin Bruggeman
Assistant Vice President, Michael Oller
Vice President, Jeffrey Wolken
Vice President, Nadine Black
Vice President Risk Manager, Holly Stiefel
Assistant Vice President, Laura Barone
Vice President Director, Bette Francis
Assistant Vice President, William Morris
Vice President Director Of Wisd Vendor Management, Bill Cunnion
Vice President, Arlene Moyer
Vice President, Karen Touchstone
Assistant Vice President, Liz Hudgens
Vice President, Virginia Machamer
Vice President Network And Desktop Computing, Rob Averbach
Assistant Vice President, Beth Power
Vice President Director Client Services Institu, Amy Roe
Vice President, Robert Quinn
Vice President, Jane Snyder
Assistant Vice President, Greg Cherewko
Vice President And Portfolio Manager, Luke Betterly
Vice President, Joe Fahey
Vice President Wealth Advisory Senior Private Client Fiduciary Advisor, Latonya Hubbard
Vice President, Steven Kochie
Vice President Marketing Manager, Andrea Spahr
Vice President, Thomas Herring
Vice President And Senior Private Client Fiduciary Advisor, Cindy White
Vice President Esop Services, Kristy Britsch
Vice President, Kara Partin
Assistant Vice President, Ryan Thompson
Vice President, Jason Johnson
Executive Vice President, Bill Farrell
Regional Vice President, John Breda
Assistant Vice President, Rachel Simpson
Vice President And Senior Client Development Officer For Wtris, Robert Barnett
Vice President Senior Fiduciary Advisor, Lori Brodbeck
Vice President, Chris Slaybaugh
Assistant Vice President, Thomas Kalafut
Assistant Vice President, Elizabeth Bothner
Vice President Senior Investment Advisor, Mark Stevenson
Assistant Vice President Of Lending, Mary Fisher
Vice President, Rebecca Rogers
Vice President, Glenn Best
Vice President, Clay Weisenberg
Assistant Vice President Loan Agency Group, Jennifer Anderson
Executive Vice President Of The Company Mandt Bank And Wilmington Trust Investment Advisors, Doris Meister
Vice President, John Kelley
Vice President Equity Management, Mark Horst
Vice President Corporate Capital Markets, Aaron Soper
Assistant Vice President, Michael Moorehead
Assistant Vice President, Barry Butina
Vice President, Robert Reynolds
Assistant Vice President, Bonnie Metcalfe
Vice President, Carl Robinson
Assistant Vice President, Chad May
Vice President And Private Client Fiduciary Advisor, Karen Kiley
Vice President, Robert Collins
Assistant Vice President Global Capital Markets, Clarice Wright
Group Vice President, Laura Havranek
Assistant Vice President, Melissa Jalace-vasold
Vice President Senior Private Client Advisor, Sandra Besso Plowinske

Vice President, Ann Harris-johnson
Vice President, Christopher Guardino
Vice President Director Of Sales, Gregory Hasty
Vice President, Mark Gerstenschlager
Vice President Regional Marketing Director, Laura Cleveland
Assistant Vice President, Joann Petry
Avp, Lisa Lewis
Assistant Vice President, Carleen Terranova
Vice President Wealth Advisory Services, Paul Bartkowski
Assistant Vice President Commercial Real Estate, Rachel Skrabak
Vice President Channel Management, John J Hurley
Assistant Vice President, Greg Golden
Assistant Vice President, Melissa Marion
Vice President, Karen Bonn
Vice President And Senior Private Client Investment Advisor, Sue Schnaars
Vice President Private Banking, Julia Odonnell
Assistant Vice President, Brenda Parker
Vice President, Al Miller
Vice President, Barbara Obrien
Vice President, Charlie Buehler
Vice President And Senior Investment Advisor, Andrew Cloud
Assistant Vice President, Andrea Rybczynski
Vice President, Joseph Odonnell
Vice President, Renee Buchner
Assistant Vice President, Nancy Hagner
Assistant Vice President, Catherine Chandler
Vice President, Kyle Barry
Assistant Vice President, Maureen Auld
Vice President, Denise Sbraccia
Assistant Vice President, Sophie Pendolino
Assistant Vice President, Christopher Hickok
Assistant Vice President, Ruth Ann Mcmillen
Assistant Vice President, Jose Paredes
Vice President, Howard Gordon
Vice President, David Bagley
Vice President Private Client Advisor, Ed Barone
Vice President, Jeffrey Ritchie
Vice President, Kaye Crouch
Assistant Vice President, Kevin Ebert
Vice President, Nickole Garrison
Vice President Senior Private Banker, Nicholas Macechko
Assistant Vice President, Russell Whitley
Assistant Vice President, Matthew Lyndaker
Vice President And Investment Advisor, Darren Jordan
Vice President, Erin Miller
Vice President, William Gering
Vice President, Joseph Baker
Vice President, Stephen Seivold
Vice President, Theresa Drew
Assistant Vice President, Tammy Krawczyk
Vice President, Todd Bemiller
Vice President, Brooks Von Arx Jr
Vice President And Team Leader, Donald Hargadon

LOCATIONS

HQ: WILMINGTON TRUST COMPANY
1100 N MARKET ST, WILMINGTON, DE 198900001
Phone: 302 651-1000
Web: WWW.WILMINGTONTRUST.COM

HISTORICAL FINANCIALS

Company Type: Private

Income Statement — FYE: December 31

	ASSETS ($ mil.)	NET INCOME ($ mil.)	INCOME AS % OF ASSETS	EMPLOYEES
12/17	4,960	30	0.6%	1,818
12/16	3,685	17	0.5%	—
12/15	1,928	36	1.9%	—
Annual Growth	60.4%	(9.0%)	—	—

2017 Year-End Financials

Return on assets: 0.6%
Return on equity: 5.7%
Sales ($ mil): 234

WINCO HOLDINGS, INC.

EXECUTIVES

Pres-Ceo, Steven Goddard
Vp-Cfo-Sec-treas, David Butler
Vp-Coo, Richard Charrier
Chb, Gary R Piva
Vice-President Engineering, Dick Vanderlinden
Business Analyst, Dustin Earl
Engineer, Matthew Sabin
Administrator, Jason Murphy
Vice-President Engineering, David V Etten
Director Private Brands, Susan Barry
Buyer Deli, Stephan Bosch
Auditors: KPMG LLP BOISE ID

LOCATIONS

HQ: WINCO HOLDINGS, INC.
650 N ARMSTRONG PL, BOISE, ID 837040825
Phone: 208 377-0110

HISTORICAL FINANCIALS

Company Type: Private

Income Statement — FYE: March 28

	REVENUE ($ mil.)	NET INCOME ($ mil.)	NET PROFIT MARGIN	EMPLOYEES
03/09	4,104	225	5.5%	14,000
03/08	3,515	132	3.8%	—
03/07	2,976	106	3.6%	—
Annual Growth	17.4%	45.5%	—	—

2009 Year-End Financials

Return on assets: 15.2%
Return on equity: 24.4%
Current ratio: 1.30
Cash ($ mil.): 146

WINDSTREAM EAGLE HOLDINGS, LLC

EXECUTIVES

Ceo-Pres, Tony Thomas
Cfo, Bob Gunderman
Ezec V Pres-CHR, John Fletcher
Cmo, Joe Harding
Exec V Pres-Enterprises Sales, Jeff Howe
Pres-Consumer, Sarah Day
Pres-Wholesale, Mike Shippey
Exec V Pres-Access, John Dobbins
Exec V Pres, Engr, Jeff Small
Auditors: ERNST & YOUNG LLP ATLANTA GE

LOCATIONS

HQ: WINDSTREAM EAGLE HOLDINGS, LLC
4001 N RODNEY PARHAM RD, LITTLE ROCK, AR 722122459
Phone: 501 748-5839
Web: WWW.CORP.EARTHLINK.COM

HISTORICAL FINANCIALS

Company Type: Private

Income Statement — FYE: December 31

	REVENUE ($ mil.)	NET INCOME ($ mil.)	NET PROFIT MARGIN	EMPLOYEES
12/16	959	7	0.8%	60
12/15	1,097	(43)	—	—
12/14	1,176	(72)	—	—
Annual Growth	(9.7%)	—	—	—

2016 Year-End Financials

Return on assets: 1.2%
Return on equity: 38.0%
Current ratio: 1.00
Cash ($ mil.): 51

WIPRO, LLC

EXECUTIVES

Ceo, Abidali Neemuchwala
Pres*, Mallathur Balasubramanian
SEC*, Mitchell Mackler
Cfo-Treas*, Ashish Chawla
Head of Marketing, Alex Beal
Global Head of Martech, Andy Coghlan
Project Manager, Aravinth Thatchanamoorth
Information Technology Departm, Fernando Cardoza
E Commerce, George Ioannou
Vice President, Jayraj Nair
Head of Strategy, Jeremy Leach
Auditors: FOR DELOITTE HASKINS & SELLS L

LOCATIONS

HQ: WIPRO, LLC
2 TOWER CENTER BLVD # 2200, EAST BRUNSWICK, NJ 088161100
Phone: 732 509-1664
Web: WWW.WIPRO.COM

HISTORICAL FINANCIALS

Company Type: Private

Income Statement — FYE: March 31

	REVENUE ($ mil.)	NET INCOME ($ mil.)	NET PROFIT MARGIN	EMPLOYEES
03/18	585	(45)	—	800
03/13	120	(17)	—	—
Annual Growth	37.1%	—	—	—

2018 Year-End Financials

Return on assets: (-4.8%)
Return on equity: (-20.4%)
Current ratio: 0.70
Cash ($ mil.): 22

WISCONSIN MILWAUKEE COUNTY

EXECUTIVES

Ceo, Chris Abele
County Clerk*, Joseph Czarnezki
District Attorney*, John Chisholm
Clerk of Courts*, John Barrett

Register of Deeds*, John La Fave
County Exec*, Scott Walker
Chairman of Board*, Marina Dimitrijevic
Treasurer*, David Cullen
Managing Director*, Teig Whaley-Smith
Controller*, Scott Manske
Supervisor, Anthony Staskunas
Auditors: BAKER TILLY VIRCHOW KRAUSE

LOCATIONS

HQ: WISCONSIN MILWAUKEE COUNTY
901 N 9TH ST STE 306, MILWAUKEE, WI 532331425
Phone: 414 278-4211
Web: WWW.LASMILWAUKEE.COM

HISTORICAL FINANCIALS

Company Type: Private

Income Statement — FYE: December 31

	REVENUE ($ mil.)	NET INCOME ($ mil.)	NET PROFIT MARGIN	EMPLOYEES
12/19	877	16	1.9%	4,400
12/18	851	2	0.3%	—
12/17	852	5	0.7%	—
12/16	1,009	(32)	—	—
Annual Growth	(4.6%)	—	—	—

WORKFORCE COMMISSION, TEXAS

The Texas Workforce Commission (TWC) supports economic development in the Lone Star State by developing its workforce. The state government agency with 28 regional workforce boards offers a number of services benefiting employers (recruiting retention and outplacement services) and workers (training and job-search resources). The agency also provides support services such as child care for targeted groups employment and training services for veterans publishes labor law and labor market information and administers the state's unemployment insurance program. Texans receive most of TWC's services for free; the agency is funded primarily by the federal government.

EXECUTIVES

Director Workforce Development Division, Larry Jones
Executive Director, Larry Temple
Director Unemployment Insurance And Regulation Division, LaSha Lenzy
Director External Relations Division, Jesse Lewis
Director Information Technology Division, Dee Meador
Director Employer Initiatives, Doug Ridge
Director Civil Rights Division, Robert Gomez
Director Regulatory Enforcement Division, John Moore

LOCATIONS

HQ: WORKFORCE COMMISSION, TEXAS
101 E 15TH ST, AUSTIN, TX 787781442
Phone: 512 463-9729
Web: WWW.TWC.TEXAS.GOV

PRODUCTS/OPERATIONS

Program / Service
Adult Education & Literacy
Appeals
Apprenticeship
Career Schools & Colleges
Child Care Services
Choices
Civil Rights
Employment Services
Foreign Labor Certification
Labor Law
Labor Market & Career Information
Noncustodial Parent Choices
Rapid Reemployment Services
Self Sufficiency
Senior Community Service Employment Program
Skills Development
Skills for Small Businesses
Skills for Veterans
Supplemental Nutrition Assistance Program Employment & Training
Trade Adjustment Assistance
Unemployment Benefits
Unemployment Tax
Veterans' Services
Workforce Investment Act

HISTORICAL FINANCIALS

Company Type: Private

Income Statement — FYE: August 31

	REVENUE ($ mil.)	NET INCOME ($ mil.)	NET PROFIT MARGIN	EMPLOYEES
08/19	1,898	46	2.5%	4,600
08/18	1,822	134	7.4%	—
08/11	1,466	3	0.2%	—
Annual Growth	3.3%	38.7%	—	—

2019 Year-End Financials

Return on assets: 9.3%
Return on equity: 11.6%
Current ratio: 5.00
Cash ($ mil.): 360

WORLD WIDE TECHNOLOGY HOLDING CO., LLC

EXECUTIVES

Ceo, James P Kavanaugh
Chb*, David Steward
Cfo*, Tom Strunk
Director, Holly Kriegesmann
Project Coordinator, Jennifer Barrett
Business Manager, Nicole Reichert
Specialist, Jennifer Geisler
Client Director, Scott Wilson
Engineer, Rob Walters
Human Resources Business Partn, Abby Baker
Regional Manager, Doug Warner
Auditors: ERNST & YOUNG LLP ST LOUIS

LOCATIONS

HQ: WORLD WIDE TECHNOLOGY HOLDING CO., LLC
1 WORLD WIDE WAY, SAINT LOUIS, MO 631463002
Phone: 314 919-1400
Web: WWW.WWT.COM

HISTORICAL FINANCIALS

Company Type: Private

Income Statement — FYE: December 31

	REVENUE ($ mil.)	NET INCOME ($ mil.)	NET PROFIT MARGIN	EMPLOYEES
12/14	6,702	88	1.3%	1,052
12/13	6,392	77	1.2%	—
12/12	5,041	68	1.3%	—
Annual Growth	15.3%	14.2%	—	—

2014 Year-End Financials

Return on assets: 6.4%
Return on equity: 38.0%
Current ratio: 1.20
Cash ($ mil.): 109

WORLD WIDE TECHNOLOGY, LLC

World Wide Technology (WWT) has a broad view of its business. The company primarily provides such IT services as network design and installation systems and application integration and license consulting. It works with trusted brands such as Cisco VMware NetApp Dell EMC HPE and several others but also include emerging tech players like Tanium and Dedrone. WWT serves businesses in the retail oil and gas energy and utilities industries as well as public sectors. With more than 300 labs the company has over 200 technology partners in the Advanced Technology Center (ATC). WWT was founded in 1990.

Operations

WWT provides consulting ATC lab application supply chain and integration infrastructure EA+ and strategic staffing services.

The company partner with the world's leading technology manufacturers and maintain the highest levels of certification to bring hardware and software solutions. These manufacturers can be evaluated in one environment its ATC and range from Silicon Valley heavyweights like Hewlett Packard Enterprise Microsoft Intel Nvidia Apple and Veritas among others.

Geographic Reach

Headquartered in St. Louis Missouri WWT has about 45 facilities throughout the world and about 4 million-sq.ft. of warehouse and distribution space worldwide. It also has three distribution outlets in Brazil Mexico and Singapore as well as facilities in London; Amsterdam; Hong Kong; and Chengdu China.

Sales and Marketing

WWT serves customers in energy and utility financial global service provider healthcare life sciences and manufacturing industries.

Strategy

World Wide Technology Cisco and Altiostar an innovator in open virtual RAN (vRAN) technology announced the companies are working together on an Open vRAN blueprint that will accelerate the deployment of 4G/5G OpenRAN solutions in service provider networks. The combined solution will help service providers deploy fully integrated open cloud-based virtualized RAN solutions based on technologies created by Cisco and Altiostar and that will be brought to market using the sales integration and deployment capabilities of WWT.

The blueprint is a major step towards the realization of the industry's 5G vision by delivering an open agile software-driven network that enables richer services with greater flexibility at a lower cost. The Open vRAN blueprint will be validated in WWT's state-of-the-art Advanced Technology Center (ATC) a one-of-a-kind testing and validation facility equipped with roughly $1 billion in hardware and software and take advantage of WWT's deep integration and deployment expertise through its global integration centers in Mumbai Singapore St. Louis and Amsterdam. The ATC is a key enabler to solution innovation and can help operators make critical technology decisions faster than ever ? from designing and conceptualizing solutions to validating new industry architectures. WWT will then take the Open vRAN blueprint to market as a fully integrated solution that will be available for customers to test and deploy in their networks with the support of services from WWT and Cisco.

EXECUTIVES

Ceo, James P. (Jim) Kavanaugh
Vp Enterprise Commercial & Service Provider Sales, Mark J. Catalano
Cfo, Thomas W. (Tom) Strunk
Vp Corporate Properties, Dan B. Svoboda
President, Joseph G. (Joe) Koenig
Vp And General Manager U.s. East And Europe Sales & Operations, Matt Horner
Vp Supply Chain Operations, Kurt Grimminger
Vp Global Supply Chain, Mark Franke
Vice President Of Information Technology, Mike P. Taylor
Area Vice President Of Professional Services, Tim Henderson
Vice President Advanced Technology, Brian Ortbals
Vice President Professional Services, Tom Gain
Vice President Of Sales, John Lynch
Vice President Of Federal Sales, Bill Mckeon
Vice President Global Accounts, Leo Makhlin
Vice President Head Of Asia Pacific, Nilesh Mistry
Vice President Security Solutions, Michael Mcglynn
Senior Vice President, Kraig Ecker
Vice President Of Federal Strategy, Robert Ferrell
Vice President, Jeree Hanavec
Chairman, David L. Steward

LOCATIONS

HQ: WORLD WIDE TECHNOLOGY, LLC
1 WORLD WIDE WAY, SAINT LOUIS, MO 631463002
Phone: 314 569-7000
Web: WWW.WWT.COM

PRODUCTS/OPERATIONS

Selected Services

IT Products and Solutions
- Facilities Infrastructure
- Integration and Staging
- Leasing
- Managed Services
- Order Management and Reporting

Pre-Sales Support

- Value Added Reseller

Professional Services
- Configuration
- Implementation
- Planning and Design
- Training

Supply Chain Services
- Business Process Outsourcing
- Logistics/Warehousing
- Material Planning and Scheduling
- Outsourced Procurement
- Supplier Management

COMPETITORS

Accenture
Black Box
Computer Sciences Corp.
DataSpan
Dynamics Research
En Pointe
HP Enterprise Services
IBM Global Services
PC Mall
Rose International
Unisys
WebLinc

HISTORICAL FINANCIALS

Company Type: Private

Income Statement — FYE: December 31

	REVENUE ($ mil.)	NET INCOME ($ mil.)	NET PROFIT MARGIN	EMPLOYEES
12/15	5,927	95	1.6%	1,052
12/14	5,057	95	1.9%	—
12/13	4,545	77	1.7%	—
12/12	3,396	57	1.7%	—
Annual Growth	20.4%	18.3%	—	—

2015 Year-End Financials

Return on assets: 5.7%
Return on equity: 18.8%
Current ratio: 1.40
Cash ($ mil.): 46

WORLEY & OBETZ, INC.

Auditors: HOROVITZ RUDOY & ROTEMAN LLC

LOCATIONS

HQ: WORLEY & OBETZ, INC.
85 WHITE OAK RD, MANHEIM, PA 175458550
Phone: 717 665-6891
Web: WWW.WORLEYOBETZ.COM

HISTORICAL FINANCIALS

Company Type: Private

Income Statement — FYE: August 31

	REVENUE ($ mil.)	NET INCOME ($ mil.)	NET PROFIT MARGIN	EMPLOYEES
08/17	677	2	0.4%	68
08/16	584	1	0.3%	—
08/15	520	2	0.4%	—
08/14	466	1	0.4%	—
Annual Growth	13.2%	14.0%	—	—

2017 Year-End Financials

Return on assets: 3.0%
Return on equity: 16.3%
Current ratio: 1.50
Cash ($ mil.): —

WTG GAS PROCESSING, L.P.

EXECUTIVES

Gen Ptnr, Ealmoor GP
Gen Ptnr, James L Davis
Safety Director, Bobby Roach
Vice President Business Develo, Dave Freeman
Producer Accounting Manager, Joey Farquhar
Safety Manager, Kendall McCasland
Director of Gas Supply, Rick Watkins
Supervisor Right of Way, Tom Segulja

LOCATIONS

HQ: WTG GAS PROCESSING, L.P.
211 N COLORADO ST, MIDLAND, TX 797014607
Phone: 432 682-4349
Web: WWW.WTGGASPROCESSING.COM

HISTORICAL FINANCIALS

Company Type: Private

Income Statement — FYE: December 31

	REVENUE ($ mil.)	NET INCOME ($ mil.)	NET PROFIT MARGIN	EMPLOYEES
12/07	588	85	14.5%	25
12/06	498	64	13.0%	—
12/05	484	69	14.4%	—
12/04	342	39	11.5%	—
Annual Growth	19.7%	29.2%	—	—

2007 Year-End Financials

Return on assets: 29.8%
Return on equity: 37.2%
Current ratio: 2.90
Cash ($ mil.): 45

XMED OXYGEN & MEDICAL EQUIPMENT, LP

EXECUTIVES

Ptnr-Pres, Russel Scott Phillips
Pntr-V Pres, Ali Mutlu
Ptnr-Ceo, John Skono
Store Manager, Kendall Moore

LOCATIONS

HQ: XMED OXYGEN & MEDICAL EQUIPMENT, LP
15230 SURVEYOR BLVD, ADDISON, TX 750014338
Phone: 972 416-5502
Web: WWW.XMED4U.COM

HISTORICAL FINANCIALS

Company Type: Private

Income Statement — FYE: December 31

	REVENUE ($ mil.)	NET INCOME ($ mil.)	NET PROFIT MARGIN	EMPLOYEES
12/18	4,060	227	5.6%	24
12/08	3	0	7.2%	—
12/06	0	0	—	—
12/05	4	0	11.7%	—
Annual Growth	68.6%	59.3%	—	—

2018 Year-End Financials

Return on assets: 19.1%
Return on equity: —
Current ratio: 1.00
Cash ($ mil.): 13

YALE NEW HAVEN HOSPITAL, INC.

Yale-New Haven supports its community and the brainiacs at Yale. Yale-New Haven Hospital (YNHH) is the flagship member of the Yale New Haven Health System. It provides tertiary care in more than 100 medical specialties to residents of southwestern Connecticut. The not-for-profit hospital has more than 1500 beds on two campuses. Its main location includes the Yale-New Haven Children's Hospital and the Yale-New Haven Psychiatric Hospital. Smilow Cancer Hospital with 170 beds is also part of the hospital complex. YNHH provides cardiac and cancer care performs organ transplants and offers a variety of outpatient clinics. The medical center serves as the primary teaching hospital for Yale University's medical school.

Operations

YNHH handles some 80000 inpatient admissions each year including more than 5000 births. It also has more than 150000 emergency room and urgent care encounters. The hospital's campuses employ some 4250 medical staffers.

A key component of the main hospital facility is the Smilow Cancer Hospital which conducts cancer care and research in partnership with Yale University's Cancer Center.

Financial Performance

YNHH's patient services contribute the bulk of the hospital's total operating revenue. In fiscal 2016 (ended September) operating revenue increased 5% to $2.7 billion as patient volume rose. However operating expenses also increased that year; supplies and other expenses rose to $1.3 billion (versus $1.2 billion in fiscal 2015). Total operating expenses in 2016 reached $2.6 billion. All told the hospital's excess of revenue over expenses increased 50% to $158.5 million.

Strategy

Despite facing challenges including state budget cuts YNHH has been working on the integration of its second campus Saint Raphael. The hospital has also invested some $100 million towards capital improvements at the campus. The combined organization allows YNHH to increase coordination of care and reduce redundancies for area communities.

EXECUTIVES

Evp Coo And Trustee, Marna P. Borgstrom
Svp Patient Services And Chief Nursing Officer, Patricia Sue Fitzsimons
Svp Operations; Executive Director Women's And Children's Services, Cynthia N. Sparer
President And Trustee, Richard D'Aquila
Svp Patient Safety And Quality And Chief Medical Officer, Thomas J. Balcezak
Svp Operations; Executive Director Smilow Cancer Hospital, Abe Lopman
Evp And Cfo Yale New Haven Health System And Cfo Yale New Haven Hospital (ynhh), Vincent Tammaro
Vice President Executive Director Cardiovascular Services, Keith Churchwell
Medical Director, Robert Ostroff
Legal Secretary, Mohamed Ramadan
Assistant Vice President Outcomes Management, Peggy Parniawski
Associate Medical Director, Kevin Burns
Vice Chairman, Julia M. McNamara, age 78
Chair, Mary C. Farrell, age 70
Secretary Administrative Assistant, Adria Coleman
Secretary, Stephanie Pane
Secretary, Sheryl Raffile
Adm Secretary, Shaun Epps
Medical Secretary, Jenifer Yoston

LOCATIONS

HQ: YALE NEW HAVEN HOSPITAL, INC.
20 YORK ST, NEW HAVEN, CT 065103220
Phone: 203 688-4242
Web: WWW.YNHH.ORG

PRODUCTS/OPERATIONS

Selected Services

Ambulatory (outpatient) services
Bariatric surgery
Blood draw stations
Dental center
Diabetes and endocrinology
Diagnostic radiology
Ear nose and throat
Emergency services
Endocrine surgery
Gastroenterology
Geriatrics
Kidney disease
Maternity
Psychiatry
Pulmonology
Urology

COMPETITORS

Bristol Hospital
Connecticut Children's Medical Center
Griffin Hospital
Hartford Health Care
New Milford Hospital
St. Vincent's Health Services
Waterbury Hospital
Western Connecticut Health Network

HISTORICAL FINANCIALS

Company Type: Private

Income Statement — FYE: September 30

	REVENUE ($ mil.)	NET INCOME ($ mil.)	NET PROFIT MARGIN	EMPLOYEES
09/15	2,388	107	4.5%	22,000
09/14	2,360	120	5.1%	—
09/13	2,360	120	5.1%	—
09/09	1,237	52	4.3%	—
Annual Growth	11.6%	12.5%	—	—

2015 Year-End Financials

Return on assets: 3.6%
Return on equity: 9.8%
Current ratio: 3.40
Cash ($ mil.): 101

YALE UNIVERSITY

What do former President George W. Bush and actress Meryl Streep have in common? They are Yalies. Yale University is one of the nation's most prestigious private liberal arts institutions as well as one of its oldest (founded in 1701). Yale comprises an undergraduate college a graduate school and more than a dozen professional schools. Programs of study include architecture law medicine and drama. Its 12 residential colleges (a system borrowed from Oxford) serve as dormitory dining hall and social center. The school has around 12000 students and nearly 4000 faculty members.

Operations

Yale's graduate students of which there are more than 6500 outnumber its more than 5300 undergrads. Undergraduate tuition runs at around $42000 per year plus $13000 in room and board. Graduate tuition is about $35000 per year. The university has some 4000 faculty members.

The university has extensive research programs affiliated with its graduate school and its graduate-level professional schools which cover architecture art divinity drama engineering and applied science forestry and environmental studies law management medicine music nursing and public health.

Yale also operates the Yale University Press which publishes works of academics and professionals including e-books and traditional books. It published 475 titles during 2012 and has produced about 9000 titles in total.

Geographic Reach

Yale's facilities cover a total of 1100 acres including a 340-acre central campus with 260 buildings in New Haven Connecticut; a 140-acre West Campus on the edge of New Haven; and 600 acres of athletic fields and natural preserve areas outside of town. Yale's students come from all 50 US states and about 110 foreign countries.

Financial Performance

Sales for Yale have grown over the last five years and the university showed a 1% increase in revenues to more than $2.8 billion in 2012 due to higher student income grants and contracts (for research and training programs) medical service revenues and other income sources. Endowment income and grants and contracts are the largest source of revenue.

Yale's annual operating budget is about $2.7 billion.

Yale's roughly $19 billion endowment ranks as one of the largest in the US. Yale's Endowment grew about 9% in 2010 producing a gain of $1.4 billion.

Company Background

Yale was founded in 1701 through the vision of a group of colonial clergymen who began planning for a university in the 1640s. It was named Yale College in 1718 after a Welsh merchant Elihu Yale who made a sizable donation to the institution.

EXECUTIVES

Chair Department Of Physics, Paul Tipton
Medical Director, Matthew Ellman
Co President Emergency Medicine Interest Group Emig, Tyler Phelan
Medical Director, Karen Santucci
Senior Vice President Operations And Interim Chief Information Officer, Jack Callahan
Senior Vice President Chief Medical Officer, Thomas Balcezak
Vice Chairman, John Geibel
Assistant Secretary, ERIN JOHNSON
Auditors: PRICEWATERHOUSECOOPERS LLP HA

LOCATIONS

HQ: YALE UNIVERSITY
105 WALL ST, NEW HAVEN, CT 065118917
Phone: 203 432-2550
Web: WWW.YALE.EDU

PRODUCTS/OPERATIONS

Colleges and Schools

Graduate School of Arts and Sciences
Professional schools
- School of Architecture
- School of Art
- Divinity School
- School of Drama
- School of Engineering & Applied Science
- School of Forestry & Environmental Studies
- Law School
- School of Management
- School of Medicine
- School of Music
- School of Nursing
- School of Public Health
- Institute of Sacred Music

Yale College (undergraduate studies)
Residential Colleges

Berkeley College
Branford College
Calhoun College
Davenport College
Ezra Stiles College
Jonathan Edwards College
Morse College
Pierson College
Saybrook College
Silliman College
Timothy Dwight College
Trumbull College

HISTORICAL FINANCIALS

Company Type: Private

Income Statement — FYE: June 30

	REVENUE ($ mil.)	NET INCOME ($ mil.)	NET PROFIT MARGIN	EMPLOYEES
06/20	4,246	(509)	—	11,000
06/19	4,105	(15)	—	—
06/18	3,848	3,270	85.0%	—
06/17	3,647	2,447	67.1%	—
Annual Growth	5.2%	—	—	—

2020 Year-End Financials

Return on assets: (-1.1%)
Return on equity: (-1.6%)
Current ratio: —
Cash ($ mil.): 1,011

YATES GROUP, INC.

E-Z Mart Stores aims to make filling gas tanks and stomachs EZR for small-town America. The regional convenience store chain operates about 295 stores across four neighboring states including Arkansas Louisiana Oklahoma and Texas. Rather than build its own stores the company usually expands through acquisitions. In addition to the standard hot dogs sodas coffee and cigarettes most E-Z Mart locations also offer Shell Conoco Phillips 66 or CITGO gasoline. E-Z Mart was founded in 1970 by Jim Yates in Nashville Arkansas. Yates died in 1998 when the plane he was piloting crashed leaving his daughter Sonja Hubbard at the company's helm as CEO.

Geographic Reach

Ranked #35 on Convenience Store News ' "Top 100 Convenience Stores Report" E-Z Mart is a regional c-store chain that primarily serves Texas and Arkansas as well as Oklahoma and Louisiana.

Sales and Marketing

Aiming to offer the chain's customers access to updated fuel prices a list of locations and in-store promotions among other items E-Z Mart partnered with OpenStore by GasBuddy to roll out a new E-Z Mart website and mobile app. The fully integrated mobile app enables consumers to send feedback from their mobile phones and receive time-sensitive electronic mobile coupons.

Strategy

While E-Z Mart has trimmed its store count during the past decade or so including exiting markets such as Missouri it continues to make strategic acquisitions. Like other convenience store operators seeking to boost in-store sales E-Z Mart is expanding its food and beverage offering adding fresh-brewed iced tea to all of its stores and installing freezers. Outside the company has a deal with Redbox to place its movie rental kiosks outside of E-Z Mart stores.

EXECUTIVES

Vice President, Lifford Luthringer
Auditors: BKD LLP FORT SMITH ARKANSAS

LOCATIONS

HQ: YATES GROUP, INC.
2015 GALLERIA OAKS DR, TEXARKANA, TX 755034618
Phone: 903 336-6246
Web: WWW.GPMINVESTMENTS.COM

2014 Stores

	No.
Texas	96
Arkansas	95
Oklahoma	80
Louisiana	18
Total	289

COMPETITORS

7-Eleven
Allsup's
Brookshire Grocery
Chevron
Exxon Mobil
Krause Gentle
Love's Country Stores
QuikTrip
Racetrac Petroleum
Susser Holdings
Valero Energy

HISTORICAL FINANCIALS

Company Type: Private

Income Statement — FYE: December 31

	REVENUE ($ mil.)	NET INCOME ($ mil.)	NET PROFIT MARGIN	EMPLOYEES
12/16	786	16	2.1%	2,100
12/15	827	16	2.0%	—
12/14	1,026	19	1.9%	—
12/13	1,003	15	1.5%	—
Annual Growth	(7.8%)	3.2%	—	—

2016 Year-End Financials

Return on assets: 7.9%
Return on equity: 12.6%
Current ratio: 1.30
Cash ($ mil.): 7

YORK HOSPITAL

York Hospital operating as WellSpan York Hospital takes its name from the community whose health it seeks to preserve. Part of WellSpan Health the medical center has about 570 beds and serves residents of York and surrounding area of south-central Pennsylvania. It is a regional leader in cardiovascular and orthopedic care and has programs in other specialty areas including oncology behavioral health and geriatrics. Additionally WellSpan York Hospital operates a Level 1 trauma center offers outpatient surgery emergency home health and diagnostic imaging services. It is also has teaching and research programs. The hospital was founded in 1880.

Operations

WellSpan York Hospital has been recognized as a top 100 US hospital by US News for more than five years in a row. It is also recognized for its cardiovascular and orthopedic programs. The center employs about 700 doctors.

The hospital's education programs include five allied health schools and seven residency programs. Affiliated organizations include the medical schools of Drexel University Pennsylvania State University and University of Maryland.

Strategy

WellSpan York Hospital is working to improve its specialist programs to meet the growing medical needs of area residents. In 2011 for instance it collaborated with technology firm Cerner and pharmaceuticals firm Hospira to form an infusion management program for its intensive care unit; the program aims to reduce infusion-related errors. In addition it launched a urinary catheter removal protocol to reduce infection rates and it implemented an aortic valve replacement program (making it one of three facilities in Pennsylvania to offer the open-heart surgery alternative).

EXECUTIVES

Vice President Of Sales, Richard Brown
Vice President, Peter Hartmann
Medical Director, Pradeep Alur
Senior Vice President, Michael Oconnor
Pharmacy Manager, Courtney Rodgers
Medical Director, Creston Tate
Managing Director General Surgeon, Matthew Souder
Pharmacist Manager, Tony Bixler
Medical Director, Rachelle Ambrose
Vice President, John Holmes
Senior Vice President And General Counsel, Glen Moffett
Senior Vice President, Charles Chodroff
Vice President Treasury Management Services, Richard Harley
Medical Director Neurosciences, Todd Barron
Vice President Of Medical Affairs Wellspan Gettysburg Hospital, Charles Marley
Vice President Planning, William Lafferty
Pharmacist Manager, Kim Oconnor

LOCATIONS

HQ: YORK HOSPITAL
1001 S GEORGE ST, YORK, PA 174033645
Phone: 717 851-2345
Web: WWW.WELLSPAN.ORG

COMPETITORS

Ascension Health
Catholic Health Initiatives
Geisinger Health System
Guthrie Healthcare
Hanover Healthcare
Hershey Medical Center
Holy Spirit
Lancaster General Memorial Hospital (PA)
PinnacleHealth System

HISTORICAL FINANCIALS

Company Type: Private

Income Statement — FYE: June 30

	REVENUE ($ mil.)	NET INCOME ($ mil.)	NET PROFIT MARGIN	EMPLOYEES
06/20	1,163	15	1.4%	6,200
06/18	1,063	181	17.0%	—
06/16	990	17	1.8%	—
06/15	925	82	9.0%	—
Annual Growth	4.7%	(28.3%)	—	—

2020 Year-End Financials

Return on assets: 0.7%
Return on equity: 1.2%
Current ratio: 1.20
Cash ($ mil.): 249

ZEN-NOH GRAIN CORPORATION

EXECUTIVES

Ceo, Charles Colbert
Ceo*, John D Williams
Exec V Pres*, Shin Inoue
Sr. V Pres*, Charles E Colbert
Ctlr*, Robin Gerarve

Dir*, Hiroyuki Kawasaki
Dir*, Yoshihiro Sugiyama
Dir*, Yoshinori Ohara
Executive Vice-President, Osamu Yako
Feed Ingredients Manager, Jeigh Hymel
Sales Manager, Akira Hayashi
Auditors: KPMG LLP NEW ORLEANS LA

LOCATIONS

HQ: ZEN-NOH GRAIN CORPORATION
1127 HWY 190 E SERVICE RD, COVINGTON, LA 704334929
Phone: 985 867-3500
Web: WWW.CGB.COM

HISTORICAL FINANCIALS

Company Type: Private

Income Statement FYE: May 31

	REVENUE ($ mil.)	NET INCOME ($ mil.)	NET PROFIT MARGIN	EMPLOYEES
05/20	5,930	44	0.7%	188
05/19	5,983	53	0.9%	—
05/18	6,971	101	1.5%	—
05/17	7,047	67	1.0%	—
Annual Growth	(5.6%)	(13.2%)	—	—

2020 Year-End Financials

Return on assets: 2.8%
Return on equity: 7.6%
Current ratio: 1.30
Cash ($ mil.): 12

Hoover's Handbook of

Private Companies

Index of Executives

Index of Executives

A

Index of Executives

Index of Executives

B

Index of Executives

Index of Executives

Index of Executives

Index of Executives

Index of Executives

C

Index of Executives

Index of Executives

Index of Executives

Index of Executives

Index of Executives

D

Index of Executives

Index of Executives

E

Index of Executives

Index of Executives

Index of Executives

Index of Executives

Index of Executives

Index of Executives

Index of Executives

H

Index of Executives

Index of Executives

Index of Executives

Index of Executives

I

J

Index of Executives

Index of Executives

K

Index of Executives

Index of Executives

Index of Executives

Index of Executives

Index of Executives

Index of Executives

M

Index of Executives

Index of Executives

Index of Executives

Index of Executives

Index of Executives

N

Index of Executives

O

Index of Executives

P

Index of Executives

Index of Executives

Index of Executives

Q

R

Index of Executives

Index of Executives

Index of Executives

S

Index of Executives

Index of Executives

Index of Executives

Index of Executives

Index of Executives

Index of Executives

T

Index of Executives

Index of Executives

U

V

Index of Executives

W

Index of Executives

Index of Executives

Index of Executives

X

Y

Index of Executives